MIDDLE AND JUNIOR HIGH SCHOOL
LIBRARY CATALOG

NINTH EDITION

STANDARD CATALOG SERIES

JOHN GREENFIELDT, GENERAL EDITOR

CHILDREN'S CATALOG

FICTION CATALOG

MIDDLE AND JUNIOR HIGH SCHOOL LIBRARY CATALOG

PUBLIC LIBRARY CATALOG

SENIOR HIGH SCHOOL LIBRARY CATALOG

MIDDLE AND JUNIOR HIGH SCHOOL LIBRARY CATALOG

NINTH EDITION

EDITED BY

ANNE PRICE

NEW YORK • DUBLIN

THE H. W. WILSON COMPANY

2005

Printed in the United States of America

Abridged Dewey Decimal Classification and Relative Index, Edition 14 is © 2004-2005 OCLC Online Computer Library Center, Incorporated. Used with Permission. DDC, Dewey, and Dewey Decimal Classification are registered trademarks of OCLC.

ISBN 0-8242-1053-0

Library of Congress Cataloging-in-Publication Data

Middle and junior high school library catalog / edited by Anne Price. — 9th ed.
    p. cm. — (Standard catalog series)
Includes index.
Kept up to date between editions by annual supplements.

ISBN 0-8242-1053-0 (alk. paper)

1. Young adult literature—Bibliography. 2. Children's literature—Bibliography. 3. Junior high school libraries—United States—Book lists. 4. Middle school libraries—United States—Book lists. I. Price, Anne, 1946- II. Series.

Z1037.J854 2005
011.62'5—dc22

2005023123

Visit H.W. Wilson's Web site at: www.hwwilson.com

CONTENTS

Preface vii

Acknowledgments ix

Directions for Use of the Catalog xi

Outline of Classification xv

Part 1. Classified Catalog 1

    Nonfiction. 1

    Fiction. 557

    Story Collections 736

Part 2. List of Recommended Periodicals 749

Part 3. List of Recommended Electronic Resources . . 755

Part 4. Author, Title, Subject, and Analytical Index . . 773

PREFACE

Middle and Junior High School Library Catalog is a selective list of fiction and nonfiction books recommended for young people in grades five through nine. In addition to this volume, the service unit comprises annual supplements for 2006, 2007, and 2008 without further charge.

New in This Edition

There are three features of the *Middle and Junior High School Library Catalog* that are new in this edition. The list of recommended CD-ROMs in the eighth edition has been replaced by a list of recommended electronic resources, mostly Web resources, reflecting the changes in information technology in the past five years. An entirely new feature is the list of recommended periodicals, which is given in two sections, one a list of journals for teachers, librarians, and media specialists, and the other a list of periodicals for children and young adults, with emphasis on their educational value. The third new feature is a selection of recommended graphic novels. These graphic novels have been chosen by a well-known expert in the field with special attention to their suitability for a middle and junior high school audience.

History

Junior High School Library Catalog, first published in 1965, was developed to address the unique needs of younger adolescents. It developed from the *Standard Catalog for High School Libraries*, which was subsequently modified in scope and retitled *Senior High School Library Catalog*. With the seventh edition in 1995 the title of the Catalog was changed from *Junior High School Library Catalog* to *Middle and Junior High School Library Catalog* to reflect the prevalence of middle school programs and the extension of coverage to grades five and six.

Preparation

An advisory committee of distinguished librarians assisted in the compilation of this Catalog. The committee reaffirmed the selection policy, reevaluated titles from the previous edition of the Catalog and its supplements, and proposed many new titles. The committee represents a diversity of backgrounds in librarianship for young people and a wealth of experience on national juries and American Library Association committees.

Scope and Purpose

Middle and Junior High School Library Catalog lists books for youth in grades five through nine, along with review sources and other professional aids for the librarian or school media specialist. This edition includes 5,968 book titles and 3,034 analytical entries for parts of books. Entries for works other than reference works that are most likely to be of interest to young people in grades seven and higher are given the notation "7 and up." Special sections are devoted to electronic resources and periodicals. Libraries and media centers serving large systems and those with special curriculum needs will wish to supplement this Catalog.

All the books listed are published in the United States, or published in Canada or the United Kingdom and distributed in the United States. A small number of out-of-print titles that are considered essential to a well-rounded collection have been included at the suggestion of the advisory committee. They are noted as o.p. All other titles were in print at the time of listing. For some books, paper is the only available binding.

Because of the lack of uniform national standards and the movement away from a set curriculum, the Catalog does not aim to support any particular middle level curriculum but rather to cover a broad spectrum of topics. In the nonfiction section special importance is given to works devoted to technology, personal values, and current social and political issues, with special emphasis on ethnic diversity and minorities. New topics of particular importance are cloning and other new technologies, bioethics, terrorism, and politics in the post-September 11 world. The fiction section contains a wide range of literary works that are of interest to youth and many that are frequently included in the school curriculum—classics as well as contemporary fiction and genre literature. A generous selection of recommended graphic novels suitable for the middle and junior high school library can be found in the Classified Catalog at 741.5 (Graphic arts).

Among the works for the librarian or media specialist are bibliographies, professional journals, and other resources for the selection and evaluation of print and nonprint materials and the use of the Internet in instruction.

The section devoted to periodicals recommends in separate lists both professional materials for teachers and librarians and periodicals for the students in middle and junior high schools. The titles are chosen for their educational value, and no purely entertainment magazines are listed.

The section of recommended electronic resources is devoted primarily to reference works and educational materials in support of the curriculum in the areas of science, social studies, geography, and mathematics. The items in this section were chosen on the basis of accuracy of content, scope of coverage, quality of multimedia elements, ease of navigation, and usefulness of supporting documentation. It is not intended to be a comprehensive list and can be augmented according to the needs of individual collections. Where a CD-ROM version of a printed book is available, that information is noted at the entry for the book in the Classified Catalog.

The Catalog excludes the following: nonprint materials other than Web-based resources; non-English-language materials, with the exception of dictionaries and similar items; works of adult fiction, except for books originally written for adults but read by young people or books widely used in the curriculum; textbooks; and books about specific vocations, individual computer programs or versions of programs, and other topics that quickly become outdated.

ACKNOWLEDGMENTS

This Catalog could not have been published without the cooperative efforts of publishers and the library community. The H. W. Wilson Company is indebted to the publishers who generously supplied copies of their books, as well as information about editions and prices. The Company also acknowledges its gratitude to the librarians of its advisory committee, who gave so generously of their time and expertise in advising the editors in the choice of materials to include in the Catalog.

Members of the Advisory Committee:

Raymond W. Barber, Chair
Director of Libraries
The William Penn Charter School
Philadelphia, PA

Danielle J. Ford
Assistant Professor, Science Education
School of Education
University of Delaware
Newark, DE

Randall Enos
Youth Services Consultant
Ramapo Catskill Library System
Middletown, NY

Melinda Greenblatt
Program Director, Library Connections
Archdiocese of New York
New York, NY

Kathie Fitch
Head Librarian
Rachel Carson Middle School
Herndon, VA

Mari Hardacre
Manager of Young Adult Services
Allen County Public Library
Fort Wayne, IN

Consultant on Electronic Resources:

Frances B. Bradburn
Director, Instructional Technologies
North Carolina Department of Public Instruction
Raleigh, NC

Consultant on Graphic Novels:

Katharine L. Kan
Reviewer and consultant
Panama City, FL

DIRECTIONS FOR USE OF THE CATALOG

USES OF THE CATALOG

Middle and Junior High School Library Catalog is designed to serve a number of purposes:

As an aid in purchasing. The Catalog is designed to assist in the selection and ordering of titles. Annotations are provided for each title along with information concerning publisher, ISBN, price, and availability. Since Part 1, the Classified Catalog, is arranged according to the Dewey Decimal Classification, the Catalog may be used to identify parts of the library collection that should be updated or strengthened. In evaluating the suitability of a work each library will want to consider the special character of the school and community it serves.

As an aid to the reader's advisor. The work of the reader's advisor is furthered by the information about sequels and companion volumes and the descriptive and critical annotations in the Classified Catalog, and by the subject access in the Index. The analytical entries in the Index augment the library's catalog by providing access to parts of composite works.

As an aid in verification of information. For this purpose full bibliographical data are provided in the Classified Catalog. Entries also include recommended subject headings based upon *Sears List of Subject Headings* and a suggested classification derived from the *Abridged Dewey Decimal Classification and Relative Index*. Notes describe editions available, awards, publication history, and other titles in the series.

As an aid in curriculum support. The classified approach, subject indexing, and annotations are helpful in identifying materials appropriate for classroom use.

As an aid in collection maintenance. Information about the titles available on a subject facilitates decisions to rebind, replace, or discard items. If a book has been deleted from the Catalog in this edition because it is no longer in print, that deletion is not intended as a sign that the book is no longer valuable or that it should necessarily be weeded from the collection.

As an instructional aid. The Catalog is useful in courses that deal with literature and book selection for young people.

ORGANIZATION

The Catalog consists of four parts:

Part 1. Classified Catalog
Part 2. List of Recommended Periodicals

Part 3. List of Recommended Electronic Resources
Part 4. Author, Title, Subject, and Analytical Index

Part 1. CLASSIFIED CATALOG

The Classified Catalog is arranged with the nonfiction books first, classified according to the Dewey Decimal Classification in numerical order from 000 to 999. Individual biographies are classed at 92 and follow the 920's (collective biography). Fiction books, denoted by the symbol "Fic," follow the nonfiction. Short story collections, denoted by "S C," follow fiction. The information supplied for each book includes bibliographic description, suggested subject headings, an annotation, and an evaluation, frequently from a quoted source.

An Outline of Classification, which serves as a table of contents to the Classified Catalog, is reproduced on page xv. It should be remembered that many subjects are treated in more than one discipline and so are found in various parts of the classification. If a particular title is not found where it might be expected, the Index should be consulted to determine if the work is classified elsewhere.

Within classes, books are arranged alphabetically under main entry, usually the author. An exception is made for works of individual biography, classed at 92, which are arranged alphabetically under the name of the person written about.

The following is an example of a typical entry and a description of its components:

> **Houghton, Gillian**
> The Transcontinental Railroad; a primary source history of America's first coast-to-coast railroad. Rosen Central 2002 64p il map (Primary sources in American history) lib bdg $29.25 **385**
> 1. Union Pacific Railroad Company 2. Railroads—United States
> ISBN 0-8239-3684-8 LC 2001-8530
> Describes the people, circumstances, and events surrounding the building of the railway system across the continent in the mid-nineteenth century.
> "Clearly written [text is] accompanied by numerous reproductions of handbills, maps, period photographs, portraits, political cartoons, the National Republican platform of 1860, blueprints, and letters. . . . [This] will be useful to students and their teachers." SLJ
> Includes glossary and bibliographical references

The name of the author, Gillian Houghton, is given in conformity with *Anglo-American Cataloguing Rules*, 2nd edition, 2002 revision. It is inverted and printed in dark or bold face type.

The title of the book is *The Transcontinental Railroad; a primary source history of America's first coast-to-coast railroad*. The book was published by Rosen Central in 2002.

The book has 64 pages and contains illustrations and at least one map. It is published in the "Primary sources in American history" series, in a library binding, and sells for $29.25. (Prices given were current when the Catalog went to press.)

At the end of the last line of type in the body of the entry is the figure 385 in bold face type. This is the classification number derived from the fourteenth edition of the *Abridged Dewey Decimal Classification*. The number 385 is the classification number for "Railroad transportation."

The numbered term "1. Union Pacific Railroad Company" is a corporate name subject, again established in conformity with *Anglo-American Cataloguing Rules*. The second term, "2. Railroads—United States", is a recommended topical subject heading for this book based on *Sears List of Subject Headings*.

The ISBN (International Standard Book Number) is included to facilitate ordering. The Library of Congress control number is provided when available.

Following are three notes supplying additional information about the book. The first is a description of the book's content. The second is a critical note from *School Library Journal*. Such annotations are useful in evaluating books for selection and in determining which of several books on the same subject is best suited for the individual reader. The final note describes special features, in this case a glossary and a bibliography. Notes are also made to describe sequels and companion volumes, editions available, awards, and publication history.

Part 2. LIST OF RECOMMENDED PERIODICALS

The List of Recommended Periodicals is divided into two parts: Part I, Professional journals for teachers and librarians, and Part II, Periodicals for children and young adults. Within each part the journals are listed alphabetically by title. The information given for each periodical consists of title, publisher, price, ISSN, a note indicating frequency of publication, and a brief annotation.

Part 3. LIST OF RECOMMENDED ELECTRONIC RESOURCES

The List of Recommended Electronic Resources is arranged alphabetically by title. Subscription-based and free resources are included in a single alphabet. For each item the following information is given: title, publisher, price (or an indication that it is free), a telephone number for subscription resources, a URL, and an annotation. Where the price is too variable to list, a note directs the user to contact the publisher for pricing information. The annotation describes the general contents and features of the resource and includes a quotation from a reviewing source where available.

Part 4. AUTHOR, TITLE, SUBJECT, AND ANALYTICAL INDEX

This Index is a comprehensive key to the Classified Catalog. Each book is entered under author, title (if distinctive), series, subject, and other added entries as necessary. Following the name of the series all the titles in that series are listed. Also included are subject, author, and title analytics for parts of composite works. The classification number in bold face type is the key to the location of the main entry of the book in the Classified Catalog. Works classed at 92, individual biography, will be found under the name of the person written about. Analytical entries provide indexing for parts of works and are an important feature of the Catalog in that they maximize use of the library's holdings, especially for plays and short stories contained in anthologies and collections.

Cross-references are made in the Index from variant forms of names, from terms not used as subject headings to the term that is used, and from terms used as subject headings to related or more specific headings.

The following are examples of Index entries for the book cited above:

Author   **Houghton, Gillian**
                The Transcontinental Railroad   **385**

Title   The **Transcontinental** railroad. Houghton, G.   **385**

Subject   **Union Pacific Railroad Company**
                Houghton, G. The Transcontinental Railroad (5 and up)
                                                                       385

Examples of other types of entries:

Joint Author   **Baguley, Kitt**
                (jt.auth) Winter, J. K. Venezuela   **987**

Author Analytic
                Aiken, Joan, 1924-2004
                Cousin Alice
                    In Visions: nineteen short stories by outstanding
                        writers for young adults p152-69   **SC**

Title Analytic
                Something old, something new. Sweeney, J.
                    In Destination unexpected: short stories   **SC**

Subject Analytic
                Exercise
                See/See also pages in the following book(s):
                    Schwager, T. The right moves (7 and up)   **613.7**

Outline of Classification

Reproduced below is the Second Summary of the Dewey Decimal Classification. * It will serve as a table of contents for the nonfiction section of the Classified Catalog. (Fiction and Story Collections follow the nonfiction.) Note that the inclusion of this outline is not intended as a substitute for consulting the Dewey Decimal Classification itself.

000 Computer science, knowledge & systems
010   Bibliographies
020   Library & information sciences
030   Encyclopedias & books of facts
040   [Unassigned]
050   Magazines, journals & serials
060   Associations, organizations & museums
070   News media, journalism & publishing
080   Quotations
090   Manuscripts & rare books

100 Philosophy
110   Metaphysics
120   Epistemology
130   Parapsychology & occultism
140   Philosophical schools of thought
150   Psychology
160   Logic
170   Ethics
180   Ancient, medieval & eastern philosophy
190   Modern western philosophy

200 Religion
210   Philosophy & theory of religion
220   The Bible
230   Christianity & Christian theology
240   Christian practice & observance
250   Christian pastoral practice & religious orders
260   Christian organization, social work & worship
270   History of Christianity
280   Christian denominations
290   Other religions

300 Social sciences, sociology & anthropology
310   Statistics
320   Political science
330   Economics
340   Law
350   Public administration & military science
360   Social problems & social services
370   Education
380   Commerce, communications & transportation
390   Customs, etiquette & folklore

400 Language
410   Linguistics
420   English & Old English languages
430   German & related languages
440   French & related languages
450   Italian, Romanian & related languages
460   Spanish & Portuguese languages
470   Latin & Italic languages
480   Classical & modern Greek languages
490   Other languages

500 Science
510   Mathematics
520   Astronomy
530   Physics
540   Chemistry
550   Earth sciences & geology
560   Fossils & prehistoric life
570   Life sciences; biology
580   Plants (Botany)
590   Animals (Zoology)

600 Technology
610   Medicine & health
620   Engineering
630   Agriculture
640   Home & family management
650   Management & public relations
660   Chemical engineering
670   Manufacturing
680   Manufacture for specific uses
690   Building & construction

700 Arts
710   Landscaping & area planning
720   Architecture
730   Sculpture, ceramics & metalwork
740   Drawing & decorative arts
750   Painting
760   Graphic arts
770   Photography & computer art
780   Music
790   Sports, games & entertainment

800 Literature, rhetoric & criticism
810   American literature in English
820   English & Old English literatures
830   German & related literatures
840   French & related literatures
850   Italian, Romanian & related literatures
860   Spanish & Portuguese literatures
870   Latin & Italic literatures
880   Classical & modern Greek literatures
890   Other literatures

900 History
910   Geography & travel
920   Biography & genealogy
930   History of ancient world (to ca. 499)
940   History of Europe
950   History of Asia
960   History of Africa
970   History of North America
980   History of South America
990   History of other areas

* Reproduced from Edition 14 of the Abridged Dewey Decimal Classification and Relative Index, published in 2004, by permission of OCLC Online Computer Library Center, Inc., owner of copyright.

MIDDLE & JUNIOR HIGH SCHOOL LIBRARY CATALOG

NINTH EDITION
CLASSIFIED CATALOG

000 COMPUTER SCIENCE, INFORMATION & GENERAL WORKS

001.4 Research; statistical methods

The **Nobel** book of answers; the Dalai Lama, Mikhail Gorbachev, Shimon Peres, and other Nobel Prize winners answer some of life's most intriguing questions for young people; edited by Bettina Stiekel; translated by Paul De Angelis and Elisabeth Kaestner. Atheneum Bks. for Young Readers 2003 254p $14.95 (5 and up)

001.4

1. Nobel Prizes
ISBN 0-689-86310-1   LC 2003-8721
"Will I soon have a clone? Why are leaves green? Why are some people rich and others poor? Why does 1 + 1 = 2? Why is there war? What is love? Nobel Prize winners honored for their work for peace and in science, economics, medicine, and literature speak to children about elemental issues. . . . Most of these intellectuals do an amazing job of explaining complex ideas . . . . This will be especially welcome as a discussion opener in science and social studies classrooms." Booklist

Valenza, Joyce Kasman
Power research tools; learning activities & posters; illustrated by Emily Valenza. American Lib. Assn. 2003 113p il pa $55   **001.4**
1. Research 2. Internet resources 3. Internet searching 4. Report writing
ISBN 0-8389-0838-1   LC 2002-8972
Contents: Searching; Ethics; Evaluation; Organizing and communicating
A collection of "lessons, rubrics, graphic organizers, and curriculum designed to help students become successful users of information. Beginning with the first steps of research, the development of a thesis, the material progresses logically through the succeeding steps, covering Boolean operators; search tools and strategies; subject and keyword searching; ethics; plagiarism; documenting and citing resources; creating source and note cards; the process of writing the paper; and quoting, paraphrasing, and summarizing. . . . This is an invaluable resource for teaching information skills in any subject area, in middle school or high school." SLJ

001.9 Controversial knowledge

Blackwood, Gary L.
Extraordinary events and oddball occurrences. Benchmark Bks. (Tarrytown) 1999 80p il (Secrets of the unexplained) lib bdg $29.93   **001.9**
1. Parapsychology 2. Curiosities and wonders
ISBN 0-7614-0748-0   LC 98-30261
Discusses the details and possible explanations of mysterious events throughout human history, including strange things falling out of the sky, the teleportation of objects, and unexplained appearances and disappearances
Includes bibliographical references

Floyd, E. Randall
Great American mysteries; raining snakes, fabled cities of gold, strange disappearances, and other baffling tales. August House 1991 190p hardcover o.p. paperback available $9.95 (7 and up)   **001.9**
1. Curiosities and wonders
ISBN 0-87483-170-9 (pa)   LC 91-6566
A collection of "legends of the weird and bizarre in American life. Unsolved murders, buildings with no exits, tales from the Bermuda Triangle, and the mysterious moving rocks of Death Valley . . . make for absorbing, sometimes spooky, reading. Great for browsers." Booklist
Includes bibliographical references

Nardo, Don, 1947-
Atlantis; by Don Nardo. Lucent Books 2004 112p il map (Mystery library) $28.70

001.9

1. Atlantis
ISBN 1-590-18287-1   LC 2003-13854
Contents: Plato's original account of Atlantis; The modern world rediscovers Atlantis; Searching for Atlantis around the globe; The Atlantean empire and Minoan Crete; Thera and the blast that shook history; Myths as memories: the making of a legend
Discusses the mystery and theories surrounding Atlantis, a legendary lost continent which Plato wrote about in 399 B.C.
"Although the mystery may never be solved, the story of Atlantis will continue to be a source of fascination." SLJ
Includes bibliographical references

Netzley, Patricia D.
Alien abductions: opposing viewpoints.
Greenhaven Press 1996 128p il (Great mysteries)
lib bdg $27.45 (7 and up)   **001.9**
1. Unidentified flying objects 2. Extraterrestrial beings
ISBN 1-56510-352-1   LC 95-25106
Explores reports of UFO sightings and alleged kidnapping of humans by extraterrestrials
Includes bibliographical references

004   Data processing. Computer science

Barrett, Joanne R., 1960-
Teaching and learning about computers; a classroom guide for teachers, librarians, media specialists, and students. Scarecrow Press 2002 255p il $45   **004**
1. Computers 2. Data processing
ISBN 0-8108-4450-8   LC 2002-8350
"The 14 chapters in increasing complexity include information about word processing, spreadsheets, charts and graphics, databases, multimedia presentations, the Internet, the World Wide Web, creating Web pages, learning programming, and viruses and copyright law. . . . Every computer teacher should be in possession of this book, and it would make a terrific textbook for those who are teaching teachers." SLJ

Billings, Charlene W., 1941-
Supercomputers; charting the future of cybernetics; {by} Charlene W. Billings and Sean M. Grady. New ed. Facts on File 2004 228p $29.95   **004**
1. Supercomputers
ISBN 0-8160-4730-8   LC 2003-3628
First published 1995
"Defining 'supercomputers' as 'usually . . . the fastest, and most expensive, computers available at any given time,' the authors present a thorough history of data storage and manipulation devices, from ancient Sumerian clay tablets through Charles Babbage's 'Difference Engine' to ENIAC, the sexy-looking creation of Seymour Cray, and the recent growth of multiple-unit cluster systems—not to mention the Internet. The development of office machines in general and the many uses to which computers have been put in business, science, military pursuits, and film animation are also examined." SLJ
Includes bibliographical references

McAlpine, Margaret
Working with computers; Margaret McAlpine. Gareth Stevens Pub 2005 64p il (My future career)
lib bdg $26   **004**
1. Computer science 2. Vocational guidance
ISBN 0-8368-4242-1   LC 2004-45227
This describes seven computer-related careers including basic responsibilities and qualifications, and offers examples of a real-life professional's workday.
This "excellent [book] will be attractive to browsers. . . . The writing is clear and interesting." SLJ
Includes bibliographical references

004.6   Interfacing and communications. Networks

Benson, Allen C.
Connecting kids & the Web; a handbook for teaching Internet use and safety. Neal-Schuman 2003 xxi, 346p il map (Neal-Schuman netguide series) pa $59.95   **004.6**
1. Internet 2. Internet searching—Study and teaching 3. World Wide Web
ISBN 1-55570-460-3   LC 2002-38698
Replaces Connecting kids and the Internet, 2nd edition published 1999
Includes CD-ROM
This handbook covers "Internet basics, browsers, e-mail, chat rooms, virtual libraries; search engines and subject trees; sound, streaming video, and other Web media; Web safety, resources and more." Publisher's note
"This book is replete with practical suggestions and quality Web sites. . . . In clear, easy-to-understand language, Benson's directions and explanations cover every basic possibility that new and experienced Internet users might encounter and answers many questions they never thought to ask. The accompanying CD consolidates many of the links mentioned in the book." SLJ

Neal-Schuman complete Internet companion for librarians. 2nd ed. Neal-Schuman 2001 xxxi, 566p il (Neal-Schuman net-guide series) pa $85
                                   004.6
1. Internet
ISBN 1-55570-414-X   LC 2001-30033
First published 1995 with title: The complete Internet companion for librarians
Includes CD-ROM
This covers such library related topics as "Internet basics . . . digital library design, intranets, extranets, metadata, computer security, information architecture, filters, copyright, operations, domain name registration, the Linux, {and} e books." Publisher's note
"The abundance of practical information will make this a well-thumbed addition to any library media specialist's personal or professional collection." Book Rep {review of 1997 edition}

Johnson, Doug, 1952-
Learning right from wrong in the digital age; an ethics guide for parents, teachers, librarians, and others who care about computer-using young people. Linworth Pub. 2003 122p pa $44.55
                                   004.6
1. Internet 2. Computers and children 3. Cheating (Education)
ISBN 1-586-83131-3   LC 2003-43320
"After an overview of the difference between the physical and virtual world in regard to ethical codes, several sections are devoted to scenarios of various behaviors that involve privacy, property, and appropriate use of information. Each scenario provides discussion topics as well as the relationship to National Learning Standards." Lib Media Connect
"Johnson's '3 P's of Technology Ethics,' Privacy,

Johnson, Doug, 1952-—*Continued*
Property, and a(P)propriate use, are effectively and excitingly addressed through both discussion and instructional scenarios." SLJ
Includes bibliographical references

Souter, Gerry
Researching on the Internet using search engines, bulletin boards, and listservs; {by} Gerry, Janet, and Allison Souter. Enslow Pubs. 2003 64p il (Internet library) lib bdg $22.60 (4 and up)
004.6
1. Internet resources 2. Research
ISBN 0-7660-2081-9   LC 2002-152959
Contents: Preparing to research the Internet; Web browsers and search engines; "Ask an Expert" sites; Mailing lists and newsgroups; Chat rooms, homework helpers, and Webcasts
The authors describe how use the Internet "when doing research. They explore the various search engines that are available, bulletin boards, listservs, and chat rooms. They help the reader figure out which methods and options will work best for them and . . . describe the uses and possible dangers of each suggestion." Publisher's note
Includes glossary and bibliographical references

Wolinsky, Art
Safe surfing on the Internet. Enslow Pubs. 2003 64p il (Internet library) $22.60 (4 and up)
004.6
1. Internet 2. Computer crimes
ISBN 0-7660-2030-4   LC 2002-12336
Contents: When did you learn your first rule?; From transportation revolution to information revolution; Acceptable use policies and schools; Finding what you want; E-mail use and abuse; Bandwidth and hoses; Sharing or piracy?
Explores the many safety issues involved in using the Internet, including the relevant laws, especially CIPA and COPPA, acceptable use policies (AUPs), and other protection and privacy issues
"The no-nonsense discussion of Acceptable Use Policy, copyright, and plagiarism gives a clear understanding of how to use the Internet. . . . A highly readable presentation." SLJ
Includes bibliographical references

005 Computer programming, programs, data

The **Software** encyclopedia. Bowker 2v pa set $379   **005**
1. Computer software
Annual. First published 1985
Contents: v1 Titles, publishers; v2 System compatibility/applications
A guide to currently available microcomputer software packages including publishing-related programs, word processing programs, database programs and spreadsheet programs
"This annually updated work is considered the most comprehensive and current list available." Nichols. Guide to Ref Books for Sch Media Cent. 4th edition

005.7 Data in computer systems

Lindsay, Dave
Dave's quick n' easy web pages; an introductory guide to creating web sites; written by Dave Lindsay; illustrated by Sean Lindsay; edited by Bruce Lindsay. 2nd ed. Erin Publs. 2001 116p il pa $11.95   **005.7**
1. Web sites
ISBN 0-9690609-8-X
First published 1999
Basic information on creating, testing, editing, and maintaining web pages with HTML

Smith, Susan S.
Web-based instruction; a guide for libraries; {by} Susan Sharpless Smith. American Lib. Assn. 2001 194p il pa $40   **005.7**
1. Bibliographic instruction 2. Computer-assisted instruction 3. Web sites 4. Library information networks
ISBN 0-8389-0805-5   LC 2001-22050
"Starting with an introduction to the concept of web-based instruction, {the author} then discusses the types of web-based library instruction and the designing and development cycle; selecting project development tools, including software and hardware; designing the user interface; using multimedia; introducing interactivity; and evaluation and testing." Libr J
Includes bibliographical references

006.3 Artificial intelligence

Margulies, Phillip
Artificial intelligence; written by Phillip Margulies. Blackbirch Press 2004 48p il (Science on the edge) $23.70 (5 and up)   **006.3**
1. Artificial intelligence
ISBN 1-56711-783-X   LC 2002-13160
Contents: History of artificial intelligence; The quest for artificial intelligence; The future of artificial intelligence
Discusses the definition of artificial intelligence, the development of "thinking" machines, and what computers may be able to do in the future
Includes glossary and bibliographical references

006.6 Computer graphics

Souter, Gerry
Creating animation for your Web page; [by] Gerry, Janet and Allison Souter. Enslow Pubs. 2003 64p il (Internet library) $22.60 (4 and up)
006.6
1. Computer animation 2. Web sites
ISBN 0-7660-2083-5   LC 2002-152960
Contents: Types of animation; GIF animations; Animating with GIF Construction Set; Animating with GifBuilder; Java Applets; JavaScript; Flash and QuickTime

Souter, Gerry—*Continued*
The authors "explore the many options and possibilities in adding animation to a Web page. Instructions are provided . . . and software for both PCs and Macs is covered. The authors explore ways to borrow animation for free, as well as the different methods for creating your own animations, from the simple to the complex." Publisher's note
Includes glossary and bibliographical references

006.8   Virtual reality

Grady, Sean M., 1965-
Virtual reality; simulating and enhancing the world with computers. new ed. Facts on File 2002 226p il (Science & technology in focus) $29.95 (7 and up)   **006.8**
1. Virtual reality
ISBN 0-8160-4686-7   LC 2002-4380
First published 1998
Contents: A quick tour of VR; Creating practical computers; Developing better interfaces; Precursors to VR; A new view of data; A new course for indoor flight training; Mimicking reality; Reality simulators: supercomputers to PCs; Graphics: polygons and perspectives; Displays: looking and listening in VR; Manipulators: gloves, wands and trackers; The larger view: caves, walls and desks; VR as a research tool; VR as a training tool; VR as a teaching tool; VR as a design tool; VR as a healing tool; Developing VR as a business; Drawbacks to VR; Virtual philosophy; VR's future
Includes glossary and bibliographical references

Wyborny, Sheila, 1950-
Virtual reality; written by Sheila Wyborny. Blackbirch Press 2003 48p il (Science on the edge) lib bdg $23.70   **006.8**
1. Virtual reality
ISBN 1-567-11789-9   LC 2002-11926
Discusses the history, present uses, and future of the technology of virtual reality
"Exemplary in [its] balanced, easy-to-grasp coverage of complex issures." Booklist
Includes bibliographical references

011   Bibliographies

Recommended reference books for small and medium-sized libraries and media centers. Libraries Unlimited $70   **011**
1. Reference books—Bibliography 2. Reference books—Reviews
ISSN 0277-5948
Annual. First published 1981
Editor: 2005 Shannon Graff Hysell
Each annual volume includes reviews of about 550 titles chosen by the editor as the most valuable reference titles published during the previous year
"Where budget restrictions are a consideration, this is an invaluable asset; for small libraries, a superior selection/acquisitions tool. Highly recommended." Voice Youth Advocates

011.6   General bibliographies of works for specific kinds of users and libraries

Best books for young adult readers; Stephen J. Calvert, editor. Bowker 1997 xx, 744p $63
011.6
1. Best books 2. Young adult literature—Bibliography
ISBN 0-8352-3832-6   LC 97-478
Combines and updates Best books for Junior high readers and Best books for senior high readers
This volume lists and annotates about 6,500 titles published between 1990 and 1996. Each entry provides bibliographic information, awards, review citations, etc.

Children's catalog. 18th ed, edited by Anne Price and Juliette Yaakov. Wilson, H.W. 2001 1265p (Standard catalog series) $185   **011.6**
1. Children's literature—Bibliography 2. Classified catalogs 3. School libraries—Catalogs
ISBN 0-8242-1009-3   LC 2001-46599
Also available online
First published 1909
Kept up to date by annual supplements included in the price of main volume
This collection of recommended materials includes approximately 7,000 entries of books for children from preschool to grade six. Entries contain full bibliographic information, Dewey Decimal Classification number, subject headings, reading level, descriptive, and when possible, critical annotations. A list of recommended Web resources is also included
"The most comprehensive bibliography in its field." Guide to Ref Books. 11th edition

Culturally diverse videos, audios, and CD-ROMS for children and young adults; edited by Irene Wood. Neal-Schuman 1999 276p $49.95
011.6
1. Motion pictures—Catalogs 2. Videotapes—Catalogs 3. CD-ROMs—Catalogs
ISBN 1-55570-377-1   LC 99-48572
"A chapter on multicultural videos is followed by chapters on videos by and/or about African Americans, Asian Americans, Hispanic Americans, and Native Americans. Also included are chapters about audio materials: music, storytelling and folklore, audiobooks, and Spanish-language read-alongs. Another section lists CD-ROMs available in languages other than English and those that address multicultural themes. The book concludes with a comprehensive list of distributors and subject and title indexes." SLJ

Jones, Patrick
A core collection for young adults; [by] Patrick Jones, Patricia Taylor, Kirsten Edwards. Neal-Schuman 2003 xxix, 405p (Teens @ the library series) pa $65   **011.6**
1. Young adult literature—Bibliography 2. Best books
ISBN 1-55570-458-1   LC 2002-45237
The authors "have selected and annotated over 1,000 titles, including adult and young adult fiction and nonfiction; biographies and personal narratives; graphic novels

Jones, Patrick—*Continued*
and illustrated works; underground classics; humor; science fiction/fantasy; Web sites; databases, and other electronic formats. Brief annotations . . . identify the primary audience for each book. Core collection entries include call numbers, full bibliographic information, and grade/audience level. . . . An accompanying title-checker disk allows librarians to . . . compare catalog holdings to the core collection." Publisher's note
"A useful book for both novice and experienced librarians who want to build a teen collection that actually circulates." SLJ
Includes bibliographical references

Matulka, Denise I.
Picture this; picture books for young adults: a curriculum-related annotated bibliography. Greenwood Press 1997 xx, 267p $39.95
011.6
1. Picture books for children—Bibliography
ISBN 0-313-30182-4   LC 97-2234
"This bibliography introduces 424 titles. . . . It is organized according to curriculum-content areas—the arts, health, literature, mathematics, science, and social sciences and history. Each annotation lists bibliographic information, summarizes the book, discusses artistic style and mediums employed, suggests companion titles, and provides ideas for classroom use." SLJ

New York Public Library
Books for the teen age. New York Public Lib.
$10   **011.6**
1. Young adult literature—Bibliography 2. Best books
Annual. First published 1929
A list of approximately 1,000 books of interest to teenagers arranged in broad categories. Many of the titles address current concerns

Rosow, La Vergne
Light 'n lively reads for ESL, adult, and teen readers; a thematic bibliography. Libraries Unlimited 1996 xxxvii, 343p il pa $42
011.6
1. English as a second language—Bibliography
2. Young adult literature—Bibliography
ISBN 1-56308-365-5   LC 96-7084
"This bibliography is arranged by themes such as arts, sports and science. Within each theme, recommended books are listed in order of difficulty with easier titles first. Each entry includes a thoughtful and motivating annotation. . . . An author, illustrator, title and subject index adds further access. Recommended for all levels to support reading guidance." Safford. Guide to Ref Materials for Sch Libr Media Cent. 5th edition

Safford, Barbara Ripp
Guide to reference materials for school media centers. 5th ed. Libraries Unlimited 1998 353p
$51.95   **011.6**
1. Reference books—Bibliography 2. School libraries—Catalogs 3. Instructional materials centers
ISBN 1-56308-545-3   LC 98-29867

First edition by Christine Gehrt Wynar published 1973 with title: Guide to reference books for school media centers
"Safford reviews more than 2,000 current information sources (most published between 1992 and 1997). . . . Organized by topics within broad subject categories, this work covers not only books but also CD-ROMs and other electronic reference sources in all curricular and some extracurricular areas. . . . Each entry gives complete bibliographic data; a grade level code; and a description of the work's content, organization, and special features." Publisher's note

Schon, Isabel
The best of Latino heritage 1996-2002; a guide to the best juvenile books about Latino people and cultures. Scarecrow Press 2003 269p $37.50
011.6
1. Children's literature—Bibliography 2. Latin America—Bibliography
ISBN 0-8108-4669-1   LC 2002-154088
Companion volume to The best of the Latino heritage, published 1997
Schon "identifies both fiction and nonfiction works useful in exposing K-12 students to Latino public figures, history, art, politics, social issues, and economics. . . . Each title receives a full bibliographic citation, suggested grade level, and a paragraph-long annotation. . . . Recommended books are in English or bilingual editions and are available from U.S. publishers. An excellent tool for collection development." Booklist

The best of the Latino heritage; a guide to the best juvenile books about Latino people and cultures. Scarecrow Press 1997 285p $37.50
011.6
1. Children's literature—Bibliography 2. Latin America—Bibliography
ISBN 0-8108-3221-6   LC 96-24249
"This is a bibliography of the books on the topic [Schon] considers the best from the last forty years or so; they range from picture books to novels to biographies to political analyses. The collection is divided by country and region, and each entry includes necessary bibliographic information and a pithy, well-turned annotation that often includes evaluative comments." Bull Cent Child Books

Recommended books in Spanish for children and young adults, 2000 through 2004. Scarecrow Press 2004 415p $45   **011.6**
1. Latin American literature—Bibliography
2. Spanish literature—Bibliography 3. Children's literature—Bibliography 4. Young adult literature—Bibliography
ISBN 0-8108-5196-2   LC 2004-11910
Also available volumes covering titles published 1991-1995 and 1996-1999
This "reference tool includes annotated entries for more than 1300 books in Spanish published between 2000 and 2004 in the U.S., Spain, Mexico, Venezuela, and Argentina. . . . Each entry includes an extensive critical annotation, title in Spanish as well as English, tentative grade level, and approximate price." Publisher's note

Senior high school library catalog. 16th ed, edited by Juliette Yaakov. Wilson, H.W. 2002 1243p (Standard catalog series) $220   **011.6**
1. Classified catalogs 2. High school libraries—Catalogs 3. Young adult literature—Bibliography
ISBN 0-8242-1008-5   LC 2002-33133
Also available online
First published 1926-28 with title: Standard catalog for high school libraries
Kept up to date by annual supplements included in price of main volume
This collection of recommended materials includes 5,321 titles and 9,123 analytical entries of books for grades nine through twelve. Entries contain full bibliographic information, Abridged Dewey Decimal Classification number, subject headings, descriptive, and when available, critical annotations. Includes a list of recommended web resources

The World through children's books; edited by Susan Stan. Scarecrow Press 2002 324p il pa $36.95   **011.6**
1. Children's literature—Bibliography 2. Children's literature—History and criticism
ISBN 0-8108-4198-3   LC 2001-45863
Companion volume to Children's books from other countries (1998)
"This annotated bibliography of international books published in the U.S. from 1996 through 2000 is sponsored by the U.S. Board on Books for Young People (USBBY). . . . Beginning with a lengthy introduction to international children's literature, it also includes lists of international awards, organizations, publishers, and sources of foreign-language and bilingual books. The main portion of the book, the bibliography, is arranged by region and subdivided by country. . . . A very useful volume for multicultural collection development." Booklist
Includes bibliographical references and indexes

Wright, Cora M.
More hot links; linking literature with the middle school curriculum. Libraries Unlimited 2002 212p tab pa $33.95   **011.6**
1. Children's literature—Bibliography 2. Books and reading
ISBN 1-56308-942-4   LC 2002-11278
Companion to: Hot links
Contents: Biographies -- English : classics -- English : use of language -- Fine arts -- Greatest of the latest -- Humor -- Mathematics -- Multicultural -- Myths, folktales, and legends -- Picture books for all ages -- Poetry -- Read alouds -- Science -- Series -- Social studies : ancient and early cultures -- Social studies : United States history -- Sports and games -- Unique presentations
"This companion to . . . Hot Links by the same author provides . . . annotations for an additional 300+ fiction and nonfiction books . . . that support and enhance the middle school curriculum." Publisher's note
Includes bibliographical references

Your reading; an annotated booklist for middle school and junior high; Jean E. Brown and Elaine C. Stephens, editors, and the Committee on the Middle School and Junior High Booklist; foreword by Joan Bauer; afterword by Joyce Hansen. 11th ed. National Council of Teachers of English 2003 387p (NCTE bibliography series) pa $33.95   **011.6**
1. Children's literature—Bibliography 2. Young adult literature—Bibliography 3. Best books
ISBN 0-8141-5944-3
First published 1954
This booklist offers annotations of more than 1,200 fiction and non-fiction books recommended for young adults, grouped under 18 headings such as Families, Adventure and Survival, Mysteries and Suspense, Diversity, and Historical Fiction

015.73 Bibliographies and catalogs of works issued or printed in the United States

Books in print. Bowker 9v set $859   **015.73**
1. Bibliography
ISSN 0068-0214
Also available CD-ROM version and online
Annual. First published 1948
Updated by Books in print Supplement (3v) published annually in Spring, available at $459 (ISSN 0000-0310)
Contents: v1-4 Authors; v5-8 Titles; v9 Publishers
Lists titles available during the current year from American publishers, supplying such information as authors, co-authors, title, price, publisher, year of publication, and International Standard Book Numbers of cooperating publishers

Hoffmann, Frank W. (Frank William), 1949-
Guide to popular U.S. government publications; {by} Frank W. Hoffmann, Richard J. Wood. 5th ed. Libraries Unlimited 1998 xxvi, 300p $40.50   **015.73**
1. Government publications—United States—Bibliography
ISBN 1-56308-607-7   LC 98-29868
First edition compiled by LeRoy C. Schwarzkopf published 1986
This is a guide to 1,500 federal documents in print, microfiche, CD-ROM and electronic formats arranged by subject. Includes title and subject indexes. Most of the documents cited were published or printed during the 1995 and 1996 calendar years

Subject guide to Books in print. Bowker 6v set $550   **015.73**
1. Subject catalogs 2. Bibliography
ISSN 0000-0159
Annual. First published 1957
This companion publication to Books in print, lists titles currently available from United States publishers indexing them under LC subject headings

Subject guide to Children's books in print. Bowker $250 **015.73**
1. Children's literature—Bibliography 2. Subject catalogs
ISSN 0000-0167
Also available CD-ROM version
Annual. First published 1970
This publication provides a subject approach to its companion work: Children's books in print. The headings used are based on the Sears list of subject headings supplemented by headings from LC. Entries include author, title, publisher, year of publication, binding, price, ISBN, and, in some cases, grade level. A directory of publishers and distributors is included

Vertical file index; guide to pamphlets and references to current topics. Wilson, H.W. $130 per year **015.73**
1. Pamphlets—Bibliography
ISSN 0042-4439
First published 1932 with title: Vertical file service catalog. Issued monthly except August
"A list of free and inexpensive pamphlets, booklets, leaflets, and similar material considered to be of interest to general libraries. Subjects range from those suitable for school libraries to specialized technical reports. Arranged alphabetically by subject headings (deemed suitable for vertical file use) with title index." Guide to Ref Books. 11th edition

016.2 Bibliographies of religion

Dole, Patricia Pearl, 1927-
Children's books about religion. Libraries Unlimited 1999 230p $35 **016.2**
1. Religion—Bibliography
ISBN 1-56308-515-1 LC 98-33707
"A compilation of books with overt spiritual themes for preschoolers through young adults. These titles represent a variety of genres, including retellings of Bible stories, prayer books, creation stories, songbooks, holiday tales, mysteries, and biographies from both religious and trade publishers. All have been published since 1990." SLJ

016.3 Bibliographies of the social sciences

Notable social studies trade books for young people. Children's Bk. Council pa $2 **016.3**
1. Social sciences—Bibliography 2. Best books
An annual annotated list, reprinted from an issue of the periodical Social Education, of the preceding year's best trade books in the field of social studies of interest to children in grades K-8. Prepared by the Book Review Panel of the National Council for the Social Studies—Children's Book Council Joint Committee. Titles are selected for emphasis on human relations, originality, readability and, when appropriate, illustrations. General reading levels (primary, intermediate, advanced) are indicated

016.3637 Bibliographies of environmental problems and services

Dwyer, James R.
Earth works; recommended fiction and nonfiction about nature and the environment for adults and young adults; {by} Jim Dwyer. Neal-Schuman 1996 507p pa $75 **016.3637**
1. Environmental protection—Bibliography
ISBN 1-55570-194-9 LC 94-36284
Dwyer "lists 2600 entries, including about 1000 fiction titles, that were in print as of March 1995. The nonfiction titles are arranged into seven chapters by such topics as specific environments (deserts, rainforests), activities and issues (water supply, energy), and, in the largest section, environmental action (deep ecology, green business). The fiction titles are arranged by such topics as animals, ecofeminism, and the New West. . . . Entries offer standard bibliographic information . . . . a two- to three-sentence annotation discussing the scope of the work, and reading level for young adult titles." Libr J

016.3713 Bibliographies of instructional materials

El-hi textbooks and serials in print. Bowker 2v set $290 **016.3713**
1. Textbooks—Bibliography 2. Periodicals—Bibliography
ISSN 0000-0825
Annual. Title varies
"Index to textbooks, dictionaries, encyclopedias, maps, atlases, professional books, teaching aids and auxiliary AV materials for grades K-12, plus adult and special education. Subject index contains grade and reading level; also author and title indexes and series index. Lists information not in 'Books in Print.' " N Y Public Libr. Ref Books for Child Collect. 2d edition

016.4 Bibliographies of language

McCaffery, Laura Hibbets
Building an ESL collection for young adults; a bibliography of recommended fiction and nonfiction for schools and public libraries. Greenwood Press 1998 182p $49.95 **016.4**
1. English as a second language—Bibliography
2. Young adult literature—Bibliography
ISBN 0-313-29937-4 LC 98-5271
"This annotated bibliography offers more than 500 titles for grades 5 through adult. The entries are organized by genre or topic and arranged alphabetically by author. They include complete bibliographic information, ISBN, price, Fry Reading Level, interest level, and possible uses in and out of the classroom. An introduction outlines the changing need for ESL materials in the United States and explains McCaffery's selection criteria." Libr

McCaffery, Laura Hibbets—*Continued*
J
"Teachers will find this an excellent source for titles to meet specific curriculum needs." Voice Youth Advocates

016.5   Bibliographies of science

Outstanding science trade books for students K-12. Children's Bk. Council pa $2
016.5
1. Science—Bibliography 2. Best books
An annual annotated list, reprinted from an issue of the periodical Science and Children, of the preceding year's best trade books in the field of science of interest to children in grades K-8. Prepared by a Book Review Committee appointed by the National Science Teachers Association in cooperation with the Children's Book Council. Titles are selected for accuracy, readability and pleasing format. General reading levels (primary, intermediate, advanced) are indicated

016.8   Bibliographies of literature

Anderson, Vicki
Fiction sequels for readers 10 to 16; an annotated bibliography of books in succession. 2nd ed. McFarland & Co. 1998 176p pa $39.95
016.8
1. Children's literature—Bibliography 2. Young adult literature—Bibliography 3. Fiction—Bibliography
ISBN 0-7864-0185-0   LC 98-5236
First published 1990
This list contains about 3000 titles that are part of a series. "The entries are arranged by author and provide title, publisher and date of publication along with a brief annotation." Publisher's note

Day, Frances Ann
Lesbian and gay voices; an annotated bibliography and guide to literature for children and young adults; foreword by Nancy Garden. Greenwood Press 2000 xxi, 268p $38.95
016.8
1. Children's literature—Bibliography 2. Young adult literature—Bibliography 3. Homosexuality in literature—Bibliography
ISBN 0-313-31162-5   LC 00-21047
This reference "lists over 275 recommended books that incorporate various aspects of homosexuality. . . . Each chapter looks at a particular literary genre. Listed alphabetically by author, each entry includes complete bibliographic information, a detailed annotation, topics, age level specifications, mention of any strong language or explicit sex, a summary of pertinent criticism, and a listing of literary awards." Book Rep
A "much-needed, thorough guide. . . . this is an extraordinary compilation that belongs in every collection." SLJ

From biography to history; best books for children's entertainment and education; edited by Catherine Barr; foreword by James Cross Giblin; contributors, Rebecca L. Thomas, Deanna McDaniel. Bowker 1998 508p il $63
016.8
1. Biography—Bibliography
ISBN 0-8352-4012-6   LC 98-23147
"This annotated bibliography recommends biographies and related books that provide information about nearly 300 people of historical interest and the time periods in which they lived. The entries are arranged alphabetically; a brief paragraph about the individual is followed by suggested titles for 'Older Readers' (grades six to nine) and 'Younger Readers' (grades three to five). The bibliographic information is complete and most of the titles have been published in the last 10 years." SLJ

Hall, Susan, 1940-
Using picture storybooks to teach literary devices; recommended books for children and young adults. v3. Oryx Press 2002 349p $34.95
016.8
1. Children's literature—Bibliography 2. Picture books for children—Bibliography 3. Literature—Study and teaching
ISBN 1-5735-6350-1
"In this work, which updates earlier volumes published in 1990 and 1994, Hall selects picture storybooks that have received favorable reviews as resources for teaching the recognition and understanding of literary devices. Hall selects 120 picture storybooks published through the year 2000. . . . Hall's book is a useful tool for teachers in language arts programs in kindergarten through twelfth grade and for professional collections in public libraries and school library media centers." Voice Youth Advocates

Helbig, Alethea
Many peoples, one land; a guide to new multicultural literature for children and young adults; {by} Alethea K. Helbig, Agnes Regan Perkins. Greenwood Press 2001 431p $70.95
016.8
1. Children's literature—Bibliography 2. Young adult literature—Bibliography 3. Minorities—Bibliography
ISBN 0-313-30967-1   LC 00-25111
Replaces This land is our land published 1994
"This volume contains 561 entries covering works of literature published from 1994 to 1999. It offers entries for African Americans, Asian Americans, Hispanic Americans, and Native-American Indians, which are then subdivided into separate sections for books of fiction, books of poetry, and oral tradition for audiences from preschool through high school. Each numbered entry includes author, title, illustrator, publisher, publication year, ISBN, price, number of pages, age level, and grade level. A brief description of each literary work contains the major themes, plot, characters, settings, and illustration style of each work." Book Rep
"An excellent tool for readers' advisory and collection building." SLJ
Includes bibliographical references

Herald, Diana Tixier
Teen genreflecting; a guide to reading interests. 2nd ed. Libraries Unlimited 2003 275p lib bdg $40
016.8
1. Young adult literature—Bibliography
2. Teenagers—Books and reading
ISBN 1-56308-996-3   LC 2003-54610
First published 1997
"The first chapter offers an overview of teen readers' advisory services, and subsequent chapters focus on popular genres of young adult literature, including but not limited to suspense, adventure, fantasy, alternate formats (including graphic novels), and Christian fiction. Both recent and classic YA books are listed in their appropriate genres, and every entry contains the author, title, publication date, and age level of the book. . . . When appropriate, awards and any best lists on which a book might have appeared are cited. . . . In addition to its value as a readers' advisory guide, this book can serve as a key to building a core young adult fiction collection or as a guide to purchasing for a collection that is weak in some genres." Voice Youth Advocates
Includes bibliographical references

Makowski, Silk
Serious about series; evaluations and annotations of teen fiction in paperback series; edited by Dorothy M. Broderick. Scarecrow Press 1998 291p pa $35.50
016.8
1. Young adult literature—Bibliography 2. Fiction—Bibliography
ISBN 0-8108-3304-2   LC 97-48913
"Following introductory material on the genre, each chapter cites a series, explains and evaluates it, and provides an annotated title list with ISBNs and publication dates. Makowski covers more than 50 series of all types, including romance, horror, sci-fi, 'Tom Swift,' and the 'Hardy Boys.' Comparisons between series of similar nature are helpful." SLJ
Includes bibliographical references

Steiner, Stanley F.
Promoting a global community through multicultural children's literature; illustrations by Peggy Hokom; foreword by Alma Flor Ada. Libraries Unlimited 2001 179p pa $35
016.8
1. Children's literature—Bibliography 2. Minorities—Bibliography
ISBN 1-56308-705-7   LC 00-50702
This guide to developing a children's multicultural book collection lists over 800 titles for kindergarten through eighth grade
"A timely and informative guide for educators who are trying to promote an understanding of world cultures and our interconnectedness." SLJ

Ward, Marilyn
Voices from the margins; an annotated bibliography of fiction on disabilities and differences for young people. Greenwood Press 2002 154p $44.95
016.8
1. Children's literature—Bibliography 2. Young adult literature—Bibliography 3. Handicapped—Fiction—Bibliography
ISBN 0-313-31798-4   LC 2002-276832
This title "lists 200 books for children and young adults published from 1990 to 2001. . . . The juvenile fiction covered includes picture books, chapter books for middle-schoolers, and young adult novels as well as poetry. A few of the books included are nonfiction. . . . This resource is a welcome addition to the growing literature about disabilities of all kinds." Booklist

016.813 Bibliographies of American fiction

Coffey, Rosemary K.
America as story; historical fiction for middle and secondary schools; {by} Rosemary K. Coffey, Elizabeth F. Howard. 2nd ed. American Lib. Assn. 1997 xxi, 216p pa $25
016.813
1. Historical fiction—Bibliography
ISBN 0-8389-0702-4   LC 96-43453
First published 1988 under the authorship of Elizabeth F. Howard
"This is an annotated bibliography of approximately 200 recommended titles arranged by historical period. Coded according to appropriate reading levels, the entries include annotations, comments on what readers will learn about historical events, and suggestions for reports and activities." Publisher's note

Dickinson, A. T.
American historical fiction; an annotated guide to novels for adults and young adults. Oryx Press 1999 405p $65.95
016.813
1. Historical fiction—Bibliography 2. American fiction—Bibliography 3. United States—History—Fiction—Bibliography
ISBN 1-57356-067-7   LC 98-38044
Based on Dickinson's American historical fiction, 5th edition published 1986 by Scarecrow Press
"Organized by time period, the entries include author, title, date of publication, number of pages, content notes, setting, main characters, and, where applicable, genres, awards, and series/sequel information. . . . This work should be a boon to reader's advisory and collection development librarians needing to build specific areas of the collection." Libr J

VanMeter, Vandelia
America in historical fiction; a bibliographic guide; {by} Vandelia L. VanMeter. Libraries Unlimited 1997 280p $40.50
016.813
1. Historical fiction—Bibliography 2. American fiction—Bibliography 3. United States—History—Fiction—Bibliography
ISBN 1-56308-496-1   LC 96-34745

VanMeter, Vandelia—*Continued*
"Arranged in major chronological divisions of U.S. history, the annotated entries include standard bibliographic information, time period, subject, location, research base (if known), and whether the title is more appropriate for mature students or younger secondary students." Publisher's note

016.9 Bibliographies of geography and history

Adamson, Lynda G.
Literature connections to world history, 7-12; resources to enhance and entice. Libraries Unlimited 1998 511p pa $38.50   **016.9**
1. History—Bibliography 2. Audiovisual materials—Catalogs
ISBN 1-56308-505-4   LC 97-35953
Also available Literature connections to world history, K-6
This resource is divided "into two main sections. The first section lists authors and book titles in the categories of historical fiction, biography, collective biography, history trade book, CD-ROM, and videotape within specific time periods according to grade levels. The second section contains annotated bibliographies of titles listed in the first part: books, CD-ROMs, and videotapes." Introduction

Beck, Peggy
GlobaLinks: resources for world studies, grades K-8. Linworth Pub. 2002 148p pa $39.95
     016.9
1. World history—Bibliography
ISBN 1-58683-040-6   LC 2001-50718
Also available GlobaLinks: resources for Asian studies, grades K-8
This "annotated bibliography of books, videos, CD-ROMs and Web sites includes items selected on the basis of the 10 strands of social studies. . . . For each source, whether print, non-print, Web site, or key and pen pal project, complete bibliographic information is given, as well as two to four sentences about the source and its intended audience." Book Rep
"The author's strength . . . lies not only in her selections, but also in her consistently high-quality annotations. . . . This compilation is highly recommended for the professional collection of young adult sections and school media centers." Am Ref Books Annu, 2003

Wee, Patricia Hachten, 1948-
World War II in literature for youth; a guide and resource book; [by] Patricia Hachten Wee, Robert James Wee. Scarecrow Press 2004 391p (Literature for youth series) pa $48   **016.9**
1. World War, 1939-1945—Bibliography
ISBN 0-8108-5301-9   LC 2004-11087
This "offers more than 3,000 annotated bibliographies for resources on the Second World War. Entries are arranged according to well-thought-out subjects and cover multiple genres (biographies, memoirs, fiction, eyewit-

ness accounts, technical reports, etc.) and formats (monographs, reference sets, periodicals, Web sites, CDs, videos, DVDs). Annotations are succinct but informative and include both positive and negative comments." Booklist
Includes bibliographical references

016.94053 Bibliographies of World War II, 1939-1945

Rosen, Philip, 1928-
Bearing witness; a resource guide to literature, poetry, art, music, and videos by Holocaust victims and survivors; {by} Philip Rosen and Nina Apfelbaum. Greenwood Press 2002 210p $52.95
     016.94053
1. Holocaust, 1933-1945—Bibliography
ISBN 0-313-31076-9   LC 00-69153
This is a resource guide to "over 800 first-person accounts, fiction, poetry, art interpretations, and music by Holocaust victims and survivors, as well as videos relating the testimony and experiences of Holocaust survivors." Publisher's note
"This volume will be valuable to all who are researching the Holocaust. Its strength lies in the inclusion of materials not often found elsewhere." Booklist
Includes bibliographical references

016.973 Bibliographies of United States history

Adamson, Lynda G.
Literature connections to American history, 7-12; resources to enhance and entice. Libraries Unlimited 1997 624p pa $41.50   **016.973**
1. United States—History—Bibliography 2. Audiovisual materials—Catalogs 3. CD-ROMs—Reviews
ISBN 1-56308-503-8   LC 97-19560
Also available Literature connections to American history, K-6
"The first part of the book is divided into 13 time periods or topics, each of which is subdivided by grade level. . . . The books, identified only by author and title, are listed according to genre, including historical fiction, biography, collective biography, and history trade books. Multimedia listings include CD-ROMs and videos. The bulk of the volume contains short annotated bibliographies of the nearly 3,000 books, CD-ROMs, and videos." Book Rep
"This comprehensive title should be valuable as a reader's advisory tool, a purchasing guide, and a resource for curriculum enrichment." Bull Cent Child Books

Stephens, Elaine C., 1943-
Learning about—the Civil War; literature and other resources for young people; [by] Elaine C. Stephens and Jean E. Brown. Linnet Professional Publs. 1998 259p $32; pa $25   **016.973**
  1. United States—History—1861-1865, Civil War—Bibliography
  ISBN 0-208-02464-6; 0-208-02449-2 (pa)
                                              LC 98-14569
"First discussing separately both the Civil War and the role of literature in the curriculum, the authors then discuss how literature can be used to teach about the Civil War. . . . Each of the following chapters focuses on one aspect of the Civil War, providing basic information and the significance of that aspect for those with little background. 'Focus Books' directly relating to that specific aspect are then listed. Each book is briefly summarized, then fully annotated with the appropriate grade level indicated." Voice Youth Advocates

020 Library and information sciences

McCain, Mary Maude
Dictionary for school library media specialists; a practical and comprehensive guide; {by} Mary Maude McCain and Martha Merrill. Libraries Unlimited 2001 219p pa $42   **020**
  1. Library science—Dictionaries
  ISBN 1-56308-696-4   LC 01-16506
"The book defines more than 375 terms. There are two types of definitions—shorter glossary descriptions (*capital outlay, reboot*) and longer, more detailed treatments (*poetry, proximity operators*). *See* references (especially from acronyms and abbreviations) and *see also* references facilitate use." Booklist

021.2 Relationships with the community

Gillespie, Kellie M., 1960-
Teen volunteer services in libraries; Kellie M. Gillespie. VOYA Books 2004 133p il (VOYA guides) pa $26.95   **021.2**
  1. Volunteer work 2. Libraries
  ISBN 0-8108-4837-6   LC 2003-17932
Contents: Why teens as volunteers?; Getting started; Marketing, recruiting, and placement; Orientation and training; Recognition and retention; Supervising volunteers; Volunteer program variations; How do they do it?: interviews with teen volunteer managers; Successful teen volunteer programs
This offers "advice about starting and maintaining effective teen volunteer programs in school and public libraries. . . . [The author discusses] recruitment, orientation and training, recognition and retention, and supervision." Publisher's note
"If you are even considering starting a teen volunteer program, you must read this book. If you already have one in your library, this volume still has much to offer." SLJ

021.7 Promotion of libraries, information centers

Flowers, Helen F.
Public relations for school library media programs; 500 ways to influence people and win friends for your school library media center. Neal-Schuman 1998 158p pa $49.95
                                              021.7
  1. Libraries—Public relations 2. School libraries
  ISBN 1-55570-320-8   LC 98-11470
The author recommends "techniques for promoting the use of the library media services by students, faculty, building administrators, and school support staff. Readers will also learn how to target administrators, the board of education, parents, community, and legislators to maintain and increase suppport for staff, materials, equipment, and space." Publisher's note
"Writing with a sense both of purpose and of humor, Flowers turns a book of excellent lists into a good, entertaining read." Voice Youth Advocates
Includes bibliographical references

Hill, Ann
Tooting your own horn; web-based public relations for the 21st century librarian; [by] Ann Hill and Julieta Dias Fisher. Linworth Pub. 2002 130p il pa $39.95   **021.7**
  1. Libraries—Public relations 2. Web sites 3. Internet
  ISBN 1-58683-066-X   LC 2002-32440
"Hill and Fisher offer a step-by-step approach to marketing the library program by using the Internet to provide information to students, teachers, administrators, parents, and the community. . . . Enlightening, engaging and chock-full of practical tips." Libr Media Connect
Includes glossary and bibliographical references

022 Administration of physical plant

Taney, Kimberly Bolan
Teen spaces; the step-by-step library makeover. American Lib. Assn. 2003 137p il pa $35
                                              022
  1. Young adults' libraries
  ISBN 0-8389-0832-2   LC 2002-9122
Contents: Teens and their space; Ask and analyze; Plan and propose; Design and decorate; Long-term promotion
Providing "ideas for redesigning or creating new spaces for teens, this book is packed with suggestions. Examples from some American libraries are given, as is research that describes marketing to 12- through 19-year-olds. . . . This book is for every young adult librarian and administrator who works in a library with either a drab area for teens or no area at all." Booklist
Includes bibliographical references

025.04   Automated information storage and retrieval systems

Blowers, Helene
Weaving a library Web; a guide to developing children's websites; [by] Helene Blowers and Robin Bryan. American Library Association 2004 197p il pa $32   **025.04**
1. Web sites
ISBN 0-8389-0877-2   LC 2004-1806
"A detailed description of topics and issues involved in designing, implementing, and maintaining Web sites for children. . . . This book can be used as a beginner's first stop and as a webmaster's companion. It is uncomplicated and easy to read." SLJ
Includes bibliographical references

Braun, Linda W.
Hooking teens with the Net. Neal-Schuman 2003 133p (Teens @ the library series) pa $45   **025.04**
1. Internet resources 2. Internet searching—Study and teaching
ISBN 1-55570-457-3   LC 2002-45221
This is a "guide to integrating information-literacy skills into the curriculum via the Internet. Through the use of popular teen sites, the author suggests that students will make an easy transition to more traditional electronic tools. . . . Each chapter includes an overview and bulleted skills and technology requirements as well as skills taught and extension activities, and each one culminates with a resource list. . . . A detailed and useful teaching tool." SLJ
Includes bibliographical references

Diaz, Karen R.
IssueWeb: a guide and sourcebook for researching controversial issues on the Web; [by] Karen R. Diaz, Nancy O'Hanlon. Libraries Unlimited 2004 287p pa $30   **025.04**
1. Internet resources 2. Internet searching—Study and teaching
ISBN 1-591-58078-1   LC 2003-65946
The authors "open with an online research guide that concentrates on finding an appropriate topic, using the right terminology, and evaluating online research, considering bias, balance, and documentation. . . . Recommended Web sites follow, subdivided into reference, legal issues, news, data sources, and advocacy for and against." Choice
"A veritable gold mine of more than 40 well-organized, well-presented issues briefs follows three remarkably clear, concise chapters on finding, evaluating, and incorporating Internet resources." SLJ

Gordon, Rachel Singer
Teaching the Internet in libraries. American Lib. Assn. 2001 143p pa $38   **025.04**
1. Internet searching—Study and teaching
2. Computer networks
ISBN 0-8389-0799-7   LC 00-52564

"Chapters cover the reasons and methods to initiate programs, including convincing others of the necessity of such training, the importance of choosing proper trainers and how to do so; techniques for reaching diverse audiences such as parents, senior citizens, and Hispanics; training techniques and considerations such as lists of popular searches requested by patrons; and criteria for evaluating the program. Each section of the book concludes with resources for further information." Book Rep
An "excellent and readable volume." Voice Youth Advocates
Includes bibliographical references

Haycock, Ken
Neal-Schuman authoritative guide to kids' search engines, subject directories, and portals; by Ken Haycock, Michelle Dober, and Barbara Edwards. Neal-Schuman 2003 234p il pa $55   **025.04**
1. Web sites 2. Internet resources 3. Internet searching 4. Computers and children
ISBN 1-555-70451-4   LC 2002-35766
"Focusing on children in grades 4-9, the book begins with descriptions of search tools and the way children search the Web. The authors identify elements of search engines, present a checklist for evaluating them, and then recommend 20 of the best. . . . The book concludes with coverage of online tutors and homework help sites and a section on critical issues confronting children's use of the Internet. . . . Useful for any school or public librarian who wants to better serve his or her students using the Internet." Booklist
Includes bibliographical references

Johnson, Carolyn
Using internet primary sources to teach critical thinking skills in the sciences. Libraries Unlimited 2003 339p (Libraries Unlimited professional guides in school librarianship) $39.95   **025.04**
1. Science—Study and teaching 2. Internet in education
ISBN 0-313-31851-4   LC 2003-47722
Also available: Using internet primary sources to teach critical thinking skills in world literature by Roxanne M. Kent-Drury; Using internet primary sources to teach critical thinking skills in visual arts by Pamela J. Eyerdam; Using internet primary sources to teach critical thinking skills in government, economics, and contemporary world issues by James M. Shiveley and Phillip J. VanFossen
"A navigation tool for steering students to excellent scientific resources available on the Internet. The sites included are principally primary documents and other sites that provide reliable data. . . . Each lesson begins with a URL and a site summary. A series of tasks follows that would serve as a starting point for science teachers to expand upon, and are designed to trigger discussion and analytical thinking and writing. . . . The 10 appendixes offer such helpful topics as subject guides to Web sites, career data, information available in journals and other periodicals, and Web guides to standards." SLJ
Includes bibliographical references

Kuntz, Jerry, 1956-
The KidsClick! Web searching skills guide with CD-ROM. Neal-Schuman 2001 123p (Neal-Schuman net-guide series) pa $49.95
025.04
1. Internet searching—Study and teaching
ISBN 1-55570-396-8   LC 00-45074
"An Internet searching curriculum made up of . . . lessons designed to introduce and reinforce skills for students in grades three through eight to make them more proficient Web users. Topics include alphabetizing, subject hierarchies, symbolic classification, keyword searching, Boolean operators, search commands, indexes and directories, evaluating, and citing sites. There are 9 reproducible activity sheets for each of 10 chapters. . . . Electronic versions of each sheet are included on the accompanying CD-ROM." SLJ

Managing the Internet controversy; edited by Mark L. Smith. Neal-Schuman 2000 226p (Neal-Schuman net-guide series) pa $49.95
025.04
1. Library information networks 2. Internet
ISBN 1-55570-395-X   LC 00-62516
This is a "compilation of 12 essays. . . . Topics range from the historical and philosophical underpinnings of intellectual freedom to strategies for building public support for library policies to handling media interviews. Although the core of the discussion is the Internet and the concerns raised by its widespread use in libraries, the end product is a seminar on the key issues of library management. . . . Thought-provoking analysis by respected library professionals coupled with practical tools for addressing difficult issues makes this a valuable resource for school and public librarians." Book Rep
Includes bibliographical references

Minkel, Walter
Delivering Web reference services to young people; {by} Walter Minkel and Roxanne Hsu Feldman. American Lib. Assn. 1998 121p il $32
025.04
1. Children's libraries 2. World Wide Web 3. Library information networks
ISBN 0-8389-0743-1   LC 98-26112
"Webliography": p. 101-115; Includes index
"Minkel and Feldman have written a book designed to guide both school and public librarians through using, teaching, and developing the Web for youth. . . . Descriptions of search tools are given in a manner that anyone trained in research will be able to understand and use easily." J Youth Serv Libr
Includes bibliographical references

Raatma, Lucia
Safety on the Internet; by Lucia Raatma. Child's World 2005 32p il (Living well) lib bdg $25.64 (4 and up)
025.04
1. Internet and children 2. Safety education
ISBN 1-59296-242-4   LC 2003-27212
Contents: Daniel's school report; Safe surfing; E-mail, IMS, and netiquette; Knowing to whom you are talking; Guarding your computer; When it's time to sign off;

Glossary; Questions and answers about Internet safety; Helping a friend learn about Internet safety; Did you know?; How to learn more about Internet safety
This is an "overview of online safety, including choosing age-appropriate sites, e-mailing, instant messaging, netiquette, and maintaining one's privacy." SLJ
Includes glossary

Stephens, Michael T., 1965-
The library Internet trainer's toolkit. Neal-Schuman 2001 223p il (Neal-Schuman net-guide series) pa $149.95
025.04
1. Internet searching—Study and teaching 2. Computer-assisted instruction 3. Computer networks
ISBN 1-55570-415-8   LC 2001-30805
This book "presents 12 modules or sets of instruction programs to be used in conjunction with a CD-ROM that offers more than 400 slides, directions, handouts, and fliers. Each module begins with a brief introduction, anticipated outcomes for attendees, and tips for presentation. They cover navigating the Internet and the Web, using e-mail and WWW e-mail services, and security issues and safety tips. Module 12 discusses the consumption of memory by digital images and provides excellent ideas for selection and use of digital images and cameras. . . . The CD-ROM also provides the scripts for each instructional program in Microsoft Word format." SLJ

Wolinsky, Art
Internet power research using the Big6 approach; . rev ed. Enslow Publishers 2005 64p il (Internet library) lib bdg $22.60 (5 and up)
025.04
1. Information systems 2. Research
ISBN 0-7660-1563-7   LC 2004-22185
First published 2002
Provides instructions for using the "Big6" research method and scenarios for applying the technique to research conducted on the Internet
"The book's conversational tone and simple, direct text, with its touches of humor and its real-life situations, will appeal to students, while its kid-friendly vocabulary makes comparisons and explanations relevant and understandable." {Review of 2002 ed.} Book Rep
Includes glossary and bibliographical references

025.1 Library administration

Anderson, Cynthia
Write grants, get money. Linworth Pub. 2002 146p il pa $44.95
025.1
1. Grants-in-aid
ISBN 1-58683-025-2   LC 2001-38555
The author "begins with identifying the need for a grant, making a plan, and asking the right questions to help stimulate the generation of proposal ideas. Then she explains how to identify donors. . . . This title offers an excellent analysis of the grant-writing process for both novice and veteran grant writers." Book Rep
Includes glossary and bibliographical references

Grantsmanship for small libraries and school library media centers; {by} Sylvia D. Hall-Ellis {et al.}; edited by Frank W. Hoffman. Libraries Unlimited 1999 173p pa $34 **025.1**
1. Grants-in-aid
ISBN 1-56308-484-8　　　　LC 98-31247
This "guide outlines each step of the process for obtaining grants, providing examples and definitions along the way. . . . This helpful and easy-to-use handbook should be a part of every professional collection." SLJ
Includes bibliographical references

Hall-Ellis, Sylvia Dunn, 1949-
Grants for school libraries; [by] Sylvia D. Hall-Ellis and Ann Jerabek. Libraries Unlimited 2003 197p il pa $35 **025.1**
1. Grants-in-aid 2. School libraries
ISBN 1-59158-079-X　　　　LC 2003-54630
"Hall-Ellis and Jerabek provide a systematic approach to every aspect of the grant process. Each section breaks down important concepts and is clearly supported by reproducible forms, examples, and lists. Two important segments address budget and personnel considerations. The project-evaluation section includes data-collection instruments and time lines, while a final chapter discusses practical suggestions such as publicity and writing letters of appreciation. . . . . This surprisingly readable guide should be on every school library media specialist's professional shelf." SLJ
Includes bibliographical references

025.2　Acquisitions and collection development

Doll, Carol Ann
Managing and analyzing your collection; a practical guide for small libraries and school media centers; {by} Carol A. Doll, Pamela Petrick Barron. American Lib. Assn. 2002 93p il pa $30 **025.2**
1. Libraries—Collection development
ISBN 0-8389-0821-7　　　　LC 2001-53747
This guide to collection development is divided into chapters covering management objectives, gathering and analyzing collection data, and weeding
This is a "book that librarians will actually read from cover to cover. . . . {It} isn't overwhelming and technical. Instead, it is rather chatty with solid, useful information." Book Rep
Includes bibliographical references

Lyga, Allyson A. W.
Graphic novels in your media center; a definitive guide; by Allyson A. W. Lyga with Barry Lyga. Libraries Unlimited 2004 180p il pa $35 **025.2**
1. Graphic novels 2. Book selection 3. Books and reading
ISBN 1-59158-142-7　　　　LC 2004-46517

In the first section the authors "make cogent arguments for the inclusion of graphic novels. A second section introduces common terms and includes an extremely useful 'how to read' subsection, complete with sample pages. The remaining sections provide recommended titles for all ages, testimonials from teachers and comic book store proprietors, resource lists, and a set of 17 lesson plans." Booklist
"This indispensable, well-organized guide willl provide school librarians with all of the necessary information for implementing and developing a graphic-novels collection." SLJ

Reichman, Henry, 1947-
Censorship and selection; issues and answers for schools. 3rd ed. American Lib. Assn. 2001 223p pa $37 **025.2**
1. Censorship 2. School libraries 3. Academic freedom
ISBN 0-8389-0798-9　　　　LC 00-67657
First published 1988
The author "covers the different media (including books, school newspapers, and the Internet), the important court cases (including recent litigations involving Harry Potter, the Internet, and Huck Finn), the issues in dispute (including violence, religion, and profanity), and how the laws on the books can be incorporated into selection policies." Publisher's note
"Reichman's manual provides sound practical advice on how to handle this complex and emotionally charged subject." Voice Youth Advocates
Includes bibliographical references

Slote, Stanley J.
Weeding library collections; library weeding methods. 4th ed. Libraries Unlimited 1997 xxi, 240p il $69 **025.2**
1. Libraries—Collection development
ISBN 1-56308-511-9　　　　LC 96-54865
First published 1975
"The author demonstrates how weeding strengthens a collection and increases circulation. . . . Four weeding methods are presented: the book card method, the spine-marking method, the historical reconstruction method, and the computer-assisted method. Slote gives precise instructions for each method, enhanced with illustrations." Book Rep
Includes bibliographical references

Symons, Ann K.
Protecting the right to read; a how-to-do-it manual for school and public librarians; {by} Ann K. Symons, Charles Harmon; illustrations by Pat Race. Neal-Schuman 1995 211p il (How-to-do-it manuals for libraries) pa $55 **025.2**
1. Libraries—Censorship 2. Intellectual freedom
ISBN 1-55570-216-3　　　　LC 95-42444
"The authors take readers from discussion of the policies and principles of intellectual freedom to considerations specific to school and public libraries to the protection of freedom on the Internet. . . . Appendixes consist of reprints of documents put out by the ALA and the Minnesota Coalition Against Censorship." Book Rep

Symons, Ann K.—*Continued*
"Intellectual freedom issues and guiding principles get a thorough and comprehensive treatment. . . . An essential book." Voice Youth Advocates
Includes bibliographical references

Walker, Barbara J.
Developing Christian fiction collections for children and adults; selection criteria and a core collection. Neal-Schuman 1998 224p pa $45
025.2
1. Christian fiction—Bibliography
ISBN 1-55570-292-9   LC 98-5881
"Areas covered include an overview of Christian fiction, establishing a solid selection process, and promoting this category in your library. Detailed appendixes feature annotated bibliographies of recommended books for children, adults, and young adults; listings of the Gold Medallion Fiction award winners from 1978 to present; biographies of prominent authors; and a selected, annotated videography on the best Christian videos." Publisher's note
Includes bibliographical references

025.3   Bibliographic analysis and control

Anglo-American cataloguing rules; prepared under the direction of the Joint Steering Committee for Revision of AACR, a committee of the American Library Association {et al.}. 2nd ed, 2002 revision. American Lib. Assn. 2002 . unp loose-leaf $62   **025.3**
1. Cataloging
ISBN 0-8389-3530-3   LC 2002-73596
Also available loose leaf pages with binder and tabs
First published 1967
This volume provides rules that cover the description of, and the provision of access points for, library materials. Included are 1999 and 2001 amendments and revisions approved and finalized through 2002
Includes bibliographical references

Fritz, Deborah A. (Deborah Angela), 1955-
Cataloging with AACR2 and MARC21; for books, electronic resources, sound recordings, videorecordings, and serials. 2nd ed. American Library Association 2004 various paging il loose leaf $68   **025.3**
1. Anglo-American cataloguing rules 2. Cataloging
ISBN 0-8389-0884-5   LC 2004-6535
First published 1998 with title: Cataloging with AACR2R and USMARC
In this guide Fritz "provides the hands-on cross-references between AACR2 and MARC21 required for easy online cataloging. Designed to streamline the process and avoid errors, the book is organized in order of MARC tags." Publisher's note
"Although it does not present every rule or MARC tag, this fairly comprehensive and handy reference addresses all levels of cataloging expertise. Catalogers and instructors should add this to their collection." Libr J

Gorman, Michael, 1941-
The concise AACR2, 2004 revision; prepared by Michael Gorman. American Library Association 2004 179p pa $40   **025.3**
1. Anglo-American cataloguing rules 2. Cataloging
ISBN 0-8389-3548-6   LC 2004-16088
On cover: Fourth edition
"This practical guidebook . . . has been fully revised and is now in concordance with AACR2, 2002 Revision 2004 Update. Michael Gorman . . . explains the more generally applicable AACR2 rules for cataloging library materials in simplified terms that make the rules more accessible and practical for practitioners and students who are in less complex library and bibliographic environments." Publisher's note

Intner, Sheila S., 1935-
Standard cataloging for school and public libraries; {by} Sheila S. Intner and Jean Weihs. 3rd ed. Libraries Unlimited 2001 346p il $47.50
025.3
1. Cataloging 2. Library classification
ISBN 1-56308-781-2   LC 2001-18615
First published 1990
This explains the Anglo-American Cataloging Rules (AACR2), Sears and Library of Congress subject headings, Dewey decimal and Library of Congress classification systems, MARC format, large computer networks, policy manuals, and how to manage a cataloging department
Includes bibliographical references

025.4   Subject analysis and control

Dewey, Melvil, 1851-1931
Abridged Dewey decimal classification and relative index; devised by Melvil Dewey. ed 14, edited by Joan S. Mitchell, Julianne Beall, Giles Martin, Winton E. Matthews, Jr., Gregory R. New. OCLC 2004 1050p $99   **025.4**
1. Dewey Decimal Classification
ISBN 0-910608-73-3   LC 2003-542823
Also available online
First abridged edition published 1894
The 14th Abridged Edition is an abridgement of the four volume 22nd Edition. Adapted to the needs of small and growing libraries, the 14th Abridged Edition is designed primarily for school and public libraries with collections of up to 20,000 titles

Sears list of subject headings. 18th ed, Joseph Miller, editor; Joan Goodsell, associate editor. Wilson, H.W. 2004 864p $115   **025.4**
1. Subject headings
ISBN 0-8242-1040-9
Also available Canadian companion. 6th edition published 2001
First published 1923 with title: List of subject headings for small libraries, by Minnie Earl Sears
In addition to the inclusion of five hundred new subject headings, this edition has updated the suggested classification numbers to conform to the 14th edition of the

Sears list of subject headings—*Continued*
Abridged Dewey Decimal classification. The new subject headings reflect developments in areas such as computers, technology, personal relations, politics, and popular culture

025.5   Services to users

Cooper, Gail, 1950-
New virtual field trips; {by} Gail Cooper and Garry Cooper. Libraries Unlimited 2001 155p pa $27.50   **025.5**
1. Internet 2. World Wide Web 3. Field trips
ISBN 1-56308-887-8   LC 00-45091
Replaces virtual field trips, published 1997
This is an "annotated guide to 440 web sites . . . that were selected to tie in to National Science Standards and inquiry-based learning, and to encourage independent studies. Organized into 13 topics covered in most K-12 school curricula, the entries include museums, libraries, schools, scientific labs, and government and university sites. . . . An accessible, useful resource." SLJ
Includes bibliographical references

Developing an information literacy program, K-12; a how-to-do-it manual and CD-ROM package; developed by the Iowa City Community School District ; edited by Mary Jo Langhorne. 2nd ed. Neal-Schuman 2004 432p (How-to-do-it manuals for libraries) pa $89.95   **025.5**
1. Bibliographic instruction 2. School libraries 3. Library information networks
ISBN 1-55570-509-X   LC 2004-46046
"Over twenty lessons . . . cover keyword research, library and library materials organization, using nonfiction books, using the library catalog, using online databases, using the Internet, note-taking, creating bibliographies, and more. You will also find planning and assessment forms, checklists, tables, and worksheets for developing, implementing, and instructing your information literacy programs—all reproduced in the book and accompanying CD-ROM." Publisher's note

Heiligman, Deborah
The New York Public Library kid's guide to research. Scholastic Ref. 1998 134p il hardcover o.p. paperback available $8.95 (5 and up)   **025.5**
1. Research 2. Libraries
ISBN 0-590-30716-9 (pa)   LC 97-28939
Provides guidance on how to do research, including how to use libraries and their resources, the Internet, and other sources such as interviews and surveys
"Short and complete, this book contains a wealth of material for young researchers. . . . A book that is appealing and informative, with content appeal across the grades." SLJ

Lanning, Scott
Essential reference services for today's school media specialists; [by] Scott Lanning and John Bryner. Libraries Unlimited 2004 129p il pa $40   **025.5**
1. Reference services (Libraries) 2. School libraries
ISBN 1-59158-137-0   LC 2004-40833
This book "covers not only how to develop a quality reference section for school library media specialists, but also how to complete a reference interview and work with teachers to reach the most students. . . . All librarians will find something useful in this book." Libr Media Connect
Includes bibliographical references

Yucht, Alice H.
Flip it! an information skills strategy for student researchers. Linworth Pub. 1997 105p il (Professional growth series) $29.95   **025.5**
1. Bibliographic instruction 2. School libraries
ISBN 0-938865-62-5   LC 97-3887
The author "presents a new information skills strategy for librarians and teachers to use with students. . . . FLIP IT is a mnemonic for research processes: Focus— on the topic; Link—new information to what is already known; Input—implement the information; Payoff—put it all together (finished product)." Voice Youth Advocates
Includes bibliographical references

027   General libraries, information centers

Trumble, Kelly
The Library of Alexandria; illustrated by Robina MacIntyre Marshall. Clarion Bks. 2003 72p il maps $17 (5 and up)   **027**
1. Alexandrian Library (Egypt) 2. Egypt—Civilization 3. Ancient civilization
ISBN 0-395-75832-7   LC 2003-150
Contents: A city of learning; Collecting books; Pergamum; Astronomy; Geography; Mathematics; Medicine; Decline and destruction; The fate of the Library of Alexandria
An introduction to the largest and most famous library in the ancient world, discussing its construction in Alexandria, Egypt, its vast collections, rivalry with the Pergamum Library, famous scholars, and destruction by fire
This is a "well-organized and thorough resource." SLJ
Includes glossary and bibliographical references

027.4   Public libraries

Mediavilla, Cindy
Creating the full-service homework center in your library. American Lib. Assn. 2001 141p pa $35   **027.4**
1. Libraries and students 2. Public libraries 3. Latchkey children
ISBN 0-8389-0800-4   LC 00-52163

Mediavilla, Cindy—*Continued*

The author "describes what constitutes an effective homework center, a separate space in the library, with set hours, clearly defined services, and an assigned staff member. With real-life examples from actual homework centers, this how-to-do-it manual has . . . sample surveys, goals, objectives, publicity and recruitment flyers, homework helper application forms and contracts, staff and volunteer job descriptions, grant applications, and focus group questions." Publisher's note

"There are no other books available solely on this topic, and this resource is surely definitive." Voice Youth Advocates

Includes bibliographical references

027.6   Libraries for special groups and organizations

Lerch, Maureen T.

Serving homeschooled teens and their parents. Libraries Unlimited 2004 242p (Libraries Unlimited professional guides for young adult librarians) pa $39   **027.6**

1. Home schooling 2. Young adults' libraries

ISBN 0-313-32052-7   LC 2004-46518

"After introductory chapters that dispel many myths about homeschooling and delve into adolescent psychology, the two experts give sound advice and great examples for service plan creation, collection development, programming, and promotion of services." Libr Media Connect

Includes bibliographical references

027.62   Libraries for young people

Braun, Linda W.

Technically involved; technology-based youth participation activities for your library. American Library Association 2003 138p il pa $34

027.62

1. Young adults' libraries

ISBN 0-8389-0861-6   LC 2003-12021

Contents: Youth participation - the what and the why; Getting teens involved; On the road to greatness; Bringing generations together; Reading, writing, and youth participation; Getting things done at the library; Overcoming obstacles

In this "title, Braun encourages librarians to involve teens in technology-related activities and projects that will benefit them and others. She responds to questions regarding participation, benefits to patrons and libraries, and training. The author provides numerous suggestions for activities. . . . This excellent volume is a must for libraries with teen groups, and a consideration for those that don't have them." SLJ

Includes bibliographical references

Teens.library; developing internet services for young adults. American Lib. Assn. 2002 82p pa $30   **027.62**

1. Internet 2. Young adults' libraries

ISBN 0-8389-0824-1

This "resource for librarians in both the public and school environment provides insight as to why teens gravitate to the Internet and which sites are their favorites. . . . The book offers the clueless as well as the knowledgeable librarian steps to take in developing library Web sites for teens and designing and maintaining these sites. . . . Detailed descriptions of the cites Web resources are included. A must-read for all librarians who work with teenagers." Booklist

Includes bibliographical references

Curriculum connections through the library; edited by Barbara K. Stripling and Sandra Hughes-Hassell. Libraries Unlimited 2003 xxi, 229p (Principles and practice series) pa $37.50

027.62

1. School libraries

ISBN 1-56308-973-4   LC 2003-54628

The editors have chosen "essays that sample existing scholarship and direct professionals in ways to affect curriculum, collections, and collaboration across disciplines and to aid students who must perform under the scrutiny of the national standards movement. The book contains some suggestions for joint projects, but primarily promotes open-ended, inquiry-based learning. . . . The writing is clear and purposeful. . . . A stimulating choice for practicing librarians and students of library science." SLJ

Includes bibliographical references

Edwards, Kirsten, 1965-

Teen library events; a month-by-month guide. Greenwood Press 2002 166p (Greenwood professional guides for young adult librarians) $52.95   **027.62**

1. Young adults' libraries 2. Public libraries

ISBN 0-313-31482-9   LC 00-52430

The author "presents step-by-step procedures covering January through December, from developing booktalks using the Printz Award titles to bookmaking (with detailed diagrams) to designing a Teen Read Week contest." Booklist

"This is an excellent, no-nonsense guide that describes programs that can be executed with a minimum amount of effort." SLJ

Includes bibliographical references

Honnold, RoseMary, 1954-

101+ teen programs that work. Neal-Schuman 2003 xxi, 195p il (Teens @ the library series) pa $49.95   **027.62**

1. Young adults' libraries 2. School libraries—Activity projects 3. Teenagers—Books and reading

ISBN 1-55570-453-0   LC 2002-29385

Program plans cover activities such as summer reading games, contests, crafts, coffeehouse style poetry and Mike nights

"Those who work with teens will find plenty of year-round programming ideas in this useful volume. The author has incorporated tried-and-true activities complete with instructions on how to plan and present each one." SLJ

Includes bibliographical references

Information literacy skills, grades 7-12; Catherine M. Andronik, compiler. 3rd ed. Linworth Pub. 1999 315p pa $39.95   **027.62**

1. Young adults' libraries

ISBN 0-938865-82-6

First published 1990 with title: Library research skills workbook, grades 7-12

This is a compilation of articles "gathered from *The Book Report* and *Library Talk*. The 11 thematic chapters cover both practical and theoretical aspects of secondary librarianship, with topics ranging from research models and Internet skills, to assessment and literature." Booklist

Jones, Patrick

Connecting young adults and libraries; a how-to-do-it manual for librarians; [by] Patrick Jones, Michele Gorman, Tricia Suellentrop. 3rd ed. Neal-Schuman Publishers 2004 xxix, 438p il (How-to-do-it manuals for libraries) pa $75   **027.62**

1. Young adults' libraries 2. Young adult literature— Bibliography 3. Books and reading

ISBN 1-55570-508-1   LC 2004-46008

"Not only are the building blocks of library services such as collection development, outreach, programs, booktalking, and teen space included, but the authors also discuss why they are important and why they work. Peppered throughout are examples of libraries successfully connecting with teens. . . . An upbeat, well-organized must-have for anyone working with this audience." SLJ

Do it right! best practices for serving young adults in school and public libraries; {by} Patrick Jones and Joel Shoemaker. Neal-Schuman 2001 182p il (Teens @ the library series) pa $45   **027.62**

1. Young adults' libraries 2. Public libraries

ISBN 1-55570-394-1   LC 2001-30718

"In the first half of the book, Shoemaker concentrates on turning the school library media center into 'library heaven,' while in the second half Jones addresses the challenges and rewards of working with young adults in the public library. . . . The book . . . provides plenty of training ideas, sample surveys, action plans, job descriptions, library policies, and interview questions." SLJ

Includes bibliographical references

Kan, Katharine

Sizzling summer reading programs for young adults; {by} Katherine L. Kan, for the Young Adult Library Services Association. American Lib. Assn. 1998 60p il pa $25   **027.62**

1. Young adults' libraries 2. Teenagers—Books and reading

ISBN 0-8389-3480-3   LC 97-52973

This "book is divided by subject: type of program (general incentive or thematic); participation opportunities (volunteers, teen advisory board, etc.); programs for teens with special needs. A solid introduction explains how to connect with YAs. Each program is thoroughly described and includes graphics of such things as give-aways and posters. Some of the programs give insights into difficulties other libraries might run up against." Booklist

Mondowney, JoAnn G.

Hold them in your heart; successful strategies for library services to at-risk teens. Neal-Schuman 2001 139p (Teens @ the library series) pa $45   **027.62**

ISBN 1-55570-393-3   LC 00-58413

"This book focuses on specific services for teens. . . . It includes sections on gaining support, needs assessment, funding, and planning and evaluation." SLJ

New directions for library service to young adults; Young Adult Library Services Association with Patrick Jones; edited by Linda Waddle. American Lib. Assn. 2002 146p pa $32   **027.62**

1. Young adults' libraries

ISBN 0-8389-0827-6   LC 2002-3377

This "covers guidelines on planning, implementing, and evaluating services with youth involved in each step of the process. Twelve goal statements for YA services and ten core values upon which these goals are built are presented. . . . Besides his usual clear writing, ubiquitous lists, and deft editorial organization, Jones writes a manifesto for how services for young adults should be conceptualized." Voice Youth Advocates

Includes bibliographical references

O'Dell, Katie

Library materials and services for teen girls. Libraries Unlimited 2002 179p il (Libraries Unlimited professional guides for young adult librarians) pa $45   **027.62**

1. Young adults' libraries 2. Libraries—Collection development 3. Girls—Books and reading

ISBN 0-313-31554-X   LC 2002-7609

Contents: Girls in the spotlight: a short history; Collection development; Programming; Girls and technology; Volunteers; Collaboration; Outreach to teen girls

In this "guide to providing library services to teen girls in a public library setting, chapters cover such topics as collection development . . . programming; girls and technology; volunteers; collaboration; and outreach." Booklist

"This book will be useful to librarians with the very specific goal of attracting adolescent girls to the library." SLJ

Includes bibliographical references

Rankin, Virginia

The thoughtful researcher; teaching the research process to middle school students. Libraries Unlimited 1999 211p il (Information literacy series) $30.50   **027.62**

1. School libraries 2. Bibliographic instruction 3. Research

ISBN 1-56308-698-0   LC 98-55916

Rankin "offers concrete suggestions (and 16 reproducible handouts) for researching a topic, generating questions, planning a project, managing time, searching for information, evaluating sources, note taking, mastering thinking skills, selecting a presentation format, and assessing the product and the process. . . . A must-have resource for school libraries serving grades 5-9, this will

Rankin, Virginia—*Continued*
be welcomed by classroom teachers and teacher-librarians." Booklist
Includes bibliographical references

Reid, Rob
Something funny happened at the library; how to create humorous programs for children and young adults. American Lib. Assn. 2003 163p $32
027.62
1. Children's libraries 2. Young adults' libraries 3. Storytelling
ISBN 0-8389-0836-5   LC 2002-8970
Contents: Tricks of the trade; Humor programs for younger children: preschool and primary school age; Humor programs for intermediate school age children; Humor programs for middle and high school students; Reader's theater; Lively library tours & visits to schools; Raps and closings; The funniest books in the library; Two last treats
This is "an excellent resource for adding wit to your library repertoire." SLJ
Includes bibliographical references

Sima, Judy
Raising voices; creating youth storytelling groups and troupes. Libraries Unlimited 2003 xxviii, 241p pa $32.50   **027.62**
1. Storytelling
ISBN 1-563-08919-X   LC 2003-47631
This offers a "blueprint for beginning and sustaining a successful group or troupe of storytellers from grades 4 to 12. . . . . The book includes reproducible forms that will save a lot of work and lists of valuable resources. . . . . Raising Voices is the complete, and essential, handbook for this special group of storytellers." SLJ
Includes bibliographical references

027.8   School libraries

American Association of School Librarians
Information power; building partnerships for learning; prepared by the American Association of School Librarians {and} Association for Educational Communications and Technology. American Lib. Assn. 1998 205p il pa $37
027.8
1. School libraries 2. Instructional materials centers
ISBN 0-8389-3470-6   LC 98-23291
First published 1988
This resource "relates the library-media program to the entire educational infrastructure. The authors explicate their themes in terms of standards, indicators, levels of proficiency, goals, principles, and examples of student activities. The appendixes contain essential information on Library Power, AASL's ICON-nect project, the Library Bill of Rights, confidentiality, censorship, access equity, and ethics." SLJ
Includes bibliographical references

Bradburn, Frances Bryant
Output measures for school library media programs. Neal-Schuman 1999 95p pa $55
027.8
1. School libraries 2. Instructional materials centers
ISBN 1-55570-326-7   LC 98-45557
"Bradburn's handbook is intended to guide school library specialists in collecting data on budgets, staff, and services and in using the data to evaluate programs and argue for increased funding. Forms and work sheets as well as three case studies are included." Booklist
Includes bibliographical references

Church, Audrey P., 1957-
Leverage your library program to help raise test scores; a guide for library media specialists, principals, teachers, and parents. Linworth Pub 2003 123p il pa $39.95   **027.8**
1. School libraries 2. Instructional materials centers
ISBN 1-586-83120-8   LC 2003-40080
"In chapter one, recent research on school libraries is provided and briefly explains the results in layman terms. This is followed by a chapter each for the administrators, teachers, and parents that describes what each needs to know about the library and librarian's roles. A chapter is included for the librarian on what they need to do. The final chapter pulls the book together with perspectives from principals and librarians . . . This book can serve as a means to start a dialog with the administration and at the same time as a reference book for the school librarian." Lib Media Connect
Includes bibliographical references

Craver, Kathleen W.
Creating cyber libraries; an instructional guide for school library media specialists. Libraries Unlimited 2002 xxvi, 222p (Libraries Unlimited professional guides in school librarianship) pa $40
027.8
1. Internet resources 2. School libraries
ISBN 0-313-32080-2   LC 2001-55619
"Nine chapters cover guidelines; policies to consider; Web-design issues; the use of portals; and strategies for maintaining, evaluating, and promoting a library Web site. Special-interest areas, such as providing a virtual reading room and online instruction, are also discussed. . . . This title is a one-stop-shopping bonanza of wonderful, useful ideas on how to create a cyber library that will meet the information needs of our patrons." Libr J
Includes bibliographical references

Donham, Jean
Enhancing teaching and learning; a leadership guide for school library media specialists. 2nd ed. Neal-Schuman Publishers 2005 337p il pa $59.95
027.8
1. School libraries 2. Instructional materials centers
ISBN 1-55570-516-2   LC 2004-53173
First published 1998
This attempts to show "how to develop and implement an effective library media program by integrating it into the total education environment. Part One covers all as-

Donham, Jean—_Continued_
pects of the school environment: students, curriculum and
instruction, principals, school district administrators, and
the community. Part Two shows you how to use interaction and collaboration to make the school library media
program integral to all of these communities." Publisher's note

Erikson, Rolf
Designing a school library media center for the
future; {by} Rolf Erikson, Carolyn Markuson.
American Lib. Assn. 2000 109p il pa $40
              027.8
1. Instructional materials centers—Design and construction 2. School libraries—Design and construction
ISBN 0-8389-0790-3   LC 00-42025
"For the American Association of School Librarians"
"This book covers researching, planning, constructing,
and moving into a new school media center. The chapters dealing with overseeing specification and bidding
processes and meeting accessibility guidelines are particularly helpful." SLJ
Includes bibliographical references

Everhart, Nancy
Evaluating the school library media center;
analysis techniques and research practices.
Libraries Unlimited 1998 262p pa $37
              027.8
1. School libraries 2. Instructional materials centers
ISBN 1-56308-085-0   LC 98-6949
"The author describes qualitative and quantitative
techniques for evaluating in areas of curriculum, personnel, facilities, collections, usage, and technology. She
also provides step-by-step instructions on how to create
in-house surveys, conduct interviews, and use observation
to gather data." Publisher's note
Includes bibliographical references

Exploring science in the library; resources and
activities for young people; edited by Maria
Sosa and Tracy Gath. American Lib. Assn. 1999
236p pa $32
              027.8
1. Elementary school libraries 2. Science—Study and
teaching
ISBN 0-8389-0768-7   LC 99-41496
This "resource helps public and school librarians develop science, math, and technology resources for K-12
students, supporting the recent national efforts toward
achieving science literacy." SLJ
Includes bibliographical references

Farmer, Lesley S. Johnson, 1949-
Student success and library media programs; a
systems approach to research and best practice;
[by] Lesley S. J. Farmer. Libraries Unlimited 2003
180p bibl tab pa $45
              027.8
1. School libraries 2. Academic achievement
ISBN 1-59158-058-7   LC 2003-53881
"Designed for school library media specialists, this
book focuses on library media programs and examines
the factors that influence student achievement." Publish-

er's note
This is a "comprehensive and thoroughly researched
book. . . . An invaluable guide for media specialists."
SLJ
Includes bibliographical references

Foundations for effective school library media
programs; Ken Haycock, editor. Libraries
Unlimited 1999 331p hardcover o.p. paperback
available $47.50   **027.8**
1. School libraries 2. Instructional materials centers
3. Bibliographic instruction
ISBN 0-56308-368-X (pa)   LC 98-40343
Explores the role of library media specialists in school
improvement, curriculum design, collaboration with
teachers, and building information literacy. Articles discuss learning theories, flexible scheduling, new technologies, and thematic units
Includes bibliographical references

The **Information-powered** school; {by} Public
Education Network, American Association of
School Librarians; edited by Sandra
Hughes-Hassell, Anne Wheelock. American Lib.
Assn. 2001 138p il pa $35   **027.8**
1. Library Power (Program) 2. School libraries
3. Instructional materials centers
ISBN 0-8389-3514-1   LC 2001-22561
"This volume presents a variety of articles highlighting various aspects and activities of Information Powered
Schools and giving tips for putting the principles and
practices to work. . . . Checklists, surveys, and planning
forms are included to determine the status of current
practices. The collaborative planning worksheets, request
forms, unit evaluation and collaborative-unit evaluation
forms will be of special interest to librarians already involved in this process." SLJ
Includes bibliographical references

Job, Amy G.
The school library media specialist as manager;
a book of case studies; {by} Amy G. Job and
Mary Kay W. Schnare. Scarecrow Press 1997
195p (School librarianship series) pa $29.95
              027.8
1. School libraries 2. Instructional materials centers
ISBN 0-8108-3363-8   LC 97-20841
"Chapters are devoted to broad topics—leadership,
planning, and management; personnel; resources and
equipment; facilities; and district, regional, and state
leadership—with specific scenarios for elementary, middle, and high school media centers. The most practical
feature of this book is the appendix section, which contains the American Association of School Librarians' position statements on various subjects." SLJ
Includes bibliographical references

Jweid, Rosann, 1933-
The library-classroom partnership; teaching library media skills in middle and junior high school; {by} Rosann Jweid and Margaret Rizzo. 2nd ed. Scarecrow Press 1998 238p il pa $42.95
                                                        027.8
1. School libraries 2. Instructional materials centers 3. Bibliographic instruction
ISBN 0-8108-3476-6   LC 98-21206
First published 1988
The authors describe ways to coordinate library media skills with classroom subjects. English, mathematics, social studies, science, art, music, home economics, vocational guidance, physical education, technology and foreign language curricula are covered. Reading enrichment and accessing of information electronically are also discussed
Includes bibliographical references

Kearney, Carol A.
Curriculum partner; redefining the role of the library media specialist. Greenwood Press 2000 xxiv, 180p (Greenwood professional guides in school librarianship) $46.95   **027.8**
1. School libraries 2. Instructional materials centers
ISBN 0-313-31025-4   LC 99-462341
The author "includes chapters on leadership, change, vision, partnering, collaborative planning, staff development, and advocacy and provides examples from the experiences of practitioners to support her ideas." SLJ
Includes bibliographical references

Mendrinos, Roxanne Baxter
Using educational technology with at-risk students; a guide for library media specialists and teachers. Greenwood Press 1997 227p il map $46.95   **027.8**
1. School libraries 2. Computer-assisted instruction 3. Instructional materials centers
ISBN 0-313-29369-4   LC 96-50290
"Mendrinos explores the uses and appeal of technology-based education in various subject areas, particularly in terms of reaching 'the average and below-average student who is in danger of dropping out, or who does not have the skills to enter and succeed in the information technology job market of today.' . . . Chapters focus on technology applications in library media centers, and in language arts, social studies, and science classrooms. Specific projects and Web sites are cited frequently." SLJ
Includes bibliographical references

Morris, Betty J.
Administering the school library media center. 4th ed, rev and expanded. Libraries Unlimited 2004 683p $70; pa $55   **027.8**
1. School libraries 2. Instructional materials centers
ISBN 0-313-32261-9; 1-59158-183-4 (pa)
                                LC 2004-41797
First published 1973 under the authorship of John T. Gillespie and Diana L. Spirt with title: Creating a school media program

"This volume covers library media center programming, facilities and technologies, student learning, policies and procedures, and library media specialist roles. . . . Highlights include budget planning and justification, library media job descriptions, and information on the bid process. The chapter on facilities contains infrequently found information on the psychology of color, URLs for Web sites with floor plans, and guidelines for space planning." Booklist

Ray, Virginia Lawrence
School wide book events; how to make them happen; Virginia Lawrence Ray. Libraries Unlimited 2003 133p pa $25   **027.8**
1. School libraries 2. Books and reading
ISBN 1-591-58038-2   LC 2003-47724
"The author's intent is to present ideas on how to celebrate reading across grade levels and curriculum, involving teachers, administration, faculty, and students both in preparation and actual activities. She proposes that school libraries have a Book Event for the whole school. . . . All events require simple resources and are easy to follow even for school systems with extremely limited budgets." SLJ
Includes bibliographical references

Schuckett, Sandy
Political advocacy for school librarians; you have the power! by Sandy Schuckett. Linworth Pub 2004 128p pa $39.95   **027.8**
1. School libraries 2. Libraries and community 3. Lobbying
ISBN 1-58683-158-5   LC 2004-4869
"Schuckett motivates and explicitly details an exciting 'how-to' of political lobbying at all levels–from the school site and local board all the way to the national level. . . . School librarians need political clout, and Schuckett shows us how to get it." SLJ
Includes bibliographical references

Skaggs, Gayle
On display; 25 themes to promote reading. McFarland & Co. 1999 162p il pa $29.95
                                        027.8
1. School libraries 2. Libraries—Exhibitions
ISBN 0-7864-0657-7   LC 98-54964
The emphasis is "on simple themes that will attract kids, such as rock and roll, basketball, and outer space. Along with the ideas there are directions for bulletin boards and simple displays: a jukebox, a freestanding basketball hoop, a bookworm." Booklist

Smith, Jane Bandy
Achieving a curriculum-based library media center program; the middle school model for change. American Lib. Assn. 1995 146p pa $25
                                        027.8
1. School libraries 2. Instructional materials centers 3. Bibliographic instruction
ISBN 0-8389-0660-5   LC 95-20014
First published 1989 with title: Library media center programs for middle schools

Smith, Jane Bandy—*Continued*

The author "stresses the importance of connecting information skills with district outcomes and curricula as well as the necessity for library media specialists to become involved in curriculum planning and to view themselves as instructional consultants. . . . For school districts just beginning the process of restructuring curricula, Smith's work will be invaluable. Her program is carefully reasoned, practical, student centered, and thoroughly readable. Reproducible forms are included." Booklist

Valenza, Joyce Kasman

Power tools recharged; 125+ essential forms and presentations for your school library information program; illustrated by Emily Valenza. American Library Association 2004 various paging .p il pa $55   **027.8**

1. School libraries 2. Libraries—Public relations
ISBN 0-8389-0880-2   LC 2004-5853

This offers a compilation of customizable, reproducible forms and handouts for school library administration and assessment, teaching information literacy, making presentations. Included are such items as templates for a gift book program, letters to parents and faculty members, a checklist of tasks, library equipment sign-out forms, and a reading interest survey.

Includes bibliographical references

The **Whole** school library handbook; edited by Blanche Woolls and David V. Loertscher. American Library Association 2005 448p pa $45   **027.8**

1. School libraries 2. Instructional materials centers
ISBN 0-8389-0883-7 (pa)   LC 2004-20198

This reference resource to the school media center includes "facts, . . . articles, checklists, organization contact information, trivia, [and] advice from the field's experts. . . . [It also features] information on fundraising, grant writing, flexible scheduling, promoting the school library, and advocating its value in the school community." Publisher's note

Includes bibliographical references

Wilson, Patricia J. (Patricia Jane)

Center stage; library programs that inspire middle school patrons; [by] Patricia Potter Wilson and Roger Leslie. Libraries Unlimited 2002 xx, 204p il pa $35   **027.8**

1. School libraries 2. Instructional materials centers
ISBN 1-56308-796-0   LC 2002-3185

"Wilson and Leslie discuss the purpose and benefits of programming and carefully delineate the stages of planning, implementation, and evaluation and include bulleted lists, checklists, and evaluative handouts. . . . *Center Stage* is well organized and written in a way that is easy to understand and put into practice." SLJ

Includes bibliographical references

Woolls, E. Blanche

The school library media manager. 3rd ed. Libraries Unlimited 2004 352p (Library and information science text series) $60; pa $45   **027.8**

1. School libraries 2. Instructional materials centers
ISBN 1-591-58144-3; 1-591-58182-6 (pa)
          LC 2004-48478

First published 1994

This provides an "overview of the profession and all aspects of school library management. . . . The new National Board for Professional Teaching Standards certification for school librarians is discussed as are budget, facilities, cataloging, copyright, selection of materials, staff evaluation, and all the other basic managerial functions. The book is current with discussions of the AASL national guidelines and standards, the USA Patriot Act, and the effect of Internet filtering on school libraries." Publisher's note

Yesner, Bernice L.

Operating and evaluating school library media programs; a handbook for administrators and librarians; {by} Bernice L. Yesner and Hilda L. Jay. Neal-Schuman 1998 xxi, 424p pa $59.95   **027.8**

1. School libraries 2. Instructional materials centers
ISBN 1-55570-250-3   LC 98-11469

"Yesner and Jay attempt to clarify for school administrators everything a school librarian should be doing in an exemplary school library media program. They cover staffing, programming, collection management, instructional strategies, and technology use. . . . For each topic, they provide a brief philosophy of current practices followed by checklists of positive, negative, and missing elements and possible solutions." Booklist

Zweizig, Douglas

Lessons from Library Power; enriching teaching and learning: final report of the evaluation of the national library power initiative: an initiative of the DeWitt Wallace-Reader's Digest Fund; {by} Douglas L. Zweizig and Dianne McAfee Hopkins; with Norman Lott Webb and Gary Wehlage. Libraries Unlimited 1999 281p pa $39.50   **027.8**

1. Library Power (Program) 2. School libraries
ISBN 1-56308-833-9   LC 99-52025

The authors "examine the specific goals and accomplishments of Library Power, the school library funding project initiated in 1988 by the DeWitt Wallace—Reader's Digest Fund. Having analyzed surveys collected from teachers, librarians, and principals, and case studies of media center practices, they conclude that collaborative planning, flexible scheduling, collection development, and professional growth can make a positive difference in libraries and the students that they support." Booklist

Includes bibliographical references

028.1 Reviews of books and other media

Baxter, Kathleen A.
Gotcha! nonfiction booktalks to get kids excited about reading; by Kathleen A. Baxter {and} Marcia Agness Kochel. Libraries Unlimited 1999 183p pa $28 **028.1**
1. Books and reading
ISBN 1-56308-683-2   LC 99-34279
This guide to booktalking discusses more than 350 titles for grades one through eight
The books are presented in a "conversational style that is extremely readable and entertaining; useful bibliographies following each section assign appropriate grade levels to the books. The authors also give general tips on organizing booktalks." SLJ

Carter, Betty, 1944-
Best books for young adults. 2nd ed, {by} Betty Carter, with Sally Estes and Linda Waddle; Young Adult Library Services Association. American Lib. Assn. 2000 229p pa $35 **028.1**
1. Young adult literature—Bibliography 2. Best books
ISBN 0-8389-3501-X   LC 00-35583
First published 1994
This volume lists over 1,800 titles that have been selected by the Best Books for Young Adults Committee of the American Library Association. "These titles are intended for classroom teachers, librarians, and parents who want to reach young adult or teenage readers. In part 1 there are detailed chapters on how the titles were selected and trends in young adult publishing. There is also a very useful and practical chapter that contains topical lists of titles arranged in a format that is easy to copy and distribute. Among the topics covered are adventure, animals, family, fantasy, friendship, historical fiction, romance, sports, survival, war, westerns, and youths in trouble. Part 2 consists of the book lists from 1966 through 1999." Am Ref Books Annu, 2001
Includes bibliographical references and index

Cooper-Mullin, Alison
Once upon a heroine; 400 books for girls to love; {by} Alison Cooper-Mullin and Jennifer Marmaduke Coye. Contemporary Bks. 1998 349p pa $16.95 **028.1**
1. Girls—Books and reading
ISBN 0-8092-3020-8   LC 97-32121
The authors "have gathered books whose heroines are smart and strong-willed. Nontraditional roles, interesting plots, meaningful character development, and rich language were some of their criteria for inclusion. Organized from 'early readers' to 'young adults,' their book includes a resource list for finding the books mentioned." SLJ

Dodson, Shireen
100 books for girls to grow on; lively descriptions of the most inspiring books for girls, terrific discussion questions to spark conversation, great ideas for book-inspired activities, crafts, and field trips. HarperCollins Pubs. 1998 334p pa $14 **028.1**
1. Girls—Books and reading
ISBN 0-06-095718-2   LC 98-27606
The author summarizes "books that girls ages nine to thirteen might enjoy reading on their own or sharing in a book discussion group. . . . Organized alphabetically by title, each book is broken down into several categories including the summary, reading time, themes, discussion questions, information about the author, activities to do beyond the book, and recommended further reading." Voice Youth Advocates

Horning, Kathleen T.
From cover to cover; evaluating and reviewing children's books. HarperCollins Pubs. 1997 230p hardcover o.p. paperback available $14.99 **028.1**
1. Books—Reviews 2. Children's literature—History and criticism
ISBN 0-06-446167-X (pa)   LC 96-27281
The author "begins with an overview of how children's books are published in the United States, the physical parts of the book, and categories of children's books. The next six chapters are devoted to the definition and scope of those categories." Bull Cent Child Books
"Anyone entering the field of children's book reviewing, or indeed, the wider field of children's literature, will find *From Cover to Cover* an excellent guide to analyzing books and presenting clear, useful reviews." Booklist
Includes bibliographical references

Into focus; understanding and creating middle school readers; editors: Kylene Beers, Barbara G. Samuels. Christopher-Gordon Pubs. 1998 xx, 490p il pa $44.95 **028.1**
1. Reading 2. Literature—Study and teaching
ISBN 0-926842-64-1
In this "handbook, 24 experts from the fields of reading theory, library science, response theory, children's literature, and middle school philosophy present strategies, describe programs, and provide lists that foster academic success and a lifelong love of reading." SLJ

Odean, Kathleen
Great books for boys; more than 600 books for boys 2 to 14. Ballantine Bks. 1998 384p pa $13.95 **028.1**
1. Boys—Books and reading
ISBN 0-345-42083-7   LC 97-45926
This annotated bibliography offers recommended titles and strategies for parents, teachers, and librarians to promote reading among boys
"An excellent resource!" SLJ

028.5　Reading and use of other information media by young people

Author talk; conversations with Judy Blume [et al.]; compiled and edited by Leonard S. Marcus. Simon & Schuster Bks. for Young Readers 2000 103p il $22 (4 and up)　　　**028.5**
1. Authors
ISBN 0-689-81383-X　　　LC 99-39777
Presents interviews with fifteen well-known children's writers, including Judy Blume, Karen Cushman, Russell Freedman, James Howe, Lois Lowry, Gary Paulsen, and Laurence Yep
"In addition to the editor's well-crafted introductions to the writers, the volume contains contemporary photos and childhood snapshots, reproductions of edited manuscript pages and a selected bibliography of each author's oeuvre. An excellent choice for aspiring writers and avid readers." Publ Wkly

Barker, Keith, d. 1998
Outstanding books for children and young people; the LA guide to Carnegie/Greenaway winners 1937-1997. Library Assn. Pub.; distributed by Bernan Assocs. 1998 135p il pa $35
　　　028.5
1. Children's literature—Bibliography 2. Carnegie medal 3. Kate Greenaway medal
ISBN 1-85604-287-1
An annotated list of the prestigious British book awards winners
"The gossip and strong opinions (Barker makes no bones about which books he thinks were good choices and which books he thinks were inferior) makes this survey informative as well as readable, and it's fascinating to see the trends both in awards and in responses." Bull Cent Child Books

Bodart, Joni Richards
Radical reads; 101 YA novels on the edge. Scarecrow Press 2002 376p pa $34.95
　　　028.5
1. Teenagers—Books and reading 2. Young adult literature—Bibliography
ISBN 0-8108-4287-4　　　LC 2001-57705
This resource examines "the 'edgy, raw, and relevant' in contemporary YA literature. The entries, arranged alphabetically by title, include bibliographic information, suggested reading and interest levels, and an extensive list of keywords that helps describe each book's content. . . . Detailed booktalk and discussion tips and ideas, a well-written and informative booktalk, and excerpts from reviews are provided. . . . The 101 selections, dating from 1994 to 2001, offer a balanced depiction of the literature and its authors." SLJ
Includes bibliographical references

Bromann, Jennifer
Booktalking that works. Neal-Schuman 2001 155p (Teens @ the library series) pa $35
　　　028.5
1. Book talks 2. Young adults' libraries 3. Teenagers—Books and reading
ISBN 1-55570-403-4　　　LC 2001-18340
This presents "a variety of booktalking techniques, selection tips for booktalk titles, and how to write and prepare for booktalks. The book begins by addressing who today's teenagers are, what they want, and what they need. There are specific magazines, catalogs, and on-line Web sites mentioned for selection." Book Rep
"Practical, smart, hip, and irreverent. . . . A fun read that will encourage you to find your own personal style." Booklist
Includes bibliographical references

Brown, Joanne, 1933-
Declarations of independence; empowered girls in young adult literature, 1990-2001; {by} Joanne Brown, Nancy St. Clair. Scarecrow Press 2002 194p (Scarecrow studies in young adult literature) lib bdg $32.50　　　**028.5**
1. Young adult literature—History and criticism
ISBN 0-8108-4290-4　　　LC 2002-17585
"The authors describe and critically evaluate the representation of female protagonists in fiction and memoirs written by Americans for young adults. . . . This nice introduction to feminist approaches in young adult literature is highly recommended for all those working with teens and their literature." Voice Youth Advocates
Includes bibliographical references

Children's books from other countries; {sponsored by} United States Board on Books for Young People; Carl M. Tomlinson, editor. Scarecrow Press 1998 304p il pa $32.95　　　**028.5**
1. Children—Books and reading 2. Children's literature—Bibliography
ISBN 0-8108-3447-2　　　LC 97-41768
This is a "reference guide to children's titles originally published outside of the U.S. and translated into English. This resource is divided into three sections, containing a broad overview of the field, advice on how to use the books, and signed evaluative annotations for over 700 titles, arranged by genre." SLJ
"An excellent tool that shows and tells the importance of global reach." Booklist
Includes bibliographical references

Children's books in children's hands; an introduction to their literature; [by] Charles Temple ... {et al.} ; with contributions by Evelyn B. Freeman. 2nd ed. Allyn and Bacon 2002 xxvi, 612p il $97.20　　　**028.5**
1. Children's literature—History and criticism 2. Books and reading
ISBN 0-205-31846-0　　　LC 2001-33671
First published 1998
Includes CD-ROM
Part I covers the intellectual development of children, literary elements of children's literature, and reader response criticism. Part II surveys the literature by genre.

Children's books in children's hands—*Continued*

Part III shows how to create a literature-based classroom through activities, classroom libraries, and book discussions. This edition ends with a new chapter on teaching both literary and literature-based content units. Appendices list award-winning titles, professional organizations, publishers, children's periodicals and Web sites

Includes bibliographical references

Closter, Kathryn, 1950-

Fiction, food, and fun; the original recipe for the Read 'n' Feed Program; [by] Kathryn Closer, Karen L. Sipes, and Vickie Thomas; foreword by Caroline B. Cooney. Libraries Unlimited 1998 xx, 224p il pa $30.95 **028.5**

1. Books and reading

ISBN 1-56308-519-4   LC 98-9511

This "resource provides detailed information—activities, publicity, discussion questions, author background, and more—for 10 titles. . . . The program is designed to introduce young people to quality literature, actively involve them in discussion, and encourage them to become lifelong readers. Each chapter includes bibliographic information, suggested interest level, plot summary, and a booktalk." SLJ

Includes bibliographical references

The **Coretta** Scott King Awards book, 1970-1999; edited by Henrietta M. Smith. American Lib. Assn. 1999 135p pa $40 **028.5**

1. Coretta Scott King Award 2. Children's literature—History and criticism 3. American literature—African American authors 4. African Americans in literature

ISBN 0-8389-3496-X   LC 99-25046

First published 1994

"Coretta Scott King Task Force, Social Responsibilities Round Table" --p.viii

This work begins with discussions of the 1994-1999 award winners and honor books and then goes back year by year to 1969

"The text is broken up with quotes from the winning titles, and the book ends with photos and biographies of the authors and artists. An essential resource." Booklist

Includes index

The **Dictionary** of characters in children's literature; Beverly Ann Chin, general editor. Watts 2002 128p il $34 **028.5**

1. Children's literature—Dictionaries 2. Characters and characteristics in literature

ISBN 0-531-11984-X   LC 2001-17771

This reference describes over 550 characters in children's literature and includes brief book summaries, book jackets and illustrations, author anecdotes, and review excerpts

"Beverly Ann Chin does an admirable job of choosing characters from traditional and contemporary literature, as well as different cultures and time periods. The content is well organized and easy to understand." Book Rep

Includes bibliographical references

Donelson, Kenneth L.

Literature for today's young adults; [by] Kenneth L. Donelson, Alleen Pace Nilsen. 7th ed. Pearson/Allyn and Bacon 2004 c2005 478p il $93.33 **028.5**

1. Young adult literature—History and criticism 2. Books and reading

ISBN 0-205-41035-9   LC 2004-44306

First published 1980

Authors' names appear in reverse order in 6th ed

This is an "introduction to young adult literature framed within . . . literary, historical, and social context. It also provides . . . criteria for evaluating books of all genres, from poetry and nonfiction to mysteries, science fiction, and horror. [It includes] coverage of . . . issues, such as pop culture and mass media." Publisher's note

Includes bibliographical references

Gillespie, John Thomas

The Newbery companion; booktalk and related materials for Newbery Medal and Honor books; [by] John T. Gillespie, Corinne J. Naden. 2nd ed. Libraries Unlimited 2001 465p $59 **028.5**

1. Newbery Medal 2. Children's literature—History and criticism 3. Authors

ISBN 1-56308-813-4   LC 00-45092

First published 1996

This "covers Newbery winners and honor books from 1922 through 2001. Each entry includes a plot summary, themes and subjects, incidents for booktalking, related titles, and a bibliography about the author. Honor books are each given only a plot summary. . . . This work supersedes the first edition and is essential for public, school, academic, and other libraries serving students of children's literature." Booklist

Includes bibliographical references

Jweid, Rosann, 1933-

Building character through literature; a guide for middle school readers; [by] Rosann Jweid, Margaret Rizzo. Scarecrow Press 2001 232p $34.50 **028.5**

1. Best books 2. Children's literature—Bibliography 3. Young adult literature—Bibliography 4. Characters and characteristics in literature

ISBN 0-8108-3951-2   LC 00-46401

"This book describes fifty young adult novels chosen for their protagonists' trials of character. The entry for each book includes awards, characters, setting, plot summary, discussion questions, supplemental projects, vocabulary lists, and author biography; sometimes there are comments from the author. The books span more than a century." Voice Youth Advocates

"This book is an invaluable tool for booktalks, book reports, and unit/lesson plans." Book Rep

Includes bibliographical references

Keane, Nancy J.

Booktalking across the curriculum; the middle years. Libraries Unlimited 2002 217p il pa $30 **028.5**

1. Books and reading 2. Children's literature 3. Book talks

ISBN 1-56308-937-8   LC 2002-12171

Keane, Nancy J.—*Continued*

"More than 170 booktalks and an additional 330 suggested books for middle-school students are organized by subject. . . . Most of the books are fiction, but 10 percent are nonfiction. Brief booktalks are followed by learning extensions and suggestions for further reading." Booklist

"The booktalks are well written, easy to use, and encourage critical thinking." Libr Media Connect

Knowles, Elizabeth, 1946-

Reading rules! motivating teens to read; {by} Elizabeth Knowles, Martha Smith. Libraries Unlimited 2001 168p pa $33.50 **028.5**

1. Teenagers—Books and reading 2. Young adult literature—Bibliography

ISBN 1-56308-883-5   LC 2001-29738

"Some of the strategies discussed are literature circles, book clubs, booktalks, interdisciplinary and thematic units, and reading in the content areas. Each chapter has the same format: identification of the problem or strategy, professional development questions, practical application suggestions, annotated young adult literature titles, annotated professional journal articles, annotated professional books, and Web sites." Book Rep

Includes bibliographical references

Krashen, Stephen D.

The power of reading; insights from the research; by Stephen D. Krashen. 2nd ed. Libraries Unlimited 2004 199p bibl diag tab $25

028.5

1. Reading 2. Literacy

ISBN 1-59158-169-9 (pa)   LC 2004-44207

First published 1993

The author presents research for "the argument that free voluntary reading (FVR) is the most effective tool available for increasing literacy. . . . Some of the topics he explores include the research surrounding second language acquisition, reading rewards and incentives programs, and some of today's popular 'electronic reading products.' " Publisher's note

Includes bibliographical references

Langemack, Chapple

The booktalker's bible; how to talk about the books you love to any audience; Chapple Langemack. Libraries Unlimited 2003 199p pa $30

028.5

1. Book talks

ISBN 1-563-08944-0   LC 2003-47543

"This book reminds readers that booktalks . . . are an effective way to present books and can be aimed at all types of settings . . . and age groups. It explains why booktalks are needed, tells how to hold one, and offers tips for a fail-safe presentation. Each chapter provides practical examples and closes with additional reading. Appendixes include sample talks and ideas for titles as well as other helpful resources." Booklist

Includes bibliographical references

Larson, Jeanette C.

Bringing mysteries alive for children and young adults; [by] Jeanette Larson. Linworth Pub. 2004 134p il pa $39.95   **028.5**

1. Children—Books and reading 2. Teenagers—Books and reading 3. Mystery fiction

ISBN 1-586-83012-0   LC 2003-22064

Contents: Introducing mystery; Defining mystery; Appreciating mysteries; Looking at series mysteries; Suggestions for integrating mysteries into the curriculum; Programming with mysteries

"The book has excellent ideas for beginning as well as seasoned professionals." SLJ

Includes bibliographical references

The **Newbery** & Caldecott medal books, 1986-2000; a comprehensive guide to the winners; [by] the Horn Book, Association for Library Service to Children. American Lib. Assn. 2001 368p il   **028.5**

1. Newbery Medal 2. Caldecott Medal 3. Children's literature—History and criticism 4. Authors 5. Illustrators

ISBN 0-8389-3505-2   LC 00-53430

This volume "chronologically presents the Newbery and Caldecott acceptance speeches, biographical essays on the authors and artists, and the original 'Horn Book Magazine' and 'Booklist' reviews of the award winners." Horn Book

Includes bibliographical references

Newbery and Caldecott Medal books, 1966-1975; with acceptance papers, biographies and related material chiefly from The Horn Book magazine; edited by Lee Kingman. Horn Bk. 1975 xx, 321p il $22.95   **028.5**

1. Newbery Medal 2. Caldecott Medal 3. Children's literature—History and criticism 4. Authors 5. Illustrators

ISBN 0-87675-003-X

Continues Newbery Medal books, 1922-1955, Caldecott Medal books, 1938-1957 (o.p.), and Newbery and Caldecott Medal books, 1956-1965 (o.p.)

"Gives for each Newbery or Caldecott award winner his acceptance speech, a biographical note, and a book note. An excerpt from each Newbery book gives an example of the writer's style; a sample illustration from each Caldecott book is supplemented by notes on size, medium, printing process, number of illustrations and type used." Choice

Newbery and Caldecott Medal books, 1976-1985; with acceptance papers, biographies, and related material chiefly from The Horn Book magazine; edited by Lee Kingman. Horn Bk. 1986 358p il $24.95   **028.5**

1. Newbery Medal 2. Caldecott Medal 3. Children's literature—History and criticism 4. Authors 5. Illustrators

ISBN 0-87675-004-8   LC 86-15223

This volume "compiles the winning speeches, biographies and book notes for the 1976 through 1985 awards. It includes essays by Barbara Bader, Ethel Heins and Zena Sutherland." Bookbird

Newbery Medal books, 1922-1955; with their authors' acceptance papers & related material chiefly from The Horn Book magazine; edited by Bertha Mahony Miller and Elinor Whitney Field. Horn Bk. 1955 458p il $22.95

028.5

1. Newbery Medal 2. Children's literature—History and criticism 3. Authors

ISBN 0-87675-000-5

Companion volume to Caldecott Medal books, 1938-1957

"Largely biographical notes about award recipients and the acceptance papers." Ref Sources for Small & Medium-sized Libr. 5th edition

Stephens, Claire Gatrell

Coretta Scott King Award books; using great literature with children and young adults. Libraries Unlimited 2000 238p pa $27.50

028.5

1. Coretta Scott King Award 2. Children's literature—History and criticism 3. Young adult literature—History and criticism 4. American literature—African American authors 5. African Americans in literature

ISBN 1-56308-685-9   LC 99-51955

"Both author and illustrator award lists are followed by annotated bibliographies. Twelve of the author entries also feature biographical information. The book is chock-full of curricular units for 15 selected titles. The units include discussion questions, crossword puzzles, vocabulary exercises, performance activities, and integrated curriculum ideas. Additionally, lists of related materials and Internet sites are provided." Book Rep

Includes bibliographical references

Sullivan, Edward T.

Reaching reluctant young adult readers; a handbook for librarians and teachers. Scarecrow Press 2002 121p $24.50

028.5

1. Teenagers—Books and reading 2. Young adult literature—Bibliography

ISBN 0-8108-4343-9   LC 2002-21219

"Sullivan explains his concern over the preponderance of 'aliterate' (able to read, but choosing not to) young adults. He defines young adult readers as those between the ages of 10 and 15. . . . He places responsibility for the problem on teachers, librarians, and parents and then offers strategies to reverse the trend. The bulk of the book concentrates on overlooked resources including fiction series and short stories, comics and graphic novels, nonfiction, magazines, picture books, and audiobooks. . . . A bibliography of professional resources completes the practical information provided. . . . A valuable tool to combat the nonreader." Booklist

Sutherland, Zena, 1915-2002

Children and books; [by] Zena Sutherland, May Hill Arbuthnot; chapters contributed by Dianne L. Monson. Longman il $110.80

028.5

1. Children's literature—History and criticism

First edition by May Hill Arbuthnot published 1947 by Scott, Foresman. (9th edition 1997) Periodically revised

"This children's literature textbook emphasizes the best books and authors. The introductory sections about children and books in general are followed by genre overviews which emphasize the major authors in each category. A third section discusses ways to bring children and books together, while a final section covers issues such as censorship. Lavish color illustrations, viewpoint boxes, extensive bibliographies and useful appendices make this an attractive and stimulating work." Safford. Guide to Ref Materials for Sch Libr Media Cent. 5th edition

Trelease, Jim

The read-aloud handbook. 5th ed. Penguin Bks. 2001 xxvi, 402p il pa $15

028.5

1. Books and reading 2. Children's literature—Bibliography

ISBN 0-14-100161-5   LC 2001-21012

First published 1982

This handbook explains the importance of reading aloud to children, offers guidance on how to set up a read-aloud atmosphere in the home or classroom, and "shows readers how to take full advantage of recent cultural and technological developments. A new chapter explores important lessons from Oprah, Harry Potter, and the Internet, and an updated appendix lists key Internet sites for children's literature and education." Publisher's note

Includes bibliographical references

York, Sherry, 1947-

Children's and young adult literature by Latino writers; a guide for librarians, teachers, parents, and students. Linworth Pub. 2002 184p pa $36.95

028.5

1. American literature—Hispanic American authors—Bibliography 2. Young adult literature—Bibliography 3. Children's literature—Bibliography 4. Books and reading

ISBN 1-58683-062-7   LC 2002-67112

This guide includes "bibliographic information for a variety of titles in various genres including novels, chapter books, short stories, folklore, drama, poetry, and nonfiction. A list of additional resource materials, as well as publisher information and an index, is also included." Publisher's note

"This publication fills a necessary void for professionals looking for all forms of Latino literature for primary grades through high school. . . . This book should provide the framework for building a solid collection." SLJ

028.7 Use of books and other information media as sources of information

Riedling, Ann Marlow, 1952-

Learning to learn; a guide to becoming information literate; introduction by Michael Eisenberg. Neal-Schuman 2002 129p pa $24.95

028.7

1. Research 2. Internet resources 3. Internet searching

ISBN 1-55570-452-2   LC 2002-26532

Riedling, Ann Marlow, 1952-—*Continued*
This is a "guide to the research/learning process. Chapters lead researchers step-by-step through the information maze to find what they are looking for. Numerous URLs and exercises are included, as is material on copyright, plagiarism, and basic citation styles. . . . The section on evaluating Web sites is particularly valuable. As an added bonus, all mentioned sites are updated and hyperlinked at the publisher's Web site. This is a practical guide for all librarians, but particularly for those teaching research skills." SLJ
Includes bibliographical references

031   General encyclopedic works in American English

Compton's encyclopedia & fact-index. Success Pub. Group, P.O. Box 1167, Elmhurst, Il 60126 26v il maps set $649   **031**
1. Encyclopedias and dictionaries
First published 1922 with title: Compton's pictured encyclopedia. Frequently revised
Supplemented by: Compton's yearbook
"Recommended for home and school use by young people ages nine through eighteen. The main text, consisting of more than 5,000 articles, is supported by nearly 30,000 brief articles among the 70,000 entries in the 'fact-index.' This volume presents brief dictionary entries, biographical sketches, statistics, and capsule treatments of topics not considered in the main text." Ref Sources for Small & Medium-sized Libr. 6th edition

The **Encyclopedia** Americana. Grolier 30v il maps
                                                            031
1. Encyclopedias and dictionaries
ISBN apply to publisher for price
Also available online
First published 1829. Frequently revised
"An encyclopedia suitable for junior and senior high school students as well as adults and college-level students. Cross-references are plentiful throughout the 45,000 articles. The index is comprehensive and analytical. *Americana* contains an exceptionally large number of U.S. place-names and biographies. The sciences, mathematics, American history, and the social sciences are particularly well developed. There are bibliographies at the end of major articles, nearly 400 of which have been updated for this edition." Ref Sources for Small & Medium-sized Libr. 6th edition
For a review of 2004 edition see: Booklist, Sept. 15, 2004

Hirsch, E. D. (Eric Donald), 1928-
The new dictionary of cultural literacy; [by] E.D. Hirsch, Joseph F. Kett, James Trefil. Completely rev and updated, 3rd ed. Houghton Mifflin 2002 647p il maps $29.95   **031**
  1. Civilization—Dictionaries 2. English language—Dictionaries
ISBN 0-618-22647-8   LC 2002-27609
First published 1988 with title: The dictionary of cultural literacy

"The text is divided into sections by subject—e.g., fine arts, world politics, life sciences—each with a brief introduction; access is also aided by a thorough index. The entries themselves are complete, concise, and clearly written as well as extensively and effectively cross-referenced." Libr J

The **New** Grolier children's encyclopedia. Grolier Educ. 1999 10v il $225   **031**
1. Encyclopedias and dictionaries
ISBN 0-7172-9373-4   LC 98-7378
First published 1994 with title: The Grolier children's encyclopedia
Topics range "from science-related areas such as astronomy and wolves to social studies considerations such as geographic information and historical milestones. Each topic is clearly defined initially, and then subtopics are identified and described in the text. . . . Information is vibrantly enhanced through an effective display of illustrations, charts, and graphics." Sci Books Films

Oxford American children's encyclopedia. 2nd ed. Oxford University Press 2002 9v il map set $325   **031**
1. Encyclopedias and dictionaries
ISBN 0-19-515568-8   LC 2002-728277
First published 1998
This encyclopedia "includes more than 2,000 entries. . . . Listed alphabetically and color coded by letter, the entries {offer} information {with} . . . photos, . . . illustrations, diagrams, maps, charts, and sidebars. The set includes a separate volume of nearly 500 biographies." Publisher's note

Scholastic children's encyclopedia. Scholastic Reference 2004 710p il map $19.95 (4 and up)
                                                            031
1. Encyclopedias and dictionaries
ISBN 0-439-43816-0   LC 2003-45591
"More than 600 entries are arranged alphabetically and range in length from one-half page to just over four pages. Entries are illustrated with more than 2,000 photographs, diagrams, charts, time lines, and maps. Longer entries include subheadings that divide text into easy-to-read sections. . . . Libraries serving younger students will want multiple copies of this highly usable and user-friendly tool." Booklist

The **World** Book encyclopedia. World Bk. 22v il maps   **031**
1. Encyclopedias and dictionaries
ISBN apply to publisher for price
Also available CD-ROM version, The World Book multimedia encyclopedia, and online
First published 1917-1918 by Field Enterprises. Frequently revised
Supplemented by: World Book's year in review; another available annual supplement is World Book's science year in review
"Curriculum-oriented, this superior encyclopedia is well-edited and produced to meet the reference and informational needs of students from grade four through high school. Long standing tradition of excellence for readability, accuracy, authoritativeness, objectivity, judicious and extensive use of outstanding graphics and timeli-

The World Book encyclopedia—*Continued*
ness." N Y Public Libr. Ref Books for Child Collect
For a review of 2004 edition see: Booklist, Sept. 15,
2004

031.02   American books of miscellaneous facts

Ash, Russell
The top 10 of everything. DK Pub. $27; pa $19
031.02
1. Curiosities and wonders 2. World records
Annual. First published 1994
This illustrated collection of facts and trivia features
1,000 lists encompassing human achievements and the
natural world
"This book is sure to get lots of browsing attention
and has much supplemental information for report writers." SLJ

Encyclopaedia Britannica almanac. Encyclopaedia
Britannica pa $11.95 **031.02**
1. Almanacs 2. Statistics 3. United States—Statistics
Annual. First published 2002
"Features include biographies of notable figures, from
the past as well as the present; a lookup of thousands of
facts covering various branches of knowledge (e.g., science, business, history, entertainment, sports, and the
arts). . . . There are also entries for countries and their
leaders, with maps, flags, and various statistics; for
awards and award winners; for sporting events; and
much more." Libr J
For a fuller review see: Booklist, May 15, 2003

Information please almanac, atlas & yearbook.
Houghton Mifflin il maps $24.95 $10.95
031.02
1. Almanacs 2. Statistics 3. United States—Statistics
ISSN 0073-7860
Annual. First published 1947 by Doubleday. Publisher
varies
"Statistical and factual material organized by subject
area; contains special articles by experts. Illustrated, with
a color map section and detailed index." N Y Public Libr
Book of How & Where to Look It Up

Kane, Joseph Nathan, 1899-2002
Famous first facts; a record of first happenings,
discoveries, and inventions in American history;
by Joseph Nathan Kane, Steven Anzovin, Janet
Podell. 5th ed. Wilson, H.W. 1997 xxix, 1122p
$160 **031.02**
1. Encyclopedias and dictionaries 2. United States—
History—Dictionaries
ISBN 0-8242-0930-3   LC 97-31252
Also available CD-ROM version and online
First published 1933
"Aims to establish the earliest date of various occurrences, achievements, inventions, etc. Dictionary arrangement with many cross-references. Gives brief description
or explanation together with the date; some references to
sources." Guide to Ref Books. 11th edition

The New York Times almanac. Penguin Ref. il
maps $11.95 **031.02**
1. Almanacs 2. Statistics 3. United States—Statistics
Annual. First published 1997
Edited by John W. Wright
This almanac contains a "chronology of the year; major news stories of the year; U.S. history; U.S. presidential biographies; world history; world geography; economic and climate data; major awards in the arts, sciences, and sports; and a wide variety of U.S. demographic information. . . . It is well organized, the table layout
is easy to read, and the typeface does not invite eye
strain." Am Ref Books Annu, 1998

Packard, Mary
Ripley's believe it or not! by Mary Packard and
the editors of Ripley Entertainment; illustrations by
Leanne Franson. Special ed. Scholastic 2001 143p
il lib bdg $14.95 **031.02**
1. Curiosities and wonders
ISBN 0-439-26040-X   LC 2001-20936
This is a collection of more than 700 hard to believe
stories under such chapter headings as "The Sporting
Life," "Out of the Odd-inary," and "Downright Spooky,"
from Ripley's the "Believe It or Not" newspaper cartoon
panel

Pascoe, Elaine
Scholastic kid's almanac; facts, figures, and
stats; written by Elaine Pascoe, Deborah Kops, and
Jenifer Morse ; illustrated by Bob Italiano and
David C. Bell. rev. ed. Scholastic Reference 2004
il map pa $12.95 (4 and up) **031.02**
1. Encyclopedias and dictionaries
ISBN 0-439-56078-0
"A Georgian Bay book"
First published 1999
This is a compilation of facts, illustrations, graphs,
and statistics alphabetically arranged under 38 topics
such as aerospace, animals, arts and music, calendars and
holidays, energy, environment, health, math, religion,
sports, and zodiac.

The World almanac and book of facts. World
Almanac Educ. il maps $32.95; pa $12.95
031.02
1. Almanacs 2. Statistics 3. United States—Statistics
ISSN 0084-1382
Annual. First published 1868. Publisher varies
"This is the most comprehensive and well-known of
almanacs. . . . Contains a chronology of the year's
events, consumer information, historical anniversaries,
annual climatological data, and forecasts. Color section
has flags and maps. Includes detailed index." N Y Public
Libr Book of How & Where to Look It Up

The World almanac for kids. World Almanac il
maps $21.95; pa $11.95 **031.02**
1. Almanacs
Annual. First published 1995 for 1996
This volume contains information on animals, art, religion, sports, books, law, language, science and computers. Includes a section of full-color maps and flags. Illustrated throughout with pictures, diagrams, and charts

032.02 English books of miscellaneous facts

Guinness book of records. Guinness Media il
$27.95 **032.02**
1. Curiosities and wonders
ISSN 1057-4557
Also available in paperback from Bantam Bks.
Annual. First published 1955 in the United Kingdom;
in the United States 1962. Variant titles: Guinness book
of world records; Guinness world records
Editors and publisher vary
"Ready reference for current record holders in all
fields, some esoteric. Index provides access to information arranged in broad subject categories. Must be replaced annually." N Y Public Libr. Ref Books for Child
Collect

051 General serial publications in American English

Abridged readers' guide to periodical literature.
Wilson, H.W. $205 per year **051**
1. Periodicals—Indexes
ISSN 0001-334X
First published July 1935. Monthly except June, July,
and August (The indexing for these months is included
in the September issue). Permanent bound annual cumulations
An index to over 80 periodicals of general interest
which have been chosen by the subscribers to the index
from the approximately 200 periodicals covered by the
unabridged Readers' guide to periodical literature. The
form of indexing is the same as that used in the unabridged Readers' guide
"Designed especially for school and small public libraries unable to afford the regular Readers' guide."
Sheehy. Guide to Ref Books. 11th edition

Readers' guide to periodical literature. Wilson,
H.W. $385 per year **051**
1. Periodicals—Indexes
ISSN 0034-0464
Also available online
First published 1900. Monthly. Permanent bound annual cumulations
A free pamphlet: How to use the Reader's guide to
periodical literature, is available upon request
A cumulative author and subject index to over 300 periodicals. Coverage includes computers, business, health,
fashion, politics, education, science, sports, arts and literature with criticism of individual dramatic works,
videodiscs and videotapes, operas, ballets, musicals, movies, phonograph records, dance, and television and radio
programs
"This is a modern index of the best type." Sheehy.
Guide to Ref Books. 10th edition

060.4 General rules of order (Parliamentary procedure)

Riddick, Floyd M.
Riddick's Rules of procedure; a modern guide
to faster and more efficient meetings; [by] Floyd
M. Riddick & Miriam H. Butcher. Scribner 1985
224p o.p. Madison Bks. paperback available $30
060.4
1. Parliamentary practice
ISBN 0-8191-8064-5 (pa) LC 85-18470
"Since most people find *Robert's Rules of Order* difficult to use, this simplified guide to parliamentary procedure is recommended. It discusses various processes alphabetically, making it easier to locate a specific rule.
. . . The work is authoritative." Safford. Guide to Ref
Materials for Sch Libr Media Cent. 5th edition

Robert, Henry Martyn, 1837-1923
The Scott, Foresman Robert's Rules of order
newly revised. a new and enl ed, by Sarah Corbin
Robert, with the assistance of Henry M. Robert III,
William J. Evans. Scott, Foresman $35; pa $16.95
060.4
1. Parliamentary practice
A simplified paperback version with title: The new
Robert's Rules of order, by Mary A. De Vries, is avail-
able from New Am. Lib.
First published 1876 as: Pocket manual of rules of or-
der for deliberate assemblies. Later editions have title:
Robert's Rules of order
"Long the standard compendium of parliamentary law,
explaining methods of organizing and conducting the
business of societies, conventions, and other assemblies.
Includes convenient charts and tables." Ref Sources for
Small & Medium-sized Libr. 6th edition

070.1 News media

Garner, Joe
We interrupt this broadcast; the events that
stopped our lives—from the Hindenburg explosion
to the attacks of September 11. Updated 3rd ed.
Sourcebooks 2002 178p il + 2 sound discs $49.95
070.1
1. Television broadcasting of news 2. Broadcast journalism 3. Disasters
ISBN 1-57071-974-8 LC 2003-265013
First published 1998
"This book and double-CD set documents, in text, audio and black-and-white photographs, the moments when
history, for better or for worse (though usually for
worse), was made in an instant. . . . In addition to the
CDs' reports and sound bites dramatically introduced and
explained . . . each event gets about four pages of coverage, with an efficient summary and at least half a doz-
en photos. . . . These are the kinds of moments that still
shock and amaze. This moving book is 'a tribute of
sorts' to the events that defined eras, the journalists who
reported on them and the media television, radio that
made us all witnesses." Publ Wkly

Spangenburg, Ray, 1939-
TV news; can it be trusted? [by] Ray
Spangenburg and Kit Moser. Enslow Pubs. 2003
112p il (Issues in focus) lib bdg $20.95 (7 and up)
070.1
1. Television broadcasting of news
ISBN 0-7660-1942-X   LC 2002-12523
Discusses what makes a story newsworthy, the different
people who are part of television newscasts, the reli-
ability and distortions of these broadcasts, and how to
use critical thinking when watching the news
"This book does a good job of exploring the forces
that have gradually compromised the quality of television
journalism." SLJ
Includes glossary and bibliographical references

Wakin, Edward
How TV changed America's mind. Lothrop, Lee
& Shepard Bks. 1996 248p il $17.95 (7 and up)
070.1
1. Broadcast journalism
ISBN 0-688-13482-3   LC 94-22542
This book surveys television "news and documentary
reports—decade by decade from the '50s through the
'90s, examining ways in which the medium changed his-
tory or affected Americans' views of themselves. . . .
This is a clear, persuasive, and useful synthesis of the
immense significance of television in recent history."
Bull Cent Child Books
Includes bibliography

070.4 Journalism

Colman, Penny
Where the action was; women war
correspondents in World War II. Crown 2002 118p
il maps $17.95; lib bdg $19.99   **070.4**
1. Women journalists 2. World War, 1939-1945—
Women 3. World War, 1939-1945—Journalists
ISBN 0-517-80075-6; 0-517-80076-4 (lib bdg)
LC 2001-28689
This describes the work of such journalists as Margaret Bourke-White, Martha Gellhorn, Dickey Chapelle,
and Marguerite Higgins
"The text is briskly readable, and the 70 black-and-
white photos are impressive and well chosen. . . . This
well-handled book profoundly captures both the times
and the struggle of women who had the talent to do the
job male reporters did, but had to fight harder to do it."
Booklist
Includes bibliographical references

Flash!: the Associated Press covers the world;
introduction by Peter Arnett; edited by Vincent
Alabiso, Kelly Smith Tunney, and Chuck
Zoeller. Abrams 1998 200p il hardcover o.p.
paperback available $24.95   **070.4**
1. Associated Press 2. Journalism 3. Photojournalism
ISBN 0-8109-2793-4 (pa)   LC 97-40307
"A collection of notable news photos 'from the AP
wire' marks the 150th anniversary of the news cooperative begun in 1848, which was the first wire service to

provide photographs. . . . The text here includes Peter
Arnett's appreciation of the AP's ethos and achievements
and a history of the service by Charles J. Hanley." Booklist
"The human side of history is especially evident in
this book in the faces of refugees, movie stars, soldiers,
athletes, and politicians. . . . This outstanding work will
be eagerly pored over in all libraries." Voice Youth Advocates

070.5 Publishing

Brookfield, Karen
Book; written by Karen Brookfield;
photographed by Laurence Pordes. Dorling
Kindersley 2000 63p il (DK eyewitness books)
$15.95; lib bdg $19.99 (4 and up)   **070.5**
1. Books
ISBN 0-7894-5892-6; 0-7894-6597-3 (lib bdg)
First published 1993 by Knopf
Text and photographs trace the evolution of the written word, how the alphabet grew out of pictures, the development of papermaking, bookbinding, children's
books, and more.

100 PHILOSOPHY & PSYCHOLOGY

Weate, Jeremy
A young person's guide to philosophy; "I think,
therefore I am". DK Pub. 1998 64p il $16.99 (5
and up)   **100**
1. Philosophy 2. Philosophers
ISBN 0-7894-3074-6   LC 97-33454
Socrates, Aquinas, Descartes, Nietzsche, Simone de
Beauvoir and Herbert Marcuse are among the thinkers
discussed. Schools of thought and philosophical concepts
are covered
"Teens who have thought about and questioned the
hows, whats, and whys of human existence will find this
introduction fascinating." Booklist

130 Parapsychology and occultism

Steiger, Brad
Gale encyclopedia of the unusual and
unexplained; {by} Brad E. Steiger and Sherry
Hansen Steiger. Thomson/Gale 2003 3v .p il map
set $205   **130**
1. Parapsychology 2. Occultism 3. Supernatural
ISBN 0-7876-5382-9   LC 2003-3995
"These volumes cover broad concepts from 'Afterlife
Mysteries' to 'Invaders from Outer Space.' . . . [This is]
an encyclopedia for believers. The volumes are meant to
'explore and describe the research of those who take
such phenomena seriously.'. . . The work covers material of interest to a large segment of the public in a way
that is clear and readable." Booklist
Includes bibliographical references

Paranormal phenomena: opposing viewpoints; Mary E. Williams, book editor. Greenhaven Press/Thomson Gale 2003 205p il lib bdg $21.95; pa $14.96 (7 and up)   **133**
1. Parapsychology
ISBN 0-7377-1238-4 (lib bdg); 0-7377-1237-6 (pa)
LC 2002-66461
"Opposing viewpoints series"
Replaces the edition published 1997 under the editorship of Paul A. Winters
"Four chapters of four to six essays each offer opinions on the reality of ghosts, psychic ability, extraterrestrial life, UFO's, near-death experiences, reincarnation, and changing concepts of eternal life. Each essay is preceded by an introduction, which poses questions to be answered in the article." SLJ
Includes bibliographical references

133.3 Divinatory arts

Cohen, Daniel, 1936-
Prophets of doom. millennium ed. Millbrook Press 1999 160p il lib bdg $24.90 (7 and up)
133.3
1. End of the world 2. Prophecies
ISBN 0-7613-1317-6   LC 98-38462
First published 1992
This "survey of doomsayers touches on Bible prophecy, the oracles of ancient Greece, and the predictions of Nostradamus. . . . [Cohen discusses] apocalyptic groups such as the Branch Davidians, the portentous nature of the Hale-Bopp comet, and the millennial madness that has fueled terrorist groups." Horn Book Guide
A "nonsensational book about a topic that's a perennial favorite." Booklist
Includes bibliographical references

133.4 Demonology and witchcraft

Black magic and witches; Tamara L. Roleff, book editor. Greenhaven Press 2003 127p (Fact or fiction) $29.95; pa $21.20   **133.4**
1. Witchcraft 2. Magic
ISBN 0-7377-1318-6; 0-7377-1319-4 (pa)
LC 2002-378
Explores both sides of the question of whether or not witchcraft is destructive, looking at issues related to the Harry Potter books, wiccans serving in the military, and the validity of magic
"This is a useful introduction to current debate over witchcraft." SLJ
Includes bibliographical references

Fremon, David K.
The Salem witchcraft trials in American history. Enslow Pubs. 1999 128p il map (In American history) lib bdg $26.60   **133.4**
1. Witchcraft 2. Salem (Mass.)—History
ISBN 0-7660-1125-9   LC 98-6240
Discusses the issues and controversy surrounding the trials, highlighting possible causes and the key figures
Includes bibliographical references

Kallen, Stuart A., 1955-
The Salem witch trials. Lucent Bks. 1999 96p il (World history series) $27.45 (7 and up)
133.4
1. Witchcraft 2. Salem (Mass.)—History
ISBN 1-56006-544-3   LC 98-52010
"Kallen borrows heavily from firsthand accounts such as trial notes and diary excerpts to provide a real sense of these chaotic times. With its exceptional organization and ample background information, this is an excellent resource." SLJ
Includes bibliographical references

Meltzer, Milton, 1915-
Witches and witch-hunts; a history of persecution. Blue Sky Press (NY) 1999 128p $16.95 (4 and up)   **133.4**
1. Witchcraft
ISBN 0-590-48517-2   LC 97-36999
The author "crams a lot of ideas and insights into this ambitious, unusually meaty survey." Publ Wkly
Includes bibliographical references

Roach, Marilynne K.
In the days of the Salem witchcraft trials. Houghton Mifflin 1996 92p il map $16 (4 and up)
133.4
1. Witchcraft 2. Salem (Mass.)—History
ISBN 0-395-69704-2   LC 94-32383
"After discussing the Salem Witchcraft trials in one short chapter, this attractive volume explores the social history of the times to show the context that made such events possible. Topics include the law and punishment, magic, social status, clothing, food, household goods, occupations, recreation, common activities, government, and the political troubles leading to widespread tension and unrest. Readers will come away with a much fuller picture of who lived in Salem and how they lived. Small ink drawings decorate the pages." Booklist
Includes bibliographical references

133.8 Psychic phenomena

ESP; Terry O'Neill, book editor. Greenhaven Press 2003 160p (Fact or fiction) lib bdg $21.96; pa $14.96   **133.8**
1. Extrasensory perception
ISBN 0-7377-1066-7 (lib bdg); 0-7377-1065-9 (pa)
LC 2002-73859
Examines the arguments for and against the existence and usefulness of ESP
"The well-structured introduction provides solid background information on the subject, and the epilogue walks readers through a logical method for analyzing the essays. This work brings a careful, thoughtful balance to a sometimes emotional field." SLJ
Includes bibliographical references

150   Psychology

Gardner, Robert, 1929-
Health science projects about psychology; {by} Robert Gardner and Barbara Gardner Conklin. Enslow Pubs. 2002 112p il (Science projects) $26.60 (7 and up)   **150**
1. Psychology 2. Science projects
ISBN 0-7660-1439-8   LC 2001-3425
Uses science projects to explore such areas of psychology as personality, emotions, perception, learning, memory, and parapsychology
"Schools with psychology classes should find this title helpful as well as schools whose students participate in science fair competitions." Book Rep
Includes bibliographical references

152.14   Visual perception

Jennings, Terry
101 amazing optical illusions; fantastic visual tricks; illustrated by Alex Pang. Sterling 1996 87p il hardcover o.p. paperback available $10.95
                152.14
1. Optical illusions
ISBN 0-8069-9463-0 (pa)   LC 96-37628
"The illusions are divided into three sections that deal with sight . . . perception . . . and movement." SLJ
"Familiar and lesser-known optical illusions are featured in an attractive, informative book. . . . The easy-to-follow instructions and large format make the book a noteworthy choice for the curious minded." Booklist
Includes glossary

Wick, Walter, 1953-
Walter Wick's Optical tricks. Cartwheel Bks. 1998 43p il $13.95 (4 and up)   **152.14**
1. Optical illusions
ISBN 0-590-22227-9   LC 97-35672
Presents a series of optical illusions and explains what is seen
The author "has produced a stunning picture book of optical illusions. With crystal-clear photographs, he creates a series of scenes that fool the eye and the brain." Booklist

152.4   Emotions

Andrews, Linda Wasmer
Emotional intelligence; . Franklin Watts 2004 80p il (Life balance) $19.50   **152.4**
1. Emotions
ISBN 0-531-12335-9   LC 2003-19772
Contents: Dealing with feeling; Name that emotion!; Understanding yourself; Handling Your emotions; Managing relationships
"This book explains that the ability to manage one's emotions and to understand those of others is important for success in life. . . . This title will help young people

to understand themselves and others better, and the tools for managing relationships and one's own emotions will promote maturity and development of social skills." SLJ
Includes glossary and bibliographical references

Crist, James J.
What to do when you're scared & worried; a guide for kids; James Crist. Free Spirit Pub. 2004 128p il pa $9.95 (5 and up)   **152.4**
1. Fear 2. Worry
ISBN 1-575-42153-4
"Part one deals with normal anxiety, offering detailed steps for developing 10 coping mechanisms. Expert help is needed to deal with the more serious problems discussed in Part two (e.g., phobias, separation anxiety, obsessive-compulsive disorder). Throughout, the author provides information, case histories, and coping skills in a manner that is both reassuring and encouraging. . . . Illustrations lighten the tone of the subject matter. " SLJ
Includes bibliographical references

Tym, Kate
Coping with your emotions; {by} Kate Tym and Penny Worms. Raintree 2005 48p il (Get real) $29.93   **152.4**
1. Emotions
ISBN 1-4109-0575-6   LC 2004-8069
Contents: Painfully shy; Feeling blue; Depression; Scaredy cats; Blow your top; Love bug; Lots to smile about
"Chapters consist of a spread presenting an overview of a topic such as depression . . . followed by three case studies about teens dealing with the problem. On the same page, three 'experts' . . . offer advice. . . . The advice of professionals lends credibility to the information presented. . . . Sure to appeal to readers looking for advice." SLJ
Inlcudes glossary and bibliographical references

153.8   Will (Volition)

Bachel, Beverly K., 1957-
What do you really want? how to set a goal and go for it! A guide for teens. Free Spirit 2000 134p il pa $12.95   **153.8**
1. Success 2. Motivation (Psychology)
ISBN 1-57542-085-6   LC 00-57286
The book discusses various ways for teenagers to set goals, build support networks, keep themselves motivated in the process and reap the harvest of their successes
Bachel's "helpful advice is well supported by quotations from teens who have tried some of the techniques, and simple, appealing graphics keep things light. . . . Back matter includes goal-setting resources and some helpful organizations and Web sites." Booklist

153.9   Intelligence and aptitudes

Armstrong, Thomas
You're smarter than you think; a kid's guide to multiple intelligences; edited by Jennifer Brannen. Free Spirit 2003 186p il pa $15.95   **153.9**
1. Intellect
ISBN 1-57542-113-5   LC 2002-2687
Contents: The many ways of being smart; Picture Smart, visualizing your artistic ways; Body Smart, displaying your physical fabulousness; Music Smart, singing out your melodic and rhythmic nature; People Smart, shining forth with your social graces; Self Smart, reflecting on your radiant personality; Nature Smart, exploring the wide world of the outdoors; Number Smart, calculating your math science expertise; Word Smart, verbalizing your literary gifts; Using all your smarts in school; Playing it smart eight ways outside of school; Being smart for the future; MI Pizza
The author "covers eight different intelligences—word, music, logic, picture, body, people, self, and nature—and talks about what they mean." Booklist
"A self-help book that's clear, concise, and fun to peruse." SLJ
Includes bibliographical references

155.5   Psychology of young people

Wells, Donna Koren
Live aware, not in fear; the 411 after 9-11: a book for teens; {by} Donna K. Wells, Bruce C. Morris. Health Communications 2002 160p il pa $9.95 (7 and up)   **155.5**
1. September 11 terrorist attacks, 2001 2. Terrorism 3. Adolescent psychology 4. Stress (Psychology)
ISBN 0-7573-0013-8   LC 2002-19993
A collection of facts, concrete advice, and thought-provoking questions designed to help teens cope with the aftermath of the September 11th, 2001, terrorist attacks, as well as other dangers in today's world
"This book, which is divided into informative text and well-selected question and answers . . . fulfills its purpose." Booklist

155.9   Environmental psychology

Altman, Linda Jacobs, 1943-
Death: an introduction to medical-ethical dilemmas. Enslow Pubs. 2000 112p il (Issues in focus) lib bdg $26.60   **155.9**
1. Death
ISBN 0-7660-1246-8   LC 99-32714
The author "addresses a variety of topics, including the actual physiology of dying, the ethics and legal issues involved in prolonging life, euthanasia, rituals surrounding death, and how various cultures perceive an afterlife. Scattered black-and-white illustrations, a Webliography, and a useful glossary round out the presentation." SLJ
Includes bibliographical references

Cobain, Bev, 1940-
When nothing matters anymore; a survival guide for depressed teens; edited by Elizabeth Verdick. Free Spirit 1998 165p il pa $13.95 (7 and up)   **155.9**
1. Depression (Psychology)
ISBN 1-57542-036-8   LC 98-24911
A guide to understanding and coping with depression, discussing the different types, how and why the condition begins, how it may be linked to substance abuse or suicide, and how to get help
"Cobain has written a book that ought to be on every teacher's desk and in every place teens gather." Book Rep
Includes bibliographical references

Death and dying: opposing viewpoints; Paul A. Winters, book editor. Greenhaven Press 1998 191p il lib bdg $26.20; pa $19.95 (7 and up)   **155.9**
1. Death
ISBN 1-56510-671-7 (lib bdg); 1-56510-670-9 (pa)   LC 97-21804
"Opposing viewpoints series"
A collection of essays which "debate a variety of death-related issues, including appropriate treatment for terminally ill or severely disabled patients and the right to specify the manner and timing of one's death, . . . arguments for and against cryogenic preservation of dead humans are included with discussions of the meaning of near-death experiences. . . . A rich resource for debates as well as opinion." SLJ
Includes bibliographical references

Dennison, Amy
Our dad died; the true story of three kids whose lives changed; as told and illustrated by Amy, Allie, and David Dennison. Free Spirit Pub. 2003 107p pa $9.95 (4 and up)   **155.9**
1. Bereavement 2. Fathers 3. Loss (Psychology)
ISBN 1-57542-135-6   LC 2003-4440
Contents: Finding out that dad died; The night he died; The day before the funeral; The funeral; After the funeral; The first week; Two weeks; Six weeks; Two months; Three months; Four months; Six months; Eight months; The cemetery; One year; Fifteen months; Seventeen months; A year and a half; Twenty-two months; Messages from dad; Grandparents; The future; Suggestions; Letters to dad
"When Amy and Allie were eight and David was four, their father died unexpectedly in his sleep. For the next two years, with their mother's help and encouragement, they kept journals about their reactions to their loss. The chapters are organized chronologically from the time they learned the news through their return to school and other activities. . . . The book is a valuable resource not only for children who have lost a parent but also for the adults who interact with them." SLJ

Gootman, Marilyn E., 1944-
When a friend dies; a book for teens about grieving & healing. Free Spirit 1994 107p pa $9.95 (7 and up)   **155.9**
1. Death 2. Bereavement
ISBN 0-915793-66-0   LC 93-37992

Gootman, Marilyn E., 1944-—*Continued*
This book "aids teenagers who are grieving the loss of a friend, someone of their own generation. The reader is addressed alternately by the author and by teenagers who have experienced such a loss. . . . The young mourner accesses what he or she needs from the book through the questions that are the table of contents." Voice Youth Advocates
Includes bibliographical references

Myers, Edward
When will I stop hurting? teens, loss, and grief; illustrations by Kelly Adams. Scarecrow Press 2004 159p il (It happened to me) $34.50 (7 and up) **155.9**
1. Bereavement 2. Loss (Psychology)
ISBN 0-8108-4921-6   LC 2003-23698
"Outlining the phases of the grieving process, Myers incorporates . . . personal accounts and quotes from young adults who have experienced the death of a family member into the text. He discusses the range of emotions young people may have from anger and fear to relief and sadness and assures readers that these feelings are normal." SLJ
This book "will be extremely helpful for teens struggling to understand their emotions following the loss of a loved one. Grieving is well explained and the individual nature of grief is stressed." Libr Media Connect
Includes bibliographical references

Schleifer, Jay
Everything you need to know when someone you know has been killed. Rosen Pub. Group 1998 64p il (Need to know library) lib bdg $25.25 (7 and up) **155.9**
1. Death 2. Bereavement
ISBN 0-8239-2779-2   LC 98-16193
Discusses death and the fear of death, explains the emotions experienced when someone you know is killed, and gives strategies to cope with them
"For students seeking help for themselves or others, this resource offers a valuable first step toward identifying emotional reactions to untimely death and taking action to begin healing." Booklist
Includes bibliographical references

Sneddon, Pamela Shires
Body image; a reality check. Enslow Pubs. 1999 112p il (Issues in focus) lib bdg $26.60 (7 and up) **155.9**
1. Self-acceptance 2. Self-perception
ISBN 0-89490-960-6   LC 98-35120
Discusses the problems with body image, the reasons why some people have a poor body image, and how self-perception and self-acceptance are affected by society
Includes bibliographical references

158   Applied psychology

Andrews, Linda Wasmer
Meditation; Linda Wasmer Andrews. F. Watts 2004 79p (Life balance) $19.50; pa $6.95 (5 and up) **158**
1. Meditation
ISBN 0-531-12219-0; 0-531-16609-0 (pa)
LC 2003-7153
Contents: Meditation myth-busters; The relaxation response; The mind\body\spirit link; Minding your mindfulness
"Andrews emphasizes that meditation is not a flaky practice, or a particularly religious one, but one that's designed to reduce stress and help individuals manage their lives. Four chapters explain the why and how of meditating. . . . [This offers] solid, easy-to-understand information" SLJ
Includes bibliographical references

Canfield, Jack, 1944-
Chicken soup for the teenage soul {I-III}; {by} Jack Canfield, Mark Victor Hansen, Kimberly Kirberger. Health Communications 1997-2000 3v il ea $24 **158**
1. Interpersonal relations 2. Emotions
ISBN 1-55874-468-1 ({I}; 1-55874-615-3 ({II}; 1-55874-761-3 ({III}
Available in paperback ca $12.95
These books cover "teenage subjects running the gamut from love, family ties, and self-esteem to developing values and life crises, such as a death in the family. . . . Teenagers not only helped select the poems, stories, and accounts that have been included but also have written some of them . . . with a few contributions by well-known people, including Sandra Cisneros, Helen Keller, and Robert Fulghum. . . . This isn't a religious book, but it is an inspirational and motivational one, sometimes funny, sometimes poignant." Booklist {review of 1997 volume}
Includes bibliographical references

Chicken soup for the kid's soul; 101 stories of courage, hope, and laughter; {compiled by} Jack Canfield {et al.}. Health Communications 1998 xxv, 398p il $24; pa $12.95 **158**
1. Interpersonal relations 2. Emotions
ISBN 1-55874-608-0; 1-55874-609-9 (pa)
LC 98-16871
A collection of short stories, anecdotes, poems, and cartoons which present a positive outlook on life

Kreiner, Anna
Everything you need to know about creating your own support system. Rosen Pub. Group 1996 64p il (Need to know library) lib bdg $25.25 (7 and up) **158**
1. Interpersonal relations
ISBN 0-8239-2215-4   LC 95-10753
Discusses how teenagers can create their own support system, a group of people in their lives to whom they feel connected and who can help them build skills and

Kreiner, Anna—_Continued_
solve problems

This offers "valuable information in easily understood
language, illustrated with appealing black-and-white and
full-color photographs with a nice mix of genders and
ethnic groups." SLJ

Includes glossary and bibliographical references

McIntyre, Thomas
The behavior survival guide for kids; how to
make good choices and stay out of trouble;
Thomas McIntyre. Free Spirit Pub. 2003 167p pa
$14.95 (5 and up)   **158**
1. Interpersonal relations 2. Conduct of life
ISBN 1-57542-132-1   LC 2003-4565
"The author provides skills and activities to learn and
practice so that new behaviors can replace those that
have resulted in getting students into trouble. . . . Those
motivated to make better choices for how they behave in
school or with friends and family will find much to help
them." Voice Youth Advocates

Romain, Trevor
Cliques, phonies & other baloney. Free Spirit
1998 129p il pa $9.95   **158**
1. Social groups 2. Interpersonal relations
3. Friendship
ISBN 1-57542-045-7   LC 98-36248
Discusses cliques, what they are and their negative aspects, and gives advice on forming healthier relationships
and friendships
"With a sense of ease and lighthearted humor. . . the
author serves up solid advice in friendly, reassuring
prose." SLJ
Includes bibliographical references

Taylor, Julie, 1971-
The girls' guide to friends; straight talk on
making close pals, creating lasting ties, and being
an all-around great friend. Three Rivers Press
(NY) 2002 222p pa $12   **158**
1. Friendship
ISBN 0-609-80857-5   LC 2002-18123
Explores the comforts and confusions of friendship,
discussing the different kinds of friends, keeping in touch
with friends, mixing romance and friendship, the impact
of friendship, saving a friendship, and more
"In her practical guide, journalist Taylor maintains the
format and bouncy voice of teen-oriented magazines,
with slang, cutesy wordplay, and plenty of how-tos."
Booklist

170   Ethics (Moral philosophy)

Robinson, Sharon, 1950-
Jackie's nine; Jackie Robinson's values to live
by; courage, determination, teamwork, persistence,
integrity, citizenship, justice, commitment,
excellence. Scholastic 2001 181p il $15.95; pa
$4.99   **170**
1. Robinson, Jackie, 1919-1972 2. Values
ISBN 0-439-23764-5; 0-439-38550-4 (pa)
                                          LC 2001-269598
"Written by Jackie Robinson's daughter, this book
contains nine sections, each focusing on one of nine
values the ballplayer lived by (courage, determination,
and so on). Each section contains a scene from the author's life, one from her father's (by various writers,
including Robinson himself), and a sketch of one of her
heroes." Horn Book Guide
"The glimpses into Robinson's life and that of her famous father are stirringly honest, and the hero stories are
thought provoking. . . . The short essays are readable,
and the generous number of photos enhances the collection nicely." Voice Youth Advocates

174   Occupational ethics

Ethics in school librarianship; a reader; edited by
Carol Simpson. Linworth Pub 2003 164p pa
$44.95   **174**
1. School libraries 2. Librarians—Ethics
ISBN 1-586-83084-8   LC 2003-7956
Contents: An ethical dilemma by Carol Simpson; Ethical issues in collection development by Kay Bishop; Ethics in access by Mary Ann Bell; Confidentiality in the
school library by Harry Willems; Ethics in the use of
technology by Doug Johnson; Ethics and intellectual
freedom by Carrie Gardner; Ethics in intellectual property by Carol Simpson; Ethics in the administration of
school library media centers by Nancy Everhart; Ethics
in Internet use by Nancy Willard; Ethics in professional
realtionships by Frank Hoffman
This is a compilation of "articles dealing with the ethical aspects of collection development, access, confidentiality, technology, intellectual freedom, intellectual property, administration, Internet use, and professional relationships. . . . School librarians and administrators
would do well to have this thought and discussion-
provoking book on hand." SLJ
Includes bibliographical references

174.2   Medical ethics

Biomedical ethics: opposing viewpoints; Tamara
L. Roleff, book editor. Greenhaven Press 1998
252p lib bdg $31.20; pa $19.95 (7 and up)
                                                  174.2
1. Medical ethics 2. Bioethics
ISBN 1-56510-793-4 (lib bdg); 1-56510-792-6 (pa)
                                          LC 97-51374
"Opposing viewpoints series"
Replaces the edition published 1994 under the
editorship of Terry O'Neill

Biomedical ethics: opposing viewpoints—*Continued*

Presents opposing viewpoints on biomedical ethics issues such as human cloning, genetic research and engineering, organ transplants and reproductive technologies

Includes glossary and bibliographical references

Cloning; Paul A. Winters, book editor. Greenhaven Press 1998 89p (At issue) lib bdg $27.45; pa $18.70 (7 and up) **174.2**
1. Cloning
ISBN 1-56510-753-5 (lib bdg); 1-56510-752-7 (pa)
LC 97-28560
"Opposing viewpoints series"
Scientists, theologians and philosophers debate the cloning of animals and humans. Included is an interview with Ian Wilmut, who cloned Dolly the sheep
Includes bibliographical references

Goodnough, David
The debate over human cloning; a pro/con issue. Enslow Pubs. 2003 64p il (Hot pro/con issues) lib bdg $27.93 **174.2**
1. Cloning 2. Genetic engineering
ISBN 0-7660-1818-0
LC 2002-5702
Provides an overview of the technology and history of cloning and presents arguments for and against human cloning
"Explains the cloning process in a simple and comprehensible manner. . . . The information is presented in a way that allows readers to see both sides of the debate and to draw their own conclusions. Colorful charts, photographs, and a few helpful diagrams are included." SLJ
Includes glossary and bibliographical references

O'Neill, Terry, 1944-
Biomedical ethics. Greenhaven Press 1999 144p il (Opposing viewpoints digests) lib bdg $27.45; pa $17.45 (7 and up) **174.2**
1. Medical ethics 2. Bioethics
ISBN 1-56510-875-2 (lib bdg); 1-56510-874-4 (pa)
LC 98-37239
Presents opposing viewpoints on various issues of biomedical ethics, including animal testing, human testing, organ transplants, genetic testing, gene therapy, and cloning
Includes bibliographical references

Snedden, Robert
Medical ethics; changing attitudes 1900-2000. Raintree Steck-Vaughn Pubs. 1999 64p il (20th century issues series) lib bdg $32.79 **174.2**
1. Medical ethics
ISBN 0-8172-5893-0
LC 99-26790
Surveys the most significant medical advances of the twentieth century and the ethical questions they have posed, presenting both sides of such issues as reproductive rights, organ transplants, euthanasia, and genetic engineering
"This is a complex issue and Snedden does a good job of explaining it. . . . The author points out all sides of issues, and is up-to-date on facts and philosophies." SLJ
Includes bibliographical references

179 Other ethical norms

Animal rights movement; Kelly Wand, book editor. Greenhaven Press 2003 224p il (American social movements) $33.70; pa $22.45 **179**
1. Animal rights movement
ISBN 0-7377-1046-2; 0-7377-1045-4 (pa)
LC 2002-21476
"Following an introductory overview, excerpts from books and periodicals published between 1972 and 2000 cover such topics as the founding of the ASPCA, the People for the Ethical Treatment of Animals (PETA) movement, and four landmark cases. Differing viewpoints allow for a balanced perspective, and the contents page contains annotations for each essay. Useful for research and reports." SLJ
Includes bibliographical references

Day, Nancy, 1953-
Animal experimentation; cruelty or science? rev ed. Enslow Pubs. 2000 128p il (Issues in focus) lib bdg $26.60 **179**
1. Animal experimentation 2. Animal rights
ISBN 0-7660-1244-1
LC 99-49334
First published 1994
Discusses issues surrounding animal experimentation, including animal rights, medical breakthroughs, and alternatives to animal experimentaion
"Great for reports or debates." Voice Youth Advocates
Includes glossary and bibliographical references

The **Rights** of animals; Tamara L. Roleff, book editor; Jennifer A. Hurley, assistant editor. Greenhaven Press 1999 223p (Current controversies) lib bdg $20.96; pa $12.96 (7 and up) **179**
1. Animal rights
ISBN 0-7377-0069-6 (lib bdg); 0-7377-0068-8 (pa)
LC 98-45934
Includes chapters on animal experimentation, the breeding of animals for human consumption, the ethics of hunting, and animal use in the entertainment industry
"The essays, footnoted and subdivided for easy reference use, provide impassioned, balanced arguments from scientific, religious, and social viewpoints. Bibliography; list of organizations to contact." Booklist

179.7 Respect and disrespect for human life

Euthanasia: opposing viewpoints; James Torr, editor. Greenhaven Press 2000 208p lib bdg $28.70; pa $22.45 (7 and up) **179.7**
1. Euthanasia
ISBN 0-7377-0127-7 (lib bdg); 0-7377-0126-9 (pa)
LC 99-16488
"Opposing viewpoints series"
"The four chapters explore whether euthanasia is ethical, if it should be legalized, if legalization would lead to involuntary killing, and under what circumstances, if any, doctors should assist in suicide." Booklist
Includes bibliographical references

Rebman, Renee C.
Euthanasia and the "right to die"; a pro/con issue. Enslow Pubs. 2002 64p il (Hot pro/con issues) lib bdg $27.93   **179.7**
1. Euthanasia 2. Right to die
ISBN 0-7660-1816-4   LC 2001-5251
The author discusses "the right to die by choice rather than by nature. . . . Rebman steps into the debate by asking what is a 'good death.' . . . She goes on to offer a variety of possible answers without bias, and she paints a historic picture of the controversy and how technology has complicated our definitions of life and death. . . . Objectivity makes this a good reference." Booklist
Includes bibliographical references

181   Eastern philosophy

Slavicek, Louise Chipley, 1956-
Confucianism. Lucent Bks. 2002 128p il maps (Religions of the world) $27.45   **181**
1. Confucianism
ISBN 1-56006-984-8   LC 2001-5773
Discusses what Confucianism is, the life, times, and teachings of Confucius, and the spread and practice of Confucianism in modern times
"Informative and well organized. The writing is clear and the 'Works Consulted' lists include a healthy helping of Web sites." SLJ

200   RELIGION

Birdseye, Debbie Holsclaw
What I believe; kids talk about faith; by Debbie Holsclaw Birdseye and Tom Birdseye; photographs by Robert Crum. Holiday House 1996 32p il $15.95 (4 and up)   **200**
1. Religions
ISBN 0-8234-1268-7   LC 96-11240
Six children of different religious backgrounds tell about their faith and what it means to them; includes background information on each religious tradition
"These simple personal portraits show kids who have made a strong place for religion in their everyday world. . . . An affirmation of faith that goes beyond any single faith." Booklist
Includes bibliographical references

Gaskins, Pearl, 1957-
I believe in—; Christian, Jewish, and Muslim young people speak about their faith; Pearl Gaskins. Cricket Books 2004 205p il $18.95
                    200
1. Faith 2. Teenagers—Religious life
ISBN 0-8126-2713-X   LC 2004-1146
This is a "collection of excerpts from interviews conducted with almost 100 Chicago-area teens—Jews, Christians, and Muslims. Individual chapters include such topics as religious symbols . . . ; following (and breaking) religious laws; women's issues; and the idea of 'many

faiths, one world.'" Booklist
"From this well-structured, open-ended presentation of viewpoints, stereotypes are challenged, moral and ethical conflicts are discussed, and varied perspectives emerge on current issues." SLJ
Includes bibliographical references

Gellman, Marc
How do you spell God? answers to the big questions from around the world; [by] Marc Gellman & Thomas Hartman; illustrated by Jos. A. Smith; with a foreword by his Holiness the Dalai Lama. Morrow Junior Bks. 1995 206p il $17.99; pa $6.95 (5 and up)   **200**
1. Religions
ISBN 0-688-13041-0; 0-688-15296-1 (pa)
                    LC 94-28770
The authors "show how the various religions—Judaism, Christianity, Islam, Buddhism, and Hinduism—deal with the soul-searching questions central to all people. . . . There is also information on each religion's teachers, holy days and places, sanctuaries, and prayers, among other topics." Booklist
This book "is warm, friendly and, most of all, respectful of the importance and variety of belief." Book Rep

Joselit, Jenna Weissman
Immigration and American religion. Oxford Univ. Press 2001 138p il (Religion in American life) lib bdg $28 (7 and up)   **200**
1. Immigrants—United States 2. United States—Religion
ISBN 0-19-511083-8   LC 00-60645
"A chapter each is devoted to Protestantism, Catholicism, Judaism, and the Asian religions. The interesting, well-written text, rich in quotations from immigrants and their religious leaders, tells as much about these new Americans as it does about their religions. . . . Carefully chosen period illustrations round out the volume." SLJ
Includes bibliographical references

Langley, Myrtle
Religion. Dorling Kindersley 2000 61p il (DK Eyewitness books) $15.99   **200**
1. Religion
ISBN 0-7894-5886-1
First published 1996 by Knopf
An illustrated introduction to the religions of the world, including images of "a Passover meal, a lama's headdress, the Wheel of Existence, a picture of Christ's Crucifixion, a Buddhist monk and a shaman's mask. . . . [and text about such topics as] why Buddhists meditate, who Mahavira was, what the five pillars of Islam are, what the Tao is, why Sikhs wear turbans and what Confucius taught." Publisher's note

Murphy, Larry
African-American faith in America; [by] Larry G. Murphy. Facts on File 2003 128p il (Faith in America) $30   **200**
1. African Americans—Religion
ISBN 0-8160-4990-4   LC 2002-28593

Murphy, Larry—*Continued*
"In-depth coverage of diverse religious worship practiced among African Americans is presented. Murphy examines popular Christian religions, but also explores Judaism, Islam, Buddhism, and more. The well-written account begins with the religious experiences of the first Africans in America, moves to the establishment of pioneer religious institutions, and culminates with a chapter on the current status of diverse congregations. . . .Students will find ample material on well-known historical figures and current leaders" SLJ
Includes bibliographical references

The **Wilson** chronology of the world's religions; edited by David Levinson with contributions from John Bowman {et al.}. Wilson, H.W. 2000 688p $110   **200**
1. Religion—History—Chronology
ISBN 0-8242-0978-8   LC 99-52362
"The entries cover religion in the prehistoric and ancient world; world religions, sects, and cults; religious tolerance and intolerance; state religions; and many other topics. The chronology is supplemented by 250 informational sidebars which provide coverage of religions and sects, religious leaders, texts, and major events." Publisher's note
Includes bibliographical references

200.3   Religion--Encyclopedias and dictionaries

The **Encyclopedia** of world religions; Robert S. Ellwood, general editor; Gregory D. Alles, associate editor. Facts on File 1998 390p il maps $45 (7 and up)   **200.3**
1. Religions
ISBN 0-8160-3504-0   LC 97-39529
"Nearly 500 entries cover topics from prehistoric and ancient religions, major contemporary world religions, concepts, symbols, and personages." Booklist
"This encyclopedia presents discussions that are unbiased and succinct, reflects modern scholarship and current problems, and includes areas related to religious practices as well as definitions of the religions themselves. And it's interesting to read." SLJ

200.9   Religion--Historical and geographic treatment

Balmer, Randall Herbert
Religion in twentieth century America; {by} Randall Balmer. Oxford Univ. Press 2001 142p il (Religion in American life) $28 (7 and up)
200.9
1. United States—Religion
ISBN 0-19-511295-4   LC 00-60674
The author "traces the evolution of various movements, including the Pentecostal, Fundamentalist, Evangelical, and New Age movements, the emergence of the Religious Right, Promise Keepers, and televangelism." Booklist

"This title is accessible and reliable, brief and lively, and makes a fine addition to most libraries." SLJ
Includes bibliographical references

Braude, Ann
Women and American religion; Jon Butler & Harry S. Stout, general editors. Oxford Univ. Press 2000 141p il (Religion in American life) lib bdg $28 (7 and up)   **200.9**
1. Women—Religious life 2. United States—Religion
ISBN 0-19-510676-8   LC 99-32968
Braude discusses "how women from various groups, including African Americans, immigrants, and social crusaders, shaped the face of religion in the U.S. . . . Included are individuals such as colonist Margaret Winthrop and African American preacher Jarena Lee, as well as religious leaders such as Mary Baker Eddy and Mother Elizabeth Seaton. Black-and-white illustrations and historical engravings pepper the text." Booklist
Includes bibliographical references

Religion in America: opposing viewpoints; William Dudley, book editor. Greenhaven Press 2002 218p il lib bdg $34.95; pa $23.70 (7 and up)   **200.9**
1. United States—Religion
ISBN 1-56510-003-4 (lib bdg); 1-56510-002-6 (pa)
LC 2001-18806
"Opposing viewpoints series"
Replaces the edition published 1989 under the editorship of Julie S. Bach and Tom Modl
"The book is divided into four broad sections that address the questions: Is America a religious nation? Can religion solve America's problems? What should be done to accommodate religious freedom? What role should religion play in public school? . . . The writings are both thoughtful and provocative." Booklist
Includes bibliographical references

201   Religious mythology & social theology

Barnes, Trevor
The Kingfisher book of religions; festivals, ceremonies, and beliefs from around the world. Kingfisher (NY) 1999 160p il map $23
201
1. Religions
ISBN 0-7534-5199-9   LC 98-53303
Explains the origins, development, beliefs, festivals, and ceremonies of various world faiths and where they are practiced, including Hinduism, Buddhism, Judaism, Christianity, Islam, and traditional religions of Australian aborigines and Native Americans
"This volume is recommended as an attractive introduction for libraries serving intermediate and middle-school students." Booklist

Breuilly, Elizabeth

Religions of the world; the illustrated guide to origins, beliefs, traditions & festivals; {by} Elizabeth Breuilly, Joanne O'Brien, Martin Palmer. Facts on File 1997 160p il map $29.95 (7 and up)

201

1. Religions
ISBN 0-8160-3723-X   LC 97-22829

This "overview of 10 major faiths is divided into three sections: the Abrahamic faiths (Judaism, Christianity, and Islam), the Vedic faiths (Hinduism, Buddhism, and Jainism), and the other major traditions (Shinto, Taoism, Sikhism, and Baha'i). The history, development, ways of worship, and celebrations are given for each. The material is particularly well arranged in a large, handsome format and lavishly illustrated. . . . The writing is scholarly, lucid, and nonpartisan." SLJ

Includes glossary and bibliographical references

Bulfinch, Thomas, 1796-1867

Bulfinch's mythology   **201**

1. Mythology 2. Folklore—Europe 3. Chivalry

Hardcover and paperback editions available from various publishers

First combined edition published 1913 by Crowell. Originally published in three separate volumes 1855, 1858 and 1862 respectively

Contents: The age of fable; The age of chivalry; Legends of Charlemagne

"The classic work on mythology, Bulfinch's gives brief summations of Greek, Roman, Norse, Arthurian, and other miscellaneous myths and includes notes on the 'Iliad', the 'Odyssey', and the 'Aeneid'." N Y Public Libr Book of How & Where to Look It Up

Comparative religions on file; by the Diagram Group. Facts on File 2000 il map loose-leaf $185   **201**

1. Religions 2. Rites and ceremonies
ISBN 0-8160-4254-3   LC 00-39396

This loose-leaf binder of reproducible pages covers "origins, symbols, places of worship, festivals, rituals, leaders, religious groups, and myths. It also includes maps, charts, images, a chronology of religions, the current world population of religions, the basic teachings of certain beliefs, and a description of differences among Christian sects." Book Rep

Glick, Susan

War and peace; Susan Glick. Lucent Books 2004 112p il map (Discovering mythology) $28.70

201

1. Mythology 2. War 3. Peace
ISBN 1-560-06903-1   LC 2004-6290

Contents: Ancient battles between the Babylonian gods of creation; Power struggles in the Aegean; Warrior magic and the Celtic otherworld; War and peace in the wild land of the giants; Vishnu and other demon-fighters of Hindu myth; The hero twins and their fight against the forces of the darkness

This examines the meaning and cultural significance behind the myths concerning war and peace in ancient world cultures

Includes bibliographical references

Hamilton, Virginia, 1936-2002

In the beginning; creation stories from around the world; told by Virginia Hamilton; illustrated by Barry Moser. Harcourt Brace Jovanovich 1988 161p il lib bdg $28; pa $20 (5 and up)

201

1. Creation 2. Mythology
ISBN 0-15-238740-4 (lib bdg); 0-15-238742-0 (pa)

LC 88-6211

A Newbery Medal honor book, 1989

"Hamilton has gathered 25 creation myths from various cultures and retold them in language true to the original. Images from the tales are captured in Moser's 42 full-page illustrations, tantalizing oil paintings that are rich with somber colors and striking compositions. Included in the collection are the familiar stories (biblical creation stories, Greek and Roman myths), and some that are not so familiar (tales from the Australian aborigines, various African and native American tribes, as well as from countries like Russia, China, and Iceland). At the end of each tale, Hamilton provides a brief commentary on the story's origin and originators." Booklist

Includes bibliographical references

Kallen, Stuart A., 1955-

Shamans; by Stuart A. Kallen. Lucent Books 2004 112p il (Mystery library) $28.70

201

1. Shamanism
ISBN 1-59018-628-1   LC 2004-12665

Contents: Introduction: The mystery of Shamanism; An enduring tradition; Communicating with the spirits; Shamanistic healing; Shamans who kill; Shamans in a new age

"The methods employed by shamans to visit the realm of spirits in order to learn how to effect cures are described in some detail. . . . Activities of Siberian and North, Central, and South American shamans receive the most attention. Chinese, Australian aboriginal, Greenlander, ancient Greek, and a few other practitioners are mentioned. . . . Halftone photographs make textual descriptions real while numerous shaded sidebars offer considerable supplementary material. . . . This title provides a varied, understandable introduction to the spiritual side of many human cultures." SLJ

Includes bibliographical references

Keenan, Sheila

Gods, goddesses, and monsters. Scholastic Ref. 2000 128p il $19.95; lib bdg $24.95   **201**

1. Mythology
ISBN 0-439-04289-5; 0-439-55497-7 (lib bdg)

LC 99-46838

Discusses the characters and themes of the myths of peoples from Asia to Africa to North and South America

"Photographs of paintings and artifacts from museum collections . . . support the text. They contribute greatly to the reader's understanding of the impact on culture these stories have had. The complete index and bibliography by region could help students research a specific character." Book Rep

Mass, Wendy, 1967-
Gods and goddesses. Lucent Bks. 2002 112p (Discovering mythology) $27.45 **201**

1. Gods and goddesses 2. Mythology
ISBN 1-56006-852-3 LC 2001-5775
Examines the origins and nature of Egyptian, Hindu, Celtic, Greek, Roman, Viking, and Aztec gods and goddesses as revealed in the mythologies of these cultures
"This is a good overview for study of mythology that may spark interest in further study." Book Rep
Includes bibliographical references

Osborne, Mary Pope, 1949-
One world, many religions; the ways we worship. Knopf 1996 86p il map $19.95 (4 and up) **201**

1. Religions
ISBN 0-679-83930-5 LC 96-836
This is an "overview of major world religions—Judaism, Christianity, Islam, Hinduism, Buddhism, Confucianism, and Taoism. . . . Each of six essay-styled chapters addresses themes of religious tenets, deities, morality, and ritual only as they are pertinent to a particular faith." Bull Cent Child Books
"The presentation is notable for its respect to each group, succinctness, and clarity. . . . The artful, full-page, color and black-and-white photographs tell much of the story." SLJ
Includes glossary and bibliographical references

Philip, Neil
The illustrated book of myths; tales & legends of the world; retold by Neil Philip; illustrated by Nilesh Mistry. Dorling Kindersley 1995 192p il $19.99 (5 and up) **201**

1. Mythology
ISBN 0 7894-0202-5 LC 95-2156
"This collection represents a wide variety of world cultures and stories. Selections are grouped by type (creation myths, fertility and cultivation, visions of the end), which helps readers understand the commonality of the tales. The standard Greek and Norse myths are here, but what makes this volume special is its inclusion of less frequently anthologized stories of the Aztecs, Haitians, Africans, and Japanese, to name a few." SLJ

Mythology; written by Neil Philip. Dorling Kindersley 2000 61p il (DK Eyewitness books) $15.99; lib bdg $19.99 **201**

1. Mythology 2. Religions
ISBN 0-7894-6288-5; 0-7894-6627-9 (lib bdg)
First published 1999 by Knopf
Surveys the treatment of gods, goddesses, the heavens, creation, death, and evil as expressed in various mythologies around the world.

Wilkinson, Philip, 1955-
Illustrated dictionary of mythology; heroes, heroines, gods, and goddesses from around the world; written by Philip Wilkinson; consultant, Neil Philip. DK Pub. 1998 128p il map $25 **201**

1. Mythology—Dictionaries
ISBN 0-7894-3413-X LC 98-22992

Includes index
This volume describes myths and deities from cultures around the world divided into nine geographic regions including Japan, North America, Australia, Greece and Rome. 2000 illustrations accompany the text

World mythology; Roy Willis, general editor; foreword by Robert Walter. Holt & Co. 1993 311p il map (Henry Holt reference book) hardcover o.p. paperback available $30 **201**

1. Mythology
ISBN 0-8050-4913-4 (pa) LC 93-3045
This book describes "the myths of Egypt, the Middle East, India, China, Tibet, Mongolia, Japan, Greece, Rome, the Celtic lands, Northern and Eastern Europe, the Arctic, North and South America, Mesoamerica, Africa, Australia, Oceania, and Southeast Asia." Libr J

Zeitlin, Steven J.
The four corners of the sky; creation stories and cosmologies from around the world; [by] Steve Zeitlin; pictures by Chris Raschka. Holt & Co. 2000 135p il lib bdg $17 (5 and up) **201**

1. Creation 2. Cosmology 3. Mythology
ISBN 0-8050-4816-2 LC 00-22546
A collection of folk stories from around the world, each accompanied by background information, that explain the various perspectives of different peoples on how the universe and their world came to be
"Raschka's stylish, culture-specific graphic designs enliven the text without literally translating the stories. A conclusion calling for tolerance across cultures and extensive source notes round out this intriguing volume that will find wide curricular support." Booklist

203 Public worship and other practices

Sturges, Philemon
Sacred places; illustrated by Giles Laroche. Putnam 2000 38p il $16.99 (4 and up) **203**

1. Shrines 2. Religions
ISBN 0-399-23317-2 LC 98-31086
Describes various types of space which are sacred to different religions, including churches, mosques, synagogues, temples, and other shrines
"Sturges' approach is respectful and impartial, and the selection of sites offers some thought-provoking diversity. . . . The intricate paper construction of everything from Chartres to the River Ganges is impressive and visually absorbing." Bull Cent Child Books

204   Religious experience, life, practice

Philip, Neil

In the house of happiness; a book of prayers and praise; selected by Neil Philip; illustrated by Isabelle Brent. Clarion Bks. 2003 unp il $17

204

1. Prayers

ISBN 0-618-23481-0   LC 2002-10269

A collection of short prayers from major religions—Christianity, Judaism, Hinduism, Buddhism, and Islam—along with tribal chants, folk rhymes, and poems of praise and devotion

"The beautiful art encourages readers to pick up the book. Brent, who was inspired by the *Book of Hours*, lavishly employs illumination to highlight her pictures of nature. . . . This book offers the opportunity for quiet moments of reflection in a lovely setting." Booklist

209   Sects and reform movements

Barghusen, Joan D., 1935-

Cults. Lucent Bks. 1998 96p il (Lucent overview series) lib bdg $28.70 (7 and up)

209

1. Cults

ISBN 1-56006-199-5   LC 97-26652

Describes the nature and history of cults and the different aspects of living in a cult, including the difficulty of leaving it

"A balanced and informative look at the subject. . . . A smooth prose style and careful use of transitions contribute to the book's readability. . . . Detailed notes and a list of works consulted reflect the breadth of the author's research." SLJ

Includes bibliographical references (p.

Stein, Stephen J.

Alternative American religions. Oxford Univ. Press 1999 156p il (Religion in American life) lib bdg $28 (7 and up)   **209**

1. Sects 2. Cults 3. United States—Religion

ISBN 0-19-511196-6   LC 99-42370

Examines various alternative religions, or New Religious Movements, that have existed in the United States from colonial times through the twentieth century and from the perspectives of both insiders and outsiders

"The tone throughout is nonjudgmental and the emphasis is on people and their ideas. Black-and-white photos and reproductions add information and perspective to the presentation." SLJ

Zeinert, Karen, 1942-2002

Cults. Enslow Pubs. 1997 128p il (Issues in focus) lib bdg $26.60 (7 and up)   **209**

1. Cults

ISBN 0-89490-900-2   LC 96-40886

Describes various types of cults including their history, characteristics, and danger to American society

"This is a thought-provoking title with an engaging narrative on a fascinating subject." Booklist

Includes bibliographical references

220   Bible

Brown, Alan

The Bible and Christianity; by Alan Brown. Smart Apple Media 2003 30p il (Sacred texts) $27.10 (5 and up)   **220**

1. Bible 2. Bible (as subject) 3. Christianity

ISBN 1-583-40243-8   LC 2003-41645

Explains how the Old and New Testaments came to be part of the Bible used by Christians and discusses some of the important messages found in the holy scriptures.

"Colorful strips of symbolic patterns adorn the pages and accent the informative text boxes. . . . The clear captioned . . . illustrations (photos and historical art) provide additional background." Horn Book Guide

Includes glossary

220.3   Bible--Encyclopedias and topical dictionaries

The **Oxford** companion to the Bible; edited by Bruce M. Metzger, Michael D. Coogan. Oxford Univ. Press 1993 xxi, 874p il map $70

220.3

1. Bible (as subject)—Dictionaries

ISBN 0-19-504645-5   LC 93-19315

This volume "contains more than 700 signed entries treating the formation, transmission, circulation, sociohistorical situation, interpretation, theology, uses, and influence of the Bible." Libr J

"The many contributors read as a veritable who's who among biblical scholars. Although this companion is not meant to be an exhaustive reference, it is a highly reliable guide." Booklist

220.5   Bible--Modern versions

Bible.

The Holy Bible; containing the Old and New Testaments; translated out of the original tongues and with the former translations diligently compared and revised; King James Version, 1611. American Bible Soc. maps   **220.5**

Available in various bindings and editions including large print edition

This version first published 1982

This King James or Authorized version was first published 1962 by the American Bible Society; it includes a concordance of 3,700 key words, including about 45,000 specially chosen context lines

"Protestant. This edition replaces 17th Century verb forms and second person pronouns. Updates archaic terms. Psalms and Job appear as poetry." N Y Public Libr. Ref Books for Child Collect. 2d edition

Bible.
Good news Bible; today's English version.
American Bible Soc. **220.5**
Available in various bindings and editions
"Begun in 1964 with the Gospel of Mark, The New Testament was completed in 1966, with rev. eds. in 1971 and 1976. The whole Bible was published in 1976. An extremely popular, inexpensive translation using contemporary American English. . . . Especially useful for youth or lay Bible study as well as for private reading." Bollier. Lit of Theology

The Holy Bible: new revised standard version; containing the Old and New Testaments with the Apocryphal/Deuterocanonical books. Nelson, T. **220.5**
Available in various bindings and editions
This version first published 1989
"Intended for public reading, congregational worship, private study, instruction, and meditation, it attempts to be as literal as possible while following standard American English usage, avoids colloquialism, and prefers simple, direct terms and phrases." Sheehy. Guide to Ref Books. 10th edition. suppl

The new American Bible; with revised New Testament; translated from the original languages, with critical use of all the ancient sources by members of the Catholic Biblical Association of America; sponsored by the Bishops' Committee of the Confraternity of Christian Doctrine **220.5**
Available in various bindings and editions from various publishers
First published 1970 by Kenedy
"Roman Catholic version based on modern English translations; replaces the Douay edition." N Y Public Libr Book of How & Where to Look It Up

The new Jerusalem Bible. Doubleday **220.5**
Available in various bindings and editions
First published in this format 1966 with title: The Jerusalem Bible
General editor: Henry Wansbrough
"Derives from the French version edited at the Dominican Ecole Biblique de Jerusalem and known as 'La Bible de Jerusalem.' The introductions and notes are 'a direct translation from the French, though revised and brought up to date in some places' but translation of the Biblical text goes back to the original languages." Guide to Ref Books. 11th edition

The Holy Bible; containing the Old and New Testaments; translated out of the original tongues; and with the former translations diligently compared and revised by King James's special command, 1611. Oxford Univ. Press **220.5**
Available in various bindings and editions
The authorized or King James Version originally published 1611

220.7 Bible--Commentaries

Asimov, Isaac, 1920-1992
Asimov's guide to the Bible; maps by Rafael Palacios. Doubleday 1968-1969 2v maps o.p. Random House Value Pub. $14.95 **220.7**
1. Bible—Commentaries 2. Bible (as subject)—Commentaries
ISBN 0-517-34582-X (reprint available)
Also available in paperback from Avon Bks.
Contents: v1 The Old Testament; v2 The New Testament
The author discusses the Bible book by book, verse by verse, letting us in on the actual historical, geographical, and biographical aspects of Biblical history
"Asimov is relaxed, down-to-earth, calmly analytical, not irreverent but also not 'pious' in his approach." Publ Wkly

220.9 Bible--Geography, history, biography, stories

Daughters of the desert; stories of remarkable women from Christian, Jewish, and Muslim traditions; {by} Claire Rudolf Murphy . . . {et al.}. SkyLight Paths Pub. 2003 178p $19.95 **220.9**
1. Women in the Bible 2. Women in the Koran
ISBN 1-89336-172-1 LC 2002-153821
"Using sacred writings as their basis, the five women authors have reshaped the stories of such individuals as Sarah, Mary Magdalene, Eve, and Khadiji, the wife of Mohammed. . . . The stories are short and simply told, but they are intriguing and invite discussion." Booklist
Includes bibliographical references

Tubb, Jonathan N.
Bible lands. Dorling Kindersley 2000 63p il map (DK eyewitness books) $15.99; lib bdg $19.99 **220.9**
1. Bible—Antiquities 2. Bible (as subject)—Antiquities
ISBN 0-7894-5770-9; 0-7694-6579-5 (lib bdg)
Photographs and text document life in Biblical times, surveying the clothing, food, and civilizations of a wide variety of cultures, including the Israelites, Babylonians, Persians, and Romans.

221.9 Bible. Old Testament--Geography, history, biography, stories

Gellman, Marc
Does God have a big toe? stories about stories in the Bible; paintings by Oscar de Mejo. Harper & Row 1989 88p il hardcover o.p. paperback available $7.99 (4-6) **221.9**
1. Bible stories
ISBN 0-06-440453-6 (pa) LC 89-1893

Gellman, Marc—Continued

This is a collection of twenty "tales that use familiar characters and situations from the Bible, but which imagine events and feelings and consequences the Bible never recorded. . . . Oscar de Mejo's primitive-style paintings suit the text exactly. Adam and Eve, for example, pop up behind the bushes in the Garden of Eden, just as a child might imagine them. These tales have the ring of genuine folk-fables and the wit of a single, affectionate heart." N Y Times Book Rev

McKissack, Patricia C., 1944-

Let my people go; Bible stories told by a freeman of color to his daughter, Charlotte, in Charleston, South Carolina, 1806-16; by Patricia and Fredrick McKissack; illustrated by James Ransome. Atheneum Bks. for Young Readers 1998 134p il $20 (4 and up) **221.9**

1. African Americans—Fiction 2. Bible stories 3. Slavery—Fiction

ISBN 0-689-80856-9   LC 97-19983

"An Anne Schwartz book"

Charlotte, the daughter of a free black man who worked as a blacksmith in Charleston, South Carolina, in the early 1800s recalls the stories from the Bible that her father shared with her, relating them to the experiences of African Americans

"The poignant juxtaposition of the Biblical characters and Charlotte's personal narrative is authentic and moving. . . . The occasional illustrations are powerful oil paintings in rich colors, emotional and evocative." SLJ

Includes bibliographical references

Ward, Elaine M.

Old Testament women; [by] Elaine Ward. Enchanted Lion 2004 32p il (Art revelations) $18.95 (5 and up) **221.9**

1. Women in the Bible

ISBN 1-59270-011-x

These Old Testament stories about women include "explanatory paragraphs, sidebars, and captions by the author. Art masterpieces . . . illustrate each story. . . . The captions provide background on the artist and the significance of each painting or mosaic. . . . The 18 women . . . include Rachel, Leah, Ruth, and Bathsheba. . . . Bosch, Botticelli, and Poussin are among the painters whose work appears here. . . . Visually stunning. " SLJ

222 Historical books of Old Testament

Cato, Vivienne

The Torah and Judaism; by Vivienne Cato. Smart Apple Media 2003 30p il (Sacred texts) $27.10 (5 and up) **222**

1. Torah 2. Judaism

ISBN 1-583-40244-6   LC 2003-41644

This explains the origins of the Torah, its structure and contents, its message and teachings, and its place in Jewish life and worship.

"Colorful strips of symbolic patterns adorn the pages and accent the informative text boxes. . . . The clear, captioned . . . illustrations (photos and historical art) provide additional background." Horn Book Guide

Feiler, Bruce S.

Walking the Bible; an illustrated journey for kids through the greatest stories ever told; by Bruce Feiler ; illustrated by Sasha Meret. 1st ed. HarperCollinsPublishers 2004 108p il map $16.99; lib bdg $17.89 **222**

1. Middle East 2. Bible (as subject)

ISBN 0-06-051117-6; 0-06-051118-4 (lib bdg)
       LC 2003-15861

Includes index

Contents: Walking the Bible; Creating the world; Noah's ark; Abraham; Abraham in the promised land; Abraham and Isaac; Joseph in Egypt; Moses parts the Red Sea; The burning bush; Climbing Mt. Sinai

The author describes his journey through places mentioned in the Old Testament.

"In this version of his adult book with the same title (Morrow, 2001), Feiler largely succeeds in slimming rather than dumbing down his account of his trip across the 10,000-mile setting of the earliest Bible stories. The author's unpretentious . . . tone and astute pacing help make the volume accessible, and his sincerity is palpable." SLJ

Goldin, Barbara Diamond

Journeys with Elijah; eight tales of the Prophet; retold by Barbara Diamond Goldin; paintings by Jerry Pinkney. Harcourt Brace & Co. 1999 77p il $20 (4 and up) **222**

1. Elijah (Biblical figure) 2. Jewish legends 3. Bible stories

ISBN 0-15-200445-9   LC 96-9278

"Gulliver books"

Presents eight stories about the Old Testament prophet Elijah, set in a variety of time periods and in places all over the world where Jews have lived

"Goldin's storytelling is every bit as colorful as Pinkney's radiant, masterfully composed paintings, and both text and art testify to careful historical research." Publ Wkly

Includes bibliographical references

223 Poetic books of Old Testament

Bible. O.T. Ecclesiastes.

To every thing there is a season; verses from Ecclesiastes; illustrations by Leo and Diane Dillon. Blue Sky Press (NY) 1998 unp il $16.95 **223**

ISBN 0-590-47887-7   LC 97-35124

Presents that selection from Ecclesiastes which relates that everything in life has its own time and season

"The Dillons compellingly convey the relevance of the Ecclesiastes verse throughout history, via a stunning array of artwork that embraces motifs from cultures the world over." Publ Wkly

226 Gospels and Acts

Connolly, Sean
New Testament miracles; Sean Connolly. 1st American ed. Enchanted Lion Books 2004 32p il (Art revelations) $18.95 **226**
1. Miracles—Christianity 2. Christian art
ISBN 1-59270-012-8   LC 2003-49414
"The 12 miracles discussed . . . include Jesus healing the man born blind, Jesus raising Lazarus from the dead, and the conversion of Paul. Each one is told from verses in the four Gospels or the Book of Acts, with explanatory paragraphs, sidebars, and captions by the author. Art masterpieces . . . illustrate each story. Works by El Greco, Rembrandt, Tintoretto, and Witz, among others, are featured. . . . Visually stunning." SLJ

230 Christianity. Christian theology

Lace, William W.
Christianity; by William W. Lace. Lucent Books 2004 128p il map (Religions of the world) $28.70 **230**
1. Christianity
ISBN 1-59018-141-7   LC 2004-10844
Contents: Birth and growth; Persecution to prominence; Heresy and schism; Power and perversion; Reformation and counter reformation; Expansion and enlightenment; Beliefs and worship; Christianity in the new millennium
This offers a history of Christianity, outlining the life of Jesus, Saint Paul's role in spreading the faith, the rise of Christianity, persecutions, heresies, and schisms, the Reformation and Counter-Reformation, world expansion of the faith, beliefs and worship, and Christian faiths today.
Includes bibliographical references

230.003 Christianity--Encyclopedias and dictionaries

The **Oxford** dictionary of the Christian Church; edited by F. L. Cross and E. A. Livingstone. Oxford Univ. Press 1997 3rd ed xxxvii, 1786p $125 **230.003**
1. Christianity—Dictionaries
ISBN 0-19-211655-X
First published 1957
"The authoritative one-volume dictionary of the Christian Church. More than 6,000 entries presented in an alphabetical arrangement provide extensive information on the history, beliefs, practices, people, and traditions of the 2,000-year-old Christian world." Ref Sources for Small & Medium-sized Libr. 6th edition

232.9 Family and life of Jesus

Bible. N.T. Selections.
The Christmas story; according to the Gospels of Matthew and Luke from the King James Version; paintings by Gennady Spirin. Holt & Co. 1998 32p il $19.95 **232.9**
1. Jesus Christ—Nativity
ISBN 0-8050-5292-5   LC 97-50417
Presents the story of the birth of Christ, from Mary's meeting with the angel Gabriel to the birth of baby Jesus in a stable and the visit of the shepherds and three Wise Men
"The beautiful illustrations, with angels everywhere and Christian symbols such as lilies, are illuminated by an appropriate golden glow that gives an air of religiosity and holiness to the art." Booklist

L'Engle, Madeleine, 1918-
The glorious impossible; illustrated with frescoes from the Scrovegni Chapel by Giotto; afterword by A. Richard Turner. Simon & Schuster Bks. for Young Readers 1990 il $24.95 **232.9**
1. Jesus Christ
ISBN 0-671-68690-9   LC 89-6104
Describes the life of Jesus Christ and presents twenty-four paintings showing scenes from the life of Christ by the fourteenth-century Italian artist Giotto

Lottridge, Celia Barker
Stories from the life of Jesus; retold from the Bible by Celia Barker Lottridge; illustrated by Linda Wolfsgruber. Douglas & McIntyre 2004 140p il $24.95 (4 and up) **232.9**
1. Jesus Christ 2. Bible stories
ISBN 0-88899-497-4
"A Groundwood book"
A retelling of selected events from the life of Christ based on biblical accounts
This is an "exceptional collection. . . . Each story is retold in three or four pages of clear, concise prose that is meant to be read aloud. . . . Each selection is enhanced by dramatic and atmospheric, mixed-media illustrations that are executed in warm earth tones." SLJ

270 History of Christianity and Christian church

The **Rise** of Christianity; Don Nardo, book editor. Greenhaven Press 1999 224p (Turning points in world history) hardcover o.p. paperback available $19.95 (7 and up) **270**
1. Church history
ISBN 1-56510-962-7 (pa)   LC 98-17499
"Among the topics covered are the Jewish background of Christianity; the life of Jesus; the growth of Christianity, with emphasis on the work of the apostles; Roman persecution of Christians and the impact of rival religions on the early church; and the spread of Christianity across

The Rise of Christianity—*Continued*
Europe and the role of Christianity as the official religion of Rome. The lucid and thought-provoking essays are presented in a crisply designed format." Booklist
Includes bibliographical references

272   Persecutions in church history

Worth, Richard, 1945-
The Spanish Inquisition in world history. Enslow Pubs. 2002 112p il map (In world history) lib bdg $26.60 (7 and up)   **272**
1. Inquisition 2. Spain—History
ISBN 0-7660-1825-3   LC 2001-8516
Examines the events that led to the persecution of accused heretics against the Catholic Church, focusing on the Inquisition in medieval Spain
"Thoroughly researched. . . . [This] volume will be useful, especially for reports." SLJ
Includes bibliographical references

274   Christian Church in Europe

Hinds, Kathryn, 1962-
The church. Benchmark Bks. 2004 95p il (Life in the Renaissance) lib bdg $20.95   **274**
1. Reformation 2. Renaissance 3. Europe—Church history
ISBN 0-7614-1679-X   LC 2003-8258
Contents: Christian roots and branches; Power and protest; Community life; Men of God; Women and the church; Holy days and every day; Learning tolerance
A description of the religious controversies of the Renaissance and Reformation with a focus on what life was like for ordinary people, both Catholic and Protestant
"Informative and beautifully illustrated. . . . Quality period reproductions of paintings and clear, color photos appear throughout." SLJ
Includes glossary and bibliographical references

280   Christian denominations and sects

Brown, Stephen F.
Protestantism. Facts on File 2002 127p il (World religions) $30 (7 and up)   **280**
1. Protestantism
ISBN 0-8160-4614-X   LC 01-40278
A narrative history of Protestantism, tracing its growth and customs from its beginning to the present
Includes glossary and bibliographical references

Noll, Mark A.
Protestants in America; general editors, Jon Butler and Harry S. Stout. Oxford Univ. Press 2000 155p il (Religion in American life) lib bdg $28 (7 and up)   **280**
1. Protestant churches
ISBN 0-19-511034-X   LC 00-27271

Discusses the origins of Protestantism, the diversity of Protestant churches in the United States, and the role of Protestants in American life from colonial times to the present
"This volume is especially valuable for its discussion of the church in the African-American community and its coverage of smaller sects, like the Shakers. The many black-and-white photographs and reproduction add immensely to the text." SLJ
Includes bibliographical references

289   Other denominations and sects

Williams, Jean Kinney
The Shakers. Watts 1997 111p il (American religious experience) lib bdg $25 (7 and up)   **289**
1. Shakers
ISBN 0-531-11342-6   LC 96-51498
Examines the history, beliefs, way of life, and current status of this devout Christian group
"Williams gives a lucid account of the movement's history and beliefs. . . . An accessible and interesting introduction." Booklist
Includes bibliographical references

289.3   Latter-Day Saints (Mormons)

Book of Mormon.
The Book of Mormon. Herald House   **289.3**
1. Mormons
Available in various bindings and editions
First published 1830
"Based on golden plates which Joseph Smith claimed were revealed to him, and which he unearthed from Cumorah Hill, New York, this book is roughly similar in structure to the *Bible*. . . . Emphasized are the doctrines of pre-existence, perfection, the after-life, and Christ's second coming." Haydn. Thesaurus of Book Dig

Bushman, Claudia L.
Mormons in America; {by} Claudia Lauper Bushman and Richard Lyman Bushman. Oxford Univ. Press 1998 142p il (Religion in American life) $28 (7 and up)   **289.3**
1. Church of Jesus Christ of Latter-day Saints
ISBN 0-19-510677-6   LC 98-18605
Chronicles the history of the Church of Jesus Christ of Latter-Day Saints beginning in America in the early 1800s and continuing to the present day throughout the world
"A solid resource for libraries. Illustrated with historical material and black-and-white photos. Time line and bibliography appended." Booklist

289.5 Church of Christ, Scientist (Christian Science)

Williams, Jean Kinney
The Christian Scientists. Watts 1997 109p il (American religious experience) lib bdg $25 (7 and up) **289.5**
1. Eddy, Mary Baker, 1821-1910 2. Christian Science
ISBN 0-531-11309-4 LC 96-9878
Provides a history of Christian Scientists, covering their doctrines and practices, organization, place in American society, and changes in beliefs, as well as discussing the work of Mary Baker Eddy
"Large black-and-white photographs and art reproductions appear throughout. The author's research is thorough, and her prose style is straightforward and skilled." SLJ
Includes bibliographical references

289.6 Society of Friends (Quakers)

Williams, Jean Kinney
The Quakers. Watts 1998 110p il (American religious experience) $25 (7 and up) **289.6**
1. Society of Friends
ISBN 0-531-11377-9 LC 97-35133
Examines the history, notable individuals, beliefs, way of life, and current status of this longstanding Christian group
"Those studying William Penn will find an insightful chapter on his 'Holy Experiment.'. . . The research in this well-documented title is sound." SLJ
Includes bibliographical references

289.7 Mennonite churches

Kenna, Kathleen
A people apart; photographs by Andrew Stawicki. Somerville House Pub. 1995 64p il $18 (4 and up) **289.7**
1. Mennonites
ISBN 0-395-67344-5 LC 94-18545
"A Nick Harris book"
This photo-essay "shows various aspects of life in Old Order Mennonite communities, including home, work, education, and worship. The well-written text does a good job of explaining the Mennonites' lifestyle and the reasons they choose to live as they do. It also explains how groups splinter off or individuals leave or are expelled because of disagreements about what is acceptable and unacceptable. . . . The full-page black-and-white photographs are marvelous and reflect the same respect for the way of life expressed in the narrative." SLJ
Includes bibliographical references

Williams, Jean Kinney
The Amish. Watts 1996 111p il (American religious experience) lib bdg $25 (7 and up) **289.7**
1. Amish
ISBN 0-531-11275-6 LC 96-33830
Includes a history of the Amish, their general doctrines, practices, social structure, place in American society, changes in beliefs, and issues facing them in modern society
"Students working on reports will be well served by the thorough discussion of the key players and precepts, as well as by the endnotes, lists of further reading, indexes, and Internet sites. . . . Large, well-reproduced black-and-white captioned photographs and prints are attractive and informative." SLJ

292 Classical religion (Greek and Roman religion)

Greek and Roman mythology; Don Nardo, book editor. Greenhaven Press 2002 304p il (Greenhaven encyclopedia of) lib bdg $76.20 (7 and up) **292**
1. Classical mythology
ISBN 0-7377-0719-4 LC 2001-40864
This is an overview of classical mythology, its heroes, and its influence on the history of Western civilization
Includes bibliographical references

Hamilton, Edith, 1867-1963
Mythology; illustrated by Steele Savage. Little, Brown 1942 497p il $27.95; pa $13.95 **292**
1. Classical mythology 2. Norse mythology
ISBN 0-316-34114-2; 0-316-34151-7 (pa)
A retelling of Greek, Roman and Norse myths

Hinds, Kathryn, 1962-
Religion. Benchmark Books 2004 c2005 87p il (Life in the Roman empire) lib bdg $20.95 **292**
1. Rome—Religion 2. Rome—Civilization
ISBN 0-7614-1657-9 LC 2004-8400
Contents: A world of gods and spirits; Beliefs and ceremonies; Sacred places; Religious roles for men; Women and worship; Through life's stages; Roman holiday; Conflict and tolerance
This considers the religion of the Roman empire, describing beliefs in gods and spirits, ceremonies and sacred places, religious roles of men and women, and religious conflict and tolerance.
Includes glossary and bibliographical references

McCaughrean, Geraldine, 1951-
Odysseus; retold by Geraldine McCaughrean. 1st American ed. Cricket Books 2004 148p il (Heroes) (5 and up) **292**
1. Odysseus (Greek mythology) 2. Classical mythology
ISBN 0-8126-2721-0 LC 2004-10734

McCaughrean, Geraldine, 1951——Continued
This is a retelling of the "adventures of Odysseus, including his encounters with the evil Cyclops, the monsters Scylla and Charybdis, the beautiful sorceress Circe, and . . . Poseidon." Publisher's note
"With mounting suspense, wild action, and simple, rhythmic prose, this dramatic retelling of Homer's classic makes a gripping read-aloud as well as an exciting introduction to the story." Booklist

Perseus; retold by Geraldine McCaughrean. Cricket Books 2005 118p (Heroes) $15.95 (5 and up)   **292**
1. Perseus (Greek mythology) 2. Classical mythology
ISBN 0-8126-2735-0
This follows the story of "Perseus as he lives the fate the oracles have declared, an impossible quest to kill the hideous, snake-haired Medusa to save his mother from marriage to an evil king." Publisher's note
This "makes a thrilling read-aloud. . . . McCaughrean blends the colloquial and contemporary into the heroic quest." Booklist

293   Germanic religion and religious mythology

Philip, Neil
Odin's family; myths of the Vikings; retold by Neil Philip; illustrated by Maryclare Foa. Orchard Bks. 1996 124p il $19.95 (4-6)   **293**
1. Norse mythology
ISBN 0-531-09531-2   LC 96-1965
"Philip tells the stories of the origin of the gods and frost giants, how Odin got his wisdom, the death of Baldur, the coming of Ragnarok, and eleven other Norse myths. What distinguishes Philip's anthology is its design: large print, a generous amount of white space, and full-page color art make this an eminently accessible, easily promoted collection. Foa's oil paintings (with a preponderance of red, gold and blue) have a primitive vigor." Bull Cent Child Books
Includes bibliographical references

294   Religions of Indic origin

Mann, Gurinder Singh
Buddhists, Hindus, and Sikhs in America; {by} Gurinder Singh Mann, Paul David Numrich & Raymond B. Williams. Oxford Univ. Press 2001 158p il (Religion in American life) lib bdg $28 (7 and up)   **294**
1. Buddhism 2. Hinduism 3. Sikhism 4. Asian Americans—Religion
ISBN 0-19-512442-1   LC 2001-45151
Presents the basic tenets of these three Asian religions and discusses the religious history and experience of their practitioners after immigration to the United States
"Solid information, a large selection of historical and contemporary photographs, interesting readings from primary sources, and accounts from school-age Buddhists, Hindus, and Sikhs combine to make this is a valuable resource." Booklist
Includes bibliographical references

294.3   Buddhism

Demi, 1942-
Buddha. Holt & Co. 1996 unp il $21.95 (4-6)
                                    294.3
1. Gautama Buddha
ISBN 0-8050-4203-2   LC 95-16906
The author "tells the story of Siddhartha's birth and the prophecies surrounding it, touches upon his childhood, and then follows his path to enlightenment." Booklist
Demi "uses clear, uncomplicated storytelling to present complex philosophical concepts. . . . The gilded illustrations (based, according to the jacket, on 'Indian, Chinese, Japanese, Burmese, and Indonesian paintings, sculptures, and sutra illustrations') are delicate, yet the colors and composition are bold, with central figures and action cascading beyond the careful borders." Bull Cent Child Books

Ganeri, Anita, 1961-
The Tipitaka and Buddhism. Smart Apple Media 2003 30p il (Sacred texts) $27.10 (5 and up)
                                    294.3
1. Buddhism
ISBN 1-583-40246-2   LC 2003-42354
A discussion of Buddhism and some of its sacred texts.
"Attractive illustrations, including photographs and reproductions of religious art, make for a nice design, and students will find a wealth of information for reports." Booklist

Lee, Jeanne M.
I once was a monkey; stories Buddha told. Farrar, Straus & Giroux 1999 unp il $16 (4 and up)   **294.3**
1. Jataka stories
ISBN 0-374-33548-6   LC 98-17651
A retelling of six Jatakas, or birth stories, which illustrate some of the central tenets of Buddha's teachings, such as compassion, honesty, and thinking clearly before acting
"The appealing character of the monkey will pull children into the tales, which convey lessons in a direct yet gentle way that is never preachy. The accompanying linocut illustrations are lovely." Booklist

Wangu, Madhu Bazaz
Buddhism. rev ed. Facts on File 2002 128p il map (World religions) $30   **294.3**
1. Buddhism
ISBN 0-8160-4728-6   LC 2002-19997
First published 1993
Presents the story of Buddhism's origins and growth through the centuries, discussing its basic philosophy and the evolution of the three major schools of Buddhist thought

Wilkinson, Philip, 1955-
Buddhism; written by Philip Wilkinson; photographed by Steve Teague. DK Pub 2003 64p il (DK eyewitness guides) $15.99; lib bdg $19.99 (4 and up) **294.3**
1. Buddhism
ISBN 0-7894-9833-2; 0-7894-9834-0 (lib bdg)
LC 2003-51656
"This introduction to Buddhism presents a series of topics on double-page spreads, each with a paragraph of text and many excellent color photographs, accompanied by lengthy captions in small type. . . . The book provides a visually appealing introduction to Buddhism and is a good source of photos of Buddhist sites, art, and artifacts." Booklist

Winston, Diana
Wide awake: a Buddhist guide for teens. Perigee Bk. 2003 290p pa $13.95 **294.3**
1. Buddhism
ISBN 0-399-52897-0
LC 2002-192666
"Switching between anecdotes of her own journey in Buddhism and advice on how teens can apply the Buddha's teachings to their lives, Winston offers a personal and thoughtful introduction to Buddhist thought and practice." Booklist

294.5   Hinduism

Ganeri, Anita, 1961-
The Ramayana and Hinduism. Smart Apple Media 2003 30p il (Sacred texts) $27.10 (5 and up) **294.5**
1. Hinduism
ISBN 1-583-40242-X
LC 2003-42352
Contents: Origins; Texts and teaching; In daily life
Explains the history and practices of the religion of Hinduism, especially as revealed through its sacred book, the Ramayana.

Wangu, Madhu Bazaz
Hinduism. rev ed. Facts on File 2001 128p (World religions) $30 (7 and up) **294.5**
1. Hinduism
ISBN 0-8160-4400-7
LC 00-51857
First published 1991
Presents the history, customs, and beleifs of Hinduism, describing the mysteries and the myths that sustained it growth over the centuries. Also includes information on the Hindu national movement, conflict in Kashmir, and India's first nuclear bombs
Includes bibliographical references

296   Judaism

Buxbaum, Shelley M.
Jewish faith in America; [by] Shelley M. Buxbaum, Sara E. Karesh. Facts on File 2003 128p il (Faith in America) $30 (7 and up) **296**
1. Judaism 2. Jews—United States 3. United States—Ethnic relations
ISBN 0-8160-4986-6
LC 2002-29392
This offers a history of the Jewish people in America "from the early days . . . and their participation in the Revolutionary and Civil Wars, to the impact of World War II and the Holocaust on Jewish life in America. . . . [It also covers] the various ways Judaism is practiced in the U.S. as well as the contributions Jews have made to American society." Publisher's note
"Thoroughly researched and heavily illustrated." Libr Media Connect
Includes glossary and bibliographical references

Fisher, Leonard Everett, 1924-
To bigotry, no sanction; the story of the oldest synagogue in America. Holiday House 1998 64p il $16.95 (4 and up) **296**
1. Touro Synagogue (Newport, R.I.) 2. Jews—United States
ISBN 0-8234-1401-9
LC 98-12834
The author discusses "the history of the Jews in America in general and the building of the Touro Synagogue, the oldest in the U.S. in particular. Fisher does his usual excellent job of bringing history to life." Booklist
Includes bibliographical references

296.03   Judaism--Encyclopedias and dictionaries

The **Oxford** dictionary of the Jewish religion; editors in chief, R.J. Zwi Werblowsky, Geoffrey Wigoder. Oxford Univ. Press 1997 764p $110 **296.03**
1. Judaism—Dictionaries
ISBN 0-19-508605-8
LC 96-45517
"The 2400 entries in this dictionary include unsigned but revised articles from the editors' Encyclopedia of the Jewish Religion (1966), as well as . . . new signed articles covering [topics] . . . and biographies related to the Jewish religion and interfaith relations." Libr J

296.1   Judaism--Sources

Chaikin, Miriam
Angels sweep the desert floor; Bible legends about Moses in the wilderness; illustrated by Alexander Koshkin. Clarion Bks. 2002 102p il $19 (4 and up) **296.1**
1. Moses (Biblical figure) 2. Angels—Fiction 3. Jewish legends 4. Bible stories
ISBN 0-395-97825-4
LC 2001-47501

Chaikin, Miriam—*Continued*

A collection of eighteen stories based on the Bible which tell how angels respond to God's commands to ease the way for Moses and the Israelites as they cross the wilderness after being freed from slavery in Egypt

"The full-page watercolor, tempera, and gouache illustrations have a fanciful formality that complements the narrative. Capable of exciting the creative, as well as the spiritual imagination, these wonderful stories make great read-alouds." SLJ

Includes bibliographical references

Lester, Julius

When the beginning began; stories about God, the creatures, and us; illustrations by Emily Lisker. Silver Whistle Bks. 1999 100p il $17 (4 and up)
296.1

1. Creation 2. Bible stories 3. Jewish legends
ISBN 0-15-201238-9   LC 97-37352

A collection of traditional and original Jewish tales interpreting the Biblical story of the creation of the world

"Lester fuses two traditions here—the 'loving irreverence' of African-American storytelling and the imaginative inquiry of midrashim. . . . Lisker's paintings capture the stories' primal essence (and a bit of their playfulness) in bold, archetypal forms. A reverent, wise, witty, and wonderfully entertaining book." Horn Book Guide

Includes bibliographical references

296.4 Judaism--Traditions, rites, public services

Adler, David A., 1947-

The kids' catalog of Jewish holidays. Jewish Publ. Soc. 1996 283p il pa $15.95   **296.4**

1. Jewish holidays 2. Handicraft
ISBN 0-8276-0581-1   LC 96-17784

Presents stories, poems, songs, recipes, crafts, and other activities for special days that are significant to Jews

Berger, Gilda

Celebrate! stories of the Jewish holidays; paintings by Peter Catalanotto. Scholastic 1998 114p il hardcover o.p. paperback available $8.99 (4 and up)   **296.4**

1. Jewish holidays
ISBN 0-439-43052-6 (pa)   LC 97-40150

"Berger examines the history of the major holidays of the Jewish faith and the Bible story that lies behind the celebration of each, as well as the customs that make these special days. The lively writing coupled with Catalanotto's dramatic watercolors ensure that this volume will become a treasured family favorite." Publ Wkly

Kimmel, Eric A.

Wonders and miracles; a Passover companion; illustrated with art spanning three thousand years; written and compiled by Eric A. Kimmel. Scholastic Press 2004 136p il $18.95 (4 and up)
296.4

1. Passover
ISBN 0-439-07175-5   LC 2002-4732

Presents the steps performed in a traditional Passover Seder, plus stories, songs, poetry, and pictures that celebrate the historical significance of this holiday to Jews all over the world

"The marvelous selection of art— paintings, photographs, artifacts, and illustrations from historical Haggadahs—illuminates each step in the service. . . . Both the presentation of information and the overall design attest to the careful and loving attention given to every detail. This inviting, handsome, and informative compendium should find a place of honor in every library." SLJ

Includes bibliographical references

Musleah, Rahel

Why on this night? a Passover haggadah for family celebration; illustrated by Louise August. Simon & Schuster Bks. for Young Readers 2000 112p $24.95; pa $12.99   **296.4**

1. Passover
ISBN 0-689-81356-2; 0-689-83313-X (pa)
LC 97-2570

Includes the basic elements of a traditional seder as well as many creative facets intended to involve children in this Jewish liturgy through song, dance, drama, explanation, and action

"A useful addition to Jewish holiday collections." SLJ

Schecter, Ellen

The family Haggadah; illustrated by Neil Waldman. Viking 1999 66p il music pa $13.99
296.4

1. Passover
ISBN 0-670-88341-7   LC 98-28597

"This book interweaves original writing with traditional Haggadah, prayer book, and biblical texts, as well as with midrash (rabbinic stories and commentaries)." Verso of title page

"Although really intended for parents to use with their children at a family Passover seder, this attractive book may also be useful to children wanting to plan their own model celebration." Booklist

297 Islam, Babism, Bahai Faith

Clark, Charles

Islam. Lucent Bks. 2002 128p il (Religions of the world) lib bdg $27.45   **297**

1. Islam
ISBN 1-56006-986-4   LC 2001-4872

Discusses the history, beliefs, popularity, practices, politics, and challenges of one of the world's major religions, Islam

Includes glossary and bibliographical references

Demi, 1942-

Muhammad; written and illustrated by Demi. Margaret K. McElderry Bks. 2003 unp il $19.95 (4 and up)   **297**

1. Muḥammad, d. 632 2. Islam
ISBN 0-689-85264-9   LC 2002-2985

Demi, 1942-—*Continued*
"With dramatic scenes extending past the borders of the intricately patterned frames, the art will be a continual source of interest for young people. . . . {An} excellent retelling of the Prophet's life that combines beauty and scholarship." Booklist
Includes bibliographical references

Gordon, Matthew
Islam; by Matthew S. Gordon. rev ed. Facts on File 2001 128p il (World religions) $30 (7 and up)
297
1. Islam
ISBN 0-8160-4401-5   LC 00-51858
An overview of Islam chronicling the religion's impact historically and in the modern world and discussing its origins, basic beliefs, structure, places of worship, and rites of passage
"The book is enhanced by well-chosen, full-color photographs and illustrations. . . . Overall, this is a handy, informed and attractive primer." Publ Wkly
Includes bibliographical references

Hartz, Paula
Baha'i Faith. Facts on File 2002 128p il (World religions) $30 (7 and up)   297
1. Bahai Faith
ISBN 0-8160-4729-4   LC 2002-3529
Contents: The Baha'i Faith and its people; Foundations of the Baha'i Faith; Baha'u'llah, the founder of the Baha'i Faith; The Baha'i scriptures; The spread of the Baha'i Faith; Baha'i belief and worship; The Baha'i community; The Baha'i Faith today
"Excellent organization and clear writing are the hallmarks of this text. . . . This book will be especially useful for schools in which world religions are taught or in any library in which religion is a popular topic." SLJ
Includes bibliographical references

The **Muslim** almanac; a reference work on the history, faith, culture, and peoples of Islam; Azim A. Nanji, editor. Gale Res. 1996 xxxv, 581p il map $120   297
1. Islam 2. Islamic countries
ISBN 0-8103-8924-X   LC 95-17324
This "basic reference on Islam contains 39 chapters, each contributed by a recognized scholar and each discussing a broad topic area of Islamic history, belief, or culture. Chapters conclude with useful topical bibliographies. A general bibliography, a chronology of Islamic history, and a glossary of Islamic terms also appear." Libr J

Oliver, Marilyn Tower, 1935-
Muhammad. Lucent Bks. 2003 112p il maps (Importance of) lib bdg $27.45 (7 and up)
297
1. Muḥammad, d. 632 2. Muslims
ISBN 1-59018-232-4   LC 2002-11291
Contents: The beginning: before the revelations; A messenger for God; The early Muslims meet with opposition; Hijra, the flight to Yathrib (Medina); Raids and battles; The return to Mecca; The final years

Profiles the life of Muhammad and his founding of the religion known as Islam
"A solid and balanced look at the 'last prophet.'" SLJ
Includes glossary and bibliographical references

Wormser, Richard, 1933-
American Islam; growing up Muslim in America. Walker & Co. 1994 130p il hardcover o.p. paperback available $8.95 (7 and up)
297
1. Islam
ISBN 0-8027-7628-0 (pa)   LC 94-12335
"A portrait of Muslim American youth and their faith. Wormser describes the cultural, literary, and scientific heritage of Islamic civilization; their traditional tolerance of unbelievers; and the history of Muslim settlement in the Christian West. He also offers a concise summary of the religion's origins, its Sunni and Shia branches, and its basic beliefs." SLJ
"Although historical background is interlaced within the text, much of the information comes from interviews. This anecdotal method lends an immediacy that will appeal to young people." Book Rep
Includes bibliographical references

297.1 Sources of Islam

Koran.
The Koran   297.1
Available in various bindings and editions
"The sacred scripture of Islam, regarded by Muslims as the Word of God, and except in sūra I.—which is a prayer to God—and some few passages in which Muhammad or the angels speak in the first person, the speaker throughout is God." Ency Britannica

299 Religions not provided for elsewhere

Matson, Gienna
Celtic mythology A to Z; Gienna Matson. Facts on File 2004 114p il map (Mythology A to Z) $40
299
1. Celtic mythology
ISBN 0-8160-4890-8   LC 2004-47111
This is an "illustrated guide to the characters, objects, and places that make up the mythic lore of the Celtic peoples." Publisher's note
"This title is an excellent introduction to the mythology of Celtic cultures and should be in most public and school libraries." Booklist
Includes bibliographical references

Remler, Pat
Egyptian mythology A to Z; a young reader's companion. Facts on File 2000 180p il $35 (7 and up)
299
1. Egyptian mythology
ISBN 0-8160-3984-4   LC 99-58590

Remler, Pat—*Continued*
This work begins with an "introductory section on the Nile Valley and Egyptian history. The alphabetical entries that follow discuss philosophical concepts, gods and goddesses, sites, and influences, and provide diverse details on the culture, including types of royal crowns and symbols. Some names or expressions in hieroglyphics are incorporated into the text." SLJ
Includes bibliographical references

299.5   Religions of East and Southeast Asian origin

Hartz, Paula
Taoism; by Paula R. Hartz. Updated ed. Facts on File 2004 128p il (World religions) $30
                                                              299.5
1. Taoism
ISBN 0-8160-5724-9   LC 2004-43224
First published 1993
This book "traces the progress of Taoist thought, from the great *Tao Te Ching* or 'The Book of the Way and Its Power,' by Laozi to the contemporary *Tao of Physics* by Fritjof Capra. It also examines the restoration of Taoism under China's religious freedom clause, the slow rebirth of Taoist monasticism, renewed interest in Taoism in China and abroad, and the impact of tourism on the monastic tradition." Publisher's note
Includes bibliographical references

Kallen, Stuart A., 1955-
Shinto. Lucent Bks. 2002 128p il map (Religions of the world) lib bdg $27.45
                                                              299.5
1. Shinto
ISBN 1-56006-988-0   LC 2001-6120
Discusses historical origins, the teachings, practices, and the spread of Shinto into modern times
Includes glossary and bibliographical references

Roberts, Jeremy
Chinese mythology A to Z; a young reader's companion; by Jeremy Roberts. 1st ed. Facts on File 2004 160p il map (Mythology A to Z) $40
                                                              299.5
1. Asian mythology
ISBN 0-8160-4870-3   LC 2004-5341
"Alphabetically arranged entries describe {Chinese} historical and mythological figures, places, objects, themes, and story cycles. . . . . The inviting {format features} generous white space and large headings plus numerous drawings, reproductions, and sharp halftone photographs. The clarity of wording, well-chosen bibliographic sources, and detailed {index makes this title an} excellent {resource}. " SLJ
Includes bibliographical references

299.6   Religions originating among Black Africans and people of Black African descent

Lynch, Patricia Ann
African mythology A to Z; Patricia Ann Lynch. Facts on File 2004 xx, 137p il map (Mythology A to Z) $40
                                                              299.6
1. African mythology
ISBN 0-8160-4892-4   LC 2004-47109
This is a "reference to the deities, places, events, animals, beliefs, and other subjects that appear in the myths of various African peoples." Publisher's note
"This title is an excellent introduction to the mythologies of African cultures and should be in most public and school libraries." Booklist
Includes bibliographical references

299.7   Religions of North American native origin

Bierhorst, John, 1936-
The mythology of Mexico and Central America; with a new afterword. Oxford University Press 2002 249p il map pa $18.95 (7 and up)
                                                              299.7
1. Native Americans—Mexico—Religion 2. Native Americans—Central America—Religion
ISBN 0-19-514621-2   LC 2001-55441
The author collects twenty basic myths of the Aztec and Mayan people and examines their influence on the culture and political life of the region
Includes bibliographical references

The mythology of North America; with a new afterword. Oxford University Press 2001 c2002 268p il map pa $10.95 (7 and up)   **299.7**
1. Native Americans—Religion
ISBN 0-19-514623-9   LC 2001-55440
First published 1985 by Morrow
The author "delineates eleven mythological regions—from the Arctic to the Southwest and from California to the East Coast—presenting the gods, heroes, and primary myths of each area." Publisher's note

Hartz, Paula
Native American religions; by Paula R. Hartz. updated edition. Facts on File 2004 128p il (World religions) $30   **299.7**
1. Native Americans—Religion 2. Native Americans—Rites and ceremonies
ISBN 0-8160-5727-3   LC 2004-46907
First published 1997
"Presents the common traits shared among the diverse Native American tribes, the ceremonies and rituals that are an intrinsic part of the lives of tribe members, the ethical and religious principles that guide believers to living a harmonious and balanced life, and the relationship between Native American religions and Christianity." Publisher's note
Includes bibliographical references

Martin, Joel
Native American religion. Oxford Univ. Press 1999 157p il (Religion in American life) $28 (7 and up)   **299.7**
1. Native Americans—Religion
ISBN 0-19-511035-8   LC 98-50155
An "examination of religious life and practices from ancient times through the Colonial period and the Western Expansion, and into the 20th century. Martin acknowledges the importance of religion in all aspects of Native American daily life and explores some of the differences among the various cultures. He also addresses the impact of the arrival of Europeans on spiritual life." SLJ
Includes bibliographical references

299.8 Religions of South American native origin

Bierhorst, John, 1936-
The mythology of South America; with a new afterword; John Bierhorst. Oxford University Press 2002 279p il map pa $18.95 (7 and up)
                                               299.8
1. Native Americans—South America—Religion
ISBN 0-19-514625-5   LC 2001-55420
Discusses Indian mythology of various regions of South America, describing origins, comparing similar tales, and presenting some of the myths themselves
Includes bibliographical references

300 SOCIAL SCIENCES

301 Sociology and anthropology

Batten, Mary
Anthropologist: scientist of the people; with photographs by A. Magdalena Hurtado and Kim Hill. Houghton Mifflin 2001 64p il maps (Scientists in the field) $16 (4 and up)
                                               301
1. Hurtado, A. Magdalena 2. Hill, Kim 3. Anthropology 4. Guayaki Indians
ISBN 0-618-08368-5
This book "introduces readers to Magdalena {Hurtado} and Kim Hill, a husband-and-wife team who study the Aché of Paraguay. . . . Batten's graceful text covers basic science concepts (what an anthropologist really does; what evolutionary biology is) in accessible, clear language and examples just right for kids, offering fascinating hypotheses along the way." Booklist

302 Social interaction

Erlbach, Arlene
The kids' volunteering book. Lerner Publs. 1998 64p il lib bdg $22.60; pa $9.95 (4-6)   **302**
1. Volunteer work
ISBN 0-8225-2415-5 (lib bdg); 0-8225-9820-5 (pa)
                                        LC 97-23356

Presents some opportunities for young people to perform volunteer service, and briefly profiles some children who are volunteers
"The profiles are interesting and inspiring, and substantial information is provided on the practical details of . . . a volunteer enterprise." Horn Book Guide
Includes glossary and bibliographical references

Worth the risk; true stories about risk takers plus how you can be one, too. Free Spirit 1999 127p il pa $12.95   **302**
1. Risk-taking (Psychology)
ISBN 1-57542-051-1   LC 98-38615
Discusses the value of taking risks and different kinds of risk-taking, both good and bad, and offers advice on and examples of this type of behavior and how to learn from both successes and mistakes
"The narratives are sure to provoke discussion about various types of behavior." SLJ
Includes bibliographical references

302.2 Communication

Liungman, Carl G.
Dictionary of symbols. ABC-CLIO 1991 596p o.p. Norton paperback available $21.95
                                               302.2
1. Signs and symbols 2. Picture writing
ISBN 0-393-31236-4 (pa)   LC 91-36657
Original Swedish edition, 1974
This dictionary groups "icons according to their graphical style rather than their meaning. For example, all symbols based upon the cross are included in one chapter, those based upon the triangle in another, and those based upon the circle in yet another. Each symbol is succinctly defined and a source of origin (if known) is given. To enhance access, both name and form indexes are provided. This work will certainly become one of the key sources for tracing symbols and their meanings." Am Libr
Includes bibliographical references

Zielin, Lara, 1975-
Make things happen; the key to networking for teens. Lobster Press 2003 107p il $18.75
                                               302.2
1. Teenagers—Employment 2. Interpersonal relations
ISBN 1-894222-43-1
"Defining networking for teens as learning about oneself in relation to a life purpose, Zielin proposes healthy ways to assess interests, skills, and personality traits while developing career goals. . . . Specific suggestions for organizing information, obtaining hands-on experience, becoming confident and assertive, and developing, acquiring, and using networking resources such as résumés, cover letters, business cards, and thank-you letters make this small book an asset for teens and those who advise them. . . . This book combines information and common sense." Voice Youth Advocates

302.23   Media (Means of communication)

Cohen, Daniel, 1936-
Yellow journalism; scandal, sensationalism, and gossip in the media. 21st Cent. Bks. (Brookfield) 2000 128p il lib bdg $24.90 (7 and up)

302.23

1. Mass media 2. Journalism
ISBN 0-7613-1502-0   LC 99-48934
"A history of sensational news reporting, beginning with the story of life on the moon as described by the New York Sun in 1835." SLJ
"Enhanced by vivid if occasionally gruesome photos, this is nonfiction so riveting it's almost impossible to put down." Booklist
Includes bibliographical references

Mass media: opposing viewpoints; William Dudley, book editor. Greenhaven Press 2005 218p il $33.70; pa $22.45   302.23
1. Mass media
ISBN 0-7377-2242-8; 0-7377-2243-6 (pa)
                                    LC 2004-42401
"Opposing viewpoints series"
Presents opposing viewpoints on various aspects of mass media including television's affect on society, whether or not advertising is harmful, the influence of media on politics, whether or not pornography on the Internet should be regulated, and the regulation of television for children
Includes bibliographical references

Petley, Julian
Media; the impact on our lives. Raintree Steck-Vaughn Pubs. 2001 64p il (21st century debates) $22.95 (7 and up)   302.23
1. Mass media
ISBN 0-7398-3175-5   LC 00-62647
"Petley looks at the influence that newspapers, radio, television, film, and advertising have on our view of the world. He discusses who is in control of knowledge, who regulates the media, propaganda, politics, and whether the media contributes to and/or causes criminal behavior. . . . There is a great deal of material here for reports, and many topics may lead students to further research." SLJ
Includes glossary and bibliographical references

302.3   Social interaction within groups

Hinojosa, Maria
Crews: gang members talk to Maria Hinojosa; photographs by German Perez. Harcourt Brace & Co. 1995 168p il hardcover o.p. paperback available $12 (7 and up)   302.3
1. Gangs
ISBN 0-15-200283-4 (pa)   LC 94-12173

A "look at Latino gang members in New York City. Shank, Coki, Cindy, Tre, Smooth b, and their friends answer the interviewer's questions to reveal lives driven overwhelmingly by some common threads: the need for acceptance, suppressed anger, dysfunctional families, poverty, violence, and drugs. . . . Hinojosa's open-ended questioning style encourages young men and women to tell their own stories." SLJ

303.3   Coordination and control

Senker, Cath
Why are people prejudiced? Raintree Steck-Vaughn Pubs. 2002 48p il (Exploring tough issues) lib bdg $28.70   303.3
1. Prejudices 2. Discrimination
ISBN 0-7398-4959-X   LC 2001-48628
Contents: What is prejudice?; Historical reasons for prejudice; The fear of the unknown; Scapegoating as a form of prejudice; Institutional racism; Feeling superior; What can we do?
This "does an excellent job of giving students a solid background and well-written explanation of {prejudice}." Voice Youth Advocates
Includes glossary and bibliographical references

Spangenburg, Ray, 1939-
Propaganda; understanding the power of persuasion; {by} Ray Spangenburg and Kit Moser. Enslow Pubs. 2002 64p il (Teen issues) lib bdg $22.60 (7 and up)   303.3
1. Propaganda
ISBN 0-7660-1664-1   LC 2001-8627
Includes bibliographical references
"The authors define [propaganda], show how it is used in various situations, and suggest ways in which people can test information for accuracy and defend themselves against unwanted persuasion. . . . The section on the language of propaganda gives excellent definitions of terms . . . used to sway an audience's thinking. The chapter on ways to protect oneself from daily propaganda is enlightening." SLJ

303.4   Social change

The **information** revolution; opposing viewpoints; Laura K. Egendorf, book editor. Greenhaven Press 2004 202p il $33.70; pa $22.45
                                            303.4
1. Information technology 2. Information society
ISBN 0-7377-1693-2; 0-7377-1694-0 (pa)
                                    LC 2003-44813
"Opposing viewpoints series"
"This title looks at how the Internet and the Information Revolution have changed society, education, our individual rights, and the future . . . Students will find short, accurate articles here for their research, and they will be aided by the discussion questions, bibliographies, organizations to contact, and excellent index . . . The easily digested format is welcome as many resources on this topic are dense and scholarly. A solid addition for most libraries." SLJ
Includes bibliographical references

The **Internet:** opposing viewpoints; James D. Torr, book editor. Greenhaven Press 2005 204p il lib bdg $34.95; pa $23.70 **303.4**
1. Internet
ISBN 0-7377-2941-4 (lib bdg); 0-7377-2942-2 (pa)
LC 2004-59699
"Opposing viewpoints series"
"The authors in this volume examine the diverse effects of the Internet revolution—and suggest ways in which the technology can be harnessed for the better." Publisher's note
Includes bibliographical references

Kronenwetter, Michael
Protest! 21st Cent. Bks. (NY) 1996 126p il lib bdg $23.40 (7 and up) **303.4**
1. Dissent 2. Demonstrations
ISBN 0-8050-4103-6 LC 96-9866
This is an "introduction to and overview of the history of protest in the U.S. and elsewhere. . . . Particularly attention-getting are the chapters on the birth of the women's rights movement and the persistence of the suffragists; on the heroism of Gandhi and his consistent practice of nonviolent protest throughout his long life; and on the role of unions and strikes within the labor movement." SLJ
Includes glossary and bibliographical references

Yount, Lisa
Biotechnology and genetic engineering. rev ed. Facts on File 2004 316p $45 **303.4**
1. Biotechnology 2. Genetic engineering
ISBN 0-8160-5059-7 LC 2003-64223
First published 2000
This provides "medical, political, and ethical viewpoints behind headline stories about DNA research and fingerprinting, the Human Genome Project, cloning, and the patenting of living organisms. The author also includes a chronology, a glossary of technical terms, and short biographical sketches of the scientists and others involved in the history and current issues surrounding the new science. . . . She completes the volume with addresses and Web sites of biotechnical agencies and organizations as well as abstracts of landmark Court cases." Voice Youth Advocates {review of 2000 edition}
"In one comprehensive volume, Yount provides the ultimate resource for students, teachers, and library media specialists." Booklist {review of 2000 edition}
Includes bibliographical references

303.6 Conflict

Currie, Stephen, 1960-
Terrorists and terrorist groups. Lucent Bks. 2002 96p il maps (Lucent terrorism library) lib bdg $21.96 (7 and up) **303.6**
1. Terrorism
ISBN 1-59018-207-3 LC 2001-7843
Contents: The terrorists; Hamas; Abimael Guzman and Shining Path; The Irish Republican Army; Timothy McVeigh; Osama bin Laden and Al-Qaeda

Discusses the formation, political agenda, actions, and religious beliefs of various groups that use violent means to achieve their ends
This "is an excellent resource that demonstrates thorough research and opens up issues for discussion." Booklist
Includes bibliographical references

Drew, Naomi
The kids' guide to working out conflicts; how to keep cool, stay safe, and get along; Naomi Drew. Free Spirit Pub 2004 146p il pa $13.95 **303.6**
1. Conflict management
ISBN 1-575-42150-X LC 2003-21108
Describes common forms of conflict, the reasons behind conflicts, and various positive ways to deal with and defuse tough situations at school, at home, and in the community without getting physical.
"In clean, respectful language, {the author} offers youth a highly doable eight-step plan to overcome anger issues. . . . The thoughtful encouraging tone of this important book . . . embraces children all along the conflict spectrum, from tortured victims of bullying to those who endure sustained stress and from moderate levels of conflict to full-blown bullies. . . . Highly recommended." Voice Youth Advocates
Includes bibliographical references

Edgar, Kathleen J.
Everything you need to know about media violence; Kathleen J. Edgar. rev ed. Rosen Pub. Group 2000 64p il (The need to know library) $25.95 **303.6**
1. Violence 2. Mass media
ISBN 0-8239-3108-0 LC 2001-268462
First published 1998
"This book examines how the media portrays violence while also offering kids advice on how to protect themselves from these disturbing messages." Publisher's note

Gelletly, LeeAnne
Violence in the media; by LeeAnne Gelletly. Lucent Books 2005 112p il (Lucent Overview series) $28.70 (7 and up) **303.6**
1. Violence 2. Mass media
ISBN 1-560-06508-7 LC 2004-10692
Contents: Violence in film and television; Violence in music; Violence in interactive media; Linking media violence with real-life violence; Regulating the media
Explores the issue of violence in television, films, music, and other forms of media, with an examination of the link between media violence and real-life violence and discussion of the steps that have been taken to regulate violent media
Includes bibliographical references

Grant, R. G.
Genocide. Raintree Steck-Vaughn Pubs. 1999 64p il (Talking points) $32.79 **303.6**
1. Genocide
ISBN 0-8172-5314-9 LC 98-38347

Grant, R. G.—*Continued*
Explains the nature, history, effects, and various causes of genocide

The author "uses facts, statistics, and case studies to examine the phenomenon of cultural and racial extermination. His concluding section suggests a realistic view of this issue." Sci Books Films

Includes glossary and bibliographical references

Innes, Brian, 1928-
International terrorism; Brian Innes. Mason Crest Publishers 2003 96p il (Crime and detection) lib bdg $22.95; pa $9.95   **303.6**
1. Terrorism
ISBN 1-590-84371-1; 1-590-84592-7 (pa)
LC 2003-485
Contents: Introduction; The rise of terrorism; The rise of the PLO; Urban guerrillas; Terrorism and religion; Osama bin Laden and al Qaeda; Counter-terrorist organizations

Includes bibliographical references

Media violence: opposing viewpoints; Louise I. Gerdes, book editor. Greenhaven Press 2004 191p il lib bdg $33.70; pa $22.45 (7 and up)
303.6
1. Violence 2. Mass media
ISBN 0-7377-2011-5 (lib bdg); 0-7377-2012-3 (pa)
LC 2003-44810
"Opposing viewpoints series"

Replaces the edition published 1999 under the editorship of William Dudley

"This volume opens with a history of the nationwide debate over violent content in television, video games, music, and film. . . . The following chapters address the impact of violent media, government intervention, and societal response. . . . The articles provide a truly diverse and divergent set of opinions. Short in length . . . and strong on substance, the essays will appeal to students preparing papers and debate topics." SLJ

Meltzer, Milton, 1915-
Ain't gonna study war no more; the story of America's peace seekers. Random House 2002 290p il lib bdg $10.99; pa $5.99   **303.6**
1. Pacifism 2. Draft resisters
ISBN 0-375-92260-1 (lib bdg); 0-375-82260-7 (pa)
LC 2001-57815
First published 1985 by Harper & Row

This "provides an authoritative and quite readable history of the peace movement and nonviolent resistance in America." Booklist

Includes bibliographical references

The day the sky fell; a history of terrorism. Random House 2002 290p lib bdg $10.99; pa $5.99 (7 and up)   **303.6**
1. Terrorism
ISBN 0-375-92250-4 (lib bdg); 0-375-82250-X (pa)
LC 2001-57816
"Originally published in slightly different form under the title *The Terrorists* by Harper & Row, Publishers, Inc., in 1983." Verso of title page

This study of terrorism includes chapters on September 11, 2001; the religion of Islam; the troubles in Ireland; and the terrorist state. A discussion guide is also included

Includes bibliographical references

Stewart, Gail, 1949-
Guns and violence; [by] Gail B. Stewart. KidHaven Press 2002 48p il (Understanding issues) $23.70   **303.6**
1. Violence 2. Firearms
ISBN 0-7377-0952-9   LC 2001-3361
"The connection between guns and violent crime, especially school violence, is examined in this title." Publisher's note

"Facts, statistics, and other information are interwoven with personal examples in a way that lets readers associate the material with their own circumstances. . . . Colorful illustrations and charts make the pages attractive." Book Rep

Includes bibliographical references

Terrorism. KidHaven Press 2002 48p il map (Understanding issues) lib bdg $23.70 (4 and up)
303.6
1. Terrorism 2. September 11 terrorist attacks, 2001
ISBN 0-7377-1287-2   LC 2001-6215
Uses the terrorist attacks of September 11, 2001 to explore the historical, political, and religious origins of political violence, its effects on individuals, and what governments can do to stop it

"Clear, colorful photographs appear on nearly every page and illustrate the text effectively. . . . A succinct, balanced presentation that can serve as a good starting point for both research and discussion." Booklist

Taylor, Robert, 1948-
History of terrorism. Lucent Bks. 2002 96p il map (Terrorism library) $28.70 (7 and up)
303.6
1. Terrorism
ISBN 1-590-18206-5   LC 2002-1910
Contents: Zealots, assassins, and the reign of terror; Propaganda of the bomb; Anti-colonial terrorism; Terrorism and the Left; Separatist terrorism; Holy War

Examines the political agendas, actions, and religious beliefs of individuals and groups who, throughout history, have resorted to violent actions in order to generate fear and gain their objectives

This "is an excellent resource that demonstrates thorough research and opens up issues for discussion." Booklist

Includes bibliographical references

Violence: opposing viewpoints; Laura K. Egendorf, book editor. Greenhaven Press 2001 192p il $31.20; pa $19.95 (7 and up)
303.6
1. Violence
ISBN 0-7377-0660-0; 0-7377-0659-7 (pa)
LC 00-50319
"Opposing viewpoints series"

Violence: opposing viewpoints—*Continued*
Explores the causes and consequences of violence and offers possible solutions

This work "covers a lot of ground, and its extensive cross references will prove useful for assignments on a variety of social issues." Booklist

Includes bibliographical references

304.8 Movement of people

Flanders, Stephen A.
Atlas of American migration. Facts on File 1998 214p il maps $93.50   **304.8**
1. Internal migration
ISBN 0-8160-3158-4

This source "is divided into 10 thematic chapters, from 'A Shifting Mosaic: America and Migration,' to 'The Suburban Frontier: Migration since 1945.' Intervening chapters cover such topics as slavery, Native American migration, the settlement of the West, and the move to the cities after 1890. . . . The most important features of the atlas are the many tables, graphs, and maps." Booklist

305.23 Young people

Benson, Peter L.
What teens need to succeed; proven, practical ways to shape your own future; [by] Peter L. Benson, Judy Galbraith, and Pamela Espeland. Free Spirit 1998 361p il pa $15.95 (7 and up)
305.23
1. Life skills 2. Conduct of life
ISBN 1-57542-027-9   LC 98-6036

Describes forty "developmental assets" that teenagers need to succeed in life, such as family support, positive peer influences, and religious community, and suggests ways to acquire these assets

"A useful resource for teens and those who work with them." SLJ

Includes bibliographical references

Colman, Penny
Girls! the history of growing up female in America. Scholastic 2000 192p il hardcover o.p. paperback available pa $12.95 (5 and up)
305.23
1. Girls
ISBN 0-590-37130-4 (pa)   LC 99-28150

Traces the history of growing up female in America as told by the girls themselves in journals, household manuals, letters, slave narratives, and other primary sources

"The author's thorough research, inclusiveness, and accessible style make this book an essential resource for libraries serving young people." SLJ

Includes bibliographical references

Daldry, Jeremy, 1969-
The teenage guy's survival guide. Little, Brown 1999 136p il pa $8.99 (7 and up)   **305.23**
1. Boys 2. Adolescence 3. Sex education
ISBN 0-316-17824-1   LC 98-40816

First published 1997 in the United Kingdom with title: Boys behaving badly

This book is "designed to answer questions . . . about dating, physical changes, emotional problems, and social survival. . . . Other concerns addressed include safe sex, being gay, pornography, alcohol, drugs, tobacco, and fighting. That is a lot of information packed into these pages, but that information, while not exhaustive, is certainly sound and clearly presented." Voice Youth Advocates

Includes bibliographical references

Girls know best; advice from girls for girls on just about everything! written by girls just like you!; compiled by Michelle Roehm; designed and illustrated by Marci Doane Roth. Beyond Words Pub. 1997 160p il pa $8.95   **305.23**
1. Girls 2. Interpersonal relations
ISBN 1-88522-363-3   LC 97-19942

Thirty-eight different girls respond to questions on specific issues including siblings, school, homework, parents, divorce, stepfamilies, boys, race, religion, and personal appearance

The "advice is on-target and mature, and the perspective is fresh and welcome." SLJ

Includes bibliographical references

Gray, Heather M.
Real girl/real world; tools for finding your true self; by Heather M. Gray & Samantha Phillips. Seal Press 1998 221p il pa $14.95 (7 and up)
305.23
1. Girls 2. Adolescence 3. Sex education
ISBN 1-58005 005-0   LC 98-8612

Provides information for teenage girls about sexuality, birth control, health, body image, eating disorders, and feminism

This is a "highly recommended resource book that belongs in every young adult collection. . . . Fun and readable, this is a highly accessible discussion of the issues." Voice Youth Advocates

Includes bibliographical references

Gurian, Michael
From boys to men; all about adolescence and you; illustrated by Brian Floca. Price/Stern/Sloan 1999 86p il (Plugged in) hardcover o.p. paperback available $5.99   **305.23**
1. Boys 2. Adolescence 3. Sex education
ISBN 0-8431-7483-8 (pa)   LC 98-37025

This offers "advice for preteens on how to cope with the emotional and physical changes that typically accompany adolescence. Gurian . . . addresses such subjects as developing romantic and sexual relationships, friendships, peer pressure, and even nutrition and wellness. The writing is direct, personal, and conversational. The tone is always positive and empathetic." SLJ

Hartman, Holly

Girlwonder; every girl's guide to the fantastic feats, cool qualities, and remarkable abilities of women and girls; {by} Holly Hartman with the editors of Information Please. Houghton Mifflin 2003 234p il pa $9.95 (5 and up)   **305.23**

1. Women—United States 2. Teenagers

ISBN 0-618-31939-5

An updated and expanded edition of The Information Please girls' almanac by Margo McLoone and Alice Siegel, published 1995

"After opening with a day-by-day calendar of events in women's history, Hartman divides the information into topical sections, including chapters on American history, sports, literature, science, and careers. Famous women are highlighted throughout the pages. . . . There are also scattered bits of advice about health issues and relationships, as well as interesting tidbits about love and romance, mythological characters, and fashion trends. Readers will enjoy thumbing through this fact-packed text." SLJ

Jones, Carolyn

Every girl tells a story; a celebration of girls speaking their minds; by Carolyn Jones in collaboration with Girl Scouts of the USA; foreword by First Lady Laura Bush. Simon & Schuster Bks. for Young Readers 2002 86p il $19.95   **305.23**

1. Teenagers 2. Girls

ISBN 0-689-84872-2   LC 2001-55117

Presents the attitudes and achievements of a diverse group of girls between the ages of thirteen and eighteen living across the United States through portraits and their own words

"Jones has done a good job of preserving each speaker's individuality. . . . The format is very appealing, with lots of white space and color photos showing each girl, and there's a good deal of ethnic diversity evident in both the pictures and the text." Booklist

Jukes, Mavis

The guy book; an owner's manual for teens: safety, maintenance, and operating instructions for teens. Crown 2002 152p il lib bdg $18.99; pa $12.95 (7 and up)   **305.23**

1. Boys 2. Adolescence 3. Sex education

ISBN 0-679-99028-3 (lib bdg); 0-679-89028-9 (pa)
     LC 2001-47073

Provides information for boys on changes that occur in their bodies during puberty and offering advice on sexual topics, nutrition, drugs, girls, and more

"In a jokey premise that will appeal to teens, the book follows the format of a car owner's manual with a retro look. . . . Much of this information is available in other sources, but the added sense of fun will make this a first choice for a lot of young men." Booklist

Includes bibliographical references

It's a girl thing; how to stay healthy, safe, and in charge; illustrations by Debbie Tilley. Knopf 1996 135p il hardcover o.p. paperback available $5.99 (5 and up)   **305.23**

1. Adolescence 2. Girls 3. Sex education

ISBN 0-679-88771-7 (pa)   LC 93-40296

"Jukes discusses a wide variety of subjects from buying a bra to sexual harassment and abuse. In a warm, conversational style, she covers body changes in both boys and girls, menstruation, general health, drinking and drugs, sexual feelings, pregnancy, contraceptives, and sexually transmitted diseases including AIDS. The text is sometimes humorous, but always conveys caring, respect, and concern." SLJ

Includes bibliographical references

Muharrar, Aisha

More than a label; why what you wear and who you're with doesn't define who you are. Free Spirit 2002 144p il pa $13.95 (7 and up)
   305.23

1. Adolescent psychology 2. Conduct of life

ISBN 1-57542-110-0   LC 2001-7386

Drawn from a survey of more than one thousand teenagers, first-person stories help to address the problems inherent in labeling people

"The enthusiastic, conversational tone will make the compassionate message very acceptable to teen readers." Booklist

Includes bibliographical references

Parks, Rosa, 1913-

Dear Mrs. Parks; a dialogue with today's youth; by Rosa Parks, with Gregory J. Reed. Lee & Low Bks. 1996 111p il $16.95; pa $9.95 (5 and up)
   305.23

1. African American children

ISBN 1-880000-45-8; 1-880000-61-X (pa)
     LC 96-18389

Presents correspondence between Rosa Parks and various children in which the "Mother of the Modern Day Civil Rights Movement" answers questions and encourages young people to reach their highest potential

"Parks responds to young people with boundless compassion, respect, and hope." Booklist

Piquemal, Michel, 1954-

When life stinks; how to deal with your bad moods, blues, and depression; [by] Michel Piquemal with Melissa Daly; illustrated by Olivier Tossan ; {translated by Jane Moseley}. Amulet Boooks 2004 112p il pa $9.95   **305.23**

1. Teenagers 2. Depression (Psychology)

ISBN 0-8109-4932-6   LC 2004-13001

This "book examines dark moods and mental illness, and gives young people tools for coping, plus advice on when, where, and how to get help." Publisher's note

"The pleasing use of blocks of color and cartoon illustrations enhances the text. . . . Using the common-sense suggestions provided, readers will more successfully navigate the turmoil of adolescence." SLJ

Includes bibliographical references

Rimm, Sylvia B., 1935-

See Jane win for girls; a smart girl's guide to success; {by} Sylvia Rimm. Free Spirit 2003 131p il pa $13.95 (5 and up)   **305.23**

1. Girls 2. Success 3. Conduct of life

ISBN 1-575-42122-4   LC 2002-155780

Rimm, Sylvia B., 1935-—*Continued*

Adapted from the author's title for adults See Jane win, published 1999 by Crown

Presents tips, quizzes, activities, and words of wisdom from successful women for girls trying to make positive changes and choices in all areas of their lives and develop confidence, inner strength, and the desire to learn

"The message is strong and simple, the advice is practical, and readers looking for guidance and direction will respond positively to the book's format. . . . A useful self-help book and practical guide to life." SLJ

Includes bibliographical references

Rutledge, Jill Zimmerman

Dealing with the stuff that makes life tough; the 10 things that stress girls out and how to cope with them; Jill Zimmerman Rutledge. Contemporary Books 2004 224p pa $14.95 (7 and up)   **305.23**

1. Interpersonal relations 2. Stress (Psychology) 3. Women—Psychology

ISBN 0-07-142326-5   LC 2003-46047

"Using quotes from women in history and anecdotal stories of adolescent girls, 'Dr. Jill' gives prescriptions for dealing with difficult situations. The chapters address relationships, drug addiction, stress, body image, parental divorce, insomnia, bullies, and having a crush on another girl. . . . Although the anecdotes are generic and include only a first name, they are broad in scope and right on target." SLJ

Shandler, Sara

Ophelia speaks; adolescent girls write about their search for self. HarperPerennial 1999 285p pa $12.95 (7 and up)   **305.23**

1. Girls 2. Adolescence

ISBN 0-06-095297-0   LC 99-13534

Also available Thorndike Press large print edition

"Shandler collected writings from adolescent girls all over the country on topics that include sexuality, eating disorders, feminism, family dynamics, and friendship; their words, framed by Shandler's own reflections, are riveting and revealing." Libr J

Sherrow, Victoria

Encyclopedia of youth and war; young people as participants and victims. Oryx Press 2000 366p il $68.95   **305.23**

1. Children and war

ISBN 1-57356-287-4   LC 99-43452

"Beginning with the Thirty-Year War in the mid-1600s, this single volume containing over three hundred individual entries addresses the impact of war on young people from the perspectives of both victim and participant. . . . Students will find valuable and interesting information on broad subjects such as volunteers, land mines, disease, or resistance movements as they relate specifically to children aged eighteen or younger." Voice Youth Advocates

Weston, Carol

For teens only; quotes, notes, & advice you can use. HarperTrophy 2003 248p pa $8.99   **305.23**

1. Life skills 2. Conduct of life 3. Quotations

ISBN 0-06-000214-X   LC 2002-6381

The author "offers counsel for both boys and girls. Quick, one-page bits on various topics are contained in seven chapters, 'Mind,' 'Body,' 'Friends,' 'Relationships,' 'School,' 'Family,' and 'Work.'. . . The information is sound, catchy, and fun to read, but the quotes are the true attention-getters. They are from famous people, dead and living, from Shakespeare to Chris Rock." Voice Youth Advocates

Private and personal; questions and answers for girls only. HarperCollins Pubs. 2000 345p pa $10.99   **305.23**

1. Girls

ISBN 0-380-81025-5   LC 99-96353

The author "adds responses to short, sharp letters she's received from girls, grouping them together in obvious categories: family, friendship, boyfriends, and growing up. . . . She's absolutely straightforward, like a loving older sister, and she's always encouraging." Booklist

You be me; friendship in the lives of teen girls; edited by Susan Musgrave. Annick Press 2002 123p $18.95; pa $7.95 (7 and up)   **305.23**

1. Teenagers 2. Girls 3. Friendship

ISBN 1-550-37739-6; 1-550-37738-8 (pa)

LC 2003-427230

"In this series of vignettes, teen friendship and its accompanying emotions are examined from the personal perspectives of seven women. The well-written pieces capture the joy and the hurt, the fun and the responsibility, and the memories shared. . . . A valuable addition." SLJ

305.3   Men and women

Male/female roles: opposing viewpoints; Auriana Ojeda, book editor. Greenhaven Press 2005 219p il lib bdg $33.70; pa $22.45   **305.3**

1. Sex role

ISBN 0-7377-2240-1 (lib bdg); 0-7377-2241-X (pa)

LC 2004-40605

"Opposing viewpoints series"

"Authors in this anthology debate whether gender is biological or culturally determined, if male and female roles have changed for the better, and how best to improve relationships between men and women." Publisher's note

Includes bibliographical references

McGowan, Keith, 1968-

Sexual harassment. Lucent Bks. 1999 112p il (Lucent overview series) lib bdg $27.45 (7 and up)   **305.3**

1. Sexual harassment

ISBN 1-56006-507-9   LC 98-14683

McGowan, Keith, 1968——*Continued*
An overview of sexual harassment, including its aspects in the law, the workplace, education, and the military
"McGowan does a steady job of defining and differentiating complex and weighted terms. . . . Quick, basic, informative, and detailed enough without being overwhelming." SLJ
Includes bibliographical references

305.4   Women

33 things every girl should know about women's history; from suffragettes to skirt lengths to the E.R.A.; edited by Tonya Bolden. Crown 2002 240p il lib bdg $18.99; pa $12.95 (5 and up)   **305.4**
1. Women—United States—History 2. Feminism 3. Women's rights
ISBN 0-375-91122-7 (lib bdg); 0-375-81122-2 (pa)
LC 2001-47131
Uses poems, essays, letters, photographs and more to present the actions and achievements of women in the United States, from its beginnings up through the twentieth century
"This is a very strong, highly readable offering that gives context to the feminist movement." Booklist

Adams, Colleen
Women's suffrage; a primary source history of the women's rights movement in America. Rosen Pub. Group 2003 64p il map (Primary sources in American history) lib bdg $29.95   **305.4**
1. Women's rights 2. Women—Suffrage 3. Women—United States
ISBN 0-8239-3685-6   LC 2002-4476
Contents: Women's influence on early social reform movements; Leaders of the women's rights movement in the 1850s; Elizabeth Cady Stanton makes a difference; Susan B. Anthony and the fight for women's suffrage; The struggle for the vote continues
This "leads off with a discussion of the role of women in early reform movements, then moves into a more detailed consideration of the women's movement, including profiles of individual pioneers. Highlighting chapters are photographs of original documents, declarations from the first Women's Rights Convention, excerpts from a pamphlet, and more." Booklist
Includes glossary and bibliographical references

Bausum, Ann
With courage and cloth; winning the fight for a woman's right to vote; by Ann Bausum. National Geographic 2004 111p il $21.95; lib bdg $32.90
305.4
1. Women—Suffrage 2. Women—United States—History
ISBN 0-7922-7647-7; 0-7922-6996-9 (lib bdg)
LC 2004-1191
Contents: Introduction; Parade, 1913; Rights, 1848-1906; Momentum, 1906-1916; Protest, 1917; Prison, 1917; Action, 1918-1919; Victory, 1919-1920

This is a history of the movement for women's suffrage in the United States.
"Vintage photographs, some never before published, depict key figures in the movement speaking, protesting, parading, picketing, and going to jail. Bausum's careful research is evident throughout, with sources thoroughly cited and a text studded with original source quotations." SLJ

Coppens, Linda Miles, 1944-
What American women did, 1789-1920; a year-by-year reference. McFarland & Co. 2001 259p il $38.50 (7 and up)   **305.4**
1. Women—United States—History 2. Women—Social conditions
ISBN 0-7864-0899-5   LC 00-64010
"A chronological account of women's accomplishments in the areas of domesticity, work, education, religion, the arts, law and politics, and reform efforts. . . . This work will prove useful for students wishing to gain a better perspective of history, particularly social history, as it pertained to women." SLJ
Includes bibliographical references

Cullen-DuPont, Kathryn
Encyclopedia of women's history in America. 2nd ed. Facts on File 2000 418p il $71.50
305.4
1. Women—United States—History 2. Feminism
ISBN 0-8160-4100-8   LC 99-87498
First published 1996
This work highlights the lives and contributions of women in American history ranging from Pocahontas to Hillary Clinton and Madeleine Albright. Entries cover individuals, movements, court cases and women's issues from Colonial times to the present
"Well-written and informative . . . . An excellent quick reference source . . . recommended . . . ." Choice

Franck, Irene M.
The Wilson chronology of women's achievements; a record of women's achievements from ancient times to present; by Irene M. Franck and David M. Brownstone. Wilson, H.W. 1998 507p $110 (7 and up)   **305.4**
1. Women—History
ISBN 0-8242-0936-2   LC 97-34394
First published 1995 by HarperPerennial with title: Women's world
This chronicle of women's history ranges "from the Egyptian queen Nefertiti and the Greek poet Sappho to Susan B. Anthony, Marie Curie, Eleanor Roosevelt, and Janet Reno." Publisher's note
Includes bibliographical references

Harik, Ramsay M.
Women in the Middle East; tradition and change; {by} Ramsay M. Harik and Elsa Marston. rev ed. Watts 2003 192p il map lib bdg $29.50
305.4
1. Women—Middle East
ISBN 0-531-12222-0   LC 2002-8510

Harik, Ramsay M.—*Continued*
First published 1996
Contents: The Middle East; Growing up; School days; Religion and tradition; Becoming a wife; Married life; Family and home: women's world; Veiling; Women's health; Women at work; Women in the arts and athletics; Women in public life; Is there a Middle Eastern women's movement?; A woman's later years; Afghanistan: the extremes of oppression; Looking toward tomorrow
Discusses the lives of women in the Middle East today including the traditions that shape these lives, the present day religious, social and political realities, and changing expectations
"A fine and timely revision. . . . A colorful and inviting new dust jacket along with a well-researched and well-written text combine to make this an important purchase for general readers and student researchers alike." SLJ
Includes bibliographical references

Heinemann, Sue, 1948-
The New York Public Library amazing women in American history; a book of answers for kids. Wiley 1998 192p (New York Public Library answer books for kids series) pa $12.95 (5 and up)
305.4
1. Women—United States—History 2. Women—Social conditions
ISBN 0-471-19216-3   LC 97-18465
"A Stonesong Press book"
Consists of short answers to questions about the roles and achievements of women in America from prehistory to the end of the twentieth century
"The text is succinct, easy to read, and informative. . . . Pertinent black-and-white photos appear throughout." SLJ
Includes glossary and bibliographical references

Kendall, Martha E., 1947-
Failure is impossible! the history of American women's rights. Lerner Publs. 2001 96p il (People's history) lib bdg $26.60   **305.4**
1. Women's rights 2. Feminism 3. Women—United States—History
ISBN 0-8225-1744-2   LC 00-9707
This volume "reviews the history of the women's rights movement in America, beginning with a discussion of women's legal status among the Puritans of Boston, then highlighting developments to the present." Booklist
"A well-organized, well-documented resource." SLJ
Includes bibliographical references

Macdonald, Fiona
Women in 19th-century America. Bedrick Bks. 1999 48p il (Other half of history) $17.95
305.4
1. Women—United States—History 2. Women—Social conditions
ISBN 0-87226-566-8   LC 98-42644
Examines the everyday life of women in the United States during the 1800s, contrasting society's ideal view of women with their real lives
Includes glossary and bibliographical references

Women in 19th-century Europe. Bedrick Bks. 1999 48p il (Other half of history) $17.95
305.4
1. Women—Europe 2. Women—Social conditions
ISBN 0-87226-565-X   LC 98-42170
Examines the reality of women's lives in Europe during the 1800s and how change slowly occurred
"The pages are a panorama of illustrations from black-and-white woodcuts to line drawings and full-color reproductions, each accompanied by a succinct caption. . . . A delight to browse, and should lead readers to more extensive exploration." SLJ
Includes glossary and bibliographical references

Matthews, Glenna
American women's history; a student companion. Oxford Univ. Press 2000 368p il (Oxford student companions to American history) lib bdg $60   **305.4**
1. Women—United States—History
ISBN 0-19-511317-9   LC 99-87245
Alphabetical articles on major events, documents, persons, social movements, and political and social concepts connected with the history of women in America
"Articles vary in length and are easy to read. Many articles are accompanied by a photograph. . . . This is a helpful reference tool that will be useful to students needing information about American women and their contributions to U.S. history." Booklist

Miller, Brandon Marie
Good women of a well-blessed land; women's lives in colonial America. Lerner Publs. 2003 96p il (People's history) lib bdg $25.26   **305.4**
1. Women—United States—History 2. United States—Social life and customs—1600-1775, Colonial period
ISBN 0-8225-0032-9   LC 2002-8902
Contents: The naturall inhabitants; In this new discovered Virginia; Goodwives to New England; Weary, weary, weary, o; Up to their elbows in housewifery; Daughters of Eve; A changing world
A social history of the American colonial period with a focus on the daily lives of women, including European immigrants, Native Americans, and slaves
"The well-written account offers enough solid information to give readers a good sense of the period and enough fascinating detail to keep them interested." Booklist
Includes bibliographical references

Stearman, Kaye, 1951-
Feminism; Kaye Stearman. Raintree 2004 64p il (Ideas of the modern world) lib bdg $32.79 (7 and up)   **305.4**
1. Feminism
ISBN 0-7398-6415-7   LC 2003-2068
Contents: What is feminism?; Raising the issues; Campaigning for the vote; The forgotten years of feminism; Feminism becomes women's liberation; I'm not a feminist but . . . ; Beijing and beyond
"Stearman discusses the history of women's rights with connections made to other political movements such

Stearman, Kaye, 1951-—*Continued*
as abolitionism and temperance. . . . The author looks at
new interpretations of feminism and issues such as
sweatshop labor, countries with controversial social laws
against women's rights, and female genital mutilation.
{This book has} a balance of ideas and nonjudgmental
language. Black-and-white and full-color photos appear
throughout." SLJ
Includes bibliographical references

Women in history on file; {by} the Diagram
Group. Facts on File 2002 various paging
loose-leaf $185   **305.4**
1. Women—History
ISBN 0-8160-4646-8   LC 2001-40267
Also available CD-ROM version
A loose-leaf compilation of charts, graphs, line drawings, and chronologies which may be photocopied relating to women's history worldwide from prehistory to the
20th century

Women's almanac; edited by Linda Schmittroth &
Mary Reilly McCall. U.X.L 1997 3v il set $159
                                                  305.4
1. Women 2. Almanacs
ISBN 0-7876-0656-1   LC 96-25681
Contents: v1 History; v2 Society; v3 Culture
This almanac focuses on "women throughout his-
tory—their social concerns and cultural contributions.
. . .Twenty-five chapters examine topics such as 'Civil
Rights and Legal Status,' 'Women in Developing Coun-
tries,' 'Women's Movements,' 'Jobs and Money,' 'Edu-
cation,' 'Health, ' 'Family,' 'Literature,' 'Music,' and
'Science and Exploration.' Each chapter presents a historical overview and current information on women's
roles, achievements, and influences in these areas." SLJ

305.8   Ethnic and national groups

The **African** American almanac. Gale Res. il $220
                                                  305.8
1. African Americans
ISSN 1071-8710
First edition under the editorship of Harry A. Ploski
published 1967 by Bellwether with title: The Negro almanac. (9th edition 2002) Periodically revised. Editors
vary
"Reference covering the cultural and political history
of Black Americans. Includes generous amount of statistical information and biographies of Black Americans,
both historical and contemporary." N Y Public Libr.
Book of How & Where to Look It Up

African American breakthroughs; 500 years of
black firsts; Jay P. Pederson and Jessie Carney
Smith, editors. U.X.L 1995 280p il (African
American reference library) $58   **305.8**
1. African Americans—History
ISBN 0-8103-9496-0   LC 95-122049
Also available adult version entitled Black firsts
(1994) published by Visible Ink Press
"Organized by subject, events are then listed
chronologically. Subjects include *Business and Labor*;
Justice, Law Enforcement, and Public Safety; *Religion*;

and *Science, Medicine, and Invention.* . . . Each of the
500 entries consists of three or four sentences on the person or event with the original source or sources cited."
Booklist

African-American culture and history; a student's
guide; Jack Salzman, editor-in-chief. Macmillan
Ref. USA 2001 4v il set $415   **305.8**
1. African Americans—Encyclopedias
ISBN 0-02-865531-1   LC 00-61657
Adapted from the five-volume Encyclopedia of
African American culture and history published by Macmillan in 1996; revised for sixth- to seventh-grade, middle school audience
"The 852 alphabetically arranged articles include biographies of notable African-Americans, events, historical
eras, legal cases, areas of cultural achievement, professions, sports, and places. . . . The final volume includes
supplemental material such as a detailed chronology of
African-American history from 1444 through 2000, a
glossary; list of suggested resources, and comprehensive
index." Book Rep
"This is a good choice for a comprehensive, readable
resource about African American culture and history."
Booklist

The **African** American encyclopedia. 2nd ed,
managing editor, R. Kent Rasmussen. Marshall
Cavendish 2001 10v il maps set $599.93
                                                  305.8
1. African Americans—Encyclopedias
ISBN 0-7614-7208-8   LC 00-31526
First published 1993
This source contains some 1,950 essays on many aspects of the African American experience such as religion, music, films, art, literature, dance, food, politics,
the military, family life, and sports

The **African-American** experience on file. Facts
on File 1999 various paging il maps loose-leaf
$140   **305.8**
1. African Americans—History
ISBN 0-8160-3697-7   LC 98-29845
Executive editor, Carter Smith
A collection of over 300 maps, charts, graphs, and il-
lustrations with explanatory text covering African
American history from ancient Africa to the present
Includes bibliographical references

Altman, Susan
Encyclopedia of African-American heritage;
special writing and research by Joel Kemelhor.
2nd ed. Facts on File 2000 353p il $45; pa $18.95
                                                  305.8
1. African Americans—Encyclopedias 2. Africa—En-
cyclopedias
ISBN 0-8160-4125-3; 0-8160-4126-1 (pa)
                                      LC 00-49449
First published 1997
This "relates the history of those living on the African
continent as well as those who were sold into slavery or
who voluntarily migrated to other continents." Book Rep
"A welcome addition to any collection or classroom."
SLJ
Includes bibliographical references

Arab American encyclopedia; {by the} Arab Community Center for Economic and Social Services (ACCESS); Anan Ameri and Dawn Ramey, editors. U.X.L 1999 various paging il lib bdg $58 (7 and up)   **305.8**
1. Arab Americans—Encyclopedias
ISBN 0-7876-2952-9   LC 99-37499
"Surveys history, immigration, languages, religions, education, culture, and political activities in 19 chapters. . . . Each chapter presents its information in easy-to-read prose. Sidebars provide definitions of unfamiliar vocabulary words and facts that reinforce information found in the text. A bibliography, often with Web sites, is found at the end of each section." Booklist

The **Asian-American** experience on file; Carter Smith II, executive editor. Facts on File 1998 various paging il maps loose-leaf $140
                                         305.8
1. Asian Americans
ISBN 0-8160-3696-9   LC 98-33466
A collection of over 300 maps, charts, graphs, and illustrations with explanatory text covering Asian American history and cultures from China, South and Southeast Asia, Hawaii and the Pacific Islands, Japan, and Korea
"Upper-elementary and secondary teachers and students looking for supplementary materials for units on diversity, the California Gold Rush, Hawaii, and Chinese history will certainly find it here." Booklist
Includes bibliographical references

Asian Americans: opposing viewpoints; William Dudley, book editor. Greenhaven Press 1997 240p (American history series) lib bdg $32.45; pa $22.45 (7 and up)   **305.8**
1. Asian Americans
ISBN 1-56510-524-9 (lib bdg); 1-56510-523-0 (pa)
                                         LC 96-30439
"This collection of speeches and articles . . . provides in-depth primary material about how this country has looked on Asian immigrants. There are arguments from the 1850s onward about whether Chinese immigration should be restricted, whether Japanese residents can be assimilated, whether Asian Americans have been accepted in Hawaii. Policy makers in the 1940s argue for and against the internment of Japanese Americans during World War II. A final section looks at Asian Americans in the years after 1965." Booklist
Includes bibliographical references

Bair, Barbara
Though justice sleeps; African Americans, 1880-1900. Oxford Univ. Press 1997 142p il (Young Oxford history of African Americans) lib bdg $25 (7 and up)   **305.8**
1. African Americans—History 2. United States—History—1865-1898
ISBN 0-19-509343-7   LC 96-8472
Chronicles the lives of African Americans during the late 1800's
This book "gives a detailed account of how blacks coped with racism; terrorism; and the gradual stripping away of hard-won economic, political, and social gains.

Illustrations are copious, consisting of period photographs, documents, and drawings." SLJ
Includes bibliographical references

Birdseye, Debbie Holsclaw
Under our skin; kids talk about race; by Debbie Holsclaw Birdseye and Tom Birdseye; photographs by Robert Crum. Holiday House 1997 30p il $15.95 (4 and up)   **305.8**
1. United States—Race relations 2. Ethnic relations
ISBN 0-8234-1325-X   LC 97-9395
Six young people discuss their feelings about their own ethnic backgrounds and about their experiences with people of different races
"This book provides an excellent starting point for discussion. It gives readers a chance to see what life is like through someone else's eyes, and in someone else's skin." SLJ
Includes bibliographical references

Bode, Janet
The colors of freedom; immigrant stories. Watts 1999 144p il $25; pa $9.95   **305.8**
1. Minorities 2. Immigrants—United States 3. Teenagers 4. United States—Immigration and emigration
ISBN 0-531-11530-5; 0-531-15961-2 (pa)
                                         LC 98-29608
Newly arrived teenaged immigrants describe their experiences in America, recount traditions of their native countries, and present short stories, poems, recipes, and artwork. Also provides interviews with native born American teenagers who share their family histories
"A stellar treatment of complex immigration issues presented in an accessible format." Booklist
Includes bibliographical references

Bolden, Tonya
Tell all the children our story; memories and mementos of being young and Black in America. Abrams 2001 128p il $24.95 (5 and up)
                                         305.8
1. African American children 2. United States—Race relations
ISBN 0-8109-4496-0   LC 2001-1353
"This compilation of the African American experience, from colonial times through the twentieth century, reads and looks like a family scrapbook. . . . Photographs, excerpts from diaries and memoirs, and reproductions of artwork by black artists such as Charles Altson beautifully bring the story of each generation to life. Bolden vibrantly delivers her historical message through a contemporary perspective." Booklist
Includes bibliographical references

Boyle, David
African Americans. Barron's 2003 128p il (Coming to America) $14.95   **305.8**
1. African Americans—History
ISBN 0-7641-5628-4   LC 2002-112400

Boyle, David—*Continued*
"Boyle discusses the horrific Atlantic passage experienced by those in chains and incorporates a number of firsthand accounts of slavery. He also covers the African-American fight for freedom and civil rights. . . . [This book] has an excellent chapter on 'Family and Community.' The [book is] rich in quality color and black-and-white archival photographs and reproductions." SLJ

Byers, Ann
African-American history from emancipation to today; rising above the ashes of slavery; foreword by series advisor Henry Louis Gates. Enslow Publishers 2004 128p il map (Slavery in American history) lib bdg $26.60 (7 and up) **305.8**
1. African Americans—History
ISBN 0-7660-2153-X   LC 2003-24558
Contents: Free at last?: 1865-1866; Free but not equal: 1865-1877; Equal but separate: 1877-1915; Separate but proud: 1915-1941; Equal rights: 1941-1965; Equal power: 1966-1972; Righting the wrongs
"Byers brings together the issues and their impact from 1865 to 2002 by discussing such topics as Reconstruction, sharecropping, Jim Crow, the Harlem Renaissance, Brown v. Board of Education, Malcolm X, Black Panthers, and reparation debates. . . . [This book] will be useful in American-history collections." SLJ
Includes bibliographical references

Deignan, Tom
Irish Americans. Barron's Educ. Ser. 2003 128p il (Coming to America) $14.95 (7 and up) **305.8**
1. Irish Americans
ISBN 0-7641-5627-6   LC 2002-112399
Book created by the Ivy Press
This discusses Irish immigration to the United States and the lives of Irish Americans
This is "particularly well thought out, with informative graphics complementing the well-written [text]." Booklist
Includes bibliographical references

Diner, Hasia R.
Jews in America. Oxford Univ. Press 1999 158p il (Religion in American life) lib bdg $28 (7 and up) **305.8**
1. Jews—United States
ISBN 0-19-510678-4   LC 98-17645
Examines the migration and background of those Jews who came to America, their adaptations to their new life, the rituals, traditions, and organizations of Jewish Americans, and their contemporary situation
"The coverage is brief, but the text is clear and lively. A host of archival photos and reproductions enhance the presentation." SLJ
Includes glossary and bibliographical references

Discrimination: opposing viewpoints; Mary E. Williams, book editor. Greenhaven Press 1997 223p il $34.95; pa $21.20 (7 and up) **305.8**
1. Discrimination 2. Minorities
ISBN 1-56510-657-1; 1-56510-656-3 (pa)
LC 96-49920

"The extent to which discrimination is a national problem, its causes, the validity of claims of reverse discrimination, and ways society can fight to end it are addressed by writers, scholars, and media personalities. . . . The collection offers an evenhanded overview. . . . A solid choice for students doing research, preparing for debates, or those simply interested in the many aspects of this complex issue." SLJ
Includes bibliographical references

Frankel, Noralee, 1950-
Break those chains at last: African Americans, 1860-1880. Oxford Univ. Press 1996 143p il map (Young Oxford history of African Americans) lib bdg $25 **305.8**
1. African Americans—History 2. Slavery—United States
ISBN 0-19-508798-4   LC 95-1848
After a chapter on the Civil War, this volume addresses such topics as suffrage and political participation; economic and educational opportunities; and marriage and family life of the newly freed slaves
"Frankel makes especially good use of quotations from interviews with former slaves done in the 1930s; Reconstruction Era pension examiners' interviews with Black Civil War widows; Freedmen's Bureau records, etc." SLJ
Includes bibliographical references

Gay, Kathlyn, 1930-
Cultural diversity; conflicts and challenges : the ultimate teen guide. Scarecrow Press 2003 121p (It happened to me) pa $25.95 (7 and up) **305.8**
1. Multiculturalism 2. Prejudices 3. Racism 4. Toleration
ISBN 0-8108-4805-8   LC 2003-7709
Contents: Out of many, one?; Challenges in a diverse society; Prejudice and racism amidst diversity; Racist images and stereotypes; Religious diversity and conflicts; From intolerance to hatred to violence; Reducing bigotry, racism, and hate crimes; Respecting diversity; Speaking out
The author discusses prejudice, racism, religious intolerance, stereotypes, and hate crimes and how to reduce them
"The author does an outstanding job of tackling an emotionally charged topic and relates violent and destructive situations with grace and intelligence. Cultural Diversity should be in all libraries." SLJ

Golay, Michael, 1951-
Reconstruction and reaction; the emancipation of slaves, 1861-1913. Facts on File 1996 158p il (Library of African-American history) $25 (7 and up) **305.8**
1. African Americans—History 2. Reconstruction (1865-1876) 3. Slavery—United States
ISBN 0-8160-3318-8   LC 96-1881
This "explores how former slaves struggled to find their place in American society as free people following the Civil War. Author Golay relates the advancements of

Golay, Michael, 1951——*Continued*
African Americans immediately following the war. . . .
The book concludes with a brief discussion of the Civil
Rights Movement." Publisher's note
Includes bibliographical references

Grossman, James R.
A chance to make good; African Americans,
1900-1929. Oxford Univ. Press 1997 157p (Young
Oxford history of African Americans) lib bdg $25
(7 and up) **305.8**
1. African Americans—History
ISBN 0-19-508770-4 LC 96-8471
Chronicles the lives of African Americans from the
turn of the twentieth century to the Great Depression
Includes bibliographical references

Hall, Loretta
Arab American voices. U.X.L 2000 233p il $58
305.8
1. Arab Americans
ISBN 0-7876-2956-1 LC 99-37500
Twenty primary source documents from speeches,
memoirs, poems, novels, and autobiographies present the
words of Americans with roots in Lebanon, Syria, Palestine, Iraq, Egypt, and other Arab nations
"The works selected, from Kahlil Gibran's 'Dead Are
My People' to the text of the U.S. government's
Antiterrorism and Effective Death Penalty Act of 1986,
should provide many new openings for discussions with
students." Booklist
Includes glossary and bibliographical references

Haskins, James, 1941-2005
Out of the darkness; the story of Blacks moving
North, 1890-1940; by James Haskins and Kathleen
Benson. Benchmark Bks. 2000 112p (Great
journeys) lib bdg $32.79 (5 and up)
305.8
1. Bricktop, 1894-1984 2. Jones, Joe, 1896-1987
3. African Americans—History 4. United States—Race
relations
ISBN 0-7614-0970-X LC 99-19882
Uses the experiences of two individuals, Ada
"Bricktop" Smith and Joe Jones, to present the story of
the Great Migration of Southern Blacks to northern cities
from the late 1800s to the years after World War I.
This "delivers a compelling account of the 'Great Migration' from the South to the North. . . . Black-and-
white photos and quotes greatly enhance the narrative."
SLJ
Includes bibliographical references

Hispanic American almanac; Bryan Ryan and
Nicolás Kanellos, editors. U.X.L 1995 213p il
maps $60 (5 and up) **305.8**
1. Hispanic Americans
ISBN 0-8103-9823-0 LC 95-196496
Also available adult version with same title published
1993 by Gale Res.
This volume "provides information about 'the heritage,
the communities and the growing influence of hispanics

on U.S. culture.'. . . Fourteen chapters cover Spanish
exploration, immigration to the U.S. from Mexico, Puerto
Rico, and Cuba; family structure and the role of religion;
the workplace and education; and contributions in the
arts and sports." Booklist

Hispanic-American experience on file; {edited
by} Carter Smith III and David Lindroth. Facts
on File 1999 il map loose-leaf $140
305.8
1. Hispanic Americans
ISBN 0-8160-3695-0 LC 99-13666
Also available CD-ROM version
A collection of maps, charts, graphs and illustrations
with explanatory text covering Hispanic-Americans of
Latin American and Caribbean background. Coverage
ranges from Columbus's rule in Hispanola and the Texas
independence movement to the Mariel boatlift and the
Immigration Act of 1986
Includes bibliographical references

Hoobler, Dorothy
The African American family album; {by}
Dorothy and Thomas Hoobler; introduction by
Phylicia Rashad. Oxford Univ. Press 1995 127p il
(American family albums) hardcover o.p.
paperback available $16.95 (5 and up)
305.8
1. African Americans
ISBN 0-19-512419-7 (pa) LC 94-34697
"Beginning with life in pre-colonial Africa, the
Hooblers make superb use of personal histories, autobiographies, slave narratives, and other original documents
to paint a vivid picture of life in medieval Africa, in Africa during the slave trade, and of the lives of slaves and
former slaves in the U.S. Readers are introduced to a
complex set of historical events, presented in a simple,
yet moving manner. . . . An excellent addition to any
collection." SLJ
Includes bibliographical references

The Chinese American family album; {by}
Dorothy and Thomas Hoobler; introduction by
Bette Bao Lord. Oxford Univ. Press 1994 128p il
map (American family albums) hardcover o.p.
paperback available $16.95 **305.8**
1. Chinese Americans
ISBN 0-19-512421-9 (pa) LC 93-11873
"This sourcebook on the Chinese immigrant experience is divided into six topics: the homeland, the voyage
to America, arrival in America, first-generation life, the
integration of . . . generations, and Chinese Americans
today. The authors introduce each chapter with a summary essay, then let the immigrants and their descendents
speak for themselves in excerpts from oral reminiscences,
written histories, and fiction spanning the years from the
Gold Rush to the 1980s. Period photographs and drawings, maps, and sidebars enhance the text. The result resembles a well-organized, handsomely designed scrapbook. . . . A valuable resource." SLJ
Includes bibliographical references

Hoobler, Dorothy—*Continued*

The Cuban American family album; {by} Dorothy and Thomas Hoobler; introduction by Oscar Hijuelos. Oxford Univ. Press 1996 127p il (American family albums) hardcover o.p. paperback available $16.95   **305.8**
1. Cuban Americans
ISBN 0-19-512425-1 (pa)   LC 95-38103
Interviews, excerpts from diaries and letters, newspaper accounts, profiles of famous individuals, and pictures from family albums portray the Cuban American experience
Includes bibliographical references

The German American family album; {by} Dorothy and Thomas Hoobler; introductions by Werner Klemperer. Oxford Univ. Press 1996 127p il (American family albums) hardcover o.p. paperback available $16.95 (5 and up)   **305.8**
1. German Americans
ISBN 0-19-512422-7 (pa)   LC 95-14448
Traces the history of German immigrants to the United States through letters, diaries and newspaper accounts
Includes bibliographical references

The Irish American family album; {by} Dorothy and Thomas Hoobler; introduction by Joseph P. Kennedy II. Oxford Univ. Press 1995 128p il (American family albums) hardcover o.p. paperback available $16.95 (5 and up)   **305.8**
1. Irish Americans
ISBN 0-19-512418-9 (pa)   LC 94-19569
"Selections from diaries, letters, interviews, newspaper and magazine articles, and books provide an arresting picture of what it has meant to be of Irish heritage in America. . . . Topics such as prejudice, working conditions and labor unions; politics; and the importance of family, friends, and the Catholic Church are touched upon." SLJ
Includes bibliographical references

The Italian American family album; {by} Dorothy and Thomas Hoobler; introduction by Governor Mario M. Cuomo. Oxford Univ. Press 1994 127p il map (American family albums) hardcover o.p. paperback available $16.95 (5 and up)   **305.8**
1. Italian Americans
ISBN 0-19-512420-0 (pa)   LC 93-46918
This volume includes selections from "diaries, letters, and oral histories. . . . Each of the six chapters begins with background information and then goes on to discuss life in the old country, coming to America, first impressions, working, forming a new life, and becoming a part of America." SLJ
Includes bibliographical references

The Japanese American family album; {by} Dorothy and Thomas Hoobler. Oxford Univ. Press 1995 127p il map (American family albums) hardcover o.p. paperback available $16.95 (5 and up)   **305.8**
1. Japanese Americans
ISBN 0-19-512423-5 (pa)   LC 94-43466
"Organized chronologically, this book captures the broad sweep of the Japanese-American experience. Each of the six chapters offers a succinct historical presentation followed by first-person accounts. Relying on oral histories and original documents, both pictorial and written, the Hooblers have truly humanized historical events." SLJ
Includes bibliographical references

The Mexican American family album; {by} Dorothy and Thomas Hoobler; introduction by Henry G. Cisneros. Oxford Univ. Press 1994 127p il (American family albums) hardcover o.p. paperback available $16.95 (5 and up)   **305.8**
1. Mexican Americans
ISBN 0-19-512426-x (pa)   LC 94-7785
"Using almost exclusively first-person accounts, the Hooblers present vignettes of history, culture, and experience from the first Mexican American settlers to the Chicano Movement. . . . Gathered together, these accounts present a powerful portrait of a strong people, rich in history and culture. A must for multicultural studies." Book Rep
Includes bibliographical references

Hornsby, Alton, Jr.
Chronology of African American history; from 1492 to the present; {by} Alton Hornsby, Jr. 2nd ed. Gale Res. 1997 720p il $99 (7 and up)   **305.8**
1. African Americans—History—Chronology
ISBN 0-8103-8573-2   LC 97-10558
First published 1991
This work traces African Americans over a period of 400 years. Starting with Estevanico, a black explorer who left Spain in 1527 to explore the Gulf of Mexico, the author provides an historical overview of the African Americans experience concluding with Douglas Wilder's victory as the first elected black governor in U.S. history
Includes bibliographical references

Isserman, Maurice
Journey to freedom; the African-American great migration. Facts on File 1997 131p il maps (Library of African-American history) $25 (7 and up)   **305.8**
1. African Americans—History 2. United States—Race relations
ISBN 0-8160-3413-3   LC 96-52160
Discusses the northward journey of Black southerners, the greatest internal mass migration of people in American history
"This book uses primary source material copiously. . . . The black and white photographs are clearly repro-

Isserman, Maurice—*Continued*
duced. . . . {The book} is well-written and the historical
detail is fascinating." Book Rep
Includes bibliographical references

Katz, William Loren
Black Indians; a hidden heritage. Atheneum
Pubs. 1986 198p il $17.95; pa $10 **305.8**
1. African Americans 2. Native Americans
ISBN 0-689-31196-6; 0-689-80901-8 (pa)
LC 85-28770
Traces the history of relations between blacks and
American Indians, and the existence of black Indians,
from the earliest foreign landings through pioneer days
The author "has provided a valuable addition to titles
on American Indians. Excellent for assignments, it con-
tains important information many history instructors may
be unaware of. His sections on black Indians and the
Seminoles of Florida and their views about living togeth-
er are particularly good." Child Book Rev Serv
Includes bibliographical references

Littlefield, Daniel C.
Revolutionary citizens; African Americans,
1776-1804. Oxford Univ. Press 1997 141p (Young
Oxford history of African Americans) lib bdg $25
(7 and up) **305.8**
1. African Americans—History 2. United States—His-
tory—1775-1783, Revolution 3. United States—His-
tory—1783-1865
ISBN 0-19-508715-1 LC 96-8470
Chronicles the lives of African Americans during the
Revolutionary War and the early years of the nation
Includes bibliographical references

Mason, Antony
People around the world. Kingfisher (NY) 2002
256p il map $24.95 **305.8**
1. Ethnology 2. Human geography
ISBN 0-7534-5497-1 LC 2002-72935
Includes index
"This volume presents the cultural, social, and economic aspects of selected countries and explains the geographical reasons for their uniqueness. At the same time,
the author emphasizes the interaction of world cultures,
their influences upon each other, and the inevitability of
globalization. . . . The writing is clear and engaging and
the statistical information is useful. . . . While the book
will be of limited use for reports, it's a browser's delight. " SLJ

Moreno, Barry
Italian Americans; Barry Moreno. . Barron's
Educational Series, Inc 2003 128p il (Coming to
America) $14.95 (7 and up) **305.8**
1. Italian Americans 2. United States—Immigration
and emigration
ISBN 0-7641-5624-1 LC 2002-108726
Book created by the Ivy Press
This describes the reasons for Italian immigration to
the U.S., Italian American history and culture, and in-

cludes brief biographical sketches.
The book is "illustrated with many photographs, both
color and black and white, as well as reproductions,
maps, cartoons, and charts, all well placed and captioned.
. . . [This title] will enhance world and American history shelves and be useful for students researching immigration issues." SLJ
Includes bibliographical references

Myers, Walter Dean, 1937-
Now is your time! the African-American
struggle for freedom. HarperCollins Pubs. 1991
292p il hardcover o.p. paperback available $12.99
(6 and up) **305.8**
1. African Americans—History
ISBN 0-06-446120-3 (pa) LC 91-314
Coretta Scott King Award for text, 1992
A history of the African-American struggle for freedom and equality, beginning with the capture of Africans
in 1619, continuing through the American Revolution,
the Civil War, and into contemporary times
"Myers's unique episodic approach makes this history
a compelling exploration of the African-American experience. . . . This fascinating book will engender pride in
heritage for young African Americans and provide insight into American history for all of us." Horn Book
Includes bibliographical references

Ochoa, George
Atlas of Hispanic-American history. Facts on
File 2001 214p il maps (Facts on File library of
American history) $85 (7 and up) **305.8**
1. Hispanic Americans—History
ISBN 0-8160-3698-5 LC 00-49077
This reference covers "Hispanic America, from its origins, and European, Native American and African influences, through the present, and from the arrival of the
conquistadors to the impact of U.S. Manifest Destiny,
and on through the battle over Puerto Rican independence." Publ Wkly
"While scholarly in content, the well-written and well-
researched text holds the reader's attention. Historical
maps, photographs, paintings, and graphs put history into
perspective and sidebars highlight important events and
people." Book Rep
Includes bibliographical references

The New York Public Library amazing Hispanic
American history; a book of answers for kids.
Wiley 1998 192p il maps pa $12.95
305.8
1. Hispanic Americans
ISBN 0-471-19204-X LC 98-23797
"A Stonesong Press book"
Consists of questions and answers about Latinos, revealing the common history which unites them while
also showing how they differ depending upon their country of origin
"Recommended for purchase as a bargain buy and extremely handy source for frequently requested and sometimes hard-to-find information about Hispanic Americans." Booklist
Includes glossary and bibliographical references

Omoto, Susan, 1955-
Hmong milestones in America; citizens in a new world. Burke, J.G. 2002 64p il map (To know the land) $27; pa $15   **305.8**
1. Hmong Americans
ISBN 0-934272-57-3; 0-934272-56-5 (pa)
                                LC 2002-10431
Contents: Hmong history; Life in Laos; Celebrations; The war years; Leaving Laos for Thailand; Life in the camps; Dr. Xoua Thao, first Hmong medical doctor; Ying Vang, first Hmong Catholic priest in the United States; Choua Lee, first elected Hmong official in the United States; Rev. Bea Vue-Benson, first Hmong woman Lutheran minister; Christopher Thao, first Hmong attorney in the United States; Afterward: bridging two worlds
This "book introduces the background of the Hmong people and their immigration to the U.S. . . . The last chapters profile five individuals who emigrated as children or teenagers and were the first Hmong to become, respectively, a medical doctor, a Catholic priest, an elected official, a Lutheran minister, and an attorney in the U.S. . . . A good addition to many libraries, this is one of the few books available for children that reflect the experience of the Hmong in America." Booklist
Includes glossary and bibliographical references

Patrick, Diane, 1955-
The New York Public Library amazing African American history; a book of answers for kids. Wiley 1998 170p il (New York Public Library answer books for kids series) pa $12.95 (5 and up)
                                305.8
1. African Americans—History
ISBN 0-471-19217-1   LC 97-16938
"A Stonesong Press book"
Presents questions and answers relating to important periods in African American history including the Revolution, Civil War, Reconstruction, Migration, and the Civil Rights Movement
"Enhanced by black-and-white photographs, this useful resource provides information in a formal but readable style. . . . A well-organized, objective, accessible guide for students." SLJ
Includes glossary and bibliographical references

Peoples of North America. Grolier 2003 10v il maps set $299   **305.8**
1. North America—Population 2. Minorities 3. Immigrants
ISBN 0-7172-5777-0   LC 2003-42395
Includes indexes
Contents: v1 Afghans-Bosnians; v2 Brazilians-Colombians; v3 Colonial America-Egyptians; v4 Emigrés and refugees-Guyanese; v5 Gypsies (Romany)-Irish; v6 Iroquois confederacy-local politics, Canada; v7 Local politics, U.S.-Native Americans, Southeast; v8 Native Americans, Southwest and Mexico-Puerto Ricans; v9 Quebec separatism-social mobility and race; v10 South Africans-World War II
Profiles the native and immigrant groups that have peopled North America, focusing on the modes and monitoring of immigration
"The writing is clear and neutral in tone. The appealing layout features numerous maps and color photo-

graphs. Multitoned insets offer statistics and additional, often fascinating, information. . . . This will be a highly useful reference tool for students studying immigration." SLJ

Perl, Lila
North across the border; the story of the Mexican Americans. Benchmark Bks. 2002 112p il (Great journeys) lib bdg $32.79   **305.8**
1. Mexican Americans
ISBN 0-7614-1226-3   LC 00-57017
The author "begins by describing the monumental effect the arrival of Europeans had on Mexican civilizations. She then discusses the impact, on both countries, of the great migration to the U.S., which began in the twentieth century. . . . {This book is} filled with crisp, well-selected photographs and historical illustrations." Booklist
Includes bibliographical references

To the Golden Mountain; the story of the Chinese who built the transcontinental railroad. Benchmark Bks. 2002 112p il music (Great journeys) lib bdg $32.79   **305.8**
1. Chinese—United States 2. Railroads—United States 3. United States—Immigration and emigration
ISBN 0-7614-1324-3   LC 2001-6241
Contents: From the land of the celestials; Gold fields and Chinatowns; Working on the railroad; Blasting through the mountains; The race to the finish; The Chinese must go; The door to the Golden Mountain closes
"More than the story of Chinese workers' contributions to building the transcontinental railroad, this book is also a brief history of China's contacts with the West, focusing on the financial despair that drove many men to emigrate, beginning in the 1840s. The anti-Chinese sentiment that rose in California after their success in the gold rush is discussed, as is life in the Chinatowns that were established." SLJ
Includes bibliographical references

Race relations: opposing viewpoints; James D. Torr, book editor. Greenhaven Press 2005 208p il lib bdg $34.95; pa $23.70   **305.8**
1. United States—Race relations
ISBN 0-7377-2955-4 (lib bdg); 0-7377-2956-2 (pa)
                                LC 2004-59763
"Opposing viewpoints series"
This book explores race-related "topics in the following chapters: What Is the State of Race Relations in America? Is Racism a Serious Problem? What Should the Government Do to Improve Race Relations? How Can Society Improve Race Relations?" Publisher's note
Includes bibliographical references

Rasmussen, R. Kent
Farewell to Jim Crow; the rise and fall of segregation in America. Facts on File 1997 168p il maps (Library of African-American history) $25 (7 and up)   **305.8**
1. African Americans—Segregation 2. African Americans—Civil rights 3. United States—Race relations
ISBN 0-8160-3248-3   LC 96-48329

Rasmussen, R. Kent—*Continued*

This book "deals with the origins and causes of segregation in America. There is a chapter devoted to the definition of Jim Crow and how the unjust practice affected African Americans' lives from housing to entertainment to education. The author then begins the history of segregation in colonial times and covers the slavery issue in the South. . . . He also covers the blacks and their part in the Civil War, the Reconstruction period, and the beginnings of segregation in the South." Book Rep

"This is a solidly written and thoroughly researched book that inspires the reader to learn more." Voice Youth Advocates

Includes bibliographical references

Reef, Catherine

Africans in America: the spread of people and culture. Facts on File 1999 136p il (Library of African-American history) lib bdg $25

305.8

1. African Americans—History

ISBN 0-8160-3772-8 LC 98-11793

Describes the spread of Africans to the western hemisphere and the influences and development of their culture

"Written with clarity and depth, this is an excellent account of the 'African diaspora.' " Booklist

Includes bibliographical references

Rubin, Susan Goldman, 1939-

L'chaim! to Jewish life in America! Susan Goldman Rubin. Harry N. Abrams 2004 176p il map $24.95 (7 and up) **305.8**

1. Jews—United States

ISBN 0-8109-5035-9 LC 2004-5848

"Rubin focuses on particular individuals to show how European immigrants have found ways to be both Jewish and American." SLJ

This is an "exceptionally attractive package, packed with quotes, personal stories, and photos of art from The Jewish Museum. . . . The art is gorgeous, and Rubin . . . writes with clarity and enthusiasm." Booklist

Includes bibliographical references

Stein, Robert

Jewish Americans. Barron's Educ. Ser. 2003 128p il maps (Coming to America) $14.95 (7 and up) **305.8**

1. Jews—United States

ISBN 0-7641-5626-8 LC 2002-108727

Book created by the Ivy Press

In this history of Jewish Americans "Stein addresses oppression and poverty in Russia, Poland, Germany, and other parts of Europe. Discussions of the transatlantic journey, passing through Ellis Island, and the process of immigrants establishing themselves as Americans are also included. [The] book presents information on writers, singers, actors, sports figures, politicians, and other individuals." SLJ

This is "particularly well thought out, with informative graphics complementing the well-writtten [text]." Booklist

Includes bibliographical references

Student almanac of African American history; Media Project, Inc. Greenwood Press 2003 2v v cmp il map (Middle school reference) set $80

305.8

1. African Americans—History

ISBN 0-313-32596-0 LC 2002-35332

Contents: v1 From slavery to freedom, 1492-1876; v2 From Reconstruction to today, 1877-present

"This basic overview covers the history of African Americans in the U.S. from 1492 to the present. Each straightforward chapter introduces a time period through a short narrative essay followed by an A-to-Z section outlining the important figures and terms." SLJ

"This attractive almanac provides information on topics of interest to users in middle school and up. . . . It will be a welcome addition to school and public libraries where there is a need for additional information about African Americans." Booklist

Includes bibliographical references

Trotter, Joe William, 1945-

From a raw deal to a New Deal? African Americans, 1929-1945; {by} Joe William Trotter, Jr. Oxford Univ. Press 1995 125p il (Young Oxford history of African Americans) lib bdg $25 (7 and up) **305.8**

1. African Americans—History 2. United States—Race relations

ISBN 0-19-508771-2 LC 95-17348

The author "examines the important events and major forces of 1929-1945 in the U.S. from the perspective of African Americans. He notes that while they made sociopolitical, economic, and cultural advancements through a plethora of New Deal-created opportunities, many blacks were concurrently being treated as second-class citizens and suffering racial violence at the hands of disgruntled, fearful working-class whites. He concludes that it wasn't until 1935 that the 'raw deal' began to be transformed into a 'new deal.' " SLJ

"A concise, well-researched, readable account of African American life. . . . The text is amply illustrated with excellent photographs, documents, and political cartoons." Booklist

Includes bibliographical references

What are you? voices of mixed-race young people; {edited by} Pearl Fuyo Gaskins. Holt & Co. 1999 273p il $18.95 (7 and up)

305.8

1. Racially mixed people 2. Teenagers 3. United States—Race relations

ISBN 0-8050-5968-7 LC 98-37381

Many young people of racially mixed backgrounds discuss their feelings about family relationships, prejudice, dating, personal identity, and other issues

"While underscoring the complexity of the mixed-race experience, these unadorned voices offer a genuine, poignant, enlightening and empowering message to all readers." SLJ

Includes bibliographical references

White, Deborah Gray
Let my people go: African Americans, 1804-1860. Oxford Univ. Press 1996 141p il (Young Oxford history of African Americans) lib bdg $25 (7 and up)   305.8
1. African Americans—History 2. Slavery—United States
ISBN 0-19-508769-0   LC 95-38104
Discusses the lives of African Americans from the early years of the nineteenth century to the start of the Civil War
"History comes alive for students when reading the words of the people who lived it. This volume does just that and is recommended for all American history students." Voice Youth Advocates
Includes bibliographical references

Wormser, Richard, 1933-
The rise and fall of Jim Crow; the African-American struggle against discrimination, 1865-1954. Watts 1999 144p il map lib bdg $23 (7 and up)   305.8
1. African Americans—Segregation 2. African Americans—Civil rights 3. United States—Race relations
ISBN 0-531-11443-0   LC 99-28254
Discusses the laws and practices that supported discrimination against African Americans from Reconstruction to the Supreme Court decision that found segregation to be illegal
Wormser "writes quietly, without sensationalism, in an immediate present-tense narrative illustrated with occasional black-and-white photos." Booklist
Includes bibliographical references

306   Culture and institutions

The **Baby** boom; Stuart A. Kallen, book editor. Greenhaven Press 2001 220p il (Turning points in world history) lib bdg $34.95; pa $23.70 (7 and up)   306
1. United States—Social life and customs 2. United States—Social conditions
ISBN 0-7377-0925-1 (lib bdg); 0-7377-0924-3 (pa)
                                        LC 2001-37224
This title considers the generation of Americans born after World War II and their affect on American culture from the 1950s to the 21st century
Includes bibliographical references

Bowling, beatniks, and bell-bottoms; pop culture of 20th-century America; Sara Pendergast and Tom Pendergast, editors. U.X.L 2002 5v il set $250   306
1. Popular culture—United States 2. United States—Civilization
ISBN 0-7876-5675-5   LC 2002-1829
Contents: v1 1900s and 1910s; v2 1920s and 1930s; v3 1940s and 1950s; v4 1960s and 1970s; v5 1980s and 1990s
The editors "track trends in American popular culture through 750 entries arranged chronologically by decade over five volumes. Within decades, entries are divided into nine major areas: 'Commerce,' 'Fashion,' 'Film and

Theater,' 'Food and Drink,' 'Music,' 'Print Culture,' 'Sports and Games,' Television and Radio,' and 'The Way We Lived'. . . . Informative, entertaining, and clearly presented." Libr J
Includes bibliographical references

Culture wars: opposing viewpoints; Mary E. Williams, book editor. Greenhaven Press 2003 224p il $33.70; pa $22.45   306
1. Popular culture—United States
ISBN 0-7377-1679-7; 0-7377-1680-0 (pa)
                                        LC 2002-42611
"Opposing viewpoints series"
Replaces the edition published 1994 under the editorship of Fred Whitehead
"This anthology . . . spotlights current debates on American morality, social values, religion, and popular culture. Chapters include: Is American Culture in Decline? What Political and Cultural Influences Benefit Society?" Publisher's note
Includes bibliographical references

Junior Worldmark encyclopedia of world cultures. U.X.L 1999 9v il maps set $315 (5 and up)
                                        306
1. Ethnology—Encyclopedias
ISBN 0-7876-1756-3   LC 98-13810
Timothy L. Gall and Susan Bevans Gall, editors
Arranges countries around the world alphabetically, subdivides these countries into 250 culture groups, and provides information about the ethnology and human geography of each group
"The short and engaging articles are based on entries in the *Worldmark Encyclopedia of Cultures and Daily Life* and targeted to appeal to a younger audience. . . . This is a valuable and timely resource with considerable assignment value." SLJ
Includes bibliographical references

Rap and hip hop; Jared Green, book editor. Greenhaven Press 2003 175p (Examining pop culture) lib bdg $25.96; pa $16.96 (7 and up)
                                        306
1. African American youth 2. Rap music 3. Popular culture—United States
ISBN 0-7377-1064-0 (lib bdg); 0-7377-1063-2 (pa)
                                        LC 2002-1147
Contents: Bring the noise: the roots of rap and hip hop; Blowing up: the rise of the hip-hop nation; Does rap glorify sex and violence?; Case study in controversy: Eminem and gay bashing
"In this anthology of excerpted articles and essays, rap music and hip hop are summarized, contextualized, and analyzed. . . . Particular emphasis is given to charges that rap music glorifies violence and gang life and to media reports that it is sexist, racist, homophobic, and anti-semitic. The book also includes a four-chapter 'case study' of Eminem. . . . A good beginning resource for research on this now-mainstream genre of music and an integral part of our popular culture." SLJ
Includes bibliographical references

306.4 Specific aspects of culture

Hinds, Maurene J.
Focus on body image; how you feel about how you look. Enslow Pubs. 2002 64p il (Teen issues) lib bdg $22.60 **306.4**
1. Self-esteem 2. Personal appearance
ISBN 0-7660-1915-2 LC 2001-7714
Discusses how young people feel about the way they look, the impact of society and advertisers on an individual's body image, problems with poor self-esteem, and maintaining a healthy body image
Includes glossary and bibliographical references

306.7 Sexual relations

Sex: opposing viewpoints; Mary E. Williams, book editor. Greenhaven Press 2000 218p lib bdg $33.70; pa $18.70 **306.7**
1. Sexual behavior
ISBN 0-7377-0352-0 (lib bdg); 0-7377-0351-2 (pa)
LC 99-59374
"Opposing viewpoints series"
This collection of articles presents varying viewpoints on such issues as the state of sexual ethics in America, Alfred Kinsey's research on sexuality, premarital sex, sex education, co-habitation before marriage, sexual attitudes of youth, contraception, pornography, prostitution, and monogamy
Includes bibliographical references

306.76 Sexual orientation

Homosexuality: opposing viewpoints; Auriana Ojeda, editor. Greenhaven Press 2004 240p lib bdg $34.95; pa $23.70 (7 and up)
306.76
1. Homosexuality
ISBN 0-7377-1687-8 (lib bdg); 0-7377-1688-6 (pa)
LC 2003-44859
"Opposing viewpoints series"
Replaces the edition published 1999 under the editorship of Mary E. Williams
This presents opposing viewpoints answering such questions as "Should Society Encourage Increased Acceptance of Homosexuality?" and "Is Homosexuality Immoral?"
"This well-researched, unbiased anthology includes a variety of provocative articles and essays that are sure to invite criticism, discussion, and debate." SLJ
Includes bibliographical references

Huegel, Kelly
GLBTQ (Gay, Lesbian, Bisexual, Transgender, Questioning); the survival guide for queer & questioning teens. Free Spirit 2003 224p il pa $15.95 **306.76**
1. Homosexuality 2. Transsexualism 3. Bisexuality
ISBN 1-57542-126-7 LC 2002-156692

Contents: GLBTQ basics; Homophobia; Coming out; Life at school; GLBTQ friends; Dating and relationships; Sex; Your health; Drugs, alcohol and tobacco; Religion and culture; Work, college & beyond; Transgender teens
Describes the challenges faced by gay, lesbian, bisexual, and transgendered teens, offers practical advice, real-life experiences, and accessible resources and support groups
"Huegel has written an indispensable guide for gay, lesbian, bisexual, transgender, and questioning teens, as well as for their straight peers and parents." Booklist
Includes bibliographical references

306.8 Marriage and family

The **Family:** opposing viewpoints; Mary E. Williams, book editor. Greenhaven Press 1998 224p il lib bdg $33.70; pa $22.45 (7 and up)
306.8
1. Family
ISBN 1-56510-669-5 (lib bdg); 1-56510-668-7 (pa)
LC 97-19211
"Opposing viewpoints series"
The articles and essays in this volume "examine the state of the family, how divorce-law reforms and work-related policies have affected it, adoption policies, and how public policy and values impact upon it . . . The selections are well chosen, clearly written, and thought-provoking." SLJ
Includes bibliographical references

In my grandmother's house; award-winning authors tell stories about their grandmothers; compiled & illustrated by Bonnie Christensen. HarperCollins Pubs. 2003 195p il $18.99; lib bdg $19.89 **306.8**
1. Grandmothers
ISBN 0-06-029109-5; 0-06-029110-9 (lib bdg)
LC 2002-151601
Contents: The naked truth, by C. L Smith; Rhizomes, by Minfong Ho; The grannies, by P. Cummings; The doctor's daughter, by D. Stanley; Grandma and her needle, by B. Cleary; A visit to Grandma's, by G. C. Levine; And then another locust came and took away another grain of corn, by J. C. George; Granny was a gambler, by B. Naidoo; Fairy grandmother, by B. Christensen; To my Nai Nai, by J. Jiang; The best parts, by J. Abelove; My abuelita, my paradise, by A. F. Ada
This "powerful anthology of family stories . . . will encourage teens to reflect on their own families and recognize the individuals behind the family roles." Booklist

Marriage and divorce; Tamara L. Roleff, Mary E. Williams, book editors. Greenhaven Press 1997 190p (Current controversies) lib bdg $33.70; pa $23.70 (7 and up) **306.8**
1. Marriage 2. Divorce
ISBN 1-56510-568-0 (lib bdg); 1-56510-567-2 (pa)
LC 97-4941
This title "addresses several issues: premarital cohabitation, divorce's effect upon children, child custody, and same-sex marriage. The 32 reprinted articles present several sides of the issues, including Andrew Sullivan's piece on gay marriage from the New Republic, and an

Marriage and divorce—*Continued*

argument made by Commonweal, a Catholic magazine, that marriage is for procreation. . . . The book ends with an annotated list of organizations dealing with marriage and divorce." SLJ

Includes bibliographical references

Presma, Frances

Straight talk about today's families; {by} Frances Presma and Paula Edelson. Facts on File 1999 136p $27.45 (7 and up)   **306.8**

1. Family

ISBN 0-8160-3905-4   LC 98-44901

Discusses the nature, importance, and challenges of being part of a family and explains ways to deal with family stress and dysfunction

Includes bibliographical references

Schultz, Margaret A.

Teens with single parents; why me? Enslow Pubs. 1997 128p (Teen issues) lib bdg $26.60 (7 and up)   **306.8**

1. Single parent family 2. Children of divorced parents

ISBN 0-89490-913-4   LC 96-39439

Examines the effects of living in a single-parent family, discussing such topics as emotional aspects and economic factors

"Interviews with teens, parents, and psychologists offer young people excellent coping strategies and a chance to see that their anger and frustration are hardly unique." Booklist

Includes bibliographical references

Snow, Judith E.

How it feels to have a gay or lesbian parent; a book by kids for kids of all ages. Harrington Park Press 2004 110p $19.95; pa $12.95 (5 and up)   **306.8**

1. Parent-child relationship 2. Homosexuality

ISBN 1-56023-419-9; 1-56023-420-2 (pa)
                    LC 2003-18008

In their own words, children of different ages talk about how and when they learned of their gay or lesbian parent's sexual orientation and the effect it has had on them.

"This inspirational, eye-opening title gives readers who have gay and lesbian parents a much-deserved voice." SLJ

Trapani, Margi

Listen up! teenage mothers speak out. Rosen Pub. Group 1997 64p il (Teen pregnancy prevention library) lib bdg $17.95 (7 and up)   **306.8**

1. Teenage mothers 2. Teenage pregnancy

ISBN 0-8239-2254-5   LC 95-42449

"Seven young mothers describe the reality of their lives before and since the birth of their babies. None of them have maintained a relationship with their child's father. They all voice regret for lost youth and forgone opportunities." SLJ

Includes glossary and bibliographical references

Reality check; teenage fathers speak out. rev ed. Rosen Pub. Group 1999 64p il (Teen pregnancy prevention library) lib bdg $23.95 (7 and up)
                    306.8

1. Teenage fathers 2. Parenting

ISBN 0-8239-2995-7   LC 95-42450

First published 1997

Teenage fathers highlight the challenges of being a teen parent, discussing responsibility, economic hardship, and emotional issues involved in parenting at a young age

This book presents "a true picture of the hardships of being a teenage parent." Voice Youth Advocates {review of 1997 edition}

Includes glossary and bibliographical references

306.89   Separation and divorce

Bode, Janet

For better, for worse; a guide to surviving divorce for preteens and their families; by Janet Bode and Stan Mack. Simon & Schuster Bks. for Young Readers 2001 164p $16   **306.89**

1. Divorce 2. Remarriage

ISBN 0-689-81945-5   LC 99-462105

Uses first-person accounts from young people to describe the effects of divorce and remarriage and how to handle them. Includes a section for adults discussing how to minimize both the short- and long-term impact of divorce

"Readers will recognize and appreciate the honesty here, and the fact that no one offers easy answers. . . . A useful resource for preteens who need to know they are not alone." SLJ

Includes bibliographical references

Sanders, Pete

Divorce and separation; {by} Pete Sanders and Steve Myers. Copper Beech Bks. 1997 32p il (What do you know about) lib bdg $23.90
                    306.89

1. Divorce

ISBN 0-7613-0574-2   LC 96-35822

Discusses the meaning of separation and divorce and some of the reasons that relationships come to an end. Also examines the effects that divorce and separation can have on people's lives

"The clear writing style and open format {makes this} useful for reports and for general interest reading." SLJ

Stewart, Gail, 1949-

Divorce; by Gail B. Stewart. KidHaven Press 2002 48p il (Understanding issues) $23.70
                    306.89

1. Divorce

ISBN 0-7377-0950-2   LC 2001-2952

Discusses the understanding, fears, courts, custody, communication, and problems that young children must face and deal with when their parents get a divorce

"Facts, statistics, and other information are interwoven with personal examples in a way that lets readers asso-

Stewart, Gail, 1949-—*Continued*
ciate the material with their own circumstances. . . .
Colorful illustrations and charts make the pages attractive." Book Rep
Includes glossary and bibliographical references

306.9   Institutions pertaining to death

Stewart, Gail, 1949-
Death; [by] Gail B. Stewart. KidHaven Press 2002 48p il (Understanding issues) $23.70
306.9
1. Death
ISBN 0-7377-0949-9   LC 2001-2308
"This title examines aspects of dying, from the aging process and clinical death, to funerals and grief." Publisher's note
"Facts, statistics, and other information are interwoven with personal examples in a way that lets readers associate the material with their own circumstances. . . .
Colorful illustrations and charts make the pages attractive." Book Rep
Includes glossary and bibliographical references

307.7   Specific kinds of communities

Collier, Christopher, 1930-
The rise of the cities, 1820-1920; [by] Christopher Collier, James Lincoln Collier. Benchmark Bks. (Tarrytown) 2001 95p il maps (Drama of American history) lib bdg $31.36
307.7
1. Cities and towns—United States
ISBN 0-7614-1051-1   LC 99-38409
This "traces the development, problems, and increasing prominence of cities in America between 1820 and 1920. Illustrations, many in color, include period photographs and engravings as well as maps and charts. . . .
Highly readable and informative." Booklist
Includes bibliographical references

310.5   General statistics--Serial publications

The **Statesman's** year-book; the politics, cultures, and economies of the world. St. Martin's Press $170
310.5
1. Statistics 2. Political science
ISSN 0081-4601
Also available online
Annual. First published 1864
"Descriptive and statistical information about international organizations and countries of the world—brief history, area, political status, economy, etc." N Y Public Libr. Ref Books for Child Collect. 2d edition

317.3   General statistics of the United States

United States. Bureau of the Census
Statistical abstract of the United States. U.S. Govt. Ptg. Office $39
317.3
1. United States—Statistics 2. Statistics
Also available CD-ROM version and online
Annual. First published for the year 1878
"Compendium of statistics on the social, political and economic organization of the U.S. presented in tables. Lists other sources of such information." N Y Public Libr. Ref Books for Child Collect. 2d edition

320   Political science

Ventura, Jesse
Jesse Ventura tells it like it is; America's most outspoken governor speaks out about government; [by] Jesse Ventura with Heron Marquez. Lerner Publs. 2002 64p il $15.95
320
1. United States—Politics and government—1989-
ISBN 0-8225-0385-9   LC 2001-6822
Contents: Introduction; What is government?; Freedom and the Constitution; The many levels of government; Voting and election campaigns; Cutting the pie; What can kids do?
The author "presents a simple overview and history of the United States government, with an emphasis on ideals, checks and balances, and documents such as the Constitution and Bill of Rights. . . . Ventura incorporates his personal experience as a campaigner and politician. He delivers facts objectively but does not hesitate to offer his own viewpoint on a variety of issues. . . .
The narrative is engagingly readable with well-placed captioned photos." Voice Youth Advocates
Includes bibliographical references

Zeinert, Karen, 1942-2002
Women in politics; in the running. 21st Cent. Bks. (Brookfield) 2002 112p il lib bdg $29.90
320
1. Women in politics
ISBN 0-7613-2253-1   LC 2001-52253
Examines the contributions women have made at every level of American politics throughout the history of the United States, as well as the struggles they have encountered
"Zeinert does a solid job of introducing these pioneering women, and her overview makes a good starting point for research." Booklist
Includes bibliographical references

320.03   Political science-- Encyclopedias and dictionaries

Encyclopedia of American government; consulting editor, Joseph M. Bessette; project editor, R. Kent Rasmussen. Salem Press 1998 4v il maps set $221   **320.03**
1. United States—Politics and government—Encyclopedias
ISBN 0-89356-117-7   LC 98-28986
Contents: v1 Accountability in government—criminal justice system; v2 Declaration of independence—juvenile justice; v3 Labor law—right to die; v4 School law—women in politics
"Two hundred alphabetically arranged essays make up this. . . set that covers the basics of American government. Well-written, illuminating articles range from broad subjects such as Federalism to more specific topics such as 'Iron Triangles' and reflect an awareness for gender and minority issues." SLJ
Includes bibliographical references

320.4   Structure and functions of government

American government at work. Grolier Educ. 2000 9v set $319 (7 and up)   **320.4**
1. State governments 2. Local government 3. United States—Politics and government
ISBN 0-7172-9557-5   LC 00-34083
Contents: v1 Federal Legislative Branch; v2 Federal Executive Branch; v3 Federal Judicial Branch; v4 Federal Bureaucracy; v5 State Legislative Branch; v6 State Executive Branch; v7 State Judicial Branch; v8 Local Legislative Branch; v9 Local Executive Branch
"Separate volumes examine each of the three branches of government on the local, state, and federal level and the federal bureaucracy. Historical background, including origins, roles, and quotes from primary documents, is provided as well as detailed text on the day-to-day business of the government. . . . An attractive and useful reference set." SLJ

Tomaselli-Moschovitis, Valerie
Government on file. Facts on File 1998 various paging il maps loose-leaf $185   **320.4**
1. United States—Politics and government
ISBN 0-8160-3560-1   LC 97-45171
Also available CD-ROM version
"Among the topics are how a bill becomes a law, the electoral college, the organization of the federal court system, the history of immigration and immigration policy, and foreign exchange and balance of trade." Booklist
Includes bibliographical references

320.5   Political ideologies

Tames, Richard
Nationalism; Richard Tames. Raintree 2004 64p il (Ideas of the modern world) $32.79 (7 and up)
                                        320.5
1. Nationalism
ISBN 0-7398-6417-3   LC 2003-913
Contents: What is nationalism?; The birth of modern nationalism; Nations and empires; Empires into nations; Nationalism and communism; Beyond the nation-state; Nationalism : today and tomorrow
This "begins with a succinct definition of [nationalism] and includes historical examples to clarify it. . . '. The American and French Revolutions, are discussed [as well as] the unification of Italy, Greek independence, and Scotland's evolution into a free, independent state. . . . Conflicts, such as those in East Timor, Sri Lanka, and Kurdistan, are part of the discussion. Pan-Slavism, Pan-Arabism, and Pan-Africanism are also included. The author has taken a complex subject, simplified it, and made it accessible to students." SLJ
Includes bibliographical references

323   Civil and political rights

Altman, Linda Jacobs, 1943-
Human rights; issues for a new millennium. Enslow Pubs. 2002 128p il (Issues in focus) lib bdg $20.95 (7 and up)   **323**
1. Human rights
ISBN 0-7660-1689-7   LC 2002-6050
Partial contents: The foundations of human rights; Rights and revolutions; The struggle against slavery; In time of war; Human rights and civil disobedience; The activist sixties
Explores the history of concern for human rights around the world, looking particularly at the internationalism begun in the last quarter of the twentieth century and its influence on human rights issues
"This book is a good introduction and overview of the subject." BAYA Book Rev
Includes glossary and bibliographical references

Banks, Deena
Amnesty International; by Deena Banks. World Almanac Library 2004 48p (International organizations) $30; pa $15.93   **323**
1. Amnesty International
ISBN 0-8368-5517-5; 0-8368-5526-4 (pa)
                                    LC 2003-45030
Contents: Human rights: a vision; Goals and organization to achieve them; How Amnesty International works; Current campaigns and urgent actions; Success stories
This describes the history and goals of "Amnesty International, which is dedicated to persuading governments around the world to free prisoners of conscience or those who have been imprisoned for disagreeing with their actions." Publisher's note
This provides "ample material for reports." SLJ
Includes bibliographical references

Civil liberties: opposing viewpoints; Auriana Ojeda, book editor. Greenhaven Press 2004 204p il $33.70; pa $22.45 (7 and up)

323

1. Civil rights
ISBN 0-7377-1675-4; 0-7377-1676-2 (pa)
LC 2003-59647

"Opposing viewpoints series"

Replaces the edition published 1999 under the editorship of Tamara L. Roleff

"This volume examines the pros and cons of such issues as regulation of hate speech, flag burning, banning of child pornography, posting of the Ten Commandments in public places, public surveillance cameras, the war on terrorism, and ethnic profiling. Twenty-two essays from contributors ranging from the ACLU to John Ashcroft and from such publications as the 'Humanist', the 'Seattle Times', and 'Midstream' offer arguments from a variety of perspectives. . . . This highly accessible book will prove useful for opinion and research papers." SLJ

Includes bibliographical references

Human rights; Laura Hitt, book editor. Greenhaven Press 2002 224p il (Great speeches in history series) lib bdg $34.95; pa $23.70

323

1. Human rights
ISBN 0-7377-0875-1 (lib bdg); 0-7377-0874-3 (pa)
LC 2001-50175

This is an anthology of speeches about human rights from the 13th up to the 21st century from such historical figures as Mahatma Gandhi, Nelson Mandela, and Eleanor Roosevelt

Includes bibliographical references

Human rights: opposing viewpoints; opposing viewpoints; Laura K. Egendorf, book editor. Greenhaven Press 2003 208p lib bdg $34.95; pa $23.70 (7 and up)

323

1. Human rights
ISBN 0-7377-1689-4 (lib bdg); 0-7377-1690-8 (pa)
LC 2002-192800

"Opposing viewpoints series"

"In this anthology, the authors address the definition of human rights, the state of these rights, and ways in which the United States and the rest of the world should respond to human rights abuses." Publisher's note

Includes bibliographical references

Stewart, Gail, 1949-

Human rights in the Middle East; by Gail B. Stewart. Lucent Books 2004 c2005 112p il map (Lucent library of conflict in the Middle East) $28.70

323

1. Human rights 2. Middle East
ISBN 1-59018-488-2
LC 2004-10836

Contents: Introduction; Systems of injustice; Women and injustice; The right of expression; Children's rights; Persecution of minorities

This discusses such human rights issues in the Middle East as the forced labor of children, discrimination against women and ethnic minorities, torture and executions, and censorship.

Includes bibliographical references

323.1 Civil and political rights of nondominant groups

Alonso, Karen

Korematsu v. United States; Japanese-American internment camps. Enslow Pubs. 1998 128p il (Landmark Supreme Court cases) lib bdg $26.60 (7 and up)

323.1

1. Korematsu, Fred, 1919-2005 2. Japanese Americans—Evacuation and relocation, 1942-1945 3. World War, 1939-1945—Reparations
ISBN 0-89490-966-5
LC 97-29582

Profiles the case of Fred Korematsu, who sought compensation from the American government for his time spent in a Japanese-American internment camp during World War II

"The book makes the operations of the judicial branch intelligible. . . . It offers many possible topics for classroom discussion." SLJ

Includes glossary and bibliographical references

American civil rights: primary sources; {compiled by} Phillis Engelbert; edited by Betz Des Chenes. U.X.L 1999 xl, 200p il $58

323.1

1. Civil rights
ISBN 0-7876-3170-1
LC 99-27167

Presents fifteen documents, including speeches, autobiographical texts, and proclamations, related to the civil rights movement and arranged by category under economic rights, desegregation, and human rights

"The uniqueness of this set lies in the range of people covered. Students will find it an excellent resource for reports and interesting reading." Booklist

Includes bibliographical references

Bullard, Sara

Free at last; a history of the Civil Rights Movement and those who died in the struggle; introduction by Julian Bond. Oxford Univ. Press 1993 112p il map $28; pa $12.95

323.1

1. African Americans—Civil rights 2. United States—Race relations
ISBN 0-19-508381-4; 0-19-509450-6 (pa)
LC 92-38174

An illustrated history of the civil rights movement, including a timeline and profiles of forty people who gave their lives in the movement

Includes bibliographical references

Civil rights; edited by Mary E. Williams. Greenhaven Press 2002 94p il (Examining issues through political cartoons) lib bdg $24.95; pa $16.20 (7 and up)

323.1

1. African Americans—Civil rights—Cartoons and caricatures
ISBN 0-7377-1100-0 (lib bdg); 0-7377-1099-3 (pa)
LC 2001-55743

The author provides "readers with an overview of African Americans' struggle for those rights enjoyed by other citizens and of the historical role of the political cartoon. . . . Four chapters ('The Struggle for Justice,'

Civil rights—*Continued*

'Has the Civil Rights Movement Benefited Minorities?' 'How Has Affirmative Action Affected Civil Rights?' and 'What Is the Legacy of the Civil Rights Movement?') examine three to six cartoons each. All are reproduced in the book, and information about the artist is provided." SLJ

"Facts, statistics, and historical perspectives are presented in easy-to-understand terms. . . . This title is an excellent resource for history, government, and debate classes." Book Rep

Includes bibliographical references

Civil rights; Jill Karson, book editor. Greenhaven Press 2003 238p il map (Great speeches in history series) lib bdg $33.70; pa $22.45 (7 and up)   **323.1**
1. African Americans—Civil rights 2. United States—Race relations 3. Speeches
ISBN 0-7377-1593-6 (lib bdg); 0-7377-1594-4 (pa)
LC 2002-32209

"A collection of the speeches of well-known individuals who participated in or supported the American Civil Rights Movement from early pioneers through the 1960s up until today. Selections from Frederick Douglass, Malcolm X, Fannie Lou Hamer, Jesse Jackson, and Nelson Mandela emphasize the power of oratory to inform, persuade, and make an impact." SLJ

Includes bibliographical references

Engelbert, Phillis

American civil rights: almanac. U.X.L 1999 2v il set $110   **323.1**
1. Civil rights
ISBN 0-7876-3172-8   LC 98-52526
Contents: v1 African Americans, Asian Americans; v2 Hispanic Americans, Native Americans, selected immigrant groups, selected nonethnic groups

"The format of both volumes is identical. Following an introduction, a time line chronicles major events from the first signing of U.S. government and Native American treaties in 1778 to the April 20, 1999, award of the Congressional Gold Medal to Rosa Parks." Booklist

Includes bibliographical references

Finlayson, Reggie

We shall overcome; the history of the American civil rights movement. Lerner Publs. 2003 96p il (People's history) lib bdg $25.26   **323.1**
1. African Americans—Civil rights 2. United States—Race relations
ISBN 0-8225-0647-5   LC 2002-954
Contents: We shall overcome; This little light; Ain't gonna ride; The walls come a tumblin' down; The fires of frustration and discord; On my way; Selma, Bloody Sunday; Solving the American problem; Timeline; In their own words

Uses the words of spirituals and other music of the time to frame a discussion of the civil rights movement in the United States, focusing on specific people, incidents, and court cases

The author "ably places events in their historical con-

text and tells a linear, inspiring story of the crucial era. Compelling black-and-white photos . . . bring the events up close." Booklist

Includes bibliographical references

George, Linda

Civil rights marches; [by] Linda and Charles George. Children's Press 1999 30p il (Cornerstones of freedom) lib bdg $21; pa $5.95   **323.1**
1. African Americans—Civil rights 2. United States—Race relations
ISBN 0-516-21183-8 (lib bdg); 0-516-26516-4 (pa)
LC 98-41943

Describes the peaceful marches in the United States on behalf of civil rights for blacks from the 1950s to the 1990s, including the March on Washington and other important marches

King, Casey

Oh, freedom! kids talk about the Civil Rights Movement with the people who made it happen: illustrated with photographs; by Casey King and Linda Barrett Osborne; foreword by Rosa Parks; portraits by Joe Brooks. Knopf 1997 137p il lib bdg $19; pa $10.99 (5 and up)   **323.1**
1. African Americans—Civil rights 2. United States—Race relations
ISBN 0-679-85856-3 (lib bdg); 0-679-89005-X (pa)
LC 96-13014

Interviews between young people and people who took part in the civil rights movement accompany essays that describe the history of efforts to make equality a reality for African Americans

"King and Osborne present a carefully unbiased overview of the civil rights movement. . . . But most impressive is the way the authors use interesting interviews by students . . . [that] humanize history and add depth to the bare facts of the historical account." Book Rep

Includes bibliographical references

King, Martin Luther, 1929-1968

The words of Martin Luther King, Jr.; selected by Coretta Scott King. Newmarket Press 1983 112p il $15.95; pa $11.95   **323.1**
1. African Americans—Civil rights 2. United States—Race relations
ISBN 0-937858-28-5; 1-55704-483-X (pa)
LC 83-17306

This "volume of selections from Dr. King's speeches and writings . . . focuses on seven areas of his concerns: 'The Community of Man, Racism, Civil Rights, Justice and Freedom, Faith and Religion, Nonviolence, and Peace' " Publisher's note

Includes bibliographical references

Linda Brown, you are not alone; the Brown v. Board of Education decision: a collection; edited by Joyce Carol Thomas; illustrations by Curtis James. Jump at the Sun/Hyperion Books for Children 2003 114p il $15.99 (5 and up)   **323.1**

Linda Brown, you are not alone—*Continued*
1. School integration 2. African Americans—Civil rights 3. United States—Race relations
ISBN 0-7868-0821-7

A collection of personal reflections, stories and poems of 10 well-known children's authors, such as Jerry Spinelli, Eloise Greenfield, Lois Lowry, Michael Cart, and Katherine Paterson, who were themselves young people in 1954 when the Supreme Court handed down the decision to desegregate public schools.

The authors' "personal reminiscences capture a spectrum of powerfully expressed emotions. . . . James's closely focused, lifelike pastel illustrations feature striking portraits and memorable images." Publ Wkly

McWhorter, Diane
A dream of freedom; the Civil Rights Movement from 1954 to 1968; foreword by Reverend Fred Shuttlesworth. Scholastic Nonfiction 2004 160p il $19.95 (5 and up)
323.1
1. African Americans—Civil rights 2. United States—Race relations
ISBN 0-439-57678-4

The author discusses "the national civil rights movement from Brown v. the Board of Education to the assassination of Martin Luther King Jr. . . . This account is both factual and personal. She discusses her feelings as a white child in the South, and she focuses in on the many ways in which both white and black children were involved in the movement. . . . The breadth and depth of McWhorter's book is exemplary." Booklist

Meltzer, Milton, 1915-
There comes a time: the struggle for Civil Rights. Random House 2001 193p il hardcover o.p. paperback available pa $8.99 (5 and up)
323.1
1. African Americans—Civil rights 2. United States—Race relations
ISBN 0-375-80414-5   LC 99-89550
"Landmark books"

Presents an overview of the events in African American history that culminated in the United States during the 1950s and 1960s and represented a striving for equal rights

"The writing is clear and straightforward, making it accessible and appealing. . . . This is nonfiction at its best." SLJ
Includes bibliographical references

Ritchie, Nigel
The civil rights movement. Barron's 2003 64p il map (Lives in crisis) $14.95; pa $8.95
323.1
1. African Americans—Civil rights 2. United States—Race relations
ISBN 0-7641-5602-0; 0-7641-2416-1 (pa)
          LC 2002-106927

This "opens with the crisis in Little Rock, AR, followed by discussions of the history of slavery, the early civil rights movement, the development of the modern movement, its successes, and its legacy....{The book contains} numerous well-captioned photos, illustrations, and maps as well as excerpts from primary sources." SLJ

Sirimarco, Elizabeth, 1966-
American voices from the civil rights movement; by Elizabeth Sirimarco. Benchmark Books 2004 xxi, 134p il (American voices from--) lib bdg $34.21
323.1
1. African Americans—Civil rights 2. United States—Race relations
ISBN 0-7614-1697-8   LC 2003-7952

Presents the history of the civil rights movement in the United States, from Reconstruction to the late 1960s, through excerpts from letters, newspaper articles, speeches, songs, and poems of the time.

This "excellent [resource stands] out . . . because [it deals] strictly with primary sources, [contains] topnotch illustrations, and [enables] students to grasp the concepts without being overwhelmed." SLJ
Includes bibliographical references

Walsh, Frank
The Montgomery bus boycott. World Almanac Library 2003 48p il map (Landmark events in American history) lib bdg $26.60; pa $11.95
323.1
1. African Americans—Civil rights 2. Montgomery (Ala.)—Race relations
ISBN 0-8368-5375-X (lib bdg); 0-8368-5403-9 (pa)
          LC 2002-36020

Contents: Slavery in America; Segregation and racism; The spark; The boycott; The Civil Rights Movement

Describes how the black community of Montgomery, Alabama, staged the 1955 boycott to end segregation on public buses and discusses that struggle in the context of the Civil Rights Movement

"Brief but informative. . . . [The book is] heavily illustrated with well-chosen and carefully placed archival photographs and . . . reproductions of historical documents." SLJ
Includes glossary and bibliographical references

Wexler, Sanford
The civil rights movement; an eyewitness history; introduction by Julian Bond. Facts on File 1993 356p il maps (Eyewitness history series) $75 (7 and up)
323.1
1. African Americans—Civil rights 2. United States—Race relations
ISBN 0-8160-2748-X   LC 92-28674

Uses speeches, articles, and other writings of those involved to trace the history of the civil rights movement in the United States, primarily from 1954 to 1965

"This very readable source deserves a place in every public and middle and high school library, though it may fit better in the circulating collection." Booklist
Includes bibliographical references

Williams, Juan
Eyes on the prize: America's civil rights years, 1954-1965; {by} Juan Williams with the Eyes on the prize production team; introduction by Julian Bond. Viking 1987 300p il hardcover o.p. paperback available $20 (7 and up)   **323.1**
1. African Americans—Civil rights 2. United States—Race relations
ISBN 0-14-009653-1 (pa)   LC 86-40271
"A Robert Lavelle book"
"This companion volume to the PBS TV series of the same name is an . . . account of black America's struggle for social and political equality, covering the civil rights battle from the landmark Brown v. Board of Education decision in 1954 to the Selma protest marches, and Voting Rights Act of 1965." Libr J
"Highly recommended both as a socio-historical document and as a heartfelt, poignant remembrance of a movement and its activists." Booklist
Includes bibliographical references

323.44   Freedom of action (Liberty)

Bridegam, Martha A.
The right to privacy. Chelsea House 2003 117p il (Point-counterpoint) lib bdg $26.95
    323.44
1. Right of privacy
ISBN 0-7910-7373-4   LC 2002-152056
Contents: Defining and valuing the right to privacy; Not everyone can be safely "let alone"; Too much official invasion of privacy harms the public interest; Civilized life requires the exchange of information; Institutions and businesses are exploiting personal information unfairly; A free society depends on the right to learn and share information; Some kinds of information should always be protected; Drawing lines
"This book explores the right to privacy from various perspectives, including the rights of criminal suspects, witnesses, and even those subjected to extra security measures regardless of whether or not they're suspected of a crime. Special emphasis has been given to the heightened debate over civil liberties in the post-9/11 United States." Publisher's note
Includes bibliographical references and index

Intellectual freedom manual; compiled by the Office for Intellectual Freedom of the American Library Association. American Lib. Assn. il $45
    323.44
1. Intellectual freedom 2. Libraries—Censorship
First published 1974. (6th edition 2001) Periodically revised
This guide to preserving intellectual freedom includes: ALA interpretations to the Library Bill of Rights; recommendations for special libraries and specific situations; information about legal decisions affecting school and public libraries; a section on the ALA's Intellectual Freedom Action Network
"This manual details the professional standards to which librarians aspire and offers practical information about how to achieve those goals; it's a must for any librarian's professional library." Book Rep
Includes bibliographical references

MccGwire, Scarlett
Surveillance; the impact on our lives. Raintree Steck-Vaughn Pubs. 2001 64p il (21st century debates) lib bdg $32.79 (7 and up)
    323.44
1. Right of privacy 2. Electronic surveillance 3. Eavesdropping
ISBN 0-7398-3172-0   LC 00-33281
"Chapters discuss the development of surveillance techniques and equipment; their use by the government, police, and corporations; and their impact on private citizens. Also covered are modern surveillance equipment and methods such as cameras, e-mail interception through satellite relays, cable-tapping operations, and the use of DNA databases for solving violent crimes. Commentary on future techniques, developments, and the use of the Internet to gather and compile information will provoke thought and discussion among students." SLJ
Includes glossary and bibliographical references

Scales, Pat R.
Teaching banned books; 12 guides for young readers. American Lib. Assn. 2001 134p pa $28
    323.44
1. Books—Censorship 2. Children's literature—Study and teaching 3. School libraries
ISBN 0-8389-0807-1   LC 01-22340
The author "offers twelve strategies for teaching books that have been challenged or censored in the United States. Designed to accompany teaching about the First Amendment, 'each strategy includes a summary of the novel, a pre-reading activity, discussion questions to encourage critical thinking, and activities to broaden students' knowledge of topics in the novel.'" Bull Cent Child Books
"Scales knows her material inside out. She also knows how to inspire others to take up this cause and gives them an effective handbook to do just that." Booklist
Includes bibliographical references

324   The political process

Archer, Jules
Special interests; how lobbyists influence legislation. Millbrook Press 1997 144p il lib bdg $24.90   **324**
1. Lobbying
ISBN 0-7613-0060-0   LC 96-27076
"A Lucas-Evans book"
Describes the concept of lobbying, the history of its development, and the efforts of present-day lobbyists to influence state and federal legislators in such areas as tobacco, oil, and firearms
"Archer enlivens what could have been a dull read with clear, concise writing, well-placed political cartoons, and intriguing examples of dirty politics from the birth of the U.S. to the present." Booklist
Includes bibliographical references

The **Election** of 2000 and the administration of George W. Bush; editor, Arthur M. Schlesinger, Jr.; associate editors, Fred L. Israel & Jonathan H. Mann. Mason Crest Publs. 2003 128p il (Major presidential elections and the administrations that followed) lib bdg $24.95 (7 and up) **324**

1. Bush, George W. 2. Presidents—United States—Election—2000 3. United States—Politics and government—1989-

ISBN 1-59084-365-7 LC 2002-13397

A discussion of the presidential election of 2000 and the subsequent administration of George W. Bush, based on source documents

"An exemplary, evenhanded discussion of the election and of the Bush administration, through the Trade Bill of 2002." SLJ

Includes bibliographical references

324.6 Election systems and procedures; suffrage

Frost-Knappman, Elizabeth
Women's suffrage in America; an eyewitness history, [by] Elizabeth Frost and Kathryn Cullen-DuPont. Facts on File 1992 452p il (Eyewitness history series) $75 (7 and up) **324.6**

1. Women—Suffrage 2. Women—United States—History

ISBN 0-8160-2309-3 LC 91-31177

Chronicles the struggle of American women for the right to vote, from 1800 to their victory in 1920. Includes quotations from contemporary witnesses through memoirs, letters, and other documents of the period

This is "a lively and important sourcebook for students of American political and cultural history." SLJ

Includes bibliographical references

Marzilli, Alan, 1970-
Election reform. Chelsea House 2004 123p il (Point-counterpoint) lib bdg $29.95 (7 and up) **324.6**

1. Elections 2. Politics

ISBN 0-7910-7698-9 LC 2003-11607

"This volume addresses three important issues: voter fraud, campaign contributions, and political advertising. . . . An excellent resource for assignments." SLJ

Includes bibliographical references

Monroe, Judy
The Susan B. Anthony women's voting rights trial; a headline court case. Enslow Pubs. 2002 112p il (Headline court cases) lib bdg $26.60 **324.6**

1. Anthony, Susan B., 1820-1906 2. Women—Suffrage

ISBN 0-7660-1759-1 LC 2001-4528

Examines the efforts to gain the right for women in the United States to vote, focusing on the trial of Susan

B. Anthony for illegally voting in the presidential election in 1872

"Simple syntax, insightful quotes, and logical organization make the information easily accessible." SLJ

Includes glossary and bibliographical references

325.73 Immigration to the United States

Anderson, Dale, 1953-
Arriving at Ellis Island. World Almanac Library 2002 48p il map (Landmark events in American history) lib bdg $26.60; pa $11.95 (5 and up) **325.73**

1. Ellis Island Immigration Station 2. United States—Immigration and emigration

ISBN 0-8368-5337-7 (lib bdg); 0-8368-5351-2 (pa) LC 2002-24627

Discusses immigration to the United States during the nineteenth and early twentieth centuries and describes the small island in New York harbor that served as the point of entry for millions of immigrants from 1892 to 1954

The "design is attractive, with drawings, maps, paintings, and photos; primary sources, such as excerpts from diaries, letters, and newspapers, support and enhance the {text}. . . . Informative, competently written." Booklist

Includes glossary and bibliographical references

Collier, Christopher, 1930-
A century of immigration, 1820-1924; by Christopher Collier, James Lincoln Collier. Benchmark Bks. (Tarrytown) 2000 95p il (Drama of American history) lib bdg $31.36 **325.73**

1. United States—Immigration and emigration

ISBN 0-7614-0821-5 LC 98-33858

Discusses the economic, social, and religious reasons why immigrants, predominantly from northern Europe, and then from eastern and southern Europe, came to the United States. Considers incidents of prejudice experienced by these immigrants as well as contributions made by those of immigrant background

"By focusing on broad themes, the Colliers are able to show cause and effect over several decades and to make the sweep of time 'bite-sized' and intelligible. The frequent full-color and black-and-white period photographs and engravings effectively supplement and enrich the text." SLJ

Includes bibliographical references

Daniels, Roger
American immigration; a student companion. Oxford Univ. Press 2000 303p (Oxford student companions to American history) lib bdg $60 (7 and up) **325.73**

1. United States—Immigration and emigration 2. Immigrants—United States

ISBN 0-19-511316-0 LC 00-56673

"Following an essay that provides an overview of the book, students find immigration statistics, areas of settlement, major periods of immigration, and the predominant

Daniels, Roger—*Continued*

religion of the immigrant groups. Key pieces of legislation . . . are discussed. . . . The appendices cover important dates in immigration history; immigration, ethnic,
and refugee organizations." Book Rep

"This resource would be ideal for young adults seeking brief overviews of particular ethnic groups." Voice
Youth Advocates

Includes bibliographical references

Hoobler, Dorothy

We are Americans; voices of the immigrant
experience; by Dorothy and Thomas Hoobler.
Scholastic Ref. 2003 194p il $21.95 (5 and up)

325.73

1. United States—Immigration and emigration

ISBN 0-439-16297-1   LC 2001-49612

A history of immigration to America, from speculation
about the earliest immigrants to the present day

"This thoughtful, well-researched overview will be a
solid addition to most collections and is most notable for
the diverse array of voices that it contains." SLJ

Includes bibliographical references

I was dreaming to come to America; memories
from the Ellis Island Oral History Project;
selected and illustrated by Veronica Lawlor;
foreword by Rudolph W. Giuliani. Viking 1995
38p il pa $6.99 hardcover o.p. (4 and up)

325.73

1. Ellis Island Immigration Station 2. United States—
Immigration and emigration

ISBN 0-14-055622-2 (pa)   LC 95-1281

In their own words, coupled with hand-painted collage
illustrations, immigrants recall their arrival in the United
States. Includes brief biographies and facts about the Ellis Island Oral History Project

"There is a flavor of Chagall in the peasant figures
dancing above the ship or hopping ashore near the turret-
ed towers of the huge building on Ellis Island. The elegant rendering offers a timeless view of this significant
journey that is at once personal and universal." Horn
Book

Illegal immigration: opposing viewpoints; William
Dudley, book editor. Greenhaven Press 2002
206p il lib bdg $31.20; pa $19.95 (7 and up)

325.73

1. Illegal aliens 2. United States—Immigration and
emigration

ISBN 0-7377-0911-1 (lib bdg); 0-7377-0910-3 (pa)

LC 2001-40733

"Opposing viewpoints series"

Replaces the edition published 1997 under the
editorship of Charles P. Cozic

"Dudley begins with a brief overview of U.S. immigration policy, followed by more than 20 essays that represent both liberal and conservative points of view, all
written between 1995 and 2001. Students will find the
articles helpful in examining these controversial and often emotional issues." SLJ

Includes bibliographical references

Immigration; Jeff Hay, book editor. Greenhaven
Press 2001 252p il (Turning points in world
history) lib bdg $34.95; pa $23.70 (7 and up)

325.73

1. United States—Immigration and emigration

ISBN 0-7377-0639-2 (lib bdg); 0-7377-0638-4 (pa)

LC 00-52800

"This anthology covers the history of immigration to
the United States from the first great wave of immigrants
through Ellis Island to problems of assimilation and the
rise of anti-immigrant sentiment. Chapters also discuss
immigrant destinations, restricting immigration, and
Asian and Mexican immigrants." Publisher's note

Includes bibliographical references

Kosof, Anna

Living in two worlds; the immigrant children's
experience. 21st Cent. Bks. (NY) 1996 112p il lib
bdg $23.40 (7 and up)   **325.73**

1. United States—Immigration and emigration
2. Children of immigrants

ISBN 0-8050-4083-8   LC 96-13004

After a brief history of immigration, the author "introduces teen immigrants that she interviewed in schools
around the country. Cultural differences, from food, to
dress, to ways to show respect are easily understood
from these vignettes about young people who came here
from around the world." SLJ

Includes bibliographical references

Meltzer, Milton, 1915-

Bound for America; the story of the European
immigrants. Benchmark Bks. 2002 112p il (Great
journeys) $32.79 (5 and up)   **325.73**

1. United States—Immigration and emigration

ISBN 0-7614-1227-1   LC 00-51875

This history of immigration to the United States focuses on Europeans who arrived in the late 19th and early
20th century

Includes bibliographical references

The **Newest** Americans. Greenwood Press 2003 5v
il maps (Middle school reference) set $200

325.73

1. United States—Immigration and emigration—Encyclopedias 2. Minorities—Encyclopedias

ISBN 0-313-32553-7   LC 2002-35214

Contents: v1 A-D, Afghans to Dominicans; v2 E-H,
Ecuadoreans to Hatians; v3 I-L, Indians to Laotians; v4
M-P, Mexicans to Puerto Ricans; v5 R-V, Russians to
Vietnamese

Provides historical, social, political, and cultural information about immigrant groups that have been changing
the face of the United States from 1960 to the present,
as well as facts about immigrants in general

"These volumes present thorough and accessible information. . . . A good choice for contemporary immigration assignments." SLJ

Sandler, Martin W.
Island of hope; the story of Ellis Island and the journey to America. Scholastic Nonfiction 2004 144p il $18.95 (5 and up)   325.73
1. Ellis Island Immigration Station 2. United States—Immigration and emigration
ISBN 0-439-53082-2   LC 2003-54448
Relates the story of immigration to America through the voices and stories of those who passed through Ellis Island, from its opening in 1892 to the release of the last detainee in 1954.
"This engagingly written, inspirational account will give children, particularly immigrants or descendants of immigrants, some sharp insight into the trials and triumphs of their predecessors." Booklist
Includes bibliographical references

Wepman, Dennis
Immigration; from the founding of Virginia to the closing of Ellis Island. Facts on File 2002 430p il maps (Eyewitness history series) $75 (7 and up)   325.73
1. United States—Immigration and emigration
ISBN 0-8160-3999-2   LC 2001-33083
This history offers "firsthand accounts of the period—from diary entries, letters, speeches, and newspaper articles. . . . Each chapter provides an introductory essay and a chronology of events. The book also includes such . . . documents as the Alien and Sedition Acts, the Chinese Exclusion Act, the Johnson-Reed Act, and the McCarran-Walter Act as well as capsule biographies of 95 key figures." Publisher's note
"This resource will serve as an excellent addition to reference collections. . . . The comprehensive index is an excellent ready-reference tool for finding relevant information within the fascinating pages." Voice Youth Advocates
Includes bibliographical references

326   Slavery and emancipation

Altman, Linda Jacobs, 1943-
The politics of slavery; fiery national debates fueled by the slave economy; foreword by series advisor Henry Louis Gates. Enslow 2004 128p il map (Slavery in American history) lib bdg $26.60 (7 and up)   326
1. Slavery—United States 2. United States—Politics and government 3. United States—Race relations
ISBN 0-7660-2150-5   LC 2003-26532
Contents: The beginnings of American slavery; From servants to slaves; Slavery and the founding freedoms; Compromise and the Constitution; Slavery in a growing nation; Missouri and the westward expansion; Slavery and manifest destiny; North and South : a clash of cultures; The road to disunion
"Altman relates the beginning of 'the peculiar institution' and the constitutional, historical, and political issues and figures surrounding it from 1619 to the ratification of the Thirteenth Amendment in 1865. . . . [This book] will be useful in American-history collections." SLJ

American slavery; William Dudley, book editor. Greenhaven Press 2000 255p il (Turning points in world history) lib bdg $33.70; pa $22.45 (7 and up)   326
1. Slavery—United States
ISBN 0-7377-0213-3 (lib bdg); 0-7377-0212-5 (pa)
LC 99-55866
This "volume traces the effects of slavery in the New World and discusses its economic, political, social, and cultural effects on the United States. . . . Each chapter begins with a valuable summary, and discussion questions appear at the end. The extensive appendix contains reprints of 20 historical documents." SLJ
Includes bibliographical references

Bial, Raymond
The strength of these arms; life in the slave quarters. Houghton Mifflin 1997 40p il $16 (4 and up)   326
1. Slavery—United States 2. Plantation life 3. African Americans—Social life and customs
ISBN 0-395-77394-6   LC 96-39860
Describes how slaves were able to preserve some elements of their African heritage despite the often brutal treatment they experienced on Southern plantations
"This volume features clear, color photographs of plantation sites and artifacts, as well as a few early photos of people living under slavery. . . . This makes slavery in America more concrete than many other books on the subject." Booklist
Includes bibliographical references

The Underground Railroad. Houghton Mifflin 1995 48p il map $17; pa $6.95 (4 and up)   326
1. Underground railroad 2. Slavery—United States
ISBN 0-395-69937-1; 0-395-97915-3 (pa)
LC 94-19614
Using first-person accounts, historical documents, and his own photographs, the author "focuses on the history of the Underground Railroad, building on the experiences of both riders and conductors as he outlines the political climate and the moral beliefs that allowed slavery to thrive and those that helped bring about its downfall." Publ Wkly
"Although the text covers ground often trodden by other works on this popular subject, Bial's shots of places and things which now appear tidy and innocent conjure spirits of desperate freedom-seekers as handily as do more detailed narratives." Bull Cent Child Books
Includes bibliographical references

Cloud Tapper, Suzanne
Voices from slavery's past; yearning to be heard; foreword by series advisor Henry Louis Gates. Enslow Publishers 2004 128p il map (Slavery in American history) lib bdg $26.60 (7 and up)   326
1. Abolitionists 2. Slavery—United States
ISBN 0-7660-2157-2   LC 2003-25134
This profiles escaped slave Henry Bibb, slave trader John Newton, captured African Olauda Equiano, racist scientist Joseph Le Conte, slave mistress Letitia Burwell,

Cloud Tapper, Suzanne—*Continued*
escaped slave Harriet Jacobs, and abolitionists William
Lloyd Garrison and Frederick Douglass
This title is "consistently solid, with many informative
period photographs and drawings, excerpts from primary-
source documents, and strong back matter." SLJ
Includes glossary and bibliographical references

The **Complete** history of American slavery; James
Miller, book editor. Greenhaven Press 2001
642p il map (Complete history of) lib bdg $99
(7 and up)   **326**
1. Slavery—United States 2. African Americans—History
ISBN 0-7377-0424-1   LC 00-39332
This anthology includes more than 90 entries and "begins with the Atlantic slave trade and ends with the Civil
War, with entries by Frederick Douglass, Nat Turner,
Mary Chestnut, and many others. It is organized into 16
chapters on a number of topics, including a fascinating
discussion of whether the Underground Railroad actually
existed." Booklist
Includes bibliographical references

Currie, Stephen, 1960-
Escapes from slavery; Stephen Currie. Lucent
Books 2003 112p il map (Great escapes) $28.70
    326
1. Slavery—United States
ISBN 1-590-18276-6   LC 2002-154078
Contents: Introduction: fugitive slaves; Ellen and Wil-
liam Craft; Josiah Henson; Harriet Tubman; William
Wells Brown; Henry Brown
"These exciting tales are written in lively language
and are accompanied by black-and-white illustrations and
informative sidebars." SLJ
Includes bibliographical references

Slavery. Greenhaven Press 1999 111p il
(Opposing viewpoints digests) lib bdg $29.95; pa
$19.95 (7 and up)   **326**
1. Slavery—United States
ISBN 1-56510-881-7 (lib bdg); 1-56510-880-9 (pa)
    LC 98-36198
Contributors discuss slavery in the United States from
historical, political, economic and sociological perspec-
tives
Includes bibliographical references

Edwards, Judith
Abolitionists and slave resistance; breaking the
chains of slavery; foreword by Henry Louis Gates.
Enslow Publishers 2004 128p il map (Slavery in
American history) lib bdg $26.60 (7 and up)
    326
1. Abolitionists 2. Slavery—United States
ISBN 0-7660-2155-6   LC 2003-13457
Contents: Events leading to abolition -- Slavery and
the Revolution -- The anti-slavery movement gathers
force -- Abolitionists organize -- The Amistad and the
new decade -- The rebels and the runaways -- Escape
from slavery -- John Brown's raid -- On the antislavery
side -- From slave to soldier

"Edwards examines the growth of the abolition movement and provides examples of some of the ways slaves
themselves protested, including theft, work slowdowns,
and destruction of property. Rebellions, runaways, and
the Underground Railroad are also covered. The sensitive
and respectful approach leads to an understanding of the
social issues that remain as a legacy of slavery in
American society today." SLJ
Includes bibliographical references

Eskridge, Ann E.
Slave uprisings and runaways; fighting for
freedom and the Underground Railroad; foreword
by series advisor Henry Louis Gates. Enslow 2004
128p il map (Slavery in American history) lib bdg
$26.60   **326**
1. Slavery—United States 2. Underground railroad
ISBN 0-7660-2154-8   LC 2003-26533
This history of slave rebellions and escapes covers
such topics as Nat Turner, John Brown, Harriet Tubman,
Frederick Douglass, The Fugitive Slave Act, and The
Underground Railroad.

Fradin, Dennis B.
Bound for the North Star; true stories of fugitive
slaves; [by] Dennis Brindell Fradin. Clarion Bks.
2000 206p il $20 (7 and up)   **326**
1. Slavery—United States 2. Underground railroad
3. Abolitionists
ISBN 0-395-97017-2   LC 00-29052
"Fradin here draws on more than 16 slaves' personal
experiences to show what slavery was like: the unrelent-
ing racism; the physical brutality, including rape and
flogging; the anguish of family separation. . . . The narrative is direct, with no rhetoric or cover-up. . . . This
is painful reading about legal racist cruelty and those
who resisted it." Booklist
Includes bibliographical references

Grant, R. G. (Reg G.)
The African-American slave trade. Barron's
Educational Series 2003 64p il map (Lives in
crisis) $14.95; pa $8.95   **326**
1. Slavery—United States 2. Slave trade 3. African
Americans—History
ISBN 0-7641-5604-7; 0-7641-2423-4 (pa)
    LC 2002-107467
This "opens with a discussion of slavery as it existed
in 1776. . . . Grant continues with a description of the
growth of the slave trade, the roles played by both Europeans and Africans, working conditions for slaves in differing parts of the New World, and the abolition and aftermath of this institution. The author provides background information and analyzes events in the context of
the era." SLJ
This does "an excellent job of setting American history within an international context. {It avoids} vague
generalization, and numerous, heartrending eyewitness
accounts . . . personalize the politics." Booklist
Includes bibliographical references

Hamilton, Virginia, 1936-2002
Many thousand gone; African Americans from slavery to freedom; illustrated by Leo and Diane Dillon. Knopf 1993 151p il lib bdg $18.99; pa $12.95 (5 and up)   **326**
   1. Underground railroad 2. Slavery—United States
   ISBN 0-394-92873-3 (lib bdg); 0-679-87936-6 (pa)
                        LC 89-19988
In this book the author tells "the story of slavery through a series of dramatic biographical vignettes. . . . Her book includes such famous historical figures as Frederick Douglass, Sojourner Truth and Harriet Tubman. She also presents some more obscure individuals. . . . All of these profiles drive home the sickening realities of slavery in a personal way. . . . These are powerful stories eloquently told." N Y Times Book Rev
Includes bibliographical references

Haskins, James, 1941-2005
Bound for America; the forced migration of Africans to the New World; {by} James Haskins & Kathleen Benson; illustrated by Floyd Cooper. Lothrop, Lee & Shepard Bks. 1999 48p il $17; lib bdg $17.89 (5 and up)   **326**
   1. Slave trade 2. Slavery—History
   ISBN 0-688-10258-1; 0-688-10259-X (lib bdg)
                        LC 98-24101
"This combination of clear text and judicious use of primary-source material makes crystalline the inhumanity and commercialism that kept the trade in slaves alive for 350 years." SLJ
Includes bibliographical references

Get on board: the story of the Underground Railroad. Scholastic 1993 152p il map hardcover o.p. paperback available $4.50 (5 and up)
                              326
   1. Tubman, Harriet, 1815?-1913 2. Brown, John, b. ca. 1810 3. Underground railroad 4. Slavery—United States
   ISBN 0-590-45419-6   LC 92-13247
The author "relates the history of the Underground Railroad in the U.S., and introduces those who made it a success." SLJ
"Weaving together poignant personal stories and carefully researched historical data, Haskins has produced a stirring account of the founding and the workings of the Underground Railroad." Publ Wkly
Includes bibliographical references

Hulm, David
United States v. the Amistad; the question of slavery in a free country. Rosen Pub. Group 2004 64p il (Supreme Court cases through primary sources) lib bdg $29.25   **326**
   1. Amistad (Schooner) 2. Slavery—United States
   ISBN 0-8239-4013-6   LC 2003-5938
Contents: A mutiny changes American history; Trials and tribulations; District Court and Circuit Court; Forged in the fires of adversity; Free, but not home
This is an account of the mutiny aboard the slave ship Amistad and the court cases which followed.
This "deserves a place in every library. . . . Copious

and well-chosen primary source documents give extra value to this [book]. . . . Each document adds human drama to the already engaging text." Lib Media Connect
Includes glossary and bibliographical references

Katz, William Loren
Breaking the chains; African-American slave resistance. Atheneum Pubs. 1990 194p il (7 and up)   **326**
   1. Slavery—United States
   ISBN 0-689-31493-0; 0-689-81919-6 (pa)
                        LC 89-36355
Describes slavery in the United States, the harsh conditions under which slaves lived, the active and passive resistance with which they fought for their rights, the revolts, and the involvement of slaves in the Civil War
"This book will force many readers to reexamine their assumptions about American history. . . . The power of the text's content is made even more impressive by the many black-and-white photographs and reproductions." SLJ
Includes bibliographical references

Lester, Julius
From slave ship to freedom road; paintings by Rod Brown. Dial Bks. 1998 40p il $17.99; pa $6.99 (4 and up)   **326**
   1. Slavery—United States
   ISBN 0-8037-1893-4; 0-14-056669-4 (pa)
                        LC 96-44422
"Lester uses empathy-provoking exercises, open-ended questions, and the paintings of Rod Brown to help readers understand the experience of African-American slaves." Bull Cent Child Books
"Lester's impassioned questions grow from his visceral response to Brown's narrative paintings. . . . The combination of history, art, and commentary demands interaction." Booklist

McKissack, Patricia C., 1944-
Rebels against slavery; by Patricia C. McKissack and Fredrick McKissack. Scholastic 1996 181p il $15.95 (5 and up)   **326**
   1. Slavery—United States
   ISBN 0-590-45735-7   LC 94-41089
   A Coretta Scott King honor book for text, 1997
The authors "explore slave revolts and the men and women who led them, weaving a tale of courage and defiance in the face of tremendous odds. Readers learn not only about Nat Turner and Denmark Vesey, but also about Cato, Gabriel Prosser, the maroons, and the relationship between escaped slaves and Seminole Indians. The activities of abolitionists are described as well. The authors' careful research, sensitivity, and evenhanded style reveal a sad, yet inspiring story of the will to be free." SLJ

McNeese, Tim
The rise and fall of American slavery; freedom denied, freedom gained; foreword by series advisor Dr. Henry Louis Gates, Jr. Enslow Publishers 2004 128p il map (Slavery in American history) lib bdg $26.60 (7 and up)   **326**
1. Slavery—United States
ISBN 0-7660-2156-4   LC 2003-13459
Contents: The story of Josiah Henson; The slave trade; Slavery in the colonies; Slavery and revolution; King Cotton; Abolition and emancipation
This is a history of American slavery from colonial times to emacipation.
"Drawing on personal slave narratives as well as the commentary and analysis of eminent scholars, [this title] . . . [brings] immediacy and depth to crucial events and [assesses] their lasting impact on America's economy, politics, and culture. . . . The documentation is exemplary." Booklist
Includes glossary and bibliographical references

Meltzer, Milton, 1915-
They came in chains; the story of the slave ships. Benchmark Bks. 2000 96p il map (Great journeys) lib bdg $32.79   **326**
1. Slavery—United States 2. Slave trade
ISBN 0-7614-0967-X   LC 98-47456
"Firsthand accounts, black-and-white photos and reproductions, and excerpts from newspapers and speeches dramatically convey the horrors of slavery." SLJ
Includes bibliographical references

Myers, Walter Dean, 1937-
Amistad: a long road to freedom. Dutton Children's Bks. 1998 99p il maps $16.99; pa $9.99 (5 and up)   **326**
1. Amistad (Schooner) 2. Slavery—United States
ISBN 0-525-45970-7; 0-14-130004-3 (pa)
This is an "account of the capture in West Africa, the hellish journey aboard the slave ship on the Middle Passage, the sale in Cuba, the mutiny led by Sengbe on the *Amistad* as it sailed from Cuba, the forced landing in Connecticut, the subsequent court trials in the U.S., and the final struggle to return home. The design is clear and readable. . . . Myers includes considerable detail drawn from primary reports. . . . The narrative is exciting, not only the account of the uprising but also the tension of the court arguments." Booklist
Includes bibliographical references

Rappaport, Doreen, 1939-
Escape from slavery; five journeys to freedom; illustrated by Charles Lilly. HarperCollins Pubs. 1991 117p il $15.95; pa $5.99 (4 and up)
                                                    326
1. Underground railroad 2. Slavery—United States
ISBN 0-06-021631-X; 0-06-446169-6 (pa)
                                      LC 90-38170
"These accounts of a courageous and daring people deserve a wide readership. Readable, clear and precise, the book shows evidence of careful research and is an excellent addition to books on Black History." Child Book Rev Serv
Includes bibliographical references

Sawyer, Kem Knapp
The underground railroad in American history. Enslow Pubs. 1997 128p il maps (In American history) lib bdg $26.60   **326**
1. Underground railroad 2. Slavery—United States
ISBN 0-89490-885-5   LC 96-30901
Describes the Underground Railroad and the historical events surrounding it and presents the stories of some of its conductors
Includes bibliographical references

Slave narratives; the journey to freedom; {compiled} by Elaine Landau. Watts 2001 95p il (In their own voices) lib bdg $24
                                                    326
1. Slavery—United States 2. African Americans—Biography
ISBN 0-531-11743-X   LC 00-32515
Contents: Austin Steward; Louis Huges; Bethany Veney; James L. Smith
"Landau has chosen excerpts from four accounts of life under slavery and how these individuals obtained their freedom. . . . Each narrative is compelling in its details of the hardships that slaves faced in their daily lives and the risks and sacrifices they made to obtain their freedom. Photographs and period illustrations complement the moving text." SLJ
Includes bibliographical references

Slavery; James D. Torr, book editor. Greenhaven Press 2004 240p map (Opposing viewpoints in world history series) $33.70; pa $22.45
                                                    326
1. Slavery—United States
ISBN 0-7377-1705-X; 0-7377-1706-8 (pa)
                                      LC 2003-44812
This book offers "perspectives on American slavery through a selection of primary sources. The excerpts, culled from speeches, pamphlets, and scholarly texts, are divided into four sections that cover moral issues, slave resistance, abolitionists, and events that led to the Civil War. . . . The entries that are included . . . will greatly enhance students' understanding of the issues. . . . An important, useful addition to the high-school history curriculum." Booklist
Includes bibliographical references

Tackach, James, 1954-
The abolition of American slavery. Lucent Bks. 2002 112p il maps (World history series) lib bdg $27.45 (7 and up)   **326**
1. Abolitionists 2. Slavery—United States
ISBN 1-59018-002-X   LC 2001-5301
Discusses the introduction of slaves into American society, the beginnings of the abolitionist movement, the national conflict over slavery and the resulting Civil War, emancipation of the slaves, and slavery's legacy
"There is a good deal of information packed into the brief text and both report writers and general readers will be well served. The book is illustrated with archival photographs and reproductions of prints and broadsides." SLJ
Includes bibliographical references

Thomas, Velma Maia
Lest we forget; the passage from Africa to slavery and emancipation. Crown 1997 32p il $29.95 (7 and up)   **326**
1. Slavery—United States 2. African Americans—History 3. Slave trade
ISBN 0-609-60030-3   LC 96-54240
"A three-dimensional interactive book with photographs and documents from the Black Holocaust Exhibit." Title page
"By combining highly effective and readable text with photographs, news clippings, drawings, and facsimilies of documents, Thomas shares with her readers the details of virtually every aspect of slave life. . . . Throughout the assortment of pop-out and pull-out replicas, points are raised that will lead to classroom discussion." SLJ

Watkins, Richard Ross
Slavery: bondage throughout history; written and illustrated by Richard Watkins. Houghton Mifflin 2001 136p il $18 (7 and up)   **326**
1. Slavery—History
ISBN 0-395-92289-5   LC 00-40752
"The author discusses how people have been owned as property through history and across the world. . . . He takes a number of comprehensive subjects—capture, trading, law, escape, revolt, etc.—and talks about each one across cultures and civilizations." Booklist
"A brilliantly written treatment of an abhorrent topic." SLJ
Includes glossary and bibliographical references

Worth, Richard, 1945-
Slave life on the plantation; prisons beneath the sun. Enslow Publishers 2004 128p il (Slavery in American history) lib bdg $26.60 (7 and up)   **326**
1. Slavery—United States 2. Plantation life
ISBN 0-7660-2152-1   LC 2003-24291
Contents: A slave's life; Slavery in the 1600s; Plantation life in 1700s; King Cotton; Relationships between owners and slaves; African-American culture on the plantation; Freedom
"Worth frames his account within the sweep of history, but his focus is on daily life - the work, the hardship (especially the breakup of family life), punishment, and resistance - and he discusses the relationship between owners and slaves, the importance of cotton, and African American culture. [This title includes] several stirring page-long slave narratives as well as black-and-white drawings and photos. The documentation is exemplary." Booklist
Includes glossary and bibliographical references

The slave trade in America; cruel commerce; foreword by series advisor Dr. Henry Louis Gates, Jr. Enslow Publishers 2004 128p il map (Slavery in American history) lib bdg $26.60 (7 and up)   **326**
1. Slave trade 2. Slavery—United States
ISBN 0-7660-2151-3   LC 2003-12079
Contents: Stories of the slave trade; Origins of the slave trade; The slave trade in the 1600s; The slave trade

in the 1700s; The slave trade and the law; Slave trade within the South; Major centers of internal slave trade; End of the slave trade
This is a history of the slave trade in America from colonial times to emancipation
This "clearly written, well-researched [book presents] solid coverage of the subject." SLJ
Includes glossary and bibliographical references

327.1   Foreign policy and international relations

Blohm, Craig E., 1948-
Weapons of peace; the nuclear arms race. Lucent Bks. 2003 128p il map (American war library, Cold War) $27.45   **327.1**
1. Nuclear weapons 2. Arms race 3. Arms control 4. World politics—1945-
ISBN 1-59018-212-X   LC 2002-11035
Discusses the development of nuclear weapons, the race for nuclear supremacy, deployment of these weapons during the Cold War, and disarmament
Includes bibliographical references

327.12   Espionage and subversion

Gifford, Clive
Spies; foreword by Dame Stella Rimington. Kingfisher 2004 63p il (Kingfisher knowledge) $11.95 (5 and up)   **327.12**
1. Spies
ISBN 0-7534-5777-6
This "book provides a history of the trade, includes memorable spy stories, and discusses the future of espionage. The facts come fast and furiously, interspersed with attractive color photographs. . . . An eye-catching introduction, best for browsers." SLJ
Includes glossary

Keeley, Jennifer, 1974-
Espionage. Lucent Bks. 2003 112p il map (American war library, Cold War) $27.45
                    327.12
1. Espionage 2. Cold war
ISBN 1-59018-210-3   LC 2002-2218
Discusses the agents, communications, technological advances, covert actions, and double agents during the Cold War
Includes bibliographical references

Kupperberg, Paul
Spy satellites. Rosen Pub. Group 2003 63p il (Library of satellites) lib bdg $26.50
                    327.12
1. Espionage 2. Artificial satellites
ISBN 0-8239-3854-9   LC 2002-10747
Contents: A cold war in space; CORONA; Inside a spy satellite; Eyes in the sky

Kupperberg, Paul—Continued
Examines the history, technology, and uses of spy satellites, looking especially at the various reconnaissance satellite programs of the United States, from the mid-twentieth century to the present
"Clear and topical photographs enliven the [presentation]. While packed with information, the [text is] easy to read." SLJ
Includes glossary and bibliographical references

Platt, Richard, 1953-
Spy; written by Richard Platt; photographed by Geoff Dann and Steve Gorton. Knopf 1996 59p il (Eyewitness books) $19; lib bdg $20.99
327.12
1. Espionage 2. Intelligence service
ISBN 0-679-88122-0; 0-679-98122-5 (lib bdg)
LC 96-11003
Available from DK Pub. edition $15.99; $19.99
"A Dorling Kindersley book"
Numerous photos, drawings and maps illustrate this history of espionage. "Every aspect of spy culture is examined, including equipment and its concealment, methods of bugging and tapping, codes and ciphers, double agents and defectors, and industrial espionage and surveillance. Famous past and present spy personalities, as well as fictional spies, are discussed. The book is eye-catching." Booklist

327.73   United States--Foreign relations

Collier, Christopher, 1930-
The United States in the Cold War: 1945-1989; {by} Christopher Collier, James Lincoln Collier. Benchmark Bks. 2001 95p il maps (Drama of American history) $31.36   **327.73**
1. Cold war 2. World politics—1945-1991 3. United States—Foreign relations—Soviet Union 4. Soviet Union—Foreign relations—United States
ISBN 0-7614-1317-0   LC 00-68010
The author discusses such topics as the Berlin Wall, the Korean and Vietnam Wars, the arms race, and other conflicts between the United States and the Soviet Union and other communist countries
This is written in "engaging narrative style . . . {and is} easy to read and informative." Book Rep
Includes bibliographical references

Pascoe, Elaine
Mexico and the United States; cooperation and conflict. 21st Cent. Bks. (NY) 1996 126p il map lib bdg $24.90 (7 and up)   **327.73**
1. United States—Foreign relations—Mexico 2. Mexico—Foreign relations—United States
ISBN 0-8050-4180-X   LC 96-11430
This discussion of the relationship between the two nations focuses on political, economic and environmental issues as well as immigration and drug trafficking
"The strong narrative and balanced point of view recommend the text to students needing more information

about Mexico-U.S. relations than textbooks normally can supply." Booklist
Includes bibliographical references

Ross, Stewart
The causes of the Cold War. World Almanac 2002 64p il maps (Cold War) lib bdg $32.67
327.73
1. Cold war 2. World politics—1945- 3. United States—Foreign relations—Soviet Union 4. Soviet Union—Foreign relations—United States
ISBN 0-8368-5272-9   LC 2001-46604
First published 2001 in the United Kingdom
Explores the rivalry and tensions between the United States and the Soviet Union stemming from their differing ideologies and discusses the resulting events during the decade after World War II
This does "an excellent job of explanation and context setting. {It does} . . . extremely well at introducing the chief players of the times, and how their personalities influenced events." Booklist
Includes glossary and bibliographical references

Speakman, Jay
The Cold War. Greenhaven Press 2001 128p il (Opposing viewpoints digests) $29.95; pa $19.95 (7 and up)   **327.73**
1. Cold war 2. World politics—1945-1991 3. United States—Foreign relations—Soviet Union 4. Soviet Union—Foreign relations—United States
ISBN 0-7377-0421-7; 0-7377-0420-9 (pa)
LC 00-11681
This explores the causes and consequences of the Cold War and whether the cost was justified, using primary and secondary sources to place each viewpoint in the context of its supporters and detractors
Includes bibliographical references

Spencer, William
The United States and Iran. 21st Cent. Bks. (Brookfield) 2000 128p il map lib bdg $24.90 (7 and up)   **327.73**
1. United States—Foreign relations—Iran 2. Iran—Foreign relations—United States 3. Iran—Politics and government
ISBN 0-7613-1554-3   LC 99-41426
"Spencer briefly mentions Iran's long history, but concentrates on the problems dominating its relationship with the U.S. . . . His clear, direct explanations and illustrative comments will be understandable to students who have little knowledge of the conflicts or religions involved. . . . Up-to-date information presented in an accessible format." SLJ
Includes bibliographical references

328 The legislative process

Horn, Geoffrey
The Congress; by Geoffrey M. Horn. World Almanac Library 2003 48p il (World Almanac Library of American government) lib bdg $30; pa $11.95 (5 and up)   **328**
  1. United States. Congress
  ISBN 0-8368-5457-8 (lib bdg); 0-8368-5462-4 (pa)
                       LC 2002-514111
  Contents: Congress and the Capitol; What the Constitution says; Getting elected and reelected; House and Senate; How a bill becomes a law; Landmark legislation; Congress in the spotlight
  This describes "how the Constitution gives different jobs to each chamber of Congress, the extent and limits of their powers, and the roles each performs in the making of federal laws. . . . . [It also discusses] the important officials in Congress, the legislative process, and some important laws Congress has passed. Special sections explain concepts such as pork-barrel spending, lameduck sessions, and filibusters." Publisher's note
  Includes bibliographical references

328.73 The legislative process in the United States

Christianson, Stephen G.
Facts about the Congress; with an introduction by Richard Allan Baker. Wilson, H.W. 1996 xxvii, 635p il $115   **328.73**
  1. United States. Congress 2. United States—Politics and government
  ISBN 0-8242-0883-8   LC 95-53691
  This volume describes "the structure, function, and history of both houses of the U.S. Congress. An opening section discusses how the Congress operates in the passage of legislation, including the details of its committee and subcommittee structure, leadership and seniority, and relations with the President. The main part of the book consists of chapters devoted to the activities of every Congress, from the First (1789-1791) to the One Hundred Fourth (1995)." Publisher's note
  Includes glossary and bibliographical references

330.9 Economic situation and conditions

Outman, James L., 1946-
Industrial Revolution: almanac; [by] James L. Outman, Elisabeth M. Outman. UXL 2003 242p il (Industrial revolution reference library) $55
                             330.9
  1. Industrial revolution
  ISBN 0-7876-6513-4   LC 2002-155422
  Contents: Origins of the Industrial Revolution; The revolution begins: steam engines, railroads, steamboats; New machines and the factory system; The social and political impact of the Industrial Revolution, part 1; The age of petroleum and electricity; The new business models; The social and political impact of the Industrial Revolution, part 2; Globalization
  "This is an excellent adjunct to American and world history units and classes on economics and labor movements." Booklist
  Includes bibliographical references

Industrial Revolution: primary sources; [by] James L. Outman, Elisabeth M. Outman. UXL 2003 212p il (Industrial revolution reference library) $55   **330.9**
  1. Industrial revolution
  ISBN 0-7876-6515-0   LC 2002-155420
  Contents: Economic theory; Adam Smith; The Wealth of Nations; Andrew Ure; The philosophy of manufacturers; Karl Marx; The Communist Manifesto; Andrew Carnegie; The gospel of wealth; Technological advances and criticisms; Thomas Savery; Uses of the fire engine; Leeds letters; Luddites; Samuel Morse; On the telegraph; J. Stillman; The last tie; The Industrial Revolution and working conditions; Sadler Report; Samuel Gompers; Germinal Zola and coal miners; Upton Sinclair; Excerpt from The Jungle; Triangle Shirtwaist fire; Jane Addams; Excerpt from Hull House; Carmen Teoli; Congressional testimony; Politics and law in the Industrial Revolution; United States Supreme Court; Northern Securities v. United States; Theodore Roosevelt; Progressive Party platform
  "This is an excellent adjunct to American and world history units and classes on economics and labor movements." Booklist
  Includes bibliographical references

Ross, Stewart
The industrial revolution. Watts 2001 62p il maps (Documenting history) lib bdg $22 (7 and up)   **330.9**
  1. Industrial revolution
  ISBN 0-531-14609-X   LC 00-51347
  First published 2000 in the United Kingdom
  This history of the Industrial Revolution cites primary sources such as newspaper accounts, letters, government documents and individuals' commentary, and summarizes the global effects of industrialization in the 20th century
  "Economic history is well defined, and the role of industrialization comes alive within the short but detailed text. . . . Textual aids and an abundance of identified black-and-white and color art reproductions and useful maps accompany the narrative. . . . This title is a solid resource for quick reference." SLJ

330.973 United States--Economic conditions

The **Industrial** revolution: opposing viewpoints; William Dudley, editor. Greenhaven Press 1998 282p il (American history series) lib bdg $33.70; pa $22.45 (7 and up)   **330.973**
  1. Industrial revolution 2. United States—Economic conditions
  ISBN 1-56510-707-1 (lib bdg); 1-56510-706-3 (pa)
                       LC 97-48274

The Industrial revolution: opposing view-points—*Continued*

"This anthology traces the evolution of the United States from a collection of small agricultural colonies to an industrial giant—a development that radically changed how Americans worked and lived. The views of industrialists, labor organizers, and social critics of industrialism are featured." Publisher's note

Includes bibliographical references

331.2 Conditions of employment

Woog, Adam, 1953-
A sweatshop during the industrial revolution. Lucent Bks. 2003 112p il (Working life) lib bdg $21.96   **331.2**
1. Labor—United States 2. Industrial revolution 3. United States—Economic Conditions—1865-1918 4. United States—Social conditions
ISBN 1-59018-179-4   LC 2002-5162
Contents: Who worked in sweatshops?; Daily life in a sweatshop; Dangers in the sweatshop; Life outside the sweatshop; The role of organized labor; The reformers and the sweatshops

This "gives information on the evolving technology of . . . [the Industrial Revolution], how both gender and race were factors in the workaday world, the role of organized labor, and the reformers who were instrumental in helping to improve working conditions. Frequent boxed excerpts from newspaper articles and quotes add authenticity. Students will find plenty of research material in [this title]." SLJ

Includes bibliographical references

331.3 Workers by age group

Bartoletti, Susan Campbell, 1958-
Growing up in coal country. Houghton Mifflin 1996 127p il $17; pa $7.95 (5 and up)
    331.3
1. Child labor 2. Coal mines and mining
ISBN 0-395-77847-6; 0-395-97914-5 (pa)
    LC 96-3142
This is an "account of working and living conditions in Pennsylvania coal towns. The first half of the volume details various duties in the mines, from jobs performed by the youngest boys to the tasks of adult miners, while the second half describes the company village, common customs and recreational activities, and the accidents and diseases that frequently beset the workers." Horn Book

"With compelling black-and-white photographs of children at work in the coal mines of northeastern Pennsylvania about 100 years ago, this handsome, spacious photo-essay will draw browsers as well as students doing research on labor and immigrant history." Booklist

Includes bibliographical references

Freedman, Russell
Kids at work; Lewis Hine and the crusade against child labor; with photographs by Lewis Hine. Clarion Bks. 1994 104p il $20; pa $9.95 (5 and up)
    331.3
1. Hine, Lewis Wickes, 1874-1940 2. Child labor
ISBN 0-395-58703-4; 0-395-79726-8 (pa)
    LC 93-5989
"Using the photographer's work throughout, Freedman provides a documentary account of child labor in America during the early 1900s and the role Lewis Hine played in the crusade against it. He offers a look at the man behind the camera, his involvement with the National Child Labor Committee, and the dangers he faced trying to document unjust labor conditions." SLJ

Freedman "does an outstanding job of integrating historical photographs with meticulously researched and highly readable prose." Publ Wkly

Includes bibliographical references

Kuklin, Susan
Iqbal Masih and the crusaders against child slavery. Holt & Co. 1998 133p il $18.95 (7 and up)
    331.3
1. Masih, Iqbal, d. 1995 2. Child labor
ISBN 0-8050-5459-6   LC 98-5100
An account of the former Pakistani child labor activist whose life and unexplained murder has brought to the attention of the world the evil of child bondage

"Kuklin's thorough research makes this an excellent resource for anyone interested in child welfare issues. The names, addresses, and Web sites of many child labor information sources are provided, along with how to contact various activists groups and heads of state. . . . This book belongs in every library." Voice Youth Advocates

Includes glossary and bibliographical references

Parker, David L., 1951-
Stolen dreams; portraits of working children; by David L. Parker with Lee Engfer and Robert Conrow; photographs by David L. Parker. Lerner Publs. 1998 112p il map lib bdg $19.93
    331.3
1. Child labor
ISBN 0-8225-2960-2   LC 97-4939
Photographs and text document working children especially in Nepal, India, Bangladesh, and Mexico. Includes a chapter on Iqbal Masih, the child labor activist from Pakistan

"This hard-hitting exploration, set in a handsome volume, is a sobering reflection on contemporary childhood." Horn Book Guide

Includes bibliographical references

Springer, Jane
Listen to us; the world's working children. Douglas & McIntyre; distributed by Publishers Group West 1997 96p il $24.95; pa $16.95 (7 and up)
    331.3
1. Child labor
ISBN 0-88899-291-2; 0-88899-307-2 (pa)
This "photo-essay looks at the hazardous work children do in developing and industrialized countries, in ag-

Springer, Jane—*Continued*
riculture, industry, the home, the military, on the street, and in sex work. . . . There are easy-to-read sidebars, charts, and maps, but it is the personal accounts that have the most authority. The pictures of small brickmakers, garbage pickers, migrant workers, and bonded laborers are heartbreaking, and the voices are authentic." Booklist

Includes glossary and bibliographical references

331.4 Women workers

Colman, Penny
Rosie the riveter; women working on the home front in World War II. Crown 1995 120p il hardcover o.p. paperback available $10.99 (5 and up)   **331.4**
1. Women—Employment 2. World War, 1939-1945—United States
ISBN 0-517-59791-8 (pa)   LC 94-3614
This is an account of women's employment in wartime industry during the Second World War. "Colman looks at the jobs women took, the impact women had on the workplace, and what happened to working women at war's end. . . . {She also discusses} the public relations campaign that not only 'wooed' women into the workplace, but also sought to change firmly entrenched attitudes about women's role in society." Booklist
"A thoughtfully prepared look at women's history and wartime society, this dynamic book is characterized by extensive research." Horn Book
Includes bibliographical references

Dash, Joan
We shall not be moved; the women's factory strike of 1909. Scholastic 1996 165p il hardcover o.p. paperback available $5.99 (7 and up)   **331.4**
1. Women—Employment 2. Labor unions 3. Strikes
ISBN 0-590-48410-9 (pa)   LC 95-19404
Describes the conditions that gave rise to efforts to secure better working conditions for the women working in the garment industry in early twentieth-century New York and led to the formation of the Women's Trade Union League and the first women's strike in 1909
"Dash brings a novelist's skill to her descriptions of Lower East Side streets, and she conveys the general excitement of the movement by focusing on key individuals, memorably presenting them as impassioned agents for social change." Publ Wkly
Includes bibliographical references

331.5 Special categories of workers other than by age or sex

Ancona, George, 1929-
Harvest. Marshall Cavendish 2001 48p il lib bdg $15.95 (4 and up)   **331.5**
1. Agricultural laborers 2. Migrant labor 3. Mexicans—United States
ISBN 0-7614-5086-6   LC 2001-17497

"This photo-documentary focuses on the lives and work of Mexican migrant workers as they pick various crops on the West coast." SLJ
"Ancona puts a face on Mexican migrant workers and uses their own words to explain their lives, also including a great deal of information about the crops they pick. . . . Ancona's photos are insightful, with scenes and subjects deftly chosen and shot." Booklist

Atkin, S. Beth
Voices from the fields; children of migrant farmworkers tell their stories; interviews and photographs by S. Beth Atkin. Little, Brown 1993 96p il $18.95; pa $13.99 (5 and up)   **331.5**
1. Migrant labor 2. Agricultural laborers 3. Mexican Americans 4. Children's writings
ISBN 0-316-05633-2; 0-316-05620-0 (pa)
                                          LC 92-32248
"Joy Street books"
Photographs, poems in Spanish and English, and interviews with children reveal the hardships and hopes of Mexican American migrant farm workers and their families
"The Spanish is accurate, the English expressive, and the whole is a thoughtful tribute to the migrant experience. The black-and-white photographs are crisp and clear, frequently transcending the representational to achieve art." SLJ
Includes bibliographical references

331.7 Labor by industry and occupation

Barter, James, 1946-
A worker on the transcontinental railroad. Lucent Bks. 2003 112p il map (Working life) $27.45   **331.7**
1. Railroad engineering 2. Railroads—History
ISBN 1-59018-247-2   LC 2002-9883
This presents a history of the construction of the Union Pacific and Central Pacific railroads focusing on the lives and labor of the construction workers
Includes bibliographical references

Career discovery encyclopedia. 5th ed. Ferguson 2003 8v il set $175   **331.7**
1. Vocational guidance 2. Occupations
ISBN 0-8160-5469-X   LC 2003-616322
First published 1990
Contents: 1. Accountants; Border patrol officers; 2. Botanists; Dental laboratory technicians; 3. Dentists; Furniture manufacturing workers; 4. Gaming workers; landscape architects; 5. Landscapers; Nurse assistants; 6. Nurse practitioners; Printing Press operators; 7. Private investigators; Sports facility designers; 8. Sports facility managers; Zoologists
Presents articles describing over 650 jobs or career fields, discussing personal, educational, and professional requirements; ways of exploring the career; salary statistics; job outlook; and how to obtain more information about the career
This is a "reliable, succinct source." SLJ

The **Encyclopedia** of careers and vocational guidance. Ferguson, J.G. 4v il set $199.95

331.7

1. Occupations 2. Vocational guidance

First published 1967. (12th edition 2002) Periodically revised. Editors vary

The first volume of this "reference provides articles on career preparation, the job search process, and industries, the remaining three volumes offer lengthy essays on . . . occupations arranged within . . . industry fields." Libr J

Heading out; the start of some splendid careers; edited by Gloria Kamen. Bloomsbury Pub. 2003 236p $16.95 (7 and up)   **331.7**

1. Vocational guidance 2. Occupations

ISBN 1-58234-787-5   LC 2002-19113

Excerpts from the writings of famous and successful artists, athletes, writers, political activists, and scientists reveal the defining moment that led each to make a career decision

"The 24 contributors include a wide range, from Sidney Poitier, Beverly Sills, and Boris Yeltsin to Katherine Paterson, Julia Alvarez, Lance Armstrong, and Sammy Sosa. . . . The anthology provides insight and inspiration for teens." Booklist

Includes bibliographical references

Unger, Harlow G., 1931-

But what if I don't want to go to college? a guide to success through alternative education. rev ed. Facts on File 1998 216p il $30; pa $21.55 (7 and up)   **331.7**

1. Occupational training 2. Vocational education 3. Vocational guidance

ISBN 0-8160-3793-0; 0-8160-3861-9 (pa)

LC 97-50278

First published 1992

The author describes opportunities available to young adults through alternative and vocational education, discussing the various positions available, the minimum education requirements needed to land the job and positions available for youth with special skills and abilities

United States. Bureau of Labor Statistics

Occupational outlook handbook. U.S. Govt. Ptg. Office il $57; pa $53   **331.7**

1. Occupations 2. Vocational guidance

Also available Occupational outlook handbook and Career guide to industries on CD-ROM

Biennial. First published 1949. Supplemented by Occupational Outlook Quarterly, subscription $15

"Gives information on employment trends and outlook in more than 800 occupations. Indicates nature of work, qualifications, earnings and working conditions, how to enter, where to go for more information, etc." Guide to Ref Books. 11th edition

Young person's occupational outlook handbook. 5th ed. Jist Works 2005 319p il $19.95

331.7

1. Occupations 2. Vocational guidance

ISBN 1-593-57125-9   LC 2004-13091

This "career reference includes 277 jobs employing 88 percent of the workforce. . . . Each entry includes a short description of duties and working conditions; suggested academic preparation; hands-on activites simulating actual job aspects; related personal habits and preferences or sources for further investigation; and additional related jobs. . . . The book is a strong starting point for student research." Voice Youth Advocates

331.8   Labor unions and labor-management relations

Bartoletti, Susan Campbell, 1958-

Kids on strike! Houghton Mifflin 1999 208p il $20; pa $8.95 (5 and up)   **331.8**

1. Jones, Mother, 1830-1930 2. Strikes 3. Child labor

ISBN 0-395-88892-1; 0-618-36923-6 (pa)

LC 98-50575

Describes the conditions and treatment that drove workers, including many children, to various strikes, from the mill workers strikes in 1828 and 1836 and the coal strikes at the turn of the century to the work of Mother Jones on behalf of child workers

"This well-researched and well-illustrated account creates a vivid portrait of the working conditions of many American children in the 19th and early 20th centuries." SLJ

Includes bibliographical references

332.024   Personal finance

Godfrey, Neale S.

Neale S. Godfrey's ultimate kids' money book; illustrated by Randy Verougstraete. Simon & Schuster Bks. for Young Readers 1998 122p il $19 (5 and up)   **332.024**

1. Personal finance 2. Money

ISBN 0-689-81717-7   LC 97-35433

Provides an overview of economics and money, including earning, spending, saving, checks and credit cards, banks, and the history of money

"Facts, fables, advice, strategies, games, history, vocabulary, and more are energetically packaged with cartoon art, photos, and archival documents in this exciting treatment of money and economics for kids. The eye-catching pages playfully combine bold colors and varied sizes of print with lighthearted illustrations and commendably cogent text." Booklist

Includes glossary

Menhard, Francha Roffe

Teen consumer smarts; shop, save, and steer clear of scams. Enslow Pubs. 2002 64p il (Teen issues) lib bdg $22.60   **332.024**

1. Consumer education

ISBN 0-7660-1667-6   LC 2001-3675

Provides advice on developing good financial and consumer skills

This "is a basic primer that may well lead interested teens to seek out further information on investment or financial management." SLJ

Includes glossary and bibliographical references

332.4 Money

Cribb, Joe
Money; written by Joe Cribb. rev ed. DK Pub. 2005 72p il (DK eyewitness books) $15.99; lib bdg $19.99 (4 and up)   **332.4**
1. Money
ISBN 0-7566-1389-2; 0-7566-1398-1 (lib bdg)
First published 1990 by Knopf
Examines, in text and photographs, the symbolic and material meaning of money, from shekels, shells, and beads to gold, silver, checks, and credit cards. Also discusses how coins and banknotes are made, the value of money during wartime, and how to collect coins

332.6 Investment

Blumenthal, Karen
Six days in October; the stock market crash of 1929. Atheneum Bks. for Young Readers 2002 156p il $17.95 (7 and up)   **332.6**
1. New York Stock Exchange, Inc. 2. Great Depression, 1929-1939 3. United States—Economic conditions—1919-1933
ISBN 0-689-84276-7   LC 2001-46360
"A Wall Street Journal book"
A comprehensive review of the events, personalities, and mistakes behind the Stock Market Crash of 1929, featuring photographs, newspaper articles, and cartoons of the day
"This fast-paced, gripping . . . account of the market crash of October 1929 puts a human face on the crisis." Publ Wkly
Includes bibliographical references

Liebowitz, Jay
Wall Street wizard; sound ideas from a savvy teen investor. Simon & Schuster Bks. for Young Readers 2000 143p $16   **332.6**
1. Investments 2. Personal finance
ISBN 0-689-83401-2   LC 00-32931
"After briefly introducing the basic concepts of investment, stocks, markets, and brokerages, Liebowitz gives investment tips and financial-planning guidance. . . . The tone is sufficiently insouciant to attract teen readers, and the use of language is fairly colorful and engaging. The author's practical attitude and constant suggestions to seek more information from reliable sources allow him to avoid oversimplification of complex topics." SLJ

McGowan, Eileen Nixon
Stock market smart; [by] Eileen Nixon McGowan & Nancy Lagow Dumas. Millbrook Press 2002 64p lib bdg $23.90   **332.6**
1. Investments 2. Stocks
ISBN 0-7613-2113-6   LC 2001-32694
"Short chapters in a question-and-answer format discuss 'Setting Up a Portfolio,' 'Buying and Selling Stocks,' 'Piggy Banks to Government Bonds,' and other related topics. . . . Clear, color photos, varied fonts in different colors, and plenty of white space result in an attractive presentation. This well-organized book will be welcome in collections needing material on the topic." SLJ
Includes glossary and bibliographical references

333.7 Land, recreational and wilderness areas, energy

Gallant, Roy A.
Resources; nature's riches. Benchmark Bks. 2002 c2003 80p il (Earthworks) lib bdg $28.50   **333.7**
1. Natural resources—Management 2. Conservation of natural resources
ISBN 0-7614-1369-3   LC 2002-911
Describes the importance of Earth's natural resources and discusses how their misuse and depletion endanger life on the planet
Includes glossary and bibliographical references

Macmillan encyclopedia of the environment; general editor, Stephen R. Kellert; associate editors, Matthew Black, Richard Haley. Macmillan Lib. Ref. USA 1997 6v il maps set $445   **333.7**
1. Environmental protection—Encyclopedias
ISBN 0-02-897381-X   LC 96-29045
"These volumes provide a snapshot of the current state of the environment and human efforts to exploit or protect it. Types of pollution, environmental law and regulation, and the interaction of human populations with the environment are just some of the topics covered in this excellent set. Useful appendixes list major environmental legislation, organizations, and U.S. governmental agencies with environmental responsibilities, while outstanding indexing facilitates access. Lavishly illustrated, the encyclopedia will appeal to students and laypersons interested in environmental topics, legislation, ecology, and evolution." Am Libr

Netzley, Patricia D.
Issues in the environment. Lucent Bks. 1998 95p il (Contemporary issues) lib bdg $27.45 (7 and up)   **333.7**
1. Environmental protection 2. Environmental policy—United States
ISBN 1-56006-475-7   LC 97-25894
"This book looks at our government's environmental policies regarding the protection of endangered species, management of federal wilderness areas, and the disposal of garbage. . . . Netzley concludes with a short discussion of the ozone layer. . . . This title could be useful for balance and support in libraries serving students researching these controversial questions." SLJ
Includes bibliographical references

333.71 General topics of natural resources and energy

Global resources: opposing viewpoints; Helen Cothran, book editor. Greenhaven Press 2004 224p il lib bdg $34.95; pa $23.70
333.71
1. Natural resources—Management 2. Conservation of natural resources
ISBN 0-7377-1681-9 (lib bdg); 0-7377-1682-7 (pa)
LC 2002-41629
"Opposing viewpoints series"
"In this volume, scientists, activists, and policy makers debate what resources are being threatened and the best ways to protect them." Publisher's note

333.72 Conservation and protection

Conserving the environment; Laura K. Egendorf, book editor. Greenhaven Press 1999 208p (Current controversies) lib bdg $33.70; pa $22.45 (7 and up) **333.72**
1. Environmental protection 2. Biological diversity 3. Pollution
ISBN 1-56510-951-1 (lib bdg); 1-56510-950-3 (pa)
LC 98-35009
This offers opposing viewpoints on such issues as whether or not an environmental crisis exists, preserving biodiversity, reducing pollution, and whether or not free-market solutions are effective in protecting the environment
Includes bibliographical references

Malaspina, Ann, 1957-
Saving the American wilderness. Lucent Bks. 1999 96p il (Our endangered planet) lib bdg $28.70 **333.72**
1. Wilderness areas 2. Conservation of natural resources
ISBN 1-56006-505-2 LC 98-31959
Discusses saving the American wilderness, including preservation and conservation, environmental activism, recreation in the wilderness, and the future of wilderness management
Includes bibliographical references

333.79 Energy

Bowden, Rob
Energy; by Rob Bowden. KidHaven Press 2004 48p (Sustainable world) $23.70 (5 and up)
333.79
1. Renewable energy resources 2. Energy development
ISBN 0-7377-1897-8 LC 2003-52953
This "briefly introduces various forms of sustainable energy - water, wind, sun, geothermal sources - and takes a look at where sustainable technology is headed. . . . Bowden writes with admirable simplicity about complicated subjects, and he's careful to separate facts from opinions when he quotes others. [This book in-

cludes] excellent color photos . . . and gripping statistics." Booklist
Includes glossary and bibliographical references

Juettner, Bonnie, 1968-
Energy; by Bonnie Juettner. KidHaven Press 2004 48p il map (Our environment) $23.70 (5 and up) **333.79**
1. Energy resources
ISBN 0-7377-1821-8 LC 2003-876
Contents: What does the world use for energy?; How is energy managed?; Are we running out of energy?; What will happen in the future?
"The liberal use of vibrant colors, the inclusion of a photograph or diagram on most pages, and the generous print size will appeal to reluctant readers. [This title] will help students examine cause and effect (and possible solutions), and challenge them to live green." SLJ
Includes glossary and bibliographical references

333.91 Water and lands adjoining bodies of water

Vogel, Carole Garbuny
Human impact; Carole G. Vogel. F. Watts 2003 95p il (Restless sea) $29.59; pa $12.95 (5 and up)
333.91
1. Marine pollution 2. Human influence on nature
ISBN 0-531-12323-5; 0-531-16680-5 (pa)
LC 2003-5301
Contents: Troubled waters; Sea sick; Too many fishermen; The impact of global warming; The human footprint
This "provides a detailed description of the results of population growth, global warming, and the development of coastal areas. The devastation to marine life resulting from occurrences such as oil spills and the dead zones caused by oxygen-depleted water are described through both heart-wrenching photographs and informative text." SLJ
Includes bibliographical references

333.95 Biological resources

The **Atlas** of endangered species; editor, John A. Burton; pictures supplied by Bruce Coleman Ltd. 2nd ed. Macmillan Lib. Ref. USA 1999 272p il maps lib bdg $140 **333.95**
1. Endangered species 2. Wildlife conservation 3. Environmental protection
ISBN 0-02-865034-4 LC 98-44328
First published 1991
Describes the various animals and plants throughout the world whose survival is being threatened and the steps being taken to save them from extinction
Includes bibliographical references

Bortolotti, Dan
Tiger rescue; changing the future for endangered wildlife. Firefly 2003 64p il map lib bdg $19.95; pa $9.95 (4 and up) **333.95**

Bortolotti, Dan—*Continued*
1. Tigers 2. Wildlife conservation
ISBN 1-55297-599-1 (lib bdg); 1-55297-558-4 (pa)
This describes the tiger's "natural habitat, habits,
physiology, and behavior in captivity. [It also includes]
a time line of conservation efforts, profiles of conservationists in the field, and forecasts of the animals' future.
Throughout, the author makes clear the factors that can
threaten animal populations, and discusses human attitudes toward the animals throughout history. . . . Written in accessible, lively language and nicely illustrated
with exciting color photos, [this] will be useful for reports and browsing." Booklist

Burnie, David
Endangered planet; David Burnie. 1st ed.
Kingfisher 2004 63p il (Kingfisher knowledge)
$11.95 (5 and up) **333.95**
1. Human influence on nature 2. Environmental degradation
ISBN 0-7534-5776-8 LC 2004-478
This "explores the delicate web of natural cycles that
supports millions of species . . . and reveals how our
ever-growing demand for food, fuel, and living space
threatens to damage Earth's habitats beyond repair." Publisher's note
"Children will be immediately drawn to the high-
quality graphics artfully laid out on brightly colored
spreads. . . . The [narrative is] logically arranged into
three chapters, each containing a broad overview as well
as more detailed subtopics." SLJ
Includes glossary

Endangered animals. Grolier Educ. 2002 10v il
maps set $469 **333.95**
1. Endangered species
ISBN 0-7172-5584-0 LC 00-69134
Contents: v1 What is an endangered animal?; v2 Ad-
dax - blackbuck; v3 Boa, Jamaican - danio, barred; v4
Darter, Watercress - frog, gastric-brooding; v5 Frog,
green and golden bell - kestrel, lesser; v6 Kestrel, Mauri-
tius - Mulgara; v7 Murrelet, Japanese - Pupfish, Devil's
Hole; v8 Pygmy-possum, mountain - Siskin, red; v9
Skink, pygmy blue-tongued - tragopan, Temminck's; v10
Tree-kangaroo, Goodfellow's - zebra, mountain
This reference "provides information for over 400 extinct or threatened animals all over the world, including
all the major animal groups. . . . This set has much to
recommend it. The writing is solidly researched, highly
accessible, and imbued with a clearness of purpose. The
textual information is strengthened by a copious amount
of supplementary material and further enhanced by the
exquisitely beautiful photography." Booklist

Gallant, Roy A.
The wonders of biodiversity. Benchmark Bks.
2003 80p il maps (Story of science) lib bdg
$19.95 (5 and up) **333.95**
1. Biological diversity
ISBN 0-7614-1427-4 LC 2002-916
Partial contents: Beetles, bacteria, and biodiversity;
Critters galore, what they are; Critters galore, where they
live; Major ecosystems; Tragedy of the rain forests; Gaia

Discusses the many different life forms that have existed on Earth, their importance, and how they have
changed over time
"Readers will find accurate, readable explanations for
the scientific principles here addressed. . . . Up-to-date
controversies and predictions conclude the [book] . . . illustrated with well-captioned photos." Horn Book Guide
Includes glossary and bibliographical references

Patent, Dorothy Hinshaw
Biodiversity; photographs by William Muñoz.
Clarion Bks. 1996 109p il $18; pa $7.95 (5 and
up) **333.95**
1. Biological diversity 2. Nature conservation
ISBN 0-395-68704-7; 0-618-31514-4 (pa)
LC 95-49982
Provides a global perspective on environmental issues
while demonstrating the concept which encompasses the
many forms of life on earth and their interdependence on
one another for survival
"Patent imbues her lucid scientific discussion with
many examples of her personal experience both in childhood and as an adult, and she employs a wide array of
examples from many parts of the world to demonstrate
current problems and scientific and conservation activity.
Illustrated with plentiful and helpful photos." Horn Book
Includes glossary

Salmansohn, Pete, 1947-
Saving birds; heroes around the world; [by] Pete
Salmansohn and Stephen W. Kress. Tilbury House
2003 39p il $16.95 (5 and up) **333.95**
1. Birds—Protection 2. Wildlife conservation
3. Endangered species
ISBN 0-88448-237-5 LC 2002-6710
Profiles adults and children working in six habitats
around the world to save wild birds, some of which are
on the brink of extinction.
"As a teaching aid, this volume is an exceptional supplement. The six articles relating the heroic rescue of the
endangered birds are accurate and enhanced by appropriate color photographs." Sci Books Films

Swinburne, Stephen R.
Once a wolf; how wildlife biologists fought to
bring back the gray wolf; with photographs by Jim
Brandenburg. Houghton Mifflin 1999 48p il $16 (4
and up) **333.95**
1. Wolves 2. Wildlife conservation
ISBN 0-395-89827-7 LC 98-16865
Surveys the history of the troubled relationship between wolves and humans, examines the view that these
predators are a valuable part of the ecosystem, and describes the conservation movement to restore them to the
wild
The "crisp color photographs showing wolves in their
natural environment are exceptional. Swinburne's text
adds suspense and excitement to the story. . . . This is
an involving study . . . which makes fascinating reading." Bull Cent Child Books
Includes bibliographical references

Thomas, Peggy

Big cat conservation. 21st Cent. Bks. (Brookfield) 2000 64p il (Science of saving animals) lib bdg $25.90 **333.95**

1. Wild cats 2. Wildlife conservation

ISBN 0-7613-3231-6   LC 99-37434

Examines how scientists and zoos around the world are managing wild and captive big cats like panthers, cheetahs, tigers, and lions by radio tracking, scat examination, zoo breeding programs, and habitat conservation

This offers "well-written {text}; open, easy-to-read page design; and attractive, good-quality, full-color photographs of wildlife and scientists conducting fieldwork." SLJ

Includes bibliographical references

Bird alert. 21st Cent. Bks. (Brookfield) 2000 64p il (Science of saving animals) lib bdg $25.90 **333.95**

1. Birds 2. Wildlife conservation

ISBN 0-7613-1457-1   LC 00-25028

Surveys programs and individuals dedicated to preserving birds and bird habitats.

"The text is highly readable. . . . Good-quality, color photographs are well integrated with text." SLJ

Includes glossary and bibliographical references

Turner, Pamela S.

Gorilla doctors; saving endangered great apes. Houghton Mifflin 2005 64p il map (Scientists in the field) $17 (5 and up) **333.95**

1. Gorillas 2. Wildlife conservation

ISBN 0-618-44555-2   LC 2004-9213

This describes The Mountain Gorilla Veterinary Project which works to save the mountain gorilla population in Rwanda and Uganda.

This offers "readable text . . . . accompanied by striking, full-color photographs." SLJ

Includes bibliographical references

336.3 Public debt and expenditure

Garlake, Teresa

Global debt. Raintree 2003 64p il (21st century debates) lib bdg $28.56 (7 and up) **336.3**

1. Public debts 2. Developing countries—Economic conditions

ISBN 0-7398-6035-6   LC 2002-15214

Contents: What is debt?; How did the debt problem start?; The effects of debt on education; The effects of debt on health; The debt boomerang; Is aid the answer?; Debt and trade; Debt relief

"Garlake describes the relationship between global debt and the quality of life of ordinary people. . . . [She] examines the issues involved in giving aid to debt-ridden countries, and concludes with a look to the future. [The title has] many well-placed sidebars with facts, debates, and viewpoints [and] . . . good-quality color photographs." SLJ

Includes bibliographical references

337 International economics

January, Brendan, 1972-

Globalize it! the stories of the IMF, the World Bank, the WTO, and those who protest. Twenty-First Century Books 2003 143p il map lib bdg $26.90 (7 and up) **337**

1. World Trade Organization 2. World Bank 3. International Monetary Fund 4. Globalization

ISBN 0-7613-2417-8   LC 2002-152509

Contents: The battle of Seattle; A world order : the foundations of globalization; I don't want to be like Mike; Globalization is good for the globe ; Killing the world to save it?; Whose culture?; Protest; The IMF faces a meltdown : economic crisis in Mexico, Russia, and Asia; Mistakes and resolve; A new world

"Following a history of globalization, {the author} presents the arguments for and against this trend, taking stories from the headlines . . . to illustrate the passions surrounding the subject. . . . {The book covers} issues such as the Asian monetary crisis, the AIDS crisis, and an analysis of September 11." SLJ

"The clear writing, up-to-date primary sources, photographs, and maps provide a comprehensible look at the specialized procedures and terminology that govern the complicated world of economics, finance, and trade." Bull Cent Child Books

Includes bibliographical references

338 Production

McCormick, Anita Louise

The industrial revolution in American history. Enslow Pubs. 1998 128p il (In American history) lib bdg $26.60 **338**

1. Industrial revolution

ISBN 0-89490-985-1   LC 97-23479

Traces the history of the industrial revolution from its roots in eighteenth-century England, through its beginnings in the United States, to its decline in the twentieth-century

"This book competently surveys the topic. . . . The illustrations include black-and-white reproductions of period photos, portraits, and documents." Booklist

Includes bibliographical references

338.2 Mineral industries

Gunderson, Cory Gideon

The need for oil; [by] Cory Gunderson. Abdo Pub 2004 48p il map (World in conflict, Middle East) $25.65 **338.2**

1. Petroleum industry 2. World politics—1991- 3. Middle East—Politics and government

ISBN 1-591-97417-8   LC 2003-44376

Contents: An overview of oil; Who has oil?; Who needs oil?; Organization of Petroleum Exporting Countries (OPEC); Middle East conflicts and oil; The future of oil

Gunderson, Cory Gideon—*Continued*
Examines the importance of oil, how it is formed and obtained, the dependence of industrialized nations on oil, and why it has become a bargaining chip between Middle Eastern and Western nations.

This title offers "current, factual information in an eye-catching, hi/lo format. Although chapters and sentences are brief, the [text is] politically balanced. Maps and photographs are clear, colorful, and up-to-date." SLJ
Includes glossary and bibliographical references

338.5 General production economics

Fremon, David K.
The Great Depression in American history. Enslow Pubs. 1997 128p il (In American history) lib bdg $26.60 **338.5**
1. Great Depression, 1929-1939 2. United States—Economic conditions—1933-1945
ISBN 0-89490-881-2 LC 96-34289
Describes the history surrounding the Great Depression, highlighting the causes and key figures
Includes bibliographical references

341.23 United Nations

Ross, Stewart
The United Nations. Heinemann Lib. 2003 48p il maps (20th-century perspectives) lib bdg $25.64 **341.23**
1. United Nations
ISBN 1-4034-0152-7 LC 2002-4550
Contents: What is the United Nations?; The League of Nations; A new beginning; A world parliament; Struggling secretaries; International law and justice; The Security Council; Working for peace; Enforcement; The blue helmets; The Gulf War; Disarmament and arms limitation; Closing the economic gap; World health; Emergency!; Human rights; The rights of women; The environment; Kyoto; Past and future; Timeline
Discusses the establishment of the United Nations, its function in preventing war and eliminating poverty, and its role in various international conflicts
This is a "timely overview. . . . Black-and-white and clear color photographs of the U.N. peacekeeping troops and relief workers throughout its history will provide students with a sense of those places in which the organization has been and is an active presence." SLJ
Includes glossary and bibliographical references

342 Constitutional and administrative law

Alonso, Karen
Schenck v. United States; restrictions on free speech. Enslow Pubs. 1999 128p il (Landmark Supreme Court cases) lib bdg $26.60 (7 and up) **342**
1. Schenck, Charles 2. Freedom of speech
ISBN 0-7660-1089-9 LC 98-34010

Describes the landmark case which limited free speech in cases of "clear and present danger" to national security, as well as later cases which continued working out the limits of freedom of speech
Includes glossary and bibliographical references

Anderson, Wayne, 1966-
Plessy v. Ferguson; legalizing segregation. Rosen Pub. Group 2004 64p il (Supreme Court cases through primary sources) lib bdg $29.25 **342**
1. Plessy, Homer 2. Discrimination in public accommodations 3. Segregation—Law and legislation 4. United States—Race relations
ISBN 0-8239-4011-X LC 2002-154574
Contents: The social environment; A ride into history; The case for Plessy; The case for Louisiana; The decision; The aftermath
This examines the Supreme Court case that challenged a state's right to allow separate but equal railroad accommodations for different races.
This "deserves a place in every library. . . . Copious and well-chosen primary source documents give extra value to this [book]. . . . Each document adds human drama to the already engaging text." Lib Media Connect
Includes glossary and bibliographical references

Cate, Fred H.
The Internet and the First Amendment; schools and sexually explicit expression. Phi Delta Kappa Educ. Foundation 1998 103p pa $10.95 **342**
1. Freedom of speech 2. Internet 3. Computer networks
ISBN 0-87367-398-0 LC 97-75653
The author provides "a legal history of First Amendment rights, particularly as pertaining to the Internet and minors. He identifies the legal issues surrounding minors' access to sexually explicit material and discusses the ramifications of controlling and regulating that access, citing many court rulings and statutes." SLJ
Includes bibliographical references

Collier, Christopher, 1930-
Creating the Constitution, 1787; {by} Christopher Collier, James Lincoln Collier. Benchmark Bks. (Tarrytown) 1999 95p il map (Drama of American history) lib bdg $31.36 **342**
1. United States. Constitutional Convention (1787) 2. Constitutional history—United States 3. United States—Politics and government—1783-1809
ISBN 0-7614-0776-6 LC 97-1788
Examines the events and personalities involved in creating the Constitution of the United States in 1787, a document which has been the foundation of American democracy for over 200 years
"Most spreads are brightened by at least one illustration, a painting or print from the period, a photo of a site or artifact, or a map. Useful for school reports and surprisingly readable." Booklist
Includes bibliographical references

The **Constitution** and its amendments; Roger K. Newman, editor in chief. Macmillan Lib. Ref. USA 1998 4v set $415   **342**
1. United States. Constitution 2. Constitutional history—United States 3. Constitutional law—United States
ISBN 0-02-864858-7   LC 98-8570
Provides a chronological history of the Constitution's seven articles and twenty-seven amendments to date, placing them in the context of the social, political, and judicial events that formed them, and examining contemporary issues and court cases where constitutional interpretation plays a key role
"This will be a useful addition to school and public libraries serving students at the middle-school level and up." Booklist

The **Constitutional** Convention; Richard Haesly, book editor. Greenhaven Press 2002 240p il maps (History firsthand) lib bdg $34.95; pa $23.70 (7 and up)   **342**
1. Constitutional history—United States
ISBN 0-7377-1072-1 (lib bdg); 0-7377-1071-3 (pa)
    LC 2001-23832
This is a "study of the historical and political events that led up to the ratification of the U.S. Constitution. Using accounts and opinions by actual delegates and other prominent figures such as Patrick Henry and Thomas Jefferson, Haesly outlines the concepts of the Declaration of Independence, the Articles of Confederation, and the Constitution/Bill of Rights. The volume is enlivened by personal stories of those who lived through and influenced the events depicted, and includes discussions on slavery and the nature of the presidency. . . . Well suited for reports." SLJ
Includes bibliographical references

Farish, Leah
Tinker v. Des Moines; student protest. Enslow Pubs. 1997 128p il (Landmark Supreme Court cases) lib bdg $26.60 (7 and up)   **342**
1. Tinker, John Frederick 2. Des Moines Independent Community School District 3. Freedom of speech 4. Vietnam War, 1961-1975—Protest movements
ISBN 0-89490-859-6   LC 96-25704
Considers the landmark case that dealt with the rights of students to wear arm bands to protest U.S. involvement in the Vietnam War
Includes glossary and bibliographical references

Feinberg, Barbara Silberdick, 1938-
The Articles of Confederation; the first constitution of the United States. 21st Cent. Bks. (Brookfield) 2002 110p il maps lib bdg $24.90 (7 and up)   **342**
1. United States. Articles of Confederation 2. Constitutional history—United States 3. United States—Politics and government—1775-1783, Revolution
ISBN 0-7613-2114-4   LC 2001-27441
"Feinberg introduces the history and text of 'The Articles of Confederation and Perpetual Union,' the constitution that guided the U.S. government from 1776 to 1787.

. . . Attractively laid out, this solid choice includes many black-and-white illustrations, including portrait paintings, engravings, and maps." Booklist
Includes bibliographical references

The dictionary of the U.S. Constitution; preface by Jack N. Rakove. Watts 1999 214p il $33
    342
1. Constitutional law—United States—Dictionaries
ISBN 0-531-11570-4   LC 99-14775
"A Franklin Watts library edition"
Entries in this alphabetically arranged reference work "cover a variety of terms related to the U.S. Constitution; examples include Civil liberties; Executive branch; Federalist Papers; Habeas corpus, writ of; Pardons and reprieves; and Speech, freedom of. Most entries end with a list of see also references. A preface answering the question 'What is the Constitution?' begins the volume." Booklist
"This resource offers students readable, easily understood information for reports and general background knowledge." Libr J
Includes bibliographical references

Fireside, Harvey, 1929-
New York Times v. Sullivan; affirming freedom of the press. Enslow Pubs. 1999 128p il (Landmark Supreme Court cases) lib bdg $26.60 (7 and up)   **342**
1. Sullivan, L. B. 2. New York Times Company 3. Freedom of the press
ISBN 0-7660-1085-6   LC 98-36959
Describes the Supreme Court decision in the case of New York Times v. Sullivan, preventing public officials from receiving damages for false statements unless they can prove actual malice
Includes glossary and bibliographical references

Free speech; Scott Barbour, book editor. Greenhaven Press 2000 206p (Current controversies) lib bdg $33.70; pa $22.45 (7 and up)   **342**
1. Freedom of speech
ISBN 0-7377-0143-9 (lib bdg); 0-7377-0142-0 (pa)
    LC 99-29107
"Censorship, flag burning, pornography, and funding for the arts are covered from many points of view, giving readers a solid, usually enlightening look at why some individuals and groups become so angered by opposition to their opinions." Booklist
Includes bibliographical references

Freedman, Russell
In defense of liberty; the story of America's Bill of Rights. Holiday House 2003 196p il $24.95
    342
1. United States. Constitution. 1st-10th amendments 2. Civil rights
ISBN 0-8234-1585-6   LC 2002-191918
Describes the origins, applications of, and challenges to the ten amendments to the United States Constitution that comprise the Bill of Rights
"This excellent study of the continually evolving

Freedman, Russell—*Continued*
meaning and interpretation of the Bill of Rights . . . is
an essential purchase for all libraries." SLJ
Includes bibliographical references

Fridell, Ron, 1943-
Privacy vs. security; your rights in conflict; Ron
Fridell. Enslow Publishers 2004 128p il (Issues in
focus) lib bdg $26.60   **342**
1. Right of privacy
ISBN 0-7660-2161-0   LC 2003-14755
Contents: Privacy's widening scope; Watchers and lis-
teners; Searches and seizures; Intrusions and exposures;
Students: a special case; Privacy for sale; Privacy stolen;
Privacy and terrorism
This is an "overview of specific topics like searches
and seizures, credit-card fraud, identity theft, student rec-
ords, drug testing, medical records, and library records.
There are warnings about protecting personal informa-
tion, and case studies regarding challenges to students'
rights in high schools." SLJ
Includes glossary and bibliographical references

Gold, Susan Dudley, 1949-
The Pentagon papers; national security or the
right to know; by Susan Dudley Gold. Benchmark
Books 2004 144p il lib bdg $25.95   **342**
1. New York Times Company v. United States
2. Freedom of the press
ISBN 0-7614-1843-1   LC 2004-8583
Contents: The Pentagon study; The leak; Prior restraint : censorship versus censure; *The New York Times*
goes to press; *The Washington Post* : keeping up the momentum; Before the Supreme Court; The decision; Aftermath
An examination of the Supreme Court decision regarding the New York Times decision to publish articles
about United States government's "secret war" in Cambodia and Vietnam.
"The format of the [book] makes [it] easy to read and
understand. [A] valuable [resource] for reports." SLJ
Includes bibliographical references

Herda, D. J., 1948-
The Dred Scott case; slavery and citizenship.
Enslow Pubs. 1994 104p il (Landmark Supreme
Court cases) lib bdg $26.60 (7 and up)
                                              342
1. Scott, Dred, ca. 1795-1858 2. Slavery—United
States
ISBN 0-89490-460-4   LC 93-22402
This volume "examines the pivotal pre-Civil War case
in which a slave was denied his freedom and the Mis-
souri Compromise was deemed unconstitutional, and it
also shows the personal and historical consequences of
the Supreme Court decision." Booklist
Includes bibliographical references

New York Times v. United States; national
security and censorship. Enslow Pubs. 1994 104p
il (Landmark Supreme Court cases) lib bdg $26.60
(7 and up)   **342**
1. New York Times Company v. United States
2. Pentagon Papers 3. Freedom of the press
ISBN 0-89490-490-6   LC 93-32156
This examination of the conflict between the public's
right to information and the government's desire to maintain national security focuses on the New York Times
decision to publish articles about the United States government's "secret war" in Cambodia and Vietnam. The
author follows the case through the Supreme Court
Includes bibliographical references

Hudson, David L., 1969-
Gay rights; David L. Hudson, Jr. Chelsea House
2004 114p (Point-counterpoint) $37.50 (7 and up)
                                              342
1. Lesbians—Civil rights 2. Gay men—Civil rights
ISBN 0-7910-8094-3   LC 2004-13828
Contents: Point : same-sex couples have a fundamental right to marry; Counterpoint : marriage is between a
man and a woman; Point : gays and lesbians should not
face discrimination as parents; Counterpoint : states have
the power to protect children by giving preference to het-
erosexual parents; Point : employers should not be able
to discriminate against gays and lesbians; Counterpoint :
gays and lesbians don't need special treatment in the
workforce; Point : the military should end its discrimina-
tory policy toward gays and lesbians; Counterpoint : the
military can prohibit homosexual conduct in the military
"Gay marriage, adoption rights, workplace rights, and
service in the armed forces are all argued pro and con
in a clear, journalistic style. Both sides of an issue are
reinforced with sidebars of pertinent U.S. court case decisions and provocative questions. Well-organized footnotes and an index provide easy access to more specific
perspectives on each argument, and a section on 'Beginning Legal Research' is also included." SLJ
Includes bibliographical references

January, Brendan, 1972-
The Dred Scott decision. Children's Press 1998
30p il maps (Cornerstones of freedom) lib bdg
$19.50; pa $5.95   **342**
1. Scott, Dred, ca. 1795-1858 2. Slavery—United
States
ISBN 0-516-20833-0 (lib bdg); 0-516-26457-5 (pa)
                                       LC 97-11713
Places the events relating to the 1857 Supreme Court
decision regarding rights of slaves into the larger context
of the conflict about slavery among the states
"Those with an interest in the case will be captivated
by the account and researchers will find more than
enough information for a report." SLJ

Krull, Kathleen, 1952-
A kid's guide to America's Bill of Rights;
curfews, censorship, and the 100-pound giant;
illustrated by Anna DiVito. Avon Bks. 1999 226p
il $15.99 (4 and up)   **342**
  1. United States. Constitution. 1st-10th amendments
  2. Civil rights
  ISBN 0-380-97497-5   LC 99-17324
"After describing how the first 10 amendments came
to be added to the Constitution, the book considers each
one from a historical point of view, examining Supreme
Court cases and famous challenges, and explaining in
what ways each amendment applies to children and
teenagers. Anna Divito's cartoonlike drawings add a visually appealing touch." Booklist
  Includes bibliographical references

McKissack, Patricia C., 1944-
To establish justice; citizenship and the
Constitution; [by] Patricia McKissack and Arlene
Zarembka. Alfred A. Knopf 2004 154p il map
$18.95; lib bdg $22.99   **342**
  1. Discrimination—Law and legislation
  ISBN 0-679-89308-3; 0-679-99308-8 (lib bdg)
    LC 2003-27929
The authors "examine issues of justice and equality in
American history by focusing on the Supreme Court's
role in defining rights of minority groups and citizens.
. . .This book covers a broad spectrum of cases, and the
authors do a fine job of providing the history, background, and events surrounding each Supreme Court decision." SLJ

Moehn, Heather
The U.S. Constitution; a primary source
investigation into the fundamental law of the
United States. Rosen Primary Source 2003 144p il
map (Great American political documents) $26.50
    342
  1. Constitutional history—United States 2. United
States—Politics and government—1775-1783, Revolu-
tion
  ISBN 0-8239-3804-2   LC 2002-11223
  Contents: American constitutional experience prior to
1787; The Philadelphia Convention; The main issues;
The three branches of government; Ratification
  A historical review of the people, issues, and events
that led to the drafting and ratification of the United
States Constitution
  "The Constitution of the United States has been so
clearly explained here that even the most reluctant reader
will be caught up in the history. The reader almost feels
as if he or she was there in Philadelphia with the founding fathers. Historical illustrations add to the completeness of the book." Libr Media Connect
  Includes bibliographical references

Naden, Corinne J.
Dred Scott; person or property? [by] Corinne J.
Naden and Rose Blue. Benchmark Books 2004
128p il (Supreme Court milestones) lib bdg $25.95
(7 and up)   **342**
  1. Scott, Dred, ca. 1795-1858 2. Slavery—United
States
  ISBN 0-7614-1841-5   LC 2003-25568
  Contents: A slave asks for freedom; The way it was;
A case for judicial restraint; The "worst" decision; The
long, bloody path to justice
  The is an account of the 1857 Supreme Court decision
regarding Dred Scott, who sued for his freedom from
slavery
  The authors "sandwich a clear account of the case's
course, arguments, and participants between summaries
of prior and subsequent historical events and an analysis
of the decision's place in Supreme Court history. Illustrated with images of documents and oil portraits and
supplemented by boxed essays. " Booklist

Patrick, John J.
The Bill of Rights; a history in documents.
Oxford Univ. Press 2003 205p il map (Pages from
history) lib bdg $32.95 (7 and up)   **342**
  1. United States. Constitution. 1st-10th amendments
  2. Civil rights
  ISBN 0-19-510354-8   LC 2002-6294
  Contents: The roots of American rights; Rights revolu-
tion and in America; The birth of the Bill of Rights; The
Bill of Rights marginalized; Rights renewed and denied;
A resurgence of rights; Nationalization of the Bill of
Rights; Political cartoons on the right to bear arms; Con-
sensus and controversy
  Uses contemporary documents to explore the history
of the first ten amendments to the U.S. Constitution, the
British traditions on which they were based, and their
impact on American society
  "This attractive and informative volume will be a
valuable resource for most collections." SLJ
  Includes bibliographical references

Pendergast, Tom, 1964-
Constitutional amendments: from freedom of
speech to flag burning; [by] Tom Pendergast, Sara
Pendergast, and John Sousanis; Elizabeth Shaw
Grunow, editor. U.X.L 2001 3v set $165 (7 and
up)   **342**
  1. United States. Constitution. 1st-10th amendments
  2. Constitutional law—United States 3. Civil rights
  ISBN 0-7876-4865-5   LC 00-67236
  "Covering each of the 27 amendments, this 3-vol. resource provides the history and social context of the
amendment process. Entries range in length from 10 to
15 pages and begin with the full text of the amendment
followed by an essay on the social and political climate
that gave rise to its proposal." Publisher's note
  "Presentation is very clear. . . . This is definitely a
set that belongs in school and public libraries." Booklist
  Includes glossary and bibliographical references

Schleichert, Elizabeth, 1945-
The Thirteenth Amendment; ending slavery. Enslow Pubs. 1998 128p il (Constitution) lib bdg $19.95 (7 and up) **342**
1. Slavery—United States
ISBN 0-89490-923-1   LC 97-34082
Presents an overview of the history of slavery in the United States, its abolition by constitutional amendment in 1865, and the Reconstruction and its aftermath
"A title that will shed light on the efforts to reconcile past inequities in our government." SLJ
Includes bibliographical references

Sergis, Diana K.
Bush v. Gore; controversial presidential election case; Diana K. Sergis. Enslow Publishers 2003 128p il (Landmark Supreme Court cases) $26.60 **342**
1. Bush, George W. 2. Gore, Albert, Jr. 3. Presidents—United States—Election—2000
ISBN 0-7660-2095-9   LC 2002-154646
Contents: Building a case; Electing a president as set by the constitution; The road to the Supreme Court; The case for George W. Bush; The case for Al Gore; The decision; Where do we stand today?
An account of the Supreme Court decision which decided the outcome of the 2000 presidential election.
"Hewing closely to the legal aspects of the contest, the book nevertheless gives some of the atmosphere surrounding the decision, maintaining a balanced tone without avoiding the tough questions." Horn Book Guide
Includes bibliographical references

Steffens, Bradley
Censorship; by Bradley Steffens. Lucent Books 2004 112p il (Lucent overview series) $27.45 (7 and up) **342**
1. Censorship
ISBN 1-59018-187-5   LC 2004-10852
Discusses the history of censorship, what is and is not protected under the First Amendment, and regulations and standards for the Internet
"Interestingly written chapters are short but comprehensive. Well-chosen illustrations add visual interest and provide additional information." SLJ
Includes bibliographical references

Vile, John R.
The United States Constitution; questions and answers. Greenwood Press 1998 316p il $39.95 (7 and up) **342**
1. United States. Constitution 2. Constitutional law—United States
ISBN 0-313-30643-5   LC 97-32008
The author examines each section of the U.S. Constitution "and provides a question-and-answer format that allows for easy explanation of a complicated document. The amendments are addressed in detail. . . . The book is easy to read and well laid out." Book Rep
Includes bibliographical references

343   Military, tax, trade, industrial law

Freedman, Suzanne, 1932-
Clay v. United States; Muhammad Ali objects to war. Enslow Pubs. 1997 112p il (Landmark Supreme Court cases) lib bdg $19.95 (7 and up) **343**
1. Ali, Muhammad, 1942- 2. Conscientious objectors
ISBN 0-89490-855-3   LC 97-9985
Describes the trial of Muhammad Ali, the first three-time boxing Heavyweight Champion of the world, for refusing to serve in the Vietnam War
Includes bibliographical references

Levinson, Isabel Simone
Gibbons v. Ogden; controlling trade between states. Enslow Pubs. 1999 112p il (Landmark Supreme Court cases) lib bdg $19.95 (7 and up) **343**
1. Gibbons, Thomas, 1757-1826 2. Ogden, Aaron, 1756-1839 3. Interstate commerce
ISBN 0-7660-1086-4   LC 98-34011
Describes the Supreme Court case concerning the steamboat monopoly between New York State and New Jersey, which established the right of Congress to regulate interstate commerce
Includes glossary and bibliographical references

344   Labor, social service, education, cultural law

Anderson, Wayne, 1966-
Brown v. Board of Education; the case against school segregation. Rosen Pub. Group 2004 64p il (Supreme Court cases through primary sources) lib bdg $29.95 **344**
1. Brown, Oliver, 1919-1961 2. Topeka (Kan.). Board of Education 3. Segregation in education
ISBN 0-8239-4009-8   LC 2003-219
Contents: Jim Crow; The NAACP challenges segregation; The NAACP's case against segregation; The case for the states; Rearguments and a decision; Implementation and impact
This is a discussion of the Supreme Court decision which ended racial segregation in public schools.
This "deserves a place in every library. . . . Copious and well-chosen primary source documents give extra value to this [book]. . . . Each document adds human drama to the already engaging text." Lib Media Connect
Includes glossary and bibliographical references

Andryszewski, Tricia, 1956-
School prayer; a history of the debate. Enslow Pubs. 1997 104p il (Issues in focus) lib bdg $19.95 (7 and up) **344**
1. Religion in the public schools 2. Church and state
ISBN 0-89490-904-5   LC 96-51951

Andryszewski, Tricia, 1956-——*Continued*
"Beginning with a discussion of the concept of separation of church and state, the author discusses the Supreme Court cases and laws dealing with school prayer." Horn Book Guide
"With clear, concise language, difficult and often ambiguous concepts, such as tolerance, equal access, and separation of church and state, are delineated and elucidated." Voice Youth Advocates
Includes bibliographical references

Banfield, Susan
The Bakke case; quotas in college admissions. Enslow Pubs. 1998 128p il (Landmark Supreme Court cases) lib bdg $26.60 (7 and up)
    344
1. Bakke, Allan Paul 2. Discrimination in education—Law and legislation
ISBN 0-89490-968-1   LC 97-21309
Provides background and discussion of the case brought by a white male student who challenged the affirmative action policy used in admitting students to the University of California medical school
Includes glossary and bibliographical references

Donnelly, Karen J.
Cruzan v. Missouri; the right to die; by Karen Donnelly. Rosen Pub. Group 2004 64p il (Supreme Court cases through primary sources) lib bdg $29.25   **344**
1. Cruzan, Nancy 2. Cruzan, Joe, d. 1996 3. Right to die—Law and legislation
ISBN 0-8239-4014-4   LC 2002-156162
Contents: The accident; The history behind the case; The Cruzans argue their case; Missouri's case; Appealing the decision; The Supreme Court; After the decision
"Donnelly covers the . . . right-to-die trials of the Cruzan family, whose adult daughter lingered in a vegetative state for many years before she was taken off life support." SLJ
This "deserves a place in every library. . . . Copious and well-chosen primary source documents give extra value to this [book]. . . . Each document adds human drama to the already engaging text." Lib Media Connect
Includes glossary and bibliographical references

Dudley, Mark E.
Engel v. Vitale (1962); religion in the schools. 21st Cent. Bks. (NY) 1995 96p il (Supreme Court decisions) $18.90 (7 and up)   **344**
1. Engel, Stephen 2. Vitale, William J. 3. Religion in the public schools 4. Church and state
ISBN 0-8050-3916-3   LC 95-19435
The author points out that although a 1962 Supreme Court case decided that official prayers in public schools are unconstitutional, the issue of separation of church and state remains
This volume is "clearly written and well organized." SLJ
Includes bibliographical references

Fridell, Ron, 1943-
Cruzan v. Missouri and the right to die debate; debating Supreme Court decisions; Ron Fridell. 1st ed. Enslow Publishers 2005 128p il (Debating Supreme Court decisions) lib bdg $26.60 (7 and up)   **344**
1. Cruzan, Nancy 2. Cruzan, Joe, d. 1996 3. Right to die—Law and legislation
ISBN 0-7660-2356-7   LC 2004-20028
Contents: Legal questions; The changing face of death; Through supporters' eyes; Through opponents' eyes; Right to die laws; Lower court cases; U.S. Supreme Court cases; The issues today; Debating the issues
This examines both sides of the debate concerning assisted suicide and related Supreme Court decisions.
Includes glossary and bibliographical references

Fuller, Sarah Betsy, 1946-2004
Hazelwood v. Kuhlmeier; censorship in school newspapers. Enslow Pubs. 1998 128p il (Landmark Supreme Court cases) lib bdg $26.60 (7 and up)
    344
1. Censorship 2. Freedom of the press 3. Students—Law and legislation
ISBN 0-89490-971-1   LC 98-13336
Examines the 1988 Supreme Court case which dealt with the question of whether the censorship of student newspapers by school administrators violated the students' first amendment rights to freedom of speech and freedom of the press
"Fuller offers thought-provoking ideas. . . . Sections devoted to the Supreme Court case and residual effects of the decision are balanced, compelling, and relevant." Booklist
Includes bibliographical references

Gold, John Coopersmith
Board of Education v. Pico (1982); book banning. 21st Cent. Bks. (NY) 1994 93p il (Supreme Court decisions) $18.90 (7 and up)
    344
1. Pico, Steven A. 2. Island Trees Public Schools (Levittown, N.Y.) 3. Censorship
ISBN 0-8050-3660-1   LC 94-21861
This discusses the Supreme Court decision "ensuring students the right to read what they choose. . . . [It] presents the pivotal issue and then reviews the historical context and complicated chain of legal decisions leading up to the ultimate ruling. . . . [It adds] depth and perspective to the current literature." SLJ
Includes bibliographical references

Gold, Susan Dudley, 1949-
Brown v. Board of Education; separate but equal? by Susan Dudley Gold. Benchmark Books 2004 c2005 143p il (Supreme Court milestones) lib bdg $25.95   **344**
1. Brown, Oliver, 1919-1961 2. Topeka (Kan.). Board of Education 3. Segregation in education
ISBN 0-7614-1842-3   LC 2004-5866
Contents: A girl and a dream; Civil War legacy; Separate but not equal; Through the court system; To the Supreme Court; A momentous decision; A new day; Darkness and light

Gold, Susan Dudley, 1949-—*Continued*
An overview of the Supreme Court decision which struck down racial segregation in schools.
"The format of the [book] makes [it] easy to read and understand. [A] valuable [resource] for reports." SLJ

Roe v. Wade; a woman's choice? by Susan Dudley Gold. Benchmark Books 2004 144p il (Supreme Court milestones) lib bdg $25.95
344
1. McCorvey, Norma 2. Wade, Henry, 1914-2001 3. Abortion—Law and legislation
ISBN 0-7614-1839-3   LC 2003-25567
Contents: A fundamental right; Two women's stories; Bans on abortion; A case and a plaintiff; Filing suit; Making a case for abortion; Supreme Court arguments; A momentous decision
An overview of the Supreme Court decision which made abortion legal.
"The format of the [book] makes [it] easy to read and understand. [A] valuable [resource] for reports." SLJ
Includes bibliographical references

Hanson, Freya Ottem, 1949-
The Second Amendment; the right to own guns. Enslow Pubs. 1998 128p il (Constitution) lib bdg $26.60 (7 and up)
344
1. Gun control
ISBN 0-89490-925-8   LC 97-30805
Presents an overview of the Second Amendment of the United States Constitution and examines the debate which has surrounded the right to bear arms
The author "presents an intelligent and studied case for a wide debate of the issue, and includes accounts of both sides of the argument." SLJ
Includes bibliographical references

Payment, Simone
Roe v. Wade; the right to choose. Rosen Pub. Group 2004 64p il (Supreme Court cases through primary sources) lib bdg $29.25
344
1. McCorvey, Norma 2. Wade, Henry, 1914-2001 3. Abortion—Law and legislation
ISBN 0-8239-4012-8   LC 2002-155346
Contents: A historic case begins in Texas; Abortion goes on trial; Next stop: Supreme Court; Another trip to the Supreme Court; Finally, a decision; After Roe v. Wade
This examines the Supreme Court decision which legalized abortion.
This "deserves a place in every library. . . . Copious and well-chosen primary source documents give extra value to this [book]. . . . Each document adds human drama to the already engaging text." Lib Media Connect
Includes glossary and bibliographical references

Romaine, Deborah S., 1956-
Roe v. Wade; abortion and the Supreme Court. Lucent Bks. 1998 112p il (Famous trials) lib bdg $22.45 (7 and up)
344
1. McCorvey, Norma 2. Wade, Henry, 1914-2001 3. Abortion—Law and legislation
ISBN 1-56006-274-6   LC 98-2540

A "look at the watershed case that legalized abortion. . . . While sharing a great deal of legal and historical information, Romaine manages to examine the people, events, and questions connected to the case in a way that makes the story read like a gripping courtroom drama." SLJ
Includes glossary and bibliographical references

Spitzer, Robert J.
The right to bear arms; rights and liberties under the law. ABC-CLIO 2001 xxii, 263p (America's freedoms) lib bdg $55
344
1. Gun control 2. Constitutional history—United States
ISBN 1-57607-347-5   LC 2001-5143
This reference offers an "examination of the Second Amendment to the U.S. Constitution, with chapters on the history, politics, laws, and contemporary controversies of the right to bear arms. . . . This purchase is recommended for both reference and circulation for all public and school libraries." Voice Youth Advocates
Includes bibliographical references

Torrans, Lee Ann, 1952-
Law for K-12 libraries and librarians. Libraries Unlimited 2003 250p pa $25
344
1. Libraries—Law and legislation 2. School libraries
ISBN 1-59158-036-6   LC 2003-2592
Contents: Copyright; The scope of copyright; The fair use of material protected by copyright in education; Library archiving and section 108 of the DMCA; Tracing copyright; Library bibliographies criteria for selection and the legal implications and limitations of linking; Faculty created web sites: who owns them?; Patron privacy and filtering in the school library: guarding outgoing data, monitoring incoming data; Library bibliographies: student web pages, metatags in websites and the law; Licensing in the library; Americans with disabilities and the school library; Employment in the library; Policies and procedures: a difference with significance
"Advice and regulations addressing what can be copied, taped, and used on school Web sites will be helpful for both media specialists and teachers. Comprehensive yet readable, this guide is logically organized and solidly supported by examples and references. An indispensable resource." SLJ
Includes bibliographical references

Trespacz, Karen L.
Ferrell v. Dallas I.S.D.; hairstyles in schools. Enslow Pubs. 1998 128p il (Landmark Supreme Court cases) lib bdg $26.60 (7 and up)
344
1. Ferrell, L. W. 2. Dallas Independent School District (Tex.) 3. Students—Law and legislation
ISBN 0-7660-1054-6   LC 97-28930
Discusses the case in which three students in the Dallas Independent School District were suspended from school in 1966 because of their hairstyles
"Trespacz presents a highly readable account of the issues surrounding this landmark case." SLJ
Includes glossary and bibliographical references

345 Criminal law

Aaseng, Nathan, 1953-
You are the juror. Oliver Press (Minneapolis) 1997 160p (Great decisions) lib bdg $18.95
345
1. Trials 2. Jury
ISBN 1-88150-840-4   LC 96-53046
The reader assumes the role of a juror in eight famous trials of the twentieth century: the Lindbergh kidnapping, Sullivan v. New York Times, the Chicago Seven, Patty Hearst's trial for armed robbery, and others
"For each case, the author presents just enough information for readers to assume the role of juror, with three options from which to choose. He then reveals the actual results and analyzes the consequences. This format balances the passions of those on all sides of these cases and allows Aaseng to present controversial views in a palatable way." SLJ
Includes bibliographical references

Alonso, Karen
The Chicago Seven political protest trial; a headline court case. Enslow Pubs. 2002 112p il (Headline court cases) lib bdg $20.95   **345**
1. Riots 2. Trials
ISBN 0-7660-1764-8   LC 2002-384
Contents: Two faces of America; The convention; The trial; The prosecution's case; Bobby Seale objects; The defense; The decision; The appeal; After the decision; The Chicago Seven today
Discusses the trial of Abbie Hoffman, Jerry Rubin, Tom Hayden, Rennie Davis, David Dellinger, John Froines, and Lee Weiner for activities during the Democratic National Convention of 1968
Includes glossary and bibliographical references

Fireside, Harvey, 1929-
The "Mississippi Burning" civil rights murder conspiracy trial; a headline court case. Enslow Pubs. 2002 112p il (Headline court cases) lib bdg $26.60   **345**
1. Trials (Homicide) 2. African Americans—Civil rights
ISBN 0-7660-1762-1   LC 2002-389
Examines the trials of the men accused of murdering three civil rights workers in Mississippi in 1964, including the Supreme Court decision to try the defendants in a federal rather than a state court and the final verdicts which marked the first time, in Mississippi, that a jury convicted white men for killing African Americans or civil rights workers
"A straightforward, riveting account. . . . The roles of the people involved are clearly delineated. . . . Well researched and documented, this readable text is a solid addition to most libraries." SLJ
Includes bibliographical references

Gold, Susan Dudley, 1949-
In re Gault (1967); juvenile justice. 21st Cent. Bks. (NY) 1995 96p il (Supreme Court decisions) lib bdg $18.90 (7 and up)   **345**
1. Gault, Gerald 2. Juvenile courts 3. Children—Law and legislation
ISBN 0-8050-3917-1   LC 95-19446
Discusses the case involving fifteen-year-old Gerald Gault and its impact on children's rights and due process of law for juveniles
This is "clearly written and well organized." SLJ
Includes bibliographical references

Miranda v. Arizona (1966); suspects' rights. 21st Cent. Bks. (NY) 1995 96p il (Supreme Court decisions) lib bdg $25.90 (7 and up)   **345**
1. Miranda, Ernesto
ISBN 0-8050-3915-5   LC 94-45045
On June 13, 1966, a divided Supreme Court ruled that suspects must be informed of their rights, including the right to remain silent and the right to counsel, before they are questioned by the police
"Carefully detailed background notes and quotations from lawyers, suspects, and judges are included. In a straightforward text, the entire process is explained, as well as the workings of the Supreme Court itself." SLJ
Includes bibliographical references

Herda, D. J., 1948-
Furman v. Georgia; the death penalty case. Enslow Pubs. 1994 104p il (Landmark Supreme Court cases) lib bdg $26.60 (7 and up)
345
1. Furman, William Henry 2. Capital punishment
ISBN 0-89490-489-2   LC 93-37512
Herda presents "the account of William Furman—convicted in 1967 and sentenced with the death penalty—and his legal attempts to appeal. The story highlights the author's goal of dealing with the issue of capital punishment in the United States, including the history of capital punishment and suspected bias according to race." Sci Books Films
Includes bibliographical references

Hile, Kevin S.
The trial of juveniles as adults; {by} Kevin Hile. Chelsea House 2003 128p il (Point-counterpoint) lib bdg $25.95; pa $11.95
345
1. Administration of justice 2. Juvenile delinquency
ISBN 0-7910-7374-2; 0-7910-7506-0 (pa)
LC 2002-15638
This gives a brief history of the juvenile justice system, and offers arguments for and against trying juveniles as adults.
Includes bibliographical references

Jacobs, Thomas A.
They broke the law, you be the judge; true cases of teen crime; edited by Al Desetta. Free Spirit Pub 2003 213p il pa $15.95 (7 and up)
345
1. Administration of justice 2. Juvenile courts
ISBN 1-575-42134-8   LC 2003-4814

Jacobs, Thomas A.—*Continued*

"This book details 21 cases ranging from truancy to auto theft. Following a description of events leading up to and including the crime itself, readers are given background about the individual, sentencing options, and questions to consider before sentencing, and then asked to make a decision about the case." SLJ

"An excellent introduction to how juvenile justice works, this will be a great resource for classroom and group discussions." Booklist

Kuklin, Susan

Trial: the inside story. Holt & Co. 2001 194p il $17.95 (7 and up) **345**

1. Trials (Kidnapping) 2. Illegal aliens

ISBN 0-8050-6457-5   LC 00-27783

This "account chronicles a criminal trial involving Chinese illegal aliens, beginning with double kidnappings in New York City during the summer of 1995." Voice Youth Advocates

"Eminently readable and information rich, this absorbing work will have wide appeal." SLJ

Includes glossary and bibliographical references

Pellowski, Michael, 1949-

The O.J. Simpson murder trial; a headline court case; {by} Michael J. Pellowski. Enslow Pubs. 2001 112p il (Headline court cases) lib bdg $26.60 **345**

1. Simpson, O. J., 1947- 2. Trials (Homicide)

ISBN 0-7660-1480-0   LC 00-11907

"This book provides background information, the cases for the prosecution and for the defense, and a follow-up to one of the most controversial murder trials of all time. . . . The author presents the elements of the investigation in an objective manner. . . . Excerpts of public opinion and legal analysis are included as well as a page of questions to be used as springboard for discussion. . . . Well done and worthy of shelf space." SLJ

Includes glossary and bibliographical references

Persico, Deborah

Mapp v. Ohio; evidence and search warrants; [by] Deborah A. Persico. Enslow Pubs. 1997 128p il (Landmark Supreme Court cases) lib bdg $19.95 (7 and up) **345**

1. Mapp, Dollree 2. Right of privacy

ISBN 0-89490-857-X   LC 96-21295

The landmark Supreme Court case that dealt with drawing the line between legal and illegal searches of private residences and what evidence obtained from such searches is admissible in court

This "contains information useful for reports and questions for subsequent discussion." SLJ

Includes bibliographical references

Ruschmann, Paul

Legalizing marijuana. Chelsea House 2004 129p il (Point-counterpoint) $25.95 (7 and up) **345**

1. Marijuana 2. Drugs—Law and legislation

ISBN 0-7910-7483-8   LC 2003-9497

Contents: Marijuana and prohibition; Marijuana use is harmless enough to be considered a personal choice; Laws are needed to protect uninformed people from the dangers of marijuana; Enforcement of marijuana laws is uneven, ineffective, and wasteful; Marijuana laws should be strictly enforced; Heavily regulated marijuana is a better alternative than the black market; Relaxing marijuana laws would lead to too many problems; The future of marijuana policy

This presents arguments for and against legalization of marijuana, including whether or not the drug is dangerous, how marijuana laws are enforced, and whether or not relaxing the laws would be good for society.

Includes bibliographical references

Sherrow, Victoria

Gideon v. Wainwright; free legal counsel. Enslow Pubs. 1995 104p il (Landmark Supreme Court cases) lib bdg $18.95 (7 and up)
345

1. Gideon, Clarence Earl 2. Wainwright, Louie L. 3. Legal aid

ISBN 0-89490-507-4   LC 93-45981

This "volume details the genesis of the case that established the right to free legal counsel, the Supreme Court decision, and the arguments presented by the lawyers for each side. A fine addition to the thought-provoking series." Horn Book Guide

Includes bibliographical references

Sonneborn, Liz

Miranda v. Arizona. Rosen Pub. Group 2004 64p il (Supreme Court cases through primary sources) lib bdg $29.95 **345**

1. Miranda, Ernesto

ISBN 0-8239-4010-1   LC 2002-154575

Contents: A rape in Arizona; Confessing to the crime; The rights of the accused; Making a case; The Supreme Court decision; The legacy of Miranda

This discusses the case in which the Supreme Court ruled that suspects must be informed of their rights to remain silent and the right to counsel when they they are being questioned by the police.

This "deserves a place in every library. . . .Copious and well-chosen primary source documents give extra value to this [book]. . . . Each document adds human drama to the already engaging text. " Lib Media Connect

Includes glossary and bibliographical references

Sorensen, Lita

The Scottsboro Boys Trial; a primary source account; by Lita Sorensen. 1st ed. Rosen Publishing Group 2004 64p il (Great trials of the 20th century) lib bdg $29.25 **345**

1. Trials 2. African Americans—Civil rights

ISBN 0-8239-3975-8   LC 2002-153356

Contents: Background : a journey interrupted; The story of two white girls; A court in the Old South; The role of the NAACP and the ILD; Appeals, outcomes, and a landmark decision; A long road to justice; Impact of the Scottsboro Boys Trial in American history

Sorensen, Lita—_Continued_
An account of the 1931 trial in which African
American youths were charged with rape
This is "packed with information. . . . [An] attractive,
intelligent offering." SLJ
Includes bibliographical references

Wetterer, Charles M.
The Fourth Amendment; search and seizure.
Enslow Pubs. 1998 128p il (Constitution) lib bdg
$19.95 (7 and up)   345
1. Right of privacy
ISBN 0-89490-924-X   LC 97-29946
Shows how the Fourth Amendment of the United
States Constitution has been historically interpreted by
the judicial system and presents cases which illustrate
how it is currently being applied
This volume is "clearly written [and] evenhanded."
Horn Book Guide
Includes glossary and bibliographical references

Wormser, Richard, 1933-
Defending the accused; stories from the
courtroom. Watts 2001 127p $25 (7 and up)
                                                345
1. Criminal procedure 2. Administration of criminal
justice 3. Lawyers
ISBN 0-531-11378-7   LC 00-33036
Presents case histories that illustrate the role of and
techniques used by defense lawyers in the American judicial system
"The writing is lively and accessible. . . . This solid
introduction to the subject will stimulate class discussion." SLJ
Includes glossary and bibliographical references

Worth, Richard, 1945-
The insanity defense. Chelsea House 2001 99p
il (Crime, justice, and punishment) lib bdg $22.95
(7 and up)   345
1. Insanity defense
ISBN 0-7910-4294-4   LC 00-40507
"This title examines the history of the insanity defense
and uses case studies to examine the ways the argument
is used. In discussing cases to illuminate this legal defense, Worth also examines how public reaction has impacted the laws and the use of an insanity plea." Voice
Youth Advocates
Includes bibliographical references

346   Private law

Alonso, Karen
Loving v. Virginia; interracial marriage. Enslow
Pubs. 2000 112p il (Landmark Supreme Court
cases) lib bdg $26.60 (7 and up)   346
1. Loving, Richard 2. Loving, Mildred Jeter
3. Interracial marriage—Law and legislation
ISBN 0-7660-1338-3   LC 99-50541

Explores the Supreme Court case that challenged and
eventually overturned Virginia's law forbidding interra-
cial marriages
This is a "carefully researched and documented book."
SLJ
Includes glossary and bibliographical references

Frost-Knappman, Elizabeth
Women's rights on trial; 101 historic trials from
Anne Hutchinson to the Virginia Military Institute
cadets; {by} Elizabeth Frost-Knappman and
Kathryn Cullen-DuPont. Gale Res. 1997 xxxi,
478p il $95   346
1. Trials 2. Women—Law and legislation
ISBN 0-7876-0384-8   LC 96-43656
"A New England Publishing Associates book"
This describes legal cases relating to women's rights
from colonial times to the present. Each entry lists major
facts of the trial and includes an essay discussing the
case's historical significance and legal issues
"This outstanding resource will give any student of
this country's judicial system or the profound changes in
the legal status of American women a strong, up-to-date
foundation." SLJ
Includes glossary and bibliographical references

Greenberg, Keith Elliot, 1959-
Adolescent rights; are young people equal under
the law? {by} Keith Greenberg. 21st Cent. Bks.
(NY) 1995 64p il (Issues of our time) $22.90 (7
and up)   346
1. Youth—Law and legislation 2. Children—Law and
legislation
ISBN 0-8050-3877-9   LC 94-41753
An illustrated overview of how the legal system has
treated children in the past and discusses the rights
young people have today
This is "clearly written and well rounded." SLJ
Includes glossary and bibliographical references

Jacobs, Thomas A.
What are my rights? 95 questions and answers
about teens and the law. Free Spirit 1997 199p il
pa $14.95 (7 and up)   346
1. Youth—Law and legislation
ISBN 1-57542-028-7   LC 97-8599
Provides information to help the reader understand
laws, recognize responsibilities, and appreciate rights especially in relation to parents, school, job, and personal
matters
"In clear, everyday language, with just a sprinkling of
legal terms, Jacobs presents useful guidelines and background on a variety of topically organized concerns related to teens' rights." Booklist
Includes glossary and bibliographical references

Landau, Elaine
Your legal rights; from custody battles to school
searches, the headline-making cases that affect
your life. Walker & Co. 1995 84p $13.95 (7 and
up)   346
1. Children—Law and legislation
ISBN 0-8027-8359-7   LC 94-42718

Landau, Elaine—_Continued_
"Beginning with the history of the treatment of children from ancient times through today, Landau goes on to discuss court cases that made headlines: the adoption of baby Jessica, the murder of Lisa Steinberg, Michael Fay's caning in Singapore, Gregory Kingsley's attempt to divorce his mother, and Kimberly May's effort to sever her ties with her biological parents." Book Rep
Includes bibliographical references

Sherrow, Victoria
Cherokee Nation v. Georgia; Native American rights. Enslow Pubs. 1997 128p il (Landmark Supreme Court cases) lib bdg $26.60 (7 and up) **346**
1. Native Americans—Government relations
ISBN 0-89490-856-1   LC 96-39651
Discusses the cases brought by the Cherokee Nation and its supporters against the state of Georgia beginning in the 1830s to protect the rights of the Cherokee living there
This offers "cogently written prose." Horn Book Guide
Includes bibliographical references

346.03 Torts (delicts)

Sergis, Diana K.
Cipollone v. Liggett Group; suing tobacco companies. Enslow Pubs. 2001 128p (Landmark Supreme Court cases) lib bdg $26.60 (7 and up) **346.03**
1. Cipollone, Rose, d. 1984 2. Liggett & Myers Tobacco Company 3. Trials 4. Liability (Law) 5. Tobacco industry
ISBN 0-7660-1343-X   LC 00-9787
"This volume focuses on the Supreme Court case concerning whether or not cigarette companies are protected from litigation by warning labels mandated by federal law. The text contains clear and useful background information on previous cases, explanations of the legal issues, and a discussion of repercussions of the case." Horn Book Guide
Includes glossary and bibliographical references

346.04 Property law

Butler, Rebecca P.
Copyright for teachers and librarians. Neal-Schuman Publishers 2004 248p il pa $59.95 **346.04**
1. Copyright 2. Fair use (Copyright)
ISBN 1-55570-500-6   LC 2004-46013
"The five chapters in Part I are . . . reviews of copyright law, the concept of fair use, determining what is in public domain, how to obtain permissions, and other general guidelines on such topics as licensing, loaning, penalties, plagiarism, and exemptions. The bulk of the book is in Part II, which deals with specific applications, such as Internet and public access, videos and DVDs, televi-sion, software, music, multimedia, distance learning and—oh, yes!—print! . . . An indispensable addition." SLJ
Includes bibliographical references

Crews, Kenneth D.
Copyright essentials for librarians and educators; {by} Kenneth D. Crews with contributions from Dwayne K. Buttler {et al.}. American Lib. Assn. 2001 143p pa $45 **346.04**
1. Copyright
ISBN 0-8389-0797-0   LC 00-59421
This reference is "designed to instruct today's information providers on the fundamentals of current copyright law. . . . {It answers such questions as}: What makes a work copyright-protected or not? How long do copyrights last? What are the rights of copyright owners? How can I determine what qualifies as fair use? What are the need-to-knows regarding copyright and the Internet?" Publisher's note

347 Civil procedure and courts

Brannen, Daniel E., 1968-
Supreme Court drama; cases that changed America; {by} Daniel E. Brannen & Richard Clay Hanes; Elizabeth M. Shaw, editor. U.X.L 2001 4v il set $215 (7 and up) **347**
1. United States. Supreme Court 2. Constitutional law—United States
ISBN 0-7876-4877-9   LC 00-56380
"The 159 cases included span the years 1803 to 2000 and are organized under major legal topics such as 'Individual Liberties' and 'Equal Protection and Civil Rights.' Each entry, ranging from three to five pages, is introduced by a profile listing the appellant and appellee or petitioner and respondent, attorneys, and justices along with a brief description of the case and its significance. . . . Each volume contains alphabetical and chronological lists of the cases, a guide to how the Supreme Court works, a list of Supreme Court Justices, and the text of the U.S. Constitution." SLJ
"This set will be an especially useful reference when students need to retrieve concise information on Supreme Court cases." Book Rep
Includes glossary and bibliographical references

Courtroom drama; 120 of the world's most notable trials; Elizabeth Frost-Knappman, Edward W. Knappman, and Lisa Paddock, editors. U.X.L 1998 3v il set $135 (7 and up) **347**
1. Trials
ISBN 0-7876-1735-0   LC 97-23014
Covers 120 notable trials that occurred around the world, from Socrates to Timothy McVeigh
"The authors have done an excellent job of identifying relevant information and describing the significance of the legal process. What makes this resource so useful is the broad coverage that spans many countries and historical periods." SLJ
Includes glossary and bibliographical references

DeVillers, David
Marbury v. Madison; powers of the Supreme Court. Enslow Pubs. 1998 112p il (Landmark Supreme Court cases) lib bdg $19.95 (7 and up) **347**
1. Marbury, William, 1761?-1835 2. Madison, James, 1751-1836 3. United States. Supreme Court
ISBN 0-89490-967-3   LC 97-24865
Discusses the case Marbury v. Madison in which the idea of judicial review became part of the federal government's system of checks and balances
Includes glossary and bibliographical references

Fireside, Harvey, 1929-
The Fifth Amendment; the right to remain silent. Enslow Pubs. 1998 128p il (Constitution) lib bdg $19.95 (7 and up)   **347**
1. Criminal procedure
ISBN 0-89490-894-4   LC 97-33476
An overview of the Fifth Amendment of the United States Constitution, which defines and protects a citizen's rights within the legal system
Includes glossary and bibliographical references

Horn, Geoffrey
The Supreme Court; by Geoffrey M. Horn. World Almanac Library 2003 48p il (World Almanac Library of American government) lib bdg $30; pa $11.95 (5 and up)   **347**
ISBN 0-8368-5459-4 (lib bdg); 0-8368-5464-0 (pa)
                                            LC 2002-38091
Contents: First Monday in October; What the Constitution says; Getting Confirmed; Arguing a case; The Chief Justices; Great dissenters; Finding a balance
This describes "the organization of the Court, the extent and limits of its powers, and how it checks and balances the president and Congress. . . . the history of the Court, how a person becomes a Supreme Court justice, how cases come before the Court, the role of the chief justice, and the importance of dissenting opinions." Publisher's note
"An amazing array of historical photos, statistics, primary-source documents, tables, graphs, and case studies supports the [text]." SLJ
Includes bibliographical references

The **Supreme** Court A to Z; Kenneth Jost, editor. 3rd ed. CQ Press 2003 576p $125   **347**
1. United States. Supreme Court
ISBN 1-56802-802-4
First published 1993
"Topics, which range from abortion to zoning, are arranged alphabetically with appropriate cross references to sections that provide further information. For most issues discussed, a historical overview essay is provided for all relevant cases, as is an explanation of how the Court's decisions have changed (or not changed) over the years as interpretations evolve." Libr J {review of 1993 edition}

352.2 Organization of administration

United States government manual; Office of the Federal Register, National Archives and Records Service, General Services Administration. Claitor's Law Bks. $52   **352.2**
1. United States—Politics and government—Handbooks, manuals, etc.
Annual. First published 1935. Variant title: United States government organization manual
"Official handbook of the Federal government describing the purposes and programs of most Government agencies and listing the top personnel." N Y Public Libr. Ref Books for Child Collect. 2d edition

352.23 Chief executives

Horn, Geoffrey
The presidency; by Geoffrey M. Horn. World Almanac Library 2003 48p il (World Almanac Library of American government) lib bdg $30; pa $11.95 (5 and up)   **352.23**
1. Presidents—United States 2. United States—Politics and government
ISBN 0-8368-5458-6 (lib bdg); 0-8368-5463-2 (pa)
                                            LC 2002-33129
Contents: A presidential inauguration; What the Constitution says; Getting elected; Using presidential power; Life in the White House; The first family; Leaving office
This discusses the jobs of the president, the history of the presidency, presidential elections and the electoral college, the transfer of power from one president to the next, the vice presidency, life in the White House, impeachment, and the role of the first lady.
"An amazing array of historical photos, statistics, primary-source documents, tables, graphs, and case studies supports the [text]. Highly readable for casual information seekers, yet perfect for research." SLJ
Includes bibliographical references

My fellow Americans; the most important speeches of America's presidents, from George Washington to George W. Bush; {compiled} by Michael Waldman; CDs narrated by George Stephanopoulos. Sourcebooks 2003 337p il $45 (7 and up)   **352.23**
1. Presidents—United States 2. United States—Politics and government 3. American speeches
ISBN 1-402-20027-7   LC 2003-6879
This "resource contains 43 speeches from 17 presidents, nearly all unabridged, each with an introduction explaining its historical context and significance. Two companion CDs allow listeners to hear all 43 speeches, including the actual voices of presidents from Teddy Roosevelt to George W. Bush. . . . Waldman's stated purpose in putting together this volume is to show how the actions, the dreams, and the big ideas presented by these addresses furthered the American democratic spirit. Some early drafts are included, including several versions of the opening paragraph of JFK's Inaugural Address. The most recent entry is President Bush's Address on

My fellow Americans—*Continued*
Iraq given on March 17, 2003, accompanied by the April news photo showing the fall of the Saddam Hussein statue in Baghdad. A fine addition." SLJ
Includes bibliographical references

The **Presidency** A to Z; Michael Nelson, advisory editor. 3rd ed. CQ Press 2003 603p (CQ's American government A to Z series) $125
                                    352.23
1. Presidents—United States—Encyclopedias
ISBN 1-56802-803-2   LC 2003-9464
First published 1992
"Approximately 300 entries describe the background of the presidents, their public experiences, daily and family life, powers and life in the White House, and deaths. Extensive essays explore concepts relating to the presidency such as Constitutional powers, the budget process, diplomatic activity, the cabinet, and the relationship of the presidency to Congress and the courts." Libr J {review of 1992 edition}
Includes bibliographical references

352.24 Cabinets and cabinet-level committees

Feinberg, Barbara Silberdick, 1938-
The cabinet. 21st Cent. Bks. (NY) 1995 64p il (Inside government) $18.90   **352.24**
1. Cabinet officers
ISBN 0-8050-3421-8   LC 94-41760
Provides a historical perspective for the development of the cabinet with heads of executive departments of government as advisers to the president
"Excellent-quality black-and-white and full-color photographs and reproductions accompany the interesting and lively text." SLJ
Includes bibliographical references

355 Military science

Ashabranner, Brent K., 1921-
A date with destiny; the Women in Military Service for America Memorial; [by] Brent Ashabranner; photographs by Jennifer Ashabranner. 21st Cent. Bks. (Brookfield) 2000 64p il lib bdg $25.90   **355**
1. Women in Military Service for America Memorial (Arlington, Va.) 2. Women in the armed forces
ISBN 0-7613-1472-5   LC 99-36384
Describes the planning and creation of the Women in Military Service for America Memorial, profiles some of the servicewomen involved, and presents a general history of women in military service
"The excellent, full-color photographs include many images featuring the memorial as well as others showing related exhibits and events. A good, readable introduction to a subject barely represented in library collections." Booklist
Includes bibliographical references

Brownlie, Ali
Why do people fight wars? [by] Ali Brownlie & Chris Mason. Raintree Steck-Vaughn Pubs. 2002 48p il (Exploring tough issues) lib bdg $25.69
                                    355
1. War 2. Military history
ISBN 0-7398-4961-1   LC 2001-48372
Explores issues related to war, such as causes, types, results, and peacekeeping efforts, illustrated by examples of armed conflicts throughout history and throughout the world
This "does an excellent job of giving students a solid background and well-written explanation of [the subject]." Voice Youth Advocates
Includes glossary and bibliographical references

Buckley, Gail Lumet, 1937-
American patriots; the story of Blacks in the military from the Revolution to Desert Storm; by Gail Buckley; adapted for young people by Tonya Bolden. Crown 2003 233p il $15.95; lib bdg $17.99 (7 and up)   **355**
1. African American soldiers 2. United States—Military history 3. United States—Race relations
ISBN 0-375-82243 7; 0-375-92243-1 (lib bdg)
                                    LC 2002-73713
Adapted from the title for adults published 2001 by Random House
Presents the story of the Black experience in United States military history
"This is an informative, enlightening introduction, offering unusual perspectives on the American military experience through the lens of its black patriots." Booklist
Includes bibliographical references

Chrisp, Peter
Warfare; by Peter Chrisp. Lucent Books 2004 48p il map (Medieval realms) $28.70   **355**
1. Military history 2. Medieval civilization 3. Knights and knighthood
ISBN 1-59018-537-4   LC 2003-18308
Contents: 1. Warrior nobles; War and the Church; The Normans; 1066: the year of three battles; Castles; 2. Holy war; Siege warfare; Warrior Monks of Outremer; Muslim holy war; Chivalry; The dead of Visby; 3. The Hundred Years War; English victory; The Campaign of Crecy; 4. The Black Prince's War, Chivalry in Decline; 5. Joan of Arc; Gunpowder; Swiss footsoldiers; 6. The Wars of the Roses; New armies
This briefly describes wars and warfare in the Middle Ages, including the Norman invasions, the Crusades, knighthood and chivalry, the Hundred Years War, the campaign of Crécy, the Black Prince's War, and the Wars of the Roses.
Inlcudes glossary and bibliographical references

Clinton, Catherine, 1952-
The Black soldier; 1492 to the present. Houghton Mifflin 2000 117p il $17 (5 and up)
                                    355
1. African American soldiers
ISBN 0-395-67722-X   LC 99-48935

Clinton, Catherine, 1952-—*Continued*

Chronicles the military accomplishments of African Americans who fought for the independence and preservation of the United States while struggling to be treated as equals and recognized for their valor and achievement

"Numerous black-and-white archival photographs and reproductions appear throughout this well-organized, readable resource." SLJ

Includes bibliographical references

Gay, Kathlyn, 1930-

After the shooting stops; the aftermath of war; [by] Kathlyn Gay and Martin Gay. 21st Cent. Bks. (Brookfield) 1998 128p il lib bdg $22.40 (7 and up) **355**

1. War and civilization 2. United States—Military history

ISBN 0-7613-3006-2　　　　　　LC 98-11387

Discusses the major social, political, and technological changes that occured in the United States as a result of various wars from the Revolution to the Gulf War

This is "an insightful, balanced, and impressively comprehensive overview of U.S. history." Booklist

Includes bibliographical references

Gravett, Christopher

Going to war in Viking times. Watts 2001 32p il (Armies of the past) lib bdg $24.50; pa $6.95 **355**

1. Vikings 2. Military history 3. Naval art and science

ISBN 0-531-14592-1 (lib bdg); 0-531-16353-9 (pa)
　　　　　　LC 00-42642

This describes the weaponry, dress, transportation, and military and naval strategies of Viking times

This volume is "wonderfully attractive, highly visual, and historically accurate." Book Rep

Includes glossary

Meltzer, Milton, 1915-

Weapons & warfare; from the stone age to the space age; illustrated by Sergio Martinez. HarperCollins Pubs. 1996 85p il $16.95; lib bdg $16.89 (5 and up) **355**

1. Weapons 2. Military art and science

ISBN 0-06-024875-0; 0-06-024876-9 (lib bdg)
　　　　　　LC 95-48464

"A concise, tautly written, introductory survey of an ever-popular subject. In straightforward, seemingly effortless prose, Meltzer presents readers with essential facts and figures." SLJ

Includes bibliographical references

Nathan, Amy

Count on us; American women in the military. National Geographic 2004 89p il $21.95
　　　　　　355

1. Women in the armed forces

ISBN 0-7922-6330-8　　　　　　LC 2003-14189

Reviews the history of American women's involvement in the Armed Forces from the Revolutionary War to the present

This is a "clearly written, well-organized book. . . . Readers will find this book valuable for research and interesting for browsing." SLJ

Inlcudes bibiographical references

War: opposing viewpoints; Louise Gerdes, book editor. Greenhaven Press 2005 239p il lib bdg $34.95; pa $23.70　　　　　　**355**

1. War

ISBN 0-7377-2591-5 (lib bdg); 0-7377-2592-3 (pa)
　　　　　　LC 2004-54283

"Opposing viewpoints series"

In this anthology the authors "debate controversies surrounding the causes and conduct of war, including under what circumstances war is justified, how prisoners and civilians should be treated, and what measures, if any, will prevent wars." Publisher's note

Includes bibliographical references

355.7　Military installations

Adams, Simon

Castles & forts; foreword by Clifford J. Rogers. Kingfisher (NY) 2003 63p il (Kingfisher knowledge) $11.95 (5 and up)　　　　**355.7**

1. Fortification 2. Castles

ISBN 0-7534-5620-6　　　　　　LC 2003-44631

An illustrated exploration of a wide array of castles and fortifications throughout the world, from Norman mottes to Maori forts, including how and why they were built and their importance in history

This title includes "stunning, captioned photos and illustrations that emphasize the many intriguing factual details in the text." SLJ

Includes glossary

355.8　Military equipment and supplies

The **Atom** bomb; Tamara L. Roleff, book editor. Greenhaven Press 2000 272p (Turning points in world history) lib bdg $33.70; pa $22.45
　　　　　　355.8

1. Atomic bomb 2. Hiroshima (Japan)—Bombardment, 1945 3. Nagasaki (Japan)—Bombardment, 1945

ISBN 0-7377-0215-X (lib bdg); 0-7377-0214-1 (pa)
　　　　　　LC 99-34739

"The authors in this anthology discuss the development of the bomb and the scientists who worked on it, the decision to drop the bomb on Japan, and the atom bomb's impact and legacy." Publisher's note

Includes bibliographical references

Byam, Michéle

Arms & armor; written by Michéle Byam. rev ed. DK Pub 2004 72p il (DK eyewitness books) $15.99; lib bdg $19.99 (4 and up)　　　**355.8**

1. Weapons 2. Armor

ISBN 0-7566-0654-3; 0-7566-0653-5 (lib bdg)
　　　　　　LC 2004-558979

First published 1988 by Knopf

Byam, Michéle—*Continued*
A photo essay examining the design, construction, and uses of hand weapons and armor from a Stone Age axe to the revolvers and rifles of the Wild West.

Making and using the atomic bomb; Mark McKain, book editor. Greenhaven Press 2003 240p (History firsthand) lib bdg $25.96; pa $16.96 (7 and up)   **355.8**
1. Manhattan Project 2. Atomic bomb
ISBN 0-7377-1412-3 (lib bdg); 0-7377-1413-1 (pa)
                                    LC 2002-27880
"This collection of writings surveys the history of the atomic bomb, its use, and its destructive capability. . . . The volume is divided into four chapters—'Discovery of Fission,' 'The Manhattan Project,' 'Using the Bomb,' and 'The Aftermath'—with several contemporary narratives and reminiscences in each." SLJ
Includes bibliographical references

358   Air and other specialized forces and warfare

Gay, Kathlyn, 1930-
Silent death; the threat of chemical and biological terrorism. 21st Cent. Bks. (Brookfield) 2001 128p il lib bdg $24.90 (7 and up)
                                    358
1. Chemical warfare 2. Biological warfare 3. Terrorism
ISBN 0-7613-1401-6   LC 00-41807
"Citing examples of military and civilian persons exposed to chemical biological agents, primarily from World War I to the Persian Gulf War, Gay argues for the need to understand and curtail the use of agents that often cannot be detected until the damage is done. . . . Relevant, engrossing." Booklist
Includes bibliographical references

Judson, Karen, 1941-
Chemical and biological warfare. Benchmark Bks. 2004 144p il (Open for debate) lib bdg $25.95 (7 and up)   **358**
1. Biological warfare 2. Chemical warfare
ISBN 0-7614-1585-8   LC 2003-7768
This describes various types of biological and chemical weapons, their histories and effects, and their development, testing, and control, and their effects on current events and policies.
"Well-organized and informative." SLJ
Includes bibliographical references

Levine, Herbert M.
Chemical & biological weapons in our times. Watts 2000 127p il $23 (7 and up)   **358**
1. Biological warfare 2. Chemical warfare
ISBN 0-531-11852-5   LC 99-49982
Examines the history and development of chemical and biological weapons and discusses their proliferation, association with terrorism, and efforts to control their use.

"This is a balanced exploration of the subject, combining science, history, and philosophical commentary to provide an interesting, informative look at a multifaceted issue." Booklist
Includes bibliographical references

Weapons of mass destruction: opposing viewpoints; James D. Torr, book editor. Greenhaven Press 2005 207p il lib bdg $33.70; pa $22.45   **358**
1. Weapons
ISBN 0-7377-2250-9 (lib bdg); 0-7377-2251-7 (pa)
                                    LC 2004-47587
"Opposing viewpoints series"
"The viewpoints in the volume examine WMD threats from terrorist groups and 'axis of evil' nations in the following chapters: How Likely Is an Attack Involving Weapons of Mass Destruction? How Should the United States Deal with Countries that Threaten to Develop Weapons of Mass Destruction? What Policies Should the United States Adopt Toward Nuclear Weapons? How Can the United States Defend Itself Against Weapons of Mass Destruction?" Publisher's note
Includes bibliographical references

Wolny, Philip
Weapons satellites. Rosen Pub. Group 2003 63p il (Library of satellites) lib bdg $26.50
                                    358
1. Space warfare 2. Space weapons 3. Artificial satellites
ISBN 0-8239-3855-7   LC 2002-10746
Contents: From space race to arms race and back again; The high ground and its perils; Inside weapons satellites; The future
Examines the development of weapons satellites which are not yet in use but which, when deployed, can use laser beams to attack large targets, disrupt the weather, or eliminate nuclear missiles in flight
"Clear and topical photographs enliven the [presentation]. While packed with information, the [text is] easy to read." SLJ
Includes glossary and bibliographical references

359.8   Naval equipment and supplies

Myers, Walter Dean, 1937-
USS Constellation; pride of the American navy. Holiday House 2004 86p il $16.95   **359.8**
1. Constellation (Frigate)
ISBN 0-8234-1816-2   LC 2003-56764
This "book traces the history of the USS Constellation, which was built as a frigate, launched in 1797, and initially charged with battling privateers that threatened U.S. trade with Europe. She was rebuilt as a sloop in 1854 and, in 1999, restored to her 1854 glory and docked in Baltimore Harbor. . . . The volume features an attractive design and many black-and-white reproductions of period photographs, drawings, paintings, and documents . . . A unique addition to American history collections." Booklist
Includes glossary and bibliographical references

361.2 Social action

Halpin, Mikki
It's your world—if you don't like it, change it; activism for teenagers. Simon Pulse 2004 305p pa $8.99 (7 and up)   **361.2**
1. Social action
ISBN 0-689-87448-0
"Animal rights, racism, war protest, AIDS, school violence and bullying, women's rights, and promoting tolerance are among the topics covered here. Halpin provides basic information about each one and then makes myriad suggestions for action at home, in the community, the 'five-minute activist,' etc. The ideas are easy to implement. . . . . This is an important book that will empower any young adult who would like to make a difference." SLJ
Includes bibliographical references

361.3 Social work

Gay, Kathlyn, 1930-
Volunteering; the ultimate teen guide. Scarecrow Press 2004 127p il (It happened to me) $32.50 (7 and up)   **361.3**
1. Volunteer work
ISBN 0-8108-4922-4   LC 2004-8174
Contents: Being a volunteer; Building and repairing; Closing the generation gap; Helping with health care; Helping the homeless, feeding the hungry; Protecting the environment and animals; Preserving the past; Counseling, teaching, and tutoring; Reducing bigotry, prejudice, and racism; Campaigning, communicating, and collecting; Getting started, reaping rewards
"This is a useful tool in that it provides a one-stop resource for teens interested in locating volunteer opportunities." SLJ
Includes bibliographical references

361.6 Governmental action

Welfare reform; Charles P. Cozic, book editor. Greenhaven Press 1997 112p il (At issue) lib bdg $18.70; pa $11.20 (7 and up)   **361.6**
1. Public welfare 2. United States—Social policy
ISBN 1-56510-546-X (lib bdg); 1-56510-545-1 (pa)
LC 96-33567
"This book presents a collection of essays that juxtapose opinions of various experts in the field. A selection by The Women's Alliance entitled 'Welfare Reform is a Mistake' is opposed by Robert Rector in 'Welfare Reform is Necessary' and Michael Tanner's 'Welfare Should Be Eliminated.' Other essays deal with women and children, illegitimacy, and immigrants as recipients of welfare benefits." SLJ
Includes bibliographical references

361.7 Private action

Perkins, Ralf
International Red Cross. Watts 2001 32p il (World organizations) $23; pa $6.95
361.7
1. Red Cross
ISBN 0-531-14623-5; 0-531-14812-2 (pa)
LC 2001-24889
Introduces the history, structure, goals, and projects of the International Red Cross and Crescent

362.1 Physical illness

Fleischman, John
Phineas Gage: a gruesome but true story about brain science. Houghton Mifflin 2002 86p il $16
362.1
1. Gage, Phineas P., d. 1861 2. Brain—Wounds and injuries
ISBN 0-618-05252-6   LC 2001-39253
"Phineas, a railroad construction foreman, was blasting rock near Cavendish, Vermont, in 1848 when a thirteen-pound iron rod was shot through his brain. Miraculously, he survived to live another eleven years and become a textbook case in brain science." Publisher's note
"The author deftly introduces readers to a diverse range of relevant scientific history as well as more specific beliefs that influenced the medical establishment's understanding of Gage, then goes on to examine subsequent neurological discoveries that have changed and enhanced our understanding of Gage's fate. The book's present-tense narrative is inviting and intimate, and the text is crisp and lucid." Bull Cent Child Books
Includes glossary and bibliographical references

Foley, Ronan
World health; the impact on our lives. Raintree Steck-Vaughn Pubs. 2003 64p il map (21st century debates) lib bdg $28.56 (7 and up)   **362.1**
1. World Health Organization 2. Health 3. Public health
ISBN 0-7398-5507-7   LC 2002-151937
Contents: A healthy world?; Measuring health; World diseases; The HIV/AIDS crisis; Health inequalities around the world; Health and environment; Food, poverty, development, and health; The future of world health
Provides an overview of global health issues, as well as the health problems that arise from economic and social situations in particular parts of the world, and explores the work of the World Health Organization
This title has "many well-placed sidebars with facts, debates, and viewpoints . . . [and] good-quality color photographs." SLJ
Includes bibliographical references

Gray, Susan H.
Living with cerebral palsy. Child's World 2003 32p il (Living well) lib bdg $25.64 (4 and up)
362.1
1. Cerebral palsy
ISBN 1-567-66101-7   LC 2002-2865

Gray, Susan H.—*Continued*

This title "leads off with an introduction to a young person who has [cerebral palsy]. Subsequent chapters explain the physiology of the illness, what causes it, and what it's like to live with it. [The concluding section looks] at possible treatments and potential cures. The [text is] clear and simple, double spaced, and punctuated by colorful exemplary photos of kids dealing with the disease. Gray provides a surprising amount of information and develops considerable empathy in readers." SLJ

Includes glossary and bibliographical references

Mintzer, Richard

The National Institutes of Health; [by] Rich Mintzer. Chelsea House 2002 64p il (Your government—how it works) lib bdg $20.75

362.1

1. National Institutes of Health (U.S.)

ISBN 0-7910-6793-9   LC 2002-43

Presents an overview of the history of infectious disease epidemics in the United States, as well as the history of the National Institutes of Health, the structure and role of that institution, and current major health concerns that are its focus

"This is a complete and fascinating overview of not just a government agency but also a complex organization that plays an important role in all of our lives." SLJ

Includes glossary and bibliographical references

Terminal illness: opposing viewpoints; Mary E. Williams, book editor. Greenhaven Press 2001 208p il lib bdg $34.95; pa $23.70 (7 and up)

362.1

1. Terminal care

ISBN 0-7377-0526-4 (lib bdg); 0-7377-0525-6 (pa)

     LC 00-56044

"Opposing viewpoints series"

This "title addresses hospice, home, and hospital care; discusses pain management (or lack of), including opinions on the legalization of marijuana; looks at varying positions on the withdrawal of life support and euthanasia; and offers varying viewpoints on a patient's right to die." SLJ

"This text will prove useful for a wide range of research topics." Booklist

Includes bibliographical references

Winick, Judd, 1970-

Pedro and me; friendship, loss, and what I learned. Holt & Co. 2000 187p il pa $16 (7 and up)

362.1

1. Zamora, Pedro, 1972-1994 2. Real world (Television program) 3. AIDS (Disease) 4. Friendship

ISBN 0-8050-6403-6   LC 99-40729

In this "volume—part graphic novel, part memoir—professional cartoonist Winick pays tribute to his *Real World* housemate and friend Pedro Zamora, an AIDS activist who died of the disease in 1994." Publ Wkly

"The author does a stellar job of marrying image to word to form a flowing narrative. . . . This is an important book for teens and the adults who care about them. Winick handles his topics with both sensitivity and a thoroughness that rarely coexist so seamlessly." SLJ

362.2 Mental and emotional illnesses and disturbances

Mental illness: opposing viewpoints; Tamara L. Roleff, Laura K. Egendorf, book editor. Greenhaven Press 2000 191p il lib bdg $33.70; pa $22.45 (7 and up)   **362.2**

1. Mental illness

ISBN 0-7377-0348-2 (lib bdg); 0-7377-0347-4 (pa)

     LC 99-55632

"Opposing viewpoints series"

Replaces the edition published 1995 under the editorship of William Barbour

The editors "offer essays and conference speeches . . . that explore the abstract elements of trying to define, diagnose, and treat mental illness. Teens, drawn to the topic for research or personal interest, should relish the heated debates that grow more multidimensional as the book progresses." Booklist

Includes bibliographical references

362.28 Suicide

Suicide: opposing viewpoints; Tamara L. Roleff, book editor. Greenhaven Press 1998 192p lib bdg $31.20; pa $19.95 (7 and up)

     362.28

1. Suicide

ISBN 1-56510-665-2 (lib bdg); 1-56510-664-4 (pa)

     LC 97-6697

"Opposing viewpoints series"

Replaces the edition published 1992 under the editorship of Michael D. Biskup and Carol Wekesser

Sections of this collection of articles deal with "individual rights in regard to suicide, including the influence that Christianity has had on such thinking and actions, the causes of teen suicide, the issue of assisted suicide. . . . The juxtaposition of popular and unpopular opinions is particularly helpful for students preparing to debate." SLJ

Includes bibliographical references

362.29 Substance abuse

Addiction: opposing viewpoints; Louise I. Gerdes, book editor. Greenhaven Press 2005 189p il $33.70; pa $22.45   **362.29**

1. Drug abuse 2. Alcoholism 3. Tobacco habit

ISBN 0-7377-2216-9; 0-7377-2217-7 (pa)

     LC 2003-67520

"Opposing viewpoints series"

"Authors in this . . . anthology debate controversies surrounding the concept of addiction, including what behaviors should be considered addictive, what causes addiction, what treatments are most effective, and whether the government should intervene to reduce the costs associated with addiction." Publisher's note

Includes bibliographical references

Barter, James, 1946-
Hallucinogens. Lucent Bks. 2002 112p il (Drug
education library) lib bdg $27.45 (7 and up)
362.29
1. Hallucinogens 2. Drug abuse
ISBN 1-56006-915-5   LC 2001-5776
Discusses the development of hallucinogens, their use
for spiritual, medicinal, and recreational purposes, and
the laws governing their use
"This intelligently written, objective title provides students with detailed information." SLJ
Includes bibliographical references

Chemical dependency: opposing viewpoints; Carol
Wekesser, book editor. Greenhaven Press 1997
192p lib bdg $31.20; pa $19.95 (7 and up)
362.29
1. Drug abuse 2. Alcoholism
ISBN 1-56510-552-4 (lib bdg); 1-56510-551-6 (pa)
LC 96-48030
"Opposing viewpoints series"
Replaces the edition published 1991 under the
editorship of Charles P. Cozic and Karin Swisher
Articles debate the following issues: How great a
problem is chemical dependency? What causes chemical
dependency? What treatments are effective for chemical
dependency? Should drug laws be reformed?
Includes bibliographical references

Drug abuse: opposing viewpoints; Tamara L.
Roleff, book editor. Greenhaven Press 2005
221p il lib bdg $33.70; pa $22.45 (7 and up)
362.29
1. Drug abuse
ISBN 0-7377-2226-6 (lib bdg); 0-7377-2227-4 (pa)
LC 2004-42406
A collection of articles and speeches, book excerpts
and quotations on various aspects of the drug abuse
problem
Includes bibliographical references

Drugs, alcohol, and tobacco; learning about
addictive behavior; Rosalyn Carson-DeWitt,
editor in chief. Macmillan Ref. USA 2003 3v
set $295 (7 and up)   362.29
1. Drug abuse—Encyclopedias
ISBN 0-02-865756-X   LC 2002-9270
Based on the Encyclopedia of drugs, alcohol & addictive behavior, 2nd edition, published 2001
"The 190 alphabetically arranged articles range from
one to six pages in length and yield a comprehensive
look at the nature of, treatments for, and social issues
surrounding addictive substances and behaviors. Topics
include specific drugs, diagnoses, treatments, legal and
social implications, drug trafficking, cultural pressures,
and related compulsive behaviors." SLJ

Drugs and sports; edited by William Dudley.
Greenhaven Press 2001 93p (At issue) lib bdg
$28.70; pa $19.95 (7 and up)   362.29
1. Athletes—Drug use
ISBN 1-56510-697-0 (lib bdg); 1-56510-696-2 (pa)
LC 00-59632

This collection of essays addresses "drug abuse among
athletes and the ethical erosion of sports by unscrupulous
athletes, trainers, doctors, and pharmacists who keep
finding ways to outwit drug testers. . . . The information
is eye-opening enough to give readers much to consider."
Booklist

Goodwin, William, 1943-
Marijuana. Lucent Bks. 2002 110p il maps
(Drug education library) lib bdg $27.45 (7 and up)
362.29
1. Marijuana 2. Drug abuse
ISBN 1-56006-916-3   LC 2001-4401
Discusses the history of marijuana, its physiological
and societal effects, laws regulating its medicinal and
recreational uses, and the continuing controversy which
surrounds those regulations
"A detailed, well-sourced portrait of the medical, legal, historical, and societal aspects of drug use in America." Booklist
Includes bibliographical references

Gottfried, Ted, 1928-
The facts about marijuana; by Ted Gottfried.
Benchmark Books 2004 c2005 109p il (Drugs) lib
bdg $37.07   362.29
1. Marijuana
ISBN 0-7614-1806-7   LC 2004-5578
Contents: What is marijuana?; Highs and lows; Go di-
rectly to jail; Pot, pain and punishment; Tests that count!
The author describes the effects of marijuana use,
varying opinions about legalization, marijuana laws, and
drug testing in schools.
Includes glossary and bibliographical references

LeVert, Suzanne
The facts about ecstasy; Suzanne Levert.
Benchmark Books 2004 c2005 96p il (Drugs) lib
bdg $37.07   362.29
1. Ecstasy (Drug)
ISBN 0-7614-1807-5   LC 2004-9341
Contents: Ecstasy: number one club drug; Drugs by
design; Risky business: the body and brain on X; Ecstasy
and the law; Designing a drug-free life
The author describes the drug MDMA, commonly
known as ecstasy, and how it is abused, its health risks,
the laws against it, and how to recover from the habit
Inlcudes glossary and bibliographical references

The facts about steroids; Suzanne Levert.
Benchmark Books 2004 c2005 96p il (Drugs) lib
bdg $37.07   362.29
1. Steroids 2. Athletes—Drug use
ISBN 0-7614-1808-3   LC 2004-11852
Contents: The game of steroids; Steroids and your
body; The health risks of taking steroids; Steroids and
the law; Treatment, prevention, and healthy fitness
The author "discusses the effects of steroids on the
body, health risks, the law, prevention, and treatment.
The medicinal use of steroids is very briefly mentioned.
. . . [This title has a] readable, well-organized [text], and
good use of color, graphics, photographs, tables, dia-
grams, and labels helps to spark readers' interest." SLJ
Includes glossary and bibliographical references

Menhard, Francha Roffe

The facts about inhalants; Francha Roffe Menhard. Benchmark Books 2004 c2005 92p il (Drugs) lib bdg $37.07 **362.29**

1. Solvent abuse

ISBN 0-7614-1809-1 LC 2004-11858

Contents: Introduction; What are inhalants?; A history of inhalant abuse; The dangers of inhalant abuse; Help for inhalant abusers; Inhalants and the law

The author "addresses the types of inhalants, the history, dangers, effects, available help for abuse of these drugs, and the laws regulating them. . . . [This title has a] readable, well-organized [text], and good use of color, graphics, photographs, tables, diagrams, and labels helps to spark readers' interest." SLJ

Includes glossary and bibliographical references

Smoking; Carol Wekesser, book editor. Greenhaven Press 1997 192p (Current controversies) lib bdg $26.20; pa $16.20 (7 and up) **362.29**

1. Smoking 2. Tobacco habit

ISBN 1-56510-534-6 (lib bdg); 1-56510-533-8 (pa) LC 96-36098

This is a compilation of articles regarding such questions as "'Are the health risks of smoking exaggerated?'; 'Is the tobacco industry to blame for leading people to smoke?'; 'How can smoking be reduced?'; 'Are increased measures needed to combat teen smoking?'; and 'Should government regulation of smoking be increased?' . . . A fascinating and authoritative debate on many aspects of a complicated subject." SLJ

Includes bibliographical references

Sonder, Ben, 1954-

All about heroin. Watts 2002 128p il $25 (7 and up) **362.29**

1. Heroin 2. Drug abuse

ISBN 0-531-11541-0 LC 2001-28914

This offers information about what heroin is, how it is made, what it is like to take it, facts about withdrawal and overdosing, users, attempts to stop trafficking, ways to recover from addiction, case histories, and relevant organizations and online resources

"Sonder's book gives readers a thorough, well-documented introduction to the drug in five nicely written chapters." Booklist

Includes bibliographical references

Stewart, Gail, 1949-

Drugs; by Gail B. Stewart. KidHaven Press 2002 48p il (Understanding issues) $23.70 **362.29**

1. Drug abuse

ISBN 0-7377-0951-0 LC 2001-2964

Discusses the social pressures, family instability, health risks, and treatments involved with drugs

"Facts, statistics, and other information are interwoven with personal examples in a way that lets readers associate the material with their own circumstances. . . . Colorful illustrations and charts make the pages attractive." Book Rep

Includes glossary and bibliographical references

Tobacco and smoking: opposing viewpoints; Karen F. Balkin, book editor. Greenhaven Press 2005 188p il lib bdg $33.70; pa $22.45 **362.29**

1. Tobacco habit 2. Smoking 3. Tobacco industry

ISBN 0-7377-2248-7 (lib bdg); 0-7377-2249-5 (pa) LC 2003-67502

"Opposing viewpoints series"

"Many twenty-first century health and social issues surrounding tobacco and smoking are examined. . . . The anthology includes [an] international chapter that explores the worldwide health and economic impacts of tobacco use." Publisher's note

Includes bibliographical references

362.292 Alcoholism

Alcoholism; James D. Torr, book editor. Greenhaven Press 2000 202p (Current controversies) lib bdg $33.70; pa $22.45 (7 and up) **362.292**

1. Alcoholism

ISBN 0-7377-0139-0 (lib bdg); 0-7377-0138-2 (pa) LC 99-37265

This "selection of primary source materials . . . is used to debate such topics as the effectiveness of Alcoholics Anonymous and the alcohol industry's responsibility for its marketing program. . . . A solid, invaluable resource on its subject." Booklist

Includes bibliographical references

Gottfried, Ted, 1928-

The facts about alcohol; by Ted Gottfried. Benchmark Books 2004 c2005 111p il (Drugs) lib bdg $37.07 **362.292**

1. Drinking of alcoholic beverages 2. Alcoholism 3. Youth—Alcohol use

ISBN 0-7614-1805-9 LC 2004-5388

Contents: What's in a drink?; The noble experiment; Liquor: lobbies and laws; A problem in the family; Help, hope, and healing

The author "includes historical aspects of alcohol and society, including humans' first experimentations with fermentation, Prohibition, and the temperance movement; related laws and legislation; and definition, causes, treatment, and effects. . . . [This title has a] readable, well-organized [text], and good use of color, graphics, photographs, tables, diagrams, and labels helps to spark readers' interest." SLJ

Includes glossary and bibliographical references

Hyde, Margaret Oldroyd, 1917-

Alcohol 101; an overview for teens; {by} Margaret O. Hyde and John F. Setaro. 21st Cent. Bks. (Brookfield) 1999 128p lib bdg $24.90 (7 and up) **362.292**

1. Alcoholism

ISBN 0-7613-1274-9 LC 99-17926

Discusses alcohol use in the United States, including the physical effects, the origin of the drinking age, societal mixed messages, and the sociological impacts

Includes bibliographical references

Teen alcoholism; Laura K. Egendorf, book editor. Greenhaven Press 2001 138p (Contemporary issues companion) lib bdg $22.96; pa $14.96 (7 and up)   **362.292**
1. Teenagers—Alcohol use 2. Alcoholism
ISBN 0-7377-0683-X (lib bdg); 0-7377-0682-1 (pa)
LC 00-68181
A collection of essays on such topics as the risk factors of teen alcoholism, the effects of parental drinking, social pressures, and advertising on teen drinking, and the dangers of alcohol abuse
The editor includes "an entire chapter of personal essays from people who have actually struggled with teen alcoholism or seen effects on a friend or family member. This chapter alone is worth the entire volume. . . . The rest of the book, which includes charts and sometimes staggering facts, will help in standard research." Booklist
Includes bibliographical references

The **truth** about alcohol; Mark J. Kittleson, general editor; William Kane, adviser; Richelle Rennegarbe, adviser; Barry Youngerman, principal author. Facts on File 2004 196p $35 (7 and up)   **362.292**
ISBN 0-8160-5298-0   LC 2004-509
Includes index
This discusses such topics as binge drinking, underage drinking, the prevalence of drinking on college campuses, drunken driving, dealing with alcohol abuse in the family, alcohol advertising and counter-advertising, and seeking help for an alcohol problem
This title does "an excellent job of providing accurate information for teens. For reports or for self-help, [it belongs] in any library serving young adults." SLJ

362.4 Problems of and services to people with physical disabilities

Alexander, Sally Hobart
Do you remember the color blue? and other questions kids ask about blindness. Viking 2000 78p il $16.99 (4 and up)   **362.4**
1. Blind
ISBN 0-670-88043-4   LC 99-34130
Children ask questions of an author who lost her vision at the age of twenty-seven, including "How did you become blind?" "How can you read?" and "Was it hard to be a parent when you couldn't see your kids?"
"The author's clearheaded and pragmatic approach . . . refreshingly resists mythologizing, and her balanced account will give kids a feeling for a life that on the one hand seems very different and on the other could be anybody's." Bull Cent Child Books

362.5 Problems of and services to poor people

Criswell, Sara Dixon, 1945-
Homelessness. Lucent Bks. 1998 112p il (Lucent overview series) lib bdg $22.45 (7 and up)   **362.5**
1. Homeless persons
ISBN 1-56006-180-4   LC 97-42439
Discusses the causes of homelessness, life on the streets, homeless children, the shelter system, and help for the homeless
"Criswell does justice to the complexity of the problem. . . . Well-chosen black-and-white photographs complement the text." Booklist
Includes bibliographical references

The **Homeless:** opposing viewpoints; Jennifer A. Hurley, book editor. Greenhaven Press 2002 186p lib bdg $34.95; pa $23.70 (7 and up)   **362.5**
1. Homeless persons
ISBN 0-7377-0750-X (lib bdg); 0-7377-0749-6 (pa)
LC 2001-23916
"Opposing viewpoints series"
Replaces the edition published 1995 under the editorship of Tamara L. Roleff
This collection of essays addresses the causes and seriousness of homelessness and possible remedies
Includes bibliographical references

Inner-city poverty; Tamara L. Roleff, book editor. Greenhaven Press 2002 176p (Contemporary issues companion) $22.45; pa $16.96 (7 and up)   **362.5**
1. Poverty 2. Public welfare 3. Inner cities 4. United States—Economic conditions
ISBN 0-7377-0841-7; 0-7377-0840-9 (pa)
LC 2002-23639
"A number of writers contributed to this collection of articles about the severity of the urban poverty dilemma. All aspects of the problem are clearly presented. Proposed solutions are suggested. The effectiveness of these solutions in dealing with the urban poor is discussed. Several personal accounts shed illuminating perspectives on living the life of the inner city poor." Libr Media Connect
Includes bibliographical references

Kowalski, Kathiann M., 1955-
Poverty in America; causes and issues. Enslow Pubs. 2003 128p il (Issues in focus) lib bdg $26.60   **362.5**
1. Poor 2. Poverty
ISBN 0-7660-1945-4   LC 2002-156034
Contents: Unequal wealth; Who are the poor?; What has America done about poverty?; The war over welfare; Homelessness and housing issues; Help for low-income workers; The bigger picture
Explores the issues of poverty in the United States through real-life stories of poor people and the agencies and organizations available to help them

Kowalski, Kathiann M., 1955-—*Continued*
"Kowalski tackles a tough topic and makes balanced sense of it. . . . Well organized, this book provides fundamental information and perspectives for vital classroom discussion." SLJ
Includes bibliographical references

Poverty: opposing viewpoints; Laura K. Egendorf, book editor. Greenhaven Press 1999 224p il lib bdg $31.20; pa $19.95 (7 and up)
362.5
1. Poverty 2. United States—Economic conditions 3. Public welfare
ISBN 1-56510-947-3 (lib bdg); 1-56510-946-5 (pa)
LC 98-17866
"Opposing viewpoints series"
Replaces the edition published 1994 under the editionship of Katie de Koster
A collection of articles which present differing viewpoints on the problem of poverty in America, its causes, and possible remedies
Includes bibliographical references

Stewart, Gail, 1949-
Homeless teens; by Gail B. Stewart; photographs by Carl Franzén. Lucent Bks. 1999 112p il (Other America) lib bdg $22.45 (7 and up)
362.5
1. Homeless persons
ISBN 1-56006-398-X
LC 98-37997
Discusses the numbers of homeless teenagers, their situation and behavior, and looks at the lives of four of them
"The attention-grabbing stories highlight a variety of scenarios and readers are likely to develop a new understanding about the unfortunate situations that dominate the lives of these young people." SLJ
Includes bibliographical references

362.7 Problems of and services to young people

Adoption: opposing viewpoints; Roman Espejo, book editor. Greenhaven Press 2002 206p il lib bdg $34.95; pa $23.70 (7 and up)
362.7
1. Adoption
ISBN 0-7377-0790-9 (lib bdg); 0-7377-0789-5 (pa)
LC 2001-40358
"Opposing viewpoints series"
"Issues discussed include adoption as an alternative to abortion, transracial adoptions, and adoptions by gay and lesbian couples. . . . Sometimes complementary, sometimes contradictory, the many views clearly articulated here make this volume an excellent starting place for any thoughtful discussion of adoption." Booklist
Includes bibliographical references

Blue, Rose
Staying out of trouble in a troubled family; [by] Rose Blue and Corinne J. Naden. 21st Cent. Bks. (Brookfield) 1998 112p lib bdg $21.40 (7 and up)
362.7
1. Family
ISBN 0-7613-0365-0
LC 98-15625
Case studies and interviews present ways to cope with life in a troubled family, including such problems as drug abuse, divorce, child abuse, alcoholism, disability, and adoption
"Interspersed within each story are analyses by trained professionals who dignify and make comprehensible to teens the reactions of each study's central character. The comments are articulated simply but effectively." Booklist

Bode, Janet
Kids still having kids; talking about teen pregnancy; art by Stan Mack and Ida Marx Blue Spruce. rev ed. Watts 1999 159p il lib bdg $23; pa $9.95
362.7
1. Teenage pregnancy 2. Teenage mothers
ISBN 0-531-11588-7 (lib bdg); 0-531-11593-6 (pa)
LC 98-45477
First published 1992
Presents interviews with teenage mothers and provides information about adoption, parenting, abortion, and foster care
"Bode provides a valuable resource for young adults making decisions about pregnancy, as well as those researching the issue for school projects. . . . A lively design, which includes cartoon strips and snippets from current newspaper and magazine articles, adds to the dynamic presentation." Horn Book Guide
Includes bibliographical references

Child abuse; Bryan J. Grapes, book editor. Greenhaven Press 2001 176p (Current controversies) lib bdg $31.20; pa $19.95 (7 and up)
362.7
1. Child abuse
ISBN 0-7377-0679-1 (lib bdg); 0-7377-0678-3 (pa)
LC 2001-23407
The first section "establishes the controversy surrounding the issue. Ensuing sections delve into specifics—causes, concerns about substance abuse, family preservation law, foster care, and cohabitation of the unmarried parents. There's a scattering of frank though not gratuitous reminiscences from abuse victims, some of whom repeated the behavior with their own children." Booklist
Includes bibliographical references

Child abuse: opposing viewpoints; Jennifer Hurley, book editor. Greenhaven Press 1999 206p lib bdg $31.20; pa $19.95 (7 and up)
362.7
1. Child abuse
ISBN 1-56510-935-X (lib bdg); 1-56510-173-1 (pa)
LC 98-16387
"Opposing viewpoints series"
A collection of articles which present differing viewpoints about the causes of child abuse, false allegations of child abuse, how the legal system should deal with

Child abuse: opposing viewpoints—*Continued*
child molesters, and how to reduce child abuse
Includes bibliographical references

Child and youth security sourcebook; edited by
Chad T. Kimball. Omnigraphics 2003 646p il
(Security reference series) $68   **362.7**
1. Safety education 2. Youth—Health and hygiene
3. School violence
ISBN 0-7808-0613-1   LC 2002-45010
This is an "examination of safety and security issues
in the lives of children and teenagers geared toward parents, teachers, and students. . . . The nine sections discuss how to protect young people from school crime and
violence, physical/sexual/emotional abuse and neglect,
drug use and abuse, gangs, Internet sex offenders, and
mental and emotional health risks. . . . This successful
blend of clear writing, quality research, and meticulous
attention to detail conveys much of the information
through user-friendly outlines, checklists, and lists of key
points. . . . An essential purchase for all libraries serving
youth." SLJ
Includes bibliographical references

Dean, Ruth, 1947-
Teen prostitution; by Ruth Dean and Melissa
Thomson. Lucent Bks. 1998 96p il (Teen issues)
lib bdg $22.45   **362.7**
1. Juvenile prostitution
ISBN 1-56006-512-5   LC 97-27452
Presents an overview of the problem of teenage prosti-
tutes, including some of the causes and consequences of
this phenomenon and what can be done to prevent it
Includes glossary and bibliographical references

Edelson, Paula
Straight talk about teenage pregnancy. Facts on
File 1999 136p il lib bdg $27.45 (7 and up)
    362.7
1. Teenage pregnancy 2. Teenage mothers
ISBN 0-8160-3717-5   LC 98-7268
"Topics covered include male and female reproductive
systems and stages of pregnancy; sexual abstinence and
methods of delaying sexual intercourse; responsible sexuality; contraceptive choices; options for pregnant teens;
realities of teenage parenting; and a brief discussion of
U.S. national and local attempts to prevent teen pregnancy. . . . This clearly written, informative, gritty book
fills a definite need." Booklist
Includes bibliographical references

Hurley, Jennifer A., 1973-
Teen pregnancy. Greenhaven Press 2000 96p il
(Opposing viewpoints digests) lib bdg $28.70; pa
$18.70 (7 and up)   **362.7**
1. Teenage pregnancy
ISBN 0-7377-0366-0 (lib bdg); 0-7377-0365-2 (pa)
    LC 00-37135
Examines the differing viewpoints on issues related to
teen pregnancy, including factors that contribute to this
problem, its effects on teenagers' lives, and possible
ways to prevent teen pregnancy

"Debaters will find this a useful tool, both for its concise summations of differing views, and its occasional inclusion of an unpopular viewpoint." Booklist
Includes bibliographical references

Jocelyn, Marthe, 1956-
A home for foundlings. Tundra Books 2005
128p il pa $15.95 (7 and up)   **362.7**
1. Foundling Hospital (London, England)
2. Abandoned children
ISBN 0-88776-709-5
"A Lord Museum book"
"Published in cooperation with Foundling Museum
and LORD Cultural Resources Planning and Management."
A "history of Foundling Hospital, a London orphanage
that took in more than 27,000 children from the time it
was established in the eighteenth century as a home for
abandoned babies." Booklist
"Black-and-white reproductions of early admission
documents and ledgers as well as period photographs and
engravings appear throughout. This is a useful resource."
SLJ

Kaminker, Laura
Everything you need to know about being
adopted. Rosen Pub. Group 1999 64p il (Need to
know library) $23.95 (7 and up)   **362.7**
1. Adoption
ISBN 0-8239-2834-9   LC 98-45629
"Kaminker gives legal facts about adoption and brings
up many of the problems adolescent adoptees face. . . .
The author's suggestions are sensible." SLJ
Includes glossary and bibliographical references

Kim, Henny H., 1968-
Child abuse. Greenhaven Press 2000 144p il
(Opposing viewpoints digests) lib bdg $28.70; pa
$18.70 (7 and up)   **362.7**
1. Child abuse
ISBN 1-56510-867-1 (lib bdg); 1-56510-866-3 (pa)
    LC 99-47464
Presents differing views on various aspects of the top-
ic of child abuse, including defining what child abuse is,
the seriousness of the problem, and ways to handle and
prevent it
Includes bibliographical references

Pledge, Deanna S., 1956-
When something feels wrong; a survival guide
about abuse for young people. Free Spirit 2003
214p il pa $14.95 (7 and up)   **362.7**
1. Child abuse 2. Domestic violence
ISBN 1-575-42115-1   LC 2002-14060
Contents: What is abuse?; Taking action; Your healing
journey
Provides checklists, journaling ideas, and other positive ways of dealing with being physically, sexually,
and/or emotionally abused, emphasizing the importance
of talking about what has happened and getting help
"This book will be a godsend for those struggling

Pledge, Deanna S., 1956-—*Continued*
with any type of abuse. . . . The tone is light and encouraging, yet straightforward. The advice is seasoned and workable." SLJ
Includes bibliographical references

Pregnancy; William Dudley, book editor. Greenhaven Press 2001 191p il (Teen decisions) lib bdg $33.70; pa $22.45 (7 and up)
362.7
1. Teenage pregnancy 2. Youth—Sexual behavior
ISBN 0-7377-0492-6 (lib bdg); 0-7377-0491-8 (pa)
LC 00-32162
"This volume features the stories of teens who chose adoption, abortion, or parenthood, and the advice they offer to others." Publisher's note
Includes bibliographical references

Prior, Katherine
UNICEF. Watts 2001 32p il (World organizations) lib bdg $23; pa $9.75
362.7
1. UNICEF
ISBN 0-531-14625-1 (lib bdg); 0-531-14813-0 (pa)
LC 2001-17764
This introduction to the United Nations International Children's Emergency Fund "opens with a short description and mission statement of the organization along with the emblem. A boxed 'Checklist' is used to summarize documents and lists into small, easy-to-read outlines. 'Spotlights' give brief historical accounts of key events, and 'Problem Boxes' delineate areas of concern." Book Rep
Includes glossary

Reef, Catherine
Alone in the world; orphans and orphanages in America; by Catherine Reef. Clarion Books 2005 135p il $18
362.7
1. Orphanages 2. Orphans
ISBN 0-618-35670-3
LC 2004-20179
Contents: Thrown upon the world; Asylum children; Saving youthful hearts; Let society beware!; Soldiers' orphans; Everyone's business; This army of children; Afterword: where life led some of the children who appeared in this book
This is a history of orphanages "in the U.S. beginning in 1729, when a place for girls was founded in New Orleans. . . . [The author] ends with a discussion of the challenges the U.S. faces today in caring for growing numbers of homeless, abused, or neglected children. Illustrated with archival photographs and reproductions." SLJ
Includes bibliographical references

Rue, Nancy N., 1951-
Everything you need to know about abusive relationships. rev ed. Rosen Pub. Group 1998 64p il (Need to know library) lib bdg $23.95
362.7
1. Date rape 2. Dating (Social customs)
ISBN 0-8239-2832-2
LC 00-266280
First published 1996

Discusses different kinds of abuse that occurs between teens who are dating and offers advice on how to handle abusive situations
Includes bibliographical references

Teenage pregnancy: opposing viewpoints; Stephen P. Thompson, book editor. Greenhaven Press 1997 190p lib bdg $27.45; pa $19.96 (7 and up)
362.7
1. Teenage pregnancy 2. Teenage mothers
ISBN 1-56510-562-1 (lib bdg); 1-56510-561-3 (pa)
LC 96-48031
"Opposing viewpoints series"
A collection of articles representing varying opinions about teenage pregnancy including whether or not it is a serious problem, its causes and prevention, and possible solutions
Includes bibliographical references

Teens at risk: opposing viewpoints; Laura K. Egendorf, book editor; Jennifer A. Hurley, book editor. Greenhaven Press 1999 190p il lib bdg $31.20; pa $19.95 (7 and up)
362.7
1. Teenagers
ISBN 1-56510-949-X (lib bdg); 1-56510-948-1 (pa)
LC 98-23191
"Opposing viewpoints series"
This collection of articles presents differing viewpoints about the causes, possible prevention, and remedies for such problems as teenage crime, pregnancy, and drug use
Includes bibliographical references

Veladota, Christina
Teen runaways; by Christina Veladota. Lucent Books 2004 112p il (Teen issues) $28.70 (7 and up)
362.7
1. Runaway teenagers
ISBN 1-560-06780-2
LC 2003-2057
Contents: Who runs away and why do they run?; Life on the streets; Runaways face serious health risks; Runaways and the law; Help for runaways; Alternatives and prevention
"Who are teen runaways and why do they run? What risks do they face on the streets? What happens to runaways when the law gets involved? These questions, along with facts about prevention and alternatives to running away, are explored." Publisher's note
Includes bibliographical references

Warren, Andrea
Orphan train rider; one boy's true story. Houghton Mifflin 1996 80p il $16; pa $7.95 (4 and up)
362.7
1. Nailling, Lee, 1917- 2. Orphans 3. Abandoned children
ISBN 0-395-69822-7; 0-395-91362-4 (pa)
LC 94-43688
"From 1854 to 1930, the orphan trains took homeless children from cities in the East to new homes in the West, the Midwest, and the South. In Warren's book, one man's memories of his childhood abandonment and adoption give a personal slant on the subject. Chapters telling the story of Lee Nailing, who took an orphan

Warren, Andrea—*Continued*
train west in 1926, alternate with chapters filling in background information about the trains and the experiences of other children who rode them to their destinies." Booklist

"An excellent introduction to researching or discussing children-at-risk in an earlier generation. The book is clearly written and illustrated with numerous black-and-white photographs and reproductions." SLJ
Includes bibliographical references

We rode the orphan trains. Houghton Mifflin 2001 132p il $18; pa $8.95 (4 and up)

362.7
1. Orphans
ISBN 0-618-11712-1; 0-618-11712-1 (pa)
LC 00-47279

The author "interviews eight orphan train riders concerning their childhood experiences during 'the largest children's migration in history' between 1854 and 1929 as part of a 'placing out' program run by the Children's Aid Society of New York City." Publ Wkly
"This is powerful nonfiction for classroom and personal reading and for discussion." Booklist
Includes bibliographical references

Weiss, Ann E., 1943-
Adoptions today; questions and controversies. 21st Cent. Bks. (Brookfield) 2001 144p il lib bdg $24.90 (7 and up)   362.7
1. Adoption
ISBN 0-7613-1914-X   LC 00-53633
"Following a brief history of adoption, Weiss discusses nontraditional adoption (interracial, interfaith, gay and lesbian), international adoption, and changing attitudes on such aspects as open adoption and searches for birth parents. Her perspective on adoption is overwhelmingly positive . . . but she does offer information on the adoption black market and the problems of Internet adoptions." Booklist
Includes bibliographical references

362.82   Problems of and services to families

Battered women; Lane E. Volpe, book editor. Greenhaven Press 2004 138p (Contemporary issues companion) $33.70; pa $22.45

362.82
1. Domestic violence 2. Abused women
ISBN 0-7377-1617-7; 0-7377-1618-5 (pa)
LC 2003-56877

Replaces the edition published 1999 under the editorship of Louise Gerdes
"Contributors to this . . . anthology investigate the nature of domestic violence and examine various measures that can protect battered women. Personal profiles of individuals whose lives have been touched by domestic violence round out this look at a disturbing but important issue." Publisher's note
Includes bibliographical references

Domestic violence: opposing viewpoints; David M. Haugen, book editor. Greenhaven Press 2005 186p il lib bdg $33.70; pa $22.45

362.82
1. Domestic violence
ISBN 0-7377-2224-X (lib bdg); 0-7377-2225-8 (pa)
LC 2004-41168

"Opposing viewpoints series"
"This volume examines the prevalence of domestic violence in America, its causes, and its remedies." Publisher's note
Includes bibliographical references

Family violence; J. D. Lloyd, book editor. Greenhaven Press 2000 138p (Current controversies) lib bdg $33.70; pa $22.45 (7 and up)   362.82
1. Domestic violence
ISBN 0-7377-0452-7 (lib bdg); 0-7377-0451-9 (pa)
LC 00-27984

This "title examines violence in the home, mainly against spouses and children, but also against the elderly and gay and lesbian partners. . . . The 19 selections, mainly magazine articles and book excerpts . . . do justice to the complexity of the issues. A helpful resource for students." Booklist

362.87   Problems of and services to victims of oppression

Gay, Kathlyn, 1930-
Leaving Cuba; from Operation Pedro Pan to Elian. 21st Cent. Bks. (Brookfield) 2000 144p il maps lib bdg $24.90 (7 and up)   362.87
1. Cuban Americans 2. Cuban refugees
ISBN 0-7613-1466-0   LC 99-462149
Considers the various ways children have escaped from Communist Cuba and found refuge in the United States through different plans set up to help them, from the early 1960s to the present
The author "uses biographical sketches to put a human face on the agonies of family separation as well as the readjustment to life in a new country and culture. The book concludes with an unbiased reporting of the Elian Gonzalez case." SLJ
Includes bibliographical references

362.88   Problems of and services to victims of crimes

Bode, Janet
Voices of rape. rev ed. Watts 1998 160p il lib bdg $25; pa $9.95 (7 and up)   362.88
1. Rape
ISBN 0-531-11518-6; 0-531-15932-9 (0a)
LC 97-41225

First published 1990
This volume includes "first-person accounts by rape victims, counselors, health-care providers, law-enforcement officials, and offenders. . . . The author of-

Bode, Janet—*Continued*
fers her interviewees' statements with little editorial comment. . . . While valuable information is provided in addition to the interviews (sections on crisis centers and emergency-room procedures are particularly noteworthy), it is the words of the people directly involved that carry the greatest power." SLJ
Includes bibliographical references

Faherty, Sara
Victims and victims' rights. Chelsea House 1999 111p il (Crime, justice, and punishment) lib bdg $19.95 (7 and up)   **362.88**
1. Victims of crimes
ISBN 0-7910-4308-8   LC 98-36531
Explores victims and victims' rights from various perspectives, including the psychological consequences of victimization, the divergent responses of victims seeking justice and emotional healing, and the tension between granting the wishes of victims and protecting the rights of criminal defendants
Includes bibliographical references

363.1   Public safety programs

Bryan, Nichol, 1958-
Bhopal; chemical plant accident. World Almanac Library 2004 48p il map (Environmental disasters) lib bdg $29.27; pa $11.95 (5 and up)
                    363.1
1. Chemical industry—Accidents 2. Bhopal Union Carbide Plant Disaster, Bhopal, India, 1984
ISBN 0-8368-5503-5 (lib bdg); 0-8368 5510-8 (pa)
                    LC 2003-49718
Presents an account of the 1984 chemical accident at the Union Carbide plant in Bhopal, India, and its aftermath
Includes glossary and bibliographical references

Cole, Michael D.
TWA flight 800; explosion in midair. Enslow Pubs. 1999 48p il (American disasters) lib bdg $18.95   **363.1**
1. Aircraft accidents
ISBN 0-7660-1217-4   LC 98-30265
Describes the explosion that caused TWA Flight 800 to break apart in midair, killing 230 people on July 17, 1996, and examines some possible causes for the disaster
Includes bibliographical references

Hampton, Wilborn
Meltdown; a race against nuclear disaster at Three Mile Island: a reporter's story. Candlewick Press 2001 104p il maps $19.99   **363.1**
1. Three Mile Island Nuclear Power Plant (Pa.) 2. Nuclear power plants 3. Nuclear energy
ISBN 0-7636-0715-0   LC 00-37959
The author "offers an account of his experiences covering the near meltdown at the Three Mile Island nuclear power plant near Harrisburg, PA, in 1979." SLJ

"Hampton's compelling account . . . both objectively portrays the history of nuclear energy leading up to that day and offers an engaging, personal perspective. Readers are left pondering weighty ethical questions about the future of atomic power." Publ Wkly
Includes glossary and bibliographical references

Mayell, Mark
Tragedies of space exploration. Lucent Books 2004 112p il (Manmade disasters) $27.45 (5 and up)   **363.1**
1. Space vehicle accidents 2. Astronautics
ISBN 1-590-18508-0   LC 2003-15618
Contents: Into the dead zone; A pair of shuttle disasters; Rescue efforts; Challenging investigations; Preventing future accidents
Analyzes the inherent risks and dangers of human space exploration, from those that affect the health of astronauts to those that result in shuttle explosions, and examines ways of reducing safety-related incidents.
"Behind-the-headlines details are fresh and thought-provoking. . . . Halftone photographs and clear drawings speak to the reality of these events. . . . [This is] rich in content and detail." SLJ

Mintzer, Richard
The National Transportation Safety Board; [by] Rich Mintzer. Chelsea House 2002 64p il (Your government—how it works) lib bdg $20.75
                    363.1
1. United States. National Transportation Safety Board 2. Traffic accidents
ISBN 0-7910-6794-7   LC 2002-44
Contents: The early growth of transportation in America; The need for safer transportation; The National Transportation Safety Board: how it works; Investigating accidents: the go-team; Investigating Flight 587; Making safety recommendations; Safety concerns of the future
Describes the workings and history of the National Transportation Safety Board as part of the United States government, including how it investigates transportation accidents and makes safety recommendations
Includes glossary and bibliographical references

Riddle, John
Bhopal. Chelsea House 2002 84p il map (Great disasters, reforms and ramifications) lib bdg $22.95 (7 and up)   **363.1**
1. Bhopal Union Carbide Plant Disaster, Bhopal, India, 1984 2. Chemical industry—Accidents
ISBN 0-7910-6741-6   LC 2002-1416
Contents: Danger lies ahead; An unthinkable accident; What happened next; Union carbide responds; A long period of suffering; A look at Bhopal today
Presents an account of the 1984 chemical accident at the Union Carbide plant in Bhopal, India, and explores how the investigation of such accidents can lead to safety reform
This "book is enhanced by eyewitness accounts. . . . Readable and informative. The format is handsome with many photographs to break up the text." Voice Youth Advocates
Includes bibliographical references

Vogt, Gregory
Disasters in space exploration; {by} Gregory L.
Vogt. rev ed. Millbrook Press 2003 79p il lib bdg
$25.90   **363.1**
1. Space vehicle accidents
ISBN 0-7613-2895-5   LC 2003-10864
First published 2001
Examines the failed missions, accidents, and destroyed
vehicles of various world space programs, including the
explosion of the space shuttle Columbia in 2003
"The writing is interesting and succinct without leav-
ing out any of the details. Brimming with clearly repro-
duced full-color and black-and-white photographs." SLJ
Includes bibliographical references

363.2   Police services

Bell, Suzanne
Encyclopedia of forensic science; foreword by
Barry A.J. Fisher; preface by Max M. Houck.
Facts on File 2003 350p il $75   **363.2**
1. Forensic sciences—Encyclopedias
ISBN 0-8160-4811-8   LC 2002-154971
"In addition to explaining the science of forensics,
Bell . . . reviews various disciplines related to forensic
science, among them entomology, odontology, and psychology. Other entries cover professional organizations,
government agencies, famous names in the field of forensics, evidence, and legal issues. . . . With its clear
language and brief entries [this] volume will provide
readers with a nuts-and-bolts understanding of the real
world of forensic science." Booklist
Includes bibliographical references

Campbell, Andrea
Forensic science; evidence, clues, and
investigation. Chelsea House 2000 135p il (Crime,
justice, and punishment) lib bdg $19.95 (7 and up)
                                                363.2
1. Forensic sciences 2. Criminal investigation
ISBN 0-7910-4950-7   LC 99-19454
Examines forensic science and how it can be used to
apprehend criminals by finding clues in rug fibers, the
way a bone is broken, DNA "fingerprints," and more
"A rich compilation of current criminal-investigation
techniques." SLJ
Includes bibliographical references

Friedlander, Mark P.
When objects talk; solving a crime with science;
{by} Mark P. Friedlander, Jr., and Terry M.
Phillips. Lerner Publs. 2001 120p il lib bdg $27.93
                                                363.2
1. Forensic sciences 2. Criminal investigation
ISBN 0-8225-0649-1   LC 00-10247
"This book explains the latest techniques and technology for DNA testing, ballistics, autopsies, bloodstain-
pattern interpretation, and much more, but combines it
with 'The Case,' a fictional account of how forensics is
used to solve a hypothetical murder." Book Rep
"The readable, informative text gives students an understanding of the scientific methods and how they are
used to help police, lawyers, judges, and juries bring
criminals to justice." SLJ
Includes glossary and bibliographical references

Innes, Brian, 1928-
Forensic science. Mason Crest Publs. 2003 96p
il (Crime and detection) lib bdg $22.95 (7 and up)
                                                363.2
1. Forensic sciences 2. Criminal investigation
ISBN 1-59084-373-8   LC 2003-479
Contents: Every contact leaves a trace; Finger of fate;
Deadly poison; Telltale blood; The smoking gun; Fragments of evidence
"The minute details of crime-scene investigation and
painstaking laboratory examination of evidence are described. . . . The large format allows clear views of fingerprinting, bloody footprints, and police examining the
scene of a bombing. The features that separate this treatment from earlier titles . . . are the abundance of color
photographs and the international scope. . . . This is a
detailed and thorough package." SLJ
Includes bibliographical references

Mattern, Joanne, 1963-
Forensics; written by Joanne Mattern.
Blackbirch Press 2004 48p il (Science on the
edge) $23.70 (5 and up)   **363.2**
1. Forensic sciences
ISBN 1-567-11785-6   LC 2003-12995
Contents: Forensics through history; Forensics today;
The future of forensics
Discusses the investigation by scientists and detectives
of deaths that occur under mysterious circumstances,
including how forensic science developed and how tech-
nology is transforming the field.
Includes glossary and bibliographical references

Meltzer, Milton, 1915-
Case closed; the real scoop on detective work.
Orchard Bks. 2001 88p il $18.95 (5 and up)
                                                363.2
1. Detectives 2. Police 3. Criminal investigation
ISBN 0-439-29315-4   LC 2001-16293
"Meltzer's book covers the day-to-day work of detectives, the crime lab, and investigators outside the police
force. Separate chapters provide information . . . on
handwriting and DNA analysis, organized crime, the Pin-
kertons, and the efforts of investigative journalists. . . .
A good choice for career reports or for anyone interested
in the fascinating world of criminal investigation." SLJ
Includes bibliographical references

Owen, David, 1939-
Police lab; how forensic science tracks down
and convicts criminals. Firefly Bks. 2002 128p il
$19.95; pa $9.95 (7 and up)   **363.2**
1. Forensic sciences 2. Criminal investigation
ISBN 1-55297-620-3; 1-55297-619-X (pa)
                                      LC 2002-512986

Owen, David, 1939-—*Continued*

The author explains "how forensics experts gather, analyze, and assess data on forgery, poisoning, suicides, explosions, and murder by fire, water, suffocation, and various weapons. Detailed descriptions of the forensics process are always put into historical context, with brief, gripping summaries of many famous cases and historical events. . . . An exciting, enlightening read." Booklist

Includes glossary

Pentland, Peter

Forensic science; {by} Peter Pentland and Pennie Stoyles. Chelsea House 2003 c2002 32p il (Science and scientists) lib bdg $18.95 (4 and up)
363.2

1. Forensic sciences 2. Criminal investigation
ISBN 0-7910-7010-7   LC 2002-1279
First published 2002 in Australia
Contents: Have you ever wondered . . .?; Questions and clues; Tools of the trade; Would you make a good witness?; Making faces; Leaving your fingerprints; Why are other prints useful?; Is all blood the same?; What is DNA profiling?; Clues in your cleaning up; Teeth tell stories too; Paper and ink; Autopsies; Meet a forensic technician; Forensic science timeline

Surveys some of the scientific principles used in investigating crime scenes and suspects

This title has "colorful illustrations and {uses} sidebars to present interesting tidbits of relevant information." SLJ

Includes glossary

Platt, Richard, 1953-

Crime scene; the ultimate guide to forensic science. DK Publishing 2003 144p il $25
363.2

1. Forensic sciences 2. Criminal investigation
ISBN 0-7894-8891-4   LC 2003-271170
"Techniques such as fingerprint analysis, shoe prints and tire tracks, tool marks and fabric prints, insect analysis, nuclear and mitochondrial DNA evidence, and other tools used by scene-of-the crime investigators are described; details of the collaborative roles of the medical examiner, law enforcement officers, and officers of the court are also included." Sci Books Films

"This is a solid, thorough, well-organized, and beautifully illustrated treatment of the subject of forensic science . . . This book would be invaluable for law classes and reports, as well as for mystery readers and writers." Libr Media Connect

Police brutality: opposing viewpoints; Helen Cothran, book editor. Greenhaven Press 2001 154p il lib bdg $34.95; pa $23.70 (7 and up)
363.2

1. Police brutality 2. Race discrimination
ISBN 0-7377-0516-7 (lib bdg); 0-7377-0515-9 (pa)
LC 00-32996
"Opposing viewpoints series"
"Citing examples overwhelmingly from Los Angeles and New York City, the various contributors to this volume . . . argue heatedly about issues concerning police brutality, especially in relation to alleged abuse of teen

suspects. Four chapters explore whether or not police misconduct truly is a serious problem, what factors cause police brutality, whether modern police methods cause police misconduct, and who should police the police." Booklist

Includes bibliographical references

Schulman, Arlene

Cop on the beat; officer Steven Mayfield in New York City; text & photographs by Arlene Schulman. Dutton Bks. 2002 120p il $18.99; pa $12.99
363.2

1. Mayfield, Steven 2. Police 3. New York (N.Y.)
ISBN 0-525-47064-6; 0-525-46527-8 (pa)
LC 2002-2591
Presents the experiences of Steven Mayfield, a New York City police officer whose beat includes the neighborhoods of Washington Heights and Inwood

"Short and fast-paced, the book includes vivid descriptions of people and events juxtaposed with Mayfield's commentary, creating clear mental images of street-cop life." Voice Youth Advocates

Includes glossary and bibliographical references

Wiese, Jim, 1948-

Spy science; 40 secret-sleuthing, code-cracking, spy-catching activities for kids; illustrations by Ed Shems. Wiley 1996 120p il pa $12.95
363.2

1. Espionage 2. Intelligence service
ISBN 0-471-14620-X   LC 96-7019
Describes the skills, equipment, and techniques that spies use. Includes activities and experiments

Includes glossary

Wirths, Claudine G.

Coping with confrontations and encounters with the police; [by] Claudine G. Wirths, Mary Bowman-Kruhm. Rosen Pub. Group 1998 155p lib bdg $17.95 (7 and up)
363.2

1. Police 2. Law enforcement
ISBN 0-8239-2431-9   LC 97-19059
A practical guide to minimize risks when dealing with police officers and law enforcement procedures

This book "is well written and easy to read, and the real-life examples feel authentic." Voice Youth Advocates

Includes glossary and bibliographical references

363.3   Other aspects of public safety

Campbell, Geoffrey A.

A vulnerable America; an overview of national security; by Geoffrey A. Campbell. Lucent Books 2004 112p il (Lucent library of homeland security) $28.70 (7 and up)
363.3

1. Civil defense 2. Terrorism 3. National security
ISBN 1-590-18383-5   LC 2003-8150
Contents: Safeguarding the nation's transportation system; Bracing for bioterrorism and other weapons; Racial profiling and the battle against terrorism; A consolidation of power; A changing way of life.

Campbell, Geoffrey A.—*Continued*
"Campbell examines America's response to the terrorist attacks of September 11, 2001, and explores the measures taken to increase security and the new challenges to our personal freedoms." SLJ
"Current, informative, and well researched." Booklist
Includes bibliographical references

363.32   Control of violence and terrorism

Terrorism: opposing viewpoints; .; Laura K. Egendorf, book editor. Greenhaven Press 2004 204p il lib bdg $34.95; pa $23.70
363.32
1. Terrorism
ISBN 0-7377-2246-0 (lib bdg); 0-7377-2247-9 (pa)
LC 2003-49497
"Opposing viewpoints series"
Replaces the edition published 2000
This anthology includes essays and writings on terrorism by John Ashcroft, Noam Chomsky, Michelle Malkin, and others. Chapters include: Is terrorism a serious threat?; What are the causes of terrorism?; How should America's domestic war on terrorism be conducted?; How should the international community respond to terrorism?
Includes bibliographical references

363.33   Control of explosives and firearms

Guns and violence; Laura K. Egendorf, book editor. Greenhaven Press 2005 202p (Current controversies) lib bdg $34.95; pa $23.70
363.33
1. Gun control 2. Violence
ISBN 0-7377-2206-1 (lib bdg); 0-7377-2207-X (pa)
LC 2004-52287
Replaces the edition published 1999 under the editorship of Henny H. Kim
Presents differing viewpoints on the seriousness of gun violence, whether or not gun control reduces crime and its constitutionality, the effectiveness of gun ownership as self defense, and what measures would reduce gun violence
Includes bibliographical references

O'Neill, Terry
Gun control. Greenhaven Press 2000 144p il (Opposing viewpoints digests) lib bdg $29.95 (7 and up)
363.33
1. Gun control
ISBN 1-56510-879-5 (lib bdg)
LC 99-48707
Presents opposing arguments on gun control, including gun availability and its influence on society, the constitutionality of gun control, effective measures in reducing gun violence, and the effects of a gun ban on society
Includes bibliographical references

363.34   Disasters

Barnard, Bryn
Dangerous planet; natural disasters that changed history; written and illustrated by Bryn Barnard. Crown Pubs. 2003 48p il maps $17.95; lib bdg $19.99
363.34
1. Natural disasters
ISBN 0-375-82249-6; 0-375-92249-0 (lib bdg)
LC 2002-17545
Describes specific occurrences of natural disasters such as meteor impacts, landslides, typhoons, volcanic eruptions, and earthquakes, and their impact on human history
This is "an absorbing narrative that includes touches of humor. . . . Teachers will find many uses for this, but the book is so engaging it will also attract browsers—and hold them." Booklist
Includes bibliographical references

Bryan, Nichol, 1958-
Los Alamos wildfires. World Almanac Library 2004 48p il map (Environmental disasters) lib bdg $29.27; pa $11.95 (5 and up)
363.34
1. Los Alamos wildfires 2. Wildfires
ISBN 0-8368-5507-8 (lib bdg); 0-8368-5514-0 (pa)
LC 2003-53536
Describes the events surrounding the wildfire that raged in New Mexico in 2000 and the resulting debate over the policy of prescribed burning, or purposely setting fires as a means of forest management.
Includes glossary and bibliographical references

Engelbert, Phillis
Dangerous planet; the science of natural disasters. U.X.L 2001 3v il maps set $165
363.34
1. Natural disasters
ISBN 0-7876-2848-4
LC 98-54422
Contents: v1 Avalanche to El Niño; v2 Flow to mud flow; v3 Tornado to volcano
This set "explains the science behind earthquakes, volcanoes, tornadoes, avalanches, mudslides and other devastating natural disasters. Alphabetically arranged entries typically include a definition of the type of disaster; a summary, including coverage of particularly well-known or destructive occurrences; a discussion of the causes of the disaster; technology's role in predicting and measuring a disaster; {and} a list of further reading." Publisher's note
"The science is accurate, and the technical terms are explained well. The illustrations are clear and well placed." Booklist
Includes bibliographical references

363.4 Controversies related to public morals and customs

Newton, David E.
Drug testing; an issue for school, sports, and work. Enslow Pubs. 1999 128p il lib bdg $19.95 (7 and up) **363.4**
1. Drug testing
ISBN 0-89490-954-1 LC 98-21607
Examines differing opinions on the topic of drug testing by employers, in schools, and in sports as a means of curbing drug abuse
"The writing is clear, succinct, and objective. The text is well organized." SLJ
Includes bibliographical references

Pornography: opposing viewpoints; Helen Cothran, book editor. Greenhaven Press 2002 186p il lib bdg $34.95; pa $23.70 (7 and up) **363.4**
1. Pornography
ISBN 0-7377-0761-5 (lib bdg); 0-7377-0760-7 (pa) LC 2001-16036
"Opposing viewpoints series"
Replaces the edition published 1997 under the editorship of Carol Wekesser
This collection of essays "addresses both sides of the following questions: 'Is Pornography Harmful?' 'Should Pornography Be Censored?' 'How Should Internet Pornography Be Regulated?' 'What Should Be the Feminist Stance on Pornography?'" SLJ
Includes bibliographical references

Smoking; Auriana Ojeda, book editor. Greenhaven Press 2002 175p (Current controversies) lib bdg $31.20; pa $19.95 (7 and up) **363.4**
1. Smoking
ISBN 0-7377-0857-3 (lib bdg); 0-7377-0856-5 (pa) LC 2001-51247
"Selections debate whether the health risks of smoking are exaggerated, consider the impact of advertising by tobacco companies, look at government regulation, and more. . . . Researchers will appreciate the bibliography and the extensive, annotated list of organizations." Booklist

The **war** on drugs; opposing viewpoints; Tamara L. Roleff, book editor. Greenhaven Press 2004 222p il lib bdg $34.95; pa $23.70 **363.4**
1. Drug abuse
ISBN 0-7377-2284-3 (lib bdg); 0-7377-2285-1 (pa) LC 2003-63063
"Opposing viewpoints series"
"Chapters in this . . . anthology include Is the War on Drugs Succeeding? Is There a Link Between the War on Drugs and Terrorism? Which Policies Are Working in the War on Drugs? [and] Should Illegal Drugs Be Legalized?" Publisher's note
Includes bibliographical references

363.46 Abortion

Abortion: opposing viewpoints; Mary E. Williams, book editor. Greenhaven Press 2001 224p il lib bdg $34.95; pa $23.70 (7 and up) **363.46**
1. Abortion
ISBN 0-7377-0778-X (lib bdg); 0-7377-0777-1 (pa) LC 2001-18762
"Opposing viewpoints series"
This work addresses various issues of the abortion debate, including whether abortion is immoral, whether abortion rights should be restricted, if abortion can ever be justified and if abortion is safe
Includes bibliographical references

363.6 Public utilities and related services

Bowden, Rob
Water supply; our impact on the planet. Raintree Steck-Vaughn Pubs. 2003 64p il (21st century debates) lib bdg $28.56 **363.6**
1. Water supply
ISBN 0-7398-5506-9 LC 2002-151938
Contents: A thirsty world; Water as a resource; Water is life; The well runs dry; Polluted water; Water conservation; Water conflicts; A new water economy; Water for tomorrow
This title "looks at the problem of water scarcity, how we use and misuse this precious resource, and what can be done to conserve it, both now and in the future." Publisher's note
The author packs "in a dense amount of data, made accessible by the attractive page design, full-color photos, sidebars, and boxes that extend the scope of [the] volume." Booklist
Includes bibliographical references

363.7 Environmental problems

Barbour, Scott
The environment. Greenhaven Press 2000 144p (Opposing viewpoints digests) lib bdg $28.70; pa $18.70 (7 and up) **363.7**
1. Environmental protection
ISBN 1-56510-873-6 (lib bdg); 1-56510-872-8 (pa) LC 99-49960
Presents opposing views on the state of the environment, discussing global warming, pollution, the consumer culture, federal regulation, and America's role in environmental problems
Includes bibliographical references

Bowden, Rob
Waste; by Rob Bowden. KidHaven Press 2004 48p il (Sustainable world) lib bdg $23.70 **363.7**
1. Refuse and refuse disposal
ISBN 0-7377-1902-8 LC 2003-52951

Bowden, Rob—*Continued*

This "discusses innovations in reuse and recycling, ingenious ways to use what would be discarded, and changes in taxation policy. The many full-color photographs clarify the {text}. {This} will be highly useful for both reports and in classroom discussions." SLJ

Includes bibliographical references

Bryan, Nichol, 1958-

Chernobyl; nuclear disaster. World Almanac Library 2004 48p il map (Environmental disasters) lib bdg $29.27; pa $11.95 (5 and up)

                363.7

1. Chernobyl Nuclear Accident, Chernobyl, Ukraine, 1986 2. Nuclear power plants—Environmental aspects

ISBN 0-8368-5504-3 (lib bdg); 0-8368-5511-6 (pa)

                LC 2003-42291

Discusses the disastrous 1986 accident at the Chernobyl nuclear power plant in the Ukraine.

Includes glossary and bibliographical references

Danube; cyanide spill; by Nichol Bryan. World Almanac Library 2004 48p il map (Environmental disasters) lib bdg $29.27; pa $11.95 (5 and up)

                363.7

1. Chemical spills 2. Water pollution

ISBN 0-8368-5505-1 (lib bdg); 0-8368-5512-4 (pa)

                LC 2003-57694

Discusses the disastrous year 2000 overflow of a Romanian reservoir that held heavy metals and cyanide, pouring the deadly mix into rivers that feed the Danube and killing all living creatures in its path.

Includes glossary and bibliographical references

Exxon Valdez oil spill. World Almanac Library 2004 48p il map (Environmental disasters) lib bdg $29.27; pa $11.95 (5 and up)   **363.7**

1. Exxon Valdez (Ship) 2. Oil spills

ISBN 0-8368-5506-X (lib bdg); 0-8368-5513-2 (pa)

                LC 2003-47991

Describes the oil tanker Exxon Valdez, the events that led up to its disastrous oil spill in 1989, and the effects of the spill on the Alaskan environment.

This is "well-illustrated. . . . {It does} a fine job of placing {the} disaster within a larger context by including detailed background about America's industrial and environmental history; quotes from eyewitnesses, politicians, and journalists; and clear explanations of the changes in policy that {the} disaster instigated." Booklist

Includes glossary and bibliographical references

Love Canal; pollution crisis. World Almanac Library 2004 48p il map (Environmental disasters) lib bdg $29.27; pa $11.95 (5 and up)

                363.7

1. Love Canal Chemical Waste Landfill (Niagara Falls, N.Y.) 2. Pollution

ISBN 0-8368-5508-6 (lib bdg); 0-8368-5515-9 (pa)

                LC 2003-57162

Traces the history and eventual cleanup of the ecological disaster known as Love Canal, which resulted from building a neighborhood over a chemical dumpsite that poisoned the environment and endangered the health of residents.

This is "well-illustrated. . . . [It does] a fine job of placing [the] disaster within a larger context by including detailed background about America's industrial and environmental history; quotes from eyewitnesses, politicians, and journalists; and clear explanations of the changes in policy that [the] disaster instigated." Booklist

Includes glossary and bibliographical references

Davis, Lee Allyn

Environmental disasters; a chronicle of individual, industrial, and governmental carelessness; [by] Lee Davis. Facts on File 1998 246p il $49.50 (7 and up)   **363.7**

1. Pollution 2. Human influence on nature 3. Industrial accidents 4. Disasters

ISBN 0-8160-3265-3   LC 98-29134

"This volume chronicles nearly 100 different environmental tragedies. Although the concentration is on the twentieth century, Davis has also included some events, such as deforestation, that began earlier. . . . The strength of this work is in its coverage of events that did not have the international impact of Chernobyl or Bhopal. Davis makes a strong effort to include the underlying causes of these disasters." Booklist

Includes bibliographical references

The **Environment** encyclopedia; acid rain - zoning; edited by Ruth A. Eblen, William R. Eblen. Marshall Cavendish 2000 11v il maps set $459.95 (7 and up)   **363.7**

1. Environmental sciences—Encyclopedias 2. Ecology—Encyclopedias 3. Earth sciences—Encyclopedias

ISBN 0-7614-7182-0   LC 99-86986

This reference includes 400 articles and over 1,400 color photographs covering such subjects as "natural ecosystems; cultural ecosystems; the history of environmentalism; law, government and education; art, literature and ethics; and biographies." Publisher's note

"This is an attractive, useful set that's sure to hold readers' attention." SLJ

The **environment:** opposing viewpoints; Laura K. Egendorf, book editor. Greenhaven Press 2005 202p il $33.70; pa $26.20   **363.7**

1. Pollution 2. Human ecology 3. Environmental policy—United States

ISBN 0-7377-2230-4; 0-7377-2231-2 (pa)

                LC 2004-49292

"Opposing viewpoints series"

This collection of essays offers varying viewpoints on environmental pollution and protection

Includes bibliographical references

Gardner, Robert, 1929-

Science projects about the environment and ecology. Enslow Pubs. 1999 112p il (Science projects) lib bdg $20.95 (7 and up)   **363.7**

1. Environmental protection 2. Ecology 3. Science—Experiments 4. Science projects

ISBN 0-89490-951-7   LC 98-35049

Presents experiments and projects suitable for science fairs, dealing with such aspects of the environment and

Gardner, Robert, 1929-—*Continued*
ecology as the atmosphere, soil, water, plants, animals, and climate
"Each project is clearly outlined with a list of generally available supplies. The text [is] concise and informative." SLJ
Includes bibliographical references

Global warming: opposing viewpoints; James Haley, editor. Greenhaven Press 2002 224p il $34.95; pa $23.70 (7 and up)   **363.7**
1. Greenhouse effect
ISBN 0-7377-0909-X; 0-7377-0908-1 (pa)
           LC 2001-45128
"Opposing viewpoints series"
Replaces the edition published 1997 under the editorship of Tamara L. Roleff, Scott Barbour and Karin L. Swisher
A collection of articles exploring the scientific evidence for global warming and what, if any, measures should be taken to combat it. Preservation of the world's rain forests is also discussed
Includes bibliographical references

Hall, Eleanor J.
Recycling; by P.M. Boekhoff and Stuart A. Kallen. KidHaven Press 2004 c2005 48p il (Our environment) $23.70 (5 and up)   **363.7**
1. Recycling
ISBN 0-7377-1517-0   LC 2003-21682
Contents: What is recycling?; The challenges of recycling; The benefits of recycling; What does the future hold?
"The liberal use of vibrant colors, the inclusion of a photograph or diagram on most pages, and the generous print size will appeal to reluctant readers. [This title] will help students examine cause and effect (and possible solutions), and challenge them to live green." SLJ
Includes glossary and bibliographical references

Hirschmann, Kris, 1967-
Pollution. Kidhaven Press 2004 c2005 48p il (Our environment) $23.70 (5 and up)
           363.7
1. Pollution
ISBN 0-7377-1563-4
Contents: What is pollution?; Air pollution; Water pollution; Garbage
This briefly describes the sources and effects of air and water pollution and refuse disposal and suggests possible solutions.
Includes glossary and bibliographical references

Kidd, J. S. (Jerry S.)
Into thin air; the problem of air pollution; [by] J.S. Kidd and Renee A. Kidd. Facts on File 1998 134p il maps (Science and society) $25 (7 and up)
           363.7
1. Air pollution
ISBN 0-8160-3585-7   LC 98-9886
Examines the causes of atmospheric pollution, acid rain, ozone depletion, and global warming and explains

how these conditions affect our health and economic prosperity
"The complexity of issues is not glossed over. Students will find the book . . . accessible and useful for research." Booklist
Includes glossary and bibliographical references

Shades of green; the clash of agricultural science and environmental science; [by] J.S. Kidd and Renee A. Kidd. Facts on File 1998 136p il (Science and society) lib bdg $19.95 (7 and up)
           363.7
1. Agriculture 2. Environmental movement
ISBN 0-8160-3583-0   LC 97-15968
This book "examines the struggle between agriculture and the environment. In addition to offering readers a historical perspective of this social conflict, the authors also introduce some of the scientists responsible for the growth in agricultural technology, and individuals, such as Rachel Carson, who have struggled to preserve an uncontaminated environment. . . . Designed for curricular use, this concise overview is a solid supplement and reference source." Booklist
Includes glossary and bibliographical references

Oxlade, Chris
Global warming. Bridgestone Bks. 2003 32p il (Our planet in peril) lib bdg $22.60 (5 and up)
           363.7
1. Greenhouse effect
ISBN 0-7368-1361-6   LC 2002-9823
Contents: About global warming; The atmosphere and the weather; The greenhouse effect; Greenhouse gases; Upsetting the balance; Gathering evidence; Changing climates; More causes of climate change; Modeling the future; Effects of global warming; Problems for us; Stopping global warming; Waking up to global warming
"Double-page chapters introduce topics such as 'The atmosphere and the weather' . . . through brief paragraphs of information. Numerous colorful photographs, graphs, and diagrams with informative captions add details on each spread." SLJ
Includes bibliographical references

Parks, Peggy J., 1951-
Global warming. KidHaven Press 2004 48p il (Our environment) $23.70 (5 and up)
           363.7
1. Greenhouse effect
ISBN 0-7377-1822-6   LC 2002-156050
Contents: What is global warming?; Caused by humans or caused by nature?; Signs and effects of global warming; What can be done?
"The liberal use of vibrant colors, the inclusion of a photograph or diagram on most pages, and the generous print size will appeal to reluctant readers. [This title] will help students examine cause and effect (and possible solutions), and challenge them to live green." SLJ
Includes glossary and bibliographical references

Pollution: opposing viewpoints; Tamara L. Roleff, book editor. Greenhaven Press 2000 224p il lib bdg $33.70; pa $22.45 (7 and up)

363.7

1. Pollution
ISBN 0-7377-0135-8 (lib bdg); 0-7377-0134-X (pa)
LC 99-17677
"Opposing viewpoints series"
"Authors debate the physical effects of pollution on human health and the environment and possible ways to protect both in the following chapters: Is Pollution a Serious Problem? Do Chemical Pollutants Pose a Health Risk? Is Recycling an Effective Response to Pollution? How Can Air Pollution be Reduced? How Should Pollution Be Managed?" Publisher's note
Includes bibliographical references

Pringle, Laurence P.
Global warming; the threat of Earth's changing climate; {by} Laurence Pringle. SeaStar Bks. 2001 48p il $16.95; pa $6.95 (4 and up)   363.7
1. Greenhouse effect
ISBN 1-58717-009-4; 1-58717-28-3 (pa)
LC 00-63740
Replaces the edition published 1990 by Arcade Pub.
"Pringle covers the science of global warming . . . from detailed discussion of atmospheric phenomena to concerns about human production of emissions." Horn Book Guide
"Well-illustrated . . . this offers students a solid, factual overview of the subject." Booklist
Includes glossary and bibliographical references

Reed, Jennifer
Love Canal; [by] Jennifer Bond Reed. Chelsea House 2002 114p il (Great disasters, reforms and ramifications) lib bdg $22.95 (7 and up)

363.7

1. Pollution 2. Love Canal Chemical Waste Landfill (Niagara Falls, N.Y.)
ISBN 0-7910-6742-4   LC 2001-8373
Contents: A mother's crusade; Before the Love Canal crises; Breaking news; Children at risk; The great escape; The great debate; Now what?
This "tells of the unsuspecting residents whose homes and school sat on top of a hazardous-waste site, giving background and context to the issue. It also identifies the major political, medical, scientific, and industrial players, as well as the mother-turned-activist, Lois Gibbs. . . . [This] will give students ample information for reports." SLJ
Includes bibliographical references

Scarborough, Kate
Nuclear waste. Bridgestone Bks. 2003 32p il (Our planet in peril) lib bdg $22.60 (5 and up)

363.7

1. Radioactive waste disposal 2. Nuclear energy
ISBN 0-7368-1362-4   LC 2002-10139
Contents: What is nuclear waste?; The world's energy needs; Fossil fuels; Nuclear energy; Background radiation; Nuclear power stations; Nuclear waste; Low level

and intermediate waste; High level waste; Further research; Nuclear fusion; Public concerns; The future of nuclear power
"Chapters introduce topics such as . . . 'What is nuclear power?' through brief paragraphs of information. Numerous colorful photographs, graphs, and diagrams with informative captions add details on each spread." SLJ
Includes glossary and bibliographical references

Sherrow, Victoria
The Exxon Valdez; tragic oil spill. Enslow Pubs. 1998 48p il (American disasters) lib bdg $18.95   363.7
1. Exxon Valdez (Ship) 2. Oil spills
ISBN 0-7660-1058-9   LC 97-39182
Details the grounding of the Exxon Valdez oil tanker in Prince William Sound, discusses why this disaster happened, describes the cleanup effort, and suggests lessons learned from the event
This "is well documented with citations for all of the statistics and quotes. . . . Reluctant readers will be drawn to . . . [this title] for the simplicity of language and the full-color photos." SLJ
Includes glossary and bibliographical references

Silverstein, Alvin
Global warming; [by] Alvin Silverstein, Virginia Silverstein, Laura Silverstein Nunn. 21st Cent. Bks. (Brookfield) 2002 64p il (Science concepts) lib bdg $26.90   363.7
1. Greenhouse effect
ISBN 0-7613-2256-6   LC 2002-239
Contents: Heating up; Our planet earth; The greenhouse effect; Our changing climate; Is global warming for real?; The effects of global warming; Can global warming be stopped?
Examines global warming and the greenhouse effect, changes in earth's climate since its formation, the effects of these changes, and whether anything can be done to reverse them
This title is "authoritatve, objective, and broadly based. . . . [It is] beautifully designed and well illustrated." SLJ
Includes bibliographical references

363.8   Food supply

Bowden, Rob
Food and farming; by Rob Bowden. KidHaven Press 2004 il map (Sustainable world) lib bdg $23.70   363.8
1. Food 2. Agriculture
ISBN 0-7377-1899-4   LC 2003-52952
This "first presents conventional techniques of food production, but focuses primarily on sustainable agriculture methods. . . . Bowden writes with admirable simplicity about complicated subjects, and he's careful to separate facts from opinions when he quotes others. . . . {The book includes} excellent color photos, and gripping statistics." Booklist
Includes glossary and bibliographical references

363.9 Population problems

Zeaman, John
Overpopulation. Watts 2002 128p il map lib bdg
$25 (7 and up)   **363.9**
1. Population 2. Human ecology
ISBN 0-531-11893-2   LC 2001-17579
The author "discusses factors that have contributed to
overpopulation, including better health care, fewer wars,
and improved grain crops, as well as destructive behaviors that are harming the ecosystems, and offers suggestions for preventing a catastrophic planetary future. . . .
{The book} will be useful for students searching for debate material or researching the future of life on Earth."
SLJ
Includes bibliographical references

364 Criminology

Lane, Brian
Crime & detection; written by Brian Lane;
photographed by Andy Crawford. Knopf 1998 59p
il (Eyewitness books) (4 and up)   **364**
1. Crime 2. Forensic sciences 3. Criminal investigation
LC 97-32376
Available DK Pub. edition $15.95; lib bdg $19.99
(ISBN 0-7894-5882-9; 0-7894-6622-8)
Explores the many different methods used to solve
crimes, covering such topics as criminal, detectives, and
forensics

364.1 Criminal offenses

Blackwood, Gary L.
Gangsters. Benchmark Bks. 2002 72p il (Bad
guys) lib bdg $29.93   **364.1**
1. Criminals
ISBN 0-7614-1016-3   LC 00-57154
This profiles Monk Eastman, James Colosimo, Al
Capone, Clyde Barrow, John Dillinger, and Alvin Karpis
"Useful for research and pleasure reading. . . . There
is an attractive mix of illustrations, photos, maps, and re-
productions." Book Rep
Includes glossary and bibliographical references

Highwaymen. Benchmark Bks. 2002 72p il (Bad
guys) lib bdg $29.93   **364.1**
1. Thieves
ISBN 0-7614-1017-1   LC 99-86663
Describes the lives and careers of such European and
American highwaymen as Claude Duval, Mary Frith, and
Joseph Thompson Hare
"Well written and well designed. . . . {This book is}
illustrated with reproductions of period artwork, docu-
ments, and photographs." Booklist
Includes glossary and bibliographical references

Outlaws. Benchmark Bks. 2002 72p il (Bad
guys) lib bdg $29.93   **364.1**
1. Thieves 2. West (U.S.)—History
ISBN 0-7614-1015-5   LC 00-57161

This profiles seven outlaws of the Old West including
Joaquin Murieta, Jesse James, John Wesley Hardin, Billy
the Kid, Black Bart, Pearl Hart, and Henry Starr
"Vivid photographs, reproductions, and illustrations effectively complement the text. . . . Entertaining and informative reading." SLJ
Includes glossary and bibliographical references

Pirates. Benchmark Bks. 2002 72p il maps (Bad
guys) lib bdg $29.93   **364.1**
1. Pirates
ISBN 0-7614-1019-8   LC 99-86674
Discusses notable pirates and their activities over four
centuries, from Africa to the Caribbean
"Their colorful stories, which often come to violent
conclusions, are related in accessible, engaging prose and
illustrated with reproductions in both black and white
and color." Horn Book Guide
Includes glossary and bibliographical references

Swindlers. Benchmark Bks. 2002 72p il (Bad
guys) lib bdg $29.93   **364.1**
1. Swindlers and swindling
ISBN 0-7614-1031-7   LC 00-57153
"*Swindlers* traces the concept of cheating to the biblical story of Jacob and Esau but focuses on historical personages such as William Henry Ireland, an English forg-
er of Shakespearean plays; Soapy Smith, a con artist of
the American West; and Joseph 'Yellow Kid' Weil, a
swindler on a grand scale. Well written and well designed. . . . Illustrated with reproductions of period artwork, documents, and photographs." Booklist
Includes glossary and bibliographical references

Crowe, Chris
Getting away with murder: the true story of the
Emmett Till case. Phyllis Fogelman Bks. 2003
128p il map $18.99 (7 and up)   **364.1**
1. Till, Emmett 2. Lynching 3. Racism 4. Trials
(Homicide) 5. Mississippi—Race relations
ISBN 0-8037-2804-2   LC 2002-5736
Contents: The boy who triggered the civil rights
movement; Kicking the hornets' nest; The boy from Chicago; The wolf whistle; Setting the stage; Getting away
with murder; Aftershocks
This is the story of "the black 14-year-old from Chicago who was brutally murdered while visiting relatives
in the Mississippi Delta in 1954. . . . The gruesome, racially motivated crime and the court's failure to convict
the white murderers was a powerful national catalyst for
the civil rights movement. . . . Crowe's powerful, terrifying account does justice to its subject in bold, direct
telling, supported by numerous archival photos and
quotes from those who remember." Booklist
Includes bibliographical references

DeAngelis, Gina
White-collar crime. Chelsea House 1999 81p
(Crime, justice, and punishment) $19.95 (7 and up)
364.1
1. White collar crimes
ISBN 0-7910-4279-0   LC 99-26299

DeAngelis, Gina—*Continued*

Discusses such white-collar crimes as fraud, computer crimes, and insider stock trading and how these crimes should be deterred and punished

"The direct text argues that betraying the public trust is as much a crime as cold-blooded murder. Appropriate photos give face to these often victimless crimes." Booklist

Includes bibliographical references

Fooks, Louie

The drug trade; the impact on our lives; Louie Fooks. Raintree 2003 64p il (21st century debates) lib bdg $32.79　　　　　　　　　　**364.1**

1. Drug traffic 2. Drugs and crime
ISBN 0-7398-6033-X　　　　　LC 2003-3593

Contents: The global drug trade; Illegal drugs; Production of illegal drugs; Traffic!; Who uses illegal drugs?; Looking toward solutions; What else can be done?

This "looks at global drug production and trafficking, types of illegal drugs, who uses them, and possible solutions. The book includes information about drug crops and the economic implications that make it difficult for governments around the world to control their sale and abuse. . . . Color photographs are plentiful and color-keyed boxes include opposing viewpoints, facts, and topics to debate." SLJ

Hate groups: opposing viewpoints; Tamara L. Roleff, book editor; Brenda Stalcup, assistant editor; Mary E. Williams, assistant editor. Greenhaven Press 1999 192p il lib bdg $31.20; pa $19.95 (7 and up)　　　　　　**364.1**

1. Hate crimes 2. Militia movements
ISBN 1-56510-943-0 (lib bdg); 1-56510-942-2 (pa)
LC 98-36586

"Opposing viewpoints series"

This collection of articles is divided in four chapters titled: Are hate crimes a serious problem? Do certain groups promote hate and violence? Does the militia movement present a serious threat? and How can hate crimes and terrorism be reduced?

Includes bibliographical references

Illegal drugs; Charles P. Cozic, book editor. Greenhaven Press 1998 173p (Current controversies) lib bdg $26.20; pa $16.20 (7 and up)　　　　　　　　　　　　　**364.1**

1. Drug abuse
ISBN 1-56510-683-0 (lib bdg); 1-56510-682-2 (pa)
LC 97-29281

A collection of essays providing varying viewpoints on drug abuse, drug testing, antidrug programs, and drug legalization

Includes bibliographical references

Johnson, Julie

Why do people join gangs? Raintree Steck-Vaughn Pubs. 2001 48p il (Exploring tough issues) lib bdg $29.93　　　　　　　**364.1**

1. Gangs
ISBN 0-7398-3236-0　　　　　　LC 00-51750

This attempts to explain the attraction of gangs with sections on bullying, rites and rituals, gang mentality, and drug and protection rackets

"Concise and well written, this book provides an overview of the problem, focusing on the United States, but discussing other countries as well." SLJ

Includes glossary and bibliographical references

Kaminker, Laura

Everything you need to know about dealing with sexual assault. Rosen Pub. Group 1998 64p il (Need to know library) lib bdg $17.95

364.1

1. Rape
ISBN 0-8239-2837-3　　　　　　LC 98-7048

Discusses the myths and facts surrounding sexual assault and rape, the physical and psychological consequences, suggests ways to stay safe, and explains what to do if sexually assaulted

Includes glossary and bibliographical references

Roleff, Tamara L., 1959-

Hate groups; by Tami Roleff. Greenhaven Press 2001 112p il (Opposing viewpoints digests) $29.95; pa $19.95 (7 and up)　　　　　**364.1**

1. Hate crimes
ISBN 0-7377-0677-5; 0-7377-0676-7 (pa)
LC 00-12170

This book "poses three basic questions about hate groups and hate speech (Are these groups a problem? Should hate speech be restricted? Are hate crimes laws necessary?) before unveiling documented pro and con essays that explore each question's complexities. Roleff's crisp, journalistic writing combines anecdotes and facts in a dense, but easily readable style." Booklist

Includes bibliographical references

Schroeder, Andreas, 1946-

Scams! ten stories that explore some of the most outrageous swindlers and tricksters of all time. Annick Press 2004 154p (True stories from the edge) $18.95; pa $7.95 (5 and up)　　　**364.1**

1. Fraud 2. Swindlers and swindling
ISBN 1-55037-853-8; 1-55037-852-X (pa)

This is a "collection of stories about forgers, con artists, and other individuals who duped the public for fame, money, love, or power. . . . Schroeder's lively narration with undocumented dialogue breathes life into characters whom readers can't help but marvel at for their sheer ingenuity. . . . Schroeder's page-turning stories are suspenseful." SLJ

Includes bibliographical references

Sherrow, Victoria

The Oklahoma City bombing; terror in the heartland. Enslow Pubs. 1998 48p il (American disasters) lib bdg $18.95　　　　　　**364.1**

1. Oklahoma City (Okla.) bombing, 1995
2. Terrorism
ISBN 0-7660-1061-9　　　　　　LC 97-45750

Sherrow, Victoria—*Continued*

Details the events surrounding the 1995 terrorist bombing of the federal building in Oklahoma City, as well as the investigation and trial of those responsible for the blast

"A vivid accounting. . . . Chapters are brief and punctuated with photographs, which, though not gory, bring the disaster to life in horrifying color." Booklist

Includes glossary and bibliographical references

Shields, Charles J., 1951-

The 1993 World Trade Center bombing. Chelsea House 2002 120p il (Great disasters, reforms and ramifications) lib bdg $23.95; pa $9.95

364.1

1. World Trade Center Bombing, New York, N.Y., 1993 2. Terrorism 3. Bombings

ISBN 0-7910-5789-5 (lib bdg); 0-7910-6915-X (pa)

LC 2001-28794

This is an account "of the tangled web of events surrounding the 1993 Twin Towers bombing—from the planning and execution to the investigation, arrests, and trials that followed. . . . A three-page epilogue describing the events of September 11 adds to the book's value." Booklist

Includes bibliographical references

Silverstein, Herma

Kids who kill. 21st Cent. Bks. (NY) 1997 128p il lib bdg $25.90 (7 and up) **364.1**

1. Homicide 2. Juvenile delinquency

ISBN 0-8050-4369-1 LC 97-8706

Examines the causes, cases, and social and personal impact of the increasing incidence of murders being committed by children and teenagers

"A thoroughly researched, insightful look at the histories, motives, and tragic results of juvenile murders in our society." SLJ

Includes bibliographical references

St. George, Judith, 1931-

In the line of fire; presidents' lives at stake. Holiday House 1999 144p il lib bdg $22.95 (4 and up) **364.1**

1. Kennedy, John F. (John Fitzgerald), 1917-1963 2. McKinley, William, 1843-1901 3. Garfield, James A., 1831-1881 4. Lincoln, Abraham, 1809-1865 5. Presidents—United States—Assassination

ISBN 0-8234-1428-0 LC 98-39030

"The first of the two main sections concerns the four slain U.S. presidents as well as their respective assassins, and also discusses the effects of these fatal events on the country. Each chapter preface relays the day's events preceding the murder in a dramatic fashion. The second half concerns the assassination attempts on six presidents and their would-be assassins. St. George includes intriguing anecdotes. . . . Nicely placed illustrations and photos add power to the text." SLJ

Includes bibliographical references

What is a hate crime? Roman Espejo, book editor. Greenhaven Press 2002 106p (At issue) lib bdg $28.70; pa $19.95 (7 and up) **364.1**

1. Hate crimes

ISBN 0-7377-0813-1 (lib bdg); 0-7377-0812-3 (pa)

LC 2001-23817

This presents a range of opinions about hate crimes from a variety of sources

Includes bibliographical references

364.36 Juvenile delinquents

Youth violence; Henny H. Kim, book editor. Greenhaven Press 1998 204p (Current controversies) lib bdg $34.95 (7 and up)

364.36

1. Juvenile delinquency 2. Violence

ISBN 1-56510-811-6 LC 98-5784

Replaces the edition published 1992 under the editorship of Michael D. Biskup and Charles P. Cozic

This collection of articles "examines the problem of violence among the nation's young people. Chapters include: Is youth violence a serious problem? What causes youth violence? How can youth violence be reduced? Should violent youths receive harsh punishment?" Publisher's note

Includes bibliographical references

364.6 Penology

Kerrigan, Michael

The history of punishment; Michael Kerrigan. Mason Crest Publishers 2003 96p il (Crime and detection) $22.95 (7 and up) **364.6**

1. Punishment

ISBN 1-590 84386-X LC 2003-488

Contents: Introduction; The wages of sin; A debt to society; Corporal punishment; Capital punishment; The rise of rehabilitation

This covers punishment "from the beginning of time, taking into account secular and religious laws and rules of conduct, and the various means people have employed to punish those who violate the laws, including corporal punishment, imprisonment, capital punishment, and rehabilitation efforts. . . . {This book provides} no-nonsense, straightforward, gritty information, accompanied by good-quality, full-color photos, reproductions, and illustrations." SLJ

364.66 Capital punishment

The **Death** penalty: opposing viewpoints; Mary E. Williams, book editor. Greenhaven Press 2001 208p il lib bdg $34.95; pa $23.70 (7 and up)

364.66

1. Capital punishment

ISBN 0-7377-0792-5 (lib bdg); 0-7377-0791-7 (pa)

LC 2001-40456

"Opposing viewpoints series"

This collection of essays presents varying points of view about capital punishment

Includes bibliographical references

Does capital punishment deter crime? Stephen E. Schonebaum, book editor. Greenhaven Press 1998 95p il (At issue) lib bdg $27.45; pa $18.70 (7 and up) **364.66**
1. Capital punishment
ISBN 1-56510-791-8 (lib bdg); 1-56510-091-3 (pa)
LC 98-9752
"This collection includes 10 articles by politicians, lawyers, and human rights activists, who debate the relative power of the death penalty versus life in prison. . . . This volume provides a serious introduction to one aspect of a crucial controversial issue." Booklist
Includes bibliographical references

365 Penal and related institutions

America's prisons: opposing viewpoints; Roman Espejo, book editor. Greenhaven Press 2002 202p il lib bdg $34.95; pa $23.70 (7 and up) **365**
1. Prisons—United States
ISBN 0-7377-0788-7 (lib bdg); 0-7377-0787-9 (pa)
LC 2001-23814
"Opposing viewpoints series"
This "volume tackles four general questions concerning the topic: Are prisons effective? How should prisons treat inmates? Should prisons use inmate labor? What are the alternatives to prisons? . . . Privatization of prisons, chain gangs, inmate labor, creative sentencing, and shame-based punishment all come under discussion. . . . This is a well-balanced approach to the issues, argued with studied analysis rather than blind emotion." Booklist
Includes bibliographical references

Lock, Joan
Famous prisons; Joan Lock. Mason Crest Publishers 2003 96p il (Crime and detection) $22.95 (7 and up) **365**
1. Prisons
ISBN 1-590-84380-0 LC 2003-477
Contents: Alcatraz Federal Penitentiary, California; Up river: Sing Sing Prison, New York State; Halfway to Hell: Dartmoor Prison; The big house: San Quentin State Penitentiary, California; Ireland's model prison: Mountjoy, Dublin; Going around in circles: Stateville Penitentiary, Joliet, Illinois
"Lock takes readers on a tour of famous U.S. prisons . . . as well as one in England . . . and another in Ireland . . . . She includes a history of each one, and the conditions over time, as well as interesting stories about each prison, and some of its famous inmates. . . . [The book provides] no-nonsense, straightforward, gritty information, accompanied by good-quality, full-color photos, reproductions, and illustrations." SLJ
Includes bibliographical references

Rabiger, Joanna
Daily prison life; Joanna Rabiger. Mason Crest Publishers 2003 96p il (Crime and detection) $22.95 (7 and up) **365**
1. Prisons 2. Prisoners
ISBN 1-590-84384-3 LC 2003-364

"Rabiger concentrates on the U.S. prison system and gives readers a closeup and grimly realistic view of living in one. . . . {This book provides} no-nonsense, straightforward, gritty information, accompanied by good-quality, full-color photos, reproductions, and illustrations." SLJ
Includes bibliographical references

370 Education

Fridell, Ron, 1943-
Education for all; floating schools, cave classrooms, and backpacking teachers. 21st Cent. Bks. (Brookfield) 2002 80p il (In a perfect world) lib bdg $26.90 **370**
1. Education—Developing countries
ISBN 0-7613-2624-3 LC 2002-3305
Explains the lack of education in countries around the world and discusses the organizations that help children receive schooling
This is a "well-researched book. . . . Valuable for gaining a better understanding of the living conditions in the third world." Voice Youth Advocates
Includes bibliographical references

370.25 Education--Directories

The **Handbook** of private schools; an annual descriptive survey of independent education. Sargent Pubs. il map $95 **370.25**
1. Private schools—Directories 2. Education—United States—Directories
ISSN 0072-9884
Annual. First published 1915 with title: Handbook of the best private schools of the United States and Canada
"Describes more than 1,700 boarding and day schools, providing information on age and grade ranges, whether co-educational or for boys or girls, enrollment, faculty size and background, academic orientation and curriculum, and where graduates attend college. 'Features classifield' section lists institutions offering military programs, elementary boarding divisions, programs for students with learning differences, international and bilingual schools, and schools with more than 500 or fewer than 100 students." Guide to Ref Books. 11th edition

370.9 Education--Historical and geographic treatment

Loeper, John J., 1929-
Going to school in 1776. Atheneum Pubs. 1973 79p il $16 (4 and up) **370.9**
1. Education—United States—History 2. United States—Social life and customs—1600-1775, Colonial period 3. Schools—United States—History
ISBN 0-689-30089-1 LC 72-86940
The author tells what it was like to be a child and to go to school in America in 1776. He describes children's dress, schools, teachers, school books, lessons, discipline and after-school recreation
Includes bibliographical references

371.1   Teachers, teaching, and related activities

Harada, Violet H.
Inquiry learning through librarian-teacher partnerships; {by} Violet H. Harada and Joan M. Yoshina. Linworth Pub 2004 172p il pa $39.95
371.1
1. Teaching teams 2. School libraries
ISBN 1-586-83134-8   LC 2004-662
"The authors describe what happens in an inquiry-based classroom and library media center and show teachers/librarians how to develop a curriculum that incorporates essential questions and important habits of mind, all aligned with content standards. . . . The volume contains everything a teacher-librarian team would need to create, teach, research, and assess major interdisciplinary units." SLJ
Includes bibliographical references

371.2   School administration

Gilbert, Sara D.
How to do your best on tests; {by} Sara Dulaney Gilbert. rev ed. Morrow Junior Bks. 1998 128p il hardcover o.p. paperback available $4.99 (7 and up)   **371.2**
1. Examinations 2. Study skills
ISBN 0-688-16090-5 (pa)   LC 98-14297
First published 1983 with title: How to take tests
Discusses effective ways to successfully study for and take tests, including quizzes, final exams, and standardized tests, emphasizing the methods of preview, view, review

Terkel, Marni
What's an "A" anyway? how important are grades? by Marni Terkel and Susan Neiburg Terkel. Watts 2001 143p il lib bdg $25 (7 and up)
371.2
1. Grading and marking (Education) 2. Educational tests and measurements
ISBN 0-531-11417-1   LC 00-43731
This book "looks at a variety of ranking-related issues in school—among them, the effect of grading on curriculum and performance, multiple intelligences, grade inflation, and schools that don't give grades. There are even some study and homework tips. . . . A solid resource on a topic that is important to students but rarely addressed at their level." Booklist
Includes glossary and bibliographical references

371.3   Methods of instruction and study

Barron, Ann E.
Technologies for education; a practical guide; [by] Ann E. Barron [et al.] 4th ed. Libraries Unlimited 2002 234p il pa $48   **371.3**
1. Teaching—Aids and devices
ISBN 1-56308-779-0   LC 2001-50746
First published 1993 with title: New technologies for education
This discusses such educational technologies as graphics and digital audio
"This useful, practical guide will be a boon for teachers and librarians. . . . The book is clearly written and easy to understand." Libr Media Connect
Includes bibliographical references

Directory of distance learning opportunities, K-12; compiled by Modoc Press, Inc. Greenwood Press 2003 302p $69.95   **371.3**
1. Distance education—Directories 2. Correspondence schools and courses
ISBN 1-573-56515-6   LC 2002-35210
"An Oryx book"
"Designed for librarians, parents, and school counselors looking for information on specific K-12 distance learning courses of study, this work contains an overview of the current status of distance education in the U.S. and in-depth information on more than 6,000 courses offered by 154 U.S. institutions and consortia. . . . Both print-based (correspondence study) and electronic (via the Internet, satellite broadcast, or interactive television) programs are included. . . . This directory is sure to be a welcome addition in public and school libraries. Nothing else pulls so much information together in one print source." Booklist

Wood, Gail
How to study; use your personal learning style to help you succeed when it counts. 2nd ed. LearningExpress 2000 176p il pa $14.95 (7 and up)   **371.3**
1. Study skills
ISBN 1-576-85308-X   LC 00-32720
First published 1998
This offers advice on developing such skills as overcoming procrastination, time management, reading comprehension, listening and note-taking, class participation and discussion, and preparing for tests.

371.7   Student welfare

Hester, Joseph P.
Public school safety; a handbook, with a resource guide. McFarland & Co. 2003 200p pa $35   **371.7**
1. School violence 2. Education—Government policy
ISBN 0-7864-1483-9   LC 2003-2511

Hester, Joseph P.—*Continued*

Contents: The state of youth violence and its roots; Public school safety, government initiatives; Strategies for building a school safety program; Measures to ensure school safety, model programs; Building a leadership culture; National resources for safe school programs; Resources for the Surgeon General's report

This "begins by discussing a number of important government reports that have identified the problems and causes of youth violence and some ideas for combating it. . . . The myriad strategies involving the community, parents, and teachers are discussed and both ineffective and effective programs are evaluated. . . . This is a solid and thorough guide." SLJ

Includes bibliographical references

Orr, Tamra

Violence in our schools; halls of hope, halls of fear. Franklin Watts 2003 192p il $29.50 (7 and up)   **371.7**

1. School violence

ISBN 0-531-12268-9   LC 2003-104

Chronicles school violence and discusses its causes, perpetrators, and solutions, including "Questions to ponder" and specific advice for individual action

"This book takes an evenhanded, enlightening look at the problem of, and possible solutions for, school violence. . . . For students doing research, the book offers succinct summaries of incidents of school violence dating back to the 1920s, and it includes an overview of the Columbine tragedy. . . . For sociology research and for schools seeking proactive ideas for creating safe and inclusive campuses, this is an excellent resource." Booklist

Includes bibliographical references

371.8   Students

Cruz, Bárbara

School dress codes; a pro/con issue; {by} Bárbara C. Cruz. Enslow Pubs. 2001 64p il (Hot pro/con issues) $27.93   **371.8**

1. Dress codes

ISBN 0-7660-1465-7   LC 00-21972

The author gives a "presentation of the cases for and against dress codes, and the cases for and against school uniforms. Citing real-life situations in schools across the nation, she gives readers insight into the controversy. Written clearly and including chapter notes and a resource list for related Web sites, the book will be useful for reports or debates." SLJ

Tym, Kate

School survival; a guide to taking control of your life; [by] Kate Tym and Penny Worms. Raintree 2005 48p il (Get real) $29.93
                                              371.8

1. Socialization 2. Schools 3. Peer pressure

ISBN 1-4109-0577-2   LC 2004-8070

Contents: It's what I go to school for; A friend in need; Peer pressure; Misfit city; Bully boys and girls; I'm in trouble; Moving on

"Chapters consist of a spread presenting an overview of a topic such as . . . peer pressure, followed by three case studies about teens dealing with the problem. On the same page, three 'experts' . . . offer advice. . . . The advice of professionals lends credibility to the information presented. . . . [This volume is] sure to appeal to readers looking for advice." SLJ

371.9   Special education

Kent, Deborah, 1948-

Athletes with disabilities. Watts 2003 63p il lib bdg $24; pa $8.95 (4 and up)   **371.9**

1. Sports for the handicapped

ISBN 0-531-12019-8 (lib bdg); 0-531-16664-3 (pa)
                                        LC 2002-8883

"Watts library"

Contents: The love of the game; Beating the odds; Brave in the attempt; Going for the Gold; A level playing field

Explores the people and events involved in sports competitions for people with disabilities and discusses people with disabilities who play professional sports

"Information is effectively conveyed through clear, straightforward prose and accounts of individual athletes. . . . {This is} informative, often inspirational and thought-provoking." Booklist

Includes bibliographical references

Paquette, Penny Hutchins

Learning disabilities; the ultimate teen guide; [by] Penny Hutchins Paquette, Cheryl Gerson Tuttle. Scarecrow Press 2003 301p il (It happened to me) lib bdg $32.50   **371.9**

1. Learning disabilities

ISBN 0-8108-4261-0   LC 2002-17588

This provides an "overview of the most common disabilities. . . . The book also teaches students how to advocate for themselves, informing them of their rights under law both during the school years and after high school graduation. . . . Assistive technology that can help students improve their learning abilities such as Optical Character Recognition (OCR) systems, screen reading software, books on tape, electronic notebooks, and other tools that aid student learning are covered." Publisher's note

"Far more detailed than similiar books from other publishers." Voice Youth Advocates

Includes bibliographical references

Stanley, Jerry, 1941-

Children of the Dust Bowl; the true story of the school at Weedpatch Camp. Crown 1992 85p il maps hardcover o.p. paperback available $9.95 (5 and up)   **371.9**

1. Migrant labor 2. Great Depression, 1929-1939 3. Education—Social aspects

ISBN 0-517-88094-6 (pa)   LC 92-393

Describes the plight of the migrant workers who traveled from the Dust Bowl to California during the Depression and were forced to live in a federal labor camp and discusses the school that was built for their children

Stanley, Jerry, 1941-—*Continued*
"Stanley's text is a compelling document. . . . The story is inspiring and disturbing, and Stanley has recorded the details with passion and dignity." Booklist
Includes bibliographical references

372.4 Reading

Bouchard, Dave
The gift of reading; [by] David Bouchard, with Wendy Sutton. Orca Bk. Pubs. 2001 158p il pa $16.95   **372.4**
1. Reading 2. Books and reading
ISBN 1-55143-214-5   LC 2001-92682
This "overview of what young people need to become independent readers . . . targets families, teachers, and school administrators, claiming that nothing extravagant is required to promote reading. . . . All groups will find the grade-level reading lists and abundant literacy strategies helpful." Voice Youth Advocates

Knowles, Elizabeth, 1946-
Talk about books! a guide for book clubs, literature circles, and discussion groups, grades 4-8. Libraries Unlimited 2003 147p il pa $30
                                                            372.4
1. Books and reading
ISBN 1-591-58023 4   LC 2003-51582
"Each of the fifteen chapters focuses on a different book that serves as a prototype for a particular subject or genre. . . . Each focal book is briefly summarized, followed by a bit of biographical information about its author. Then a list of discussion questions is offered. . . . The questions nicely probe both concrete and abstract understanding of the book. . . . In addition, each chapter includes activities for all areas of the curriculum, an annotated list of related books, an annotated list of the author's other works, dozens of Web site suggestions, and the publisher's information." Voice Youth Advocates
Includes bibliographical references

372.6 Language arts (Communication skills)

Ellis, Sarah, 1952-
From reader to writer; teaching writing through classic children's books. Douglas & McIntyre 2000 176p $24.95   **372.6**
1. Rhetoric—Study and teaching 2. Children's literature—Study and teaching
ISBN 0-88899-372-2
"A Groundwood book"

.
The author discusses the work of seventeen British, Canadian and American authors of children's literature. "With each classic book, there's a 'sneak preview' (i.e., booktalk), a suggested read-aloud, exercises to help students and adult writers find their own stories, and a short annotated bibliography of related children's books." Booklist

Hopkins, Lee Bennett, 1938-
Pass the poetry, please! 3rd ed. HarperCollins Pubs. 1998 277p $25; pa $!5.99   **372.6**
1. Poetry—Study and teaching
ISBN 0-06-027746-7; 0-06-446199-8 (pa)
                                                    LC 98-19617
First published 1972
"Written for teachers and librarians seeking ways of getting poetry into the lives of children. . . . Throughout, many poets are cited, from Langston Hughes to Nikki Giovanni and from Jack Prelutsky to Robert Frost." Booklist
"This a must-purchase." SLJ
Includes bibliographical references

373 Secondary education

Somerlott, Robert, 1928-
The Little Rock school desegregation crisis in American history. Enslow Pubs. 2001 128p il (In American history) lib bdg $26.60   **373**
1. Central High School (Little Rock, Ark.) 2. School integration 3. African Americans—Civil rights
ISBN 0-7660-1298-0   LC 00-11444
This book discusses the desegregation of Central High School in Little Rock Arkansas in 1957
This is a "well-researched and well-documented account. . . . Somerlott clearly captures the courage of the students and their families in the face of violent threats. He also presents a broader view of the impact of this event on the city of Little Rock, the state of Arkansas, and the nation." SLJ
Includes bibliographical references

373.1 Organization and activities in secondary education

Erlbach, Arlene
The middle school survival guide; illustrations by Helen Flook. Walker & Co. 2003 150p il pa $8.95   **373.1**
1. Life skills 2. Middle schools 3. Teenagers
ISBN 0-8027-8852-1   LC 2002-34784
Contents: A new school, a new environment; Teachers; Academics; Peers; The opposite sex; Home life; Puberty; Really serious stuff; Being yourself
A guidebook to help deal with changes in school, families, social lives, and bodies that come during the middle school years, with specific advice for a variety of situations
"Erlbach's advice is sound, but the real gems are the quotes from kids. There are some explicit content and frank discussion, with Erlbach using the same no-nonsense language whether covering drugs, sexual harassment, crushes, cheating, oral sex, or pregnancy. . . . Strong, and well-delivered, often necessary medicine." Booklist

Farrell, Juliana

High school, the real deal; from GPAs to graduation; {by} Juliana Farrell, Colleen Rush. HarperCollins Pubs. 2001 142p il pa $7.95

373.1

1. High schools

ISBN 0-380-81314-9 LC 00-66219

This offers "advice about the academic, extracurricular, and social changes faced by students entering high school." Booklist

This is "well organized, and the funky format will keep the interest of even the most reluctant reader." Voice Youth Advocates

Middle school, the real deal; from cafeteria food to combination locks; {by} Juliana Farrell, Beth Mayall. HarperCollins Pubs. 2001 139p il pa $7.99

373.1

1. Middle schools

ISBN 0-380-81313-0 LC 00-66218

"New middle school students are given advice about living through the first day of school, handling the changing classroom schedule after being in a single elementary classroom, the benefits of extracurricular activities, making and keeping friends, and how to get along with parents." Voice Youth Advocates

"This is a must-have book for middle schoolers. . . . With a very appealing cover, this book contains just the right amount of information and is reader friendly." BAYA Book Rev

Lieberman, Susan Abel

The real high school handbook; how to survive, thrive, and prepare for what's next. Houghton Mifflin 1997 130p pa $13 (7 and up)

373.1

1. High schools

ISBN 0-395-79760-8 LC 97-26558

"A Mariner original"

This book provides information about courses, grades, testing, communicating with teachers, and postgraduation options

"The book is chockablock with information. . . . A good book that does exactly what it sets out to do: help YAs start thinking clearly about school as it impacts on the rest of their lives." Booklist

Pipkin, Gloria

At the schoolhouse gate; lessons in intellectual freedom; [by] Gloria Pipkin and ReLeah Cossett Lent; foreword by Susan Ohanian. Heinemann (Portsmouth) 2002 xx, 235p pa $21 **373.1**

1. Academic freedom 2. Censorship 3. Public schools

ISBN 0-325-00395-5 LC 2001-39909

"Two English teachers share their . . . personal battle to support students intellectual rights in the Bay County School District in Florida in the 1980s when censorship cases were looming in schools throughout the nation. . . . This book is one of inspiration, and teachers, librarians, and school administrators may find it encouraging as they face similar battles." SLJ

Includes bibliographical references

Serritella, Judy, 1948-

Look again! appealing bulletin board ideas for secondary students. Linworth Pub. 2002 160p pa $36.95 **373.1**

1. Bulletin boards 2. Teenagers—Books and reading

ISBN 1-58683-053-8 LC 2002-16181

"Basic practical tips suggest ways to liven up board displays, for example, by using three-dimensional materials such as corrugated cardboard or wallpaper. Ideas focus on providing students with information they need, as well as on promoting reading and library services." Book Rep

Includes bibliographical references

Shostak, Jerome

How to prepare for the SSAT/ ISEE: Secondary School Admissions Test/Independent School Entrance Exam; [by] Jerome Shostak, Max Peters. Barron's Educ. Ser. il $13.95 pa $14.95

373.1

1. High schools—Entrance requirements

First published 1961 with title: Barron's how to prepare for high school entrance examinations, SSAT, ISEE. (9th edition 2001) Periodically revised

This book attempts to prepare students for qualifying exams required by prep schools, parochial high schools and specialized public high schools. It reviews basic verbal and mathematical skills as well as abstract reasoning. Answers are provided for all questions, and step-by-step solutions are demonstrated for mathematics problems

379 Public policy issues in education

Haskins, James, 1941-2005

Separate, but not equal; the dream and the struggle. Scholastic 1998 184p il hardcover o.p. paperback available $4.99 (5 and up) **379**

1. African Americans—Education 2. School integration 3. Segregation in education

ISBN 0-590-45911-2 LC 96-51507

The author traces "the history of the African American struggle for equal rights to education, from the enforced illiteracy of slavery times to the present debate about affirmative action." Booklist

"With his knack for blending historical facts and thoughtful interpretation, Haskins offers an informative, closeup look at the course of black education in America." SLJ

Includes bibliographical references

384 Communications. Telecommunication

Graham, Ian, 1953-

Global networks. Raintree Steck-Vaughn Pubs. 2001 47p il (Communications close-up) $20.95

384

1. Computer networks 2. Telecommunication

ISBN 0-7398-3188-7 LC 00-33285

Graham, Ian, 1953——*Continued*
A brief introduction to telecommunications and computer networks and their applications
The author "provides a compelling look at communications in the 21st century. Graham is not only knowledgeable about his subject but also adept at clearly explaining complex information. The colorful, attractive illustrations add to the textual explanations." Book Rep
Includes glossary and bibliographical references

384.5 Wireless communication

Byers, Ann
Communications satellites. Rosen Pub. Group 2003 58p il (Library of satellites) lib bdg $26.50
384.5
1. Artificial satellites in telecommunication
ISBN 0-8239-3851-4   LC 2002-7527
Contents: How satellites work; The "global village"; The business of satellite communication; What comes next?
This discusses the history, development, and applications of communications satellites
"Clear and topical photographs enliven the [presentation]. While packed with information, the [text is] easy to read." SLJ
Includes bibliographical references

385 Railroad transportation

Houghton, Gillian
The Transcontinental Railroad; a primary source history of America's first coast-to-coast railroad. Rosen Central 2002 64p il map (Primary sources in American history) lib bdg $29.25 (5 and up)
385
1. Union Pacific Railroad Company 2. Railroads—United States
ISBN 0-8239-3684-8   LC 2001-8530
Describes the people, circumstances, and events surrounding the building of the railway system across the continent in the mid-nineteenth century.
"Clearly written [text is] accompanied by numerous reproductions of handbills, maps, period photographs, portraits, political cartoons, the National Republican platform of 1860, blueprints, and letters. . . . [This] will be useful to students and their teachers." SLJ
Includes glossary and bibliographical references

Meltzer, Milton, 1915-
Hear that train whistle blow! how the railroad changed the world. Random House 2004 157p il $18.95; lib bdg $20.95 (5 and up)   **385**
1. Railroads
ISBN 0-375-81563-5; 0-375-91563-X (lib bdg)
LC 2003-13255
"Landmark books"
"Illustrated with numerous archival photographs, this excellent, comprehensive history will be a welcome addition." SLJ

Zimmermann, Karl R.
Steam locomotives; whistling, chugging, smoking iron horses of the past. Boyds Mills Press 2004 48p il $19.95 (4 and up)   **385**
1. Locomotives 2. Steam engines
ISBN 1-59078-165-1
"In this photo-essay, Zimmermann shares his excitement for steam locomotives with young readers, tracing the development of the early engines and their impact on the history of the U.S. He includes a clear explanation . . . of how a steam engine works. The photographs, some archival and some from the present day, are excellent. . . . The engaging text clearly imparts the author's enthusiasm and love for the subject." SLJ
Includes glossary

386 Inland waterway and ferry transportation

Bial, Raymond
The canals. Benchmark Bks. 2002 56p il map (Building America) lib bdg $27.07   **386**
1. Canals
ISBN 0-7614-1336-7   LC 00-65078
This describes the history of canals in America from colonial times to the 19th century
This book is "marked by strong research, clear writing, good organization, and very handsome color photographs." Booklist
Includes glossary and bibliographical references

McNeese, Tim
The Panama Canal. Lucent Bks. 1997 96p il maps (Building history series) lib bdg $22.45 (7 and up)   **386**
1. Panama Canal
ISBN 1-56006-425-0   LC 96-45623
Describes the planning and building of the Panama Canal
"McNeese describes in detail the great effort that was required to complete this project, from the political conniving to the physical construction of the canal itself. Historical black-and-white photographs illustrate this monumental venture. . . . A solid choice for libraries wanting to provide support for research reports." SLJ
Includes bibliographical references

387.2 Ships

Kentley, Eric
Boat; written by Eric Kentley. Knopf 1992 63p il (Eyewitness books) (4 and up)   **387.2**
1. Ships 2. Boats and boating
LC 91-53136
Available DK Pub. edition $15.95; lib bdg $19.99 (ISBN 0-7894-5758-X; 0-7894-6585-X)
"A Dorling Kindersley book"
A history of the development and uses of boats, ships, and rafts, from birch-bark canoes to luxury liners

Macaulay, David, 1946-
Ship. Houghton Mifflin 1993 96p il $19.95; pa
$12.95 (4 and up)   **387.2**
1. Shipwrecks 2. Underwater exploration
3. Caribbean region—Antiquities
ISBN 0-395-52439-3; 0-395-74518-7 (pa)
LC 92-1346
This book "opens with an underwater find in the Caribbean and, in story and illustration, follows the work of
marine archeologists in studying the wreck. As part of
the background research in Spain, one of the team finds
a diary recording the building of a caravel in 1504. The
rest of the book contains a 'translation' of the diary with
accompanying illustrations. Though a fictional account,
the narrative gives a good feel for the maritime technology of the early 16th century." Sci Books Films

Sandler, Martin W.
On the waters of the USA; ships and boats in
American life. Oxford Univ. Press 2004 63p il
(Transportation in America) $19.95 (5 and up)
387.2
1. Shipping—United States 2. Ships 3. Boats and
boating
ISBN 0-19-513227-0
Explores the evolving role of boats and ships in
American history, from the dugout and birchbark canoes
of Native Americans to twenty-first century container
ships and supertankers.
This is a "fascinating account. . . . Drawings, maps,
and photographs are well placed and fully captioned.
. . . The large type is reader friendly, and the writing is
clear and engaging." SLJ
Includes bibliographical references

388   Transportation. Ground transportation

Macmillan Encyclopedia of transportation.
Macmillan Ref. USA 2000 6v il map set $450
388
1. Transportation—Encyclopedias
ISBN 0-02-865361-0   LC 99-33371
Contents: v1 Accidents—Aviation, history of; v2 Bal-
last—European Space Agency; v3 Exploration—Motor-
boats; v4 Motorcycles—Sailboats and sailing ships; v5
Sailing—Tankers; v6 Tanks—Zeppelins
An encyclopedia covering different methods of transportation and key events, people, and social, economic,
and political issues in the history of transportation
Entries present "information in a readable and entertaining manner. . . .This set will be useful in school and
public libraries." Booklist

388.4   Local transportation

DuTemple, Lesley A., 1952-
The New York subways. Lerner Publs. 2003
80p il (Great building feats) lib bdg $27.93 (5 and
up)   **388.4**
1. Subways 2. New York (N.Y.)—History
ISBN 0-8225-0378-6   LC 2001-6143

Traces the history of the underground transportation
system in New York City, discussing the politics involved, how it was financed, the men who built it, and
the construction techniques
"DuTemple does a fine job. . . . [Photos] sidebars,
maps, and archival material work beautifully together to
supplement the information." Booklist
Includes bibliographical references

Sandler, Martin W.
Straphanging in the USA; trolleys and subways
in American life. Oxford Univ. Press 2003 61p il
(Transportation in America) lib bdg $19.95 (5 and
up)   **388.4**
1. Subways 2. Street railroads 3. City and town life
ISBN 0-19-513229-7
An illustrated look at how the problem of moving
large numbers of people within cities has been addressed
through a series of vehicles and systems, from horse-
drawn cars to the modern subway.
"The fascinating narrative is embellished with reproductions of historical photos and illustrations and period
quotes from newspapers, magazines, and books. This offering will capture the interest of casual readers and provide researchers with plenty of information." SLJ
Includes bibliographical references

391   Costume and personal appearance

Fashions of a decade [series] Facts on File
1991-1992 8v il set $200   **391**
1. Costume
ISBN 0-8160-2464-2
Volumes also available separately ea $25
Contents: The 1920s by Jacqueline Herald; The 1930s
by Marie Costantino; The 1940s by Patricia Baker; The
1950s by by Patricia Baker; The 1960s by Yvonne
Connikie; The 1970s by Jacqueline Herald; The 1980s by
by Vicky Carnegy; The 1990s by Elane Feldman
This set describes clothing styles of the 20th century
in the context of world events, social movements, and
cultural movements of each decade.
"Almost every page in these . . . volumes includes at
least one vivid full-color fashion drawing or photograph.
. . . These titles . . . will be fun for browsers and those
interested in an introduction to the concept of clothing
design in the context of contemporary events." SLJ

Finley, Carol
The art of African masks; exploring cultural
traditions. Lerner Publs. 1999 64p il map (Art
around the world) $23.93 (5 and up)   **391**
1. Masks (Facial) 2. African art
ISBN 0-8225-2078-8   LC 98-10570
Describes how different types of masks are made and
used in Africa and how they reflect the culture of their
ethnic groups
"Clear, sharp full-color photographs of museum artifacts are well placed on the pages. . . . Pictures of modern members of still-existing cultures add to the attractiveness of this volume." SLJ
Includes bibliographical references

Graydon, Shari

In your face; the culture of beauty and you. Annick 2004 176p il pa $14.95 (7 and up)

391

1. Personal appearance
ISBN 1-55037-856-2

The author "looks at fashion across time and cultures, and analyzes the underlying messages in today's focus . . . on thinness, long nails, and high heels. Along the way, she warns both young men and women of the very real dangers of eating disorders, plastic surgery, liposuction, and other body-image 'solutions.' . . . Graydon will make readers laugh as well as think about the issues." Booklist

Includes bibliographical references

Hoobler, Dorothy

Vanity rules; a history of American fashion and beauty; {by} Dorothy and Thomas Hoobler. Millbrook Press 1999 160p il lib bdg $28.90

391

1. Costume 2. Personal appearance 3. United States—Social life and customs
ISBN 0-7613-1258-7   LC 99-12820

Describes the shifting ideal of beauty in the United States, from colonial times to the present, and how it influenced and was influenced by societal and economic changes

"Quotations give voice to Americans from different periods, while the many well-told anecdotes keep the writing from becoming too dry or simply descriptive. . . . An engaging volume of social history for browsing or research." Booklist

Includes bibliographical references

Mason, Paul, 1967-

Body piercing and tattooing. Heinemann Lib. 2003 56p il (Just the facts) lib bdg $25.64

391

1. Tattooing 2. Body piercing
ISBN 1-4034-0817-3   LC 2002-10936

Contents: Body piercing and tattooing ; What is body piercing?; What is tattooing?; The first tattoos; Tatau; Piercing; Into the West; How tattooing and piercing work; Does it hurt?; Safe tattoos and piercings; Possible problems; Caring for a tattoo; Permanence; Impermanent tattoos; Living with tattoos and piercings: motivations and decisions; Positive reactions; Negative reactions; Cosmetic tattooing; Getting help; Treatment and removal; Legal issues

Describes the history of body piercing and tattooing, as well as what motivates people to get a piercing or a tattoo, how to care for them, problems that can arise, and legal issues surrounding them

"The writing is clear and frank. . . . Students will find much to like and make use of in {this book}." Libr Media Connect

Includes glossary and bibliographical references

Miller, Brandon Marie

Dressed for the occasion; what Americans wore 1620-1970. Lerner Publs. 1999 96p il $26.60

391

1. Costume
ISBN 0-8225-1738-8   LC 98-22668

Examines the history, manufacture, and care of American clothing from colonial times to the 1970s and discusses its relationship to the social milieu

"An excellent overview. . . . Interesting tidbits, such as what was under those hoop skirts, enliven the presentation. The text is highlighted with sepia-toned reproductions and photographs." SLJ

Includes bibliographical references

Pendergast, Sara

Fashion, costume, and culture; clothing, headwear, body decoration, and footwear through the ages; {by} Sara Pendergast and Tom Pendergast. UXL 2004 5v il set $275   391

1. Costume—History 2. Clothing and dress 3. Fashion
ISBN 0-7876-5417-5

This set "surveys how people have covered and adorned themselves through the ages and around the world. . . . There are 430 entries in all, ranging from a paragraph or two to a page. . . .The work is notable for its organization, breadth of coverage, and attractive design. Strongly recommended for school and public libraries." Booklist

Rowland-Warne, L.

Costume; written by L. Rowland-Warne. Knopf 1992 63p il (Eyewitness books) (4 and up)

391

1. Costume 2. Clothing and dress
          LC 91-53135

Available DK Pub. edition $15.99 (ISBN 0-7894-5586-2; lib bdg $19.99 (ISBN 0-7894-6584-1)

"A Dorling Kindersley book"

Photographs and text document the history and meaning of clothing, from loincloths to modern children's clothes

This "fascinating historical overview . . . blends close-up, full-color photographs of period clothing and accessories with brief snippets of text that explain the item's significance and purpose." SLJ

Sills, Leslie

From rags to riches; a history of girls' clothing in America; Leslie Sills. 1st ed. Holiday House 2005 48p il $16.95 (5 and up)   391

1. Children's clothing 2. Girls
ISBN 0-8234-1708-5   LC 2003-67600

A history of the clothing of American girls from colonial times to the present.

"The sparkling design of Sills' overview makes this a pleasure to page through. . . . A marvelous collection of paintings and photographs show off the apparel." Booklist

Includes glossary and bibliographical references

392   Customs of life cycle and domestic life

King, Elizabeth, 1953-
Quinceañera; celebrating fifteen. Dutton Children's Bks. 1998 40p il $16.99 (5 and up)
392
1. Quinceañera (Social custom) 2. Mexican Americans—Social life and customs
ISBN 0-525-45638-4   LC 97-44539
Also available Spanish language edition
Focuses on describing the celebration of this rite of passage in the life of a specific Mexican American girl, while also presenting historical background for the occasion
"The photographs are so full of spectacle and genuine warmth that we feel as though we have been invited, too." Booklist

393   Death customs

Colman, Penny
Corpses, coffins, and crypts; a history of burial. Holt & Co. 1997 212p il $17.95 (7 and up)
393
1. Funeral rites and ceremonies 2. Burial
ISBN 0-8050-5066-3   LC 97-7842
Documents the burial process throughout the centuries and in different cultures
The author "is both candid and detailed in her handling of the gruesome nitty-gritty. . . . Many of the photographs in the liberally illustrated text are from her own explorations, and all are captioned, some in great detail. . . . She's filled her sensitive, solid book with answers to questions people often need and want to know but are too reluctant to ask." Booklist
Includes glossary and bibliographical references

Kallen, Stuart A., 1955-
Mummies. KidHaven Press 2003 48p il map (Wonders of the world) $23.70 (4 and up)
393
1. Mummies
ISBN 0-7377-1031-4   LC 2002-5388
Contents: The golden age of mummies; King Tut and his amazing tomb; Bog bodies; Otzi the iceman
"Kallen discusses accidental mummification as well as the art and science practiced in different civilizations around the world. . . . The mummification process is described in great detail." SLJ
"There's plenty of information to support reports, all of which is presented in . . . Kallen's straightforward, sometimes lively language." Booklist
Includes glossary and bibliographical references

Malam, John, 1957-
Mummies; foreword by Ron Beckett and Gerald Conlogue. Kingfisher 2003 63p il (Kingfisher knowledge) $11.95 (5 and up)   **393**
1. Mummies
ISBN 0-7534-5623-0   LC 2003-44630

Contents: Two ways to make a mummy; Egypt, the land of mummies; Mummy world; Mummies today
"Malam covers Egyptian mummies; the discovery of a variety of preserved bodies throughout history and the world in bogs, deserts, and ice; animal mummies; and mummies today. {The title includes} stunning, captioned photos and illustrations that emphasize the many intriguing factual details in the text." SLJ
Includes glossary and bibliographical references

Pemberton, Delia
Egyptian mummies; people from the past. Harcourt 2001 48p il lib bdg $18 (4 and up)
393
1. Mummies 2. Egypt—Civilization
ISBN 0-15-202600-2   LC 00-44882
First published 2000 in the United Kingdom
"Seven mummies from the British Museum are used as an organizing device to look at the historical and medical significance of mummification. . . . Following a general overview, there are discussions of grave goods, tombs, coffins and sarcophagi, medical uses of mummies (past and present), archaeology and excavation, hieroglyphics, etc. The text is brisk and readable, and is enhanced by an abundance of well-placed color photographs." SLJ
Includes glossary and bibliographical references

Perl, Lila
Mummies, tombs, and treasure; secrets of ancient Egypt; drawings by Erika Weihs. Clarion Bks. 1987 120p il lib bdg $16; pa $8.95 (4 and up)   **393**
1. Mummies 2. Funeral rites and ceremonies 3. Egypt—Antiquities
ISBN 0-89919-407-9 (lib bdg); 0-395-54796-2 (pa)
LC 86-17646
The author incorporates "information on burial customs, religious beliefs, and historical background along with specifics of the mummification process and the archeological finds that have kept the study of the dead a dynamic one." Bull Cent Child Books
This "book is attractive, readable, plentifully illustrated with drawings and black-and-white photographs. . . . Phonetic pronunciations throughout make this easily accessible." Appraisal
Includes bibliographical references

Sloan, Christopher
Bury the dead; tombs, corpses, mummies, skeletons, & rituals; foreword by Bruno Frohlich. National Geographic Soc. 2002 64p il $18.95 (5 and up)   **393**
1. Funeral rites and ceremonies 2. Burial
ISBN 0-7922-7192-0   LC 2001-7507
Examines the customs and practices related to burial that have existed from ancient times to the present
The author "does a terrific job of providing an intriguing, reader-friendly text that is not overshadowed by the fabulous color photographs." Booklist
Includes bibliographical references

Tanaka, Shelley
Secrets of the mummies; uncovering the bodies of ancient Egyptians; illustrations by Greg Ruhl; historical consultation by Peter Brand. Hyperion Bks. for Children 1999 48p il hardcover o.p. paperback available pa $7.99 (4 and up)

393

1. Mummies 2. Egypt—Civilization
ISBN 0-7868-1539-6 (hardcover out of print)
LC 99-11012

"An I was there book"
Describes the ancient Egyptian practice of preserving the dead through the process of mummification and explains what scientists have learned from unwrapping and examining mummies

Wilcox, Charlotte
Mummies, bones & body parts. Carolrhoda Bks. 2000 64p il $25.26; pa $7.95 (5 and up)

393

1. Mummies 2. Funeral rites and ceremonies
ISBN 1-57505-428-0; 1-57505-486-8 (pa)
LC 99-50516

"Wilcox touches on many aspects of how death is treated in various cultures, including the indigenous peoples of the Americas. Embalming techniques and cryonics are discussed, as well as the fascinating jobs of experimental archaeologists and artists trained in anthropology. Scattered liberally throughout the text are uncompromising photos of important finds and scientists at work piecing together mysteries." Booklist
Includes bibliographical references

394.1   Eating, drinking; using drugs

Whitman, Sylvia, 1961-
What's cooking? the history of American food. Lerner Publs. 2001 88p il (People's history) lib bdg $22.60 (5 and up)
394.1
1. Food—History 2. United States—Social life and customs
ISBN 0-8225-1732-9
LC 00-9168
A look at food in the United States from colonial times to the present, describing what we have eaten, where it came from, and how it reflected events in American history
"The text is very accessible, and there are many interesting black-and-white photographs. . . . Intriguing as well as informative." Booklist
Includes bibliographical references

394.2   Customs--Special occasions

Heath, Alan
Windows on the world; multicultural festivals for schools and libraries. Scarecrow Press 1995 392p il hardcover o.p. paperback available $42.95
394.2
1. Festivals 2. Multiculturalism
ISBN 0-8108-3958-X (pa)
LC 94-10032

This guide "promotes reading through thematic festive activities centered around diverse cultural celebrations. Students explore varied art forms, from sculpture, printmaking, batik, and puppetry to drama, music, dancing, cooking, and writing. . . . The book is profusely illustrated with photographs, diagrams, activity sheets, maps, bulletin board ideas, and . . . instructions for arts and crafts projects." Publisher's note
Includes bibliographical references

394.26   Holidays

The **American** book of days; compiled and edited by Stephen G. Christianson. 4th ed. Wilson, H.W. 2000 xxvi, 945p $140
394.26
1. Holidays 2. Festivals—United States
ISBN 0-8242-0954-0
LC 99-86611
First edition, by George William Douglas, published 1937

This work "consists of essays that are a day-to-day recounting of selective American historic events, including those of festivals and celebrations. . . . The topics of these essays vary, with the editor highlighting notable activities from military, scientific, ethnic, political, and cultural occurrences. Not limited strictly to events, essays are also devoted to individuals who played a significant role in American history. . . . A comprehensive index and table of contents provide excellent means for finding specific topics." Am Ref Books Annu, 2001

Bowler, Gerald, 1948-
The world encyclopedia of Christmas; [by] Gerry Bowler. McClelland & Stewart 2000 257p il
394.26
1. Christmas—Encyclopedias
ISBN 0-7710-1531-3; 0-7710-1535-6 (pa)
This "provides more than 1,000 entries on worldwide secular and religious Christmas practices expressed in song, literature, events, film, arts, and trivia and is aimed at young adult and adult readers as well as researchers. Entries are primarily descriptive, but a number of them, especially those on films, contain critical commentary. . . . The book is enticing reading with its many descriptions of exotic customs and its blend of the ancient and the modern. It is written well and concisely." Booklist

Breuilly, Elizabeth
Festivals of the world; the illustrated guide to celebrations, customs, events, and holidays; {by} Elizabeth Breuilly, Joanne O'Brien, Martin Palmer. Checkmark Bks. 2002 160p il maps $29.95
394.26
1. Festivals 2. Religious holidays
ISBN 0-8160-4481-3
LC 2001-59876
The religions featured include Judaism, Christianity, Islam, Hinduism, Buddhism, Sikhism, Taoism, and Zoroastrianism
"A unique approach to holidays, organized by religion rather than alphabet, marks this thoughtful reference book. The introduction relates world festivals to the universal human search for meaning, and offers thematic re-

Breuilly, Elizabeth—*Continued*
lationships between seemingly disparate events. . . .
Beautiful full-color photographs, diagrams, and maps
bring the celebrations to life, and informative text boxes
offer additional facts. . . . This book deserves to be in
every reference collection." SLJ
Includes glossary and bibliographical references

Festivals and holidays. Macmillan Lib. Ref. USA
1999 479p (Macmillan profiles) $90

394.26
1. Festivals 2. Holidays
ISBN 0-02-865378-5   LC 99-26394
"Entries describe the history and significance of more
than 100 rituals, feast days, festivals, and fairs. International in scope, articles cover both religious and national
holidays. . . . Three helpful appendixes supplement the
main text: a discussion of lunar and solar calendars, a
day-by-day listing of national holidays around the world,
and an inclusive list of religious holidays." Booklist

The **Folklore** of the American holidays; Hennig
Cohen and Tristram Potter Coffin, editors. 3rd
ed. Gale Res. 1998 c1999 573p $150

394.26
1. Holidays 2. Festivals—United States 3. Folklore—
United States
ISBN 0-8138-8642-2   LC 98-37035
First published 1987
"A compilation of more than 600 beliefs, legends, superstitions, proverbs, riddles, poems, songs, dances,
games, plays, pageants, fairs, foods, and processions associated with over 140 American calendar customs and
festivals." Title page

The **Folklore** of world holidays; Robert Griffin
and Ann H. Shurgin, editors. 2nd ed. Gale Res.
1998 c1999 841p $150   **394.26**
1. Holidays 2. Festivals 3. Folklore
ISBN 0-8103-8901-0   LC 98-37030
First published 1992 under the editorship of Margaret
Read MacDonald
"Provides descriptive information on nearly 2,000 beliefs, stories, superstitions, proverbs, recipes, games, pageants, fairs, processions and other lore related to more
than 350 special dates from 150 countries." Publisher's
note
Includes bibliographical references

Holidays, festivals and celebrations of the world
dictionary; detailing 2,500 observances from all
50 states and more than 100 nations; edited by
Helene Henderson and Sue Ellen Thompson. 3rd
ed. Omnigraphics 2001 1000p $110

394.26
1. Holidays 2. Festivals
ISBN 0-7808-0422-8
First edition published 1994 compiled by Sue Ellen
Thompson and Barbara W. Carlson
This "describes 2,500 holidays, festivals, commemora-
tions, holy days, feasts and fasts, and other observances
from all parts of the world. The entries cover popular,
secular, and religious events." Publisher's note

Junior worldmark encyclopedia of world holidays;
{edited by Robert Griffin and Ann H. Shurgin}.
U.X.L 2000 4v il set $185   **394.26**
1. Holidays 2. Festivals
ISBN 0-7876-3927-3   LC 00-23425
Alphabetically arranged entries provide descriptions of
celebrations around the world of some thirty holidays
and festivals, including national and cultural holidays,
such as Independence Day and New Year's Day, which
are commemorated on different days for different reasons
in a number of countries
Includes bibliographical references

Marks, Diana F.
Let's celebrate today; calendars, events, and
holidays; illustrated by Donna L. Farrell. 2nd ed.
Libraries Unlimited 2003 340p il pa $38.95

394.26
1. Holidays 2. Festivals 3. Calendars
ISBN 1-591-58060-9   LC 2003-47723
First published 1998
.
This is a "day-by-day calendar . . . for planning . . .
activities and classroom units based on national and international holidays, multicultural and historic events, famous firsts, inventions, birthdays of important individuals
(including authors), and more. The entries are annotated
and include contact information and Web site addresses
to facilitate further research and learning. In addition,
three suggested learning activities are provided for each
day of the year." Publisher's note
Includes bibliographical references

Matthew, Kathryn I.
Neal-Schuman guide to celebrations & holidays
around the world; [by] Kathryn I. Matthew, Joy L.
Lowe. Neal-Schuman Publishers 2004 xx, 452p il
pa $65   **394.26**
1. Holidays—Bibliography 2. Festivals—Bibliography
3. Children's literature—Bibliography
ISBN 1-555-70479-4   LC 2003-59940
"The first section provides bibliographic information
and suggested grade levels for titles on specific days.
Sections that follow offer longer, more detailed explanations of the meaning and significance of a holiday and
a . . . description of the content of each recommended
book or media choice. 'Explorations,' or activities for
sharing specific titles with students, are included." SLJ
"Selecting books that represent favorite authors who
will appeal to children, the authors have designed a work
that will be useful to elementary librarians and teachers
looking for culturally sensitive resources and activities to
teach K-8 students about more than 80 holidays." Booklist

McKissack, Patricia C., 1944-
Christmas in the big house, Christmas in the
quarters; by Patricia C. McKissack and Fredrick L.
McKissack; illustrated by John Thompson.
Scholastic 1994 68p il pa $6.99 hardcover o.p. (4
and up)   **394.26**
1. Plantation life 2. Christmas 3. Slavery—United
States
ISBN 0-590-43028-9 (pa)   LC 92-33831

McKissack, Patricia C., 1944-—*Continued*
Coretta Scott King award for text, 1995
"The authors view the holiday from the perspectives of both slaveholder and his household in the 'Big House' and the slaves in the 'Quarters.' Rich descriptions of preparations fill the text—recipes and menus from both groups are provided—and colorful paintings reflect the antebellum period. Sprinkled throughout the book are lyrics of traditional spirituals, carols, and poetry. . . . Use of authentic language of the time helps the narrative flow, and carefully documented notes illuminate the interesting text." Horn Book
Includes bibliographical references

Rajtar, Steve, 1951-
United States holidays and observances; by date, jurisdiction, and subject, fully indexed. McFarland & Co. 2003 165p $45 **394.26**
1. Holidays 2. Festivals
ISBN 0-7864-1446-4   LC 2002-154293
Includes indexes
This "concentrates on observances and holidays established by statute in the U.S. and American Samoa, District of Columbia, Guam, the Northern Mariana Islands, Puerto Rico, and the U.S. Virgin Islands. In addition, UN-designated holidays are included. . . . The text is arranged by month, and chapters for each month are divided into 'Observances with Variable Dates' and 'Observances with Fixed Dates.' Each entry identifies the observance as federal or specific to a state and offers a description that ranges in length from three or four lines to a quarter page. . . . {This} would be a good addition to ready-reference desks in public libraries and information centers in schools." Booklist
Includes indexes

Walter, Mildred Pitts, 1922-
Kwanzaa: a family affair. Lothrop, Lee & Shepard Bks. 1995 95p il hardcover o.p. paperback available $3.99 (4 and up) **394.26**
1. Kwanzaa 2. African Americans—Social life and customs
ISBN 0-380-72735-8 (pa)
This is a "guide to preparing for and celebrating Kwanzaa that encourages early planning and the sharing of family histories. The principles and symbols are clearly explained, and the directions for making simple gifts are accompanied by adequate line drawings. Walter's enthusiasm for her subject brightens this modest effort." Booklist
Includes glossary and bibliographical references

395 Etiquette (Manners)

Dougherty, Karla
The rules to be cool; etiquette and netiquette. Enslow Pubs. 2001 64p il (Teen issues) lib bdg $22.60 (7 and up) **395**
1. Etiquette
ISBN 0-7660-1607-2   LC 00-10311
"Dougherty approaches good manners as a means of showing respect and consideration for others, thereby prompting reciprocation and easing social relationships and situations. . . . Always practical and low-key, the tips and attitudes emphasize kindness and courtesy as a way of life." SLJ
Includes bibliographical references

James, Elizabeth
Social smarts; manners for today's kids; by Elizabeth James and Carol Barkin; illustrated by Martha Weston. Clarion Bks. 1996 103p il hardcover o.p. paperback available $6.95 **395**
1. Etiquette 2. Conduct of life
ISBN 0-395-81312-3 (pa)   LC 95-35613
Offers advice on how to handle all kinds of social situations and personal interactions, presented with letters from two eighth graders to an etiquette advice columnist, K. T. Answers
"The writing throughout is clear; and it's noteworthy that the authors do more than simply tell readers how to behave—they usually explain why." Booklist

Packer, Alex J., 1951-
How rude! the teenagers' guide to good manners, proper behavior, and not grossing people out. Free Spirit 1997 465p il pa $19.95 (7 and up) **395**
1. Etiquette
ISBN 1-57542-024-4   LC 97-13015
This guide to etiquette for teenagers covers such areas as sex etiquette, toilet etiquette, net etiquette (cyberspace behavior) as well as the correct way to answer invitations and standard protocols for life in a "proper" society
"This volume not only uses humor to make the subject palatable but also makes good sense in terms of most young poeple's everyday lives." Booklist
Includes bibliographical references

Post, Elizabeth L.
Emily Post's teen etiquette; {by} Elizabeth L. Post and Joan M. Coles. HarperPerennial 1995 177p il pa $13 (7 and up) **395**
1. Etiquette
ISBN 0-06-273337-0   LC 95-18503
Replaces Emily Post talks with teens about manners and etiquette (1986)
"Practical, commonsense advice on dealing with your family, communicating with others, mealtime manners, your appearance, social survival (friendship and dating), money, and getting a job. The basics of how to write a thank you note and which fork to use are covered as well as dealing with call waiting and beepers. The family section recognizes divorce and stepfamilies as well as situations involving abuse." Voice Youth Advocates

Post, Peggy, 1945-
Emily Post's etiquette. HarperCollins Pubs. il $38 (7 and up) **395**
1. Etiquette
ISBN 0-39.95
First published 1922 under the authorship of Emily Post. Periodically revised and updated. Title varies. 11th-

Post, Peggy, 1945-—*Continued*
15th editions revised by Elizabeth Post; 16th-17th editions revised by Peggy Post
"The classic reference for which fork to use has been expanded to include such modern situations as dating, living together, second marriages, and co-ed business traveling." N Y Public Libr Book of How & Where to Look It Up

Emily Post's The guide to good manners for kids; by Peggy Post & Cindy Post Senning. HarperCollins 2004 144p il $15.99; lib bdg $16.89 (5 and up) **395**
1. Etiquette
ISBN 0-06-057196-9; 0-06-057197-7 (lib bdg)
LC 2003-26426
This offers advice on etiquette at home, at school, and other places, including letter writing and on-line communication, table manners, phone answering, and behavior at social gatherings, and public places.
"The writing is clear, friendly, and sometimes clever. . . . The advice is consistently practical and simple." SLJ

398 Folklore

Buller, Laura
Myths and monsters; from dragons to werewolves; consultant, Philip Wilkinson. DK Pub. 2003 96p il (DK secret worlds) $14.99; pa $5.99 (5 and up) **398**
1. Mythical animals 2. Monsters
ISBN 0-7894-9703-4; 0-7894-9226-1 (pa)
LC 2003-268994
This guide to myths and monsters includes "photographs of artifacts such as Egyptian mummies . . . {as well as} movie stills from Shrek, Lord of the Rings, and Harry Potter and the Sorcerer's Stone. . . . The text provides origins of characters such as Dracula and Medusa and describes a wide variety of creatures." SLJ
"Action photographs, authentic artwork and maps, inset Weird World facts, action captions, and highlighted Web sites work together with snappy vocabulary and intriguing facts to capture a reader's interest from the first sentence on." Libr Media Connect
Includes glossary and bibliographical references

The **Dictionary** of folklore; David Adams Leeming, general editor. Watts 2002 128p il $34 (4 and up) **398**
1. Folklore—Dictionaries
ISBN 0-531-11985-8
LC 2001-22034
This work answers such questions as "Why was Abraham Lincoln known as 'Honest Abe?' Did George Washington really cut down his father's cherry tree? How much truth is there to the tall tale of John Henry, the 'natural-born steel-driving man,' or Paul Bunyon and Babe the Blue Ox?" Publisher's note
"The layout of the book is pleasing. It is organized in alphabetical order and the content is understandable with many cross-references. The illustrations complement the text. . . . Leeming does an excellent job of enticing the reader to be curious." Book Rep

Drake, Ernest
Dr. Ernest Drake's Dragonology; the complete book of dragons; edited by Dugald A. Steer. Candlewick 2003 il map $19.99 **398**
1. Dragons
ISBN 0-7636-2329-6
"Replete with large foldout pages, small inset foldouts, and maps . . . the book covers everything from dragon habitats, physiology, and behavior to finding, tracking, taming, and flying them. . . . All in all, a delightful treatment for readers fascinated by dragons." Booklist

Hughes, Mary
Popular superstitions. Chelsea House 1999 64p il (Costume, tradition and culture) lib bdg $20.75 **398**
1. Superstition 2. Folklore
ISBN 0-7910-5172-2
LC 98-36081
Explores twenty-five superstitions and how they may have started, including those about walking under a ladder, breaking a mirror, and opening an umbrella indoors
Includes bibliographical references

Myths and legends. Macmillan Lib. Ref. USA 2000 436p (Macmillan profiles) $95 **398**
1. Folklore—Dictionaries 2. Mythology—Dictionaries
ISBN 0-02-865376-9
LC 99-51558
Entries in this volume "are drawn from the mythologies of numerous cultures, ranging from antiquity (*Astarte*) to more modern times (*Paul Bunyan*). Some articles focus on groups: *Centaurs Leprechauns, Mermaids*. Some profile real-life heroes: *Casey Jones* and *Davy Crockett* among others. More than 40 of the articles cover classical Greek and Roman mythology." Booklist
This volume "contains informative, accurate, and detailed information." SLJ

Nigg, Joe
Wonder beasts; tales and lore of the phoenix, the griffin, the unicorn, and the dragon. Libraries Unlimited 1995 160p il $27.50 (7 and up) **398**
1. Animals—Folklore
ISBN 1-56308-242-X
LC 94-46797
The author "has compiled material ranging from Herodotus, Ovid, Pliny the Elder, to Chinese and Native American folk tales, and fantasies by Edith Nesbit. Each entry is carefully documented and a reference list at the end provides dozens of full citations for those who'd like to delve deeper. Wonder Beasts will be useful to students who are researching myth and folklore, and to librarians and scholars who are looking for a comprehensive source list on the topic." Voice Youth Advocates

Van Laan, Nancy
With a whoop and a holler; a bushel of lore from way down south; illustrated by Scott Cook. Atheneum Bks. for Young Readers 1998 102p il map pa $10 hardcover o.p. (4 and up) **398**
1. Folklore—Southern States
ISBN 0-689-84473-3 (pa)
LC 96-24336

Van Laan, Nancy—_Continued_

"An Anne Schwartz book"

A collection of tales, rhymes, riddles, superstitions, and sayings organized around the three distinct regions of the South: the Bayou, the Deep South, and Appalachia

"Cook's caricature-like illustrations draw out the fun-loving humor with an affectionate wink-and-a-nod style." Horn Book Guide

398.2 Folk literature

Sagas, romances, legends, ballads, and fables in prose form, and fairy tales, folk tales, and tall tales are included here, instead of with the literature of the country of origin, to keep the traditional material together and to make it more readily accessible. Modern fairy tales are classified with Fiction, Story collections (SC)

African folktales; traditional stories of the black world; selected and retold by Roger D. Abrahams. Pantheon Bks. 1983 354p il (Pantheon fairy tale & folklore library) hardcover o.p. paperback available $18

398.2

1. Folklore—Africa

ISBN 0-394-72117-9 (pa)   LC 83-2474

This collection contains almost one hundred tales gleaned from the storytelling traditions of Africa, south of the Sahara

Includes bibliographical references

American Indian myths and legends; selected and edited by Richard Erdoes and Alfonso Ortiz. Pantheon Bks. 1984 527p il hardcover o.p. paperback available $18   **398.2**

1. Native Americans—Folklore 2. Native Americans—Religion

ISBN 0-394-74018-1 (pa)   LC 84-42669

"This volume comprises 160 tales of native folklore and myth ranging from one geographical end of our continent to the other. The book is organized according to type of myth. . . . Erdoes and Ortiz seek to keep Indian myth intact and pure through their retellings, using, as often as possible, primary sources." Booklist

Includes bibliographical references

Bedard, Michael, 1949-

The painted wall and other strange tales; selected and adapted from the Liao-chai of Pu Sung-ling by Michael Bedard. Tundra Books 2003 109p $16.95 (7 and up)   **398.2**

1. Folklore—China

ISBN 0-88776-652-8

Contents: Planting a pear tree; Tiger of Chao-cheng; Princess Lily; Missing silver ; Wonderful stone; Taoist priest of Lao Shan; Pianpian, the leaf fairy; Past lives; Paper robes; Jen Shui, the gambler; Invisible priest; Man who was changed into a crow; Glass eyes; Two friends; Talking eye pupils; Theft of the peach; Assistant to the Thunder God; Case of possession; Supernatural wife; Pigeon collector; Arrival of the Buddhist monks; Magic path; Painted wall

"Known as the Liao-chai, these . . . stories were first collected by a scholar named Pu Sung-ling. . . . Wildly popular in China but little known in the West, they draw on the supernatural or unusual to cast their spell. . . . The stories are short and accessible to reluctant readers." SLJ

Bodger, Joan

Tales of court and castle; illustrated by Mark Lang. Tundra Books 2003 88p il pa $9.95 (5 and up)   **398.2**

1. Folklore—Great Britain

ISBN 0-88776-614-5

This presents "retellings of seven English, Irish, and Welsh tales. Tristan, Iron John, Burd Janet, Tamlane, and others come to life with language that speaks to the stories' origins, but will engage modern readers. . . . Lang's illustrations are detailed and wonderfully moody, adding to the otherworldly appeal of the book." SLJ

Brown, Dee Alexander

Dee Brown's folktales of the Native American; retold for our times; illustrated by Louis Mofsie. Holt & Co. 1993 174p il pa $12   **398.2**

1. Native Americans—Folklore

ISBN 0-8050-2607-X   LC 93-12449

"An Owl book"

First published 1979 by Holt, Rinehart & Winston with title: Teepee tales of the American Indian

This is a collection of 36 folktales from Native American tribes, including the Seneca, Hopi, Navaho, Creek, Cheyenne, Cherokee, and Blackfoot, grouped by themes such as tricksters and magicians, heroes and heroines, and ghost stories

Includes bibliographical references

Bruchac, Joseph, 1942-

When the Chenoo howls; native American tales of terror; {by} Joseph and James Bruchac; illustrations by William Sauts Netamuxwe Bock. Walker & Co. 1998 136p $16.95; lib bdg $17.85; pa $10.95 (4-6)   **398.2**

1. Native Americans—Folklore

ISBN 0-8027-8638-3; 0-8027-8639-1 (lib bdg); 0-8027-7576-4 (pa)   LC 97-48715

"Twelve monster tales from a variety of American Indian tribes. . . . These pithily retold tales are short enough for reading aloud and easy enough to learn to tell quickly. Brief notes at the end of each tale give cultural context as well as specific written and oral sources. Full-page black-and-white pen and ink drawings and spot art effectively evoke the spooky but concrete creepiness of the tales. . . . A successful, accessible collection." Bull Cent Child Books

Includes bibliographical references

Bryan, Ashley, 1923-

Ashley Bryan's African tales, uh-huh; retold and illustrated by Ashley Bryan. Atheneum Bks. for Young Readers 1998 198p il $22 (4-6)

398.2

1. Folklore—Africa

ISBN 0-689-82076-3   LC 97-77743

Bryan, Ashley, 1923— *Continued*

This volume combines three previously published titles: The ox of the wonderful horns and other African folktales (1971), Beat the story-drum, pum-pum (1980), Lion and the ostrich chicks and other African folktales (1986)

This collection of African folktales is "told with Bryan's distinctive rhythmic word patterns and filled with humor, life lessons, and the antics of trickster Ananse. . . . Quality reproductions of the original woodcuts enrich this handsome volume." Horn Book Guide

Climo, Shirley, 1928-

Magic & mischief; tales from Cornwall; retold by Shirley Climo; illustrated by Anthony Bacon Venti. Clarion Bks. 1999 127p il $17 (4 and up)

         398.2

1. Folklore—Great Britain

ISBN 0-395-86968-4   LC 97-34091

Drawn from Robert Hunt's Popular romances of the west of England and from William Bottrell's Traditions and hearthside stories of West Cornwall

"Ten tales of Cornwall featuring supernatural beings . . . are accompanied by explanatory bits of traditional lore . . . in this handsomely presented volume. . . . Climo's style is polished and literary, and her selection of tales to retell from detailed sources leans toward the humorous happy ending with just the occasional creepy shiver." Bull Cent Child Books

Curry, Jane Louise, 1932-

Hold up the sky: and other Native American tales from Texas and the Southern Plains; illustrated by James Watts. Margaret K. McElderry Bks. 2003 159p il $17.95 (4 and up)

         398.2

1. Native Americans—Folklore 2. Folklore—Southern States

ISBN 0-689-85287-8   LC 2002-16519

Retells twenty-six tales from Native Americans whose traditional lands were in Texas and the Southern Plains, and provides a brief introduction to the history of each tribe

"Curry has carefully researched and sensitively retold tales from fourteen Native American nations. Attractive pencil drawings enhance the stories." Horn Book Guide

Includes bibliographical references

De Vos, Gail

New tales for old; folktales as literary fictions for young adults; {by} Gail de Vos, Anna E. Altmann. Libraries Unlimited 1999 xxi, 408p pa $41   **398.2**

1. Folklore—Study and teaching

ISBN 1-56308-447-3   LC 99-33150

The authors analyze reworkings of classic folktales according to format: short story, film, poetry, opera and picture book. Chapters are devoted to Cinderella, The Frog King, Hansel and Gretel, Little Red Riding Hood, Rapunzel, Rumpelstiltskin, Sleeping Beauty, and Snow White. Themes such as leaving home, finding self, and dealing with adult sexuality are emphasized. Internet resources are discussed and bibliographic information included

Delacre, Lulu, 1957-

Golden tales; myths, legends, and folktales from Latin America; {retold by} Lulu Delacre. Scholastic 1996 73p pa $5.99 hardcover o.p. (5 and up)   **398.2**

1. Folklore—Latin America 2. Native Americans—Folklore

ISBN 0-439-24398-X (pa)   LC 94-36724

This includes 12 "stories from four native cultures (Taino, Zapotec, Muisca, and Quechua), including pourqu*io tales*, legends of the conquistadores, and folktales from before and after the age of Columbus. . . . {The author's} . . . retellings are done in a clear and confident voice and are accompanied by her robust, colorful oil paintings. . . . This impressively presented and referenced collection will inspire readers and tellers alike." Booklist

Includes bibliographical references

Forest, Heather

Wisdom tales from around the world; retold by Heather Forest. August House 1996 156p $28; pa $17.95   **398.2**

1. Folklore

ISBN 0-87483-478-3; 0-87483-479-1 (pa)

       LC 96-31141

A collection of traditional stories from around the world, reflecting the cumulative wisdom of Sufi, Zen, Taoist, Buddhist, Jewish, Christian, African, and Native American cultures

"Forest retells folktales, proverbs, and parables in a thoughtful and satisfying style that amuses as it deftly imparts lessons for living." SLJ

Includes bibliographical references

Gerson, Mary-Joan

Fiesta femenina; celebrating women in Mexican folktale; retold by Mary-Joan Gerson; illustrated by Maya Christina Gonzalez. Barefoot Bks. (NY) 2001 64p il map $19.99 (4 and up)   **398.2**

1. Folklore—Mexico 2. Women—Folklore

ISBN 1-8414-8365-6   LC 00-12965

A collection of folktales from various cultures in Mexico, all focusing on the important roles of women, such as Rosha, a young girl who rescues the sun; the goddess Tangu Yuh; Kesne, a Zapotec princess; and the Virgin Mary

"Gerson's prose is lively and engaging, drawing readers in and conveying pictures of believable people in fantastic situations. Gonzalez's primitive acrylic paintings are strong and vigorous, and their riotous use of color enhances the stories tremendously." SLJ

Includes glossary and bibliographical references

Hamilton, Virginia, 1936-2002

Her stories; African American folktales, fairy tales, and true tales; told by Virginia Hamilton; illustrated by Leo & Diane Dillon. Blue Sky Press (NY) 1995 112p il $22.95 (4 and up)

         398.2

1. African American women—Folklore

ISBN 0-590-47370-0   LC 94-33055

Coretta Scott King award for text, 1996

Hamilton, Virginia, 1936-2002—*Continued*

"Nineteen African-American fairy tales, animal stories, supernatural tales, legends and true narratives of a female kind are presented in this single volume." Child Book Rev Serv

"Retold from a variety of sources, the stories flow smoothly in Hamilton's expertly measured prose. The full-color illustrations, one per story, are lush and detailed. . . . These are tales to be read over and over again." Publ Wkly

Includes bibliographical references

The people could fly; American black folktales; illustrated by Leo and Diane Dillon. Knopf 1985 178p il lib bdg $18.99; pa $13 (5 and up)
398.2

1. African Americans—Folklore
ISBN 0-394-96925-1 (lib bdg); 0-679-84336-1 (pa)
LC 84-25020
Also available with audio CD $24.95 (ISBN 0-375-80471-4)

"Hamilton retells 24 representative black folktales. . . . The stories are organized into four sections: tales of animals; the supernatural; the real, extravagent, and fanciful; and freedom tales." Booklist

The author "has been successful in her efforts to write these tales in the Black English of the slave storytellers. Her scholarship is unobtrusive and intelligible. She has provided a glossary and notes concerning the origins of the tales and the different versions in other cultures. Handsomely illustrated." N Y Times Book Rev

Includes bibliographical references

Hearne, Betsy Gould, 1942-

Beauties and beasts; by Betsy Hearne; illustrated by Joanne Caroselli. Oryx Press 1993 179p il (Oryx multicultural folktale series) pa $33.95
398.2

1. Fairy tales 2. Folklore 3. Mythology
ISBN 0-89774-729-1
LC 93-16

"The theme of a lonely beast who is transformed by the magic of human love is threaded throughout worldwide variations of the 'Beauty and the Beast' folktale. Author Betsy G. Hearne presents 28 versions of the beloved fable with minimal adaptations from around the world." Publisher's note

"Professionals will be very grateful for this sensitively written, thoughtful, and accessible interpretive collection." J Youth Serv Libr

Includes bibliographical references

Helbig, Alethea

Myths and hero tales; a cross-cultural guide to literature for children and young adults; {by} Alethea K. Helbig and Agnes Regan Perkins. Greenwood Press 1997 288p $49.95
398.2

1. Mythology—Bibliography
ISBN 0-313-29935-8
LC 97-8778

"Brief, incisive critical reviews of 189 books, published between 1985 and 1996, that contain 1455 myths and hero tales form the heart of this . . . sourcebook. Scholarly accuracy and literary quality are the authors'

chief criteria for inclusion, but they also comment trenchantly on illustrations. Indexes list stories by writer, tale type, culture, character and place name, grade level, title, or illustrator." SLJ

Index to fairy tales; including folklore, legends, and myths in collections. Scarecrow Press 1985-1994 4v
398.2

1. Folklore—Indexes

Volumes covering 1949-1972 and 1973-1977 first published by Faxon 1973 and 1979 respectively

A continuation of Index to fairy tales, myths and legends and its two supplements, compiled by Mary Huse Eastman, published 1926-1952 by Faxon (o.p.)

Volume covering 1949-1972 compiled by Norma Olin Ireland $78 (ISBN 0-8108-2011-0); volume covering 1973-1977 compiled by Norma Olin Ireland $45 (ISBN 0-8108-1855-8); volume covering 1978-1986 compiled by Norma Olin Ireland and Joseph W. Sprug $88 (ISBN 0-8108-2194-X); volume covering 1987-1992 compiled by Joseph W. Sprug $88 (ISBN 0-8108-2750-6)

"Although this is an essential reference book for the children's department, it is also a valuable source for the location of much folklore and fairy-tale material and should be available in adult book collections as well." Ref Sources for Small & Medium-sized Libr. 6th edition

Jaffe, Nina

The cow of no color: riddle stories and justice tales from around the world; {by} Nina Jaffe and Steve Zeitlin; pictures by Whitney Sherman. Holt & Co. 1998 159p il $17 (4 and up)
398.2

1. Folklore
ISBN 0-8050-3736-5
LC 98-14167

In each of these stories, collected from around the world, a character faces a problem situation which requires that he make a decision about what is fair or just

"Sherman's black-and-white line drawings have a stark gracefulness that complements the tales' form and structure; the tales themselves are simply told with little embellishment." Bull Cent Child Books

Includes bibliographical references

Krasno, Rena, 1923-

Cloud weavers; ancient Chinese legends; [by] Rena Krasno and Yeng Fong Chiang; illustrations from the collection of Yeng-Fong Chiang. Pacific View Press 2003 96p il $22.95 (5 and up)
398.2

1. Folklore—China
ISBN 1-88189-626-9
LC 2002-35911

Presents legends and tales from China, including ancient folktales, stories that reflect Chinese traditions and virtues, historical tales, and selections from literature

This collection "provides a showcase for some remarkable pieces of Chinese calendar art and advertising posters from the 1920s and 1930s. . . . Prefaces provide cultural insight for some stories, and the brisk retellings weave important background unobtrusively into the narrative." Booklist

Lester, Julius
The last tales of Uncle Remus; as told by Julius
Lester; illustrated by Jerry Pinkney. Dial Bks.
1994 156p il $18.99 (4 and up)   **398.2**
1. African Americans—Folklore 2. Animals—Fiction
ISBN 0-8037-1303-7   LC 93-7531
Also available Uncle Remus: the complete tales $30
(ISBN 0-8037-2451-9)
"Thirty-nine selections . . . drawn from the African
American tradition are reclaimed and retold in this fourth
and . . . final volume in Lester's Uncle Remus series.
Lester's ability to communicate the oral rhythm of the
stories is compelling, and his storyteller's voice offers
commentary and asides in a nearly perfect combination
of traditional and modern vernacular. Humor bubbles
from the characterizations, plot, and language. . . . With
8 color and 26 black-and-white illustrations by Pinkney,
this roundup is as refreshing and down-to-earth as was
the first book in the series." Booklist
Other Uncle Remus tales in this series are:
Further tales of Uncle Remus (1989)
More tales of Uncle Remus (1988)
The tales of Uncle Remus (1987)

Livo, Norma J., 1929-
Folk stories of the Hmong; peoples of Laos,
Thailand, and Vietnam; {by} Norma J. Livo and
Dia Cha. Libraries Unlimited 1991 135p il $26
    398.2
1. Hmong Americans
ISBN 0-87287-854-6   LC 91-370
This is a collection of folktales of the Hmong people
of Asia which also includes a description of Hmong his-
tory and culture, with 16 pages of color photographs of
Hmong dress and needlework
Includes bibliographical references

Martin, Rafe, 1946-
The world before this one; a novel told in
legend; with paper sculpture by Calvin Nicholls.
Levine Bks. 2002 195p il $16.95 (4 and up)
    398.2
1. Seneca Indians—Folklore
ISBN 0-590-37976-3   LC 2001-23403
"Written in the style of a novel, this collection of 14
Seneca tales is presented through the retelling of one
central story into which all of the others are artfully
woven. . . . Martin offers sources for the tales along
with an introductory note by Seneca Elder Peter Jemison.
Each chapter includes a painstakingly detailed white paper sculpture of a character (often an animal) from one
of the stories." SLJ

Mayer, Marianna, 1945-
Women warriors; myths and legends of heroic
women; illustrated by Julek Heller. Morrow Junior
Bks. 1999 80p il $17.95 (5 and up)
    398.2
1. Women—Folklore
ISBN 0-688-15522-7   LC 98-45697
A collection of twelve traditional tales about female
military leaders, war goddesses, women warriors, and

heroines from around the world, including such countries
as Japan, Ireland, and Zimbabwe
These stories "are told in accessible, rhythmic prose.
. . . Each three-to six page selection is prefaced by comments on its origin and history and accompanied by a
full-page watercolor painting showing the protagonist in
action." SLJ
Includes bibliographical references

McCaughrean, Geraldine, 1951-
The epic of Gilgamesh; retold by Geraldine
McCaughrean; illustrated by David Parkins.
Eerdmans Bks. for Young Readers 2003 c2002
95p il $18 (5 and up)   **398.2**
1. Gilgamesh 2. Folklore—Iraq
ISBN 0-8028-5262-9   LC 2003-1086
Cover title: Gilgamesh the hero
A retelling, based on seventh-century B.C. Assyrian
clay tablets, of the wanderings and adventures of the god
king, Gilgamesh, who ruled in ancient Mesopotamia
(now Iraq) in about 2700 B.C., and of his faithful companion, Enkidu
This is "clearly a telling for our time, but one that
honors its source. Parkins captures the epic's primitive
power and universal emotions in rough, broadly rendered
portraits." Horn Book

McKinley, Robin
The outlaws of Sherwood. Greenwillow Bks.
1988 282p $17   **398.2**
1. Robin Hood (Legendary character)
ISBN 0-688-07178-3   LC 88-45227
Also available in paperback from Ace Bks.
"McKinley takes a fresh look at a classic, changing
some of the events or deviating from standard characterization to gain new dimensions. Her afterword explains
her artistic compromise with myth and history, her wish
to write a version that is 'historically unembarrassing.'
With a few exceptions, she has done that admirably, creating a story that has pace and substance and style, and
that is given nuance and depth by the characterization."
Bull Cent Child Books

Molnár, Irma
One-time dog market at Buda and other
Hungarian folktales; translated and retold by Irma
Molnár; illustrations by Georgeta-Elena Eneşel.
Linnet Bks. 2001 129p il lib bdg $25
    398.2
1. Folklore—Hungary
ISBN 0-208-02505-7   LC 01-38836
Presents twenty-three Hungarian folktales, featuring
historical figures such as King Matthias, legends about
the founding of Hungary and the Mongol raids, Turkish
tales, Gypsy stories, and tales that reflect Hungary's geo-
graphical position as a meeting and fighting place in
east-central Europe
These "folktales are filled with cleverness and quick
wit. . . . The language is rich." Booklist
Includes bibliographical references

Morpurgo, Michael

Sir Gawain and the Green Knight; as told by Michael Morpurgo ; illustrated by Michael Foreman. Candlewick Press 2004 114p il $18.99 (5 and up) **398.2**

1. Arthurian romances 2. Gawain (Legendary character)

ISBN 0-7636-2519-1   LC 2003-65527

The quest of Sir Gawain for the Green Knight teaches him a lesson in pride, humility, and honor

"Morpurgo's sprightly writing brings out all the humor as well as the horror of the original tale, and Foreman's profuse, evocative watercolor-and-pastel illustrations highlight the drama in each scene." SLJ

Myths, legends, and folktales of America; an anthology; {edited by} David Leeming and Jake Page. Oxford Univ. Press 1999 221p il hardcover o.p. paperback available $21.50 **398.2**

1. Folklore—United States 2. United States—Social life and customs

ISBN 0-19-511784-0 (pa)   LC 97-48607

This presents "beliefs, myths, sketches, and tall tales that reflect the American experience. Though modest in length, it effectively covers America's polyglot society. . . . Deftly arranged and clearly written." Libr J

Includes bibliographical references

Norman, Howard

Between heaven and earth; bird tales from around the world; illustrated by Leo & Diane Dillon. Harcourt 2004 78p il lib bdg $22 (4 and up) **398.2**

1. Folklore 2. Birds—Fiction

ISBN 0-15-201982-0   LC 2003-7874

"Gulliver books"

A collection of folktales from around the world, all of which have a bird as a main character.

This is "a collection of stories that are rich in cultural references from the lands of their origins. . . . The Dillons' luminous watercolor-and-pencil illustrations, detailed with patterns drawn from each tale's culture of origin, will draw readers and listeners back to the stories." Booklist

The girl who dreamed only geese, and other tales of the Far North; told by Howard Norman; illustrated by Leo & Diane Dillon. Harcourt Brace & Co. 1997 147p il $22 (4 and up) **398.2**

1. Inuit—Folklore

ISBN 0-15-230979-9   LC 96-20880

"Gulliver books"

A collection of stories retold from Inuit folklore

"The narratives have a marvelous vitality and excitement. They capture the sound and cadence of the spoken word. . . . The plots reflect the diversity and humor of Inuit culture. . . . Each tale is accompanied by several large, full-color acrylic illustrations in addition to outstanding black-and-white friezes that run across the top of each page." SLJ

Olson, Arielle North, 1932-

Ask the bones: scary stories from around the world; selected and retold by Arielle North Olson and Howard Schwartz; illustrated by David Linn. Viking 1999 145p il $15.99; pa $5.99 (4 and up) **398.2**

1. Folklore

ISBN 0-670-87581-3; 0-14-230140-X (pa)

LC 98-19108

A collection of scary folktales from countries around the world including China, Russia, Spain, and the United States

"David Linn's bone-chilling black-and-white illustrations. . . will stay with the reader long after the book is closed. Excellent for reading aloud, this collection will satisfy even jaded genre fans." Booklist

Includes bibliographical references

Osborne, Mary Pope, 1949-

Favorite medieval tales; retold by Mary Pope Osborne; illustrated by Troy Howell. Scholastic 1998 86p il pa $7.99 hardcover o.p. (4 and up) **398.2**

1. Folklore—Europe

ISBN 0-439-14134-6 (pa)   LC 96-17285

A collection of well-known tales from medieval Europe, including "Beowulf," "The Sword in the Stone," "The Song of Roland," and "Gudren and the Island of the Lost Children"

"Inspired by medieval art and illuminated manuscripts, Howell's paintings complement the well-researched text." Horn Book Guide

Includes bibliographical references

Philip, Neil

Celtic fairy tales; retold with an introduction by Neil Philip; illustrated by Isabelle Brent. Viking 1999 137p il $21.99 (4 and up) **398.2**

1. Fairy tales 2. Celts—Folklore 3. Folklore—Great Britain

ISBN 0-670-88387-5   LC 98-50081

An illustrated collection of twenty stories from many Celtic regions, including "The Battle of the Birds," "Finn MacCool and the Scotch Giant," and "The Ship that Went to America"

"There's a mix of the almost familiar and nicely exotic in this collection, which is lavishly illustrated with a glowing full-page painting for each tale and Celtic motifs on every page." Booklist

Myths & legends. DK Pub. 1999 128p il (Annotated guides) $25 (7 and up) **398.2**

1. Mythology 2. Legends

ISBN 0-7894-4117-9   LC 98-48836

"Philip uses art in various forms—from Chinese plates to Norwegian wooden church doors to the paintings of Raphael—to illustrate and illuminate 56 myths and legends. . . . Each page is colorful and informative, with details of the artwork sidebarred for further explanation and arrows with captions pointing out details relevant to the myths." Libr J

Philip, Neil—*Continued*

The story of Robin Hood; illustrated by Nick Harris. DK Pub. 1997 64p il maps (Eyewitness classics) $14.99   **398.2**

1. Robin Hood (Legendary character)

ISBN 0-7894-1490-2   LC 96-39117

Also available with Audio cassette

Recounts the life and adventures of Robin Hood, who, with his band of followers, lived in Sherwood Forest as an outlaw dedicated to fighting tyranny. Illustrated notes throughout the text explain the historical background of the story

"This retelling stays true to the tale of Robin Hood, handed down through 14th-century ballads. Philip's version is fast-moving, readable, and child-friendly without becoming inane." SLJ

Pyle, Howard, 1853-1911

The merry adventures of Robin Hood of great renown in Notinghamshire; as written and illustrated by Howard Pyle (7 and up)

    398.2

1. Robin Hood (Legendary character)

Available from various publishers

First published 1883

Twenty-two stories of Robin Hood and his adventures with the King's foresters in Sherwood Forest. This band of outlaws made a practice of robbing the rich to help the poor. Set during the reign of Henry II of England

"Of all the books of Robin Hood this is best for literary style, adherence to the spirit and events of the old ballads and wealth of historical background." Toronto Public Libr

The story of King Arthur and his knights; written and illustrated by Howard Pyle. Scribner 1984 312p il $22.95 (7 and up)   **398.2**

1. Arthur, King 2. Arthurian romances

ISBN 0-684-14814-5   LC 84-50167

Also available in paperback from Dover Publs.

A reissue of the title first published 1903

The first of a four-volume series retelling the Arthurian legends

This is an account of the times "when Arthur, son of Uther-Pendragon, was Overlord of Britain and Merlin was a powerful enchanter, when the sword Excalibur was forged and won, when the Round Table came into being." Publisher's note

The story of Sir Launcelot and his companions. Scribner 1985 340p il (7 and up)   **398.2**

1. Lancelot (Legendary character) 2. Arthurian romances

Available in paperback from Dover Publs.

A reissue of the title first published 1907

This third book of the series follows "Sir Launcelot's adventures as he rescues Queen Guinevere from the clutches of Sir Mellegrans, does battle with the Worm of Corbin, wanders as a madman in the forest and is finally returned to health by the Lady Elaine." Best Sellers

The story of the champions of the Round Table; written and illustrated by Howard Pyle. Scribner 1984 328p il (7 and up)   **398.2**

1. Arthurian romances

Available in hardcover from Amereon and in paperback from Dover Publs.

A reissue of the title first published 1905

Contents: The story of Launcelot; The book of Sir Tristram; The book of Sir Percival

"Pyle's second volume of Arthurian legends will be of interest to motivated students of literature and history, as well as useful in professional collections for comparisons and source work. In spite of the archaic language . . . the narrative depth and graphic force . . . will draw in readers." Booklist

The story of the Grail and the passing of Arthur. Scribner 1985 258p il (7 and up)

    398.2

1. Arthur, King 2. Arthurian romances 3. Grail—Fiction

    LC 85-40302

Available in paperback from Dover Publs.

A reissue of the title first published 1910

This fourth volume of the series follows the adventures of Sir Geraint, Galahad's quest for the holy Grail, the battle between Launcelot and Gawaine, and the slaying of Mordred

Rogasky, Barbara, 1933-

The golem; a version; illustrated by Trina Schart Hyman. Holiday House 1996 96p il $18.95 (4 and up)   **398.2**

1. Jewish legends

ISBN 0-8234-0964-3   LC 94-13040

This is "the legend of the golem—a monster created of clay—who, under the guidance of the chief rabbi of Prague, rescued the Jews from persecution by anti-Semitic Christians in the late 16th century. Rogasky's strong storytelling skills are evident. . . . Hyman's colorful, fairy tale-like illustrations bring the story to life." SLJ

San Souci, Robert, 1946-

Cut from the same cloth; American women of myth, legend, and tall tale; collected and told by Robert D. San Souci; illustrated by Brian Pinkney; introduction by Jane Yolen. Philomel Bks. 1993 140p il $21.99; pa $6.99 (4 and up)

    398.2

1. Folklore—United States 2. Tall tales 3. Women—Folklore

ISBN 0-399-21987-0; 0-698-11811-1 (pa)

    LC 92-5233

A collection of fifteen stories about legendary American women from Anglo-American, African American, and Native American folklore

"San Souci's language is vigorous and action verbs abound; Pinkney's black-and-white block prints match the strength of the telling. The inclusion of notes on the sources and a general bibliography make this an academic resource as well as a good collection of rolicking stories." Child Book Rev Serv

San Souci, Robert, 1946-—*Continued*

A terrifying taste of short & shivery; thirty creepy tales; retold by Robert D. San Souci; illustrated by Lenny Wooden. Delacorte Press 1998 159p il $14.95; pa $10.95 (4 and up)

398.2

1. Ghost stories 2. Folklore
ISBN 0-385-32635-1; 0-385-32255-0 (pa)

LC 98-5551

"Drawing on urban legends, myths, folktales, and ghost stories from around the world and across time, the reteller serves up 30 tales of the supernatural that range from eerie to downright scary. . . . Suspenseful, accessible, and energetic, the tales are uniformly brief and gripping." SLJ

Includes bibliographical references

Schwartz, Alvin, 1927-1992

More scary stories to tell in the dark; collected & retold from folklore by Alvin Schwartz; drawings by Stephen Gammell. Lippincott 1984 100p il $15.99; lib bdg $16.89; pa $5.99 (4 and up)

398.2

1. Ghost stories 2. Horror fiction 3. Folklore—United States
ISBN 0-397-32081-7, 0-397-32082 5 (lib bdg); 0-06-440177-4 (pa)

LC 83-49494

This volume contains stories of ghosts, murders, graveyards and other horrors

"The stories are all short and lively, very tellable, and greatly enhanced by the gray, ghoulish, horrifying illustrations of dismembered bodies, hideous creatures, and mysterious lights. A fine compendium by a well-known collector, easily accessible to young readers." Horn Book

Includes bibliographical references

Scary stories 3; more tales to chill your bones; collected from folklore and retold by Alvin Schwartz; drawings by Stephen Gammell. HarperCollins Pubs. 1991 115p il music $15.99; lib bdg $16.89; pa $5.99 (4 and up)

398.2

1. Ghost stories 2. Horror fiction 3. Folklore—United States
ISBN 0-06-021794-4; 0-06-021795-2 (lib bdg); 0-06-440418-8 (pa)

LC 90-47474

Traditional and modern-day stories of ghosts, haunts, superstitions, monsters, and horrible scary things

"The book is well paced and continually captivates, surprises, and entices audiences into reading just one more page. Gammell's gauzy, cobwebby, black-and-white pen-and-ink drawings help to sustain the overall creepy mood." SLJ

Includes bibliographical references

Scary stories to tell in the dark; collected from American folklore by Alvin Schwartz; with drawings by Stephen Gammell. Lippincott 1981 111p il $15.99; lib bdg $16.89; pa $5.99 (4 and up)

398.2

1. Ghost stories 2. Horror fiction 3. Folklore—United States
ISBN 0-397-31926-6; 0-397-31927-4 (lib bdg); 0-06-440170-7 (pa)

LC 80-8728

"A collection of scary, semi-scary, and humorous stories about ghosts and witches collected from American folklore. Most of the stories (poems and songs also) are very short and range from the traditional to the modern. The author includes suggestions on how to tell scary stories effectively." Bull Cent Child Books

"The scholarship in the source notes and bibliography will be useful to serious literature students." SLJ

Schwartz, Howard, 1945-

The day the Rabbi disappeared: Jewish holiday tales of magic; retold by Howard Schwartz; illustrated by Monique Passicot. Viking 2000 80p il o.p. Jewish Publication Society paperback available pa $9.95 (4 and up)

398.2

1. Jews—Folklore 2. Jewish holidays—Fiction
ISBN 0-827-60757-1 (out of print)

LC 99-42061

Retellings of twelve traditional tales from Jewish folklore featuring elements of magic and relating to holidays, including Rosh Hodesh, Sukkot, Tu bi-Shevat, and Shabbat

"Schwartz follows these brief, clear, and simply told tales with rich and highly readable notes about the history of the holiday, the importance of the rabbi, and the sources of the story." Horn Book

Sherman, Josepha

Merlin's kin; world tales of the hero magician. August House 1998 192p $21.95; pa $11.95

398.2

1. Folklore 2. Magicians—Folklore
ISBN 0-87483-523-2; 0-87483-519-4 (pa)

LC 98-24524

"Sherman presents 30 international folktales that feature heroic magicians. Among her sorcerers are Gwydion of Wales, King Solomon of ancient Israel, Clever Aja of the Ashante in Ghana, and Glooscap of the Wabanaki of New England and Canada." Booklist

"This is a good book for collections of folklore, or for fantasy readers who love classic tales of magic." Voice Youth Advocates

Includes bibliographical references

Spencer, Ann, 1955-

And round me rings; bell tales and folklore; Illustrated by Lindsay Grater. Tundra 2003 225p il pa $11.95 (7 and up)

398.2

1. Folklore 2. Bells—Fiction
ISBN 0-88776-597-1

"Spencer assembles a variety of traditional tales, true accounts, and poetry about bells. The selections are arranged by broad themes, such as bells used to herald nature, those related to the performing of miracles, those that ring away evil, and those that reflect the rhythm of life." SLJ

"Spencer's smooth writing style brings continuity to the dozens of entries. . . . The variety of material and its attractive presentation make this well-rounded volume a good source for storytelling as well as individual reading." Booklist

Sutcliff, Rosemary, 1920-1992

The light beyond the forest; the quest for the Holy Grail; decorations by Shirley Felts. Dutton 1980 143p hardcover o.p. paperback available $5.99 (4 and up)   **398.2**

1. Arthur, King 2. Grail—Fiction 3. Arthurian romances

ISBN 0-14-037150-8 (pa)   LC 79-23396

First published 1979 in the United Kingdom

This is a retelling of the adventures of King Arthur's knights as they search for the Holy Grail. "After a vision of the Cup from the Last Supper appears, Sir Lancelot, Sir Galahad, Sir Bors, and Sir Percival quit Camelot to look for the Grail, knowing that only the world's most perfect knight will succeed. The individual adventures, which take on a loftier meaning as the journeys also become the knights' personal searches for God, will be most appreciated by special readers interested in King Arthur and his time." Booklist

Followed by The sword and the circle

The road to Camlann; decorations by Shirley Felts. Dutton 1982 142p hardcover o.p. paperback available $5.99 (4 and up)   **398.2**

1. Arthur, King 2. Arthurian romances

ISBN 0-14-037147-8 (pa)   LC 82-9481

First published 1981 in the United Kingdom

"This book completes Rosemary Sutcliff's Arthurian trilogy, begun with 'The Light Beyond the Forest' and 'The Sword and the Circle'. Here Sutcliff describes the events from the coming of Mordred to the death of Lancelot. The title refers to The Last Battle, in which Arthur and his civilization perish. Sutcliff writes with her usual economy and rich prose, with a touch of archaic diction in the speeches. . . . Other than Malory, I can think of no better introduction to the whole sweep of Arthurian stories and values." SLJ

The sword and the circle; King Arthur and the Knights of the Round Table. Dutton 1981 260p hardcover o.p. paperback available $5.99 (4 and up)   **398.2**

1. Arthur, King 2. Arthurian romances

ISBN 0-14-037149-4 (pa)   LC 81-9759

The second volume in the author's Arthurian trilogy, begun with: The light beyond the forest. The events in this volume precede those in the earlier volume

"The author has brought together thirteen stories associated with the Arthurian cycle, beginning with 'The Coming of Arthur' and concluding not with the passing of Arthur but with 'The Coming of Perceval.' Although she has relied on Malory's 'Morte d'Arthur' for most of her material, she has drawn upon other medieval sources for some of her best storytelling: For example 'Sir Gawain and the Green Knight' comes from a Middle English poem, and the twenty-nine-page 'Tristan and Iseult' is indebted to Godfrey of Strasburg's version." Horn Book

Followed by The road to Camlann

Talk that talk: an anthology of African-American storytelling; edited by Linda Goss & Marian E. Barnes. Simon & Schuster 1989 521p hardcover o.p. paperback available $24.95   **398.2**

1. African Americans—Folklore

ISBN 0-671-67168-5 (pa)   LC 89-10582

The selections included range "from slave stories and the animal legends of Brer Rabbit and Brer Fox to the comedy monologues of Dick Gregory and rap routines. . . . Interspersed throughout are brief sections of commentary and analysis." Booklist

Includes bibliographical references

Taylor, C. J. (Carrie J.), 1952-

Peace walker; the legend of Hiawatha and Tekanawita. Tundra Books 2004 45p il $15.95   **398.2**

1. Iroquois Indians—Folklore

ISBN 0-88776-547-5

"The events surrounding the collaboration of two chiefs, the Onandaga Hiawatha and Tekanawita of the Mohawk, to upset the tyrant Atotarho are related simply and abound with graphic details of Native life. . . . Each chapter includes one full-page illustration done in acrylic on canvas in a slightly naive style. . . . The writing is eloquent and poetically rhythmic." SLJ

Tchana, Katrin Hyman, 1963-

The serpent slayer: and other stories of strong women; retold by Katrin Tchana; illustrated by Trina Schart Hyman. Little, Brown 2000 113p il $19.95   **398.2**

1. Women—Folklore

ISBN 0-316-38701-0   LC 95-35077

"These 18 folktales emphasize feminine strength, courage, and wit. . . . The selections come from places as diverse as China, Scotland, and the Gambia." SLJ

"Tchana offers solid retellings of the oft-anthologized ('Kate Crackernuts') and the not oft-anthologized ('Sister Lace'). . . . The thematic variety of the stories provides something for everyone. . . . Humor, suspense, romance, and horror are reflected through the medium of Hyman's powerful art." Bull Cent Child Books

Includes bibliographical references

Tingle, Tim

Walking the Choctaw road. Cinco Puntos Press 2003 142p il $16.95 (7 and up)   **398.2**

1. Choctaw Indians—Folklore 2. Folklore—Southern States

ISBN 0-938317-74-1   LC 2003-1069

A collection of stories of the Choctaw people, including traditional lore arising from beliefs and myths, historical tales passed down through generations, and personal stories of contemporary life

"Sophisticated narrative devices and some subtle character nuances give these stories a literary cast, but the author's evocative language, expert pacing, and absorbing subject matter will rivet readers and listeners both." Booklist

Yeoman, John

The Seven voyages of Sinbad the Sailor; illustrated by Quentin Blake; retold by John Yeoman. Margaret K. McElderry Bks. 1997 c1996 119p il (5 and up)   **398.2**

Yeoman, John—_Continued_
1. Fairy tales 2. Arabs—Folklore
ISBN 0-689-81368-6
Available in paperback from Chrysalis Books $6.95
(ISBN 1-8436-5040-1)
First published 1996 in the United Kingdom
"Yeoman's first-person narration . . . leads readers
through Sinbad's seven shipwrecks while introducing
them to the amazing inhabitants of the islands on which
the sailor is inevitably stranded." SLJ
"Blake's ink drawings with watercolors . . . illustrate
the story with style and grace. A handsome edition in every way, this book features good storytelling, lively illustrations, and excellent design." Booklist

Yep, Laurence
The rainbow people; {retold by} Laurence Yep;
illustrated by David Wiesner. Harper & Row 1989
194p il hardcover o.p. paperback available $5.99
(4 and up)   **398.2**
1. Folklore—China
ISBN 0-06-440441-2 (pa)   LC 88-21203
"Twenty Chinese fokltales, selected and retold by Yep
from those collected in the 1930s in the Oakland
Chinetown as part of a WPA project. . . . The tales,
while drawn from the depicting Chinese culture, present
a variety of familiar motifs and types: wizards and saints,
shape changing and magical objects, pourquoi tales and
lessons. An 'Afterword' provides suggestions for further
reading on Chinese folktales. This is an excellent introduction to Chinese and Chinese-American folklore." SLJ
Includes bibliographical references

Yolen, Jane
Mightier than the sword; world folktales for
strong boys; collected and told by Jane Yolen;
with illustrations by Raul Colón. Silver
Whistle/Harcourt 2003 112p il $19 (4 and up)
                                                 398.2
1. Folklore
ISBN 0-15-216391-3   LC 2002-9886
A collection of folktales from around the world which
demonstrate the triumph of brains over brawn
Yolen's "versions of these stories are lively, expres-
sively written, ready for reading aloud or telling, and illustrative of her point." SLJ
Includes bibliographical references

398.8   Rhymes and rhyming games

Mother Goose on the loose; cartoons from the
New Yorker; edited by Bobbye S. Goldstein.
Abrams 2003 106p il $18.95   **398.8**
1. Nursery rhymes 2. Cartoons and comics
ISBN 0-8109-4239-9   LC 2002-9802
"Goldstein brings together familiar nursery rhymes
and children's stories with cartoons from The New Yorker Cartoon Bank that reflect humorous and satirical commentary on contemporary life. . . . Allusions to courts
and lawyers, divorce, the movie industry, grouchy
spouses, sex, diets, advertising, and the stock market provide plenty of snickers and guffaws to adults and older

children. An afterword introduces aspects of cartooning
history and Goldstein's research on using cartoons and
comic strips to teach reading." SLJ

400   LANGUAGE

419   Verbal language not spoken and written

Butterworth, Rod R.
The Perigee visual dictionary of signing; an
A-to-Z guide to over 1,350 signs of American
Sign Language; {by} Rod R. Butterworth and
Mickey Flodin. rev & expanded 3rd ed. Berkley
Pub. Group 1995 478p il pa $15.95   **419**
1. Sign language
ISBN 0-399-51952-1   LC 95-1380
"A Perigee book"
First published 1983
This guide to American Sign Language features more
than 1,350 alphabetically arranged signs with directions
on how to form them. Illustrations show precise hand po-
sitions and movements. Includes memory aids

The **Comprehensive** signed English dictionary;
edited by Harry Bornstein, Karen L. Saulnier,
Lillian B. Hamilton; illustrated by Ralph R.
Miller, Sr. Gallaudet College Press 1983 456p il
$39.95   **419**
1. Sign language—Dictionaries
ISBN 0-913580-81-3   LC 82-82830
"An introductory essay about learning Signed English
is followed by 3,100 words and 14 markers representing
English usage. The words are arranged in alphabetical
order with illustrations and descriptions." Safford Guide
to Ref Materials for Sch Libr Media Cent. 5th edition
Includes bibliographical references

Costello, Elaine
Random House American sign language
dictionary; illustrated by Lois Lenderman, Paul M.
Setzer, Linda C. Tom. Random House 1994 xxxiv,
1067p il $55; pa $20   **419**
1. Sign language
ISBN 0-394-58580-1; 0-679-78011-4 (pa)
Also available Random House Webster's concise
American sign language dictionary pa $7.99 (ISBN 0-
553-58474-X)
Costello "has compiled over 5000 signs in this massive dictionary. Each sign is illustrated with a full-torso
picture showing hand configuration and movement, and
both the common and alternate meanings are given
where necessary. Arranged like a typical dictionary, this
work is easy to use and very detailed." Libr J

Kelly, Michael
Native American talking signs. Chelsea House 1997 64p il (Looking into the past: people, places, and customs) $20.75   **419**
1. Native Americans—Sign language 2. Native Americans—Social life and customs
ISBN 0-7910-4681-8   LC 97-26194
Directions for the signs for twenty-five words used by various Native Americans accompanies information about the customs, daily life, religious beliefs, and history of these peoples
Includes bibliographical references

Riekehof, Lottie L.
The joy of signing; the illustrated guide for mastering sign language and the manual alphabet. 2nd ed. Gospel Pub. House 1987 352p il $23.99
    419
1. Sign language
ISBN 0-88243-520-5   LC 86-80173
First published 1963 with title: Talk to the deaf
This manual presents over 1300 signs used for communicating with deaf adults, and provides basic vocabulary needed for entering interpreter training programs. Signs are arranged in 25 categories with an alphabetical index. For each sign there is a line drawing, description of how to make the sign, origin (concept) and notes on usage
Includes bibliographical references

Sternberg, Martin L. A.
American Sign Language; a comprehensive dictionary; illustrated by Herbert Rogoff. Unabridged. HarperCollins Pubs. 1998 xxi, 983p il $60; pa $24   **419**
1. Sign language
ISBN 0-06-271608-5; 0-06-273634-5 (pa)
    LC 98-26649
Also available American sign language concise dictionary pa $12 (ISBN 0-06-274010-5)
First published 1981
Arranged alphabetically, this dictionary features 7,000 sign entries, with cross-references and more than 12,000 illustrations
Includes bibliographical references

422   Etymology of standard English

Baker, Rosalie F.
In a word; 750 words and their fascinating stories and origins; by Rosalie Baker ; illustrated by Tom Lopes. 1st American ed. Cobblestone Pub 2003 221p il $17.95 (5 and up)   **422**
1. English language—Etymology
ISBN 0-8126-2710-5   LC 2003-25582
Includes index
Contents: Cultural creations; Worldly words & power people; Math magic & science synergy; Religious rituals, fabulous folklore, & marvelous myths; Exceptional expressions; Clothing collection; Glorious gizmos & great grub; Spectacular sports; Joyful journeys; Natural neces-

sities; Awesome archaeology; Political powerhouse; Military madness; Tantalizing tidbits; Fickle finances; Fantastic foreigners
"The entries in this book discuss the meanings and derivations of 750 words and phrases. . . . While exploring word origins, Baker also touches on interesting facets of European history and Greek mythology. The jaunty illustrations are reproduced in black and shades of gray. . . . This informative book fosters an appreciation for the richness of the English language." Booklist

422.03   Etymology of standard English--Dictionaries

The **Barnhart** dictionary of etymology; Robert K. Barnhart, editor; Sol Steinmetz, managing editor. Wilson, H.W. 1988 xxvii, 1284p $110
    422.03
1. English language—Etymology
ISBN 0-8242-0745-9   LC 87-27994
Also available The Barnhart concise dictionary of etymology (HarperCollins Pubs. 1995)
This dictionary "focuses on words used in contemporary American English and words of American origin and incorporates current American scholarship. Entries give spelling variations, pronunciation for difficult words, part of speech, definition, and information on word origins. Written for a wide audience, this is a very attractive, readable work suited for most library users." Ref Sources for Small & Medium-sized Libr. 6th edition

Morris, William, 1913-1994
Morris dictionary of word and phrase origins; {by} William and Mary Morris; foreword by Isaac Asimov. 2nd ed. Harper & Row 1988 669p $38
    422.03
1. English language—Etymology 2. English language—Terms and phrases
ISBN 0-06-015862-X   LC 87-45651
Original three volume edition published 1962-1971; one volume edition first published 1977
"Traces the origins of several thousand words and phrases commonly used in the English language, including slang terms and clichés not usually found in more formal works. Entries are listed alphabetically by the first word in the phrase, with an index at the end." Ref Sources for Small & Medium-sized Libr. 6th edition

423   Dictionaries of standard English

The **American** Heritage student dictionary. Houghton Mifflin $18   **423**
1. English language—Dictionaries
First published 1977 with title: The American Heritage school dictionary (2003 edition). Periodically revised
The more than 65,000 entries are accompanied by over 2000 photographs and illustrations. Includes geographical and biographical entries, usage notes, word histories, synonym paragraphs, and regionalisms. Computer and Internet terms are featured

Bartlett's Roget's thesaurus. Little, Brown 1996
xxxii, 1415p $21.95 **423**
1. English language—Synonyms and antonyms
2. Americanisms
ISBN 0-316-10138-9 LC 96-18343
This thesaurus "reflects the current state of American English, including terminology from the worlds of composers and television, with such sub-categories as 'Living Things,' 'The Arts,' 'Feelings.' But what really makes the book a joy to use is the tremendously useful lists—everything from phobias to styles and periods of furniture." Am Libr

Corbeil, Jean-Claude
The Facts on File visual dictionary. Facts on File 1986 797p il $29.95 **423**
1. Encyclopedias and dictionaries 2. Picture dictionaries
ISBN 0-8160-1544-9 LC 86-6261
Corbeil "compiled careful diagrams, architectural in their completeness, of almost everything imaginable, and then labeled the parts. He has organized the book by 28 themes, covering astronomy, the animal kingdom, and creative leisure activities. Then he adds a general index, thematic indexes, and special indexes that provide excellent access from the word to the picture." Libr J
Includes bibliographical references

DK dictionary/thesaurus. DK Pub. 1999 512p
$11.99 **423**
1. English language—Dictionaries 2. English language—Synonyms and antonyms
ISBN 0-7894-3949-2 LC 98-52899
This combined dictionary and thesaurus for school-aged children is alphabetically arranged with more than 20,000 dictionary entries and 50,000 synonyms

The **Facts** on File student's thesaurus; {edited by} Marc McCutcheon. 2nd ed. Facts on File 2000 504p (Facts on File library of language and literature) $43.95 **423**
1. English language—Synonyms and antonyms
ISBN 0-8160-4058-3 LC 99-30711
First published 1991
Provides synonyms and antonyms and usage examples for more than 7000 words listed in alphabetical order

Hellweg, Paul
The American Heritage children's thesaurus; by Paul Hellweg with the editors of the American Heritage dictionaries. Houghton Mifflin 2003 279p il $17.95 **423**
1. English language—Synonyms and antonyms
ISBN 0-618-28024-3
First published 1997
Presents over 4000 alphabetically arranged words with several synonyms and an illustrative sentence for each

Merriam-Webster's dictionary of synonyms.
Merriam-Webster $22.95 **423**
1. English language—Synonyms and antonyms
First published 1942 with title: Webster's dictionary of synonyms. (1993 edition) Periodically revised

"This synonym dictionary is an outstanding work. . . . Synonyms and similar words, alphabetically arranged, are carefully defined, discriminated, and illustrated with thousands of quotations. The entries also include antonyms and analogous words." Nichols. Guide to Ref Books for Sch Media Cent. 4th edition

Merriam-Webster's school thesaurus.
Merriam-Webster 1994 690p $15.95
423
1. English language—Synonyms and antonyms
ISBN 0-87779-178-3
First published 1978 with title: Webster's student thesaurus
This alphabetically arranged volume includes more than 43,000 synonyms, antonyms, idiomatic phrases, related words, and contrasted words

Random House Webster's unabridged dictionary.
3rd ed. Random House 2005 il $59.95
423
1. English language—Dictionaries
ISBN 0-375-42599-3
This dictionary contains over 315,000 entries. A new-words section and an essay on the growth of English are included. 2,400 spot maps and illustrations complement the text

Roget's 21st century thesaurus in dictionary form; the essential reference for home, school, or office; edited by the Princeton Language Institute; Barbara Ann Kipfer, head lexicographer. 3rd ed. Bantam Dell 2005 962p $15; pa $5.99 **423**
1. English language—Synonyms and antonyms
ISBN 0-385-33895-3; 0-440-24269 X (pa)
"A Delta book"
First published 1992
"Produced by the Philip Lief Group, Inc."
This thesaurus, cross referencing each word with the same concept, provides 500,000 synonyms and antonyms in a dictionary format and includes recently coined and common slang terms and commonly used foreign terms.

Roget's II; the new thesaurus. 3rd ed. Houghton Mifflin 1995 1280p $21 **423**
1. English language—Synonyms and antonyms
LC 94-42879

Includes index
This is a new "edition of Houghton Mifflin's 1988 edition of Roget's. . . . {The} number of synonyms provided for each word in the 1988 edition has been . . . increased, . . . and the use of cross-references to words in a category index provides antonyms and lists of synonym groups related to a particular sense of the headword." Booklist

Roget's international thesaurus. 6th ed. edited by Barbara Ann Kipfer; Robert L. Chapman, consulting editor. HarperResource 2001 xxv, 1248p $20.95; pa $16.95 **423**
1. English language—Synonyms and antonyms
ISBN 0-06-273693-0; 0-06-093544-8 (pa)
LC 2002-276277
Also available thumb-indexed edition

Roget's international thesaurus—*Continued*
First copyright edition published 1911 with title: The
standard thesaurus of English words and phrases classified and arranged so as to facilitate the expression of
ideas and assist in literary composition

This edition includes 330,000 words and phrases organized into 1,075 categories and a pinpoint reference system that directs the user from a comprehensive index to
the numbered category of the right word. Cross-
references throughout lead to other categories. Also included are supplemental word lists that supply the names
of things which have no synonyms (measurements,
wines, state mottoes) as well as quotations that amplify
the meanings of selected words

Simon & Schuster thesaurus for children; {edited
by} Jonathan P. Latimer and Karen Stray
Nolting. Simon & Schuster Bks. for Young
Readers 2001 288p $16.95   **423**
1. English language—Synonyms and antonyms
ISBN 0-689-84322-4   LC 2001-31083
"This volume offers cross-references leading to a
number of related terms. The main entries generally focus on one thread of meaning; for example, for 'correct,'
the entry lists 'adjust' and 'revise' as synonyms with a
see-also for 'change' and 'fix.' Each main entry word
and synonym are separately defined and include a sample
sentence. . . . Different colors highlight sidebars and distinguish main-entry words from synonyms. There is a
useful 23-page index. Clear print and an easy-to-use format make this serviceable resource a good choice for
novices." SLJ

Terban, Marvin
Scholastic dictionary of idioms. Scholastic 1996
245p il hardcover o.p. paperback available $8.95
(4 and up)   **423**
1. English language—Idioms
ISBN 0-590-38157-1 (pa)   LC 95-16593
"Terban explains the meanings and origins (if known)
of more than 600 idioms and proverbs. . . . Each page
includes one lightly comical line drawing of a child expressing feelings such as quizzical, annoyed, amused, or
distressed. Not only is this a good resource for teachers
who discuss idioms in the classroom but it also has some
appeal for browsers." Booklist

Webster's third new international dictionary of the
English language, unabridged. Merriam-Webster
il   **423**
1. English language—Dictionaries
Prices vary according to binding; Also available print
and CD-ROM edition
Original edition by Noah Webster published 1828 with
title: An American dictionary of the English language.
Has also appeared under various other titles. First published with present title 1961. Frequently reprinted with
additions and changes to keep it up to date
"Clear, accurate definitions are given in historical order. Outstanding for its numerous illustrative quotations,
impeccable authority, and etymologies, *Webster's third* is
regarded as the most reliable, comprehensive general unabridged dictionary." Ref Sources for Small & Medium-
sized Libr. 6th edition

Young, Sue
The new comprehensive American rhyming
dictionary. Morrow 1991 622p o.p. Avon Bks.
paperback available $14.95   **423**
1. English language—Rhyme 2. Americanisms
ISBN 0-380-71392-6 (pa)   LC 90-19165
This book contains over 65,000 words and phrases
categorized by sound, rather than spelling. It includes
many colloquialisms and slang expressions

427   English language variations

Dictionary of American slang; edited by Robert L.
Chapman. 3rd ed. HarperCollins Pubs. 1995
xxii, 617p $42.95   **427**
1. English language—Slang 2. Americanisms
ISBN 0-06-270107-X   LC 97-2771
First published 1960 by Crowell. Variant title: New
dictionary of American slang
This dictionary defines over 17,000 terms. Examples
of usage are provided and derivations noted. Particular
emphasis has been placed on language pertaining to technology, business and the media

428   Standard English usage

Ostler, Rosemarie
Dewdroppers, waldos, and slackers; a
decade-by-decade guide to the vanishing
vocabulary of the twentieth century; Rosemarie
Ostler. Oxford University Press 2003 239p il $25
                                           428
1. English language—Slang
ISBN 0-19-516146-7   LC 2003-8302
"This reference work is not simply a slang dictionary.
Along with definitions . . . Ostler includes in each decade's chapter both brief discussions of relevant cultural
topics and a few photos. These short, often humorous essays are a way to provide examples for the terms defined. . . . Ostler's work is fun for browsing; it offers a
unique presentation of recent cultural history." Libr J
Includes bibliographical references

Terban, Marvin
Building your vocabulary. Scholastic Ref. 2002
188p il (Scholastic guides) $12.95; pa $7.95 (4
and up)   **428**
1. Vocabulary
ISBN 0-439-28561-5; 0-439-28562-3 (pa)
                                 LC 2001-20838
"Chapters are devoted to prefixes, roots, and suffixes;
word families; homonyms and homographs; understanding the meaning of words using context clues; how to
use a dictionary and thesaurus; and how to increase one's
vocabulary using techniques such as games. . . . Explanations and examples are clear and often amusing. . . .
This easy-to-read, enjoyable guide says a great deal
about language." SLJ

Terban, Marvin—*Continued*
Scholastic dictionary of spelling; over 15,000 words. Scholastic Ref. 1998 223p il $15.95; pa $8.95 (4 and up) **428**
1. Spellers
ISBN 0-590-30697-9; 0-439-14496-5 (pa)
LC 97-18020
The words in this speller are "arranged alphabetically (i.e., ladies comes before lady) broken into syllables with the accented syllables in boldface, on attractively laid-out pages, with occasional cartoonish illustrations. Homophones include pronunciation help, and a parenthetical sentence illustrates proper use. The first 26 pages are a treasure trove of helpful hints. . . . The book concludes with the 'Misspeller's Dictionary,' 600 words with tricky beginnngs listed in matched pairs of the common misspelling and the correct one." Book Rep

433   German language--Dictionaries

Cassell's German-English, English-German dictionary; completely revised by Harold T. Betteridge. Macmillan 2v in 1 thumb-indexed $27 **433**
1. German language—Dictionaries
First compiled 1888 by Elizabeth Weir and published by Heath. Periodically revised. Previous American editions published by Funk & Wagnalls with title: The New Cassell's German dictionary
This dictionary incorporates "many new words and usages. Gives phonetic transcriptions of headwords. One of the most useful bilingual dictionaries." Guide to Ref Books. 11th edition

443   French language--Dictionaries

Cassell's French dictionary; French-English, English-French; completely revised by Denis Girard with the assistance of Gaston Dulong, Oliver Van Oss, and Charles Guinness. Wiley 2002 762, 655p thumb-indexed $24.95
443
1. French language—Dictionaries
ISBN 0-02-522620-7
First published 1920 with title: Cassell's French-English, English-French dictionary. Previous American editions published by Funk & Wagnalls with title: The New Cassell's French dictionary
"New words including colloquialisms, slang, American English and French-Canadian terms {are included}. . . . There are also sections on French verbs and French and English abbreviations. Reliable, standard dictionary. A first choice." N Y Public Libr. Ref Books for Child Collect. 2d edition

453   Italian language--Dictionaries

Cassell's Italian dictionary; Italian-English, English-Italian; compiled by Piero Rebora, with the assistance of Francis M. Guercio and Arthur L. Hayward. Wiley 2002 xxi, 1128p thumb-indexed $24.95 **453**

ISBN 0-02-522540-5
First published 1958 in the United Kingdom with title: Cassell's Italian-English, English-Italian dictionary. Previous United States editions published by Funk & Wagnalls
"A general dictionary of the Italian language as currently written and spoken." Ref Sources for Small & Medium-sized Libr. 5th edition

463   Dictionaries of standard Spanish

Cassell's Spanish-English, English-Spanish dictionary. Completely rev and reset ed, completely rev by Anthony Gooch, Angel Garcia de Paredes. Macmillan 1978 xxv, 1109p thumb-indexed $22.95 **463**
1. Spanish language—Dictionaries
ISBN 0-02-522910-9 LC 77-18453
Also available in a concise edition for $13 (ISBN 0-02-522660-6)
First published 1959 in the United Kingdom. First American edition published 1960 by Funk & Wagnall's with title: Cassell's Spanish dictionary
This dictionary emphasizes the Spanish of Latin America, and includes both classical and literary Spanish as well as the language of the modern Spanish-speaking world

473   Dictionaries of classical Latin

Cassell's Latin dictionary; Latin-English, English-Latin; by D. P. Simpson. Macmillan 1977 c1959 883p thumb-indexed $24.95
473
1. Latin language—Dictionaries
ISBN 0-02-522580-4
Also available in a concise paperback edition for $7.99 (ISBN 0-02-013340-5)
First published 1854. This edition first published 1959. Previous United States editions published by Funk & Wagnalls with title: Cassell's New Latin dictionary
"Cassell's incorporates current English idiom and Latin spelling into the traditional presentation of classical Latin. The 30,000 entries include generic terms, geographical and proper nouns. Etymological notes and illustrative quotations are provided within entries." Wynar. Guide to Ref Books for Sch Media Cent. 3d edition

493   Non-Semitic Afro-Asiatic languages

Donoughue, Carol, 1935-
The mystery of the hieroglyphs; the story of the Rosetta stone and the race to decipher Egyptian hieroglyphs. Oxford Univ. Press 1999 48p il lib bdg hardcover o.p.; pa $7.99 hardcover o.p. (4 and up) **493**

Donoughue, Carol, 1935-—*Continued*
1. Rosetta stone 2. Egyptian language
3. Hieroglyphics
ISBN 0-19-521553-2 (lib bdg); 0-19-521850-7 (pa)
This is a history of the discovery and deciphering of
the Rosetta stone which led to the understanding of
Egyptian hieroglyphics
"What makes this book so involving is that readers
must do their own learning, translating, and reading of
hieroglyphics. . . . Crisp color photos, reproductions,
and sidebars enrich the text. An enticing volume." SLJ
Includes glossary and bibliographical references

Giblin, James, 1933-
The riddle of the Rosetta Stone; key to ancient
Egypt; [by] James Cross Giblin. Crowell 1990 85p
il hardcover o.p. paperback available $7.99 (5 and
up)   **493**
1. Rosetta stone 2. Egyptian language
3. Hieroglyphics
ISBN 0-06-446137-8 (pa)   LC 89-29289
Describes how the discovery and deciphering of the
Rosetta Stone unlocked the secret of Egyptian hieroglyphics
"Suspense keeps the reader glued to this fine piece of
nonfiction as the mystery of hieroglyphs is slowly unrav-
eled. . . . The author has done a masterful job of distill-
ing information, citing the highlights, and fitting it all together in an interesting and enlightening look at a puzzling subject." Horn Book
Includes bibliographical references

495.6 Japanese language

Basic Japanese-English dictionary. 2nd ed. Oxford
University Press, Bonjinsha 2004 1000p pa
$19.95   **495.6**
1. Japanese language—Dictionaries
ISBN 0-19-860859-4   LC 2004-54786
First published 1986 in Japan; 1989 by Oxford University Press
This "dictionary contains over 3,000 entries which,
along with providing basic meanings and grammatical information, also distinguish between senses, list compounds, and give sample sentences and idiomatic expressions. . . . It presents all the Japanese words and phrases
in roman script with standard Japanese script alongside.
. . . . Cross-references direct the user to words of contrasting or related meaning, and, where necessary, the
dictionary provides notes on special usage. It also includes [an] appendix which gives an introduction to Japanese grammar." Publisher's note

The **Oxford-Duden** pictorial Japanese and English
dictionary. Oxford Univ. Press 1997 880p il pa
$25   **495.6**
1. Japanese language—Dictionaries 2. Picture dictionaries
ISBN 0-19-860119-0
First published 1983 with title: The Oxford-Duden
pictorial English-Japanese dictionary
"Pictures of hospitals and doctor's and dentist's of-
fices, clothing, houses and furniture, supermarkets, air-

ports and libraries (and about 380 more items) are labeled with numbers which are keys for the terms printed
below in each language. Complete indexes in each language provide quick access." Safford. Guide to Ref Materials for Sch Libr Media Cent. 5th edition

500 SCIENCE

Thimmesh, Catherine
The sky's the limit; stories of discovery by
women and girls; illustrated by Melissa Sweet.
Houghton Mifflin 2002 73p il $16; pa $7.95 (5
and up)   **500**
1. Science 2. Women scientists
ISBN 0-618-07698-0; 0-618-49489-8 (pa)
                                       LC 2001-39111
"This collection highlights a variety of women discoverers from the well known, including Jane Goodall and
Mary Leakey, to budding pioneers, such as eleven-year-
old science-lover Katie Murray." Voice Youth Advocates
"The lively design and the mixed-media collage artwork is a creative delight, and the intricate ink-and-
watercolor borders, inventive paintings, and childlike pictures will draw readers in. The best thing about the book,
however, is Thimmesh's sparkling writing style. . . . Report writers will appreciate this, but the book will also
charm browsers." Booklist
Includes bibliographical references

U.X.L science fact finder; Phillis Engelbert, editor.
U.X.L 1997 3v il set $165   **500**
1. Science 2. Technology
ISBN 0-7876-1727-X   LC 97-24046
Adapted from The handy science answer book, 2nd
edition, published 1996 by Visible Ink Press
Contents: v1 The natural world; v2 The physical
world; v3 The technological world
This set "answers more than 750 FAQs (frequently
asked questions) from all areas of science: natural, physical, and technological. The three volumes are arranged
by subject, with numerous sidebars, photos, diagrams,
and charts. There is a further reading list repeated at the
beginning of each volume, divided into books, journals
and periodicals, online sources, and CD-ROMs. . . . A
fun, interesting, and helpful resource." Booklist
Includes bibliographical references

500.5 Space sciences

Pentland, Peter
Space science; [by] Peter Pentland and Pennie
Stoyles. Chelsea House 2003 c2002 32p il
(Science and scientists) lib bdg $18.95 (4 and up)
                                                        500.5
1. Space sciences
ISBN 0-7910-7011-5   LC 2002-1284
First published 2002 in Australia
Contents: Have you ever wondered ... ?; Sight and
light; Telescopes; Telescopes can find more than planets;
How do you send things into space?; Rocket science;
What is sent into space and why?; Probing the planets;

Pentland, Peter—*Continued*
What are satellites?; How does science help people survive in space?; What is it like to live in space?; Meet a NASA scientist; Is it possible to live on other planets?; Space science timeline

This briefly explains such phenomena as light, telescopes, rockets, space vehicles, and space exploration
Includes glossary

Space science. Grolier 2004 8v il map set $289 (5 and up)   **500.5**
1. Space sciences
ISBN 0-7172-5825-4   LC 2003-61836

Contents: v1 How the universe works; v2 Sun and solar system; v3 Earth and Moon; v4 Rocky planets; v5 Gas giants; v6 Journey into space; v7 Shuttle to space station; v8 What satellites see

This set "provides general coverage of astronomy and cosmology, . . . [discusses] the technology and engineering aspects of understanding and exploring space, and [covers] the solar system and its central star. . . . The books all make excellent use of fantastic photographs and drawings. . . .The text is well-written and complete. . . . [This is] a must-have set." Sci Books Films

Space sciences; Pat Dasch, editor in chief. Macmillan Ref. USA 2002 4v il set $395
500.5
1. Space sciences
ISBN 0-02-865546-X   LC 2002-1707

"The Macmillan science library." On cover

Contents: v1 Space business; v2 Planetary science and astronomy; v3 Humans in space; v4 Our future in space

"The entries in each volume are in alphabetical order and range from a single paragraph to several pages in length, with most being one or two pages long. The front and back matter are the same in each volume and include a few pages of reference tables such as conversion charts, time lines of milestones in space history and human achievements in space, a list of contributors, a table of contents for the set, and a glossary." Booklist

"A comprehensive and usable survey of space exploration, this marvelous encyclopedia works equally well as a multivolume set and as four standalone volumes. . . . The photographs are excellent." Libr J

502   Science--Miscellany

Ochoa, George
The Wilson chronology of science and technology; {by} George Ochoa and Melinda Corey. Wilson, H.W. 1997 440p $110
502
1. Science—History 2. Technology—History
ISBN 0-8242-0933-8   LC 97-22060

This chronology begins in 2,500,000 B.C. and continues into 1997. "Within each year, entries are arranged alphabetically according to one of 13 categories: archaeology; astronomy; space science, and space exploration; biology; biochemistry, agriculture, and ecology; chemistry; earth sciences (geology, oceanography, meteorology) and earth exploration; mathematics; medicine; miscellaneous; paleontology; physics; psychology, neuroscience, and ar-

tificial intelligence; social sciences (anthropology, sociology, economics, political science) and linguistics; and technology and engineering." Publisher's note
Includes bibliographical references

502.8   Science--Auxiliary techniques and procedures; apparatus, equipment, materials

Kramer, Stephen
Hidden worlds: looking through a scientist's microscope; photographs by Dennis Kunkel. Houghton Mifflin 2001 57p il (Scientists in the field) $16; pa $5.95 (4 and up)   **502.8**
1. Kunkel, Dennis 2. Microscopes
ISBN 0-618-05546-0; 0-618-35405-0 (pa)
LC 00-58083

This book takes a "look at the work of a microscopist. Kunkel works with microscopes to explore science. . . . This book contains many of his photos, most taken with electron microscopes. . . . Several opening pages, along with the front and back endpapers, are visually dazzling. The heart of the book, though, is what readers learn about how Kunkel produces these images, and to what uses scientists put them. . . . This title offers a wealth of scientific information along with an insightful look at the world of an individual scientist." SLJ
Includes bibliographical references

Levine, Shar
The microscope book; [by] Shar Levine & Leslie Johnstone; illustrations by David Sovka. Sterling 1996 80p il $19.95; pa $9.95
502.8
1. Microscopes 2. Science—Experiments
ISBN 0-8069-4898-1; 0-8069-4899-X (pa)
LC 95-43239

An introduction to microscopes and magnification with experiments using such easily obtained materials as comic books, leaves, hair, and potatoes

"An excellent introduction. . . . The attractive, well-designed format features colorful drawings and full-color microscopic photographs that are helpful in illustrating and explaining projects." SLJ

Simon, Seymour, 1931-
Out of sight; pictures of hidden worlds. SeaStar Bks. 2000 unp il lib bdg $16.50; pa $6.95 (4 and up)   **502.8**
1. Science—Pictorial works 2. Photography—Scientific applications
ISBN 1-58717-012-4 (lib bdg); 1-58717-149-X (pa)
LC 00-25684

Shows pictures of objects which are too small, too far away, or too fast to see without mechanical assistance such as microscopes, telescopes, X-rays, and other techniques

"The text serves primarily as extended captions to the photos, providing information on the ways the pictures were taken and a basic explanation of what the images represent. The large, bright illustrations are beautifully reproduced and present some fascinating views of the world." SLJ

503 Science--Encyclopedias and dictionaries

The **American** Heritage children's science dictionary. Houghton Mifflin 2003 280p il $17.95 **503**
1. Science—Dictionaries
ISBN 0-618-35401-8   LC 2003-10476
"The 2,600 entries were selected to represent different areas of science such as astronomy, biology, and physics as well as areas like weather and computer technology. . . . One nice feature is the 'Did You Know?' boxes that are interspersed throughout the book and contain extra information. . . . School and public libraries that serve upper-elementary and middle-school patrons will find this a useful addition to their reference collections. It is well bound, attractive, and accessible and has the types of definitions a young patron needs." Booklist

The **American** Heritage science dictionary. 1st ed. Houghton Mifflin 2005 695p il $19.95
503
1. Science—Dictionaries
ISBN 0-618-45504-3   LC 2004-19696
This "science dictionary includes 8500 terms in anthropology, biology, chemistry, earth science, mathematics, medicine, physics, and technology. There are also 320 biographical entries of noted scientists as well as 30 biographical notes that explain how certain researchers found answers to major scientific problems. Written in clear, simple prose that general readers can understand, the entries are often more than simple definitions, offering in-depth discussions of scientific ideas." Libr J

The **American** Heritage student science dictionary. Houghton Mifflin 2002 376p il $18
503
1. Science—Dictionaries
ISBN 0-618-18919-X   LC 2002-22726
Entries with definitions of basic scientific terms are accompanied by illustrations, "Did You Know" sidebars, and explanatory notes

The **DK** science encyclopedia. new rev ed. DK Pub. 1998 448p il maps $39.99; pa $9.99 (5 and up) **503**
1. Science—Encyclopedias
ISBN 0-7894-2190-9; 0-7894-2871-7 (pa)
LC 97-20881
First published 1993 with title: The Dorling Kindersley science encyclopedia
"Entries are grouped into 12 topical sections ('Weather,' 'Ecology,' 'Reactions,' etc.). Each one-to-two page article is drizzled with small, clipped color photos and paintings supplemented by boxed capsule biographies, brief side excursions, and see-also references. The book concludes with a relatively dense 'Fact Finder Section' into which are gathered charts, statistics, and specialized terms." SLJ

The **Kingfisher** science encyclopedia; [general editor, Charles Taylor] Kingfisher (NY) 2000 488p il $39.95 **503**
1. Science—Encyclopedias
ISBN 0-7534-5269-3   LC 00-24556

Topical chapters present "basic surveys of physics, geology, chemistry, biology, anatomy, the environment, and space. . . . Articles are generally, though not rigidly, confined to a spread each, and all have see-also references. . . . The illustrations are a plus; they are crisply reproduced, finely detailed, and labeled, enhancing the text rather than competing with it." SLJ

Prescott, Chris
Barron's science study dictionary. Barron's Educ. Ser. 2001 xxvi, 262p il pa $11.95 (7 and up) **503**
1. Science—Dictionaries
ISBN 0-7641-1652-5   LC 00-103329
"The more than 2500 entries in this resource are arranged alphabetically by subject. Each topical two-page spread contains approximately 15 precisely defined scientific words, many of which are accompanied by a labeled black-and-white diagram or illustration or a chart. Coverage includes communications, chemical equations, energy, genetics, machines, bacteria, plants, reproduction, and more. . . . This useful volume is a must for public and school libraries." SLJ

U.X.L encyclopedia of science. 2nd ed, Rob Nagel, editor. U.X.L 2002 10v il maps set $395
503
1. Science—Encyclopedias
ISBN 0-7876-5432-9   LC 2001-35562
First published 1997
Includes 600 topics in the life, earth, and physical sciences as well as in engineering, technology, math, environmental science, and psychology
It's "difficult to find fault with this clearly written resource that uses simple, nontechnical terms to explain scientific concepts at a basic level." Booklist

Ultimate visual dictionary of science. DK Pub. 1998 448p il $30 **503**
1. Science—Dictionaries
ISBN 0-7894-3512-8   LC 98-11900
At head of title: Dorling Kindersley
"Much of this title is a compilation of several previously published volumes. *The Visual Dictionary of Physics* (1995), *The Visual Dictonary of Chemistry* (1996), and *The Visual Dictionary of Human Anatomy* (1996, all DK) have been virtually reprinted page by page, illustration by illustration, and shrunk to fit a smaller format . . . . Other sections include medical science, life sciences and ecology, earth sciences, astronomy and astrophysics, electronics and computer science, and mathematics. Here, the information has been synthesized from earlier books and updated." SLJ

Visual science encyclopedia. Grolier Educ. 2001 12v set $279 (5 and up) **503**
1. Science—Encyclopedias
ISBN 0-7172-5595-6   LC 2001-23704

Contents: v1 Weather; v2 Elements; v3 Rocks, minerals, and soil; v4 Forces; v5 Light and sound; v6 Water; v7 Plants; v8 Electricity and magnetism; v9 Earth and space; v10 Computers and the Internet; v11 Volcano [sic] and earthquakes; v12 Heat and energy

Visual science encyclopedia—*Continued*
This set defines main terms and concepts in science with over 500 full color illustrations and cross references
"This is a useful resource for students seeking quick definitions and clear illustrations that help explain terms." Booklist

The **World** Book encyclopedia of science. World Bk. 8v il set $337   **503**
1. Science—Encyclopedias
First published 1985 in seven volumes. (2001 edition) Periodically revised
Accompanied by CD-ROM
Contents: v1 Astronomy; v2 Physics; v3 Chemistry; v4 The planet earth; v5 The plant world; v6 The animal world; v7 The human body; v8 Men and women of science. Index
"An overall excellent and affordable effort to present science clearly to a wide range of ages and abilities." Am Ref Books Annu, 1998

The **Young** Oxford Library of science. Oxford Univ. Press 2003 11v il maps set $275
    503
1. Science—Encyclopedias
ISBN 0-19-521906-6
Contents: v1 Mind and body, by B. Walpole; v2 Plants and animals, by B. Taylor; v3 Land, sea, and air, by M. Carruthers; v4 Atoms and elements, by D. Bradley and I. Crofton; v5 Materials, by R. Kerrod; v6 Light and sound, by J. Allday; v7 Electricity and electronics, by P. Marks; v8 Energy and forces, by N. Ardley; v9 Science in action, by R. Kerrod; v10 Stars and planets, by J. Mitton; v11 Reference volume and series index
"A basic introduction to the physical, chemical, and biological sciences and how they apply to our daily lives." SLJ
"This is an engaging set that will almost certainly be used frequently." Libr Media Connect

507.8   Science--Use of apparatus and equipment in study and teaching

Adams, Richard C., 1945-
More ideas for science projects; {by} Richard Adams and Robert Gardner. rev. Watts 1998 128p llustration(s) (Experimental science series) lib bdg $23 (7 and up)   **507.8**
1. Science projects 2. Science—Experiments
ISBN 0-531-11380-9   LC 97-5792
First published 1989 under the authorship of Robert Gardner
This volume "offers over 100 ideas in a variety of scientific disciplines. In some cases, detailed instructions are given for projects; in others, an idea is presented with a number of questions to be considered. . . . This is a good resource for class assignments and science-fair projects." SLJ
Includes glossary and bibliographical references

Bazler, Judith A.
More science projects for all students. Facts on File 2002 various paging il (Facts on File science library) loose-leaf $185   **507.8**
1. Science—Experiments 2. Science projects
ISBN 0-8160-4518-6   LC 2002-1463
Also available CD-ROM version
Companion volume to Science projects for all students by Marty Berda and Mary Jean Blaisdell, published 1998
"More than 55 large-print experiments are presented in binder format and illustrated with clear, accurate pen-and-ink drawings. . . . Changes in equipment and presentation have been made so that children with learning disabilities or visual or motor impairment can be successful. Areas covered include earth science, weather, space science, life science, and physical science." SLJ
Includes glossary and bibliographical references

Bochinski, Julianne Blair, 1966-
The complete handbook of science fair projects; illustrated by Judy DiBiase. Newly rev and updated. J. Wiley 2004 228p il $29.95; pa $14.95
    507.8
1. Science projects
ISBN 0-471-45767-1; 0-471-46043-5 (pa)
    LC 2003-19494
First published 1991
Discusses various aspects of science fair projects including advice on choosing a topic, doing research, developing experiments, organizing data results, and presenting a project to the judges
"An excellent resource for students looking for ideas." Booklist

More award-winning science fair projects; illustrated by Judy J. Bochinski-DiBiase. J. Wiley 2004 228p il $29.95; pa $14.95 (7 and up)
    507.8
1. Science projects 2. Science—Experiments
ISBN 0-471-27338-4; 0-471-27337-6 (pa)
    LC 2003-9477
Presents forty award-winning science fair projects, a section on how to do a science fair project, updates to science fair rules and science supply resources, as well as new material on useful web sites.

Bombaugh, Ruth J.
Science fair success; {by} Ruth Bombaugh. rev & expanded. Enslow Pubs. 1999 128p il lib bdg $26.60 (7 and up)   **507.8**
1. Science projects 2. Science—Experiments
ISBN 0-7660-1163-1   LC 98-3297
First published 1989
A guide for choosing, designing, and completing an investigative science fair project, with an appendix listing prize winning projects
Includes bibliographical references

Chahrour, Janet

Zap! blink! taste! think! exciting life science for curious minds; illustrated by Abe Gurvin. Barron's Educ. Ser. 2003 211p il $14.95 (5 and up)

507.8

1. Science—Experiments 2. Science projects
ISBN 0-7641-1912-5   LC 2002-28036
Contents: Your senses; Food science; Create your own; Inspections and dissections; Psychology and beliefs

Presents the procedures and concepts involved in twenty-four science experiments that can be done at home with readily available materials, exploring psychology, food chemistry, crime-solving, and horoscopes

"This volume is an excellent book for any elementary school, junior high, or home library. The colorful illustrations, large print, and clear directions make it easy to use and a pleasure to look at. . . . Goofy jokes and inspiring quotes are scattered throughout the book." Sci Books Films

Includes bibliographical references

Cobb, Vicki, 1938-

Science experiments you can eat; illustrated by David Cain. rev & updated. HarperCollins Pubs. 1994 214p il lib bdg $15.89; pa $5.95 (5 and up)

507.8

1. Science—Experiments 2. Cooking
ISBN 0-06-023551-9 (lib bdg); 0-06-446002-9 (pa)
LC 93-13679
First published 1972
Experiments with food demonstrate various scientific principles and produce an eatable result. Includes rock candy, grape jelly, cupcakes, and popcorn

Includes glossary

You gotta try this! absolutely irresistible science; by Vicki Cobb and Kathy Darling; illustrated by True Kelley. Morrow Junior Bks. 1999 144p il $15.99 (4 and up)   **507.8**

1. Science—Experiments 2. Scientific recreations
ISBN 0-688-15740-8   LC 98-29556
A collection of science experiments and activities, arranged in such categories as "Physical Attractions," "Curious Chemistry," and "Freaky Fluids"

"True Kelley's line-and-gray-wash illustrations clarify the directions and add their own good-natured visual appeal. A fine addition to science collections." Booklist

Experiment central; understanding scientific principles through projects; John T. Tanacredi & John Loret, general editors. U.X.L 2000 4v set $165 (7 and up)   **507.8**

1. Science—Experiments
ISBN 0-7876-2892-1   LC 99-54142
Also available additional two volume set published 2003, designated volume five and six $99 (ISBN 0-7876-7615-2)

Demonstrates scientific concepts by means of experiments, including step-by-step instructions, lists of materials, troubleshooter's guide, and interpretation and explanation of the results

Gardner, Robert, 1929-

Light, sound, and waves science fair projects; using sunglasses, guitars, CDs, and other stuff. Enslow Publishers 2004 128p il (Physics! best science projects) lib bdg $20.95 (7 and up)

507.8

1. Light 2. Sound 3. Science projects 4. Science—Experiments
ISBN 0-7660-2126-2   LC 2003-13713
Contents: Some properties of sound and waves; Some properties of light; Light, sound, and reflection; Light, sound, and refraction; Dispersion, light, and color; Sound, light, and waves; Transverse waves and polarized light

These science fair projects attempt to answer such questions as "why dogs can hear things that humans cannot? Why a flame gives off light? Why certain mirrors make you look shorter or taller?"

"This is a very good book, as both a practical and a reference resource." Sci Books Films

Includes glossary and bibliographical references

Science fair projects—planning, presenting, succeeding. Enslow Pubs. 1999 104p il (Science projects) lib bdg $26.60 (7 and up)   **507.8**

1. Science projects 2. Science—Experiments
ISBN 0-89490-949-5   LC 98-8667
Provides information on choosing and planning a science fair project, carrying it out, recording your findings, writing a report, and exhibiting the project

Includes bibliographical references

Science project ideas in the house. rev ed. Enslow Pubs. 2002 128p il (Science project ideas) $26.60   **507.8**

1. Physics 2. Science—Experiments 3. Science projects
ISBN 0-7660-1705-2   LC 2001-700
First published 1985 by Messner with title: Science around the house

"This volume is a primer in physics presenting more than 40 simple experiments and activities with objects easily found in most homes. Topics include balances, weights and density, condensation, evaporation, motion and gravity, force, matter, friction, and acceleration." Book Rep

Includes bibliographical references

Science projects about physics in the home. Enslow Pubs. 1999 112p il (Science projects) lib bdg $26.60 (5 and up)   **507.8**

1. Physics 2. Science—Experiments 3. Science projects
ISBN 0-89490-948-7   LC 98-6822
Presents instructions for physics projects and experiments that can be done at home and exhibited at science fairs

"This volume is well organized with lots of hands-on activities that use relatively simple pieces of equipment. . . . A good starting point in the understanding of the physics of objects and events in our daily life." Sci Books Films

Includes bibliographical references

Goodstein, Madeline

Plastics and polymers science fair projects; using hair gel, soda bottles, and slimy stuff. Enslow Publishers 2004 128p il (Chemistry! best science projects) lib bdg $20.95 (7 and up)
507.8

1. Plastics 2. Polymers 3. Science projects 4. Science—Experiments

ISBN 0-7660-2123-8   LC 2003-12825

Contents: Plastics and polymers are all around us; Some properties of polymers; Testing plastics; The mysterious case of natural rubber

This "is a compilation of 20 hands-on activities having to do with the chemical compositon of plastics and common polymers. . . . The directions for the activities are clear and concise while addressing key safety considerations. . . . The book is an excellent example of cross-disciplinary science." Sci Books Films

Includes glossary and bibliographical references

Haduch, Bill

Science fair success secrets; how to win prizes, have fun, and think like a scientist; illustrated by Philip Scheuer. Dutton 2002 134p il pa $10.99 (5 and up)
507.8

1. Science projects 2. Science—Experiments

ISBN 0-525-46534-0   LC 2002-23536

Explains the scientific method and describes a variety of actual science fair projects in such fields as engineering, botany, behavioral science, and chemistry

"The often jaunty tone of the text and the cartoon-style drawings make this an unusually appealing book on the topic, while the respect for science and the solid presentation make it a highly useful book as well." Booklist

Includes bibliographical references

Kerrod, Robin, 1938-

The way science works; discover the secrets of science with exciting, accessible experiments; by Robin Kerrod and Sharon Ann Holgate. DK Pub. 2002 160p il $24.99 (7 and up)
507.8

1. Science—Experiments

ISBN 0-7894-8562-1   LC 2002-83510

This "science book explores the key theories involving matter, atoms and elements, forces and energy, heat and sound, light and color, electricity, and magnetism by giving detailed experiments, while including history, principles, and procedures for each." Book Rep

"This terrific resource explains key theories in clear and accessible language, and highlights even the smallest of detail with clear and vivid images." ALAN

Includes glossary

Krieger, Melanie Jacobs

How to excel in science competitions. rev and updated ed. Enslow Pubs. 1999 128p il (Science fair success) lib bdg $26.60
507.8

1. Science projects 2. Science—Experiments

ISBN 0-7660-1292-1   LC 98-31754

First published 1991

This is a "resource for preparing for science competitions. Students are guided from start to finish, including

beginning a project, writing and presenting a paper, and answering judges' questions. . . . This well-researched, clearly written book will encourage exploration and experimentation." SLJ

Includes bibliographical references

Parker, Steve

Science experiments. Sterling 1998 96p il $19.95; pa $12.95
507.8

1. Science—Experiments

ISBN 0-8069-6295-X; 0-8069-5914-2

LC 99-162341

"A Quarto children's book"

Cover title: Shocking, slimy, stinky, shiny science experiments

"A collection of 73 . . . projects. Each chapter begins with a brief introduction followed by a number of experiments. The first chapter, 'Shiny Science,' covers light and sight, including reflections, lenses, and rainbows. 'Shocking Science' begins with static electricity and progresses to electromagnetism. The last two chapters, 'Slimy Science' and 'Stinky Science,' invite children to create, observe, and analyze a variety of slimes and smells." SLJ

Includes glossary

Pentland, Peter

Party science; [by] Peter Pentland and Pennie Stoyles. Chelsea House 2003 c2002 32p il (Science and scientists) lib bdg $18.95 (4 and up)
507.8

1. Science

ISBN 0-7910-7015-8   LC 2002-1281

First published 2002 in Australia

Contents: Have you ever wondered ...?; Where do soft drink bubbles come from?; Party food that pops and fizzes; Making an insulated cake; How cool is ice cream?; What makes ice cream taste good?; Gelatin: wobbly, foamy and chewy; Balloons; Candles; What is your star sign?; Party lights; Fireworks; Meet a science communicator; Party noise; Party tricks and illusions; Laughter; Too much fun; Party science timeline

Discusses the scientific principles behind various objects and activities at a party including balloons, fireworks, magic, and laughter

"These authors have a knack for offering concise, easy-to-understand explanations of common phenomena. . . . [This book is] sound, highly educational, and entertaining." SLJ

Includes glossary

Pilger, Mary Anne

Science experiments index for young people. 3rd ed. Libraries Unlimited 2002 xxx, 294p $65
507.8

1. Science—Experiments—Indexes

ISBN 1-563-08899-1   LC 2001-54369

First published 1988

"This volume indexes science experiments from more than 500 books published from 1990 through 2000. Experiments are grouped under topics, from *3-D viewers* to *Zoology*." Booklist

"The arrangement of the book and the formatting of

Pilger, Mary Anne—*Continued*
the text on the page make it very easy to use. . . . It is highly recommended." Am Ref Books Annu, 2003
Includes bibliographical references

Rhatigan, Joe
Sure-to-win science fair projects; {by} Joe Rhatigan with Heather Smith. Lark Bks. 2001 128p il $21.95; pa $14.95 (5 and up)   **507.8**
1. Science projects 2. Science—Experiments
ISBN 1-57990-238-3; 1-57990-374-6 (pa)
LC 2001-16505
The authors give "directions for choosing a topic and an . . . assessment of the time and effort a good experiment will take, along with . . . instructions for record keeping, the use of constant and variable controls, and the successful presentation of results. A variety of research venues is suggested, including interviews, print, and the Internet." SLJ
Students "will find a gold mine of instructions in this well-written, easy-to-grasp volume that includes nearly 60 amusing, sometimes ingenious biology, physical science, and chemistry projects." Booklist

Rosner, Marc Alan
Science fair success using the Internet. Enslow Pubs. 1999 112p il (Science fair success) lib bdg $26.60 (7 and up)   **507.8**
1. Science projects 2. Science—Experiments 3. Internet
ISBN 0-7660-1172-0   LC 98-25945
Explains how to use Internet resources, including e-mailing experts and using search engines, to enhance science projects, with sample projects in biology, chemistry, physics, environment and earth science, and astronomy
Includes bibliographical references

Science activities. Grolier Educ. 2002 10v set $365 (4 and up)   **507.8**
1. Science—Experiments
ISBN 0-7172-5608-1   LC 2001-40519
Contents: v1 Electricity and magnetism; v2 Everyday chemistry; v3 Force and motion; v4 Heat and energy; v5 Inside matter; v6 Light and color; v7 Our environment; v8 Sound and hearing; v9 Using materials; v10 Weather and climate
Each volume in this set presents 10 experiments, each with an introduction, step-by-step instructions, follow-up activities, and analysis

Science experiments on file; experiments, demonstrations, and projects for school and home; edited by Judith A. Bazler. rev ed. Facts on File 2000 2v il loose-leaf set $330   **507.8**
1. Science—Experiments
ISBN 0-8160-3998-4   LC 99-52951
First published 1988
Contents: v1 Earth science; weather; space; biology; v2 Chemistry; physics
This offers 200 science experiments, listing time required, safety precautions, materials, procedure, principles illustrated, data tables, connections, and additional activities, which may be reproduced for classroom use

Science fairs: ideas and activities. World Bk. 1997 80p il $14.95; pa $9.95   **507.8**
1. Science projects
ISBN 0-7166-4498-3; 0-7166-4497-5 (pa)
LC 97-29786
Ideas for hands-on science fair projects in the areas of space, earth, machines, plants, and time
"Great care has been taken to make the experiments attractive and accessible." SLJ
Includes bibliographical references

Tocci, Salvatore
How to do a science fair project. rev ed. Watts 1997 127p il (Experimental science series) lib bdg $23   **507.8**
1. Science projects 2. Science—Experiments
ISBN 0-531-11346-9   LC 96-50019
First published 1986
A step-by-step guide for creating a variety of projects suitable for entry in a science fair with suggestions for choosing a subject, performing the experiment, and polishing the presentation
"The author provides sage advice on how to select a project, conduct the research, and present the results. A good list of dos and don'ts includes a nice discussion of what works as a project topic and what doesn't. . . . The author also provides a good list of science supply companies." SLJ
Includes glossary and bibliographical references

VanCleave, Janice Pratt
Janice VanCleave's 203 icy, freezing, frosty, cool & wild experiments. Wiley 1999 122p il pa $12.95 (4 and up)   **507.8**
1. Science—Experiments
ISBN 0-471-25223-9   LC 98-49721
This includes "experiments in astronomy, biology, chemistry, earth science, and physics. . . . Each activity includes a purpose, a list of materials, a step-by-step procedure, results, and an explanation. Experiments address such topics as the Moon's 'changing' size, how environment affects body temperature, and why ice pops are softer than ice. An excellent resource." SLJ

Janice VanCleave's guide to more of the best science fair projects. Wiley 2000 156p il pa $14.95 (5 and up)   **507.8**
1. Science projects 2. Science—Experiments
ISBN 0-471-32627-5   LC 99-25575
This volume includes "fifty experiments . . . in the areas of astronomy, biology, earth science, engineering, physical science, and mathematics. . . . A valuable addition to science collections." SLJ
Includes bibliographical references

Janice VanCleave's guide to the best science fair projects; {by} Janice VanCleave. Wiley 1997 156p il pa 14.95 (4 and up)   **507.8**
1. Science projects 2. Science—Experiments
ISBN 0-471-14802-4   LC 96-27512
"In the first section, VanCleave discusses scientific methodology: how to organize a project from selecting a topic through the investigatory process, the importance of

VanCleave, Janice Pratt—*Continued*

keeping records, writing a final report, and the value of a nicely crafted presentation. . . . The next section—the largest by far—presents a number of double-page projects in a variety of fields. . . . A clear and informative addition." SLJ

Includes glossary and bibliographical references

Vecchione, Glen

100 award-winning science fair projects. Sterling 2001 208p il $21.95; pa $14.95 (7 and up)

507.8

1. Science projects 2. Science—Experiments
ISBN 0-8069-4261-4; 0-8069-7377-3 (pa)

LC 2001-20189

"Students will find projects on physics, chemistry, biology, earth science, mechanics, astronomy, and more here. . . . A reliable, useful purchase." SLJ

508 Natural history

Burnie, David

The Kingfisher illustrated nature encyclopedia; David Burnie. Kingfisher 2004 320p il $24.95 (5 and up)

508

1. Natural history 2. Nature
ISBN 0-7534-5576-5

LC 2003-61914

"Three major sections discuss the formation of the Earth, the biosphere, and climate change; focus on life from microscopic plants through the shapes, senses, and categories of animals, including habitats; and consider biomes. Highly detailed color photography, including many full-page, spectacular spreads, illuminates the concepts and discussions. Clear, colorful diagrams explain the unseen processes of nature." SLJ

DK nature encyclopedia. DK Pub. 1998 304p il maps $29.99

508

1. Natural history—Encyclopedias
ISBN 0-7894-3411-3

LC 98-16657

"The book is divided into six sections. 'The Natural World' describes the origins and evolution of life on earth. 'How Living Things Work' examines the basic characteristics shared by all living things—respiration, reproduction, life cycles, etc. 'Ecology' surveys the major types of habitats around the world and discusses topics such as food chains and endangered species. A short section explains 'How Living Things Are Classified,' while the final chapters look at specific groups of plants. . . . Well organized, clearly written, and with an amazing scope, this encyclopedia makes a valuable guide to nature." SLJ

509 Science--Historical and geographic treatment

Beshore, George W.

Science in ancient China; {by} George Beshore. Watts 1998 63p il map (Science of the past) lib bdg $26; pa $8.95 (4 and up)

509

1. Science—China—History 2. Science and civilization
ISBN 0-531-11334-5 (lib bdg); 0-531-15914-0 (pa)

LC 97-3519

First published 1988 in the First book series

Surveys the achievements of the ancient Chinese in science, medicine, astronomy, and cosmology, and describes such innovations as rockets, wells, the compass, water wheels, and movable type

Includes glossary and bibliographical references

Science in early Islamic culture; {by} George Beshore. Watts 1998 64p il maps (Science of the past) lib bdg $26; pa $8.95 (4 and up)

509

1. Science—History 2. Science and civilization
3. Islamic countries—Civilization
ISBN 0-531-20355-7 (lib bdg); 0-531-15917-5 (pa)

LC 97-5012

First published 1988 in the First book series

Discusses the extraordinary scientific discoveries and advancements in the Islamic world after the birth of Mohammed in 570 and their impact on Western civilization in subsequent centuries and today

"The writing is crisp and lively. . . . Numerous full-color and black-and-white photographs, reproductions, and drawings illuminate the text." SLJ

Includes glossary and bibliographical references

Gay, Kathlyn, 1930-

Science in ancient Greece. Watts 1998 64p il (Science of the past) lib bdg $26; pa $8.95 (4 and up)

509

1. Science—Greece—History 2. Science and civilization
ISBN 0-531-20357-3 (lib bdg); 0-531-15929-9 (pa)

LC 97-24029

First published 1988 in the First book series

Discusses the theories of ancient Greek philosopher-scientists such as Ptolemy, Pythagoras, Hippocrates, and Aristotle, and describes some of the scientific discoveries attributed to the Greeks and their impact on modern science

"Useful for reports, and there's also much to interest science students." SLJ

Includes glossary and bibliographical references

Hakim, Joy

Aristotle leads the way. Smithsonian 2004 282p il map (Story of science) $21.95 (5 and up)

509

1. Science—History 2. Ancient civilization
ISBN 1-58834-160-7

"In the first book of her three part Story of Science Joy Hakim invites readers . . . to meet the forebearers

Hakim, Joy—*Continued*

of modern science—Thales, Pythagoras, Archimedes, Aristotle, Arab and Chinese thinkers, Thomas Aquinas, Roger Bacon, and many others—and share in their . . . discoveries in astronomy, math, and physics." Publisher's note

"Hakim has interwoven creation myths, history, physics, and mathematics to present a seamless, multifaceted view of the foundation of modern science. . . . The entire volume is beautifully organized." SLJ

Includes bibliographical references

Harris, Jacqueline L., 1929-

Science in ancient Rome. Watts 1998 64p il map (Science of the past) lib bdg $26; pa $8.95 (4 and up)   **509**

1. Science—Rome—History 2. Science and civilization

ISBN 0-531-20354-9 (lib bdg); 0-531-15916-7 (pa)
LC 97-1901

First published 1988 in the First book series

Describes how the Romans put to use and expanded the scientific achievements of earlier civilizations

This "includes clear, easy-to-read text; simple yet effective topic headings; excellent-quality, full-color photographs and reproductions; and Internet sites." SLJ

Includes glossary and bibliographical references

Hatt, Christine

Scientists and their discoveries. Watts 2001 62p il (Documenting history) lib bdg $23.50 (7 and up)
509

1. Scientists 2. Science—History

ISBN 0-531-14614-6   LC 2001-17574

This "highlights an assortment of astronomers, chemists, physicists, geologists, and biologists, profiling their lives and contributions and explaining the basics of their theories and discoveries." Booklist

January, Brendan, 1972-

Science in colonial America. Watts 1999 64p il (Science of the past) lib bdg $26; pa $8.95 (4 and up)   **509**

1. Science—United States—History 2. Science and civilization

ISBN 0-531-11525-9 (lib bdg); 0-531-15940-X (pa)
LC 98-10450

Describes the scientific contributions made by people in colonial America, including natural history, medicine, astronomy, and electricity

"Attractive and accessible. . . . Plentiful, accurate material." SLJ

Includes glossary and bibliographical references

Llewellyn, Claire

Great discoveries & amazing adventures. Kingfisher 2004 76p il $18.95 (4 and up)
509

1. Science 2. Curiosities and wonders

ISBN 0-7534-5783-0

An "introductory look at a swath of discoveries, and at some of the people who made them. Divided into four

areas . . . the heavily illustrated two-page units present 31 various finds. . . . This factoid-loaded title will lure interested readers and propel the seriously curious into further, more detailed investigations. Inviting, exciting, and eminently browsable." SLJ

Moss, Carol (Carol Marie)

Science in ancient Mesopotamia. Watts 1998 63p il (Science of the past) hardcover o.p. paperback available $8.95 (4 and up)   **509**

1. Science—Iraq—History 2. Science and civilization

ISBN 0-531-15930-2 (pa)   LC 97-24030

First published 1988 in the First book series

Describes the enormous accomplishments of the Sumerians and Babylonians of ancient Mesopotamia in every scientific area, a heritage which affects our own everyday lives

"Clearly written. . . . Black-and-white and full-color photographs and reproductions . . . are well captioned." SLJ

Includes glossary and bibliographical references

Popular science: science year by year; discoveries and inventions from the last century that shape our lives. Scholastic Ref. 2001 240p il $19.95
509

1. Science—History 2. Technology—History

ISBN 0-439-28438-4   LC 00-50476

One illustrated page per each year from 1900 to 2000 chronicles important discoveries and inventions in such fields as medicine, earth sciences, space exploration, computers, mathematics, and biology

Science, technology, and society: the impact of science in the 20th century; Phillis Engelbert, editor. U.X.L 2002 3v il set $159   **509**

1. Science—History 2. Science and civilization 3. Technology—History 4. Technology and civilization

ISBN 0-7876-5649-6   LC 2002-4668

Also available 2 volume companion set covering the impact of science in the 19th century and a 3 volume companion set covering the impact of science from 2000 B.C. to the 18th century

"Each volume begins with the same table of contents, chronology, and list of words to know. Volumes cover specific fields of science: volume 1, *Life Science*; volume 2, *Mathematics and Medicine*; volume 3, *Physical Science and Technology*. The format for each of the five topics is the same: 'Chronology,' 'Overview,' 'Essays' on specific discoveries and inventions, 'Biographies' (nine or ten two-page profiles), 'Brief Biographies' (additional paragraph-length treatments), 'Research and Activity Ideas,' and a bibliography for more information." Booklist

Spangenburg, Ray, 1939-

The age of synthesis: 1800-1895; [by] Ray Spangenburg and Diane Kit Moser. Facts on File 2004 208p (History of science) $35 (7 and up)
509

1. Science—History

ISBN 0-8160-4853-3   LC 2003-21409

First published 1994 with title: The history of science in the nineteenth century

Spangenburg, Ray, 1939——*Continued*

Examines the role of science in the Industrial Revolution, its establishment as a popular discipline, and discoveries in the areas of atoms and the elements, chemistry, evolution, and energy

This "is a valuable resource." Voice Youth Advocates [review of 1994 edition]

Includes glossary and bibliographical references

The birth of science: ancient times to 1699; [by] Ray Spangenburg and Diane Kit Moser. Facts on File 2004 256p (History of science) $35 (7 and up) **509**

1. Science—History

ISBN 0-8160-4851-7   LC 2003-19470

First published 1993 with title: The history of science from the ancient Greeks to the scientific revolution

Discusses major scientists as well as scientific knowledge and discoveries from ancient times through the seventeenth century

"Very well written and thoroughly understandable, the book succeeds hugely in its objective to introduce the development of science in an interesting fashion to the intended audience without patronizing or oversimplifying." Sci Books Films [review of 1993 edition]

Includes glossary and bibliographical references

Modern science, 1896-1945; [by] Ray Spangenburg and Diane Kit Moser. rev ed. Facts on File 2004 206p (History of science) $35 (7 and up) **509**

1. Science—History 2. Life sciences

ISBN 0-8160-4854-1   LC 2003-22974

First published 1994 with title: The history of science from 1895 to 1945

Discusses major scientists and scientific issues and discoveries of the first half of the twentieth century

Consider this title an "essential support for any studies in the nature or history of modern science." SLJ

Includes glossary and bibliographical references

The rise of reason: 1700-1799; -; [by] Ray Spangenburg and Diane Kit Moser. Facts on File 2005 224p (History of science) $35 (7 and up) **509**

1. Science—History

ISBN 0-8160-4852-5   LC 2003-19471

Discusses major scientists and scientific issues and discoveries of the eighteenth and early nineteenth centuries

Consider this title an "essential support for any studies in the nature or history of modern science." SLJ

Includes glossary and bibliographical references

Science frontiers, 1946 to the present; [by] Ray Spangenburg and Diane Kit Moser. Facts on File 2004 272p (History of science) $35 (7 and up) **509**

1. Science—History

ISBN 0-8160-4855-X   LC 2003-24290

First published 1994 with title: The history of science from 1946 to the 1990s

The authors provide "descriptions of complex scientific theories and lines of research in the latter part of the 20th century—but only in the natural sciences: physics (new particles, lasers, and superconductors), astronomy (quasars, black holes, cosmology, dark matter, planetary geology, and SETI), geology (evolution, plate tectonics, and environmental change), and biology (DNA, biotechnology, the human genome, and retroviruses)." Sci Books Films [review of 1994 edition]

Includes glossary and bibliographical references

Stewart, Melissa, 1968-

Science in ancient India. Watts 1999 64p il map (Science of the past) lib bdg $26 (4 and up) **509**

1. Science—India—History 2. Science and civilization

ISBN 0-531-11626-3   LC 98-18536

An overview of the scientific contributions of ancient India including Arabic numerals, ayurveda, basic chemistry and physics, and celestial observations

"A useful and unique resource." SLJ

Includes glossary and bibliographical references

Whitfield, Peter

History of science. Grolier 2003 10v il set $279 **509**

1. Science—History

ISBN 0-7172-5729-0   LC 2002-29844

Contents: v1 Science in ancient civilizations; v2 Islamic and western medieval science; v3 Traditions of science outside Europe; v4 The European Renaissance; v5 The Scientific Revolution; v6 The eighteenth century; v7 Physical science in the nineteenth century; v8 Biology and geology in the nineteenth century; v9 Atoms and galaxies: modern physical science; v10 Twentieth-century life sciences

This set provides a brief history of physical and life sciences from ancient civilizations to the twentieth century worldwide, and is illustrated with numerous photographs, diagrams, and drawings

Woods, Geraldine, 1948-

Science in ancient Egypt. Watts 1998 64p il (Science of the past) lib bdg $26; pa $8.95 (4 and up) **509**

1. Science—Egypt—History 2. Science and civilization

ISBN 0-531-20341-7 (lib bdg); 0-531-15915-9 (pa) LC 97-649

First published 1988 in the First book series

Discusses the achievements of the ancient Egyptians in science, mathematics, astronomy, medicine, agriculture, and technology

"Well-researched and easy-to-understand. . . . Woods offers a fascinating look at the ancient Egyptians' accomplishments." SLJ

Includes glossary and bibliographical references

Woods, Geraldine, 1948——*Continued*

Science of the early Americas. Watts 1999 64p il (Science of the past) lib bdg $26; pa $8.95 (4 and up) **509**

1. Science—History 2. Science and civilization 3. Native Americans

ISBN 0-531-11524-0 (lib bdg); 0-531-15941-8 (pa)
LC 97-44047

Discusses the scientific accomplishments in such fields as medicine, mathematics, engineering, and astronomy of various groups of American Indians

Includes glossary and bibliographical references

510   Mathematics

Bazin, Maurice

Math and science across cultures; activities and investigations from the Exploratorium; [by] Maurice Bazin, Modesto Tamez, and the Exploratorium Teacher Institute. New Press 2002 176p il maps pa $19.95 **510**

1. Mathematics 2. Science

ISBN 1-56584-541-2   LC 00-136455

This book provides "activities that integrate geography, math, and science into a multicultural curriculum. . . . Each topic provides a hands-on, minds-on activity that enriches thinking skills and the application-research-based process." Sci Books Films

Includes bibliographical references

Mathematics; Barry Max Brandenberger, Jr., editor in chief. Macmillan Ref. USA 2002 4v set $395 **510**

1. Mathematics

ISBN 0-02-865561-3   LC 00-45593

This alphabetically arranged encyclopedia includes "articles about the history of mathematics, prominent scientists from Hypatia to Grace Hopper, technology, and mathematics-related careers, as well as such everyday applications as culinary math." SLJ

This reference "meets its goal of presenting mathematics in a realistic, practical manner." Booklist

510.7   Mathematics--Education and related topics

Salvadori, Mario George, 1907-1997

Math games for middle school; challenges and skill-builders for students at every level; {by} Mario Salvadori and Joseph P. Wright. Chicago Review Press 1998 168p il pa $16.95

510.7

1. Mathematics—Study and teaching

ISBN 1-55652-288-6   LC 97-51422

Uses explanations, word problems, and games to cover some mathematical topics that middle school students need to know, including the invention of numerical notations, basic arithmatical operations, measurements, geometry, graphs, and probability

513   Arithmetic

Julius, Edward H., 1952-

Arithmetricks; 50 easy ways to add, subtract, multiply, and divide without a calculator; illustrations by Dale M. Gladstone. Wiley 1995 142p il pa $12.95 **513**

1. Arithmetic

ISBN 0-471-10639-9   LC 94-41836

This book "offers fifty ways to do simple arithmetic calculations in one's head. . . . Each trick is covered on two facing pages. The first page presents the problem and gives two examples of how to use the trick. The facing page has a black and white cartoon and extra exercises to practice. The correct answers are given at the end of the book. This would be a fun book for mathematically inclined Middle-Schoolers and up. Math teachers will enjoy using this book for extra-curricular activities." Appraisal

520   Astronomy and allied sciences

Astronomy. Reader's Digest Assn. 1998 159p il (Reader's Digest explores) $24.95 (7 and up)
520

1. Astronomy 2. Outer space—Exploration

ISBN 0-7621-0042-7   LC 97-46925

This illustrated volume discusses such topics as space exploration, moon landings, space probes, shuttles, and space stations

Bond, Peter, 1948-

DK guide to space. DK Pub. 1999 63p il $19.99 (4 and up) **520**

1. Astronomy

ISBN 0-7894-3946-8   LC 98-42054

Presents discoveries, observations, and theories about the planets and other phenomena in our solar system as well as in outer space, using text, illustrations, and photographs from NASA

"This book demonstrates both the author's enthusiasm and his knowledge of astronomy. The photographs are beautiful, well chosen, and up to date." Sci Books Films

Bramwell, Martyn

Mapping the planets and space; illustrated by George Fryer. Lerner Publs. 1998 48p il (Maps & mapmakers) lib bdg $22.60 **520**

1. Astronomy 2. Planets 3. Outer space

ISBN 0-8225-2922-X   LC 97-12188

Explains what our study of outer space has revealed to us about the planets and other heavenly bodies

Includes glossary

Dickinson, Terence

NightWatch; a practical guide to viewing the universe; foreword by Timothy Ferris; illustrations by Adolf Schaller, Victor Costanzo and Roberta Cooke; principal photography by Terrance Dickinson. 3rd ed, rev and expanded. Firefly Bks. (Buffalo) 1998 176p il hardcover o.p. paperback available $29.95 (7 and up) **520**
1. Astronomy
ISBN 1-55209-302-6 (pa)
First published 1983
This "handbook for amateur astronomers combines a text both meaty and hard to put down with a great array of charts, boxes, tables, and dazzling full-color photos of the sky." SLJ
Includes bibliographical references

Furniss, Tim

The atlas of space exploration. Friedman/Fairfax Pubs. 2002 96p il $14.95 **520**
1. Space sciences 2. Outer space—Exploration
ISBN 1-5866-3346-5   LC 2002-80913
First published 2001 in the United Kingdom
This "book is divided into three parts: 'Voyages into the Unknown,' 'Discovering New worlds,' and 'To the Stars and beyond.' . . . The layout is attractive and easy to read, and the content is enhanced by an assortment of superb photographs, clear diagrams, illustrations and artist's impressions, and actual X-ray and satellite imagery." Sci Books Films

Lippincott, Kristen, 1954-

Astronomy; written by Kristen Lippincott. rev ed. DK Pub. 2004 72p il map (DK eyewitness books) $15.99 **520**
1. Astronomy
ISBN 0-7566-0656-X
First published 1994
This covers a history of astronomy and telescopes, the planets and stars, galaxies, and modern research.
Includes glossary

Mechler, Gary

National Audubon Society first field guide: night sky; sky maps by Wil Tirion. Scholastic 1999 159p il maps $17.95; pa $8.95 (4 and up) **520**
1. Astronomy
ISBN 0-590-64085-2; 0-590-64086-0 (pa)
            LC 98-51876
A field guide to the night sky, explaining through text and maps how to locate and identify stars, planets, meteors, comets, and constellations
Includes bibliographical references

Redfern, Martin

The Kingfisher young people's book of space. Kingfisher (NY) 1998 95p il $21.95 **520**
1. Astronomy 2. Outer space—Exploration
ISBN 0-7534-5136-0   LC 97-51122

Examines our exploration of outer space and discusses the solar system, stars, galaxies, and the universe in general
"The book's layout, with outstanding pictures and text, complements this engaging journey through our space." Sci Child
Includes glossary

Reed, George

Eyes on the universe. Benchmark Bks. 2001 80p il (Story of science) lib bdg $29.93 (5 and up)
520
1. Astronomy
ISBN 0-7614-1150-X   LC 00-31527
This survey examines the history of astronomy from ancient times to the present. Aristotle, Ptolemy, Galileo, Newton, Copernicus, William Hubble and Karl Jansky are among the major figures discussed
Includes glossary and bibliographical references

Rhatigan, Joe

Out-of-this-world astronomy; 50 amazing activities & projects; {by} Joe Rhatigan & Rain Newcomb; with Gregg Doppmann, special consultant. Lark Books 2003 128p il $19.95 (5 and up) **520**
1. Astronomy
ISBN 1-579-90410-6   LC 2003-5196
Contents: The view from here; The Moon; The Sun; The solar system; The stars and beyond
Introduces the study of "stuff in space," providing statistics, quizzes, activities, and experiments about the stars and planets
"An excellent introduction to astronomy. . . . Most [of the projects] are interesting, informative, and well within the abilities of the intended audience. . . . Spectacular color photos and other graphics, useful charts, and graphs augment the text." SLJ
Includes glossary

Ridpath, Ian

Facts on File stars & planets atlas. updated ed. Facts on File 2001 80p il $18.95 **520**
1. Astronomy 2. Stars 3. Planets
ISBN 0-8160-4800-2   LC 2001-40827
First published 1993 with title: The Facts on File atlas of stars and planets
An overview of the solar system, including such topics as the earth and other planets, the sun, moon, asteroids, comets, meteors, and black holes.

Scagell, Robin, 1946-

Children's night sky atlas; written by Robin Scagell. Dorling Kindersley Pub 2004 96p il spiral bdg $19.99 (5 and up) **520**
1. Astronomy
ISBN 0-7566-0284-X   LC 2004-131
"This atlas illustrates . . . constellations, the evolution of stars and galaxies, and the planets in the solar system. Acetate overlays highlight special points of interest." Publisher's note

Scagell, Robin, 1946- — *Continued*
"A visually stunning and informative introduction to astronomy and stargazing." SLJ
Inlcudes glossary

Silverstein, Alvin
The universe; [by] Alvin Silverstein, Virginia Silverstein, Laura Silverstein Nunn. 21st Cent. Bks. (Brookfield) 2003 64p il (Science concepts) lib bdg $26.90 **520**
1. Astronomy 2. Universe
ISBN 0-7613-2255-8 LC 2002-240
Contents: Our vast universe; Our solar system; The planet; Starry skies; Exploring the universe; Our future in the universe
Explores the universe and all of its elements, including the Milky Way, our solar system, the stars, and other astronomical bodies, and examines why it is important to continue studying the cosmos
"Authoritative, objective, and broadly based. . . . Beautifully designed and well illustrated." SLJ
Includes bibliographical references

Simon, Seymour, 1931-
Destination: space. HarperCollins Pubs. 2002 unp il $15.99; lib bdg $16.89; pa $6.99 (4 and up) **520**
1. Astronomy 2. Hubble Space Telescope
ISBN 0-688-16289-4; 0-688-16290-8 (lib bdg); 0-06-059681-3 (pa) LC 2001-24773
Explains new discoveries about the universe made possible by the Hubble Telescope
This book is "handsome and fascinating. . . . On each spread, the large-print, easy-to-understand text is supported by a stunning, full-page color photograph. The author explains what discovery each image produced and how the information fits into our existing knowledge. His enthusiastic descriptions create vivid pictures in and of themselves." SLJ

Space and astronomy on file; {by} The Diagram Group. Facts on File 2001 various paging loose-leaf $185 **520**
1. Astronomy 2. Space sciences
ISBN 0-8160-4545-3 LC 2001-24663
Also available CD-ROM version
This looseleaf volume offers 300 reproducable line illustrations, charts, tables, and graphs for classroom use about astronomy and space exploration

Stott, Carole
New astronomer; editorial consultant, Amie Gallagher. DK Pub. 1999 144p il maps $25 (7 and up) **520**
1. Astronomy
ISBN 0-7894-4175-6 LC 98-45283
This introduces astronomical tools and techniques, combines photographs from the Hubble Space Telescope with surface-contour maps from space probes, and includes charts and advice for observing planets and stars and other astronomical phenomena
"Beautifully illustrated with clear photographs and dia-

grams. . . . Cross-referencing within the text is excellent, explanations are in-depth, and the sky maps in the Star section are exemplary." Voice Youth Advocates
Includes glossary

VanCleave, Janice Pratt
Janice VanCleave's A+ projects in astronomy; winning experiments for science fairs and extra credit. Wiley 2002 216p il $32.50; pa $12.95 (7 and up) **520**
1. Astronomy 2. Science projects 3. Science—Experiments
ISBN 0-471-32816-2; 0-471-32820-0 (pa) LC 2001-24708
This "has seven sections: Measurements, Optical Instruments, the Sun, the Planets, Moons, and Stars, Meteors, and Artificial Satellites. Project descriptions include purpose, needed materials, procedure, results, and a 'Why?' section. . . . The materials needed are all readily available." Book Rep

520.3 Astronomy--Encyclopedias and dictionaries

The **Facts** on File dictionary of astronomy. 4th ed, edited by Valerie Illingworth and John O. E. Clark. Facts on File 2000 490p (Facts on File science library) $55; pa $19.95 **520.3**
1. Astronomy—Dictionaries
ISBN 0-8160-4283-7; 0-8160-4284-5 (pa) LC 00-55553
First published 1979
This dictionary includes "more than 3,700 entries . . . that reflect all aspects of astronomy, together with associated terms in spectroscopy, photometry, and particle physics." Publisher's note
"The information is concise and to the point. . . . Valuable for quick reference. The entries are accurate." Book Rep

522 Techniques, equipment, materials of astronomy

Cole, Michael D.
Hubble Space Telescope; exploring the universe. Enslow Pubs. 1999 48p il (Countdown to space) lib bdg $23.93 (4 and up) **522**
1. Astronomy 2. Hubble Space Telescope 3. Astronautics
ISBN 0-7660-1120-8 LC 98-3298
Details the initiation of the Hubble Space Telescope in April 1990 and the repair and servicing missions which followed; explains the telescope's role in answering questions about the universe
"Illustrated with color photographs, the book provides solid basic information." Horn Book
Includes glossary and bibliographical references

Matloff, Gregory L.
More telescope power; all new activities and projects for young astronomers; with drawings by C. Bangs. Wiley 2002 118p il pa $12.95
522
1. Telescopes 2. Astronomy 3. Science—Experiments
ISBN 0-471-40985-5   LC 2001-46738
Presents various astronomy activities using a telescope, including constructing a simple telescope, tracking satellites, and sketching details of the moon
This "book is well-written, interesting, and suitable for anyone who wants to learn more about astronomy." Book Rep
Includes glossary and bibliographical references

Spangenburg, Ray, 1939-
The Hubble Space Telescope; {by} Ray Spangenburg and Kit Moser. Watts 2002 128p il (Out of this world) lib bdg $33.50; pa $14.95
522
1. Hubble Space Telescope
ISBN 0-531-11894-0 (lib bdg); 0-531-15565-X (pa)
LC 2001-17563
This "begins by tracing the origins of stargazing and the development of the first telescopes. Eventually, after great technological advances and a few setbacks, the Hubble is completed and put into place. Dramatic photos of faraway galaxies underline the significant contributions that it has made to understanding the universe. The book includes the telescope's specifications and brief biographies of historical figures and present-day scientists, as well as a time line of discoveries and achievements that led to its creation." Voice Youth Advocates
Includes bibliographical references

523 Specific celestial bodies and phenomena

Chartrand, Mark R.
The Audubon Society field guide to the night sky; astronomical charts by Wil Tirion. Knopf 1991 714p il maps $19.95   **523**
1. Astronomy
ISBN 0-679-40852-5   LC 91-52708
"A Chanticleer Press edition. The Audubon Society field guide series"
This guide "begins with monthly star charts and constellation star charts . . . then gives photographs of the constellations; and finally, provides detailed information on each constellation including stars, galaxies, and nebulae. . . . Other information includes hints on observing ther sky; dates of solar and lunar eclipses, meteor showers, and comets, and the Messier catalog. . . . Students interested in astronomy will find lots of observing tips and information." Voice Youth Advocates
Includes bibliographical references

Miller, Ron, 1947-
Extrasolar planets. 21st Cent. Bks. (Brookfield) 2002 96p il (Worlds beyond) lib bdg $27.90
523
1. Planets
ISBN 0-7613-2354-6   LC 2001-31685

Chronicles the discoveries of all the planets within our solar system, as well as planets beyond our system
The author "makes the complicated idea of the solar system approachable enough for even the most reluctant science student. . . . The writing is simple and straightforward. The format is open, with lots of white space peppered with NASA photographs and Miller's own stunning illustrations to complement the text." Booklist
Includes glossary and bibliographical references

Pasachoff, Jay M.
A field guide to the stars and planets. 4th ed, Jay M. Pasachoff; with monthly star maps and atlas charts by Wil Tirion. Houghton Mifflin 2000 578p il maps (Peterson field guide series) $30; pa $19   **523**
1. Astronomy
ISBN 0-395-93432-X; 0-395-93431-1 (pa)
LC 99-27354
First published 1964 under the authorship of Donald H. Menzel and Jay M. Pasachoff
This guide contains 24 monthly sky maps, 54 atlas charts, information and numerous color photographs from NASA and other sources, and time-sensitive material through 2010
Includes bibliographical references

Simon, Seymour, 1931-
The universe. Morrow Junior Bks. 1998 unp il $16.95; pa $6.99 (4 and up)   **523**
1. Cosmology
ISBN 0-688-15301-1; 0-06-443752-3 (pa)
LC 97-20489
"Matching full-color, full- and double-page-spread-sized light and radio photographs of nebulas, galaxies, and sundry deep-space phenomena with two or three paragraphs of explanatory text {Simon} covers a wide range of topics, from the Big Bang to quasars, from star formation to extrasolar planets. . . . The choice of detail is guaranteed to whet youngster's appetites for a more thorough, narrowly focused treatment." SLJ

523.2 Planetary systems

Ride, Sally K.
Exploring our solar system; [by] Sally Ride and Tam O'Shaughnessy. Crown 2003 110p il $19.95 (4 and up)   **523.2**
1. Solar system 2. Planets
ISBN 0-375-81204-0   LC 2002-17471
Describes what we have learned about our solar system from telescopes and spacecraft, focusing on the characteristics of the planets and their moons
"In this copiously illustrated volume, astronaut Ride and educator O'Shaughnessy offer a thrilling introduction to our solar system. . . . Visually arresting and clearly presented." Booklist
Includes glossary

VanCleave, Janice Pratt
Janice VanCleave's solar system; mind-boggling experiments you can turn into science fair projects. Wiley 2000 90p il map pa $10.95 (4 and up)
523.2
1. Solar system 2. Science projects 3. Science—Experiments
ISBN 0-471-32204-0   LC 99-15479
Provides instructions for a variety of experiments and science fair projects exploring the solar system, including the sun, moon, planets, comets, and meteorites
"Welcome and valuable." SLJ
Includes glossary

523.3 Moon

Bredeson, Carmen
The moon. Watts 1998 63p il hardcover o.p. paperback available $6.95 (4 and up)
523.3
1. Project Apollo 2. Moon 3. Apollo project
ISBN 0-531-15911-6 (pa)   LC 96-40226
"A First book"
Describes what people have believed about the moon and what has been learned over time and presents an overview of the Apollo space program
"Clear, effective illustrations, most in color, appear throughout the book. . . . A good resource for science collections." Booklist
Includes glossary and bibliographical references

Gardner, Robert, 1929-
Science project ideas about the moon. Enslow Pubs. 1997 96p il (Science project ideas) lib bdg $25.26   **523.3**
1. Moon 2. Science projects 3. Science—Experiments
ISBN 0-89490-844-8   LC 97-6486
Introduces the phases and other characteristics of the moon through a series of experiments, most of which can be used to start a science fair project
"Includes a wealth of information about the moon, as well as telescopes." Sci Books Films
Includes bibliographical references

Kerrod, Robin, 1938-
The moon. Carolrhoda Bks. 2000 32p il lib bdg $21.27   **523.3**
1. Moon
ISBN 0-8225-3900-4   LC 98-34703
"Kerrod discusses the Moon's origin and physical description, its orbit and phases, its effect on tides, its craters, eclipses, and its exploration, with an emphasis on the *Apollo* missions. There are also good-quality maps of the Moon's surface." SLJ

Simon, Seymour, 1931-
The moon. {rev ed}. Simon & Schuster Bks. for Young Readers 2003 unp il $17.95 (4 and up)
523.3
1. Moon
ISBN 0-689-83563-9   LC 2001-31303

First published 1984 by Four Winds Press
A basic introduction to Earth's closest neighbor, its composition, and man's missions to it
"The digitally remastered color photographs in this update are incredible. . . . The text has undergone minimal change. . . . The facts remain true and relevant, and the writing reflects the graphics: beautiful. This is a must-have for astronomy sections." SLJ

523.4 Planets

Bortolotti, Dan
Exploring Saturn. Firefly Bks. 2003 64p il $19.95; pa $9.95 (5 and up)   **523.4**
1. Saturn (Planet)
ISBN 1552977668; 155297765X (pa)
This "introduction to the sixth planet [describes]...what we know, don't know, and hope to find out soon. The author . . . lays out Saturn's probable origins and inner structure, provides . . . glimpses of [its] rings, and describes each moon in turn - including one, as yet unnamed, discovered in 2003. He then covers the Cassini-Huygens mission in detail." SLJ
"This appealing presentation features a well-organized and engaging text as well as many exceptionally clear, colorful illustrations: photographs, space-telescope images, paintings, and drawings." Booklist

Bredeson, Carmen
Pluto. Watts 2001 63p il $24.50; pa $8.95
523.4
1. Pluto (Planet)
ISBN 0-531-11784-7; 0-531-13988-3 (pa)
LC 00-35179
"Watts library"
This describes the planet Pluto "beginning with a historical account of its formation and discovery. About half of {the} book focuses on modern exploration of the {planet} using earth-based and space-based telescopes and spacecraft. . . . {This volume is} well illustrated with both diagrams and photographs . . . {and} difficult concepts are presented in an easy-to-understand fashion." Sci Books Films
Includes glossary and bibliographical references

Fradin, Dennis B.
The planet hunters; the search for other worlds; {by} Dennis Brindell Fradin. Margaret K. McElderry Bks. 1997 148p il $19.95 (5 and up)
523.4
1. Astronomers 2. Astronomy 3. Planets
ISBN 0-689-81323-6   LC 96-29721
Provides historical information on astronomy, the discovery of the planets, and the people who have made such discoveries
This is "a well-researched book. . . . Black-and-white photographs appear throughout the book, with a section of color plates inserted in the middle. . . . The immediacy of the writing will carry readers along in the narrative flow of this often dramatic story." Booklist
Includes bibliographical references

Miller, Ron, 1947-
Jupiter. 21st Cent. Bks. (Brookfield) 2002 72p
il (Worlds beyond) lib bdg $27.90   **523.4**
1. Jupiter (Planet)
ISBN 0-7613-2356-2   LC 2001-36790
Chronicles the discovery and explorations of the planet Jupiter and discusses each of its moons, its place in the solar system, and more
Illustrated "with a mix of NASA photos and big, amazingly realistic, digitally produced, color images." SLJ
Includes glossary and bibliographical references

Mercury and Pluto; Ron Miller. Twenty-First Century Books 2003 80p il (Worlds beyond) lib bdg $27.90 (5 and up)   **523.4**
1. Mercury (Planet) 2. Pluto (Planet)
ISBN 0-7613-2361-9   LC 2002-14099
Contents: The limits of the solar system; New worlds; The planet hunt; Worlds of fire and ice; Pluto
Contrasts the discovery, creation, orbit, atmosphere, composition, surface features, and rotation of the nearest and farthest planets from the sun.
"Concepts are explained clearly, and helpful diagrams and carefully chosen illustrations assist understanding." SLJ
Includes bibliographical references

Saturn. Twenty-First Century Books 2003 80p il (Worlds beyond) lib bdg $27.90 (5 and up)
523.4
1. Saturn (Planet)
ISBN 0-7613-2360-0   LC 2002-14098
Contents: Lord of the rings; Exploring Saturn; The crown jewel of the solar system; Moons, moons, and more moons; The future of Saturn
Chronicles the discovery and exploration of the planet Saturn and discusses its rings and moons, its place in the solar system, and more.
"Concepts are explained clearly, and helpful diagrams and carefully chosen illustrations assist understanding." SLJ
Includes bibliographical references

Schwabacher, Martin
Jupiter. Benchmark Bks. 2001 c2002 64p il (Blastoff!) lib bdg $28.50   **523.4**
1. Jupiter (Planet)
ISBN 0-7614-1236-0   LC 2001-25640
This describes astronomers' present knowledge of the planet Jupiter "with considerable attention given to the sources of information (visiting spacecraft, the Hubble telescope, ground-based observation, mathematical inference. . . . {It includes} many well-captioned photos, illustrations, and diagrams." Horn Book Guide
Includes glossary and bibliographical references

Simon, Seymour, 1931-
Destination: Jupiter. rev ed. Morrow Junior Bks. 1998 unp il $16.89; pa $6.99 (4 and up)
523.4
1. Jupiter (Planet)
ISBN 0-688-15620-7; 0-06-443759-0 (pa)
LC 97-20488

First published 1985 with title: Jupiter
This is a "guide to the planet and its four Galilean moons, Io, Europa, Ganymede, and Callisto. The complete planetary portrait is achieved by combining classic *Voyager* spacecraft images and more recent *Galileo* mission photographs." Horn Book Guide
"Expertly balancing the verbal and visual presentation, Simon . . . demonstrates his ability to inform and entertain simultaneously." SLJ

Skurzynski, Gloria, 1930-
Discover Mars. National Geographic Soc. 1998 44p il $17.95   **523.4**
1. Mars (Planet)
ISBN 0-7922-7099-1   LC 98-13190
Includes two pairs of 3-D glasses
Reviews results from the study of Mars, from Copernicus through the Viking and Pathfinder missions, and speculates on a future human landing
"Scattered throughout this thoroughly illustrated report are specially printed photos that, when viewed through cardboard 'anaglyph' glasses, appear as 3-D. . . . The book makes an inviting package, with plenty of big, bright photographs and artists' conceptions for standard illustrations, a concise but specific summary of what is now known about Mars, and a generous selection of Web sites at the end." SLJ

Spangenburg, Ray, 1939-
A look at Mercury; [by] Ray Spangenburg and Kit Moser. Watts 2003 110p il map (Out of this world) lib bdg $33.50; pa $14.95   **523.4**
1. Mercury (Planet)
ISBN 0-531-11928-9 (lib bdg); 0-531-16673-2 (pa)
LC 2002-8508
Describes the discovery and observation of the planet nearest the sun, Mercury, including the findings of the Mariner 10 fly-by mission of 1974-75
Includes glossary and bibliographical references

Mercury; {by} Ray Spangenburg and Kit Moser. Watts 2001 63p il $24.50; pa $8.95   **523.4**
1. Mercury (Planet)
ISBN 0-531-11766-9; 0-531-13986-7 (pa)
LC 00-38201
"Watts library"
Describes the orbit, temperature, surface formations, composition, and theories of formation of the planet Mercury, and the probe Mariner X that took pictures of it in 1974 and 1975
"Difficult concepts are presented in an easy-to-understand fashion. . . . Well written and edited for accuracy." Sci Books Films
Includes glossary and bibliographical references

Venus; {by} Ray Spangenburg and Kit Moser. Watts 2001 63p il $24.50; pa $8.95   **523.4**
1. Venus (Planet)
ISBN 0-531-11768-5; 0-531-13992-1 (pa)
LC 00-35902
"Watts library"
This provides a description of the planet Venus "beginning with a historical account of its formation and

Spangenburg, Ray, 1939- —*Continued*
discovery. About half of {the} book focuses on modern exploration of . . . {Venus} using earth-based and space-based telescopes and spacecraft. . . . Well illustrated with both diagrams and photographs. . . . *Venus* contains an excellent discussion of the greenhouse effect and explains its significance on the Earth." Sci Books Films
Includes glossary and bibliographical references

Stefoff, Rebecca, 1951-
Neptune. Benchmark Bks. 2001 c2002 64p il (Blastoff!) lib bdg $28.50   **523.4**
1. Neptune (Planet)
ISBN 0-7614-1232-X   LC 00-59643
This is a study of the planet Neptune from its discovery in 1846 to recent and future space probes
"Students will find {this book} useful for science projects and gathering information for class presentations." Book Rep
Includes glossary and bibliographical references

Stone, Tanya Lee
Mars. Benchmark Bks. 2001 c2002 64p il (Blastoff!) lib bdg $28.50   **523.4**
1. Mars (Planet)
ISBN 0-7614-1233-6   LC 00-46775
This is a study of the planet Mars from ancient times to the present that also discusses future space missions
"Students will find {this book} useful for science projects and gathering information for class presentations." Book Rep
Includes glossary and bibliographical references

Saturn. Benchmark Bks. 2001 c2002 64p il (Blastoff!) lib bdg $28.50   **523.4**
1. Saturn (Planet)
ISBN 0-7614-1234-4
This is a study of the planet Saturn and its moons from early astronomers such as Galileo, Huygens, and Cassini to recent space probes
"Students will find {this book} useful for science projects and gathering information for class presentations." Book Rep
Includes glossary and bibliographical references

Tabak, John
A look at Neptune. Watts 2003 107p il (Out of this world) lib bdg $33.50; pa $14.95
                                    523.4
1. Neptune (Planet)
ISBN 0-531-12267-0 (lib bdg); 0-531-15584-6 (pa)
                                    LC 2002-2023
Describes the discovery and observation of the planet Neptune and what has been learned about it, particularly from the Voyager spacecraft mission
Overall this "conveys the material well. Outstanding color photos contribute to the content." SLJ
Includes glossary and bibliographical references

Tocci, Salvatore
A look at Pluto. Watts 2003 107p il (Out of this world) lib bdg $33.50; pa $14.95   **523.4**
1. Pluto (Planet)
ISBN 0-531-12245-X (lib bdg); 0-531-15569-2 (pa)
                                    LC 2002-2022
Describes the discovery and observation of the ninth planet, Pluto, and what has been learned about its orbit, its makeup, and its moon
This "does everything it should to be both interesting to young people and informative. . . . The graphic material is excellent." Sci Books Films
Includes glossary and bibliographical references

A look at Uranus. Watts 2003 109p il (Out of this world) lib bdg $33.50; pa $14.95
                                    523.4
1. Uranus (Planet)
ISBN 0-531-12250-6 (lib bdg); 0-531-15570-6 (pa)
                                    LC 2002-156020
Looks at the history and discovery of the planet Uranus
This "does everything it should to be both interesting to young people and informative. . . . The graphic material is excellent." Sci Books Films
Includes glossary and bibliographical references

523.5   Meteoroids, solar wind, zodiacal light

Aronson, Billy
Meteors; the truth behind shooting stars. Watts 1996 63p il hardcover o.p. paperback available $6.95 (4 and up)   **523.5**
1. Meteors
ISBN 0-531-15813-6 (pa)   LC 95-48846
"A First book"
Explains such things as the difference between a meteor, a meteoroid, and a meteorite and what happens when an asteroid or comet gets too close to the earth
"Offers a clear and concise explanation of a . . . common phenomenon. . . . The well-chosen photographs of assorted meteorites and their effects will appeal to readers." SLJ
Includes glossary and bibliographical references

Koppes, Steven N.
Killer rocks from outer space; asteroids, comets, and meteorites. Lerner Publications Co 2004 112p il (Discovery!) $26.60   **523.5**
1. Asteroids 2. Comets 3. Meteorites
ISBN 0-8225-2861-4   LC 2003-10077
Describes the role that collisions with meteors, comets, and asteroids have played in the history of Earth and other planets in the solar system and examines what is being done to protect Earth from future collisions
"A catchy title, colorful cover, and well-written and interesting information combine to make this unusual science book one that students will find to be very readable and extremely useful for research projects. . . . This book will find many readers and should inspire students to further study astronomy." Lib Media Connect
Includes bibliographical references

Spangenburg, Ray, 1939-
Meteors, meteorites, and meteoroids; {by} Ray Spangenburg and Kit Moser. Watts 2002 112p il (Out of this world) $33.50; pa $14.95
                                                    523.5
1. Meteors 2. Meteorites
ISBN 0-531-11925-4; 0-531-15567-6 (pa)
                                    LC 2002-17
Contents: Space rocks!; Meteors: nature's fireworks; Meteorites: rocks from the sky; The great hunt; Big impacts and earth's scars; Meteoroids: source material; Keeping watch; Clues to the universe
Explores the mysteries of rocks that travel vast distances through space, sometimes passing through Earth's atmosphere and sometimes landing on the surface
This "includes scientific facts and personal touches that give the text warmth. The conversational style makes for easy reading and high interest. The illustrations are accurate and colorful and significantly provide understanding to the text." Book Rep
Includes glossary and bibliographical references

523.6 Comets

Bonar, Samantha
Comets. Watts 1998 63p il hardcover o.p. paperback available $6.95 (4 and up)
                                                    523.6
1. Comets
ISBN 0-531-15907-8 (pa)   LC 96-53502
"A First book"
Describes what has been learned about the composition, orbits, and the existence of several well-known comets
"Attractive, colorful illustrations are numerous and complement the text. . . . An excellent reference book for young readers." Sci Books Films
Includes glossary and bibliographical references

Cole, Michael D.
Comets and asteroids; ice and rocks in space. Enslow Pubs. 2003 48p il (Countdown to space) lib bdg $18.95 (4 and up)   **523.6**
1. Comets
ISBN 0-7660-1954-3   LC 2002-8520
Explores what comets and asteroids are, how scientists have studied them throughout history, and the effects of space debris on the Earth when it enters our atmosphere
Includes glossary and bibliographical references

523.7 Sun

Gardner, Robert, 1929-
Science project ideas about the sun. Enslow Pubs. 1997 96p il (Science project ideas) lib bdg $25.26   **523.7**
1. Sun 2. Science projects 3. Science—Experiments
ISBN 0-89490-845-6   LC 96-42693
Uses experiments to illustrate the phases and patterns of the sun as well as the reasons for its importance as an energy source
"A mixture of mostly simple experiments, facts, and activities that utilize easy-to-find objects. . . . The diagrams and drawings are clear and helpful." SLJ
Includes bibliographical references

Miller, Ron, 1947-
The sun. 21st Cent. Bks. (Brookfield) 2002 64p il (Worlds beyond) lib bdg $27.90   **523.7**
1. Sun
ISBN 0-7613-2355-4   LC 2001-35811
Presents information about the sun's origins, characteristics, future, and importance to the earth
"Both the writing and the visuals go beyond stating the facts to help readers imagine the ideas and processes described. Some of the colorful, well-reproduced illustrations are images from NASA, but others are original art created by Miller. The diagrams are usually clear and attractive." Booklist
Includes bibliographical references

Spangenburg, Ray, 1939-
The sun; {by} Ray Spangenburg and Kit Moser. Watts 2001 63p il map $24.50; pa $8.95
                                                    523.7
1. Sun
ISBN 0-531-11767-7; 0-531-13991-3 (pa)
                                    LC 00-39924
"Watts library"
This describes the sun "beginning with a historical account of its formation and discovery. About half of {the} book focuses on modern exploration . . . using earth-based and space-based telescopes and spacecraft. . . . {This book is} well illustrated with both diagrams and photographs . . . {and} difficult concepts are presented in an easy-to-understand fashion." Sci Books Films
Includes glossary and bibliographical references

523.8 Stars

Gallant, Roy A.
The life stories of stars. Benchmark Bks. (Tarrytown) 2000 80p il (Story of science) lib bdg $29.93   **523.8**
1. Stars 2. Astronomy
ISBN 0-7614-1152-6   LC 99-86675
This book "describes how the very purpose of studying the heavens changed, from a desire to link the stars to events on Earth to curiosity about what sky phenomena actually are and how we went about refining techniques for finding out. . . . {This} will strenghten any science collection." SLJ
Includes glossary and bibliographical references

Rükl, Antonín
Constellation guidebook. Sterling 1998 223p il $17.95; pa $14.95 (7 and up)   **523.8**
1. Constellations
ISBN 0-8069-4299-1; 0-8069-3979-6 (pa)
                                    LC 98-22850

Rükl, Antonín—*Continued*

"After a brief introduction and detailed directions on how to find constellations, Rukl begins his celestial guide. The guide explains what stars are and how scientists measure their brightness, luminosity and temperature. Maps of the whole sky and of individual constellations are provided. With each constellation map there is the story of how the constellation was named, where to look for the constellation and information about the stars that make up the constellation. . . . This book will be useful to budding astronomers and students seeking information on a specific constellation." Appraisal

Includes glossary

Sasaki, Chris

Constellations: the stars and stories; illustrations by Joe Boddy. Sterling 2002 128p il $24.95; pa $12.95   **523.8**

1. Constellations 2. Stars

ISBN 0-8069-7635-7; 1-40270-800-9 (pa)

LC 2002-726870

"Beginning with an introduction to stargazing and how to read star maps, the author relates how figures and creatures came to be represented in the patterns called constellations. The 88 alphabetical entries are often a page in length and are accompanied by large, sometimes full-page illustrations. The descriptions include information about the myths behind the patterns and note where and when it is best to view them." SLJ

This is a "useful, accessible resource that is written in relaxed, teen-friendly language." Booklist

525   Earth (Astronomical geography)

Miller, Ron, 1947-

Earth and the moon. 21st Cent. Bks. (Brookfield) 2003 96p il (Worlds beyond) lib bdg $25.90 (5 and up)   **525**

1. Earth 2. Moon

ISBN 0-7613-2358-9   LC 2001-8479

Contents: Discovering a planet; The beginning; The story of the moon; Earth, air, fire, and water; The birth of life; The first animals; Earth takes shape; The rise and fall of the dinosaurs; Earth today; Earth around us; A planet on the move; A visit to the moon; The end of the world

Chronicles the origin, evolution, and exploration of the Earth and the Moon, and discusses their composition, their place in our solar system, and more

This is illustrated "with a mix of NASA photos and wide-angle, computer-generated art. . . . Students with a serious interest in the physical history of the Earth and its moon will be engrossed by his account of our planet's first few billion years, the Moon's probable origin, and the rise of life." SLJ

Includes glossary and bibliographical references

Simon, Seymour, 1931-

Earth: our planet in space. {rev ed}. Simon & Schuster Bks. for Young Readers 2003 unp il $17.95 (4 and up)   **525**

1. Earth

ISBN 0-689-83562-0   LC 2001-31304

First published 1984 by Four Winds Press

This describes the relationship between the Earth, the sun, and the moon and explains the seasons, day and night, the atmosphere, and changes in the planet's surface. Illustrated with photographs taken from space

529   Chronology

Farndon, John

Time. Benchmark Bks. 2003 32p il (Science experiments) lib bdg $24.21   **529**

1. Time 2. Science—Experiments

ISBN 0-7614-1470-3   LC 2002-4846

Contents: What is time?; Dividing the day; Solar time; Sun clock; Clocks; Beating time; Calendars; Seasons; Months; Standard time; Time zones and the date line; Life times; Time and space; Experiments in science

Includes glossary

530   Physics

Cooper, Chris

Matter; written by Christopher Cooper. DK Pub 1999 64p il (Eyewitness science) $15.99

530

1. Matter 2. Atoms 3. Molecules

ISBN 0-7894-4886-6   LC 00-267041

First published 1992
.

Examines the elements that make up the physical world and the properties and behavior of different kinds of matter.

The **Facts** on File physics handbook; [by] the Diagram Group. Facts on File 2000 223p il $35 (7 and up)   **530**

1. Physics

ISBN 0-8160-4082-6   LC 99-52837

Also covering mathematics and computer science, this reference "contains, in separate sections, a dictionary of around 1500 entries; 250-400 thumbnail biographies; a multipage chronology; and an array of field-specific charts, tables, and diagrams." SLJ

Physics matters! {edited by} John O. E. Clark. Grolier Educ. 2001 10v set lib bdg $359

530

1. Physics

ISBN 0-7172-5509-3   LC 00-55160

Contents: v1 Matter; v2 Mechanics; v3 Heat; v4 Light; v5 Sound; v6 Electric charges; v7 Electric current; v8 Magnetism; v9 Electronics; v10 Nuclear physics

This set surveys key concepts and scientists in physics. Projects are included

"The narrative is very clear, avoiding the use of com-

Physics matters!—*Continued*
plicated terminology. . . . This is an excellent set for every school and public library. . . . The projects are simple, and most won't require adult supervision." Booklist

530.4   States of matter

Farndon, John
Solids, liquids, and gases. Benchmark Bks. 2001 32p il (Science experiments) lib bdg $25.64
530.4
1. Matter 2. Science—Experiments
ISBN 0-7614-1338-3   LC 00-68017
This presents six experiments involving melting points, crystals, hydraulic power, gases and volume, freezing, and solutions
Includes glossary

530.8   Measurement

Clark, John O. E. (John Owen Edward), 1937-
Under the microscope: science tools. Grolier Educ. 2002 9v il set $239   **530.8**
1. Weights and measures 2. Measuring instruments 3. Scientific apparatus and instruments
ISBN 0-7172-5628-6   LC 2002-2598
Contents: v1 Length and distance; v2 Measuring time; v3 Force and pressure; v4 Electrical measurement; v5 Using visible light; v6 Using invisible light; v7 Using sound; v8 Scientific analysis; v9 Scientific classification
Describes the fundamental units and measuring devices that scientists use to bring systematic order to the world around them
This "series does not talk down to young people. . . . The many color illustrations include photographs and exceptionally clear diagrams that heighten the books' visual appeal and usefulness to students. An interesting and potentially helpful addition to reference or circulating collections." Booklist

531   Classical mechanics. Solid mechanics

Farndon, John
Energy. Benchmark Bks. 2003 32p il (Science experiments) lib bdg $25.64   **531**
1. Force and energy 2. Power (Mechanics) 3. Science—Experiments
ISBN 0-7614-1469-X   LC 2002-4631
Contents: What is energy?; Kinds of energy; Stored energy; Movement energy; Energy changes; Putting energy to work; Conserving energy; Losing energy; Energy sources; Solar energy; Human energy; Nuclear energy; Alternative energy; Experiments in science
Includes glossary

Gravity. Benchmark Bks. 2002 32p il lib bdg $25.64   **531**
1. Gravitation 2. Science—Experiments
ISBN 0-7614-1340-5   LC 2001-25965

This presents six experiments titled Falling first, Falling faster, Fighting gravity, Up and down, Centrifugal force, and Tides
Includes glossary

Motion. Benchmark Bks. 2003 32p il (Science experiments) lib bdg $25.64   **531**
1. Motion 2. Science—Experiments
ISBN 0-7614-1471-1   LC 2002-5010
Contents: What is motion?; How fast?; Measuring speed; Getting faster; Understanding acceleration; Starting to move; Beating inertia; Force and acceleration; Friction; Rough and smooth; Action and reaction; Reaction rockets; High speed motion; Experiments in science
Includes glossary

Gardner, Robert, 1929-
Bicycle science projects; physics on wheels; Robert Gardner. Enslow Publishers 2004 112p il (Science fair success) lib bdg $26.60   **531**
1. Physics 2. Bicycles 3. Cycling 4. Science—Experiments 5. Science projects
ISBN 0-7660-1630-7   LC 2003-26961
Contents: The emergence of bicycles; Bikes, gears, and speed; Using your bicycle to measure distance and speed; Forces every cyclist must overcome or apply; Working on your bicycle
"Gardner demonstrates the principles of physics through 22 projects and many related activities using bicycles. An introductory chapter, which features advice about experiments, science fairs, and safety, is followed by a brief section on bicycle history. Gardner then clearly explains a series of progressively more difficult projects. . . . The black-and-white drawings that illustrate the projects are unusually clear, accurate, and expressive." Booklist
Includes bibliographical references

Forces and motion science fair projects; using water balloons, pulleys, and other stuff. Enslow Publishers 2004 128p il (Physics! best science projects) lib bdg $20.95   **531**
1. Motion 2. Force and energy 3. Science—Experiments 4. Science projects
ISBN 0-7660-2129-7   LC 2003-11107
Motion: measuring distance and time -- Forces and motion -- Pendulums and springs: oscillating motion -- Motions that curve or circle -- Forces, machines, and muscles
This describes experiments for science fairs which attempt to answer such questions as "Why don't you fall out of a roller coaster when it goes upside down? Which is stronger—your arms or your legs? Why do skydivers spread out their bodies when they jump from a plane?" Publisher's note
Includes bibliographical references

Parker, Barry R.
The mystery of gravity. Benchmark Bks. 2003 78p il (Story of science) lib bdg $28.50 (5 and up)
531
1. Gravitation
ISBN 0-7614-1428-2   LC 2002-970

175

Parker, Barry R.—*Continued*
Defines gravity and discusses how our knowledge of the natural force has broadened and evolved
"Readers will find accurate, readable explanations for the phenomenon of gravity. The text moves from classical attempts to understand why and how objects fall to the work of Kepler, Galileo, Newton, and Einstein's general theory of relativity. The book is ably illustrated by well-captioned photos and clear diagrams, such as the wormhole of a black hole." Horn Book Guide
Includes glossary and bibliographical references

Pentland, Peter
Toy and game science; [by] Peter Pentland and Pennie Stoyles. Chelsea House 2003 c2002 32p il (Science and scientists) lib bdg $18.95 (4 and up)
531
1. Mechanics 2. Toys
ISBN 0-7910-7013-1   LC 2002-1285
First published 2002 in Australia
Contents: Have you ever wondered ... ?; How do toys balance?; Construction toys; Meet the K'Nex events coordinator; Why do toy cars move the way they do?; Spinning toys; How can air move toys?; Why can some toys fly?; Why do some toys float and others sink?; Toys with springs; Toys that make noise; What is the difference between noise and music?; Toys that use light; Magnetic toys; Electric toys; Toy science timeline
Describes different kinds of toys and the scientific principles that explain how they work
"These authors have a knack for offering concise, easy-to-understand explanations of common phenomena. . . . [This book is] sound, highly educational, and entertaining." SLJ
Includes glossary

532 Fluid mechanics

Farndon, John
Buoyancy. Benchmark Bks. 2002 32p il (Science experiments) lib bdg $25.64   **532**
1. Water 2. Science—Experiments
ISBN 0-7614-1467-3   LC 2002-19571
Contents: Floating and sinking; Floaters and sinkers; Why things float; Measuring buoyancy; How ships float; Floating steadily; How fish swim; Floating liquids; Hovercrafts and hydrofoils; Making a hovercraft; Submarines and submersibles; Floating rocks; Floating in the air; Experiments in science
Presents information on floating and sinking in liquids or air, providing instructions for relevant scientific experiments
Includes glossary

Meiani, Antonella
Water. Lerner Publs. 2003 40p il (Experimenting with science) lib bdg $23.93 (4 and up)   **532**
1. Water 2. Science—Experiments
ISBN 0-8225-0083-3   LC 2001-50773
Contents: The force of water; To float or not to float?; The transformation of water; Water solutions; The force of water; Fact finder; Metric conversion chart

Describes experiments with water which answer such questions as "Why are water droplets round?" and "Why do some things, like salt, dissolve in water and other things, like fish, don't?"
This offers "straightforward, well-designed experiments. . . . Numerous clear diagrams, some photos, and occasional historical sidebars extend this material, which is notable for its substance." Horn Book Guide
Includes glossary and bibliographical references

533 Gas mechanics (Pneumatics)

Gardner, Robert, 1929-
Science project ideas about air. Enslow Pubs. 1997 96p il (Science project ideas) lib bdg $25.26
533
1. Air 2. Science projects 3. Science—Experiments
ISBN 0-89490-838-3   LC 97-7389
Presents experiments that reveal the properties of air, with special attention to those that would make good science fair projects
"The author does a nice job of choosing materials that will be readily accessible to most readers or that can be made at home; however, some adult assistance will be necessary. 'Did you know' fact boxes offer informative tidbits." SLJ
Includes bibliographical references

Meiani, Antonella
Air. Lerner Publs. 2003 40p il (Experimenting with science) lib bdg $23.93 (4 and up)
533
1. Air 2. Science—Experiments
ISBN 0-8225-0082-5   LC 2001-37730
Explains the properties of air through experiments which feature such topics as what air is, how much force wind has, what shape is best for flying, and how sound travels
This offers "straightforward, well-designed experiments. . . . Numerous clear diagrams, some photos, and occasional historical sidebars extend this material, which is notable for its substance." Horn Book Guide
Includes glossary and bibliographical references

535 Light and infrared and ultraviolet phenomena

Burnie, David
Light. Dorling Kindersley 1992 64p il (Eyewitness science) $15.95; lib bdg $19.99 (4 and up)   **535**
1. Light
ISBN 0-7894-4885-8; 0-7894-6709-7 (lib bdg)
    LC 92-7661
A guide to the origins, principles, and historical study of light
"Each double-page spread is lavishly illustrated with full-color photographs and diagrams, and each contains a wealth of information." Booklist

Meiani, Antonella
Light. Lerner Publs. 2003 40p il (Experimenting with science) lib bdg $23.93 (4 and up)
535
1. Light 2. Science—Experiments
ISBN 0-8225-0084-1   LC 2001-38947
Experiments with light explain shadows and colors, and demonstrate such concepts as reflection and refraction
This offers "straightforward, well-designed experiments. . . . Numerous clear diagrams, some photos, and occasional historical sidebars extend this material, which is notable for its substance." Horn Book Guide
Includes glossary and bibliographical references

536 Heat

Gardner, Robert, 1929-
Science projects about temperature and heat; {by} Robert Gardner and Eric Kemer. Enslow Pubs. 1994 128p il lib bdg $26.60 (7 and up)
536
1. Temperature 2. Heat 3. Science—Experiments
ISBN 0-89490-534-1   LC 93-48800
The authors suggest "investigations about heat and how it is measured as temperature. Some of the experiments cover the rules of temperature change, how different materials conduct heat, and how heat is made by friction." Publisher's note
Includes bibliographical references

537 Electricity and electronics

Meiani, Antonella
Electricity. Lerner Publs. 2003 40p il (Experimenting with science) lib bdg $23.93 (4 and up)
537
1. Electricity 2. Science—Experiments
ISBN 0-8225-0086-8   LC 2001-50517
Experiments and text illustrate characteristics of static electricity, circuits and switches, and electrical currents
This offers "straightforward, well-designed experiments. . . . Numerous clear diagrams, some photos, and occasional historical sidebars extend this material, which is notable for its substance." Horn Book Guide
Includes glossary and bibliographical references

Parker, Steve
Electricity; written by Steve Parker. Dorling Kindersley 1992 64p il (Eyewitness science) $15.95; lib bdg $19.99 (4 and up)
537
1. Electricity
ISBN 0-7894-5577-3; 0-7894-6711-9 (lib bdg)
LC 92-6926
Discusses the properties of electricity and describes how it is made and used
"Pictures and text work together to offer a lucid chronicle of pertinent experiments, discoveries and inventions from ancient times to the present." Publ Wkly

Woodford, Chris, 1943-
Electricity; Chris Woodford. Blackbirch Press 2004 40p il (Routes of science) $23.70; pa $18.70 (5 and up)
537
1. Electricity
ISBN 1-4103-0165-6; 1-4103-0304-7 (pa)
LC 2004-301790
Contents: The mysteries of electric fluid; From frogs' legs to batteries; Electricity meets magnetism; The power of electricity; Electricity makes waves; The electronic age; Into the future
"This book traces the history of electrical discovery from ancient Greek experiments with static electricity to Benjamin Franklin's famous kite experiment to today's work with superconductivity. " Publisher's note
This "volume contains color photographs, illustrations, and diagrams to help explain the important concepts and discoveries. [This volume] would be [an] excellent [supplement] to the science curriculum." SLJ
Includes glossary and bibliographical references

538 Magnetism

Meiani, Antonella
Magnetism. Lerner Publs. 2003 40p il (Experimenting with science) lib bdg $23.93 (4 and up)
538
1. Magnetism 2. Science—Experiments
ISBN 0-8225-0085-X   LC 2001-50464
Describes a variety of experiments that explore the world of magnets and magnetism, arranged in the categories "Magnets," "Magnetic Poles," "Magnetic Force," and "Magnetism and Electricity"
This offers "straightforward, well-designed experiments. . . . Numerous clear diagrams, some photos, and occasional historical sidebars extend this material, which is notable for its substance." Horn Book Guide
Includes glossary and bibliographical references

539.7 Atomic and nuclear physics

Bortz, Alfred B., 1944-
The library of subatomic particles [series] Rosen Publishing 2004 6v il ea $19.95; set $119.70
539.7
1. Particles (Nuclear physics)
ISBN 0-8239-4528-6 (The electron); 0-8239-4529-4 (The neutrino); 0-8239-4530-8 (The neutron); 0-8239-4531-6 (The photon); 0-8239-4532-4 (The proton); 0-8239-4533-2 (The quark)
Contents: The electron; The neutrino; The neutron; The photon; The proton; The quark
"These titles offer the history behind the discovery of specific subatomic particles, as well as a discussion of their importance and current applications. . . . Excellent additions for research and reports." SLJ

Gallant, Roy A.
The ever changing atom. Benchmark Bks. 1999 80p il (Story of science) lib bdg $29.93 (5 and up)
539.7
1. Atoms 2. Atomic theory 3. Nuclear physics
ISBN 0-7614-0961-0   LC 98-35420
Introduces atoms, the tiny particles which make up everything in the world, discussing their different parts, how they were discovered, and how they can be used as a source of energy
Includes glossary and bibliographical references

Henderson, Harry, 1951-
Nuclear physics. Facts on File 1998 132p il (Milestones in discovery and invention) $25 (7 and up)
539.7
1. Nuclear physics 2. Physicists
ISBN 0-8160-3567-9   LC 97-17380
This book profiles physicists Marie and Pierre Curie, Ernest Rutherford, Niels Bohr, Lise Meitner, Richard Feynman, and Murray Gell-Mann, explains their scientific discoveries, and outlines questions in current physics research
Includes bibliographical references

540   Chemistry & allied sciences

The **Facts** on File chemistry handbook; {by} the Diagram Group. Facts on File 2000 223p il $35 (7 and up)
540
1. Chemistry
ISBN 0-8160-4080-X   LC 99-48563
In addition to a dictionary of around 1500 entries, this source also includes hundreds of thumbnail biographies and an extensive chronology. Charts, tables, and diagrams are included

Gardner, Robert, 1929-
Chemistry science fair projects using acids, bases, metals, salts, and inorganic stuff; Robert Gardner. Enslow Publishers 2004 128p il (Chemistry! best science projects) lib bdg $26.60 (7 and up)
540
1. Chemistry 2. Science—Experiments 3. Science projects
ISBN 0-7660-2210-2   LC 2003-27476
Contents: Identifying substances; Conservation of matter; Some chemical reactions and their reaction speeds; Energy in chemical and physical changes; Acids, bases, ions, and an electric cell
"An introduction offers a short explanation of inorganic chemistry and then discusses the materials required for the more than 25 experiments presented. . . . The text is clear and concise and includes many questions to be considered for further research. Simple black-and-white illustrations accompany the text. A solid addition to any collection." SLJ
Includes bibliographical references

Meiani, Antonella
Chemistry. Lerner Publs. 2003 40p il (Experimenting with science) lib bdg $23.93 (4 and up)
540
1. Chemistry 2. Science—Experiments
ISBN 0-8225-0087-6   LC 2001-50503
Uses experiments to explore such topics as how heat changes a substance, the purpose of chemical analysis, and how the human stomach digests food
"This book makes chemistry both accessible and exciting." Sci Books Films
Includes glossary and bibliographical references

Woodford, Chris, 1943-
Atoms and molecules; {by} Chris Woodford and Martin Clowes. Blackbirch Press 2004 40p il (Routes of science) $23.70; pa $18.70 (5 and up)
540
1. Atoms 2. Molecules
ISBN 1-4103-0295-4; 1-4103-0324-1 (pa)
Contents: Philosophers and alchemists; Discovering the elements; The periodic table; Molecules, matter, and motion; Inside the atom; Into the future
"This book traces the history of atomic discovery from ancient Greek theories about four basic elements to today's research into nanotechnology." Publisher's note
This "volume contains color photographs, illustrations, and diagrams to help explain the important concepts and discoveries. [This] up-to-date [volume] would be [an] excellent [supplement] to the science curriculum." SLJ

540.7   Chemistry--Education and related topics

Bonnet, Robert L.
Science fair projects: chemistry; {by} Bob Bonnet & Dan Keen; illustrated by Frances Zweifel. Sterling 2001 c2000 95p il $17.95; pa $9.95
540.7
1. Chemistry 2. Science projects 3. Science—Experiments
ISBN 0-8069-7771-X; 0-8069-7799-X (pa)
LC 99-87099
Presents projects and experiments covering chemical principles in sciences such as geology, electronics, environmental science, and health, with dozens of ideas for science fair chemistry projects
"This is a marvelous start-up experience for the young scientist." Sci Books Films
Includes glossary

Farndon, John
Chemicals. Benchmark Bks. 2003 32p il (Science experiments) lib bdg $25.64
540.7
1. Chemistry 2. Science—Experiments
ISBN 0-7614-1466-5   LC 2002-108284
Presents information on chemicals and chemistry, providing instructions for relevant scientific experiments
Includes glossary

Gardner, Robert, 1929-
Science project ideas about kitchen chemistry.
rev ed. Enslow Publishers 2002 128p il lib bdg
$26.60   **540.7**
1. Chemistry 2. Science projects 3. Science—Experiments
ISBN 0-7660-1706-0   LC 2001-704
First published 1988 with title: Kitchen chemistry

Presents experiments suitable for science fair projects,
dealing with the chemistry involved with foods and activities related to the kitchen
Includes bibliographical references

Oxlade, Chris
Chemistry; photography by Chris Fairclough.
Raintree Steck-Vaughn Pubs. 1999 48p il (Science
projects) $29.93   **540.7**
1. Chemistry 2. Science projects 3. Science—Experiments
ISBN 0-8172-4948-6   LC 97-46796
Introduces basic concepts of chemistry through a variety of experiments, exploring such topics as changes of
state, distillation, and catalysts
"A colorful and commonsensical introduction to major
topics in chemistry." Sci Books Films
Includes glossary and bibliographical references

546 Inorganic chemistry

Blashfield, Jean F.
Sparks of life; chemical elements that make life
possible. Raintree Steck-Vaughn Pubs. 1999-2002
12v il ea $22.95; set $275.40   **546**
1. Chemical elements
ISBN 0-7398-4362-1 (set)
Contents: Calcium; Carbon; Chlorine; Hydrogen; Iron
and the Trace Elements; Magnesium; Nitrogen; Oxygen;
Phosphorus; Potassium; Sodium; Sulfur
"Each volume begins with the complete periodic table
of elements, with that volume's element highlighted, and
discusses such topics as atomic weight and element
groups. The following chapters focus on the element's
history. . . . The way the element reacts with other elements, how and where it is found in the world and in
outer space, and how it is used in industry." Booklist

Elements. Grolier Educ. 1996-2002 18v set $299
(5 and up)   **546**
1. Chemical elements
ISBN 0-7172-7572-8   LC 95-82222
Contents: v1 Hydrogen and the noble gases; v2 Sodium and potassium; v3 Calcium and magnesium; v4 Iron,
chromium, and manganese; v5 Copper, silver, and gold;
v6 Zinc, cadmium, and mercury v7 Aluminum; v8 Carbon; v9 Silicon; v10 Lead and tin; v11 Nitrogen and
phosphorus; v12 Oxygen; v13 Sulfur; v14 Chlorine, fluorine, bromine, and iodine; v15 Uranium and other radioactive elements; v16 Actinium-Fluorine; v17 Francium-Polonium; v18 Potassium-Zirconium
This set "discusses each element's discovery, forms,
extraction, industrial uses, and unique character. In a

one-topic-per-spread format, text blocks surround several
large, clear, full-color photos or, more rarely, schematics.
. . . This resource will strengthen both school labs and
library collections." SLJ

The **Elements**. Benchmark Bks. 1999-2004 28v il
ea $25.64 (5 and up)   **546**
1. Chemical elements
Contents: Aluminum, by J. Farndon; Calcium, by J.
Farndon; Carbon, by G. Sparrow; Chlorine, by S. Watt;
Copper, by R. Beatty; Flourine by T. Jackson; Gold, by
S. Angliss; Hydrogen, by J. Farndon; Iodine by L. Gray;
Iron, by G. Sparrow; Lead by S. Watt; Magnesium, by
C. Uttley; Manganese by R. Beatty; Mercury by S. Watt;
Nickel by G. Sparrow; Nitrogen, by J. Farndon; Noble
gases, by J. Thomas; Oxygen, by J. Farndon; Phosphorus, by R. Beatty; Platinum by I. Wood; Potassium, by
C. Woodford; Silicon, by A. O'Daly; Silver, by S. Watt;
Sodium, by A. O'Daly; Sulfur, by R. Beatty; Tin, by L.
Gray; Titanium, by C. Woodford; Tungsten by K. Turrell
These "titles cover where these substances are found,
how they were discovered, their characteristics and reactions, and their importance in the human body and the
environment. Each volume includes a double-page spread
on the element's position in the periodic table. The captioned, full-color drawings, photographs, and diagrams
clarify the text while boxed 'Did you Know?' items offer
interesting extensions to it. . . . Informative, accessible
science books that will be of interest for both general
reading and report writing." SLJ
Includes glossaries

Newton, David E.
Chemical elements; from carbon to krypton;
Lawrence W. Baker, editor. U.X.L 1999 3v set
$165   **546**
1. Chemical elements
ISBN 0-7876-2844-1   LC 98-31207
In this reference "the 112 elements of the periodic table are arranged alphabetically by chemical name. . . .
{Each entry includes} 'basic information about the chemical element: its chemical symbol, atomic number, atomic
mass, family and pronunciation.'. . . The entry then discusses the element's discovery and naming, physical and
chemical properties, occurrence in nature, isotopes, methods of extraction, important compounds and uses, and
health effects." Booklist

547 Organic chemistry

Gardner, Robert, 1929-
Chemistry science fair projects using french
fries, gumdrops, soap, and other organic stuff; [by]
Robert Gardner and Barbara Gardner Conklin.
Enslow Publishers 2004 128p il (Chemistry! best
science projects) lib bdg $26.60 (7 and up)
                                                547
1. Chemistry 2. Science—Experiments 3. Science
projects
ISBN 0-7660-2211-0   LC 2004-2465
Contents: Organic chemistry in your life; Compounds
of carbon; Polar and nonpolar compounds; Food : organic compounds; Baking : organic chemistry in the kitchen

Gardner, Robert, 1929—*Continued*
"How does invisible ink work? Why does detergent remove dirt from your clothing? How much fat is in a French fry? What makes bread rise? This book is filled with experiments to help you discover the world of organic chemistry." Publisher's note
"Simple black-and-white drawings complement the text, and illustrations of chemical structures help to demonstrate reactions. A sound addition to science collections." SLJ
Includes bibliographical references

548 Crystallography

Symes, R. F.
Crystal & gem; written by R. F. Symes and R. R. Harding. rev ed. DK Pub. 2004 72p il (DK eyewitness books) $15.99 (5 and up)   **548**
1. Crystals 2. Precious stones
ISBN 0-7566-0664-0
First published 1991
Describes how crystals form in nature, how crystals are grown artificially, and how crystals are used in industry. Numerous color photos with text identify the various gemstones.

549 Mineralogy

Chesterman, Charles W.
The Audubon Society field guide to North American rocks and minerals; scientific consultant, Kurt E. Lowe. Knopf 1979 c1978 850p il $19.95
          549
1. Minerals 2. Rocks
ISBN 0-394-50269-8   LC 78-54893
"Pocket guide providing color photos and descriptions of some 232 mineral species and forty types of rocks. Includes guide to mineral environments, glossary, bibliography, and indexes by name and locality." Ref Sources for Small & Medium-sized Libr. 5th edition

Farndon, John
Rocks and minerals. Benchmark Bks. 2003 32p il (Science experiments) lib bdg $25.64
          549
1. Rocks 2. Minerals 3. Science—Experiments
ISBN 0-7614-1468-1   LC 2002-908
Discusses the physical properties of various rocks and minerals and gives instructions for experiments that identify their unique characteristics
Includes glossary

Pough, Frederick H. (Frederick Harvey), 1906-
A field guide to rocks and minerals; photographs by Jeffrey Scovil. Houghton Mifflin pa $20   **549**
1. Minerals 2. Rocks
          LC 94-49005
"The Peterson field guide series"
First published 1953. (5th edition 1996) Periodically revised

"Sponsored by the National Audubon Society, the National Wildlife Federation, and the Roger Tory Peterson Institute"
This illustrated guide utilizes traditional identification methods and includes discussions of crystallography, mineralogy and home laboratory techniques
Includes bibliographical references

Simon and Schuster's guide to rocks and minerals; edited by Martin Prinz, George Harlow, and Joseph Peters. Simon & Schuster 1978 607p il hardcover o.p. paperback available $17
          549
1. Minerals 2. Rocks
ISBN 0-671-24417-5 (pa)   LC 78-8610
Original Italian edition, 1977
"Half of this book consists of color plates; the other half is an authoritative text which describes the elements of mineralogy and petrology. Crystal system or family, physical and chemical properties, occurrence, uses, and rarity are included for each species." Libr J

Symes, R. F.
Eyewitness rocks & minerals; written by R. F. Symes and the staff of the Natural History Museum, London. rev ed. DK Pub. 2004 72p il (DK eyewitness books) $15.99 (5 and up)
          549
1. Rocks 2. Minerals
ISBN 0-756-0719-1
First published 1988
Text and photographs examine the creation, importance, erosion, mining, and uses of rocks and minerals

550 Earth sciences

Campbell, Ann
The New York Public Library incredible Earth; a book of answers for kids; {by} Ann-Jeanette Campbell and Ronald Rood; illustrated by Jessica Wolk-Stanley. Wiley 1996 186p il maps pa $12.95
          550
1. Earth sciences
ISBN 0-471-14497-5   LC 96-22112
"A Stonesong Press book"
Presents 1000 questions and answers on such topics as rocks and minerals, fossils, oceans, seasons, earthquakes, and volcanoes
This is an "accessible, fact-rich book for the science-minded." Booklist
Includes glossary and bibliographical references

Day, Trevor, 1955-
DK guide to savage Earth. DK Pub. 2001 64p il $15.95   **550**
1. Earth 2. Natural disasters
ISBN 0-7894-7919-2   LC 2001-275872
The author takes us on a "journey from Earth's violent beginnings to possible future destruction from such forces as asteroid strikes and other natural disasters, global warming, or a depletion of the forests and fisheries

Day, Trevor, 1955-—*Continued*
of the world. Each chapter focuses on one force of nature, discussing how and why it has shaped the Earth in the past and how it is changing the shape of the Earth in the present. . . . The text is concise, authoritative, and very interesting and easy to read." Book Rep
Includes glossary

Earth; editor-in-chief, James F. Luhr. DK Pub. 2003 520p il map $50 **550**
1. Earth
ISBN 0-7894-9643-7 LC 2003-51573
At head of title: Smithsonian Institution
This guide to Earth's physical dynamics is "divided into five major sections—Planet Earth, Land, Ocean, Atmosphere and Tectonic Earth—the book explores the planet's environment, weather systems and general physical makeup." Publ Wkly
"The writing is clear, animated, and engrossing. . . . This superb and stunning volume should be kept handy along with atlases and dictionaries." Booklist

Earth science on file; [by] the Diagram Group. rev ed. Facts on File 1999 various paging il maps loose-leaf $249 **550**
1. Earth sciences
ISBN 0-8160-3873-2 LC 98-55739
Also available CD-ROM version
First published 1988
A looseleaf "compilation of 300 charts, all intended to be copied, covering the earth, astronomy, geology, tectonics, earthquakes, the atmosphere, oceans, weather, climate, erosion processes, paleontology, evolution, and earth resources. The pages are on heavy card-stock to withstand repeated copying." Malinowsky. Best Sci & Technol Ref Books for Young People [entry for 1988 edition]

Earth sciences for students; E. Julius Dasch, editor in chief. Macmillan Ref. USA 1999 4v set $325 (7 and up) **550**
1. Earth sciences
ISBN 0-02-865308-4 LC 99-26905
Based on the Encyclopedia of earth sciences (1996)
This resource "covers the physics, chemistry, and biology of Earth and space. The alphabetically arranged articles begin with brief definitions, explain basic concepts, outline natural processes, and conclude with cross-references to other articles." SLJ

The **Facts** on File earth science handbook; [by] the Diagram Group. Facts on File 2000 224p il $35 (7 and up) **550**
1. Earth sciences
ISBN 0-8160-4081-5 LC 99-48564
This guide to earth sciences "contains, in separate sections, a dictionary of around 1500 entries; 250-400 thumbnail biographies; a multipage chronology; and an array of field-specific charts, tables, and diagrams." SLJ

Knapp, Brian J.
Earth science; discovering the secrets of the earth; [author, Brian Knapp; illustrations David Woodroffe and Julian Baker] Grolier 2000 8v set $269 **550**
1. Earth sciences
ISBN 0-7172-7499-3 LC 99-86995
Contents: v1 Minerals; v2 Rocks; v3 Fossils; v4 Earthquakes and volcanoes; v5 Plate tectonics; v6 Landforms; v7 Geological time; v8 The earth's resources
"Each book provides easy-to-access detailed factual information. The writing is straightforward and direct, and easy to read without sounding condescending. . . . The text is supported by excellently labeled color diagrams, color photographs, tables, maps, and sidebars." Book Rep

Patent, Dorothy Hinshaw
Shaping the earth; photographs by William Muñoz. Clarion Bks. 2000 88p il maps $18 (4 and up) **550**
1. Geology
ISBN 0-395-85691-4 LC 99-37093
Explains the forces that have created the geological features on the earth's surface
"This concise, attractive volume succeeds in a daunting task—to present the history of Earth in 88 pages of compelling, age-appropriate text. . . . William Muñoz's full-color photographs, well-chosen and reproduced, will draw young readers into the text. . . . A glossary and a list of further references, including Web sites, are appended." Booklist

Pentland, Peter
Earth science; [by] Peter Pentland and Pennie Stoyles. Chelsea House 2003 c2002 32p il (Science and scientists) lib bdg $18.95 (4 and up) **550**
1. Earth sciences
ISBN 0-7910-7012-3 LC 2002-1283
First published 2002 in Australia
Contents: Have you ever wondered ...?; How was earth formed and what is it made of?; Is earth's crust all in one piece?; What is an earthquake?; How can you measure an earthquake?; Tsunamis: what are they?; What is a volcano?; How are volcanoes formed?; Meet a volcanologist; What is there between here and space?; Weather; Why does it rain, hail and snow?; What are lightning and thunder?; Wild winds; Earth science timeline
This explains such phenomena as the earth's crust, earthquakes, tsunamis, volcanoes, atmosphere, and weather
"The information is correct and presented in a well-organized manner." Sci Books Films
Includes glossary

Redfern, Martin
The Kingfisher young people's book of planet earth. Kingfisher (NY) 1999 96p il maps $21.95 **550**
1. Earth sciences
ISBN 0-7534-5180-8 LC 98-53276

Redfern, Martin—*Continued*
Examines the geology, atmosphere, and weather of the
planet Earth and how they affect its life forms
"Vivid, full-color maps, charts, graphs, drawings, and
photographs effectively enhance the text and are exceptionally well done." SLJ

Science smart; cool projects for exploring the
marvels of the planet Earth; [by] Gwen Diehn
[et al.] Main Street 2003 400p il $19.95

550

1. Earth sciences 2. Handicraft
ISBN 1-4027-0514-X   LC 2003-273228
A compilation of Geology crafts for kids, Science
crafts for kids, and Geography crafts for kids published
1998, 1997, and 2002 respectively by Lark
Contents: Geology crafts for kids by Alan Anderson,
Gwen Diehn, and Terry Krautwurst; Science crafts for
kids by Gwen Diehn & Terry Krautwurst; Geography
crafts for kids by Joe Rhatigan and Heather Smith
"Step-by-sep instructions and simple black-and-white
illustrations clearly outline how to construct the projects,
while color photographs make them attractive. . . . From
a solar food dryer to a primitive kiln, the selection of
crafts is outstanding." SLJ

Stefoff, Rebecca, 1951-
Earth and the moon. Benchmark Bks. 2001
c2002 64p il (Blastoff!) lib bdg $28.50

550

1. Earth 2. Moon
ISBN 0-7614-1235-2   LC 00-54710
This describes astronomers' present knowledge of the
planet Earth "and Earth's moon, with considerable attention given to the sources of information (visiting spacecraft, the Hubble telescope, ground-based observations,
mathematical inference). . . . {It includes} many well-
captioned photos, illustrations, and diagrams." Horn
Book Guide
Includes glossary and bibliographical references

Tabak, John
A look at earth. Watts 2003 109p il map (Out
of this world) lib bdg $33.50; pa $14.95

550

1. Earth
ISBN 0-531-12266-2 (lib bdg); 0-531-15583-8 (pa)
LC 2002-1728
An in-depth look at the Earth's composition, environ-
ment, and biomes
Includes glossary and bibliographical references

VanCleave, Janice Pratt
Janice VanCleave's A+ projects in earth science;
winning experiments for science fairs and extra
credit. Wiley 1999 234p il $32.50; pa $12.95 (7
and up)   **550**
1. Earth sciences 2. Science projects 3. Science—Experiments
ISBN 0-471-17769-5; 0-471-17770-9 (pa)
LC 98-14795

Presents thirty sample science projects as well as ideas
for small changes to the original experiments thereby encouraging creativity and increased learning
"Students will appreciate the clear, organized instructions and the fact that most of the projects use such ordinary household items as soda bottles, kitchen utensils,
rulers, and strings. . . . A rock-solid addition to library
collections." SLJ
Includes glossary

550.3   Earth sciences--Encyclopedias and dictionaries

Exploring earth and space science. Marshall
Cavendish 2002 11v il maps set $329.95 (7 and
up)   **550.3**
1. Earth sciences—Encyclopedias 2. Space sciences—
Encyclopedias 3. Astronomy—Encyclopedias
ISBN 0-7614-7219-3   LC 00-65801
Contents: v1 Acid and base-Calcium; v2 Calendar-
Continental shelf; v3 Copper-El Niño and La Niña; v4
Energy-Gondwana; v5 Grassland -Laser; v6 Light-
Meteor; v7 Meteorology-Ordovician period; v8 Ore-
Prospecting; v9 Protein-Star; v10 Stratosphere-X-ray; v11
Index
"There is much to recommend about this set. The for-
mat is user friendly and very accessible to students.
Many of the illustrations are excellent and support the ar-
ticles very well." Am Ref Books Annu, 2002
Includes bibliographical references

551.1   Gross structure and properties of the earth

Gallant, Roy A.
Dance of the continents. Benchmark Bks. 2000
80p il (Story of science) lib bdg $29.93 (5 and up)
551.1
1. Plate tectonics 2. Geology
ISBN 0-7614-0962-9   LC 98-28046
Describes the development of geological theory from
the ancient Greek philosophers to the discovery of plate
tectonics, which explains the forming of geological structures
"This book is a good brief description of continental
drift as it is now perceived by most geologists." Sci
Books Films
Includes glossary and bibliographical references

Plates; restless earth. Benchmark Bks. 2002
c2003 80p il map (Earthworks) lib bdg $29.93 (5
and up)   **551.1**
1. Plate tectonics
ISBN 0-7614-1370-7   LC 2002-915
Discusses plate tectonics, the theory that the surface of
the earth is always moving, and the connection of this
phenomenon to earthquakes and volcanoes
Includes glossary and bibliographical references

Gallant, Roy A.—*Continued*

Structure; exploring the earth's interior. Benchmark Bks. 2002 c2003 80p il map (Earthworks) lib bdg $29.93 (5 and up)

551.1

1. Geology 2. Earth—Internal structure
ISBN 0-7614-1368-5   LC 2001-43858

Describes the formation of the earth, the composition of its surface and interior, and the effects of earthquakes and volcanoes

Includes glossary and bibliographical references

Sattler, Helen Roney

Our patchwork planet; the story of plate tectonics; illustrated by Giulio Maestro, and with photographs. Lothrop, Lee & Shepard Bks. 1995 48p il maps $16 (5 and up)   **551.1**

1. Plate tectonics 2. Continental drift 3. Geology
ISBN 0-688-09312-4   LC 90-32623

"Sattler discusses the formation of the Earth's plates, their locations, and how their movements affect what happens on our planet's surface. She explains how earthquakes and volcanoes occur, and gives detailed descriptions of 'hot spots' in the world." SLJ

"Report writers and students seeking material to supplement textbook lessons will particularly appreciate Maestro's comprehensible diagrams and maps. . . . This title will claim a place even in basic science collections and will be useful to readers well into junior high." Bull Cent Child Books

Includes bibliographical references

Silverstein, Alvin

Plate tectonics; {by} Alvin Silverstein, Virginia Silverstein {and} Laura Silverstein Nunn. 21st Cent. Bks. (Brookfield) 1998 64p il maps (Science concepts) lib bdg $26.90 (5 and up)

551.1

1. Plate tectonics 2. Earthquakes 3. Volcanoes
ISBN 0-7613-3225-1   LC 98-24934

Discusses plate tectonics, the theory that the surface of the earth is always moving, and the connection of this phenomenon to earthquakes and volcanoes

"The inviting layout includes many colorful photographs, maps, and diagrams, as well as some interesting informational sidebars." Booklist

Includes glossary and bibliographical references

551.2 Volcanoes, earthquakes, thermal waters and gases

Burleigh, Robert, 1936-

Volcanoes; journey to the crater's edge; photographs by Philippe Bourseiller; adapted by Robert Burleigh; text by Helene Montardre; drawings by David Giraudon. H.N. Abrams 2003 75p il map $14.95 (4 and up)   **551.2**

1. Volcanoes
ISBN 0-8109-4590-8   LC 2003-971

Over thirty photographs and accompanying text reveal the facts about the world's volcanoes

"Photographer Bourseiller takes young readers to the crater's edge with truly spectacular full-color photographs. . . . The book does an excellent job of documenting the effect of volcanoes on the lives of those who live close to them, and small watercolor paintings further enliven the sense of human history." Booklist

Christian, Spencer

Shake, rattle, and roll; the world's most amazing volcanoes, earthquakes, and other forces; {by} Spencer Christian and Antonia Felix. Wiley 1997 122p il pa $12.95   **551.2**

1. Earthquakes 2. Volcanoes
ISBN 0-471-15291-9   LC 97-5541

The author "covers technical details such as plate tectonics, P and S seismic waves, and types of volcanic eruptions. There is . . . a section on volcanoes on other planets and moons, and another linking geologic activity to geysers and hot springs." SLJ

"Everything young readers want to know about . . . the movements of the earth is explained clearly and with a sense of humor." Appraisal

Includes glossary

Grace, Catherine O'Neill

Forces of nature; the awesome power of volcanoes, earthquakes, and tornadoes; by Catherine O'Neill Grace. National Geographic Society 2004 62p il $17.95 (4 and up)

551.2

1. Stein, Ross S. 2. Wurman, Joshua 3. Edmonds, Marie 4. Herd, Richard 5. Volcanoes 6. Earthquakes 7. Tornadoes
ISBN 0-792-26328-6   LC 2003-18929

Contents: On the rim of a volcano; In an earthquake zone; In the path of a storm

"A companion volume to the National Geographic film of the same title, this book presents the basics of these phenomena with a focus on the work of four scientists who study them: Richard Herd, Marie Edmonds, Ross Stein, and Joshua Wurman. . . . Outstanding color and black-and-white photos and diagrams augment the very readable text." SLJ

Lauber, Patricia, 1924-

Volcano: the eruption and healing of Mount St. Helens. Bradbury Press 1986 60p il $17.99; pa $8.99 (4 and up)   **551.2**

1. Mount Saint Helens (Wash.) 2. Volcanoes
ISBN 0-02-754500-8; 0-689-71679-6 (pa)

LC 85-22442

A Newbery Medal honor book, 1987

"A clearly written account of the volcano's 1980 eruption in Washington State, with handsome color photographs of every phase of the eruption and its aftermath. Perhaps most interesting is the detailed description of the healing process—what flora and fauna survived and how." N Y Times Book Rev

Lindop, Laurie
Probing volcanoes. Twenty-First Century Books 2003 80p il map (Science on the edge) lib bdg $26.90 (5 and up)   **551.2**
1. Volcanoes
ISBN 0-7613-2700-2   LC 2002-14251
Contents: Predicting eruptions; Eruption! Volcanologists on the edge; History of volcano monitoring; Looking to the future; Becoming a volcanologist
This "examines the work of volcanologists, whose main goal is to determine how to predict volcanic eruptions. A great deal of scientific information is included, beginning with a basic explanation of the subject and what the scientists are trying to discover. . . . [The book is] profusely illustrated with well-placed color photographs." SLJ
Includes bibliographical references

Reed, Jennifer
Earthquakes; disaster & survival; Jennifer Bond Reed. Enslow Publishers 2004 48p il map (Deadly disasters) $23.93 (4 and up)   **551.2**
1. Earthquakes
ISBN 0-7660-2381-8   LC 2004-11698
Contents: Living dangerously; What is an earthquake?; Devastation in Central and South America; Asia and the Middle East; On shaky ground : North America; Saving lives; Top ten deadliest earthquakes ever
This explains the causes of earthquakes, tells stories of survivors and rescuers, and offers safety advice
This is an "attractive and straightforward volume. . . . Illustrations include dramatic full-color photos, as well as maps and diagrams." SLJ
Includes glossary and bibliographical references

Trueit, Trudi Strain
Earthquakes. Watts 2003 63p il maps $24; pa $8.95   **551.2**
1. Earthquakes
ISBN 0-531-12197-6; 0-531-16243-5 (pa)
                                      LC 2002-6150
"Watts library"
Contents: Moment of terror; On shaky ground; Sizing up shocks; Triggering disaster; Predicting and preparing
This describes earthquakes including their measurement on the Mercalli and Richter scales and by movement magnitude and includes a brief description of the work of a woman seismologist
This includes "attention-grabbing photography, excellent charts and diagrams, short articles with or without photographs, and vocabulary terms that appear in bold and are explained in context." Sci Books Films
Includes glossary and bibliographical references

Volcanoes. Watts 2003 63p il map $24; pa $8.95   **551.2**
1. Volcanoes
ISBN 0-531-12198-4; 0-531-16244-3 (pa)
                                      LC 2002-11647
"Watts library"
Discusses the formation and characteristics of volcanoes, the causes and effects of their eruption, and describes specific volcanic eruptions such as that of Mount

St. Helen's in 1980
This includes "attention-grabbing photography, excellent charts and diagrams, short articles with or without photographs, and vocabulary terms that appear in bold and are explained in context." Sci Books Films
Includes bibliographical references

Walker, Sally M.
Earthquakes. Carolrhoda Bks. 1996 48p il (Carolrhoda earth watch book) lib bdg $21.27 (3-6)   **551.2**
1. Earthquakes
ISBN 0-87614-888-7   LC 94-36178
The author offers "explanations for how and where earthquakes occur, how scientists are working to predict them, and how to survive if one strikes. In addition to photographs, a number of informative charts and graphs extend the text. . . . This book is informative enough for reports, yet readable and visually appealing to browsers." SLJ
Includes glossary

551.3 Surface and exogenous processes and their agents

Winner, Cherie
Erosion; written and photographed by Cherie Winner. Carolrhoda Bks. 1999 48p il (Carolrhoda earth watch book) $21.27   **551.3**
1. Erosion
ISBN 1-57505-223-7   LC 98-16456
Describes the forces of erosion as caused by glaciers, water, and wind, how they affect the earth's surface, and how their destructive effects can be prevented

551.4 Geomorphology and hydrosphere

Erickson, Jon, 1948-
Making of the earth; geologic forces that shape our planet; foreword by Donald R. Coates. Facts on File 2000 257p il map (Living earth) $55 (7 and up)   **551.4**
1. Geology
ISBN 0-8160-4276-4   LC 00-39343
The author provides an "overview of geomorphology, the branch of geology that focuses on landforms, the structures that endow the earth with its myriad landscapes. . . . Charts, maps, photographs, a glossary, and bibliography make this enjoyable read an extremely useful resource." Booklist
Includes bibliographical references

Simon, Seymour, 1931-
Mountains. Morrow Junior Bks. 1994 unp il hardcover o.p. paperback available $6.99 (3-6)
                                              551.4
1. Mountains
ISBN 0-688-15477-8 (pa)   LC 93-11398

Simon, Seymour, 1931-—Continued

Introduces various mountain ranges, how they are formed and shaped, and how they affect vegetation and animals, including humans

"The striking color photographs work well with the clear text to illustrate key points and highlight the diversity among the Earth's mountain ranges." Horn Book Guide

551.46 Hydrosphere and submarine geology. Oceanography

Burleigh, Robert, 1936-

The sea; exploring life on an ocean planet; photographs by Philip Plisson; adapted by Robert Burleigh; text by Yvon Mauffret; drawings by Emmanuel Cerisier. Harry N. Abrams 2003 79p il $14.95 (5 and up)   **551.46**

1. Ocean

ISBN 0-8109-4591-6

Originally published in French

Text and photographs of storms, ports, pollution, diving, rescues, surfing, lighthouses, tides, and many kinds of boats, plants, and animals reveal the world's oceans and the people who live on or near them

"Each photograph is a work of art. Plisson's innate love the sea is obvious, and he shares this feeling with his audience. . . . Text explains the significance of each photograph. . . . This book is a deep-sea treasure chest." Libr Media Connect

Carson, Rachel, 1907-1964

The sea around us; {by} Rachel L. Carson; introduction by Ann H. Zwinger; afterword by Jeffrey S. Levinton. Oxford Univ. Press 1989 xxvii, 250p hardcover o.p. paperback available $15.95 (7 and up)   **551.46**

1. Ocean

ISBN 0-19-506997-8 (pa)   LC 89-16333

First published 1951; revised edition published 1961; this is a reissue of the 1979 edition which added the introduction and afterword

Beginning with a description of how the earth acquired its oceans, the book covers such topics as how life began in the primeval sea, the hidden lands, the life discovered in the abyss by highly delicate sounding apparatus, currents and tides, the formation of volcanic islands, and mineral resources

Includes bibliographical references

Day, Trevor, 1955-

Oceans. Facts on File 1999 216p il maps (Ecosystem) $65 (7 and up)   **551.46**

1. Oceanography

ISBN 0-8160-3647-0   LC 98-18110

This volume describes the oceans of the world with regard to their geography, geology, history, chemistry, exploration, relationship to the atmosphere, economic resources, and management

Includes bibliographical references

Erickson, Jon, 1948-

Marine geology; exploring the new frontiers of the ocean; foreword by Timothy Kusky. rev ed. Facts on File 2003 317p il (Living earth) $55 (7 and up)   **551.46**

1. Submarine geology 2. Marine biology

ISBN 0-8160-4874-6   LC 2002-1295

"Facts on File science library"

First published 1996

This "examines the interrelationship between water and its life forms and geologic structures. It looks at several ideas for the origins of the Earth, continents and oceans, and how these processes fit into the origin of the universe." Publisher's note

Includes glossary and bibliographical references

Matsen, Bradford

The incredible record-setting deep-sea dive of the bathysphere; {by} Brad Matsen. Enslow Pubs. 2003 48p il map (Incredible deep-sea adventures) lib bdg $18.95 (4 and up)   **551.46**

1. Beebe, William, 1877-1962 2. Barton, Otis 3. Underwater exploration 4. Ocean bottom

ISBN 0-7660-2188-2   LC 2002-13822

Contents: Heroes of the deep; The voyage into the depths; A record is broken, a record is set; Explorers of the abyss; The ultimate dive to the bottom of the sea

Describes the 1934 dive of a bathysphere, or "sphere of the deep," in which two explorers, William Beebe and Otis Barton, set the world depth record and saw mysterious creatures of the deep ocean

"Attractive color photos contribute to the content." SLJ

Includes glossary and bibliographical references

Scholastic atlas of oceans. Scholastic Reference 2004 96p il map $18.95 (4 and up)

551.46

1. Ocean

ISBN 0-439-56128-0

This presents an "overview of the origins and workings of [ocean] ecosystems and examines some of the unique characteristics and features of the five oceans and the five major seas. Marine inhabitants and their activities are included as are humankind's effects on these fragile resources. . . . The illustrations are eye-catching and appealing for browsing. The organization and factual approach make the title useful for reports." SLJ

551.48 Hydrology

Allaby, Michael, 1933-

Floods. Facts on File 1998 135p il maps (Dangerous weather) $35 (7 and up)

551.48

1. Floods

ISBN 0-8160-3520-2   LC 97-18374

The author describes: floodplains and meanders; aquifers, springs, and wells; natural drainage; floods and agriculture; latent heat and dewpoint; tsunamis; tidal surges; coastal erosion; prevention, warning, and survival. Illustrated with black-and-white photographs, drawings, charts and graphs

551.5 Meteorology

Engelbert, Phillis
The complete weather resource. U.X.L
1997-2000 4v il v1-3 set $135; v4 $52
                                                           551.5
1. Weather 2. Meteorology
ISBN 0-8103-9787-0; 0-7876-4834-5   LC 97-6930
Contents: v1 Understanding weather; v2 Weather phe-
nomenas; v3 Forecasting & climate; v4 Recent developments in world weather
This resource "makes weather and forecasting understandable. . . . The information is fascinating, readable,
and accessible for young adults." Booklist

Gardner, Robert, 1929-
Science projects about weather; by Robert
Gardner and David Webster. Enslow Pubs. 1994
128p il (Science projects) lib bdg $26.60 (7 and
up)   **551.5**
1. Weather 2. Science projects 3. Science—Experi-
ments
ISBN 0-89490-533-3   LC 93-48720
Black-and-white line drawings accompany instructions
on how to make weather stations and to do experiments
with wind speed, precipitation and temperature
"This title will not disappoint students and teachers
looking for interesting, challenging projects on an ever-
fascinating subject." SLJ
Includes bibliographical references

Kahl, Jonathan D.
National Audubon Society first field guide:
weather. Scholastic 1998 159p il hardcover o.p.
paperback available $8.95 (4 and up)
                                                           551.5
1. Weather 2. Meteorology
ISBN 0-590-05488-0 (pa)   LC 98-2938
Provides an overview of various weather conditions,
how they develop, and how they are studied
Includes glossary and bibliographical references

Oxlade, Chris
Weather; photography by Chris Fairclough.
Raintree Steck-Vaughn Pubs. 1999 48p il (Science
projects) $29.93   **551.5**
1. Weather 2. Science projects 3. Science—Experi-
ments
ISBN 0-8172-4949-4   LC 97-41171
Introduces basic concepts of weather, discussing such
topics as atmospheric pressure, clouds, rain, and wind
and includes experiments
This is "a colorful and commonsensical introduction."
Sci Books Films
Includes glossary and bibliographical references

Scholastic atlas of weather. Scholastic Reference
2004 80p il $17.95 (5 and up)   **551.5**
ISBN 0-439-41902-6   LC 2002-26915
Contents: The ABCs of weather; When weather runs
wild; A planet under many influences; Predictions . . .
for better or worse

A guide to weather phenomena and climate which explains precipitation, ocean currents, weather prediction,
pollution, and global warming, plus activities, weather
facts, records, and statistics.
"Replete with a multitude of colorful illustrations and
diagrams (and data-packed captions) and a plethora of
sidebars, the conversational text is limited to a paragraph
or so on each topic. . . . This offering presents a fresh
face in the weather lineup." SLJ
Includes glossary

Silverstein, Alvin
Weather and climate; {by} Alvin Silverstein,
Virginia Silverstein, and Laura Silverstein Nunn.
21st Cent. Bks. (Brookfield) 1998 64p il maps
$26.90   **551.5**
1. Weather 2. Meteorology
ISBN 0-7613-3223-5   LC 98-24932
Examines the changes in the atmosphere that produce
various weather phenomena and how weather patterns
over a period of time determine the climates of the
Earth's various regions
Includes bibliographical references

Stein, Paul, 1968-
Macmillan encyclopedia of weather. Macmillan
Ref. USA 2001 295p il lib bdg $150
                                                           551.5
1. Weather 2. Meteorology
ISBN 0-02-865473-0   LC 00-48682
In this volume "150 entries are arranged alphabetically
and vary in length from two or three paragraphs to almost 10 pages for *Hurricanes* and *Tornadoes*. Most entries are devoted to meteorological terms . . . but a
handful of individuals . . . are also included. The text is
readable and does not overwhelm the reader with technical jargon. . . . The illustrations are superior. The photographs are often dramatic." Booklist

Weather and climate on file; [by] the Diagram
Group. Facts on File 2001 various paging il
maps loose-leaf $185   **551.5**
1. Meteorology
ISBN 0-8160-4396-5   LC 00-62299
Also available CD-ROM version
.
A loose-leaf compilation of charts, graphs, maps, and
drawings which may be photocopied for studying topics
in weather and climate

551.51 Composition, regions, dynamics of atmosphere

Friend, Sandra
Earth's wild winds. 21st Cent. Bks. (Brookfield)
2002 32p il maps (Exploring planet earth) lib bdg
$24.90 (5 and up)   **551.51**
1. Winds
ISBN 0-7613-2673-1   LC 2001-6515

Friend, Sandra—*Continued*
Examines different aspects of the wind, including its measurement, effects on weather, potential destructiveness, and uses
"This attractive and fact-filled book will be useful for earth-science reports. . . . The full-color charts, maps, and photos contribute immeasurably to the success of the presentation." SLJ
Includes bibliographical references

Gallant, Roy A.
Atmosphere; sea of air. Benchmark Bks. 2002 79p il (Earthworks) lib bdg $19.95 (5 and up)
                                                      551.51
1. Atmosphere 2. Meteorology
ISBN 0-7614-1366-9   LC 2001-43301
Describes the atmosphere which makes life on earth possible, explores its effects on weather and climate, and examines what causes air pollution and what can be done it
"Gallant's prose is nearly conversational in its easy delivery, but his facts are always thorough and his ideas clearly explained. . . . Crisp graphs, maps, and excellent color photos illustrate {this} fine {volume}." Booklist
Includes glossary and bibliographical references

551.55 Atmospheric disturbances and formations

Allen, Jean, 1964-
Tornadoes. Capstone Press 2001 48p il (Natural disasters) lib bdg $21.26   **551.55**
1. Tornadoes
ISBN 0-7368-0588-5   LC 00-21319
Describes how and why tornadoes happen, the damage they can cause, and some of the most destructive tornadoes of the past
"The illustrations are excellent and the explanations clear." Sci Books Films
Includes glossary and bibliographical references

Ceban, Bonnie J.
Tornadoes; disaster & survival; Bonnie J. Ceban. Enslow Publishers 2005 48p il map (Deadly disasters) $23.93 (4 and up)
                                                      551.55
1. Tornadoes
ISBN 0-7660-2383-4   LC 2004-11700
This explores the causes of tornadoes, how people survive these storms, and how they are predicted.
Includes glossary and bibliographical references

Lindop, Laurie
Chasing tornadoes. Twenty-First Century Books 2003 80p il map (Science on the edge) lib bdg $26.90   **551.55**
1. Tornadoes
ISBN 0-7613-2703-7   LC 2002-14250
Contents: Tornado!; Tornado research; Project Vortex; History of tornado science; When a tornado strikes

In this title "researchers chase tornadoes and waterspouts using many different modes of transportation in order to document the weather conditions that cause these deadly storms. . . . A great deal of scientific information is included. . . . {The book is} profusely illustrated with well-placed color photographs." SLJ
Includes bibliographical references

Longshore, David
Encyclopedia of hurricanes, typhoons and cyclones. Facts on File 1998 372p il maps $55; pa $19.95 (7 and up)   **551.55**
1. Hurricanes 2. Typhoons 3. Cyclones
ISBN 0-8160-3398-6; 0-8160-4291-8 (pa)
                                   LC 97-20860
This encyclopedia describes named hurricanes, typhoons and cyclones, explains meteorological terms and instruments, and includes biographical data, a chronology, and a list of hurricane safety procedures

Sherrow, Victoria
Hurricane Andrew; nature's rage. Enslow Pubs. 1998 48p il (American disasters) lib bdg $23.93
                                                      551.55
1. Hurricanes
ISBN 0-7660-1057-0   LC 97-39193
Details the course of Hurricane Andrew, which hit the southeastern United States in 1992, and describes the recovery efforts that followed the storm
"Quotes from individuals who survived the hurricane add credence to the descriptions of its destructiveness. Numerous colored photos vividly portray the damage inflicted by the storm." Sci Books Films
Includes glossary and bibliographical references

Simon, Seymour, 1931-
Hurricanes. HarperCollins Pubs. 2003 unp il $15.99; lib bdg $16.89 (4 and up)   **551.55**
1. Hurricanes
ISBN 0-688-16291-6; 0-688-16292-4 (lib bdg)
                                   LC 2002-151603
Discusses where and how hurricanes are formed, the destruction caused by legendary storms, and the precautions to take when a hurricane strikes
"Pairing a simply phrased narrative with arresting, eye-catching color photos, Simon explains what hurricanes are and imparts a vivid sense of their destructive potential." Booklist

Tornadoes. Morrow Junior Bks. 1999 unp il map $16.95; pa $6.99 (4 and up)   **551.55**
1. Tornadoes
ISBN 0-688-14646-5; 0-06-443791-4 (pa)
                                   LC 98-27953
Describes the location, nature, development, measurement, and destructive effects of tornadoes, as well as how to stay out of danger from them
"Incredible full-color photographs and diagrams, clearly portraying the different formations and devastating power of the windstorms, complement the text perfectly." Booklist

551.56　Atmospheric electricity and optics

Simon, Seymour, 1931-
Lightning. Morrow Junior Bks. 1997 unp il $16; pa $6.99 (4 and up)　　　　　551.56
1. Lightning
ISBN 0-688-14638-4; 0-688-16706-3 (pa)
　　　　　　　　　　　　　LC 96-16962
Photographs and text explore the natural phenomenon of lightning
"The subject is exciting, the information is amazing, and the full-color photographs are riveting. . . . Simon's explanations are concise but thorough." Booklist

551.57　Hydrometeorology

Allaby, Michael, 1933-
Droughts; illustrations by Richard Garratt. rev ed. Facts on File 2003 212p il map (Dangerous weather) $35 (7 and up)　　　　　551.57
1. Droughts
ISBN 0-8160-4793-6　　　　LC 2002-13035
First published 1997
This examination of droughts and their impact includes "coverage of topics such as the geography of deserts; climate cycles and oscillations. . . . [Sidebars explain concepts] from atmospheric science, such as adiabatic cooling and warming, potential temperature, lapse rates, and the intertropical convergence and equatorial trough, as well as biological processes." Publisher's note

Gardner, Robert, 1929-
Science project ideas about rain. Enslow Pubs. 1997 96p il (Science project ideas) lib bdg $25.26
　　　　　　　　　　　　　551.57
1. Rain 2. Clouds 3. Science projects 4. Science—Experiments
ISBN 0-89490-843-X　　　　LC 96-42411
Uses experiments to illustrate the properties of rain as well as the reasons that water is such an important part of life
"This useful collection of demonstrations, experiments, and information . . . is clearly written and well illustrated with charts and diagrams that assist in the understanding of the text." Voice Youth Advocates
Includes bibliographical references

551.6　Climatology and weather

Arnold, Caroline, 1944-
El Niño; stormy weather for people and wildlife. Clarion Bks. 1998 48p il $16; pa $5.95 (4 and up)
　　　　　　　　　　　　　551.6
1. El Niño Current 2. Climate
ISBN 0-395-77602-3; 0-618-55110-7 (pa)
　　　　　　　　　　　　　LC 98-4826

Explores the nature of the El Niño current and its effects on people and wildlife
This book has a "readable, informative text. . . . Full-color photos, a computer-image series, diagrams, and Internet sources bolster the narrative." SLJ
Includes glossary and bibliographical references

Weather almanac. Gale Res. il maps $165 $185
　　　　　　　　　　　　　551.6
1. United States—Climate—Statistics 2. Weather—Statistics
First published 1974. (11th edition 2003) Periodically revised
Editors vary
"Definitions and articles on major weather events and meteorological issues. Includes layperson's guide to 'weather fundamentals' and a glossary. Provides meteorological and climatological information and statistics for major U.S. and world cities." N Y Public Libr Book of How & Where to Look It Up

551.7　Historical geology

Gallant, Roy A.
History; journey through time. Benchmark Bks. 2002 c2003 80p il (Earthworks) lib bdg $19.95
　　　　　　　　　　　　　551.7
1. Stratigraphic geology
ISBN 0-7614-1367-7　　　　LC 2001-43253
An overview of the history of the Earth, the life that evolved on it, and known periods of mass extinctions, from the planet's origin to the present
Includes glossary and bibliographical references

552　Petrology

Trueit, Trudi Strain
Rocks, gems, and minerals. Watts 2003 63p il $24; pa $8.95　　　　　552
1. Rocks 2. Minerals 3. Precious stones
ISBN 0-531-12195-X; 0-531-16241-9 (pa)
　　　　　　　　　　　　　LC 2001-7222
"Watts library"
Contents: World of wonders; Mineral magic; The circle of stone; A rocky road; Where do you stand?
"The formation of basic rocks - sedimentary, igneous, and metamorphic - are covered, as are rock crystals and crystallization. Chemical symbols for elements, charts such as the Mohs scale and the geographic location of major gem finds, and fun facts are included." SLJ
This includes "attention-grabbing photography, excellent charts and diagrams, short articles with or without photographs, and vocabulary terms that appear in bold and are explained in context." Sci Books Films
Includes glossary and bibliographical references

553.7 Water

Gallant, Roy A.
Water; our precious resource. Benchmark Bks. 2002 c2003 79p il map (Earthworks) lib bdg $29.93 (5 and up)   **553.7**
1. Water
ISBN 0-7614-1365-0   LC 2001-43290
Contents: What is water?; Some properties of water; Where is all the water?; Our needs for water; Water pollution and purification; Whose water is it?
An in-depth look at Earth's waters and mankind's uses of water throughout history which includes ideas about planning better use of this critical resource in the future
"Gallant's prose is nearly conversational in its easy delivery, but his facts are always thorough and his ideas clearly explained. Best of all, he raises informed points that will help readers rethink their habits and realize the complexity of the issues. . . . Crisp graphs, maps, and excellent color photos illustrate {this} fine {volume}." Booklist
Includes glossary and bibliographical references

553.8 Gems

Kallen, Stuart A., 1955-
Gems. KidHaven Press 2003 48p il (Wonders of the world) $23.70 (4 and up)   **553.8**
1. Precious stones
ISBN 0-7377-1028-4   LC 2002-6025
Contents: Gems from rocks; Gems from plants and animals; History of gem mining; Amazing gems
This "explains how mineral (diamonds, rubies) and organic (amber, pearls) precious materials are formed. Later chapters introduce legends behind famous stones such as the Hope Diamond and describe how gems are mined. . . . There's plenty of information to support reports, all of which is presented in . . . Kallen's straightforward, sometimes lively language." Booklist

560 Paleontology. Paleozoology

Gallant, Jonathan R.
The tales fossils tell. Benchmark Bks. 2000 80p il (Story of science) lib bdg $29.93 (5 and up)   **560**
1. Fossils 2. Prehistoric animals
ISBN 0-7614-1153-4   LC 00-20077
Describes fossils, how they are formed, and what they can tell us about life in the past
This "will strengthen any science collection." SLJ
Includes glossary and bibliographical references

Taylor, Paul D., 1953-
Fossil; written by Paul D. Taylor. rev ed. DK Pub. 2004 72p il map (DK eyewitness books) $15.99; lib bdg $19.99 (4 and up)   **560**
1. Fossils
ISBN 0-7566-0682-9; 0-7566-0681-0 (lib bdg)
First published 1990 by Knopf

This book describes different types of fossils, from algae to birds and mammals.

Trueit, Trudi Strain
Fossils. Watts 2003 63p il $24; pa $8.95   **560**
1. Fossils
ISBN 0-531-12196-8; 0-531-16242-7 (pa)
                      LC 2001-8285
"Watts library"
Contents: Yesterday's world; Fossils forever; Digging into the past; Fascinating fossils; Dinosaurs and beyond; Treasure hunters
Presents information on fossils, including how different types are formed, how they have been used to date periods in Earth's history, and major areas of the world where fossil hunting is going on today
This includes "attention-grabbing photography, excellent charts and diagrams, short articles with or without photographs, and vocabulary terms that appear in bold and are explained in context." Sci Books Films
Includes glossary and bibliographical references

567.9 Fossil reptiles. Dinosaurs

Barrett, Paul M.
National Geographic dinosaurs; illustrated by Raul Martin; introduction by Kevin Padian. National Geographic Soc. 2001 192p il $29.95
                      567.9
1. Dinosaurs
ISBN 0-7922-8224-8   LC 00-45263
"The opening chapters offer a chronology of the age of dinosaurs, a brief history of key discoveries, and . . . information about the creatures' habits and characteristics in general. The heart of the book is the 50 or so profiles of individual dinosaur genera, divided into the two major groups (bird-hipped and lizard-hipped)." SLJ
"Clearly distinguishing fact from theory, this book provides an exciting guide to the life and times of the dinosaurs." Sci Child
Includes glossary

Bishop, Nic
Digging for bird-dinosaurs; an expedition to Madagascar. Houghton Mifflin 2000 48p il $16; pa $4.95 (4 and up)   **567.9**
1. Forster, Cathy 2. Dinosaurs 3. Birds 4. Fossils 5. Madagascar
ISBN 0-395-96056-8; 0-618-1982-X (pa)
                      LC 99-36145
The story of Cathy Forster's experiences as a member of a team of paleontologists who went on an expedition to the island of Madagascar in 1998 to search for fossil birds
"Throughout the engaging, personal story, Bishop presents a great deal of information in highly readable, age-appropriate language, well matched by exceptional full-color images of scientists at work and the Malagasy landscape and people." Booklist
Includes bibliographical references

Clark, Neil
1,001 facts about dinosaurs; written by Neil Clark and William Lindsay, with additional material from Dougal Dixon. DK Pub. 2002 192p il (DK backpack books) pa $8.95   **567.9**
1. Dinosaurs
ISBN 0-7894-8448-X   LC 2002-277303
This "begins with general discussions of the three periods when dinosaurs ruled the Earth, covering 160 million years before talking about how man discovered the fossil record, and finally giving specific, detailed descriptions of individual dinosaur species. . . . [The illustrations] comprise a nice balance between photographs of actual fossilized skeletons, artists' renderings, and three-dimensional models." Voice Youth Advocates

Dinosaurs of the world; with an introduction by Mark Norell; consultants, Michael Benton, Tom Holtz; edited by Chris Marshall. Marshall Cavendish 1998 11v 704p il map lib bdg set $471.36   **567.9**
1. Dinosaurs—Encyclopedias
ISBN 0-7614-7072-7   LC 97-43365
"The first 10 volumes contain more than 200 articles on dinosaurs and related topics. Volume 11 has been designated the 'reference' volume, and features a brief history of the earth, time lines, a list of famous fossil sites and digs, dinosaur family trees, brief biographies of 24 dinosaur hunters, museums with pertinent collections, and a section called 'Things to Do,' which lists resources and activities." Booklist
"This superb set is current, well organized, and provides interesting and comprehensive coverage of life in prehistoric times." SLJ
Includes bibliographical references

Farlow, James Orville, 1951-
Bringing dinosaur bones to life; how do we know what dinosaurs were really like? {by} James O. Farlow; with illustrations by James E. Whitcraft. Watts 2001 63p il lib bdg $25 (5 and up)   **567.9**
1. Dinosaurs 2. Fossils
ISBN 0-531-11403-1   LC 00-38150
This "describes how paleontologists draw conclusions from the dinosaur fossils they study. Separate chapters examine physical appearance, diet, fighting, and reproduction." SLJ
"Clearly written and well organized, this book will interest children intrigued by the process of scientific thinking as well as its results." Booklist
Includes glossary and bibliographical references

Halls, Kelly Milner, 1957-
Dinosaur mummies; beyond bare-bone fossils; illustrated by Rick Spears. Darby Creek 2003 48p il $17.95 (5 and up)   **567.9**
1. Dinosaurs 2. Fossils
ISBN 1-58196-000-X
After "explaining the fossilization process, the book spotlights six significant dinosaur mummies. . . . Halls' enthusiasm shines through in this well-researched and clearly written book. Drawings washed with color show

how the dinosaurs might have looked, while many excellent color photos illustrate the fossilized finds, and dinosaur diggers and paleontologists at work." Booklist
Includes bibliographical references

Kelsey, Elin
Canadian dinosaurs 2004 96p il $29.95; pa $19.95   **567.9**
1. Dinosaurs
ISBN 1-894379-55-1; 1-894379-56-X (pa)
"A Wow Canada! book"
"The main text discusses topics such as the types of dinosaurs that lived in Canada, recent discoveries as well as the country's history of paleontology, and the art of creating dinosaur exhibits. The many sidebars introduce individual researchers, events, and information of special interest. The colorful pages feature many excellent photos of fossils and sites as well as images of how the dinosaurs may have looked. . . . A treasure trove for . . . dinosaur fans." Booklist
Includes glossary

Lambert, David, 1932-
DK guide to dinosaurs. DK Pub. 2000 64p il maps $19.95   **567.9**
1. Dinosaurs
ISBN 0-7894-5237-5   LC 99-39207
Depicts how dinosaurs lived and died, covering such topics as habitats, size, hunting techniques, self-defense, courtship, and family life

Lessem, Don
Scholastic dinosaurs A to Z; the ultimate dinosaur encyclopedia; illustrated by Jan Sovak. Scholastic 2003 224p il $22.95 (4 and up)   **567.9**
1. Dinosaurs
ISBN 0-439-16591-1   LC 00-41304
This reference "lists dinosaurs in alphabetical order and gives their pronunciation. Other information includes what each dinosaur's name means, its complete taxonomic classification, length, time period, place, diet, and other details. Icons beside each name tell the reader to which class of dinosaur it belongs. . . . The text is thorough and interesting. . . . This is an excellent purchase for every school and public library, and many children will want their own copies." Booklist
Includes glossary and bibliographical references

Patent, Dorothy Hinshaw
In search of the maiasaurs. Benchmark Bks. (Tarrytown) 1999 64p il (Frozen in time) lib bdg $28.50   **567.9**
1. Horner, John R. 2. Dinosaurs 3. Fossils
ISBN 0-7614-0787-1   LC 97-46733
Describes John R. Horner's discovery and study of fossil records revealing the herding and nesting behavior of the dinosaur known as Maiasaura
"This offers clear expository style, accuracy, informative sidebars, time lines, {and} maps. . . . {It is} heavily illustrated with crisp full-color photos and a few paintings." SLJ
Includes glossary and bibliographical references

Relf, Patricia

A dinosaur named Sue: the story of the colossal fossil: the world's most complete T. rex; by Pat Relf; with the SUE Science Team of The Field Museum. Scholastic 2000 64p il $15.95 (5 and up)

567.9

1. Fossils 2. Dinosaurs
ISBN 0-439-09985-4   LC 00-38038

"Sue, named after discoverer Susan Hendrickson, is the most complete *Tyrannosaurus Rex* in existence. The reader follows the scientific journey from the fossil excavation in 1990 to its display at Chicago's Field Museum." Sci Child

"Readers will get a real sense of the team effort that science can be. . . . Many color photographs, as well as diagrams and paintings, appear throughout the book." Booklist

Sloan, Christopher

Feathered dinosaurs; introduction by Philip J. Currie. National Geographic Soc. 2000 64p il $17.95 (5 and up)   **567.9**

1. Dinosaurs 2. Birds 3. Fossils
ISBN 0-7922-7219-6   LC 00-27001

Looks at the evidence of dinosaurs with skeletal structures and feathers so similar to birds and why that is convincing many scientists that birds evolved from dinosaurs

"This exciting title combines an accurate, readable text and excellent drawings, photos, and diagrams." SLJ

Supercroc and the origin of crocodiles; introduction by Paul Sereno. National Geographic Soc. 2002 55p il maps $18.95 (5 and up)

567.9

1. Fossil reptiles 2. Crocodiles
ISBN 0-7922-6691-9   LC 2001-3976

Discusses prehistoric crocodiles, including the discovery of SuperCroc in the Sahara Desert, and the lifestyles, habitats, and conservation of modern crocodiles

"Fans of paleontology or of crocodiles will find a great deal of information clearly explained. The illustrations are up to the high National Geographic standard." Booklist

Includes glossary

Tanaka, Shelley

Graveyards of the dinosaurs; what it's like to discover prehistoric creatures; paleontological consultation by Philip J. Currie, Mark Norell, and Paul Sereno; featuring illustrations by Alan Barnard. Hyperion Bks. for Children 1998 48p il maps hardcover o.p. paperback available $7.99 (4-6)   **567.9**

1. Fossils 2. Dinosaurs
ISBN 0-7868-1540-x (pa)   LC 97-31286

"An I Was There book; A Hyperion/Madison Press book"

Discusses the work of paleontologists who have found dinosaur bones and fossils in Canada, Argentina, and the Gobi Desert

"Full-color photos of the sites and of important finds

and dramatic re-creations of dinosaurs in action enhance the readable text." Horn Book Guide

Includes glossary and bibliographical references

Yates, Adam

Guide to wild dinosaurs; illustrated by Jon Hughes. Sterling 2002 255p il maps $19.95; pa $5.95   **567.9**

1. Dinosaurs
ISBN 0-8069-9646-4; 1-4027-0856-4 (pa)

"For each of the 120 dinosaur species and the other prehistoric animals that lived alongside them, there's a double-page spread that includes a color portrait, a distribution map, a designation showing the group the animal belongs to, an 'ID Fact File,' and a few paragraphs of essential information. The style is clear and direct." Booklist

Includes bibliographical references

Zoehfeld, Kathleen Weidner

Dinosaur parents, dinosaur young; uncovering the mystery of dinosaur families; with full-color paintings by Paul Carrick and line drawings by Bruce Shillinglaw. Clarion Bks. 2001 58p il map $17 (4 and up)   **567.9**

1. Dinosaurs 2. Fossils
ISBN 0-395-91338-1   LC 00-43101

The author "guides readers through the complex historical trail of evidence collection and theory development that make up what we currently believe we know about dinosaur family life." Horn Book Guide

"High-quality, color photographs of fossils of eggs and embryos and of paleontologists at work as well as line drawings and full-color paintings add to this inviting, thought-provoking book." SLJ

Includes glossary and bibliographical references

569   Fossil mammals

Agenbroad, Larry D.

Mammoths; ice-age giants; {by} Larry D. Agenbroad and Lisa Nelson. Lerner Publs. 2002 120p il (Discovery!) lib bdg $27.93; pa $7.95

569

1. Mammoths
ISBN 0-8225-2862-2 (lib bdg); 0-8225-0470-7 (pa)
LC 2001-1147

"Chapters discuss what is currently known about {mammoths} . . . when and where they lived, and the discovery of remains. The authors present several theories as to why mammoths might have died out. The book is well documented, and the many photos and drawings add clarity to the text." Horn Book Guide

Includes glossary and bibliographical references

Giblin, James, 1933-

The mystery of the mammoth bones; and how it was solved. HarperCollins Pubs. 1999 97p il lib bdg $16.89 (4 and up)   **569**

1. Peale, Charles Willson, 1741-1827 2. Mastodon 3. Fossil mammals
ISBN 0-06-027494-8   LC 98-6701

Giblin, James, 1933-—_Continued_

Describes the efforts of the artist, museum curator, and self-taught paleontologist, Charles Willson Peale, to excavate, study, and display the bones of a prehistoric creature that is later named "mastodon"

"Giblin's research is superb, and he turns to Peale's actual notes for details. He also includes recent information about the mammoth (and mastodon)." SLJ

Includes bibliographical references

Hehner, Barbara, 1947-

Ice Age cave bear; the giant beast that terrified ancient humans; illustrations by Mark Hallett; scientific consultation by Mark Engstrom and Kevin Seymour. Crown 2002 32p il hardcover o.p. lib bdg available $18.99 (5 and up)   **569**

1. Bears 2. Fossil mammals
ISBN 0-375-91329-7 (lib bdg)   LC 2001-52953
"A Madison Press book"

Describes how and where cave bears lived, possible reasons for their extinction, and what kind of relationship might have existed between these huge creatures and prehistoric man

"Accompanied by full-color photographs and Hallett's rich, realistic illustrations, the book is eye-catching and informative." SLJ

Includes glossary and bibliographical references

Ice Age mammoth; will this ancient giant come back to life? illustrated by Mark Hallett. Crown 2001 32p il hardcover o.p. paperback available $8.99 (5 and up)   **569**

1. Mammoths
ISBN 0-375-82192-9 (pa)   LC 00-66023
"A Madison Press book"

Beginning with the "find in 1997 of the Jarkov Mammoth frozen into the Siberian permafrost, Hehner presents what is positively known about such Ice Age creatures and what is surmised by studies of their modern-day cousins, the elephants. . . . The author discusses the possibility of cloning a mammoth should the Jarkov find provide usable DNA or even undamaged frozen sperm. . . . The brief, readable text is larded with information boxes, maps, and color photos." SLJ

Includes glossary and bibliographical references

Ice Age sabertooth; the most ferocious cat that ever lived; illustrations by Mark Hallett; scientific consultation by Mark Engstrom and Kevin Seymour. Crown 2002 32p il hardcover o.p. paperback available $8.99 (5 and up)   **569**

1. Saber-toothed tigers
ISBN 0-375-82193-7 (pa)   LC 2001-28539
"A Madison Press book"

The "text presents what is known about these big cats from their fossilized remains, and discusses what paleontologists surmise about their outward appearance, behavior, and hunting techniques." SLJ

"The dramatic pictures grab attention and the detailed, straightforward text fills in the astonishing facts." Booklist

Includes glossary and bibliographical references

Turner, Alan

National Geographic prehistoric mammals; illustrated by Mauricio Antón. National Geographic 2004 192p il map $29.95; lib bdg $49.90 (5 and up)   **569**

1. Fossil mammals
ISBN 0-7922-7134-3; 0-7922-6997-7 (lib bdg)
   LC 2004-1189

This describes the Age of Mammals and profiles over 100 prehistoric mammals, including time lines, fact boxes, distribution maps, photos of fossils, and illustrations

"Dramatic full-color pictures . . . and captions enhance the brief, informative text." SLJ

570   Life sciences. Biology

Biology; Richard Robinson, editor in chief. Macmillan Ref. USA 2002 4v set $395
   570

1. Biology
ISBN 0-02-865551-6   LC 2001-40211

This set "provides 432 signed entries on a broad range of topics pertaining to biology, including basic concepts . . . history of the science . . . related fields . . . and issues . . . as well as topics of interest to young adults, such as smoking, birth control, alcohol, and STDs. . . . The eye-pleasing layout features many colorful photographs and diagrams that will appeal to casual browsers and the articles contain more than enough information to meet the needs of students. This informative set is highly recommended." Booklist

Bottone, Frank G., Jr.

The science of life; projects and principles for beginning biologists; {by} Frank G. Bottone, Jr. Chicago Review Press 2001 126p il pa $14.95
   570

1. Biology 2. Science—Experiments
ISBN 1-556-52382-3   LC 00-65873

"An introduction to the fundamentals of biology through different activities. Arranged by the five kingdoms of life, the text includes 25 projects. The book begins with a thorough section on safety and an introduction to the scientific method. The experiments range from creating a compost bin to observing and growing carnivorous plants to growing mushroom spores on a potato medium. Most of the activities are somewhat complicated and would require adult supervision, but students should find them intriguing. . . . The volume provides a thorough introduction to this area of science and would be useful in most collections." SLJ

Includes bibliographical references

The **Facts** on File biology handbook; [by] the Diagram Group. Facts on File 2000 223p il $35; pa $17.95 (7 and up)   **570**

1. Biology
ISBN 0-8160-4079-6; 0-8160-4584-4 (pa)
   LC 99-52953

Topics covered include: amniocentesis, synthesis, hormones, glands, embryo, ventricle, and zygote. Francis Bacon, Edwin Hubble, and Linus Pauling are among the

The Facts on File biology handbook—*Continued*
400 scientists profiled. Includes a chronology of significant developments and discoveries from ancient Greece to the present day. Illustrated with tables, charts, and diagrams

570.3 Life sciences--Encyclopedias and dictionaries

Encyclopedia of life sciences. 2nd ed. Marshall Cavendish 2003 13v il set $459.95
570.3
1. Life sciences—Encyclopedias 2. Biology—Encyclopedias
ISBN 0-7614-7442-0   LC 2002-31157
First published 1996 in 11 volumes
Editor-in-chief Anne O'Daly
Contents: v1 Abdomen-Arthropods; v2 Artificial life Camouflage and mimicry; v3 Cancer-Conservation; v4 Continental shelves-Echolocation; v5 Ecology and ecosystems-Fertilizers; v6 Fibers-Hallucinogens; v7 Hands-Larvae and pupae; v8 Leaf crops Mollusks; v9 Molting-Pheromones; v10 Phobias-Rodents; v11 Roots and tuber crops-Symbiosis; v12 Taiga biomes Zoos; v13 Index volume
This illustrated encyclopedia covers agriculture, anatomy, biochemistry, biology, genetics, medicine, and molecular biology. Volume 13 includes "a comprehensive index, as well as indexes on specific topics in life sciences, including biochemistry, biotechnology, ecology, genetics, psychology, and zoology. Volume 13 also includes a 'Classification' of organisms within the five kingdom taxonomic scheme; a 'Glossary,' which gives definitions of biological terms; and a 'bibliography,' divided into the main branches of the life sciences." Publisher's note
"This attractively laid-out set provides up-to-date information that will be in demand at report time. Budding scientists will enjoy delving into various volumes." Booklist {review of 1996 edition}

571.3 Anatomy and morphology

Animal anatomy on file; {by} the Diagram Group. New ed. Facts on File 2003 various paging il loose-leaf $185   **571.3**
1. Comparative anatomy
ISBN 0-8160-5102-X   LC 2003-49145
Also available CD-ROM version
First published 1990
This looseleaf volume offers 270 labeled photocopiable charts and diagrams of the internal and external anatomy of animals, divided into the following categories: lower groups; annelids and mollusks; anthropods and echinoderms; lower chordates and fish; amphibians and reptiles; birds; mammals
Includes glossary and bibliographical references

571.8 Reproduction, development, growth

Cohen, Daniel, 1936-
Cloning. [rev. and updated ed.] Twenty-First Century Books 2002 144p il $25.90 (7 and up)
571.8
1. Cloning 2. Genetic engineering
ISBN 0-7613-2802-5
First published 1998 by Millbrook Press
Examines the history, current developments, future, and ethical ramifications of cloning, recombinant DNA, and gene therapy
"Cohen succeeds in covering the ethical questions and social ramifications surrounding this issue." SLJ [review of 1998 edition]
Includes bibliographical references

576.5 Genetics

Allan, Tony, 1946-
Understanding DNA; a breakthrough in science. Heinemann Lib. 2002 32p il (Point of impact) lib bdg $27.79   **576.5**
1. DNA 2. Genetics
ISBN 1-58810-557-1   LC 2001-3481
Examines the events and circumstances leading to the discovery of DNA and the impact of this discovery on the scientific and medical communities
This "would be of interest to researchers and science students who are curious about the history of great discoveries." SLJ
Includes glossary and bibliographical references

Day, Trevor, 1955-
Genetics; by Trevor Day. Blackbirch Press 2004 40p il (Routes of science) $23.70; pa $18.70 (5 and up)   **576.5**
1. Genetics
ISBN 1-410-30301-2; 1-410-30300-4 (pa)
LC 2003-15949
Contents: Early ideas about inheritance; Genetics is born; From peas to fruit flies to people; The DNA story; Genetics goes molecular ; Genes helping people; Into the future
"This book traces the history of genetic discoveries from ancient beliefs about spontaneous generation to modern-day advances in cloning." Publisher's note
This "volume contains color photographs, illustrations, and diagrams to help explain the important concepts and discoveries. [This] up-to-date [volume] would be [an] excellent [supplement] to the science curriculum." SLJ
Includes glossary and bibliographical references

Fridell, Ron, 1943-
Decoding life; unraveling the mysteries of the genome; written by Ron Fridell. Lerner Publications 2005 112p il (Discovery!) lib bdg $27.93   **576.5**
1. Genetics
ISBN 0-8225-1196-7   LC 2004-4710

Fridell, Ron, 1943-—*Continued*
Contents: Exploring the unknown; Searching for damaged genes; Repairing damaged genes; Stems and snips; Living longer; Engineering ourselves; How far should we go?; Privacy and justice; Engineering nature
This offers an overview of modern genetics from Gregor Mendel to genetic engineering, and discusses the Human Genome Project.
Includes bibliographical references

Gallant, Roy A.
The treasure of inheritance. Benchmark Bks. 2003 78p il (Story of science) lib bdg $19.95 (5 and up)   **576.5**
1. Genetics 2. Heredity
ISBN 0-7614-1426-6   LC 2002-10
Discusses how living things inherit traits, chronicles the history of the study of heredity, and examines current research on genetic engineering and mapping the human gene
"Readers will find accurate, readable explanations for the scientific principles here addressed. . . . Up-to-date controversies and predictions conclude the [book] . . . . illustrated with well-captioned photos." Horn Book Guide
Includes glossary and bibliographical references

Kidd, J. S. (Jerry S.)
Life lines; the story of the new genetics; {by} J.S. Kidd and Renee A. Kidd. Facts on File 1999 152p il (Science and society) $25 (7 and up)   **576.5**
1. Genetics
ISBN 0-8160-3586-5   LC 98-22219
Surveys the field of genetics, discussing genetic analysis, cloning, other new research and developments, and their ethical aspects
Includes glossary and bibliographical references

Tagliaferro, Linda
Genetic engineering; progress or peril? Lerner Publs. 1997 128p il (Pro/Con) lib bdg $25.26 (7 and up)   **576.5**
1. Genetic engineering 2. Bioethics
ISBN 0-8225-2610-7   LC 95-25667
Discusses current and potential uses of genetic engineering in fields such as medicine, criminal investigation, and agriculture and examines some of the ethical questions involved
"Tagliaferro makes a complex, difficult subject understandable without oversimplification." Booklist
Includes glossary and bibliographical references

Walker, Richard, 1951-
Genes & DNA; foreword by Steve Jones. Kingfisher 2003 63p il (Kingfisher knowledge) $11.95 (5 and up)   **576.5**
1. Genetics
ISBN 0-7534-5621-4   LC 2004-269108
This briefly discusses such topics as the role of genes in inheritance, the structure of the DNA molecule, mutations, The Human Genome Project, and genetic technolo-gy such as DNA fingerprinting, gene therapy, genetic engineering, and cloning
Includes glossary and bibliographical references

576.8   Evolution

Ackroyd, Peter
The beginning. DK Pub. 2003 143p il (Voyages through time) $19.99 (7 and up)   **576.8**
1. Evolution
ISBN 0-7894-9836-7
"Ackroyd traces the history of life on Earth from the big bang to the emergence of Homo sapiens. Chapters are divided to reflect major eons, eras, periods, and epochs within this vast time span. . . . The story of evolution is simply and beautifully laid out. The engaging text reflects the most recent research on prehistoric life. . . . Eye-catching, relevant illustrations bring the prehistoric world to life." SLJ
Includes glossary

Dixon, Dougal, 1947-
The future is wild; [by] Dougal Dixon, John Adams. Firefly Bks. 2003 160p il maps $35; pa $24.95   **576.8**
1. Evolution 2. Forecasting
ISBN 1-55297-724-2; 1-55297-723-4 (pa)
"A natural history of the future." Cover; Companion book to the Discovery Channel television series
"This work speculates on the evolution of the Earth and its beings, minus human life, over the next 5, 100, and 200 million years." SLJ
"The computer-generated illustrations of the hypothetical species are gorgeous and detailed. . . . The clever, creative forces behind this work have a real chance of opening some young adults' eyes to the possibilities of science." Voice Youth Advocates

Gallant, Roy A.
The origins of life. Benchmark Bks. 2001 80p il (Story of science) lib bdg $29.93 (5 and up)   **576.8**
1. Life—Origin
ISBN 0-7614-1151-8   LC 99-86435
Explores the many different myths, theories, and experiments which explain the origin of life, including spontaneous generation, the development of planets, chemical evolution of matter, and the various places in the solar system where life exists or may exist
Includes glossary and bibliographical references

Gamblin, Linda
Evolution; written by Linda Gamblin. Dorling Kindersley 1993 64p il map (Eyewitness science) $15.99; lib bdg $19.99 (4 and up)   **576.8**
1. Evolution
ISBN 0-7894-5579-X; 0-7894-6719-4 (lib bdg)
    LC 92-54478
Text about and photography of experiments, animals, plants, bones, and fossils reveal the ideas and discoveries

Gamblin, Linda—*Continued*

that have changed our understanding of the natural world and how life began

This offers "a wealth of outstanding color photographs and drawings and interesting information in a format that is particularly attractive for browsing." SLJ

Jackson, Ellen B., 1943-

Looking for life in the universe; the search for extraterrestrial intelligence; by Ellen Jackson; with photographs by Nic Bishop. Houghton Mifflin 2002 57p il (Scientists in the field) $16 (4 and up)
576.8

1. Tarter, Jill Cornell, 1944- 2. Life on other planets
ISBN 0-618-12894-8   LC 2001-51312

Investigates how scientists, particularly Jill Tarter, Director of the SETI Institute in Mountain View, California, use twenty-first century technology to investigate whether life exists on other planets

"An exciting, visually awesome look at frontier science." SLJ

Includes glossary and bibliographical references

Skurzynski, Gloria, 1930-

Are we alone? scientists search for life in space. National Geographic Society 2004 92p il $18.95 (5 and up)
576.8

1. Life on other planets
ISBN 0-7922-6567-x   LC 2003-17732

The author begins with a "history of how the idea of flying saucers and extraterrestrials became part of the American consciousness. Later chapters trace specific quests . . . for signs of life beyond earth. . . . The text remains readable even while explaining intricate scientific concepts and complex. . . ideas. The vibrant full-color photos enhance the work impressively." Booklist

Includes glossary and bibliographical references

577 Ecology

Allaby, Michael, 1933-

Biomes of the world. Grolier Educ. 1999 9v .p il map lib bdg set $299 (5 and up)   **577**

1. Ecology
ISBN 0-7172-9341-6   LC 98-37524

Contents: v1 The Polar regions; v2 Deserts; v3 Oceans; v4 Wetlands; v5 Mountains; v6 Temperate forests; v7 Tropical forests; v8 Temperate grasslands; Tropical grasslands

Explores each of the earth's major ecological regions, defining important features, animals, and environmental issues

This "is a well designed nine-volume set of books providing an excellent introduction to the principal biomes of planet Earth. The books are an outstanding resource for students and teachers." Sci Books Films

Includes bibliographical references

The **Dictionary** of the environment and its biomes; Chris Myers, general editor; Marilee Foglesong, Paul L. Sieswerda advisers. Watts 2001 128p il maps lib bdg $34   **577**

1. Ecology—Dictionaries
ISBN 0-531-11983-1   LC 00-65438

"Focusing on geographic regions that share similar characteristics, this dictionary provides definitions of terms that are helpful for an elementary understanding of important environmental concepts. . . . The attractive presentation, useful introductory instructions, clear language and organization, and readable type all contribute to making this a useful addition for most collections." SLJ

Includes bibliographical references

Guiberson, Brenda Z., 1946-

Exotic species; invaders in paradise. 21st Cent. Bks. (Brookfield) 1999 80p il lib bdg $24.90
577

1. Biological invasions 2. Ecology
ISBN 0-7613-1319-2   LC 98-41508

The author discusses species that have been introduced into a new environment and have subsequently harmed the established species. Included are starlings, zebra mussels, kudzu, and mountain goats

"The text is well written in clear, lively language. The accompanying color photos help to illustrate the subject under discussion." SLJ

Includes glossary and bibliographical references

Silverstein, Alvin

Food chains; {by} Alvin Silverstein, Virginia Silverstein, Laura Silverstein Nunn. 21st Cent. Bks. (Brookfield) 1998 63p il lib bdg $26.90
577

1. Food chains (Ecology)
ISBN 0-7613-3002-X   LC 97-52147

Explains various components of a food chain and discusses the concepts of food webs, umbrella species, biogeochemical cycles, and more

"Clearly written, dependable material. Utilitarian. Useful." SLJ

Includes glossary and bibliographical references

Snedden, Robert

The environment; photography by Chris Fairclough. Raintree Steck-Vaughn Pubs. 1999 48p il (Science projects) $29.93   **577**

1. Ecology 2. Science projects 3. Science—Experiments
ISBN 0-8172-4964-8   LC 97-46789

Describes the various elements that make up an environment, including the carbon cycle, the water cycle, and food chains. Experiments are included

Includes glossary and bibliographical references

Sussman, Art

Dr. Art's guide to planet earth; for earthlings ages 12 to 120. Chelsea Green 2000 122p il maps pa $14.95   **577**

1. Environmental sciences 2. Ecology
ISBN 1-89013-273-X   LC 00-23731

Sussman, Art—Continued

"Dr. Art's systems-based Earth guide introduces three easy-to-understand principles that explain how our planet works—Matter Cycles, Energy Flows, and Life Webs. This full-color, engaging guide will help us better understand Earth's systems." Sci Child

Includes glossary

VanCleave, Janice Pratt

Janice Vancleave's ecology for every kid; easy activities that make learning science fun. Wiley 1996 219p il maps (Science for every kid series) $32.50; pa $10.95 (4 and up)   **577**

1. Ecology 2. Habitat (Ecology) 3. Science—Experiments

ISBN 0-471-10100-1; 0-471-10086-2 (pa)

LC 95-6112

This book of science activities covers "25 topics, ranging from plant and animal food chains to the effect of plastics on the environment. Subjects are introduced in a 'What You Need to Know' section that gives explanation of the scientific principles, plus plenty of everyday examples. A brief preparatory exercise follows, usually in the form of an imaginative game. . . . Simple black-line drawings are crisp, uncluttered, and well placed. . . . Solid information and a generous portion of fun are combined to elevate this selection above the standard collection of experiments." SLJ

Includes glossary

577.2   Specific factors affecting ecology

Patent, Dorothy Hinshaw

Fire: friend or foe; photographs by William Muñoz. Clarion Bks. 1998 80p il $16 (4 and up)   **577.2**

1. Forest fires 2. Forest ecology

ISBN 0-395-73081-3   LC 98-11754

Discusses forest fires and the effect that they have on both people and the natural world

"The text offers rich science support. . . . Muñoz's full-color photographs are a nice complement to the text." Booklist

Simon, Seymour, 1931-

Wildfires. Morrow Junior Bks. 1996 unp il hardcover o.p. paperback available $6.99 (3-6)   **577.2**

1. Forest fires 2. Forest ecology

ISBN 0-688-17530-9 (pa)   LC 95-12653

"Exploring the place of fire in nature, Simon explains that . . . forest fires have important functions in the ecosystem. With a brilliantly clear and colorful photograph facing each page of text, the book describes the causes and the progression of the wildfires that burned areas of Yellowstone National Park in 1988, explains how the fires were beneficial in many ways. . . . Lucid writing and excellent book design." Booklist

577.3   Forest ecology

Allaby, Michael, 1933-

Temperate forests. Facts on File 1999 216p il maps (Ecosystem) $65 (7 and up)   **577.3**

1. Forest ecology 2. Forests and forestry

ISBN 0-8160-3678-0   LC 98-23458

This book "explores the ecology, biology, chemistry, history, and economics of the forest." Publisher's note

Includes bibliographical references

Burnie, David

Shrublands. Raintree Steck-Vaughn Pubs. 2003 64p il maps (Biomes atlases) lib bdg $31.42 (5 and up)   **577.3**

1. Forest ecology

ISBN 0-7398-5514-X   LC 2002-68093

A comprehensive look at the shrubland biome, describing the climate, plants, animals, people, and future of these areas, and providing detailed views of some major shrubland regions

"Especially effective are the maps. Brief notes for 10 to 12 highlights appear on each one, commenting on the diversity of flora, fauna, and landforms that occurs. . . . [The book includes] excellent-quality, full-color photographs and related sidebars." SLJ

Includes glossary and bibliographical references

Castner, James L.

Layers of life. Benchmark Bks. 2002 64p il (Deep in the Amazon) lib bdg $28.50

577.3

1. Rain forest ecology 2. Amazon River valley

ISBN 0-7614-1130-5   LC 2001-25472

"Castner discusses the many parts of the {Amazon} forest and their complex connections, from the litter on the ground to the canopy high above, conveying excitement about the spectacular things he has seen. . . . {This title is} attractive and informative." Booklist

Includes glossary and bibliographical references

Partners and rivals. Benchmark Bks. 2002 64p il (Deep in the Amazon) lib bdg $28.50

577.3

1. Rain forest ecology 2. Amazon River valley

ISBN 0-7614-1131-3   LC 2001-25977

This account of the ecology of the Amazon River valley "provides illustrations of commensalism, mutualism, and parasitism by discussing the fascinating relationships among species. . . . The interesting accounts of plant and animal life will keep most readers involved beyond a mere search for facts to add to reports." SLJ

Includes glossary and bibliographical references

Surviving in the rain forest. Benchmark Bks. 2002 64p il (Deep in the Amazon) lib bdg $28.50

577.3

1. Rain forest ecology 2. Animal defenses 3. Amazon River valley

ISBN 0-7614-1126-7   LC 99-57013

Describes the ecology of the Amazon rainforest and the different ways animals there protect themselves

"Attractive and informative." Booklist

Includes glossary and bibliographical references

Fielding, Eileen
The Eastern forest. Benchmark Bks. (Tarrytown) 1999 64p il (Ecosystems of North America) lib bdg $28.50   **577.3**
1. Forest ecology
ISBN 0-7614-0895-9   LC 97-33115
Examines the forests of eastern North America, their ecosystems, and their responses to temperature and weather
Includes glossary and bibliographical references

Jackson, Tom, 1972-
Tropical forests. Raintree Steck-Vaughn Pubs. 2003 64p il maps (Biomes atlases) lib bdg $31.42 (5 and up)   **577.3**
1. Rain forest ecology
ISBN 0-7398-5250-7   LC 2002-68094
A comprehensive look at the tropical forest biome, examining its climate, plants, animals, people, and future, plus detailed views of some particular tropical forest locations
"Especially effective are the maps. Brief notes for 10 to 12 highlights appear on each one, commenting on the diversity of flora, fauna, and landforms that occurs. . . . [The book includes] excellent-quality, full-color photographs and related sidebars." SLJ
Includes glossary and bibliographical references

Lasky, Kathryn
The most beautiful roof in the world; exploring the rainforest canopy; photographs by Christopher G. Knight. Harcourt Brace & Co. 1997 unp il $18; pa $9 (4 and up)   **577.3**
1. Lowman, Margaret 2. Rain forest ecology
ISBN 0-15-200893-4; 0-15-200897-7 (pa)
                                       LC 95-48193
"Gulliver Green"
Describes the work of Meg Lowman in the rainforest canopy, an area unexplored until the last ten years and home to previously unknown species of plants and animals
"Fresh in out-look and intriguing in details, this memorable book features colorful photographs that reflect the you-are-there quality of the text." Booklist
Includes glossary

Martin, Patricia A. Fink, 1955-
Woods and forests; illustrations by Bob Italiano and Steve Savage. Watts 2000 143p il (Exploring ecosystems) lib bdg $24; pa $6.95 (7 and up)
                                       577.3
1. Forest ecology 2. Science—Experiments
ISBN 0-531-11697-2 (lib bdg); 0-531-16459-4 (pa)
                                       LC 99-33044
"In six chapters with 20 projects and 13 investigations, Martin starts students on a journey of understanding and appreciating our woods and forests. Topics in this book include tree identification, forest wildlife, and life cycles in the forest. . . . Appended are a glossary, an index, and a listing of books, videos, organizations, Web sites, and equipment suppliers." Book Rep

Pipes, Rose
Rain forests. Raintree Steck-Vaughn Pubs. 1998 32p il map (World habitats) $25.64   **577.3**
1. Rain forest ecology
ISBN 0-8172-5003-4   LC 97-9070
"A Zoe book"
Introduces some notable rain forests around the world, including those of South America, Congo, and Central America

Quinlan, Susan E., 1954-
The case of the monkeys that fell from the trees; and other mysteries in tropical nature. Boyds Mills Press 2003 171p il map $15.95
                                       577.3
1. Rain forest ecology 2. Natural history
ISBN 1-56397-902-0   LC 2002-108914
This "presents a number of questions or 'mysteries' concerning plants and animals in the tropical forests of South and Central America and explains how scientists answered those questions." Booklist
"Quinlan's book is well organized and clearly written. . . . Besides presenting some fascinating case studies in a style that conveys the thrill of the scientific chase, it also provides information on the different kinds of tropical forests and how they function." SLJ
Includes bibliographical references

Rain forests of the world. Benchmark Bks. 2002 11v il maps set $329.95   **577.3**
1. Rain forests—Encyclopedias
ISBN 0-7614-7254-1   LC 2001-28460
Contents: v1 Africa-bioluminescence; v2 Biomass-clear-cutting; v3 Climate and weather-emergent; v4 Endangered species-food web; v5 Forest fire-iguana; v6 Indonesia-manatee; v7 Mangrove forest-orangutan; v8 Orchid-red panda; v9 Reforestation-spider; v10 Squirrel-Yanomami people; v11 Index
"Within each volume, alphabetically arranged entries are placed into five color coded categories: types and characteristics; peoples; animals; plants, algae, and microorganisms; and general topics." Book Rep
"This comprehensive encyclopedia is easily accessible and provides a nice introduction to topics not easily found in other sources. An excellent purchase for school and public libraries." Booklist
Includes bibliographical references

Sayre, April Pulley
Taiga. 21st Cent. Bks. (NY) 1994 64p il maps (Exploring Earth's biomes) lib bdg $25.90 (5 and up)   **577.3**
1. Forest ecology
ISBN 0-8050-2830-7   LC 94-19388
The author describes the taiga environments of open lichen woodland and closed forests, including weather and climate, geology, plants and animals, and the effects of human habitation. Includes experiments
"An excellent resource book. . . . Appropriately illustrated with color photos and sketches and written in a refreshing style, the pages are loaded with information about the taiga biome." Sci Books Films
Includes glossary and bibliographical references

Sayre, April Pulley—*Continued*
Temperate deciduous forest. 21st Cent. Bks.
(NY) 1994 64p il maps (Exploring Earth's biomes)
lib bdg $25.90 (5 and up)   **577.3**
1. Forest ecology
ISBN 0-8050-2828-5   LC 94-25425
This locates temperate deciduous forests geographically "giving an overall description and treating the plants,
animals, and people found there. Individual chapters,
which are broken into small units, are brief and well illustrated and include suggestions for experiments using
easily obtainable materials." Booklist
Includes glossary and bibliographical references

Tropical rain forest. 21st Cent. Bks. (NY) 1994
64p il maps (Exploring Earth's biomes) lib bdg
$25.90 (5 and up)   **577.3**
1. Rain forest ecology
ISBN 0-8050-2826-9   LC 94-25427
Also available in paperback from Scholastic Ref.
This geographically locates and describes tropical rain
forests of the world and their plants and animals, and the
effects of human habitation on the flora and fauna
"Filled with facts and interesting science projects. . . .
Most illustrations are in full color, and the many charts
and graphs add to the presentation." SLJ
Includes glossary and bibliographical references

Staub, Frank J.
America's forests; written and photographed by
Frank Staub. Carolrhoda Bks. 1998 48p il map
(Carolrhoda earth watch book) lib bdg $21.27 (4
and up)   **577.3**
1. Forests and forestry 2. Forest ecology
ISBN 1-57505-265-2   LC 98-7291
Examines the growth and changing nature of forests,
the plants and animals living there, and the uses to which
these lands are put
"Solid, accessible information presented in an attractive format. . . . Even students with little interest in nature will be drawn to the numerous full-color photographs that depict the beauty and variety of our country's
woodlands." SLJ
Includes glossary

577.4   Grassland ecology

Hoare, Ben
Temperate grasslands. Raintree Steck-Vaughn
Pubs. 2003 64p il maps (Biomes atlases) lib bdg
$31.42 (5 and up)   **577.4**
1. Grassland ecology
ISBN 0-7398-5249-3   LC 2002-12818
Contents: Biomes of the world; Temperate grasslands
of the world; Grassland climate; Grassland plants; Grassland animals; People and grasslands; The future
This offers a look at temperate grasslands of the world
describing their climate, plants, animals, people, and future
"Especially effective are the maps. Brief notes for 10
to 12 highlights appear on each one, commenting on the
diversity of flora, fauna, and landforms that occurs. . . .

[The book includes] excellent-quality, full-color photographs and related sidebars." SLJ
Includes glossary and bibliographical references

Martin, Patricia A. Fink, 1955-
Prairies, fields, and meadows. Watts 2002 144p
il map (Exploring ecosystems) $23 (7 and up)
                                           577.4
1. Prairie ecology 2. Grassland ecology
ISBN 0-531-11859-2   LC 2001-17570
"Martin follows theories about how the prairies
formed with an overview of plants and animals, including species and anatomy, and a consideration of the
types of grasslands, how species coexist, and conservation efforts. Throughout, the author suggests activities."
Booklist
"One can glean a great deal of useful information
from this text." Libr Media Connect
Includes glossary and bibliographical references

Ormsby, Alison
The prairie. Benchmark Bks. (Tarrytown) 1999
64p il (Ecosystems of North America) $28.50
                                           577.4
1. Prairie ecology
ISBN 0-7614-0897-5   LC 97-39444
Examines the prairies of central North America, their
ecosystems, and their responses to temperature, weather,
and agriculture
This title is "well-written {and} well-organized." SLJ
Includes glossary and bibliographical references

Sayre, April Pulley
Grassland. 21st Cent. Bks. (NY) 1994 64p il
maps (Exploring Earth's biomes) lib bdg $25.90 (5
and up)   **577.4**
1. Grassland ecology 2. Prairie ecology
ISBN 0-8050-2827-7   LC 94-19389
This book "reviews the similarities and differences in
the grasslands that occur on every continent except Antarctica. The author examines the impact of the unique
combination of the abiotic factors of weather, climate,
and geology on the creation of conditions conducive for
the various types of grasslands." Sci Books Films
"The experiments and observations noted are interesting and within the range of most students' understanding.
. . . Full-color photos are scattered throughout." SLJ
Includes glossary and bibliographical references

577.5   Ecology of miscellaneous environments

Allaby, Michael, 1933-
Deserts. Facts on File 2001 214p il maps
(Ecosystem) $65 (7 and up)   **577.5**
1. Deserts
ISBN 0-8160-3929-1   LC 00-41749
"This book explains why deserts form in particular re-
gions. It describes their climates and the ways plants and
animals have adapted to them. It also offers a historical

Allaby, Michael, 1933-—*Continued*
perspective, covering periods when different climates allow crops to grow and how climatic changes triggered major historical events. The author devotes one-half of the book to accounts of desert peoples, their ways of life, and their possible future." Publisher's note
Includes bibliographical references

Mudd-Ruth, Maria
The deserts of the Southwest. Benchmark Bks. (Tarrytown) 1999 64p il (Ecosystems of North America) lib bdg $28.50   **577.5**
1. Desert ecology
ISBN 0-7614-0899-1   LC 97-49842
Examines the deserts of the Southwest, their ecosystems, and their responses to temperature and weather
Includes glossary and bibliographical references

Sayre, April Pulley
Desert. 21st Cent. Bks. (NY) 1994 64p il maps (Exploring Earth's biomes) lib bdg $25.90 (5 and up)   **577.5**
1. Desert ecology
ISBN 0-8050-2825-0   LC 94-21427
This describes deserts of the world, their plants and animals, and the effects of human habitation
"Lively and interesting. . . . Adept and well presented." Booklist
Includes glossary and bibliographical references

577.6   Aquatic ecology. Freshwater ecology

Bredeson, Carmen
Tide pools. Watts 1999 61p il hardcover o.p. paperback available $6.95   **577.6**
1. Seashore ecology 2. Marine biology
ISBN 0-531-15958-2 (pa)   LC 97-41630
Describes the physical characteristics of tide pools and the organisms that inhabit them
"Illustrated with many full-color photographs, this book presents basic information in an accessible format." Booklist
Includes glossary and bibliographical references

Castner, James L.
River life. Benchmark Bks. 2002 64p il (Deep in the Amazon) lib bdg $28.50   **577.6**
1. Amazon River 2. River ecology
ISBN 0-7614-1127-5   LC 99-57015
Describes the geology, topography, and fishes of the Amazon River Region
"Attractive and informative." Booklist
Includes glossary and bibliographical references

Goodman, Susan, 1952-
Ultimate field trip 3; wading into marine biology; photographs by Michael J. Doolittle. Atheneum Bks. for Young Readers 1999 46p il $17; pa $6.99   **577.6**
1. Seashore ecology 2. Marine biology 3. Natural history—Maine
ISBN 0-689-81963-3; 0-689-83890-5 (pa)
LC 98-13985
A middle school class from Boston visits Cobscook Bay, Maine, to learn about the marine biology of the Bay's tidal zone
"This celebrates the pleasures of hands-on, outdoor science with an inviting mix of fact and frolic." Booklist
Includes glossary and bibliographical references

Josephs, David
Lakes, ponds, and temporary pools. Watts 2000 127p il (Exploring ecosystems) lib bdg $24; pa $6.95   **577.6**
1. Lake ecology 2. Pond ecology
ISBN 0-531-11698-0 (lib bdg); 0-531-16506-X (pa)
LC 99-57578
Explains the importance of preserving and protecting slow-moving water habitats and provides instructions for related projects and activities
Includes bibliographical references

Katz, Sharon
The Great Lakes. Benchmark Bks. (Tarrytown) 1999 64p il (Ecosystems of North America) $28.50   **577.6**
1. Lake ecology
ISBN 0-7614-0898-3   LC 97-32693
Describes the formation of the Great Lakes, the varied lifeforms that are part of this ecosystem, the interactions among the plants and animals that live there, and threats to this environment
Includes glossary and bibliographical references

Martin, Patricia A. Fink, 1955-
Rivers and streams. Watts 1999 143p il maps (Exploring ecosystems) lib bdg $23.50; pa $6.95 (7 and up)   **577.6**
1. River ecology 2. Science—Experiments
ISBN 0-531-11523-2 (lib bdg); 0-531-15969-8 (pa)
LC 98-10117
Provides instructions for projects and activities that explore river and stream habitats and explains why these environments should be preserved and protected
"The well-written, generally well illustrated text provides abundant information beyond the activities." Booklist
Includes glossary and bibliographical references

Sayre, April Pulley
Lake and pond. 21st Cent. Bks. (NY) 1996 78p il (Exploring Earth's biomes) lib bdg $25.90 (5 and up)   **577.6**
1. Lake ecology 2. Pond ecology
ISBN 0-8050-4089-7   LC 95-36228

Sayre, April Pulley—*Continued*
Discusses the lake and pond biomes and how each is affected by the environment and people
"The writing style, lively and precise, makes this . . . unusually readable." Booklist

River and stream. 21st Cent. Bks. (NY) 1996 80p il (Exploring Earth's biomes) lib bdg $25.90 (5 and up)   **577.6**
1. River ecology
ISBN 0-8050-4088-9   LC 95-34458
Describes aquatic biomes, focusing on life in rivers and streams, and explains the effect of pollution on these biotic communities and on the lives of people everywhere
"Exceptionally well-focused, well-organized." SLJ

577.7   Marine ecology

Carson, Rachel, 1907-1964
The edge of the sea; with illustrations by Bob Hines. Houghton Mifflin 1955 276p il hardcover o.p. paperback available $14 (7 and up)
                                              577.7
1. Marine biology 2. Seashore
ISBN 0-395-28519-4 (pa)
Also available in hardcover from P. Smith
"The seashores of the world may be divided into three basic types: the rugged shores of rock, the sand beaches, and the coral reefs and all their associated features. Each has its typical community of plants and animals. The Atlantic coast of the United States [provides] clear examples of each of these types. I have chosen it as the setting for my pictures of shore life." Preface

Cerullo, Mary M., 1949-
Coral reef; a city that never sleeps; text by Mary M. Cerullo; photographs by Jeffrey L. Rotman. Cobblehill Bks. 1996 58p il $18.99 (4 and up)   **577.7**
1. Coral reefs and islands 2. Marine ecology
ISBN 0-525-65193-4   LC 95-6635
This describes the ecosystem of coral reefs and their inhabitants
"As fascinatingly fact-filled as the text is, it's even more outstanding because of Rotman's spectacular, full-color photographs." SLJ
Includes glossary and bibliographical references

Collard, Sneed B., III
Lizard Island; science and scientists on Australia's Great Barrier Reef. Watts 2000 143p il $25; pa $12.95   **577.7**
1. Coral reefs and islands 2. Marine ecology 3. Great Barrier Reef (Australia)
ISBN 0-531-11719-7; 0-531-1619-1 (pa)
                                      LC 99-55149
Describes the biologists who manage the Lizard Island Research Station and their activities studying and protecting the Great Barrier Reef
"The author ends with an ominous account of the

tragic destruction of many of the world's coral reefs and a direct plea for more ecologically responsible behavior. . . . This is a readable, enthusiastic visit with the practicing scientists in the field." Booklist
Includes bibliographical references

Endangered oceans: opposing viewpoints; William Dudley, book editor. Greenhaven Press 1999 208p il lib bdg $33.70; pa $22.45 (7 and up)   **577.7**
1. Marine ecology 2. Environmental policy 3. Marine pollution
ISBN 0-7377-0063-7 (lib bdg); 0-7377-0062-9 (pa)
                                      LC 98-45933
"This volume addresses how endangered the world's oceans and coastlines are, potential management and conservation practices, how the world's fisheries can be protected, and how whales can be protected. . . . A welcome addition." SLJ
Includes bibliographical references

Gowell, Elizabeth Tayntor
Fountains of life; the story of deep sea vents. Watts 1998 63p il $23; pa $6.95   **577.7**
1. Ocean bottom 2. Marine ecology
ISBN 0-531-20369-7; 0-531-15908-6 (pa)
                                      LC 97-10924
"A First book"
Discusses the formation and discovery of hydrothermal vents and the unusual animals and plants that can be found near them
"Color diagrams of the formation of new sea floor and tectonic plates are clear and understandable, and the computer-generated map of the ocean floor pulsates in vibrant color. Full-color illustrations amplify the descriptions, definitions, and explanations." SLJ
Includes glossary and bibliographical references

Kricher, John C.
Peterson first guide to seashores; {by} John Kricher; illustrated by Gordon Morrison. Houghton Mifflin 1992 128p il (6 and up)   **577.7**
1. Seashore 2. Marine biology
                                      LC 91-38829
Available 1998 edition with title: Peterson first guide to the seashore $5.95 (ISBN 0-395-91180-X)
This is a guide to identification of plants and animals found at the seashore
This is "sure to satisfy the curiosity of novices and inspire a deeper interest in nature. . . . The selections, grouped geographically and by habitat, are limited to those most commonly discovered by hikers or beachcombers. The clear, full-color pictures are simply labeled for easy identification." SLJ

Parker, Steve
Seashore; written by Steve Parker. rev ed. DK Pub. 2004 72p il (DK eyewitness books) $15.99; lib bdg $19.99 (4 and up)   **577.7**
1. Seashore 2. Marine animals 3. Marine plants
ISBN 0-7566-0721-3; 0-7566-0720-5 (lib bdg)
First published 1989 by Knopf

Parker, Steve—*Continued*
Brief text and photos introduce the animal inhabitants of the seashore, including fish, crustaceans, snails, and shorebirds.

Sayre, April Pulley
Ocean. 21st Cent. Bks. (NY) 1996 80p il (Exploring Earth's biomes) lib bdg $25.90 (5 and up)   **577.7**
1. Ocean
ISBN 0-8050-4084-6   LC 96-2419
Describes the physical features of the ocean biome, as well as ocean life, human use, and conservation efforts
"Presents clear, accurate information. Almost every page has a small color picture or color diagram, nicely captioned, to augment the text." Voice Youth Advocates

World Book looks at the sea and its marvels. World Bk. 1997 64p il (World Book looks at) $10.95; pa $6.95   **577.7**
1. Marine biology
ISBN 0-7166-1803-6; 0-7166-1811-7 (pa)
                                          LC 96-61142
This look at the ocean and marine life is based on information and illustrations contained in the World Book encyclopedia

577.8 Synecology and population biology

Silverstein, Alvin
Symbiosis; {by} Alvin Silverstein, Virginia Silverstein, Laura Silverstein Nunn. 21st Cent. Bks. (Brookfield) 1998 64p il lib bdg $26.90
                                             577.8
1. Symbiosis
ISBN 0-7613-3001-1   LC 97-52149
Discusses the three kinds of symbiosis: mutualism, commensalism, and parasitism and describes examples of these relationships
"Well researched and interesting and the format is inviting for both general-interest reading and research." SLJ
Includes glossary and bibliographical references

U.X.L encyclopedia of biomes; Marlene Weigel, Julie L. Carnagie, editor. U.X.L 1999 3v set $165 (7 and up)   **577.8**
1. Ecology
ISBN 0-7876-3732-7   LC 99-23395
Contents: v1 Coniferous forests, continental margins, deciduous forests, and deserts; v2 Grasslands, lakes and ponds, oceans, and rainforests; v3 Rivers, seashores, tundras, and wetlands
"Alphabetically arranged entries on land biomes and water biomes range from 35 to 45 pages each and cover climate, elevation, soil water bodies, vegetation, animal life, food web, plant and animal adaptations, endangered species, human effects on the biome and the effects of the environment on humans' culture and economy." Publisher's note

578 Natural history of organisms and related subjects

Kerrod, Robin, 1938-
Facts on File wildlife atlas; {by} Robin Kerrod and John Stidworthy. 2nd ed. Facts on File 1997 80p il maps $18.95   **578**
1. Habitat (Ecology) 2. Animals 3. Plants 4. Ecology
ISBN 0-8160-3714-0   LC 97-15967
First published 1992 in the United Kingdom with title: Philip's wildlife atlas
Describes the different types of wild animals and plants in the world and explains how and why each region has its own unique mix of creatures. Habitats, evolution, migratory patterns, and danger of extinction are discussed
This volume "offers an attractive, informal introduction." Booklist

Wildlife and plants of the world. Marshall Cavendish 1998 17v set $471.36   **578**
1. Animals 2. Plants
ISBN 0-7614-7099-9   LC 97-32139
First published 1994 with title: Wildlife of the world
Edited by Deborah Evans and Leon Gray
Alphabetically-arranged illustrated articles introduce nearly 400 animals, plants and habitats
"The books are easy to use. . . . The set will be useful for research by upper-elementary and middle-school students." Booklist
Includes bibliographical references

578.68 Rare and endangered species

Endangered species: opposing viewpoints; Helen Cothran, book editor. Greenhaven Press 2000 156p il lib bdg $34.95; pa $23.70 (7 and up)
                                           578.68
1. Endangered species
ISBN 0-7377-0506-X (lib bdg); 0-7377-0505-1 (pa)
                                          LC 99-85752
"Opposing viewpoints series"
Replaces the edition published 1995 under the editorship of Brenda Stalcup
This collection of articles offers varying viewpoints on extinction, preservation, property rights, and international cooperation
Includes bibliographical references

Vergoth, Karin
Endangered species; {by} Karin Vergoth & Christopher Lampton. rev ed. Watts 1999 111p il lib bdg $25; pa $12.95   **578.68**
1. Endangered species 2. Wildlife conservation
ISBN 0-531-11480-5; 0-531-16438-1 (pa)
                                          LC 98-8197
First published 1988 under the authorship of Christopher Lampton

Vergoth, Karin—*Continued*

Explains what species are, how they become extinct, and the effect of extinction on the ecology, and surveys endangered species of plants and animals and possible solutions

This is "a compact, valuable overview of the subject." Booklist

Includes bibliographical references

578.7 Organisms characteristic of specific kinds of environments

Aquatic life of the world. Marshall Cavendish 2001 11v set $471.36 (4 and up)   **578.7**
1. Marine biology 2. Freshwater animals
ISBN 0-7614-7170-7   LC 99-86128

Arranged alphabetically, the more than 200 articles in volumes 1-10 cover mammals, fish, amphibians reptiles, birds, plants and their habitats. Biogeography, global warming and scuba diving are among the general topics discussed. Volume II contains a comprehensive index and nine subject indexes. Over 900 full-color photographs, illustrations and maps accompany the text

Conlan, Kathy

Under the ice; a Canadian museum of nature book. Kids Can Press 2002 55p il $16.95; pa $8.95 (4 and up)   **578.7**
1. Marine biology 2. Marine pollution 3. Polar regions
ISBN 1-55337-001-5; 1-55337-060-0 (pa)

"In this photo-essay, Conlan details her three-month stay in Antarctica, highlighting some of her experiences and her involvement in ongoing experiments relating to the effects of human waste on marine life." SLJ

"The first-person text creates a feeling of immediacy. . . . Well-captioned, color photos appear throughout the book. . . . Conlan . . . offers readers an engaging account of her adventurous career in scientific field research." Booklist

Encyclopedia of the aquatic world. Marshall Cavendish 2004 11v il map lib bdg set $459.95   **578.7**
1. Marine biology—Encyclopedias
ISBN 0-7614-7418-8   LC 2003-40948

Contents: v1 Algae, bacteria, and protist--Barnacle; v2 Barracuda and relatives--Carp and relatives; v3 Catfish--Crab; v4 Deep-sea fish--Flying fish and relatives; v5 Frog and toad--Mudskipper and relatives; v6 Newt and salamander--Piranha and relatives; v7 Plankton--Sea anemone; v8 Seabird--Sea turtle; v9 Sea urchin and sand dollar--Sponge; v10 Starfish--Worm; v11 Index

"The pleasing layout and abundant illustrations will satisfy researchers and browsers alike." SLJ

Includes bibliographical references

579 Microorganisms, fungi, algae

Farrell, Jeanette

Invisible allies; microbes that shape our lives. Farrar, Straus, and Giroux 2005 165p il lib bdg $17   **579**
1. Microorganisms
ISBN 0-374-33608-3   LC 2004-53750

This describes the roles of microbes in the making of cheese, bread, and chocolate, in digestion and killing harmful microbes, and in decomposition for waste treatment.

This is "a fascinating, broad-ranging and imminently readable book. . . . Illustrations include photos as well as interesting archival material." Booklist

Includes glossary and bibliographical references

579.5 Fungi

Pascoe, Elaine

Slime, molds, and fungi; text by Elaine Pascoe; photographs by Dwight Kuhn. Blackbirch Press 1999 48p il (Nature close-up) lib bdg $23.70 (4 and up)   **579.5**
1. Fungi
ISBN 1-56711-182-3   LC 97-36751

Using hands-on natural science projects, explores and explains different types and characteristics of fungi

This is "clearly written and well organized, and the photographs are outstanding in their clarity and composition." SLJ

Includes glossary and bibliographical references

Souza, D. M. (Dorothy M.)

What is a fungus? Watts 2002 63p il lib bdg $24.50; pa $8.95 (5 and up)   **579.5**
1. Fungi
ISBN 0-531-11979-3 (lib bdg); 0-531-16223-0 (pa)   LC 2001-17565

"Watts library"

This explains "how a fungus lives, what it eats, and how it reproduces. The writing is accessible and entertaining enough to keep readers engaged." SLJ

Includes glossary and bibliographical references

579.6 Mushrooms

Lincoff, Gary

The Audubon Society field guide to North American mushrooms; {by} Gary H. Lincoff; visual key by Carol Nehring. Knopf 1981 926p il flexible bdg $19.95   **579.6**
1. Mushrooms
ISBN 0-394-51992-2   LC 81-80827

"A Chanticleer Press edition. The Audubon Society field guide series"

This guide to 703 species of common mushrooms provides 762 color photographs and descriptions as keys to identifying these plants

Lincoff, Gary—*Continued*
"The author is an expert on mushroom toxins and instills responsible cautions. The photos are uncommonly beautiful." SLJ

580 Plants

Bailey, Jill
Plants and plant life. Grolier Educ. 2001 10v il maps set $279   **580**
1. Plants 2. Botany
ISBN 0-7172-9510-9   LC 99-56140
Volumes 4, 5, 8, 9, and 10 by Michael Allaby
Contents: v1 Roots, stems, and leaves; v2 Flowers and fruits; v3 Life processes; v4 Plant ecology; v5 Plants used by people; v6 Algae and fungi; v7 Mosses and ferns; v8 Conifers; v9 Flowering plants—the Monocotyledons; v10 Flowering plants—the Dicotyledons
"This set shows how plants came into being, evolved, and now live in every conceivable environment. It explores how people use plants now and in the past, breeding for ornament, food, clothing, and other applications. And it helps students identify the common and intriguing plants they are likely to find anywhere around them." Publisher's note
"Everything you've always wanted to know about plants is packed into this beautifully illustrated and easy-to-read set of books." Book Rep
Includes bibliographical references

Plant sciences; Richard Robinson, editor in chief. Macmillan Ref. USA 2001 4v il set $415 (7 and up)   **580**
1. Botany 2. Plants
ISBN 0-02-865434-X   LC 00-46064
This set covers "plant-related topics from acid rain to wood products. While this set includes complex information . . . it also offers basic facts on biomes, leaves, cells, individual scientists, related careers, and other subjects. The writing is clear and well organized, and depending on the topic, it's concise or very detailed." SLJ

Silverstein, Alvin
Plants; {by} Alvin, Virginia, and Robert Silverstein. 21st Cent. Bks. (NY) 1996 64p il (Kingdoms of life) lib bdg $25.90   **580**
1. Plants 2. Botany
ISBN 0-8050-3519-2   LC 95-45673
Begins with a general description of the plant kingdom and its classification before going on to discuss specific kinds of plants
"This easy-to-read and-understand book containing accurate information will be of interest to children at the junior high school level." Sci Books Films
Includes glossary

580.7 Plants--Education, research, related topics

Gardner, Robert, 1929-
Science projects about plants. Enslow Pubs. 1999 112p il (Science projects) lib bdg $26.60 (7 and up)   **580.7**
1. Plants 2. Science projects 3. Science—Experiments
ISBN 0-89490-952-5   LC 98-6821
Provides instructions for over thirty experiments appropriate for science fairs, involving plant physiology, reproduction, and growth
"The book offers solid ideas for projects." Booklist
Includes bibliographical references

Perry, Phyllis J., 1933-
Science fair success with plants. Enslow Pubs. 1999 104p il (Science fair success) lib bdg $26.60 (7 and up)   **580.7**
1. Botany 2. Plants 3. Science projects 4. Science—Experiments
ISBN 0-7660-1170-4   LC 98-25944
Details twenty-five experiments demonstrating the structure, environmental needs, and life processes of plants
Includes glossary and bibliographical references

VanCleave, Janice Pratt
Janice VanCleave's plants; mind-boggling experiments you can turn into science fair projects. Wiley 1997 90p il (Spectacular science projects series) pa $10.95 (5 and up)   **580.7**
1. Botany 2. Plants 3. Science projects 4. Science—Experiments
ISBN 0-471-14687-0   LC 96-2744
Presents facts about plants and includes experiments, projects, and activities related to each topic
This book "is inspiring without being flashy. . . . The black-and-white line drawings are sketchy but helpful. . . . This is a fine example of helpful information that is neither academically dry nor ingratiatingly slangy." SLJ
Includes glossary

582 Plants notable for specific vegetative characteristics and flowers

Pascoe, Elaine
Seeds and seedlings; text by Elaine Pascoe; photographs by Dwight Kuhn. Blackbirch Press 1997 48p il (Nature close up) lib bdg $23.70
582
1. Seeds
ISBN 1-56711-178-5   LC 95-25178
Describes how seeds are formed, how they grow, what they look like, how they reproduce, and how they make food. Instructions for related hands-on science projects is included
"The clearly written, interesting text is enhanced by numerous high-quality, full-color photographs." SLJ
Includes glossary and bibliographical references

582.13   Plants noted for their flowers

Niehaus, Theodore F.
A field guide to Pacific states wildflowers; illustrated by Charles L. Ripper. Houghton Mifflin 1976 xxxii, 432p il map hardcover o.p. paperback available $19   **582.13**
1. Wild flowers
ISSN `
ISBN 0-395-91095-1 (pa)   LC 76-5873
"The Peterson field guide series"
"Sponsored by the National Audubon Society and National Wildlife Federation"
"Field marks of species found in Washington, Oregon, California and adjacent areas; a visual approach arranged by color, form, and detail." Title page
"This offering identifies 1492 common wildflowers. . . . Common and scientific name, habitat, and recognition features are given for each plant." Libr J

Ryden, Hope
Wildflowers around the year; photographs and text by Hope Ryden. Clarion Bks. 2001 90p il $17 (5 and up)   **582.13**
1. Wild flowers
ISBN 0-395-85814-3   LC 00-43011
"Ryden introduces the reader to 38 species of wildflowers. . . . The flowers are identified by both their common names and the genus-species nomenclature. The months during which they are expected to be in full bloom are given as well." Sci Books Films
"Accompanied by exquisite, sharply focused photos. . . . Filled with interesting tidbits, Ryden's lyrical text meanders appealingly through moments of wonder, experience, explanation, and speculation." Horn Book Guide
Includes bibliographical references

Souza, D. M. (Dorothy M.)
Freaky flowers. Watts 2002 63p il lib bdg $24.50; pa $8.95 (5 and up)   **582.13**
1. Flowers
ISBN 0-531-11981-5 (lib bdg); 0-531-16221-4 (pa)
LC 2001-17573
"Watts library"
"The book begins with a short course in botany that stresses vocabulary and processes. Subsequent chapters discuss different ways plants attract pollinators through colors, odors, and habitats. The last chapter acts as a warning that many plants are endangered because their pollinators are threatened, emphasizing the balance of nature. The outstanding full-color photos feature some of the most spectacular flowers found anywhere. Small sidebars offer interesting bits of trivia about similar plants. The text is packed with biological information and pertinent vocabulary." SLJ
Includes bibliographical references

Spellenberg, Richard
National Audubon Society field guide to North American wildflowers, western region. 2nd ed rev. Knopf 2001 862p il map $19.95   **582.13**
1. Wild flowers
ISBN 0-375-40233-0   LC 2001-269242
"A Chanticleer Press edition"
First published 1979
"More than 940 . . . full-color images show the wildflowers of western North America close-up and in their natural habitats. . . . Images are grouped by flower color and shape and keyed to . . . descriptions that reflect current taxonomy." Publisher's note

Thieret, John W.
National Audubon Society field guide to North American wildflowers: eastern region; revising author, John W. Thieret; original authors, William A. Niering and Nancy C. Olmstead. Knopf 2001 879p il map (National Audubon Society field guide series) $19.95   **582.13**
1. Wild flowers
ISBN 0-375-40232-2   LC 2001-269241
"A Chanticleer Press edition"
First published 1979 under the authorship of William A. Niering and Nancy C. Olmstead
Spine title: Field guide to wildflowers, eastern region
"Covers the area east of the Rockies and east of the Big Bend area of Texas to the Atlantic. Color photographs together with family and species descriptions make this a most useful field guide." Sci News {review of 1979 edition}

582.16   Trees

Brockman, C. Frank (Christian Frank), 1902-
Trees of North America; a field guide to the major native and introduced species north of Mexico; illustrated of Rebecca Merrilees; under the editorship of Herbert S. Zim. Golden Press Bks. 1968 280p il hardcover o.p. paperback available $11.95   **582.16**
1. Trees—North America
ISBN 0-307-13658-2 (pa)   LC 68-23523
"A Golden field guide"
This book identifies 594 species of trees "native to North America north of Mexico, plus some important foreign species that have become naturalized, and some that are grown commercially or as ornamentals. Each of the 730 species is illustrated and described briefly. Technical terms are held to a minimum and the brief descriptions emphasize only the most obvious field characteristics that may not be apparent in the illustrations." Appraisal

Burnie, David
Tree; written by David Burnie. rev ed. DK Pub. 2005 72p il (DK eyewitness books) $15.99; lib bdg $19.99 (4 and up)   **582.16**
1. Trees
ISBN 0-7566-1094-X; 0-7566-1093-1 (lib bdg)
First published 1988 by Knopf

Burnie, David—*Continued*
Photographs and text explore the anatomy and life cycle of trees, examining the different kinds of bark, seeds, and leaves, the commercial processing of trees to make lumber, and the creatures that live in trees.

Gardner, Robert, 1929-
Science project ideas about trees. Enslow Pubs. 1997 96p il (Science project ideas) lib bdg $25.26 (5 and up)   **582.16**
1. Trees 2. Science projects 3. Science—Experiments
ISBN 0-89490-846-4   LC 97-6515
Contains many experiments introducing the processes that take place in plants and trees
The directions "are easy to understand, and the vocabulary is fairly accessible. The accompanying diagrams are particularly sharp and clear." SLJ
Includes bibliographical references

Petrides, George A.
A field guide to trees and shrubs; northeastern and north-central United States and southeastern and south-central Canada; illustrations by George A. Petrides, Roger Tory Peterson. 2nd. Houghton Mifflin 1986 xxxii, 428p il hardcover o.p. paperback available $19   **582.16**
1. Trees—North America 2. Shrubs 3. Climbing plants
ISBN 0-395-35370-X (pa)   LC 76-157132
"The Peterson field guide series"
First published 1958
"Field marks of all trees, shrubs, and woody vines that grow wild in the northeastern and north-central United States and in southeastern and south-central Canada." Title page
"Descriptions and clear drawings compare similar species. Includes silhouettes showing typical branching of many of the trees." AAAS. Sci Book List. 3d edition

590   Animals

Lewin, Ted, 1935-
Tooth and claw; animal adventures in the wild. HarperCollins Pubs. 2003 97p il maps $15.99; lib bdg $16.89 (4 and up)   **590**
1. Wildlife 2. Dangerous animals
ISBN 0-688-14105-6; 0-688-14106-4 (lib bdg)
                                          LC 2002-4588
Contents: Beach master; Grizzly; Macaco meojor; Waiting for puff adder; Bears, bears, bears; Roar; The meat eaters of Kibale; Barnstorming; Sleeping with bison; Rattler; Deputy Dawg; Downwind of a dung beetle; The joker; Garbage elephants
Author/illustrator Ted Lewin relates fourteen of his experiences with wild animals while travelling the world, following each anecdote with facts about the featured animal and its habitat
"This is outstanding nature storytelling, related in a distinctive voice imbued with humor and personality; it's even better when read aloud." Horn Book
Includes glossary

Myers, Jack
On the trail of the Komodo dragon and other explorations of science in action; scientists probe 11 animal mysteries; illustrated by John Rice. Boyds Mills Press 1999 63p il $17.95; pa $9.95
                                                    590
1. Animals
ISBN 1-56397-761-3; 1-59078-279-8 (pa)
Based on science reporting columns published in Highlights for Children
"Each article answers an intriguing question about a particular animal: How do horses sleep? Why do snakes flick their tongues? What helps cats fall safely? Information is clearly presented in succinct chapters; frequent illustrations, sidebars, and section titles further break up the text." Booklist
Includes bibliographical references

Staub, Frank J.
The signs animals leave; {by} Frank Staub. Watts 2001 63p il $24.50; pa $8.95   **590**
1. Animal behavior 2. Animal tracks
ISBN 0-531-11863-0; 0-531-16575-2 (pa)
                                          LC 00-43603
"Watts library"
This describes traces left by animals which reveal their behavior including tracks and scents
Includes bibliographical references

Taylor, Barbara, 1954-
Animal giants. Kingfisher 2004 63p il (Kingfisher knowledge) $11.95 (5 and up)
                                                    590
1. Animals
ISBN 0-7534-5770-9   LC 2003-61898
Provides information on the largest animals of land, air, and sea
This offers "a concise, fact-filled text. . . .The clear color photos are appealing." Horn Book Guide

590.3   Animals--Encyclopedias and dictionaries

Animal; editors-in-chief, David Burnie & Don E. Wilson. DK Pub. 2001 624p il maps $50
                                                  590.3
1. Animals—Encyclopedias
ISBN 0-7894-7764-5   LC 2001-28346
"The book is divided into three sections. The first is a general introduction to animals and their lives. The second looks at animal habitats, describing each habitat in terms of its climate, plant life, and the animals found there. The main part of the book profiles over 2000 species of animals, from the familiar to the extremely rare, and includes some newly recognized species. . . . Each individual listing gives the animal's range, habitat, size, and social unit and includes a full-color illustration and descriptive paragraph. . . . An outstanding publication appropriate for all types of libraries. . . . This is unique for its comprehensiveness and its coverage of animal habitats and major evolutionary developments." Libr J

Animal sciences; Allan B. Cobb, editor in chief. Macmillan Ref. USA 2002 4v il (Macmillan science library) set $395   **590.3**
1. Animals—Encyclopedias
ISBN 0-02-865556-7   LC 2001-26627
This "work contains approximately 300 signed entries on a variety of topics relating to animal science, including animal development, functions, behavior, ecology, and evolution. The connection between animals and humans is also explored. . . . Also included are biographies of noted scientists who have made 'significant contributions' to the field. . . . Articles appear in alphabetical order and range in length from several paragraphs to several pages. . . . Articles are clear and well written, and the appealing layout includes many colorful photographs, diagrams, and sidebars. . . . This set contains sufficient information to serve the needs of a variety of student users and will appeal to the casual browser as well." Booklist

Burnie, David
The Kingfisher illustrated animal encyclopedia. Kingfisher (NY) 2000 319p il $27.95
590.3
1. Animals—Encyclopedias
ISBN 0-7534-5283-9   LC 00-27058
An illustrated encyclopedia describing the physical characteristics, behavior, and habitats of a variety of animals
"Each bewitching photo attracts the reader to read the description, and Burnie's descriptions are interesting." Booklist

The **encyclopedia** of animals; a complete visual guide; [text, Jenni Bruce . . . et al.] University of California Press 2004 608p il map $39.95
590.3
1. Animals—Encyclopedias
ISBN 0-520-24406-0   LC 2004-303646
"The book starts with an introduction to animal evolution, biology, behavior, classification, habitats, and current conservation issues. This is followed by a survey of animals, divided into the standard taxonomic classifications of mammals, birds, reptiles, amphibians, fishes, and invertebrates. . . . Icons and symbols indicate habitat, size, weight, and social and reproductive habits of the various species." Libr J
"This lavishly illustrated chronicle of Earth's biodiversity is a visual delight." Booklist

International wildlife encyclopedia. 3rd ed. Marshall Cavendish 2002 22v il map set $499.95   **590.3**
1. Wildlife—Encyclopedias
ISBN 0-7614-7266-5   LC 2001-17458
First published 1970
"All forms of world wildlife are covered—insects, fish, amphibians, reptiles, birds, and mammals. Although most of the entries deal with individual species, 'guidepost' articles . . . discuss animals such as apes or owls as a group. 'Fact file' boxes, color-coded according to whether an animal is a mammal, reptile, and so on, provide a summary of the important characteristics of the animal or group of animals; in addition, a color range

map is usually included. . . . {The 1,200} articles, ranging from about two to four pages in length are arranged in alphabetical order by the animal's most common English name." Booklist
"Accessible and well-researched. . . . A visual and verbal feast." SLJ
Includes bibliographical references

Visual encyclopedia of animals. DK Pub. 2001 512p il maps pa $17.99   **590.3**
1. Animals—Encyclopedias
ISBN 0-7894-7871-4
First published 1999 in the United Kingdom with title: Animals of the world
This visual reference to animals is divided into seven sections: Introduction, Insects, Fish, Amphibians, Reptiles, Birds, Mammals, and Domestic Animals. Illustrated with over 1,000 color photographs, diagrams, and artwork

591.4 Physical adaptation

The **Visual** dictionary of animals. Dorling Kindersley 1991 64p il (Eyewitness visual dictionaries) $18.95 (4 and up)   **591.4**
1. Animals
ISBN 1-879431-19-X   LC 91-60901
This volume "begins with introductory pages on animal bodies and animal heads. . . . The book then proceeds from butterflies and moths through mammals. Almost every page shows a skeleton and often a photograph or diagram of a dissected animal. . . . The book closes with animal tracks and a chart of animal classification." Booklist

591.47 Protective and locomotor adaptations, color

Perry, Phyllis J., 1933-
Armor to venom; animal defenses. Watts 1997 63p il hardcover o.p. paperback available $6.95
591.47
1. Animal defenses
ISBN 0-531-15884-5 (pa)   LC 96-37289
"A First book"
Describes how animals survive by using their armor, camouflage, horns, stings, and other natural protective devices and strategies
"A readable compendium. . . . Six well-organized chapters are interspersed with captioned, full-color photographs. . . . Useful for report writers and browsers, this is a book that most libraries will want to stock." SLJ
Includes glossary and bibliographical references

591.5 Behavior

Gardner, Robert, 1929-
Science project ideas about animal behavior; {by} Robert Gardner and David Webster. Enslow Pubs. 1997 96p il (Science project ideas) lib bdg $25.26 **591.5**
1. Animal behavior 2. Science projects 3. Science—Experiments
ISBN 0-89490-842-1   LC 97-13136
Presents facts about animal behavior and includes related experiments, projects, and activities
"The authors provide a well-written and -illustrated guide to experiments in animal behavior with just enough original science to give background and pique interest." Sci Books Films
Includes bibliographical references

Settel, Joanne
Exploding ants; amazing facts about how animals adapt. Atheneum Bks. for Young Readers 1999 40p il $16.95 (4 and up) **591.5**
1. Animal behavior
ISBN 0-689-81739-8   LC 97-35395
Describes examples of animal behavior that may strike humans as disgusting, including the "gross" ways animals find food, shelter, and safety in the natural world
"This attractive volume presents its material as wondrous science instead of sensational effect." Booklist
Includes glossary and bibliographical references

591.56 Behavior relating to life cycle

Perry, Phyllis J., 1933-
Animals that hibernate. Watts 2001 63p il lib bdg $24.50 **591.56**
1. Hibernation
ISBN 0-531-11864-9   LC 00-43511
"Watts library"
This describes the hibernation habits of a variety of animals including gray bats and grizzly bears
Includes bibliographical references

Animals under the ground; {by} Phyllis Perry. Watts 2001 63p il lib bdg $24.50 **591.56**
1. Animal behavior
ISBN 0-531-11759-6   LC 00-43601
"Watts library"
This describes the behavior and adaptations of animals that go underground including moles, pocket gophers, kangaroo rats, prairie dogs, and badgers
Includes bibliographical references

591.59 Animal communication

Sayre, April Pulley
Secrets of sound; studying the calls and songs of whales, elephants, and birds. Houghton Mifflin 2002 63p il (Scientists in the field) $16 (4 and up) **591.59**
1. Animal communication
ISBN 0 618 01514-0   LC 2001-51877
Examines the work of several bioacousticians, scientists who study the sounds made by living creatures, discussing the results and importance of their research
"This fascinating title shows the thrill of scientific discovery up close. . . . Lots of well-edited quotes from the scientists convey their contagious enthusiasm for what they do, and sharp color photos, sound charts, and activity boxes break up the text, making it even more readable." Booklist
Includes glossary and bibliographical references

591.6 Miscellaneous nontaxonomic kinds of animals

Aaseng, Nathan, 1953-
Poisonous creatures. 21st Cent. Bks. (NY) 1997 95p il map (Scientific American sourcebooks) lib bdg $28.90 **591.6**
1. Poisonous animals
ISBN 0-8050-4690-9   LC 97-8728
Describes various species from every animal family that use some kind of venom to protect themselves or as a means of acquiring food
"The crisply written text is matched by a clean format enhanced by lots of intriguing color photos." Booklist
Includes bibliographical references

Wilkes, Angela
Dangerous creatures; foreword by Steve Leonard. Kingfisher 2003 63p il (Kingfisher knowledge) $11.95 (5 and up) **591.6**
1. Dangerous animals
ISBN 0-7534-5622-2   LC 2003-40063
Describes various kinds of dangerous animals, such as lions, piranhas, killer bees, and vampire bats

591.68 Rare and endangered animals

Pringle, Laurence P.
Strange animals, new to science; {by} Laurence Pringle. Marshall Cavendish 2002 64p il $16.95 (4 and up) **591.68**
1. Rare animals
ISBN 0-7614-5083-1   LC 2001-28185
"Text covers seventeen unusual animals that have been newly discovered or previously thought to be extinct. Pringle describes their habitats, which are often in remote and inaccessible places, as well as how the ani-

Pringle, Laurence P.—*Continued*

mals came to be discovered." Horn Book Guide

"Many of the animals discussed in the short chapters are shown in intriguing color photos. An informative book on an unusual topic that will open kids' minds." Booklist

591.7 Animal ecology, animals characteristic of specific environments

Johnson, Jinny

Simon & Schuster children's guide to sea creatures. Simon & Schuster Bks. for Young Readers 1998 80p il $21.95 (4 and up)

           591.7

1. Marine animals

ISBN 0-689-81534-4   LC 97-8227

Describes the major groups of marine animals, including fish, birds, mammals, and crustaceans

"A beautifully illustrated guide, with a full-color drawing of each animal. . . . The book has enough information to be a useful research tool in the library. The organization, by habitat, is outstanding." Book Rep

Includes glossary

Lavies, Bianca

Compost critters; text and photographs by Bianca Lavies. Dutton Children's Bks. 1993 unp il $15.99 (4 and up)   **591.7**

1. Compost 2. Soil ecology

ISBN 0-525-44763-6   LC 92-35651

Examines how creatures, from bacteria and mites to millipedes and earthworms, aid in the process of turning compost into humus

"The author is to be commended for her excellent use of basic taxonomy in reference to animals. . . . The writing is very well done, and almost every page has a beautiful full-color photograph." Sci Books Films

Swinburne, Stephen R.

The woods scientist; with photographs by Susan C. Morse. Houghton Mifflin 2002 41p il map (Scientists in the field) $16 (4 and up)

           591.7

1. Morse, Susan 2. Forest animals

ISBN 0-618-04602-X   LC 2002-302

A devoted nature lover and animal tracker, Sue Morse shares her knowledge and love of some of the creatures that inhabit America's woodlands

"The language is immediate, clear, and filled with moment-by-moment observations and well-presented facts. . . . Readers will come away with a much more informed view of wildlife at risk, enriched by Morse's superb color photographs." Booklist

Includes glossary and bibliographical references

Vogel, Carole Garbuny

Ocean wildlife. Franklin Watts 2003 95p il $29.50; pa $12.95 (5 and up)   **591.7**

1. Marine animals

ISBN 0-531-12324-3; 0-53116681-3 (pa)

            LC 2003-5302

Discusses how various underwater creatures have adapted to their environment in order to keep themselves safe from dangerous predators

This offers "magnificent, full-color photographs. . . . The clearly written narrative introduces the many creatures that have adapted to the harsh conditions of the ocean. The disastrous effects of overfishing, contamination, and pollution are briefly examined." SLJ

592 Invertebrates

Meinkoth, Norman August, 1913-

The Audubon Society field guide to North American seashore creatures; {by} Norman A. Meinkoth. Knopf 1981 799p il maps flexible bdg $19.95   **592**

1. Invertebrates 2. Marine biology

ISBN 0-394-51993-0   LC 81-80828

"A Chanticleer Press edition. The Audubon Society field guide series"

This "unique field guide covers some 850 marine invertebrate animals living in or around the shallow waters of the temperate seacoasts of the United States and Canada. Excellent color photographs are grouped at the beginning of the book, followed by text that gives, for each animal, a short description, common and scientific names, habitat, range, and comments." Malinowsky. Best Sci & Technol Ref Books for Young People

Pascoe, Elaine

Earthworms; text by Elaine Pascoe; photographs by Dwight Kuhn. Blackbirch Press 1997 48p il (Nature close up) lib bdg $23.70   **592**

1. Worms

ISBN 1-56711-177-7   LC 95-25177

Describes the digging habits, physical characteristics, reproduction process, and habitat of the earthworm and provides instructions for related hands-on science projects

Written "in a chatty, enthusiastic style and with extraordinary close-up color photographs and clear instructions for activities and experiments." Booklist

Includes glossary and bibliographical references

594 Mollusks and mollusk-like animals

Arthur, Alex

Shell; written by Alex Arthur. Knopf 1989 62p il (Eyewitness books) $19; lib bdg $19.99 (4 and up)   **594**

1. Shells

ISBN 0-394-82256-0; 0-394-92256-5 (lib bdg)

            LC 88-13449

Available DK Pub. edition $15.99; $19.99 (0-7894-5830-6; 0-7894-6558-2)

Arthur, Alex—*Continued*
"Arthur showcases varieties of shelled mollusks, echinoderms, crustaceans, turtles, tortoises, and terrapins, illustrating how shells and pearls form and comparing species that inhabit such different environments as freshwater bodies and coral reefs." Booklist

Douglass, Jackie Leatherbury
Peterson first guide to shells of North America; illustrations by John Douglass. Houghton Mifflin 1989 128p il pa $5.95   **594**
1. Shells
ISBN 0-395-91182-6   LC 88-32884
"Shell collectors will enjoy the basic descriptions of shell types. Douglass has included the 'most colorful, not necessarily the most common, shells.' . . . Filled with precise color drawings and concise identification information." Booklist

Pascoe, Elaine
Snails and slugs; text by Elaine Pascoe; photographs by Dwight Kuhn. Blackbirch Press 1999 48p il (Nature close-up) lib bdg $23.70 (4 and up)   **594**
1. Snails 2. Slugs (Mollusks)
ISBN 1-56711-181-5   LC 97-29159
Describes the physical characteristics, reproduction processes, habitats, and metamorphoses of snails and slugs and provides instructions for related hands-on science projects
"The interesting, clearly written {text is} enhanced by numerous high-quality, full-color photographs." Sci Books Films
Includes glossary and bibliographical references

Rehder, Harald Alfred, 1907-1996
The Audubon Society field guide to North American seashells; {by} Harald A. Rehder; with photographs by James H. Carmichael, Jr.; visual key by Carol Nehring and Mary Beth Brewer. Knopf 1981 894p il flexible bdg $19.95
                                                      594
1. Shells 2. Mollusks
ISBN 0-394-51913-2   LC 80-84239
"A Chanticleer Press edition. The Audubon Society field guide series"
"The more than 700 color plates are arranged according to shape and color rather than family or genus, making identification very simple for even the rankest amateur. . . . The text gives the common name, scientific name, description, habitat, range, and comments for each species. This is the most comprehensive field guide to North American seashells." Libr J

595.3   Crustaceans

Lassieur, Allison
Crabs, lobsters, and shrimps. Watts 2003 47p il (Animals in order) $25 (4-6)   **595.3**
1. Crustaceans
ISBN 0-531-12265-4   LC 2002-11293

Explores the relationship between members of the decapoda order, including descriptions of several types of lobsters, crabs, and shrimp
This book makes "for fascinating reading. . . . Photographs are glorious." Libr Media Connect
Includes glossary and bibliographical references

595.4   Chelicerates. Arachnids

Montgomery, Sy
The tarantula scientist; text by Sy Montgomery; photographs by Nic Bishop. Houghton Mifflin Co 2004 80p il map (Scientists in the field) $18 (4 and up)   **595.4**
1. Marshall, Samuel D. 2. Tarantulas
ISBN 0-618-14799-3   LC 2003-20125
Describes the research that Samuel Marshall and his students are doing on tarantulas, including the largest spider on earth, the Goliath birdeating tarantula
"Enthusiasm for the subject and respect for both Marshall and his eight-legged subjects come through on every page of the clear, informative, and even occasionally humorous text. Bishop's full-color photos . . . are amazing." Booklist
Includes glossary and bibliographical references

Simon, Seymour, 1931-
Spiders. HarperCollins 2003 unp il $15.99; lib bdg $16.89 (4 and up)   **595.4**
1. Spiders
ISBN 0-06-028391-2; 0-06-028392-0 (lib bdg)
                                      LC 2002-14922
An introduction to the physical characteristics, behavior, and life cycle of different kinds of spiders
"In his now familiar picture-book format that pairs incredible photographs with graceful, clear prose, Simon provides a wealth of information." Booklist

595.7   Insects

Discovery Channel insects & spiders; an explore your world-handbook. Discovery Bks. (NY) 2000 192p il pa $14.95   **595.7**
1. Insects 2. Spiders
ISBN 1-56331-841-5   LC 99-87177
This covers insect evolution, anatomy, physiology, behavior, and insects and spiders as pets. Includes an identification guide to 160 insects and spiders and more than 300 full-color photos and illustrations
"Incredible photographs and illustrations are sure to catch the eye of even the most reluctant reader, weaving important concepts amidst the illustrations." Voice Youth Advocates
Includes glossary and bibliographical references

Insects and other invertebrates. Grolier 2004 10v il (World of animals) lib bdg set $499
                                                      595.7
1. Insects 2. Invertebrates
ISBN 0-7172-5894-7   LC 2003-63100
Volume numbering of this set continues previous 10v sets in this series: Mammals (2003) and Birds (2004)

Insects and other invertebrates—*Continued*

Contents: v21 Simple and wormlike animals: protozoans, sea anemones, worms . . . by Amy-Jane Beer; v22 Insects 1: millipedes and unusual insects by Rod Preston-Mafham; v23 Insects 2: crickets, grasshoppers, flies. . . by Rob Preston-Mafham; v24 Insects 3: true bugs by Rod Preston-Mafham; v25 Insects 4: beetles by Ken Preston-Mafham; v26 Insects 5: butterflies and moths by Ken Preston-Mafham; v27 Insects 6: wasps, ants, and bees by Ken Preston-Mafham; v28 Crustaceans: shrimps, crabs, lobsters . . . by Amy-Jane Beer; v29 Arachnids: spiders and scorpions by Ken Preston-Mafham; v30 Mollusks and echinoderms: slugs, snails, starfish . . . by Andrew Campbell

This "set groups species that share similar characteristics or have similar lifestyles, such as simple and wormlike animals, crustaceans, arachnids, mollusks, and echinoderms. . . . Well-written entries range in length from two to six pages and include numerous full-color photographs and illustrations. These detailed, vivid, and captioned pictures enhance the highly appealing and browsable layout." Booklist

Insects and spiders of the world. Marshall Cavendish 2003 11v il maps set $329.95 (5 and up)   **595.7**
1. Insects 2. Spiders
ISBN 0-7614-7334-3   LC 2001-28882
"Nearly 200 entries are arranged alphabetically and range in length from one to six pages. Each entry is color coded into one of four categories: insects (Ant, Bedbug, Termite); spiders (Black widow, House spider, Tarantula); other arthropods (Centipede, Millipede, Scorpion); and overview (Arachnology, Communication, Metamorphosis). Many articles include a 'Key Facts' box with basic details concerning habitat, breeding, and so on as well as a distribution map that indicates where the insect or spider lives in the world. . . . Entries are further enhanced by diagrams, illustrations, and vivid color photographs." Booklist
Includes bibliographical references

Jackson, Donna M., 1959-

The bug scientists; by Donna M. Jackson. Houghton Mifflin 2002 48p il (Scientists in the field) $16 (4 and up)   **595.7**
1. Insects
ISBN 0-618-10868-8   LC 2001-39256
Bug scientists, called entomologists, present information on insects and explain how they use that information in their work
"The much-maligned world of insects becomes fascinating in this . . . entry in the excellent Scientists in the Field series. . . . The highly readable text weaves in plenty of science. . . . With its crisp photos and lively story angles and language, this is sure to attract young readers." Booklist
Includes glossary and bibliographical references

Lasky, Kathryn

Monarchs; photographs by Christopher G. Knight. Harcourt Brace & Co. 1993 63p il hardcover o.p. paperback available $12 (4 and up)   **595.7**
1. Butterflies 2. Wildlife conservation
ISBN 0-15-255297-9 (pa)   LC 92-33972
"A Gulliver Green book"
Describes the life cycle and winter migrations of the eastern and western monarch butterflies and towns that protect their winter habitats including Pacific Grove, California and El Rosario, Mexico
"Vibrant description melds with fascinating full-color photographs in a book that strikes a perfect balance between science and humanity." SLJ

Latimer, Jonathan P.

Butterflies; {by} Jonathan P. Latimer, Karen Stray Nolting; illustrations by Amy Bartlett Wright; foreword by Virginia Marie Peterson. Houghton Mifflin 2000 48p il (Peterson field guides for young naturalists) $15; pa $5.95 (4 and up)   **595.7**
1. Butterflies
ISBN 0-395-97943-9; 0-395-97944-7 (pa)
                                       LC 99-38605
A guide to help identify various butterflies, using the Peterson System of identification

Caterpillars; {by} Jonathan P. Latimer, Karen Stray Nolting; illustrations by Amy Bartlett Wright; foreword by Virginia Marie Peterson. Houghton Mifflin 2000 48p il (Peterson field guides for young naturalists) $15; pa $5.95 (4 and up)   **595.7**
1. Caterpillars
ISBN 0-395-97942-0; 0-395-97945-5 (pa)
                                       LC 99-38944
Describes the physical characteristics, behavior, and habitat of a variety of caterpillars, arranged by the categories "Smooth," "Bumpy," "Sluglike," "Horned," "Hairy," "Bristly," and "Spiny"

Milne, Lorus Johnson, 1912-

The Audubon Society field guide to North American insects and spiders; {by} Lorus and Margery Milne; visual key by Susan Rayfield. Knopf 1980 989p il $19.95   **595.7**
1. Insects 2. Spiders
ISBN 0-394-50763-0   LC 80-7620
"A Chanticleer Press edition. The Audubon Society field guide series"
The authors "have based their field guide on 702 excellent color photographs (75 of which are of spiders and other arachnids). In addition to some general information, the text (two thirds of the book) is made up of brief comments on each kind of arthropod pictured." Choice
Includes glossary

Pascoe, Elaine

Ants; text by Elaine Pascoe; photographs by Dwight Kuhn. Blackbirch Press 1999 48p il (Nature close-up) lib bdg $23.70 (4 and up)

595.7

1. Ants

ISBN 1-56711-183-1   LC 97-43571

Describes the physical characteristics, habitats, and life cycle of ants

"With its excellent visuals and simple experiments, Ants will be a useful supplement to other material about the topic." SLJ

Includes glossary and bibliographical references

Beetles; text by Elaine Pascoe; photographs by Dwight Kuhn. Blackbirch Press 2000 48p il (Nature close-up) lib bdg $23.70   595.7

1. Beetles

ISBN 1-56711-175-0   LC 99-53770

Explains the characteristics, habits, life cycle, and appearance of the many species of beetles. Includes experiments

This book is "well organized and clearly written." SLJ

Includes glossary and bibliographical references

Butterflies and moths; text by Elaine Pascoe; photographs by Dwight Kuhn. Blackbirch Press 1997 48p il lib bdg $23.70   595.7

1. Butterflies 2. Moths

ISBN 1-56711-180-7   LC 95-42704

Investigates the physical characteristics, reproductive processes, habitats, and metamorphoses of butterflies and moths through hands-on projects

This volume is "attractively designed and heavily illlustrated with bright, full-color, close-up photos." SLJ

Includes glossary and bibliographical references

Crickets and grasshoppers; text by Elaine Pascoe; photographs by Dwight Kuhn. Blackbirch Press 1999 48p il (Nature close-up) lib bdg $23.70 (4 and up)   595.7

1. Crickets 2. Grasshoppers

ISBN 1-56711-176-9   LC 97-43572

Describes the physical characteristics, habitats, and life cycle of crickets and grasshoppers. Includes related activities

This offers "clear, readable text and striking close-up photos." Horn Book Guide

Includes glossary and bibliographical references

Flies; text by Elaine Pascoe; photographs by Dwight Kuhn. Blackbirch Press 2000 48p il (Nature close-up) lib bdg $23.70   595.7

1. Flies

ISBN 1-56711-149-1   LC 99-53769

Explains the characteristics, habits, life cycle, and appearance of the many species of flies. Includes experiments

This book is "well organized and clearly written." SLJ

Includes glossary and bibliographical references

Pringle, Laurence P.

A dragon in the sky; the story of a green darner dragonfly; by Laurence Pringle; paintings by Bob Marstall. Orchard Bks. 2001 64p il maps $18.95 (4 and up)   595.7

1. Dragonflies

ISBN 0-531-30315-2   LC 00-39156

This is the "story of one green darner dragonfly, Anax, and his journey from hatching in a New York state swamp to mating and dying in a Florida pond." Horn Book Guide

"There's a great deal about dragonflies to be learned from this well-written account. Marstall's paintings include beautiful landscapes as well as many clear, enlarged views of Anax and the creatures around him." Booklist

Includes bibliographical references

An extraordinary life; the story of a monarch butterfly; by Laurence Pringle; paintings by Bob Marstall. Orchard Bks. 1997 64p il $18.95 (5 and up)   595.7

1. Butterflies

ISBN 0-531-30002-1   LC 96-31482

Introduces the life cycle, feeding habits, migration, predators, and mating of the monarch butterfly through the observation of one particular monarch named Danaus

"The narrative is scientifically sound and includes information from the most recent research. . . . The attractive, oversized book is lavished with realistic, full-color paintings." SLJ

Includes bibliographical references

Pyle, Robert Michael

The Audubon Society field guide to North American butterflies; visual key by Carol Nehring and Jane Opper. Knopf 1981 916p il $19.95

595.7

1. Butterflies

ISBN 0-394-51914-0   LC 80-84240

"A Chanticleer Press edition. The Audubon Society field guide series"

This guide "introduces more than 600 species of North American butterfly, including those native to the Hawaiian Islands. A section of brilliant color plates (more than 1,000 of them) featuring butterflies in their natural habitats, follows a general introduction and notes on text organization and use." Booklist

Whalley, Paul Ernest Sutton

Butterfly & moth; written by Paul Whalley. Knopf 1988 63p il (Eyewitness books) (4 and up)

595.7

1. Butterflies 2. Moths

LC 88-1574

Available DK Pub. edition $15.99; lib bdg $19.95 (ISBN 0-7894-5832-2; 0-7894-6556-6)

This book "explores the changes that occur at each stage of the life cycles of these insects. Temperate, mountain, and exotic species are described as are shapes, camouflage, and mimicry." Sci Teach

"This is an impressive, informative, and high-quality book." Sci Books Films

Wilsdon, Christina
National Audubon Society first field guide: insects; written by Christina Wilsdon. Scholastic 1998 159p il hardcover o.p. paperback available $8.95 (4 and up) **595.7**
1. Insects
ISBN 0-590-05483-X (pa)   LC 97-17990
A visual guide to the natural science of insects which includes information on the ten most common orders, pollination, and life-cycles; also works as a field guide
This offers "sharp, clear full-color photos. . . . Inviting and easy-to-use." SLJ
Includes glossary and bibliographical references

596   Chordates

Animals; edited by Philip Whitfield. Macmillan Lib. Ref. USA 1999 3v il (Macmillan illustrated encyclopedia) set $310   **596**
1. Vertebrates 2. Animals—Encyclopedias
ISBN 0-02-865420-X   LC 99-41055
Contents: v1 Mammals; v2 Birds; v3 Reptiles, amphibians, and fish
A guide to vertebrate species and their habitats around the world. Environmental and conservation issues are addressed. Full-color illustrations accompany the text
Includes bibliographical references

Silverstein, Alvin
Vertebrates; {by} Alvin, Virginia, and Robert Silverstein. 21st Cent. Bks. (NY) 1996 64p il (Kingdoms of life) lib bdg $25.90 (5 and up)   **596**
1. Vertebrates
ISBN 0-8050-3517-6   LC 95-45672
"Using a minimal amount of scientific terminology, the authors . . . provide a successful introduction for young readers to the basic principles of the taxonomy of vertebrates. . . . Color photographs that are suitably placed throughout the text aid in making the subject matter clear." Sci Books Films
Includes glossary

597   Cold-blooded vertebrates. Fishes

Buttfield, Helen
The secret life of fishes; from angels to zebras on the coral reef; watercolors & text by Helen Buttfield. Abrams 1999 72p il map $19.95
    597
1. Fishes 2. Coral reefs and islands
ISBN 0-8109-3933-9   LC 99-10892
Alphabetical entries introduce more than 250 fishes native to coral reefs around the world. Behavior, mating, and feeding habits are discussed. Illustrated with full-color photographs

Capuzzo, Mike
Close to shore; the terrifying shark attacks of 1916. Crown 2003 140p il $16.95; lib bdg $18.99
    597
1. Sharks
ISBN 0-375-82231-3; 0-375-92231-8 (lib bdg)
    LC 2002-29918
An adaptation of the title for adults published 2001 by Broadway Bks.
Details the first documented cases in American history of sharks attacking swimmers, which occured along the Atlantic coast of New Jersey in 1916
"This book has a rich assortment of photos and news clippings. . . . Capuzzo reconstructs events with a novelist's flair and a scientist's attention to detail, and his pacing is relentless." Booklist
Includes bibliographical references

Cerullo, Mary M., 1949-
The truth about great white sharks; written by Mary M. Cerullo; photographs by Jeffrey L. Rotman; illustrations by Michael Wertz. Chronicle Bks. 2000 48p il $14.95 (4 and up)   **597**
1. Sharks
ISBN 0-8118-2467-5   LC 00-31506
This provides information "about shark anatomy, senses, eating habits, and their relationships with humans. . . . The book also contains unusual information such as how these fish are measured and photographed and why they are not able to survive in an aquarium. The attractive layout blends line drawings, full-color photographs, varied typefaces, and eye-catching graphics. Rotman's pictures are clear and informative. . . . This title will be accessible to reluctant readers and is a must for most collections." SLJ
Includes bibliographical references

Fish. Grolier 2005 10v il (World of animals) set $499   **597**
1. Fishes
ISBN 0-7172-5905-6   LC 2004-47333
Volume numbering of this set continues previously published sets in the World of animals series
Contents: v31 Primitive fish by John Dawes; v32 Sharks by John Dawes; v33 Rays, chimaeras, and eels by David Alderton; v34 Carp, minnows, and allies by John Dawes; v35 Salmon, trout, and allies by John Dawes; v36 Cod, herring, and allies by Amy-Jane Beer; v37 Catfish by John Dawes; v38 Piranhas, guppies, and allies by John Dawes; v39 Spiny-finned fish 1 by John Dawes; v40 Siny-finner fish 2 by John Dawes
This set describes the characteristics of fishes in general and includes specific information and color photos of many species.

Macquitty, Miranda
Shark; written by Miranda MacQuitty. rev. ed. DK Pub. 2004 72p il (DK eyewitness books) $15.99; lib bdg $19.99 (4 and up)   **597**
1. Sharks
ISBN 0-7566-0725-6; 0-7566-0724-8 (lib bdg)
First published 1992 by Knopf
Describes, in text and photographs, the physical characteristics, behavior, and life cycle of various types of sharks.

Mallory, Kenneth
Swimming with hammerhead sharks. Houghton
Mifflin 2001 48p il (Scientists in the field) $16 (4
and up) **597**
1. Klimley, A. Peter 2. Sharks
ISBN 0-618-05543-6   LC 00-61401
"A New England Aquarium book"
This book follows "marine biologist Pete Klimley and
an IMAX film team to seamounts off Cocos Island in the
Pacific Ocean to observe and film schooling hammerhead
sharks. . . . A fascinating record of research and investi-
gation, this inviting book is larded with numerous dra-
matic color photos." SLJ
Includes bibliographical references

Page, Lawrence M.
A field guide to freshwater fishes: North
America north of Mexico; {by} Lawrence M.
Page, Brooks M. Burr; illustrations by Eugene C.
Beckham III, John Parker Sherrod, Craig W.
Ronto. Houghton Mifflin 1991 432p il maps
hardcover o.p. paperback available $19 (7 and up)
597
1. Fishes—North America
ISBN 0-395-91091-9 (pa)   LC 90-42049
"The Peterson field guide series"
"Sponsored by the National Audubon Society, the Na-
tional Wildlife Federation, and the Roger Tory Peterson
Institute"
This guide "covers all 790 species known in North
America north of Mexico. Over 700 illustrations, most in
color, show identifying marks. Also includes 377 distri-
bution maps and additional line drawings of key details."
Publisher's note
Includes bibliographical references

Robins, C. Richard
A field guide to Atlantic coast fishes of North
America; {by} C. Richard Robins, G. Carleton
Ray; illustrations by John Douglass and Rudolf
Freund. Houghton Mifflin 1986 354p il hardcover
o.p. paperback available $19   **597**
1. Fishes—North America
ISBN 0-395-97515-8 (pa)   LC 85-18144
"The Peterson field guide series"
"Sponsored by the National Audubon Society and the
National Wildlife Federation"
This guide describes and illustrates 1,100 species that
inhabit the waters between the Canadian Arctic and the
Gulf of Mexico
Includes bibliographical reference

Walker, Sally M.
Fossil fish found alive; discovering the
coelacanth. Carolrhoda Bks. 2002 72p il maps lib
bdg $17.95 (5 and up)   **597**
1. Coelacanth
ISBN 1-57505-536-8   LC 2001-3815
Describes the 1938 discovery of the coelacanth, a fish
previously believed to be extinct, and subsequent research about it
"Walker writes well, making this relatively unknown

area of science history an exciting story of exploration
and discovery. Excellent, full-color photos illustrate the
text." Booklist
Includes bibliographical references

597.8 Amphibians

Fridell, Ron, 1943-
The search for poison-dart frogs. Watts 2001
48p il maps lib bdg $23.50; pa $6.95 (4-6)
597.8
1. Frogs 2. Wildlife conservation 3. Suriname
ISBN 0-531-11888-6 (lib bdg); 0-531-16570-1 (pa)
LC 00-36507
"Wildlife Conservation Society books"
This describes a scientific "expedition as a team trav-
els to Suriname to study the electric blue amphibians.
Written with vivid detail, the text explains environmental
issues and shows why preservation of the area is so cru-
cial." Booklist
Includes glossary and bibliographical references

Miller, Sara Swan
Amazing amphibians. Watts 2001 63p il lib bdg
$24.50; pa $8.95   **597.8**
1. Amphibians
ISBN 0-531-11793-6 (lib bdg); 0-531-13980-8 (pa)
LC 99-57309
"Watts library"
Portrays several amphibian species with unusual ap-
pearances, habitats, or behaviors, including caecilians, to-
mato frogs, and midwife toads
Includes bibliographical references

Pascoe, Elaine
Tadpoles; text by Elaine Pascoe; photographs by
Dwight Kuhn. Blackbirch Press 1997 48p il
(Nature close-up) lib bdg $23.70   **597.8**
1. Frogs
ISBN 1-56711-179-3   LC 95-40848
Explores the physical characteristics, reproduction,
habitat, and metamorphosis of tadpoles. Includes hands-
on activities
"The full-color photographs are of excellent quality."
SLJ
Includes glossary and bibliographical references

597.9 Reptiles

Amphibians and reptiles. Grolier 2005 10v il map
(World of animals) lib bdg set $499
597.9
1. Amphibians 2. Reptiles
ISBN 0-7172-5916-1
Volume numbering of this set continues previous 10v
sets in this series: Mammals (2003), Birds (2004), Insects
and other invertebrates (2004) and Fish (2004)
Contents: v41 Salamanders, newts, and caecilians by
Chris Mattison; v42 Frogs and toads 1 by Chris
Mattison; v43 Frogs and toads 2 by Chris Mattison; v44

Amphibians and reptiles—*Continued*

Lizards 1 by Chris Mattison, Valerie Davies; v45 Lizards 2 by Chris Mattison; v46 Lizards 3 by Valerie Davies, Chris Mattison; v47 Turtles and crocodilians by David Alderton; v48 Snakes 1 by Chris Mattison; v49 Snakes 2 by Chris Mattison; v50 Snakes 3 byChris Mattison

This set describes the characteristics of amphibians and reptiles in general and includes specific information and color photos of many species.

Crump, Martha L.

Amphibians, reptiles, and their conservation. Linnet Bks. 2002 149p il $25 (7 and up)

597.9

1. Amphibians 2. Reptiles

ISBN 0-208-02511-1   LC 2002-73072

Provides an overview of amphibians and reptiles, discussing common perceptions about these species, phobias, how humans impact their survival, and more

"The style is informal without being cute ('about 260 species of turtle share the planet with us today'). The science is focused and rigorous, with detailed text and occasional photos as well as boxed charts about the classification, the habitat, and the behavior of a wide range of amphibians and reptiles . . . This is an excellent title for reports, with an extensive glossary, a bibliography, and listings of further resources, including Web sites and conservation organizations for those who want to get involved." Booklist

Greenberg, Daniel A.

Lizards; [by] Dan Greenberg. Benchmark Bks. 2003 112p il (Animalways) lib bdg $21.95

597.9

1. Lizards

ISBN 0-7614-1580-7   LC 2003-2566

Contents: All sizes and shapes; What is a lizard?; The lizard body; Lizards in action; Getting to know lizards; Reproduction; Lizards, today and tomorrow

This provides information on the physical characteristics, behavior, and habitats of lizard species

Includes glossary and bibliographical references

Mattison, Christopher

Snake; by Chris Mattison. DK Pub. 1999 192p il $30; pa $8.99

597.9

1. Snakes

ISBN 0-7894-4660-X; 0-7894-6068-8 (pa)

LC 99-19957

An illustrated guide to "more than 60 types of snakes, ranging from adders to yellow anacondas. This richly formatted book features each snake in detailed entries with informative, readable text." Sci Child

Includes glossary

McCarthy, Colin, 1951-

Reptile; written by Colin McCarthy. Knopf 1991 63p il (Eyewitness books) (4 and up)

597.9

1. Reptiles

LC 90-4890

Available DK Pub. edition $15.99; lib bdg $19.99 (ISBN 0-7894-5786-5; 0-7894-6575-2)

Photographs and text depict the many different kinds of reptiles, their similarities and differences, habitats, and behavior

This book "stands out because of the fascinating photographs, which are brilliantly lifelike and well-chosen to demonstrate concepts discussed. . . . The text is nicely balanced between straightforward factual data and intriguing bits of trivia." SLJ

McDonald, Mary Ann, 1956-

Pythons; by Mary Ann and Joe McDonald; illustrated with photographs by the authors. Capstone Press 1996 48p il (Animals & the environment) lib bdg $21.26   597.9

1. Pythons

ISBN 1-56065-296-9   LC 95-438

Describes the physical characteristics, habitat, and different varieties of pythons

Includes bibliographical references

Rattlesnakes; by Mary Ann and Joe McDonald; illustrated with photographs by the authors. Capstone Press 1996 48p il (Animals & the environment) lib bdg $21.26   597.9

1. Rattlesnakes

ISBN 1-56065-294-2   LC 95-436

Describes the physical characteristics, behavior, and different varieties of rattlesnakes

Includes bibliographical references

Miller, Sara Swan

Radical reptiles. Watts 2001 63p il lib bdg $24.50; pa $8.95   597.9

1. Reptiles

ISBN 0-531-11794-4 (lib bdg); 0-531-13989-1 (pa)

LC 99-57020

"Watts library"

Describes several species of reptiles that have unusual appearances, habitats, or behaviors

This is "well-organized . . . {and} includes numerous, well-placed color photographs." SLJ

Includes glossary and bibliographical references

Montgomery, Sy

The snake scientist; photographs by Nic Bishop. Houghton Mifflin 1999 48p il map $16; pa $5.95 (4 and up)   597.9

1. Mason, Bob 2. Snakes

ISBN 0-395-87169-7; 0-618-11119-0 (pa)

LC 98-6124

Discusses the work of Bob Mason and his efforts to study and protect snakes, particularly red-sided garter snakes

"The lively text communicates both the meticulous measurements required in this kind of work and the thrill of new discoveries. Large, full-color photos of the zoologist and young students at work, and lots of wriggly snakes, pull readers into the presentation." SLJ

Includes bibliographical references

Reptiles and amphibians. Marshall Cavendish 2003 11v il maps set $459.95   597.9

1. Reptiles 2. Amphibians

ISBN 0-7614-7390-4   LC 2002-67556

Reptiles and amphibians—*Continued*

Contents: v1 African reed frogs-Boas and pythons; v2 Caecilians-Darwin's frogs; v3 Disk-tongued frogs-Gharials; v4 Ghost frogs-Harlequin frogs; v5 Hellbenders-Monitor lizards; v6 Mudpuppies-River turtles; v7 Salamandrids-Side-necked turtles; v8 Sirens-Squeakers; v9 Sunbeam snakes-Tropical frogs; v10 True frogs-Worm lizards; v11 Index volume

This "resource is organized alphabetically by the common family names of animals as used in the U.S. Each section . . includes an illustrated family tree that shows the relationship within the species, a profile giving important basic facts, some highlighted insights, and a 'Focus On' section that details a specific aspect of both common and rarely seen creatures. Anatomy, habitats, food, reproduction, and survival are all covered. The clear writing style makes this set valuable for a wide range of age and ability levels. The abundant mix of full-color photographs . . . and drawings offers great detail, and a habitat map is provided for each animal." SLJ

Ripple, Jeff, 1963-
Sea turtles. Voyageur Press 1996 85p il (World life library) pa $16.95 (7 and up)   **597.9**
1. Sea turtles
ISBN 0-89658-315-5   LC 95-22059
This book covers sea turtle distribution, biology, behavior, historical background and conservation techniques. The text is "lavishly illustrated with more than 50 full-color photographs that bring these animals to vibrant life." SLJ
Includes bibliographical references

Simon, Seymour, 1931-
Crocodiles & alligators. HarperCollins Pubs. 1999 unp il $15.95; lib bdg $16.89; pa $6.99 (4 and up)   **597.9**
1. Crocodiles 2. Alligators
ISBN 0-06-027473-5; 0-06-027474-3 (lib bdg); 0-06-443829-5 (pa)   LC 98-34705
Describes the physical characteristics and behavior of various members of the family of animals known as crocodilians
"The book is filled with interesting information, and the vivid, well-composed, full-color photographs and entertaining text will draw in browsers." SLJ

Snakes. HarperCollins Pubs. 1992 unp il pa $6.99 hardcover o.p. (4 and up)   **597.9**
1. Snakes
ISBN 0-06-446165-3   LC 91-15948
Describes, in text and photographs, the physical characteristics, habits, and natural environment of various species of snakes
"Once again Simon demonstrates his skill in molding a lucid discussion and striking photographs into a compelling, informative overview." Horn Book

The **Snake** book; photography by Frank Greenaway and Dave King. DK Pub. 1997 unp il $12.99; pa $8.99 (4-6)   **597.9**
1. Snakes
ISBN 0-7894-1526-7; 0-7894-6068-8 (pa)
LC 96-38294

Written and edited by Mary Ling and Mary Atkinson
The "creators of the book have used a stark white box as a background for some spectacular life-size photographs of 12 varieties of snakes. . . . Text containing very basic information about each snake sweeps around and inside the reptiles' coils, with the font varying in size from large to very small." Booklist

Stebbins, Robert C. (Robert Cyril), 1915-
A field guide to Western reptiles and amphibians; text and illustrations by Robert C. Stebbins. 3rd ed newly rev. Houghton Mifflin 2003 533p il maps $22   **597.9**
1. Reptiles 2. Amphibians
ISBN 0-395-98272-3   LC 2002-27561
"The Peterson field guide series"
First published 1966
"Sponsored by The National Wildlife Federation and the Roger Tory Peterson Institute"
This "covers all the species of reptiles and amphibians found in western North America. More than 650 full-color paintings and photographs show key details for making accurate identifications. . . . Color range maps give species' distributions. . . . [Includes] information on conservation efforts and survival status." Publisher's note
Includes bibliographical references

598 Birds

Arnold, Caroline, 1944-
On the brink of extinction; the California condor; photographs by Michael Wallace. Harcourt Brace Jovanovich 1993 48p il $20 (4 and up)   **598**
1. Condors 2. Endangered species 3. Wildlife conservation
ISBN 0-15-257990-7   LC 92-14914
"A Gulliver Green book"
Describes the history of the condor in North America and the efforts to capture and breed the few remaining California condors to save them from extinction
"Author and photographer have collaborated to describe, with a clearly written text and outstanding, informative photographs, the efforts to save the condor." Sci Books Films

Bailey, Jill
Birds of prey. Facts on File 1988 61p il (Nature watch series) $15.95   **598**
1. Birds of prey
ISBN 0-8160-1655-0   LC 88-45088
This book "covers birds of all continents, dealing with topics such as the differences between owls and other raptors, beak and feet adaptations, migration, vision, nesting and mating behavior, and endangered species. A quick check list helps distinguish between the various raptors, and a good bibliography is included." Sci Books Films

Barghusen, Joan D., 1935-
The bald eagle. Lucent Bks. 1999 96p il maps
(Endangered animals & habitats) lib bdg $28.70 (7
and up)   **598**
1. Bald eagle 2. Endangered species
ISBN 1-56006-254-1   LC 98-19034
Describes the physical characteristics and habits of
bald eagles, threats to their existence, changes in their
habitats, and efforts to protect these birds
Includes glossary and bibliographical references

Birds. Grolier 2003 10v il maps (World of
animals) set $499   **598**
1. Birds
ISBN 0-7172-5731-2   LC 2003-48308
Volume numbering of this set continues previous 10v
set in this series: Mammals (2003)
Contents: v11 Ground birds by Rob A. Hume; v12
Seabirds by Jonathan Elphick; v13 Shorebirds by Derek
W. Niemann, Euan Dunn; v14 Waterbirds by Tony
Whitehead, Derek W. Niemann, David Chandler; v15
Hunting birds by John Woodward; v16 Seed-, fruit-, and
nectar-eating birds by Dominic Couzens; v17 Insectivo-
rous birds by Rob A. Hume; v18 Omnivorous birds by
Derek W. Niemann, David Chandler, Tony Whitehead;
v19 Tropical forest birds by Jonathan Elphick; v20 Unusual birds by Dominic Couzens
This set "displays more than 250 characteristic species
in full. It points out their special nesting, breeding, feeding, and seasonal behaviors. . . . The set locates each
species geographically with world range maps and
biologically with full Latin names and subspecies lists.
The range maps show breeding, wintering, and resident
distributions." Publisher's note

Bull, John L.
The National Audubon Society field guide to
North American birds, Eastern region; {by} John
Bull and John Farrand, Jr.; revised by John
Farrand, Jr.; visual key by Amanda Wilson and
Lori Hogan. rev ed. Knopf 1994 797p il maps pa
$19.95   **598**
1. Birds—North America
ISBN 0-679-42852-6   LC 94-7768
Companion volume to National Audubon Society field
guide to North American birds, Western region, by
Miklos D. F. Udvardy
"A Chanticleer Press edition"
First published 1977
This pictorial guide to 508 eastern species arranges
birds by color and shape to simplify identification. It also
includes information on bird-watching and conservation
status
Includes bibliographical references

Burnie, David
Bird; written by David Burnie. rev ed. DK Pub.
2004 72p il (DK eyewitness books) $15.99; lib
bdg $19.99 (4 and up)   **598**
1. Birds
ISBN 0-7566-06586; 0-7566-0657-8 (lib bdg)
First published 1988 by Knopf

A photo essay on the world of birds examining such
topics as body construction, feathers and flight, the adaptation of beaks and feet, feeding habits, courtship, nests
and eggs, and bird watching.

Collard, Sneed B., III
Birds of prey; a look at daytime raptors; {by}
Sneed B. Collard III. Watts 1999 64p il lib bdg
$24.50; pa $8.95   **598**
1. Birds of prey
ISBN 0-531-20363-8; 0-531-16419-5 (pa)
     LC 98-38196
Discusses the physical features and behavior of daytime raptors, including eagles, harriers, kites, Old World
vultures, caracaras, and falcons
"Illustrated with many color photographs and designed
with fairly large type and generous use of white space,
the book provides an attractive, clearly written
overview." Booklist
Includes bibliographical references

DuTemple, Lesley A., 1952-
North American cranes. Carolrhoda Bks. 1999
48p il (Carolrhoda nature watch book) $25.26 (4
and up)   **598**
1. Cranes (Birds)
ISBN 1-57505-302-0   LC 98-4519
Describes the physical characteristics, diet, natural
habitat, and life cycle of these large wading birds, and
tells about the efforts of scientists to establish resident
flocks
"Colorful and informative. . . . Illustrated with many
excellent, full-color photos." Booklist

Griggs, Jack L.
All the birds of North America; American Bird
Conservancy's field guide; concept and design by
Jack L. Griggs. HarperPerennial 1997 172p il
maps pa $19.95   **598**
1. Birds—North America
ISBN 0-06-52770-6   LC 96-49679
This identification guide to North American birds uses
a system based on how and where birds collect food,
with icons, color bars, key numbers, and color illustrations

Grzimek's student animal life resource, Birds;
Melissa C. McDade, project editor: Birds. UXL
2005 5v .p il map set $260   **598**
1. Birds
ISBN 0-7876-9235-2   LC 2004-15729
Based on Grzimek's Animal Life Encyclopedia (2d.
ed, Gale, 2002)
Contents: v1 Tinamous to falcons; v2 Ducks to auks;
v3 Sandgrouse to woodpeckers; v4 Perching birds; v5
Monarch flycathcers to crows
This reference to birds "treats 166 families and 316
species from around the world. . . . Each entry includes
sections on physical characteristics, geographic range,
habitat, diet, behavior and reproduction, animals and people, and conservation status. . . . Each entry concludes
with a list of books, periodicals, and Web sites . . . for

Grzimek's student animal life resource, Birds—
Continued
further research. There are more than 500 colorful photographs, illustrations, and charts. . . . Layout is open and appealing, and the writing is clear and easily understood." Booklist

Harrison, Colin, 1926-2003
Birds of the world; by Colin Harrison and Alan Greensmith. Dorling Kindersley 1993 416p il maps (Eyewitness handbooks) pa $20 hardcover o.p. (7 and up) **598**
1. Birds
ISBN 0-7894-9390-X LC 93-7065
This book "starts with a how-to-section, then discusses anatomy, variations within species, watching birds, flight patterns, and, finally, presents a user-friendly identification key. . . . In addition, there are very readable range maps, pictures of alternative plumages, and scale drawings of each bird." Sci Books Films

Hoose, Phillip M., 1947-
The race to save the Lord God Bird; [by] Phillip Hoose. Farrar, Straus and Giroux 2004 196p il map $20 (7 and up) **598**
1. Woodpeckers 2. Endangered species
ISBN 0-374-36173-8
Tells the story of the ivory-billed woodpecker's extinction in the United States, describing the encounters between this species and humans, and discussing what these encounters have taught us about preserving endangered creatures
"Sharp, clear, black-and-white archival photos and reproductions appear throughout. The author's passion for his subject and high standards for excellence result in readable, compelling nonfiction." SLJ
Includes glossary and bibliographical references

Kaufman, Kenn
Lives of North American birds. Houghton Mifflin 1996 xxv, 675p il maps (Peterson natural history companions) $35 (7 and up) **598**
1. Birds—North America
ISBN 0-395-77017-3 LC 96-20285
This "is the print version of the previously issued CD-ROM, *Peterson Multimedia Guides: North American Birds*. Organized like the CD-ROM, the book presents 600 species of birds in taxonomic order and groups them by family. Small color photographs and range maps accompany concise, plain-language information regarding nesting, feeding, migration, courtship, habitat, clutch size, and conservation status. Upping the included species to 900 are brief descriptions of nonendemic vagrant birds." Libr J
Includes bibliographical references

Latimer, Jonathan P.
Backyard birds; {by} Jonathan P. Latimer, Karen Stray Nolting; illustrations by Roger Tory Peterson; foreword by Virginia Marie Peterson. Houghton Mifflin 1999 48p il (Peterson field guides for young naturalists) pa $5.95 hardcover o.p. (4 and up) **598**
1. Birds
ISBN 0-395-92276-3 LC 98-35509
This is an identification guide to birds "'you are likely to see where you live'. . . . [It] includes a . . . selection of about 20 creatures . . . grouped by color. . . . Bright, full-color photographs and drawings clearly indicate distinguishing features. Useful, accessible." SLJ

Birds of prey; {by} Jonathan P. Latimer, Karen Stray Nolting; illustrations by Roger Tory Peterson; foreword by Virginia Marie Peterson. Houghton Mifflin 1999 48p il (Peterson field guides for young naturalists) $15; pa $5.95 (4 and up) **598**
1. Birds of prey
ISBN 0-395-95211-5; 0-395-92277-1 (pa)
LC 98-35516
This illustrated volume introduces the physical characteristics, behavior, and habitats of such birds of prey as eagles, hawks, falcons, and owls.

Bizarre birds; {by} Jonathan P. Latimer, Karen Stray Nolting; illustrations by Roger Tory Peterson; foreword by Virginia Marie Peterson. Houghton Mifflin 1999 48p il (Peterson field guides for young naturalists) $15; pa $5.95 (4 and up) **598**
1. Birds
ISBN 0-395-95213-1; 0-395-92279-8 (pa)
LC 98-35512
A field guide to odd birds such as roseate spoonbills, snail kites, anhimas, burrowing owls, and greater prairie chickens.
"Bright, full-color photographs and drawings clearly indicate distinguishing features. Useful, accessible." SLJ

Shorebirds; {by} Jonathan P. Latimer, Karen Stray Nolting; illustrations by Roger Tory Peterson; foreword by Virginia Marie Peterson. Houghton Mifflin 1999 48p il (Peterson field guides for young naturalists) $15; pa $5.95 (4 and up) **598**
1. Birds
ISBN 0-395-95212-3; 0-395-92278-X (pa)
LC 98-35510
This is an illustrated field guide to shorebirds, including gulls, coots, sandpipers, and egrets.
"Bright, full-color photographs and drawings clearly indicate distinguishing features. Useful, accessible." SLJ

Latimer, Jonathan P.—*Continued*

Songbirds; [by] Jonathan P. Latimer, Karen Stray Nolting; illustrations by Roger Tory Peterson; foreword by Virginia Marie Peterson. Houghton Mifflin 2000 48p il (Peterson field guides for young naturalists) $15; pa $5.95 (4 and up) **598**

1. Birds 2. Birdsongs

ISBN 0-395-97941-2; 0-395-97946-3 (pa)

LC 99-38293

Describes the physical characteristics, habitats, feeding habits, and voices of a variety of songbirds, arranged under the categories "Simple Songs," "Complex Songs," "Whistling Songs," "Warbling Songs," "Trilling Songs," "Name-sayers," and "Mimics"

Laubach, Christyna M.

Raptor! a kid's guide to birds of prey; by Christyna & René Laubach and Charles W.G. Smith. Storey Bks. 2002 118p il maps $21.95; pa $14.95 (4 and up) **598**

1. Birds of prey

ISBN 1-58017-475-2; 1-58017-445-0 (pa)

LC 2001-54980

This is an "overview of North American raptors. . . . After describing their characteristics and behavior, the book introduces individual species within family groups: vultures, hawks, falcons, barn owls, and true owls. . . . There is also advice on bird-watching and efforts to save endangered species. Well-designed projects . . . are followed by a glossary and extensive lists of hawk-watching sites, raptor centers, banding demonstration sites, books, videos, organizations, and Web sites related to birds in general and raptors in particular." Booklist

Lerner, Carol, 1927-

On the wing; American birds in migration. HarperCollins Pubs. 2001 47p il maps $16.95; lib bdg $17.89 (4 and up) **598**

1. Birds—Migration

ISBN 0-688-16649-0; 0-688-16650-4 (lib bdg)

LC 00-38831

This book discusses "the migration of birds living in the Americas, particularly in North America. . . . Lerner illustrates the clearly written discussions with precise, delicate paintings of birds as well as maps of migratory routes." Booklist

National Audubon Society first field guide: birds. Scholastic 1998 159p il maps pa $8.95 hardcover o.p. (4 and up) **598**

1. Birds

ISBN 0-590-05482-1   LC 97-17989

A visual guide to the natural science of birds as well as a field guide to over 150 species found in North America

This offers "a great deal of information in a handy format . . . {and} large, beautifully colored photos of each bird." Booklist

Includes glossary and bibliographical references

Osborn, Elinor, 1939-

Project UltraSwan; written and photographed by Elinor Osborn. Houghton Mifflin 2002 64p il maps (Scientists in the field) $16 (4 and up) **598**

1. Swans

ISBN 0-618-14528-1   LC 2002-223

Describes the life of large trumpeter swans, how they nearly became extinct, and efforts to reintroduce them to the Northeastern United States and to help them relearn migration routes

"Beautifully illustrated with crisp, colorful photographs and maps, *Project UltraSwan* describes in clear, succinct language all that the scientists must take into account in their work, as well as what they have learned about their subject so far." Booklist

Patent, Dorothy Hinshaw

The bald eagle returns; [by] Dorothy Hinshaw Patent; [photographs by] William Muñoz. Clarion Bks. 2000 68p il map $15 (4 and up) **598**

1. Bald eagle 2. Birds—Protection

ISBN 0-395-91416-7   LC 00-21751

"A revised version of the author's and photographer's earlier book *Where the Bald Eagles Gather.*" Title page

Describes how bald eagles have recovered from the threat of extinction, how they raise their families, and why they are the national bird of the United States

This offers "exciting new information about the status of our national bird; and crisp, beautiful, full-color photos." SLJ

Eagles of America; photographs by William Muñoz. Holiday House 1995 40p il $15.95 (4 and up) **598**

1. Eagles

ISBN 0-8234-1198-2   LC 95-6083

"The only two native species of North American eagles, the bald and golden, are treated in this comparative presentation. Patent describes how their numbers declined dramatically during the 19th and 20th centuries. . . . She also discusses the work of wildlife rehabilitators and conservation efforts. Splendid full-color photographs illustrate the lively text and clarify descriptions." SLJ

Peterson, Roger Tory, 1908-1996

A field guide to the birds of eastern and central North America; by Roger Tory Peterson and Virginia Marie Peterson. 5th ed. Houghton Mifflin 2002 xxii, 427p il maps $30 **598**

1. Birds—North America

ISBN 0-395-74047-9   LC 2001-51879

Also available large print edition $24 (ISBN 0-395-96371-0)

"The Peterson field guide series"

First published 1934 with title: A field guide to the birds

"Sponsored by the National Audubon Society, the National Wildlife Federation, and the Roger Tory Peterson Institute"

This guide to birds found east of the Rocky Mountains contains colored illustrations painted by the author,

Peterson, Roger Tory, 1908-1996—*Continued*
with a description of each species on the facing page.
Views of young birds and seasonal variations in plumage
are included. Birds are arranged in eight major groups of
body shape

A field guide to western birds; text and
illustrations by Roger Tory Peterson; maps by
Virginia Marie Peterson. 3rd ed, completely rev
and enl. Houghton Mifflin 1998 432p il maps $27;
pa $18 **598**
1. Birds—West (U.S.)
ISBN 0-395-91174-5; 0-395-91173-7 (pa)
LC 89-31517
Also available vinyl-bound edition (ISBN 0-618-
13218-X) $20
"The Peterson field guide series"
First published 1941
"Sponsored by the National Audubon Society, the National Wildlife Federation, and the Roger Tory Peterson
Institute"
"A completely new guide to field marks of all species
found in North America west of the 100th meridian and
north of Mexico." Title page
This guide illustrates over 1,000 birds (700 species)
on 165 color plates. In addition, over 400 distribution
maps are included

Quinlan, Susan E., 1954-
Puffins; photographs by Bud Lehnhausen.
Carolrhoda Bks. 1999 48p il (Carolrhoda nature
watch book) lib bdg $25.26 **598**
1. Puffins
ISBN 1-57505-090-0 LC 97-38983
Discusses the physical characteristics, life cycle, and
ecology of Atlantic puffins, tufted puffins, and horned
puffins
"A solid introduction to this seabird. . . . The large,
clear, full-color photographs with their informative captions add to the book's appeal and make it a good choice
for recreational reading and reports." SLJ
Includes glossary

Rauzon, Mark J.
Hummingbirds. Watts 1997 63p il pa $6.95
hardcover o.p. **598**
1. Hummingbirds
ISBN 0-531-15849-7 LC 96-36156
Describes the physical characteristics, behavior, and
habitat of the smallest bird in the world
"The book is scientifically accurate, well written, and
well illustrated." Sci Books Films
Includes glossary and bibliographical references

Vultures. Watts 1997 63p il pa $6.95 hardcover
o.p. **598**
1. Vultures
ISBN 0-531-15853-5 LC 96-31019
"A First book"
Describes the physical characteristics, behavior, and
different species of these scavenger birds
This "is well written and illustrated and contains much
good science." Sci Books Films
Includes glossary and bibliographical references

Robbins, Chandler S., 1918-
Birds of North America; a guide to field
identification; by Chandler S. Robbins, Bertel
Bruun, and Herbert S. Zim; illustrated by Arthur
Singer. expanded rev ed. Golden Bks. (NY) 1983
360p il maps $15.95; pa $11.95 (4 and up)
598
1. Birds—North America
ISBN 0-307-37002-X; 0-307-33656-5 (pa)
LC 83-60422
"A Golden field guide"
First published 1966
"Water birds are presented first, followed by land
birds; within each of these two main divisions, arrangement is by related groups of species. Featured are carefully made, full-color illustrations, clear textual descriptions, and detailed range maps." Booklist

Sattler, Helen Roney
The book of North American owls; illustrated
by Jean Day Zallinger. Clarion Bks. 1995 64p il
maps $17; pa $7.95 (4 and up) **598**
1. Owls
ISBN 0-395-60524-5; 0-395-90017-4 (pa)
LC 91-43626
This volume "includes owl classification and history,
hunting and habitat, courtship and nesting, and the complex relationship between owls and humans. The
comprehensive glossary includes all of the 21 North
American species." Sci Child
This "is a superb ornithological primer. . . . The book
is lavishly illustrated." Appraisal
Includes bibliographical references

Udvardy, Miklos D. F., 1919-1998
National Audubon Society field guide to North
American birds, Western region; revised by John
Farrand, Jr.; visual key by Amanda Wilson and
Lori Hogan. rev ed. Knopf 1994 822p il maps pa
$19.95 **598**
1. Birds—North America
ISBN 0-679-42851-8 LC 94-7415
Companion volume to National Audubon Society field
guide to North American birds, Eastern region by John
L. Bull
"A Chanticleer Press edition"
First published 1977
This pictorial guide to 544 western species arranges
birds by color and shape to simplify identification. It also
includes information on bird-watching and conservation
status
Includes bibliographical references

Warhol, Tom
Eagles; [by] Tom Warhol and Chris Reiter.
Benchmark Bks. 2004 112p il map (Animalways)
lib bdg $31.36 **598**
1. Eagles
ISBN 0-7614-1578-5 LC 2002-155814
Contents: Eagles, honored and feared; Eagle origins;
The family of eagles; How eagles work; Flight, hunting,
and migration; The life cycle; The fate of eagles

Warhol, Tom—*Continued*
This discusses the evolution of eagles, their places in human culture, their life cycles, anatomy, and protection. Includes glossary and bibliographical references

Webb, Sophie, 1958-
Looking for seabirds; journal from an Alaskan voyage. Houghton Mifflin Co 2004 48p il $16

598

1. Birds 2. Alaska
ISBN 0-618-21235-3   LC 2003-12420
A journal of the author's observations and adventures while working on a research vessel counting seabirds through Alaska's Aleutian Island chain.
The "immediacy of the narrative . . . and the clear and colorful watercolor-and-gouache landscapes and drawings of the birds form an appealing travelogue that is as exciting as it is informative." SLJ

My season with penguins; an Antarctic journal. Houghton Mifflin 2000 48p il map $15; pa $5.95 (4 and up)

598

1. Penguins 2. Antarctica
ISBN 0-395-92291-7; 0-618-43234-5 (pa)
LC 99-54781
Describes the author's two-month stay in Antarctica to study and draw penguins
"Webb presents a great deal of scientific information through an effective blend of journal entries and illustrations. . . . Done in gouache and watercolor, the paintings range from scenes of mountains and moving ice to depictions of penguins engaged in typical behaviors. . . . Webb offers a fine look at the scientific method in action." SLJ
Includes glossary

599 Mammals

Bateman, Robert, 1930-
Safari; [by] Robert Bateman and Rick Archbold. Little, Brown 1998 unp il $17.95 (4 and up)

599

1. Animals—Africa
ISBN 0-316-08265-1   LC 98-6139
"A Madison Press book"
Paintings and brief text present some of the animals found in Africa, including elephants, giraffes, cheetahs, wildebeests, lions, ostriches, and zebras
"At least one full page per spread is devoted to Bateman's spectacular oil paintings that are photographic in detail and perfectly capture the essence and beauty of their subjects. These illustrations combined with the text create a sort of travel diary that clearly conveys the artist's love of wildlife." SLJ

Grzimek's student animal life resource, Mammals; Melissa C. McDade, project editor. UXL 2005 5v .p set $260

599

1. Mammals
ISBN 0-7876-9183-6   LC 2004-15604
Contents: v1 Echindas to armadillos; v2 Hedgehogs to bats; v3 Primates to true seals; v4 Dolphins to antelopes; v5 Pangolins to sengis

This reference to mammals "offers coverage of 141 families and 265 species. . . . Each entry includes sections on physical characteristics, geographic range, habitat, diet, behavior and reproduction, animals and people, and conservation status. . . . There are more than 500 colorful photographs, illustrations, and charts. . . . Layout is open and appealing, and the writing is clear and easily understood." Booklist

Hare, Tony
Animal fact-file; head-to-tail profiles of more than 100 mammals. Facts on File 1999 191p il $40

599

1. Mammals
ISBN 0-8160-3921-6   LC 98-42092
This is "an alphabetical guide to mammals from aardvarks to wombats. The full-color illustrations are excellent. Pictures show external and internal views of the animals as a whole and highlight distinctive body parts. Interesting comparison drawings abound. . . . And there is, for every entry, an easy reference chart giving the mammal's classification, size, coloration, and features. . . . The book provides a lot of easily accessed information in digestible bits." SLJ

Morris, Pat
Mammals; {by} Pat Morris, Amy-Jane Beer. Grolier 2003 10v il maps (World of animals) set $499

599

1. Mammals
ISBN 0-7172-5742-8   LC 2002-73860
Contents: v1 Small carnivores; v2 Large carnivores; v3 Sea mammals; v4 Primates; v5 Large herbivores; v6 Ruminant (horned) herbivores; v7 Rodents 1; v8 Rodents 2 and lagomorphs; v9 Insectivores and bats; v10 Marsupials
"The first volume of this reference set begins with an article that describes the general features that define an animal as a mammal. . . . An introductory article in each volume first describes the major characteristics of one of the orders of mammals. This entry is followed by a set of articles about a families or group of related families within the order. Each family article is followed by a series of articles about representative members (particular species) of the family. Each species article begins with a data panel that highlights information about classification, key features, distribution, and the conservation status of the animal. . . . The data panel is followed by a two- to six page in-depth discussion about the animal. Excellent photographs and drawings complement the text. . . . The reading level of this set makes it accessible to a wide range of students." Sci Books Films
For a fuller review see: Booklist, August 2003

Whitaker, John O., Jr.
National Audubon Society field guide to North American mammals. rev ed. Knopf 1996 937p il maps pa $19.95

599

1. Mammals
ISBN 0-679-44631-1   LC 95-81456
First published 1980
This field guide describes 390 species of mammals of North America and includes keys for identification, range maps, information on tracks and anatomy, and 375 color photos

599.2 Marsupials and monotremes

Malaspina, Ann, 1957-
The koala. Lucent Bks. 2002 112p il maps (Endangered animals & habitats) lib bdg $27.45 (7 and up) **599.2**
1. Koalas 2. Endangered species
ISBN 1-56006-876-0 LC 2001-1768
"Information about the koala's behavior and natural habitat is included, but the emphasis of this book is on measures to protect the animals and to preserve their environment. . . . This is a well-researched presentation." SLJ
Includes glossary and bibliographical references

599.3 Miscellaneous orders of placental mammals

Patent, Dorothy Hinshaw
Prairie dogs; photographs by William Muñoz. Clarion Bks. 1993 63p il hardcover o.p. paperback available $7.95 (4 and up) **599.3**
1. Prairie dogs 2. Prairie ecology
ISBN 0-395-52601-9 (pa) LC 92-34724
Discusses the habits and life cycle of prairie dogs and examines their place in the ecology of their grassland environment
"The text and illustrations work together, each enlarging the other and both enlightening the reader. Appearing on nearly every page, the full-color photographs take readers out to the prairie to see its plants and animals clearly." Booklist
Includes bibliographical references

599.5 Cetaceans and sea cows

Carwardine, Mark
Whales, dolphins, and porpoises; illustrated by Martin Camm; editorial consultants: Peter Evans, Mason Weinrich. Dorling Kindersley 1995 256p il maps (Eyewitness handbooks) (7 and up)
599.5
1. Whales 2. Dolphins 3. Porpoises
ISBN 1-56458-621-9; 1-56458-620-0 (flexible bdg); 0-78942-968-3 (pa) LC 94-33301
This book is "arranged by species. Each entry has a drawing of the animal; drawings of body parts, such as teeth and fins; and a map showing the distribution of the species. Information is given on status, population size, threats to survival, birth and adult weight, and diet. The introduction discusses cetacean behavior and where and how to observe the animals. An identification key helps in distinguishing among various species." Booklist
"A book with efficient organization, concise information, and loads of illustrations." SLJ
Includes bibliographical references

Cerullo, Mary M., 1949-
Dolphins; what they can teach us; text by Mary M. Cerullo; photographs by Jeffrey L. Rotman. Dutton Children's Bks. 1998 42p il $17.99
599.5
1. Dolphins
ISBN 0-525-65263-9 LC 97-34424
Focuses on the behavior of these large sea animals, their interactions with humans, and ways in which dolphins and people can benefit each other
"Eye-catching full-color photos, many of dolphins and humans together do much to add to the book's appeal. . . . This title is a good supplemental source. It has lots of appeal for casual readers and fans of this popular animal." SLJ
Includes glossary and bibliographical references

Greenberg, Daniel A.
Dolphins; [by] Dan Greenberg. Benchmark Bks. 2003 112p il (Animalways) lib bdg $21.95
599.5
1. Dolphins
ISBN 0-7614-1576-9 LC 2002-155246
Contents: Mysterious travelers; What is a dolphin?; Dolphin habitats; Dolphins up close; Dolphins in action; The life of a dolphin; Dolphins, today and tomorrow
This provides information on the physical characteristics, behavior, and habitats of dolphin species
Includes glossary and bibliographical references

Whales; {by} Dan Greenberg. Benchmark Bks. 2002 110p il (Animalways) lib bdg $21.95
599.5
1. Whales
ISBN 0-7614-1389-8 LC 2001-43883
Describes in detail the physical characteristics, behavior, and migration and life cycle of various kinds of whales, among the largest creatures ever known to have lived on Earth, and discusses the history of human interaction with these animals
"Written in engaging language. . . . Sharp color photos of the animals in the wild mix with archival images, helpful charts, and artists' renderings." Booklist
Includes glossary and bibliographical references

Montgomery, Sy
Encantado; pink dolphin of the Amazon; with photographs by Dianne Taylor-Snow. Houghton Mifflin 2002 73p il $18 (4 and up) **599.5**
1. Dolphins 2. Amazon River valley
ISBN 0-618-13103-5 LC 2001-39251
Introduces the world of the freshwater dolphins called Encantados, or Enchanted, by the people who live near them in the region of the Amazon and Orinoco rivers in South America
"The book contains remarkable descriptions and color photos of the Amazonian rainforest and its inhabitants." Horn Book Guide
Includes bibliographical references

Price-Groff, Claire
The manatee. Lucent Bks. 1999 112p il (Endangered animals & habitats) lib bdg $27.45 (7 and up) **599.5**
1. Manatees 2. Endangered species
ISBN 1-56006-445-5 LC 98-53230
Discusses the physical characteristics, behavior, habitats, and endangered status of the manatee and the closely related dugong
Includes glossary and bibliographical references

Woog, Adam, 1953-
The whale. Lucent Bks. 1998 112p il (Endangered animals & habitats) lib bdg $28.70 (7 and up) **599.5**
1. Whales 2. Endangered species
ISBN 1-56006-460-9 LC 97-21349
Presents an overview of various species of whale, how they have become endangered, and what is being done to protect them from extinction
This book is "packed with facts and statistics {and} . . . well-researched. . . . Illustrated with dark black-and-white photos, editorial cartoons, diagrams, maps, and reproductions." Horn Book Guide
Includes glossary and bibliographical references

599.65 Deer

Patent, Dorothy Hinshaw
Deer and elk; photographs by William Muñoz. Clarion Bks. 1994 77p il maps $17 (4 and up) **599.65**
1. Deer 2. Elk
ISBN 0-395-52003-7 LC 93-25894
"The text describes in detail the lives, enemies, and survival of North American whitetail deer, mule deer, and elk, among others. The color photographs of the shy, gentle creatures are effective, crisp, and clear." Horn Book Guide
"Numerous full-color photographs enhance the presentation; each includes a caption. A great addition to the animal science section of any library." SLJ
Includes bibliographical references

599.66 Odd-toed ungulates

Ryden, Hope
Wild horses I have known. Clarion Bks. 1999 90p il $18 (4 and up) **599.66**
1. Horses
ISBN 0-395-77520-5 LC 97-49021
Text and photographs depict mustang social behavior observed by the author, as well as an account of how the mustang established itself and adapted to being a wild horse in the American West
"A carefully crafted book that features abundant use of strikingly beautiful photographs. . . . A nice combination of elegance and sound information." Horn Book

599.67 Elephants

Levine, Stuart P., 1968-
The elephant. Lucent Bks. 1998 96p il maps (Endangered animals & habitats) lib bdg $28.70 (7 and up) **599.67**
1. Elephants 2. Endangered species
ISBN 1-56006-522-2 LC 97-28532
Presents an overview of elephants, how they have become endangered, and what is being done to protect them from extinction
Includes glossary and bibliographical references

Redmond, Ian
Elephant; photographed by Dave King. Knopf 1993 63p il (Eyewitness books) $15.99; lib bdg $19.95 **599.67**
1. Elephants
ISBN 0-679-83880-5; 0-679-93880-X (lib bdg)
LC 92-20855
"A Dorling Kindersley book"
Text and numerous illustrations portray elephants, their physiology, behavior, evolution, relatives, uses by humans, and conservation
"The photography is excellent with pictures that are exciting to the eye. The information, while not definitive, is interesting." Appraisal

Schlaepfer, Gloria G.
Elephants; {by} Gloria Schlaepfer. Benchmark Bks. 2002 112p il (Animalways) lib bdg $21.95
599.67
1. Elephants
ISBN 0-7614-1390-1 LC 2001-5592
Contents: The world of elephants; Elephant ancestors; The remarkable nature of elephants; Elephant behavior; Special characteristics;The cycle of life; Conservation
Provides information on the physical characteristics, behavior, and habitats of elephant species
"Written in engaging language. . . . Sharp color photos of the animals in the wild mix with archival images, helpful charts, and artists' renderings." Booklist
Includes glossary and bibliographical references

599.7 Carnivores. Land carnivores

North, Sterling, 1906-1974
Rascal; illustrated by John Schoenherr. Dutton 1984 c1963 189p il $16.99; pa $5.99 (5 and up)
599.7
1. Raccoons
ISBN 0-525-18839-8; 0-14-034445-4 (pa)
LC 84-10292
A Newbery Award honor book, 1964
First published 1963 with subtitle: A memoir of a better era
A book about Rascal "a young raccoon, Sterling North's pet the year he was eleven, in rural Wisconsin. . . . The book calls up a series of marvelous pictures; boy fishing in peaceful company of raccoon, boy riding

North, Sterling, 1906-1974—_Continued_
on bike with raccoon (a demon for speed) standing up in the bike basket, raccoon with friend, a prize trotting horse, raccoon helping boy to win a pie-eating contest. A central episode is about an idyllic camping trip." Publ Wkly

599.75 Cat family

Adamson, Joy, 1910-1980
Born free; a lioness of two worlds. Pantheon Bks. 1987 220p il hardcover o.p. paperback available $14.95   **599.75**
1. Lions 2. Kenya—Description and travel
ISBN 0-375-71438-3 (pa)   LC 86-42972
A reissue of the title first published 1960
This is the "story of a lioness who bridged the gulf between two worlds, that of the jungle and of man. The author and her husband, a Kenya game warden, reared a cub to kill and fend for herself when she was returned to the jungle. At the same time they were able to preserve the bond of confidence and affection established with her as a pet." Cincinnati Public Libr

Alderton, David
Wild cats of the world; photographs by Bruce Tanner. Facts on File 1993 192p il maps $35 (7 and up)   **599.75**
1. Wild cats
ISBN 0-8160-2736-6   LC 92-38774
"A broad, comprehensive overview of the world's wild felines. The first half of the book covers the animals' anatomy, way of life, and interaction with humans. The second half is a species-by-species look at the specific cats. A map and a description indicates where they can be found. The author's ecological concerns are evident throughout. The full-color photographs are detailed and intriguing and amount to perhaps a third of the book." SLJ
Includes bibliographical references

Bonar, Samantha
Small wildcats. Watts 2002 63p il $24; pa $8.95
                                599.75
1. Wild cats
ISBN 0-531-11965-3; 0-531-16632-5 (pa)
                          LC 2001-17581
"Watts library"
In this title "the reader learns terms, including species and genus, with various species examined more closely in chapters devoted to a particular region such as Africa, Europe and Asia, and the Americas. In addition, this book also provides conservation facts and ways in which the reader can help the endangered cats of the world." Libr Media Connect
Includes glossary and bibliographical references

Gamble, Cyndi
Leopards; natural history & conservation; text by Cyndi Gamble; photography by Rodney Griffiths. Voyageur Press 2004 48p il map (World life library) pa $12.95 (7 and up)   **599.75**
1. Leopards
ISBN 0-89658-656-1   LC 2004-14316
"The text offers a comprehensive look at these endangered animals and raises awareness of various efforts to preserve their habitats and to save them from extinction. Excellent-quality photographs appear throughout. . . . An attractive and informative addition." SLJ
Includes bibliographical references

Levine, Stuart P., 1968-
The tiger. Lucent Bks. 1999 96p il (Endangered animals & habitats) lib bdg $28.70 (7 and up)
                                599.75
1. Tigers 2. Endangered species
ISBN 1-56006-465-X   LC 98-27237
Discusses the various species of tigers and their behavior and examines how they have become endangered through habitat loss, hunting, research, and captivity
Includes glossary and bibliographical references

Montgomery, Sy
The man-eating tigers of Sundarbans; with photographs by Eleanor Briggs. Houghton Mifflin 2001 57p il maps $16; pa $6.95 (4 and up)
                                599.75
1. Tigers
ISBN 0-618-07704-9; 0-618-49490-1 (pa)
                          LC 00-32031
"The author introduces readers to the geography of India and the ecology of Sundarbans, gives a brief overview of tiger behavior . . . discusses the man-eating habits of the tigers of Sundarbans, and puts forth some possible explanations for their unusual behavior." Bull Cent Child Books
"To draw readers into this scientific puzzle, Montgomery integrates science, storytelling, anthropology, and adventure in a unique treatment, illustrated with excellent color photos and diagrams." Horn Book Guide
Includes bibliographical references

Saign, Geoffrey, 1955-
The African cats. Watts 1999 64p il lib bdg $23
                                599.75
1. Wild cats 2. Animals—Africa
ISBN 0-531-20365-4   LC 97-41629
"A First book"
Describes the physical characteristics and behavior patterns of ten types of cats found in Africa
"This combines dramatic wildlife color photographs with a lively, informative text." Booklist
Includes glossary and bibliographical references

Thompson, Sharon Elaine, 1952-
Built for speed; the extraordinary, enigmatic cheetah. Lerner Publs. 1998 88p il lib bdg $27.93 (5 and up)   **599.75**
1. Cheetahs
ISBN 0-8225-2854-1   LC 96-51094

Thompson, Sharon Elaine, 1952— *Continued*
Describes the habitat, physical characteristics, and behavior of the cheetah, as well as efforts to ensure the continued existence of this fastest land mammal
This "includes and explains many fascinating details of the animals' lives in a comprehensive, well-organized, and attractive way." Sci Books Films
Includes glossary and bibliographical references

599.78   Bears

Barghusen, Laura, 1964-
The bear. Lucent Bks. 1999 96p il (Endangered animals & habitats) lib bdg $27.45 (7 and up)
           599.78
1. Bears 2. Endangered species
ISBN 1-56006-394-7   LC 98-50214
Discusses the bears of the world and threats to their existence, such as hunting and international trade, habitat destruction, and captivity, as well as the future of bears
Includes glossary and bibliographical references

Montgomery, Sy
Search for the golden moon bear; science and adventure in the Asian tropics. Houghton Mifflin 2004 80p il $17 (5 and up)   **599.78**
1. Bears
ISBN 0-618-35650-9   LC 2004-5236
The author reports on an expedition into Laos and Thailand in search of a rare species of bear
"The exciting narrative is complemented by an array of full-color photos. . . . This attractive and informative offering is an intelligent reportage of science as it happens." SLJ
Includes bibliographical references

Ovsyanikov, Nikita
Polar bears. Voyageur Press 1998 72p il maps (World life library) pa $16.95 (7 and up)
           599.78
1. Polar bear
ISBN 0-89658-358-9   LC 98-3431
This describes the polar bear's habits, behavior, and biology
"Approachable. . . . Written by an expert on the species. . . . Well illustrated with many excellent photos." Booklist
Includes bibliographical references

Patent, Dorothy Hinshaw
A polar bear biologist at work. Watts 2001 48p il maps lib bdg $23.50 (4 and up)   **599.78**
1. Jonkel, Charles 2. Polar bear
ISBN 0-531-11850-9   LC 00-38151
"A Wildlife Conservation Society book"
.
Describes the work of Charles Jonkel, a biologist who studied polar bears in the Arctic and primarily in Churchill, Manitoba
"Patent's lucid text is brimming with enough data on

habitat, physiology, and behavior to satisfy the needs of report writers. . . . Patent's book is important not only for the basic 'critter data' it contains, but also for its picture of a scientist at work in the field. . . . Approachable and appealing." SLJ
Includes glossary and bibliographical references

Presnall, Judith Janda
The giant panda. Lucent Bks. 1998 96p il maps (Endangered animals & habitats) lib bdg $27.45 (7 and up)   **599.78**
1. Giant panda 2. Endangered species
ISBN 1-56006-463-3   LC 97-27276
Discusses the forces pushing the giant panda toward extinction and the efforts being made to counter those forces
This book is "packed with facts and statistics {and is} . . . well-researched." Horn Book Guide
Includes glossary and bibliographical references

Silverstein, Alvin
The grizzly bear; {by} Alvin and Virginia Silverstein and Laura Silverstein Nunn. Millbrook Press 1998 64p il (Endangered in America) lib bdg $24.90   **599.78**
1. Grizzly bear 2. Endangered species
ISBN 0-7613-0265-4   LC 97-45026
Describes the physical characteristics and behavior of the grizzly bear, its decline in numbers due to human population growth and activities, and the efforts being made to maintain its population
"Large color photographs and a highly readable text characterize this presentation of the once-feared American ursine." Horn Book Guide
Includes bibliographical references

Stonehouse, Bernard
Bears; a visual introduction; illustrated by Martin Camm. Checkmark Bks. 1998 46p il maps (Animal watch) $16.95   **599.78**
1. Bears
ISBN 0-8160-3923-2   LC 98-25083
This describes 10 types of bears throughout the world, as well as pandas and prehistoric cave bears, with color illustrations, facts about classification, size, and range, environment, and behavior, endangered species and conservation efforts
Includes glossary

Ward, Paul, 1959-
Wild bears of the world; {by} Paul Ward and Suzanne Kynaston. Facts on File 1995 191p il maps $32.95   **599.78**
1. Bears
ISBN 0-8160-3245-9   LC 95-12487
This book "starts by explaining how and why bears have meant so much from early in our evolutionary history. . . . It then describes the bears' position and uniqueness among carnivores, introduces the living species, charts their evolutionary history, tells how they live, what they eat, how they cope with their habitats, and

Ward, Paul, 1959-—*Continued*
looks at their behavior. It concludes with a re-examination of the interrelationship they have with us."
Publisher's note
Includes glossary and bibliographical references

599.79 Marine carnivores

DuTemple, Lesley A., 1952-
Seals and sea lions. Lucent Bks. 1999 112p il maps (Endangered animals & habitats) lib bdg $27.45 (7 and up)   **599.79**
1. Seals (Animals) 2. Endangered species
ISBN 1-56006-473-0   LC 98-30303
Describes the physical characteristics and behavior of seals and sea lions, how they differ from each other, how they relate to humans, how they have become endangered, and what is being done to protect them
Includes glossary and bibliographical references

599.8 Primates

Goodall, Jane, 1934-
The chimpanzees I love; saving their world and ours. Scholastic Press 2001 80p il map $17.95 (4 and up)   **599.8**
1. Chimpanzees
ISBN 0-439-21310-X   LC 00-47080
"A Byron Preiss book"
"Goodall presents her long involvement with the chimpanzees of Gombe, describing the amazing discoveries she has made over 40 years." SLJ
"Striking an admirable balance between scientific reporting and deep affection, Goodall's . . . impassioned introduction to the creatures to whom she's dedicated her life's work may well ignite in readers a similar appreciation." Publ Wkly
Includes bibliographical references

With love; illustrated by Alan Marks. North-South Bks. 1998 unp il $15.95; lib bdg $15.88 (4 and up)   **599.8**
1. Chimpanzees
ISBN 1-55858-911-2; 1-55858-912-0 (lib bdg)
                    LC 97-49948
First published 1994 by the Jane Goodall Institute
Illustration on end-papers
A collection of stories based on the author's experiences with chimpanzees in Gombe Stream National Park in Tanzania over a period of almost forty years
"Children will love these stories because they are sometimes silly or gross and because they are always tender, and young humans will recognize aspects of themselves in the younger chimps. . . . Marks' watercolor-and-ink paintings capture both action and stasis beautifully and without affectation or sentimentality." Booklist

Lewin, Ted, 1935-
Gorilla walk; {by} Ted & Betsy Lewin. Lothrop, Lee & Shepard Bks. 1999 48p il map lib bdg $16.89 (4 and up)   **599.8**
1. Gorillas
ISBN 0-688-16510-9   LC 98-44727
Describes an expedition into the field in southern Uganda to observe mountain gorillas in their native habitat
"Briefly captioned, thumbnail watercolors picture the jungle trek, and magnificent double-page spreads replicate the exotic surroundings and show the animals close up." Booklist

Redmond, Ian
Gorilla; written by Ian Redmond; photographed by Peter Anderson & Geoff Brightling. Knopf 1995 63p il maps (Eyewitness books) (4 and up)   **599.8**
1. Primates
                    LC 95-3241
Available DK Pub. edition $15.99; lib bdg $19.99 (ISBN 0-7894-6036-X; 0-7894-6613-9)
"A Dorling Kindersley book"
An illustrated look at primates, including lemurs, monkeys, and apes
This offers "the same fabulous layout, interesting photographs, and fascinating facts that have made the series so popular. . . . Fun to browse through." SLJ

Saign, Geoffrey, 1955-
The great apes; {by} Geoffrey C. Saign. Watts 1998 63p il pa $6.95 hardcover o.p.
                    599.8
1. Apes
ISBN 0-531-15902-7   LC 97-1189
"A First book"
Describes and compares the four great apes: chimpanzees, bonobos, orangutans, and gorillas through a discussion of their physical, intellectual, emotional, and social characteristics
This is an "appealing, involving introduction. . . . The many color photographs are well chosen for their clarity and sensitivity as well as for their clear illustration of the text." Booklist
Includes glossary and bibliographical references

599.9 Hominids. Humans

Tocci, Salvatore
High-tech IDs; from finger scans to voice patterns. Watts 2000 127p il lib bdg $20; pa $8.95 (7 and up)   **599.9**
1. Biometry 2. Fingerprints 3. DNA fingerprinting
ISBN 0-531-11752-9 (lib bdg); 0-531-116462-4 (pa)
                    LC 99-37380
Describes a variety of devices and systems used for identifying individuals, including finger and hand scans, iris and retinal scans, fingerprinting, DNA fingerprinting, and voice pattern recognition, and gives examples of how they are used

Tocci, Salvatore—*Continued*
"This title fills a need for topical and timely information on current technology. It is easy to read, and the information is presented in a clear and logical style." SLJ
Includes bibliographical references

599.93 Genetics, sex and age characteristics, evolution

Boon, Kevin A.
The human genome project; what does decoding DNA mean for us? {by} Kevin Alexander Boon. Enslow Pubs. 2002 128p il (Issues in focus) lib bdg $26.60 (7 and up)   **599.93**
1. Human Genome Project 2. DNA 3. Genetics
ISBN 0-7660-1685-4   LC 2001-3388
Discusses genes, genetics, and the legal and ethical issues involved in mapping DNA in the human body
"Opposing viewpoints are presented and a great deal of well-documented information that could be used by debate teams is included. . . . A good update for science shelves." SLJ
Includes glossary and bibliographical references

Gallant, Roy A.
Early humans. Benchmark Bks. 1999 c2000 80p il maps (Story of science) lib bdg $29.93 (5 and up)   **599.93**
1. Fossil hominids 2. Human origins 3. Evolution
ISBN 0-7614-0960-2   LC 98-28037
Discusses human evolution and the search for the earliest forms of humans, examining the Neanderthals, Homo erectus, the variety of fossils found in Africa, and the early apelike hominids
"Richly illustrated with color photos, drawings, and charts. . . . Gallant writes clearly and provides readers with balanced, informative discussions." Booklist
Includes glossary and bibliographical references

Gardner, Robert, 1929-
Human evolution. Watts 1999 144p il lib bdg $21 (7 and up)   **599.93**
1. Human origins 2. Evolution
ISBN 0-531-11528-3   LC 98-20859
Traces past and present theories of human origins and development
The "author makes the subject fascinating. . . . A wonderful text for the classroom, but the curious general reader will learn plenty by thumbing through its pages." Voice Youth Advocates
Includes glossary and bibliographical references

Sloan, Christopher
The human story; our evolution from prehistoric ancestors to today; foreword by Meave Leakey and Louise Leakey; photographs by Kenneth L. Garrett; art by Kennis and Kennis. National Geographic Society 2004 80p il $21.95 (7 and up)   **599.93**
1. Evolution 2. Human origins
ISBN 0-7922-6325-1   LC 2003-13978

Contents: Of bones and genes; Our next of kin; Out of Africa; Becoming modern; Being human today
Explores the origins of humans, including how such developments as Linnaeus' classification system and recent understanding of the human genome have improved scientists' comprehension of evolution
"What many . . . readers will find most exciting is how today's cutting-edge technology helps us learn about the prehistoric connections all humans share. Great for classroom discussion." Booklist
Includes glossary and bibliographical references

600 TECHNOLOGY

Inside a—. Grolier Educ. 2000 16v lib bdg set $349   **600**
1. Machinery 2. Technology
ISBN 0-7172-9521-4   LC 00-29415
Contents: v1 Car; v2 Clock; v3 Compact disk; v4 Computer; v5 Construction machine; v6 Helicopter; v7 High-speed train; v8 Jet plane; v9 Powerboat; v10 Rocket; v11 Satellite; v12 Skyscraper; v13 Stove; v14 Telephone; v15 Television; v16 Web site
"Each volume looks at the past, internal structure, and possible future of a common machine or artifact. . . . Each book also includes one or two simple activities." SLJ
"The information in each text is accurate, up to date, and clear. Each volume includes a brief glossary {and} a short list of helpful Internet links." Sci Books Films

Macaulay, David, 1946-
The new way things work; {by} David Macaulay with Neil Ardley. Houghton Mifflin 1998 400p il $35 (4 and up)   **600**
1. Technology 2. Machinery 3. Inventions
ISBN 0-395-93847-3   LC 98-14224
First published 1988 with title: The way things work
Arranged in five sections this volume provides information on "the workings of hundreds of machines and devices—holograms, helicopters, airplanes, mobile phones, compact disks, hard disks, bits and bytes, cash machines. . . . Explanations {are also given} of the scientific principles behind each machine—how gears make work easier, why jumbo jets are able to fly, how computers actually compute." Publisher's note

603 Technology--Encyclopedias and dictionaries

Encyclopedia of technology and applied sciences. Marshall Cavendish 2000 11v il set $459.95   **603**
1. Technology—Encyclopedias
ISBN 0-7614-7116-2   LC 99-14520
In this encyclopedia, some "400 entries, on topics from *Abacus* to *Wood and woodworking*, range in length from two to ten pages. The index volume offers 33 pages of tables and lists, among which are measurement conversions, the periodic table, prefixes, Nobel Prize winners, a glossary, suggested Web sites, addresses, inventors, and a scientific time line. . . . The set is generously illustrated with more than 1,400 photographs, diagrams, and other illustrations, most in color." Booklist

Engelbert, Phillis
Technology in action; science applied to everyday life; edited by Jane Hoehner. U.X.L 1999 3v set $165　　　　　**603**
1. Technology—Encyclopedias
ISBN 0-7876-2809-3　　　　　LC 98-15377
Contents: v1. Communications, electronics & computers; v2. Energy, food & agriculture, health & medicine; v3. Civil engineering, manufacturing & materials, transportation
Contains information on approximately 120 technological terms such as computers, fiberoptics, and biochemistry. Includes sidebars and inserts of famous firsts, trivia items, and unusual facts
"Technology is explained in terms that any middle- or junior-high-school student will understand and most adults will appreciate. An excellent resource." Booklist

Exploring technology. Marshall Cavendish 2004 11v il set $329.95 (5 and up)　　　　**603**
1. Technology—Encyclopedias
ISBN 0-7614-7406-4　　　　　LC 2002-71510
"The set offers 280 articles pertaining to all facets of technology. . . . The history of invention and innovation are also included in the coverage. . . . The colorful and eye-catching presentation, featuring many color photographs and diagrams as well as the boxed features, will especially appeal to casual browsers. . . . The articles contain enough information to meet the needs of most upper-elementary and middle-school students." Booklist

How it works: science and technology. 3rd ed. Marshall Cavendish 2003 20v set $499.95
　　　　603
1. Technology—Encyclopedias 2. Science—Encyclopedias
ISBN 0-7614-7314-9　　　　　LC 2001-28771
Replaces the second edition, published 1978
"Within the set there are over 80 entries spanning the field of astronomy, chemistry, physics, geography, geology, biology and medicine. All entries include 'See Also' boxes containing alphabetical lists of cross-references to other articles. Many entries feature . . . 'Fact File' boxes to elaborate on special topics. . . . Illustrated with 2,800 illustrations . . . the set also offers . . . cutaway diagrams showing in detail the inner workings of various inventions, such as airplanes and coffeemakers." Publisher's note
"Enhanced by plenty of sharp, color photos, side boxes, and see-also references, and thoroughly indexed in the final volume." SLJ

608　Inventions and patents

Erlbach, Arlene
The kids' invention book. Lerner Publs. 1997 64p il lib bdg $22.60; pa $9.95 (4 and up)
　　　　608
1. Inventions
ISBN 0-8225-2414-7 (lib bdg); 0-8225-9844-2 (pa)
　　　　LC 96-27105
Profiles eleven inventors between the ages of eight and fourteen, describes the steps involved in inventing a new product, and discusses contests, patents, lawyers, and clubs
"Readers will enjoy the stories behind such clever creations as an edible pet-food spoon, an adjustable jump-rope belt, and a portable wheelchair ramp; and the accounts serve as wonderful encouragement for kids who want to pursue ideas of their own." Booklist
Includes bibliographical references

609　Technology--Historical and geographic treatment

Bender, Lionel
Invention; written by Lionel Bender. rev ed. DK Pub. 2005 72p il (DK eyewitness books) $15.99; lib bdg $19.99 (4 and up)　　　　**609**
1. Inventions
ISBN 0-7566-1076-1; 0-7566-1075-3 (lib bdg)
First published 1991 by Knopf
Photographs and text explore such inventions as the wheel, gears, levers, clocks, telephones, and rocket engines.

Bridgman, Roger Francis, 1940-
1,000 inventions & discoveries; written by Roger Bridgman. DK Pub. 2002 256p il $24.99 (5 and up)　　　　**609**
1. Inventions—History
ISBN 0-7894-8826-4　　　　　LC 2002-23742
Summarizes 1000 notable inventions and discoveries of ancient and modern times, from 3,000,000 B.C. to the beginning of the twenty-first century A.D
This offers "color photos, highly informative and readable text, and easy-to-read layouts." ALAN

Cole, David J.
Encyclopedia of modern everyday inventions; [by] David J. Cole, Eve Browning, and Fred E.H. Schroeder. Greenwood Press 2003 285p il $49.95 (7 and up)　　　　**609**
1. Inventions—History
ISBN 0-313-31345-8　　　　　LC 2002-69620
"Profiles of approximately 150 20th-century inventions, from Post-Its to Murphy beds, gumball machines to the Internet. . . . The articles include specific but nontechnical discussions of the invention's development, principles, and components, and conclude with a short list of both print and electronic resources." SLJ
"The analysis of each invention is thorough and lively. . . . This book . . . would make an excellent addition to any school or public library needing books on technology and inventions in the modern world." Voice Youth Advocates

Crosher, Judith
Technology in the time of ancient Egypt. Raintree Steck-Vaughn Pubs. 1998 48p il lib bdg $29.93　　　　**609**
1. Technology—History 2. Egypt—Civilization
ISBN 0-8172-4875-7　　　　　LC 97-13922

Crosher, Judith—*Continued*

Describes many of the innovative inventions that the Egyptians incorporated into their daily life, including ground looms, glass pots, and wooden sledges

Includes bibliographical references

Technology in the time of ancient Greece. Raintree Steck-Vaughn Pubs. 1998 48p il lib bdg $29.93   **609**

1. Technology—History 2. Greece—Civilization

ISBN 0-8172-4877-3   LC 97-19067

Describes many of the innovative discoveries that the ancient Greeks incorporated into their daily lives, including the tools and technology they used to produce their clothes, food, pottery, statues, and temples

Includes bibliographical references

Technology in the time of the Maya. Raintree Steck-Vaughn Pubs. 1998 48p il lib bdg $29.93   **609**

1. Technology—History 2. Mayas

ISBN 0-8172-4881-1   LC 97-24119

Explores innovative tools and methods used by the Maya in the areas of food production, building, metalwork, and transportation, among others. Illustrations include photographs of artifacts and line drawings

Includes bibliographical references

Haskins, James, 1941-2005

Outward dreams; black inventors and their inventions. Walker & Co. 1991 101p il $13.95; lib bdg $14.85   **609**

1. African American inventors

ISBN 0-8027-6993-4; 0-8027-6994-2 (lib bdg)

LC 90-12973

Discusses black inventors and their contributions, including Benjamin Bradley, Madam Walker, and George Washington Carver

Includes bibliographical references

Hicks, Peter, 1952-

Technology in the time of the Vikings. Raintree Steck-Vaughn Pubs. 1998 48p il lib bdg $29.93   **609**

1. Technology—History 2. Vikings

ISBN 0-8172-4880-3   LC 97-28053

Examines many of the technological innovations that the Vikings incorporated into their daily lives in such areas as weapons and armor, transportation, and jewelery-making

Includes bibliographical references

Historical inventions on file; {by} the Diagram Group. Facts on File 1994 various paging il loose-leaf $185   **609**

1. Inventions—History

ISBN 0-8160-2911-3   LC 94-7098

This work contains "65 experiments re-creating famous inventions. The purpose of these re-creations is to assist students in understanding important concepts and innovations in science. Intended for grades 6-12, the work is multidisciplinary in approach, making use of history, science, mathematics, and abstract and applied thinking. . . . This will be a useful source for middle- and high-school students and teachers doing science projects and experiments." Booklist

Platt, Richard, 1953-

Eureka! great inventions and how they happened. Kingfisher 2003 95p il $18.95 (4 and up)   **609**

1. Inventions—History

ISBN 0-7534-5580-3   LC 2002-34029

"Platt organizes his introductions to inventors and inventions around 'eureka moments' when scientific breakthroughs occurred. Two-page topical entries include a brief biography of the scientist, an account of the pivotal event, and an explanation of what happened next." SLJ

This is a "most excellent work." Sci Books Films

Includes glossary

Sandler, Martin W.

Inventors; a Library of Congress book; introduction by James H. Billington. HarperCollins Pubs. 1996 93p il pa $10.99 hardcover o.p.   **609**

1. Inventions—History 2. Inventors

ISBN 0-06-446746-5 (pa)   LC 95-944

"Composed mainly of historical photographs, reproductions, and period writing culled from the Library of Congress archives, the volume presents an intriguing montage of the inventors, technology, and ingenuity that flourished around the turn of the twentieth century. The brief present tense narrative is informative; the illustrative material is hugely appealing." Horn Book

Snedden, Robert

Technology in the time of ancient Rome. Raintree Steck-Vaughn Pubs. 1998 48p il lib bdg $29.93   **609**

1. Technology—History 2. Rome—Civilization

ISBN 0-8172-4876-5   LC 97-13924

Describes many of the innovative inventions that the Romans incorporated into their daily lives, including aqueducts, hot baths, and central heating

Includes bibliographical references

Tomecek, Steve

What a great idea! inventions that changed the world; [by] Stephen M. Tomecek; illustrated by Dan Stuckenschneider. Scholastic Ref. 2003 112p il $18.95 (4 and up)   **609**

1. Inventions—History

ISBN 0-590-68144-3   LC 2001-20937

"Tomecek puts significant inventions and discoveries in a historical context. Dividing the text into five broad time periods, he offers a series of essays on important advances that occurred in each 'age'. . . . What emerges is a sense of interconnectedness that other books often lack. . . . Full-color diagrams and illustrations are well integrated into each spread." SLJ

Includes bibliographical references

Tucker, Tom, 1944-
Brainstorm! the stories of twenty American kid inventors; with drawings by Richard Loehle. Farrar, Straus & Giroux 1995 148p il pa $6.95 hardcover o.p. (5 and up) **609**
1. Inventors 2. Inventions
ISBN 0-374-40928-5 (pa)   LC 94-38780
The author looks at inventions devised by children since the 18th century. Ear muffs, water skis, the popsicle, colored car wax and the electronic television are among the products discussed. Includes a discussion of how the Patent Office works
Includes glossary and bibliographical references

Wulffson, Don L., 1943-
The kid who invented the trampoline; more surprising stories about inventions. Dutton Children's Bks. 2000 120p il $16.99 **609**
1. Inventions—History
ISBN 0-525-46654-1   LC 00-41699
Companion volume to The kid who invented the popsicle and other surprising stories (1997)
The author "tells us where and how we got erasers, false teeth, vending machines, snowboards, windsurfing, and 44 other common devices. This is a great book for browsing, a virtual treasure trove of trivia. The sidebars are tidbits of related wacky but interesting information." Book Rep

610 Medicine & health

Green, Jen
Medicine; by Jen Green. Blackbirch Press 2004 40p il (Routes of science) $23.70; pa $18.70 (5 and up) **610**
1. Medicine
ISBN 1-410-30168-0; 1-410-30305-5 (pa)
    LC 2003-12999
Contents: Ancient medicine; Eastern medicine; Greece and Rome; The Dark Ages and the Renaissance; A scientific approach; Modern medicine
"This book traces the history of medical discovery from trepanning (the ancient practice of drilling holes in the skull to release evil spirits) to today's . . . advances in transplants and vaccines." Publisher's note
This "volume contains color photographs, illustrations, and diagrams to help explain the important concepts and discoveries. [This] up-to-date [volume] would be [an] excellent [supplement] to the science curriculum." SLJ
Includes glossary and bibliographical references

Hyde, Margaret Oldroyd, 1917-
Medicine's brave new world; bioengineering and the new genetics; {by} Margaret O. Hyde and John F. Setaro. 21st Cent. Bks. (Brookfield) 2001 143p il lib bdg $29.90 (7 and up) **610**
1. Medical technology 2. Medical ethics
ISBN 0-7613-1706-6   LC 00-69083
"The authors present a host of medical breakthroughs and ponder the future of many versions of genetic manipulation to support medical science. Topics include fer-

tility advances, xenotransplants (the transfer of animal organs or cells to humans), stem cell research, cloning, the Human Genome Project, and genetic testing." Booklist
"What makes this work stand out is the way that incredibly complex cellular processes are lucidly explained." SLJ
Includes glossary and bibliographical references

Parker, Steve
Medicine; written by Steve Parker. Dorling Kindersley 1995 64p il (Eyewitness science) $15.95 **610**
1. Medicine
ISBN 1-56458-882-3   LC 94-34860
Available DK pub. edition $15.99; lib bdg $19.99 (ISBN 0-7894-5580-3; 0-7894-6722-4)
This book "travels from ancient times to the future, addressing alternative treatments, modern drugs, fads in health care, diagnostic techniques, etc. What really stands out are the numerous examples of tools of the trade, like the 18th-century brass enema syringe and the 20th-century electronic hand." SLJ
"Many readers will enjoy just browsing through the volume, looking at the numerous excellent illustrations and reading the text more closely if they are interested. The author makes a concerted effort to avoid controversial questions." Sci Books Films

Woolf, Alex
Death and disease; Alex Woolf. Lucent Books 2004 48p il map (Medieval realms) $28.70 (5 and up) **610**
1. Medicine—History 2. Medieval civilization
ISBN 1-590-18533-1   LC 2003-61797
This "discusses topics such as medieval theories about the body and disease, the influence of the Church on health practices, the causes and effects of bubonic plague, and the emergence of modern medicine as the medieval era drew to an end." Booklist
"Clear, well-organized {text} along with full-color reproductions of art and artifacts and photos of period structures immerse readers in . . . medieval life and offer sufficient information for reports." SLJ
Includes glossary and bibliographical references

610.3 Medical sciences--
Encyclopedias and dictionaries

Encyclopedia of health. 3rd ed. Marshall Cavendish 2003 16v il set $329.95 (4 and up) **610.3**
1. Medicine—Encyclopedias
ISBN 0-7614-7347-5   LC 2001-28883
Replaces The Marshall Cavendish encyclopedia of health published 1995 in 14 volumes
"This reference features entries on body function, fitness, diet, disease, hygiene, medicine and drugs." Publisher's note
This "combines compelling text with remarkable illustrations. Sixteen attractive, slim volumes offer . . . easy-to-read articles on a vast array of specific topics related to physical and emotional health." SLJ

610.6 Organizations, management, professions

Grahame, Deborah A.
World Health Organization; by Deborah A.
Grahame. World Almanac 2004 48p il
(International organizations) lib bdg $30; pa
$11.95   **610.6**
1. World Health Organization
ISBN 0-8368-5524-8 (lib bdg); 0-8368-5533-7 (pa)
LC 2003-47996
Describes the founding, development, and staffing of
the World Health Organization, and its focus on immuni-
zation, disease prevention, sanitation and nutrition as
well as combating disease.
This provides "ample material for reports." SLJ
Includes bibliographical references

610.9 Medical sciences--Historical and geographic treatment

Davis, Lucile
Medicine in the American West. Children's
Press 2001 30p il (Cornerstones of freedom) lib
bdg $21   **610.9**
1. Medicine—History 2. West (U.S.)—History
ISBN 0-516-22004-7   LC 00-31608
The author provides an "overview of medical practices
at the time Lewis and Clark set out, and builds from
there to include the importance of Native American herb-
als, wagon-train surgeries, traveling elixir salesmen, continuing to the introduction of ether to anesthetize patients
in surgery. . . . High-quality, full-color illustrations add
variety to the page layout." SLJ
Includes glossary

Gates, Phil
Medicine; consultant: Lawrence Ghislaine.
Candlewick Press 1997 32p il (History news)
$15.99   **610.9**
1. Medicine—History
ISBN 0-7636-0316-3   LC 97-14668
Presents in newspaper format the stories of break-
throughs in medicine in many different cultures and
lands from the year 8000 B.C. to the 1990s
Includes bibliographical references

611 Human anatomy, cytology, histology

Human anatomy on file; {by} The Diagram
Group. New ed. Facts on File 2003 unp il
loose-leaf $185   **611**
1. Human anatomy
ISBN 0-8160-5103-8   LC 2003-44821
Also available CD-ROM version
Companion volume to Human physiology on file
First published 1983 with title: The human body

This loose-leaf volume includes approximately 1500
labelled anatomical drawings and charts which may be
reproduced for classroom use
Includes glossary and bibliographical references

612 Human physiology

Beckelman, Laurie
The human body. Reader's Digest Children's
Bks. 1999 64p il (Reader's Digest pathfinders)
$16.99; pa $7.99   **612**
1. Human anatomy
ISBN 1-57584-289-0; 0-794-40371-9 (pa)
LC 98-53122
Examines the structure and function of various parts
of the human body, including skin, hair, muscles, and
bones, and describes how the various parts of the brain
sense our environment and coordinate our actions

Being human; edited by Derek Hall. Grolier Educ.
2000 8v set $229   **612**
1. Human beings
ISBN 0-7172-9419-6   LC 99-34157
Contents: v1 The human body, by D. Hall; v2 The
brain and senses, by D. Hall; v3 Health and illness, by
M. Whiteside; v4 Keeping safe, by B. Collyer; v5 Personality and behavior, by P. Carmichael; v6 Communication, by B. Medlam; v7 Relationships, by S. Benson; v8
The human race, by P. Steele
"Within each volume, 16 topics are addressed in two-
page presentations. . . . Full-color illustrations are copious and top quality, and both text and pictures are
multicultural and gender inclusive." Booklist

Gardner, Robert, 1929-
Health science projects about sports
performance; [by] Robert Gardner and Barbara
Gardner Conklin. Enslow Pubs. 2002 112p il
(Science projects) lib bdg $26.60 (7 and up)
612
1. Physiology 2. Sports medicine 3. Science projects
4. Science—Experiments
ISBN 0-7660-1441-X   LC 2001-6338
These activities address such topics as the effects of
body position, exercise, and conditioning, nutrition and
health, and sports psychology
Includes bibliographical references

Glover, David M.
The young Oxford book of the human being;
{by} David Glover. Oxford Univ. Press 1997 160p
il $25; lib bdg $30   **612**
1. Human beings
ISBN 0-19-521375-0; 0-19-521374-2 (lib bdg)
LC 97-11922
Explores the way the human body works, the origins
of human beings, and the various ways that humans live
and organize themselves socially and culturally
"The author tackles all of this material in direct, uncomplicated sentences." SLJ
Includes glossary

Human physiology on file; {by} The Diagram Group. New ed. Facts on File 2003 unp il loose-leaf $185   612
1. Physiology
ISBN 0-8160-5104-6   LC 2003-44822
Also available CD-ROM version
Companion volume to Human anatomy on file
Previously published as: Human body on file : physiology. New York : Facts On File, 1996
This loose-leaf volume includes labelled diagrams illustrating physiological functions and body systems which may be reproduced for classroom use
Includes glossary and bibliographical references

Nagel, Rob
Body by design; from the digestive system to the skeleton. U.X.L 2000 2v set $110
612
1. Physiology 2. Human anatomy
ISBN 0-7876-3897-8   LC 99-14642
Contents: v1 Cardiovascular system; Digestive system; Endocrine system; Integumentary system; Lymphatic system; Muscular system; v2 Nervous system; Reproductive system; Respiratory system; Skeletal system; Urinary system; Special senses
"Each chapter examines one of the 11 organ systems of the body; the final chapter focuses on the senses. In addition to describing each system's structure and function, the diseases commonly associated with it and suggestions for keeping it healthy are also discussed." SLJ
"Black-and-white and color photographs are plentiful, and color is used throughout to highlight headings and subheadings, sidebars, and other features." Booklist

Parker, Steve
Human body; written by Steve Parker. rev ed. DK Pub. 2004 72p il (DK eyewitness books) $15.99   612
1. Human anatomy 2. Physiology
ISBN 0-75660-688-8
First published 1993
In this book, text and illustrations present information on the parts of the body and how they work

Walker, Richard, 1951-
DK guide to the human body. Dorling Kindersley 2001 64p il $19.99   612
1. Physiology 2. Human anatomy
ISBN 0-7894-7388-7   LC 00-55519
"Multiple imaging techniques such as X-ray, MRI, and CT scans present the reader with views of the human body from the microscopic to the macroscopic level. Each image helps to explain the complex functions of the body systems." Sci Child
Includes glossary

Encyclopedia of the human body. DK Pub 2002 304p il $29.99   612
1. Human anatomy 2. Physiology
ISBN 0-7894-8672-5   LC 2002-73489

This "volume contains 116 entries divided into 5 categories: 'Working Parts,' 'Moving Framework,' 'Control and Sensation,' 'Supply and Maintenance,' and 'New Generations.' Within these sections each spread takes a closer look at an aspect of the topic ('Cells,' 'Cell Structure,' 'Cell Chemistry,' etc.). Almost 900 . . . illustrations, photographs, models, diagrams, and electron micrographs are incorporated into this work." SLJ
"This encyclopedia is attractive and a good beginning reference source for basic information or quick answers. Browsers will appreciate the appealing layout, especially the closeup images of various body structures." Booklist
Includes bibliographical references

612.1   Blood and circulation

Brynie, Faith Hickman, 1946-
101 questions about blood and circulation, with answers straight from the heart. 21st Cent. Bks. (Brookfield) 2001 176p il lib bdg $27.90 (7 and up)   612.1
1. Cardiovascular system 2. Blood 3. Heart
ISBN 0-7613-1455-5   LC 00-32570
"The book is divided into five chapters in a question-and-answer format: 'That Should Come First' (on the structure and function of the circulatory system), 'The Heart,' 'Blood', 'When Things Go Wrong'. . . and 'Your Healthy Heart'. . . . Comprehensive, informative, and highly instructional. . . . The reader will appreciate the many graphs, diagrams, tables, and photomicrographs." Sci Books Films
Includes bibliographical references

Parker, Steve
Heart, blood, and lungs. Gareth Stevens Pub 2005 32p il (Understanding the human body) lib bdg $24.67   612.1
1. Cardiovascular system 2. Heart 3. Respiratory system
ISBN 0-8368-4206-5   LC 2004-45328
This describes the anatomy and physiology of the human cardio-pulmonary system.
"Entertaining and informative. . . . Full-color photos and diagrams, computer-generated images, microscopic pictures, posed skeletons, X rays, and PET scans appear throughout." SLJ

Simon, Seymour, 1931-
The heart. Morrow Junior Bks. 1996 unp lib bdg $18.89; pa $6.99 (4 and up)   612.1
1. Cardiovascular system 2. Heart
ISBN 0-688-11407-5 (lib bdg); 0-688-17059-5 (pa)
LC 95-38021
This "introduces the human circulatory system: the heart, the blood, the arteries and veins, the transfer of oxygen and carbon dioxide, the functions of various blood cells, and heart problems and their solutions. The text is succinct and direct, making the details understandable without losing the sense that the whole process of circulation is 'strange and wonderful.' . . . The often striking pictures include many computer-enhanced photographs as well as diagrams and highly enlarged images made possible by electron microscopes. Handsome and well-conceived in every way." Booklist

612.2   Respiration

Silverstein, Alvin
The respiratory system; [by] Alvin, Virginia and Robert Silverstein. 21st Cent. Bks. (NY) 1994 96p il (Human body systems) lib bdg $29.90 (5 and up)   **612.2**
1. Respiratory system
ISBN 0-8050-2831-5   LC 94-21422
This illustrated introduction to the morphology and physiology of the respiratory system also discusses respiratory diseases and their treatments
Includes glossary

612.3   Digestion

Brynie, Faith Hickman, 1946-
101 questions about food and digestion that have been eating at you . . . until now. 21st Cent. Bks. (Brookfield) 2002 176p il lib bdg $27.90
                                                    612.3
1. Digestion 2. Nutrition
ISBN 0-7613-2309-0   LC 2001-52250
Questions and answers explain the human digestive system and how it uses food for nutrition
"Presenting solid research with a lively writing style, this book provides a great deal of information and sound advice on the topic." Booklist
Includes glossary and bibliographical references

Gardner, Robert, 1929-
Health science projects about nutrition. Enslow Pubs. 2002 112p il (Science projects) lib bdg $26.60 (7 and up)   **612.3**
1. Nutrition 2. Science—Experiments 3. Science projects
ISBN 0-7660-1442-8   LC 2001-306
This is a "compilation of science projects and experiments that involve weight, food, and nutrition. Carbohydrates, fats, proteins, vitamins and minerals, digestive processes, and weight reduction are studied in a variety of projects. . . . Gardner introduces each area with sufficient background information before setting students on the path of investigation." SLJ
Includes bibliographical references

Parker, Steve
Digestion and reproduction. Gareth Stevens Pub 2004 32p il (Understanding the human body) lib bdg $24.67   **612.3**
1. Digestion 2. Reproductive system
ISBN 0-8368-4205-7   LC 2004-45329
This describes the anatomy and physiology of the human digestive and reproductive systems
"Entertaining and informative. . . . Full-color photos and diagrams, computer-generated images, microscopic pictures, posed skeletons, X rays, and PET scans appear throughout." SLJ

Simon, Seymour, 1931-
Guts; our digestive system; Seymour Simon. 1st ed. HarperCollins 2005 unp il $15.99; lib bdg $16.89 (4 and up)   **612.3**
1. Digestion
ISBN 0-06-054651-4; 0-06-054652-2 (lib bdg)
                                     LC 2004-14508
This "explains how the digestive system works. . . . [The author] describes the complex facts and processes of the physiology, from the time food enters the mouth until all the various organs transform it into energy, nutrients, and waste." Booklist
"Simon's specialty of drawing in readers through large, detailed, breathtaking photos and then entertaining them with facts is again in evidence. . . . The text is enhanced with detailed colored X rays, computer-generated pictures, and microscopic photos." SLJ

Walker, Pamela
The digestive system; {by} Pam Walker and Elaine Wood. Lucent Bks. 2003 96p il (Understanding the human body) lib bdg $27.45 (7 and up)   **612.3**
1. Digestion 2. Nutrition
ISBN 1-59018-150-6   LC 2001-6246
Contents: A journey down the food tube; Energy for the body; Interesting events in the food tube; Diseases and disorders of the digestive system; Medical tests on the digestive system
Discusses the organs and function of the human digestive system, nutrients essential for good health and how they are processed by the body, and medical treatments of digestive disorders
This title is "informative, accurate, and up-to-date." Booklist
Includes glossary and bibliographical references

612.4   Hematopoietic, lymphatic, glandular, urinary systems

Little, Marjorie
The endocrine system; introduction by C. Everett Koop; foreword by Sandra Thurman. Chelsea House 2000 112p il (21st century health and wellness) $25.95 (7 and up)   **612.4**
1. Endocrine glands 2. Hormones
ISBN 0-7910-5982-0   LC 00-30327
First published 1990 in Encyclopedia of health series
The author "explains how the endocrine system works, first in a general overview and then by focusing on each of the major glands in the system. Excellent examples of the diseases that arise from the malfunctioning of the glands give the reader a clear picture of how important each part of the endocrine system is." Sci Books Films
Includes bibliographical references

612.6 Reproduction, development, maturation

Flanagan, Geraldine Lux
Beginning life. DK Pub. 1996 120p il $20
612.6
1. Embryology 2. Pregnancy 3. Childbirth
ISBN 0-7894-0609-8   LC 95-52790
The author "describes pregnancy month by month from conception through birth. The detailed text of this oversize book is enhanced by magnified photographs, ultrasound images, and color video sequences of the baby's development in the womb." Book Rep

Gravelle, Karen
The period book; everything you don't want to ask (but need to know); by Karen Gravelle & Jennifer Gravelle; illustrations by Debbie Palen. Walker & Co. 1996 117p il pa $8.95 hardcover o.p. (4 and up)   **612.6**
1. Menstruation
ISBN 0-8027-7478-4 (pa)   LC 95-31101
"An aunt and her fifteen-year-old niece provide forthright information about tampon insertion, pelvic exams, body changes during puberty, and other topics adolescent girls might feel uncomfortable discussing with parents and friends. The cartoonlike illustrations and conversational tone make this a friendly, reassuring resource as well as a thorough one." Horn Book Guide

What's going on down there? answers to questions boys find hard to ask; [by] Karen Gravelle, with Nick and Chava Castro; illustrations by Robert Leighton. Walker & Co. 1998 150p il pa $8.95 hardcover o.p.   **612.6**
1. Adolescence 2. Boys 3. Sex education
ISBN 0-8027-7540-3 (pa)   LC 98-3686
This title "covers physical changes, sexual intercourse, peer pressure, and pregnancy and birth. Gravelle reassures readers that there are a lot of different ways to describe normal when discussing puberty, and that each person will experience changes on his own timetable. The book balances information about being a sexual person with that of being a responsible person." SLJ

Jukes, Mavis
Growing up: it's a girl thing; straight talk about first bras, first periods, and your changing body; illustrations by Debbie Tilley. Knopf 1998 72p il pa $10 hardcover o.p. (4 and up)   **612.6**
1. Adolescence 2. Girls 3. Menstruation
ISBN 0-679-89027-0 (pa)   LC 98-18113
This "covers body hair and shaving, perspiration and deodorant, and how to buy your first bra. The second half of the book is devoted to what to expect and how to plan for your first period. . . . The narration has an easy, comfortable voice and imparts accurate and important information." SLJ

Parker, Steve
The reproductive system. Heinemann Lib. 2003 48p il (Body focus: injury, illness and health) lib bdg $29.93; pa $8.50   **612.6**
1. Reproduction 2. Sex education
ISBN 1-403-40199-3 (lib bdg); 1-403-40455-0 (pa)
LC 2002-14431
Contents: Reproduction; Female reproductive organs; Female cycle; Production of egg cells; Menstrual problems; Other female reproductive problems; Male reproductive organs; Production of sperm cells; Male reproductive system problems; Reproductive infections; Reproductive health; Sperm and egg; Embryo and fetus; Childbirth; Infancy and childhood; Adolescence and puberty; Fertility problems; Fertility control; Assisted reproduction; Reproduction and genetics
"Explains the parts of the reproductive system and their functions and provides an overview of human development from birth through adolescence." Publisher's note
This is "well organized and well written. The full-color photos, diagrams, and illustrations are clear and complement the text." SLJ
Includes bibliographical references

Teen dreams; Elaine Pascoe, book editor. Blackbirch Press 2004 48p il (Body story) $23.70; pa $9.95   **612.6**
1. Puberty 2. Adolescence
ISBN 1-410-30061-7; 1-410-30182-6 (pa)
LC 2003-9640
Contents: Puberty waits; Aggression; Sexual attraction
Next-door neighbors Natalie and Darren discover the effects that gonadotrophins, testosterone, and estrogen have on their bodies and minds as they enter puberty.
This volume is "bubbling over with informative, full-color photographs. . . . The {text is} amazingly concise and {takes} extraordinarily complex processes and {makes} them clearly understandable to the intended audience." SLJ
Includes bibliographical references

612.7 Musculoskeletal system, integument

Gold, Susan Dudley, 1949-
The musculoskeletal system and the skin. Enslow Pubs. 2003 48p il (Human body library) lib bdg $18.95   **612.7**
1. Musculoskeletal system 2. Skin
ISBN 0-7660-2023-1   LC 2002-151081
Contents: What is the musculoskeletal system?; Who is on the team?; How does the system work?; Wear and tear; Staying healthy; Amazing but true
The author "examines the biology amd overall health of the musculoskeletal system. She explains what the musculoskeletal system is, how it works, and what parts of the body are involved. She also offers advice for ways to stay fit and healthy and interesting facts about this body system." Publisher's note
"The design is open and uncluttered, interspersed with occasional small, helpful, full-color diagrams. . . . A non-intimidating start to some fascinating science." Booklist
Includes bibliographical references

Parker, Steve
The skeleton and muscles; Steve Parker. Raintree 2004 48p il (Our bodies) lib bdg $29.93 (5 and up)   **612.7**
1. Musculoskeletal system
ISBN 0-7398-6622-2   LC 2003-6594
Contents: The skeleton; Inside bones; The growing skeleton (case study); Bones of the skull and face; Healthy bones (focus on health); The muscle system; More muscles; Tendons; Inside a muscle; Making movements (case study); Controlling muscles; Muscles of the face and head; Bone and muscle disorders (focus on health); How joints work; Keeping joints healthy (case study); How the hands work; The shoulder and arm (case study); The leg and foot; The back joints and muscles; Joint problems
This "takes a look at bones, muscles, and joints; how they are connected and function; and how to keep them healthy. The anatomy is accurate, and the format, with plenty of pictures, diagrams, and magnified photos, is very accessible. There are also lots of lively boxed facts." Booklist
Includes bibliographical references

Skin, muscles, and bones. Gareth Stevens Pub 2004 32p il (Understanding the human body) lib bdg $24.67   **612.7**
1. Musculoskeletal system 2. Skin
ISBN 0-8368-4207-3   LC 2004-45327
This describes the anatomy and physiology of the human musculoskeletal system and skin
"Entertaining and informative. . . . Full-color photos and diagrams, computer-generated images, microscopic pictures, posed skeletons, X rays, and PET scans appear throughout." SLJ

Simon, Seymour, 1931-
Bones; our skeletal system. Morrow Junior Bks. 1998 unp il lib bdg $16.89; pa $6.95 (4 and up)
                                               612.7
1. Bones 2. Skeleton
ISBN 0-688-14645-7 (lib bdg); 0-688-17721-2 (pa)
                                        LC 97-44751
Describes the skeletal system and outlines the many important roles that bones play in the healthy functioning of the human body
"Simon once again proves his remarkable facility for making complicated science clear and understandable." Booklist

Muscles; our muscular system. Morrow Junior Bks. 1998 unp il pa $6.95 (4 and up)
                                               612.7
1. Muscles
ISBN 0-688-17720-4 (pa)   LC 97-44758
Describes the nature and work of muscles, the different kinds, and the effects of exercise and other activities on them
"The full-paged illustrations are great and include full-color photographs, MRI scans, X rays, and excellent drawings." SLJ

612.8   Nervous functions. Sensory functions

Brynie, Faith Hickman, 1946-
Perception; by Faith Brynie. Blackbirch Press 2001 64p il (Amazing brain) lib bdg $24.95
                                               612.8
1. Senses and sensation 2. Perception
ISBN 1-56711-423-7   LC 00-12022
"Highlighting the important difference between sensing (absorbing the world around us) and perceiving (processing and interpreting information), seven chapters cover how humans experience touch, smell, taste, vision, hearing, balance, and motion." Horn Book Guide
"One-page articles throughout {the} book are interesting to read, easy-to-understand text that will appeal to students." Book Rep
Includes glossary and bibliographical references

The physical brain; by Faith Brynie. Blackbirch Press 2001 64p il (Amazing brain) lib bdg $24.95
                                               612.8
1. Brain
ISBN 1-56711-424-5   LC 00-11947
"Brynie covers the anatomy and physiology of the brain." SLJ
"The structure of the brain is expertly, yet simply, described, and at every turn the author takes the opportunity to connect the text to the reader through questions and examples." Sci Books Films
Includes glossary and bibliographical references

Newquist, H. P. (Harvey P.)
The great brain book; an inside look at the inside of your head; illustrations by Keith Kasnot and Eric Brace. Scholastic Reference 2005 c2004 160p il $18.95 (5 and up)   **612.8**
1. Brain
ISBN 0-439-45895-1   LC 2004-42955
This describes the anatomy and physiology of the brain and covers such topics as the history of brain research, neurons, learning and memory, brain diseases and mental illness, and the possible future of brain research.
"With an appealing, colorful design and a flashy cover, this in-depth introduction to the human brain and its remarkable powers will attract browsers, but strong readers are its best audience. . . . The clever, kid-friendly anecdotes amid the anatomy lessons . . . enhance accessibility." Booklist

Out of control; brain function and immune reactions; Elaine Pascoe, book editor. Blackbirch Press 2004 48p il (Body story) lib bdg $23.70; pa $9.95   **612.8**
1. Brain 2. Allergy
ISBN 1-410-30063-3 (lib bdg); 1-410-30184-2 (pa)
                                        LC 2003-9639
Contents: The brain; Signals; Allergic reactions
Explores how baby Robert's brain functions at birth and how the cerebral cortex develops to control his body, then looks at what happens to Phoebe's body when her brain cannot control an allergic reaction.

Out of control—*Continued*

This volume is "bubbling over with informative, full-color photographs. . . . {The text is} amazingly concise and {takes} extraordinarily complex processes and {makes} them clearly understandable to the intended audience." SLJ

Includes bibliographical references

Parker, Steve

Brain, nerves, and senses. Gareth Stevens Pub 2005 32p il (Understanding the human body) lib bdg $23.93   **612.8**

1. Nervous system 2. Brain 3. Senses and sensation

ISBN 0-8368-4204-9   LC 2004-45330

The describes the anatomy and physiology of the human nervous system.

"Entertaining and informative. . . . Full-color photos and diagrams, computer-generated images, microscopic pictures, posed skeletons, X rays, and PET scans appear throughout." SLJ

Rybolt, Thomas R.

Science fair success with scents, aromas, and smells; {by} Thomas R. Rybolt, Leah M. Rybolt. Enslow Pubs. 2002 112p il (Science fair success) lib bdg $26.60 (7 and up)   **612.8**

1. Smell 2. Science projects 3. Science—Experiments

ISBN 0-7660-1625-0   LC 2001-1780

This collection of science projects explores such topics as the relationships of smell to the brain, to taste, and to memories, pleasant and unpleasant smells and neutralizing odors

Includes bibliographical references

Silverstein, Alvin

Senses and sensors [series]; by Alvin Silverstein, Virginia Silverstein, and Laura Silverstein Nunn. 21st Century Books 2001-2002 4v lib bdg ea $25.90   **612.8**

1. Senses and sensation

ISBN 0-7613-1666-3 (Hearing); 0-7613-1663-9 (Seeing); 0-7613-1667-1 (Smelling and tasting); 0-7613-1668-X (Touching and feeling)

Contents: Hearing; Seeing; Smelling and tasting; Touching and feeling

These volumes explain the anatomy and physiology of the senses and the ways technology is being used to repair or enhance them.

"Color photographs, diagrams, and other images enhance the interesting, clearly presented text." Booklist

Simon, Seymour, 1931-

The brain; our nervous system. Morrow Junior Bks. 1997 unp il lib bdg $17.89; pa $6.99 (4 and up)   **612.8**

1. Brain 2. Nervous system

ISBN 0-688-14641-4 (lib bdg); 0-688-17060-9 (pa)   LC 96-36801

Describes the various parts of the brain and the nervous system and how they function to enable us to think, feel, move, and remember

Simon's "clear, concise writing style is complemented by stunning color images taken with radiological scanners, such as CAT scans, MRIs, and SEMs (scanning electron microscopes.)" SLJ

Eyes and ears. HarperCollins Pubs. 2003 unp il $15.99; lib bdg $16.89 (4 and up)   **612.8**

1. Eye 2. Ear 3. Vision 4. Hearing

ISBN 0-688-15303-8; 0-688-15304-6 (lib bdg)   LC 2002-19060

Describes the anatomy of the eye and ear, how those organs function and some ways in which they may malfunction, and how the brain is also involved in our seeing and hearing

"Simon is at his very best here. . . . The large, exquisitely reproduced photographs from a number of sources look like fiery planets, galaxies, and monster creatures. . . . The anatomy and physiology are detailed and accurate, with clear diagrams." Booklist

Viegas, Jennifer

The revolution in healing the brain. Rosen Pub. Group 2003 64p il (Library of future medicine) lib bdg $26.50   **612.8**

1. Nervous system

ISBN 0-8239-3668-6   LC 2001-6721

Contents: Anatomy of the brain; Brain cells; Learning and intelligence; Sleep and dreams; Sensory awareness; Brain healing in the future

The author provides "basic information on the brain and its functions before describing various disorders and the . . . research involved in treating them. Chapters on learning and intelligence, sleep and dreaming, and sensory awareness are included. The book cites functional magnetic resonance imaging, high-powered microscopes, stem-cell research, and better pharmaceuticals as tools for healing the brain. . . . {The book is} well illustrated with well-positioned and captioned diagrams, drawings, photographs, and color-enhanced images." SLJ

Includes glossary and bibliographical references

613 Personal health and safety

Cheung, Lillian Wai-Yin

Be healthy! it's a girl thing; food, fitness, and feeling great; {by} Lilian Cheung and Mavis Jukes. Crown Publishers 2003 117p il lib bdg $18.99; pa $12.95 (5 and up)   **613**

1. Girls—Health and hygiene 2. Nutrition 3. Physical fitness

ISBN 0-679-99029-1 (lib bdg); 0-679-89029-7 (pa)   LC 2003-10114

This "offers girls going through puberty advice on nutrition, fitness, self-image, and appearance." SLJ

"Given the alarmingly high rates of eating disorders, girls definitely need to hear some of the straight talk more often. . . . A chapter devoted to advertising is also helpful in countering the unrealistic images portrayed in the media." Booklist

Crump, Marguerite, 1955-
Don't sweat it! every body's answers to questions you don't want to ask; edited by Elizabeth Verdick. Free Spirit 2002 118p il pa $13.95   **613**
1. Adolescence 2. Youth—Health and hygiene
ISBN 1-57542-114-3   LC 2002-7021
Contents: Hair: crowning glory or constant struggle?; Face facts!; Your mouth: an amusement park for germs; Helping hands; Body odor basics; Those parts below; Sweet feet
An introduction to common concerns of adolescence, such as acne and body odor, covering the physical changes of puberty and offering tips on caring for oneself from head to toe
"The author doesn't mince words but remains empathetic throughout, and the medical information behind personal hygiene practice is accurate and up-to-date. Sidebars present interesting facts, trivia, and humorous asides." SLJ
Includes bibliographical references

Health on file; {by} Victoria Chapman & Associates. 2nd ed. Facts on File 2002 various paging il loose-leaf $185   **613**
1. Health
ISBN 0-8160-4345-0
Also available CD-ROM version
First published 1995
This is a looseleaf collection of diagrams which can be reproduced for classroom use. Topics include: mental & emotional health, social & family health, growth & development, food & nutrition, personal health choices, substance abuse, diseases & disorders, consumer health, accidents & safety, and environmental health

Levchuck, Caroline M.
Healthy living; {by} Caroline Levchuck, Michele Drohan, Jane Kelly Kosek. U.X.L 2000 3v il set $165   **613**
1. Health 2. Mental health 3. Medical care
ISBN 0-7876-3918-4   LC 99-53258
This set provides a "survey of topics and issues related to wellness: nutrition, physical fitness, personal hygiene, health-care systems and careers, alternative medicine, sexuality, and others." SLJ
"Useful as a starting point for students doing research or looking for the questions to ask on sensitive subjects." Voice Youth Advocates
Includes bibliographical references

613.2 Dietetics

Diet information for teens; edited by Karen Bellenir. Omnigraphics 2000 399p il (Teen health series) $58 (7 and up)   **613.2**
1. Nutrition 2. Teenagers—Health and hygiene
ISBN 0-7808-0441-4   LC 00-49213
"Health tips about diet and nutrition, including facts about nutrients, dietary guidelines, breakfasts, school lunches, snacks, party food, weight control, eating disorders, and more." Title page

This "is a compilation of articles on all facets of nutrition, drawn mainly from FDA documents. The information is presented in a straightforward, plainspoken manner." SLJ

Duden, Jane
Vegetarianism for teens. LifeMatters 2001 64p il (Nutrition and fitness) lib bdg $23.93
613.2
1. Vegetarianism
ISBN 0-7368-0712-8   LC 00-39092
This "discusses the reasons people choose a vegetarian life-style and the different types of vegetarian diets. The bulk of the book lays out guidelines for readers to develop their own diet, including a checklist and vegetarian food guide. An ending chapter gives young vegetarians strategies for dealing with family and friends who may not always be supportive." Booklist
"The information presented is solid." Horn Book Guide
Includes glossary and bibliographical references

Haduch, Bill
Food rules! the stuff you munch, its crunch, its punch, and why you sometimes lose your lunch; illustrated by Rick Stromoski. Dutton Children's Bks. 2001 106p il $19.99; pa $10.99
613.2
1. Food 2. Nutrition
ISBN 0-525-46419-0; 0-14-131147-9 (pa)
LC 00-42698
This book presents "information on nutrition, digestion, food-related ailments, eating customs, and genetically engineered foods." Horn Book Guide
"In an extremely well-organized format that combines the right amount of nutritional information with historical, anecdotal, and humorous facts, the fast-paced, often irreverent text quickly grabs its readers." Booklist
Includes glossary and bibliographical references

Schwartz, Ellen, 1949-
I'm a vegetarian; amazing facts and ideas for healthy vegetarians; illustrated by Farida Zaman. Tundra Bks. 2002 112p il pa $9.95   **613.2**
1. Vegetarianism
ISBN 0-88776-588-2   LC 2001-95376
"The author opens with an overview of the different types of vegetarians and the rationale behind their decisions, then moves into advice on handling parental concerns and sticky social situations that are sure to arise. A consideration of nutrition and how to achieve a healthy diet that provides all necessary nutrients follows, ending with a smattering of suggested menus and recipes. . . . She writes in a light, chatty tone, using a question-and-answer format, bulleted facts and lists, boxed information, and humor. Black-and-white drawings throughout add to the book's appeal." SLJ
Includes glossary and bibliographical references

613.6 Personal safety and special topics of health

Wiloch, Thomas
Everything you need to know about protecting yourself and others from abduction. Rosen Pub. Group 1998 64p il (Need to know library) $25.25
613.6
1. Kidnapping 2. Safety education
ISBN 0-8239-2553-6 LC 97-44784
"This title calls attention to the increasing number of abductions of teens and children. While it categorizes the different types of abductions, it focuses on those committed by strangers. . . . Preventive measures as well as strategies for escaping attempted kidnappings are described. Chapters are devoted to precautions to take at home, and while babysitting, jogging, bicycling, using the Internet, etc. The author addresses teens although there is some discussion of the vulnerability of children. Most suggestions are intelligent, practical, and easy to follow." SLJ
Includes bibliographical references

613.7 Physical fitness

Gedatus, Gus
Bicycling for fitness. LifeMatters 2001 64p il (Nutrition and fitness) lib bdg $23.93
613.7
1. Cycling 2. Physical fitness
ISBN 0-7368-0705-5 LC 00-37099
This describes the health benefits of cycling and explains how to create a fitness plan and how to choose and maintain a bike, and offers safety information
"The information is simple and well organized." Horn Book Guide
Includes glossary and bibliographical references

Exercise for weight management. LifeMatters 2001 64p il (Nutrition and fitness) lib bdg $23.93
613.7
1. Exercise 2. Physical fitness
ISBN 0-7368-0706-3 LC 00-34899
This offers information on physical fitness and setting up a healthy exercise plan
"This brief, well-designed title delivers informative and relevant material for the serious teen reader." Sci Books Films
Includes glossary and bibliographical references

Porter, David, 1960-
Winning weight training for girls; fitness and conditioning for sports; foreword by Gerard K. Green. Facts on File 2004 205p il $35; pa $16.95 (7 and up)
613.7
1. Weight lifting 2. Physical fitness
ISBN 0-8160-5185-2; 0-8160-5186-0 (pa)
LC 2003-3500
"A Mountain Lion Book"

"The book describes the benefits of weight training, the muscles of the body and how they interact, biomechanics, anaerobic versus aerobic exercises, proper use of equipment, circuit programs for different levels of ability, training for performance or injury recovery, controlling weight, and much more." Publisher's note
This is "detailed yet easy to read. . . . Safety and proper technique are stressed throughout." SLJ
Includes bibliographical references

Schwager, Tina, 1964-
The right moves; a girl's guide to getting fit and feeling good; by Tina Schwager and Michele Schuerger; edited by Elizabeth Verdick. Free Spirit 1998 273p il pa $15.95 (7 and up)
613.7
1. Girls—Health and hygiene 2. Physical fitness
ISBN 1-57542-035-X LC 98-9851
Explains how girls can achieve total fitness by focusing on three broad areas: developing a positive self-image, choosing nutritious foods, and exercising regularly
"This useful addition to the self-help genre is both cheerleader and resource, providing valuable advice and information." Booklist
Includes bibliographical references

Stiefer, Sandy
A risky prescription; sports and health. Lerner Publs. 1997 96p il (Sports issues) lib bdg $23.93
613.7
1. Sports medicine
ISBN 0-8225-3304-9 LC 96-48340
Discusses athletes and sports in today's society, focusing on mental and physical health aspects, including the use of drugs, the stress placed on professional athletes, and the pressure to win at any cost
"Full-color photos add action to the text, and boxed sidebars add additional information. The author writes clearly and without sensationalism, calmly conveying her message of caution and common sense." SLJ
Includes bibliographical references

Turck, Mary, 1950-
Healthy eating for weight management. LifeMatters 2001 64p il (Nutrition and fitness) lib bdg $23.93
613.7
1. Nutrition 2. Weight loss
ISBN 0-7368-0709-8 LC 00-39113
This book "examines diet as only one aspect of a lifestyle that will naturally yield effective weight control and encourages readers to exercise and avoid fad diets. Overall nutritional needs are spelled out, and dietary myths are dispelled." SLJ
"The volume should be required reading for teen and parent alike." Sci Books Films
Includes glossary and bibliographical references

Vedral, Joyce L.
Toning for teens; the 20-minute workout that makes you look good and feel great! Warner Bks. 2002 165p il pa $15.95 (7 and up)
613.7
1. Exercise 2. Physical fitness 3. Teenagers—Health and hygiene
ISBN 0-446-67815-5 LC 2002-101020

Vedral, Joyce L.—*Continued*
The author offers a "workout specifically aimed at helping adolescent girls tone and firm their muscles using free weights. . . . The author emphasizes sound nutrition and exercise information. . . . The exercises are clearly described, and illustrated with photos of teens performing the routines." SLJ

613.9 Birth control, reproductive technology, sex hygiene

Bell, Ruth
Changing bodies, changing lives; a book for teens on sex and relationships; {by} Ruth Bell and other co-authors of Our bodies, ourselves and Ourselves and our children, together with members of the Teen Book Project. expanded 3rd ed. Times Bks. 1998 411p il pa $24 (7 and up)

        613.9
1. Sex education
ISBN 0-8129-2990-X   LC 97-29249
First published 1980
This is a "book on sex, physical and emotional health, and personal relationships. . . . Readers . . . will find emotional support as well as specific answers to most of their questions in this nonjudgmental resource." Booklist

Brynie, Faith Hickman, 1946-
101 questions about sex and sexuality—; with answers for the curious, cautious, and confused. Twenty-First Century Books 2003 176p il lib bdg $27.90 (7 and up)   **613.9**
1. Sex education
ISBN 0-7613-2310-4   LC 2002-11209
Uses a question-and-answer format to present information about the physical, emotional, and social topics surrounding sex and sexuality
"Brynie emphasizes abstinence as the only sure way of avoiding STDs and pregnancies, but also gives detailed information on contraception. . . . The matter-of-fact style is never condescending or alarmist in tone. . . . Explicit black-and-white illustrations lend an almost clinical touch. . . . The glossary; resource list of books, articles, and Web sites; and extensive citations make Brynie's title good for reports, while the directness of the presentation will appeal to general readers." SLJ

Harris, Robie H.
It's perfectly normal; a book about changing bodies, growing up, sex, and sexual health; illustrated by Michael Emberley. 10th anniversary edition. Candlewick Press 2004 89p il $19.99; pa $10.99 (4 and up)   **613.9**
1. Sex education
ISBN 0-7636-2610-4; 0-7636-2433-0 (pa)
First published 1994
The author "explains the physical, psychological, emotional and social changes that occur during puberty—and the implications of these changes." Publ Wkly
"This caring, conscientious, and well-crafted book will be a fine library resource as well as a marvelous adjunct to the middle-school sex-education curriculum. . . . The bold color cartoon drawings are very candid: a double-page spread of nudes, which beautifully demonstrates the varied shapes and sizes humans come in; a picture of a couple making love; one of a boy masturbating as he sits on his bed; another of a girl examining her genitals with a mirror. . . . Harris' text, as forthright as Emberley's art, encompasses . . . (the structure of the reproductive system and puberty) . . . intercourse, birth, abortion, sexual responsibility and respect." Booklist

614 Forensic medicine, incidence & prevention of disease

Fridell, Ron, 1943-
DNA fingerprinting; the ultimate identity. Watts 2001 112p il lib bdg $25 (7 and up)   **614**
1. DNA fingerprinting 2. Forensic sciences
ISBN 0-531-11858-4   LC 00-26925
Discusses the discovery of DNA fingerprinting, the processes involved, its initial use, and its past and present role in forensic identification, conservation biology, and human genetics
"Fridell consistently gets right to the heart of his subject, melding scientific, forensic, and historic information in an easy-to-grasp, often eye-opening fashion." Booklist
Includes bibliographical references

Hoff, Brent H.
Mapping epidemics; a historical atlas of disease; [by] Brent H. Hoff and Carter Smith III; Charles H. Calisher, consulting editor. Watts 2000 112p il map $38.50; pa $19.95 (7 and up)   **614**
1. Epidemiology 2. Diseases
ISBN 0-531-11713-8; 0-531-16487-X (pa)
              LC 99-16502
"More than 30 potentially deadly human illnesses are profiled in this volume. . . . Each two-to-six page article includes a boxed compilation of basic facts and a map showing global distribution. Most present the causative agent, transmission systems, treatment, prevention, and control measures. The bulk of each article links the history of human experience with the illness, major outbreaks, and its *modus operandi*." SLJ
This work offers a "wealth of information expressed clearly enough for younger students and deeply enough for students doing higher-level research." Booklist
Includes glossary and bibliographical references

Jackson, Donna M., 1959-
The bone detectives; how forensic anthropologists solve crimes and uncover mysteries of the dead; by Donna M. Jackson; photographs by Charlie Fellenbaum. Little, Brown 1996 48p il lib bdg $17.95 (5 and up)   **614**
1. Forensic sciences 2. Criminal investigation
ISBN 0-316-82935-8   LC 95-19051
"Jackson follows forensic anthropologist Dr. Michael Charney and his colleagues as they solve an actual case by developing a physical profile from bones and teeth,

Jackson, Donna M., 1959-—*Continued*
reconstructing the victim's skull, and using clues from fibers and other material to make further identification." Booklist
"Laced with eye-catching full-color photos, this readable book is a fine example of the application of scientific knowledge to the 'real' world." SLJ
Includes glossary

614.4 Incidence of and public measures to prevent disease

Altman, Linda Jacobs, 1943-
Plague and pestilence; a history of infectious disease. Enslow Pubs. 1998 128p il (Issues in focus) lib bdg $26.60 **614.4**
1. Communicable diseases
ISBN 0-89490-957-6 LC 98-12677
Traces the battles that societies have waged against infectious diseases from the Black Death of the fourteenth century to the Ebola virus of more recent times
"The inclusion of large numbers of references, including Internet Web sites, will encourage further reading." Sci Books Films
Includes bibliographical references

Epidemics: opposing viewpoints; Mary E. Williams, book editor. Greenhaven Press 2005 208p il lib bdg $34.95; pa $23.70
614.4
1. Epidemics
ISBN 0-7377-2282-7 (lib bdg); 0-7377-2283-5 (pa)
LC 2004-61657
"Opposing viewpoints series"
In this "anthology, authors examine the resurgent problem of infectious disease around the world and discuss how governments and individuals should respond to the threats posed by epidemics." Publisher's note
Includes bibliographical references

Farrell, Jeanette
Invisible enemies; stories of infectious diseases. 2nd ed. Farrar, Straus and Giroux 2005 259p il $18 (7 and up) **614.4**
1. Communicable diseases
ISBN 0-374-33607-5 LC 2004-57668
First published 1998
The author "focuses on seven dreaded human diseases: smallpox, leprosy, plague, tuberculosis, malaria, cholera, and AIDS. Each chapter provides a description of the physical and psychological effects of the disease on its victims, early theories about its causes, and efforts made to avoid or cure it. Then the methods of research that revealed its cause and developed the means to control its spread are explained in fascinating detail. . . . If every science book for nonspecialists were written with such flair and attention to detail, science would soon become every student's favorite subject." SLJ
Includes glossary and bibliographical references

Friedlander, Mark P.
Outbreak: disease detectives at work; by Mark P. Friedlander Jr. {2nd ed}. Lerner Publs. 2003 128p il lib bdg $27.93 **614.4**
1. Epidemiology 2. Diseases
ISBN 0-8225-0948-2 LC 2002-6836
First published 2000
Contents: Epidemiology: the study of disease; A closer Look at microbes; Great plagues of history: bubonic plague, smallpox, and anthrax; From the Tropics to the Tundra: malaria, influenza, and diphtheria; Modern killers: Legionnaire's disease, ebola, and muerto canyon virus; AIDS: the modern pandemic; Ongoing battles; Bioterrorism; Conclusion: epidemiology and the future
Describes the field of epidemiology and its history, presenting historical and modern case studies and biological explanations of some diseases and a discussion of the microbes most likely to be used by bioterrorists
"This is a readable, intriguing overview of the destructive power of epidemics and the critical work of public health professionals." SLJ
Includes glossary and bibliographical references

614.5 Incidence & prevention of specific diseases

Corzine, Phyllis
The Black Death. Lucent Bks. 1997 112p il maps (World history series) lib bdg $27.45 (7 and up) **614.5**
1. Plague
ISBN 1-56006-299-1 LC 96-19441
Examines the causes, effects, and legacy of the epidemic that killed millions of people in Europe during the fourteenth century
"Students will find answers to homework questions in {this} clearly written volume." SLJ
Includes bibliographical references

Marrin, Albert, 1936-
Dr. Jenner and the speckled monster; the search for the smallpox vaccine. Dutton Children's Bks. 2002 120p il $17.99 (5 and up) **614.5**
1. Jenner, Edward, 1749-1823 2. Smallpox
ISBN 0-525-46922-2 LC 2002-2698
This is a "social history of smallpox, with an emphasis on Dr. Edward Jenner's contributions to eradicate the disease. . . . Marrin's writing is direct and succinct, and his scientific explanations are lucid and well detailed. Numerous black-and-white period illustrations (some appropriately gruesome) appear in most chapters, adding interest to the text." Booklist
Includes bibliographical references

Murphy, Jim, 1947-
An American plague; the true and terrifying story of the yellow fever epidemic of 1793. Clarion Bks. 2003 165p il maps $17 (5 and up) **614.5**
1. Yellow fever 2. Philadelphia (Pa.)—History
ISBN 0-395-77608-2 LC 2002-151355
A Newbery Medal honor book, 2004

Murphy, Jim, 1947——*Continued*
Contents: No one noticed; "All was not right"; Church bells tolling; Confusion, distress, and utter desolation; "It was our duty"; The prince of bleeders; "By twelve only"; "This unmerciful enemy"; "A delicate situation"; Improvements and the public gratitude; "A modern-day time bomb"
"Murphy culls from a number of historical records the story of the yellow fever epidemic that swept Philadelphia in 1793, skillfully drawing out from these sources the fear and drama of the time and making them immediate to modern readers. . . . Thoroughly documented, with an annotated source list, the work is both rigorous and inviting." Horn Book

Peters, Stephanie True, 1965-
The 1918 influenza pandemic. Benchmark Books 2004 c2005 69p il (Epidemic!) lib bdg $29.93   **614.5**
1. Influenza
ISBN 0-7614-1636-6   LC 2003-22947
Describes the 1918 influenza pandemic, from how World War I soldiers spread the disease to recent scientific efforts to understand the virus that took between twenty and forty million lives worldwide.
Includes glossary and bibliographical references

The battle against polio. Benchmark Books 2004 c2005 69p il (Epidemic!) lib bdg $29.93
614.5
1. Poliomyelitis
ISBN 0-7614-1635-8   LC 2004-3408
This is a history of the polio epidemic, early research into the disease, and the development of the polio vaccine.
"Peters makes both the science and the social history compelling in this title. . . . The book design is appealing, with wide margins and well-placed, mostly two-tone, photos. The exemplary back matter . . . includes an annotated bibliography, Web sites, and full notes for quotes." Booklist
Includes glossary

The Black Death. Benchmark Books 2004 c2005 69p il map (Epidemic!) lib bdg $29.93
614.5
1. Plague 2. Middle Ages
ISBN 0-7614-1633-1   LC 2003-743
Describes the 1347 - 1351 outbreak of plague in Europe, known as the Black Death, which killed one out of three people and changed the course of European history.
Includes glossary and bibliographical references

Cholera; curse of the nineteenth century. Benchmark Books 2004 c2005 69p il (Epidemic!) lib bdg $29.93   **614.5**
1. Cholera
ISBN 0-7614-1634-X   LC 2004-844
This is a history of cholera, including the effects of the Industrial Revolution, the epidemics of the 19th century, and the continued existance of the disease in the world today.
Includes bibliographical references

Smallpox in the new world. Benchmark Books 2004 c2005 69p il (Epidemic!) $29.93
614.5
1. Smallpox
ISBN 0-7614-1637-4   LC 2003-2646
Describes the history of smallpox in the Americas, covering the arrival of the Spanish as carriers, its spread throughout the New World, the development of the smallpox vaccine, the elimination of the disease, and its potential use as a terrorist weapon.
Includes glossary and bibliographical references

The **Black** Death; Don Nardo, book editor. Greenhaven Press 1999 173p (Turning points in world history) $32.45 paperback o.p. (7 and up)
614.5
1. Plague 2. Epidemics
ISBN 1-56510-995-3   LC 98-44752
"The two major sections, 'The Black Death Ravages Europe' and 'The Economic and Cultural Impact of the Black Death,' illustrate the focus of the text. Students are given a clear explanation of the disease and how it may have spread and some coverage of its social, economic, and cultural repercussions. The essays each speak to a specific issue. An appendix that includes 16 primary documents, a concise chronology, lists for further reading divided by content, and an index complete this valuable research tool." SLJ

615   Pharmacology and therapeutics

Barrett, Cece
The dangers of diet drugs and other weight-loss products. Rosen Pub. Group 1999 64p il (Teen health library of eating disorder prevention) $26.50
615
1. Appetite depressants 2. Eating disorders
ISBN 0-8239-2768-7   LC 98-29712
Discusses the use of over-the-counter, prescription, and herbal diet drugs as well as liquid and prepackaged diet foods and explains their relation to eating disorders and proper nutrition

Collier, James Lincoln, 1928-
Vaccines. Benchmark Bks. 2003 127p il (Great inventions) lib bdg $25.95   **615**
1. Vaccination
ISBN 0-7614-1539-4   LC 2002-156287
Contents: "And no bells tolled"; Doctor Jenner's milkhands; Death invisible; Cleaning up the cities; The forgotten plague; The great crippler; The future
Explains the diseases that led to the discovery of vaccines, how vaccines work, and how that has changed the history of medicine
"The writing is clear, and color and black-and-white illustrations appear throughout." SLJ
Includes bibliographical references

Durham, Michael, 1952-
Painkillers and tranquilizers. Heinemann Lib. 2003 56p il (Just the facts) $25.64   **615**
1. Psychotropic drugs 2. Analgesics
ISBN 1-403-40821-1   LC 2002-10941

Durham, Michael, 1952-—*Continued*
Contents: What are painkillers and tranquilizers?; Painkillers and tranquilizers; Some history; Why do we need painkillers?; Pain relief drugs today; What are anxiety & depression?; Tranquilizers and antidepressants today; The difference between painkillers and tranquilizers; How tranquilizers and antidepressants work; How drugs can help; Side effects; What is drug dependence?; Recognizing tranquilizer dependence; Effects of long-term dependence; Getting help; Alternatives; Legal matters; Treatment and counseling; People to talk to
Offers a description of drugs used to treat pain, anxiety, and depression, and discusses how these drugs work, possible side effects, long-term effects, and how to deal with dependency or addiction to them
This provides "well-organized information. . . . The writing is clear and frank." Libr Media Connect
Includes glossary and bibliographical references

Facklam, Margery, 1927-
Modern medicines; the discovery and development of healing drugs; Margery Facklam, Howard Facklam, and Seán M. Grady. Rev. ed. Facts on File 2004 226p il (Science & technology in focus) $29.95 (7 and up)   615
1. Pharmacology 2. Drugs
ISBN 0-8160-4706-5   LC 2003-11489
First published 1992 with title: Healing drugs: the history of pharmacology
Contents: Ancient remedies; A garden of simples; Patent cures and medicine shows; Formalizing pharmacology; A world of wonder drugs; Preemptive strikes; Biological systems management; Miracles in the medicine cabinet; From the laboratory to the pharmacy; Producing modern pills and potions; New uses for old drugs; When drugs go wrong; Back to the Garden?; Herbalists and scientists; Warning signs; Drug-resistant germs; The perils of medicine; Distribution woes; Future trends in pharmacology
"Straightforward, sensibly organized, and well researched, this volume . . . is an excellent introduction." Booklist

Gordon, Melanie Apel
Drug interactions; protecting yourself from dangerous drug, medication, and food combinations; {by} Melanie Gordon. Rosen Pub. Group 1999 63p il (Drug abuse prevention library) $25.25   615
1. Drugs
ISBN 0-8239-2825-X   LC 98-44974
Discusses illegal and legal drugs (both over-the-counter and prescription), alcohol, and food and explains how to prevent dangerous interactions among these substances
Includes bibliographical references

Hyde, Margaret Oldroyd, 1917-
Vaccinations; from smallpox to cancer; by Margaret O. Hyde and Elizabeth H. Forsyth. Watts 2000 127p il $20 (7 and up)   615
1. Vaccination
ISBN 0-531-11746-4   LC 99-45841

An overview of vaccinations, explaining some basic terms, their development, with an emphasis on smallpox and polio vaccines, their current and future use, controversies concerning their use, and possible negative effects
"In this easy-to-read, sometimes alarming work, the prolific authors offer a solid text that will help students interested in everything from health and medicine to history to international travel. . . . The black-and-white photos support the information well; detailed endnotes and contact sites are appended." Booklist
Includes bibliographical references

Kidd, J. S. (Jerry S.)
Mother Nature's pharmacy; potent medicines from plants; {by} J.S. Kidd and Renee A. Kidd. Facts on File 1998 134p il maps (Science and society) $25 (7 and up)   615
1. Pharmacology 2. Medical botany
ISBN 0-8160-3584-9   LC 97-37925
"The Kidds guide the reader through a general history of medicine and medical care, the nature of folk medicine, the growth of government regulation, and the role of the South American rain forests as a source of new drugs. They include biographical sketches of medical pioneers and brief histories of several significant plant-derived drugs, such as quinine, curare, ephedrine, and cortisone." Book Rep
"Well-organized and well-researched, the book is a good introduction to the history of traditional medicine, from Hippocrates to modern times." Booklist
Includes glossary and bibliographical references

Nardo, Don, 1947-
Vaccines. Lucent Bks. 2002 128p il (Great medical discoveries) lib bdg $27.45 (7 and up)   615
1. Vaccination
ISBN 1-56006-932-5   LC 2001-3198
Discusses the impact of vaccines on diseases, their history and development, current challenges in the field, and future research
This work is "refreshingly readable yet thorough. . . . Many halftone photographs, crisp diagrams, and shaded sidebars offer supplementary information in eye-appealing forms." SLJ
Includes bibliographical references

Roza, Greg
The encyclopedia of drugs and alcohol; written by Greg Roza. Watts 2001 199p il $39   615
1. Drugs 2. Drug abuse
ISBN 0-531-11899-1   LC 00-45913
This reference "covers more than 250 commonly used and abused legal and illegal drugs—prescription, over-the-counter, and recreational. The origin, history, effects, and uses of drugs are discussed in the concise A-Z format." Booklist
"A well-organized volume offering clear definitions and explanations." SLJ

615.5 Therapeutics

Billitteri, Thomas J.
Alternative medicine. 21st Cent. Bks.
(Brookfield) 2001 112p il (Twenty-first century
medical library) lib bdg $26.90 (7 and up)
                                                    615.5
1. Alternative medicine
ISBN 0-7613-0965-9   LC 00-57707
"Among the topics covered are homeopathic medicine,
hypnosis, chiropractic touch therapy, and acupuncture.
. . . This book is a solid choice for general information
and for reports." SLJ
Includes bibliographical references

Kowalski, Kathiann M., 1955-
Alternative medicine; is it for you? Enslow
Pubs. 1998 128p il (Issues in focus) $26.60 (7 and
up)   **615.5**
1. Alternative medicine
ISBN 0-89490-955-X   LC 98-12676
Analyzes different types of alternative medicine practiced today, such as homeopathy, chiropractic, herbal,
and nutritional therapies, and discusses how to make an
informed decision about medical care
"Kowalski writes clearly and directly, maintaining
both respect for the reader's intelligence and an objective
attitude toward the material." Booklist
Includes bibliographical references

Rattenbury, Jeanne
Understanding alternative medicine. Watts 1999
128p il lib bdg $20 (7 and up)   **615.5**
1. Alternative medicine
ISBN 0-531-11413-9   LC 98-15669
Introduces five alternative medical systems and five
major alternative treatments, including osteopathy, traditional Chinese medicine, acupuncture, herbal medicine,
and massage therapy
"The history, effectiveness, and variations of therapies
are clearly detailed. An extensive glossary, solid bibliography, and listing of 16 organizations related to alterna-
tive-medical systems add to the usefulness of this volume." SLJ

615.9 Toxicology

Latta, Sara L.
Food poisoning and foodborne diseases. Enslow
Pubs. 1999 128p il (Diseases and people) lib bdg
$26.60 (7 and up)   **615.9**
1. Food poisoning
ISBN 0-7660-1183-6   LC 98-36134
"The eight chapters include the history of foodborne
diseases, the various microbes involved and how they are
toxic to our bodies, diagnosis and treatment of illnesses,
the social costs of food poisoning, and methods of prevention on both a personal and societal level. . . . Appendixes include a question-and-answer section; a list of
contact organizations; extensive chapter notes; recom-

mended books, articles, videos, and Web sites; and a
helpful index." SLJ
Includes bibliographical references

616 Diseases

Day, Nancy, 1953-
Killer superbugs; the story of drug-resistant
diseases. Enslow Pubs. 2001 128p il (Issues in
focus) lib bdg $26.60 (7 and up)   **616**
1. Diseases 2. Microorganisms 3. Drugs
ISBN 0-7660-1588-2   LC 00-12458
This "overview examines the growing number of infectious diseases that are becoming impervious to drugs.
Day identifies the major drug-resistant organisms and
diseases causing harm today, explains what antibiotics
are and how they work to either kill or inhibit the
growth of microbes, and describes several ways that bacteria and other organisms fight antibiotics through gene
mutation, dormancy, etc." SLJ
"This is an excellent book on an important scientific
topic with everyday relevance to nonscientists." Sci
Books Films
Includes bibliographical references

Diseases; Bryan Bunch, editor. 2nd rev ed. Grolier
Educ. 2003 8v il set $329   **616**
1. Diseases—Encyclopedias
ISBN 0-7172-5688-X   LC 2002-728575
First published 1997
Alphabetically arranged articles present medical information on more than 400 diseases, discussing sources,
symptoms, stages of the disease, its likelihood of striking, treatments, prevention, and long-term effects
"Access is a breeze, thanks to sheaves of see references . . . and a comprehensive index at each volume's
end. Though enhanced by a sprinkling of small photos
and diagrams, this is, by and large, a textual resource.
. . . This alphabetical catalog of ailments . . . will satisfy most curiosity and assignment-driven inquiries." SLJ

Jacobs, Marian B.
Coping with hereditary diseases. Rosen Pub.
Group 1999 152p il $26.50 (7 and up)
                                                    616
1. Medical genetics 2. Diseases
ISBN 0-8239-2823-3   LC 98-48064
Examines common hereditary diseases and ways of
avoiding them, discussing diabetes, heart disease, cancer,
alcoholism, and the exploration of one's family medical
tree
Includes bibliographical references

Landau, Elaine
Joined at birth; the lives of conjoined twins.
Watts 1997 64p il $23   **616**
1. Siamese twins
ISBN 0-531-20331-X   LC 96-38707
"A First book"
Explores the issue of conjoined twins, including a dis-
cussion of the difficult decision regarding physical sepa-
ration that parents must face
Includes bibliographical references

Sick! diseases and disorders, injuries and infections; {by} David E. Newton {et al.}. U.X.L 1999 4v set $215 **616**

1. Diseases

ISBN 0-7876-3922-2 LC 99-44739

This set covers "140 illnesses, disorders, and injuries. . . . Entries ranging from three to eight pages are arranged alphabetically throughout the four volumes and are organized under the subheadings of description, causes, symptoms, diagnosis, treatment, prognosis, and prevention. Important medical terms are highlighted and explained for each article. Information is current and quite detailed." Voice Youth Advocates

Tesar, Jenny

Stem cells; written by Jenny Tesar. Blackbirch Press 2003 48p il (Science on the edge) lib bdg $23.70 (5 and up) **616**

1. Stem cell research

ISBN 1-56711-787-2

Examines the very promising but controversial use of human stem cells in treating medical conditions ranging from burned skin to damaged spinal cords to various diseases.

This "uses remarkably clear language to explain what stem cells are and to distill the arguments on both sides of the ethical debates. . . . Illustrated with sharp microscopic images as well as color photos of scientists at work. Very accessible and informative." Booklist

Includes bibiographical references

Viegas, Jennifer

Stem cell research. Rosen 2002 64p il (Library of future medicine) lib bdg $26.50 **616**

1. Cells—Research

ISBN 0-8239-3669-4 LC 2001-6263

Discusses the latest scientific breakthroughs regarding embryonic stem cells and the growing of new human tissues, and how this can help doctors treat human illnesses

The book is "well illustrated with well-positioned and captioned diagrams, drawings, photographs, and color-enhanced images." SLJ

Includes glossary and bibliographical references

616.07 Pathology

Donnellan, William Lorne, 1925-

The miracle of immunity; by William L. Donnellan. Benchmark Bks. 2002 c2003 79p il (Story of science) lib bdg $19.95 **616.07**

1. Immune system

ISBN 0-7614-1425-8 LC 2001-5939

Chronicles discoveries made since ancient times in learning about disease and how the body's immune system fights and conquers it

"Clear, black-and-white and color photos, diagrams, and photomicrographs enhance [this title]. Timely, interesting, and useful for research." SLJ

Includes glossary and bibliographical references

Edelson, Edward

The immune system. Chelsea House 2000 104p il (21st century health and wellness) lib bdg $25.95 **616.07**

1. Immune system

ISBN 0-7910-5525-6 LC 99-52117

Replaces the title first published 1989 in The Encyclopedia of health series

Examines the workings of a complex structure, the body's defense against disease and infection

McClafferty, Carla Killough, 1958-

The head bone's connected to the neck bone; the weird, wacky, and wonderful x-ray. Farrar, Straus & Giroux 2001 135p il $17 (7 and up) **616.07**

1. X-rays

ISBN 0-374-32908-7 LC 00-140218

"Beginning with Roentgen's radiation experiments and concluding with high-tech potential for the future, this volume chronicles the history of X-rays. While reading like a novel, it is filled with excellent reference material as well." Sci Child

Includes glossary and bibliographical references

Walker, Pamela

The immune system; {by} Pam Walker and Elaine Wood. Lucent Bks. 2003 96p il (Understanding the human body) lib bdg $27.45 (7 and up) **616.07**

1. Immune system

ISBN 1-59018-151-4 LC 2002-452

Contents: One: Structure of the immune system; Two: The immune system at work; Three: Allergies: false alarms for the immune system; Four: Autoimmune diseases: when the body attacks itself; Five: Vaccines

Describes the structure and function of the immune system and also discusses allergies, autoimmune diseases, and vaccines

This title is "informative, accurate, and up-to-date." Booklist

Incudes glossary and bibliographical references

616.1 Diseases of the cardiovascular system

Baldwin, Carol

Sickle cell disease. Heinemann Lib. 2003 32p il (Health matters) lib bdg $22.79 (4-6) **616.1**

1. Sickle cell anemia

ISBN 1-4034-0252-3 LC 2001-7975

Contents: What is sickle cell disease?; What causes sickle cell disease?; Diagnosing sickle cell disease; Treating sickle cell disease; Classmates with sickle cell disease; How you can help; Visiting friends with sickle cell disease; Sickle cell success stories

This "inviting, colorful [book] will attract students who need a clear, readable introduction to [sickle cell disease]." SLJ

Includes glossary and bibliographical references

Harris, Jacqueline L., 1929-
Sickle cell disease; by Jacqueline Harris. 21st Cent. Bks. (Brookfield) 2001 96p il (Twenty-first century medical library) lib bdg $26.90 (7 and up)
616.1
1. Sickle cell anemia
ISBN 0-7613-1459-8   LC 00-47932
"The author discusses the physiology of the illness, its symptoms, and its causes." SLJ
This is "lively and compassionate. The simple language, clear explanations, and personal profiles work together nicely." Booklist
Includes glossary and bibliographical references

Silverstein, Alvin
Sickle cell anemia; {by} Alvin and Virginia Silverstein and Laura Silverstein Nunn. Enslow Pubs. 1997 112p il (Diseases and people) lib bdg $26.60 (7 and up)   **616.1**
1. Sickle cell anemia
ISBN 0-89490-711-5   LC 96-22643
Explores the history of sickle cell anemia, discussing its symptoms, diagnosis, and treatment
"The text is clear and well organized, with sections on gene therapy, diagnostic techniques, research, and even ethical concerns about the possible use of fetal tissue in treatment. Informative black-and-white photos and graphics complement the presentation." SLJ
Includes glossary and bibliographical references

616.2   Diseases of the respiratory system

Greenberg, Alissa
Asthma. Watts 2000 127p il lib bdg $20 (7 and up)   **616.2**
1. Asthma
ISBN 0-531-11331-0   LC 99-86993
"Watts library"
Describes the symptoms, causes, diagnosis, and treatment of asthma, as well as guidelines for living with the disease
"The list of organizations and Web sites will be helpful. Black-and-white photos and graphics provide welcome text breaks." SLJ
Includes glossary and bibliographical references

Kittredge, Mary, 1949-
The common cold; introduction by C. Everett Koop; foreword by Sandra Thurman. Chelsea House 2001 104p il (21st century health and wellness) lib bdg $25.95 (7 and up)
616.2
1. Cold (Disease)
ISBN 0-7910-5985-5   LC 00-27515
First published 1988 in Encyclopedia of health series
Explains the common cold, including symptoms, causes, treatments and prevention
Includes glossary and bibliographical references

Landau, Elaine
Tuberculosis. Watts 1995 96p il lib bdg $20 (7 and up)   **616.2**
1. Tuberculosis
ISBN 0-531-12555-6   LC 94-39305
"A Venture book"
"Explains tuberculosis and its method of transmission, traces its etiology, and explains why it is presently resurfacing globally. In conclusion, she counters the belief of middle-class Americans that TB only affects the poor, the homeless, and AIDS patients." Booklist
"A well-organized, well-written look at the resurgence of this deadly disease that offers an extensive appendix for further information." SLJ
Includes bibliographical references

Lennard-Brown, Sarah
Asthma. Raintree Steck-Vaughn Pubs. 2002 64p il (Health issues) lib bdg $28.54 (5 and up)
616.2
1. Asthma
ISBN 0-7398-5218-3   LC 2002-16375
Examines the causes and treatment of asthma and discusses how to deal with the environmental triggers that may stimulate an attack
The book is "comprehensive and not written down for young people. The color photographs and the bright design help make the [text] more accessible." Booklist
Includes glossary and bibliographical references

Murphy, Wendy B.
Asthma. Millbrook Press 1998 112p il (Millbrook medical library) $27.93 (7 and up)
616.2
1. Asthma
ISBN 0-7613-0364-2   LC 97-52128
Examines the various causes of asthma, what happens during an attack, how the disease can be controlled, and theories of treatment
"Asthma sufferers, their families and friends, and students researching the disease will make good use of this informative title." Booklist
Includes glossary and bibliographical references

Yancey, Diane
Tuberculosis. 21st Cent. Bks. (Brookfield) 2001 128p il (Twenty-first century medical library) $26.90 (7 and up)   **616.2**
1. Tuberculosis
ISBN 0-7613-1624-8
The author begins this book with a history of tuberculosis, "tracing evidence of it back to the Neolithic Age and then explores the variety of treatments used to combat it. . . . The three personal cases related are from three different socioeconomic situations. Good-quality, black-and-white photos appear throughout." SLJ
Includes bibliographical references

616.3 Diseases of the digestive system

Clayton, L. (Lawrence)
Diet pill drug dangers. Enslow Pubs. 1999 64p il (Drug dangers) pa $13.26 hardcover o.p.
616.3
1. Appetite depressants 2. Drug abuse
ISBN 0-7660-1737-0 (pa)   LC 98-20514
Examines the history of diet pill use, focusing on society's obsession with weight loss and the dangers of abusing these drugs
Includes bibliographical references

Monroe, Judy
Cystic fibrosis. LifeMatters 2002 64p il (Perspectives on disease and illness) lib bdg $23.93
616.3
1. Cystic fibrosis
ISBN 0-7368-1026-9   LC 00-12612
This defines cystic fibrosis and discusses how it affects the body, its diagnosis and treatment and living with the disease
"Simple and well-organized." Book Rep
Includes glossary and bibliographical references

616.4 Diseases of endocrine system

Hyde, Margaret Oldroyd, 1917-
Diabetes; [by] Margaret O. Hyde & Elizabeth H. Forsyth. Franklin Watts 2003 96p il lib bdg $25
616.4
1. Diabetes
ISBN 0-531-12209-3   LC 2002-38033
Discusses the causes of diabetes, who is likely to have this condition, how to prevent diabetic problems, and the search for a cure
"A useful, well-written resource." SLJ
Includes glossary and bibliographical references

Kelly, Pat
Coping with diabetes. Rosen Pub. Group 1998 145p $17.95 (7 and up)
616.4
1. Diabetes
ISBN 0-8239-2549-8   LC 97-49084
Discusses the types and causes of diabetes, how the disease is diagnosed and treated, and ways of managing this condition and its impact on your life
"Addressing the teen reader, the author provides clear-cut, concise information about the disease and how to handle it. Teens with diabetes share their stories of problems faced and overcome." Voice Youth Advocates
Includes bibliographical references

Sheen, Barbara, 1949-
Diabetes. Lucent Bks. 2003 112p il (Diseases and disorders) lib bdg $27.45
616.4
1. Diabetes
ISBN 1-59018-244-8   LC 2002-13620

Contents: What is diabetes?; Diagnosis and treatment; Alternative and complementary treatment; Living with diabetes; What the future holds
This explains what diabetes is, its diagnosis and treatment, living with the disease, and prospects for the future
This is "well written and well organized." SLJ
Includes glossary and bibliographical references

Stewart, Gail, 1949-
Diabetes. Lucent Bks. 1999 95p il $17.95 (7 and up)
616.4
1. Diabetes
ISBN 1-56006-527-3   LC 98-31963
Discusses the history, nature, causes, symptoms, diagnosis, treatment, emergencies, and complications of diabetes and explains ways to live with it
"The well-organized and well-paced text is suitable for research or for personal information." SLJ
Includes bibliographical references

616.5 Diseases of integument

Landau, Elaine
Living with albinism. Watts 1997 63p il $23
616.5
1. Albinos and albinism
ISBN 0-531-20296-8   LC 97-1771
"A First book"
Describes albinism, the inherited condition in which the individual lacks or has a shortage of melanin, the substance responsible for the body's coloring
"A concise consideration of a medical condition and its consequences on personal health. . . . This is a positive book, written without sensationalism and illustrated with full-color and black-and-white photographs that support this approach." SLJ

Skin health information for teens; health tips about dermatological concerns and skin cancer risks; edited by Robert Aquinas McNally. 1st ed. Omnigraphics 2003 429p il (Teen health series) $58 (7 and up)
616.5
ISBN 0-7808-0446-5   LC 2003-53631
"Including facts about acne, warts, hives, and other conditions and lifestyle choices, such as tanning, tattooing, and piercing, that affect the skin, nails, scalp, and hair." Title page
"This volume bridges the gap between books with fashion-magazine appeal and serious medical reference works. . . . Well organized and comprehensive in coverage." SLJ

616.7 Diseases of the musculoskeletal system

Eisenpreis, Bettijane
Coping with scoliosis. Rosen Pub. Group 1998 164p il $26.50 (7 and up)
616.7
1. Scoliosis
ISBN 0-8239-2557-9   LC 98-37198

Eisenpreis, Bettijane—*Continued*
The author "explores the physical and emotional issues involved in the diagnosis and treatment of scoliosis. Pencil drawings include illustrations of the spine and the types of orthopedic braces patients wear." SLJ
Includes bibliographical references

Gray, Susan H.
Living with juvenile rheumatoid arthritis. Child's World 2003 32p il (Living well) lib bdg $25.64   **616.7**
1. Arthritis
ISBN 1-56766-104-1   LC 2002-2870
This title "leads off with an introduction to a young person who has [juvenile rheumatoid arthritis]. Subsequent chapters explain the physiology of the illness, what causes it, and what it's like to live with it. [The concluding section looks] at possible treatments and potential cures. [The text is] clear and simple, double spaced, and punctuated by colorful exemplary photos of kids dealing with the disease." SLJ
Includes glossary and bibliographical references

616.8 Diseases of the nervous system and mental disorders

Aaseng, Nathan, 1953-
Multiple sclerosis. Watts 2000 111p il $20
                                                616.8
1. Multiple sclerosis
ISBN 0-531-11531-3   LC 99-34864
Describes the symptoms, diagnosis, effects, and treatments of the neurological disease known as MS, multiple sclerosis, as well as the stories of several well-known people who have this disease
"Aaseng puts the medical information within the context of individual lives, and offers a clear, straightforward explanation of what is known and what is yet to be known, as well as a number of the currently held theories." Booklist
Includes bibliographical references

Brill, Marlene Targ, 1945-
Tourette syndrome. 21st Cent. Bks. (Brookfield) 2002 112p il (Twenty-first century medical library) lib bdg $26.90 (7 and up)   **616.8**
1. Tourette syndrome
ISBN 0-7613-2101-2   LC 2001-41747
Examines the tic disorder known as Tourette syndrome, its symptoms and manifestations, how it can be controlled and treated, and, through case studies, what it is like to live with Tourette's
The author covers "most of the information report writers would be seeking and a section about home and school is especially helpful to anyone trying to understand the problems faced by a person with this disorder." Book Rep
Includes glossary and bibliographical references

Burnfield, Alexander
Multiple sclerosis; Alexander Burnfield. Heinemann Library 2003 56p il (Just the facts) lib bdg $31.36 (5 and up)   **616.8**
1. Multiple sclerosis
ISBN 1-4034-4602-4   LC 2003-10913
Contents: Multiple sclerosis; What is MS?; History of MS; Types of MS; Diagnosis and investigations; Symptoms of MS; Who gets MS?; How does MS develop?; Managing MS; Treating MS; Living with MS; MS fatigue; Other problems; MS and the family; MS and society; Will a cure be found?; Information and advice
Describes the different types of MS, their symptoms, why this disease can be difficult to diagnose, various types of treatment, and other issues related to multiple sclerosis.
This is "well written and organized, and [includes] factual information without overwhelming readers." SLJ
Includes bibliographical references

Carson, Mary Kay, 1964-
Epilepsy. Enslow Pubs. 1998 112p il (Diseases and people) lib bdg $26.60 (7 and up)
                                                616.8
1. Epilepsy
ISBN 0-7660-1049-X   LC 97-34160
Explores the topic of epilepsy, discussing its history, symptoms, diagnosis, treatment, and possible ways to prevent some forms of the disease
Includes bibliographical references

Elliot-Wright, Susan
Epilepsy. Raintree 2004 64p il (Health issues) lib bdg $28.56 (7 and up)   **616.8**
1. Epilepsy
ISBN 0-7398-6423-8
Examines the causes, symptoms, and treatment of epilepsy, a neurological condition that can lead to seizures.
"Filled with color photos, text boxes, and sidebars, [this volume is] likely to attract browsers. . . . Students writing short reports will find [this title] useful." SLJ

Gay, Kathlyn, 1930-
Epilepsy; the ultimate teen guide; [by] Kathlyn Gay and Sean McGarrahan. Scarecrow Press 2002 103p il (It happened to me) lib bdg $32.50
                                                616.8
1. Epilepsy
ISBN 0-8108-4339-0   LC 2002-4718
Contents: What's epilepsy; Fact or folklore?; What's happening?; Diagnosis and treatment; Surgery for epilepsy; Living with epilepsy; School and job issues; Sports and recreation; The female factor; Finding a cure
The authors explain the various forms epilepsy takes, the history of the disease, folklore about it, and its diagnosis and treatment
"An excellent look at epilepsy and its impact on diagnosed teens, their families, friends, and communities. . . . Readable, well organized, and well documented." SLJ
Includes glossary and bibliographical references

Gold, John Coopersmith
Cerebral palsy. Enslow Pubs. 2001 48p il
(Health watch) lib bdg $23.93 (4 and up)
                                      616.8
1. Cerebral palsy
ISBN 0-7660-1663-3   LC 00-12882
This discusses what cerebral palsy is, its causes, diagnosis, and treatment, and living with the disease
Includes glossary and bibliographical references

Gold, Susan Dudley, 1949-
Multiple sclerosis. rev ed. Enslow Pubs. 2001
48p (Health watch) lib bdg $23.93 (4 and up)
                                      616.8
1. Multiple sclerosis
ISBN 0-7660-1658-7   LC 00-10515
First published 1997 by Crestwood House
This discusses what multiple sclerosis is, its causes, diagnosis, and treatment
Includes glossary and bibliographical references

Goldsmith, Connie, 1945-
Neurological disorders. Blackbirch Press 2001
64p il (Amazing brain) lib bdg $24.95
                                      616.8
1. Nervous system 2. Brain—Diseases 3. Mental illness
ISBN 1-56711-422-9   LC 00-11949
This "focuses on such diseases and conditions as Alzheimer's, autism, meningitis, cerebral palsy, schizophrenia, and Parkinson's disease. Each short section describes how the disease may damage the brain and what treatments are used. The latest research is covered, with explanations as to why many of the conditions still leave scientists baffled. . . . The information is condensed, straightforward, and readable, supplemented by excellent color diagrams." Booklist
Includes glossary and bibliographical references

Goodfellow, Gregory
Epilepsy. Lucent Bks. 2001 95p il (Diseases and
disorders series) lib bdg $27.45   **616.8**
1. Epilepsy
ISBN 1-56006-701-2   LC 00-8657
Discusses the causes, diagnosis, and treatment of epilepsy, the types of seizures, and the challenges of living with the disease
Includes bibliographical references

Harmon, Dan
Life out of focus; Alzheimer's disease and
related disorders. Chelsea House 1999 104p il
$28.95 (7 and up)   **616.8**
1. Alzheimer's disease
ISBN 0-7910-4896-9   LC 98-26537
Discusses the nature, possible causes, effects on the patient as well as family and friends, and treatment options of this deteriorative disease
Includes bibliographical references

Hyde, Margaret Oldroyd, 1917-
When the brain dies first; by Margaret O. Hyde
and John F. Setaro. Watts 2000 144p il lib bdg
$23 (7 and up)   **616.8**
1. Brain—Diseases
ISBN 0-531-11543-7   LC 99-33060
Examines the functioning of the human brain, various causes that impede its proper functioning, and research into prevention and treatment of brain injuries and disorders
"This excellent little book has a lot of information. . . . Each chapter could act as a focal point for research projects or discussion groups. The true value of the book is in its overall presentation, clarity, and timeliness." Sci Books Films
Includes glossary and bibliographical references

Johansson, Philip
Carpal tunnel syndrome and other repetitive
strain injuries. Enslow Pubs. 1999 128p il
(Diseases and people) lib bdg $26.60 (7 and up)
                                      616.8
1. Wounds and injuries
ISBN 0-7660-1184-4   LC 98-30305
"This general discussion examines the causes, symptoms, diagnosis, treatment, and prevention of some of the most common repetitive strain injuries (RSIs) such as carpal tunnel syndrome and tennis elbow. Many of the chapters begin with individual case studies that will engage readers' interest and sympathy." SLJ
Includes bibliographical references

Landau, Elaine
Parkinson's disease. Watts 1999 112p il lib bdg
$20 (7 and up)   **616.8**
1. Parkinson's disease
ISBN 0-531-11423-6   LC 98-22450
"A Venture book"
The author "explains the symptoms of Parkinson's disease, from tremors and rigidity to emotional changes and speech problems, and discusses the difficulty of diagnosing it. . . . Treatment options range from medication to brain surgery to the controversial fetal tissue transplant, and Landau carefully explains both sides of that issue." SLJ
Includes bibliographical references

Tourette syndrome. Watts 1998 95p il lib bdg
$20 (7 and up)   **616.8**
1. Tourette syndrome
ISBN 0-531-11399-X   LC 97-48736
Describes the causes, symptoms, and treatment of Tourette Syndrome and explains the challenges faced by people with the disorder
"The attractive format and accessible reading level make this an effective guide for a young person facing the symptoms, a student needing report information, or an adult needing a concise overview." Voice Youth Advocates
Includes bibliographical references

Silverstein, Alvin
Parkinson's disease; [by] Alvin and Virginia
Silverstein and Laura Silverstein Nunn. Enslow
Pubs. 2001 128p il (Diseases and people) lib bdg
$26.60 (7 and up)   **616.8**
1. Parkinson's disease
ISBN 0-7660-1593-9   LC 00-12073
This describes the history of Parkinson's disease, its
causes, symptoms, diagnosis and treatment, the disease
and society, and research
Includes glossary and bibliographical references

Polio; {by} Alvin and Virginia Silverstein and
Laura Silverstein Nunn. Enslow Pubs. 2001 128p
il (Diseases and people) lib bdg $26.60 (7 and up)
                                              616.8
1. Poliomyelitis
ISBN 0-7660-1592-0   LC 00-10993
The authors "describe the symptoms, causes, and treatments of this crippling disease. They trace its history
from evidence of polio in ancient times to the epidemics
of the first half of the twentieth century. The authors include the stories of well-known patients, such as Franklin
D. Roosevelt, and important researchers, such as Salk,
Sabin, and Sister Kenny." Publisher's note
Includes glossary and bibliographical references

Votava, Andrea
Coping with migraines and other headaches.
Rosen Pub. Group 1997 162p il $26.50 (7 and up)
                                              616.8
1. Headache
ISBN 0-8239-2566-8   LC 97-31918
The author "covers different kinds of headaches and
migraines, including their symptoms, causes, triggers,
and prevention. Medication and alternative treatments
such as yoga, meditation, massage, and acupuncture are
discussed, as are recommendations relating to sleep and
exercise. Personal stories are included. . . . Web sites
and e-mail addresses of organizations to contact for further information are listed." SLJ
Includes bibliographical references

Willett, Edward, 1959-
Alzheimer's disease. Enslow Pubs. 2002 112p il
(Diseases and people) lib bdg $26.60 (7 and up)
                                              616.8
1. Alzheimer's disease
ISBN 0-7660-1596-3   LC 2001-4517
Contents: The mind thief; The history of Alzheimer's
Disease; What is Alzheimer's Disease?; Diagnosing Alz-
heimer's Disease; Treatment of Alzheimer's Disease; So-
cial implications of Alzheimer's Disease; Preventing Alz-
heimer's Disease; Research and the future
Presents an overview of a degenerative brain disease
which alters personality, memory, thinking and behavior
and, at present, has no cure
"Personal stories add interest to this clearly written
and well-organized overview." SLJ
Includes glossary and bibliographical references

Meningitis. Enslow Pubs. 1999 112p il
(Diseases and people) lib bdg $26.60 (7 and up)
                                              616.8
1. Meningitis
ISBN 0-7660-1187-9   LC 99-12279
Discusses the history, symptoms, diagnosis, and treat-
ment of meningitis and examines ongoing research and
its effect on the future treatment of this disease
"The material is presented in an easy-to-read style."
Sci Books Films
Includes glossary and bibliographical references

616.85   Neuroses; speech and language disorders; disorders of personality, intellect, impulse control

Anorexia; Karen F. Balkin, book editor.
Greenhaven Press 2005 110p (At issue) lib bdg
$28.70; pa $19.95   **616.85**
1. Anorexia nervosa
ISBN 0-7377-2178-2 (lib bdg); 0-7377-2179-0 (pa)
                                    LC 2004-61693
Replaces the edition published 2001 under the
editorship of Daniel A. Leone
This book "considers the physical, social, and psychological aspects of this puzzling disorder and includes
. . . viewpoints exploring anorexia in men, older women,
and women throughout the world." Publisher's note
Includes bibliographical references

Beal, Eileen
Everything you need to know about
ADD\ADHD. Rosen Pub. Group 1998 64p il
(Need to know library) $25.25 (7 and up)
                                             616.85
1. Attention deficit disorder
ISBN 0-8239-2748-2   LC 97-45149
Defines both attention deficit disorder and attention
deficit hyperactivity disorder and discusses what can be
done to treat these conditions, including medication, be-
havior modification, and counseling
Includes bibliographical references

Ritalin; its use and abuse. Rosen Pub. Group
1999 64p il (Drug abuse prevention library) lib
bdg $25.25 paperback o.p. (7 and up)
                                             616.85
1. Ritalin
ISBN 0-8239-3759-3   LC 98-27089
Describes the medical uses of the prescription drug
Ritalin, the problems presented by overprescribing it, its
potential for abuse, and ways to prevent such abuse
"Parents, students, and educators may find the book
helpful for addressing the potential pressure, social stigma, and recreational Ritalin abuse that may result from
listening to uninformed classmates." Booklist
Includes glossary and bibliographical references

Campbell, Nancy M., 1944-
Panic disorders. LifeMatters 2002 64p il
(Perspectives on mental health) lib bdg $23.93
                                          616.85
1. Panic disorders
ISBN 0-7368-1030-7   LC 00-12937
This offers a definition of panic disorders "and its
causes, diagnosis, treatment, and coping with or living
with the condition, including a look at the future. . . .
The information . . . is simple and to the point, appro-
priate for a middle school or junior high audience." Book
Rep
Includes bibliographical references

Clarke, Alicia
Coping with self-mutilation; a helping book for
teens who hurt themselves. Rosen Pub. Group
1999 104p (Coping with series) $26.50 (7 and up)
                                          616.85
1. Self-mutilation
ISBN 0-8239-2559-5   LC 98-54123
Discusses self-mutilating behavior in teens, including
possible causes and avenues for recovery
"Emphasis is placed on self-help measures and available treatment. Brief, personal stories and profiles illustrate the author's points." SLJ
Includes bibliographical references

Cotter, Alison, 1963-
Anorexia and bulimia. Lucent Bks. 2001 112p il
(Diseases and disorders series) $28.70
                                          616.85
1. Anorexia nervosa 2. Bulimia
ISBN 1-56006-725-X   LC 00-12858
This discusses anorexia and bulimia and how culture
influences eating disorders, the psychology and biology
of eating disorders, its effects on athletes and others, and
treatment and recovery
Includes bibliographical references

Davis, Brangien
What's real, what's ideal; overcoming a
negative body image. Rosen Pub. Group 1999 64p
il (Teen health library of eating disorder
prevention) $26.50 (7 and up)   **616.85**
1. Eating disorders 2. Self-perception
ISBN 0-8239-2771-7   LC 98-29941
The author "defines for readers what it means to have
a negative body image, what some of the causes might
be, and suggestions for overcoming self-defeating perceptions and finding peace within one's own skin. This title
also discusses the practice of self-mutilation." Voice
Youth Advocates
Includes bibliographical references

Demetriades, Helen A.
Bipolar disorder, depression, and other mood
disorders. Enslow Pubs. 2002 112p il (Diseases
and people) lib bdg $26.60 (7 and up)
                                          616.85
1. Depression (Psychology) 2. Manic-depressive illness
ISBN 0-7660-1898-9   LC 2002-6826

Identifies the causes, symptoms, and treatment of
mood disorders such as bipolar disorder and depression,
which can have environmental, genetic, or physiological
aspects
Includes glossary and bibliographical references

Depression; Henny H. Kim, editor. Greenhaven
Press 1999 186p (Contemporary issues
companion) lib bdg $34.95; pa $23.70 (7 and
up)   **616.85**
1. Depression (Psychology)
ISBN 1-56510-889-2 (lib bdg); 1-56510-888-4 (pa)
                                  LC 98-21728
"The essays included in this volume present a general
introduction to the various types of depression, current
and potential treatments for the disorder, and the way in
which depression affects the lives of those afflicted with
it." Publishers's note
Includes bibliographical references

Drohan, Michele Ingber
Weight-loss programs; weighing the risks and
realities. Rosen Pub. Group 1998 64p il (Teen
health library of eating disorder prevention) $26.50
(7 and up)   **616.85**
1. Eating disorders 2. Weight loss
ISBN 0-8239-2770-9   LC 98-4418
Discusses the relationship between health and diet and
examines a variety of commercial weight-loss programs
and the health risks that they pose to their members
"The book may not find favor with national weight-
loss chains, but it provides youth with important information regarding weight-loss programs and alternatives."
Booklist
Includes glossary and bibliographical references

Eating disorders; Myra H. Immell, book editor.
Greenhaven Press 1999 191p (Contemporary
issues companion) lib bdg $33.70; pa $21.20 (7
and up)   **616.85**
1. Eating disorders
ISBN 1-56510-895-7 (lib bdg); 1-56510-894-9 (pa)
                                  LC 98-35418
"In this anthology, contributing authors explore issues
related to anorexia nervosa, bulimia, compulsive overeat-
ing, and other eating disorders. Through . . . essays and
personal narratives, readers gain insight into the causes,
effects, and treatments of the different types of eating
disorders." Publisher's note
Includes bibliographical references

Eating disorders: opposing viewpoints; Jennifer A.
Hurley, book editor. Greenhaven Press 2001
173p lib bdg $34.95; pa $23.70 (7 and up)
                                          616.85
1. Eating disorders
ISBN 0-7377-0652-X (lib bdg); 0-7377-0651-1 (pa)
                                  LC 00-69183
"Opposing viewpoints series"
This collection of essays offers various points of view
about eating disorders
Includes bibliographical references

Frankenberger, Elizabeth

Food and love; dealing with family attitudes about weight. Rosen Pub. Group 1998 64p il (Teen health library of eating disorder prevention) $26.50 (7 and up)   **616.85**

1. Eating disorders 2. Food—Psychological aspects

ISBN 0-8239-2760-1   LC 98-16922

Examines the role that food plays in the home and how the family affects self-image, and provides suggestions for healthy living to protect against eating disorders

"This is an excellent title for someone who may have food issues but needs a gentle introduction to the topic." Voice Youth Advocates

Includes bibliographical references

Frissell, Susan

Eating disorders and weight control; {by} Susan Frissell & Paula Harney. Enslow Pubs. 1998 128p il (Teen issues) lib bdg $26.60 (7 and up)
    616.85

1. Eating disorders 2. Weight loss

ISBN 0-89490-919-3   LC 97-12489

Discusses weight control, body image, and eating disorders including the social pressures which may cause them; presents information about diet, nutrition, and exercise

The authors "offer information about symptoms as well as organizations that give treatment and support. Chapter notes, a glossary, and an extensive bibliography round out an excellent resource." Booklist

Girod, Christina M.

Down syndrome. Lucent Bks. 2001 96p il (Diseases and disorders series) lib bdg $27.45
    616.85

1. Down syndrome

ISBN 1-56006-824-8   LC 00-9933

"Girod offers a thorough description of Down syndrome, especially how it affects children and their families. The tone is optimistic, emphasizing mainstreaming and integration over sheltered workshops and institutions." SLJ

Includes bibliographical references

Harmon, Dan

Anorexia nervosa; starving for attention. Chelsea House 1998 87p il (Encyclopedia of psychological disorders) $28.45 (7 and up)   **616.85**

1. Anorexia nervosa 2. Bulimia

ISBN 0-7910-4901-9   LC 98-25197

Explores the truth and misconceptions regarding anorexia nervosa by examining its history, causes, considerations, treatment, and related eating disorders

"The special articles found within the text offer chilling case studies of anorexia victims such as actress Tracey Gold, gymnast Christy Henrich, and author Marya Hornbacher. The photographs of these young women are startling testaments to anorexia's effects." Voice Youth Advocates

Includes glossary and bibliographical references

Hyman, Bruce M.

Obsessive-compulsive disorder; by Bruce M. Hyman and Cherry Pedrick. Twenty-First Century Books 2003 96p (The Twenty-first century medical library) $26.90   **616.85**

1. Obsessive-compulsive disorder

ISBN 0-7613-2758-4   LC 2002-14252

Contents: What is OCD?; The symptoms of OCD; Treatment of OCD; The impact on family and friends; Living with OCD

Examines the anxiety disorder known as OCD, its symptoms and manifestations, how it can be controlled and treated, and, through case studies, what it is like to live with obsessive-compulsive disorder

"With little else written specifically for young adults on this topic—which has risen to prominence recently in the popular media—this will be useful to report writers as well as to those concerned about their own anxieties." Booklist

Includes glossary and bibliographical references

Landau, Elaine

Dyslexia; by Elaine Landau. Franklin Watts 2004 79p (Life balance) lib bdg $19.50; pa $6.95 (5 and up)   **616.85**

1. Dyslexia

ISBN 0-531-12217-4 (lib bdg); 0-531-16612-0 (pa)
    LC 2003-7142

Contents: Being dyslexic; Dyslexia; Getting help; Questions and answers about dyslexia

"Narration by dyslexics combines with an overview of the disorder to give readers an informative and thought-provoking look at this often misunderstood condition. Beginning with the struggles of a young student to cover for his difficulties, the book goes on to describe the various manifestations of dyslexia, therapies, and outcomes." SLJ

Includes glossary and bibliographical references

Moragne, Wendy

Depression. 21st Cent. Bks. (Brookfield) 2001 112p il (Twenty-first century medical library) lib bdg $26.90 (7 and up)   **616.85**

1. Depression (Psychology)

ISBN 0-7613-1774-0   LC 00-36424

"Moragne presents the stories of seven teens diagnosed with different forms of depression, following the kids from the onset of their condition to successful treatment. Her profiles are respectful as well as thorough, including a surprising amount of information about symptoms, kinds of depression, causative factors, treatment . . . and the impact on one's self-esteem and personal relationships. . . . Difficult medical information . . . is presented clearly and without condescension." Booklist

Includes glossary and bibliographical references

Ng, Gina
Everything you need to know about self-mutilation; a helping book for teens who hurt themselves. Rosen Pub. Group 1998 64p il (Need to know library) lib bdg $25.25 (7 and up)
616.85
1. Self-mutilation 2. Adolescent psychology
ISBN 0-8239-2758-X   LC 98-20115
Explores ways of dealing with the anger and emotional pain that may cause teens to mutilate themselves
Includes bibliographical references

Sanders, Pete
Anorexia and bulimia; by Pete Sanders and Steve Myers; illustrated by Mike Lacy and Liz Sawyer. Copper Beech Bks. 1999 32p il (What do you know about) lib bdg $23.90   **616.85**
1. Anorexia nervosa 2. Bulimia
ISBN 0-7613-0914-4   LC 98-47318
First published 1995 in the United Kingdom with title: Anorexia, bulimia, and other eating disorders
This look at the nature, causes, and effects of anorexia and bulimia focuses on "Nicky, who looks about 12 or 13, decides she's too fat and stops eating on a regular basis. In addition to her self-image problem, the girl misses her father after her parents' recent divorce. She resorts to lying about when and where she eats and finally gets caught. Her mother eventually seeks professional help for her daughter." SLJ

Sheen, Barbara, 1949-
Attention deficit disorder. Lucent Bks. 2001 96p il (Diseases and disorders series) $27.45
616.85
1. Attention deficit disorder
ISBN 1-56006-828-0   LC 00-10557
In her discussion of attention deficit disorder "Sheen covers its history, diagnosis, treatment, and solutions. . . . Current and future research is also mentioned. . . . A solid choice for students with a personal interest in or research requests on the topic." SLJ
Includes bibliographical references

Silverstein, Alvin
Depression; {by} Alvin and Virginia Silverstein and Laura Silverstein Nunn. Enslow Pubs. 1997 128p il (Diseases and people) lib bdg $26.60 (7 and up)   **616.85**
1. Depression (Psychology)
ISBN 0-89490-713-1   LC 97-1789
Discusses the causes, symptoms, and treatments of depression, examining the different types of depression and their effects on the individual and on society
This "is an exceptional treatment of a difficult and sometimes controversial subject. . . . The authors do a splendid job of avoiding tediousness and complication. . . . At the same time, they avoid oversimplification." Sci Books Films
Includes glossary and bibliographical references

Smith, Erica
Anorexia nervosa; when food is the enemy. Rosen Pub. Group 1999 64p il (Teen health library of eating disorder prevention) lib bdg $26.50 (7 and up)   **616.85**
1. Anorexia nervosa
ISBN 0-8239-2766-0   LC 98-29713
Describes the origins and symptoms of anorexia nervosa, who is at risk, why it develops in certain individuals, and how it can be controlled by healthy eating habits
Includes bibliographical references

Stewart, Gail, 1949-
Phobias; by Gail B. Stewart. Lucent Bks. 2001 96p il (Diseases and disorders series) lib bdg $27.45   **616.85**
1. Phobias
ISBN 1-56006-726-8   LC 00-10223
The author discusses the history, symptoms, and treatment of phobias
"A solid addition to mental-health sections." SLJ
Includes bibliographical references

Tocci, Salvatore
Down syndrome. Watts 2000 144p il lib bdg $20 (7 and up)   **616.85**
1. Down syndrome
ISBN 0-531-11589-5   LC 99-31019
"A Venture book"
This "book explores the history and causes of Down Syndrome and discusses how a child is affected during infancy, early school years, and adolescence, including sexual maturity." Book Rep
"Practical, informative, and upbeat, the book is a fine source for school and personal research." Booklist
Includes glossary and bibliographical references

Trueit, Trudi Strain
ADHD. Franklin Watts 2004 79p il (Life balance) $19.55 (5 and up)   **616.85**
1. Attention deficit disorder
ISBN 0-531-12261-1   LC 2003-7154
The author "examines the controversy surrounding ADHD, as well as the symptoms, possible causes, and methods of treatment." Publisher's note
"Trueit explains ADHD well. . . . [This book offers] solid, easy-to-understand information." SLJ

The **truth** about eating disorders; Mark J. Kittleson, general editor; William Kane, adviser; Richelle Rennegarbe, adviser; Gerri Freid Kramer, principal author. Facts on File 2004 166p il $35 (7 and up)   **616.85**
1. Eating disorders
ISBN 0-8160-5300-6   LC 2004-6389
This discusses anorexia, bulimia, fad diets, and laxative abuse, the causes of eating disorders, how to recognize the disorders, the portrayal of eating disorders in the media, and obesity and weight control.
This title does "an excellent job of providing accurate information for teens. For reports or for self-help, [it belongs] in any library serving young adults." SLJ
Includes glossary and bibliographical references

The **truth** about fear and depression; Mark J. Kittleson, general editor; William Kane, adviser; Richelle Rennegarbe, adviser; Heather Denkmire, principal author. Facts on File 2004 164p il $35 (7 and up)   **616.85**
1. Depression (Psychology) 2. Anxiety
ISBN 0-8160-5301-4   LC 2004-7364
This "title includes discussions of anxiety disorders and their treatment, causes of depression, and defense mechanisms. . . . [This title does] an excellent job of providing accurate information for teens. For reports or for self-help, [it belongs] in any library serving young adults." SLJ
Includes glossary and bibliographical references

Vollstadt, Elizabeth Weiss, 1942-
Teen eating disorders. Lucent Bks. 1999 112p il (Teen issues) lib bdg $27.45 (7 and up)
                    616.85
1. Eating disorders
ISBN 1-56006-516-8   LC 99-10031
"After defining eating disorders, Vollstadt discusses possible causes and physical consequences (there's a separate section on eating disorders among males), and clearly explains current treatments. She integrates many anecdotal stories, but the tone of text remains detached and objective." Booklist
Includes bibliographical references

Walker, Pamela
Understanding the risk of diet drugs. Rosen Pub. Group 2000 138p (Teen eating disorder prevention book) lib bdg $25.25   **616.85**
1. Appetite depressants 2. Weight loss 3. Eating disorders
ISBN 0-8239-2991-4   LC 00-9129
Discusses what diet drugs are, the difference between prescription, over-the-counter, and herbal diet drugs, and healthy alternatives to such drugs
"Walker paints a vivid portrait of teens (primarily young women) and their attitudes about weight, body image, and beauty. . . . Neither preachy nor histrionic, this book . . . has the power to really help its intended audience." Booklist
Includes bibliographical references

Wiltshire, Paula
Dyslexia. Raintree Steck-Vaughn Pubs. 2003 64p il (Health issues) lib bdg $28.54 (5 and up)
                    616.85
1. Dyslexia
ISBN 0-7398-5221-3   LC 2002-16377
Contents: The dyslexic brain: what makes someone dyslexic?; Diagnosing dyslexia: when and how to get assessed; Reading and writing: cracking the code; Math, music and maps: other effects of dyslexia; The dyslexic student: techniques for success
A comprehensive look at dyslexia, a learning disability that affects up to ten percent of the population of the Western world, covering its definitions, causes, assessment, and treatments
The book is "comprehensive and not written down for

young people. The color photographs and the bright design help make the [text] more accessible." Booklist
Includes glossary and bibliographical references

Wolff, Lisa, 1954-
Teen depression. Lucent Bks. 1999 112p il (Teen issues) lib bdg $27.45   **616.85**
1. Depression (Psychology)
ISBN 1-56006-519-2   LC 98-16379
Discusses the nature, possible causes, special problems, and both conventional and alternative treatments of depression
"Wolff's prose is clear. . . . {This} will easily satisfy class assignments." Booklist
Includes bibliographical references

616.86   Substance abuse (Drug abuse)

Banfield, Susan
Inside recovery; how the twelve step program can work for you. Rosen Pub. Group 1998 64p il (Drug abuse prevention library) $25.25
                    616.86
1. Twelve-step programs 2. Alcoholism 3. Drug abuse
ISBN 0-8239-2634-6   LC 98-11797
Describes the practices and principles of twelve-step programs, how they can be used in dealing with such problems as alcoholism and drug addiction, and how to get involved in them
"Includes a glossary, a listing of various twelve step programs, a further reading list, and an index. The book is packed with information that should be valuable to the curious, those needing help, and the researcher." Book Rep

Bridgers, Jay
Everything you need to know about having an addictive personality. Rosen Pub. Group 1998 64p il (Need to know library) lib bdg $25.25 (7 and up)   **616.86**
1. Compulsive behavior 2. Drug abuse
ISBN 0-8239-2777-6   LC 98-8496
Discusses the nature of addictions to gambling, food, sex, alcohol, and other drugs, how they form and develop, their negative effects, and how to deal with them
Includes bibliographical references

Hyde, Margaret Oldroyd, 1917-
Mind drugs; by Margaret O. Hyde with Duke D. Fisher, Elizabeth Forsyth, Allan Y. Cohen. 6th ed. Millbrook Press 1998 128p lib bdg $24.90 (7 and up)   **616.86**
1. Drugs 2. Drug abuse
ISBN 0-7613-0970-5   LC 98-20392
First published 1968 by McGraw-Hill
A "survey of and current attitudes toward the use and abuse of mind-altering substances, including LSD, uppers, downers, marijuana, and legal drugs. Also included

Hyde, Margaret Oldroyd, 1917-—*Continued*
are chapters on the legalization controversy and alternatives to drugs. Lists of organizations, hotlines, and websites are appended." Horn Book Guide
Includes bibliographical references

Papa, Susan
Addiction. Blackbirch Press 2001 64p il (Amazing brain) lib bdg $24.95 **616.86**
1. Drug abuse
ISBN 1-56711-421-0   LC 00-11948
This "examines the ways in which the chemicals in various drugs, ranging from nicotine to heroin, affect the brain and how dependency develops. . . . The information is condensed, straightforward, and readable, supplemented by excellent color diagrams." Booklist
Includes glossary and bibliographical references

Sheen, Barbara, 1949-
Teen alcoholism; by Barbara Sheen. Lucent Books 2004 112p il (Teen issues) lib bdg $28.70 (7 and up) **616.86**
1. Teenagers—Alcohol use 2. Alcoholism
ISBN 1-560-06514-1   LC 2003-8996
Examines how and why some teenagers become alcoholics and discusses the effects of teen alcoholism, as well as treatment and prevention measures.
"Graphs, diagrams, and photos enhance gripping testimonials . . . that, without becoming didactic, argue strongly against teen drinking." Booklist
Includes glossary and bibliographical references

Shepherd, K. R. (Kenneth Ronald)
Drugs and low self-esteem; {by} Kenneth R. Shepherd. Rosen Pub. Group 1998 64p il (Drug abuse prevention library) lib bdg $25.25 (7 and up) **616.86**
1. Drug abuse 2. Self-esteem
ISBN 0-8239-2826-8   LC 98-8497
Discusses various aspects of low self-esteem, how it can lead to drug abuse, the negative consequences, and where to get help for such a problem
Includes bibliographical references

616.89   Mental disorders

Baldwin, Carol
Autism. Heinemann Lib. 2003 32p il (Health matters) lib bdg $22.79 (4-6) **616.89**
1. Autism
ISBN 1-4034-0250-7   LC 2001-7973
Contents: What is autism?; What causes autism?; Diagnosing autism; Treating autism; Classmates with autism; How you can help; Visiting friends with autism; Autism success stories
This "inviting, colorful [book] will attract students who need a clear, readable introduction to [autism]." SLJ
Includes glossary and bibliographical references

Borenstein, Gerri C.
Therapy; by Gerri C. Borenstein. F. Watts 2003 79p (Life balance) $19.95 **616.89**
1. Psychotherapy
ISBN 0-531-12269-7   LC 2003-109
Also available in paperback from Scholastic
Contents: Mental health matters; Spotting a problem; Choosing a therapist; The first session; Giving therapy a try; Keeping the balance
Examines the behaviors or feelings that might lead one to seek psychotherapy, what to expect during a counseling session, getting the most out of treatment, and knowing when it is time to end therapy.
This is written "in clear, reassuring language. . . . {It is} well organized and written in an approachable manner." SLJ
Includes bibliographical references

Kent, Deborah, 1948-
Snake pits, talking cures, & magic bullets; a history of mental illness. 21st Cent. Bks. (Brookfield) 2003 160p il lib bdg $26.90 **616.89**
1. Mental illness
ISBN 0-7613-2704-5   LC 2002-11208
Looks at how the mentally ill have been treated throughout history, focusing on advances made in the 19th and 20th centuries regarding mental hospitals, medications, and social acceptance
"An excellent history peppered with fascinating accounts. . . . Black-and-white archival photographs and reproductions appear throughout. . . . This is a fine treatment of a topic not heavily covered for this audience." SLJ
Includes glossary and bibliographical references

Mental health information for teens; edited by Karen Bellenir. Omnigraphics 2001 406p (Teen health series) $58 (7 and up) **616.89**
1. Mental health 2. Teenagers—Health and hygiene 3. Adolescent psychology
ISBN 0-7808-0442-2   LC 2001-36364
"Health tips about mental health and mental illness: including facts about anxiety, depression, suicide, eating disorders, obsessive-compulsive disorders, panic attacks, phobias, schizophrenia, and more." Title page
"In both language and approach, this . . . is on target for teens needing information on mental health concerns. . . . Back matter, which includes contact resources and a section on alcohol and substance abuse, adds to the value of this handy, manageable resource." Booklist
Includes bibliographical references

Stewart, Gail, 1949-
People with mental illness; by Gail B. Stewart; photographs by Carl Franzén. Lucent Bks. 2003 96p il (Other America) lib bdg $21.96 (7 and up) **616.89**
1. Mental illness
ISBN 1-59018-237-5   LC 2002-7602
Presents the personal stories of four people with mental illness, discussing how each handles the daily demands of family, education, social life, and medical

Stewart, Gail, 1949-—*Continued*
treatment and finds the strength and courage to continue
the battle against this common debilitating condition
"An approachable, excellent resource." SLJ
Includes bibliographical references

A **student's** guide to mental health & wellness;
{by} Creative Media Applications. Greenwood
Press 2004 4v p. cmp set $160   **616.89**
1. Psychology 2. Mental health 3. Mental illness
ISBN 0-313-32548-0   LC 2003-44817
Contents: v1 Words and terms; v2 Important people;
v3 Debatable issues; v. 4 Disorders, diseases and treatments

This "set examines the evolution of psychology from
its earliest roots to its contemporary view as a well-
established and respected science. The first volume,
Words and Terms, is a well-organized collection of lucid
and relevant definitions. . . . Important People describes
the intriguing history of psychology; research methods;
types of therapy; and the pioneering work of psychologists such as Sigmund Freud, Karen Horney, William
James, Jean Piaget, and B. F. Skinner. In Debatable Issues, contemporary controversial topics, such as the ethics of animal experimentation, the relationship of violence in children and the media, and the prevalence of
the ADHD diagnosis, are discussed. The last volume,
Disorders, Diseases, and Treatments, covers mental illnesses such as depression, anxiety disorders, conduct disorders, and schizophrenia, and provides useful material
about their symptoms, diagnosis, and treatment options."
SLJ
Includes bibliographical references

616.9   Other diseases

Abrams, Liesa
Chronic fatigue syndrome. Lucent Bks. 2003
96p il (Diseases and disorders) lib bdg $27.45
                                              616.9
1. Chronic fatigue syndrome
ISBN 1-590-18039-9   LC 2002-9459
Examines the symptoms, treatment options, and mys-
tery of chronic fatigue syndrome, ongoing research into
its causes, and how to live with this disease
This title is "well written and well organized." SLJ
Includes bibliographical references

Monroe, Judy
Influenza and other viruses. LifeMatters 2002
64p il (Perspectives on disease and illness) lib bdg
$23.93   **616.9**
1. Viruses 2. Influenza 3. Cold (Disease) 4. Diseases
ISBN 0-7368-1025-0   LC 00-13233
This discusses viruses and how they attack the body
and treating and preventing colds and flu and other viral
diseases
"Simple and well-organized." Book Rep
Includes glossary and bibliographical references

Silverstein, Alvin
Chickenpox and shingles; {by} Alvin and
Virginia Silverstein and Laura Silverstein Nunn.
Enslow Pubs. 1998 128p il (Diseases and people)
lib bdg $26.60 (7 and up)   **616.9**
1. Chickenpox 2. Shingles (Disease)
ISBN 0-89490-715-8   LC 97-34041
"The book begins with a general profile of the two
diseases mentioned in the title—their causes, transmission, symptoms, treatment, and prevention. In subsequent
chapters, each disease is described in greater detail. The
relationship between these two viral infections is discussed, and how one may develop immunity to them is
examined." Sci Books Films
Includes bibliographical references

Lyme disease; {by} Alvin Silverstein, Virginia
Silverstein, Laura Silverstein Nunn. Watts 2000
63p il lib bdg $24.50; pa $8.95   **616.9**
1. Lyme disease
ISBN 0-531-11751-0 (lib bdg); 0-531-11751-0 (pa)
                                      LC 99-42674
"Watts library"
Discusses the causes, symptoms, and treatment of
Lyme disease, as well as ways to protect against it
This "will be helpful for reports as well as for answer-
ing medical questions." Booklist
Includes bibliographical references

Measles and rubella; {by} Alvin, Virginia, and
Robert Silverstein. Enslow Pubs. 1997 128p il
(Diseases and people) lib bdg $26.60 (7 and up)
                                              616.9
1. Measles 2. Rubella
ISBN 0-89490-714-X   LC 97-3785
Tracing the medical history of measles and rubella
"from ancient to modern times, this solid work considers
symptoms and transmission, including discussion about
outbreaks on college campuses and among preschool
children. . . . The authors also explore the development
of the measles vaccine and explain why the diseases continue to pose a health problem. An outstanding curricular
supplement . . . as well as a handy, readable reference
source." Booklist
Includes glossary and bibliographical references

Smart, P. (Paul), 1957-
Everything you need to know about
mononucleosis. Rosen Pub. Group 1998 63p il
(Need to know library) lib bdg $25.25 (7 and up)
                                              616.9
1. Mononucleosis
ISBN 0-8239-2550-1   LC 98-10119
Discusses the nature and diagnosis of mononucleosis
and how to protect against it or cope with having it
Includes bibliographical references

Veggeberg, Scott
Lyme disease. Enslow Pubs. 1998 104p il
(Diseases and people) lib bdg $20.95 (7 and up)
                                              616.9
1. Lyme disease
ISBN 0-7660-1052-X   LC 97-34042

Veggeberg, Scott—*Continued*
Explores the history of Lyme disease and discusses its symptoms, diagnosis, prevention, and treatment
"This book covers a wide range of information about Lyme disease. The information, accurate and up to date, is presented in ways that are clear, interesting, and imaginative." Sci Books Films
Includes glossary and bibliographical references

Willett, Edward, 1959-
Ebola virus. Enslow Pubs. 2003 112p il map (Diseases and people) $26.60   **616.9**
1. Ebola virus
ISBN 0-7660-1595-5   LC 2002-10149
Contents: Profile; A terrifying killer; The history of ebola; What is ebola hemorrhagic fever?; Diagnosing ebola hemorrhagic fever; Treatment of ebola hemorrhagic fever; Social implications of ebola hemorrhagic fever; Preventing ebola hemorrhagic fever; Research and future prospects; Q&A; Ebola hemorrhagic fever timeline
The author "explores the history and symptoms of the Ebola virus, from how it was first discovered to treatment options available for those who may contract this extremely rare—but deadly—disease. He also addresses the media attention and social factors that may add to the fear and stigma related to this virus." Publisher's note
Includes bibliographical references

616.95 Sexually transmitted diseases

Curran, Christine Perdan
Sexually transmitted diseases. Enslow Pubs. 1998 128p il (Diseases and people) lib bdg $26.60 (7 and up)   **616.95**
1. Sexually transmitted diseases
ISBN 0-7660-1050-3   LC 97-44140
Examines the history, symptoms, treatment, and prevention of such sexually transmitted diseases as syphilis, gonorrhea, herpes, AIDS, and hepatitis
Includes glossary and bibliographical references

Little, Marjorie
Sexually transmitted diseases. Chelsea House 1999 110p il (21st century health and wellness) lib bdg $25.95 (7 and up)   **616.95**
1. Sexually transmitted diseases
ISBN 0-7910-5528-0
First published 1991 in Encyclopedia of health series
Discusses the symptoms, diagnosis, treatment, and complications of such diseases as syphilis, gonorrhea, herpes, and HIV

616.97 Diseases of the immune system

Check, William A.
AIDS; introduction by C. Everett Koop. rev ed. Chelsea House 1998 c1999 128p il (Encyclopedia of health) lib bdg $25.95   **616.97**
1. AIDS (Disease)
ISBN 0-7910-4885-3   LC 98-195764

First published 1988
"Each chapter follows an AIDS-related issue from its late 1970s—early 1980s identification and discusses the social and medical changes in information, attitude, and treatment to the present. . . . The book does an excellent job of updating YA collections with current AIDS/HIV information while integrating the disease's history appropriately throughout the text." Booklist

Latta, Sara L.
Allergies. Enslow Pubs. 1998 128p (Diseases and people) lib bdg $20.95 (7 and up)
                616.97
1. Allergy
ISBN 0-7660-1048-1   LC 97-34156
Explores the history of information about allergies and discusses symptoms, diagnosis, prevention, and treatments
"Fictional case histories and true anecdotes add interest. Black-and-white photos and information boxes are included." Horn Book Guide
Includes glossary and bibliographical references

McPhee, Andrew T.
AIDS. Watts 2000 63p il lib bdg $24.50; pa $8.95 (5 and up)   **616.97**
1. AIDS (Disease)
ISBN 0-531-11779-0 (lib bdg); 0-531-16528 0 (pa)
                    LC 99-45288
"Watts library"
Discusses how AIDS is spread, diagnosed, and treated. Methods of protecting oneself from the disease are presented
Includes bibliographical references

Parker, Steve
Allergies; Steve Parker. Heinemann Library 2004 56p il (Just the facts) lib bdg $31.36 (5 and up)   **616.97**
1. Allergy
ISBN 1-4034-4598-2   LC 2003-10872
Contents: Allergies; Early history of allergies; Recent history of allergies; What is an allergy?; Different types of allergies; Who is affected?; More and more allergies; Allergies in the nose; Hay fever and similar allergies; Skin allergies; Food allergies; Drug and microbe allergies; Allergies to bites and stings; Allergy can be deadly=anaphylaxis; Is it an allergy?; Tackling an allergy; Living with an allergy; Allergy out and about; Prevention and treatment; Medical science and allergies; Complementary therapies; Can allergies be cured?; Hopes for the future; Allergies: same but different
Defines what an allergy is, various types of allergies, some prevention and treatment methods, and other issues related to allergic conditions
This is "well written and organized." SLJ
Includes bibliographical references

Shein, Lorl, 1957-
AIDS. Lucent Bks. 1998 112p il (Lucent overview series) lib bdg $28.70 (7 and up)
                616.97
1. AIDS (Disease)
ISBN 1-56006-193-6   LC 98-9461

Shein, Lori, 1957——*Continued*
An overview of AIDS including information about its discovery, methods of prevention, testing for HIV infection, the global epidemic, and what the future holds
Includes bibliographical references

616.99 Tumors and cancers

Abramovitz, Melissa
Leukemia. Lucent Bks. 2003 112p il (Diseases and disorders) lib bdg $27.45   **616.99**
1. Leukemia
ISBN 1-560-06863-9   LC 2002-3668
Contents: What is leukemia?; What causes leukemia?; Leukemia treatment; Living with leukemia; What the future holds
"Abramovitz addresses the different types of leukemia and how they are diagnosed, as well as the possible roles of electromagnetic fields, genetics, and chemicals in the development of the disease. New research techniques are described in detail, including stem cells, cytokines, replacement DNA, and Gleevec, a drug that targets a specific part of a gene." SLJ
Includes glossary and bibliographical references

Bardhan-Quallen, Sudipta
Chemotherapy; by Sudipta Bardhan. Lucent Books 2004 128p il (Great medical discoveries) $28.70 (7 and up)   **616.99**
1. Cancer—Chemotherapy
ISBN 1-560-06926-0   LC 2003-9592
Contents: Ancient hopes, modern miracles; The search for a magic bullet; Poisons that heal; The early arsenal; The problem with poison; Genetic origins, molecular cures; An alternate approach; Smart bombs
Discusses the impact of chemotherapy as a treatment for cancer, its history and development, challenges it presents, and future research.
"This fascinating exploration into the history and challenges of cancer treatment will be useful for both student researchers and cancer survivors." SLJ
Includes bibliographical references

Benowitz, Steven I.
Cancer. Enslow Pubs. 1999 128p il (Diseases and people) lib bdg $26.60 (7 and up)
616.99
1. Cancer
ISBN 0-7660-1181-X   LC 98-36123
Discusses the history, symptoms, diagnosis, treatment, prevention, and different kinds of cancer, as well as the possible impact of research on the future
Includes bibliographical references

Lamb, Kirsten
Cancer. Raintree Steck-Vaughn Pubs. 2003 64p il (Health issues) lib bdg $28.54   **616.99**
1. Cancer
ISBN 0-7398-5219-1   LC 2002-16383

Describes different types of cancer, their causes, symptoms, and effective treatments. Also discusses healthy habits that help lower the risk of contracting various cancers
This is "packed with information. . . . Boldly colored photos and diagrams abound." SLJ
Includes glossary and bibliographical references

Peacock, Judith, 1942-
Breast cancer. LifeMatters 2001 64p il (Perspectives on disease and illness) lib bdg $23.93   **616.99**
1. Breast cancer
ISBN 0-7368-1028-5   LC 00-12364
This discusses breast cancer and its types, diagnosis, and treatment
"Simple and well-organized." Book Rep
Includes glossary and bibliographical references

Hodgkin's disease. LifeMatters 2001 64p il (Perspectives on disease and illness) lib bdg $23.95   **616.99**
1. Hodgkin's disease
ISBN 0-7368-1027-7   LC 00-12614
This offers information on the definition, diagnosis, and treatment of Hodgkin's disease and on living with the disease
The information is "simple and well-organized." Book Rep
Includes glossary and bibliographical references

Yount, Lisa
Cancer. Lucent Bks. 1999 111p il (Lucent overview series) lib bdg $28.70 (7 and up)
616.99
1. Cancer
ISBN 1-56006-363-7   LC 98-54797
First published 1991
Yount presents a discussion of how "cancer cells develop and the different types of the disease. While offering information on the possible carcinogenic effects of food additives, smoking, pesticides, and even electromagnetic fields, she explains difficult concepts in simple terms. Diagnostic techniques and traditional and alternative treatment options are presented including chemotherapy, radiation, gene therapy, biofeedback, and reflexology." SLJ
Includes bibliographical references

617 Miscellaneous branches of medicine. Surgery

Giddens, Sandra
Future techniques in surgery; [by] Sandra and Owen Giddens. Rosen Pub. Group 2003 64p il (Library of future medicine) lib bdg $26.50
617
1. Surgery
ISBN 0-8239-3667-8   LC 2001-5598
Contents: Surgery past; Surgery present; The future of surgery

Giddens, Sandra—Continued

Reviews the evolution of medical surgery during two hundred years and predicts new procedures that may lead to greater safety and efficacy

This "is a competent overview of the topic supported with colorful illustrations and many photos." Libr Media Connect

Includes glossary and bibliographical references

617.1 Injuries and wounds. Sports medicine

Crash; the body in crisis; Elaine Pascoe, book editor. Blackbirch Press 2004 48p il (Body story) $23.70; pa $9.95   **617.1**

1. Wounds and injuries 2. Traffic accidents

ISBN 1-410-30062-5; 1-410-30183-4 (pa)

LC 2003-12035

Contents: Brain power; Rushed to surgery; Laura's collapse

Describes what happens when David and Laura are in a car accident and suffer serious injuries, ranging from a ruptured blood vessel near Laura's spleen to a major artery that bursts in David's brain.

This volume is "bubbling over with informative, full-color photographs. . . . The [text is] amazingly concise and [takes] extraordinarily complex processes and [makes] them clearly understandable to the intended audience." SLJ

Includes bibliographical references

Landau, Elaine

Head and brain injuries. Enslow Pubs. 2002 112p il (Diseases and people) lib bdg $26.60 (7 and up)   **617.1**

1. Brain—Wounds and injuries

ISBN 0-7660-1473-8   LC 00-12074

This describes traumatic brain injury, its causes, treatment and recovery, prevention, its relation to society, and research

Includes glossary and bibliographical references

Sports injuries information for teens; health tips about sports injuries and injury prevention; edited by Joyce Brennfleck Shannon. Omnigraphics 2004 il (Teen health series) $58 (7 and up)   **617.1**

1. Sports medicine 2. Wounds and injuries

ISBN 0-7808-0447-3

"Including facts about specific injuries, emergency treatment, rehabilitation, sports, safety, competition stress, fitness, sports nutrition, steroid risks, and more." Title page

"Along with physiological information about injuries and treatments, the special needs of teen athletes are considered in this comprehensive overview. . . . The information presented is copious and concise." SLJ

Includes bibliographical references

617.6 Dentistry

Lee, Jordan

Coping with braces and other orthodontic work. Rosen Pub. Group 1998 95p il lib bdg $26.50   **617.6**

1. Orthodontics

ISBN 0-8239-2721-0   LC 98-9276

"Lee describes various procedures involved in orthodontic care from the taking of impressions to the removal of the hardware. Discussions about the assorted accidents that can happen, how various appliances work, and how the doctor develops a plan of treatment are also included. The text is well written and reassuring, reminding readers that treatments are available to reduce or eliminate pain." SLJ

Includes bibliographical references

617.8 Otology and audiology

Landau, Elaine

Deafness. 21st Cent. Bks. (NY) 1994 64p il (Understanding illness) lib bdg $24.90   **617.8**

1. Deaf

ISBN 0-8050-2993 1   LC 94-13843

"The text opens with a series of vignettes about the varying presentations of deafness and then moves on to a discussion of the causes of hearing loss. Case histories are also used to highlight issues concerning the acceptance of individuals with deafness in our society; this is followed by a recounting of achievements of other individuals with impaired hearing. The material is clear and easy to read. . . . The book is a useful introduction to the issues presented by impaired hearing." Sci Books Films

Includes glossary and bibliographical references

617.9 Transplantation of tissue and organs

Fullick, Ann

Rebuilding the body; organ transplantation. Heinemann Lib. 2002 64p il (Science at the edge) lib bdg $32.79; pa $9.50 (7 and up)   **617.9**

1. Transplantation of organs, tissues, etc.

ISBN 1-58810-700-0 (lib bdg); 1-4034-4122-7 (pa)

LC 2001-6082

Contents: The organs of the body; Organ failure; New parts for old; How is it done?; Rejection; Life from death; Lucy's story; Pushing the boundaries; Xenotransplantation; The cutting edge; Stem cell research

This "sets the stage for understanding complex transplant procedures by first explaining how the major organs function and some of the causes of organ failure, then discussing issues related to compatibility, organ preservation, rejection, and the ethics of organ donation and transplant research. . . . {This title is} nicely written, well organized, and filled with lots of visuals." Booklist

Includes glossary and bibliographical references

McClellan, Marilyn
Organ and tissue transplants; medical miracles and challenges. Enslow Pubs. 2003 128p il (Issues in focus) lib bdg $20.95 (7 and up)

617.9

1. Transplantation of organs, tissues, etc. 2. Artificial organs
ISBN 0-7660-1943-8   LC 2002-8401
Explores the history of organ transplantation, as well as its medical, ethical, financial, and personal aspects, providing insights into the latter through stories of organ donors and recipients
"With its useful black-and-white photos, anatomical diagram, pie chart, and statistics, this book is equally approachable for curious readers and report writers." SLJ
Includes glossary and bibliographical references

Murphy, Wendy B.
Spare parts; from peg legs to gene splices; {by} Wendy Murphy. 21st Cent. Bks. (Brookfield) 2001 160p il lib bdg $24.90 (7 and up)   **617.9**
1. Artificial limbs 2. Artificial organs 3. Transplantation of organs, tissues, etc.
ISBN 0-7613-1355-9   LC 00-20883
Discusses historic and modern devices and other means of replacing damaged or missing parts in humans, including organ transplants, genetic engineering, and computer-engineered limbs
"Murphy doesn't waste a word, and her brisk presentation makes reading effortless and absorbing." Booklist
Includes bibliographical references

Rosaler, Maxine
Bionics. Blackbirch Press 2003 48p il (Science on the edge) lib bdg $23.70 (5 and up)

617.9

1. Bionics
ISBN 1-567-11784-8   LC 2002-15970
Discusses the history of replacement body parts, current accomplishments in the field, and visions of future technology.
Includes glossary and bibliographical references

Wilkinson, Beth
Coping with the dangers of tattooing, body piercing, and branding. Rosen Pub. Group 1998 126p il lib bdg $26.50   **617.9**
1. Tattooing 2. Body piercing
ISBN 0-8239-2717-2   LC 97-45683
Gives information needed to make an informed decision about body modification including the laws and safety regulations surrounding this business
"A clearly written look at body-making arts. . . . The dangers are explained and strongly emphasized throughout the book, and readers are cautioned against making decisions in haste, at too early an age, or otherwise ill-advisedly." SLJ
Includes glossary and bibliographical references

618.1   Gynecology

Diamond, Shifra N.
Everything you need to know about going to the gynecologist. Rosen Pub. Group 1999 64p il (Need to know library) lib bdg $25.25 (7 and up)

618.1

1. Gynecologists 2. Sex education 3. Women—Health and hygiene
ISBN 0-8239-2839-X   LC 98-40929
Describes what to expect in a gynecological examination, discusses birth control methods, the female reproductive system, and possible health problems and treatment
"An appendix of organization contact information, including some Web sites, may help readers find more detailed information." SLJ
Includes bibliographical references

Fullick, Ann
Test tube babies; in-vitro fertilization. Heinemann Lib. 2002 64p il (Science at the edge) lib bdg $27.86 (7 and up)   **618.1**
1. Fertilization in vitro 2. Infertility 3. Reproduction
ISBN 1-58810-703-5   LC 2001-6080
Contents: An everyday miracle; What causes infertility?; Treating infertility; The IVF story; How does IVF work?; The price of success; Doriver's story; Beyond IVF; Ethics, issues, and the law; Where do we go from here?
This "discusses the causes of infertility, the treatments, and ethical issues. The views of major religions are identified, as are laws that have been passed to deal with fertility issues. . . . [This title is] first-rate." SLJ
Includes bibliographical references

Orr, Tamra
Test tube babies; written by Tamra B. Orr. Thomson/Gale 2003 48p il (Science on the edge) lib bdg $23.70 (5 and up)   **618.1**
1. Fertilization in vitro
ISBN 1-56711-788-0   LC 2002-11928
Contents: In the beginning; The current picture; A future of possibilities
Examines the causes of infertility, the history of in vitro fertilization, the steps involved in creating a 'test tube baby,' and ethical questions the technology has raised
Includes bibliographical references

618.2   Obstetrics

Jackson, Donna M., 1959-
Twin tales; the magic and mystery of multiple birth; by Donna M. Jackson. Little, Brown 2001 48p il $16.95 (4 and up)   **618.2**
1. Multiple birth 2. Twins
ISBN 0-316-45431-1   LC 99-44741
"Megan Tingley books"

Jackson, Donna M., 1959-—_Continued_
Explores aspects of the topic of twins, including why and how they are born, twin telepathy, identical and fraternal twins, and separation of twins

"Jackson blends scientific facts with interesting personal anecdotes to create an informative and intriguing look at twins. The text is clearly written, and the tone remains lively throughout." SLJ

Includes glossary

Landau, Elaine
Multiple births. Watts 1998 64p il lib bdg $23
618.2
1. Multiple birth
ISBN 0-531-20309-3   LC 96-40224
"A First book"
Explores the phenomenon of multiple births, including those of twins, triplets, and larger groupings, discussing possible causes, medical issues, effects on the families, and other moral and practical concerns
Includes bibliographical references

620.1   Engineering mechanics and materials

Graham, Ian, 1953-
Water power. Raintree Steck-Vaughn Pubs. 1999 48p il (Energy forever?) lib bdg $29.93
620.1
1. Water power
ISBN 0-8172-5363-7   LC 98-13438
Examines the historical uses of water as a source of energy, the advantages and disadvantages, and new advances in harnessing water power
Includes bibliographical references

Kassinger, Ruth
Glass: from Cinderella's slippers to fiber optics; [by] Ruth G. Kassinger. Twenty-First Century Bks. 2003 80p il lib bdg $25.90   **620.1**
1. Glass
ISBN 0-7613-2109-8   LC 2002-5329
Describes the physical composition and characteristics of glass, and presents glassmaking techniques and the various uses made of glass throughout history
This "will catch the interest of a wide variety of readers. The color photographs are clear, interesting, and self-explanatory." Libr Media Connect
Includes bibliographical references

Knapp, Brian J.
Materials science. Grolier 2003 9v il set $319
620.1
1. Materials
ISBN 0-7172-5697-9   LC 2002-44537
Contents: v1 Plastics; v2 Metals; v3 Wood and paper; v4 Ceramics; v5 Glass; v6 Dyes, paints, and adhesives; v7 Fibers; v8 Water; v9 Air
Presents the main scientific properties of materials and how they are determined, as well as how substances can

be manipulated or modified to produce a wide array of materials with an equally wide array of applications

"The volumes are generously enhanced with photographs and appropriate illustrative figures. . . . The written presentations are all brief, but clear and understandable for anyone who has had a general science background." Sci Books Films

621   Applied physics

Adams, Richard C., 1945-
Energy projects for young scientists; {by} Richard C. Adams and Robert Gardner. rev ed. Watts 2002 160p (Projects for young scientists) lib bdg $22.50; pa $9.95 (7 and up)   **621**
1. Power (Mechanics) 2. Science—Experiments 3. Science projects
ISBN 0-531-11666-2; 0-531-16380-6 (pa)
LC 2001-3033
First published 1987 under the authorship of Robert Gardner

Instructions for a variety of projects and experiments demonstrating basic concepts of energy, work, and power, including thermal, electrical, and solar energy, energy of motion and position, and energy conservation
Includes bibliographical references

Challoner, Jack
Energy. Dorling Kindersley 1993 64p il (Eyewitness science) $19.99 (5 and up)
621
1. Energy resources 2. Force and energy
ISBN 1-56458-232-9   LC 92-54479
Surveys various sources of energy and the ways in which they have been harnessed
This "serves well as a first exploration of its topic, emphasizing historical connections but also considering technological and societal aspects. {This book's} striking visual impact will draw in even the most casual readers." SLJ

Silverstein, Alvin
Energy; {by} Alvin Silverstein, Virginia Silverstein, Laura Silverstein Nunn. 21st Cent. Bks. (Brookfield) 1998 64p il $26.90   **621**
1. Energy resources
ISBN 0-7613-3222-7   LC 98-41915
Discusses the sources and uses of different types of energy, both natural and man-made, including electrical, magnetic, light, heat, sound, and nuclear energy
Includes bibliographical references

621.3   Electrical, magnetic, optical, communications, computer engineering; electronics, lighting

Pinna, Simon de
Electricity; photography by Chris Fairclough. Raintree Steck-Vaughn Pubs. 1998 48p il (Science projects) lib bdg $29.93   **621.3**
1. Electricity 2. Science—Experiments
ISBN 0-8172-4945-1   LC 97-24637
Introduces the basic concept of electricity through simple experiments that can be performed at home or at school
Includes bibliographical references

Pollard, Michael, 1931-
The light bulb and how it changed the world. Facts on File 1995 46p il $23   **621.3**
1. Electricity 2. Inventions
ISBN 0-8160-3145-2   LC 94-15226
"This volume first reviews the electric inventions that preceded Edison's light bulb—the battery, the telegraph, and the telephone—and then explains how electricity has been generated, supplied, and used ever since." Publisher's note
Includes bibliographical references

621.36   Optical engineering

Morgan, Nina
Lasers. Raintree Steck-Vaughn Pubs. 1997 48p il (20th century inventions) lib bdg $29.93
621.36
1. Lasers
ISBN 0-8172-4812-9   LC 96-44293
Explains what lasers are and how they are used in communications, medicine, industry, and warfare, as well as possible future uses
Includes glossary

621.381   Electronics

Chorlton, Windsor
The invention of the silicon chip; a revolution in daily life. Heinemann Lib. 2002 32p il (Point of impact) lib bdg $27.79   **621.381**
1. Semiconductors 2. Microelectronics
ISBN 1-58810-554-7   LC 2001-3478
Examines the events surrounding the development of the silicon chip, its uses, and its impact on civilization
This title "would be of interest to researchers and science students who are curious about the history of great discoveries." SLJ
Includes glossary and bibliographical references

Hoare, Stephen
Digital revolution. Raintree Steck-Vaughn Pubs. 1999 48p il (20th century inventions) lib bdg $29.93   **621.381**
1. Electronics
ISBN 0-8172-4897-8   LC 97-32063
"The book is organized by category—entertainment, communications, work, home, and cars. The technologies covered include compact discs (all varieties), telephones, televisions, watches, and cameras. Cutting-edge technology such as DVD (digital videodiscs), HDTV (high-definition television), and global-positioning systems are included as well." SLJ
Includes bibliographical references

621.383   Telegraphy

Coe, Lewis, 1911-
The telegraph; a history of Morse's invention and its predecessors in the United States. McFarland & Co. 1993 184p il pa $29.95 hardcover o.p.   **621.383**
1. Morse, Samuel Finley Breese, 1791-1872
2. Telegraph
ISBN 0-7864-1808-7   LC 92-53597
This study of the development of the telegraph includes brief biographical sketches of Samuel Morse and other inventors
Includes bibliographical references

621.384   Radio and radar

Graham, Ian, 1953-
Radio and television. Raintree Steck-Vaughn Pubs. 2001 47p il (Communications close-up) $29.93   **621.384**
1. Radio 2. Television
ISBN 0-7398-3187-9   LC 00-33288
An introduction to the technology of radio and television covering cables and waves, satellites, closed circuits, digital disks and broadcasting, robot vision, radar and transponders
"Graham is not only knowledgeable about his subject but also adept at clearly explaining complex information. The colorful, attractive illustrations add to the textual explanations." Book Rep
Includes glossary and bibliographical references

621.4   Prime movers and heat engineering

Graham, Ian, 1953-
Wind power. Raintree Steck-Vaughn Pubs. 1999 48p il (Energy forever?) lib bdg $29.93
621.4
1. Wind power
ISBN 0-8172-5364-5   LC 98-25665
Discusses traditional and developing ways of using wind power as a source of energy
Includes bibliographical references

621.43   Internal-combustion engines

Miller, Ron, 1947-
The history of rockets. Watts 1999 128p il lib bdg $20   **621.43**
1. Rocketry
ISBN 0-531-11430-9   LC 97-49808
"A Venture book"
"Miller opens with homespun demonstrations of Isaac Newton's relevant principles, then retraces the chain of experiments, disasters, and refinements that began with Archytas of Tarentum's steam-driven wooden pigeon and culminated in the mighty Saturn 5. . . . Taking pains to point out how many uses rockets have beyond carrying weapons, Miller brings readers into the present era of active space exploration and space-plane designs that look beyond the shuttle, then closes with both a page of recommended books and two pages of Web sites." SLJ

621.47   Solar-energy engineering

Graham, Ian, 1953-
Solar power. Raintree Steck-Vaughn Pubs. 1999 48p il (Energy forever?) lib bdg $29.93
                                                          621.47
1. Solar energy
ISBN 0-8172-5362-9   LC 98-5839
Examines solar energy, its history, uses, advantages and disadvantages, and new developments in the field
Includes bibliographical references

621.48   Nuclear engineering

Kidd, J. S. (Jerry S.)
Quarks and sparks; the story of nuclear power; {by} J.S. Kidd and Renee A. Kidd. Facts on File 1999 146p il (Science and society) $25 (7 and up)
                                                          621.48
1. Nuclear energy
ISBN 0-8160-3587-3   LC 98-44389
Examines the people, events, and motivations leading up to modern-day discoveries and advances in nuclear physics
"Extensive scientific explanations are kept manageable, thanks to consistent references to their historical context; and descriptions of the nuclear race during the Second World War are especially riveting." Booklist
Includes bibliographical references

623.4   Ordnance

Cohen, Daniel, 1936-
The Manhattan Project. 21st Cent. Bks. (Brookfield) 1999 128p il $24.90 (7 and up)
                                                          623.4
1. Manhattan Project 2. Atomic bomb
ISBN 0-7613-0359-6   LC 98-44499

Discusses the personalities and events involved in the research, development and detonation of the atomic bombs built by the United States in the 1940s
"Historically and scientifically illuminating, this well-written, dramatic story of political intrigue and the birth of the arms race conveys the magnitude of one of the twentieth century's most profoundly defining events." Booklist
Includes bibliographical references

Collier, James Lincoln, 1928-
Gunpowder and weaponry. Benchmark Bks. 2004 124p il (Great inventions) lib bdg $37.07
                                                          623.4
1. Military art and science 2. Firearms 3. Gunpowder
ISBN 0-7614-1540-8   LC 2002-156289
Contents: Warfare before gunpowder; Gunpowder changes the ways of war; The rise of the professional army; Europeans export their weapons; The beginnings of the modern army; The Industrial Revolution in weapons; The bloody century; What does it all mean?
This is a history of warfare and weaponry with emphasis on the significance of the invention of gunpowder
Includes bibliographical references

Hamilton, John, 1959-
Weapons of war. Abdo & Daughters 2002 48p (War on terrorism) lib bdg $25.65   **623.4**
1. Military weapons
ISBN 1-57765-673-3   LC 2001-55991
.
Briefly describes the history and gives examples of military weapons and technology including various types of ships, guns, missiles, planes, tanks, and weapons of mass destruction
"Clear and well focused, this highly accessible text delivers the basic facts and the advantages of various craft. Excellent color photos show more than a dozen different planes, as well as five helicopters and other major weapons in use." Booklist

Weapons; an international encyclopedia from 5000 B.C. to 2000 A.D; {by} the Diagram Group. St. Martin's Press 1990 336p il hardcover o.p. paperback available $24.95   **623.4**
1. Weapons—History
ISBN 0-312-03950-6 (pa)   LC 90-28498
First published 1980
This "is a visual display of combat weapons of every century and culture. It is not, however, arranged alphabetically or chronologically. Instead, chapters are ordered by function. . . . The historical and regional indexes will be useful to readers who want to focus on weapons of a particular time or place. . . . The quality of illustrations is what distinguishes Diagram Group publications, and these are up to the usual standards. More than 2,500 black-and-white drawings are included." Booklist
Includes bibliographical references

623.89 Navigation

Morrison, Taylor
The coast mappers. Houghton Mifflin Co 2004
45p il map $16 (5 and up)   **623.89**
1. Davidson, George 2. Maps 3. Surveying 4. Pacific
Coast (North America)
ISBN 0-618-25408-0   LC 2003-13534
Chronicles the difficulties encountered by George Davidson and others as they attempted to create nautical
charts to complete the U.S. Coast Survey of the West
Coast in the mid-nineteenth century.
"Cartographic methods are clearly explained through
both the carefully researched text and the precise illustrations. . . . The artwork clarifies the text, depicts the
breathtaking beauty of the coastline, and adds a sense of
adventure. " SLJ
Includes glossary and bibliographical references

624 Civil engineering

Aaseng, Nathan, 1953-
Construction: building the impossible. Oliver
Press (Minneapolis) 2000 144p il (Innovators)
$21.95   **624**
1. Civil engineering
ISBN 1-88150-859-5   LC 98-51815
Profiles eight builders and their famous construction
projects, including Imhotep and the Step Pyramid,
Alexandre Eiffel and the Eiffel Tower, and William
Lamb and the Empire State Building
"The prose is clear and engaging, with a layperson's
approach to technical information. Sidebars feature relat-
ed anecdotes, fun facts, and word definitions. Historical
photos, drawings, and diagrams are fascinating and well
chosen." Booklist
Includes glossary and bibliographical references

Adkins, Jan, 1944-
Bridges; from my side to yours; written &
illustrated by Jan Adkins. Roaring Brook Press
2002 96p il $18.95; lib bdg $25.90 (4 and up)
                                                624
1. Bridges
ISBN 0-7613-2510-7; 0-7613-1542-X (lib bdg)
                              LC 2001-48297
A look at bridges throughout history, from simple ar-
rangements of stepping stones, to famous landmarks such
as London Bridge, to marvels of engineering such as
New York's Brooklyn Bridge
"Varying perspectives are used to explain technological concepts, rendering them clear and understandable.
. . . The author's fascination with his subject is well
communicated, and his knowledge of history is as daz-
zling as his understanding of engineering principles. . . .
An outstanding book for reference and or enjoyment."
Horn Book
Includes glossary

Kent, Peter
Great building stories of the past. Oxford Univ.
Press 2001 45p il maps lib bdg $18.95 (4 and up)
                                                624
1. Architecture
ISBN 0-19-521846-9   LC 2001-36557
Explains the stories and principles behind some of the
world's greatest structures, including the Great Pyramid
at Giza, the Great Wall of China, the Eiffel Tower, and
the Brooklyn Bridge
"The text is concise, yet informative, describing each
project's construction in a few pages. The illustrations
are clear, crisp, and frequently humorous." Booklist
Includes bibliographical references

Levy, Matthys
Engineering the city; how infrastructure works:
projects and principles for beginners; {by}
Matthys Levy and Richard Panchyk. Chicago
Review Press 2000 129p pa $14.95   **624**
1. Civil engineering 2. Municipal engineering
ISBN 1-55652-419-6   LC 00-31774
"Combining a study of urban infrastructure with the
history of human development, the authors examine the
topics of water, transportation, waste and garbage disposal, and pollution. A wide variety of projects include scientific experiments and extension activities. . . . Containing scientific and historical information, this book
will serve as a springboard for cross-curricular projects
in history and science, with connections to math and language arts." Book Rep
Includes glossary and bibliographical references

Macaulay, David, 1946-
Underground. Houghton Mifflin 1976 109p il
$18; pa $9.95 (5 and up)   **624**
1. Civil engineering
ISBN 0-395-24739-X; 0-395-34065-9 (pa)
In this "examination of the intricate support systems
that lie beneath the street levels of our cities, Macaulay
explains the ways in which foundations for buildings are
laid or reinforced, and how the various utilities or transportation services are constructed." Bull Cent Child
Books
Includes glossary

Malam, John, 1957-
Super structures; written by John Malam;
illustrated by Mark Bergin; created and designed
by David Salariya. Watts 2000 32p il (Fast
forward) lib bdg $28; pa $9.95   **624**
1. Buildings 2. Structural engineering 3. Architecture
ISBN 0-531-11875-4 (lib bdg); 0-531-16441-1 (pa)
                              LC 00-27640
Explores world-famous man-made structures of the ancient and modern world, discussing how they were built,
why they are important, and how architecture may
change in the future

624.1 Structural engineering and underground construction

Fantastic feats and failures; by the editors of YES magazine. Kids Can Press 2004 52p il $15.95; pa $7.95 (4 and up)   **624.1**
1. Civil engineering
ISBN 1-55337-633-1; 1-55337-634-X (pa)
This "book spotlights 20 notable highs and lows in engineering. The 'feats' celebrated include the Sydney Opera House, the Brooklyn Bridge, and Canadarm (a huge, Canadian-built robotic arm used for repairs in space). Among the 'failures' are the space shuttle Challenger, the Tacoma Narrows Bridge, and the Chernobyl nuclear power plant. . . . Well organized and engagingly written. . . . Excellent photos . . . illustrate the places and events discussed, while colorful drawings visually represent concepts " Booklist

Vanderwarker, Peter
The big dig; reshaping an American city. Little, Brown 2001 56p il maps $17.95   **624.1**
1. Central Artery/Third Harbor Tunnel Project (Mass.)
2. Highway engineering 3. Boston (Mass.)
ISBN 0-316-60598-0   LC 00-111932
This is a "chronicle of the building of Boston's underground expressway, the largest and most complex construction project any U.S. city has ever undertaken." Sci Child
"Vibrant, full-color photographs appear throughout and numerous maps and diagrams are carefully deployed to further enhance understanding of the text. . . . Vanderwarker succeeds in reducing a highly complex endeavor to comprehensible parts in a straightforward, lucid narrative." SLJ
Includes glossary

627 Hydraulic engineering

Mann, Elizabeth, 1948-
Hoover Dam; with illustrations by Alan Witschonke. Mikaya Press 2001 unp il (Wonders of the world) $19.95 (4 and up)   **627**
1. Hoover Dam (Ariz. and Nev.)
ISBN 1-931414-02-5   LC 2001-34520
Includes index
"A wonderfully readable, well-organized book filled with fascinating detail." SLJ

628.4 Waste technology

Morgan, Sally
Waste disposal. Watts 2000 32p il (Earth watch) lib bdg $22; pa $13   **628.4**
1. Refuse and refuse disposal
ISBN 0-531-14557-3 (lib bdg); 0-7496-3876-1 (pa)
                    LC 99-53857
Examines the different kinds of waste, from household trash to industrial waste, describing where it goes and how it affects the environment

628.9 Fire-fighting technology

Beil, Karen Magnuson, 1950-
Fire in their eyes; wildfires and the people who fight them. Harcourt Brace & Co. 1999 64p il pa $11 hardcover o.p. (4 and up)   **628.9**
1. Fire fighters 2. Forest fires 3. Forest ecology
ISBN 0-15-201042-4   LC 98-6378
Depicts in text and photographs the training, equipment, and real-life experiences of people who risk their lives to battle wildfires, as well as people who use fire for ecological reasons
"The ferocity of fire is forcefully depicted in both narrative and well-chosen photographs." Horn Book Guide
Includes glossary

Gorrell, Gena K. (Gena Kinton), 1946-
Catching fire; the story of firefighting. Tundra Bks. 1999 152p il $16.95   **628.9**
1. Fire fighting
ISBN 0-88776-430-4   LC 98-61435
"Beginning with fire fighting through history, the discussion turns to modern techniques, equipment, and the rescue function of fire fighting teams as well as special circumstances such as fires in forests and on ships, planes, subways. The book closes with an informative chapter on how to prevent fires and what to do when there is a fire. Full of pertinent information and intriguing anecdotes." Booklist

Masoff, Joy, 1951-
Fire! principal photography by Jack Reznicki and Barry D. Smith. Scholastic Ref. 1998 48p il pa $6.95 hardcover o.p. (4 and up)   **628.9**
1. Fire fighters
ISBN 0-439-47217-2   LC 97-10928
Presents the work done by fire fighters, including the equipment they use, the fires they fight, the rescues and investigations they perform, and the history and future of fire fighting
"Masoff's personal enthusiasm for her subject along with her attention to detail and clear, lively writing set this far above the common run of razzle-dazzle, photo-filled compendia." Horn Book Guide
Includes bibliographical references

629.13 Aeronautics

Carson, Mary Kay, 1964-
The Wright Brothers for kids; how they invented the airplane: 21 activities exploring the science and history of flight; illustrations by Laura D'Argo. Chicago Review Press 2003 146p il pa $14.95 (4 and up)   **629.13**
1. Wright, Orville, 1871-1948 2. Wright, Wilbur, 1867-1912 3. Aeronautics 4. Science—Experiments
ISBN 1-55652-477-3   LC 2002-155449
This account of the Wright brothers' invention of the airplane, explains the forces of flight-lift, thrust, gravity, and drag and includes such activities as making a Chi-

Carson, Mary Kay, 1964-—_Continued_
nese flying top, building a kite, bird watching, making a
paper glider and a rubber-band-powered flyer
"A treasure trove of activities awaits readers of this
wonderfully executed survey of the Wright brothers and
their invention. The narrative flows easily and is complemented by numerous photographs that give a sense of
history and this event. . . . This is a valuable resource
for student reports and projects, and for classroom units."
SLJ
Includes glossary and bibliographical references

Graham, Ian, 1953-
Flight. Kingfisher (NY) 2001 63p il maps
$16.95   **629.13**
1. Aeronautics 2. Airplanes
ISBN 0-7534-5326-6   LC 2001-29001
This introduction to aeronautics devotes "one section
to military uses of flight, four to civil or research aviation, then . . . {closes} with a gallery of pioneer machines. Its art, which is mostly painted or computer generated, has a clean, uncluttered look." SLJ
Includes glossary

Hart, Philip S.
Flying free; America's first black aviators;
foreword by Reeve Lindbergh. Lerner Publs. 1992
64p il pa $6.95 hardcover o.p. (4 and up)
                                                   629.13
1. African American pilots
ISBN 0-8225-9727-6   LC 91-21433
Surveys the history of black aviators, from the early
black aviation community in Chicago in the 1920s
through World War II to modern times
"Hart eloquently documents the lives of America's pioneer black aviators. . . . This well-written account, with
quotes from personal and newspaper interviews and historic photographs, brings these inspiring stories to life."
SLJ
Includes bibliographical references

Haskins, James, 1941-2005
Black eagles; African Americans in aviation.
Scholastic 1995 196p il hardcover o.p. paperback
available $4.50 (5 and up)   **629.13**
1. Coleman, Bessie, 1896?-1926 2. Davis, Benjamin
O., Jr. 3. Powell, William J., 1899-1942 4. Bluford,
Guion S., 1942- 5. African American pilots
ISBN 0-590-45913-9   LC 94-18623
"Haskins presents the . . . achievements of African-
American aviators from the beginning of the twentieth
century to the present." Horn Book Guide
"In addition to introducing the people involved,
Haskins ably sets the background scene, revealing a so-
cial context of discrimination. . . . An excellent job of
dealing with the particular and the more general aspects
of 'what it was like.'" Booklist
Includes bibliographical references

629.133   Aircraft types

Murdico, Suzanne J.
Concorde. Children's Press 2001 48p il (Built
for speed) lib bdg $22; pa $6.95 (4 and up)
                                                   629.133
1. Jet planes
ISBN 0-516-23158-8 (lib bdg); 0-516-23261-4 (pa)
                                        LC 00-63896
This describes a flight on the Concorde and gives a
brief history of the jet aircraft
This "is excellent for upper elementary students, older
reluctant readers, and ESL students. . . . The pictures
enhance the text." Book Rep
Includes glossary and bibliographical references

Nahum, Andrew
Flying machine; written by Andrew Nahum. rev
ed. DK Pub. 2004 72p il (DK eyewitness books)
$15.99; lib bdg $19.99 (4 and up)
                                                   629.133
1. Aeronautics—History
ISBN 0-7566-0680-2; 0-7566-0679-9 (lib bdg)
First published 1990 by Knopf
A photo essay tracing the history and development of
aircraft from hot-air balloons to jetliners. Includes information on the principles of flight and the inner workings
of various flying machines.

O'Brien, Patrick
The Hindenburg. Holt & Co. 2000 unp il map
$17 (4 and up)   **629.133**
1. Hindenburg (Airship) 2. Airships
ISBN 0-8050-6415-X   LC 99-46687
Describes the development and early flights of airships
and the disastrous crash of the Hindenburg at an airfield
in New Jersey in 1937
"In both pictures and text, this beautiful, fact-filled
book truly makes history come alive." Booklist

629.222   Passenger automobiles

Edmonston, Louis-Philippe
Car smarts; hot tips for the car crazy; [by] Phil
Edmonston and Maureen Sawa; illustrated by
Gordon Suavé. Tundra 2004 76p il pa $15.95
                                                   629.222
1. Automobiles
ISBN 0-88776-646-3
This offers a "look at the history and design of automobiles. . . . {It} discusses how cars work. . . . A
chapter on ownership talks about financial issues, negoti-
ating, and maintenance. The closing section covers the
automotive future, with information on ecological issues,
alternative fuels, hybrids, and fuel cells." SLJ
"Written in a lively style, the book provides solid information. . . . The many illustrations include colorful
paintings, drawings, and photos as well as excellent diagrams of a car's working parts." Booklist

Willson, Quentin
Classic American cars; photography by Matthew Ward. DK Pub. 1997 192p il $30 (7 and up)
629.222
1. Automobiles
ISBN 0-7894-2083-X   LC 97-16172
This is an illustrated history of American cars from post-World War II to the 1970s
"In this homage to the boldness and beauty of the best, or at least the most legendary, makes and models, 60 are featured in beguiling graphics: front, back, and side shots that capture both sweep and detail. . . . Textual accompaniment highlights production, sales, and design background." Booklist

The ultimate classic car book; {by} Quentin Willson with David Selby. Dorling Kindersley 1995 224p il $30   **629.222**
1. Automobiles
ISBN 0-7894-0159-2   LC 95-11903
"An introduction covers what the term 'classic car' means, goes on to discuss such models by decade, and has a section on the purchase of such a vehicle. One-paragraph profiles of innovators such as Andre Citrone, Ferdinand Porsche, and Lee Iacocca are included. But the drawing card here is the cars. There are more than 90 of them, all displayed in splendid full-color photographs." SLJ

629.228 Racing cars

Hodges, David W.
Classic racing cars; Grand Prix and Indy. Chelsea House 1998 78p il $24.95
629.228
1. Automobile racing 2. Automobiles
ISBN 0-7910-4999-X   LC 98-18188
Text and photographs present different kinds of racing cars and explore their history and future

629.4 Astronautics

Ackroyd, Peter
Escape from Earth. DK Pub. 2003 140p il (Voyages through time) $19.99 (7 and up)
629.4
1. Astronautics 2. Outer space—Exploration
ISBN 0-756-60171-1
This "book presents the history of space travel and discusses its future. . . . Ackroyd offers both a sweeping vision of what has been achieved and a great deal of interesting detail about specific space missions. . . . Ackroyd presents the space age with a fine balance of technology and humanity. The many colorful photos and diagrams illustrate the text with clarity, beauty, and occasional drama and humor." Booklist

Cole, Michael D.
Living on Mars; mission to the Red Planet. Enslow Pubs. 1999 48p il (Countdown to space) lib bdg $23.93   **629.4**
1. Space flight to Mars 2. Mars (Planet)—Exploration
ISBN 0-7660-1121-6   LC 98-13125
"Half summary account of what we know about Mars from observations and space probes, and half a speculative mission profile for the first crewed expedition that will be sent there, this book sets the stage for one of our space program's next big objectives. The text is backed by endnotes citing almost as many Web sites as print sources." SLJ

Moon base; first colony in space. Enslow Pubs. 1999 48p il (Countdown to space) lib bdg $23.93 (4 and up)   **629.4**
1. Lunar bases 2. Moon—Exploration
ISBN 0-7660-1118-6   LC 98-13126
Describes the Apollo 11 mission to the moon, explains the need for establishing a moon base, and speculates about future situations in which the base would be used
Includes glossary and bibliographical references

Johnstone, Michael
The history news in space; author, Michael Johnstone. Candlewick Press 1999 32p il $16.99
629.4
1. Astronautics 2. Outer space—Exploration
ISBN 0-7636-0490-9   LC 98-38682
Uses a newspaper format to take a look at developments that led from the ideas of Copernicus and other early scientists to the technological advances that enabled man to venture to the moon and beyond
"This breezy overview gives readers tantalizing glimpses of the history of space science." SLJ

Spangenburg, Ray, 1939-
The history of NASA; {by} Ray Spangenburg and Kit Moser. Watts 2000 127p il (Out of this world) lib bdg $33.50; pa $14.95   **629.4**
1. United States. National Aeronautics and Space Administration 2. Astronautics 3. Outer space—Exploration
ISBN 0-531-11718-9 (lib bdg); 0-531-16511-6 (pa)
LC 99-37379
Surveys the history of the National Aeronautics and Space Administration, describing the major space craft and missions launched
Includes bibliographical references

Stott, Carole
Space exploration; written by Carole Stott; photographed by Steve Gorton. rev ed. DK Pub. 2004 72p il (DK eyewitness books) $15.99; lib bdg $19.99 (4 and up)   **629.4**
1. Astronautics 2. Outer space—Exploration
ISBN 0-7566-0731-0; 0-7566-0730-2 (lib bdg)
First published 1997 by Knopf
Describes rockets, exploratory vehicles, and other technological aspects of space exploration, satellites, space stations, and the life and work of astronauts.

629.43   Unmanned flight

Cole, Michael D.
Galileo spacecraft; mission to Jupiter. Enslow
Pubs. 1999 48p il (Countdown to space) lib bdg
$23.93   **629.43**
1. Galileo Project 2. Jupiter (Planet)—Exploration
ISBN 0-7660-1119-4   LC 98-3627
Discusses the travel of the Galileo spacecraft from its
launch to its orbit around Jupiter, explaining the goals
and accomplishments of the mission
Includes bibliographical references

Sherman, Josepha
Deep space observation satellites. Rosen Pub.
Group 2003 63p il (Library of satellites) lib bdg
$26.50   **629.43**
1. Space probes 2. Outer space—Exploration
ISBN 0-8239-3852-2   LC 2002-3202
Contents: 1957-1967; 1968-1978; 1979-1989; 1990-
2000, the future
A chronological presentation of the launching of satel-
lites for observation of the solar system and deep space,
with a discussion of what we have learned from such
satellites
"A nice mix of archival and contemporary photos illustrate [this] well-organized, accessible [volume]."
Booklist
Includes glossary and bibliographical references

Wunsch, Susi Trautmann
The adventures of Sojourner; the mission to
Mars that thrilled the world. Mikaya Press 1998
60p il lib bdg $22.95; pa $9.95   **629.43**
1. Space flight to Mars 2. Mars (Planet)—Exploration
ISBN 0-9650493-5-3; 0-9650493-6-1 (pa)
                                              LC 98-7660
Tells the story of the mission that placed the Sojourner remote-control rover on Mars on July 4, 1997
"The photographs not only cover *Sojourner's movements* about the surface of Mars, but also track the entire
Mars project from its inception. In addition to an index,
there is a time line of all the Mars voyages and a page
of astronomical facts." Sci Books Films

629.44   Auxiliary spacecraft

Cole, Michael D.
The Columbia space shuttle disaster; from first
liftoff to tragic final flight. Enslow Pubs. 2003 48p
il (Countdown to space) lib bdg $18.95 (4 and up)
                                              629.44
1. Columbia (Space shuttle) 2. Space vehicle accidents
ISBN 0-7660-2295-1   LC 2003-4823
First published 1995 with title: Columbia
Contents: A new kind of spaceship; Columbia in orbit;
Flight and reentry; Welcome home, Columbia!; Colum-
bia's last mission
Details the first flight of the space shuttle Columbia,
as well as its tragic final flight

"The account offers a lot of information, helping to
make sense of a highly complicated subject. . . . The
color and b&w photographs complement the story." Libr
Media Connect
Includes glossary and bibliographical references

Spangenburg, Ray, 1939-
Onboard the space shuttle; [by] Ray
Spangenburg and Kit Moser. Watts 2002 112p il
(Out of this world) lib bdg $33.50   **629.44**
1. Space shuttles 2. Space flight 3. Space stations
ISBN 0-531-11896-7   LC 2001-5363
Examines what it is like for the crews living and
working on American space shuttles and discusses the
life of the Russian space station Mir and plans for an in-
ternational space station
"The conversational style makes for easy reading and
high interest. The illustrations are accurate and colorful
and significantly provide understanding to the text."
Book Rep
Includes glossary and bibliographical references

629.45   Manned space flight

Collins, Michael, 1930-
Flying to the moon; an astronaut's story. 2nd
ed, with a preface & a revised final chapter.
Farrar, Straus & Giroux 1994 162p il pa $6.95
                                              629.45
1. Space flight to the moon 2. Astronauts
ISBN 0-374-42356-3   LC 93-42001
"A Sunburst book"
First published 1976 with title: Flying to the moon,
and other strange places
Based in part on author's Carrying the fire (1974)
The author recounts his early days as an Air Force
test pilot, his NASA training and his experiences aboard
Gemini 10 and the Apollo 11 mission to the moon. Col-
lins also advocates continued exploration of the universe
"A well told tale, which includes a lot of easily ex-
plained science." BAYA Book Rev

Dyson, Marianne J.
Home on the moon; living on a space frontier.
National Geographic Soc. 2003 64p il $18.95 (4
and up)   **629.45**
1. Moon
ISBN 0-7922-7193-9   LC 2002-5280
Considers the moon as a frontier that has been only
partially explored, looking at its history, geography, and
weather, as well as what people would require to live
and work there. Includes activities
"Clear writing, vivid images, interesting details, and
quotes from astronauts and scientists make this a lively,
fact-filled introduction." Booklist
Includes glossary and bibliographical references

Goodman, Susan, 1952-
Ultimate field trip 5; blasting off to Space Academy; by Susan E. Goodman; photographs by Michael J. Doolittle. Atheneum Bks. for Young Readers 2001 41p il $17; $6.99 pa (4 and up)
629.45
1. U.S. Space Camp (Huntsville, Ala.) 2. Astronauts 3. Space flight
ISBN 0-689-83044-0 (0-689-84863-3); pa
LC 00-38082
"This book follows student trainees through a weeklong session at the U.S. Space Academy in Huntsville, AL, as they are exposed to what it takes to become an astronaut and to the inner workings of the entire space program. . . . Varied-colored pages, replete with outstanding full-color, captioned photos, are artistically appealing as well as informative." SLJ
Includes glossary and bibliographical references

Green, Jen
Race to the moon; the story of Apollo 11; written by Jen Green; illustrated by Mark Bergin; created and designed by David Salariya. Watts 1998 32p il (Expedition) pa $7.95 hardcover o.p.
629.45
1. Project Apollo 2. Apollo 11 (Spacecraft) 3. Space flight to the moon
ISBN 0-531-15343-6
LC 97-34691
Describes the events leading up to the Apollo 11 flight that put the first man on the moon and the technological advances that made this and later flights possible

Hehner, Barbara, 1947-
First on the moon; what it was like when man landed on the moon; illustrations by Greg Ruhl. Hyperion Bks. for Children 1999 48p il $16.99; pa $7.99 (4 and up)
629.45
1. Apollo 11 (Spacecraft) 2. Space flight to the moon
ISBN 0-7868-0489-0; 0-7868-1538-8 (pa)
LC 98-42651
"An I was there book"
An account of the first moon landing by Apollo 11 in 1969
"The informative and entertaining text is illustrated with an abundance of full-color and black-and-white photographs as well as paintings." SLJ
Includes glossary and bibliographical references

Ride, Sally K.
To space & back; by Sally Ride with Susan Okie. Lothrop, Lee & Shepard Bks. 1986 96p il $19.99; pa $14.99
629.45
1. Space flight 2. Space shuttles
ISBN 0-688-06159-1; 0-688-09112-1 (pa)
LC 85-23757
This "account of a space journey, from blastoff to landing, gives . . . details of adjusting to weightlessness, preparing and eating meals, going to the bathroom, sleeping, washing, dressing, and working on scientific projects or up-keep technology on board the shuttle. Ride gives plenty of examples from her own experience but keeps the focus generalized enough to be broadly informative." Bull Cent Child Books
Includes glossary

Vogt, Gregory
John Glenn's return to space. Millbrook Press 2000 72p il lib bdg $24.90
629.45
1. Glenn, John, 1921- 2. Space flight
ISBN 0-7613-1614-0
LC 00-20768
Details astronaut John Glenn's second flight into space in 1998 and contrasts it with his first flight in 1962, discussing training, equipment, and responsibilities
"With its well-chosen photographs, both color and black and white, this attractively designed documentation offers fascinating reading for pleasure or for school research." Booklist
Includes bibliographical references

Space mission patches; by Gregory L. Vogt. Millbrook Press 2001 78p il lib bdg $24.90
629.45
1. United States. National Aeronautics and Space Administration 2. Astronautics
ISBN 0-7613-1613-2
LC 00-41850
"Vogt provides a history of the U.S. space flight program framed around the various patches worn on the garments of the astronauts involved. The connections between the patch designs and the backgrounds or purposes of the missions will intrigue space exploration fans." Horn Book Guide
Includes glossary and bibliographical references

629.8 Automatic control engineering

Jefferis, David
Artificial intelligence; robotics and machine evolution. Crabtree 1999 32p il (Megatech) lib bdg $22.60; pa $8.95 (4 and up)
629.8
1. Robots 2. Artificial intelligence
ISBN 0-7787-0046-1 (lib bdg); 0-7787-0056-9 (pa)
LC 98-44481
An introduction to the past, present, and future of artificial intelligence and robotics, discussing early science fiction predictions, the dawn of AI, and today's use of robots in factories and space exploration
This book has "bright, full-color photographs on nearly every page." SLJ
Includes glossary

Lockman, Darcy
Robots. Benchmark Bks. (Tarrytown) 2001 48p il (Kaleidoscope) $25.64
629.8
1. Robots
ISBN 0-7614-1047-3
LC 99-58311
Provides a brief history of robotics, describes tasks for which robots are useful, and suggests future development
Includes bibliographical references

630.1 Agriculture--Philosophy and theory. Country and farm life

Bial, Raymond
Portrait of a farm family. Houghton Mifflin 1995 48p il $17 (4 and up)   630.1
1. Farm life 2. Agriculture
ISBN 0-395-69936-3   LC 94-38201
In this photo essay about the Steidinger family farm in Illinois "Bial explores the specifics of milking, raising feed-lot calves, and cutting silage and discusses the factors to be weighed before buying expensive equipment or choosing a particular kind of animal to raise. . . . Bial brings the Steidingers' everyday world to life, fitting it neatly into an excellent discussion of family-farm-based agriculture and the U.S. economy." Booklist
Includes bibliographical references

Halley, Ned
Farm; written by Ned Halley; photographed by Geoff Brightling. Knopf 1996 63p il (Eyewitness books) $19; lib bdg $20.99 (4 and up)
630.1
1. Agriculture 2. Farms
ISBN 0-679-88078-X; 0-679-98078-4 (lib bdg)
LC 95-37053
Available from DK Pub. edition $15.99; lib bdg $19.99 (0-7894-6040-8; 0-7894-6615-5)
"A Dorling Kindersley book"
Text and photographs depict different aspects of farming through the ages including the equipment, domestic animals, crops, and the future of farming
"Probably one of the better entries in the ever-growing series. . . . Lengthy captions describe the many detailed full-color illustrations, photographs, reproductions, and artifacts that are scattered around the pages." SLJ

633.5 Fiber crops

Meltzer, Milton, 1915-
The cotton gin. Benchmark Bks. 2003 c2004 123p il (Great inventions) lib bdg $25.95
633.5
1. Cotton
ISBN 0-7614-1537-8   LC 2002-15308
The author describes the invention of the cotton gin and its effects on history including "the influence of mechanized cotton processing on the growth of slavery in the United States and the increase in textile mills. . . . The author expertly describes a setting that is ripe for invention. Powerful photographs . . . historical artwork, and personal narratives make the times real and relevant to readers." SLJ
Includes bibliographical references

635 Garden crops (Horticulture)

Winckler, Suzanne, 1946-
Planting the seed; a guide to gardening. Lerner Publs. 2002 64p il lib bdg $25.26; pa $7.95
635
1. Gardening
ISBN 0-8225-0081-7 (lib bdg); 0-8225-0471-5 (pa)
LC 2001-2018
"Loosely organized into the stages of planning, planting, maintaining, and harvesting a garden, the chapters offer a basic introduction to key concepts, such as growing zones, native plants, and compost. The book also addresses Native American gardening traditions and community gardens as well as Earth-friendly topics such as organic pest control . . . and heirloom gardens. . . . Interested young people will glean some basics and find useful resources for further exploration." Booklist
Includes glossary and bibliographical references

635.9 Flowers and ornamental plants

Collard, Sneed B., III
The prairie builders; reconstructing America's lost grasslands; written and photographed by Sneed B. Collard III. Houghton Mifflin Co 2005 66p il map (Scientists in the field) $17 (4 and up)
635.9
1. Prairies 2. Nature conservation
ISBN 0-618-39687-X   LC 2004-13201
This describes an effort to restore part of the native tallgrass prairie in the the 8,000-acre Neal Smith National Wildlife Refuge in Iowa.
"The engaging text is accompanied by large, inviting color photographs. . . . An essential purchase for libraries in prairie regions and a worthwhile choice for others." SLJ
Includes bibliographical references

636.088 Animals for specific purposes

Kent, Deborah, 1948-
Animal helpers for the disabled. Watts 2003 63p il $24; pa $8.95 (4 and up)   636.088
1. Animals and the handicapped 2. Animals—Training 3. Guide dogs
ISBN 0-531-12017-1; 0-531-16663-5 (pa)
LC 2002-8885
"Watts library"
Explores the history of guide dogs, service animals, and assistance dogs, and discusses the process of training them to help people who have physical disabilities
This is an "informative, often inspirational and thought-provoking [book]." Booklist
Includes bibliographical references

636.1 Equines. Horses

Budiansky, Stephen
The world according to horses; how they run, see, and think. Holt & Co. 2000 101p il $17.95 (4 and up) **636.1**
1. Horses
ISBN 0-8050-6054-5 LC 99-31778
Discusses the interaction between people and horses, the horse as a social animal, its intelligence, abilities to communicate, athletic abilities, and physical evolution
"Intriguing premises are explained here in a straightforward and thought-provoking manner. . . . This title also will serve as a valuable resource for a beginning basic science reasoning study." Voice Youth Advocates
Includes glossary and bibliographical references

Ransford, Sandy
The Kingfisher illustrated horse & pony encyclopedia; written by Sandy Ransford; photographed by Bob Langrish. Kingfisher 2004 224p il $24.95 (4 and up) **636.1**
1. Horses 2. Horsemanship
ISBN 0-7534-5781-4 LC 2003-27293
"The first part of the book covers the life cycle, domestication, and types of horses and ponies. . . . The second part deals with how to care for these animals and discusses horsemanship from taking riding lessons to training and driving a horse. . . . Filled with appealing photos of young people interacting with their four-legged friends, this title is an extremely useful addition to any collection." SLJ

The **Visual** dictionary of the horse. Dorling Kindersley 1994 64p il (Eyewitness visual dictionaries) $18.99 (4 and up) **636.1**
1. Horses
ISBN 1-56458-504-2 LC 93-20819
"Along with spreads detailing the animal's anatomy, there are two double-page spreads illustrated with full-color photographs of the various breeds, divided into light and heavy horses. Following this overview, the guide briefly focuses on the care and activities of equines today, including grooming, shoeing, racing, jumping, and equipment." SLJ
"In this visually spectacular introduction to horses and equine and equestrian terms, the information is complete and concise; color photographs and diagrams extend the text. The anatomical drawings, with detailed labeling, are particularly instructive and useful." Horn Book Guide
Includes glossary

636.2 Ruminants. Bovines. Cattle

Freedman, Russell
In the days of the vaqueros; America's first true cowboys. Clarion Bks. 2001 70p il $18 (4 and up) **636.2**
1. Cowhands 2. Mexican Americans 3. Ranch life 4. Southwestern States
ISBN 0-395-96788-0 LC 2001-17357

"Freedman explores the often-overlooked role of the Central American cowherders who preceded by centuries the cowboys of popular lore and legend." SLJ
The author "tells the story with depth, clarity, and a vigor that conveys the thrilling excitement of the work and the macho swagger of the culture. . . . The book's design is beautiful, with spacious type on thick paper, and the dazzling illustrations—prints, paintings, and photos on almost every page." Booklist
Includes glossary and bibliographical references

Stanley, Jerry, 1941-
Cowboys & longhorns. Crown 2003 88p il map $18.95; lib bdg $20.99 **636.2**
1. Cowhands 2. Cattle 3. West (U.S.)—History
ISBN 0-375-81565-1; 0-375-91565-6 (lib bdg)
LC 2002-41229
"This account of the life of the American cowboy emphasizes the period of the Long Drive, which began in 1866 when the railroad reached Kansas, making it profitable to capture the wild longhorns of West Texas and drive them north. . . . This era ended in 1885, when the last of the Texas longhorns . . . had been driven to Kansas or absorbed into ranchers' herds." SLJ
"Illustrated with maps and photographs, this fascinating, engrossing account of a piece of American history stripped of myths is a great choice for both informational and recreational reading." Booklist
Includes bibliographical references

636.5 Poultry. Chickens

Zeaman, John
Birds; from forest to family room. Watts 1999 63p il $26 **636.5**
1. Birds 2. Cage birds
ISBN 0-531-20351-4 LC 98-2706
The author presents a "look at bird domestication, including information on bird evolution, the first human attempts at taming (including geese and jungle fowl for food, doves and pigeons for communication, and raptors for hunting), and the history of domestication of birds for pleasure. Reproductions and color photos add to the liveliness of the presentation." Horn Book Guide
Includes bibliographical references

636.7 Dogs

American Kennel Club
The complete dog book. Howell Bk. House il $32.95 **636.7**
1. Dogs
ISBN 0-8760-5047-X
First published 1935. (19th edition 1997) Periodically revised
"The official guide to 124 AKC registered breeds and their history, appearance, selection, training, care and feeding, and first aid. Some color plates." N Y Public Libr. Ref Books for Child Collect. 2d edition

The **Complete** dog book for kids; official publication of the American Kennel Club. Howell Bk. House; distributed by Hungry Minds 1996 274p il maps pa $22.95 hardcover o.p. (4 and up)   **636.7**
1. Dogs
ISBN 0-87605-460-2   LC 96-29228
This "begins with a general section that advises readers on buying a dog, responsibilities, rewards, and how to match a dog with one's situation. . . . More than 100 dogs are profiled, with information on history, appearance, health, and 'fun facts.' Crisp color photographs accompany each article. . . . A final section gives good advice about nutrition and health issues." Booklist

Gorrell, Gena K. (Gena Kinton), 1946-
Working like a dog; the story of working dogs through history. Tundra 2003 156p il pa $16.95 (4 and up)   **636.7**
1. Working dogs
ISBN 0-88776-589-0
"Gorrell begins by tracing the evolution of 'household canids' from the wild into the civilized world. Other chapters delve into the many ways in which these animals have been viewed throughout history, what makes particular breeds right for certain jobs, dogs at war, famous pooches, etc. . . . The well-captioned, black-and-white photographs and reproductions add greatly to a narrative that's packed with intriguing details." SLJ
Includes bibliographical references

636.8   Cats

Edney, A. T. B.
ASPCA complete cat care manual; {by} Andrew Edney; foreword by Roger Caras. Dorling Kindersley 1992 192p il $25   **636.8**
1. Cats
ISBN 1-56458-064-4   LC 92-52783
"Cat care is made easy through step-by-step photographs that illustrate grooming, handling, detecting illness, first aid, and other concerns. Difficult-to-explain procedures, such as how to administer medication or transport an injured cat, are clearly understandable." Libr J
Includes bibliographical references

636.9   Other mammals

McNicholas, June
Rats. Heinemann Lib. 2003 48p il (Keeping unusual pets) $24.22 (4 and up)   **636.9**
1. Rats
ISBN 1-40340-283-3   LC 2002-3164
Contents: What is a rat?; Ratty facts; Is a rat for you?; What do I need?; Routine care; Handling and play; Health issues; Major problems; A record of your rat
Describes how to select a pet rat, what to feed it, and when to take it to the vet, as well as how to keep a pet scrapbook
"A valuable, accessible resource." Booklist
Includes bibliographical references

639   Hunting, fishing, conservation, related technologies

Coborn, John
Snakes. Chelsea House 1999 64p il $22.95
639
1. Snakes
ISBN 0-7910-5085-8   LC 98-7659
Discusses the physical characteristics, health, and behavior of snakes and provides information on keeping these animals as pets

Silverstein, Alvin
Snakes & such; {by} Alvin Silverstein, Virginia Silverstein, Laura Silverstein Nunn. 21st Cent. Bks. (Brookfield) 1999 48p il lib bdg $23.90
639
1. Reptiles 2. Amphibians
ISBN 0-7613-3229-4   LC 98-41305
Discusses the positive and negative aspects of keeping such creatures as boas and pythons, chameleons, iguanas, turtles, frogs, and salamanders as pets
"The authors present the facts in an orderly, informative, and dispassionate manner, devoting four pages to each pet. A 'Fast Facts' box, imposed on a full-color photo of the creature, gives its scientific name along with cost, food, housing, and training requirements." SLJ
Includes bibliographical references

639.2   Commercial fishing, whaling, sealing

McKissack, Patricia C., 1944-
Black hands, white sails; the story of African-American whalers; {by} Patricia C. McKissack & Fredrick L. McKissack. Scholastic Press 1999 xxiv, 152p il $17.95 (5 and up)
639.2
1. Whaling 2. African Americans
ISBN 0-590-48313-7   LC 99-11439
A Coretta Scott King honor book for text, 2000
A history of African-American whalers between 1730 and 1880, describing their contributions to the whaling industry and their role in the abolitionist movement
"A well-researched and detailed book." SLJ
Includes bibliographical references

Murphy, Jim, 1947-
Gone a-whaling; the lure of the sea and the hunt for the great whale. Clarion Bks. 1998 208p il $18; pa $8.95 (7 and up)   **639.2**
1. Whaling—History
ISBN 0-395-69847-2; 0-618-43243-4 (pa)
LC 97-13051
"Murphy makes history fascinating and immediate with a lively, engrossing narrative that both informs and entertains." Voice Youth Advocates
Includes glossary and bibliographical references

639.34 Aquariums

Mills, Dick
Aquarium fish. DK Pub. 1996 72p il (101 essential tips) pa $5   **639.34**
1. Aquariums 2. Fishes
ISBN 0-7894-1074-5
This book offers advice on choosing fish for aquariums, aquarium equipment, decoration, feeding, and health care, and describes various species of tropical, coldwater, freshwater, and marine fishes
"Accurate, clear, and concise writing is enhanced with wonderful color photographs on each page." Voice Youth Advocates

639.9 Conservation of biological resources

Bortolotti, Dan
Panda rescue; changing the future for endangered wildlife. Firefly 2003 64p il map lib bdg $19.95; pa $9.95 (4 and up)   **639.9**
1. Wildlife conservation 2. Giant panda
ISBN 1552975983 (lib bdg); 1552975576 (pa)
This describes the panda's "natural habitat, habits, physiology, and behavior in captivity. [It also includes] a time line of conservation efforts, profiles of conservationists in the field, and forecasts of the animals' future. Throughout, the author makes clear the factors that can threaten animal populations, and discusses human attitudes toward the animals throughout history. . . . Written in accessible, lively language and nicely illustrated with exciting color photos, [this] will be useful for reports and browsing." Booklist

Thomas, Peggy
Marine mammal preservation. 21st Cent. Bks. (Brookfield) 2000 64p il lib bdg $25.90 (5 and up)   **639.9**
1. Marine mammals 2. Wildlife conservation
ISBN 0-7613-1458-x   LC 00-30223
This title explains "how scientific studies of animal behavior combined with public awareness can help to save lives of marine mammals. Research and rehabilitation techniques for whales, manatees, seals, and sea otters are featured." Sci Child
"Illustrated with good-quality color photographs. . . . A highly readable and informative title." SLJ
Includes glossary and bibliographical references

641 Food and drink

Pentland, Peter
Kitchen science; [by] Peter Pentland and Pennie Stoyles. Chelsea House 2003 c2002 32p il (Science and scientists) lib bdg $18.95 (4 and up)   **641**
1. Food 2. Science 3. Cooking
ISBN 0-7910-7014-X   LC 2002-1280

First published 2002 in Australia
Surveys some of the scientific principles related to foods and their preparation
This title has "colorful illustrations and [uses] sidebars to present interesting tidbits of relevant information." SLJ
Includes glossary

641.3 Food

Dunn-Georgiou, Elisha
Everything you need to know about organic foods. Rosen Pub. Group 2002 64p il (Need to know library) lib bdg $23.95 (7 and up)   **641.3**
1. Natural foods 2. Organic gardening
ISBN 0-8239-3551-5   LC 2001-3789
Discusses the organic food movement and recent information about the United States Department of Agriculture's criteria for what defines an organic food
Includes bibliographical references

Marshall, Elizabeth L.
High-tech harvest; a look at genetically engineered foods. Watts 1999 144p il lib bdg $20 (7 and up)   **641.3**
1. Agriculture 2. Food 3. Biotechnology
ISBN 0-531-11434-1   LC 98-8203
An overview of recombined DNA technology, or genetic engineering, techniques used to create crop plants and farm animals with characteristics that are attractive to farmers, food processors, and consumers
"Students looking for a discussion of the techniques and implications of gene-splicing to create new types of food plants and animals will find this just the ticket. . . . The notes, plus generous lists of books, articles and URL's, at the end will facilitate further inquiry." Booklist

Solheim, James
It's disgusting—and we ate it! true food facts from around the world—and throughout history! illustrated by Eric Brace. Simon & Schuster Bks. for Young Readers 1998 37p il $16.95; pa $6.99 (4 and up)   **641.3**
1. Food 2. Eating customs
ISBN 0-689-80675-2; 0-689-84393-3 (pa)
                    LC 96-7406
This "look at culinary culture is divided into three sections, the first discussing the global breadth of tastes, the second describing some startling dishes of history, and the third revealing some of the colorful truths behind contemporary American favorites." Bull Cent Child Books
Includes bibliographical references

641.5   Cooking

Albyn, Carole Lisa, 1955-
The multicultural cookbook for students; by
Carole Lisa Albyn and Lois Sinaiko Webb. Oryx
Press 1993 xxii, 287p maps pa $29.50

              641.5
1. Cooking
ISBN 0-89774-735-6   LC 92-41634
Presents a collection of recipes from over 120 countries and briefly discusses the culture and culinary habits
of each country

Carle, Megan
Teens cook; how to make what you want to eat;
[by] Megan and Jill Carle with Judi Carle. Ten
Speed Press 2004 146p il pa $19.95

              641.5
1. Cooking
ISBN 1-58008-584-9
This cookbook features "recipes for a variety of dishes
including chocolate chip scones, potato skins, broccoli
cheese soup, steak fajitas, baked macaroni and cheese,
and toffee bars. Because Megan is a vegetarian, there are
several vegetarian recipes or vegetarian substitutes. . . .
Attractive, engaging, and told from a teen perspective,
this cookbook will make an excellent addition to any
nonfiction collection." Voice Youth Advocates

Cook, Deanna F., 1965-
The kids' multicultural cookbook; food & fun
around the world; illustrated by Michael P. Kline.
Williamson 1995 159p il pa $12.95   **641.5**
   1. Cooking 2. Manners and customs
ISBN 0-913589-91-8   LC 94-44231
"A Williamson kids can! book"
In this "tour of 41 countries, readers are given a quick
dose of culture from each one. There are one or two recipes (their difficulty is rated by one, two, or three
spoons) for each place and an introduction to a child
who lives there. Occasional riddles and 'fun facts' are inserted, such as the world record for watermelon-seed
spitting. Foreign words are included with pronunciations." SLJ

Crespo, Clare
The secret life of food; photographs by Eric
Staudenmaier. Hyperion 2002 108p il $19.99 (4
and up)   **641.5**
   1. Cooking
ISBN 0-7868-0846-2
This includes "recipes for dishes that look remarkably
like spiders, roses, fingers, footballs, ponds, shoes—even
a chocolate moose. . . . Younger readers will need adult
help to re-create Crespo's culinary delights. The stunning
full-page color photos of each dish, posed in clever context, lend great 'ooh and aah' motivation, making this
useful for groups as well as for kids planning parties at
home." SLJ

D'Amico, Joan, 1957-
The healthy body cookbook; over 50 fun
activities and delicious recipes for kids; {by} Joan
D'Amico, Karen Eich Drummond; illustrations by
Tina Cash-Walsh. Wiley 1999 184p il pa $12.95
(4 and up)   **641.5**
   1. Cooking 2. Nutrition
ISBN 0-471-18888-3   LC 98-2776
Discusses the various parts of the human body and
what to eat to keep them healthy. Includes recipes that
contain nutrients important for the heart, muscles, teeth,
skin, nerves, and other parts of the body
"The line drawings are helpful and the writing is informal but straightforward. The recipes are clear, thoroughly explained, and tasty." SLJ

The United States cookbook; fabulous foods and
fascinating facts from all 50 states; {by} Joan
D'Amico and Karen Eich Drummond; illustrations
by Jeff Cline and Tina Cash-Walsh. Wiley 2000
186p il pa $12.95   **641.5**
   1. Cooking
ISBN 0-471-35839-8   LC 99-39548
.

Provides information about the fifty states along with
a recipe native to each of them, such as Boston baked
beans from Massachusetts, crab cakes from Maryland,
Key lime pie from Florida, corn dogs from Iowa, and
taco soup from New Mexico
"There are helpful sections on the use of equipment;
cooking skills, such as cutting, measuring, and mixing,
and safety rules." SLJ

.

Easy menu ethnic cookbooks. rev ed. Lerner
   Publs. 2002-2005 37v ea $25.26 (5 and up)
              641.5
   1. Cooking
Some titles also available in paperback
Series first published 1982-1995
Available volumes in the revised series are: Cooking
the Australian way by E. Germaine & A. L. Burchhardt;
Cooking the Austrian way by H. Hughes; Cooking the
Brazilian way by A. Behnke & K. L. Duro; Cooking the
Caribbean way, by C. D. Kaufman; Cooking the Central
American way by A. Behnke; Cooking the Chinese way,
by L. Yu; Cooking the Cuban way by A. Behnke & V.
M. Valens; Cooking the East African way, by C.
Nabwire & B. V. Montgomery; Cooking the English
way, by B. W. Hill; Cooking the French way, by L. M.
Waldee; Cooking the German way, by H. Parnell; Cook-
ing the Greek way, by L. W. Villios; Cooking the Hun-
garian way, by M. Hargittai; Cooking the Indian way, by
V. Madavan; Cooking the Indonesian way by M. Anwar
& K. Cornell; Cooking the Israeli way, by J. Bacon;
Cooking the Italian way, by A. Bisignano; Cooking the
Japanese way, by R. Weston; Cooking the Korean way,
by O. Chung and J. Monroe; Cooking the Lebanese way,
by S. Amari; Cooking the Mediterranean way by A.
Behnke; Cooking the Mexican way, by R. Coronado;
Cooking the Middle Eastern Way by A. Behnke; Cook-
ing the North African way by M. Winget & H. Cahlbi;
Cooking the Norwegian way, by S. Munsen; Cooking the
Polish way, by D. Zamojska-Hutchins; Cooking the Rus-
sian way, by G. & R. Plotkin; Cooking the Southern

Easy menu ethnic cookbooks—*Continued*

American way by H. Parnell; Cooking the Southern African way by K. Cornell & P. Thomas; Cooking the Spanish way, by R. Christian; Cooking the Thai way, by S. Harrison & J. Monroe; Cooking the Turkish way by K. Cornell & N. Turkoglu; Cooking the Vietnamese way, by C. Nguyen & J. Monroe; Cooking the West African way, by C. Nabwire & B. V. Montgomery; Desserts aroung the world by L. Engfer; Holiday cooking around the world, by R. Wolfe & D. Wolfe; Vegetarian cooking around the world, by A. Behnke

"In each volume, the front matter comprises close to half the book. Geography, history, holidays, and festivals, typical ingredients, and sample menus are all covered. . . . Each book presents about 20 recipes, mostly focusing on lunch, dinner, and holiday foods. . . . The narrative pieces are smoothly written and offer some interesting tidbits. . . . The pages are a warm buff color, and the design allows plenty of space on the pages for the text and the nicely reproduced color photos." SLJ

Erdosh, George, 1935-

The African American kitchen; food for body and soul. Rosen Pub. Group 1999 64p il (Library of African American arts and culture) lib bdg $26.50 (7 and up) **641.5**

1. African American cooking

ISBN 0-8239-1850-5   LC 98-51814

Describes the influences on and the evolution of African American cooking. Includes recipes and suggestions for healthy cooking

Includes bibliographical references

Fisher, Teresa

France. Raintree Steck-Vaughn Pubs. 1999 32p il (Food and festivals) lib bdg $24.64

641.5

1. French cooking 2. France—Social life and customs

ISBN 0-8172-5550-8   LC 98-15671

Discusses some of the foods enjoyed in France and describes special foods that are part of such specific celebrations as Christmas, Mardi Gras, and Menton's Lemon Festival. Includes recipes

Includes bibliographical references

Gillies, Judi

The jumbo vegetarian cookbook; written by Judi Gillies and Jennifer Glossop; illustrated by Louise Phillips. Kids Can Press 2002 256p il pa $14.95 (4 and up) **641.5**

1. Vegetarian cooking

ISBN 1-55074-977-3

"Much more than just a cookbook, this sprawling title introduces basic nutrition and how to achieve it with a vegetarian diet. Beginning sections cover safety tips and culinary basics . . . as well as types of vegetarianism, the environmental and health reasons that have led many to a meatless diet, and a list of common vegetarian ingredients. The recipe sections are extensive, with well-chosen dishes from breakfast foods through entrées and desserts." Booklist

Krizmanic, Judy

A teen's vegetarian cookbook; illustrations by Matthew Wawiorka. Viking 1999 186p il pa $10.99 hardcover o.p. (7 and up)   **641.5**

1. Vegetarian cooking

ISBN 0-14-038506-1 (pa)   LC 98-21856

Recipes for all types of vegetarian dishes are accompanied by information and advice on vegetarian diet and quotes from teenage vegetarians

"Recipes are laid out nicely, with ingredients listed first, followed by a numbered sequence of clear instructions. Boxed insets in Krizmanic's strong, clear voice add background on vegetarianism, and there's a helpful food chart to remind readers about nutritional values. Teens new to vegetarian cooking will find the glossary of 'unusual' foods helpful, as well." Booklist

Lagasse, Emeril

Emeril's there's a chef in my family! recipes to get everybody cooking; illustrated by Charles Yuen; photographs by Quentin Bacon. HarperCollins Publishers 2004 209p il $22.99 (5 and up)   **641.5**

1. Cooking

ISBN 0-06-000439-8   LC 2003-5612

Provides tips for having fun and keeping safe in the kitchen, along with dozens of world-famous chef Emeril Lagasse's favorite recipes that families can make and eat together

"The step-by-step directions are clearly laid out, and most of the dishes look delicious. The fresh and attractive design includes a mix of simple paintings (for the food) and photos (for the people). Emeril himself is shown throughout, conveying his enthusiasm and sense of play." SLJ

Locricchio, Matthew

Super chef {series}. Benchmark Books 2002-2004 c2003-2005 8v il map lib bdg group 1 set $119.71; lib bdg group 2 set $119.71

641.5

1. Cooking

ISBN 0-7614-1213-1 (group 1); 0-7614-1728-1 (group 2)

Also available as single volumes $29.93 each

Contents: Group 1: The cooking of China; The cooking of France; The cooking of Italy; The cooking of Mexico; Group 2: The cooking of Brazil; The cooking of Greece; The cooking of India; The cooking of Thailand

"After a quick review of the basic principles of kitchen safety, food handling and common sense nutrition, there is a region-by-region overview of the cuisine of the country. Then it's on to a variety of authentic . . . traditional recipes!" Publisher's note

"The selection of dishes is well-rounded . . . and the directions are mostly clear and thorough. Young people will gain a solid foundation in cooking techniques as well as a cultural introduction to world cuisine with these slim volumes. " Booklist

Webb, Lois Sinaiko, 1922-
Holidays of the world cookbook for students.
Oryx Press 1995 xxxiv, 297p il maps pa $36.95 (5
and up)   **641.5**
1. Cooking 2. Holidays
ISBN 0-89774-884-0   LC 95-26019
In this cookbook "more than 136 countries are represented, with 388 recipes. The U.S. is divided into six
sections with 10 recipes for regional celebrations. History
behind the holiday is included where possible, as is pertinent background information on the culture represented.
. . . A discussion of different calendars used around the
world is an interesting inclusion. The recipes' directions
are clear and include equipment lists." SLJ
Includes glossary and bibliographical references

Wilkes, Angela
Children's quick & easy cookbook; 101
delicious step-by-step recipes. DK Pub. 1997 96p
il $16.99   **641.5**
1. Cooking
ISBN 0-7894-2026-0   LC 97-15422
Discusses cooking techniques, food hygiene, and
kitchen safety, and presents step-by-step instructions for
all types of dishes
This is a "beautiful cookbook, full of eye-catching
photographs. . . . The recipes . . . are inviting and are
composed of real ingredients rather than mixes." SLJ

Zanger, Mark H.
The American ethnic cookbook for students.
Oryx Press 2001 325p il $32.50   **641.5**
1. Cooking
ISBN 1-57356-345-5   LC 00-11094
"An introduction discusses how ethnic recipes change
when they are transported to new countries. Some 400
recipes from 122 ethnic groups and 21 Native American
groups follow. Alphabetical entries for each ethnic group
include a brief introduction about the culture followed by
a few recipes." Booklist
"Using these recipes will be a great motivation for
students to learn about the varied heritage of our immigrant nation." SLJ
Includes bibliographical references

641.8   Cooking specific kinds of dishes, preparing beverages

Goss, Gary, 1947-
Blue moon soup; a family cookbook; recipes by
Gary Goss; illustrated by Jane Dyer. Little, Brown
1999 60p il $16.95 (4-6)   **641.8**
1. Soups 2. Cooking
ISBN 0-316-32991-6   LC 98-19458
This "cookbook includes eight to ten soup recipes for
each season of the year as well as several related recipes
for bread, salads, snacks, and croutons." Booklist
"The tone is lighthearted and full of quirky humor.
. . . The recipes are clear. . . . Dyer's outstanding watercolors echo the tone of the text; there are 14 fanciful
full-page illustrations, and whimsical spot art is scattered
throughout." SLJ

643   Housing and household equipment

Plante, Ellen M.
The American kitchen, 1700 to the present;
from hearth to highrise. Facts on File 1995 340p
il $32.95 (7 and up)   **643**
1. Kitchens 2. Cooking 3. United States—Social life
and customs
ISBN 0-8160-3038-3   LC 94-33235
This is a "history of the evolution of the focal point
of the American home, beginning with the colonial kitch-
en and traveling to the present. Plante gives readers not
only a clear view of how the room has changed, but also
of how the family itself has changed. The illustrations
and reproductions of advertisements make visualizing the
text interesting and easy. The 'Household Hints and Recipes' are outstanding, each worthy of the era they reflect." SLJ
Includes glossary and bibliographical references

646.7   Management of personal and family life

Busby, Cylin, 1970-
Getting dumped and getting over it! by Cylin
Busby. Price Stern Sloan 2001 135p lib bdg
$13.89; pa $4.99 (7 and up)   **646.7**
1. Dating (Social customs) 2. Teenagers 3. Love
4. Loss (Psychology)
ISBN 0-8431-7712-8 (lib bdg); 0-8431-7679-2 (pa)
                                      LC 2001-45843
Contents: It's over; Dumped; The first twenty-four
hours; He says\she says; Facing the world; What did I do
wrong?; Getting even; Getting over him; Almost over
him; But no one cares; Can we be friends?; The new guy
& other good stuff; Resources
Explores what it can feel like when a boy ends a relationship and how to deal with those feelings, including
suggestions from girls who have survived breakups.
"Filled with sound advice, unique getting-over-it activities, and real-world commentaries from the dumped (females) and dumpers (males), the book puts a new spin
on a timeworn topic." SLJ
Includes bibliographical references

Espeland, Pamela, 1951-
Life lists for teens; tips, steps, hints, and
how-tos for growing up, getting along, learning,
and having fun. Free Spirit 2003 264p pa $11.95
                                          646.7
1. Conduct of life 2. Life skills
ISBN 1-57542-125-9   LC 2002-152116
Hundreds of lists provide guidance in areas of young
adult life as diverse as selecting a book or a hair color
to selecting a mentor
"Espeland's well-organized book has lots of useful information and teen appeal." SLJ

Irons, Diane, 1949-

Teen beauty secrets; fresh, simple & sassy tips for your perfect look. Sourcebooks 2002 263p il pa $14.95 (7 and up) **646.7**

1. Personal appearance 2. Personal grooming 3. Girls—Health and hygiene

ISBN 1-57071-959-4   LC 2002-6705

"A book filled with dozens of practical beauty tips, diet and fitness suggestions, and fashion hints. With an emphasis on the natural, the former fashion model guides readers through bad-hair days, fashion faux pas, and the makeup techniques of the stars." SLJ

Morgenstern, Julie

Organizing from the inside out for teens; the foolproof system for organizing your room, your time, and your life; [by] Julie Morgenstern and Jessi Morgenstern-Colón; illustrations by Janet Pedersen. Holt & Co. 2002 238p il pa $15 (7 and up) **646.7**

1. Life skills 2. Time management

ISBN 0-8050-6470-2   LC 2002-68552

The authors "offer practical advice to teenagers who want to get organized. After considering what might be holding them back and the three steps to success (analyze, strategize, attack), the discussion shifts to the two major areas of concern: managing space and managing time. . . . Useful advice in an accessible paperback format." Booklist

Warrick, Leanne

Hair trix for cool chix; the real girl's guide to great hair; Leanne Warrick. Watson-Guptill 2004 96p il (Cool chix) pa $9.95 **646.7**

1. Hair

ISBN 0-8230-2179-3   LC 2003-22803

Contents: Get to know your hair; Hairology 101; Salon savvy; Quiz: who do you want to be today?; Everyday styles; Hang-out styles; Special styles; Hair 911; Quiz: what's your style personality?; Make your own hair accessories

A guide to hair care and hairstyles which includes quizzes, recipes for hair products, tips on how to be "salon savvy," step-by-step instructions for casual and special hairstyles, and hair accessory projects.

"Written in an upbeat, friendly style, this easy-to-follow book will have readers spending even more time in front of the bathroom mirror." SLJ

650.1   Personal success in business

Kiefer, Jeanne

Jobs for kids; a smart kid's Q & A guide; illustrations by Carol Nicklaus. Millbrook Press 2003 112p il lib bdg $25.90 (4 and up) **650.1**

1. Money-making projects for children 2. Entrepreneurship

ISBN 0-7613-2611-1   LC 2002-8353

Answers questions about the five most popular jobs for young people, as well as about other ways they can make money, with advice on the planning and marketing involved

"Packed with information, forms, and ideas, this is an ideal guide for young people looking to make money and have fun at the same time." SLJ

650.14   Success in obtaining jobs and promotions

Coon, Nora

Teen dream jobs; how to get the job you really want now! Beyond Words Pub 2003 132p il pa $9.95 (7 and up) **650.14**

1. Job hunting 2. Vocational guidance

ISBN 1-582-70093-1   LC 2003-41947

A high school freshman shares insights, practical information, and resources on conducting a job search and profiles other young people, from twelve to seventeen years old, who have found their dream jobs.

"Written in a clear, straightforward style, this title is a good choice for career-development collections." SLJ

Includes bibliographical references

Pervola, Cindy, 1956-

How to get a job if you're a teenager; [by] Cindy Pervola and Debby Hobgood. Alleyside Press 1998 62p il pa $12.95 (7 and up) **650.14**

1. Job hunting 2. Vocational guidance

ISBN 1-57950-013-7   LC 97-45843

This book provides "information on how to select the best job, where to look, how to apply, how best to prepare for the interview, how to get the job, what to expect on the first day, and what to do when leaving a job. It offers various resources like job web sites and Internet guides, and tells how to create your own job." Book Rep

"An excellent addition to career collections." SLJ

Includes bibliographical references

Schwager, Tina, 1964-

Cool women, hot jobs . . . and how you can go for it, too! {by} Tina Schwager & Michele Schuerger. Free Spirit 2002 278p il pa $15.95 (7 and up) **650.14**

1. Vocational guidance 2. Women—Employment 3. Occupations

ISBN 1-57542-109-7   LC 2001-40908

Includes index

Profiles twenty-two women and the jobs they do, from choreographer to FBI agent, describing their education, duties, personality traits, and other factors in their career success, and gives specific ways to determine one's own future work

This "is a valuable contribution to a young adult collection. The pages burst with the inspiration and motivation." Voice Youth Advocates

652   Processes of written communication

Janeczko, Paul B., 1945-
Top secret; a handbook of codes, ciphers and secret writing; illustrated by Jenna LaReau. Candlewick Press 2004 136p il $16.99 (4 and up)
         652
1. Cryptography 2. Ciphers
ISBN 0-7636-0971-4
This is a "guide to secret writing. Janeczko relates how different codes came to be and why they were needed, and gives some historical examples. The book also contains information and exercises (with answers) on deciphering codes and provides children with the tools to make their own field kit. . . . Humorous black-and-white sketches . . . are found throughout the book. The author's upbeat, positive tone is refreshing and his enthusiasm about his topic is contagious." SLJ

Singh, Simon
The code book; how to make it, break it, hack it, crack it. Delacorte Press 2002 c2001 263p il $16.95; lib bdg $18.99 (7 and up)   **652**
1. Cryptography
ISBN 0-385-72913-8; 0-385-90032-5 (lib bdg)
         LC 2001-42131
Based on the author's book of the same title for adults published 1999 by Doubleday
This is an "introduction to the underlying principles, the intriguing history, and the possible future of codes, including the issues and challenges of encrypted internet communication. . . . A challenging, but fascinating introduction to codes." Booklist
Includes bibliographical references

659.1   Advertising

Day, Nancy, 1953-
Advertising; information or manipulation? Enslow Pubs. 1999 128p il (Issues in focus) lib bdg $26.60 (7 and up)   **659.1**
1. Advertising
ISBN 0-7660-1106-2   LC 98-35032
Discusses how advertising has developed, how companies use it to entice consumers, and the impact of advertising on people, particularly young people
"The book includes tips for critically evaluating advertising, which are useful for classroom discussion on media influence, and stresses the importance of being informed before buying. . . . Readers and educators will find the book fascinating, thought-provoking, and educational, inside and outside the classroom. All in all, a top-notch culture-consumerism book, comprehensive and easy to follow." Booklist
Includes glossary and bibliographical references

Dunn, John M., 1949-
Advertising. Lucent Bks. 1997 112p il (Lucent overview series) lib bdg $27.45 (7 and up)
         659.1
1. Advertising
ISBN 1-560-06182-0   LC 96-35920
Discusses the functions, goals, and methods of advertising and examines such issues as targeting the youth market, political ads, and the right of free speech
This "offers lots of information in an attractive, well-organized, and readable format. . . . This book will be useful for school reports, and will attract interested browsers." SLJ
Includes bibliographical references

Graydon, Shari
Made you look; how advertising works and why you should know; illustrations by Warren Clark. Annick Press 2003 115p il $24.95; pa $14.95 (5 and up)   **659.1**
1. Advertising
ISBN 1-55037-815-5; 1-55037-814-7 (pa)
This "analysis seeks to raise preteens' awareness of themselves as targets and vectors of advertising messages. Brimming with anecdotes, facts, and quotes . . . the text covers controversial programs that bring ads into the schools, and describes traditional marketing methods as well as 'stealth' techniques. . . . Graydon . . . often ends sections with a provocative question . . . and she helpfully includes addresses of watchdog organizations, tips for writing effective complaints, and an impressive set of endnotes." Booklist
Includes bibliographical references

660.6   Biotechnology

Dowswell, Paul
Genetics; the impact on our lives. Raintree Steck-Vaughn Pubs. 2001 64p il (21st century debates) $22.95 (7 and up)   **660.6**
1. Genetic engineering 2. Bioethics
ISBN 0-7398-3174-7   LC 00-33279
This presents arguments for and against genetic engineering, discussing such topics as animal and human hybrids, gene therapy, designer babies, and cloning
"The factual information is presented in a pro and con format that lends itself to classroom debate. . . . Fascinating photographs, advertisments, computer images, and Web site screens add to the eye-catching appeal." Book Rep
Includes glossary and bibliographical references

Morgan, Sally
Body doubles; cloning plants and animals. Heinemann Lib. 2002 64p il lib bdg $32.79; pa $9.50   **660.6**
1. Cloning
ISBN 1-58810-698-5; 1-4034-4120-0 (pa)
         LC 2001-6078
Contents: The path to Dolly; Natural cloning; Chromosomes and DNA; Cloning in the lab; Cloning in action; Spare-part surgery; Human cloning; Future developments

Morgan, Sally—*Continued*

"Morgan presents a balanced blend of hard science and thought-provoking topics. . . . A section on chromosomes and DNA is handled especially well: it is illustrated with numerous diagrams that provide great visual aid for the well-written text." Booklist

Includes bibliographical references

Nardo, Don, 1947-

Cloning. Blackbirch Press 2003 48p il (Science on the edge) $20.95 (5 and up)   **660.6**

1. Cloning

ISBN 1-56711-782-1   LC 2002-10369

Contents: Cloning is Nothing New; Potential Benefits of Animal Cloning; The Promise of Human Cloning

Discusses the history of the concept of cloning and the pros and cons of cloning animals and humans

"Very accessible and informative . . . exemplary." Booklist

Cloning. Lucent Bks. 2002 128p il (Great medical discoveries) lib bdg $27.45 (7 and up)   **660.6**

1. Cloning

ISBN 1-56006-927-9   LC 2001-2556

This "begins with cloned plants in nature and in agriculture, then describes the turning point represented by the birth of Dolly the cloned sheep in 1996. This balanced presentation discusses not only the biological challenge of cloning species but also the ethical quandaries raised by scientists' ability to replicate individuals." Booklist

Includes bibliographical references

Spangenburg, Ray, 1939-

Genetic engineering; by Ray Spangenburg and Kit Moser. Benchmark Bks. 2003 125p il (Open for debate) $37.07 (7 and up)   **660.6**

1. Genetic engineering

ISBN 0-7614-1586-6   LC 2002-156286

Contents: Jack and the beanstalk; Genetically manufactured food crops; From douglas fir to bacterial saviors; Is it in the wind? or not?; Cloning bossy, Mickey, and the blue ox; Alliance or danger?; The human genome; The stem cell controversy; For and against; At the heart of the matter

Discusses the use of genetic engineering in plants and animals, and the hopes spurred by the mapping of human DNA by the Human Genome Project as well as the controversy over using stem cells for disease research

"Each discussion ends with a list of 'pluses' and 'minuses' that clearly presents the arguments on each side of these hot-button issues." Horn Book Guide

Includes bibliographical references

A **Student's** guide to biotechnology. Greenwood Press 2002 4v set $160 (7 and up)   **660.6**

1. Biotechnology

ISBN 0-313-32256-2   LC 2002-72693

Contents: v1 Words and terms; v2 Important people in biotechnology; v3 The history of biotechnology; v4 Debatable issues

This set "defines terms, profiles people who have made significant contributions to the field, provides a historical overview, and investigates the controversies associated with biotech research." Booklist

"This much-needed four-volume set offers readers a wealth of well-researched and clearly written information." Libr Media Connect

666   Ceramic and allied technologies

Kassinger, Ruth

Ceramics: from magic pots to man-made bones; [by] Ruth G. Kassinger. Twenty-First Century Bks. 2003 80p il map (Material world) lib bdg $25.90   **666**

1. Ceramics

ISBN 0-7613-2108-X   LC 2002-11512

Examines the discovery of pottery and ceramics and their uses throughout history, gives a scientific explanation of the properties of clay, and looks at how ceramics are used in modern technology

This "will catch the interest of a wide variety of readers. The color photographs are clear, interesting, and self-explanatory." Libr Media Connect

Includes bibliographical references

667   Cleaning, color, coating, related technologies

Kassinger, Ruth

Dyes: from sea snails to synthetics; [by] Ruth G. Kassinger. Twenty-First Century Bks. 2003 80p il map (Material world) $25.90   **667**

1. Dyes and dyeing 2. Color

ISBN 0-7613-2112-8   LC 2002-2102

Explains how dyes were developed, how they have been used throughout history and discusses the history and folklore surrounding different colors

This "will catch the interest of a wide variety of readers. The color photographs are clear, interesting, and self-explanatory." Libr Media Connect

Includes glossary and bibliographical references

669   Metallurgy

Kassinger, Ruth

Gold: from Greek myth to computer chips; [by] Ruth G. Kassinger. Twenty-First Century Bks. 2003 80p il map (Material world) lib bdg $25.90   **669**

1. Gold

ISBN 0-7613-2110-1   LC 2001-42729

An overview of the history, uses, and characteristics of gold

This "will catch the interest of a wide variety of readers. The color photographs are clear, interesting, and self-explanatory." Libr Media Connect

Includes glossary and bibliographical references

681.1   Instruments for measuring time

Collier, James Lincoln, 1928-
Clocks. Benchmark Bks. 2004 126p il (Great inventions) lib bdg $37.08   **681.1**
1. Clocks and watches 2. Time
ISBN 0-7614-1538-6   LC 2002-156288
Contents: Since the beginning of time; Timekeeping marches on; The great escapement; Springs and pendulums; Setting the year straight; Navigation time; Time for everybody; Atomic time for an atomic world
This describes the history and significance of clocks and other time-keeping devices from prehistoric times to the present
Includes bibliographical references

Duffy, Trent
The clock; fold out illustration by Toby Willes. Atheneum Bks. for Young Readers 2000 80p il (Turning point inventions series) lib bdg $17.95 (4 and up)   **681.1**
1. Clocks and watches 2. Time
ISBN 0-689-82814-4   LC 99-65242
A history of time measurement, including a short biography of John Harrison, inventor of the chronemetric clock, and the effect of the clock on the Industrial Revolution
"This accessible and thorough treatment should be welcomed by students in search of an unusual topic for the ubiquitous 'invention report.'" Bull Cent Child Books
Includes bibliographical references

686.2   Printing

Graham, Ian, 1953-
Books and newspapers. Raintree Steck-Vaughn Pubs. 2001 47p il (Communications close-up) $27.11   **686.2**
1. Printing 2. Publishers and publishing 3. Newspapers
ISBN 0-7398-3186-0   LC 00-33286
An introduction to the technology of printing, briefly covering such topics as lithography, letterpress, gravure, paper making and recycling, inks, book preservation, writing instruments, machine codes, smart cards, virtual newspapers and libraries, and mapmaking
"Graham is not only knowledgeable about his subject but also adept at clearly explaining complex information. The colorful, attractive illustrations add to the textual explanations." Book Rep
Includes glossary and bibliographical references

Meltzer, Milton, 1915-
The printing press. Benchmark Bks. 2003 c2004 125p il (Great inventions) lib bdg $25.95   **686.2**
1. Printing
ISBN 0-7614-1536-X   LC 2002-15307

Contents: Speaking, writing, and reading; Scribes and scrolls; Was China first?; How Gutenberg did it; Printing, printing, everywhere; The print shop: a cultural center; From apprentice to master; An aid to science; From Luther to Plymouth Rock; The printing press and democracy; Many voices; In love with the printed word; The power of print; The new place of print
"The author expertly describes a setting that is ripe for invention. . . . Historical artwork, and personal narratives make the times real and relevant to readers." SLJ
Includes bibliographical references

688.7   Recreational equipment

Wulffson, Don L., 1943-
Toys! amazing stories behind some great inventions; [by] Don Wulffson; with illustrations by Laurie Keller. Holt & Co. 2000 137p il $16.95 (4 and up)   **688.7**
1. Toys 2. Inventions
ISBN 0-8050-6196-7   LC 99-58440
Describes the creation of a variety of toys and games, from seesaws to Silly Putty and toy soldiers to Trivial Pursuit
"Each of the 25 chapters is illustrated with small, humorous drawings and discusses a particular toy or game's origin and development. The book ends with a bibliography and a list of Web sites. Good, readable fare for browsing or light research." Booklist
Includes bibliographical references

690   Buildings

Macaulay, David, 1946-
Mill. Houghton Mifflin 1983 128p il $18; pa $9.95 (4 and up)   **690**
1. Mills 2. Textile industry—History
ISBN 0-395-34830-7; 0-395-52019-3 (pa)
     LC 83-10652
This is an "account of the development of four fictional 19th-Century Rhode Island cotton mills. In explaining the construction and operation of a simple water-wheel powered wooden mill, as well as the more complex stone, turbine and steam mills to follow, the author also describes the rise and decline of New England's textile industry." SLJ

Unbuilding. Houghton Mifflin 1980 78p il $18; pa $9.95 (4 and up)   **690**
1. Empire State Building (New York, N.Y.) 2. Building 3. Skyscrapers
ISBN 0-395-29457-6; 0-395-45425-5 (pa)
     LC 80-15491
This fictional account of the dismantling and removal of the Empire State Building describes the structure of a skyscraper and explains how such an edifice would be demolished
"Save for the fact that one particularly stunning double-page spread is marred by tight binding, the book is a joy: accurate, informative, handsome, and eminently readable." Bull Cent Child Books

Wilkinson, Philip, 1955-
Building; written by Philip Wilkinson; photographed by Dave King & Geoff Dann. Knopf 1995 61p il (Eyewitness books) (4 and up)
690
1. Structural engineering 2. House construction 3. Building materials
LC 94-37733
Available DK Pub. edition $15.99; lib bdg $19.99 (ISBN 0-7894-6026-2; 0-7894-6607-4)
"A Dorling Kindersley book"
First published 1994 in the United Kingdom
This covers "the history of building techniques, materials, and philosophy from earth-and-thatch houses to cathedrals and skyscrapers." SLJ
An "extremely handsome volume. . . . This is an informative book, fascinating for study or browsing." Sci Books Films

700 ARTS & RECREATION

Aronson, Marc
Art attack; a short cultural history of the avant-garde. Clarion Bks. 1998 192p il $24 (7 and up)
700
1. Modern art 2. Art appreciation 3. Art and society
ISBN 0-395-79729-2
LC 97-22372
Discusses the arts, life styles, politics, and fashions while tracing the story of bohemians, radicals, hipsters, and hippies from Paris in the nineteenth century to contemporary America
"Art Attack would make an excellent resource for the secondary level student who might be interested in exploring some creative outlets or as a catalyst for discussions about aesthetics, expression, or contemporary lifestyles." ALAN
Includes bibliographical references

Chambers, Veronica
The Harlem Renaissance. Chelsea House 1997 128p il (African-American achievers) $23.95; pa $9.95
700
1. African American arts 2. Harlem Renaissance
ISBN 0-7910-2597-7; 0-7910-2598-5 (pa)
LC 97-20585
Recounts the vibrant personalities and remarkable cultural movements that flourished in America's leading Black community during the 1920s and 1930s
Includes bibliographical references

Ochoa, George
The Wilson chronology of the arts; {by} George Ochoa and Melinda Corey. Wilson, H.W. 1998 476p $110
700
1. Arts—History
ISBN 0-8242-0934-6
LC 97-23541
First published 1995 by Ballantine Books with title: The timeline book of the arts
"The authors provide a timeline detailing human creativity that progresses from ca. 43,000 B.C.E. to 1997, with 4,000 entries spread over 13 categories of artistic endeavor. . . . The chronology is global in scope and comprehensive in coverage, emphasizing well-established art forms without neglecting the oral traditions and decorative art forms of nonliterate societies and currently emerging art forms. . . . The straightforward organization of this work makes it suitable for many different uses." Recomm Ref Books for Small & Medium-sized Libr & Media Cent, 1999

Rubin, Susan Goldman, 1939-
Art against the odds; from slave quilts to prison paintings. Crown Publishers 2004 48p il $19.95; lib bdg $21.99 (5 and up)
700
1. Art
ISBN 0-375-82406-5; 0-375-92406-X (lib bdg)
LC 2003-12139
Contents: Outsider art; Captured; Pattern for freedom: women's quilts as art; Kids create art against the odds
This is a "survey of outsider art, encompassing the works of patients, slaves, concentration and internment-camp prisoners, and disadvantaged children living in modern blighted urban areas and developing nations. . . . The vivid, resilient life force radiating from these works contrasts sharply with the unimaginably bleak conditions under which they were created. . . . This unique offering is a top priority for most libraries." SLJ
Includes bibliographical references

702.8 Art--Technique, procedures, apparatus, equipment, materials

Luxbacher, Irene, 1970-
The jumbo book of art; written and illustrated by Irene Luxbacher. Kids Can Press 2003 208p il pa $14.95 (4 and up)
702.8
1. Art—Study and teaching
ISBN 1-55074-762-2
"Each of the four chapters is devoted to instructing readers in the basics of one technique—drawing, creating with color, sculpture, and mixed-media projects, respectively—and then inspires those readers to let loose and have fun making something beautiful. . . . The book features clear layouts, well-written definitions of terms, full-color illustrations, and more than 90 projects. . . . This practical, lively, and smart package is a must-have for every art and elementary school classroom, and a welcome addition to most library collections." SLJ
Includes glossary

703 Art--Encyclopedias and dictionaries

Greenway, Shirley
Art: an A-Z guide; selected and written by Shirley Greenway. Watts 2000 128p il lib bdg $33; pa $19.95
703
1. Art—Dictionaries
ISBN 0-531-11729-4; 0-531-16553-1 (pa)
LC 00-24899

Greenway, Shirley—Continued

"Greenway highlights 59 terms that are important 'to a discussion and understanding of art.' Each term is richly illustrated with examples. While there are familiar paintings, there are also lesser-known works. . . . Sidebars highlight individual artists. . . . The text is succinct and the full-color photographs and reproductions, often several per concept, are lush and informative." SLJ

International encyclopedia of art. Facts on File 1996-1997 8v set $200   **703**
1. Art—Encyclopedias
ISBN 0-8160-3327-7

Contents: African art, by W. Rea; Art of the ancient Mediterranean world, by B. Wilson; European art to 1850, by T. Lucchesi; European art since 1850, by N. Malloy; Far Eastern art, by C. Doherty; Mexican Central and South American art, by J. F. Scott; North American art to 1900, by A. Pancza-Graham; North American art since 1900, by C. M. E. P. Turner

"This set introduces world art, including both folk and fine art. . . . Arrangement is roughly chronological with 40 color and 60 black and white photographs in each volume. Sidebars and boxes are used for biographical and background information. . . . The easy reading level and attractive layout make this set useful as a basic guide to world art for all collections." Safford. Guide to Ref Materials for Sch Libr Media Cent. 5th edition

The **Oxford** dictionary of art; edited by Ian Chilvers. 3rd ed. Oxford University Press 2004 xlvi, 816p $45   **703**
1. Art—Dictionaries
ISBN 0-19-860476-9   LC 2004-41540
First published 1988

This "reference contains 3000 entries that discuss Western and Western-inspired art from antiquity on. It considers paintings, graphics, sculpture, and architecture in terms of artistic figures, periods, schools, techniques, critical terms, and museums; lesser artists are treated more concisely than major ones." Libr J

704   Art--Special topics

Bolden, Tonya

Wake up our souls; a celebration of Black American artists; Published in association with Smithsonian American Art Museum. Harry N. Abrams 2004 128p il $24.95   **704**
1. African American art
ISBN 0-8109-4527-4

Presents a history of African American visual arts and artists from the days of slavery to the present

"Bolden's writing is rich and lyrical. She smoothly incorporates the historical context, explaining pivotal events and relevant artistic movements clearly and succinctly." SLJ

Cockcroft, James D.

Latino visions; contemporary Chicano, Puerto Rican, and Cuban American artists; by James D. Cockcroft, Jr; assisted by Jane Canning. Watts 2000 143p il (Book report biography) lib bdg $27; pa $12.95 (7 and up)   **704**
1. Hispanic American art 2. Modern art
ISBN 0-531-11312-4 (lib bdg); 0-531-16523-X (pa)
   LC 99-89464

Describes the evolution of Latino art in America through discussion of various artistic movements and important Latino artists

The author "makes you value 'people's art,' to be viewed not in imposing museums but as part of public life. At the same time, he does talk about individual Latino artists . . . with stirring detail." Booklist

Includes bibliographical references

709   Art--Historical and geographic treatment

Art: a world history. DK Pub. 1998 720p il hardcover o.p. paperback available $40
   709
1. Art—History
ISBN 0-7894-8904-X (pa)   LC 97-20234
Original Italian edition, 1997

This survey consists of "brief 50- to 500-word discussions of artists, topics, styles, and historic moments, presented via multiple columns, text boxes, time lines, and the like." Libr J

Includes bibliographical references

Gardner's art through the ages. Harcourt College Publishers 2v il map ea $84.95   **709**
1. Art—History

First published 1926 under the authorship of Helen Gardner. (11th edition 2001 revised by Richard G. Tansey, Fred S. Kleiner, and Christin J. Mamiya). Periodically revised

This book surveys world art from prehistoric times to the present day. Painting, sculpture, architecture and some decorative arts are considered. Although the focus is on European art, there are also chapters on ancient Near Eastern, Asian, pre-Columbian, American Indian, African and Oceanic art

Sayre, Henry M.

Cave paintings to Picasso; the inside scoop on 50 art masterpieces; by Henry Sayre. Chronicle Books 2004 93p il $22.95 (5 and up)
   709
1. Art—History
ISBN 0-8118-3767-X   LC 2002-15583

Introduces fifty celebrated works of art, including King Tut's sarcophagus and Andy Warhol's paintings of Campbell's soup cans, with historical and interpretive information for each piece.

"The author's breezy style captures interest early on. . . . Many of the world's cultures are represented and a variety of techniques are explained. . . . A dazzling and accessible introduction to art history." SLJ

Includes glossary

709.01 Arts of nonliterate peoples, and earliest times to 499

Arnold, Caroline, 1944-
Stories in stone; rock art pictures by early Americans; photographs by Richard Hewett. Clarion Bks. 1996 48p il map $16 (4 and up)
709.01
1. Native Americans—Antiquities 2. Rock drawings, paintings, and engravings
ISBN 0-395-72092-3   LC 96-387
This focuses "on the rock art found in the Coso Range of eastern California. . . . Arnold describes the various methods that were used to create the designs. She also discusses climatic changes in the area, beginning with the last Ice Age, and surmises what life might have been like for those ancient people." Booklist
"This is a crisply written, richly photographed account of the oldest known art in the world. . . . Hewett's color photographs are finely detailed, clear, and well composed, and they enrich the text enormously." Bull Cent Child Books
Includes glossary

709.02 Art--6th-15th centuries, 500-1499

Cole, Alison
The Renaissance. Dorling Kindersley 1994 64p il (Eyewitness art) $16.95
709.02
1. Art—15th and 16th centuries
ISBN 1-56458-493-3   LC 93-21264
Available from DK Pub. edition $15.99; lib bdg $19.99 (0-7894-5582-X; 0-7894-6624-4)
A guide to the art of Northern Europe and Italy from the 14th to the 16th century. Color photographs of paintings, sculpture and architecture representative of the period include the works of Giotto, Leonardo, Dürer, Titian, Raphael and Michelangelo. Features include detailed close-ups, diagrams and charts
Includes glossary

Corrain, Lucia
The art of the Renaissance; illustrated by L.R. Galante, Simone Boni. Bedrick Bks. 1997 64p il map (Masters of art) $22.50   **709.02**
1. Art—15th and 16th centuries 2. Art appreciation
ISBN 0-87226-526-9   LC 97-19338
At head of title: Masters of art; Tr. from Italian
An illustrated survey of the art and culture of Renaissance Europe
"Despite the brevity of each entry, a surprising amount of solid information is conveyed. A typical entry consists of an introductory paragraph; a large illustration; and three-to-eight smaller illustrations, photographs, and full-color reproductions. . . . This title does a fine job of introducing young readers to this period in art history." SLJ

709.03 Art--Modern period, 1500-

Bolton, Linda
Impressionism. Bedrick Bks. 2000 32p il (Art revolutions) $16.95   **709.03**
1. Impressionism (Art)
ISBN 0-87226-611-7   LC 99-86942
This offers an introduction to the Impressionist movement with examples of works by Claude Monet, Pierre Auguste Renoir, Camille Pissarro, and others
Includes glossary and bibliographical references

709.04 Art--20th century, 1900-1999

Mason, Antony
In the time of Picasso. Copper Beech Bks. 2002 48p il (Art around the world) lib bdg $23.90; pa $8.95   **709.04**
1. Picasso, Pablo, 1881-1973 2. Art—20th century 3. Artists
ISBN 0-7613-2713-4 (lib bdg); 0-7613-1628-0 (pa)
     LC 2001-7945
Subtitle on cover: Foundations of modern art
Profiles some of the major artists of the early twentieth century and discusses such art movements of the time as Fauvism, Cubism, Expressionism, Surrealism and Dadaism in the context of the political, economic, and other changes occurring throughout the world at that time
This is "imaginative and compact . . . mighty useful for quick explorations or pre-museum-visit overviews." Bull Cent Child Books
Includes glossary

In the time of Warhol. Copper Beech Bks. 2002 48p il (Art around the world) lib bdg $23.90; pa $8.95   **709.04**
1. Art—20th century 2. Artists
ISBN 0-7613-2714-2 (lib bdg); 0-7613-1629-9 (pa)
     LC 2001-8175
Added title page has subtitle "The development of contemporary art"
Profiles major artists of the second half of the twentieth century in the context of the political, economic, and other changes occurring throughout the world at the same time
This is "imaginative and compact . . . mighty useful for quick explorations of pre-museum-visit overviews." Bull Cent Child Books
Includes glossary

709.5 Asian art

Bingham, Jane
Indian art & culture. Raintree 2004 56p il map (World art & culture) lib bdg $21.95
     709.5
1. Indic arts
ISBN 0-7398-6607-9   LC 2003-1956
This offers a history of the arts of India, including architecture, wall painting and decoration, stone and wood

Bingham, Jane—*Continued*
carving, painting, textiles, ceramics, music, dance, theater and film, and writing, and explains their roles in Indian culture.

"Every page includes interesting and vivid color photographs of the different art forms and of artists at work. {This title is} well worth purchasing for the illustrations alone." SLJ

Includes glossary and bibliographical references

709.52 Japanese art

Khanduri, Kamini
Japanese art & culture. Raintree 2004 56p il map (World art & culture) lib bdg $21.95
709.52
1. Japanese arts 2. Japan—Civilization
ISBN 0-7398-6609-5   LC 2003-1957
This offers a history of the arts of Japan including painting, woodblock prints, sculpture, metalwork, pottery, lacquerware, architecture, gardens, calligraphy, and theater, and explains their places in Japanese culture.

Includes glossary and bibliographical references

709.6 African art

Bingham, Jane
African art & culture. Raintree 2004 56p il map (World art & culture) lib bdg $21.95
709.6
1. African art
ISBN 0-7398-6606-0   LC 2003-1955
This describes a variety of art forms of the African continent and their roles in their respective cultures.

This is "stunningly illustrated. . . . Every page includes interesting and vivid color photographs of the different art forms and of artists at work. {This title is} well worth purchasing for the illustrations alone." SLJ

Includes glossary and bibliographical references

709.72 Mexican art

Lewis, Elizabeth, 1967-
Mexican art & culture. Raintree 2004 56p il map (World art & culture) lib bdg $21.95
709.72
1. Mexican art 2. Mexico—Social life and customs
ISBN 0-7398-6610-9   LC 2003-1958
This offers a history of the arts of Mexico including architecture, carvings and sculpture, pottery and ceramics, masks, lacquering, textiles and clothing, jewelry, painting, music and musical instruments, fiestas and festivals, death and burial customs, and toys, and explains their roles in Mexican culture.

The text is "straightforward and concise, but it's excellent selection of high-quality color photos that really stand out." Booklist

Includes glossary and bibliographical references

711 Area planning

Macaulay, David, 1946-
City: a story of Roman planning and construction. Houghton Mifflin 1974 112p il $18; pa $7.95 (4 and up)   **711**
1. City planning—Rome 2. Civil engineering 3. Roman architecture
ISBN 0-395-19492-X; 0-395-34922-2 (pa)
LC 74-4280
"By following the inception, construction, and development of an imaginary Roman city, the account traces the evolution of Verbonia from the selection of its site under religious auspices in 26 B.C. to its completion in 100 A.D." Horn Book

Includes glossary

720 Architecture

Corbishley, Mike
The world of architectural wonders. Bedrick Bks. 1996 45p il maps $19.95   **720**
1. Structural engineering 2. Architecture
ISBN 0-87226-279-0   LC 96-47596
First published 1996 in the United Kingdom with title: Superstructures

Examines the stories behind such wonders of the world's architecture as the pyramids of Giza, the Great Wall of China, Chartes Cathedral, the city of Venice, and Hoover Dam

"Color photographs are paired with detailed drawings. Together, the text and illustrations capture the awe and spectacle of humankind's greatest building achievement." Booklist

Includes glossary

Joseph, Leonard M.
Skyscrapers: inside and out; illustrations, Leonello Calvetti [et al.] PowerKids Press 2002 47p il (Technology—blueprints of the future) lib bdg $25.25   **720**
1. Skyscrapers
ISBN 0-8239-6109-5   LC 2001-1115
This "features a chronology of the world's tallest buildings, plus an intriguing look at how these amazing architectural pillars are designed, are constructed, and operate. Separate sections provide a closer look at such famous structures as the Empire State Building, the Chrysler Building, the World Trade Center, and the Sears Tower." Voice Youth Advocates

Includes bibliographical references

Macaulay, David, 1946-
Building big. Houghton Mifflin 2000 192p il $30; pa $12.95   **720**
1. Architecture 2. Engineering
ISBN 0-395-96331-1; 0-618-46527-8 (pa)
LC 00-28116
"Walter Lorraine books"

Macaulay, David, 1946-—_Continued_
This companion to the PBS series examines the architecture and engineering of "bridges, tunnels, dams, domes, and skyscrapers. Each section offers an implicitly chronological analysis as it focuses on several significant examples of that particular kind of structure." Bull Cent Child Books
"Macaulay combines his detailed yet vaguely whimsical illustrations with simple, straightforward prose that breaks down complex architectural and engineering accomplishments into easily digestible tidbits that don't insult the intelligence of the reader of any age." N Y Times Book Rev
Includes glossary

Ross, Stewart
Art and architecture; by Stewart Ross. Lucent Books 2004 48p il (Medieval realms) $28.70 (5 and up)   **720**
1. Medieval architecture 2. Medieval art
ISBN 1-59018-534-X   LC 2004-11491
Contents: Romanesque architecture; Romanesque art : painting; Romanesque art : tapestry; The Gothic revolution : architecture; The Gothic revolution : art; Gothic glory; High Gothic architecture; Islamic architecture; Islamic art; Picture windows; Sculpture : decoration; Sculpture : tombs and monuments; Parish churches; The monastery; Manuscript illumination; Early castles : motte and bailey; Later castles; Manors and halls; The houses of the poor; Town architecture; Towards the Renaissance; Timeline
This "discusses the role of the church in medieval art; prominent cathedrals of the Romanesque and Gothic periods; Moorish and Islamic influences in Eastern Europe; manuscript illumination; and castles, manors, and more. . . . Distinctive borders surround the top and sides of the beautifully designed spreads, and the {text is} presented in small, accessible sections with glossary words in bold, cross-references, captions, and sidebars." SLJ
Includes glossary and bibliographical references

Rubin, Susan Goldman, 1939-
There goes the neighborhood; ten buildings people loved to hate. Holiday House 2001 96p il $18.95 (7 and up)   **720**
1. Architecture
ISBN 0-8234-1435-3   LC 00-36953
This is an account of public reaction to such buildings as the Washington Monument, the Eiffel Tower, and the Pompidou Center
"Written in simple, engaging language that never condescends, the stories reveal how architects identified and solved aesthetic and engineering problems, and include fascinating tidbits about each structure's history, neighborhood, and the extreme personalities that drove some projects." Booklist
Includes bibliographical references

Severance, John B.
Skyscrapers; how America grew up. Holiday House 2000 112p $18.95   **720**
1. Skyscrapers
ISBN 0-8234-1492-2   LC 99-51842

Details some of the innovations that enabled the building of taller and taller buildings, describes the various schools of skyscraper architecture, and explores the history of several famous skyscrapers
"The many black-and-white illustrations include period prints and photos, which complement the clearly written and well-organized text." Booklist
Includes bibliographical references

722 Architecture from earliest times to ca. 300

Bentley, Diana
The seven wonders of the ancient world. Oxford Univ. Press 2002 32p il $16.95; lib bdg $18.95
                                                       722
1. Ancient architecture 2. Curiosities and wonders
ISBN 0-19-521914-7; 0-19-521913-9 (lib bdg)
                                          LC 2002-70097
Describes the architectural achievements of the ancient world known as the Seven Wonders of the World: the Pyramids at Giza, the Statue of Zeus at Olympia, the Hanging Gardens of Babylon, the Temple of Artemis at Ephesus, the Lighthouse of Alexandria, the Mausoleum of Halicarnassus, and the Colossus of Rhodes
"An appropriate sense of awe pervades the clear, straightforward prose. . . . A fascinating look at a fascinating topic." SLJ

726 Buildings for religious and related purposes

DuTemple, Lesley A., 1952-
The Pantheon. Lerner Publs. 2003 72p il (Great building feats) lib bdg $27.93 (5 and up)
                                                       726
1. Pantheon (Rome, Italy) 2. Temples 3. Roman architecture
ISBN 0-8225-0376-X   LC 2001-05694
Describes the building of the Pantheon, discussing the role of the Roman emperor Hadrian and the significance of the Pantheon in the fields of history and architecture
This offers a "clear and straightforward text. . . . There are numerous color photographs, clear diagrams, and architectural drawings of the building and its interior." SLJ
Includes bibliographical references

The Taj Mahal. Lerner Publs. 2003 88p il (Great building feats) lib bdg $27.93   **726**
1. Taj Mahal (Agra, India)
ISBN 0-8225-4694-9   LC 2002-151380
Contents: The Chosen One of the Palace (1519-1631); The origins of the Taj Mahal (1562-1632); Construction begins (1631-1632); Bricks and marble (1632-1637); The illumined tomb (1632-1643); The garden of paradise on earth (1640-1643); The fall of the Mughals (1643-present)
Recounts the history of the creation of the Taj Mahal, built as a tomb and memorial for the wife of the Mughal emperor Shah Jahan

DuTemple, Lesley A., 1952-—*Continued*
The text is "enriched with interesting sidebars, diagrams that clarify the description of the building techniques, and many color photographs and reproductions." SLJ
Includes bibliographical references

Macaulay, David, 1946-
Building the book Cathedral. Houghton Mifflin 1999 112p il $29.95 (4 and up)　　　**726**
1. Cathedrals 2. Gothic architecture
ISBN 0-395-92147-3　　　LC 99-17975
"Walter Lorraine books."
"On its twenty-fifth anniversary, the author recounts the origins of his first book and suggests revisions he'd make in light of what he's learned. . . . Most of the original *Cathedral: the story of it's construction* is reproduced in this oversized celebratory volume, along with lots of preliminary sketches, new commentary, and revised, or newly deployed, art. . . . Touches of informal humor further enliven a book that's already mesmerizing for both its original content and its insights into this author-illustrator's incisive, ebulliently creative mind." Horn Book

Cathedral: the story of its construction. Houghton Mifflin 1973 77p il $18; pa $8.95 (4 and up)　　　**726**
1. Cathedrals 2. Gothic architecture
ISBN 0-395-17513-5; 0-395-31668-5 (pa)
LC 73-6634
This is a description, illustrated with black-and-white line drawings, of the construction of an imagined representative Gothic cathedral "in southern France from its conception in 1252 to its completion in 1338. The spirit that motivated the people, the tools and materials they used, the steps and methods of constructions, all receive . . . attention." Booklist
Includes glossary

Mosque. Houghton Mifflin 2003 96p il $18 (4 and up)　　　**726**
1. Mosques—Design and construction
ISBN 0-618-24034-9　　　LC 2003-177
"Walter Lorraine books"
Using "a fictional framework to hold his nonfictional material, the author introduces readers to Admiral Suha Mehmet Pasa, a wealthy aristocrat living in Istanbul, who decides in his declining years to fund the building of a mosque and its associated buildings—religious school, soup kitchen, public baths, public fountain, and tomb. Detailing the activities of the architect and workers, Macaulay creates a from-the-ground-up look not only at the actual construction, but also at the uses of the various buildings." SLJ
"Once again Macaulay uses clear words and exemplary drawings to explore a majestic structure's design and construction. . . . In his respectful, straightforward explanation of the mosque's design, Macaulay offers an unusual, inspiring perspective into Islamic society." Booklist
Includes glossary

Pyramid. Houghton Mifflin 1975 80p il $18; pa $9.95 (4 and up)　　　**726**
1. Pyramids 2. Egypt—Civilization
ISBN 0-395-21407-6; 0-395-32121-2 (pa)
LC 75-9964
The construction of a pyramid in 25th century B.C. Egypt is described. "Information about selection of the site, drawing of the plans, calculating compass directions, clearing and leveling the ground, and quarrying and hauling the tremendous blocks of granite and limestone is conveyed as much by pictures as by text." Horn Book
Includes glossary

728　Residential and related buildings

Yue, Charlotte
The igloo; {by} Charlotte and David Yue. Houghton Mifflin 1988 117p il $16; pa $7.95 (4 and up)　　　**728**
1. Igloos 2. Inuit
ISBN 0-395-44613-9; 0-395-62986-1 (pa)
LC 88-6154
Describes how an igloo is constructed and the role it plays in the lives of the Eskimo people. Also discusses many other aspects of Eskimo culture that have helped them adapt to life in the Arctic
"This book is a tidy source of reference information, curriculum support, and just plain compelling reading." SLJ
Includes bibliographical references

728.8　Large and elaborate private dwellings

Macaulay, David, 1946-
Castle. Houghton Mifflin 1977 74p il $18; pa $9.95 (4 and up)　　　**728.8**
1. Castles 2. Fortification
ISBN 0-395-25784-0; 0-395-32920-5 (pa)
LC 77-7159
Macaulay depicts "the history of an imaginary thirteenth-century castle—built to subdue the Welsh hordes—from the age of construction to the age of neglect, when the town of Aberwyfern no longer needs a fortified stronghold." Economist
Includes glossary

730.9　Sculpture--Historical and geographic treatment

Fritz, Jean
Leonardo's horse; illustrated by Hudson Talbott. Putnam 2001 unp il $16.99 (4 and up)
730.9
1. Leonardo, da Vinci, 1452-1519 2. Dent, Charlie, 1919-1994 3. Bronzes
ISBN 0-399-23576-0　　　LC 00-41550

Fritz, Jean—*Continued*

"In 1482, Leonardo da Vinci began work on a mammoth bronze horse. But though he completed a twenty-four-foot clay model, it was never cast. . . . Half a millennium later, retired pilot Charles Dent dedicated himself to re-creating Leonardo's dream, a venture eventually realized with the help of sculptor Nina Akamu." Horn Book

"Combining biography, history, and art, Fritz's absorbing text is both a lively introduction to Leonardo and a tribute to Dent." Booklist

736 Carving and carvings. Paper cutting and folding

Boursin, Didier

Origimi paper animals. Firefly Bks. (Buffalo) 2001 64p il lib bdg $19.95; pa $9.95 (7 and up)
736

1. Origami
ISBN 1-55209-628-9 (lib bdg); 1-55209-622-X (pa)
The author of this origami book "offers some beginning information before delving into neatly outlined projects featuring airplanes or animals that are clearly labeled for difficulty." Booklist

Diehn, Gwen, 1943-

Making books that fly, fold, wrap, hide, pop up, twist, and turn; books for kids to make. Lark Bks. 1998 96p il $19.95 (4 and up)
736

1. Paper crafts 2. Handicraft
ISBN 1-57990-023-2
LC 97 41037
Presents instructions for making various kinds of books including those that carry messages across space and time as well as those that save words, ideas, and pictures

"Clear directions and diagrams and attractive full-color photographs of completed projects will make it easy for readers to duplicate 18 different folded, wrapped, and pop-up books." Booklist

Includes glossary

Nguyen, Duy

Fantasy origami. Sterling 2001 96p il $19.95; pa $9.95 (7 and up)
736

1. Origami
ISBN 0-8069-8007-9; 1-40270-117-9 (pa)
LC 2001-40081

Includes index

This origami book offers "advice for beginners, with an introduction that takes them step-by-step through the basic folds. Subsequent projects, displayed in colorful, easily followed spreads are relatively advanced. . . . Experienced and talented artists will appreciate Nguyen's suggestion to add painted details and create a 'fantasy' environment for the pieces." Booklist

741.2 Drawing--Techniques, equipment, materials

Ames, Lee J., 1921-

Drawing with Lee Ames; from the bestselling, award-winning creator of the Draw 50 series, a proven step-by-step guide to the fundamentals of drawing for all ages. Doubleday 1990 262p il pa $21
741.2

1. Drawing
ISBN 0-385-23701-4
LC 90-31436
The author "offers a compendium of samples for beginning artists. Ames explains his approach to beginning art instruction as a form of mimicry, where students copy samples in order to get a feel for the process of drawing. . . . This is definitely for the beginning student who possesses very little to no drawing experience. . . . Ames's approach offers a good base from which students can then move on to more in-depth instruction." Voice Youth Advocates

Includes bibliographical references

741.5 Cartoons, caricatures, comics

Anderson, Kevin J., 1962-

Grumpy old monsters. IDW Publishing 2004 96p il pa $13.99
741.5

1. Graphic novels
ISBN 1-932382-35-6
The old monsters Frankenstein's Monster, Dracula, the Mummy, and the Werewolf, have all retired and moved to the old monsters' home, where Nurse Wrentch terrorizes them and only little Tiffany Frankenstein, granddaughter of old Dr. F., comes to visit. But this time she comes with terrible news the Van Helsing Corporation is about to take possession of Castle Frankenstein, tear it down, and build luxury condominiums. The monsters decide they must come out of retirement and help Tiffany stop the horror if they can escape Nurse Wrentch!

Ariyoshi, Kyoko

Swan, Vol. 1. CMX/DC Comics 2004 200p il pa $9.95
741.5

1. Graphic novels
ISBN 1-4012-0535-6
This is the first in an ongoing series

"Masumi, a young girl from a rural Japanese town, dreams of becoming a prima ballerina. She is picked to take part in a national ballet competition but realizes that her training lags behind that of her peers. During the competition and the subsequent professional lessons, she fights to improve her abilities and achieve her dreams. Swan is one of the most famous shoujo (girl's manga) ever published. Although it first appeared in Japan in the mid-seventies, the art and story hold up beautifully." Booklist

Artell, Mike, 1948-
Cartooning for kids. Sterling 2001 128p il
$17.95; pa $9.95   **741.5**
1. Cartoons and caricatures 2. Drawing
ISBN 0-8069-4814-0; 1-40270-111-X (pa)
                 LC 2001-40079
A step-by-step guide for drawing animals and people,
covering alligators, bears, skunks, smiling faces, angry
faces, hairstyles, movement, and more
"This book is not for beginners as knowledge of some
of the basic shapes and positions seems to be assumed,
but it exudes confidence." SLJ

Atangan, Patrick
The yellow jar; two tales from Japanese
tradition. NBM 2003 48p il (Songs of our
ancestors) $12.92   **741.5**
1. Graphic novels
ISBN 1-561-63331-3   LC 2002-32132
"To render two magical Japanese legends, one about
a fisherman who discovers a fair maiden in a big pot, the
other about a monk whose fastidiously kept garden is invaded by two chrysanthemums, Atangan charmingly
adopts the sharp outlines, boldly juxtaposed color fields,
and striking compositions of eighteenth-century Japanese
woodblock prints." Booklist
Other titles in this series are:
Silk tapestry and other Chinese folktales (2004)
Tree of love (2005)

Avery, Ben
The hedge knight; [by] George R. R. Martin;
Ben Avery, adapter; Mike S. Miller, artist. Devil's
Due Publishing 2004 160p il pa $14.95
     741.5
1. Graphic novels
ISBN 1-932796-06-1
"Hulking young Dunk is the squire of an elderly warrior. When Dunk's master dies, he rides on to the next
tournament in hopes of winning recognition for his
knightly prowess. He acquires a squire of his own, a
bald little boy who calls himself Egg, and gives himself
the more elegant title of Duncan the Tall. . . . This heroic fantasy tale reinvigorates the tired category of sword
and sorcery fiction by emphasizing the human angle."
Publ Wkly

Beatty, Scott
Superman; the ultimate guide to the Man of
Steel; written by Scott Beatty. DK Pub. 2002 128p
il $19.99   **741.5**
1. Superman (Comic strip) 2. Comic books, strips, etc.
ISBN 0-7894-8853-1   LC 2002-19494
"Superman created by Jerry Siegel and Joe Schuster"
Surveys the nature and history of the hero Superman,
discussing his birth, career, secrets, equipment, and enemies
"The hero's universe is revealed as never before. . . .
The artwork is first-rate; classic illustrations from the
original comics blend easily with the more recent works,
some of them specially commissioned for this book. Perfect for both the die-hard and the casual fan." Booklist

Blackman, Haden
Star Wars: Clone wars adventures, Vol. 1. Dark
Horse Books 2004 96p il pa $6.95   **741.5**
1. Graphic novels
ISBN 1-59307-243-0
This volume includes several adventures featuring Star
Wars characters. Obi-Wan Kenobi and Anakin Skywalker
take on the Shadowmen on the night world of Nivek;
Jedi Master Mace Windu and Saesee Tiin face a new
droid threat; and Jedi Master Kit Fisto leads an underwater hunt for the Separatists' secret base. This series is
based on the Clone Wars Adventures cartoon series
which has aired on Cartoon Network, and fits in
chronologically between Episodes Two and Three of the
motion picture series. This is the first volume, there were
four volumes as of September 2005.

Bohl, Al
Guide to cartooning. Pelican 1997 176p il
$22.50; pa $13.95   **741.5**
1. Cartoons and caricatures 2. Drawing
ISBN 1-56554-367-X; 1-56554-177-4 (pa)
                 LC 96-44340
Provides instructions for drawing different styles of
cartooning, including political, strips, books, and illustration, and gives advice on how to get a job in the field
This "is so chockablock with information that any teen
interested in cartooning will come away with a multitude
of tips and tricks." Booklist
Includes bibliographical references

Busiek, Kurt
Shockrockets: we have ignition; [by] Kurt
Busiek, Stuart Immonen, and Wade Von
Grawbadger. Dark Horse Comics 2004 160p il pa
$14.95   **741.5**
1. Graphic novels
ISBN 1-59307-129-9
"In this graphic novel vision of 2087, Alejandro Cruz
lives in a postwar world. An alien invasion has been
averted but at a high cost, and people are rebuilding.
Alejandro loves his family, but he doesn't want to get
caught in the same dead-end jobs that his family members have had to take to survive. Then he accidentally
becomes the newest pilot for the Shockrockets, the
cream-of-the-crop, high-tech air squadron, and his entire
life changes." Booklist
"Busiek brings the same touch of character he used in
the 'Astro City' series (DC Comics), making this title as
much about Cruz's choices and challenges as about lasers and extreme fighter pilot moves." SLJ

The wizard's tale; [by] Kurt Busiek and David
Wenzel. DC Comics 1999 141p il pa $19.95
     741.5
1. Graphic novels
ISBN 1-56389-589-7
Bafflerog Rumplewhisker is the most pitiful excuse
for an evil wizard that ever lived, for all his evil spells
end up doing good. When Lord Grimthorne, head of the
Darksome Council, orders him to find the Book of
Worse, the reluctant Bafflerog heads out with the toad,
Gumpwort, to find it. Author Busiek and artist Wenzel
have crafted a tale that honors the marks of high fantasy
even while having fun with it.

Cover, Arthur Byron

Macbeth; [by] William Shakespeare; Arthur Byron Cover, adapter; Tony Leonard Tamai, illustrator. Puffin Graphics 2005 176p il pa $9.99
741.5

1. Graphic novels
ISBN 0-14-24040908

Ambitious lord Macbeth murders his king to take the throne because of the predictions of some witches, but his position is never secure, and he takes ever more violent measures to stay in power. Shakespeare's classic play is reinvented here with Japanese manga style art and a futuristic setting on a vast ringworld around a sun.

DeFalco, Tom

The Hulk: the incredible guide. DK Pub. 2003 127p il $24.99
741.5

1. Hulk (Comic strip) 2. Comic books, strips, etc.
ISBN 0-7894-9260-1
LC 2002-154785

This profiles Stan Lee's creation for Marvel Comics of the Incredible Hulk

"Various artists who have contributed to [the] series during [its] 40 years of publication fill the oversize [volume] with colorful, first-rate artwork. Every major hero and villain appearing in the series is profiled in the generous, two-page spreads. . . . Key locations (including some rarely seen in the pages of the comics) and events are meticulously detailed." Booklist

Spider-girl, Vol. 1: Legacy. Marvel Comics 2004 144p il pa $7.99
741.5

1. Graphic novels
ISBN 0-7851-1441-6

In an alternate future in the Marvel Universe, Peter Parker has retired from being Spider-Man after a crippling injury; but he and Mary Jane have a daughter, May. She has just turned sixteen, and suddenly discovers she has superpowers! Soon she finds out who her father used to be, and she decides to be a superhero but Peter knows the dangers all too well and tries to stop her. Once Mayday decides to be Spider-Girl, though, no one can stop her. This is the first of an ongoing series.

DeFilippis, Nunzio

Once in a blue moon; [by] Nunzio DeFilippis, Chistina Weir, and Jennifer Quick. Oni Press 2004 154p il pa $11.95
741.5

1. Graphic novels
ISBN 1-929998-83-X

Aeslin had a magical childhood, with loving parents who read wonderful fables from the book, The Avalon Chronicles, about a fantastic world where a brave Dragon Knight and her Prince battled an Evil Wizard. Then, her parents left on a business trip from which only her mother returned. Her mother tried to erase any aspect of fantasy from Aeslin's life from that time. Now, she happens upon a new book, Once in a Blue Moon, and when she wishes she could go to Avalon to help the people, she finds herself magically transported there and learns she is the new Dragon Knight who must save the land.

Dezago, Todd

Spider-man: Spidey strikes back Vol. 1 digest. Marvel Comics 2005 96p il pa $5.99
741.5

1. Graphic novels
ISBN 0-7851-1632-X

Tired of saving the day and getting no respect, Spider-Man considers taking a break from his superhero duties, which leaves the city wide open for the likes of the Sandman and the Enforcers. Will Spidey let it all go to pot, or will he step up to the plate and take one for the team? This volume collects Marvel Age Spider-Man issues 17-20. Previous volumes were published under the series title Marvel Age Spider-Man. The Marvel Age titles are being collected and published in the digest size, similar to manga, and at an affordable price. The Marvel Age series are aimed at younger audiences than the other superhero titles from Marvel.

Tellos, Vol. 1. Image Comics 2001 152p il pa $17.95
741.5

1. Graphic novels
ISBN 1-58240-186-1

In the magical land of Tellos, a swashbuckling boy of mysterious origins named Jarek and his tiger warrior companion Koj team up with pirate captain Serra when they are all set upon by frog soldiers and Shadow Jumpers. When they learn from a mystic that Jarek is possessed by the Warrior of the Light and is the one prophesied to defeat the evil magician Malesur, they set out on a quest and are joined by the thieves Rikk (an elf) and Hawke (a fox). The story concludes in Tellos Vol. 2: Kindred Spirits.

Dini, Paul

The Batman adventures; dangerous dames & demons; [by] Paul Dini, Bruce Timm. DC Comics 2003 190p il pa $14.95
741.5

1. Batman (Comic strip) 2. Comic books, strips, etc.
ISBN 1-56389-973-6
LC 2004-297331

Originally published in single magazine form as The Batman adventures annual 1-2, Batman adventures: mad love and Adventures in the DC universe 3

"This book collects some of the best work of . . . Paul Dini and Bruce Timm, written and illustrated in the style of the animated television series. Villainesses are the main focus here, as Batman takes on Poison Ivy, Catwoman, and others." Libr Media Connect

Dixon, Chuck, 1954-

Hobbit: an illustrated edition of the fantasy classic; [by] J. R. R. Tolkien; Chuck Dixon, adapter; David Wenzel, illustrator. Del Rey Books 2001 133p il pa $15.95
741.5

1. Graphic novels
ISBN 0-34544560-0

The tale of how dwarfs came to ask the hobbit Bilbo Baggins to leave his comfortable home in the Shire to travel with them on their quest to recover their gold from the evil dragon Smaug is adapted to comic book form, with lush, colorful illustrations by David Wenzel. All the adventures recounted in Tolkien's novel are here, retold in a format for all ages to enjoy.

Fisher, Jane Smith

WJHC: on the air! Wilson Place Comics, Inc.
2003 il pa $11.95   **741.5**
1. Graphic novels
ISBN 0-9744235-0-5

"The cast of toothy, mopheaded teens includes hard-working Janey, UFO obsessed Ciel, snotty Tara O'Toole, awkward Roland, and cool, cool The Skate. Together the teens put a school radio station on the air (thus the book's title), 'chaperone' an ill-fated sixth-grade field trip, and get into a truly hilarious tangle when a love note written by one to another of the cast works its way through the hands of each one." Booklist

Gallagher, John

Buzzboy: Trouble in paradise. Sky Dog Press
2002 144p il pa $11.95   **741.5**
1. Graphic novels
ISBN 0-8721831-0-8

Imagine a superhero who jokes constantly, watches way too many old television shows, and loves junk food, and you have Buzzboy. Years before, he was sidekick to Captain Ultra, but the evil Dr. Schism destroyed all superheroes and their sidekicks, except for Captain Ultra. Now, Ultra has declared martial law in the city of New Paradise, and his police stomp out all rebellions. Then a mysterious superhero stops the Hoppers (police) it's Buzzboy, older and back from the dead! Aided by sarcastic teen sorceress Becca and reformed mad scientist Doc Cyber, Buzzboy is here to save the day.

Another title in this series is:
Buzzboy: Monsters, dreams, & milkshakes (2003)

Gorman, Michele

Getting graphic! using graphic novels to promote literacy with preteens and teens; with a foreword by Jeff Smith. Linworth Pub 2003 100p il pa $36.95   **741.5**
1. Graphic novels
ISBN 1-586-83089-9   LC 2003-13199

"This title serves as an introduction to the world of fiction and nonfiction comics. Collection-development policies are addressed as well as cataloging, shelving, and maintaining these . . . books. Gorman provides ideas for the genre's integration into classroom curriculum and suggests promotional activities for school and public libraries." SLJ

"A must-have first resource for school and public libraries that are considering adding graphic novels to their collections but are unsure how to proceed." Booklist

Gownley, Jimmy

Amelia Rules! the whole world's crazy! ibooks
2003 176p il pa $14.95   **741.5**
1. Graphic novels
ISBN 0-7434-7503-8

"Amelia . . . is getting used to life with her newly divorced mom and her hip, young aunt Tanner; settling in at a strange new school; and finding a group of friends. Amelia is no sweet innocent, nor are her three G.A.S.P (Gathering of Awesome Superpals) buddies: Reggie, superhero in the making; Rhonda, Amelia's tough bete noire with a fourth-grade 'thing' for Reggie; and quiet, mysterious Pajamaman. Jealousy, meanness, sadness, and confusion, as well as surprising generosity, and love crisscross the pages in energetic, freewheeling, full-color cartoon art that unwraps a kid'seye view of life honestly, poignantly, and with a hefty dollop of melodrama." Booklist

Another title in this series is:
Amelia rules!: What makes you happy? (2004)

Harris, James S.

Shades of blue, Volume 1. D3 Digest/Devil's Due Publishing 2005 144p il pa $10.95
741.5
1. Graphic novels
ISBN 1-932796-26-6

The series changed artists after the second issue. This is the first volume of a series.

Heidi Page's "life takes an odd turn after she awakens with blue hair and the power to control electricity. Although she tries to keep her powers from getting in the way of her normal life, weird situations pop up, and her best friend, K. T., and Marcus (who calls himself her sidekick) insist that she's the superhero for the job. This sarcastic, funny send-up of superhero comics hinges on great characterizations and an immensely likable, believable cast." Booklist

Hart, Christopher

Christopher Hart's cartoon studio. Watson-Guptill 2003 48p il pa $7.95
741.5
1. Cartoons and caricatures
ISBN 0-8230-0624-7

First published 1996 with title: Christopher Hart's portable cartoon studio.

In this introduction to cartoon drawing "Hart explains how to draw the same characters . . . consistently from different views. He gives pointers on using action lines and drawing figures in many positions. Charts show how to create different angles of the head, design panels and dialogue boxes, create props, and choose typeface for the best impact." SLJ

How to draw comic book bad guys and gals. Watson-Guptill 1998 64p il pa $10.95
741.5
1. Comic books, strips, etc. 2. Cartoons and caricatures 3. Drawing
ISBN 0-8230-2372-9   LC 98-6411

This guide to drawing comic book villains covers such topics as head tilts, facial expressions, hands and muscle groups, the body in action, using light and shadow, composition, and storytelling

"Not for beginners, but for those who already have some knowledge of drawing and ability. . . . Boldly colored illustrations combined with the line drawings add to the professional look of the book." Voice Youth Advocates

Hart, Christopher—*Continued*

Mecha mania; how to draw the battling robots, cool spaceships, and military vehicles of Japanese comics. Watson-Guptill 2002 128p il pa $19.95 (5 and up) **741.5**

1. Comic books, strips, etc. 2. Drawing

ISBN 0-8230-3056-3 LC 2002-6402

"Hart offers budding cartoonists a mix of basic instructions and savvy technical advice for creating a wide variety of generic giant robots, robotlike craft, cyborgs of both sexes, and bad-guy types . . . then posing them for maximum visual effect. . . . His 'can-do!' tone and cogent instructions, as well as the gallery of chiseled, heavily armed, hypercomplicated machines, will make this volume appealing to both casual browsers and serious young artists." SLJ

Higuchi, Daisuke

Whistle! Volume 1. Viz Media, LLC 2004 192p il pa $7.99 **741.5**

1. Graphic novels 2. Soccer—Fiction

ISBN 1-59116-685-3

This is the first volume of an ongoing series, up to Volume 6 in July 2005.

"Although he's no Pele or David Beckham, Sho is trying to take the high school soccer world by storm. Unfortunately, he's very short and not on the first team at his new school, but he's still determined to practice as much as possible to be the best. With the rest of the second string and Tatsuya, a star player who's not into lording his ability over others like the rest of the regulars, Sho challenges the Captain to a game for leadership of the team and a starting position." Publ Wkly

Hosler, Jay

Clan Apis. Active Synapse 2000 158p il pa $15 **741.5**

1. Graphic novels

ISBN 0-9677255-0-X

"Opening with a creation myth . . . and working through the biological, sociological, and ecological changes affecting the life of Nyuki the bee, the text is a combination of authoritative science; appealing, detailed black-and-white drawings; and dialogue replete with humor, pubescent angst, political sloganeering, and more. Nyuki's colony undertakes migration to a new hive, is beset by a woodpecker, and hibernates through a winter that yields to a revitalizing spring." Booklist

The sandwalk adventures; an adventure in evolution in five chapters. Active Synapse 2003 159p il pa $20 **741.5**

1. Graphic novels

ISBN 0-9677255-1-8

An aged Charles Darwin discovers that follicle mites living in his left eyebrow believe that he is their Creator. Because he can speak with mites Mara and Willy, he sets out to explain evolution to them, as they recount their myths to him. It sounds like a crazy premise, but Hosler uses this graphic novel to clearly and succinctly explain evolutionary theory, just as he used the format in Clan Apis to describe the life cycle of honeybees.

Hotta, Yumi

Hikaru No Go, Volume 1; [by] Yumi Hotta and Takeshi Obata. Viz Media, LLC 2004 192p il pa $7.95 **741.5**

1. Graphic novels

ISBN 1-59116-222-X

Sixth-grader Hikaru Shindo is not interested in intellectual pursuits, but by a twist of fate, the spirit of Fujiwara no Sai, the ghost of an ancient Go master, manages to bond with Hikaru. Now, suddenly, Hikaru can play Go, a complex board game of strategy, better than almost anyone under 18 and most adults, too. Akira, who has been raised by his Go master father, needs to know more about the upstart Hikaru, who beats him and yet seems so casual about the game. This is the first volume of an ongoing series.

Huddleston, Courtney

Decoy; by Courtney Huddleston, Eli Williams, and Dan Jensen. Penny Farthing Press 2000 112p il pa $15.95 **741.5**

1. Graphic novels

ISBN 0-9673683-2-4

Rookie cop Bobby Luck has just stumbled into a bad situation and been shot; but, instead of dying, he ends up physically good as new, thanks to a little, green, shapeshifting alien he calls Decoy. With their symbiotic, telepathic bond, Luck and Decoy must now face Nabob and prevent him from taking over the world while keeping their bond a secret from everyone, including Luck's senior partner, Tessa. Oh, and the life of a little girl depends on them, too.

Another title in this series is:

Decoy: Storm of the century (2003)

Irwin, Jane, 1941-

Vögelein; clockwork faerie; {by} Jane Irwin with Jeff Berndt; foreword by Jennifer M. Contino. Fiery Studios 2003 167p il pa $12.95 **741.5**

1. Fairies—Comic books, strips, etc. 2. Graphic novels

ISBN 0-9743110-06

Most of the material contained within was originally printed in issues 15 of the magazine "Vögelein"

This is a "graphic novel about Vogelein, a beautiful mechanical fairy created in the seventeenth century. Although she is immortal, she must be wound every 36 hours. After her old friend and caretaker dies, she must find someone new to take care of her. . . . This modern fable is a rare treasure that weaves fanciful imagination into themes of individuality, diversity, and independence. The art is beautifully shaded black and white, and it carries the narrative impeccably." Booklist

Kirkman, Robert

Tech jacket, Vol. 1: Lost & found; [by] Robert Kirkman and E. J. Su. Image Comics 2003 144p il pa $12.95 **741.5**

1. Graphic novels

ISBN 1-58240-314-7

Teenage Zach Thompson stumbles upon a crashed space ship with a dying alien; Geldarian gives his Tech

Kirkman, Robert—*Continued*

Jacket to Zach. The Tech Jackets gave the physically weak Geldarians the ability to do their work; on the physically fit Zach, it gives him great power. But, even as his father deals with gangsters trying to take his hardware store, Zach learns that possessing the Tech Jacket gives him great responsibility, and the Geldarians need him.

Kobayashi, M. (Makoto)

What's Michael? Vol. 10: Sleepless nights. Dark Horse Manga/Dark Horse Comics 2005 88p il pa $8.95   **741.5**

1. Graphic novels 2. Cats—Fiction

ISBN 1-59307-337-2

In this volume of collected short stories, Michael the cat and his feline friends and human family entertain the reader with everyday adventures and zany fantasy. True-life cat behavior such as their sleeping habits and their tendency to find the smallest spaces to explore alternate with the ridiculous idea of cat high school, vampires, and a Mafia-like hierarchy of neighborhood cats. What's Michael? is a continuing series.

Kochalka, James

Monkey vs. Robot. Top Shelf Productions 2000 144p il pa $14.95   **741.5**

1. Graphic novels

ISBN 1-891830-15-5

"A very simply illustrated black and white pictorial narrative about a battle between a monkey community and a self-run robot factory encroaching on the monkeys' unspoiled forest domain." Publ Wkly

The book is almost wordless, allowing the reader to imagine one's own narrative. While there is violence, it's not graphic, and this little fable provides much food for thought.

Another title in this series is:

Monkey vs. Robot and the crystal of power (2003)

Konomi, Takeshi

The Prince of Tennis, Vol. 1. Viz Media, LLC 2004 192p il pa $7.95   **741.5**

1. Graphic novels 2. Tennis—Fiction

ISBN 1-59116-435-4

This is the first of an ongoing series, up to Volume 9 in September 2005

"Ryoma is a former U.S. junior tennis champion who attends a Japanese academy, where his skill and natural talent make him nearly unbeatable. The younger students are inspired by him, but he's ruffling the feathers of the older tennis team members. Then the journalists appear, trying to discover the next champion, adding to the pressure. There's lots of tennis action, dramatically illustrated, and the characters, already pretty boys, are made even more attractive with their intensity." Publ Wkly

Morse, Scott

The barefoot serpent. Top Shelf Productions 2003 128p il pa $14.95   **741.5**

1. Graphic novels

ISBN 1-891830-37-6

"A little girl journeys to Hawaii with her parents after her older brother's death. There she meets a little-boy wheeler-dealer and tags along as he hustles a mask he has carved and plays in sand and surf. Rejoining her father, she infects him with her restored spirits; the family flies home refreshed. Sandwiching that story is a child's-picture-book-like sketch of Japanese filmmaker Akira Kurosawa." Booklist

Naifeh, Ted

Courtney Crumrin and the night things. Oni Press 2005 128p il pa $11.95   **741.5**

1. Graphic novels

ISBN 1-929998-60-0

Courtney's social-climber parents take her out of her comfortable city neighborhood and move into an upscale suburb to live with her creepy Great-Uncle Aloysius in her spooky old house. She has to face uppity classmates and things that go bump in the night; but she ends up making friends with the spooks! Courtney deals with magic and the supernatural, but she's no altruistic Harry Potter; in this series, magic sometimes bites hard.

Other titles in this series are:

Courtney Crumrin and the Coven of Mystics (2003)

Courtney Crumrin in the Twilight Kingdom (2004)

Naruse, Kaori

Prétear, Volume 1. ADV Manga 2004 188p il pa $9.99   **741.5**

1. Graphic novels

ISBN 1-4139-0144-1

"Himeno's alcoholic novelist father marries a rich businesswoman with two snobby daughters. They treat [Himeno] terribly, of course, but she . . . is goodhearted, virtuous, and patient. Himeno. . . [meets] seven knights who use leafe, a substance emitted by everything in the natural world. The Princess of Disaster wants to destroy all the leafe so the world will die. The knights need Himeno to become the Prétear so they can combine with her and combat the princess." SLJ

Naruse combines elements of fairy tales such as Cinderella and Snow White with fantasy adventure in this four-volume series.

Ottaviani, Jim

Dignifying science: stories about women scientists. G. T. Labs 2003 144p il pa $16.95   **741.5**

1. Graphic novels 2. Women scientists

ISBN 0-9660106-4-7

Ottaviani provides biographical sketches of women scientists such as Lise Meitner, Rosalind Franklin, Barbara McClintock, and Hedy Lamarr (yes, the actress was also an inventor); all the stories are illustrated by women comics artists, including Lea Hernandez, Linda Medley, Anne Timmons, and others.

Pellowski, Michael, 1949-
The art of making comic books; {by} Michael Morgan Pellowski; with illustrations by Howard Bender. Lerner Publs. 1995 80p il (Media workshop) $21.27 (5 and up)   **741.5**
1. Comic books, strips, etc. 2. Cartoons and caricatures
ISBN 0-8225-2304-3   LC 94-27589
"After a brief overview of comic-book history, the text describes the making of a comic book, explaining the various jobs people hold and the various stages books must go through. . . . Serious comic fans will relish Pellowski's detail-oriented and knowledgeable pragmatism." Bull Cent Child Books
Includes glossary and bibliographical references

Peyer, Tom, 1954-
Go boy 7, Vol. 1: Ready set go! [by] Tom Peyer and Jon Sommariva. Rocket Comics/Dark Horse Comics 2004 96p il pa $12.95   **741.5**
1. Graphic novels
ISBN 1-56971-937-3
When Jonny Zero's family jet is shot down, he survives only because his uncle uses his experimental nanotech plasm to save his life. Now Jonny is more than human, which is a good thing, because Uncle Noah and his Go Base are under attack by the forces of The Cultist, an evil madman out to destroy all thinking life. The problem is, he's still just a young teen and a wee bit impulsive when taking action. The action and violence level is similar to what preteens might see in a PG rated movie.
Another title in this series is:
Go boy 7 Vol 2: The human factor, written by Brian Augustyn (2004)

Reed, Gary
Mary Shelley's Frankenstein: the graphic novel. Puffin Graphics 2005 176p il pa $9.99   **741.5**
1. Graphic novels
ISBN 0-14-240407-1
Scientist Victor Frankenstein decided to create a man, only to create something he deemed a monster.
"Reed concentrates on the emotional anguish of the story, ably capturing the rage, the hurt, and the guilt of both monster and creator. Irving . . . creates a hazy, suitably murky black-and-white backdrop, never exploiting the violence inherent in the monster's quest for vengeance." Booklist

Robbins, Trina, 1938-
Go girl!: The time team. Dark Horse Comics 95p il pa $5.95   **741.5**
1. Graphic novels
ISBN 1-59307-230-9
"Robbins, who has made a name for herself as a feminist in the comics world, creates a story about three stereotypical high school girls— the dismissive cheerleader, the misunderstood brain, and the daughter of a 1970s-era superheroine— who become stranded in pre-

history. The girls are quick-witted, the dinosaurs are cartoony, and a late appearance by Vikings offers readers a taste of what Nordic women might have been like in a confrontation. This isn't high concept, but it's definitely good, clean fun." Booklist

Robinson, James
Leave it to Chance: Shaman's rain; [by] James Robinson & Paul Smith. Image Comics 2002 unp il pa $14.95   **741.5**
1. Graphic novels
ISBN 1-58240-253-1
"Chance Falconer is a 14-year-old only child born into a family of municipal sorcerers that has protected the city of Devil's Echo for centuries. Chance can't wait to start training in the family business, but her father decides he doesn't want a girl joining the family's dangerous profession. Predictably, it's not long before she stumbles onto a dead body and a kidnapping in progress, and soon enough she's got a full-fledged mystery on her hands. . . . This is a girl power comic written with a younger audience in mind. The smartest cops are female, the violence is G-rated and the story is fast-paced, brightly colored and as wholesome as it gets." Publ Wkly
Other titles in this series are:
Leave it to Chance, Vol. 2: Trick or treat (2003)
Leave it to Chance, Vol. 3: Monster madness (2003)

Sakai, Stan
Usagi Yojimbo, Vol. 18; travels with Jotaro. Dark Horse Comics 2004 208p il $15.95   **741.5**
1. Graphic novels
ISBN 1-59307-220-1
"Usagi, the rabbit bodyguard, is traveling with his son, although Jotaro does not know that Usagi is his father. Their adventures range from the fairly straightforward defeat of two ninja assassins to fighting powerful creatures conjured by a cursed sumi (calligraphy writing) set." SLJ
"Sakai delivers plenty of martial arts action and solid storytelling . . . and his well-researched backdrop of feudal Japan makes the story seem more like a fable than a traditional comic book." Booklist

Sanderson, Peter
Ultimate X-men. updated ed. DK Pub. 2003 184p il $24.99   **741.5**
1. X-men (Comic strip) 2. Comic books, strips, etc.
ISBN 0-7894-9258-X   LC 2002-41308
First published 2000
This is an "overview of the history of the X-Men comics, detailing the stories and characters that have appeared on their pages." Publisher's note
This offers "colorful, first-rate artwork. . . . Classic illustrations blend seamlessly with more recent works." Booklist

Sava, Scott Christian
The lab: hey . . . test this! Astonish Factory 2004 120p il pa $14.95   **741.5**

Sava, Scott Christian—*Continued*
1. Graphic novels
ISBN 0-9721259-3-0
"A collection of previously published comics and original stories that highlight the working relationship between Livingston, a scientist mole, and his goofball assistant, Esteban, a weasel whose ultrasensitivity to chemicals makes him an excellent test subject for new products. With bright, colorful pictures, the stories usually consist of observing Esteban's outlandish reactions to Livingston's concoctions, such as floating to the ceiling, shrinking to microscopic size, or singing uncontrollably." SLJ

Sfar, Joann
Dungeon Vol. 1: Duck Heart; [by] Joann Sfar & Lewis Trondheim. NBM 2003 96p il pa $14.95
741.5
1. Graphic novels
ISBN 1-56163-401-8
"As a result of some unfortunate accidents, Herbert, usually a lowly messenger in the great Dungeon, is called upon to defend it from all manner of beasties. In his endeavors to become a warrior, he is helped by his friend Marvin the vegetarian dragon and by the Dungeon Keeper. Although there's a solid dose of cartoon-style violence and gore, teens will appreciate Herbert's pseudo-slacker attitude, which turns him into an accidental hero time and time again." Booklist
Other titles in this series are:
Dungeon, the early years: the night shirt (2005)
Zenith: the barbarian princess (2005)

Sizer, Paul
Little White Mouse collection 1: Dream of the ghost. Café Digital Comics 2005 144p il pa $12.95
741.5
1. Graphic novels
In a future universe, sixteen-year-old Loo is shipwrecked on a remote, automated mining satellite when the space liner on which she and her sister were traveling was destroyed. Considered an intruder by the satellite's computer, she must survive, build a robot body for her dead sister's preserved memory, and find a way home before the satellite's life support system shuts down. Creator Sizer is now self-publishing this series of four volumes and selling it at his website, www.paulsizer.com.

Smith, Ian
Emily & the intergalactic lemonade stand; [by] Ian Smith and Tyson Smith. Amaze Ink/Slave Labor Graphics 2004 96p il pa $12.95
741.5
1. Graphic novels
ISBN 0-943151-96-1
Eleven-year-old Emily runs a lemonade stand with the help of her pet robot, Juicer; she wants to earn enough money to buy a pony. Complicating matters is neighborhood rival Daisy, who wants to beat Emily because cute Jace Tanner hangs around Emily (he actually only likes robots). Then aliens invade, and the military wants Juic-

er, because they think he's the perfect weapon. And little alien warrior Pheef wants blood can he help it he's so cute and tiny? The defense of Earth depends on Emily can it survive?

Smith, Jeff
Bone: out from Boneville. Scholastic Graphix 2005 144p il $18.95; pa $9.99
741.5
1. Graphic novels
ISBN 0-439-70623-8; 0-439-70640-8 (pa)
Also available Bone: one volume edition $39.95 from Cartoon Books (ISBN 1-8889-6314-X)
"The story follows three cousins who have been thrown out of their town for cheating the citizens. Shortly thereafter, they are separated. Each Bone stumbles into a mysterious valley full of odd creatures that reveal strange happenings. The story is well paced with smooth transitions. It is dark, witty, mysterious, and exciting. The full-color art reflects that of classic comic books." SLJ
Other titles in this series are:
Bone: the great cow race (vol. 2)
Bone: eyes of the storm (vol. 3)
Bone: the dragonslayer (vol. 4)
Bone: Rock Jaw Master the Eastern Border (vol. 5)
Bone: old man's cave (vol. 6)
Bone: ghost circles (vol. 7)
Bone: treasure hunters (vol. 8)
Bone: crown of thorns (vol. 9)

TenNapel, Douglas R.
Tommysaurus Rex. Image Comics 2005 110p il pa $11.95
741.5
1. Graphic novels 2. Dinosaurs—Fiction
ISBN 1-58240-395-3
When Ely loses his dog, Tommy, in a car accident, his parents send him to Grandpa Joe's farm for the summer. He discovers a live, 40-foot Tyrannosaurus Rex in a cave on the farm, and soon the boy and his pet dinosaur cause a big ruckus in town. Ely promises to train the dinosaur he names Tommysaurus, but not if the town's bully, Randy, has his way.

Torres, J., 1969-
Alison Dare: Little Miss Adventures; by J. Torres and J. Bone. Oni Press 2002 104p il pa $8.95
741.5
1. Graphic novels
ISBN 1-929998-20-1
Meet Alison Dare, twelve-year-old boarding school student and daughter of a famous archeologist (mom) and a librarian (dad) who moonlights as the superhero, Blue Scarab. In the adventures recounted here, Alison summons a genie that causes havoc; she relates to fellow students the story of how a librarian became the Blue Scarab, and she deals with thieves in the museum who threaten her mother.
Another title in this series is:
Alison Dare, Little Miss Adventures, volume 2 (2005)

Trondheim, Lewis
Astronauts of the future; [by] Lewis Trondheim, Manu Larcenet. NBM 2004 96p il pa $14.95
741.5
1. Graphic novels
ISBN 1-561-63407-7 LC 2004-49960
This story "begins as a witty, gentle tale of two precocious youngsters, Gil and Martina, whose estrangement from their classmates and parents leads them to conclude that others are either, as Martina insists, aliens, or, according to Gil, robots. Initially wryly depicting the loneliness and alienation of brainy children and their joy at discovering simpatico souls-think Calvin and Hobbes meets To Be and to Have-the story suddenly swirls into an outrageous but compelling science-fiction epic." Booklist

Vansant, Wayne
The red badge of courage; [by] Stephen Crane; Wayne Vansant, adapter. Puffin Graphics 2005 176p il pa $9.99 **741.5**
1. Crane, Stephen, 1871-1900—Adaptations 2. Graphic novels
ISBN 0-14-240410-1
Henry Fleming had always dreamed of performing heroic deeds in battle. But as a raw recruit in the Civil War, Henry experiences fear and doubt. Will war make him a coward or a hero?
"Artist Vansant captures Fleming's uncertainty and fear quite well, sometimes through effectively understated facial expressions." Publ Wkly

Walker, Landry Q.
Little Gloomy: . . . It was a dark and stormy night; [by] Landry Q. Walker and Eric Jones. Slave Labor Graphics 2002 128p il pa $12.95
741.5
1. Graphic novels
ISBN 0-943151-64-3
In Frightsylvania, Little Gloomy is the only normal girl in a world of monsters, but that's not her problem. Mad scientist Simon, her ex-boyfriend, is her problem; he's decided to send an army of zombies against her to get revenge. Can Gloomy and her friends Larry the werewolf, Frank the lovesick monster (he's got a crush on Gloomy), and Carl Cthulhu the interdimensional octopoid demigod survive the onslaught of the undead? The monsters are all drawn to look so cute, it's hard to imagine anyone really getting scared by reading this book.

Wong, Tony
Ultraman Tiga, Vol. 1: Return of the warrior; [by] Tony Wong and Khoo Fuk Lung. Dark Horse Comics 2004 128p il pa $15.95 **741.5**
1. Graphic novels
ISBN 1-59307-119-1
A cultural icon in Hong Kong and Japan, Ultraman has punched, kicked and karate-chopped in TV shows and movies for nearly four decades. Now this incarnation of Ultraman, called Tiga, finds the 100-foot-tall hero revived in the year 2049 and finding a world ill-equipped

to handle the onslaught of gigantic beasts that are attacking all over the world. There is a second volume: Past Sins, Future Dangers.
"Wong's script moves briskly from one fight scene to the next, and Lung's art effectively uses line work and color. The duo is capable of winking knowingly at readers while still taking the story seriously enough to be compelling." Publ Wkly

741.6 Graphic design, illustration and commercial art

Marcus, Leonard S., 1950-
A Caldecott celebration; six artists and their paths to the Caldecott medal. Walker & Co. 1998 49p il $18.95 **741.6**
1. Caldecott Medal 2. Illustrators 3. Illustration of books
ISBN 0-8027-8656-1 LC 98-6616
Profiles six Caldecott award winning books and their authors, including Robert McCloskey's "Make Way for Ducklings," Marcia Brown's "Cinderella," Maurice Sendak's "Where the Wild Things Are," William Steig's "Sylvester and the Magic Pebble," Chris Van Allsburg's "Jumanji," and David Wiesner's "Tuesday"
"Marcus, who interviewed each artist, provides a lively, informative introduction to each book and its maker. A beautifully made book, this will serve as a fine resource for children interested in illustration and for teachers researching author/illustrator studies." Booklist
Includes glossary

Talking with artists {I-III}; compiled and edited by Pat Cummings. Bradbury Press 1992-1999 3v il v1 $22.95; v2 $19.95; v3 $20
741.6
1. Illustrators 2. Illustration of books
ISBN 0-02-724245-5 (v1); 0-689-80310-9 (v2 Simon & Schuster); 0-395-89132-9 (v3 Houghton Mifflin)
LC 91-9982
Volume two published by Simon & Schuster Bks. for Young Readers; volume 3 published by Clarion Bks.
Each volume presents interviews with illustrators, who discuss their lives and works. Among the 14 artists in the first volume are Victoria Chess, Leo and Diane Dillon, Amy Schwartz, Tom Feelings, and Steven Kellogg. The 13 artists represented in the second volume include Brian Pinkney, Denise Fleming, Floyd Cooper, Maira Kalman, and David Wisniewski. Samples of each illustrator's work are included

741.9 Collections of drawings

—I never saw another butterfly—; children's drawings and poems from Terezin concentration camp, 1942-1944; edited by Hana Volavková; foreword by Chaim Potok; afterword by Vaclav Havel. expanded 2nd ed, by U.S. Holocaust Memorial Mus. Schocken Bks. 1993 xxii, 106p il pa $17.50 hardcover o.p. **741.9**
1. Child artists 2. Children's writings 3. Terezin (Czechoslovakia: Concentration camp)
ISBN 0-8052-1015-6 LC 92-50477

—I never saw another butterfly——*Continued*
Original Czech edition, 1959; first American edition
published 1964 by McGraw-Hill
"Of the 15,000 children who passed through Terezin
before going to Auschwitz, only 100 lived. This book is
a collection of poems and drawings by some of them.
. . . This touching book adds another facet to library
collections on the Holocaust." SLJ

742 Perspective in drawing

DuBosque, Doug
Draw 3-D; a step-by-step guide to perspective
drawing. Peel Productions 1999 63p il pa $8.99
742
1. Perspective 2. Drawing
ISBN 0-939217-14-7   LC 98-42174
"Using easy-to-follow, step-by-step sketches,
DuBosque introduces readers to the techniques of three-
dimensional drawing. Beginning with such elementary
concepts as depth, he progresses logically through shad-
ing, reflections, and multiple vanishing points. The supportive tone encourages novices to keep trying and not
become discouraged." SLJ

743 Drawing and drawings by subject

Ames, Lee J., 1921-
[Draw 50 series] Doubleday 1974-2000 25v
prices vary (4 and up)   **743**
1. Drawing
Most titles available only in paperback
Available titles are: Draw 50 animals (1974); Draw 50
boats, ships, trucks, & trains (1976); Draw 50 airplanes,
aircraft, & spacecraft (1977); Draw 50 dinosaurs and other prehistoric animals (1977); Draw 50 famous faces
(1978); Draw 50 vehicles (1978); Draw 50 famous cartoons (1979); Draw 50 buildings and other structures
(1980); Draw 50 dogs (1981); Draw 50 monsters, creeps,
superheroes, demons, dragons, nerds, dirts, ghouls, giants, vampires, zombies, and other curiosa (1983); Draw
50 horses (1984); Draw 50 athletes (1985); Draw 50 cats
(1986); Draw 50 cars, trucks, and motorcycles (1986);
Draw 50 holiday decorations (1987); Draw 50 beasties
and yugglies and turnover uglies and things that go bump
in the night (1988); Draw 50 sharks, whales, and other
sea creatures (1989); Draw 50 creepy crawlies (1991);
Draw 50 endangered animals (1992); Draw 50 people
(1993); Draw 50 flowers, trees, and other plants (1994);
Draw 50 people of the Bible (1995); Draw 50 birds
(1996); Draw 50 aliens, UFO's galaxy ghouls, milky way
marauders, and other extraterrestrial creatures (1998);
Draw 50 animal 'toons (2000)
Each volume presents step-by-step instructions for
drawing a variety of animals, people, or objects

DuBosque, Doug
Draw insects. Peel Productions 1997 63p il pa
$8.99   **743**
1. Insects in art 2. Drawing
ISBN 0-939217-28-7   LC 97-44401

Provides step-by-step instructions for drawing insects,
including the bumblebee, giant beetle, and yellow jacket
This is a "carefully constructed drawing book. . . .
Basic information such as the order and family of each
creature and where it may be found is provided. This additional material makes this book more useful for both
observations of insects and for report writing than other
titles currently available." SLJ

Mayne, Don, 1961-
Drawing horses that look real! Williamson 2002
63p il (Quick starts for kids!) pa $8.95
743
1. Horses in art 2. Drawing
ISBN 1-88559-374-0   LC 2002-27015
.
Detailed instructions on how to use basic shapes to
draw horses in a variety of poses
"The author's friendly, encouraging tone provides support for young artists' efforts, and the hints and tips will
help youngsters organize themselves even before they begin." SLJ

745 Decorative arts

Panchyk, Richard, 1970-
American folk art for kids; with 21 activities.
Chicago Review Press 2004 118p il $16.95
745
1. Handicraft 2. American folk art
ISBN 1-556-52499-4   LC 2004-4879
"Panchyk begins with a general introduction to folk
art, and then explicates the main categories of these traditional crafts. He covers a variety of decorative arts,
including painting, fabric work, woodworking, and found
objects. Each chapter contains several related projects
ranging from reverse painting on glass to quilting, sten-
ciling, and tin-can sculpture. . . . Many quality, full-
color photos are included." SLJ

745.5 Handicrafts

Bruder, Mikyla
Button girl; more than 20 cute-as-a-button
projects; photographs by Scott Nobles. Chronicle
Books 2005 60p il spiral bdg $12.95 (5 and up)
745.5
1. Handicraft 2. Buttons
ISBN 0-8118-4553-2   LC 2004-8944
This offers instructions for creating 20 accessories
including Button Barrettes and Bobbies, Hip Ribbon Button Belts, Crazy Coasters, and more.

Doney, Meryl
Festivals. Watts 1997 32p il (World crafts) $21;
pa $6.95   **745.5**
1. Festivals 2. Handicraft
ISBN 0-531-14431-3; 0-531-15329-0 (pa)
LC 96-15838

Doney, Meryl—*Continued*
Introduces a variety of well known festivals from around the world and provides instructions for related crafts, including a dragon toy for the Chinese New Year, dancing wings for Mardi Gras, and a sugar skull for Halloween
Includes bibliographical references

Martin, Laura C.
Nature's art box; from t-shirts to twig baskets: 65 cool projects for crafty kids to make with natural materials you can find anywhere; written by Laura C. Martin; with drawings by David Cain. Storey Bks. 2003 215p il $23.95; pa $16.95 (4 and up) **745.5**
1. Nature craft
ISBN 1-58017-503-1; 1-58017-490-6 (pa)
LC 2002-154374
"Each chapter includes information about historical and ethnic uses for the natural substances. Activities are rated by level of difficulty; all have easy-to-follow instructions. Projects range from baskets, picture frames, wreaths, necklaces, and gift wrap to body paint, amulet bags, and painted stones. . . . The projects display a respect for nature and art, and a simple, subtle beauty." SLJ
Includes bibliographical references

Needham, Bobbe
Ecology crafts for kids; 50 great ways to make friends with planet earth. Sterling 1998 144p il pa $14.95 hardcover o.p. **745.5**
1. Handicraft 2. Environmental protection 3. Recycling
ISBN 0-8069-2024-6 LC 98-3565
"A Sterling/Lark book"
This "contains more than fifty projects that utilize the recycling of selected materials (i.e, twigs, gourds, used furniture, eggshells, newspapers, and rocks). . . . The text is supported by a very large number of high quality photographs. . . . One of the best publications of its kind." Appraisal

745.59 Making specific objects

Doney, Meryl
Masks. Watts 1995 32p il maps (World crafts) lib bdg $22; pa $6.95 **745.59**
1. Masks (Facial) 2. Handicraft
ISBN 0-531-14397-X (lib bdg); 0-531-15870-5 (pa)
LC 96-112757
The author presents instructions for making various masks from around the world
"Every project is presented clearly on a two-page spread along with information; a map of the country of origin; a fine, full-color photograph of the original artifact; and step-by-step illustrations that explain how to make a similar item." SLJ

745.592 Toys, models, miniatures, related objects

Doney, Meryl
Puppets. Watts 1995 32p il (World crafts) lib bdg $22; pa $6.95 **745.592**
1. Puppets and puppet plays 2. Handicraft
ISBN 0-531-14399-6 (lib bdg); 0-531-15872-1 (pa)
LC 95-11433
Color photographs and diagrams accompany step-by-step instructions for constructing a variety of puppets
Includes bibliographical references

745.594 Decorative objects

Newcomb, Rain
The Girls' World book of jewelry: 50 cool designs to make. Lark Books 2004 127p il pa $14.95 (5 and up) **745.594**
1. Jewelry 2. Handicraft
ISBN 1-57990-473-4 LC 2004-1990
This offers instructions for jewelry making projects such as bracelets made of copper washers or from old wooden game pieces, or chokers made from small metal flower embellishments to a ribbon.
"This exciting collection contains clear directions, sharp photos, and precise illustrations." SLJ

746.41 Weaving, braiding, matting unaltered vegetable fibers

Monaghan, Kathleen
You can weave! projects for young weavers; {by} Katleen Monaghan and Hermon Joyner. Davis Publs. (Worcester) 2000 96p il $19.95 (4 and up) **746.41**
1. Weaving
ISBN 0-87192-493-5 LC 2001-270107
This is a "collection of 18 step-by-step weaving projects. . . . Divided into five chapters, the text explores the basics of weaving (with photos and step-by-step instructions), loom construction (cardboard, strap looms, and more), and potential mediums. From very simple paper placemats to complex beaded designs, Monaghan tackles each project clearly." Booklist
Includes bibliographical references

746.43 Knitting, crocheting, tatting

Bradberry, Sarah
Kids knit! simple steps to nifty projects; Sarah Bradberry. Sterling Pub Co 2004 96p il $14.95 (5 and up) **746.43**
1. Knitting
ISBN 0-8069-7733-7 LC 2004-19375
Presents basic knitting techniques and instructions for making a backpack, pillow, doll, and other simple

Bradberry, Sarah—*Continued*
projects.

This "book works equally well for beginners and experienced knitters. . . . Besides the requisite information on knitting and purling, there are invaluable tips about finishing garments, fixing mistakes, and adding embellishments. The projects have been chosen with an eye toward simplicity, yet they have real appeal." Booklist

Clewer, Carolyn
Kids can knit; fun and easy projects for your small knitter. Barron's 2003 128p il pa $16.95 (4 and up)   **746.43**

1. Knitting
ISBN 0-7641-2718-7
"A Quarto book"
This "book begins by discussing types of yarn, needles, and other knitting equipment. The author explains the basic techniques of finger knitting and spool knitting, casting on, knit and purl stitches, combining stitches to create patterns, increasing and decreasing, binding off, and picking up dropped stitches. Instructions on how to make pompoms, fringes, and braiding are also provided. The 16 eye-catching projects are arranged in an orderly progression of difficulty. . . . [This is a] useful and attractive resource." SLJ

Davis, Jane
Crochet; fantastic jewelry, hats, purses, pillows & more. Lark Books 2005 112p il (Kids' crafts) $19.95 (5 and up)   **746.43**

1. Crocheting
ISBN 1-579-90477-7   LC 2004-13288
Contents: Introduction; Getting started; The projects; Ready, begin! -easy accessories and game; Shoe laces; String game; Key chain; Circle games; Scrunchies; Shape it up -rectangles, triangles, and squares; Comfy slippers; Juggling blocks; Purse; Pencil case; Phone carrier; Get around-circles and balls; Hacky sack; Large indoor ball; Space balls; Felted hat; Roly poly pig; Work fast-netting; Corner shelf; Shawl; Basic net bag; Large bag; Small lace-edged bag; Challenge yourself! -longer projects; Chemistry pillows; Pocket scarf and matching hat; Case; Zippered front summer top; Felted backpack; Shine and dazzle -beads and cord crochet; Barrette; Amulet bag; Corner bookmark; Shirt edging; Bead crochet necklace and bracelet
This describes basic crochet techniques and includes instructions for 50 projects.
"The book is a pleasure to look at. . . . Photographs are large and crisp. . . . Davis clearly knows what kids like. . . . Both visual and text explanations are very clear. . . . This is a must for your craft shelves." Booklist

Wenger, Jennifer
Teen knitting club; chill out and knit; [by] Jennifer Wenger, Carol Abrams, Maureen Lasher. Artisan 2004 142p il $17.95 (7 and up)
                                              746.43
1. Knitting
ISBN 1-57965-244-1   LC 2003-63914

"The section 'All You Need to Know' discusses materials, stitches and techniques, and problems, accompanied by . . . charts and illustrations pertaining to such matters as yarn thicknesses and labels. Instructions for scarves, hats, bags, ponchos, tank tops, and more follow, with variations." SLJ

"Although Wenger's attractive hardcover (with an inside spiral binding) explains the basics of knitting, it will appeal most to children who know how to knit. . . . The 35 projects, however, hit the mark. . . . The instructions are explicit, almost narrative in style, and they are accompanied by page references to required knitting skills." Booklist

746.46 Patchwork and quilting

Bial, Raymond
With needle and thread; a book about quilts. Houghton Mifflin 1996 48p il $16 (4 and up)
                                              746.46
1. Quilting 2. Quilts
ISBN 0-395-73568-8   LC 95-16416
"With illustrated examples of traditional patchwork patterns . . . Bial describes the processes of marking, piecing, and quilting. An historical overview ranges from the Colonial period to the famous AIDS Memorial Quilt. Highlighting the multicultural scope of this art form, Bial shows work by Amish, African-American, and Hmong quilters. The narrative is accessibly simple, the photography is clear and colorful." Bull Cent Child Books
Includes bibliographical references

750 Painting and paintings

Richardson, Joy
Looking at pictures; an introduction to art for young people; with illustrations by Charlotte Voake. Abrams 1997 80p il $19.95 (5 and up)
                                              750
1. National Gallery (Great Britain) 2. Painting 3. Art appreciation 4. Art museums
ISBN 0-8109-4252-6   LC 96-86476
This "art-appreciation book delves into the world of painting using works from London's National Gallery that span 700 years. First, the author takes readers behind the scenes, focusing on how paintings are selected and hung as well as the detailed labor of restoration. The remaining chapters present major themes in the study of art including color, light, subject matter, and perspective." SLJ

"This large-size volume makes art appreciation accessible to middle-grade readers. The text is chatty and direct. . . . {It includes} beautiful full-color pictures on every page." Booklist

750.1 Painting--Philosophy and theory

Sturgis, Alexander
Optical illusions in art. Sterling 1996 32p il $14.95 **750.1**
1. Art appreciation 2. Optical illusions
ISBN 0-8069-6135-X LC 95-46740
This volume includes "chapters on trompe l'oeil, surrealism, perspective, anamorphosis (distortions corrected by use of mirrors or acute viewing angles), reversible images and op art." Publ Wkly

759.01 Painting of nonliterate peoples, and earliest times to 499

Finley, Carol
Aboriginal art of Australia; exploring cultural traditions. Lerner Publs. 1998 56p il maps (Art around the world) $23.93 **759.01**
1. Australian painting 2. Aboriginal Australians
ISBN 0-8225-2076-1 LC 97-28467
Describes the art of the Australian Aborigines including rock painting and engraving as well as sand and bark painting; also discusses the symbolism found in these works
"Clear, full-color photographs of the art, people, and landscape illustrate the text." SLJ
Includes bibliographical references

759.05 Painting--1800-1899

Sabbeth, Carol, 1957-
Monet and the impressionists for kids; their lives and ideas, 21 activities. Chicago Review Press 2002 140p il pa $17.95 (5 and up) **759.05**
1. Impressionism (Art) 2. French art
ISBN 1-55652-397-1 LC 2001-47191
Discusses the nineteenth-century French art movement known as Impressionism, focusing on the works of Monet, Renoir, Degas, Cassatt, Cezanne, Gauguin, and Seurat
"A beautifully designed introduction to Impressionism. . . . Sabbeth also includes 21 appealing extension activities such as recipes, crafts, games, and writing suggestions. Quality color reproductions on glossy pages, and varied, attractive layouts add to the book." SLJ
Includes glossary and bibliographical references

759.13 American painting

Feelings, Tom, 1933-2003
The middle passage; white ships/black cargo; introduction by John Henrik Clarke. Dial Bks. 1995 unp il map $45 (7 and up) **759.13**
1. Blacks in art 2. Slavery—Pictorial works
ISBN 0-8037-1804-7 LC 95-13866
"Consisting entirely of Feeling's uncaptioned black-and white illustrations, this . . . picture book chronicles the inhumane conditions endured by enslaved Africans during 'four centuries of the slave trade.'" Booklist
"A book for careful study and discussion, both at home and in the classroom." N Y Times Book Rev
Includes bibliographical references

Lawrence, Jacob, 1917-2000
The great migration; an American story; paintings by Jacob Lawrence; with a poem in appreciation by Walter Dean Myers. HarperCollins Pubs. 1993 unp il hardcover o.p. paperback available $8.95 **759.13**
1. African Americans in art
ISBN 0-06-443428-1 (pa) LC 93-16788
Published by The Museum of Modern Art, The Phillips Collection, and HarperCollins Pubs.
"A noted African-American artist chronicles the 1916-1919 migration of blacks from the South through a sequence of 60 paintings and accompanying narrative captions." SLJ
"Lawrence is a storyteller with words as well as pictures: his captions and his own 1992 introduction to this book are the best commentary on his work." Booklist

759.5 Italian painting

Barter, James, 1946-
A Renaissance painter's studio; by James E. Barter. Lucent Bks. 2003 112p il (Working life) lib bdg $21.96 **759.5**
1. Artists, Italian 2. Italian painting 3. Renaissance
ISBN 1 59018-178-6 LC 2002-7892
Describes the arduous training and difficult day-to-day working lives of painters in Florence during the Renaissance and discusses how their changing approach to the art they created elevated their standing and influence in Florentine society
"Barter gives readers a fascinating glimpse . . . into the lives and work of the artists of Florence." SLJ
Includes bibliographical references

769 Prints

Owens, Tom, 1960-
Collecting baseball cards; 21st century edition; {by} Thomas S. Owens. Millbrook Press 2001 80p il lib bdg $26.60 **769**
1. Baseball cards
ISBN 0-7613-1708-2 LC 00-37998
First published 1993
Provides practical advice on building a baseball card collection, covering such topics as trading cards, preserving them, and finding rookie cards, errors, and other specialities
"Owens writes in a light, entertaining style. . . . [This is a] sure hit." SLJ

769.56   Postage stamps

Postal Service guide to U.S. stamps. U.S. Postal Service il $14.95 pa $18.95   **769.56**
1. Postage stamps
First published 1974 with title: United States stamps and stories. Revised annually
Contains reproductions and histories of U.S. postage stamps

Scott standard postage stamp catalogue. Scott Pub. Co. (Sidney) 4v il ea $35   **769.56**
1. Postage stamps—Catalogs
Annual. First published 1868. Title, publisher's name and number of volumes vary
"Gives minute details, such as date of issue, design, denomination, color, perforation, and watermark, on all the stamps of the world. Most of the stamps are given a valuation." Ref Sources for Small & Medium-sized Libr. 5th edition

770   Photography, photographs, computer art

Graham, Ian, 1953-
Film and photography. Raintree Steck-Vaughn Pubs. 2001 47p il (Communications close-up) $20.95   **770**
1. Photography 2. Cinematography
ISBN 0-7398-3185-2   LC 00-33287
.
An introduction to the technology of photography, briefly describing such topics as digital and electron cameras, laser pictures, heat images, space photography, fractals, computerized imaging, and ultrasound
"Graham is not only knowledgeable about his subject but also adept at clearly explaining complex information. The colorful, attractive illustrations add to the textual explanations." Book Rep
Includes glossary and bibliographical references

771   Photography--Techniques, equipment, materials

Johnson, Neil, 1954-
National Geographic photography guide for kids. National Geographic Soc. 2001 80p il pa $12.95 hardcover o.p. (4 and up)   **771**
1. Photography
ISBN 0-7922-6370-7   LC 00-12090
An introduction to photography covering cameras, film, lighting, film speed, lenses, depth of field, and composition
"A wonderful introduction to photography. Clear, color images and an easy-to-understand text explain concepts that will help novice photographers get started." SLJ

Price, Susanna
Click! fun with photography; {by} Susanna Price & Tim Stephens. Sterling 1997 48p il pa $7.95 hardcover o.p. (4 and up)   **771**
1. Photography 2. Cameras
ISBN 0-8069-9652-8   LC 96-37211
First published 1995 in the United Kingdom
Presents the basics of photography, from choosing a camera to making the most of the flash
"With numerous full-color photos and a brief, clearly written text, this book exposes more than just the basics. The authors include frequent checklists that summarize major points and an extensive glossary. . . . A multitude of activities complete this useful introduction." SLJ

775   Digital photography

Bidner, Jenni
The kids' guide to digital photography; how to shoot, save, play with & print your digital photos; . . Lark Books 2004 96p il $14.95; pa $9.95 (5 and up)   **775**
1. Digital photography
ISBN 1-579-90604-4; 1-579-90643-5 (pa)
                LC 2004-14465
"Beginning chapters address basics, including understanding camera features, using focus and flash functions, capturing motion, and so on. Bidner then delves into picture-editing software and even how to set up a Web site . . . . Final sections offer ideas for projects. . . . Bidner introduces sophisticated technical material in enthusiastic language that is kid-friendly without being condescending." Booklist
Includes glossary

778.5   Cinematography, video production, related activities

Lockman, Darcy
Computer animation. Benchmark Bks. (Tarrytown) 2001 48p il (Kaleidoscope) lib bdg $25.64   **778.5**
1. Animation (Cinematography)
ISBN 0-7614-1048-1   LC 99-58310
Explains how computer animation is used to make entire films, indicates how it differs from traditional animation, and includes information on the development of the technology
Includes bibliographical references

778.59   Video production (Television photography)

Shulman, Mark, 1962-
Attack of the killer video book; tips and tricks for young directors; by Mark Shulman and Hazlitt Krog; art by Martha Newbigging. Annick Press 2004 64p il $24.95; pa $12.95 (5 and up)
                778.59

Shulman, Mark, 1962-—_Continued_
1. Video recording
ISBN 1-550-37841-4; 1-550-37840-6 (pa)
This "guide explores every stage of video production, from brainstorming, to organizing a shoot, to finally piecing it all together." Publisher's note
"This lighthearted primer uses lots of humor and colorful, cartoon-style illustrations. . . . A good choice for collections in need of an updated video-production guide that won't become dated too quickly." SLJ

778.9 Photography of specific subjects

Aaseng, Nathan, 1953-
Wild shots; the world of the wildlife photographer. Millbrook Press 2001 79p il lib bdg $29.90 (5 and up)   **778.9**
1. Photography of animals
ISBN 0-7613-1551-9   LC 00-45089
In this "introduction to wildlife photography, Aaseng discusses different facets of the subject, introduces many photographers and relates their experiences in the wild. . . . Illustrating the intriguing text are many outstanding, well-captioned photos of wild animals." Booklist
Includes bibliographical references

779 Photographs

Arthus-Bertrand, Yann
Earth from above for young readers; concept and photographs by Yann Arthus-Bertrand; text by Robert Burleigh; illustrations by David Giraudon. Abrams 2002 77p il $12.95 (4 and up)
                    779
1. Aerial photography 2. Human geography
ISBN 0-8109-3486-8   LC 2002-4259
Original French edition 2001
Presents aerial photographs of various scenes from around the world including fishermen in Morocco, a farm on the island of Crete, and a mangrove forest in New Caledonia
"The 34 stunning aerial views from all over the world were snapped by photographer Arthus-Bertrand while leaning out of a helicopter. The images appeared in his earlier book for adults, Earth from Above: 365 Days (Abrams, 2001), but here they are larger and even more gorgeous. . . . Burleigh's interesting and informative text expands on each photo, explaining natural phenomena, human impact, and wildlife and human adaptations." SLJ

Life: our century in pictures for young people; edited by Richard B. Stolley; adapted by Amy E. Sklansky. Little, Brown 2000 223p il $25.95
                    779
1. Photojournalism
ISBN 0-316-81589-6   LC 00-32877
This book is based on Life: our century in pictures (1999)
"The book is divided into nine chronological chapters, each with an introductory essay, several pages of photo-graphs, a 'Turning Point' event, and a 'Requiem' for prominent men and women who died during the period. . . . Well-selected, beautifully designed, and presented with the context that young readers need, the images here convey both the misery and jubilation of a century lived at full tilt." Booklist

Myers, Walter Dean, 1937-
One more river to cross; an African American photograph album. Harcourt Brace & Co. 1995 166p il $40; pa $18 (7 and up)   **779**
1. African Americans—Pictorial works
ISBN 0-15-100191-X; 0-15-202021-7 (pa)
                    LC 95-3839
"This collection of period photography documents the African-American struggle from captivity to freedom." Book Rep
"This oversized, superbly produced album is dramatic, with spare, almost poetic narration by Myers. . . . Although there are some photos of well-known individuals, the strength of this book is the pictures of ordinary people, engaged in the everyday tasks and enjoyments of life." Voice Youth Advocates

780.3 Music--Encyclopedias and dictionaries

Barber, Nicola
Music: an A-Z guide; written by Nicola Barber. Watts 2001 128p il (Watts reference) lib bdg $33; pa $19.95 (4 and up)   **780.3**
1. Music—Dictionaries
ISBN 0-531-19236-9 (lib bdg); 0-531-15450-5 (pa)
                    LC 00-51325
"Subjects range from performers to instruments, elements to musical forms, and pop to classical. Topics are covered in one to several pages, with a brief explanation, definition, or background for the term followed by more detailed information on ancillary areas. Each page has bright, colorful photos and reproductions that aid in clarifying, creating interest in, and helping to understand the text. . . . Without getting too complicated, the book succeeds in explaining each subject well enough for readers to acquire a basic understanding of it." SLJ
Includes bibliographical references

Kennedy, Michael, 1926-
The concise Oxford dictionary of music; associate editor, Joyce Bourne. 4th ed. Oxford Univ. Press 1996 780p il pa $17.95   **780.3**
1. Music—Dictionaries 2. Musicians—Dictionaries
ISBN 0-19-860884-5
First published 1952 as a condensation of The Oxford companion to music
This volume "contains a medley of information on composers, individual works, musical theory and terminology, instruments, forms and genres, performers, orchestras, and ensembles. The articles on major composers are of particular value. . . . Many will find this tool handy for a quick lookup of instantly needed information, such as dates and places of birth and death, middle names, and so forth." Am Ref Books Annu, 1997

Story of music. Grolier Educ. 2001 10v set $329
(7 and up)   **780.3**
1. Music—Encyclopedias
ISBN 0-7172-9559-1   LC 00-23220
Contents: v1 Classical music from earliest times; v2
Classical music, Romantic to modern; v3 Music from
around the world; v4 Folk, country, and Cajun music; v5
Gospel, blues, and jazz; v6 From rock and pop to hip-
hop; v7 Music of stage and screen; v8 The music profession; v9 Musical instruments and technology; v10 The
voice and song
This set describes the world of music in all its facets
with a glossary at the end of each volume explaining the
technical terms used in the text
"The narrative is kid-friendly, and the pages beckon
readers with their numerous illustrations and photos,
many in color." Book Rep

781.6   Traditions of music. Classical music

Kallen, Stuart A., 1955-
The history of classical music. Lucent Bks.
2003 112p il (Music library) lib bdg $21.96
                                              781.6
1. Music—History and criticism
ISBN 1-59018-123-9   LC 2002-3815
Contents: Music of medieval times; The musical Renaissance; The Baroque era; The classical period; The romantic era; The modern era
This follows classical music "from Medieval times
into the present, closing with a description of avant-garde
composer John Cage's 4'33″—4 minutes and 33 seconds
of silence. . . . {The volume is} greatly enhanced by
fascinating excerpts from primary material, including articles, letters, and diaries, often in the words of the composer or musician. . . . Students reading for reports or
for personal interest will find much useful information."
Booklist
Includes bibliographical references

781.642   Country music

Kallen, Stuart A., 1955-
The history of country music. Lucent Bks. 2003
112p il (Music library) lib bdg $21.96
                                            781.642
1. Country music
ISBN 1-59018-124-7   LC 2002-664
Contents: The early years of country; The sounds of
bluegrass; Honky-tonk music; Cowboy music and western swing; Rockabilly music; The Nashville hit makers;
New sounds, new fans
A history of country music which discusses its roots,
influences, and various types including bluegrass, honky
tonk, cowboy music, western swing, and rockabilly
Includes bibliographical references

781.643   Blues music

Asirvatham, Sandy
The history of the blues. Chelsea House 2003
104p il (American mosaic: African American
contributions) lib bdg $22.95; pa $9.95
                                            781.643
1. Blues music
ISBN 0-7910-7266-5 (lib bdg); 0-7910-7490-0 (pa)
                                        LC 2002-154035
Contents: From African to African-American; Traditions in the new world; Down in the Delta; Dockery's
plantation and beyond; Ladies who hollered; The kings
eclipse the queens; Sacred or profane?; At the crossroads; Piano blues; The blues goes electric
A comprehensive look at the history of blues music,
from its origins to the present time, including the musicians involved in creating that history
This is "detailed and specific enough to attract not
only report writers, but budding musicians and music
lovers as well." SLJ
Includes bibliographical references

Elmer, Howard
Blues; its birth and growth. Rosen Pub. Group
1999 64p il (Library of African American arts and
culture) $26.50   **781.643**
1. Blues music
ISBN 0-8239-1853-X   LC 98-43705
Traces the origins of blues music, its evolution in the
United States, and its influence on jazz and rock and roll
This is "informative and interesting. . . . The artistic
photographs and reproductions, in color and in black and
white, appear on almost every page and enliven the text."
SLJ
Includes discography and bibliographical references

781.646   Reggae

Haskins, James, 1941-2005
One love, one heart; a history of reggae. Jump
at the Sun 2002 138p il $15.99   **781.646**
1. Marley, Bob 2. Reggae music 3. Jamaica
4. Rastafari movement
ISBN 0-7868-0479-3   LC 2001-16957
This is an "overview of Jamaica's music and surrounding culture. Early chapters give a brief history of
colonialism and resistance in Jamaica, Marcus Garvey
and the birth of Rastafarianism, and the musical forms
that preceded reggae. A chapter on Bob Marley follows
the singer through his life, focusing on reggae's origin
and transformation. Subsequent chapters note other major
reggae stars in Jamaica and throughout the world, as well
as the music that evolved from reggae." Booklist
The author "presents his subject in a careful, respectful, and accessible story." Voice Youth Advocates
Includes bibliographical references

781.65 Jazz music

Asirvatham, Sandy
The history of jazz. Chelsea House 2003 108p
il (American mosaic: African American
contributions) lib bdg $22.95; pa $9.95
781.65
1. Jazz music
ISBN 0-7910-7265-7 (lib bdg); 0-7910-7489-7 (pa)
LC 2002-154355
Contents: The color of jazz; The crucible of New Orleans; A soloist's art; Hot swing, sweet swing; Forgotten
women; Bebop "outsiders"; Canaries and cats; Bebop
backlash and space explorers; 'Trane to freedom; Funky
fusions and beyond
This "book presents both musical and social aspects of
jazz development, beginning with its syncopated rhythms
and improvisation. The author takes readers from the
New Orleans sound through ragtime, the lilt of swing,
and on into modal jazz and rock-jazz fusion. . . . [This
is] detailed and specific enough to attract not only report
writers, but budding musicians and music lovers as
well." SLJ
Includes bibliographical references

Collier, James Lincoln, 1928-
Jazz; an American saga. Holt & Co. 1997 104p
il $18.95 (7 and up) **781.65**
1. Jazz music
ISBN 0-8050-4121-4 LC 97-3004
Examines the possible origins of jazz, its variety,
greatness, and individual artists
"Written in a crisp, enthusiastic style. . . . The information presented will be helpful for reports, but the book
lends itself to a good nonfiction read as well." SLJ
Includes discography

Kallen, Stuart A., 1955-
The history of jazz. Lucent Bks. 2003 112p il
(Music library) lib bdg $21.96 **781.65**
1. Jazz music
ISBN 1-59018-125-5 LC 2002-2220
Contents: The roots of jazz; The swingin' jazz age;
Dancing to swing; The birth of bebop; The cool, the
hard, and the free; Fusion and beyond
This follows jazz music's "evolution from its African
roots through contemporary forms. [The volume is]
greatly enhanced by fascinating excerpts from primary
material, including articles, letters, and diaries, often in
the words of the composer or musician. . . . Students
reading for reports or for personal interest will find much
useful information." Booklist
Includes bibliographical references

Lee, Jeanne
Jam! the story of jazz music. Rosen Pub. Group
1999 64p il (Library of African American arts and
culture) $26.50 (7 and up) **781.65**
1. Jazz music
ISBN 0-8239-1852-1 LC 99-10973

Describes the history and development of jazz music
in America from its roots in Africa to the contemporary
music scene
Includes glossary and bibliographical references

781.66 Rock (Rock 'n' roll)

Kallen, Stuart A., 1955-
The history of rock and roll. Lucent Bks. 2003
128p il (Music library) lib bdg $21.96
781.66
1. Rock music
ISBN 1-59018-126-3 LC 2002-3923
Contents: The roots of rock; The Beatles and the British invasion; Sweet sixties soul; Folk rock turns psyche-
delic; Rock-and-roll superstars; The rise of punk rock;
Rock's next generation
Includes bibliographical references

The **Rolling** Stone encyclopedia of rock & roll;
edited by Holly George-Warren and Patricia
Romanowski ; consulting editor, Jon Pareles. rev
and updated for the 21st century. Fireside 2001
1114p il $27 (7 and up) **781.66**
1. Rock music—Encyclopedias
ISBN 0-7432-0120-5 LC 2001-40285
"Accompanying the biographical and discographical
information on the nearly 2,000 artists included in this
edition are . . . essays [about] the performers' musical
influences, first breaks, and critical and commercial hits
and misses, as well as evaluations of their place in rock
history. Filled with hundreds of historical photos." Publisher's note
"The scope is excellent: few works can compete in
terms of blanket coverage of the major rock'n'roll players." Libr J
Includes discographies

782.42 Songs

Cooper, Michael L., 1950-
Slave spirituals and the Jubilee Singers. Clarion
Bks. 2001 86p il music $16 **782.42**
1. Jubilee Singers (Musical group) 2. Spirituals
(Songs) 3. African American music
ISBN 0-395-97829-7 LC 00-65854
"The first half of this book traces the development of
spirituals from African musical traditions and discusses
the place of religion in the lives of the slaves. The second half focuses on Fisk University's Jubilee Singers.
. . . Illustrated with many archival prints and photographs, the book includes extensive annotated source
notes and the words and music to seven of the spirituals
popularized by the Jubilee Singers." SLJ
Includes bibliographical references

Johnson, James Weldon, 1871-1938
Lift every voice and sing; illustrations by
Elizabeth Catlett; introductions by Jim Haskins.
Walker & Co. 1993 unp il $15.95 **782.42**
1. African American music 2. Songs
ISBN 0-8027-8250-7 LC 92-27333

Johnson, James Weldon, 1871-1938—*Continued*
Includes music for voice and piano
Illustrated version of the song that has come to be
considered the African American national anthem
"Ms Catlett's woodcuts, done in the 1940's, are a per-
fect complement to the text and help make this a book
to be treasured for generations to come." Child Book
Rev Serv

Silverman, Jerry
Songs and stories from the American
Revolution. Millbrook Press 1994 71p il music lib
bdg $18.90 (6 and up)   **782.42**
1. United States—History—1775-1783, Revolution—
Songs
ISBN 1-56294-429-0   LC 94-10658
"This book presents 10 broadside ballads of the 1770s
and 1780s, with piano and chord notations and the story
behind each song. . . . An interesting combination of
music and history." Booklist

Songs and stories of the Civil War. 21st Cent.
Bks. (Brookfield) 2002 96p il music lib bdg
$29.90   **782.42**
1. United States—History—1861-1865, Civil War—
Songs
ISBN 0-7613-2305-8   LC 2001-35795
Contents: The battle cry of freedom; The battle hymn
of the republic; Dixie's land; Maryland, my Maryland;
Lincoln and liberty; Weeping sad and lonely; Tenting on
the old camp ground; When Johnny comes marching
home; Roll, Alabama, roll; The battle of Shiloh; Slavery
chain done broke at last; Free at last
Provides a history of the music and lyrics of a dozen
Civil War songs, describing the circumstances under
which they were created and performed
"Black-and-white reproductions of period photos, engravings, paintings, and drawings illustrate the text. A
good resource offering an interesting sidelight on the
times." Booklist
Includes discography and bibliographical references

784.19   Musical instruments

Baines, Anthony
The Oxford companion to musical instruments;
written and edited by Anthony Baines. Oxford
Univ. Press 1992 404p il $55 (7 and up)
                                          784.19
1. Musical instruments—Dictionaries
ISBN 0-19-311334-1   LC 92-8635
Based on The New Oxford companion to music
(1983)
This volume presents alphabetically arranged entries
for musical instruments. "The individual entries cover
specific instruments and families thereof (e.g., Wind Instruments) as well as their representation in different
countries (e.g., Africa) and time periods (e.g., Baroque).
. . . Playing techniques, a brief history, and a list of the
major repertory are {discussed}." Booklist

Kallen, Stuart A., 1955-
The instruments of music. Lucent Bks. 2003
112p il (Music library) lib bdg $27.45
                                          784.19
1. Musical instruments
ISBN 1-59018-127-1   LC 2001-6609
Contents: Percussion; Woodwinds; Brass; Strings;
Keyboards
This volume "includes history, cultural background,
and the place of individual instruments in music from
classical orchestra to rock and roll." Publisher's note
Includes bibliographical references

784.2   Full orchestra (Symphony orchestra)

Ganeri, Anita, 1961-
The young person's guide to the orchestra;
Benjamin Britten's composition on CD narrated by
Ben Kingsley; book written by Anita Ganeri.
Harcourt Brace & Co. 1996 56p il $25 (4 and up)
                                          784.2
1. Orchestra 2. Musical instruments 3. Music appreciation
ISBN 0-15-201304-0   LC 95-41478
"Accompanying this book on orchestral music is a CD
featuring Britten's *A Young Person's Guide to the Orchestra* . . . as well as Dukas' *The Sorcerer's Apprentice*. The book begins with an overview of the orchestra
and then centers around groups of instruments, explaining a bit of their history and their sound's distinctive
quality. . . . The book also introduces eight famous
composers, world music, Benjamin Britten, and the background of *The Young Person's Guide to the Orchestra*.
. . . Handsome and useful." Booklist
Includes glossary

790.1   General kinds of recreational activities

Owens, Tom, 1960-
Collecting baseball memorabilia; {by} Thomas
S. Owens. Millbrook Press 1996 96p il lib bdg
$26.90   **790.1**
1. Collectors and collecting 2. Baseball
ISBN 1-56294-579-3   LC 95-19827
"This introduction delves into a wide array of baseball
collectibles including tickets stubs, team schedules, auto-
graphs, and other items that can be obtained at little or
no cost. . . . This book has a crisp layout with full-color
photos or reproductions on nearly every page. While not
a price guide, this title will be of interest to young baseball enthusiasts." SLJ
Includes glossary

Peterson's summer opportunities for kids and
teenagers. Peterson's Guides $18.95
                                          790.1
1. Recreation—Directories 2. Camps—Directories
ISSN 0894-9417
Annual. First published 1984

Peterson's summer opportunities for kids and teenagers—*Continued*

This guide profiles more than 1600 summer programs offered by camps, independent secondary schools, colleges and universities, and private organizations. Arranged alphabetically by state, country, and travel program, each entry provides general information, principal activities, program information including dates, costs and age range, and winter contact. Other features include quick-reference charts and listings divided by activities

791.43 Motion pictures

Finch, Christopher, 1939-

The art of Walt Disney; from Mickey Mouse to the Magic Kingdoms. rev and expanded ed. Harry N. Abrams 2004 504p il $60 (7 and up)

791.43

1. Disney, Walt, 1901-1966 2. Walt Disney Company
ISBN 0-8109-4964-4   LC 2004-10016
First published 1973

Contents: Part I: A new art form. Early enterprises; Mickey Mouse and Silly Symphonies; Hyperion days; Part II: Feature animation. Snow White: the first feature; Pinocchio; Fantasia: the grand experiment; Dumbo and Bambi; Interruptions and innovations; The end of an era; New beginnings; A second flowering; The tradition continues; Digital dreams; Part III: Live-action films and Broadway. Muskets and Mouseketeers; Expanded horizons; Broadway; Part IV: The Magic Kingdoms; Beyond film; Magic Kingdoms; Themes and variations; Renewal; Roots and branches

This is the "story of Walt Disney and the company he built, from Mickey Mouse to animated feature films to theme parks. The text is illustrated with more than 800 illustrations." Publisher's note

Hahn, Don

Animation magic; a behind-the-scenes look at how an animated film is made. Millennium ed. Disney Press 2000 95p il $16.99   791.43
1. Walt Disney Company 2. Animated films
ISBN 0-7868-3261-4   LC 2001-265773
First published 1996

Discusses the techniques and people involved in creating Disney's animated films, from the first story idea to opening night

"This title focuses solely on traditional Disney cell animation, rather than on stop-motion or computer techniques. With this limitation in mind, it is of interest both to fans of animation and to budding animators." SLJ
Includes bibliographical references

Hamilton, Jake

Special effects in film and television; written by Jake Hamilton. DK Pub. 1998 63p il $17.95 (4 and up)   791.43
1. Cinematography 2. Animation (Cinematography)
ISBN 0-7894-2813-X   LC 97-43121
Presents a behind-the-scenes look at some of the magic of the movies including the puppetry techniques used

in ET, the animation in Toy Story, and much more

"Packed with lots of great movie stills, this introduction is a dazzling, but cursory, look behind the scenes. . . . Readers will be informed and possibly inspired." SLJ

Hart, Christopher

Christopher Hart's animation studio. Watson-Guptill 2003 48p il pa $7.95

791.43

1. Animated films 2. Drawing—Technique 3. Cartoons and caricatures
ISBN 0-8230-0627-1
First published 1996 with title: Christopher Hart's portable animation studio

"Christopher Hart starts with a basic overview of drawing the cartoon head and body, adding expressions, creating characters, and so on. He then takes readers on a backstage tour of a classic animation studio. . . . Future animators finish by creating an easy flip book to set their own simple sequences in motion." Publisher's note

Jones, Sarah, 1968-

Film. Smart Apple Media 2003 64p il (Media wise) $28.50 (7 and up)   791.43
1. Motion pictures 2. Vocational guidance
ISBN 1-583-40256-X   LC 2002-191173
Describes film production from idea to final product, and profiles various jobs in film, including scriptwriter, producer, composer, and stills photographer
Includes bibliographical references

O'Brien, Lisa, 1963-

Lights, camera, action! making movies and TV from the inside out; illustrated by Stephen MacEachern. Owl Bks. (Toronto); distributed by Firefly Bks. (Buffalo) 1998 64p il $19.95; pa $12.95   791.43
1. Motion pictures—Production and direction 2. Acting
ISBN 1-895688-75-2; 1-895688-76-0 (pa)
"Youngsters interested in a career in the television or film industry will find this a helpful introduction. Using a fictional character named Johnny who wants to be an actor, O'Brien reveals how to break into the business, giving tips on everything from finding an agent to creating a character and preparing for an audition. . . . O'Brien . . . {takes} readers through every facet of a production." Booklist
Includes glossary

Reynolds, David West

Star wars: the visual dictionary; written by David West Reynolds; special fabrications by Don Bies and Nelson Hall; new photography by Alexander Ivanov. DK Pub. 1998 64p il $19.95

791.43

1. Star Wars films
ISBN 0-7894-3481-4   LC 98-22877
"This oversized volume is packed with full-color photographs of the characters and costumes, equipment,

Reynolds, David West—*Continued*
weaponry, mechanical droids, and assorted creatures from the Star Wars universe. . . . 'Data Files' provide additional, often fascinating, and personal tidbits about the inhabitants of this fantasy world. . . . It is a visual treat." SLJ

792   Stage presentations

Friedman, Lise
Break a leg! the kids' guide to acting and stagecraft; photographs by Mary Dowdle. Workman 2002 222p il hardcover o.p. paperback available $14.95 (4 and up)   **792**
1. Acting 2. Theater—Production and direction
ISBN 0-7611-2590-6 (pa)   LC 2001-26986
A comprehensive manual for acting and theater, discussing improvisation, voice projection, breathing exercises, script analysis, and technical aspects of theater production
"The information is solid and presented well, and the sidebars, in which young actors offer comments and tips, add life to the text." Booklist

Jackson, Sheila, 1956-
Costumes for the stage: a complete handbook for every kind of play. Dutton 1978 144p il o.p. New Amsterdam Bks. paperback available $14.95
                                    792
1. Costume
ISBN 0-941533-36-0 (pa)   LC 77-93888
Provides practical costume ideas for use in summer camp and school productions. Choosing materials, colors, and accessories for their stage effect is discussed
Includes bibliographical references

792.09   Theater--Historical and geographic treatment

Aliki
William Shakespeare & the Globe; written & illustrated by Aliki. HarperCollins Pubs. 1999 48p il $15.95; lib bdg $15.89; pa $6.99 (4 and up)
                                    792.09
1. Shakespeare, William, 1564-1616 2. Globe Theatre (London, England) 3. Shakespeare's Globe (London, England)
ISBN 0-06-027820-X; 0-06-027821-8 (lib bdg); 0-06-443722-1 (pa)   LC 98-7903
The "text describes Shakespeare's life, the Elizabethan world and entertainments, and the ups and downs of the theatrical industry . . . including tidbits such as the Burbage brothers' piece-by-piece theft of the original Globe Theatre. A fast-forward to the twentieth century then treats Sam Wanamaker's dream of making the Globe rise again." Bull Cent Child Books
"A logically organized and engaging text, plenty of detailed illustrations with informative captions, and a clean design provide a fine introduction to both bard and theater." Horn Book Guide

Currie, Stephen, 1960-
An actor on the Elizabethan stage. Lucent Bks. 2003 96p il maps (Working life) $27.45
                                    792.09
1. Theater—History 2. Great Britain—History—1485-1603, Tudors
ISBN 1-59018-174-3   LC 2002-9460
Contents: Sharers and apprentices; Hired men; Preparing a production; The performance; On tour
Discusses various aspects of theatrical life, including staging and performance, financing, types of acting troupes, and social and economic influences
This is "well written and the [author draws on quotes] from many primary sources." Libr Media Connect
Includes bibliographical references

Woog, Adam, 1953-
A history of the Elizabethan theater. Lucent Bks. 2003 112p il maps (Lucent library of historical eras, Elizabethan England) $27.45
                                    792.09
1. Theater—History 2. English drama—History and criticism 3. Great Britain—History—1485-1603, Tudors
ISBN 1-59018-099-2   LC 2001-8205
Contents: Introduction: Queen Elizabeth, the renaissance, and the stage; A golden age of theater; The origins of the Elizabethan theater; The London theaters; Between heaven and hell: stagecraft; Ordinary poets: Elizabethan playwrights; Treading the boards: actors; The Elizabethan audience; The decline of the Elizabethan theater
Discusses the development of the English theater during the Elizabethan era, including the origins of Elizabethan theater and drama, the influence of the queen and the church, and the impact of various playwrights and actors
Includes bibliographical references

792.5   Opera

Ganeri, Anita, 1961-
The young person's guide to the opera; with music from the great operas on CD; book written by Anita Ganeri and Nicola Barber. Harcourt 2001 55p il $25 (4 and up)   **792.5**
1. Opera
ISBN 0-15-216498-7   LC 00-54105
"In association with the Royal Opera House and the San Diego Opera." Title page
The authors cover "opera, from the origins of the form to the stories behind the great works to the most famous opera singers and the venues in which they perform. . . . The accompanying CD is an excellent complement to the book. It contains an enticing mix of vocal and instrumental tracks. . . . The book and CD are an attractive and effective package that will make this often-intimidating art form more accessible." SLJ
Includes glossary

Geras, Adèle

The Random House book of opera stories; retold by Adèle Geras; illustrations by Ian Beck {et al.}; costume designs by Rosemary Vercoe. Random House 1998 127p il $29.99; lib bdg $31.99 (4 and up) **792.5**

1. Opera—Stories, plots, etc.

ISBN 0-679-89315-6; 0-679-99315-0 (lib bdg)

LC 97-51795

First published 1997 in the United Kingdom with title: The Orchard book of opera stories

This "book presents the stories of eight operas: *The Magic Flute, Aida, Carmen, The Cunning Little Vixen, Turandot, Cinderella, Hansel and Gretel, and The Love for Three Oranges*. . . . Each opera story is illustrated by a different artist, such as Emma Chichester Clark and Jane Ray. A colorful painting, border, or costume design appears on nearly every page, giving the pages an appealing look. A useful and attractive book." Booklist

Siberell, Anne

Bravo! brava! a night at the opera; behind the scenes with composers, cast, and crew; introduction by Frederica von Stade. Oxford Univ. Press 2001 64p il $19.95 (4 and up)

792.5

1. Opera

ISBN 0-19-513966-6 LC 2001-21206

This "book introduces all features of the opera, including stars, stagehands, set designers, conductors, and supernumeraries. . . . Cartoon artwork illustrates the text, and a world map highlighting the settings of well-known operas is also included, as are curtain diagrams, plot summaries of favorite operas, and sample costumes." Horn Book Guide

"An excellent resource for reports, this unusual book has an exceptional range of topics for younger students and is an essential purchase for upper elementary and middle school music programs." SLJ

Includes glossary and bibliographical references

792.8 Ballet and modern dance

Augustyn, Frank

Footnotes; dancing the world's best-loved ballets; {by} Frank Augustyn and Shelley Tanaka. Millbrook Press 2001 94p il lib bdg $24.90; pa $17.95 (5 and up) **792.8**

1. Ballet

ISBN 0-7613-2323-6 (lib bdg); 0-7613-1646-9 (pa)

LC 00-50075

"*Footnotes* uses seven classical ballets as a jumping-off point to talk about the evolution of this unique art form, partnering, dancer as actor, training, costumes, choreography, and some of the world's most well-known performers." SLJ

"Fine photographs, most in color, add enormously to the book's appeal. A well-crafted, readable volume." Booklist

Balanchine, George, 1904-1983

101 stories of the great ballets; {by} George Balanchine and Francis Mason. Dolphin Bks. (NY) 1975 541p pa $16 **792.8**

1. Ballet—Stories, plots, etc.

ISBN 0-385-03398-2

"A Doubleday Dolphin book"

This collection contains the stories of well-known 19th and 20th century ballets

793 Indoor games and amusements

Glenn, Jim

The treasury of family games; hundreds of fun games for all ages, complete with rules and strategies; [by] Jim Glenn and Carey Denton. Reader's Digest Association 2003 256p il $29.95 (5 and up) **793**

1. Games

ISBN 0-7621-0431-7 LC 2003-46602

"This compendium is divided into categories: board games, card games, party games, games to play anywhere, indoor games, and outdoor games, and then subdivided into more focused categories within each color-coded section. Each entry includes step-by-step instructions, full-color photos, and clipart decorations . . . The authors also provide the background and history of many of the games. . . . A useful and fun-packed volume." SLJ

Loeffelbein, Robert L.

The recreation handbook; 342 games and other activities for teams and individuals. McFarland & Co. 1992 237p il pa $35 **793**

1. Games 2. Sports

ISBN 0-89950-744-1 LC 92-50310

"This volume briefly describes hundreds of games and activities for teams and individuals. The author includes many traditional games along with modern variations and some newer pastimes for players age six and up. Games are arranged under basic themes. . . . Most entries note age level, organizational level, number of players, supervision (referee, scorekeeper, or none), playing time, space, and equipment. Directions for playing, scoring, and variations complete each entry." Booklist

793.7 Games not characterized by action

Kenda, Margaret

Math wizardry for kids; {by} Margaret Kenda and Phyllis S. Williams; illustrated by Tim Robinson. Barron's Educ. Ser. 1995 324p il pa $15.95 **793.7**

1. Mathematical recreations

ISBN 0-8120-1809-5 LC 94-31243

This includes over 200 mathematical puzzles and games plus a 180-degree protractor, 30-, 45-, and 60-degree triangles, a 6 ruler, compass, pencil sharpener, and eraser

Includes glossary

Wise, Leonard, 1940-
The way cool license plate book. Firefly Bks.
2002 64p il $19.95; pa $9.95 (4 and up)
793.7
1. Games
ISBN 1-55297-686-6; 1-55297-563-0 (pa)
LC 2003-279447
"The introduction explains what vanity license plates
are and how to read them. A short history discusses the
origin of license plates, the various kinds of materials
that have been used to manufacture them, and collecting
as a hobby, followed by six pages of directions for various license-plates-related games that can be played while
traveling. . . . This is one of those titles that libraries
should have just because." SLJ

793.73   Puzzles and puzzle games

Agee, Jon
Sit on a potato pan, Otis! more palindromes.
Farrar, Straus & Giroux 1999 unp il $14.41
793.73
1. Word games
ISBN 0-374-31808-5   LC 98-31783
"This volume collects more than sixty palindromes
and displays them in witty cartoon drawings, notable for
their off-center deadpan humor. Most of the entries will
have readers chuckling aloud and trying to concoct their
own palindromes." Horn Book Guide

Who ordered the jumbo shrimp? and other
oxymorons. HarperCollins Pubs. 1998 unp il
$15.99   **793.73**
1. Word games
ISBN 0-06-205159-8   LC 97-78386
Also available in paperback from Farrar Strauss &
Giroux
"Michael Di Capua books"
"This collection of oxymorons, illustrated with spirited
black-and-white cartoons, offers readers a great way to
understand the concepts while giving them a good
laugh." SLJ

Moscovich, Ivan
1000 playthinks; puzzles, paradoxes, illusions &
games; foreword by Ian Stewart ; illustrated by
Tim Robinson. Workman Pub 2001 420p il pa
$29.95 (7 and up)   **793.73**
1. Scientific recreations
ISBN 0-7611-1826-8   LC 2001-26847
The puzzles and games in this collection "are arranged
by mathematical or scientific category, and ranked by a
degree of difficulty from 1 to 10. A key further subdivides them into mind puzzles, pencil-and-paper puzzles,
those that must be traced or copied, and, finally, those
that require cutting. SLJ
"This book just might become everyone's favorite.
. . . It is big. It is bright. It is inviting and downright
happy. . . . The solutions are clear, succinct, peppered
with historical tidbits, and educational." Voice Youth
Advocates
Includes bibliographical references

794   Indoor games of skill

King, Daniel, 1963-
Games; learn to play, play to win. Kingfisher
2003 64p il $16.95 (5 and up)   **794**
1. Card games 2. Board games
ISBN 0-7534-5581-1   LC 2002-35660
Contents: Board games: Ancient games I; Ancient
games II; Nine men's morris; Fox and geese; Backgam-
mon; Go; Chess; Mancala; Checkers; Card games: The
pack; First card games; Rummy; Cribbage; Whist;
Spades; Hearts; Blackjack; Poker
Provides instructions on how to play a range of card
and board games, as well as strategy and history of the
games.
This is a "visually appealing book. . . . Great for beginners as well as seasoned players." SLJ

794.1   Chess

Basman, Michael
Chess for kids; written by Michael Basman.
Dorling Kindersley 2001 45p il $12.99 (4 and up)
794.1
1. Chess
ISBN 0-7894-6540-X   LC 00-59018
This guide to chess explains the rudiments of the
game, techniques and winning strategies
"A solid introduction for novices and good for skilled
players wanting to develop their strategies and find out
about chess clubs and tournaments." Booklist

King, Daniel, 1963-
Chess; from first moves to checkmate.
Kingfisher (NY) 2000 64p il $16.95
794.1
1. Chess
ISBN 0-7534-5387-8   LC 00-26353
Introduces the rules and strategies of chess, as well as
its history and some of the great players and matches
The author "offers training exercises, strategy quizzes,
and trivia, all of which add depth and texture to his explanations. The computer-generated graphics are staggering. The colorful, multi-image illustrations are not only
aesthetically appealing but also crystal clear and very effectively placed to enhance the text." Booklist

796   Athletic and outdoor sports and games

The **Information** please sports almanac; edited by
Mike Meserole. Houghton Mifflin pa $10.95
796
1. Sports
ISSN 1046-4980
Annual. First published 1989
Covers the major sports events of the previous year
and presents facts and records

Sports Illustrated . . . sports almanac; by the editors of Sports Illustrated. Little, Brown il pa $13   **796**
1. Sports

Annual. First published 1991

"Provides team and individual records and highlights for all major sports. . . . A brief essay opens the section on each sport, followed by page upon page of records, both current and retrospective. Interspersed throughout . . . are black-and-white and color photographs and notable quotations by sports figures." Am Ref Books Annu, 1993

Sports rules on file; {by} the Diagram Group. Facts on File 2000 various paging (Facts on File reference library) loose leaf $185   **796**
1. Sports

ISBN 0-8160-4117-2   LC 00-37137

Also available CD-ROM version

Includes index

"The coverage of each activity includes a synopsis; a competition overview; some historical background; playing field or arena diagrams; information on dress and equipment; play and scoring regulations; officials' duties; and discussion and line drawings that focus on skills, plays, and the basic rules. All of the major sports played at the U.S. high school and college level are covered. . . . An effective, easy-to-use reference tool." SLJ

Sports: the complete visual reference; François Fortin {general editor}. Firefly Bks. 2000 372p il $39.95   **796**
1. Sports

ISBN 1-55209-540-1

This is a "reference source on 120 contemporary sports . . . pulling together the history, physical environment for competitions, roles of the players and officials, specific terms and expressions, and dynamics of each. All of this is done with an emphasis on visual presentation, and each entry includes copious illustrations." Booklist

"A sure winner for any sports reference collection." Am Libr

Teitelbaum, Michael, 1953-
Great moments in women's sports. North American ed. World Almanac 2002 48p il (Great moments in sports) lib bdg $26.60; pa $11.95
796
1. Women athletes

ISBN 0-8368-5349-0 (lib bdg); 0-8368-5363-6 (pa)
LC 2002-16860

Recounts ten high points in the history of women's athletic competition, including Babe Zaharias's performance at the 1930 Olympics, the All-American Girls Professional Baseball League, and the final game in the 1999 Women's World Cup

"This is a well-written, interesting introduction that may lead young sports fans to fuller treatments." SLJ

Includes bibliographical references

796.03   Sports--Encyclopedias and dictionaries

Encyclopedia of women and sport in America; edited by Carole A. Oglesby; with {contributions by} Doreen L. Greenberg {et al.}. Oryx Press 1998 xxiii, 360p il $77.95
796.03
1. Women athletes—Encyclopedias 2. Sports—Encyclopedias

ISBN 0-89774-993-6   LC 97-52787

"This encyclopedia provides short biographical entries with time and place of birth and then spells out the women's athletic accomplishments. It also includes historical articles, such as 'Badminton and Women' and sociological/psychological entries, such as 'Goal Setting and Women'." Voice Youth Advocates

"This clearly written book offers more information about American female athletes than any other single source." SLJ

Includes bibliographical references

Rules of the game; the complete illustrated encyclopedia of all the sports of the world. {rev ed}. St. Martin's Press 1990 320p il hardcover o.p. paperback available $17.95   **796.03**
1. Sports—Encyclopedias

ISBN 0-312-11940-2 (pa)   LC 90-37196

First published 1974 with title: The rule book

This volume covers 150 sports "grouped under 13 headings such as water, court, team, wheels, and air. Each article contains a detailed discussion of major objectives, playing area and equipment, rules, timing and scoring, and participants and officials." Booklist

Scholastic visual sports encyclopedia. Scholastic Ref. 2003 224p il $19.95 (4 and up)
796.03
1. Sports—Encyclopedias

ISBN 0-439-31721-5   LC 2001-49507

Text and drawings explain the equipment and rules for approximately one hundred sports, including track and field, ball sports, and motor sports

"The book is well organized, clearly written, and effectively illustrated." Booklist

Wukovits, John F., 1944-
The encyclopedia of world sports; by John Wukovits. Watts 2001 186p il $40; pa $24.95
796.03
1. Sports—Encyclopedias

ISBN 0-531-11777-4; 0-531-16134-X (pa)
LC 00-38222

This reference offers an overview of 80 sports and sporting events

796.2   Active games requiring equipment

Chambers, Veronica
Double dutch; a celebration of jump rope, rhyme, and sisterhood. Jump at the Sun/Hyperion Bks. for Children 2002 64p il $18.99 (4 and up)
796.2
1. Rope skipping 2. Jump rope rhymes
ISBN 0-7868-0512-9
"Chambers introduces readers to the world of jump roping through personal reminiscences, wonderful action photos, and factual narratives. The book looks like a vibrant collage, a clean typeface is interspersed with pictures and inserts of the rhymes themselves. From it, readers learn not only the history of double Dutch . . . and its current state, but also experience some of the joy of jumping." SLJ

Thomas, Keltie
Blades, boards & scooters; illustrated by Steve Attoe and Allan Moon. Maple Tree Press; distributed by Firefly Books 2003 64p il (Popular mechanics for kids) $21.95; pa $12.95 (5 and up)
796.2
1. In-line skating 2. Skateboarding 3. Snowboarding
ISBN 1-894379-45-4; 1-894379-46-2 (pa)
This "volume introduces scooters, in-line skates, skateboards, and snowboards. Thomas combines sound advice for beginners with glimpses of the 'X-treme scene,' showcasing the amazing feats performed by the pros and other experienced riders. . . . Throughout the book, colorful photographs show action scenes, while very clear pictures, evidently digital, illustrate the gear and some of the moves used in the sports." Booklist

796.22   Skateboarding

Maurer, Tracy, 1965-
Skateboarding; {by} Tracy Nelson Maurer. Rourke 2002 48p il lib bdg $29.93
796.22
1. Skateboarding
ISBN 1-58952-104-8   LC 2001-41652
Surveys the history, equipment, techniques, and safety factors of skateboarding
This "combines beautiful photography with clear, commonsense and practical text." Voice Youth Advocates
Includes bibliographical references

Ryan, Pat
Extreme skateboarding. Capstone Press 1998 48p il (Extreme sports) lib bdg $21.26
796.22
1. Skateboarding
ISBN 1-560-65535-6   LC 97-9396
Describes the history, equipment, and contemporary practice of extreme skateboarding
Includes glossary and bibliographical references

796.323   Basketball

Burgan, Michael
Great moments in basketball. North American ed. World Almanac 2002 48p il (Great moments in sports) lib bdg $29.27; pa $10.95
796.323
1. Basketball
ISBN 0-8368-5345-8 (lib bdg); 0-8368-5359-8 (pa)
LC 2002-16875
Recounts ten high points in the history of basketball, including Wilt Chamberlain's 100-point game, eight consecutive NBA championships won by the Boston Celtics, and the Houston Comets win the first four WNBA championships
Includes bibliographical references

Lannin, Joanne
A history of basketball for girls and women; from bloomers to big leagues. Lerner Publs. 2000 144p il lib bdg $26.60; pa $9.95   **796.323**
1. Basketball 2. Women athletes
ISBN 0-8225-3331-6 (lib bdg); 0-8225-9863-9 (pa)
LC 99-50643
Traces the development of women's basketball, from its beginnings at Smith College to today's Women's National Basketball Association
"This well-researched, inspiring account will appeal to fans of both genders who follow the game, as well as to those interested in feminist studies and equal rights." Booklist
Includes bibliographical references

Stewart, Mark
Basketball; a history of hoops. Watts 1998 160p il (Watts history of sports) lib bdg $33.50 (7 and up)
796.323
1. Basketball
ISBN 0-531-11492-9   LC 98-25040
Discusses the origins and evolution of the sport of basketball, as well as important events and key personalities in both college and professional versions of the game
Includes bibliographical references

796.325   Volleyball

Crisfield, Deborah
Winning volleyball for girls; {by} Deborah W. Crisfield, and Mark Gola; foreword by Stacy Sykora. 2nd ed. Facts on File 2002 178p il $35; pa $10.95   **796.325**
1. Volleyball
ISBN 0-8160-4620-4; 0-8160-4621-2 (pa)
LC 2001-33473
"A Mountain Lion book"
First published 1994
This includes a brief history of volleyball followed by descriptions of the rules, court and equipment, training, techniques such as the spike, the serve, the block, and the pass, offensive and defensive play, putting a team together, and game strategies
Includes glossary and bibliographical references

Manley, Claudia B.
Competitive volleyball for girls. Rosen Pub. Group 2001 64p il (Sportsgirl) lib bdg $26.50
796.325
1. Volleyball
ISBN 0-8239-3404-7   LC 00-12210
"The author shows the players in a volleyball game, and gives a detailed look at what each player does and how she prepares. The differences between court volleyball and beach volleyball are included." Publisher's note
Includes bibliographical references

Sherrow, Victoria
Volleyball. Lucent Bks. 2002 96p il (History of sports) lib bdg $27.45   **796.325**
1. Volleyball
ISBN 1-560-06961-9   LC 2001-4233
Discusses the history and evolution of the game of volleyball, its recent popularity, and famous personalities in the game's history
This is "bound to be popular, even with reluctant readers, for reports and recreational reading. . . . The series design is readable, with clear type, black-and-white action photos, and useful sidebars." Booklist
Includes bibliographical references

796.332 American football

Buckley, James, Jr.
Football; created by NFL Publishing; written by James Buckley, Jr. DK Pub. 1999 63p il (Eyewitness books) $15.99; lib bdg $19.99 (4 and up)   **796.332**
1. Football
ISBN 0-7894-4725-8; 0-7894-6991-X (lib bdg)
LC 99-24169
Provides an illustrated look at many varied aspects of the popular sport of professional football, including the history of the game, evolution of equipment, the playing field and modern stadiums, players, fans, and more

796.334 Soccer

Coleman, Lori
Fundamental soccer; photographs by Andy King. Lerner Publs. 1995 64p il (Fundamental sports) lib bdg $22.60 (5 and up)   **796.334**
1. Soccer
ISBN 0-8225-3451-7   LC 94-11907
This "book covers the history of the sport, positions, equipment, basic and more advanced moves, rules, the merits of practice, and variations in the game. . . . King's colorful, clear, informative photographs enhance the text." SLJ
Includes glossary and bibliographical references

Hamm, Mia, 1972-
Go for the goal; a champion's guide to winning in soccer and life; {by} Mia Hamm with Aaron Heifetz. HarperCollins Pubs. 1999 222p il hardcover o.p. paperback available $12.95 (7 and up)   **796.334**
1. Soccer
ISBN 0-06-093159-0 (pa)   LC 99-19592
Personal anecdotes and both action and instructional photos illustrate soccer skills and techniques

Hornby, Hugh
Soccer; written by Hugh Hornby; photographed by Andy Crawford. rev ed. DK Pub. 2005 72p il (DK eyewitness books) $15.99; lib bdg $19.99 (4 and up)   **796.334**
1. Soccer
ISBN 0-7566-1091-5; 0-7566-1092-3 (lib bdg)
First published 2000
Examines all aspects of the game of soccer: its history, rules, techniques, tactics, equipment, playing fields, competitive play, and more.

Scott, Nina Savin
The thinking kid's guide to successful soccer; illustrations by Anne Cancvari Green. Millbrook Press 1999 96p il lib bdg $21.90 (4 and up)
796.334
1. Soccer
ISBN 0-7613-0324-3   LC 98-17201
Presents strategies for playing soccer under pressure, dealing with various situations during a game, setting goals, playing with teammates, coping with coaches, and dealing with doubts and fears
"This well-designed book, with genuinely funny cartoon illustrations, deserves a space on the shelf right next to those books on rules and techniques." Booklist
Includes bibliographical references

Stewart, Mark
Soccer; a history of the world's most popular game. Watts 1998 128p il (Watts history of sports) lib bdg $33.50 (7 and up)   **796.334**
1. Soccer
ISBN 0-531-11456-2   LC 97-17201
A comprehensive history of soccer, focusing on its evolution, momentous events, and key personalities
This book is "chock-full of outstanding full-color and black-and-white photos. There is strong coverage of memorable contests and individuals and the statistical appendix {is} useful." SLJ
Includes bibliographical references

796.34 Racket games

Swissler, Becky
Winning lacrosse for girls; foreword by Anna Maria Vesco. Facts on File 2004 192p il $35 (7 and up)   **796.34**
1. Lacrosse
ISBN 0-8160-5183-6   LC 2003-51446

Swissler, Becky—*Continued*
This "teaches the game's basic skills, strategies, and drills and how to master them. Chapters cover the history of the game, the basics of stick handling, the rules of play, passing and receiving, offense and defense, key strategies, skills and tactics, conditioning, and much more." Publisher's note
This is "well organized, clear, and concise. . . .Accurate . . . pictures accompany the instruction in a logical and clear fashion." SLJ

796.342 Tennis

Douglas, Paul
Tennis. Dorling Kindersley 1995 72p il pa $5 (7 and up)   **796.342**
1. Tennis
ISBN 0-7566-0225-4
At head of title: 101 essential tips
Aspects covered include strokes, positions, playing surfaces, dress and equipment
"This is a good text for those just picking up the sport, as well as for those seasoned players who want to brush up on their game or improve their strategy." Voice Youth Advocates

Williams, Venus, 1980-
How to play tennis; learn to play tennis with the Williams sisters; [by Venus and Serena Williams]; text editor, Laura Buller; photographer, Russell Sadur. DK Pub. 2004 95p il $19.99 (5 and up)
796.342
1. Tennis
ISBN 0-7566-0582-2   LC 2004-7187
Tennis champions "Venus and Serena Williams host this how-to book about the game of tennis, teaching readers essential rules, swings, shots, and other must-knows for winning." Publisher's note

796.357 Baseball

Buckley, James, Jr.
The visual dictionary of baseball; written by James Buckley, Jr. DK Pub. 2001 64p il maps $18.95   **796.357**
1. Baseball
ISBN 0-7894-6725-9   LC 00-31833
This is a visual guide to baseball vocabulary illustrated with color photographs and covering equipment, history, and memorabilia
Includes glossary

Geng, Don
Play-by-play baseball; photographs by Andy King. Lerner Publs. 2001 80p il pa $7.95 (5 and up)   **796.357**
1. Baseball
ISBN 0-8225-9880-9   LC 00-8879
First published 1995 with title: Fundamental baseball

Presents information on the history of baseball and the equipment used, demonstrates the basic skills involved in fielding, throwing, hitting, and baserunning, and describes how these skills are used in a game
"Not only does it have kid appeal, but there's a wealth of clearly written information in a logical format enhanced by action-packed photos." Book Rep
Includes bibliographical references

Krasner, Steven
Play ball like the pros; tips for kids from 20 big league stars; written by Steven Krasner. Peachtree Pubs. 2002 181p il pa $12.95 (4 and up)
796.357
1. Baseball
ISBN 1-56145-261-0   LC 2001-7342
Nearly two dozen professional baseball players, such as Pedro Martinez and Derek Jeter, provide insights into how they prepare for and play the game
"This title is just the sort of finely tuned analysis of baseball that many young players are looking for. . . . The tips given are detailed and insightful. . . . This is a good reference for young people working to improve their skills." Booklist

McKissack, Patricia C., 1944-
Black diamond; the story of the Negro baseball leagues; {by} Patricia C. McKissack and Fredrick McKissack, Jr. Scholastic 1994 184p il hardcover o.p. paperback available $5.99 (6 and up)
796.357
1. Baseball 2. African American athletes
ISBN 0-590-68213-X (pa)   LC 93-22691
Traces the history of baseball in the Negro Leagues and its great heroes, including Monte Irwin, Buck Leonard, and Cool Papa Bell
This is "an engaging account. . . . It includes a chronology, player profiles and wonderful photographs from the Negro Leagues." N Y Times Book Rev
Includes bibliographical references

Neft, David S.
The sports encyclopedia: baseball; {by} David S. Neft, Richard M. Cohen. St. Martin's Press $22.95 pa $22.95   **796.357**
1. Baseball—Statistics
First published 1974 by Grosset & Dunlap. (2003 edition) Periodically revised
Covers baseball from 1876 to the present and contains team statistics, alphabetical registers of batters and pitchers, and summaries of each season

Nitz, Kristin Wolden
Fundamental softball; photographs by Andy King. Lerner Publs. 1997 80p il (Fundamental sports) lib bdg $22.60   **796.357**
1. Softball
ISBN 0-8225-3460-6   LC 96-34258
Introduces the history, equipment, skills, and strategies of softball
"Clear color photographs and helpful diagrams aid in

Nitz, Kristin Wolden—*Continued*
the initial instruction of softball fundamentals. . . . The informative book provides an adequate source for more mature beginners." Horn Book Guide
Includes glossary and bibliographical references

Pellowski, Michael, 1949-
The Chicago "Black Sox" baseball scandal; a headline court case; [by] Michael J. Pellowski. Enslow Pubs. 2003 128p il (Headline court cases) lib bdg $20.95   **796.357**
1. Chicago White Sox (Baseball team) 2. Trials
ISBN 0-7660-2044-4   LC 2002-12524
Contents: "Say it ain't so, Joe"; It's a money game; A slide into the dirt; The scandal that rocked baseball; Three strikes, you're out!; Judgment day at the ballpark
Examines the 1920 trial of eight Chicago White Sox baseball players accused of conspiracy to commit an illegal act when they allegedly took money from gangsters to lose the 1919 World Series
"The facts are solid, . . . The author does a fine job of explaining some possibly unclear legal and athletic terms in context." SLJ
Includes glossary and bibliographical references

Smyth, Ian
The young baseball player; written by Ian Smyth; with a foreword by Eduardo Perez. DK Pub. 1998 37p il (Young enthusiast) $15.99 (4 and up)   **796.357**
1. Baseball
ISBN 0-7894-2825-3   LC 97-41728
Provides information on the offensive and defensive techniques of baseball as well as on the history and equipment of the game, with step-by-step instructions on individual positions
This is "filled with beautifully-reproduced full-color photos. . . . Smyth provides solid, basic information in an attractive format." SLJ
Includes glossary

Stewart, Mark
World Series. Watts 2002 159p il (Watts history of sports) $33.50   **796.357**
1. Baseball—History 2. World series (Baseball)
ISBN 0-531-11953-X   LC 2001-5727
Contents: The 19th century; The 1900s; The 1910s; The 1920s; The 1930s; The 1940s; The 1950s; The 1960s; The 1970s; The 1980s; The 1990s; 2000 and beyond
A year-by-year account of the World Series games from the 1800s through the twentieth century
This is "fast paced, brimming with photos and sidebars and sure to be a winner for browsing or reports." Libr Media Connect
Includes bibliographical references

796.4 Weight lifting, track and field, gymnastics

Brzycki, Matt, 1957-
Wrestling strength: prepare to win. Blue River Press 2002 116p il pa $12.95   **796.4**
1. Weight lifting 2. Wrestling
ISBN 0-9718959-1-0
The author outlines "information on anatomy and kinesiology, explains how to prevent injuries, and gives detailed instructions on performing weight-lifting exercises for maximum benefit. . . . Brzycki also discusses flexibility, diet, and safety in the weight room. . . . [This] should be mandatory reading for every young athlete about to begin weight training." Voice Youth Advocates

Wrestling strength: the competitive edge. Blue River Press 2002 112p il pa $12.95   **796.4**
1. Weight lifting 2. Wrestling
ISBN 0-9718959-0-2
"The author offers concrete assistance on designing the appropriate weight-lifting regimen to fit the individual and his or her sport, as well as related training activities such as conditioning and skill development. . . . [This] should be mandatory reading for every young athlete about to begin weight training." Voice Youth Advocates

796.42 Track and field

Housewright, Ed
Winning track and field for girls; foreword by Buzz Andrews. Facts on File 2004 188p il $35; pa $16.95 (7 and up)   **796.42**
1. Track athletics
ISBN 0-8160-5231-X; 0-8160-5232-8 (pa)
                    LC 2003-49241
"Housewright starts with a . . . history of women's track. The chapters are then divided into topics such as sprints, hurdles, middle and long distances, relays, jumping events, throwing events, the heptathlon, cross-country, and the triathlon. Each of these chapters then goes into detail about the individual event and concludes with a section about record holders. Helpful drills and sample workouts are also provided." SLJ
Includes bibliographical references

Macht, Norman L. (Norman Lee), 1929-
The composite guide to track & field. Chelsea House 1999 64p il (Composite guide) $20.65
                    796.42
1. Track athletics
ISBN 0-7910-4720-2   LC 97-47684
Surveys the history of track and field competitions from their origins in ancient Greece to the accomplishments of top athletes in the twentieth century
Includes bibliographical references

Manley, Claudia B.
Competitive track and field for girls. Rosen Pub. Group 2001 64p il (Sportsgirl) lib bdg $26.50
796.42
1. Track athletics
ISBN 0-8239-3408-X　　　　　LC 2001-752
This includes information about the origin of track and field athletics "as well as basic equipment requirements, and the fundamental skills and/or training needed." Book Rep
Includes glossary and bibliographical references

796.44　Sports gymnastics

Bragg, Linda Wallenberg
Fundamental gymnastics; photographs by Andy King. Lerner Publs. 1995 80p il (Fundamental sports) lib bdg $22.60 (5 and up)　　**796.44**
1. Gymnastics
ISBN 0-8225-3453-3　　　　　LC 94-40770
"Four chapters provide a brief history of gymnastics, descriptions of the six events for boys and the four events for girls, the basic moves, the general workout, and competition. The events and some of the skills are shown in excellent-quality full-color photographs on each page. Interesting facts in orange boxes appear throughout." SLJ
Includes glossary and bibliographical references

Gutman, Dan
Gymnastics. Viking 1996 187p il pa $6.99 hardcover o.p.　　**796.44**
1. Gymnastics
ISBN 0-14-130130-9　　　　　LC 95-50420
Discusses the history, competitive events, and some superstars of gymnastics, as well as problems and miscellaneous facts related to the sport
"Gutman's tone throughout is breezy and enthusiastic, and . . . he is truly bedazzled by the athletes and their skill. But he also examines the dark side of the sport: serious injuries, eating disorders, abusive coaches, and the competitive system." Booklist
Includes glossary and bibliographical references

796.48　Olympic games

Fischer, David
The encyclopedia of the Summer Olympics; written by David Fischer. F. Watts 2003 160p il (Watts reference) $19.95 (4 and up)
796.48
1. Olympic games
ISBN 0-531-11886-X　　　　　LC 2002-38024
Explores the history and traditions of the Olympics and the various events included in the competitions held every four years.
"A good assortment of full-color and archival black-and-white photos elucidates the text. With the plethora of books to choose from on the topic, this title is a worthy one." SLJ
Includes bibliographical references

Macy, Sue, 1954-
Swifter, higher, stronger; a photographic history of the Summer Olympics; foreword by Bob Costas. National Geographic Society 2004 96p il $18.95; lib bdg $28.90 (4 and up)　　**796.48**
1. Olympic games
ISBN 0-7922-6667-6; 0-7922-6980-2 (lib bdg)
LC 2003-14079
A detailed look at the history of the Olympic Games, from their origins in Ancient Greece, through their rebirth in nineteenth century France, to the present, highlighting the contributions of individuals to the Games' success and popularity.
"While other books on the topic go into more depth on specific sports, athletes, or historical events, none are as enthusiastically broad or as enjoyable to read as this one. And, it's superbly illustrated with colorful, well-chosen, and enticing photographs." SLJ
Includes bibliographical references

Olympism; a basic guide to the history, ideals, and sports of the Olympic movement; {by} the U.S. Olympic Committee. Griffin Pub.; distributed by Stevens, G. 2001 152p il (Olympic guides) lib bdg $23.33
796.48
1. Olympic games
ISBN 0-8368-2800-3　　　　　LC 00-52658
This covers "the history of the Games as well as the events and results of the 2000 Olympics in Sydney. Each sport is given a clear, up-to-date, two- to four-page description headed by the official Olympic symbol. The information . . . is accurate, well sequenced, and attractively presented." SLJ

Woff, Richard, 1953-
The ancient Greek Olympics. Oxford Univ. Press 2000 c1999 32p il $16.95 (4 and up)
796.48
1. Olympic games 2. Greece—Civilization
ISBN 0-19-521581-8　　　　　LC 99-87603
First published 1999 in the United Kingdom
Describes the history, traditions, and competitive events connected with the Olympic games held in ancient Greece
"The text brings to life the sights and sounds of the spectacle, Woff provides the sort of juicy information that students will find invaluable for research. Illustrations, including photographs of Greek art and statuary, are plentiful." Booklist
Includes bibliographical references

796.5　Outdoor life

Dewey, Jennifer
Finding your way; the art of natural navigation; {by} Jennifer Owings Dewey; photographs by Stephen Trimble. Millbrook Press 2001 63p il lib bdg $23.90　　**796.5**
1. Wilderness survival 2. Orienteering
ISBN 0-7613-0956-X　　　　　LC 00-32893

Dewey, Jennifer—*Continued*
"The author describes how it feels to be lost and disoriented, and includes tips on and clues for using nature to regain one's sense of balance and place. . . . Readers looking for real-life adventure and survival stories will enjoy this engaging account." SLJ
Includes bibliographical references

Paulsen, Gary
Woodsong. Bradbury Press 1990 132p map $17.95; pa $5.99 (7 and up)   **796.5**
1. Sled dog racing 2. Outdoor life 3. Minnesota
ISBN 0-02-770221-9; 0-689-85250-9 (pa)
                                        LC 89-70835
Also available in paperback from Puffin Bks.
For the author and his family, life in northern Minnesota is a wild experience involving wolves, deer, and the sled dogs that make their way of life possible. Includes an account of Paulsen's first Iditarod, a dogsled race across Alaska
"The book is packed with vignettes that range among various shades of terror and lyrical beauty." Voice Youth Advocates

796.51 Walking

Andryszewski, Tricia, 1956-
Step by step along the Appalachian Trail. 21st Cent. Bks. (Brookfield) 1998 64p il lib bdg $24.90
                                        796.51
1. Hiking 2. Nature study 3. Appalachian Trail
ISBN 0-7613-0273-5   LC 98-7304
An overview of the natural history of the Appalachian Trail and of historical events related to the route, an imaginary hike up the trail, and a description of what can be seen and experienced along the way
"Clear, full-color photographs give readers a sense of 'you are there' immediacy. Students using {this book} for reports are sure to get wrapped up in the vivid descriptions, while nature lovers and budding adventurers will want to pack up and start walking." SLJ
Includes bibliographical references

Hart, John, 1948-
Walking softly in the wilderness; the Sierra Club guide to backpacking; . 4th ed, complete rev and updated. Sierra Club Books 2005 508p il map (Sierra Club outdoor adventure guide) pa $16.95
                                        796.51
1. Backpacking 2. Wilderness areas
ISBN 1-578-05123-1   LC 2004-56554
First published 1977
This guide for both the novice and experienced hiker reflects the environmental concerns of the Sierra Club. Among topics covered are: clothing and equipment; making and breaking camp; problem animals and plants; hiking and camping with kids. Listings of conservation and wilderness travel organizations, map and equipment sources, land management agencies, and Internet contacts are appended.
Includes bibliographical references

796.52 Walking and exploring by kind of terrain

Jenkins, Steve
The top of the world; climbing Mount Everest. Houghton Mifflin 1999 unp il $16 (2-4)
                                        796.52
1. Mountaineering 2. Mount Everest (China and Nepal)
ISBN 0-395-94218-7   LC 98-42748
Describes the conditions and terrain of Mount Everest, attempts that have been made to scale this peak, and general information about the equipment and techniques of mountain climbing
"Jenkins' papercut illustrations are extraordinary—feathery light to catch the effect of fog radiating off the mountains, mottled and striated to replicate rocky plateaus, pebbled to look like ice flowers. . . . A very attractive book, with plenty of substance for curious children." Booklist
Includes bibliographical references

Pfetzer, Mark
Within reach: my Everest story; {by} Mark Pfetzer and Jack Galvin. Dutton 1998 224p il pa $7.99 hardcover o.p. (7 and up)   **796.52**
1. Mountaineering 2. Mount Everest (China and Nepal)
ISBN 0-14-130497-9 (pa)   LC 98-29215
Mark Pfetzer describes how he spent his teenage years climbing mountains in the United States, South America, Africa, and Asia, with an emphasis on his two expeditions up Mount Everest
"Throughout the detail-rich, briskly paced account, Pfetzer is psychologically challenging, yet always emotionally within reach." Booklist
Includes glossary

Skreslet, Laurie
To the top of Everest; {by} Laurie Skreslet with Elizabeth MacLeod. Kids Can Press 2001 56p il $16.95; pa $8.95 (4 and up)   **796.52**
1. Mountaineering 2. Mount Everest (China and Nepal)
ISBN 1-55074-721-5; 1-55074-814-9 (pa)
This is an account of Skreslet's "1982 trek up Everest when he became one of the first Canadians to make it to the top. Skreslet takes readers through every exciting, excruciating element of the climb. Beautiful color photographs abound." Booklist
Includes glossary

Venables, Stephen, 1954-
To the top; the story of Everest. Candlewick Press 2003 96p il map $17.99 (5 and up)
                                        796.52
1. Mountaineering 2. Mount Everest (China and Nepal)
ISBN 0-7636-2115-3   LC 2002-41110

Venables, Stephen, 1954-—*Continued*
Describes many of the attempts to scale Mount Everest, including the author's own experiences
"Drawing on the Royal Geographic Society's archives, familiar photos are mixed with some haunting, never-before-published images to illustrate the informed and evocative text." SLJ

796.6　Cycling and related activities

Cotter, Alison, 1963-
Cycling. Lucent Bks. 2002 112p il (History of sports) lib bdg $27.45　　**796.6**
1. Cycling
ISBN 1-590-18071-2　　　　LC 2001-6607
"*Cycling* begins with the invention of the vehicle, describes the evolution of an established sport, and sport stars and scandals. It ends with the latest craze for mountain bikes. . . . The series design is readable, with clear type, black-and-white action photos, and useful sidebars." Booklist
Includes bibliographical references

King, Andy
Play-by-play mountain biking; text and photographs by Andy King. rev ed. Lerner Publs. 2001 63p il pa $7.95　　**796.6**
1. Mountain bikes 2. Cycling
ISBN 0-8225-9879-5　　　　LC 00-8852
First published 1997 with title: Fundamental mountain biking
An introduction to the sport of mountain biking, including an explanation of the required equipment and necessary skills
"There's a wealth of clearly written information in a logical format enhanced by action-packed photos." Book Rep
Includes bibliographical references

Maurer, Tracy, 1965-
BMX freestyle; [by] Tracy Nelson Maurer. Rourke 2002 48p il lib bdg $19.95　　**796.6**
1. Bicycle racing
ISBN 1-58952-102-1　　　　LC 2001-41655
Surveys the history, equipment, techniques, and safety factors of freestyle cross-country bicycle racing
"The writing is accessible to young readers, with a bit of the sports slang thrown in for fun. . . . Sure to be popular." SLJ
Includes glossary and bibliographical references

796.72　Automobile racing

Owens, Tom, 1960-
NASCAR; [by] Thomas S. Owens and Diana Star Helmer. 21st Cent. Bks. (Brookfield) 1999 64p il lib bdg $26.90　　**796.72**
1. Automobile racing
ISBN 0-7613-1374-5　　　　LC 99-10859

Describes the fifty-year history of stock car racing, from its origins at Datona International Speedway in Florida in 1947 to current competitions among such drivers as Jeff Gordon, Dale Jarrett, and Dale Earnhardt
Includes bibliographical references

796.8　Combat sports

Bacho, Peter
Boxing in black and white; a history of the great heavyweight fights. Holt & Co. 1999 122p il $18.95 (7 and up)　　**796.8**
1. Boxing
ISBN 0-8050-5779-X　　　　LC 99-14086
This "look at the intersection between boxing and race relations is part reflection, part standard history, and part sociology. Bacho profiles a number of professional fighters, beginning with 1926 Filipino champ Sammy Santos and ending with the legendary Muhammad Ali." Booklist
Includes bibliographical references

Dallas, Kim
Fundamental karate; photographs by Andy King. Lerner Publs. 1998 64p il (Fundamental sports) lib bdg $22.60　　**796.8**
1. Karate
ISBN 0-8225-3462-2　　　　LC 97-29623
An introduction to the history, skills, and techniques of karate
Includes bibliographical references

Gallagher, Jim, 1969-
The composite guide to wrestling. Chelsea House 1999 64p il (Composite guide) lib bdg $19.65　　**796.8**
1. Wrestling
ISBN 0-7910-4721-0　　　　LC 98-5610
Explores the world of wrestling and how competitors practice it as a time-honored sport
Includes bibliographical references

796.93　Skiing and snowboarding

Lurie, Jon
Fundamental snowboarding; photographs by Jimmy Clarke. Lerner Publs. 1996 64p il (Fundamental sports) lib bdg $22.60
　　796.93
1. Snowboarding
ISBN 0-8225-3457-6　　　　LC 95-11721
Introduces the history and techniques of snowboarding
"The information is solid, and the clear photographs are eye-catching." SLJ
Includes glossary and bibliographical references

Masoff, Joy, 1951-
Snowboard! your guide to freeriding, pipe & park, jibbing, backcountry, alpine, boardercross, and more; illustrations by Jack Dickason. National Geographic Soc. 2002 64p il (Extreme sports) pa $8.95   **796.93**
1. Snowboarding
ISBN 0-7922-6740-0   LC 2001-44392
Describes different kinds of snowboarding—freeriding, in the pipe, jibbing, backcountry—and the techniques, equipment, and terminology involved
"Sharp, action-packed photos and punchy, magazine-style prose add to the appeal. . . . Relaxed, readable, and filled with helpful information." Booklist

McKenna, Lesley
The fantastic book of snow-boarding. Copper Beech Bks. 1998 40p il $10.95; lib bdg $24.40
                                              796.93
1. Snowboarding
ISBN 0-7613-0649-8; 0-7613-0717-6 (lib bdg)
                                  LC 97-35115
This introduction to snowboarding covers "clothing, equipment, instruction for beginners, and a discussion of advanced techniques. There are some nice bonuses including illustrations of how to get on and off a T-bar, an informative examination of snowboard care and repair, and an eight-page fold-out. . . . This is a solid effort." SLJ
Includes glossary

Pollack, Pam
Ski; your guide to cross-country, downhill, jumping, racing, freestyle and more; by Pamela Pollack; illustrations by Jack Dickason. National Geographic Soc. 2001 64p il (Extreme sports) pa $8.95 (7 and up)   **796.93**
1. Skiing
ISBN 0-7922-6738-9   LC 2001-54445
This guide to skiing styles offers "sharp, action-packed photos and punchy, magazine-style prose. . . . Chapters are brief but packed with information for beginners. . . . Relaxed, readable, and filled with helpful information." Booklist

796.962 Ice hockey

Foley, Mike
Fundamental hockey; photographs by Andy King. Lerner Publs. 1996 80p il (Fundamental sports) lib bdg $22.60 (5 and up)
                                              796.962
1. Hockey
ISBN 0-8225-3456-8   LC 95-7077
"A brief history of the sport is followed by an explanation of what players do during hockey practice and what occurs during a game. Finally, readers see some of the drills and variations of the game, such as broomball and sledge hockey, which is played by players with lower-body disabilities. A substantial glossary and list of places to write for more information are appended." SLJ
Includes glossary and bibliographical references

Stewart, Mark
Hockey; a history of the fastest game on ice. Watts 1998 127p il (Watts history of sports) lib bdg $33.50 (7 and up)   **796.962**
1. Hockey
ISBN 0-531-11494-5   LC 98-25039
Discusses the origins and evolution of the game of hockey, as well as memorable events and key personalities in this sport
Includes bibliographical references

Sullivan, George, 1933-
All about hockey; illustrated with photographs and diagrams. Putnam 1998 159p il $15.99 (5 and up)   **796.962**
1. Hockey
ISBN 0-399-23172-2   LC 97-38125
An introduction to the sport of ice hockey, including its history, equipment, techniques, terminology, rules, and players
"This clearly written guide provides a good, solid introduction to the sport." Booklist
Includes glossary and bibliographical references

796.98 Winter Olympic games

Wallechinsky, David, 1948-
The complete book of the Winter Olympics. Overlook Press $25.95; pa $15.95   **796.98**
1. Olympic games
First published 1984. (2005 edition) Periodically revised
"Contains national medal totals in each Olympics, and a brief history of the Winter Games. Sports are considered in separate sections, with full information on each event, lists winners (with times, scores, etc.) by year, usually with commentary on specific contests and notes on the contestants. Some sections include a glossary of terms for the particular sport. Includes discontinued events." Guide to Ref Books. 11th edition

797.1 Boating

George, Charles, 1949-
White-water rafting; by Charles and Linda George. Riverfront Bks. 1999 48p il (Sports alive!) lib bdg $21.26 hardcover o.p.   **797.1**
1. Rafting (Sports)
ISBN 0-7368-0055-7   LC 98-7188
Describes the history, equipment, and techniques of white water rafting
Includes bibliographical references

798.2 Horsemanship

Davis, Caroline
The young equestrian. Firefly Bks. (Buffalo) 2000 128p il pa $19.95 hardcover o.p.
                                              798.2

Davis, Caroline—*Continued*
1. Horsemanship
ISBN 1-55209-484-7
In this guide to horsemanship, "there are chapters devoted to riding aids and techniques and choosing schools and proper equipment. Davis also discusses buying and caring for a horse and competitions." Booklist
The author "covers the fundamentals of riding in an easily understood, step-by-step manner, illustrating each segment with photos and simple drawings that add to the reader's comprehension." Voice Youth Advocates

798.8   Dog racing

Paulsen, Gary
Winterdance; the fine madness of running the Iditarod. Harcourt Brace & Co. 1994 256p il $26; pa $15   **798.8**
1. Iditarod Trail Sled Dog Race, Alaska 2. Sled dog racing
ISBN 0-15-126227-6; 0-15-600145-4 (pa)
LC 93-42096
"This book is primarily an account of Paulsen's first Iditarod and its frequent life-threatening disasters. . . . However, the book is more than a tabulation of tribulations; it is a meditation on the extraordinary attraction this race holds for some men and women." Libr J

Wood, Ted, 1965-
Iditarod dream; Dusty and his sled dogs compete in Alaska's Jr. Iditarod. Walker & Co. 1996 48p il map $17.95; pa $8.95 (4 and up)
798.8
1. Sled dog racing
ISBN 0-8027-8406-2; 0-8027-7535-7 (pa)
LC 95-31084
This "photo essay follows 15-year-old Dusty Whittemore of Cantwell, AK, through the 1995 Jr. Iditarod Sled Dog Race—158 miles from Lake Lucille to Yentna and back." SLJ
"Clear, close-up color photographs portray every stage of the event and offer interesting information about the difficulties and hazards of this two-day competition." Booklist

799.1   Fishing

Fitzgerald, Ron
Essential fishing for teens. Children's Press 2000 48p il (Outdoor life) lib bdg $22; pa $6.95
799.1
1. Fishing
ISBN 0-516-23355-6 (lib bdg); 0-516-23555-9 (pa)
LC 00-23359
Presents information about fishing, including an explanation of the different types of fishing, the equipment needed, and safety tips
"The clear, full-color photographs depict adults of both genders." SLJ
Includes glossary and bibliographical references

800   LITERATURE

803   Literature--Encyclopedias and dictionaries

Benet's reader's encyclopedia. HarperCollins Pubs. $50   **803**
1. Literature—Dictionaries
First published 1948 under the editorship of William Rose Benet. (4th edition 1996). Periodically revised
Current editor: Bruce Murphy
This encyclopedia contains over 10,000 entries and covers world literature from early times to the present. Includes entries on authors, literary movements, principal characters, plot synopses, terms, awards, myths and legends, etc.

Brewer's dictionary of phrase and fable. HarperResource $50 $50   **803**
1. Literature—Dictionaries 2. Allusions
First published 1870. (16th edition 2000) Periodically revised
Current editor: Adrian Room
"Over 15,000 brief entries give the meanings and origins of a broad range of terms, expressions, and names of real, fictitious and mythical characters from world history, science, the arts and literature." N Y Public Libr. Ref Books for Child Collect. 2d edition

808   Rhetoric

Dragisic, Patricia
How to write a letter. Watts 1998 127p (Speak out, write on! book) lib bdg $23 hardcover o.p. (7 and up)   **808**
1. Letter writing
ISBN 0-531-15931-0   LC 97-35265
Describes the basic parts of many types of business and personal letters, offers examples of each kind, and suggests ways to write effectively for particular situations
This "is filled with easy-to-understand, useful information. . . . There is a definite need for this book in most collections." SLJ
Includes bibliographical references

Fletcher, Ralph, 1953-
How writers work; finding a process that works for you. HarperTrophy 2000 114p pa $4.99 (4 and up)   **808**
1. Authorship 2. Creative writing
ISBN 0-380-79702-X   LC 00-27573
Focuses on the skills and techniques necessary for good writing, with excerpts from established writers and samples of young people's work as examples
"The book makes youngsters feel good about their writing without making light of the work involved. . . . This is a useful resource." SLJ
Includes bibliographical references

Henderson, Kathy
The young writer's guide to getting published. Writer's Digest Bks. 2001 246p pa $18.99
808
1. Authorship—Handbooks, manuals, etc.
ISBN 1-58297-057-2   LC 2001-26176
Replaces The market guide for young writers
Provides publishing information for the young writer including tips on preparing a manuscript, profiles of published young writers, opportunities online, and market and contest listings

James, Elizabeth
How to write terrific book reports; {by} Elizabeth James and Carol Barkin. rev ed. Lothrop, Lee & Shepard Bks. 1998 80p (School survival guide) pa $4.95 hardcover o.p. (4 and up)
808
1. Report writing 2. Books—Reviews
ISBN 0-688-16140-5   LC 98-9198
First published 1986 with title: How to write your best book report
"The authors explore what a book report is, how to choose a title, writing preliminary and final drafts, giving an oral presentation, the importance of the library in finding material, and other aspects of this common assignment." SLJ

Janeczko, Paul B., 1945-
Writing winning reports and essays. Scholastic Reference 2003 224p (Scholastic guides) lib bdg $16.95; pa $7.95   **808**
1. Authorship 2. Report writing
ISBN 0-439-28717-0 (lib bdg); 0-439-28718-9 (pa)
LC 2002-30543
Provides strategies for writing successful research reports and essays, including social studies reports, book reports, persuasive essays, personal essays, and descriptive essays
"A solid and useful resource." SLJ

Nuwer, Hank
To the young writer; nine writers talk about their craft. Watts 2002 111p il lib bdg $23
808
1. Authorship 2. Authors, American
ISBN 0-531-11591-7   LC 2001-24895
Nine writers, including a Hollywood screenwriter, a novelist, and a sportswriter, talk about their craft
"A concise, practical, and accessible guide. . . . A range of topics is discussed including the thrill of reporting, editing, storytelling, and writing for student publications, different audiences, and from personal experience. Also included are tips for aspiring writers. . . . This inspiring book offers a number of options for those considering the field." SLJ
Includes bibliographical references

Shields, Nancy E., 1928-
Where credit is due; a guide to proper citing of sources, print and nonprint; {by} Nancy E. Shields, with the assistance of Mary E. Uhle. 2nd ed. Scarecrow Press 1997 189p $41.50 (7 and up)
808
1. Bibliographical citations 2. Research
ISBN 0-8108-3211-9   LC 96-6523
First published 1985
"This book is a style guide for students to properly document the vast array of sources for the research paper. It includes every possible source that could be used as a reference with examples of footnotes and bibliography entries. . . . This book is exactly what the librarian needs to provide students with up-to-date styles for documentation in their writing." Book Rep

Sullivan, Helen
Research reports; a guide for middle and high school students; by Helen Sullivan and Linda Sernoff. Millbrook Press 1996 127p lib bdg $24.90 (7 and up)   **808**
1. Report writing 2. Research
ISBN 1-56294-694-3   LC 95-21489
Also available in paperback from Copper Beech Books
This guide to report writing takes "students step by step through the process, from selecting a topic to researching, note-taking, interviewing, writing and editing, using graphics, and compiling a bibliography. Chapters are clear, short, readable, and sprinkled with examples of interest to teens." SLJ
Includes glossary and bibliographical references

Trueit, Trudi Strain
Keeping a journal; Trudi Strain Trueit. F. Watts 2004 80p (Life balance) $19.50 (5 and up)
808
1. Diaries 2. Authorship
ISBN 0-531-12262-X   LC 2003-25290
Contents: Navigating the journey; Why journal?; Time travel; Getting started; Write now! A 30-day journal
"Trueit features examples . . . to spark the imaginations of young people eager to express their unique views. Tips on how to begin, exercises designed to help overcome writer's block, and a 30-day calendar of creative ideas to get started are included. . . . The enthusiastic tone, inspirational examples, and writing prompts will help even those reluctant to express themselves to pick up a pen or pencil." SLJ
Includes bibliographical references

Young, Sue
Writing with style. Scholastic Ref. 1997 143p (Scholastic guides) hardcover o.p. paperback available $8.95 (5 and up)   **808**
1. Authorship 2. Creative writing
ISBN 0-590-25424-3 (pa)   LC 96-8772
Presents tips for writing interesting stories, passionate essays, and exciting reports, focusing on the elements of sentence structure, paragraph organization, grammar, usage, punctuation, and footnotes

Young, Sue—*Continued*
"The book is easy to comprehend, upbeat, and relevant. A must for library shelves and classrooms." SLJ
Includes bibliographical references

808.06   Writing children's literature

Peck, Richard, 1934-
Invitations to the world; teaching and writing for the young. Dial Bks. 2002 204p $16.99
808.06
1. Authorship 2. Books and reading 3. Young adult literature—Technique
ISBN 0-8037-2734-8   LC 2001-53691
First published 1994 by Delacorte Press with title: Love and death at the mall
"Peck puts down his thoughts on writing for young people and reminisces about the inspiration behind his books and his motivation to become an author. . . . The earlier version of this book addressed two questions: 'How did you get your start?' and 'Where do you get your ideas?' Here Peck adds a chapter to answer the question, 'How much longer are you going to write?'. . . Also new to this edition is a section at the end of the book called For Sharing that includes advice to encourage reading and discussion questions for novels." Voice Youth Advocates
Includes bibliographical references

808.1   Rhetoric of poetry

Fletcher, Ralph, 1953-
Poetry matters; writing a poem from the inside out. HarperCollins Pubs. 2002 142p lib bdg $15.89; pa $4.99 (4 and up)   **808.1**
1. Poetics
ISBN 0-06-623599-5 (lib bdg); 0-380-79703-8 (pa)
LC 2001-24640
"Chapters deal with images; creating 'music,' or sounds and rhythms; how to generate ideas for poems; the construction of the words on the page; and more. Tips on fine-tuning are also given. . . . Major poetic forms are defined, including haiku, ode, and free verse, and there is a section on ways to share your work. Interspersed are Fletcher's personal insights and interviews with three poets—Kristine O'Connell George, Janet S. Wong, and J. Patrick Lewis. . . . Since this thought-provoking book covers more of the internal, less-tangible aspects of poetry, it may be more suited for readers who have some experience with the genre." SLJ
Includes bibliographical references

Janeczko, Paul B., 1945-
How to write poetry. Scholastic Ref. 1999 117p il (Scholastic guides) pa $8.95 hardcover o.p. (5 and up)   **808.1**
1. Poetics
ISBN 0-590-10078-5   LC 98-26866
Provides practical advice with checklists on the art of writing poetry
"A friendly, accessible, and highly usable primer." Horn Book Guide
Includes glossary and bibliographical references

Poetry from A to Z; a guide for young writers; compiled by Paul B. Janeczko; illustrated by Cathy Bobak. Bradbury Press 1994 131p il $16.95 (5 and up)   **808.1**
1. Poetics 2. American poetry—Collections
ISBN 0-02-747672-3   LC 94-10528
"In his guide, Janeczko gives many examples and ideas to get young writers started writing poetry. The book is organized alphabetically with seventy-two poems on almost any topic you could imagine. In addition, fourteen exercises labeled 'Try This' explain how to write different types of poems and help a young writer get started." Voice Youth Advocates
Includes bibliographical references

Seeing the blue between; advice and inspiration for young poets; compiled by Paul B. Janeczko. Candlewick Press 2002 132p $18.99 (7 and up)   **808.1**
1. Poetics 2. American poetry—Collections
ISBN 0-7636-0881-5   LC 2001-25882
"Here, thirty-two established poets share their writing secrets in short letters addressed directly to the readers. Although each poet has a distinct voice . . . a familiar mantra quickly develops: read, observe, love words, write, rewrite. . . . Accompanying poems may connect directly to a letter's content, give a representative sample of an individual's body of work, or impart advice." Horn Book
"The letters are personal, friendly, and supportive. . . . A valuable addition to public and school libraries, with the potential for much classroom and personal use." SLJ
Includes index

808.2   Rhetoric of drama

Lawrence, Colton, 1968-
Big fat paycheck; a young person's guide to writing for the movies. Bantam Bks. 2004 269p il $11.99; pa $8.99   **808.2**
1. Motion picture plays—Technique
ISBN 0-553-13122-2; 0-553-13122-2 (pa)
The author addresses "the major concerns that beginning screenplay writers face—finding a voice, formatting, developing a concept and characters, plotting, rewriting, polishing, and shopping a completed script." Voice Youth Advocates
"A lively, compelling, and concisely concrete guide for creative kids with big-screen dreams." SLJ

808.3   Rhetoric of fiction

Bauer, Marion Dane, 1938-
Our stories; a fiction workshop for young authors; compiled and with commentary by Marion Dane Bauer. Clarion Bks. 1996 195p $16; pa $6.95 (5 and up)   **808.3**
1. Authorship 2. Creative writing
ISBN 0-395-81598-3; 0-395-81599-1 (pa)
LC 95-51091

Bauer, Marion Dane, 1938-—*Continued*
The author presents a selection of short fiction written by students in grades four through twelve and then critiques each piece
"This book would be an excellent resource for teachers looking for a new approach to the writing process. . . . Anyone who enjoys writing cannot help but be inspired by the remarkable talent of these young authors, and by Bauer's friendly, encouraging and helpful advice." Voice Youth Advocates

What's your story? a young person's guide to writing fiction. Clarion Bks. 1992 134p pa $7.95 hardcover o.p. (5 and up)   **808.3**
1. Authorship 2. Creative writing
ISBN 0-395-57780-2   LC 91-3816
Discusses how to write fiction, exploring such aspects as character, plot, point of view, dialogue, endings, and revising
"Bauer reveals the somber reality that writing can be hard work, though worth the effort for those who persevere. What follows is a clear, concise elucidation on the elements of fiction. . . . Bauer has taken a thorough, clear, and functional approach to this topic." Horn Book

Harrison, David L. (David Lakin)
Writing stories; fantastic fiction from start to finish. Scholastic Reference 2004 126p (Scholastic guides) $16.95; pa $7.99 (4 and up)
                                            808.3
1. Authorship 2. Creative writing
ISBN 0-439-51914-4; 0-439-51915-2 (pa)
"Harrison begins by breaking down the elements of a story and giving concrete examples for young writers to make their own. He offers basic descriptions and tools for genre writing and careful instructions on revision and rewriting. . . . Expect children to begin their writer's journal . . . immediately." Booklist

808.5   Rhetoric of speech

Otfinoski, Steven, 1949-
Speaking up, speaking out; a kid's guide to making speeches, oral reports, and conversation; illustrated by Carol Nicklaus. Millbrook Press 1996 79p il lib bdg $24.90 (5 and up)
                                            808.5
1. Public speaking
ISBN 1-56294-345-6 (lib bdg)   LC 96-509
Provides strategies and encouraging tips for speaking in social situations, reading aloud, presenting oral reports, and making speeches of all kinds
"This appealing handbook provides youngsters with just about everything they need to know about oral communication. . . . Nicklaus's cartoon illustrations are appropriately lighthearted, adding touches of humor to the text." SLJ
Includes glossary and bibliographical references

808.8   Literature--Collections

Beware!; R.L. Stine picks his favorite scary stories. HarperCollins Pubs. 2002 214p il $11.99; lib bdg $14.89 (4 and up)
                                            808.8
1. Horror fiction 2. Literature—Collections
ISBN 0-06-623842-0; 0-06-623843-9 (lib bdg)
                                         LC 2002-18938
"A Parachute Press book"
Stine "brings together 19 brief stories, folktales, poems, and cartoons from the likes of Ray Bradbury, William Sleator, Robert W. Service . . . Gahan Wilson, and Alvin Schwartz. . . . There's something in this diverse literary buffet for every taste—including enough genuine eeriness to make it a discomfiting choice for under-the-covers reading." Booklist

The **Green** Man: tales from the mythic forest; edited by Ellen Datlow & Terri Windling; introduction by Terri Windling; decorations by Charles Vess. Viking 2002 384p $18.99; pa $8.99 (7 and up)   **808.8**
1. Literature—Collections 2. Fantasy fiction
ISBN 0-670-03526-2; 0-14-240029-7 (pa)
                                         LC 2001-46976
"The stories are thematically connected yet tonally varied, and each strongly plotted tale conjures a credible fantasy world. A brief biography of and remarks by the writer are included with each story. . . . This title will be eagerly devoured." Bull Cent Child Books

Hudson, Wade
Powerful words; more than 200 years of extraordinary writing by African Americans; illustrated by Sean Qualls ; foreword by Marian Wright Edelman. Scholastic Nonfiction 2004 178p il $19.95 (5 and up)   **808.8**
1. American literature—African American authors 2. African Americans—Biography 3. African Americans—History
ISBN 0-439-40969-1   LC 2003-42792
A collection of speeches and writings by African Americans, with commentary about the time period in which each person lived, information about the speaker/writer, and public response to the words.
"Short enough to hold attention, the selections . . . are also long enough to show the writers' tone and style. Many sensitive full-page portraits are included. . . . This well-designed volume will be an excellent addition to many library collections. " Booklist
Includes bibliographical references

Leaving home: stories; selected by Hazel Rochman and Darlene Z. McCampbell. HarperCollins Pubs. 1997 231p pa $11 hardcover o.p.   **808.8**
1. Youth—Fiction 2. Short stories
ISBN 0-06-440706-3   LC 96-28979
An international anthology that reflects the thoughts and feelings of young people as they make their way into the world. Authors represented include Amy Tan, Sandra Cisneros, Tim Wynne-Jones, and Toni Morrison

Leaving home: stories—*Continued*

"The editors have varied the tones, the music, the voices, and the meanings of the pieces, which provide both humorous and heartbreaking stories of the meaning of adolescence." ALAN

Night is gone, day is still coming; stories and poems by American Indian teens and young adults; edited by Annette Pina Ochoa, Betsy Franco, and Traci L. Gourdine; with an introduction by Simon J. Ortiz. Candlewick Press 2003 145p $16.99 (7 and up)

808.8

1. American literature—Native American authors—Collections 2. Youths' writings
ISBN 0-7636-1518-8   LC 2002-74086

"In poems and short stories, young Indian writers, ages 11 to 22, tell about their lives on the reservations, in small towns, and in large cities." Booklist

"These are honest voices in a well-organized anthology that gives an excellent look into an important American culture." SLJ

Read all about it! great read-aloud stories, poems, and newspaper pieces for preteens and teens; edited by Jim Trelease. Penguin Bks. 1993 489p il pa $13.95   **808.8**

1. Young adult literature 2. Literature—Collections 3. Authors
ISBN 0-14-014655-5   LC 93-21781

This is a collection of 52 selections of fiction, poetry, and nonfiction from newspapers, magazines, and books by such authors as Cynthia Rylant, Jerry Spinelli, Howard Pyle, Rudyard Kipling, Robert W. Service, Maya Angelou, Moss Hart, Pete Hamill, and Leon Garfield. Includes biographical information about the authors

Teen sunshine reflections; words for the heart and soul; [compiled by] June Cotner. HarperCollins Pubs. 2002 187p $15.95; pa $9.95

808.8

1. Conduct of life 2. Literature—Collections
ISBN 0-06-000525-4; 0-06-000527-0 (pa)
LC 2001-51739

An interfaith collection of poems, prayers, and reflections that address challenges faced by teens, and that includes words from Mother Teresa, Mahatma Gandhi, the Dalai Lama, and teenaged authors

"Organized thematically, the selections address real-life topics relevant to the adolescent experience. . . . The result is a balanced collection that successfully fulfills Cotner's intent to harness the talents and positive energy of contemporary teens." Voice Youth Advocates

808.81   Poetry--Collections

The **Body** eclectic; an anthology of poems; edited by Patrice Vecchione. Holt & Co. 2002 192p $16.95 (7 and up)   **808.81**

1. Poetry—Collections
ISBN 0-8050-6935-6   LC 2001-51900

This collection of poetry focuses on the human body and its parts, including works by poets such as Gary Soto, Shel Silverstein, Paul Laurence Dunbar, Pablo

Neruda, Walt Whitman and Shakespeare

"Excellent notes at the back introduce each writer and suggest more books to read. A great collection to show teens that literature is about their intimate selves and their connections with people everywhere." Booklist
Includes bibliographical references

I feel a little jumpy around you; a book of her poems & his poems collected in pairs; {by} Naomi Shihab Nye and Paul B. Janeczko. Simon & Schuster Bks. for Young Readers 1996 256p pa $10 hardcover o.p. (7 and up)

808.81

1. Poetry—Collections
ISBN 0-689-81341-4   LC 95-44904

A collection of poems, by male and female authors, presented in pairings that offer insight into how men and women look at the world, both separately and together

"Though the gender counterpoint really plays little part in the juxtaposition, the pairings are piquant and provide a manageable way to start talking about a very large collection of poetry. An engaging marginal dialogue, taken from Nye's and Janeczko's collaborative fax correspondence, appears alongside the appendix and permits a revealing peek behind the scences. Highly readable notes from contributors are included, as is an index of poems and a gender-segregated index of poets." Bull Cent Child Books

I wouldn't thank you for a valentine; poems for young feminists; edited by Carol Ann Duffy; illustrated by Trisha Rafferty. Holt & Co. 1993 104p il pa $6.95 hardcover o.p.   **808.81**

1. Feminism—Poetry 2. Poetry—Collections
ISBN 0-8050-5545-2   LC 93-3172

First published 1992 in the United Kingdom

A collection of poems by women from different cultures and backgrounds, portraying the varied facets of the female experience from childhood to old age

"The anthology draws on poets from many cultures and includes well-known poets, such as Nikki Giovani, Sharon Olds, and Mary Oliver, as well as several new voices. . . . These poems open up the range of love and family." Booklist

Index to children's poetry; a title, subject, author, and first line index to poetry in collections for children and youth; compiled by John E. and Sara W. Brewton. Wilson, H.W. 1942-1965 3v

808.81

1. Poetry—Indexes

Basic volume published 1942 $105 (ISBN 0-8242-0021-7); first supplement published 1954 $75 (ISBN 0-8242-0022-5); second supplement published 1965 $75 (ISBN 0-8242-0023-3)

The main volume indexes 15,000 poems by 2,500 authors in 130 collections. The two supplements analyze another 15,000 poems by 2700 authors in 151 collections

"This tool is an invaluable reference source." Peterson. Ref Books for Child

Index to poetry for children and young people; a title, subject, author, and first line index to poetry in collections for children and young people. Wilson, H.W. 1972-1998 6v

808.81

Index to poetry for children and young people—*Continued*

1. Poetry—Indexes

A continuation of Index to children's poetry

The volume published 1972 covering 1964-1969 compiled by John E. and Sara W. Brewton and G. Meredith Blackburn III $95 (ISBN 0-8242-0435-2); 1970-1975 published 1978 compiled by John E. Brewton, G. Meredith Blackburn III and Lorraine A. Blackburn $95 (ISBN 0-8242-0621-5); 1976-1981 published 1984 compiled by John E. Brewton, G. Meredith Blackburn III and Lorraine A. Blackburn $95 (ISBN 0-8242-0681-9); 1982-1987 published 1989 compiled by G. Meredith Blackburn III and Lorraine A. Blackburn $100 (ISBN 0-8242-0773-4); 1988-1992 published 1994 compiled by G. Meredith Blackburn III $100 (ISBN 0-8242-0861-7); 1993-1997 published 1998 compiled by G. Meredith Blackburn III $105 (ISBN 0-8242-0939-7)

Each volume analyzes approximately 10,000 poems by some 2,000 authors in more than 110 collections. Over 2,000 subject headings are used in each volume

It's a woman's world; a century of women's voices in poetry; edited by Neil Philip. Dutton Children's Bks. 2000 93p il $17.99 (7 and up)
808.81

1. Poetry—Collections 2. Women poets

ISBN 0-525-46328-3   LC 99-88363

An anthology of poetry by twentieth-century women from around the world including, Sylvia Plath, Nigar Hanim, Sonia Sanchez, and Nellie Wong

"Beautifully reproduced black-and-white photos introduce each section. Overall, this book is dense, challenging, and provocative." SLJ

Light-gathering poems; edited by Liz Rosenberg. Holt & Co. 2000 146p $15.95 (7 and up)
808.81

1. Poetry—Collections

ISBN 0-8050-6223-8   LC 99-49231

Companion volume to Earth-shattering poems (1997)

"Poems were chosen for their ability to 'gather light,' some representing beauty, some joy, some fascinating imagery, and some the illusive light at the end of a dark tunnel. . . . Notable writers such as Robert Frost, Walt Whitman, Langston Hughes, Edna St. Vincent Millay, Emily Dickinson, and Allen Ginsberg share the spotlight with contemporaries such as Gary Soto, Kate Schmitt, Mary Oliver, Steven Dauer, and Henry M. Seiden." Voice Youth Advocates

Includes bibliographical references

The **Oxford** book of war poetry; chosen and edited by John Stallworthy. Oxford Univ. Press 1984 xxxi, 358p $31.95; pa $16.95
808.81

1. War poetry 2. Poetry—Collections

ISBN 0-19-214125-2; 0-19-280454-5 (pa)
          LC 83-19303

"This comprehensive anthology focuses on poetic treatment of warfare ranging from the battlefields of ancient history to the conflicts in Vietnam, Northern Ireland, and El Salvador." Univ Press Books for Second Sch Libr

This collection "reminds one of the large numbers and great variety of war poems from many centuries that are very good poems. Mr. Stallworthy's selections include most of the best, at least the best in English." N Y Times Book Rev

Includes bibliographical references

Revenge and forgiveness; an anthology of poems; edited by Patrice Vecchione. Henry Holt 2004 148p $16.95 (7 and up)
808.81

1. Poetry—Collections

ISBN 0-8050-7376-0   LC 2003-56631

A collection of nearly sixty poems dealing with revenge and forgiveness, plus suggested readings about each contributing poet

"For students who are of a philosophical bent and for teachers of poetry, this book of poems about love, hate, and war will be a useful resource." Libr Media Connect

Includes bibliographical references

The **Space** between our footsteps; poems and paintings from the Middle East; selected by Naomi Shihab Nye. Simon & Schuster Bks. for Young Readers 1998 144p il maps $19.95 (7 and up)
808.81

1. Poetry—Collections 2. Middle East—Poetry

ISBN 0-689-81233-7   LC 97-18622

"Lyrical verse about family, friendship, nature, and daily life makes up this collection of poems from 19 countries in the Middle East, with gloriously colored paintings in a wide range of styles." Booklist

Step lightly; poems for the journey; collected by Nancy Willard. Harcourt Brace & Co. 1998 99p pa $12 hardcover o.p. (7 and up)
808.81

1. Poetry—Collections

ISBN 0-15-202052-7   LC 98-5228

A collection of poems celebrating the ordinary in an unordinary way, by such authors as Emily Dickinson, Theodore Roethke, and D. H. Lawrence

"Willard weaves an anthology in which readers can find happiness, insight, inspiration, and wisdom." SLJ

Truth & lies: an anthology of poems; edited by Patrice Vecchione. Holt & Co. 2000 142p $17 (7 and up)
808.81

1. Poetry—Collections

ISBN 0-8050-6479-6   LC 00-38871

"In this multicultural anthology of poetry about truth and lies, editor Vecchione has gathered a wide-ranging, impressive assortment of poets—from classic to modern, from well-known to obscure, from Yehuda Amichai and Janet S. Wong to Sir Walter Raleigh." Booklist

This is a "quietly moving and intimate anthology." SLJ

Voices: poetry and art from around the world; selected by Barbara Brenner. National Geographic Soc. 2000 96p il $18.95
808.81

1. Poetry—Collections

ISBN 0-7922-7071-1   LC 00-20232

In this anthology "the arrangement is by continent. The large-size pages include poetry, much of it in trans-

Voices: poetry and art from around the world—*Continued*

lation, and beautifully reproduced full-color art from each region. . . . Many of the selections are compelling, beautiful in their particulars and universal in their reach. . . . With each selection there are brief facts about the artist, poet, or translator, as well as the culture and history of the place. The open design will attract browsers, and the geographical focus will make this an excellent tool for teachers across the curriculum." Booklist

War and the pity of war; edited by Neil Philip; illustrated by Michael McCurdy. Clarion Bks. 1998 96p il $20 (5 and up)   **808.81**
1. War poetry 2. Poetry—Collections
ISBN 0-395-84982-9   LC 97-32897
"The selections, covering conflicts from ancient Persia to modern-day Bosnia, are by a wide variety of poets, from the well known (Tennyson, Whitman, Sandburg, Auden), to the obscure (Anakreon from ancient Greece and 11th-century Chinese poet Bunno). . . . The stark and simple scratchboard drawings are reminiscent of the Ernie Pyle illustrations from World War II and are as memorable as the best propaganda." SLJ

What have you lost? poems; selected by Naomi Shihab Nye; photographs by Michael Nye. Greenwillow Bks. 1999 pa $9.99 hardcover o.p. (7 and up)   **808.81**
1. Poetry—Collections 2. Loss (Psychology)
ISBN 0-380-73307-2   LC 98-26674
In her "introduction, the anthologist-poet considers loss—its certainty, scope, and effect, and its ability to give rise to art. The topic is thoroughly explored by the one hundred and forty poets whose work is collected here in twenty-two unlabeled, thematically arranged sections. . . . The poets are all contemporary, with a dozen or so hailing from outside the United States." Horn Book
Includes index

808.82   Drama--Collections

The **Book** of monologues for aspiring actors; {edited by} Marsh Cassady. NTC Pub. Group 1995 212p il pa $$23.96 (7 and up)
                                           808.82
1. Monologues 2. Acting
ISBN 0-8442-5771-0   LC 94-66239
"The selections range from the classical Greeks to Sam Shepard and Oscar Wilde; they give YA's the opportunity to develop characters of like ages in many different settings. Several questions to probe the actors' imaginations appear at the end of each monologue." SLJ

Great scenes for young actors from the stage; Craig Slaight, Jack Sharrar, editors. Smith & Kraus 1991 2v v1 pa $11.95; v2 pa $14.95
                                           808.82
1. Drama—Collections 2. Acting
ISBN 0-9622722-6-4 (v1); 1-57525-107-8 (v2)
v2 has title: Great scenes for young actors
Contains scenes from classic and contemporary plays. The selections, graded according to ability level, include a range of roles for men, women, and groups. Includes a brief synopsis of each play along with special notes

Karp, Rashelle Schlessinger
Plays for children and young adults; an evaluative index and guide; {by} Rashelle S. Karp, June H. Schlessinger; editorial staff, Bernard S. Schlessinger {et al.}. Garland 1991 580p (Garland reference lib. of social science) $78
                                           808.82
1. Drama—Indexes
ISBN 0-8240-6112-8   LC 90-44195
Available: Plays for children and young adults, Supplement 1, 1989-1994 $120 (ISBN 0-8153-1493-0)
"This index provides evaluative information about 3,560 plays that may be produced by or for young people, ages 5 to 18. Coverage includes plays, choral readings, scenes, musical reviews, readers' theater, and skits published either separately or in collections between 1975 and February 1989." Booklist
"On balance, the reader will get a very clear idea of the practicality of producing any play found in this volume. . . . Professionals in libraries, schools, and theaters will find this a valuable resource indeed." J Youth Serv Libr

808.83   Fiction--Collections

Short story index. Wilson, H.W. $210 per year
                                           808.83
1. Short stories—Indexes
ISSN 0360-9774
                                           LC 75-649762
Also available Short story index: collections indexed 1900-1978 $135 (ISBN 0-8242-0643-6); Also available online version
Basic volume edited by Dorothy E. Cook and Isabel S. Monro published 1953 $210 (ISBN 0-8242-0384-4); Supplementary volumes: 1950-1954 edited by Dorothy E. Cook and Estelle A. Fidell $210 (ISBN 0-8242-0385-2); 1955-1958 edited by Estelle A. Fidell and Esther V. Flory $210 (ISBN 0-8242-0386-0); 1959-1963 edited by Estelle A. Fidell $210 (ISBN 0-8242-0387-9); 1964-1968 edited by Estelle A. Fidell $210 (ISBN 0-8242-0399-2); 1969-1973 edited by Estelle A. Fidell $210 (ISBN 0-8242-0497-2); 1974-1978 edited by Gary L. Bogart $210; 1979-1983 edited by Juliette Yaakov $210; 1984-1988 edited by Juliette Yaakov $210; 1989-1993 edited by John Greenfieldt and Juliette Yaakov $210; 1994-1998 edited by John Greenfieldt and Juliette Yaakov $210. Beginning 1974 issued annually with five-year cumulations
This index offers a single-alphabet listing of stories by author, title and subject. The List of collections indexed provides full bibliographic information. Includes a Directory of periodicals
"These indexes provide valuable access to short stories in collections published since 1900." Ref Sources for Small & Medium-sized Libr. 6th edition

808.85   Speeches--Collections

Lend me your ears; great speeches in history; selected and introduced by William Safire. rev and expanded ed. Norton 1997 1,055p $39.95
                                           808.85
1. Speeches
ISBN 0-393-05931-6   LC 96-43423

Lend me your ears—*Continued*
First published 1992
Pope Urban II, Bob Dole, Cicero, Jesus, Boris Yeltsin, Richard Nixon and Colin Powell are among the orators represented in this anthology of over 200 speeches grouped chronologically into thematic categories

808.88 Collections of miscellaneous writings

Bartlett, John, 1820-1905
Familiar quotations. Little, Brown $50 $50
808.88
1. Quotations
First published 1855. (17th edition 2003) Periodically revised. Editors vary
"Arranged chronologically by author, with exact references. Includes many interesting footnotes, tracing history or usage of analogous thoughts, the circumstances under which a particular remark was made, etc. Author and keyword indexes. One of the best books of quotations with a long history." Guide to Ref Books. 11th edition

Burleigh, Robert, 1936-
Who said that? famous Americans speak; illustrations by David Catrow. Holt & Co. 1997 45p il $16.95
808.88
1. Quotations
ISBN 0-8050-4394-2   LC 96-19985
A collection of quotations along with the story behind the words and the people who voiced them

Stretch your wings; famous black quotations for teens; selected and edited by Janet Cheatham Bell and Lucille Usher Freeman. Little, Brown 1999 150p pa $9.99 (7 and up)
808.88
1. African Americans—Quotations
ISBN 0-316-03825-3   LC 99-13045
A collection of black quotations and African proverbs, arranged in such categories as: Knowing Who I Am, Family: Joy or Nightmare, Making Better Choices, What about Racism, and Hold Fast to Dreams
"The more than 400 quotes have been garnered from successful athletes, writers, entrepreneurs, musicians, models, comics, civil rights activists, politicians, and educators. While citations for the quotes are not included, each contributor is briefly profiled in a biographical index. This compilation invites browsing and reflection." SLJ

809 Literary history and criticism

Masterpieces of world literature; edited by Frank N. Magill. Harper & Row 1989 957p $55
809
1. Literature—History and criticism
ISBN 0-06-270050-2   LC 89-45052
"The work, arranged alphabetically by title, contains plot summaries, character portrayals, and critical evalua-

tions of 270 classics of world literature (novels, plays, stories, poems, and essays), all reprints from other Magill guides." Nichols. Guide to Ref Books for Sch Media Cent. 4th edition

809.3 Fiction--History and criticism

Short stories for students; presenting analysis, context, and criticism on commonly studied short stories; Kathleen Wilson, Editor. Gale Res. 1997 2v il ea $55
809.3
1. Short stories—History and criticism
ISBN 0-7876-1690-7 (v1); 0-7876-1691-5 (v2)
LC 98-153009
"Each volume contains entries for 20 stories arranged alphabetically by title. . . . Each entry includes a brief biographical sketch of the writer; a plot summary; descriptions of characters; a discussion of the major themes and style (use of irony, symbolism, points of view, etc.); an introduction to the historical and cultural period during which the story was written; a critical overview; and an essay written for this resource along with excerpts from the work of other critics." SLJ

810.3 American literature-- Encyclopedias and dictionaries

McElmeel, Sharron L.
100 most popular children's authors; biographical sketches and bibliographies. Libraries Unlimited 1999 xxxi, 493p il (Popular authors series) $55
810.3
1. Children's literature Bio bibliography
ISBN 1-56308-646-8   LC 98-41942
"Based on a 1997 survey of both teachers and students, this volume includes such well-known authors as Beverly Clearly (most recognized by the survey respondents) and classic writers like Lewis Carroll and C. S. Lewis. Each entry provides several pages about the author and his or her writings followed by a section called 'Books and Notes,' which has details about specific books and their themes, including bibliographic information. A list of additional material about or by the author completes each entry." Booklist

810.8 American literature-- Collections

33 things every girl should know; stories, songs, poems, and smart talk by 33 extraordinary women; edited by Tonya Bolden. Crown 1998 159p il pa $13 hardcover o.p. (7 and up)
810.8
1. Girls 2. American literature—Collections
ISBN 0-517-70936-8   LC 97-29431
A mix of short stories, essays, a comic strip, a speech, an interview, poems, and more which offer insights and advice for girls
"Astute, compassionate, sometimes witty, sometimes painfully honest, the pieces are highly readable, entertaining, and educational." Booklist

911: the book of help; edited by Michael Cart; with Marianne Carus and Marc Aronson. Cricket Bks. 2002 178p $17.95; pa $9.95 **810.8**

1. September 11 terrorist attacks, 2001 2. Terrorism 3. American literature—Collections
ISBN 0-8126-2659-1; 0-8126-2676-1 (pa)

LC 2002-4707

"A Marcato book"

A collection of essays, poems, and short fiction, created in response to the terrorist attacks of September 11, 2001. Contributors include Katherine Paterson, Joan Bauer, Walter Dean Myers, Nikki Giovanni, Arnold Adoff, and Russell Freedman

This "stands out for its rich prose, its unusual reporting, its search for context, its reminder of wonders." NY Times Book Rev

American dragons: twenty-five Asian American voices; edited by Laurence Yep. HarperCollins Pubs. 1993 237p hardcover o.p. paperback available $5.95 **810.8**

1. American literature—Asian American authors—Collections
ISBN 0-06-440603-2 (pa) LC 92-28489

These "short stories, poems, and other selections are written by a cross section of Asian Americans, with roots in China, Vietnam, Japan, Korea, Tibet, and Thailand. The book is organized by theme, covering such issues of interest to adolescents as identity, family relationships, generational and cultural conflicts, and love." Horn Book

"A kaleidoscopic, occasionally brilliant, illumination of the Asian-American experience." SLJ

Includes bibliographical references

City of one; young writers speak to the world; from WritersCorps; foreword by Isabel Allende; edited by Collete DeDonato. Aunt Lute Books 2004 239p pa $10.95 (7 and up) **810.8**

1. Teenagers' writings
ISBN 1-87996-069-9 LC 2004-45089

"This anthology celebrates the 10th anniversary of WritersCorps workshops, which bring creative-writing instruction to low-income kids from public schools, youth detention centers, halfway houses, and afterschool programs. More than 150 young people ranging in age from 9 to 23 write about their lives and the state of the world. . . . Poems about family, freedom, inner peace, self-identity, and the writing process round out this remarkable anthology." SLJ

Girls got game; sports stories and poems; edited by Sue Macy. Holt & Co. 2001 152p $17.95 (5 and up) **810.8**

1. Sports 2. Women athletes 3. American literature—Collections
ISBN 0-8050-6568-7 LC 00-47297

A collection of short stories and poems written by and about young women in sports

"The lineup of authors includes heavy hitters such as Virginia Euwer Wolff and Jacqueline Woodson as well as some lesser-known talents. . . . This earnest and high-minded anthology can be dipped into or devoured in one sitting; however it is read, it should empower girls and guide them along their paths toward becoming strong, independent women." SLJ

The Great North American prairie; edited by Sara St. Antoine; maps by Paul Mirocha; illustrations by Trudy Nicholson. Milkweed Eds. 2001 262p il (Stories from where we live) $19.95; pa $12.95 **810.8**

1. American literature—Collections 2. Prairies
ISBN 1-57131-630-2; 1-57131-645-0 (pa)

LC 00-67886

This is a collection of stories, poems, and literary excerpts about the American prairie

"The varied selections include a song of a Sioux chief, a letter from Georgia O'Keeffe, and the recollections of a 92-year-old woman (Iron Teeth). Some contributors are authors who write books for children; others are scientists and lecturers. . . . Their voices ring with pride and poignancy." Book Rep

Includes bibliographical references

Growing up Latino; memoirs and stories; edited with an introduction by Harold Augenbraum and Ilan Stavans; foreword by Ilan Stavans. Houghton Mifflin 1993 xxix, 344p hardcover o.p. paperback available $15 **810.8**

1. American literature—Hispanic American authors—Collections
ISBN 0-395-66124-2 LC 92-32624

"A Marc Jaffe book"

A collection of short stories and excerpts from novels and memoirs written by twenty-five Latino authors. Among the contributors are Julia Alvarez, Oscar Hijuelos, Denise Chávez, Rolando Hinojosa, and Sandra Cisneros

Includes bibliographical references

Guys write for Guys Read; edited by Jon Scieszka. Viking 2005 272p il $16.99; pa $10.99 **810.8**

1. American literature—Collections
ISBN 0-670-06007-0; 0-670-06027-5 (pa)

This is a collection of short stories, essays, columns, cartoons, anecdotes, and artwork by such writers and illustrators as Brian Jacques, Jerry Spinelli, Chris Crutcher, Mo Willems, Chris Van Allsburg, Matt Groening, and Neil Gaiman, selected by voters at the Guys Read web site.

This is "a diverse and fast-paced anthology . . . that deserves a permanent place in any collection . . . . There's something undeniably grand about this collective celebration of the intellectual life of the common boy." SLJ

Halloween howls; spooky sounds, stories, & songs. Sourcebooks 2003 165p il pa $14.95 **810.8**

1. American literature—Collections 2. Halloween
ISBN 1-4022-0193-1 LC 2003-12719

This "includes 13 short stories, trivia, games, and decorating tips. Traditional folktales as well as selections by Edgar Allan Poe, R. L. Stine, Charles Dickens, Bram Stoker, and others are included. Following each story is a suggested activity or a song, or lists of scary movies. The tales are consistently intense and chilling. . . . The accompanying CD has five tales from the book, spooky sounds, songs, and a short history of Halloween. " SLJ

Here is my kingdom; Hispanic-American literature and art for young people; edited by Charles Sullivan; foreword by Luis R. Cancel. Abrams 1994 119p il $24.95 **810.8**

1. American literature—Hispanic American authors—Collections 2. Hispanic American art

ISBN 0-8109-3422-1   LC 93-37412

The editor "combines poetry and short prose works with art to introduce young people to selected aspects of various Hispanic cultures. More than 118 writers and artists from countries such as Mexico, Puerto Rico, Cuba, Peru and Chile are represented. A wide spectrum of history is covered, from early explorers to contemporary issues such as the Vietnam War. The works of art, reproduced in color and b&w, are skillfully combined with thematically related text." Book Rep

Sidman, Joyce, 1956-
The world according to dog; poems and teen voices; with photographs by Doug Mindell. Houghton Mifflin 2003 71p il $15 **810.8**

1. Dogs 2. Teenagers' writings

ISBN 0-618-17497-4   LC 2002-476

A collection of poems about dogs is accompanied by essays by young people about the dogs in their lives

"The teen essays are heartfelt and honest. . . . Sidman's poetic form is succinct, evoking images, memories, and even smells. . . . Readers of all ages who appreciate their canine companions will thoroughly enjoy this slim book." Voice Youth Advocates

Things I have to tell you; poems and writing by teenage girls; edited by Betsy Franco; photographs by Nina Nickles. Candlewick Press 2001 63p il $15.99; pa $8.99 (7 and up) **810.8**

1. Teenagers' writings 2. Girls

ISBN 0-7636-0905-6; 0-7636-1035-6 (pa)
     LC 99-46884

A collection of poems, stories, and essays written by girls twelve to eighteen years of age and revealing the secrets which enabled them to overcome the challenges they faced

Wáchale! poetry and prose on growing up Latino in America; edited by Han Stavans. Cricket Publs. 2001 146p $16.95 (5 and up) **810.8**

1. Hispanic Americans 2. American literature—Hispanic American authors—Collections 3. Bilingual books—English-Spanish

ISBN 0-8126-4750-5   LC 2001-47189

"This collection would make a fine classroom text, great for reading aloud and for stimulating students from everywhere to write about their roots and celebrate their shifting places across borders." Booklist

Includes glossary and bibliographical references

You hear me? poems and writing by teenage boys; edited by Betsy Franco. Candlewick Press 2000 107p $14.99; pa $6.99 (7 and up) **810.8**

1. Teenagers' writings 2. Boys

ISBN 0-7636-1158-1; 0-7636-1159-X (pa)
     LC 99-57129

This is an "anthology of poems, essays, and stories written by young men aged twelve through twenty." Harv Educ Rev

"The voices range from painfully honest to playfully ironic, but all are controlled and powerful as they speak to subjects that teen readers will be familiar with." Voice Youth Advocates

810.9 American literature--History and criticism

Drew, Bernard A. (Bernard Alger), 1950-
The 100 most popular young adult authors; biographical sketches and bibliographies. rev. Libraries Unlimited 1997 xxviii, 531p $58 **810.9**

1. Young adult literature—Bio-bibliography

ISBN 1-56308-615-8   LC 97-25882

First published 1996

A "tool for brief biographical information about authors writing books from upper elementary to adult levels which are of interest to young adults. Coverage is of mostly contemporary American authors, but other nationalities and classic writers are included as well. Arranged alphabetically, each entry gives biographical data, the types of books written and some critical analysis. Lists for further reading are appended." Safford. Guide to Ref Materials for Sch Libr Media Cent. 5th edition

Includes bibliographical references

Hill, Laban Carrick
Harlem stomp! a cultural history of the Harlem Renaissance. Little, Brown 2004 151p il $18.95 (7 and up) **810.9**

1. Harlem Renaissance 2. African Americans—Intellectual life

ISBN 0 316 81411-3   LC 2002-73067

"This is an account of cultural and intellectual life in Harlem during the first half of the 20th century." Bull Cent Child Books

"The vibrancy, energy, and color of the Harlem Renaissance come to life in this gem of a book packed with poetry, prose, song lyrics, art, and photography created by some of the period's most influential figures. . . . Informative and highly entertaining, it deserves to be shelved in any library." Voice Youth Advocates

Includes bibliographical references

811 American poetry

Adoff, Arnold, 1935-
The basket counts; illustrated by Michael Weaver. Simon & Schuster Bks. for Young Readers 2000 46p il $17 **811**

1. Basketball—Poetry

ISBN 0-689-80108-4   LC 98-47941

Illustrations and poetic text describe the movement and feel of the game of basketball

"The insider perspective of these evocative shaped-speech poems is complemented by the dynamic but straightforward street-art-inspired illustrations." Bull Cent Child Books

Adoff, Jaime

The song shoots out of my mouth; illustrated by Martin French. Dutton Children's Bks. 2002 48p il $17.99   **811**

1. Music—Poetry

ISBN 0-525-46949-4   LC 2002-284232

This is a "collection of 24 poems. Though free in form and diverse in mood and tone, all are about music, from Hip Hop to classical and from reggae to gospel. Another common element is the energy underscoring Adoff's language, which invites readers to move to the rhythm of the words. . . . All shine with the poet's obvious love of music and musicians." Booklist

Includes glossary and discography

Angelou, Maya

Maya Angelou; [compiled] by Patricia Kirkpatrick. Creative Education 2003 47p il (Voices in poetry) $19.95   **811**

1. Poets, American 2. African American women

ISBN 1-583-41281-6

Examines the life and accomplishments of the African American writer, performer, and teacher. Includes a selection of her poetry.

This is "a stunning treat for the eye. . . . Artist John Thompson creates evocative illustrations for the excerpts of Angelou's writing that capture the heart of each piece. Also included are photographs both of Angelou and of the dramatic time in which she has lived." Voice Youth Advocates

Includes bibliographical references

Appelt, Kathi, 1954-

Poems from homeroom; a writer's place to start. Holt & Co. 2002 114p $16.95 (7 and up)   **811**

1. Poetics

ISBN 0-8050-6978-X   LC 2002-67886

Appelt's "poems are at times sensual, dramatic, or violent, and always rhythmic. They are fascinating, smooth, and @with it.'" SLJ

Includes bibliographical references

Burleigh, Robert, 1936-

Hoops; illustrated by Stephen T. Johnson. Harcourt Brace & Co. 1997 unp il $16; pa $6   **811**

1. Basketball—Poetry

ISBN 0-15-201450-0; 0-15-216380-8 (pa)

    LC 96-18440

"Silver Whistle"

Illustrations and poetic text describe the movement and feel of the game of basketball

"Burleigh's staccato text is well matched by Johnson's dynamic pastels. Muted colors and a strong sense of motion as bodies leap and lift, pounce and poke, aptly complement the words." SLJ

Fields, Terri, 1948-

After the death of Anna Gonzales. Holt & Co. 2002 100p $16.95 (7 and up)   **811**

1. Suicide—Poetry

ISBN 0-8050-7127-X   LC 2002-24074

Poems written in the voices of forty-seven people, including students, teachers, and other school staff, record the aftermath of a high school student's suicide and the preoccupations of teen life

"A short book, easily read, which should generate serious thought and discussion." BAYA Book Rev

Fleischman, Paul

Big talk; poems for four voices; illustrated by Beppe Giacobbe. Candlewick Press 2000 44p il $17.99 (4 and up)   **811**

ISBN 0-7636-0636-7   LC 99-46882

A collection of poems to be read aloud by four people, with color-coded text to indicate which lines are read by which readers

"Each poem is more demanding, and more rewarding, than the last. Giacobbe highlights the humor in strips of vignettes that run along the bottom of the page. This is 'toe-tapping, tongue-flapping fun.'" Horn Book Guide

I am phoenix: poems for two voices; illustrated by Ken Nutt. Harper & Row 1985 51p il hardcover o.p. paperback available $5.95 (4 and up)   **811**

1. Birds—Poetry

ISBN 0-06-446092-4 (pa)   LC 85-42615

"A Charlotte Zolotow book"

A collection of poems about birds to be read aloud by two voices

"Devotés of the almost lost art of choral reading should be among the first to appreciate this collection. . . . Printed in script form, the selections . . . have a cadenced pace and dignified flow; their combination of imaginative imagery and realistic detail is echoed by the combination of stylized fantasy and representational drawings in the black and white pictures, all soft line and strong nuance." Bull Cent Child Books

Joyful noise: poems for two voices; illustrated by Eric Beddows. Harper & Row 1988 44p il $15.99; lib bdg $16.89; pa $5.99 (4 and up)   **811**

1. Insects—Poetry

ISBN 0-06-021852-5; 0-06-021853-3 (lib bdg); 0-06-446093-2 (pa)   LC 87-45280

Awarded the Newbery Medal, 1989

"A Charlotte Zolotow book"

"This collection of poems for two voices explores the lives of insects. Designed to be read aloud, the phrases of the poems are spaced vertically on the page in two columns, one for each reader. The voices sometimes alternate, sometimes speak in chorus, and sometimes echo each other." Booklist

"There are fourteen poems in the handsomely designed volume, with stylish endpapers and wonderfully interpretive black-and-white illustrations. Each selection is a gem, polished perfection." Horn Book

Fletcher, Ralph, 1953-

Have you been to the beach lately? poems by Ralph Fletcher; photographs by Andrea Sperling. Orchard Bks. 2001 48p il $16.95   **811**

1. Beaches—Poetry

ISBN 0-531-30330-6   LC 00-61130

Fletcher, Ralph, 1953-—*Continued*
"Short poems from the viewpoint of an 11-year-old boy trace a day his family spends at the beach. The well-written poems, some lighthearted and some more insightful, cover fairly universal themes that most middle-school-aged children can relate to." Book Rep

Frost, Robert, 1874-1963
The road not taken; illustrated by John O'Hara Cosgrave II. Holt & Co. 1951 xxxvii, 282p il $25; pa $15 **811**
    ISBN 0-8050-0529-3; 0-8050-6983-6 (pa)
    "An introduction to Robert Frost; a selection of Robert Frost's poems; with a biographical preface and running commentary by Louis Untermeyer." Title page

You come too: favorite poems for young readers; with wood engravings by Thomas W. Nason. Holt & Co. 1959 94p il $14.95; pa $10.95 **811**
    ISBN 0-8050-0299-5; 0-8050-0316-9 (pa)
    LC 59-12940
    Frost's "simplicity, wisdom, and humanity, as well as his craftsmanship, come clear in some half-hundred poems, among them 'Mending Wall,' 'The Death of the Hired Man,' and 'Tree at My Window.'" Libr J

George, Kristine O'Connell
Swimming upstream; middle school poems; illustrated by Debbie Tilley. Clarion Bks. 2002 79p il $14 **811**
    1. Schools—Poetry
    ISBN 0-618-15250-4   LC 2002-2746
    A collection of poems capture the feelings and experiences of a girl in middle school
    "Students will relate to this voice 'navigating upstream,' while they try to find their own place in the middle-school wilderness." SLJ

Giovanni, Nikki
Ego-tripping and other poems for young people; illustrations by George Ford; foreword by Virginia Hamilton. 2nd ed. Hill Bks. 1993 52p il hardcover o.p. paperback available $10.95 (5 and up) **811**
    1. African Americans—Poetry
    ISBN 1-55652-189-8 (pa)   LC 93-29578
    First published 1974
    Giovanni has added 10 new poems to her earlier "collection of 23 poems for young people. Ford's illustrations in sepia shades are bold and full of character and dreaming. As Virginia Hamilton says in her foreword, Giovanni's voice is personal and warm, she 'celebrates ordinary folks' and writes of struggle and liberation. She's upbeat and celebratory without minimizing hard times." Booklist

Glenn, Mel, 1943-
Foreign exchange; a mystery in poems. Morrow Junior Bks. 1999 159p $16.99 (7 and up) **811**
    1. City and town life—Poetry
    ISBN 0-688-16472-2   LC 98-40551

A series of poems reflect the thoughts of various people—town residents young and old, teachers, and some students visiting from the city—caught up in the events surrounding the murder of a beautiful high school student who had recently moved to the small lake-side community of Hudson Landing
    "The characters are solidly evoked and their voices are distinct." Bull Cent Child Books

Split image: a story in poems. Morrow Junior Bks. 2000 159p $15.99; pa $6.99 (7 and up) **811**
    1. Chinese Americans—Poetry 2. Suicide—Poetry
    ISBN 0-688-16249-5; 0-06-000481-9 (pa)
    LC 99-46041
    "Brief poems, written in the voices of peers and teachers, describe impressions of Chinese American high-school student Laura Li—rebellious, gifted, admired—and suggest the pressures that lead Laura to suicide." Booklist
    "A powerful look at perceptions and what lies behind them." SLJ

Grimes, Nikki
At Jerusalem's gate; poems of Easter; with woodcuts by David Frampton. Eerdmans Books for Young Readers 2005 unp il $20 (5 and up) **811**
    1. Jesus Christ—Poetry 2. Easter—Poetry
    ISBN 0-8028-5183-5   LC 2003-1089
    A collection of poems which tells the story of the first Easter.
    "Each poem is preceded by a brief synopsis of the event, often accompanied by the author's own musings and queries, which prompt readers to think and ask questions of their own. . . . Bold, handsome woodcuts reinforce the powerful drama depicted in poetry. An outstanding effort." SLJ

A dime a dozen; pictures by Angelo. Dial Bks. for Young Readers 1998 54p il $17.99 (5 and up) **811**
    1. African Americans—Poetry
    ISBN 0-8037-2227-3   LC 97-5798
    A collection of poems about an African-American girl growing up in New York
    "Free-flowing and very accessible, the poetry may inspire readers to distill their own life experiences into precise, imaginative words and phrases." Booklist

Hopscotch love; a family treasury of love poems; illustrated by Melodye Benson Rosales. Lothrop, Lee & Shepard Bks. 1999 39p il $16.99 (4 and up) **811**
    1. Love poetry 2. African Americans—Poetry
    ISBN 0-688-15667-3   LC 98-21310
    A collection of more than twenty poems speaking of different kinds of love
    "All of the poetry is simple, written with everyday language in a straightforward style that needs no analysis or search for symbolism. . . . This small treasury will lift readers' spirits and touch their hearts." SLJ

Grimes, Nikki—_Continued_
Tai chi morning; snapshots of China; [illustrated by] Ed Young. Cricket Books 2004 51p il $15.95 (5 and up)   **811**
1. China—Poetry
ISBN 0-8126-2707-5   LC 2003-16506
"In 1988, Grimes traveled to China . . . and recorded her impressions of the country. . . . She paints her personal visions of a particular area or experience in a narrative paragraph, and then knits the ideas together into a poem on the facing page. . . . Young's simple artwork complements Grimes's eloquent images. The reedy pen-and-ink drawings deftly capture the exotic and ancient culture of the country." SLJ

Grover, Lorie Ann
Loose threads. Margaret K. McElderry Bks. 2002 296p $16.95   **811**
1. Breast cancer—Poetry
ISBN 0-689-84419-0   LC 2001-44724
A series of poems describes how seventh-grader Kay Garber faces her grandmother's battle with breast cancer while living with her mother and great-grandmother and dealing with everyday junior high school concerns
"The poetic, spare language, written in Kay's self-possessed, first-person voice, is refreshingly frank about the disease. . . . Grover's book balances vivid emotional scenes with plenty of space between the words." Booklist

Harrison, David L.
Wild country; outdoor poems for young people. Boyds Mills Press 1999 48p il $14.95
    811
1. Nature poetry
ISBN 1-56397-784-2   LC 98-88337
"Forty-seven poems about the outdoors are organized under the categories 'Mountains,' 'High Country,' 'Forest,' and 'Sea.'. . . Many of the brief, mostly free verse poems . . . successfully capture nature's moments in memorable images. The collection reveals a respect for and connection to the natural world." Horn Book

Herrera, Juan Felipe, 1948-
Laughing out loud, I fly; poems in English and Spanish; drawings by Karen Barbour. HarperCollins Pubs. 1998 unp il $15.99
    811
1. Bilingual books—English-Spanish
ISBN 0-06-027604-5   LC 96-45476
"Joanna Cotler books"
A collection of poems in Spanish and English about childhood, place, and identity
"Barbour's black-and-white drawings accompany each poem, delicately underlining its images but allowing the strong sensuality of the words to seep into readers' minds." SLJ

Hopkins, Lee Bennett, 1938-
Been to yesterdays: poems of a life; illustrations by Charlene Rendeiro. Wordsong 1995 64p il $15.95; pa $9.95 (4 and up)   **811**
ISBN 1-56397-467-3; 1-56397-808-3 (pa)
    LC 94-73320

Autobiographical poems capture a thirteen-year old boy's feelings, experiences, and aspirations in one tumultuous year of his life

Hovey, Kate
Ancient voices; written by Kate Hovey ; with illustrations by Murray Kimber. Margaret McElderry Books 2004 unp il $18.95   **811**
1. Classical mythology—Poetry
ISBN 0-689-83342-3   LC 00-28359
Twenty-three poems give voice to a variety of goddesses, gods, and mortals from Greek and Roman mythology.
"These lyrical poems and dramatic picture-book-size illustrations humanize the Greek myths with flashes of contemporary realism. . . . The poetry here is both intense and accessible, with unobtrusive rhyme that adds to the music of the lines." Booklist

Hughes, Langston, 1902-1967
The collected poems of Langston Hughes; Arnold Rampersad, editor; David Roessel, associate editor. Knopf 1994 708p $39.95; pa $18   **811**
ISBN 0-679-42631-0; 0-679-76408-9 (pa)
    LC 94-14509
"The editors have attempted to collect every poem (860 in all) published by the writer in his lifetime, and have also provided a brief but informative introduction, a detailed chronology and extensive textual notes that include the original date and place of publication for each poem. . . . Although Hughes is best known for his poems celebrating African American life, he was also a passionately political poet." Publ Wkly

The dream keeper and other poems; including seven additional poems; illustrated by Brian Pinkney. Knopf 1994 83p il $14.99; pa $8.99 (5 and up)   **811**
1. African Americans—Poetry
ISBN 0-679-94421-4; 0-679-88347-9 (pa)
    LC 92-10240
First published 1932
"Langston Hughes's poems range from the romantic to the poignant, from the spiritual to the challenging. His lyrical voice asks for recognition of the Negro, offers encouragement, and reminds his African-American brothers of their glorious past. Although the pieces in _The Dream Keeper_ were written over a half-century ago . . . the words have the same strength of meaning and power as if they had been written today." Horn Book

Janeczko, Paul B., 1945-
Stardust otel; poems; illustrated by Dorothy Leech. Orchard Bks. 1993 64p il $15.95 (7 and up)   **811**
ISBN 0-531-05498-5   LC 92-44514
"A Richard Jackson book"
A series of free-verse poems in which 15-year-old Leary describes his life with his flower children parents, his friends, and neighbors
"Even students who think they hate poetry will delight in the quirky, but very human, characters who people the pages and poems of this volume." Book Rep

Johnson, Angela, 1961-
The other side; Shorter poems. Orchard Bks.
1998 44p il hardcover o.p. $6.95   **811**
1. African Americans—Poetry
ISBN 0-531-07167-7 (paperback available)
                                    LC 98-13736
A Coretta Scott King honor book for text, 1999
A collection of poems reminiscent of growing up as
an African-American girl in Shorter, Alabama
"Photographs of the author as a child emphasize the
personal nature of this captivating narrative." Horn Book

Running back to Ludie; illustrated by Angelo.
Orchard Bks. 2001 48p il $16.95   **811**
1. Mother-daughter relationship—Poetry 2. African
Americans—Poetry
ISBN 0-439-29316-2   LC 2001-16298
"Ludie's teenaged daughter voices her ambivalent
feelings about her absent mother. Each of thirty-four
free-verse vignettes adds another defining moment in the
girl's life, another dimension to her character. Johnson's
exploration of a young person's coming to terms with a
perceived rejection by an absent's parent is subtle and
beautifully wrought." Horn Book Guide

Katz, Bobbi
We the people; poems; illustrations by Nina
Crews. Greenwillow Bks. 2000 102p il $15.95 (5
and up)   **811**
1. United States—History—Poetry
ISBN 0 688 16531 1   LC 99-50009
A collection of sixty-five original poems that depict
people and events throughout the history of the United
States
"Giving voice to the diversity of American experience,
the poems are vividly imagined from the point of view
of pioneers, presidents, suffragettes, soldiers, and more.
Handsome collage pictures capture the spirit of each
century's history." Horn Book Guide

Levy, Constance, 1931-
A crack in the clouds and other poems;
illustrations by Robin Bell Corfield. Margaret K.
McElderry Bks. 1998 40p il $15 (3-5)
                                    811
1. Nature—Poetry
ISBN 0-689-82204-9   LC 98-10652
A collection of thirty-eight original poems about the
natural world
Corfield's "small, sepia-wash natural scenes strike
graceful visual notes. Levy displays a consistently distinct voice and a lively imagination . . . to go along
with the sharply attuned senses that every good poet
needs." Booklist

Lewis, J. Patrick
Freedom like sunlight; praisesongs for Black
Americans; [illustrated by] John Thompson.
Creative Eds. 2000 40p il $17.95; pa $7.95 (5 and
up)   **811**
1. African Americans—Poetry
ISBN 1-56846-163-1; 0-89812-382-8 (pa)
                                    LC 98-50909

Presents poems and brief biographical notes about
such well-known African Americans as: Arthur Ashe,
Harriet Tubman, Sojourner Truth, Louis Armstrong, Martin Luther King, Jr., "Satchel" Paige, Rosa Parks, Langston Hughes, Jesse Owens, Marian Anderson, Malcolm
X, Wilma Rudolph, and Billie Holiday
"Stunning illustrations by John Thompson take center
stage in this attractively designed poetry collection. . . .
Using a range of styles and meter, the mostly rhyming
poems are dramatic and reverential." Booklist

Monumental verses. National Geographic 2005
31p il $16.95; lib bdg $25.90 (5 and up)
                                    811
1. Monuments—Poetry
ISBN 0-7922-7135-1; 0-7922-7139-4 (lib bdg)
"Lewis offers 14 poems celebrating monumental structures. From the remnants of civilizations at Stonehenge,
Easter Island, and Machu Picchu to the more modern
achievements of the Taj Mahal, the Eiffel Tower, and the
Statue of Liberty, the subjects are varied and the accompanying photos are striking." Booklist

Longfellow, Henry Wadsworth, 1807-1882
Henry Wadsworth Longfellow; edited by
Frances Schoonmaker; illustrated by Chad
Wallace. Sterling 1998 48p il (Poetry for young
people) $14.95   **811**
ISBN 0-8069-9417-7   LC 98-14833
A collection of 27 poems, "among them, 'The Village
Blacksmith,' 'The Wreck of the Hesperus,' 'The Chil-
dren's Hour,' 'Paul Revere's Ride,' and 'Hiawatha's
Childhood' from 'The Song of Hiawatha.' A several-
page introduction to Longfellow's life also includes some
of the stories behind the poems." Booklist

Hiawatha and Megissogwon; illustrated by
Jeffrey Thompson; afterword by Joseph Bruchac.
National Geographic Soc. 2001 unp il $16.95
                                    811
1. Native Americans—Poetry
ISBN 0-7922-6676-5   LC 00-12719
"In this excerpt from *The Song of Hiawatha,* Hiawatha
engages in battle with the evil magician Megissogwon
and returns, victorious, to his people." Horn Book Guide
"Readers who persevere through the no-longer-familiar
poem will be rewarded for their efforts by Hiawatha's
exciting adventures, ferocious battles, and victorious
homecoming. The text has been capably illustrated in a
complex process utilizing original drawings, black-and-
white scratchboard, and a computer program for color."
SLJ

Mora, Pat
The desert is my mother. El desierto es mi
madre; art by Daniel Lechon. Piñata Bks. 1994
unp il $14.95   **811**
1. Deserts—Poetry 2. Bilingual books—English-
Spanish
ISBN 1-55885-121-6   LC 94-20047
English and Spanish
A poetic depiction of the desert as the provider of
comfort, food, spirit, and life

Mora, Pat—*Continued*
"Presented in both English and Spanish, the text's short verses provide opportunities for children to use their senses to explore and learn about their environment." Kaleidoscope. 2nd edition

Myers, Walter Dean, 1937-
Harlem; a poem; pictures by Christopher Myers. Scholastic 1997 unp il $16.95　　　**811**
1. African Americans—Poetry 2. Harlem (New York, N.Y.)—Poetry
ISBN 0-590-54340-7　　　LC 96-8108
A Caldecott Medal honor book, 1998
A poem celebrating the people, sights, and sounds of Harlem
"Myers's paean to Harlem sings, dances, and swaggers across the pages, conveying the myriad sounds on the streets. . . . Christopher Myers's collages add an edge to his father's words, vividly bringing to life the sights and scenes of Lenox Avenue." Horn Book Guide

Here in Harlem; poems in many voices; written by Walter Dean Myers. Holiday House 2004 88p il $16.95 (7 and up)　　　**811**
1. African Americans—Poetry 2. Harlem (New York, N.Y.)—Poetry
ISBN 0-8234-1853-7　　　LC 2003-67605
"In each poem here, a resident of Harlem speaks in a distinctive voice, offering a story, a thought, a reflection, or a memory. The poetic forms are varied and well chosen. . . . Expressive period photos from Myers' collection accompany the text of this handsome book." Booklist

Nelson, Marilyn, 1946-
Carver, a life in poems. Front St. 2001 103p il $16.95 (7 and up)　　　**811**
1. Carver, George Washington, 1864?-1943
ISBN 1-88691-053-7　　　LC 00-63624
A Newbery Medal honor book, 2002
"A series of fifty-nine poems portrays George Washington Carver as a private, scholarly man of great personal faith and social purpose. Nelson fills in the trajectory of Carver's life with details of the cultural and political contexts that shaped him even as he shaped history. As individual works, each poem stands as a finely wrought whole of . . . high caliber." Horn Book Guide

Fortune's bones; the manumission requiem. Front Street 2004 32p il $16.95　　　**811**
1. Slavery—Poetry 2. African Americans—Poetry
ISBN 1-932425-12-8　　　LC 2004-46917
"This requiem honors a slave who died in Connecticut in 1798. His owner, a doctor, dissected his body, boiling down his bones to preserve them for anatomy studies. The skeleton . . . hung in a local museum until 1970. . . . The museum . . . uncovered the skeleton's provenance, created a new exhibit, and led to the commissioning of these six poems. The selections. . . arc from grief to triumph. . . . The facts inform the verse and open up a full appreciation of its rich imagery and rhythmic, lyrical language." SLJ
Includes bibliographical references (p.)

Nye, Naomi Shihab, 1952-
19 varieties of gazelle; poems of the Middle East. Greenwillow Bks. 2002 142p $16.95; lib bdg $16.89　　　**811**
1. Middle East—Poetry
ISBN 0-06-009765-5; 0-06-009766-3 (lib bdg)
LC 2002-771
In this "volume, Nye collects her poems about growing up as an Arab American (her ancestry is Palestinian), including previously published poems and newly written pieces. This rich and varied volume offers insights into the experience of childhood in two very different worlds. . . . This volume will fill a need for classroom use, for young people seeking a more personal understanding of the Middle East, and for readers seeking a connection with their own Middle Eastern background." Bull Cent Child Books

A maze me; poems for girls; pictures by Terre Maher. 1st ed. Greenwillow Books 2005 118p il $16.99; lib bdg $17.89 (7 and up)　　　**811**
1. Girls—Poetry
ISBN 0-06-058189-1; 0-06-058190-5 (lib bdg)
LC 2004-3283
These "poems draw from Nye's observations about nature, home, school, and neighborhood to make connections to a girl's inner world. . . . Most poems . . . speak with a powerful immediacy. . . . A wide age range will respond to these deeply felt poems about everyday experiences." Booklist

Rylant, Cynthia
Something permanent; photographs by Walker Evans; poetry by Cynthia Rylant. Harcourt Brace & Co. 1994 61p il $18 (7 and up)　　　**811**
ISBN 0-15-277090-9　　　LC 93-3861
"Nearly 60 years ago, Walker Evans and James Agee documented the lives of poor Southern sharecroppers. Their efforts resulted in a devastating, legendary account of the Depression, *Let Us Now Praise Famous Men*. Here, Rylant pairs Evans's photographs with 29 short, lyrical poems." SLJ
"For students in junior high and high school, the juxtaposition of Evans' photos and Rylant's poems will demonstrate how emotions can be rooted in objects and how, to dig them out, you need to use strong, sturdy words." Booklist

Service, Robert W., 1874-1958
The cremation of Sam McGee; paintings by Ted Harrison; introduction by Pierre Berton. Greenwillow Bks. 1987 c1986 unp il $17.95 (4 and up)　　　**811**
1. Yukon Territory—Poetry
ISBN 0-688-06903-7　　　LC 86-14971
Text first published 1907. This newly illustrated edition first published 1986 in Canada
"In the tradition of tall tales, the story of Sam McGee is told here in Service's original rollicking verses. Pledged to cremate his friend Sam, the narrator tells how, after carting the frozen body for miles, he stuffs it into a ship's roaring furnace. To his surprise, when he later opens the door he discovers Sam alive . . . and

Service, Robert W., 1874-1958—*Continued*

warm for the first time 'since he left Tennessee.'" Publ Wkly

"A fine example of a 20th-Century regional ballad, one that tells of the profound cold of the Yukon and how it affected the lives of two gold miners." SLJ

Silverstein, Shel

Falling up; poems and drawings by Shel Silverstein. HarperCollins Pubs. 1996 171p il $17.99; lib bdg $18.89   **811**

1. Humorous poetry 2. Nonsense verses

ISBN 0-06-024802-5; 0-06-024803-3 (lib bdg)

      LC 96-75736

This "collection includes more than 150 poems. . . . As always, Silverstein has a direct line to what kids like, and he gives them poems celebrating the gross, the scary, the absurd, and the comical. The drawings are much more than decoration. They often extend a poem's meaning and, in many cases, add some great comedy." Booklist

A light in the attic. Harper & Row 1981 167p il lib bdg $18.89   **811**

1. Humorous poetry 2. Nonsense verses

ISBN 0-06-025674-5   LC 80-8453

Also available book with audio CD $22.99 (ISBN 0-06-623617-7)

This collection of more than one hundred poems "will delight lovers of Silverstein's raucous, rollicking verse and his often tender, whimsical, philosophical advice. . . . The poems are tuned in to kids' most hidden feelings, dark wishes and enjoyment of the silly. . . . The witty line drawings are a full half of the treat of this wholly satisfying anthology by the modern successor to Edward Lear and Hilaire Belloc." SLJ

Where the sidewalk ends; the poems & drawings of Shel Silverstein. 30th anniversary special ed. HarperCollins 2004 183p il $17.99; lib bdg $18.89   **811**

1. Humorous poetry 2. Nonsense verses

ISBN 0-06-057234-5; 0-06-058653-2 (lib bdg)

      LC 2004-269335

First published 1974

This edition contains 12 new poems

"There are skillful, sometimes grotesque line drawings with each of the 127 poems, which run in length from a few lines to a couple of pages. The poems are tender, funny, sentimental, philosophical, and ridiculous in turn, and they're for all ages." Sat Rev

Singer, Marilyn, 1948-

Central heating; poems about fire and warmth; illustrated by Meilo So. 1st ed. Alfred A. Knopf 2005 41p il $15.95; lib bdg $17.99 (4 and up)

      811

1. Fire—Poetry 2. Heat—Poetry

ISBN 0-375-82912-1; 0-375-92912-6 (lib bdg)

      LC 2004-4274

"The complicated nature of fire is explored in Singer's energetic short poems and So's deceptively simple single-color illustrations. . . . This title . . . belongs on library shelves everywhere." SLJ

Footprints on the roof; poems about the earth; illustrated by Meilo So. Knopf 2002 41p il $14.95; lib bdg $16.99 (4 and up)   **811**

1. Earth—Poetry 2. Nature poetry

ISBN 0-375-81094-3; 0-375-91094-8 (lib bdg)

      LC 2001-29407

A collection of 19 poems on such topics as caves, mud, ice, deserts, and dunes

"This elegantly presented collection of free-verse poems focuses primarily on the young narrator's emotional response to nature—its bounties, mysteries, and delights. Like the poems themselves, the black-and-white ink drawings are spare and finely crafted." Horn Book Guide

Smith, Charles R.

Hoop queens; poems. Candlewick Press 2003 35p il $14.99   **811**

1. Basketball—Poetry 2. Women athletes—Poetry

ISBN 0-7636-1422-X   LC 2002-41111

A collection of twelve poems that celebrate contemporary women basketball stars, including Yolanda Griffith, Chamique Holdsclaw, and Natalie Williams

"Action photos of the athletes are pasted large on colorful, dynamic backgrounds that barely hold the motion-filled poems to the page. Notes about each player and poem communicate the joy Smith finds both in watching the game and writing poetry. Pure pleasure for basketball fans and inspiration for kids who doubted poetry was alive." SLJ

Smith, Hope Anita

The way a door closes; [by] Hope Anita Smith; with illustrations by Shane W. Evans. Holt & Co. 2003 52p il $18.95 (4 and up)   **811**

1. Fathers—Poetry 2. Family life—Poetry 3. African Americans—Poetry

ISBN 0-8050-6477-X   LC 2002-67884

In these "poems, readers are drawn into the thoughts and feelings of a 13-year-old African American as he tries to understand and cope with a parent's departure from the family. . . . In carefully chosen, straightforward language, Smith conveys the boy's roller-coaster emotions with pinpoint accuracy. The results are poems that are heartbreaking, angry, and tender. Done in warm shades of mostly brown, blue, and gold, Evans's color spot and full-page paintings have a realistic, slightly sculptural appearance and are a perfect complement to the poems." SLJ

Soto, Gary

Canto familiar; {illustrated by Annika Nelson}. Harcourt Brace & Co. 1995 79p il $18 (4-6)

      811

1. Mexican Americans—Poetry

ISBN 0-15-200067-4   LC 94-24218

"This collection of simple free verse captures common childhood moments at home, at school, and in the street. Many of the experiences are Mexican American . . . and occasional Spanish words are part of the easy, colloquial, short lines. . . . The occasional full-page, richly colored woodcuts by Annika Nelson capture the child's imaginative take on ordinary things." Booklist

Soto, Gary—*Continued*

A natural man. Chronicle Bks. 2000 71p pa
$13.95 (7 and up)   **811**
1. Mexican Americans—Poetry
ISBN 0-8118-2518-3   LC 99-18353
"This poetry anthology offers a photographic glimpse
into the lives of California's Chicanos. But although the
titles and use of Spanish words create a very particular
setting, the characters, stories, and truths of these selections have a universal resonance." SLJ

Neighborhood odes; illustrated by David Diaz.
Harcourt Brace Jovanovich 1992 68p il $17; pa
$5.95 (4-6)   **811**
1. Hispanic Americans—Poetry
ISBN 0-15-256879-4; 0-15-205364-6 (pa)
                                         LC 91-20710
Also available in paperback from Scholastic
"Twenty-one poems, all odes, celebrate life in a Hispanic neighborhood. Other than the small details of daily
life—peoples' names or the foods they eat—these poems
could be about any neighborhood. With humor, sensitivity, and insight, Soto explores the lives of children. . . .
David Diaz's contemporary black-and-white illustrations,
which often resemble cut paper, effortlessly capture the
varied moods—happiness, fear, longing, shame, and
greed—of this remarkable collection. With a glossary of
thirty Spanish words and phrases." Horn Book

New and selected poems. Chronicle Bks. 1995
177p hardcover o.p. paperback available $14.95
                                                     811
ISBN 0-8118-0758-4 (pa)   LC 94-27081
"In one of his more striking poems, Soto stares long-
ingly at the unkempt lot in the California slum where his
family's house used to be. Elsewhere, a Mexican
American simply jogs and laughs after he has been ushered out the back door when immigration officials show
up at his workplace. With rare lyricism, gentleness, and
a touch of humor, Soto covers the ground that leads
many highly touted poets to erupt in pulsating anger.
Soto has it all—the learned craft, the intrinsic abilities
with language, a fascinating autobiography, and the storyteller's ability to manipulate memories into folklore."
Libr J

Testa, Maria

Becoming Joe DiMaggio; with illustrations by
Scott Hunt. Candlewick Press 2002 51p il $14.99;
pa $5.99 (4 and up)   **811**
1. Italian Americans—Poetry
ISBN 0-7636-1537-4; 0-7636-2444-6 (pa)
                                         LC 2001-25886
"Growing up in New York City during the 1940s and
1950s, Joseph Paul, an Italian boy, finds solace from a
difficult life by listening to baseball games with his beloved grandfather. This powerful story, told in 24 poems,
describes their relationship and their love of listening to
another Italian, Joe DiMaggio, achieve success. . . . The
beauty and the charm of the poetry—its concise language, its flow and descriptive power—add to the intensity of the experiences described. Hunt's charcoal-and-
pastel spot illustrations are scattered throughout." SLJ

Wayland, April Halprin, 1954-

Girl coming in for a landing; a novel in poems;
illustrations by Elaine Clayton. Knopf 2002 134p
il $14.95; lib bdg $16.99; pa $5.50 (7 and up)
                                                     811
1. Schools—Poetry
ISBN 0-375-80158-8; 0-375-90158-2 (lib bdg);
0-440-41903-4 (pa)   LC 2001-38107
A collection of over 100 poems recounting the ups
and downs of one adolescent girl's school year
"Wayland's spare lines and unpretentious words get
right to the heart of situations and emotions, and the familiarity and candor in the speaker's voice—warm and
authentic—will invite teens to value the small moments
in their own experiences and put them into verse." Booklist

Weatherford, Carole Boston, 1956-

Remember the bridge; poems of a people;
designed by Semador Megged. Philomel Bks. 2002
53p il $17.99   **811**
1. African Americans—Poetry
ISBN 0-399-23726-7   LC 2001-36161
"Twenty-nine poems trace African-American history
and include observations about Harriet Tubman, Marian
Anderson, and Martin Luther King, Jr." Horn Book
Guide
"The author evokes imagined and actual individual experiences of the people . . . in the historical black-and-
white photos, drawings, and etchings. . . . This
celebratory, visually striking book will be appreciated in
most collections." SLJ

Whipple, Laura

If the shoe fits; voices from Cinderella;
illustrations by Laura Beingessner. Margaret K.
McElderry Bks. 2002 67p il $17.95 (5 and up)
                                                     811
1. Cinderella—Poetry
ISBN 0-689-84070-5   LC 2001-30778
In this version of the fairy tale "the characters tell the
story in blank verses. . . . The story unfolds just as it always does, but the multiple points of view—from Cinderella's to the prince's to the rat's to the queen's—en-
large and enrich the familiar tale to win a more sophisticated audience. . . . Paintings by Beingessner achieve
just the right mixture of sorrow, beauty, and humor."
Booklist

Whitman, Walt, 1819-1892

Walt Whitman; edited by Jonathan Levin;
illustrated by Jim Burke. Sterling 1997 48p il
(Poetry for young people) $14.95 (7 and up)
                                                     811
ISBN 0-8069-9530-0   LC 97-433
An illustrated collection of twenty-six poems and excerpts from longer poems by the renowned nineteenth-
century poet
"An outstanding introduction to Whitman's life and
work. . . . This superb volume can be used to teach literature or to show a variety of poetic devices and style."
SLJ

Wong, Janet S., 1962-
Behind the wheel; poems about driving. Margaret K. McElderry Bks. 1999 44p $15.95 (7 and up) **811**
1. Automobile drivers—Poetry
ISBN 0-689-82531-5 LC 99-19079
Thirty-six poems look at various aspects of driving, including passing the written driver's test, being pulled over by a cop, and having an accident, and treat them as metaphors for life
"Wong's brief, clear lines will be accessible even to the most reluctant poetry readers, and readers of all ages will be moved by the intersection of poignancy and humor as she desribes the thrilling freedom of the car and an emerging adult's awareness that, although she's traveled, her road still leads to home." Booklist

Woodson, Jacqueline
Locomotion. Putnam 2003 100p $15.99 (4 and up) **811**
1. African Americans—Poetry 2. Foster home care—Poetry
ISBN 0-399-23115-3 LC 2002-69779
In a series of poems, eleven-year-old Lonnie writes about his life, after the death of his parents, separated from his younger sister, living in a foster home, and finding his poetic voice at school
"In a masterful use of voice, Woodson allows Lonnie's poems to tell a complex story of loss and grief and to create a gritty, urban environment. Despite the spare text, Lonnie's foster mother and the other minor characters are three-dimensional, making the boy's world a convincingly real one." SLJ

Yolen, Jane
Color me a rhyme; nature poems for young people; photographs by Jason Stemple. Boyds Mills Press 2000 unp il $19.95; pa $9.95 (4 and up) **811**
1. Nature poetry
ISBN 1-56397-892-X; 1-59078-172-4 (pa)
LC 99-68893
"Thirteen poems, each a study of a different color found in nature, accompanied by gorgeous photographs, beautifully reproduced and artfully presented. . . . There's playful yet elegant mood in the way the words and pictures merge on many of the pages. This is a visual delight." SLJ

O Jerusalem; illustrated by John Thompson. Blue Sky Press (NY) 1996 unp il pa $5.99 hardcover o.p. (4 and up) **811**
1. Jerusalem—Poetry
ISBN 0-590-48427-3 LC 95-6013
A poetic tribute to Jerusalem, in honor of the 3000th anniversary of its founding, celebrating its history as a holy city for three major religions
"Yolen captures the feelings of Judaism, Christianity, and Islam toward Jerusalem in her poetry, and Thompson brings her words to life in exquisite paintings." Booklist

Sacred places; illustrated by David Shannon. Harcourt Brace & Co. 1996 38p il $16
811
1. Religious poetry
ISBN 0-15-269953-8 LC 92-30323
"The hazy moodiness of Shannon's paintings capture the mystery Yolen explores in her text, while his dense figures and literal interpretations of a passage from each poem draw Yolen's mystical flights back down to solid ground. Appended notes offer historical information on each sacred place." Bull Cent Child Books

811.008 American poetry--Collections

The **Blackbirch** treasury of American poetry. Blackbirch Press 2001 288p il $46.20 (5 and up)
811.008
1. American poetry—Collections
ISBN 1-56711-472-5 LC 00-52899
This treasury combines volumes previously published in Sterling Publications Poetry for young people series
Contents: Carl Sandburg, illustrated by Steven Arcella; Robert Frost, illustrated by Henri Sorensen; Emily Dickinson, illustrated by Chi Chung; Edgar Allan Poe, illustrated by Carolynn Cobleigh; Walt Whitman, illustrated by Jim Burke; Henry Wadsworth Longfellow, illustrated by Chad Wallace
"This is an attractive book that will be of interest to students who are learning about American poets." Book Rep

Book poems; poems from National Children's Book Week, 1959-1998; introduction by Lee Bennett Hopkins; {ed., Mary Perrotta Rich}. Children's Bk. Council 1998 95p il pa $20
811.008
1. American poetry—Collections 2. Books and reading—Poetry
ISBN 0-933633-05-X LC 99-158017
This anthology contains four decades of poems about the importance of books and reading. Includes biographies and bibliographies of the contributing poets

Celebrate America in poetry and art; paintings, sculpture, drawings, photographs, and other works of art from the National Museum of American Art, Smithsonian Institution; edited by Nora Panzer. Hyperion Bks. for Children 1994 96p il $18.95; pa $12.99 (5 and up)
811.008
1. American poetry—Collections 2. American art 3. United States—Poetry
ISBN 1-56282-664-6; 0-7868-1360-1 (pa)
LC 93-32336
"Published in association with the National Museum of American Art, Smithsonian Institution"
A collection of American poetry that celebrates over 200 years of American life and history as illustrated by fine art from the collection of the National Museum of American Art
"There's a terrific cross-section of writers and illustrators—Maya Angelou, Robert Frost, Winslow Homer,

Celebrate America in poetry and art—*Continued*

Thomas Hart Benton—and there is special pleasure in the pairings. . . . Combined, the art and words are exhilaratingly more than the sum of their parts." Booklist

Cool salsa; bilingual poems on growing up Latino in the United States; edited by Lori M. Carlson; introduction by Oscar Hijuelos. Holt & Co. 1994 xx, 123p il $16.95 (5 and up)

811.008

1. American poetry—Hispanic American authors—Collections 2. Bilingual books—English-Spanish
ISBN 0-8050-3135-9   LC 93-45798
Also available in paperback from Fawcett Bks.

"This collection presents poems by 29 Mexican-American, Cuban-American, Puerto Rican, and other Central and South American poets, including Sandra Cisneros, Luis J. Rodriguez, Pat Mora, Gary Soto, Ana Castillo, Oscar Hijuelos, Ed J. Vega, Judith Ortiz-Cofer, and other Latino writers both contemporary and historical. Brief biographical notes on the authors are provided. All the poems deal with experiences of teenagers." Book Rep

Heart to heart; new poems inspired by twentieth-century American art; edited by Jan Greenberg. Abrams 2001 80p il map $19.95 (5 and up)   **811.008**
1. American poetry—Collections 2. American art 3. Art—20th century
ISBN 0-8109-4386-7   LC 99-462335

A compilation of poems by Americans writing about American art in the twentieth century, including such writers as Nancy Willard, Jane Yolen, and X. J. Kennedy

"From a tight diamante and pantoum to lyrical free verse, the range of poetic styles will speak to a wide age group. . . . Concluding with biographical notes on each poet and artist, this rich resource is an obvious choice for teachers, and the exciting interplay between art and the written word will encourage many readers to return again and again to the book." Booklist

I am the darker brother; an anthology of modern poems by African Americans; edited and with an afterword by Arnold Adoff; drawings by Benny Andrews; introduction by Rudine Sims Bishop; foreword by Nikki Giovanni. rev ed. Simon & Schuster Bks. for Young Readers 1997 208p il $17; pa $5.99   **811.008**
1. American poetry—African American authors—Collections
ISBN 0-689-81241-8; 0-689-80869-0 (pa)
    LC 97-144181
First published 1968

This anthology presents "the African-American experience through poetry that speaks for itself. . . . Because of the historical context of many of the poems, the book will be much in demand during Black History Month, but it should be used and treasured as part of the larger canon of literature to be enjoyed by all Americans at all times of the year. An indispensable addition to library collections." SLJ

I, too, sing America; three centuries of African American poetry; {selected and annotated by} Catherine Clinton; illustrated by Stephen Alcorn. Houghton Mifflin 1998 128p il $21 (6 and up)
    811.008
1. African Americans—Poetry 2. American poetry—African American authors—Collections
ISBN 0-395-89599-5   LC 97-46137

A collection of poems by African-American writers, including Lucy Terry, Gwendolyn Bennett, and Alice Walker

"For each poet, Clinton provides a biography and a brief, insightful commentary on the poem(s) she has chosen, including a discussion of political as well as literary connections. Alcorn's dramatic, full-page, full-color illustrations opposite each poem evoke the quiltlike patterns and rhythmic figures of folk art." Booklist

The **Invisible** ladder; an anthology of contemporary American poems for young readers with the poets' own photos and commentary; edited by Liz Rosenberg. Holt & Co. 1996 210p il $21.95 (7 and up)
    811.008
1. American poetry—Collections 2. Poets, American
ISBN 0-8050-3836-1   LC 96-12361

Features such poets as Robert Bly, Allen Ginsberg, Nikki Giovanni, and Galway Kinnell by including photos, selections of their work, and comments on their poetry

Rosenberg "introduces many exciting new adult voices to young people. Some of the poets' commentaries are sophisticated, some are pretentious; but most are immediate and extraordinarily moving, nearly as powerful as the poetry they lead into." Booklist

Is this forever, or what? poems and paintings from Texas; selected by Naomi Shihab Nye. Greenwillow Books 2004 164p il $19.99; lib bdg $20.89 (7 and up)   **811.008**
1. Texas—Poetry 2. Texas in art 3. American poetry—Collections
ISBN 0-06-051178-8; 0-06-051179-6 (lib bdg)
    LC 2003-4441

"The poems include moving family tributes, furious self-revelations, and quiet, atmospheric vignettes that find grace and beauty in sunbaked neighborhoods, basic work, and everyday faces. . . . The accompanying artworks are arresting without overpowering the words, and they echo the poems' wide range of styles." Booklist

A **Jar** of tiny stars: poems by NCTE award-winning poets; Bernice E. Cullinan, editor; illustrations by Andi MacLeod; portraits by Marc Nadel. Wordsong 1996 94p il $17.95
    811.008
1. American poetry—Collections
ISBN 1-56397-087-2   LC 93-60466

"Each poet who has won the NCTE Poetry Award—David McCord, Aileen Fisher, Karla Kuskin, Myra Cohn Livingston, Eve Merriam, John Ciardi, Lilian Moore, Arnold Adoff, Valerie Worth, and Barbara Esbensen—is pictured at the beginning of a section that includes several representative poems and a significant quote. The portraits are watercolor renditions from photographs, with

A Jar of tiny stars: poems by NCTE award-winning poets—*Continued*
cheerful pen-and-ink sketches accompanying the verse; all are in black and white." Bull Cent Child Books

A kick in the head; edited by Paul B. Janeczko ; illustrated by Chris Raschka. 1st ed. Candlewick Press 2005 61p il $17.99 **811.008**
1. Poetry—Collections
ISBN 0-7636-0662-6   LC 2004-48508
This collection offers examples of poetic forms "building from a couplet, tercet, and quatrain to the less familiar and more complex persona poem, ballad, and pantoum." SLJ
"Raschka's high-spirited, spare torn-paper-and-paint collages ingeniously broaden the poems' wide-ranging emotional tones. . . . Clear, very brief explanations of poetic forms . . . accompany each entry; a fine introduction and appended notes offer further information. . . . This is the introduction that will ignite enthusiasm." Booklist

Lives: poems about famous Americans; selected by Lee Bennett Hopkins; illustrated by Leslie Staub. HarperCollins Pubs. 1999 31p il $15.99; lib bdg $16.89 (4 and up) **811.008**
1. United States—Biography—Poetry 2. American poetry—Collections
ISBN 0-06-027767-X; 0-06-027768-8 (lib bdg)
LC 98-29851
A collection of poetic portraits of sixteen famous Americans from Paul Revere to Neil Armstrong, by such authors as Jane Yolen, Nikki Grimes, and X. J. Kennedy
"Hopkins's eloquent introduction praises the power of poetry. Concluding 'Notes on the Lives' give readers useful biographical information. Full-page portraits feature Staub's distinctive, flat, primitive style, and their backgrounds have details particular to the subject. . . . A winning combination of poems and illustrations." SLJ

Marvelous math; a book of poems; selected by Lee Bennett Hopkins; illustrated by Karen Barbour. Simon & Schuster Bks. for Young Readers 1997 31p il $17; pa $6.99 (4 and up) **811.008**
1. Mathematics—Poetry 2. American poetry—Collections
ISBN 0-689-80658-2; 0-689-84442-5 (pa)
LC 96-21597
Presents such poems as "Math Makes Me Feel Safe," "Fractions," "Pythagoras," and "Time Passes," by such writers as Janet S. Wong, Lee Bennett Hopkins, and Ilo Orleans
"Rhymed and open verse styles are represented, as are a variety of tones. . . . Barbour's lively illustrations dance and play around the poems. Her boldly outlined watercolor figures, often wearing ill-fitting hats, fill the pages with childlike whimsy." SLJ

More spice than sugar; poems about feisty females; compiled by Lillian Morrison; illustrated by Ann Boyajian. Houghton Mifflin 2001 80p il $15 (4 and up) **811.008**
1. Women—Poetry 2. American poetry—Collections
ISBN 0-618-06892-9   LC 00-31947

"Morrison's selections tell of real and imagined girls and women famous or nameless, but all true-to-life. . . . These poems are accessible, inspiring, and challenging. . . . Boyajian's black-and-white spot illustrations decorate every page without hampering the effect of the words." SLJ

My America; a poetry atlas of the United States; selected by Lee Bennett Hopkins; illustrated by Stephen Alcorn. Simon & Schuster Bks. for Young Readers 2000 83p il $21.95 (4 and up) **811.008**
1. United States—Poetry 2. American poetry—Collections
ISBN 0-689-81247-7   LC 98-47402

A collection of poems evocative of seven geographical regions of the United States, including the Northeast, Southeast, Great Lakes, Plains, Mountain, Southwest, and Pacific Coast States
"Some poems are purposive, but the best . . . capture places and people in all their diversity. Stephen Alcorn's handsome, multi-textured pictures . . . avoid literal interpretation and capture the sweep of the land and the rhythm of the words." Booklist

My black me; a beginning book of black poetry; edited by Arnold Adoff. {rev. ed.}. Dutton Children's Bks. 1994 83p $14.99; pa $6.99 (5 and up) **811.008**
1. American poetry—African American authors—Collections
ISBN 0-525-45216-8; 0-14-037443-4 (pa)
First published 1974
A compilation of poems reflecting thoughts on being black by such authors as Langston Hughes, Lucille Clifton, Nikki Giovanni, and Imamu Amiri Baraka

The New Oxford book of American verse; chosen and edited by Richard Ellmann. Oxford Univ. Press 1976 liv, 1076p $49.95 (7 and up) **811.008**
1. American poetry—Collections
ISBN 0-19-502058-8
Replaces The Oxford book of American verse, edited by F. O. Matthiessen (1950)
"This volume begins with Anne Bradstreet, who died in 1672, and ends with Imamu Amiri Baraka (LeRoy Jones), born in 1934. . . . A few ballads and folk songs, and one hymn are . . . included. Most of the poets are represented with some amplitude so as to give a sense of their range and variety." Introduction

The Oxford book of children's verse in America; edited by Donald Hall. Oxford Univ. Press 1985 xxxviii, 319p $39.95; pa $19.95 **811.008**
1. American poetry—Collections
ISBN 0-19-503539-9; 0-19-506761-4 (pa)
LC 84-20755
"Hall's intention, expressed in the introduction, is to create an anthology of American poetry actually written for or adopted by children during a particular historical period. The emphasis is on authenticity rather than personal taste." SLJ

The Oxford book of children's verse in America—*Continued*

"A fine and carefully winnowed collection of American poetry is gathered in a book that will interest students of children's literature and young people who simply enjoy browsing." Horn Book

The **Pain** tree, and other teenage angst-ridden poetry; collected and illustrated by Esther Pearl Watson and Mark Todd. Houghton Mifflin 2000 62p il $16; pa $6.95 (7 and up)

               811.008

1. Teenagers' writings 2. American poetry—Collections

ISBN 0-618-01588-2; 0-618-04758-1 (pa)

               LC 99-48905

This is a "collection of poetry culled from teen Web sites and magazines. Throughout the 25 selections, the young people address a wide range of emotions while coping with the trials of growing up, sometimes under less than ideal circumstances." SLJ

"Readers will be struck by the brutal honesty of this collection. . . . Watson and Todd have managed to compile a collection that will strike a chord with teen readers." Voice Youth Advocates

Paint me like I am; teen poems from WritersCorps. HarperTempest 2003 128p lib bdg $16.89; pa $6.99 (7 and up)   **811.008**

1. American poetry—Collections 2. Teenagers' writings

ISBN 0-06-029288-1 (lib bdg); 0-06-447264-7 (pa)

               LC 2002-5942

"The teen voices in these poems, collected from the WritersCorps youth program, are LOUD—raging, defiant, giddy, lusty, and hopeful. Grouped into arbitrary categories, the poems explore identity, creative expressions, family, neighborhood, drugs, and relationships. . . . A foreword from Nikki Giovanni rounds out this moving collection, which also includes a few thoughtful writing exercises." Booklist

The **Place** my words are looking for; what poets say about and through their work; selected by Paul B. Janeczko. Bradbury Press 1990 150p il $17.95 (4 and up)   **811.008**

1. American poetry—Collections 2. Poetics

ISBN 0-02-747671-5   LC 89-39331

"More than forty contemporary poets are included: Eve Merriam, X. J. Kennedy, Felice Holman, Gary Soto, Mark Vinz, Karla Kuskin, and John Updike, among others. Their contributions vary widely in theme and mood and style, though the preponderance of the pieces are written in modern idiom and unrhymed meter. The accompanying comments frequently are as insightful and eloquent as the poems themselves." Horn Book

A **Poem** of her own; voices of American women yesterday and today; edited by Catherine Clinton; illustrated by Stephen Alcorn. Abrams 2003 79p il $17.95   **811.008**

1. American poetry—Women authors—Collections

ISBN 0-8109-4240-2   LC 2002-12851

Presents a collection of more than twenty poems by American women published between 1678 and 2001. In-

cludes poems by Phillis Wheatley, Gertrude Stein, Lucille Clifton, Sandra Cisneros, and Naomi Shihab Nye

"The intelligent selection is matched by the fresh, open design, highlighted by Alcorn's exciting paintings, executed in light-fast casein paint." Booklist

Poetry from the masters: the pioneers; edited by Wade Hudson; illustrated by Stephan J. Hudson. Just Us Books 2003 88p il pa $9.95 (7 and up)

               811.008

1. American poetry—African American authors—Collections 2. African American authors

ISBN 0-940975-96-3

This book "focuses on a particular group of black poets, 'trailblazers' who forged a path by overcoming 'almost impossible obstacles.' Hudson puts these writers in perspective and provides a social and literary context. Eleven poets are profiled, starting with Phillis Wheatley and ending with Gwendolyn Brooks. . . . Each writer is introduced with a brief biographical sketch that highlights his or her literary significance and contributions, followed by the full text of two or more poems. . . . This is an excellent resource for students seeking research materials or just looking for wonderful examples of poetry to read." SLJ

Includes bibliographical references

A **Poke** in the I; {selected by} Paul Janeczko; illustrated by Chris Raschka. Candlewick Press 2001 35p il $16.99; pa $7.99 (4 and up)

               811.008

1. American poetry—Collections

ISBN 0-7636-0661-8; 0-7636-2376-8 (pa)

               LC 00-33675

"Thirty concrete poems of all shapes and sizes are carefully laid on large white spreads, extended by Raschka's quirky watercolor and paper-collage illustrations. . . . Beautiful and playful, this title should find use in storytimes, in the classroom, and just for pleasure anywhere." SLJ

Quiet storm; voices of young Black poets; selected by Lydia Omolola Okutoro. Jump at the Sun 1999 102p $16.99; pa $4.99 (7 and up)

               811.008

1. American poetry—African American authors—Collections 2. African Americans—Poetry

ISBN 0-7868-0461-0; 0-7868-1320-2 (pa)

               LC 98-30346

"Individual chapters include selections about Black pride, the '. . . Poets as Keeper of the Oral Tradition,' home and homelessness, spirituality, love, freedom, the future, and '. . . Our Elders.' Many of the poems will have relevance to their audience and the book could be a helpful tool when approaching the genre thematically." SLJ

Red hot salsa; bilingual poems on being young and Latino in the United States; edited by Lori Marie Carlson; introduction by Oscar Hijuelos. 1st ed. Henry Holt 2005 140p $14.95 (7 and up)

               811.008

1. American poetry—Hispanic American authors—Collections 2. Hispanic Americans—Poetry 3. Bilingual books—English-Spanish

ISBN 0-8050-7616-6   LC 2004-54005

Red hot salsa—*Continued*

This is a "bilingual collection of poems that appear in both Spanish and English. Included are many well-known writers, such as Gary Soto and Luis J. Rodriguez . . . as well as emerging poets. . . . The poems often speak about the complex challenges of being bicultural. . . . Most poems are translated by the poets themselves, and many are written in an inventive blend of languages, which English speakers will easily follow with help from the appended glossary. Powerful and immediate." Booklist

Reflections on a gift of watermelon pickle—and other modern verse; {compiled by} Stephen Dunning, Edward Lueders, Hugh Smith. Lothrop, Lee & Shepard Bks. 1967 c1966 139p il $19.99 (6 and up) **811.008**

1. American poetry—Collections

ISBN 0-688-41231-9

First published 1966 by Scott, Foresman in a text edition

"Although some of the {114} selections are by recognized modern writers, many are by minor or unknown poets, and few will be familiar to the reader. Nearly all are fresh in approach and contemporary in expression. . . . Striking photographs complementing or illuminating many of the poems enhance the attractiveness of the volume." Booklist

Roots & flowers; poets and poems on family; edited by Liz Rosenberg. Holt & Co. 2001 244p il $21.95 (7 and up) **811.008**

1. American poetry—Collections 2. Poets, American

ISBN 0-8050-6433-8   LC 00-59663

An "anthology from 40 contemporary poets (some famous, some lesser known), all touching somehow on the subject of family. As an added attraction, the poets have included a family snapshot and a brief note on their family and its effect on their poetry. The selections are well chosen, and the personal details in the notes may help to draw some readers more eagerly into the poems." SLJ

Salting the ocean; 100 poems by young poets; selected by Naomi Shihab Nye; pictures by Ashley Bryan. Greenwillow Bks. 2000 111p il $16.99 (4 and up) **811.008**

1. Children's writings 2. American poetry—Collections

ISBN 0-688-16193-6   LC 99-30590

"These poems are divided into four topics: The Self and the Inner World, Where We Live, Anybody's Family, and the Wide Imagination." Horn Book Guide

"Nye presents the exceptional work of students in grades 1 through 12. . . . Illustrated with Ashley Bryan's signature bright-hued, bold-lined paintings and multicultural imagery, the poems are varied in both sophistication and subject." Booklist

Includes bibliographical references

Shimmy shimmy shimmy like my sister Kate; looking at the Harlem Renaissance through poems; {edited by} Nikki Giovanni. Holt & Co. 1995 186p $17.95 **811.008**

1. American poetry—African American authors—Collections 2. Harlem Renaissance

ISBN 0-8050-3494-3   LC 95-38617

This anthology includes poems by such authors as Paul Laurence Dunbar, Langston Hughes, Countee Cullen, Gwendolyn Brooks, and Amiri Baraka. Commentary and a discussion of the development of African American arts known as the Harlem Renaissance is provided by editor Giovanni

Includes bibliographical references

Soul looks back in wonder; {illustrated by} Tom Feelings. Dial Bks. 1993 unp il $16.99; pa $7.99 (4 and up) **811.008**

1. American poetry—African American authors—Collections

ISBN 0-8037-1001-1; 0-14-056501-9 (pa)

LC 93-824

Coretta Scott King award for illustrations, 1994

Artwork and poems by such writers as Maya Angelou, Langston Hughes, and Askia Toure portray the creativity, strength, and beauty of their African American heritage

"This thoughtful collection of poetry is unique. . . . Feelings selected sketches done while he was in West Africa, South America, and at home in America. The original drawings were enhanced with colored pencils, colored papers, stencil cut-outs, and other techniques to give a collage effect. Marbled textures bring vibrancy to the work." Horn Book

Stone bench in an empty park; selected by Paul Janeczko; with photographs by Henri Silberman. Orchard Bks. 2000 unp il $15.95 (4 and up) **811.008**

1. City and town life—Poetry 2. Haiku 3. Poetry—Collections

ISBN 0-531-30259-8   LC 99-44282

"The poets, ranging from Buson to James Berry, capture urban sights and scenes in haiku that, while including city images of icicles, cats, and spring winds, also celebrate newsstands, car washes, traffic, and stickball." Horn Book

Silberman's black-and-white photographs "were taken in response to the selected haikus, and they offer visuals that are sometimes elucidation, sometimes illustration, and sometimes counterpoint." Bull Cent Child Books

Three centuries of American poetry, 1623-1923; edited by Allen Mandelbaum and Robert D. Richardson, Jr. Bantam Bks. 1999 733p hardcover o.p. paperback available $20 **811.008**

1. American poetry—Collections

ISBN 0-553-37518-0 (pa)   LC 98-31408

This anthology contains works by well-known poets (Bradstreet, Whitman, Dickinson, Stevens) as well as obscure names such as Ellen Sturgis Hooper and Lucretia Davidson. Spirituals, popular song lyrics and Native American poems are included

Very best (almost) friends; poems of friendship; collected by Paul B. Janeczko; illustrated by Christine Davenier. Candlewick Press 1999 37p il $12.99 (4 and up) **811.008**

1. Friendship—Poetry 2. American poetry—Collections

ISBN 0-7636-0475-5   LC 98-10782

Very best (almost) friends—*Continued*
A collection of poems celebrating the good and bad
things about friendship, giving, loneliness, and love, by
such authors as Myra Cohn Livingston, John Ciardi, and
Gwendolyn Brooks
"The jacket, with its illustration of two friends gig-
gling, hints at the fun to be found within, and the watercolors inside depict children in every possible attitude of
friendship, in all its permutations." Horn Book

When the rain sings; poems by young Native
Americans. Simon & Schuster Bks. for Young
Readers 1999 96p $16   **811.008**
1. Native Americans—Poetry 2. American poetry—
Collections 3. Children's writings
ISBN 0-689-82283-9   LC 98-31784
A collection of poems written by young Native Amer-
icans, inspired by or matched with photographs of arti-
facts and people from the National Museum of the
American Indian
"The poems vary in intensity, mood, and complexity,
but the poets' voices are unwavering in their sincerity
and passion." Booklist

Whisper and shout; poems to memorize; edited by
Patrice Vecchione. Cricket Bks. 2002 120p
$16.95 (4 and up)   **811.008**
1. American poetry—Collections
ISBN 0-8126-2656-7   LC 2002-591
A collection of poems on different subjects and in dif-
ferent styles, that lend themselves to memorization.
Among the poets represented are Jack Prelutsky, Edward
Lear, Ogden Nash, T. S. Eliot, Edna St. Vincent Millay,
Christina Rossetti, and Lewis Carroll
"With a lengthy, enthusiastic introduction and a gener-
ous final section of resources and biographies, this an-
thology will get as much use in the classroom as with in-
dividual readers." Booklist
Includes bibliographical references

Wicked poems; edited by Roger McGough;
illustrated by Neal Layton. Bloomsbury
Children's Books 2004 208p il $15 (4 and up)
            811.008
1. Good and evil—Poetry 2. Poetry—Collections
ISBN 1-582-34854-5   LC 2002-38551
"The 134 poems in this . . . collection focus on people exhibiting various degrees of wickedness. The book
includes works from well-known poets . . . and children's authors such as Shel Silverstein, Eve Merriam,
Myra Cohn Livingston, and Jack Prelutsky. . . . Childlike, black-and-white cartoons are laugh-out-loud funny.
. . . A perfect choice for reading aloud as well as independent browsing." SLJ

Words with wings; a treasury of
African-American poetry and art; selected by
Belinda Rochelle. HarperCollins Pubs. 2001 unp
il lib bdg $16.99 (4 and up)   **811.008**
1. American poetry—African American authors—Collections 2. African Americans in art 3. African Americans—Poetry
ISBN 0-688-16415-3   LC 00-26864
"Amistad"

Pairs twenty works of art by African-American artists
such as Horace Pippin and Jacob Lawrence with twenty
poems by African-American poets such as Langston
Hughes, Countee Cullen, and Lucille Clifton
"Most of the combinations are stunning. . . . Short
biographical paragraphs on each poet and artist round out
this moving presentation." SLJ

812   American drama

Gustafson, Chris, 1950-
Acting out; reader's theatre across the
curriculum. Linworth Pub. 2002 195p pa $36.95
            812
1. Readers' theater 2. Drama in education
ISBN 1-58683-064-3   LC 2002-30172
"Some of the book's pieces are adapted from current
literature for children and young adults. Others come
from works in the public domain. The rest are original
plays. . . . The book is easy to use. The introduction answers all the reader's questions about reader's theatre
including using it with classes; writing scripts; writing
character monologues; student-written reader's theatre;
and grading standards." Libr Media Connect
Includes bibliographical references

Soto, Gary
Novio boy; a play. Harcourt Brace & Co. 1997
78p pa $8 (7 and up)   **812**
1. Dating (Social customs)—Drama 2. Mexican Americans—Drama
ISBN 0-15-201531-0   LC 96-32605
Rudy anxiously prepares for and then goes out on a
first date with an attractive girl who is older than he is
"A hip, funny play. . . . Since the Mexican-American
cast spouts frequent Spanish words, several lines of dialogue could be lost on an audience unfamiliar with the
language. The visual clues of a live performance might
serve to clarify some unfamiliar words. . . . Young actors should be able to perform this entertaining play with
or without adult assistance." SLJ

Surface, Mary Hall
Short scenes and monologues for middle school
actors. Smith & Kraus 1999 183p (Young actor
series) pa $11.95   **812**
1. Acting 2. Monologues
ISBN 1-57525-179-5   LC 99-52457
A collection of original scenes and monologues written especially for middle-school actors
"A welcome find for young actors in search of material for auditions." SLJ
Includes bibliographical references

With their eyes; September 11th: the view from a high school at ground zero; edited by Annie Thoms; created by Taresh Batra [et al.]; photos by Ethan Moses. HarperTempest 2002 228p il lib bdg $17.89; pa $6.99 (7 and up)

    812

1. Stuyvesant High School (New York, N.Y.) 2. September 11 terrorist attacks, 2001—Drama
ISBN 0-06-051806-5 (lib bdg); 0-06-051718-2 (pa)
    LC 2002-4552
"The students of Stuyvesant High School watched through their classroom windows as the World Trade Center was attacked on September 11. This book contains the play that they created based on what students, teachers, janitors, and others within their school community experienced." Voice Youth Advocates

"The speakers reveal their emotions with painful honesty. . . . The book is an obvious choice for reader's theater and for use across the curriculum; its deeply affecting contents will also make compelling personal-interest reading." Booklist

812.008 American drama-- Collections

Great monologues for young actors; Craig Slaight, Jack Sharrar, editors. Smith & Kraus 1992-1999 2v v1 pa $11.95; v2 pa $14.95

    812.008

1. Monologues 2. Acting
ISBN 1-880399-03-2 (v1); 0-57525-106-X (v2)
"The Young Actors series."
These volumes provide an introduction and acting notes for monologues for men and women drawn from contemporary and classic works

Lamedman, Debbie
111 one-minute monologues; the ultimate audition book for teens. Smith & Kraus 2002 117p (Young actor series) pa $11.95   **812.008**
1. Monologues 2. Acting
ISBN 1-57525-353-4   LC 2002-30413
A collection of 111 original monologues, all about one minute long, to be used by male and female teenage actors in auditions
"Any teen looking for audition material will love this book. . . . The wording is clear, concise, and to the point in all of the selections." SLJ

Millennium monologs; 95 contemporary characterizations for young actors; edited by Gerald Lee Ratliff. Meriwether 2002 261p pa $15.95   **812.008**
1. Monologues 2. Acting
ISBN 1-56608-082-7   LC 2002-13009
An anthology of monologues by contemporary writers, divided into four categories: "Hope and Longing," "Spirit and Soul," "Fun and Fantasy," and "Doubt and Despair." Includes audition techniques
"This fine collection of American monologues is notable for its diversity as well as for the high quality of the material." Booklist

Theatre for young audiences; 20 great plays for children; edited by Coleman A. Jennings; foreword by Maurice Sendak. St. Martin's Press 1998 604p il $35; pa $19.95   **812.008**
1. Drama—Collections
ISBN 0-312-18194-9; 0-312-33714-0 (pa)
    LC 97-36542
A collection of plays, many of which are based on favorite children's tales, including such titles as: "Charlotte's Web," "Really Rosie," "Wiley and the Hairy Man," "Wise Men of Chelm," and "The Crane Wife"
"Highly recommended for school and public libraries and anyone interested in a substantial collection of plays for children." Booklist

You're on!: seven plays in English and Spanish; selected by Lori Marie Carlson. Morrow Junior Bks. 1999 139p $17 (4 and up)
    812.008
1. Hispanic Americans—Drama 2. American drama—Collections 3. Bilingual books—English-Spanish
ISBN 0-688-16237-1   LC 99-17222
This includes plays by Gary Soto, Pura Belpré, Denise Ruiz, Federico Garcia Lorca, Elena Castedo, Alfonsina Storni, and Óscar Hijuelos
"Each play is presented in both English and Spanish. Although the selections are short (anywhere from 3 to 10 pages), they vary greatly in complexity and style. . . . This unique resource will enrich any library's performing arts collection and be especially useful for those libraries serving Latino communities." Booklist

813.009 American fiction--History and criticism

Bernard, Catherine
Understanding To kill a mockingbird. Lucent Books 2003 112p il map (Understanding great literature) $27.45 (7 and up)   **813.009**
1. Lee, Harper, 1926-. To kill a mockingbird
ISBN 1-560-06860-4   LC 2002-156251
An introduction to Harper Lee's famous novel, "To Kill a Mockingbird," discussing the author's life, the historical context of the novel, its plot, themes, characters, literary criticism, and pertinence for today's audiences.
Includes bibliographical references

Bloom, Susan P.
Presenting Avi; {by} Susan P. Bloom, Cathryn M. Mercier. Twayne Pubs. 1997 206p il (Twayne's young adult authors series) $30 (7 and up)   **813.009**
1. Avi, 1937-
ISBN 0-8057-4569-6   LC 96-53878
A critical introduction to the life and work of the prolific writer of young adult and children's books
"The text shows painstakingly careful reading of Avi's work." SLJ
Includes bibliographical references

Brown, Joanne, 1933-
Presenting Kathryn Lasky. Twayne Pubs. 1998
173p il (Twayne's young adult authors series) $30
                              813.009
1. Lasky, Kathryn
ISBN 0-8057-1677-7   LC 98-35177
A critical introduction to the life and work of the author of such novels as The bone wars, The night journey,
and Memoirs of a bookbat and of nonfiction works
Includes bibliographical references

Carroll, Pamela S.
Caroline Cooney: faith and fiction; {by} Pamela
Sissi Carroll. Scarecrow Press 2001 129p
(Scarecrow studies in young adult literature) lib
bdg $31.50 (7 and up)   **813.009**
1. Cooney, Caroline B., 1947-
ISBN 0-8108-4068-5   LC 2001-31080
"Including descriptions of Cooney's writing process,
her dedication to her target audience . . . her strong personal beliefs, and her broad range of publication, the
book presents a clear picture of this popular and princi-
pled author's just-enough approach to violence, conflict,
and romance. . . . Technique, central themes, and biblical connections are part of each analysis, making this
book an excellent model for studying Cooney's subsequent works." Voice Youth Advocates
Includes bibliographical references

Crew, Hilary S.
Is it really Mommie Dearest? daughter-mother
narratives in young adult fiction. Scarecrow Press
2000 285p $51.50   **813.009**
1. Young adult literature—History and criticism
2. Mother-daughter relationships in literature
ISBN 0-8108-3692-0   LC 99-48315
"Mining a treasure trove of more than 100 young
adult novels and short stories published between 1965-
1998, Crew identifies and explains complicated relationships between mothers and daughters. . . . The author
places the literature alongside the analysis with scholarship and finesse. An outstanding offering." SLJ
Includes bibliographical references

Crowe, Chris
Presenting Mildred D. Taylor. Twayne Pubs.
1999 162p il (Twayne's United States authors
series) $35 (7 and up)   **813.009**
1. Taylor, Mildred D.
ISBN 0-8057-1687-4   LC 99-25527
Crowe "shows how much of Taylor's fiction is rooted
in her extended family's storytelling tradition and in her
personal experience growing up with racism and violence, sustained by her family's loving support and pride.
He discusses her books in their historical context, including her Newbery award winner, *Roll of Thunder, Hear
My Cry* (1976), and provides a background chapter on
the civil rights movement in Mississippi." Booklist
Includes bibliographical references

Hogan, Walter
The agony and the eggplant; Daniel Pinkwater's
heroic struggles in the name of YA literature.
Scarecrow Press 2001 159p (Scarecrow studies in
young adult literature) $28.95 (7 and up)
                              813.009
1. Pinkwater, Daniel Manus, 1941-
ISBN 0-8108-3994-6   LC 00-67047
"The book opens with a chronology of Pinkwater's
life, then is divided into chapters detailing his life and
the stages of his works. A few chapters are dedicated to
individual novels. . . . An engaging and enjoyable resource." Book Rep
Includes bibliographical references

Jones, Patrick
What's so scary about R.L. Stine? Scarecrow
Press 1998 xxvii, 249p il $35.50   **813.009**
1. Stine, R. L., 1943-
ISBN 0-8108-3468-5   LC 98-8374
"Based on interviews and articles by experts in the
fields of literature and psychology, this book includes
Jones's own viewpoint to build a powerful argument for
appreciating and evaluating Stine's style, popularity, and
contribution to young adult literature. . . . This is a sure
bet for reports." SLJ
Includes bibliographical references

Krull, Kathleen, 1952-
Presenting Paula Danziger. Twayne Pubs. 1995
109p il (Twayne's young adult authors series) $30
                              813.009
1. Danziger, Paula, 1944-2004
ISBN 0-8057-4153-4   LC 94-42014
"Open about her personal problems, Danziger told
Krull about her battles with bulimia and the problems of
a difficult early family life. Her humorous experiences as
a teacher are chronicled, as is her success as a funny and
sought-after speaker. Krull groups her discussions of
Danziger's books into six thematic chapters, covering a
total of 15 novels." Booklist
Includes bibliographical references

MacRae, Cathi Dunn
Presenting young adult fantasy fiction. Twayne
Pubs. 1998 xxx, 464p (Twayne's young adult
authors series) $30 (7 and up)   **813.009**
1. Fantasy fiction—History and criticism
ISBN 0-8057-8220-6   LC 98-12896
MacRae "examines alternate worlds, magic realism,
myth, legend, magic bestiary, and time fantasy. She includes in-depth critical analysis and interviews with four
authors: Terry Brooks, Barbara Hambly, Jane Yolen, and
Meredith Anne Pierce." Booklist
The author "is obviously enamored of her subject and
its writers; her enthusiasm is contagious, and her research outstandingly useful." Bull Cent Child Books
Includes bibliographical references

Nilsen, Alleen Pace

Presenting M.E. Kerr. updated ed. Twayne Pubs. 1997 173p il (Twayne's young adult authors series) $30 (7 and up)   **813.009**

1. Kerr, M. E., 1927-
ISBN 0-8057-9248-1   LC 96-39134
First published 1986

A critical introduction to the life and work of the young adult novelist M. E. Kerr

"The book is well researched and includes numerous quotes from two lengthy interviews. Nilsen skillfully combines biographical information and literary criticism in an inviting manner, creating a professional resource that can be enjoyed for personal reading and utilized for research." Voice Youth Advocates

Includes bibliographical references

Reed, Arthea J. S.

Norma Fox Mazer; a writer's world. Scarecrow Press 2000 140p (Scarecrow studies in young adult literature) $36 (7 and up)   **813.009**

1. Mazer, Norma Fox, 1931-
ISBN 0-8108-3814-1   LC 00-38759

"Quoting heavily from the author herself and published reviews of her work, the author provides a chronology of major events in Mazer's life and then goes into deeper detail about her subject's childhood and adolescence and how her upbringing played a vital role in her novels and partnership with her husband, Harry Mazer. Several works are comprehensively analyzed." SLJ

Includes bibliographical references

Reid, Suzanne Elizabeth

Presenting Cynthia Voigt. Twayne Pubs. 1995 133p il (Twayne's young adult authors series) $30   **813.009**

1. Voigt, Cynthia
ISBN 0-8057-8219-2   LC 94-44197

This work "provides a brief biography and then comprehensive, in-depth analysis of each of Voigt's novels. . . . Reid quotes from a range of critical reviews, but her own literary analysis is almost entirely positive. The focus is on interpretation, and she does a fine job of identifying Voigt's dominant themes—the challenge to traditional gender roles, the emphasis on work, etc.—in a style that's both scholarly and stimulating." Booklist

Includes bibliographical references

Presenting young adult science fiction. Twayne Pubs. 1998 230p (Twayne's young adult authors series) $31   **813.009**

1. Science fiction—History and criticism
ISBN 0-8057-1653-X   LC 98-35178

A critical introduction to science fiction authors Orson Scott Card, Douglas Hill, H. M. Hoover, Pamela Sargent, Octavia Butler, Pamela Service, Piers Anthony, and Douglas Adams, with chapters discussing the classical masters of science fiction, cyberpunk, Star trek, and new themes and trends

Includes filmography and bibliographical references

Stover, Lois T.

Presenting Phyllis Reynolds Naylor; {by} Lois Thomas Stover. Twayne Pubs. 1997 187p il (Twayne's young adult authors series) $30   **813.009**

1. Naylor, Phyllis Reynolds, 1933-
ISBN 0-8057-7805-5   LC 96-36022

Examines the major works of the author of the Newbery Award-winning "Shiloh," provides biographical background, and discusses some of the efforts to censor her work

"A scholarly work that provides fascinating insights into Naylor's writing." Voice Youth Advocates

Includes bibliographical references

815 American speeches

American Heritage book of great American speeches for young people; edited by Suzanne McIntire. Wiley 2001 292p il pa $14.95 (7 and up)   **815**

1. American speeches
ISBN 0-471-38942-0   LC 00-43749

This is a "compendium of more than 100 speeches that span nearly 400 years of American history, from Powhatan (1609) to Senator Charles Robb (2000). Prominent orators include Patrick Henry, Thomas Jefferson, John Kennedy, Richard Nixon, Martin Luther King, Jr., and Malcolm X. . . . The speeches inform readers and provide examples of how the spoken word has affected Americans throughout our past." SLJ

Historic speeches of African Americans; introduced and selected by Warren J. Halliburton. Watts 1993 192p il (African-American experience) lib bdg $23; pa $6.95   **815**

1. African Americans—History 2. American speeches
ISBN 0-531-11034-6 (lib bdg); 0-531-15677-x (pa)   LC 92-39318

Presents speeches by various African American religious and political leaders from the days of slavery to the present, along with biographical information and historical background

"Kids will dip into this for personal reading, and for curriculum research; they'll also find stirring pieces to read aloud and think about. The detailed sources at the end of the book make it easy to find out more about the individuals and their ideas." Booklist

UXL Asian American voices; edited by Deborah Gillan Straub. 2nd ed. UXL, Thomson\Gale 2004 xxv, 315p il $58   **815**

1. Asian Americans 2. Speeches
ISBN 0-7876-7600-4   LC 2003-110048
First published 1997 with title: Asian American voices

This "reference presents full or excerpted speeches, sermons, orations, poems, testimony and other notable spoken words of Asian Americans. Each entry is accompanied by an introduction and boxes explaining terms and events to which the speech refers. The volume is illustrated with photographs and drawings." Publisher's note

821 English poetry

Cohen, Barbara, 1932-1992
Canterbury tales; [by] Geoffrey Chaucer; selected, translated, and adapted by Barbara Cohen; illustrated by Trina Schart Hyman. Lothrop, Lee & Shepard Bks. 1988 87p il $24.99 (4 and up) **821**
1. Chaucer, Geoffrey, d. 1400—Adaptations
ISBN 0-688-06201-6 LC 86-21045
Contents: The nun's priest's tale; The pardoner's tale; The wife of Bath's tale; The franklin's tale
"Cohen's evident love and respect for Chaucer's writing keep her close to the text. Her writing retains the flavor of the times and the spirit of Chaucer's words while her prose retelling, enriched by Hyman's lively full-color paintings, enhances the book's appeal to young people. . . . An excellent introduction to *The Canterbury Tales* for young readers." Booklist

Coleridge, Samuel Taylor, 1772-1834
Samuel Taylor Coleridge; edited by James Engell; illustrated by Harvey Chan. Sterling 2003 48p il (Poetry for young people) $14.95
821
ISBN 0-8069-6951-2 LC 2003-6549
Introduces the life of author Samuel Taylor Coleridge and presents a sample of his poetry, including complete works and excerpts, with a brief, explanatory introduction to each
"Chan's enchanting paintings embellish the text and do a nice job of capturing the mood of the poetry without dominating it. . . . A useful purchase for any collection." SLJ

Hirsch, Robin
F E G: ridiculous stupid poems for intelligent children; with the assistance of Benjamin Joshua Jaglom Hirsch and a critical introduction by Alexander Max Jaglom Hirsch; illustrated by Ha. Little, Brown 2002 48p il $15.95 (5 and up)
821
1. Humorous poetry
ISBN 0-316-36344-8 LC 00-64965
"Megan Tingley books"
Title appears with "stupid" crossed out
This "collection celebrates wordplay, including acrostics, palindromes, and spoonerisms, within the confines of various poetic forms. Lengthy footnotes—usually meandering, sometimes goofy—help elucidate the clever poetry." Horn Book Guide
Includes glossary

Liu, Alan, 1953-
William Wordsworth; edited by Alan Liu; illustrated by James Muir. Sterling 2003 48p il (Poetry for young people) $14.95 (7 and up)
821
ISBN 0-8069-8277-2 LC 2003-6163

An illustrated collection of nineteen popular poems by William Wordsworth, who was the poet laureate of England in the mid-nineteenth century. Includes an introduction to the poet's life and work
The editor has "chosen well, bringing together about 20 of [the] great poet's most accessible, compelling poems. . . . The full color paintings on each page are beautiful." Booklist

821.008 English poetry--Collections

Blushing: expressions of love in poems & letters; collected by Paul B. Janeczko. Orchard Bks. 2004 98p il lib bdg $15.95 (7 and up)
821.008
1. Love poetry 2. Poetry—Collections
ISBN 0-439-53056-3 LC 2003-48697
A collection of love poetry and letters by such authors as Lord Byron, William Shakespeare, Sir Walter Scott, Nikki Giovanni, Maya Angelou, Emily Dickinson, Elizabeth Barrett Browning, and Edna St. Vincent Millay
"Janeczko chooses a subject that will certainly draw interest, and the combination of letters and poetry offers a fine glimpse of what poets do: make beautiful, disciplined work from their deepest, undisciplined feelings." Booklist

Committed to memory; 100 best poems to memorize; edited, with an introduction, by John Hollander. Academy of American Poets 1996 196p **821.008**
1. English poetry—Collections 2. American poetry—Collections
Available in hardcover from Turtle Point Press $24.95 (ISBN 1-885983-15-8) and in paperback from Riverhead Bks. $14 (ISBN 1-57322-646-7)
Hollander "has selected 100 poems by poets—including lyrics and narratives, meditations and counsels—ranging from Blake and Hughes, Bishop and Thomas, to Yeats and Hayden. These are classics that lend themselves to memory, being short; often in form, or at least metrical; always rhythmic; and delightful." Libr J

The **Kingfisher** book of funny poems; selected by Roger McGough; illustrated by Caroline Holden. Kingfisher (NY) 2002 256p il $18.95 (4 and up)
821.008
1. Humorous poetry 2. English poetry—Collections
3. American poetry—Collections
ISBN 0-7534-5480-7 LC 2001-38942
A collection of over 200 poems, limericks, and verses from such authors as Emily Dickinson, Lewis Carroll, and Shel Silverstein
"This collection is chock-full of wacky, witty, and whimsical poems that will hook readers from the first stanza to the last. . . . What really brings out the humor are the equally zany black-and-white drawings that appear on almost every page." SLJ

The **Oxford** book of story poems; {compiled by} Michael Harrison and Christopher Stuart-Clark. Oxford Univ. Press 1990 175p il $25; pa $16.95
821.008
1. English poetry—Collections 2. American poetry—Collections
ISBN 0-19-276087-4; 0-19-276212-5 (pa)
LC 89-043715
This anthology contains "narrative verse by British and American poets, from traditional ballads such as 'Sir Patrick Spens' to contemporary poems such as Judith Nicholls' 'Storytime.' . . . {The poets include} Carroll, Keats, de la Mare, Kennedy, Lear, Lindsay, Longfellow, Noyes, Poe, Southey, and Tolkien. . . . A handy collection of story poems for reading aloud or alone." Booklist

The **Oxford** book of twentieth-century English verse; chosen by Philip Larkin. Oxford Univ. Press c1973 xlii, 654p $35   **821.008**
1. English poetry—Collections
ISBN 0-19-812137-7
This anthology of more than 600 poems by more than 200 twentieth-century British writers includes works by John Masefield, T. S. Eliot, W. B. Yeats, W. H. Auden, Dylan Thomas and Alan Sillitoe
"A strong vein of neo-Georgianism runs throughout the book, resulting in a clear partiality for work that is explicitly, even documentarily, English in locale, for poems that are narrative or anecdotal, for neat, well-populated fables and for moralistic ruminations." New Statesman

The **Oxford** treasury of time poems; {edited by} Michael Harrison and Christopher Stuart-Clark. Oxford Univ. Press 1999 155p il pa $14.95 hardcover o.p.   **821.008**
1. Time—Poetry 2. English poetry—Collections 3. American poetry—Collections
ISBN 0-19-276236-2   LC 98-5382
A collection of poems about the many aspects of time, by such authors as Emily Dickinson, David McCord, and D.H. Lawrence
"Appropriately accompanying the varied types of poems are a variety of art styles, including black-and-white sketches, woodcuts, lighthearted watercolors, rich landscapes, detailed portraits, and abstract modern paintings, all from 10 different artists." SLJ
Includes index

The **Random** House book of poetry for children; selected and introduced by Jack Prelutsky; illustrated by Arnold Lobel. Random House 1983 248p il $19.95; lib bdg $21.99
821.008
1. American poetry—Collections 2. English poetry—Collections
ISBN 0-394-85010-6; 0-394-95010-0 (lib bdg)
LC 83-2990
Opening poems for each section especially written for this anthology by Jack Prelutsky
In this anthology emphasis "is placed on humor and light verse; but serious and thoughtful poems are also included. . . . Approximately two thirds of the selections were written within the past forty years—the splendid contributions of such writers as John Ciardi, Aileen Fish-

er, Dennis Lee, Myra Cohn Livingston, David McCord, Eve Merriam, and Lilian Moore. {There are} . . . samplings of earlier poets from Shakespeare and Blake to Emily Dickinson and Walter de la Mare." Horn Book

822.3   William Shakespeare

Coville, Bruce
William Shakespeare's A midsummer night's dream; retold by Bruce Coville; pictures by Dennis Nolan. Dial Bks. 1996 unp il $17.95; pa $7.99
822.3
1. Shakespeare, William, 1564-1616—Adaptations
ISBN 0-8037-1784-9; 0-14-250168-9 (pa)
LC 94-12600
A simplified prose retelling of Shakespeare's play about the strange events that take place in a forest inhabited by fairies who magically transform the romantic fate of two young couples
"Coville introduces the story and also conveys something of the poetry and drama. Nolan's framed graphite and watercolor paintings express the dreaminess and absurdity of the play, and the pictures have a theatrical flair." Booklist

William Shakespeare's Romeo and Juliet; retold by Bruce Coville; pictures by Dennis Nolan. Dial Bks. 1999 il $16.99   **822.3**
1. Shakespeare, William, 1564-1616—Adaptations
ISBN 0-8037-2462-4   LC 98-36178
A simplified prose retelling of Shakespeare's play about two young people who defy their warring families' prejudices and dare to fall in love
"Coville's treatment is generally faithful to the original and is nicely enhanced by Dennis Nolan's lushly romantic illustrations. . . . This is an accessible and enticing introduction to one of Shakespeare's most popular works." Booklist

Dunton-Downer, Leslie
Essential Shakespeare handbook; [by] Leslie Dunton-Downer, Alan Riding. DK Pub 2004 480p il pa $25   **822.3**
1. Shakespeare, William, 1564-1616
ISBN 0-7894-9333-0   LC 2004-274586
This is an "illustrated guide to every play in the Shakespeare canon, as well as a portrait of the Bard's life and the world of Elizabethan and Jacobean theater." Publisher's note
"This is an excellent basic tool for gaining insight into the Bard's poetic genius. . . . It is an informative, visually enticing introduction to the world's most famous dramatist." SLJ

Ganeri, Anita, 1961-
The young person's guide to Shakespeare; with performances on CD by the Royal Shakespeare Company; book written by Anita Ganeri. Harcourt Brace & Co. 1999 55p il $25 (7 and up)
822.3
1. Shakespeare, William, 1564-1616
ISBN 0-15-202101-9   LC 98-53785

Ganeri, Anita, 1961- —*Continued*

Provides information about William Shakespeare's family life and work as a playwright and actor, summaries of his works, and details and challenges of staging Shakespearean productions. Includes a CD with performances of selected Shakespearean plays and sonnets by Britain's Royal Shakespeare Company

Garfield, Leon, 1921-1996

Shakespeare stories {I}-II; illustrated by Michael Foreman. Houghton Mifflin 1991-1995 c1985-c1994 2v il v1 $26; pa $17; v2 $26

822.3

1. Shakespeare, William, 1564-1616—Adaptations
ISBN 0-395-56397-6 (v1); 0-395-86140-3 (pa); 0-395-70893-1 (v2)

Original volume first published 1985 by Schocken Bks.

In these volumes Garfield has rewritten twenty-one of Shakespeare's plays in narrative form, retaining much of the original language

Lamb, Charles, 1775-1834

Tales from Shakespeare; by Charles & Mary Lamb   **822.3**

1. Shakespeare, William, 1564-1616—Adaptations
Hardcover and paperback editions available from various publishers

First published 1807

A now classic collection of twenty plays by Shakespeare adapted as prose stories—the comedies by Mary Lamb, the tragedies by Charles Lamb

"The *Tales* were the first version of 'Shakespeare' to be published specifically for children. They are written in a clear, vigorous style, not often encumbered by the attempt to make the language resemble that of the original. A lot is left out. . . . But the literary quality of the *Tales* makes them outshine almost every other English children's book of this period, and they proved an immediate and lasting success." Oxford Companion to Child Lit

Nesbit, E. (Edith), 1858-1924

The best of Shakespeare; introduction by Iona Opie; afterword by Peter Hunt. Oxford Univ. Press 1997 110p il (Iona and Peter Opie library of children's literature) pa $9.95 hardcover o.p. (4 and up)   **822.3**

1. Shakespeare, William, 1564-1616—Adaptations
ISBN 0-19-513213-0   LC 97-15223

Simplified prose retellings of Romeo and Juliet, Hamlet, The Merchant of Venice, Othello, The Tempest, King Lear, Macbeth, As You Like It, Twelfth Night, and The Winter's Tale

"These stories don't recapitulate every subplot but capture the essential events and retain a little of the original wording. . . . This volume features photographs from productions by the Royal Shakespeare Company in Stratford-upon-Avon, as well as several North American companies." Booklist

Packer, Tina, 1938-

Tales from Shakespeare; retold by Tina Packer ; illustrated by Gail de Marcken . . . {et al.}. Scholastic Press 2004 192p il $24.95

822.3

1. Shakespeare, William, 1564-1616—Adaptations
ISBN 0-439-32107-7   LC 2003-42710

A collection of prose retellings of ten familiar Shakespeare plays, each illustrated by a well-known artist or artists.

This is "a treasure trove of well-told tales. In these adaptations, Packer captures the essence of the playwright's words and ideas, placing them in concise and clearly told stories. . . . Each illustrator sets the appropriate tone for and conveys the mood of the tale, and the breadth of artistic interpretations gives the book appeal to a wide audience." SLJ

Rosen, Michael, 1946-

Shakespeare; his work and his world; illustrated by Robert Ingpen. Candlewick Press 2001 96p il $19.99   **822.3**

1. Shakespeare, William, 1564-1616 2. Seafaring life—Fiction 3. Pirates—Fiction
ISBN 0-7636-1568-4   LC 00-66689

"The volume begins with plot teasers from the plays and progresses through an explanation of Shakespeare's time and the locations important to his life and works. . . . There is a plethora of historical information, as well as an explanation of the types of theaters and plays common at the time." Book Rep

"In exceptionally fresh and vivid terms, the author plies readers with abundant, accurate information. . . . The copious and engaging pencil-and-watercolor illustrations have the burnished look of old pictures and are as glorious as the text." SLJ

Includes bibliographical references

Shakespeare, William, 1564-1616

One hundred and eleven Shakespeare monologues; the ultimate audition book for teens; edited by Lisa Bansavage and L. E. McCullough; introduction by Jill K. Swanson. Smith & Kraus 2003 (Young actor series) pa $11.95 (7 and up)

822.3

1. Monologues 2. Acting
ISBN 1-57525-356-9

"These monologues are divided into three sections: those for female actors, male actors, or either. They are further subdivided into comedies, histories, and tragedies. . . . The genius of this book is in the introduction, which offers a wealth of information for teens who have never encountered Shakespeare." SLJ

Shakespeare's world and work; an encyclopedia for students; John F. Andrews, editor in chief. Scribner 2001 3v il set $340 (7 and up)

822.3

1. Shakespeare, William, 1564-1616
ISBN 0-684-80629-0   LC 00-68743

This set "complements its examination of Shakespeare as literature with glimpses of the customs, beliefs, politics, and historical personages that had an impact on his

Shakespeare's world and work—*Continued*
writing. An attractive design and many student-friendly features help make a challenging topic palatable and even appealing." Booklist
Includes bibliographical references

Shellard, Dominic
William Shakespeare. Oxford Univ. Press 1998 120p il (British Library writers' lives) pa $15.95 hardcover o.p. (7 and up)   **822.3**
1. Shakespeare, William, 1564-1616
ISBN 0-19-521655-5   LC 99-206199
Shellard "weaves the known facts of Shakespeare's life and times with archival fragments and the conjectures that have grown from them. The difference between fact and speculation is always clearly presented. . . . The information is enhanced by excellent-quality full-color and black-and-white photographs, period reproductions, and drawings." SLJ
Includes bibliographical references

Stanley, Diane, 1943-
Bard of Avon: the story of William Shakespeare; by Diane Stanley and Peter Vennema; illustrated by Diane Stanley. Morrow Junior Bks. 1992 unp il $16.99; lib bdg $17.89; pa $6.99 (4 and up)   **822.3**
1. Dramatists
ISBN 0-688-09108-3; 0-688-09109-1 (lib bdg); 0-688-16294-0 (pa)   LC 90-46564
A brief biography of the world's most famous playwright, using only historically correct information
"A remarkably rounded picture of Shakespeare's life and the period in which he lived is presented . . . together with a thoughtful attempt to relate circumstances in his personal life to the content of his plays. . . . The text is splendidly supported by the illustrations, which are stylized, yet recognizable, and present a clear view of life in the late sixteenth century. A discerning, knowledgeable biography, rising far above the ordinary." Horn Book
Includes bibliographical references

Williams, Marcia, 1945-
Tales from Shakespeare; seven plays; presented and illustrated by Marcia Williams. Candlewick Press 1998 unp il $16.99; pa $7.99   **822.3**
1. Shakespeare, William, 1564-1616—Adaptations
ISBN 0-7636-0441-0; 0-7636-2323-7 (pa)
                LC 97-42165
"Each of the seven selections, *Hamlet, Romeo and Juliet, Macbeth, The Winter's Tale, Julius Caesar, Midsummer Night's Dream*, and *The Tempest* , is told as if it were on a stage, with cartoon panels carrying the actions and direct quotations from the play. The author's narration appears below the panels." SLJ
Williams "offers an inviting taste of the Shakespearean buffet, as well as a rare glimpse into the character of Elizabethan theater." Booklist

823.009   English fiction--History and criticism

Colbert, David
The magical worlds of Harry Potter; a treasury of myths, legends, and fascinating facts. Berkeley Hills Bks. 2002 c2001 209p il pa $14 (5 and up)
                823.009
1. Rowling, J. K.—Characters—Harry Potter
2. Fantasy fiction—History and criticism
ISBN 0-425-19891-X   LC 2002-20857
First published 2001 in the United Kingdom
"The 53 entries, most of them two to six pages in length, are arranged in alphabetical order by a highlighted keyword. For example, words such as 'Alchemy,' 'Animagus,' 'Grindylows,' 'Voldemort,' and 'wizards' are defined, traced to their usage in other tales, and given an expanded description. . . . Long after the enthusiasm for Harry and friends has abated, this small volume will serve as a resource to answer questions that may result from reading other stories in the genre." SLJ
Includes bibliographical references

Kronzek, Allan Zola
The sorcerer's companion; a guide to the magical world of Harry Potter; {by} Allan Zola Kronzek and Elizabeth Kronzek. Broadway Bks. 2001 286p il pa $15.95 (4 and up)
                823.009
1. Rowling, J. K.—Characters—Harry Potter
2. Fantasy fiction—History and criticism
ISBN 0-7679-1944-0   LC 2001-35659
"The material is interesting and informative, easy to read, and fairly wide-ranging." SLJ
Includes bibliographical references

Nardo, Don, 1947-
Understanding Frankenstein. Lucent Bks. 2003 128p il (Understanding great literature) lib bdg $27.45 (7 and up)   **823.009**
1. Shelley, Mary Wollstonecraft, 1797-1851
ISBN 1-59018-147-6   LC 2002-12560
Discusses Mary Shelley's sources of ideas for the compelling plot, well-developed characters, and universal themes of "Frankenstein" which have led to its enduring popularity
"The text is easy to understand. A solid introduction for middle school students." SLJ
Includes bibliographical references

860.8   Spanish literature--Collections

The **Tree** is older than you are; a bilingual gathering of poems & stories from Mexico with paintings by Mexican artists; selected by Naomi Shihab Nye. Simon & Schuster Bks. for Young Readers 1995 111p il pa $13.95 hardcover o.p. (7 and up)   **860.8**
1. Mexican literature—Collections 2. Bilingual books—English-Spanish
ISBN 0-689-82087-9   LC 95-1565

The Tree is older than you are—*Continued*
"This bilingual anthology of poems, stories, and paintings by Mexican writers and artists brims over with a sense of wonder and playful exuberance, its themes as varied and inventive as a child's imagination." Voice Youth Advocates

883 Classical Greek epic poetry and fiction

Homer
The Iliad; translated by Robert Fagles; introduction and notes by Bernard Knox. Viking 1990 683p $35; pa $15.95 **883**
1. Trojan War
ISBN 0-670-83510-2; 0-14-027536-3 (pa)
LC 89-70695
Homer's epic of the Trojan War
This "translation is lively . . . fun, [and] . . . a worthy companion to the best. Notes, introduction, bibliography, glossary of names." Booklist

The Odyssey; translated by Robert Fagles; introduction and notes by Bernard Knox. Viking 1996 541p $35; pa $14.95 **883**
ISBN 0-670-82162-4; 0-14-026886-3 (pa)
LC 96-17280
This is a verse translation of Homer's epic poem.
"Fagles' *Odyssey* is the one to put into the hands of younger, first-time readers, not least because of its paucity of notes, which, though sometimes frustrating, is a sign that translation has been used to do the work of explanation. Altogether, an outstanding piece of work." Booklist
Includes bibliographical references

McCarty, Nick
The Iliad; retold by Nick McCarty; illustrated by Victor Ambrus. Kingfisher (NY) 2000 95p il $22.95; pa $15.95 **883**
1. Trojan War
ISBN 0-7534-5330-4; 0-7534-5321-5 (pa)
LC 00-30442
A retelling of Homer's story of the Trojan War
"An exciting text in large print and action-packed illustrations create an accessible version of a classic tale." SLJ

895.1 Chinese literature

Liu Siyu, 1964-
A thousand peaks; poems from China; [by] Siyu Liu and Orel Protopopescu; illustrated by Siyu Liu. Pacific View Press 2002 52p il $19.95
895.1
1. Chinese poetry 2. Bilingual books—English-Chinese
ISBN 1-88189-624-2 LC 2001-34008
A collection of thirty-five poems spanning nineteen centuries, representing both famous and lesser-known poets, including both the Chinese text and a literal translation
This "is an anthology of considerable fascination and broad utility. . . . The layout is neat, tidily fitting each poem's material on a single page and adding a line drawing featuring a relevant Chinese character. The wealth of material here provides a more stimulating entree to Chinese history than any dry textbook." Bull Cent Child Books
Includes bibliographical references

896 African literatures

The **Penguin** book of modern African poetry; edited by Gerald Moore and Ulli Beier. 4th ed. Penguin Bks. 1999 xxvi, 448p pa $15.95
896
1. African poetry—Collections
ISBN 0-14-118100-1
First published 1963 in the United Kingdom with title: Modern poetry from Africa
This anthology includes over 200 poems by 67 poets from 23 countries
Includes bibliographical references

Talking drums; a selection of poems from Africa south of the Sahara; edited and illustrated by Véronique Tadjo. . Bloomsbury Children's Books 2003 96p il map $15.95 (5 and up)
896
1. African poetry—Collections
ISBN 1-582-34813-8 LC 2003-52173
Contents: Our universe; The animal kingdom; Love and celebrations; People; Death; Pride and defiance; The changing times
A collection of traditional and twentieth-century poems from sub-Saharan Africa, written in or translated into English, that expresses the spirit and history of this region.
"The contemporary and the traditional are both well represented in this lively anthology. . . . Illustrated with small, black-and-white folk-art drawings, the collection ranges widely, including poems of love, sorrow, and pride. . . . This [is a] fine resource for social studies and literature classes, which will also be great for reading aloud." Booklist
Includes glossary

897 North American native literatures

Dancing teepees: poems of American Indian youth; selected by Virginia Driving Hawk Sneve, with art by Stephen Gammell. Holiday House 1989 32p il $17.95 (4 and up)
897
1. Native Americans—Poetry
ISBN 0-8234-0724-1 LC 88-11075
An illustrated collection of poems from the oral tradition of Native Americans
This is an "eclectic collection, drawn from a variety of tribal traditions. Printed on heavy paper, the book is

Dancing teepees: poems of American Indian youth—*Continued*

illustrated with a catalogue of marvelously rendered designs and motifs, ranging from those of the Northwest Coast to the intricate beadwork patterns of the Great Lakes and the zigzag geometric borders of Southwestern pottery." N Y Times Book Rev

Gleason, Katherine, 1960-

Native American literature. Chelsea House 1996 79p il (Junior library of American Indians) $17.95
897

1. American literature—Native American authors 2. Native Americans in literature

ISBN 0-7910-2477-6   LC 95-40562

Introduces Native American authors and provides a glimpse into their culture, historical perspective and world-view

"This fine introduction to the long history of Native American oral and written literature includes authors of books for children and adults." SLJ

900 HISTORY & GEOGRAPHY

902 History--Miscellany. Chronologies

Tomaselli-Moschovitis, Valerie

Junior timelines on file. Updated ed. Facts on File 2002 various paging il $185   **902**

1. Historical chronology 2. World history

ISBN 0-8160-5122-4   LC 2002-27167

Also available CD-ROM version

First published 1997

This looseleaf binder provides more than 250 reproducible timelines covering "the history of the world on a country-by-country basis; different periods of time, such as the Reorganization of Empires (300 A.D. to 1500 A.D.) and Nationalism, Imperialism, and Revolution (1700 to 1914); human thought and achievement within various fields." Publisher's note

Includes bibliographical references (p. {8.39-8.40} and index

904 Collected accounts of events

Beyer, Rick

The greatest stories never told; 100 tales from history to astonish, bewilder, & stupefy. HarperResource 2003 214p il $17.95 (7 and up)
904

1. History—Miscellanea

ISBN 0-06-001401-6   LC 2004-296419

Based on the television program: Timelab 2000

"Beginning with the year 46 B.C. and ending in 1990, Beyer presents a chronological account of one hundred unknown, partially known, and familar tales about an array of people and events that have shaped the world.

. . . They range from the mundane to the fantastic. . . . Extensive research went into the production of this charming work. Primary documents in the form of letters, laws, illustrations, and photographs bring to life these unique and incredible anecdotes." Voice Youth Advocates

Includes bibliographical references

909 World history. Civilization

Altman, Linda Jacobs, 1943-

Forever outsiders; Jews and history from ancient times to August 1935. Blackbirch Press 1998 80p il maps (Holocaust) lib bdg $26.20   **909**

1. Jews—History

ISBN 1-56711-200-5   LC 96-48179

This volume "provides a social and economic history of the Jews, shaped and punctuated by repeated acts of persecution, actions that in modern times lead to the growth of Zionism and the Holocaust." SLJ

"Authoritative, readable." Booklist

Includes glossary and bibliographical references

Burrell, R. E. C. (Roy Eric Charles), 1923-

Oxford first ancient history; {by} Roy Burrell; with many illustrations by Peter Connolly. Oxford Univ. Press 1994 c1991 320p il maps (Rebuilding the past) hardcover o.p. paperback available $22.95   **909**

1. Ancient history

ISBN 0-19-521373-4 (pa)

First published 1991 in the United Kingdom

"Beginning with prehistory, this book surveys ancient civilizations, primarily in the Mediterranean region. . . . Every page includes at least one full-color illustration, a map, a cutaway drawing, a painting re-creating the times, or a photograph of a wall painting, sculpture, artifact, site, or explorer. Not only is the format inviting, but the text is also quite readable. . . . A lively, helpful resource." Booklist

The **Kingfisher** history encyclopedia. rev ed. Kingfisher 2004 491p il map $24.95 (5 and up)
909

1. World history

ISBN 0-7534-5784-9

First published 1999

A reference guide to world history, featuring a timeline, key date boxes, and biographies of historical figures

"Students will find this tool useful and engaging." Booklist

Mann, Kenny, 1946-

The ancient Hebrews. Benchmark Bks. (Tarrytown) 1999 80p il (Cultures of the past) $28.50   **909**

1. Bible. O.T. —History of Biblical events 2. Jews—History

ISBN 0-7614-0302-7   LC 97-6551

Mann, Kenny, 1946-—*Continued*

This illustrated work "discusses the social and religious history of the Jewish people and its influence on modern Judaism, and touches on the relationship between present-day Israel and Arab countries." SLJ

Includes bibliographical references

Millard, Anne

Pyramids. Kingfisher (NY) 1996 63p il $16.95

909

1. Pyramids 2. Egypt—Antiquities

ISBN 1-85697-674-2   LC 95-39660

Describes the pyramids of Egypt and the Americas and their significance in the social, political, and religious life of long-vanished civilizations

"By combining well-captioned, clear, full-color illustrations and an engrossing narrative, this book teaches in the best way–by showing and explaining." SLJ

Includes glossary

Ochoa, George

The Wilson chronology of ideas; {by} George Ochoa and Melinda Corey. Wilson, H.W. 1998 431p $110   **909**

1. Civilization—History 2. Philosophy

ISBN 0-8242-0935-4   LC 97-17591

A chronological presentation of influential philosophical, political, theological and social thought from ancient times to the late 20th century. Sidebars feature profiles of celebrated thinkers

Roberts, J. M.

The illustrated history of the world. rev and expanded ed. Oxford Univ. Press 1999 11v il map set $275 (7 and up)   **909**

1. World history 2. Civilization—History

ISBN 0-19-521529-X   LC 00-27437

Revised and expanded edition of the author's one-volume History of the world (1993)

Contents: v1 Prehistory and the first civilizations; v2 Eastern Asia and classical Greece; v3 Rome and the classical West; v4 The age of diverging traditions; v5 The Far East and a new Europe; v6 The making of the European age; v7 The age of revolution; v8 The European empires; v9 Emerging powers; v10 The new global era; v11 Series index

"The clear design features bold headings, explanatory captions (sometimes lengthy), easy-to-read maps, explanatory boxes on essential figures or movements, and a great use of white space. Though packed with information, the pages look clean and uncluttered, and it's easy to find a quick bit of information on a certain period or person." SLJ

Sharp, Anne Wallace

The gypsies. Lucent Bks. 2003 112p il (Indigenous peoples of the world) lib bdg $27.45

909

1. Gypsies

ISBN 1-59018-239-1   LC 2002-11935

Contents: The Romaniya; Roma family and community; Spirituality and the arts; The early years; O Porraimos, the Holocaust and its aftermath; A hostile world; The Roma in the twenty-first century

Discusses the historical origins, beliefs, arts, family life, cultural clashes with white Europeans, and future hopes of the nomadic Rom, or Roma, people who were once called Gypsies

"A good choice for reports as well as for general readers." SLJ

Includes bibliographical references

World history on file. Facts on File 1999 4v il maps loose-leaf set $560   **909**

1. World history

ISBN 0-8160-3938-0

Also available CD-ROM version; v4, The 20th century, available in an updated edition

Produced by the Diagram Group/Victoria L. Chapman & David Lindroth

Contents: v1 Early civilizations (prehistory to 300 C.E.); v2 The expanding world (300 to 1750); v3 The age of revolution (1750 to 1914); v4 The 20th century

Each volume includes approximately 500 maps, charts, timelines, and line drawings with explanatory text regarding a period of world history

909.07   World history -- ca. 500-1450/1500

The **Early** Middle Ages; Jeff Hay, book editor. Greenhaven Press 2001 234p il (Turning points in world history) lib bdg $34.95; pa $23.70 (7 and up)   **909.07**

1. Medieval civilization 2. Europe—History—476-1492

ISBN 0-7377-0482-9 (lib bdg); 0-7377-0481-0 (pa)

     LC 00-34110

This is a collection of essays concerning the period marked by "the beginning of feudalism; the invention of new, more efficient farming techniques; and the shifting of European civilization away from the Mediterranean Sea." Publisher's note

Includes bibliographical references

George, Linda S., 1949-

800. Benchmark Bks. 2003 96p il maps (Around the world in—) lib bdg $28.50   **909.07**

1. Middle Ages 2. World history

ISBN 0-7614-1085-6   LC 00-50758

This "book divides its subject geographically into four parts—Europe, Asia, Africa, and the Americas. . . . 800 presents chapters on the Vikings; the Abbasid Empire, centered in Baghdad; the Golden Empire of Ghana; and the Maya." Booklist

This work is "well written, informative, attractively designed and illustrated, and logically organized." Libr Media Connect

Includes glossary and bibliographical references

Hatt, Christine

The Crusades. Watts 2001 62p il (Documenting history) $22 (7 and up)   **909.07**

1. Crusades

ISBN 0-531-14610-3   LC 00-51351

First published 1999 in the United Kingdom

Hatt, Christine—Continued

This focuses on the Crusades through primary source documents including "letters, biographies, autobiographies, speeches, newspapers, and excerpts from government documents and political commentaries. . . . This attractive [book] may encourage browsing and will be especially useful to students looking for information in a brief, inviting format, as well as for those who want a topic review or introduction." Book Rep

Knight, Judson

Middle ages: almanac; edited by Judy Galens. U.X.L 2001 lxv, 226p il map $60   **909.07**

1. Middle Ages 2. World history 3. Medieval civilization

ISBN 0-7876-4856-6   LC 00-59442

This reference's 19 chapters review world history from the fall of the Roman Empire in 500 A.D. to the beginning of the Renaissance in 1500 A.D.

"The volume's strength is its broad coverage; it includes material on India, Southeast Asia, China, Japan, the Americas, and Africa as well as Europe and the Middle East, making it unique among other books for this age group." SLJ

Includes bibliographical references

Medieval world. Grolier Educ. 2001 10v il maps set $345 (7 and up)   **909.07**

1. Middle Ages 2. Medieval civilization

ISBN 0-7172-5520-4   LC 00-46649

Contents: v1 Abelard-Burgundy; v2 The Byzantine Empire-Constantinople; v3 Copts-Feudalism; v4 Florence-Hospitals; v5 House and home-Joan of Arc; v6 Justinian-The Mediterranean; v7 Mehmet II-Painting and sculpture; v8 The papacy-Roman Empire; v9 Rome-Thomas Aquinas; v10 Tools and technology-Writing

"The 226 alphabetical entries in this set cover all aspects of the time period between 476 A.D. and 1453 A.D. . . . The set focuses on Europe, but it also shows how other civilizations were developing during this time period." Book Rep

This "is an attractive and helpful reference source that will provide information on a variety of subjects related to this complex historical period." Booklist

Includes bibliographical references

Middle ages: primary sources; {compiled by} Judson Knight; Judy Galens, editor. U.X.L 2000 xxxiv, 161p il $60   **909.07**

1. Middle Ages

ISBN 0-7876-4860-4   LC 00-59441

This volume contains "19 full or excerpted documents written during this period, including the work of celebrated writers such as St. Augustine, Marco Polo, and Dante as well as less familiar individuals such as Anna Comnena and Lo Kuan-chung. Each selection is placed in its historical context and followed by a section entitled 'What happened next'. . . . Unfamiliar words or terms are defined in sidebars. Each entry has a box profiling the author of the documents and at least two illustrations." Booklist

Includes bibliographical references

Service, Alexandra

1200; by Alexandra F. Service and Pamela F. Service. Benchmark Bks. 2003 96p il maps (Around the world in—) lib bdg $28.50   **909.07**

1. World history—13th century 2. Medieval civilization

ISBN 0-7614-1081-3   LC 00-46848

This overview of the thirteenth century "covers events happening around the world—important historical developments in Africa, Asia, Australia, Europe, and North and South America. . . . Illustrated throughout with captioned color maps and pictures. . . . [This title is] well written, informative, attractively designed and illustrated, and logically organized." Libr Media Connect

Includes glossary and bibliographical references

Stefoff, Rebecca, 1951-

The medieval world. Benchmark Books 2004 c2005 48p il map (World historical atlases) lib bdg $18.95 (5 and up)   **909.07**

1. Middle Ages 2. Medieval civilization

ISBN 0-7614-1642-0   LC 2003-22139

This history of the medieval world briefly describes the rise of European states, including the Byzantine Empire, The Franks, England, Germany, and the Papacy, the conquering powers, including Islam, the Vikings, the Crusades, the Mongols and the Turks, and the late Middle Ages, including the Black Death, peasant uprisings, merchants and trade, and the growth of cities.

The book will "prove helpful to those who know little about the subject. Sidebars, maps, and well-reproduced color art appear throughout." Horn Book Guide

Includes glossary and bibliographical references

909.08   Modern history, 1450/1500-

History of the modern world; {editor, Timothy Cooke}. Marshall Cavendish 1999 10v set $459.95   **909.08**

1. World history

ISBN 0-7614-7147-2   LC 99-14780

Contents: v1 Origins of the modern world; v2 Religion and change in Europe; v3 Old and new worlds; v4 The Age of the Enlightenment; v5 Revolution and change; v6 The changing balance of power; v7 World War I and its consequences; v8 World War II and the Cold War; v9 The world today; v10 Index

"This set covers the period from 1500 to 1999. The set generally follows a chronological sequence, from *Origins of the Modern World* to *The World Today*. Some volumes, however, take a more thematic approach. . . . Chapters are generally 10 pages long. Following the narrative portion are a volume-specific time line, glossary, bibliography, and index." Booklist

Martell, Hazel Mary

The age of discovery. Facts on File 1993 79p il maps (Illustrated history of the world) lib bdg $25   **909.08**

1. Modern history

ISBN 0-8160-2789-7   LC 92-18621

Martell, Hazel Mary—*Continued*
Explores the history of the world from 1500 to 1650, an active period which included the Renaissance in Europe, European explorations among the ancient empires of Africa and South America, and the decline of the Mogul Empire in India
Includes glossary and bibliographical references

Schomp, Virginia, 1953-
1500. Benchmark Bks. 2003 96p il maps (Around the world in—) lib bdg $28.50
909.08
1. World history—16th century
ISBN 0-7614-1082-1   LC 00-41449
This overview of the 16th century "covers events happening around the world—important historical developments in Africa, Asia, Australia, Europe, and North and South America. . . . The section on Asia in 1500 covers developments in China, Japan, and the Ottoman Middle East. . . . [This volume is] well written, informative, attractively designed and illustrated, and logically organized." Libr Media Connect
Includes glossary and bibliographical references

909.7   World history--18th century, 1700-1799

Reynoldson, Fiona
Conflict and change. Facts on File 1993 79p il maps (Illustrated history of the world) lib bdg $25
909.7
1. Modern history
ISBN 0-8160-2790-0   LC 92-20460
First published 1991 in the United Kingdom
Explores the history of the world from 1650 to 1800 with emphasis on the agricultural revolution, the Enlightenment, the Industrial Revolution, the American and French Revolutions, Manchu China, and Shogunate Japan
Includes glossary and bibliographical references

909.8   World history--1800-

Ashby, Ruth
1800. Benchmark Bks. 2003 96p il maps (Around the world in—) lib bdg $28.50
909.8
1. World history—19th century
ISBN 0-7614-1084-8   LC 00-65136
This overview of the 19th century "covers events happening around the world—important historical developments in Africa, Asia, Australia, Europe, and North and South America. . . . The section on Africa is broken down into three segments on North, West, and South Africa. . . . [This title is] well written, informative, attractively designed and illustrated, and logically organized." Libr Media Connect
Includes glossary and bibliographical references

909.81   World history--19th century, 1800-1899

Corrick, James A.
The Industrial Revolution. Lucent Bks. 1998 112p il maps (World history series) lib bdg $28.70 (7 and up)
909.81
1. Industrial revolution
ISBN 1-56006-318-1   LC 98-6922
Discusses the Industrial Revolution, including its birth in England, its spread to Europe and America, and its effects on society
"This book tells its story concisely and illustrates it with black-and-white photos, engravings, diagrams, and maps. Looking beyond the expected topics of the steam engine, cotton gin, and electric power, Corrick discusses the history, changing technology, and social impact of computers." Booklist
Includes bibliographical references

909.82   World history--20th century, 1900-1999

Burgan, Michael
Cold War. Raintree Steck-Vaughn Pubs. 2001 4v il set $148.29 (7 and up)   **909.82**
1. Cold war 2. World politics—1945-1991 3. United States—Foreign relations—Soviet Union 4. Soviet Union—Foreign relations—United States
ISBN 0-7398-1838-4   LC 00-62652
Each volume also available separately $35.68; companion videos also available
Contents: {v1} The separation; {v2} The hot conflicts; {v3} The threats; {v4} The collapse
This set discusses world politics and focuses on the relationship between the U.S. and the Soviet Union
"A wealth of information about politics, leaders, and military history is crammed into each book. The author writes in a clear, documentary style, and offers lucid explanations. . . . An excellent place to start reading about and appreciating the many complex issues of the Cold War era." SLJ
Includes bibliographical references

Children's history of the 20th century. DK Pub. 1999 352p il $29.95   **909.82**
1. World history—20th century
ISBN 0-7894-4722-3
This illustrated, chronological look at the century features special sections on the U.S. government, sports, music and theater

The **Cold** War; Louise I. Gerdes, book editor. Greenhaven Press 2003 255p (Great speeches in history series) lib bdg $32.45; pa $21.20
909.82
1. Cold war 2. Speeches 3. United States—Foreign relations—Soviet Union 4. Soviet Union—Foreign relations—United States
ISBN 0-7377-0869-7 (lib bdg); 0-7377-0868-9 (pa)
LC 2002-34718

The Cold War—*Continued*
"This collection brings together speeches by some of the most distinguished political leaders of the twentieth century together with political analysis that traces the West's volatile relationship with Communist forces. . . . The chronologically arranged selections are organized into five chapters that focus on mounting fears about Communism, the international crisis and coercion, the menace of nuclear war, the struggle for peace, and the Berlin Wall. . . . The combination of the original speeches and the present-day analysis provides a fine starting point for reports and class discussion." Booklist
Includes bibliographical references

Jennings, Peter, 1938-2005
The century for young people; {by} Peter Jennings, Todd Brewster; adapted by Jennifer Armstrong; photographs edited by Katherine Bourbeau. Random House 1999 245p il $29.95
909.82
1. World history—20th century
ISBN 0-385-32708-0
An adaptation of the authors' The century published 1998 by Doubleday
The "authors use primary sources throughout the narrative to highlight the events and people of the 1900s. . . , Excellent-quality, archival photos capture the moments on almost every page. This is a unique and valuable book." SLJ

Kallen, Stuart A., 1955-
Primary sources; edited by Stuart A. Kallen. Lucent Bks. 2003 112p il map (American war library, Cold War) $27.45
909.82
1. Cold war 2. United States—Foreign relations—Soviet Union 3. Soviet Union—Foreign relations—United States
ISBN 1-59018-243-X
LC 2002-7896
This "contains documents and essays relating to the Cold War written by some of its key players including diplomats, ambassadors, presidents, and premiers." Publisher's note
Includes bibliographical references

Sherman, Josepha
The Cold War; by Josepha Sherman. Lerner Pub. Co 2004 96p il map (Chronicle of America's wars) lib bdg $27.93
909.82
1. Cold war 2. Soviet Union—Foreign relations—United States 3. United States—Foreign relations—Soviet Union
ISBN 0-8225-0150-3
LC 2002-156559
Contents: Beginning of the Cold War, 1920-1945; The Cold War grows hotter, 1946-1948; Continuing Cold War trouble, 1949-1950s; The Cold War at home, 1950s; Thaws and freezes, 1950s; "Brinkmanship", 1960s; Hot war and a hot racehot war, Cold War, 1960s-1970s; The Cold War ends, 1980s-present
Chronicles the Cold War, from its origins in the Soviet Revolution as the twentieth century began to the collapse of the Soviet Union as the century closed.
This offers a "concise, well-written [overview] . . . .

Abundantly illustrated with color and black-and-white photographs as well as maps." Booklist
Includes bibliographical references

Sirimarco, Elizabeth, 1966-
American voices from The Cold War; by Elizabeth Sirimarco. Benchmark Books 2004 c2005 134p il (American voices from—) lib bdg $23.95
909.82
1. Cold war
ISBN 0-7614-1694-3
LC 2003-1933
Presents the history of the Cold War through excerpts from letters, newspaper articles, speeches, and songs dating from the period. Includes review questions.
This "excellent [resource stands] out . . . because [it deals] strictly with primary sources, [contains] topnotch illustrations, and [enables] students to grasp the concepts without being overwhelmed." SLJ

Taylor, David
The Cold War. Heinemann Lib. 2001 48p il maps (20th-century perspectives) lib bdg $29.93
909.82
1. Cold war 2. World politics—1945-1991
ISBN 1-57572-434-0
LC 00-63458
This book "presents a discussion of the roots of the distrust between east and west following World War II, and explains some of the major confrontations that took place between the Soviet Union and the western nations (including the Vietnam conflict). . . . Richly illustrated with photographs of the places, events, and people discussed in the {text} and {includes} a number of excellent illustrative maps and drawings." SLJ
Includes glossary and bibliographical references

Winkler, Allan M., 1945-
The Cold War; a history in documents. Oxford Univ. Press 2000 159p il maps (Pages from history) $32.95
909.82
1. Cold war 2. United States—Foreign relations—Soviet Union 3. Soviet Union—Foreign relations—United States
ISBN 0-19-512356-5
LC 00-27270
Uses contemporary documents to explore the Cold War struggle of the 1950s and 1960s and the lasting effects on American social and cultural patterns
Includes bibliographical references

910 Geography and travel

Arnold, Caroline, 1944-
The geography book; activities for exploring, mapping, and enjoying your world. Wiley 2002 108p il pa $12.95 (4 and up)
910
1. Geography
ISBN 0-471-41236-8
LC 2001-26802
"Divided into five thematic sections, the book leads children to explore topics related to maps, land formations, water, and weather. . . . Illustrated with simple line drawings, the suggested activities include making a

Arnold, Caroline, 1944-—*Continued*
relief map, creating a solar water heater, and building a
model of a dam. . . . Clearly written and illustrated."
Booklist

Includes glossary and bibliographical references

The **Blackbirch** kid's visual reference of the
world; by the editors of Blackbirch Press; maps,
charts, and graphs by Bob Italiano. Blackbirch
Press 2001 360p il maps $49.95 (5 and up)

910

1. Geography
ISBN 1-56711-579-9   LC 2001-3056
"More than 2,500 graphs, charts, maps, and photos
that cover the most important and interesting facts about
every country on the planet!" Title page
"This visually appealing resource is packed with geographic information presented in a colorful and easy-to-
follow fashion." SLJ

The **DK** geography of the world. DK 2003 304p
il map $29.99   **910**
1. Geography
ISBN 0-7894-8594-X   LC 2003-269290
First published 1996

Maps and text describe countries around the world and
the ways of life of the inhabitants
"This surprisingly comprehensive and affordable reference source is a joy to browse." Voice Youth Advocates

Stefoff, Rebecca, 1951-
Exploration. Benchmark Books 2004 c2005 48p
il map (World historical atlases) lib bdg $18.95 (5
and up)   **910**
1. Exploration
ISBN 0-7614-1640-4   LC 2003-12032
Contents: A widening world: Ancient explorers; Chinese travelers; Viking voyages; The journey of Marco
Polo; Ibn Battuta explores the Islamic world; The Great
Age of European exploration: The Portuguese navigators;
To the Indies; The unexpected Americas; Around the
World; Into the Pacific; Filling in the blanks: American
interiors; African riddles; Forbidden Asia; The frozen
north; Antarctica
This "offers a brief overview of world exploration, be-
ginning with ancient Mediterranean travelers and closing
with the polar expeditions of Shackleton and Amundsen.
. . . Numerous maps depicting travelers' routes across
the globe are noteworthy, and the text provides a solid
starting place for further research." Booklist
Includes glossary and bibliographical references

910.3 Geography--Dictionaries, encyclopedias, gazetteers

Countries of the world and their leaders yearbook.
Gale Res. 2v il maps set $205   **910.3**
1. Geography 2. Politicians 3. Political science
ISSN 0196-2809
First published 1974 with title: Countries of the world;
issued annually since 1980 with slight variations in title.
Supplementary volume published at mid-year available at
$90

A compilation of U.S. Department of State Background Notes and other government reports, this two-
volume yearbook offers geographical, social, political,
and economic data on about 170 nations. In addition, it
provides information on: overseas business services from
the Departments of State and Commerce, U.S. embassies
and consulates, travel warnings, world health, and climate

Gifford, Clive
The Kingfisher geography encyclopedia.
Kingfisher 2003 488p il map $39.95 (4 and up)

910.3

1. Geography—Encyclopedias
ISBN 0-7534-5591-9   LC 2003-47420
Contents: The physical earth; The Arctic; North Amer-
ica; Central America; The Caribbean; South America;
Europe; Russian Federation; Asia; Indian subcontinent;
Eastern Asia; Southeast Asia; Africa; Australasia; Ocea-
nia; Antarctica
Statistics, text, and color maps reveal the physical ge-
ography, peoples, politics, governments, languages, reli-
gions, and currencies of each nation of the world
"The arrangement is logical and the format accessible.
. . . Striking color photographs and informative captions
highlight the uniqueness of each locale." SLJ

Junior worldmark encyclopedia of the nations;
{Timothy L. Gall and Susan Bevan Gall,
editors}. 4th ed. UXL 2004 10v .p set $335

910.3

1. Geography—Encyclopedias 2. World history—En-
cyclopedias
ISBN 0-7876-9215-8   LC 2004-6311
First published 1996
Contents: v1 Afghanistan to Bolivia; v2 Bosnia and
Herzegovina to Congo, Democratic Republic of the; v3
Congo, Republic of the to Fiji; v4 Finland to Indonesia;
v5 Iran to Lebanon; v6 Liberia to Mozambique; v7
Myanmar to Poland; v8 Portugal to Somalia; v9 South
Africa to Tuvalu; v10 Uganda to Zimbabwe
"Articles on 193 countries are presented in alphabetical order. Each article begins with a black-and-white illustration of the nation's flag and seal and a summary
list that includes capital city, title or beginning line of
anthem, monetary unit, weights and measures, holidays,
and time. This data is followed by 35 uniform sections
of narrative covering topics such as topography, history,
government, industry, and health. Each profile ends with
names of famous people and a bibliography. . . . This is
an exemplary set for all school and public libraries."
Booklist

Lands and peoples. Grolier Educ. 6v il maps set
$279   **910.3**
1. Geography—Encyclopedias 2. World history—En-
cyclopedias 3. Civilization—Encyclopedias
Biennial. First published 1929-1930
Contents: v1 Africa; v2 Asia, Australia, New Zealand,
Oceania; v3-4 Europe; v5 North America; v6 Central and
South America, Antarctica
This is "a standard social studies reference tool for
school and public libraries. . . . {Articles} . . . include
detailed information on geography and climate, people

Lands and peoples—*Continued*
(ethnic groups, language, religion), culture (customs, arts and literature), economy, and history. . . . Positive aspects of this work, such as the up-to-date coverage, the accessibility of the information, and the attractive format, make it an extremely useful research tool." Booklist

Merriam-Webster's geographical dictionary. 3rd ed. Merriam-Webster 1997 26a, 1361p maps $32.95 **910.3**
1. Geography—Dictionaries
ISBN 0-87779-546-0 LC 96-52365
First published 1949 with title: Webster's geographical dictionary
This guide contains data about countries, cities, and physical features. More than 48,000 entries and over 250 maps provide population, size, economic data and historical notes. Pronunciations are included and a table of foreign terms used in English is provided

Worldmark encyclopedia of the nations. Gale Res. 5v il maps set $425 **910.3**
1. Geography—Encyclopedias 2. World history—Encyclopedias 3. World politics—Encyclopedias
First published 1960. (11th edition 2003) Periodically revised
"Factual and statistical information on the countries of the world, exhibited in uniform format under such rubrics as topography, population, public finance, language, and ethnic composition. Country articles appear in volumes 2 through 5, arranged geographically by continent. Volume 1 is devoted to the United Nations and its affiliated agencies. Illustrations, maps." Ref Sources for Small & Medium-sized Libr. 6th edition

910.4 Accounts of travel and facilities for travelers

Adams, Simon
Titanic; written by Simon Adams. rev ed. DK Pub. 2004 72p il (DK eyewitness books) $15.99; lib bdg $19.99 (4 and up) **910.4**
1. Titanic (Steamship) 2. Shipwrecks
ISBN 0-7566-0733-7; 0-7566-0732-9 (lib bdg)
First published 1999
Detailed descriptions of the Titanic, including its accommodations, and a retelling of its sinking in the North Atlantic in April, 1912.

Ballard, Robert D., 1942-
The discovery of the Titanic; {by} Robert D. Ballard, with Rick Archbold; introduction by Walter Lord; illustrations of the Titanic by Ken Marschall. new & updated {ed}. Madison Press Bks. 1995 287, liiip il pa $13.99 (7 and up) **910.4**
1. Titanic (Steamship) 2. Shipwrecks 3. Underwater exploration
ISBN 0-446-67174-6 LC 95-226990
"A Warner/Madison Press book"
First published 1987 by Warner Bks.

An account of the discovery and exploration of the sunken ocean liner by the leader of the joint French/American expedition

Ghost liners; exploring the world's greatest lost ships; by Robert D. Ballard and Rick Archbold; illustrations by Ken Marschall. Little, Brown 1998 64p il $19.95 (4 and up) **910.4**
1. Shipwrecks
ISBN 0-316-08020-9 LC 98-3412
"A Madison Press book"
Depicts five famous ships that have been lost at sea in modern times, the Empress of Ireland, the Lusitania, the Andrea Doria, the Brittanic, and the Titanic
"The large, attractive format and informative text combine to make this an appealing book on a subject that continues to fascinate young people." Booklist
Includes glossary and bibliographical references

Brewster, Hugh
882 ½ amazing answers to your questions about the Titanic; by Hugh Brewster and Laurie Coulter; text research by Greg Curtis; historical consultation by Don Lynch; paintings by Ken Marschall. Scholastic 1998 96p il pa $9.99 hardcover o.p. **910.4**
1. Titanic (Steamship) 2. Shipwrecks
ISBN 0-439-04296-8 LC 98 27558
"A Scholastic/Madison Press book"
Questions and answers present information about the building, passengers, launching, sailing, sinking, and rediscovery of the Titanic. Includes illustrations, archival images, and step-by-step diagrams

Fritz, Jean
Around the world in a hundred years; from Henry the Navigator to Magellan; illustrated by Anthony Bacon Venti. Putnam 1994 128p il maps $18.99; pa $6.99 (4 and up) **910.4**
1. Explorers
ISBN 0-399-22527-7; 0-698-11638-0 (pa)
LC 92-27042
"Fritz examines the voyages of ten explorers, acknowledging that their contributions, though deserving of recognition, were dearly bought. Opening and closing chapters summarize the fourteenth-century world view and indicate later expansion of geographic understanding. As always, Fritz tempers scholarship with humor in this brief volume—illustrated with drawings in pencil—which reads like an adventure story." Horn Book Guide
Includes bibliographical references

Grolier student library of explorers and exploration. Grolier Educ. 1998 10v il maps set $359 **910.4**
1. Exploration 2. Explorers
ISBN 0-7172-9135-9 LC 97-27683
This set "begins with Australopithecus and concludes with the exploration of space and the ocean. Each volume concentrates on a specific region or aspect of discovery, such as European imperial expansion in the seventeenth and eighteenth centuries (volume 3,) voyages to Asia and Australia (volume 7), and exploration of the

Grolier student library of explorers and exploration—*Continued*

North and South Poles (volume 9). . . . Highly recommended for the school and public library where students are searching for material beyond what they can find in a general encyclopedia." Booklist

Johnstone, Michael

Explorers. Gareth Stevens Pub 2001 32p il map (History news) lib bdg $24.67 **910.4**
1. Explorers
ISBN 0-8368-2875-5   LC 2001-25017
First published 1997 by Candlewick Press

Uses a newspaper format to present the adventures and accomplishments of such explorers as Columbus, Cortes, and Cook
Includes bibliographical references

Lawlor, Laurie

Magnificent voyage; an American adventurer on Captain James Cook's final expedition. Holiday House 2002 236p il maps $22.95 (7 and up)
910.4
1. Ledyard, John, 1751-1789 2. Cook, James, 1728-1779 3. Resolution (Ship) 4. Oceania
ISBN 0-8234-1575-9   LC 2002-17148
Based on the writings of John Ledyard, an American cook on the ship Resolution, tells of explorer James Cook's final voyage in search of the Northwest Passage, discovery of the Hawaiian Islands, and murder
"The author's detailed picture of the voyage, and of Ledyard's relatively brief career, makes engrossing, if gloomy, reading." Booklist
Includes glossary and bibliographical references

Marschall, Ken

Inside the Titanic; illustrated by Ken Marschall; text by Hugh Brewster. Little, Brown 1997 32p il $19.95 (4 and up)   **910.4**
1. Titanic (Steamship) 2. Shipwrecks
ISBN 0-316-55716-1   LC 97-382
"A Madison Press book"
"Color cutaway paintings of the *Titanic* in this oversize book allow readers to view every deck as they follow two 12-year-old boys exploring the vessel, and to see how the liner struck the iceberg and sank." Booklist
Includes glossary and bibliographical references

Martin, Jesse

Lionheart; a journey of the human spirit; [by] Jesse Martin with Ed Gannon. Allen & Unwin 2002 c2000 253p il maps pa $14.95 (7 and up)
910.4
1. Voyages around the world
ISBN 1-86508-347-X
First published 2000 in Australia
"In 1999, Martin sailed around the world solo and unassisted. In a 34-foot yacht named Lionheart, the 17-year-old Australian used no fossil fuels, received no supplies or visitors, and never stepped off the boat for the entire 10-month trip. His narrative is conversational in tone and unsparingly honest, revealing his insecurities as well as a quick wit. . . . The narrative form is simple, and the book hits all the marks for scope, teen appeal, and emotion." SLJ

Matsen, Bradford

The incredible search for the treasure ship Atocha; {by} Brad Matsen. Enslow Pubs. 2003 48p il map (Incredible deep-sea adventures) lib bdg $18.95 (4 and up)   **910.4**
1. Fisher, Mel 2. Nuestra Señora de Atocha (Ship) 3. Buried treasure 4. Shipwrecks
ISBN 0-7660-2193-9   LC 2002-14311
Contents: Today's the day; The sinking of the Atocha, 1622; Mel Fisher's quest for the ghost galleons; The search goes on and on and on; Atocha's treasure is worth more than money
Presents background information about the sinking of the Spanish galleon, Atocha, in 1622 and describes efforts to locate the wreck and successfully salvage its treasure more than 300 years later
"A credible title about an amazing adventure. . . . The colorful illustrations include numerous underwater photos, period reproductions, and a map." SLJ
Includes glossary and bibliographical references

Matthews, Rupert

Explorer; written by Rupert Matthews. rev ed. DK Pub. 2005 72p il map (DK eyewitness books) $15.99; lib bdg $19.99 (4 and up)   **910.4**
1. Exploration 2. Explorers
ISBN 0-7566-1072-9; 0-7566-1071-0 (lib bdg)
First published 1991 by Knopf
Photographs and text examine the history of explorers and exploration, and highlight many of their discoveries.

Meltzer, Milton, 1915-

Piracy & plunder; a murderous business; illustrated by Bruce Waldman. Dutton Children's Bks. 2001 86p il $24.99 (7 and up)
910.4
1. Pirates
ISBN 0-525-45857-3   LC 2001-32593
"Meltzer's pirates are violent thieves and murderers, and this evenhanded history doesn't shy away from the brutality (gang rape is mentioned, for example). . . . Meltzer's language is clear, engaging, and never sensationalized, offering plenty of useful context." Booklist
Includes bibliographical references

Open your eyes; extraordinary experiences in faraway places; edited by Jill Davis. Viking 2003 201p il $16.99 (7 and up)   **910.4**
1. Voyages and travels 2. Authors, American
ISBN 0-670-03616-1
A collection of memories and stories about a variety of travel experiences that changed the lives of such well-known writers as Lois Lowry, Suzie Morgenstern, and Harry Mazer
"This unusual anthology spotlights 10 people whose

Open your eyes—*Continued*

lives were changed by living or traveling abroad during their youth. . . . Though not every piece is excellent, the voices, vivid and distinctive." Booklist

Philbrick, Nathaniel

Revenge of the whale; the true story of the whaleship Essex. Putnam 2002 164p il maps $16.99; pa $7.99 (7 and up) **910.4**

1. Essex (Whale-ship) 2. Shipwrecks 3. Whaling
ISBN 0-399-23795-X; 0-14-240068-8 (pa)

LC 2002-667

Recounts the 1820 sinking of the whaleship "Essex" by an enraged sperm whale and how the crew of young men survived against impossible odds. Based on the author's adult book "In the heart of the sea"

"The story of the *Essex* crew is a compelling saga of desperation and survival that will appeal to young people. The grisly details of cannibalism necessary to the telling of the story may provoke shivers but should not give anyone nightmares." SLJ

Includes bibliographical references

Platt, Richard, 1953-

Shipwreck; written by Richard Platt; photographed by Alex Wilson and Tina Chambers. rev ed. DK Pub. 2005 72p il (DK eyewitness books) $15.99; lib bdg $19.99 (4 and up) **910.4**

1. Shipwrecks
ISBN 0-7566-1089-3; 0-7566-1090-7 (lib bdg)
First published 1997 by Knopf

Describes the history of shipwrecks, famous wrecks, causes, navigation and rescue techniques, and underwater archeology and the exploration of wrecks.

Warrick, Karen Clemens

The perilous search for the fabled Northwest Passage in American history; Karen Clemens Warrick. Enslow 2004 128p il map (In American history) lib bdg $26.60 **910.4**

1. Northwest Passage 2. Explorers 3. Arctic regions—Exploration
ISBN 0-7660-2148-3

LC 2003-26603

Contents: Franklin's final voyage; Search for a new trade route; Brave explorers in small ships; Sir John Barrow's push for Arctic exploration; Overland search for the Northwest Passage; Four winters in the Arctic; Along the coast of North America; Search and discovery; Navigating the passage; The Northwest Passage on the map

"Warrick traces the search for the Northwest Passage from the 15th to the 20th century. Describing John Cabot's and Jacques Cartier's efforts and, finally, Roald Amundsen's success in 1906, the book details the many explorers and their crews who lost their lives. . . . A worthwhile addition to history collections." SLJ

Includes bibliographical references

911 Historical geography

Leacock, Elspeth, 1946-

Places in time; a new atlas of American history; {by} Elspeth Leacock and Susan Buckley; illustrations by Randy Jones. Houghton Mifflin 2001 48p il $15; pa $6.95 (4 and up)

911

1. United States—Historical geography
ISBN 0-395-97958-7; 0-618-3113-0 (pa)

LC 00-59741

This book presents "20 sites in American history at the moment of their historical significance, beginning in 1200 (Cahokia) and ending in 1953. Places and times include New Plymouth—1627, Charlestown—1739, Saratoga—1777, Philadelphia—1787, Abilene—1871, and Chicago—1893. The detailed cutaway views of homes, forts, and mills are impressive enough to keep readers looking again and again. These fascinating slices of life stir the imagination and lead to questions and further research." SLJ

912 Atlases. Maps

Atlas of the world. Oxford Univ. Press il maps

912

1. Atlases
First published 1992. (6th edition 1998) Frequently revised

This atlas provides large-scale computer generated maps detailing political and topographical information and a 75,000-name index. Charts and graphs cover topics ranging from refuge movements and global conflicts to plate tectonics and climate patterns

"The quality and color of the maps and the 75,000 entry index make this atlas a good choice for schools. An introduction to world geography with both narrative and maps covers the earth, people, production and quality of life. There is a section of 66 city maps with its own index, followed by the world maps arranged by continent and country." Safford. Guide to Ref Materials for Sch Libr Media Cent. 5th edition [entry for 5th edition]

Atlas of the world; [prepared by National Geographic Maps for the Book Division] 8th ed. National Geographic Society 2005 various paging il map $165 **912**

1. Atlases
ISBN 0-7922-7543-8

LC 2004-45002

First published 1963

At head of title: National Geographic

This edition features 60 political maps, 17 thematic maps, and 10 panoramic satellite views of the world. Also includes views of all five ocean floors and both polar regions, the latest imagery from the Hubble Space Telescope, and new information from Mars. A world-thematic section addressing such global concerns as biodiversity, the world economy, and terrorism is also provided. The Web site that accompanies the atlas includes interactive maps

For a review see: Booklist, Feb. 15, 2005

DK student atlas. DK Pub. 1998 160p il maps $20

912

1. Atlases

ISBN 0-7566-0338-2   LC 97-45730

This atlas features "multi-colored maps, scenic photos, and topographical keys. . . . For school reports, the elevation maps, climate details, industry, farming, and land use charts, and landscape discussions will be invaluable. . . . An exciting, non-intimidating, yet factual resource for teaching basic world geography and map/chart reading skills." Sci Books Films

Europe on file; Ireland & United Kingdom; France, Spain & Portugal; Germany, Austria & Switzerland; Italy & Greece; Scandinavia. Facts on File 1997 2v loose-leaf set $185

912

1. Europe—Maps

ISBN 0-8160-3508-3

This two volume looseleaf compilation of maps, graphs and charts "is divided into 11 sections: one for each of 9 European regions . . . one for the 6 microstates (e.g., Liechtenstein, Malta, Vatican City), and one for specialized regional maps of Europe and the former Soviet Union that cover topics such as languages, deforestation, education expenditures, religions, ethnic minorities, rainfall, and energy consumption. . . . Readers will find this an accessible resource useful for locating facts quickly." SLJ

Explorer atlas of the world. Hammond 120p il maps $11.95 pa $12.95   **912**

1. Atlases

First published 1993. (1999 edition) Periodically revised

This atlas features computer-generated area maps, detailed political world maps and a color section on flags of the world. An index to over 12,000 places and geographic features is included

Geography on file. Facts on File various paging il maps loose-leaf $195   **912**

1. Atlases 2. Geography

Annual updates available for $55; CD-ROM version also available

First published 1991. Periodically revised

A collection of more than 250 maps, graphs, and statistical charts on both human and physical geography. Topics covered include demographic shifts, economic growth, language distribution, and political institutions

Johnson, Sylvia A.

Mapping the world. Atheneum Bks. for Young Readers 1999 32p il map $16.95 (4 and up)

912

1. Maps

ISBN 0-689-81813-0   LC 98-7858

"Johnson traces the history of cartography from an early Babylonian image scratched into a clay tablet to maps developed with satellite and computer technology. . . . The slender book contains a number of clear full-color reproductions that suitably illustrate Johnson's descriptions. The writing is smooth and lucid and the material is well organized." SLJ

Includes bibliographical references

Maps on file. Facts on File 2v maps loose-leaf set $250   **912**

1. Atlases

ISSN 0275-8083

Annual updates available for $75; CD-ROM version also available

First published 1981. Frequently revised

Maps copyrighted by Martin Greenwald Associates

A collection of approximately 500 black-and-white maps covering countries, every U.S. state, Canadian provinces, oceans, and continents

Oxford new concise world atlas. Oxford University Press 2003 various paging various pagingp il map $35   **912**

1. Atlases

ISBN 0-19-521983-x

A revised edition of Philip's concise world atlas, published 2000 by George Philip & Son

This atlas "opens with endpapers that provide a world and European map, a key, and an abbreviated index. . . .The . . . world statistics . . . are straightforward. An added plus is the 'Earth in Space' section. . . . The impressive photographs also include satellite images. Six sections of detailed but easy-to-read colorful maps constitute the bulk of the book. . . . This up-to-date volume offers solid information on a wealth of topics, clear visuals, and an extensive index to the maps." SLJ

Ross, Val

The road to there; mapmakers and their stories. Tundra Books 2003 146p il map $22.95

912

1. Maps

ISBN 0-88776-621-8

"Ross presents an intriguing look at several mapmakers and the way that their work reflected not only physical boundaries, but also important aspects of their lives and the times in which they lived. . . . The tone of the text is chatty, sometimes humorous, and never dry. . . . Filled with details and insights and written with a storyteller's touch, this book will simultaneously inform and fascinate readers." SLJ

Rubel, David

Scholastic atlas of the United States. new and updated. Scholastic Reference 2003 144p il map lib bdg $24.95; pa $10.95   **912**

1. United States—Maps

ISBN 0-439-55494-2 (lib bdg); 0-439-47436-1 (pa)

"An Agincourt Press book"

First published 2000

This atlas "offers students a detailed map of each of the 50 states plus the District of Columbia and Puerto Rico. {It} also features an information page about each state that uses photos, graphics, . . . facts, and a brief essay to explain what makes each state unique." Publisher's note

Scholastic atlas of the world. Scholastic Ref. 2001 224p il maps $19.95; lib bdg $24.95; pa $12.95 (4 and up)   **912**

Scholastic atlas of the world—*Continued*
1. Atlases
ISBN 0-439-08795-3; 0-439-55496-9 (lib bdg);
0-439-52797-X (pa)
In this atlas each topographical map "locates important cities, mountains, deserts, and bodies of water, indicating border countries and national capitals. The culture and geography of each country are explored through . . . essays and . . . full-color photographs." Publisher's note

917.3 Geography of and travel in the United States

The **Cambridge** gazetteer of the United States and Canada; a dictionary of places; edited by Archie Hobson. Cambridge Univ. Press 1995 743p maps $80 **917.3**
1. United States—Gazetteers 2. Canada—Gazetteers
ISBN 0-521-41579-9 LC 95-8898
The over 12,000 listings for places in the U.S. and Canada include entries for municipalities, states, countries, geographical features, notable neighborhoods, regional names, and a few legendary places. Includes definitions of about 170 geographical terms
"The inclusion of such a wide variety of places, from streets and ballparks to battlefields and forests, makes this a valuable work that will be welcome in all reference departments." Booklist

Spangenburg, Ray, 1939-
The African-American experience; by Ray Spangenburg and Diane K. Moser. Facts on File 1996 142p il maps (American historic places) $25 (7 and up) **917.3**
1. Historic sites 2. African Americans—History
ISBN 0-8160-3400-1 LC 96-27992
Explores locations that have had significant impact on the African-American experience including the homes of Harriet Tubman, Maggie Lena Walker, Mary McCloud Bethune, and Frederick Douglass; Boston's African Meeting House; the Nicodemus Historic District in Kansas, Little Rock High School, and the Martin Luther King historic district in Atlanta
Includes bibliographical references

Literature and the arts; {by} Ray Spangenburg and Diane K. Moser. Facts on File 1997 163p il maps (American historic places) $25 (7 and up) **917.3**
1. Historic sites 2. Literary landmarks—United States
ISBN 0-8160-3401-X LC 96-25939
A guidebook to the homes of writers and artists Louisa May Alcott, Charles Wilson Peale, Winslow Homer, Mark Twain, Willa Cather, Augustus St. Gaudes, Charles M. Russell, Tom Wolfe, Frank Lloyd Wright, Edith Wharton, and William Faulkner
Includes bibliographical references

Political and social movements; {by} Ray Spangenburg and Diane K. Moser. Facts on File 1998 130p il maps (American historic places) $25 (7 and up) **917.3**
1. Historic sites 2. United States—Politics and government
ISBN 0-8160-3404-4 LC 97-28096
This guide "focuses on 10 sites that are associated with American political and social movements. Valley Forge, Hancock Shaker Village, The Women's Rights National Historic Park, The Jane Addams Hull-House Museum, Wounded Knee, and the Ellis Island Immigration Center are a sampling of the places included. . . . For each site, the authors discuss the associated movement and give a brief account of how the site was preserved, a list for further reading, and related sites." SLJ
Includes bibliographical references

920 Biography

Books of biography are arranged as follows: 1. Biographical collections (920) 2. Biographies of individuals alphabetically by name of biographee (92)

Aaseng, Nathan, 1953-
Black inventors. Facts on File 1997 128p il (American profiles) $25 (7 and up) **920**
1. African American inventors 2. Inventions
ISBN 0-8160-3407-9 LC 96-40486
"Aaseng tells of 10 black inventors, the problems they overcame, and the often slow, frustrating road to ingenious achievement. A bibliography, a chronology, and photographs supplement each chapter as do patent drawings where appropriate." Booklist

Business builders in real estate. Oliver Press 2002 160p il map (Business builders) $22.95 **920**
1. Businesspeople 2. Real estate business
ISBN 1-88150-879-X LC 2001-36369
Profiles seven real estate developers, including John Nicholson, John Jacob Astor, William Levitt, Del Webb, Walt Disney, Paul Reichmann, and the Ghermezian brothers
"Each biography is complete, with enough information for a research report. The sum total paints an excellent picture of the real estate trade in America" Libr Media Connect
Includes bibliographical references

Alter, Judy
Extraordinary explorers and adventurers. Children's Press 2001 288p il (Extraordinary people) $39; pa $16.95 **920**
1. Explorers 2. Adventure and adventurers
ISBN 0-516-21693-7; 0-516-27284-5 (pa)
LC 00-30715
"This book provides short biographies of seventy-three people who explored the unknown and had adventures that were challenging and accomplishments that were admirable. The earliest entries are of Greek heroes . . . and the book concludes with biographies of such modern ad-

Alter, Judy—*Continued*

venturers as test pilot Chuck Yeager and astronaut Mae Jemison. . . . This book would be an excellent source for those readers who want to learn a bit about explorers and adventurers in general or who are interested in a particular person and what his or her life was like." Voice Youth Advocates

Includes bibliographical references

Extraordinary women of the American West. Children's Press 1999 288p il (Extraordinary people) lib bdg $39; pa $16.95   **920**
1. Women—West (U.S.)
ISBN 0-516-20974-4 (lib bdg); 0-516-26465-6 (pa)
    LC 98-5812

"Starting in the late 1700s and moving through to the present day, this title examines the lives and accomplishments of more than 60 women. Each three- to four-page entry covers the subject's childhood, work, achievements, and/or reason for her notoriety. . . . Sacajawea, Carry Nation, Annie Oakley, Willa Cather, Georgia O'Keeffe, and Pat Schroeder are among the well-known figures. Lesser-known entries include Edna Gladney, Etta Place, Esther Morris, La Tules, and Lillian Riggs." SLJ

Includes bibliographical references

Altman, Susan

Extraordinary African-Americans. Children's Press 2001 288p il (Extraordinary people) $39; pa $16.95 (5 and up)   **920**
1. African Americans—Biography
ISBN 0-516-22549-9; 0-516-25962-8 (pa)
    LC 00-52373

First published 1988 with title: Extraordinary Black Americans: from colonial to contemporary times

This "profiles more than 100 African-American achievers, including writers, artists, musicians, athletes, activists, politicians, and others who have made headlines. It also includes descriptions of important periods in African-American history, including the Harlem Renaissance, Reconstruction, the Great Northern Migration, and the civil rights movement." SLJ

"Perfect for quick reference, in an attractive layout that will appeal to even the most reluctant researchers." Voice Youth Advocates

Includes bibliographical references

Archer, Jules

They had a dream; the civil rights struggle from Frederick Douglass to Marcus Garvey to Martin Luther King and Malcolm X. Viking 1993 258p il (Epoch biographies) hardcover o.p. paperback available $5.99   **920**
1. Douglass, Frederick, 1817?-1895 2. Garvey, Marcus, 1887-1940 3. King, Martin Luther, 1929-1968 4. Malcolm X, 1925-1965 5. African Americans—Biography 6. African Americans—Civil rights
ISBN 0-14-034954-5   LC 92-40071

Traces the progression of the civil rights movement and its effect on history through biographical sketches of four prominent and influential African Americans: Frederick Douglass, Marcus Garvey, Martin Luther King, Jr., and Malcolm X

"This discussion of the contributions of four pivotal civil rights activists is balanced and substantive." Publ Wkly

Includes bibliographical references

Avery, Susan, 1949-

Extraordinary American Indians; by Susan Avery and Linda Skinner. Children's Press 1992 xx, 252p il pa $16.95 hardcover o.p.   **920**
1. Native Americans—Biography
ISBN 0-516-40583-7   LC 92-11358

This work discusses the lives and accomplishments of outstanding Native Americans from the eighteenth century to the present, including Wilma Mankiller, Billy Mills, Sacagawea, Louis Ballard, and Will Rogers

"More than a recitation of famous chiefs and war leaders from past centuries, {the book} offers students a much-needed, well-rounded look at the diversity of Indian talents and achievements." SLJ

Includes bibliographical references

Axelrod-Contrada, Joan

Women who led nations. Oliver Press (Minneapolis) 1999 160p il lib bdg $21.25 (7 and up)   **920**
1. Women politicians 2. Women in politics
ISBN 1-881508-48-X   LC 98-10958

Profiles the careers of seven women elected to head their respective countries, including Golda Meir, Indira Gandhi, Margaret Thatcher, Corazón Aquino, Benazir Bhutto, Violeta Barrios de Chamorro, and Gro Harlem Brundtland

"Black-and-white photographs adequately portray each head of state and represent highlights of the events that took place during her term of office. Fourteen other women who have ruled countries receive brief mention in the final chapter. A useful resource for reports." SLJ

Includes bibliographical references

Bausum, Ann

Our country's presidents; with a foreword by George W. Bush. rev ed. National Geographic 2005 207p il $24.95; lib bdg $45.90 (5 and up)   **920**
1. Presidents—United States
ISBN 0-7922-9329-0; 0-7922-9330-4 (lib bdg)
First published 2001

This briefly discusses such topics as "the role of vice presidents, . . . the Electoral College, past presidents as elder statesmen, presidential security, and the expanding global role of the president. The short profiles provide essential information for report writers. The book includes an appended chart of election results . . . and information on America's changing role in the world, the White House, military conflicts throughout our history, political parties and campaigns, and important historical events of the time. The beautiful illustrations . . . current information, and user-friendly layout make this title a solid addition for most libraries." SLJ

Includes bibliographical references

Benson, Sonia
Korean War: biographies; {by} Sonia G. Benson; Gerda-Ann Raffaelle, editor. U.X.L 2002 xxx, 268p il pa $60 (7 and up) **920**
1. Korean War, 1950-1953—Biography
ISBN 0-7876-5692-5   LC 2001-44241
Presents biographies of twenty-six men and women who participated in or were affected by the Korean War, including politicians, military leaders, journalists, and nurses
"An excellent starting point for researching the . . . people of the Korean War." Booklist
Includes bibliographical references

Billinghurst, Jane, 1958-
Growing up royal; life in the shadow of the British throne. Annick Press 2001 154p il $22.95; pa $15.95   **920**
1. House of Windsor 2. Princes 3. Great Britain—Kings and rulers
ISBN 1-55037-623-3; 1-55037-622-5 (pa)
This book takes a "look at childhood among the British royals. . . . The focus is on the two young princes, William and Harry, although other family members are included. Princess Diana and Prince Charles are covered but from the unique perspective of their children. . . . American students will find an engaging account of royal childhood packed with little-known facts about the customs of the British throne starring the two teen royals to whom they can best relate." Book Rep

Biography index; a cumulative index to biographical material in books and magazines. Wilson, H.W. annual subscription $340
920
1. Biography—Bibliography 2. Biography—Indexes
ISSN 0006-3053
Also available online
First issued September 1946
Published quarterly, November, February, May, and August, with bound annual and permanent two-year cumulations.
"Indexes biographical articles published in . . . periodicals, current books of individual and collected biography, obituaries, letters, diaries, memoirs, and incidental biographical material in otherwise nonbiographical books. Includes an index by professions and occupations. Annual and three-year cumulations." Ref Sources for Small & Medium-sized Libr. 6th edition

Bolden, Tonya
And not afraid to dare. Scholastic 1998 216p il pa $4.99   **920**
1. African American women
ISBN 0-439-47139-7 (pa)   LC 96-7320
Biographical portraits of ten African-American women including Leontyne Price, Toni Morrison, and Jackie Joyner-Kersee
"The writing is clear and compelling. While these biographical sketches are interesting and provocative enough to attract recreational readers, the primary use for such a title would be research." SLJ
Includes bibliographical references

Portraits of African-American heroes; paintings by Ansel Pitcairn. Dutton Children's Books 2003 88p il $18.99 (4 and up) **920**
1. African Americans—Biography
ISBN 0-525-47043-3   LC 2002-75911
Contents: Frederick Douglass; Matthew Henson; W.E.B. Du Bois; Mary McLeod Bethune; Bessie Coleman; Paul Robeson; Satchel Paige; Thurgood Marshal; Pauli Murray; Joe Louis; Gwendolyn Brooks; Jacob Lawrence; Dizzy Gillespie; Shirley Chisholm; Malcolm X; Martin Luther King, Jr.; Charlayne Hunter-Gault; Judith Jamison; Ruth Simmons; Ben Carson
"Bolden profiles 20 people, ranging from Matthew Henson, Thurgood Marshall, and Martin Luther King, Jr., to Paul Robeson, Ruth Simmons, Judith Jamison, and Charlayne Hunter-Gault." SLJ
"Each profile lists expected biographical information, but offers even more by way of keen insights into a subject's personality based on interviews and information drawn from personal memoirs. . . . Pitcairn's beautifully rendered sepia-toned portraits make each subject jump from the page, beckoning children to come ever closer and learn." Booklist

Bostrom, Kathleen Long, 1954-
Winning authors; profiles of the Newbery medalists; Kathleen Long Bostrom. Libraries Unlimited 2003 338p il (Popular authors series) $52   **920**
1. Authors, American 2. Newbery Medal
ISBN 1-563-08877-0   LC 2003-53878
This "resource opens with a brief history of the Newbery Medal. . . . Entries featuring each winner from 1922 to 2002 follow with basic information about the authors, including useful listings of all awards and honors they have won, a full listing of their books, and sources for further information. A two to three-page narrative linking life experiences to themes of their books is also included." SLJ
Includes bibliographical references

Brewster, Hugh
To be a princess; the fascinating lives of real princesses; by Hugh Brewster and Laurie Coulter; with paintings by Laurie McGaw. HarperCollins Pubs. 2001 62p il $17.95 (4 and up) **920**
1. Princesses
ISBN 0-06-029480-9   LC 2001-24164
"A Madison Press book"
A collective biography of princesses including Elizabeth and Mary Tudor of England, Ka'iulani of Hawaii, Marie Antoinette of France, Victoria, Elizabeth and Margaret of Great Britain, Gayatri Devi of India, and Anastasia of Russia
"This lushly illustrated compendium of royal biographies will appeal to a fairly wide age range. . . . Each vivid portrait will hook readers with its immediacy, rich detail, and history." Booklist

Brooks, Philip, 1963-
Extraordinary Jewish Americans. Children's
Press 1998 288p il (Extraordinary people) lib bdg
$39; pa $16.95 **920**
1. Jews—United States—Biography
ISBN 0-516-20609-5 (lib bdg); 0-516-26350-1 (pa)
LC 97-37535
Presents short biographies of more than sixty Jewish
Americans who have flourished in careers including law,
finance, entertainment, writing, politics, and science
Includes bibliographical references

Bruning, John R.
Elusive glory; African-American heroes of
World War II; {by} John Robert Bruning, Jr.
Avisson Press 2001 135p il (Avisson young adult
series) p $19.95 **920**
1. World War, 1939-1945—African Americans
2. African American soldiers
ISBN 1-88810-548-8 LC 2001-22494
"This collective biography profiles the lives of some
of the African Americans who served their country with
distinction during World War II. The first part of the
book concerns the seven men who were belatedly (in
some cases, posthumously) awarded the Medal of Honor
in 1997 for service in the U.S. Army. The second section
features six of the famous Tuskegee airmen. . . . A readable and potentially inspiring record of determined men
who had jobs to do and did them despite the limitations
of circumstance." Booklist
Includes bibliographical references

Bruno, Leonard C.
Math and mathematicians; the history of math
discoveries around the world; Lawrence W. Baker,
editor. U.X.L 1999-2002 4v il 2v set $110
920
1. Mathematicians 2. Mathematics
ISBN 0-7876-3812-9 (v1 & v2); 0-7876-6480-4 (v3);
0-7876-6481-2 (v4) LC 99-32424
Also available 4 volume set $215
Compilation of biographies, 50 to 60 per volume, of
mathematicians from throughout history and articles describing math concepts and principles
"This effective resource is marked by its attention to
detail and variety of information. Readers can readily
cross-reference concepts, people, and discoveries. Easy to
use, this wonderful reference will be appropriate for middle, high school, and public libraries." Voice Youth Advocates [review of vols 1 & 2]
Includes glossary and bibliographical references

Bussing-Burks, Marie, 1958-
Influential economists. Oliver Press 2003 160p
il (Profiles) $19.95 (7 and up) **920**
1. Economists
ISBN 1-881508-72-2 LC 2001-59310
Presents information on the lives and work of the
economists Thomas Gresham, Adam Smith, Thomas
Robert Malthus, Karl Marx, John Maynard Keynes, Milton Friedman, and Alan Greenspan
"The author discusses sometimes complex theories in
a straightforward, jargon-free text accessible to most sophisticated teen readers. . . . Informative, well-written,
and fairly interesting." Booklist
Includes glossary and bibliographical references

Byrnes, Patricia, 1942-
Environmental pioneers. Oliver Press
(Minneapolis) 1998 160p il (Profiles) lib bdg
$19.95 (7 and up) **920**
1. Environmentalists
ISBN 1-88150-845-5 LC 97-30233
Profiles people who have been influential in the envi-
ronmental movement: John Muir, Jay Norwood "Ding"
Darling, Rosalie Edge, Aldo Leopold, Olaus and Marga-
ret Murie, Rachel Carson, David Brower, and Gaylord
Nelson
"Unlike most authors of books on this topic for a
young audience, Byrnes is an experienced environmental
writer, and takes an affectionate tone in describing her
subjects." SLJ
Includes bibliographical references

Camp, Carole Ann
American astronomers; searchers and wonderers.
Enslow Pubs. 1996 104p il (Collective
biographies) lib bdg $26.60 **920**
1. Astronomers
ISBN 0-89490-631-3 LC 95-14472
This "profiles Maria Mitchell, Percival Lowell,
Williamina Fleming, Annie Jump Cannon, George Ellery
Hale, Harlow Shapley, Edwin Hubble, Cecilia Payne-
Gaposchkin, and Carl Sagan." Booklist
"A good research source for middle school students.
. . . The writing style is clear and concise in highlight-
ing the person's life and accomplishments." BAYA Book
Rev
Includes bibliographical references

Caravantes, Peggy
Petticoat spies; six women spies of the civil
war. Morgan Reynolds 2002 112p il lib bdg
$21.95 **920**
1. United States—History—1861-1865, Civil War—
Women 2. Spies
ISBN 1-88384-688-9 LC 2001-59638
Describes the lives and wartime exploits of six women
who were spies during the Civil War. Includes Sarah
Emma Edmonds, Belle Boyd, Pauline Cushman, Rose
O'Neal Greenhow, Elizabeth Van Lew, and Belle
Edmondson
The "action-packed stories include daring escapes,
clever disguises, feigned madness, and sometimes, foiled
plans." Booklist
Includes glossary and bibliographical references

Carruthers, Margaret W.
Pioneers of geology; discovering Earth's secrets;
{by} Margaret Carruthers and Susan Clinton.
Watts 2001 143p il maps (Lives in science) lib
bdg $20.50 **920**
1. Geologists
ISBN 0-531-11364-7 LC 00-27011

Carruthers, Margaret W.—*Continued*
Profiles the work of six individuals who made important contributions to the field of geology: James Hutton, Charles Lyell, G.K. Gilbert, Alfred Wegener, Harry Hess, and Gene Shoemaker
"This very readable book does an excellent job. . . . The authors pack a lot of good material between the covers of this thin volume." Sci Books Films
Includes glossary and bibliographical references

Celebrating women in mathematics and science; edited by Miriam P. Cooney. National Council of Teachers of Mathematics 1996 223p il pa $29.95   **920**
1. McClintock, Barbara 2. Women mathematicians 3. Women scientists
ISBN 0-87353-425-5   LC 96-14119
"A collective biography detailing the struggles and triumphs of women in the fields of mathematics and sciences from ancient times to the present. . . . While most of the women are mathematicians, health-care professionals, biologists, and naturalists are also represented. . . . *Celebrating Women* is a useful chronological history, ideal for short reports." SLJ
Includes bibliographical references

Chin-Lee, Cynthia, 1958-
Amelia to Zora; twenty-six women who changed the world; illustrated by Megan Halsey and Sean Addy. Charlesbridge 2005 32p il $15.95 (4 and up)   **920**
1. Women—Biography
ISBN 1-57091-522-9
"An introduction to 26 diverse, 20th-century women who have made a difference in such varied fields as the arts, sports, journalism, science, and entertainment. The entries include Dolores Huerta, Frida Kahlo, Lena Horne, Maya Lin, and Patricia Schroeder." SLJ
"The illustrations are done in a remarkable mix of media. . . . The text portions are short . . . but they are enticing. By choosing her subjects from every culture, the author introduces children to the scope of the struggles and achievements of women from many times and many places." Booklist

Danneberg, Julie, 1958-
Women artists of the West; five portraits in creativity and courage. Fulcrum 2002 84p il map pa $12.95   **920**
1. Women artists 2. American art 3. West (U.S.) in art
ISBN 1-555-91861-1   LC 2002-8400
Contents: Maria Martinez; Georgia O'Keeffe; Laura Gilpin; Dorothea Lange; Mary-Russell Colton
Narrative profiles of five notable women artists who influenced the art of the American West
"A well-researched and entertaining book that makes for an accessible entry into the world of art history." Kliatt
Includes bibliographical references

DeAngelis, Gina
Science & medicine; introduction by Roslyn Rosen. Chelsea House 1999 64p il (Female firsts in their fields) lib bdg $20.95   **920**
1. Women scientists 2. Women in medicine
ISBN 0-7910-5143-9   LC 98-31676
Chronicles the lives and accomplishments of notable women working in the fields of medicine and science in general, including Marie Curie, Rachel Carson, and Margaret Mead
Includes bibliographical references

Di Domenico, Kelly, 1977-
Super women in science. Second Story Press 2002 102p il (Women's hall of fame series) pa $10.95   **920**
1. Women scientists
ISBN 1-896764-66-5   LC 2003-430558
"This collective biography spotlights 10 women in the sciences. Though the discussion begins with Hypatia, who taught mathematics and astronomy in fifth-century Alexandria, most of the women worked during the twentieth century. These include biologist Rachel Carson, atomic physicists Maria Goeppert-Mayer and Chien-Shiung Wu, orangutan field observer Biruté Galdikas, DNA researcher Rosalind Franklin, and astronaut Mae Jemison. Each chapter in this sturdy paperback provides a clear, accessible introduction to one woman's life and work." Booklist
Includes glossary and bibliographical references

Distinguished African American scientists of the 20th century; {by} James H. Kessler {et al.}; with Sigrid Berge, portrait artist, and Alyce Neukirk, computer graphics artist. Oryx Press 1996 382p il $73.95 (7 and up)   **920**
1. Scientists 2. African Americans—Biography
ISBN 0-89774-955-3   LC 95-43880
"One hundred famous and not-so-famous African American scientists (both living and dead) are covered in this biographical reference. . . . Men and women accomplished in anthropology, biology, chemistry, engineering, geology, mathematics, medicine, and physics are included. Those profiled include lesser-known scientists such as Christine Darden (an engineer with NASA) as well as the better known, e.g., George Washington Carver." Libr J

Includes bibliographical references

Doherty, Kieran
Ranchers, homesteaders, and traders; frontiersmen of the South-Central states. Oliver Press (Minneapolis) 2001 176p il maps (Shaping America) lib bdg $22.95   **920**
1. Frontier and pioneer life—West (U.S.)
ISBN 1-88150-853-6   LC 00-52864
"Doherty traces the history of the settlement of various frontier lands through a study of the lives and achievements of seven men: Henry de Tonty (Arkansas), Auguste Chouteau (Missouri), Daniel Boone (Kentucky), John Sevier (Tennessee), Stephen Austin and Sam Houston (Texas), and Eli Thayer (Kansas)." SLJ
"There's enough personal history (and plenty of illus-

Doherty, Kieran—*Continued*

trations) to give readers a clear overview of the frontier heroes. . . . This is an excellent resource." Booklist
Includes bibliographical references

Dubovoy, Sina

Civil rights leaders. Facts on File 1997 136p il (American profiles) $25 (7 and up)   **920**
1. African Americans—Civil rights
ISBN 0-8160-3363-3   LC 96-2920
Profiles the lives and achievements of nine civil rights leaders, including Ida B. Wells, A. Philip Randolph, Thurgood Marshall, Rosa Parks, and Fannie Lou Hamer
Includes bibliographical references

Earls, Irene

Young musicians in world history. Greenwood Press 2002 139p il $44.95   **920**
1. Musicians
ISBN 0-313-31442-X   LC 2001-40559
Contents: Louis Armstrong; Johann Sebastian Bach; Ludwig van Beethoven; Pablo Casals; Sarah Chang; Ray Charles; Charlotte Church; Bob Dylan; John Lennon; Midori; Wolfgang Mozart; Niccolo Paganini; Isaac Stern
Profiles thirteen musicians who achieved high honors and fame before the age of twenty-five, representing many different time periods and musical styles
"A useful introduction to some of the musical giants of the last four centuries." SLJ
Includes glossary and bibliographical references

Engelbert, Phillis

American civil rights: biographies; Betz Des Chenes, editor. U.X.L 1999 xl, 203p il $60
                                                920
1. Civil rights 2. United States—Race relations 3. United States—Biography
ISBN 0-7876-3173-6   LC 99-20497
This collection of biographies of major civil rights figures, includes sidebars covering related events and issues
Includes bibliographical references

Fradin, Dennis B.

The signers; the fifty-six stories behind the Declaration of Independence; [by] Dennis Brindell Fradin; illustrations by Michael McCurdy. Walker & Co. 2002 164p il maps $22.95; lib bdg $23.85 (4 and up)   **920**
1. United States. Declaration of Independence 2. Statesmen—United States 3. United States—Politics and government—1775-1783, Revolution
ISBN 0-8027-8849-1; 0-8027-8850-5 (lib bdg)
                                  LC 2002-66364
Profiles each of the fifty-six men who signed the Declaration of Independence, giving historical information about the colonies they represented. Includes the text of the Declaration and its history
"Fradin gives brief, fascinating glimpses into the people who have been overlooked as well as those with whom readers might be familiar. . . . An excellent resource for report writing." SLJ
Includes bibliographical references

Freedman, Russell

Indian chiefs. Holiday House 1987 151p il lib bdg $22.95; pa $12.95 (6 and up)   **920**
1. Native Americans—Biography
ISBN 0-8234-0625-3 (lib bdg); 0-8234-0971-6 (pa)
                                  LC 86-46198
This "book chronicles the lives of six renowned Indian chiefs, each of whom served as a leader during a critical period in his tribe's history. . . . The text relates information about the lives of each chief and aspects of Indian/white relationships that illuminate his actions. Interesting vignettes and quotations are well integrated into the narrative as are dramatic accounts of battles. While the tone of the text is nonjudgmental, an underlying sympathy for the Indians' situation is apparent." Horn Book
Includes bibliographical references

George-Warren, Holly

Shake, rattle, & roll; the founders of rock & roll; words by Holly George-Warren; pictures by Laura Levine. Houghton Mifflin 2001 unp il $15; pa $5.95 (4 and up)   **920**
1. Musicians 2. Rock music
ISBN 0-618-05540-1; 0-618-43229-9 (pa)
                                  LC 00-33480
"Brief profiles of 15 men and women whose music 'created a sound that changed our culture forever,' including Bill Haley, Fats Domino, Little Richard, Elvis Presley, Carl Perkins, Wanda Jackson and Ritchie Valens." N Y Times Book Rev
"A wonderfully entertaining browsing book that will also fill a gap in most music collections." SLJ

Goldman, David J.

Presidential losers; by David J. Goldman. Lerner Publications Co 2004 72p il lib bdg $25.26
                                                920
1. Presidents—United States—Election
ISBN 0-8225-0100-7   LC 2003-11222
Contents: Aaron Burr (1756-1836) the election of 1800; Henry Clay (1777-1852) the elections of 1824, 1832 and 1844; George McClellan (1826-1885) the election of 1864; Samuel Tilden (1814-1886) the election of 1876; William Jennings Bryan (1860-1925) the elections of 1896, 1900 and 1908; Alfred M. Landon (1887-1987) the election of 1936; Thomas E. Dewey (1902-1971) the elections of 1944 and 1948; Adlai Stevenson (1900-1965) the elections of 1952 and 1956; Richard Nixon (1913-1994) and Hubert Humphrey (1911-1978) the elections of 1960 and 1968; Albert Gore (1948-) and George Bush (1946-) the election of 2000
"Covering the period from Aaron Burr's lost election in 1800 to Al Gore's in 2000, this book discusses 10 men who ran for U.S. president and lost. . . . Occasional anecdotes and vivid details enliven the smoothly written text. . . . The black-and-white illustrations include reproductions of period paintings, posters, and political cartoons as well as many photos." Booklist
Includes bibliographical references

Graham, Kevin, 1959-
Contemporary environmentalists. Facts on File 1996 178p il (Global profiles) $25 (7 and up)
920
1. Environmentalists 2. Environmental protection
ISBN 0-8160-3222-X   LC 95-35266
Profiles ten environmentalists including Jacques Cousteau, David Ross Brower, Vo Quy, Thomas Odhiambo, Gro Harlem Brundtland, Anita Roddick, Randy Hayes, Joseph Krecek, Michael Bloomfield and Neca Marcovaldi
Includes bibliographical references

Graham, Paula W.
Speaking of journals; children's book writers talk about their diaries, notebooks and sketchbooks. Boyds Mills Press 1999 226p il pa $14.95
920
1. Authors, American
ISBN 1-56397-741-9   LC 98-88261
"This collection of essays by and interviews with writers for children and young adults is a rich source of material for teachers who want to expose their students to a variety of diary, journal, and notebook-keeping practices." SLJ
Includes bibliographical references

Greenberg, Lorna
Digging into the past; pioneers of archeology; {by} Lorna Greenberg and Margot F. Horwitz. Watts 2001 127p il maps (Lives in science) lib bdg $20.50
920
1. Archeologists
ISBN 0-531-11857-6   LC 00-33032
Among the archeologists profiled are Howard Carter, Hiram Bingham, Mortimer Wheeler, Gertrude Bell, and Kathleen Kenyon
"The writing is lively enough to engage readers with an interest in the topic. The authors generally focus on the people's work and careers, yet they emerge as distinct individuals." SLJ
Includes bibliographical references (p. 120-122) and index

Growing up black; from slave days to the present: 25 African-Americans reveal the trials and triumphs of their childhoods; edited by Jay David. {rev ed}. Avon Bks. 1992 276p pa $12.50
920
1. African Americans—Biography
ISBN 0-380-76632-9   LC 92-135054
First published 1968 by Morrow
"This compelling collection of autobiographical accounts of 25 African Americans will introduce readers to some of the best black writers—from Frederick Douglass to Audre Lorde, Claude Brown, John Wideman, and Lorene Cary—and will help students write with candor and control about their own memories." Rochman
Against borders

Gulotta, Charles
Extraordinary women in politics. Children's Press 1998 288p il (Extraordinary people) pa $16.95 hardcover o.p.
920
1. Women in politics
ISBN 0-516-26399-4   LC 97-38230
This book "profiles 55 women who have been active in politics or influential in the political climate of their times. Spanning history from 69 B.C.E. to the present, the chronological coverage is international and multicultural, though women from the U.S. make up more than half of the entries." SLJ
"A good introduction to a topic seldom addressed in books for young teens." Booklist
Includes bibliographical references

Hacker, Carlotta
Nobel Prize winners. Crabtree 1998 48p il maps (Women in profile) $21.28; pa $8.95
920
1. Nobel Prizes 2. Women—Biography
ISBN 0-7787-0007-0; 0-7787-0029-1 (pa)
LC 97-53222
Chronicles the lives and achievements of women who have received Nobel Prizes in a variety of fields, including Aung San Suu Kyi, Barbara McClintock, and Nadine Gordimer
Includes glossary and bibliographical references

Hamanaka, Sheila
In search of the spirit; the Living National Treasures of Japan; by Sheila Hamanaka and Ayano Ohmi; illustrations by Sheila Hamanaka; calligraphy by Ayano Ohmi. Morrow Junior Bks. 1999 48p il $16; lib bdg $16.89 (5 and up)
920
1. Japan—Biography
ISBN 0-688-14607-4; 0-688-14608-2 (lib bdg)
LC 98-23051
This book "introduces six individuals (including a bamboo weaver, a puppet master, and a sword maker) honored in Japan for having 'devoted their lives to traditional crafts and performing arts'." Horn Book Guide
"Bold, red calligraphy and a large, full-color photo of the craft or performer at work open several pages of lyrical, informative text about each artist." SLJ

Hansen, Joyce
African princess; the amazing lives of Africa's royal women; illustrated by Laurie McGaw. . Jump at the Sun/Hyperion/Madison Press 2004 48p il lib bdg $16.99 (5 and up)
920
1. Princesses 2. Africa—Biography
ISBN 0-7868-5116-3   LC 2004-40634
This profiles six African royal women from ancient times to the present, including Hatshepsut of Egypt, Njinja of Matumba, Amina of Zaria, Tata Ajach of Dahomey, Taytu Betul of Ethiopia, and Elizabeth of Toro
"Meticulously researched and jammed with historical tidbits and surprises. . . . Each minibiography is illustrated with a stunning, golden-toned watercolor portrait." N Y Times Book Rev

Hansen, Joyce—*Continued*
Women of hope; African Americans who made
a difference; foreword by Moe Foner. Scholastic
1998 31p il $16.95 (4 and up)   **920**
1. African American women
ISBN 0-590-93973-4   LC 96-32117
Features photographs and biographies of thirteen
African-American women, including Maya Angelou,
Ruby Dee, and Alice Walker
"The book developed from a series of posters issued
by the Bread and Roses Cultural Project of the National
Health and Human Service Employees Union. . . .
Hansen has added a clear, readable, and informative sin-
gle-page commentary for each of the striking black-and-
white portraits." SLJ
Includes bibliographical references

Hardy, P. Stephen
Extraordinary people of the Harlem
Renaissance; {by} P. Stephen Hardy and Sheila
Jackson Hardy. Children's Press 2000 288p il
(Extraordinary people) lib bdg $39; pa $16.95
                                            920
1. Harlem Renaissance 2. African Americans—Biography 3. African American arts
ISBN 0-516-21201-X (lib bdg); 0-516-27170-9 (pa)
                                    LC 99-43629
Looks at the many artists, photographers, choreographers, musicians, composers, poets, writers, and other
creative people who made Harlem such an amazing place
in the 1920s and 1930s
"Appendixes include an annotated list of 40 other figures in the Harlem Renaissance, a glossary, and lists of
books and Web sites. Clearly written and designed, this
provides a good starting place for research on the period
and the people who created it." Booklist

Hasday, Judy L., 1957-
Extraordinary women athletes. Children's Press
2000 288p il (Extraordinary people) lib bdg $39;
pa $16.95   **920**
1. Women athletes
ISBN 0-516-21608-2 (lib bdg); 0-516-27039-7 (pa)
                                    LC 99-49335
Presents brief biographies of nearly fifty women athletes from the twentieth century, including Ora Washington, Althea Gibson, Tenley Albright, Wilma Rudolph,
Chris Evert, Nancy Lopez Knight, Jackie Joyner-Kersee,
and Janet Evans
"Students will find this volume interesting and inspiring because such care is taken to show each athlete's
character and drive. . . . List of women's athletic organizations and Web sites; bibliography; index." Book Rep

Haskins, James, 1941-2005
African American entrepreneurs. Wiley 1998
184p il (Black stars)   **920**
1. African American businesspeople 2. African Ameri-
cans—Biography
ISBN 0-471-14576-9   LC 97-37389
The author "has chosen his subjects well. . . .
Haskins has done a good job of individualizing his sub-

jects and catching a sense of the enormous obstacles they
had to overcome to succeed." Booklist
Includes bibliographical references

African American military heroes; {by} Jim
Haskins. Wiley 1998 182p il (Black stars) $24.95
                                            920
1. African American soldiers 2. United States—Armed
forces 3. United States—Military history
ISBN 0-471-14577-7   LC 98-14312
This "volume highlights the lives and contributions of
30 individuals who served in the military from the Revolutionary War to the present day. Well-known figures
such as Private Peter Salem, Scout Harriet Tubman,
Lieutenant Henry O. Flipper, and General Colin Powell
are here as well as others who deserve recognition." SLJ
"The broad coverage makes this an unusual resource
for teachers and researchers; there's enough information
for middle-graders, and older students can use it as a
jumping-off point for deeper studies." Booklist
Includes bibliographical references

Against all opposition; black explorers in
America; {by} Jim Haskins. Walker & Co. 1992
86p il pa $8.95 hardcover o.p. (5 and up)
                                            920
1. African Americans—Biography 2. Explorers
3. America—Exploration
ISBN 0-8027-7672-8   LC 91-30203
Surveys the lives and adventures of black explorers
who helped discover new worlds. James Beckwourth,
Matthew Henson and Ronald E. McNair are among those
profiled
This is "a readable, informative collective biography.
. . . {The author offers} crisp, flowing prose that incorporates telling details and cogent quotations, bringing his
subjects to life and giving their toils meaning and relevance." SLJ
Includes bibliographical references

Haven, Kendall F.
100 most popular scientists for young adults;
biographical sketches and professional paths; by
Kendall Haven and Donna Clark. Libraries
Unlimited 1999 526p il (Profiles and pathways
series) $59 (7 and up)   **920**
1. Scientists
ISBN 1-56308-674-3   LC 99-13755
"Well-known individuals such as Jacques Cousteau,
Sally Ride, and Carl Sagan are assembled here along
with unheralded newcomers to the field. One third of the
entries are about women and many ethnic groups are represented. . . . A bibliography concludes each entry.
Valuable appendixes include an extensive list of Web
sites and lists of scientists by their field of specialization.
The clear type and attractive layout combined with lively
writing, good organization, and curriculum-related content will make the book a useful reference source." SLJ

Henderson, Harry, 1951-
Modern mathematicians. Facts on File 1996
139p il (Global profiles) $25 (7 and up)
                                            920
1. Mathematicians
ISBN 0-8160-3235-1   LC 95-18363

Henderson, Harry, 1951-—*Continued*

This book "includes thirteen brief biographies of men and women who, through achievements in the field of mathematics, advanced modern science. . . . The biographies are arranged chronologically. . . . The coverage of women scientists and the demonstrations of how discoveries in the fields of logic, algebra, and chaos have led to a greater understanding in other scientific fields make this book a valuable resource." Voice Youth Advocates

Includes bibliographical references

Hill, Christine M.

Ten Hispanic American authors. Enslow Pubs. 2002 112p il (Collective biographies) lib bdg $26.60   **920**

1. Hispanic American authors

ISBN 0-7660-1541-6   LC 2001-307

This presents "profiles of Julia Alvarez, Rudolfo Anaya, Sandra Cisneros, Judith Ortiz Cofer, Oscar Hijuelos, Nicholasa Mohr, Richard Rodriguez, Esmeralda Santiago, Gary Soto, and Piri Thomas." SLJ

The author "writes with simple eloquence, drawing frequently on the Latino writers' own stirring memoirs to show how differently each one interprets the experience of bilingualism and of growing up in two cultures." Booklist

Includes bibliographical references

Hillstrom, Kevin

American Civil War: biographies; {by} Kevin Hillstrom and Laurie Collier Hillstrom; Lawrence W. Baker, editor. U.X.L 2000 2v il set $110   **920**

1. United States—History—1861-1865, Civil War—Biography

ISBN 0-7876-3820-X   LC 99-46920

This set "chronicles the lives of 60 famous and lesser-known men and women, including abolitionists, spies, commanders, and writers." SLJ

Vietnam War: biographies; {by} Kevin Hillstrom and Laurie Collier Hillstrom; Diane Sawinski, editor. U.X.L 2001 2v il set $110 (7 and up)   **920**

1. Vietnam War, 1961-1975—Biography 2. United States—Biography

ISBN 0-7876-4884-1   LC 00-56378

This "focuses on 60 important figures, including military and political leaders (Spiro Agnew, Ngo Dinh Diem, Pol Pot), activists (Daniel Berrigan, Jane Fonda), writers (Le Ly Hayslip, Tim O'Brien), and prominent veterans (Ron Kovic, John McCain) on both sides of the conflict. . . . A picture of each personality accompanies the informative text." Booklist

Includes bibliographical references

Howes, Kelly King

World War II: biographies; {by} Kelly K. Howes; edited by Christine Slovey. U.X.L 1999 xxxiii, 288p il $60   **920**

1. World War, 1939-1945—Biography

ISBN 0-7876-3895-1   LC 99-27166

"In addition to political and military leaders, the 31 alphabetical entries in *Biographies* include conscientious objector Franz Jaggerstatter, journalists Dorothy Thompson and Ernie Pyle, physicist J. Robert Oppenheimer, and Holocaust victim Edith Stein. The profiles range in length from 6 to 13 pages and most contain at least one black-and-white photo. Sidebars cover myriad topics such as Shintoism and examples of the Navajo code." SLJ

Includes bibliographical references

Jeffrey, Laura S.

Great American businesswomen. Enslow Pubs. 1996 112p il (Collective biographies) lib bdg $26.60   **920**

1. Businesswomen 2. Women executives

ISBN 0-89490-706-9   LC 96-1009

"Profiles of 10 20th century American women who have achieved success in the male-dominated world of business. Some are relatively unknown, such as Maggie L. Walker, an African American who was the first female banker, and Ruth Handler, who created the Barbie doll. Others, such as television-personality Oprah Winfrey and cookie-maker Debbie Fields, are well known. The other figures, Olive Ann Beech, Madam C.J. Walker, Katharine Graham, Eileen Ford, Alice Rivlin, and Elaine Garzarelli, excelled in a wide variety of fields. . . . This title would be a good choice for reports or for special units on women's history." SLJ

Includes bibliographical references

Jones, Veda Boyd, 1948-

Government & politics. Chelsea House 1999 64p il (Female firsts in their fields) lib bdg $20.65   **920**

1. Women in politics 2. Women—Biography

ISBN 0-7910-5140-4   LC 98-45391

Profiles women who have been active in politics and government, including Barbara Jordan, Geraldine Ferraro, Sandra Day O'Connor, and Madeleine Albright

Includes bibliographical references

Kallen, Stuart A., 1955-

Native American chiefs and warriors. Lucent Bks. 1999 112p il maps (History makers) $27.45 (7 and up)   **920**

1. Native Americans—Biography

ISBN 1-56006-364-5   LC 99-13227

Discusses the lives and achievements of five famous and influential Native American chiefs: King Philip, Chief Pontiac, Geronimo, Crazy Horse, and Wilma Mankiller

Includes bibliographical references

Kaminsky, Marty

Uncommon champions; fifteen athletes who battled back. Boyds Mills Press 2000 147p $14.95; pa $9.95   **920**

1. Athletes

ISBN 1-56397-787-7; 1-59078-005-1 (pa)

"Kaminsky profiles 15 athletes who have dealt with adversity (either physical or mental) and fought back.

Kaminsky, Marty—*Continued*
The subjects, a mix of male and female athletes, represent a variety of sports. . . . A full-page, black-and-white photo is included for most subjects, a few of whom are still well known today (Michelle Akers, Chris Zorich, Zina Garrison)." Booklist

Kane, Joseph Nathan, 1899-2002
Facts about the presidents; Janet Podell & Steven Anzovin {editors}. 7th ed. Wilson, H.W. 2001 721p il $120 **920**
1. Presidents—United States
ISBN 0-8242-1007-7   LC 2001-26261
First published 1959
The main part of this work provides an individual chapter on each President, from Washington through George W. Bush, presenting such information as family, education, election, Vice President, main events and accomplishments of his administration, and First Lady. Part two contains tables and lists presenting comparative data on all the Presidents
Includes bibliographical references

Katz, William Loren
Black pioneers; an untold story. Atheneum Bks. for Young Readers 1999 193p il maps $19.95
920
1. African Americans—History 2. Frontier and pioneer life 3. Abolitionists 4. Underground railroad
ISBN 0-689-81410-0   LC 98-19104
"The narration is clear, fluid, and enlivened with quotes from the pioneers themselves." Horn Book Guide
Includes bibliographical references

Kennedy, John F. (John Fitzgerald), 1917-1963
Profiles in courage. HarperCollins Pubs. 2003 xxii, 245p $19.95 **920**
1. Politicians—United States 2. Courage
ISBN 0-06-053062-6   LC 2003-40676
A reissue of the title first published 1956

This series of profiles of Americans who took courageous stands at crucial moments in public life includes John Quincy Adams, Daniel Webster, Thomas Hart Benton, Sam Houston, Edmund G. Ross, Lucius Q. C. Lamar, George Norris, Robert A. Taft and others
Includes bibliographical references

Kennedy Cuomo, Kerry
Speak truth to power; human rights defenders who are changing our world; photographs by Eddie Adams; edited by Nan Richardson. Crown 2000 256p il $50 (7 and up) **920**
1. Human rights
ISBN 0-8129-3062-2   LC 00-34557
"An Umbrage editions book"
This book "is composed of fifty three-page interviews with people who have made strides in the global fight to ensure basic human rights for everyone. . . . The Dalai Lama, Desmond Tutu, and Elie Wiesel are included, but most subjects are everyday people who have survived

imprisonment, death threats, and torture to bring about change. . . . Their reports are sad but inspiring. . . . The haunting photographs and stories are gripping." Voice Youth Advocates

Kent, Deborah, 1948-
Extraordinary people with disabilities; by Deborah Kent & Kathryn A. Quinlan. Children's Press 1996 288p il (Extraordinary people) pa $16.95 hardcover o.p. **920**
1. Handicapped
ISBN 0-516-26074-X   LC 96-11895
Profiles seven dozen people throughout history with various physical or mental disabilities. Additional articles provide historical background on the disability rights movement
"Many of the names are obvious, such as Beethoven, Helen Keller, FDR; others are not usually associated with a disability, such as Tom Cruise (dyslexia). . . . A fine combination of biography and the history of the disability-rights movement." SLJ
Includes bibliographical references

Kent, Jacqueline, 1947-
Business builders in fashion. Oliver Press (Minneapolis) 2003 160p il (Business builders) lib bdg $22.95 **920**
1. Fashion design 2. Businesspeople
ISBN 1-88150-880-3   LC 2001-59313
"Drawing from a multitude of sources on Charles Worth, Levi Strauss, Coco Chanel, Christian Dior, Mary Quant, Ralph Lauren, and Vera Wang, Kent describes the lives and businesses of these high-profile names in the industry." SLJ
"This provides a well-focused consideration of a topic." Booklist
Includes glossary and bibliographical references

Kenyon, Karen, 1938-
The Brontë family; passionate literary geniuses; [by] Karen Smith Kenyon. Lerner Publs. 2003 128p il (Lerner biography) lib bdg $25.26 (7 and up) **920**
1. Brontë family 2. Authors, English
ISBN 0-8225-0071-X   LC 2001-4957
Contents: Setting the record straight; Storyteller; Cowan bridge; The twelve soldiers; Roe head; Seeking and searching; Brussels and after; Never was better stuff penned; Gone like dreams; Charlotte alone; Charlotte and Mr. Nicholls
A joint biography of Charlotte, Emily, Branwell, and Anne Bronte, exploring how the siblings sparked creativity in each other and how their lives were woven into their novels
This title is "well-written and solidly researched. . . . A boon for report writers and fascinating pleasure reading as well." SLJ
Includes bibliographical references

Ketchum, Liza, 1946-
Into a new country; eight remarkable women of the West. Little, Brown 2000 135p il maps $18.95 (7 and up) **920**
1. Frontier and pioneer life—West (U.S.) 2. West (U.S.)—History 3. Women—West (U.S.)
ISBN 0-316-49597-2 LC 99-52358
Presents the history of the West through eight biographies of women, including Susan Magoffin, Lotta Crabtree, and Biddy Mason
"Examining the varied roles women played in the nineteenth-century western expansion, the smoothly written text is accompanied by occasional black-and-white photos of the subjects." Horn Book Guide

Kimmel, Elizabeth Cody
The look-it-up book of explorers. Random House 2004 128p il map $17.99; pa $10.99 (5 and up) **920**
1. Explorers 2. Exploration
ISBN 0-375-92478-7; 0-375-82478-2 (pa)
"Beginning with Leif Ericksson and his trip to Greenland and the Americas to Robert Ballard's 1985 expedition to search for the *Titanic*, the chronlogically arranged spreads give readers a better understanding of how the world was explored. . . . Informative black-and-white photos and reproductions appear throughout. . . . This is an excellent quick resource that will appeal to researchers and general readers alike." SLJ

Knight, Judson
Middle ages: biographies; edited by Judy Galens. U.X.L 2000 2v set $110 **920**
1. Middle ages—Biography 2. Medieval civilization
ISBN 0-7876-4857-4 LC 00-64864
Among the 50 people profiled are Eleanor of Aquitaine, Henry the Navigator, Kublai Khan, Montezuma I, and St. Patrick
Each "entry contains illustrations, date spans and pronunciations of names for individuals, sidebars, and a bibliography of books, periodicals, and Web sites." Booklist

Kozar, Richard
Inventors and their discoveries. Chelsea House 1999 64p il (Costume, tradition, and culture) $20.95 **920**
1. Scientists 2. Inventors
ISBN 0-7910-5163-3 LC 98-33701
Highlights twenty-five notable achievements in science, medicine, and industry and the individuals responsible, including Alexander Graham Bell, Madame Curie, and Samuel F. B. Morse
Includes bibliographical references

Kramer, Sydelle
The look-it-up book of first ladies; by S. A. Kramer. Random House 2001 c2000 128p pa $9.95 **920**
1. Presidents' spouses—United States
ISBN 0-679-89347-4 LC 00-35306
Provides profiles of the women who influenced the history of the United States as wives of its presidents

Krull, Kathleen, 1952-
Lives of extraordinary women; rulers, rebels (and what the neighbors thought); written by Kathleen Krull; illustrated by Kathryn Hewitt. Harcourt 2000 95p il $20 (4 and up) **920**
1. Women in politics
ISBN 0-15-200807-1 LC 99-6840
"The subjects range from Cleopatra in ancient Egypt to contemporary activists Wilma Mankiller, Aung San Suu Kyi, and Rigoberta Menchu." Voice Youth Advocates
"Each entry offers a tightly written biography, often filled with delicious anecdote. . . . Each biographical essay is accompanied by one of Hewitt's full-page, full-color caricatures. Both artful and witty, the illustrations provide perfect accompaniments to the often breezy and accessible text." N Y Times Book Rev
Includes bibliographical references

Lives of the presidents; fame, shame (and what the neighbors thought); illustrated by Kathryn Hewitt. Harcourt Brace & Co. 1998 96p il $20 **920**
1. Presidents—United States
ISBN 0-15-200808-X LC 97-33069
Also available from Raintree Steck-Vaughn Pubs.
Focuses on the lives of presidents as parents, husbands, pet-owners, and neighbors while also including humorous anecdotes about hairstyles, attitudes, diets, fears, and sleep patterns
"Packed with enough detail for brief reports, these articles are also just plain entertaining. . . . Hewitt's spirited watercolor cartoons add to the presentation immensely." SLJ
Includes bibliographical references

Lanier, Shannon
Jefferson's children; the story of one American family; by Shannon Lanier and Jane Feldman; with photographs by Jane Feldman; and an introduction by Lucian K. Truscott IV. Random House 2000 144p il $19.95 (7 and up) **920**
1. Jefferson, Thomas, 1743-1826 2. Hemings, Sally, 1773-1835 3. Jefferson family 4. Hemings family 5. African Americans—Biography 6. Racially mixed people 7. United States—Race relations
ISBN 0-375-80597-4 LC 00-44551
This is an "anthology of personal meditations by a variety of Jefferson's living descendants. Edited by Shannon Lanier, a descendant through Sally's son Madison Hemings's line, the portraits that emerge are as generous and jumbled as America itself. The statements range from hostile to conciliatory to indifferent to eloquent." NY Times Book Rev
Includes bibliographical references

Lester, Julius
The blues singers; ten who rocked the world; illustrated by Lisa Cohen. Jump at the Sun 2001 47p il $15.99; lib bdg $16.49 (5 and up)
      920
1. Blues music 2. African American singers
ISBN 0-7868-0463-7; 0-7868-2405-0 (lib bdg)
      LC 00-59019
"Lester profiles 10 blues, or blues-inspired, legends including Bessie Smith, Muddy Waters, B. B. King and Billie Holiday as well as Mahalia Jackson . . . and Little Richard. . . . Lester's anecdotal approach, his leisurely pacing and abundance of colorful, down-home similes give the famous figures a tangible presence." Publ Wkly
Includes discography and bibliographical references

Lindop, Laurie
Scientists and doctors. 21st Cent. Bks. (NY) 1997 128p il (Dynamic modern women) lib bdg $24.90 (7 and up)
      920
1. Women scientists 2. Women in medicine
ISBN 0-8050-4166-4
      LC 96-41923
Biographies of ten women in the fields of medicine and science including "Biruté Galdikas . . . Mae Jemison . . . Mildred Dresselhaus, Mary-Claire King, Mary Leakey, Rita Levi-Montalcini, Susan Love, Helen Taussig, Chien-Shiung Wu, and Rosalyn Yalow. . . . The subjects are presented in a lively, entertaining manner and are accompanied by a full-page photograph." SLJ
Includes bibliographical references

Lyman, Darryl, 1944-
Holocaust rescuers; ten stories of courage. Enslow Pubs. 1999 128p il (Collective biographies) lib bdg $26.60
      920
1. World War, 1939-1945—Jews 2. Holocaust, 1933-1945
ISBN 0-7660-1114-3
      LC 98-21584
Discusses the efforts of ten individuals who did what they could to save Jews from the Nazis, including Anna Borkowska, Varian Fry, Irene Gut Opdyke, Mustafa Hardaga, Jorgen Kieler, Oskar Schindler, Andrew Sheptitsky, Sempo Sugihara, Marion van Binsbergen Pritchard, and Raoul Wallenberg
Includes bibliographical references

Major, John S., 1942-
Caravan to America; living arts of the Silk Road; [by] John S. Major and Betty J. Belanus. Cricket Bks. 2002 130p il map $24.95; pa $15.95 (4 and up)
      920
1. Arts
ISBN 0-8126-2666-4; 0-8126-2677-X (pa)
      LC 2002-5477
"A Marcato book"
Contents: Qi Shu Fang: Peking opera performer; Doug Kim: Korean American martial artist; Yeshi Dorjee: Tibetan artist-monk; Abdul Khaliq Muradi: Turkmen rug restorer; Tamara Katayev: Bukharan singer; Najmieh Batmanglij: Iranian American cook; La Verne J. Magarian: Armenian American calligrapher and paper artist; Peter Kyvelos, Greek American oud maker

Profiles eight artists and artisans now living in America who are originally from the "Silk Road," an ancient network of caravan trails through which trade goods, ideas, and arts pass between Asia and the Mediterranean
"Full of colorful and informative archival and contemporary photographs and drawings. . . . Each person's story is told in an interesting manner, and information about their specialty and its history is woven throughout the text. . . . Not only is the work informative, but it is handsome as well." SLJ
Includes glossary and bibliographical references

Martin, Marvin
Extraordinary people in jazz; by Marvin Martin. Children's Press 2004 288p il (Extraordinary people) $39
      920
1. Jazz musicians 2. Jazz music
ISBN 0-516-22275-9
      LC 2003-7059
Contents: The profiles; Duke Ellington; Louis Armstrong; Count Basie; Coleman Hawkins; Benny Carter; Lionel Hampton; Benny Goodman; Lester Young; Art Tatum; Django Reinhardt ; Gil Evans; Kenny Clarke; Billie Holiday; Charlie Christian; Nat King Cole; Ella Fitzgerald; Thelonious Monk; Dizzy Gillespie; Marion McParland; George Shearing; Art Blakley; Anita O'Day; Charlie Parker; Billy Taylor; Lambert, Hendricks, and Ross; Charles Mingus, Jr.; Oscar Pettiford; Modern Jazz Quartet; Milt Jackson; John Lewis; Percy Heath; Connie Kay; Buddy DeFranco ; The Jones Boys, Thad, Elvin, and Hank; Max Roach; Sarah Vaughan; Tito Puente; Oscar Peterson; Miles Davis; John Coltrane; Ray Brown, Jr.; Gerry Mulligan; Cannonball Adderly; Bill Evans; Joe Pass; Ornette Coleman; Betty Carter; Clifford Brown; Cecil Taylor; McCoy Tyner; Ron Carter; Chick Corea; Gary Burton
"This book provides 60 profiles of innovators of jazz music's many iterations. . . . The profiles are accessible to those who need quick information but also include enough data for an assignment." SLJ

Matuz, Roger
Complete American presidents sourcebook; Lawrence W. Baker, editor. U.X.L 2001 5v il set $250
      920
1. Presidents—United States 2. United States—Politics and government—Sources
ISBN 0-7876-4837-X
      LC 00-56794
Contents: v1 George Washington through Martin Van Buren, 1789-1841; v2 William Henry Harrison through Andrew Johnson, 1841-1869; v3 Ulysses S. Grant through William Howard Taft, 1869-1913; v4 Woodrow Wilson through Dwight D. Eisenhower, 1913-1961; v5 John F. Kennedy through George W. Bush, 1961-2001
This set provides a "selection of biographies covering all 43 presidents. Featuring both biographies and primary source documents, profiles also include a 2,000- to 3,400-word essay covering the president's life, career and legacy; an emphasis on the long-term impact of each president's administration; one or more full or excerpted speeches or inaugural addresses {and} a 1,200- to 1,800-word biography of the first lady." Publisher's note

McConnell, Stacy A.

Ancient civilizations: biographies; Stacy McConnell and Lawrence W. Baker, editors. U.X.L 2000 xlvii, 207p il map $60 (7 and up) **920**

1. Ancient civilization

ISBN 0-7876-3985-0   LC 99-45751

Profiles sixty men and women who shaped the ancient civilizations in Egypt, Mesopotamia, Israel, China, Asia Minor, and other places

"The accessible, alphabetically arranged profiles include black-and-white photos and reproductions. Following each entry is a list of further reading and, sometimes, Web sites." SLJ

McLean, Jacqueline

Women of adventure. Oliver Press (Minneapolis) 2003 160p il maps (Profiles) lib bdg $19.95 (7 and up) **920**

1. Kingsley, Mary Henrietta, 1862-1900 2. David-Neel, Alexandra, 1868-1969 3. Adams, Harriet Chalmers, 1875-1937 4. Harrison, Marguerite Elton Baker, 1879-1967 5. Boyd, Louise Arner, 1887-1972 6. Stark, Freya, 1893-1993 7. Bancroft, Ann 8. Women—Biography 9. Adventure and adventurers

ISBN 1-88150-873-0   LC 2001-59312

"McLean profiles seven women who explored the world from the 19th century to the present day. . . . Written in a lively, narrative style, these accounts will please and entertain readers." SLJ

Includes bibliographical references

Meltzer, Milton, 1915-

Ten kings; and the worlds they ruled; illustrated by Bethanne Andersen. Orchard Bks. 2002 132p il maps $21.95 (5 and up) **920**

1. Kings and rulers

ISBN 0-439-31293-0   LC 2001-33202

This "volume comprises biographies of ten legendary leaders, including Hammurabi, Alexander the Great, Attila, Kublai Khan, and Peter the Great. Meltzer's sources for discussing these lives and their cultural contexts are impeccable, and he writes knowledgeably and thoughtfully." Horn Book Guide

Includes bibliographical references

Ten queens; portraits of women of power; illustrated by Bethanne Andersen. Dutton Children's Bks. 1998 134p il maps (5 and up) **920**

1. Queens

ISBN 0-525-45643-0; 0-525-47158-8 (pa)

LC 97-36428

"The 10 women Meltzer showcases are Esther, Cleopatra, Boudicca, Zenobia, Eleanor of Aquitaine, Isabella of Spain, Elizabeth I, Christine of Sweden, Maria Theresa, and Catherine the Great." Booklist

Meltzer "has a storyteller's flair and an eye for the small details and anecdotes that bring these queens to life. . . . Colorful expressionistic paintings, boldly stroked onto unframed panels, enrich the pages." SLJ

Includes bibliographical references

Mendoza, Patrick M.

Extraordinary people in extraordinary times; heroes, sheroes, and villains. Libraries Unlimited 1999 142p il pa $21 (7 and up) **920**

1. United States—Biography

ISBN 1-56308-611-5   LC 99-14238

Stories of little-known historical characters from American history. Subjects range from that of the first woman to receive the Congressional Medal of Honor to the first woman to be hanged in the United States. Jeanette Rankin, Jose Marti and two survivors of the Sand Creek Massacre are among those profiled

Includes bibliographical references

Mour, Stanley I.

American jazz musicians. Enslow Pubs. 1998 128p il (Collective biographies) lib bdg $26.60 **920**

1. Jazz musicians 2. Jazz music

ISBN 0-7660-1027-9   LC 97-27173

Profiles ten notable jazz musicians, including Louis Armstrong, John Coltrane, Miles Davis, Duke Ellington and Wynton Marsalis

Includes discography and bibliographical references

Mulvihill, Margaret

The treasury of saints and martyrs. Viking 1999 80p il $19.99 (5 and up) **920**

1. Christian saints

ISBN 0-670-88789-7   LC 99-70893

"Oversize and illustrated with museum art, the book introduces more than 40 saints, from the beginning of Christianity to the modern day. The life of each saint is discussed in a page or two of straightforward text that also features several illustrations. . . . A pleasure to look at and often inspiring. A calendar of saints and glossary are appended." Booklist

Nardo, Don, 1947-

Great Elizabethan playwrights. Lucent Bks. 2003 112p il (Lucent library of historical eras, Elizabethan England) lib bdg $27.45 **920**

1. English drama—History and criticism 2. Dramatists 3. Theater—History 4. Great Britain—History—1485-1603, Tudors

ISBN 1-59018-017-8   LC 2001-6602

Contents: Introduction: Birth of the English-speaking theater; "On Your Imaginary Forces Work": the Elizabethan theater; The courtly dreamer: John Lyly; Father of the revenge tragedy: Thomas Kyd; Poet of pageant and drama: George Peele; A man at war within himself: Robert Greene; Risk-taker and mystery-maker: Christopher Marlowe; A playwright for all time: William Shakespeare; Shrewd critic of human follies: Ben Jonson

Discusses the origins of English-speaking theater and includes facts about seven early Elizabethan playwrights, including William Shakespeare

Includes bibliographical references

Northrup, Mary
American computer pioneers. Enslow Pubs.
1998 112p il (Collective biographies) lib bdg
$26.60   **920**
1. Computers 2. Inventors
ISBN 0-7660-1053-8   LC 97-24155
Profiles some of the people who have made contributions to the computer industry including Herman Hollerith, Johnny von Neumann, Grace Hopper, John W. Mauchly, J. Presper Eckert, Jr., and An Wang
"Students will find the text easy to read, nontechnical, and filled with enough information for reports and enough appeal to spark further investigation." SLJ
Includes bibliographical references

Oleksy, Walter G., 1930-
Hispanic-American scientists; {by} Walter Oleksy. Facts on File 1998 120p il (American profiles) $25 (7 and up)   **920**
1. Hispanic Americans 2. Scientists 3. Engineers
ISBN 0-8160-3704-3   LC 98-6558
"A look at 10 Hispanic Americans who have made important contributions in various fields of science since the end of World War II. Luis Alvarez, Francisco Dallmeier, Adriana Ocampo, Margarita Colmenares, and Ellen Ochoa are among the individuals profiled." SLJ
This "book provides a useful general introduction to many interesting areas of scientific study and what they entail, via the often-overlooked contributions of an important ethnic group." Booklist
Includes bibliographical references

Orgill, Roxane
Shout, sister, shout! the girl singers who shaped a century. Margaret K. McElderry Bks. 2001 148p il $19.95 (6 and up)   **920**
1. Popular music 2. Singers
ISBN 0-689-81991-9   LC 99-54374
"The lives of ten 'girl singers,' representing different genres of popular music, from vaudeville to blues to jazz to country, are arranged by decade. Profiles of Sophie Tucker, Ma Rainey, Bessie Smith, Ethel Merman, Judy Garland, Anita O'Day, Joan Baez, Bette Midler, Madonna, and Lucinda Williams are included." Voice Youth Advocates
Includes discography and bibliographical references

Outman, James L., 1946-
Industrial Revolution: biographies; {by} James L. Outman, Elisabeth M. Outman. UXL 2003 218p il (Industrial revolution reference library) $55   **920**
1. Industrial revolution
ISBN 0-7876-6514-2   LC 2002-155421
Contents: Henry Bessemer; Andrew Carnegie; Henry Ford; Robert Fulton; Samuel Gompers; Jay Gould; James J. Hill; Mother Jones; Karl Marx; Rockefeller; Theodore Roosevelt; Adam Smith; George Stephenson; Ida Tarbell; James Watt; George Westinghouse; Eli Whitney
"The 25 essays in {this volume} provide biographical information with an emphasis on each person's contribution or impact on the Industrial Revolution. . . . More

than 50 black-and-white photographs complement the text. . . . This is an excellent adjunct to American and world history units and classes on economics and labor movements." Booklist
Includes bibliographical references

Pendergast, Tom, 1964-
Westward expansion: biographies. U.X.L 2001 xxv, 251p il maps $60 (7 and up)   **920**
1. Frontier and pioneer life 2. West (U.S.)—Biography
ISBN 0-7876-4863-9   LC 00-109475
This collective biography profiles a number of legendary figures of the Wild West, including Buffalo Bill, George Custer, Wyatt Earp, Kit Carson, Annie Oakley, Andrew Jackson, Sarah Winnemucca, and Belle Starr

World War I: biographies; [by] Tom Pendergast and Sara Pendergast; Christine Slovey, editor. U.X.L 2002 183p il $58 (7 and up)   **920**
1. World War, 1914-1918—Biography
ISBN 0-7876-5477-9   LC 2001-53162
A collection of thirty biographies of world figures who played important roles in World War I, including Mata Hari, T.E. Lawrence, and Alvin C. York
Includes bibliographical references

Pinkney, Andrea Davis
Let it shine; stories of Black women freedom fighters; illustrated by Stephen Alcorn. Harcourt 2000 107p il $20 (4 and up)   **920**
1. African American women 2. African Americans—Civil rights 3. United States—Race relations
ISBN 0-15-201005-X   LC 99-42806
"Gulliver books"
This "collective biography tells of 10 extraordinary black women. From Sojourner Truth to Shirley Chisholm, this is also a view of African American history through individual lives. . . . Stephen Alcorn's allegorical oil portraits are dramatic and beautiful. . . . The immediacy of the text and the spacious design of the large volume make this a natural for reading aloud." Booklist
Includes bibliographical references

Price-Groff, Claire
Extraordinary women journalists. Childrens Press 1997 272p il (Extraordinary people) lib bdg $39   **920**
1. Women journalists
ISBN 0-516-20474-2   LC 96-50341
Profiles the life and work of notable women journalists, including Sarah Hale, Margaret Fuller, and Nellie Bly
"Chapters are short but full of useful information and are accompanied by large black-and-white photos. Because these women's chosen field intersects with so many other subjects, students learn about American and world history, politics, and culture as they read these short biographies. . . . Good for reports or leisure reading." SLJ
Includes glossary and bibliographical references

Price-Groff, Claire—_Continued_

Twentieth-century women political leaders. Facts on File 1998 142p il (Global profiles) $25 (7 and up) **920**
1. Women politicians 2. Women in politics
ISBN 0-8160-3672-1 LC 97-32373
Presents biographies of twelve women who have held positions of political leadership around the world, including Golda Meir, Margaret Thatcher, Winnie Mandela, Corazon Aquino, Wilma Mankiller, and Benazir Bhutto
"The detailed index provides easy points of access for students doing research, and the variety of women included make this title a useful reference resource." SLJ
Includes bibliographical references

Reed, Jennifer
The Saudi royal family; {by} Jennifer Bond Reed. Chelsea House 2003 111p il map (Major world leaders) lib bdg $22.95; pa $9.95 **920**
1. Saudi Arabia—Kings and rulers
ISBN 0-7910-7063-8 (lib bdg); 0-7910-7187-1 (pa)
LC 2002 7455
Contents: Humble origins; Desert kingdom; King Abdul Aziz: a new kingdom; King Saud, the black sheikh: 1953-1964; King Faisal, the hero: 1964-1975; King Khalid, the quiet one: 1975-1982; King Fahd; Friend or foe: the future of Saudi Arabia
This "follows the rise of the Saud family and its radical Wahabist interpretation of Islam in the early-twentieth century and then introduces the various kings who have followed." Booklist
This book is "extensively illustrated with captioned, full-color photographs . . . informative, useful." SLJ
Includes glossary and bibliographical references

Renaissance & Reformation: biographies; Peggy Saari & Aaron Saari, editors. U.X.L 2002 2v il set $105 **920**
1. Renaissance—Biography
ISBN 0-7876-5470-1 LC 2001-8609
Profiles fifty people who played a significant role during the Renaissance and Reformation periods in Europe, including John Calvin, Peter Paul Rubens, Catherine de Medici, and Johannes Kepler
Includes bibliographical references

Reynolds, Moira Davison
American women scientists; 23 inspiring biographies, 1900-2000. McFarland & Co. 1999 149p il $35; pa $24.95 (7 and up) **920**
1. Women scientists
ISBN 0-7864-0649-6; 0-7864-2161-4 (pa)
LC 99-14603
"Four-to-six page profiles of 23 of the century's premier women scientists, representing a wide variety of disciplines. The entries are arranged chronologically beginning with Cornelia Clapp (1849-1934) and ending with Mary Good (1931-). . . . Each entry includes a black-and-white portrait." SLJ
Includes bibliographical references

Richie, Jason, 1966-
Space flight; crossing the last frontier. Oliver Press (Minneapolis) 2002 144p il (Innovators) lib bdg $21.95 **920**
1. Scientists 2. Space flight
ISBN 1-88150-877-3 LC 2001-36507
Profiles seven engineers and scientists who made space flight possible, including Robert Goddard, Sergei Korolev, and Wernher von Braun
"The biographies are readable, entertaining, and informative." SLJ
Includes glossary and bibliographical references

Roberts, Russell
Leaders and generals. Lucent Bks. 2001 112p il (American war library, Vietnam War) lib bdg $27.45 **920**
1. Vietnam War, 1961-1975—Biography
ISBN 1-56006-717-9 LC 00-12859
"Roberts covers the principal civilian and military leaders who were involved in the Vietnam War: Ho Chi Minh, Ngo Dinh Diem, Lyndon B. Johnson, William Westmoreland, Richard Nixon, and Henry Kissinger. Personal and political details combine to give insight into the personality, successes, and failures of each man." SLJ
Includes bibliographical references

Ross, Stewart
Leaders of World War II. Raintree Steck-Vaughn Pubs. 2000 64p il (World Wars) lib bdg $32.79 **920**
1. World War, 1939-1945—Biography
ISBN 0-7398-2756-1 LC 00-59216
This profiles Winston Churchill, Franklin Roosevelt, Joseph Stalin, Adolph Hitler, Dwight D. Eisenhower, George S. Patton, Bernard L. Montgomery, Georgii Zhukov, Erwin Rommel, Hideki Tojo, and Benito Mussolini
"Captioned black-and-white photographs, original documents, maps, and sidebars border the clear and engaging text." Horn Book Guide
Includes glossary and bibliographical references

Rubel, David
Scholastic encyclopedia of the presidents and their times; with a foreword by James M. McPherson. Scholastic Reference 2005 244p il $19.95 (5 and up) **920**
1. Presidents—United States
ISBN 0-439-28323-X LC 2004-52564
First published 1994
This reference "documents the tenure of each of the American presidents. It also includes information about the headlines, people, and fads that were defining America during each presidency. . . . Each profile includes a fact box that lists the president's birthday, birthplace, vice president, wife, children, and nickname." Publisher's note
"This is an attractive, inexpensive resource . . . providing concise information in an easy-to-read format." Booklist [review of 1997 edition]

Saari, Peggy
  Colonial America: biographies; Julie L. Carnagie, editor. U.X.L 1999 2v set $110
                  920
  1. United States—Biography 2. United States—History—1600-1775, Colonial period
  ISBN 0-7876-3760-2   LC 99-20707
  Profiles sixty men and women from the American colonial era, including explorers, founders of colonies, religious leaders, landowners, artists, and more
  "Each of the articles gives name, birth and death dates and places, a phrase describing the person's contribution, and a quotation by or about the person. . . . The volumes include a time line that highlights events in the lives of the biographees. All illustrations here and throughout the set are black and white." Booklist
  Includes bibliographical references

Schmittroth, Linda
  American Revolution: biographies; {by} Linda Schmittroth and Mary Kay Rosteck; Stacy A. McConnell, editor. U.X.L 2000 2v il set $110 (5 and up)   **920**
  1. United States—History—1775-1783, Revolution 2. United States—Biography
  ISBN 0-7876-3792-0   LC 99-46941
  Profiles sixty men and women who were key players on the British or American side of the American Revolution, from John Adams, who became the second president, to Eliza Wilkinson, who wrote of the day British soldiers looted her South Carolina home

Shipton, Alyn
  Jazz makers; vanguards of sound. Oxford Univ. Press 2002 263p il (Oxford profiles) $39.95 (7 and up)   **920**
  1. Jazz musicians 2. Jazz music
  ISBN 0-19-512689-0   LC 2001-53148
  "The book is divided into six sections that represent particular jazz styles or eras. Each section contains biographies of musicians who played a significant role in the development of jazz during that period. . . . The introductions and biographies are written in a lively style, which includes personal glimpses, quotations, and anecdotes." Libr Media Connect
  Includes discography and bibliographical references

Sills, Leslie
  In real life: six women photographers. Holiday House 2000 80p il $19.95; pa $9.95 (7 and up)
                  920
  1. Women photographers
  ISBN 0-8234-1498-1; 0-8234-1752-5 (pa)
               LC 99-51832
  "The book explores the lives of Imogen Cunningham, Dorothea Lange, Lola Alvarez Bravo, Carrie Mae Weems, Elsa Dorfman, and Cindy Sherman. . . . Each artist is featured in a clearly written, easy-to-understand chapter, and the chapters include numerous and excellent examples of each artist's work, in both color and b&w." Book Rep
  Includes bibliographical references

  Visions; stories about women artists: Mary Cassatt, Betye Saar, Leonora Carrington, Mary Frank. Whitman, A. 1993 58p il lib bdg $18.95 (5 and up)   **920**
  1. Women artists
  ISBN 0-8075-8491-6   LC 92-32909
  Presents the lives and works of four pioneering women artists
  "Written with clarity, simplicity, and insight. . . . Full-color reproductions of each artist's work are included. The text is further broken up by black-and-white photos of the subjects. Design and layout are carefully planned, resulting in a beautiful book worth sharing with many readers." SLJ
  Includes bibliographical references

Sinnott, Susan
  Extraordinary Asian Americans and Pacific Islanders. rev ed. Children's Press 2003 288p il (Extraordinary people) lib bdg $39; pa $16.95 (5 and up)   **920**
  1. Asian Americans—Biography
  ISBN 0-516-22655-X (lib bdg); 0-516-29355-9 (pa)
              LC 2002-11220
  First published 1993 with title: Extraordinary Asian-Pacific Americans
  Biographical sketches of notable Asian Americans and Pacific Islander Americans, from the nineteenth century up to the present
  "This well-written resource is accompanied by black-and-white photographs, and will be useful for both browsers and report writers." SLJ
  Includes bibliographical references

  The **Smithsonian** book of the First Ladies; their lives, times, and issues; Edith P. Mayo, general editor; foreword by Hillary Rodham Clinton. Holt & Co. 1996 302p il $29.95 (7 and up)
                  920
  1. Presidents' spouses—United States
  ISBN 0-8050-1751-8   LC 94-6147
  This "book gives a brief account of the life and White House doings of first ladies from Martha Washington to Hillary Rodham Clinton; it also mentions White House hostesses who were not presidential wives (such as James Buchanan's niece) and gives a quick précis of those women who didn't live long enough to see their husbands attain the highest office in the land." Bull Cent Child Books
  "Well illustrated and punctuated with tidbits of useful information, this is both an excellent reference book for studying America's First Ladies and an informative look at women's history." Voice Youth Advocates
  Includes bibliographical references

Stewart, Gail, 1949-
  Great women comedians. Lucent Bks. 2003 96p il (History makers) lib bdg $27.45   **920**
  1. Comedians 2. Women—Biography
  ISBN 1-56006-953-8   LC 2001-5695
  Discusses the careers of Gracie Allen, Lucille Ball, Whoopi Goldberg, Roseanne, and Ellen DeGeneres and the impact they had on comedy

Stewart, Gail, 1949-—*Continued*
"A useful addition to collective-biography collections."
SLJ
Includes bibliographical references

Stille, Darlene R., 1942-
Extraordinary women of medicine. Childrens
Press 1997 288p il (Extraordinary people) lib bdg
$39; pa $16.95   **920**
1. Women physicians 2. Women in medicine
ISBN 0-516-20307-X (lib bdg); 0-516-26145-2 (pa)
LC 96-43196
Presents biographical sketches highlighting the contributions of women, mostly American, to the field of medicine in the nineteenth and twentieth centuries
"The thick volume, which spans two centuries of history, is made user-friendly by large type, occasional
black-and-white photographs, and short biographical
chapters." Booklist
Includes glossary and bibliographical references

Streissguth, Thomas
Legendary labor leaders. Oliver Press
(Minneapolis) 1998 160p il (Profiles) $19.95 (7
and up)   **920**
1. Labor movement
ISBN 1-881508-44-7   LC 97-29017
Traces the history of the labor movement in the Unit-
ed States through brief biographies of labor leaders:
Samuel Gompers, Eugene Debs, William Haywood,
"Mother" Jones, John Lewis, A. Philip Randolph, Jimmy
Hoffa, and Cesar Chavez
Includes bibliographical references

Strickland, Michael R., 1965-
African-American poets. Enslow Pubs. 1996
112p il (Collective biographies) lib bdg $26.60
                                                                       920
1. Poets, American 2. African American authors
3. American poetry—African American authors
ISBN 0-89490-774-3   LC 96-2016
Profiles the lives and work of ten African American
poets: Phillis Wheatley, Gwendolyn Brooks, Haki R.
Madhubuti, Rita Dove, Eloise Greenfield, Langston
Hughes, Imamu Amiri Baraka, Maya Angelou, Paul Laurence Dunbar, and Nikki Giovanni
"The clear, focused writing makes this a solid choice
for reports, especially in multicultural units." SLJ
Includes bibliographical references

Sullivan, George, 1933-
Power football; the greatest running backs.
Atheneum Bks. for Young Readers 2001 60p il
$18   **920**
1. Football—Biography
ISBN 0-689-82432-7   LC 00-45146
This profiles eighteen 20th century football running
backs
"Sullivan's lively writing, the concise three- to four-
page biographies, and the excellent color photographs
will draw readers to this book. It is great for browsing
and for finding quick information." SLJ

Sullivan, Otha Richard, 1941-
African American inventors; Jim Haskins,
general editor. Wiley 1998 164p il (Black stars)
$24.95 (5 and up)   **920**
1. African American inventors
ISBN 0-471-14804-0   LC 97-46932
Profiles the lives of twenty-five African American inventors who made significant scientific contributions
from the eighteenth century to modern times
This is "a particularly engaging book to read; Sullivan
highlights those aspects of the subjects' lives that will interest readers the most and writes about them with insight. The book is attractive, too, with lots of historical
engravings and photographs." Booklist
Includes bibliographical references

African American millionaires. John Wiley &
Sons 2004 c2005 158p il (Black stars) $24.95
                                                                       920
1. African Americans—Biography
ISBN 0-471-46928-9   LC 2004-14694
Contents: William Alexander Leidesdorff, 1810-1848;
Mary Ellen Pleasant, 1814-1904; Bridget "Biddy" Mason, 1818-1891; Anthony Overton, 1864-1946; Abraham
Lincoln Lewis, 1865-1947; Madame C.J. Walker, 1867-
1919; Annie Turnbo Malone, 1869-1957; Robert S. Ab-
bott, 1870-1940; George Baker "Father Divine", 1879-
1965; Arthur George Gaston, 1892-1906; S.B. Fuller,
1905-1988; John H. Johnson, 1918; Crispus Attucks
Wright, 1913-2001; Matel "Mat" Dawson, 1922-2002;
Ray Charles, 1930; Quincy Jones, 1933; Earl G. Graves,
1935; Joe L. Dudley, 1937; Bill and Camille Cosby,
1937, 1944; Eddie Brown, 1940; Reginald F. Lewis,
1942-1993; Don Barden, 1943; Robert L. Johnson, 1946;
Willie Gary, 1947; Oprah Winfrey, 1954; Spike Lee,
1957; Russell Simmons, 1957; Earvin Magic Johnson,
1959; Kenneth "Babyface" Edmonds, 1959; Trish Mil-
lines, 1958; Sean "Puffy" Combs (P. Diddy), 1969; Tyra
Banks, 1973; Tiger Woods, 1975
This profiles 25 African American millionaires
"Sullivan offers an exemplary compilation of a relatively unexplored subject area. . . . The book is well organized, highly readable, and inspiring." SLJ
Includes bibliographical references

African American women scientists and
inventors; Jim Haskins, general editor. Wiley 2002
150p il (Black stars) $24.95   **920**
1. African American inventors 2. Women scientists
3. African American women
ISBN 0-471-38707-X   LC 2001-17924
This profiles 25 African American women "such as
Ellen Elgin, who invented the clothes-wringer in the
1880s; Madame C.J. Walker, who produced her secret
haircare formula; and Dr. Jane Wright, who worked in
the field of cancer tissue studies and was the first woman
elected president of the New York Cancer Society. These
historical biographies . . . provide a unique glimpse into
the struggle of the African-American woman." Book Rep
Includes bibliographical references

Tate, Eleanora E., 1948-
African American musicians; Jim Haskins, general editor. Wiley 2000 70p il (Black stars) $24.95 **920**
1. African American musicians
ISBN 0-471-25356-1   LC 99-51360
"Many genres and skills are represented from spirituals, gospel, ragtime, blues, jazz, and soul. Scott Joplin, Marian Anderson, Duke Ellington, and Aretha Franklin are here as well as Michael Jackson and a few lesser-known individuals. Each entry includes a black-and-white photo or reproduction and sidebars on pertinent topics." SLJ
Includes bibliographical references

Thimmesh, Catherine
Girls think of everything; illustrated by Melissa Sweet. Houghton Mifflin 2000 57p $16; pa $6.95 (5 and up) **920**
1. Women inventors 2. Inventions
ISBN 0-395-93744-2; 0-618-19563-7 (pa)
LC 99-36270
"Ten women and two girls are given a few pages each. Included are Mary Anderson, who invented the windshield wiper (after she was told it wouldn't work); Ruth Wakefield, who, by throwing chunks of chocolate in her cookie batter, gave Toll House cookies to the world; and young Becky Schroeder who invented Glo-paper because she wanted to write in the dark. The text is written in a fresh, breezy manner, but it is the artwork that is really outstanding." Booklist

Uschan, Michael V., 1948-
Political leaders. Lucent Bks. 2003 112p il map (American war library, Cold War) $27.45
920
1. Cold war
ISBN 1-59018-211-1   LC 2002-1837
This profiles Cold War political leaders, Joseph Stalin, Harry Truman, Mao Tse-tung, John F. Kennedy, Ho Chi Minh, Ronald Reagon, and Fidel Castro
Includes bibliographical references

World Book of America's presidents. World Bk. 2v il set $99 **920**
1. Presidents—United States
First published 1982. (5th edition 2002) Periodically revised
Contents: v1 The President's world; v2 Portraits of the Presidents
Volume one describes the duties, privileges, and power of the chief executive. The second volume offers profiles of the presidents and their administrations

Wren, Laura Lee
Pirates and privateers of the high seas. Enslow Pubs. 2002 104p il map (Collective biographies) lib bdg $20.95 **920**
1. Pirates
ISBN 0-7660-1542-4   LC 2002-6617
Describes the lives of the pirates Sir Francis Drake, Sir Henry Morgan, Henry Avery, Samuel Bellamy, Ed-

ward Teach, Anne Bonny, Mary Read, Bartholomew Roberts, John Paul Jones, Jean Laffite, and Cheng I Sao
"The history reads like an adventure story. . . . However, the author is careful not to romanticize the actions." SLJ
Includes glosssary and bibliographical references

Yount, Lisa
Asian-American scientists. Facts on File 1998 112p il (American profiles) lib bdg $25 (7 and up)
920
1. Scientists 2. Asian Americans—Biography
ISBN 0-8160-3756-6   LC 98-10804
Profiles twelve Asian-American scientists, including Subrahmanyan Chandrasekhar, Paul Chung-wu Chu, and Constance Tom Noguchi
The author writes "succinctly, developing a series of interesting narratives highlighting scientific accomplishments." Booklist
Includes bibliographical references

920.003   Biographical reference works

African American biography. U.X.L 1994-2001 7v (African American reference library) v1-4 set $215; v5,6,7 ea $60 **920.003**
1. African Americans—Biography
ISBN 0-8103-9234-8 (v1-4); 0-7876-3562-6 (v5); 0-7876-3563-4 (v6); 0-7876-3564-2 (v7)
LC 93-45651
"Individuals were selected from sports, entertainment, politics, literature, religion, and science areas as well as from history. For each person there is a picture, a quote, a summary significance, a life history which emphasizes their career. Controversy is not ignored. . . . A classified index to all volumes is in each volume. This is an attractive and useful set." Safford. Guide to Ref Materials for Sch Libr Media Cent. 5th edition

African biography; Virginia Curtin Knight, editor. U.X.L 1998 3v il set $165 **920.003**
1. Africa—Biography—Dictionaries
ISBN 0-7876-2823-9   LC 98-14069
Presents biographical entries on seventy-five noteworthy Africans, historical and contemporary, in a variety of fields, from a wide range of sub-Saharan countries
"A well-researched resource that is inviting and easy to use." SLJ

Allaby, Michael, 1933-
Makers of science; {by} Michael Allaby & Derek Gjertsen. Oxford Univ. Press 2002 5v il maps set $185 **920.003**
1. Scientists 2. Science—History
ISBN 0-19-521680-6   LC 2001-48396
"This set incorporates the political and social setting as well as the scientific achievements of each scientist. Volumes are arranged chronologically, beginning with Aristotle and ending with Stephen Hawking. In between are biographies of more than 40 European and U.S. scientists 'whose discoveries were crucial to the develop-

Allaby, Michael, 1933-—*Continued*
ment of science,' ranging in length from 8 to 16 pages.
. . . Scientific principles are clearly explained, often
with diagrams. Intriguing personal stories are also woven
in." Booklist
Includes bibliographical references

Almanac of famous people; Susan L. Stetler,
editor. Gale Res. 3v set $185   **920.003**
ISSN 1040-127X
First published 1981 with title: Biography almanac.
Periodically revised
Contents: v1-2 Biographies; v3 Indexes, chronological,
geographic, occupation
"Provides citations to biographical information for
over 25,000 past and present notables in sports, politics,
business, science, and a wide range of other activities.
Despite the claim to being a biographical dictionary, its
information is limited to pseudonym, real name, or nickname; nationality; occupation; and birth and death dates
and places. The book's primary purpose is to cite biographical sketches and articles that appear in over 300
biographical sources." Nichols. Guide to Ref Books for
Sch Media Cent. 4th edition

American authors, 1600-1900; a biographical
dictionary of American literature; edited by
Stanley J. Kunitz and Howard Haycraft. Wilson,
H.W. 1938 846p il (Authors series) $120
    920.003
1. Authors, American—Dictionaries 2. American literature—Bio-bibliography
ISBN 0-8242-0001-2
"Complete in one volume with 1300 biographies and
400 portraits." Title page
"This volume contains biographies of 1,300 authors
who contributed to the development of American literature, from the founding of Jamestown (1607) to the end
of the nineteenth century. Each essay describes the author's life, discusses past and present significance, and
evaluates principal works." Safford. Guide to Ref Materials for Sch Media Cent. 5th edition

American men & women of science; a
biographical directory of today's leaders in
physical, biological and related sciences. Gale
Group 8v set $1025   **920.003**
1. Scientists—Dictionaries
ISSN 0192-8570
Irregular. First published 1906 by Science Press with
title: American men of science. Some editions were divided into two sections: Physical and biological sciences
and Social sciences
"Brief biographical sketches of . . . scientists and engineers active in the United States and Canada. Arranged
alphabetically, with discipline index." Ref Sources for
Small & Medium-sized Libr. 6th edition

American presidents in world history; [by]
Creative Media Applications. Greenwood Press
2003 5v il (Middle school reference) set $200
    920.003
1. Presidents—United States 2. United States—Politics
and government 3. United States—Foreign relations
ISBN 0-313-32564-2   LC 2002-35205

Contents: v1 George Washington to Martin Van Buren; v2 William Henry Harrison to Abraham Lincoln; v3
Andrew Johnson to William H. Taft; v4 Woodrow Wilson to John F. Kennedy; v5 Lyndon B. Johnson to
George W. Bush
This set "examines each president's actions and policies from a global perspective. . . . With its unique emphasis on foreign relations, *American Presidents in
World History* is a wonderful supplement to reference
sources." Booklist

The **American** scene: lives. Grolier Educ. 2001
12v il maps set $329   **920.003**
1. United States—Biography
ISBN 0-7172-9572-9   LC 00-63671
"Covering more than 1,200 men and women from
American history {this set} gives a one-page synopsis of
each person's life. Each page includes a fact box that
gives the key events in the person's life or discusses
what made that person famous. It also includes an illustration or picture of the person, a map of where the person lived or how many states were in the Union at the
time of the person's fame. . . . This is an excellent addition to any collection." Book Rep

Authors & artists for young adults. Gale Res. il
ca $98   **920.003**
1. Authors—Dictionaries 2. Artists—Dictionaries
3. Literature—Bio-bibliography
ISSN 1040-5682
Semi-annual. First published 1988
Editors vary
"Each volume contains 20-25 entries offering personal,
behind-the-scenes information, . . . sidelights, portraits,
movie stills, bibliographies, cumulative index and much
more. Its international scope ranges from contemporary
to classic, fantasy to nonfiction." Publisher's note

Biography today; profiles of people of interest to
young readers. Omnigraphics apply to publisher
for subscription options   **920.003**
1. Biography—Periodicals
ISSN 1058-2347
Three issues a year with bound annual cumulations.
First published 1992
"This periodical provides short, biographical profiles
of people of current interest. Four-to-six page entries are
arranged alphabetically. . . . There is at least one photograph of the subject, a contact address, and a bibliography of accessible books and articles. . . . Useful name,
subject, and place of birth indexes will cumulate with
each new issue. Written in a friendly, almost chatty tone,
the profiles offer quick and objective information." SLJ

Creative & performing artists for teens. Gale
Group 1999 4v set $350   **920.003**
1. Arts—Biography
ISBN 0-7876-3973-7   LC 99-35562
Biographical entries of approximately 300 creative and
performing artists from the fields of literature, music, the
visual arts, and film and television. Beck, Ethan Hawke,
LL Cool J, Calude Monet, William Golding, Frank Lloyd
Wright, and Stephen King are among those profiled
"Each entry includes a photograph, biographical infor-
mation, personal data, a well-chosen quote from the sub-

Creative & performing artists for teens—*Continued*

ject, an essay detailing the person's career, thematic considerations and controversies, a boxed sidebar listing of major works, a short listing of sources for further information, and in most cases, an online Web site address." Voice Youth Advocates

Includes bibliographical references

Current biography yearbook. Wilson, H.W. il $130   **920.003**
1. Biography—Periodicals
ISSN 0084-9499

Also available online; Current biography: cumulated index, 1940-2000 available $65 (ISBN 0-8242-0997-4)

Annual. First published 1940 with title: Current biography

Also issued monthly except December at a subscription price of $130 per year (ISSN 0011-3344). Yearbooks 1940-2002 available ea $120

"Biographies of prominent people written in lively, popular prose. Emphasis is on entertainers, star athletes, politicians, and other celebrities. Series is cumulative, with biographies revised and updated occasionally. Each volume has seven-year index." N Y Public Libr Book of How & Where to Look It Up

Encyclopedia of world biography. 2nd ed. Gale Res. 1998 17v il set $1255   **920.003**
ISBN 0-7876-2221-4   LC 97-42327
Kept up-to-date by yearly supplements. Volumes available 1998-2005 designated volumes 18-25 at $136 ea

First published 1973 with title: McGraw-Hill encyclopedia of world biography

Presents brief biographical sketches which provide vital statistics as well as information on the importance of the person listed. Volumes 1-16 are arranged alphabetically; volume 17 is the index

Ergas, G. Aimée
Artists: from Michelangelo to Maya Lin. U.X.L 1995-2001 4v il 4v set $215; 2v sets [vols 1&2 or vol 3&4] ea $110   **920.003**
1. Artists—Biography
ISBN 0-8103-9862-1 (v1&2); 0-7876-5363-2 (v3&4)
LC 95-186053
"Biographies of 62 artists, arranged alphabetically. . . . The scope of the work concentrates on North America and Europe from the Renaissance to the present. Each 5-10 page entry contains a portrait of the artist, birth and death dates, and a quote by or about the subject. There are nearly 140 black-and-white illustrations throughout. Each volume begins with an index of artists by field and media (architecture, cartoons, ceramics, etc.); a timeline; and a glossary of key art terms. As an introductory text, this title is useful for students since the focus is on the individual rather than an artistic movement or period." SLJ [review of vol 1 & 2]

Explorers; from ancient times to the space age; consulting editors, John Logan Allen, E. Julius Dasch, Barry M. Gough. Macmillan Ref. USA 1999 3v il maps set $370 (5 and up)
920.003
1. Explorers—Dictionaries
ISBN 0-02-864893-5   LC 98-8809
"This set profiles 333 world explorers, including cartographers, merchants, navigators, botanists, archaeologists, treasure hunters, and astronauts. . . . Well-selected, high-quality black-and-white portraits and maps abound. . . . This is a solid resource with considerable browsing appeal." SLJ

Explorers & discoverers; from Alexander the Great to Sally Ride; [edited by] Peggy Saari, Daniel B. Baker. U.X.L 1995-1999 7v il maps v1-7 set $350; v1-4 set $215; v5, v6, & v7 ea $60   **920.003**
1. Explorers—Dictionaries 2. Adventure and adventurers
ISBN 0-8103-9787-8 (v1-4 set); 0-7876-1990-6 (v5); 0-7876-2946-4 (v6); 0-7876-3681-9 (v7)
LC 95-166826
V5-7 edited by Nancy Pear and Daniel B. Baker
Profiles men and women explorers from ancient Greek scholars and travelers to contemporary astronauts and oceanographers

Favorite children's authors and illustrators; E. Russell Primm, III, editor-in-chief. Tradition Bks. 2003 6v il set $357   **920.003**
1. Authors—Dictionaries 2. Illustrators—Dictionaries
ISBN 1-59187-026-7   LC 2002-7129
Contents: v1 Verna Aardema to Brock Cole; v2 Joanna Cole to Jack Gantos; v3 Carmen Lomas Garza to Edward Lear; v4 Ursula K. Le Guin to Helen Oxenbury; v5 Barbara Park to Peter Sis; v6 David Small to Gene Zion

Provides biographical information about authors and illustrators of books for children and young adults, arranged in dictionary form

"Each essay is a brief but informative four pages in length and contains a wealth of information useful to student researchers. All entries include a photograph of the author or illustrator, dates of birth and death (if applicable), quotes from and about the subject, reproductions of book covers, and footnotes of interesting facts. . . . This set is well designed and easily accessible." Booklist

Great American writers: twentieth century; editor, R. Baird Shuman. Marshall Cavendish 2002 13v il set $459.95   **920.003**
1. Authors, American—Dictionaries 2. Literature—Bio-bibliography
ISBN 0-7614-7240-1   LC 2001-28461
Contents: v1 Agee-Bellow; v2 Benét-Cather; v3 Cormier-Dylan; v4 Eliot-Frost; v5 Gaines-Hinton; v6 Hughes-Lewis; v7 London-McNickle; v8 Miller-O'Connor; v9 O'Neill-Rich; v10 Salinger-Stein; v11 Steinbeck-Walker; v12 Welty-Zindel; v13 Index

"Each volume profiles seven or eight writers in chapters that are up to 25 pages long. The illustrations that enhance most pages are a blend of photographs and well-chosen examples of American artwork." Booklist

Great American writers: twentieth century—
Continued
This "is a good introductory resource to many of the writers that are commonly studied in today's curriculum." Am Ref Books Annu, 2003

Great world writers: twentieth century; editor, Patrick M. O'Neil. Marshall Cavendish 2003 c2004 13v il set $459.95 **920.003**
1. Authors—Dictionaries 2. Literature—Bio-bibliography
ISBN 0-7614-7468-4   LC 2003-40922
This reference set profiles the lives and works of 93 novelists, poets, dramatists, journalists, and essayists from around the world
"This is an exemplary resource for literary-criticism collections." SLJ

Keenan, Sheila
Scholastic book of outstanding Americans. Scholastic Reference 2003 256p il $19.95 (5 and up) **920.003**
1. United States—Biography
ISBN 0-439-28358-2   LC 2002-73341
Brief biographies of nearly 500 men and women who shaped United States history including, for each, a photograph or picture, birth and death dates, and a brief essay describing why that person is notable
"There is good balance between the historical and contemporary entries. There is also a good mix of cultural backgrounds and professions. . . . Although no entry is detailed enough for reports, this book is a good starting point." Booklist

Kings and queens. Macmillan Lib. Ref. USA 1999 500p (Macmillan profiles) $95 **920.003**
1. Kings and rulers 2. Queens
ISBN 0-02-865375-0   LC 99-37943
Profiles of 170 rulers
This reference profiles 170 rulers ranging from Tutankhamen and Xerxes I to Prince Rainier and Juan Carlos I
Includes bibliographical references

Kranz, Rachel
The biographical dictionary of African Americans; {by} Rachel Kranz and Philip Jo Koslow. Facts on File 1999 310p il $44 **920.003**
1. African Americans—Biography—Dictionaries
ISBN 0-8160-3903-8   LC 98-12355
First published 1992 with title: The biographical dictionary of black Americans
This work "covers 230 individuals and ranges chronologically from Colonial times to the present and represents many fields of endeavor. . . . The black-and-white photographs and drawings are well chosen. All entries include books for further reading, and an extensive list of recommended resources is appended. Indexes organize the listings by area of activity, year of birth, and subject. A worthwhile purchase." SLJ

MacNee, Marie J.
Outlaws, mobsters & crooks; from the Old West to the Internet; edited by Jane Hoehner. U.X.L 1998-2002 5v il v1-3 set $165 v4-5 ea $60 **920.003**
1. Criminals—Dictionaries
ISBN 0-7876-2803-4 (v1-3); 0-7876-6482-0 (v4); 0-7876-6483-9 (v5)   LC 98-14861
Contents: v1 Mobsters, racketeers & gamblers, robbers; v2 Computer criminals, spies, swindlers, terrorists; v3 Bandits & gunslingers, bootleggers, pirates; v4 From the Old West to the Internet [1] ; v5 From the Old West to the Internet [2]
Presents the lives of seventy-five North American criminals including the nature of their crimes, their motivations, and information relating to the law officers who challenged them
"Browsers and researchers alike will make good use of this enjoyable reference set due to its fact-filled content and peek into the lives of such a wide variety of outlaws." Voice Youth Advocates

Meyer, Nicholas E.
Biographical dictionary of Hispanic Americans. 2nd ed. Facts on File 2001 324p (Facts on File library of American history) $44; pa $19.95 **920.003**
1. Hispanic Americans—Dictionaries
ISBN 0-8160-4330-2; 0-8160-4331-0 (pa)
   LC 00-49046
First published 1997
This reference profiles approximately 250 Hispanic Americans throughout history from many fields of endeavor

Nelson, Lyle Emerson, 1924-
American presidents; year by year; Lyle Emerson Nelson. M.E. Sharpe 2004 3v .p il set $225 **920.003**
1. Presidents—United States 2. United States—Politics and government
ISBN 0-7656-8046-7   LC 2002-30898
Contents: v1 1732-1860; v2 1861-1932; v3 1933-2000
This set chronicles "the lives of the U.S. presidents from George Washington to the election of George W. Bush. . . . Filled with personal, political, and professional details, the set not only provides valuable reference information but also is interesting to read." Booklist

The **ninth** book of junior authors and illustrators; edited by Connie C. Rockman. H.W. Wilson 2004 [i.e. 2005] 583p il $105 **920.003**
1. Authors—Dictionaries 2. Illustrators—Dictionaries 3. Children's literature—Bio-bibliography
ISBN 0-8242-1043-3   LC 2004-61627
Previous volumes in Junior authors and illustrators series available in print and electronic editions
This volume covers some 200 authors and illustrators of books for children and young adults including Kate DiCamillo, Pura Belpré, Julia Alvarez and Kadir Nelson. For 20 authors and artists whose careers include significant new works and honors since their profile in earlier editions of the series, newly written entries are featured

The ninth book of junior authors and illustrators—*Continued*

This "offers solid and appealing information for students, librarians, and educators. . . . School and public libraries would be well served by this informative and easy-to-read text." Booklist

Notable mathematicians; from ancient times to the present; Robyn V. Young, editor; Zoran Minderovic, associate editor. Gale Res. 1998 xxi, 612p il $120 (7 and up) **920.003**
1. Mathematicians—Dictionaries
ISBN 0-7876-3071-3   LC 97-33662
This work profiles "300 mathematicians chosen for their historical importance, discoveries, familiarity to the public, awards and prizes, and involvement in mathematics education. . . . Female and minority mathematicians have been expressly represented." Libr J
Includes bibliographical references

Notable women scientists; Pamela Proffitt, editor. Gale Group 1999 xxvi, 668p il $120 (7 and up) **920.003**
1. Women scientists
ISBN 0-7876-3900-1   LC 99-35741
Biographical profiles of 500 women around the world who have made significant contributions to the field of science, from antiquity to the present
"Each alphabetically arranged entry includes basic biographical information (dates, nationality, and specialty), an essay of 400-to-2000 words, a list of selected writings by the subject, and a list of further reading. The informative, clearly written essays present excellent material for reports." SLJ
Includes bibliographical references

People of the Holocaust; {edited by} Linda Schmittroth and Mary Kay Rosteck. U.X.L 1998 2v il set $110 **920.003**
1. Holocaust, 1933-1945 2. Jews—Biography
ISBN 0-7876-1743-1   LC 98-4988
Profiles sixty women and men who were caught up in the Holocaust, including Nazi perpetrators and their victims, world leaders and policy makers, and those who showed their humanity and courage by resisting Hitler's reign of genocidal terror
"This unique resource will be in constant demand." SLJ

Podell, Janet
Old worlds to new; the age of exploration and discovery; {by} Janet Podell and Steven Anzovin. Wilson, H.W. 1993 286p il maps (They changed the world) $75 **920.003**
1. Explorers—Dictionaries 2. Scientists—Dictionaries
ISBN 0-8242-0838-2   LC 92-19264
This "compilation of important discoveries begins with approximately 1000 and continues through 1800. The book is divided into logical areas of discovery with individual explorers covered in chronological order within the division. Section topics include the empires of Spain and Portugal, mariners and pirates, the exploration of Africa, and the age of scientific discovery. Individuals are treated in articles of two to four pages. Portraits, maps and period art are included." Book Rep

Scientists: their lives and works; Peggy Saari and Stephen Allison, editors. U.X.L 1996-2002 7v il v1-7 set $350; v1-3 set $165; v4, 5, 6, & 7 ea $60 **920.003**
1. Scientists—Dictionaries
ISBN 0-7876-0959-5 (v1-3); 0-7876-1874-8 (v4); 0-7876-2797-6 (v5);   0-7876-3682-7 (v6); 0-7876-6383-2 (v7)   LC 96-25579
Volume 4-6 edited by Marie C. Ellavich; volume 7 edited by Tanya Lee Stone; original 3 volume set has subtitle: the lives and works of 150 scientists
"The alphabetically arranged volumes profile figures . . . ranging from the Industrial Revolution to the present. Each entry lists birth and death dates and birthplace, followed by an accessible, fact-filled text that accurately chronicles the subject's early life, educational background, career milestones, discoveries, and awards." SLJ {review of original 3 volume set}

Something about the author; facts and pictures about authors and illustrators of books for young people. Gale Res. il ea $140 **920.003**
1. Authors—Dictionaries 2. Illustrators—Dictionaries 3. Children's literature—Bio-bibliography
ISSN 0276-816X
Also available Major authors and illustrators for children and young adults: a selection of sketches from Something about the author, 8 volume set $605 (ISBN 0-7876-1234-0)
First published 1971. Frequency varies
Editors vary
"This important series gives comprehensive coverage of the individuals who write and illustrate books for children. Each new volume adds about 100 profiles. Entries include career and personal data, a bibliography of the author's works, information on works in progress and references to further information." Safford. Guide to Ref Materials for Sch Libr Media Cent. 5th edition

Something about the author: autobiography series. Gale Res. il ea $149 **920.003**
1. Authors—Dictionaries 2. Illustrators—Dictionaries 3. Children's literature—Bio-bibliography
ISSN 0885-6842
First published 1986
Editors vary
An "ongoing series in which juvenile authors discuss their lives, careers, and published works. Each volume contains essays by 20 established writers or illustrators (e.g., Evaline Ness, Nonny Hogrogian, Betsy Byars, Jean Fritz) who represent all types of literature, preschool to young adult. . . . Some articles focus on biographical information, while others emphasize the writing career. Most, however, address young readers and provide family background, discuss the writing experience, and cite some factors that influenced it. Illustrations include portraits of the authors as children and more recent action pictures and portraits. There are cumulative indexes by authors, important published works, and geographical locations mentioned in the essays." Safford. Guide to Ref Books for Sch Libr Media Cent. 5th edition

Sonneborn, Liz
A to Z of Native American women. Facts on File 1998 228p il (Encyclopedia of women) $45
920.003
1. Native American women
ISBN 0-8160-3580-6   LC 97-36674
This "reference source features more than 100 fascinating profiles of notable Native American women from the 1500s to the present. Detailed entries include biographical sketches, photographs, descriptions of individual challenges and accomplishments, and recommended reading for each woman profiled." Libr J

UXL encyclopedia of world biography; Laura B. Tyle, editor. U.X.L 2003 10v il set $475
920.003
1. Biography—Dictionaries
ISBN 0-7876-6465-0   LC 2002-4316
A collection of 750 biographies and portraits of notable historic and current figures in American and world history, literature, science and math, arts and entertainment, and the social sciences
"The biographies are well written and, although brief, provide information that will be interesting to young adults." Am Ref Books Annu, 2003

Woolum, Janet, 1955-
Outstanding women athletes; who they are and how they influenced sports in America. 2nd ed. Oryx Press 1998 412p $75.95   **920.003**
1. Women athletes—Dictionaries
ISBN 1-57356-120-7   LC 98-17076
First published 1992
This resource is "organized into three parts: history, biographies of individual athletes and teams, and resources/appendixes. . . . An excellent reference for students, middle school through college, that would prove useful and enjoyable for general readers as well." Libr J

World authors, 1900-1950; editors, Martin Seymour-Smith and Andrew Kimmens. Wilson, H.W. 1996 4v il (Authors series) set $620
920.003
1. Authors—Dictionaries
ISBN 0-8242-0899-4   LC 96-16380
Replaces Twentieth century authors (1942) and its First supplement (1955)
Contents: v1 Abbot-Doyle; v2 Dreiser-Ledwidge; v3 Lee-Saintsbury; v4 Saki-Zweig
Provides almost 2700 articles on twentieth-century authors from all over the world who wrote in English or whose works are available in English translation

World authors, 1950-1970; a companion volume to Twentieth century authors; edited by John Wakeman; editorial consultant: Stanley J. Kunitz. Wilson, H.W. 1975 1594p il (Authors series) $160   **920.003**
1. Authors—Dictionaries 2. Literature—Bio-bibliography
ISBN 0-8242-0419-0
This volume includes 959 "authors who came into prominence between 1950 and 1970. . . . Authors were chosen for literary importance or outstanding popularity." Wilson Libr Bull

World authors, 1970-1975; editor, John Wakeman; editorial consultant, Stanley J. Kunitz. Wilson, H.W. 1980 894p il (Authors series) $140
920.003
1. Authors—Dictionaries 2. Literature—Bio-bibliography
ISBN 0-8242-0641-X   LC 79-21874
This volume provides biographical or autobiographical sketches for 348 of the most influential and popular men and women of letters who have come into prominence between 1970 and 1975

World authors, 1975-1980; editor, Vineta Colby. Wilson, H.W. 1985 829p il (Authors series) $140   **920.003**
1. Authors—Dictionaries 2. Literature—Bio-bibliography
ISBN 0-8242-0715-7   LC 85-10045
This work profiles the lives and works of 379 writers

World authors, 1980-1985; editor, Vineta Colby. Wilson, H.W. 1990 938p il (Authors series) $140   **920.003**
1. Authors—Dictionaries 2. Literature—Bio-bibliography
ISBN 0-8242-0797-1   LC 90-49782
This volume covers 320 contemporary writers

World authors, 1985-1990; a volume in the Wilson authors series; editor, Vineta Colby. Wilson, H.W. 1995 970p il (Authors series) $140   **920.003**
1. Authors—Dictionaries 2. Literature—Bio-bibliography
ISBN 0-8242-0875-7   LC 95-41656
This volume covers 345 novelists, playwrights, poets, and other authors who have risen to prominence in the late 1980s

World authors, 1990-1995; editor, Clifford Thompson. Wilson, H.W. 1999 863p il $155
920.003
1. Authors—Dictionaries 2. Literature—Bio-bibliography
ISBN 0-8242-0956-7   LC 99-48161
The 317 authors treated in this volume include novelists, playwrights, and poets who have published significant work in the early 1990s. Also covers essayists, historians, biographers, critics, philosophers, and social scientists who have made exceptional contributions to the literature of our time

World authors, 1995-2000; editors, Clifford Thompson, Mari Rich {et al.}. Wilson, H.W. 2003 872p il $160   **920.003**
1. Authors—Dictionaries 2. Literature—Bio-bibliography
ISBN 0-8242-1032-8   LC 2003-45062
This reference includes 320 novelists, poets, dramatists, essayists, social scientists, and biographers who have published significant works from 1995 through 2000. Each profile details the author's life and career, the circumstances under which their works were produced, and their literary significance
Includes bibliographical references

World Book's biographical encyclopedia of scientists. World Bk. 2003 8v il set $289

920.003

1. Scientists—Dictionaries
ISBN 0-7166-7600-1   LC 2002-33087

Contents: v1 Abbe-Borodin; v2 Bosch-DeBakey; v3 De Bono-Goddard; v4 Gödel-Kekule von Stradonitz; v5 Kelvin-Mercator; v6 Merensky-Richthoven; v7 Rideal-Tinbergen; v8 Ting-Zworykin/Resources

This set "covers more than 1,300 individuals from ancient times to the present. The alphabetically arranged entries vary in length from around one-half to two double-columned pages. Each begins with a brief summary of basic facts: date and place of birth and, where relevant, death; nationality; and occupation. The readable essays clearly state the scientist's importance in the first sentence or two and provide personal as well as professional information." Booklist

Writers for young adults; Ted Hipple, editor. Scribner 1997 3v il set $295   **920.003**
1. Authors, American—Dictionaries 2. Young adult literature
ISBN 0-684-80474-3   LC 97-6890

Also available Writers for young adults, supplement I $100 (ISBN 0-684-80618-5)

Contains articles on writers whose works are popular with young adults, including contemporary authors, such as Francesca Lia Block and Maya Angelou, and classic authors, such as Sir Arthur Conan Doyle and Louisa May Alcott

"This set is an extremely valuable tool for every reference librarian serving young adults or those who teach and care for them." Libr J

Yount, Lisa
A to Z of women in science and math. Facts on File 1999 254p il (Encyclopedia of women) $45

920.003

1. Women scientists—Dictionaries 2. Women mathematicians—Dictionaries
ISBN 0-8160-3797-3   LC 98-46093

Profiles over 150 women "who have made contributions in a wide range of fields—medicine, genetics, ecology, archaeology, astronomy, botany, mathematics, physics, computer science, zoology, chemistry, and related scientific fields. The selections cover women from antiquity to the present. . . . Essays on each woman are generally 300 to 1000 words, recounting essential biographical information: education, career, contributions to the field, and, perhaps most interestingly, obstacles they faced in male-dominated careers." Libr J

92   Individual biography

Lives of individuals are arranged alphabetically under the name of the person written about. Some subject headings have been added to aid in curriculum work.

Adams, Abigail, 1744-1818
Bober, Natalie. Abigail Adams; witness to a revolution; [by] Natalie S. Bober. Atheneum Bks. for Young Readers 1995 248p il maps (7 and up)

92

1. Presidents' spouses—United States
ISBN 0-689-31760-3; 0-689-81916-1 (pa)

LC 94-19259

"By interweaving excerpts from Adams's correspondence into a coherent biography, Bober creates a vibrant, three-dimensional portrait of a fascinating person whose comments on women's place have reverberated throughout history. This scholarly, thoroughly documented study will appeal to more mature readers, but it is more formidable in appearance than in presentation. Black-and-white reproductions are included." Horn Book Guide

Includes bibliographical references

Adams, Samuel, 1722-1803
Fradin, Dennis B. Samuel Adams; the father of American Independence; {by} Dennis Brindell Fradin. Clarion Bks. 1998 182p il $18 (6 and up)

92

1. United States—History—1775-1783, Revolution
ISBN 0-395-82510-5   LC 97-20027

"Archival reproductions effectively complement a descriptive and accurate narrative that imaginatively integrates details of Adams's life with the social and political milieu of the time." Horn Book Guide

Includes bibliographical references

Irvin, Benjamin. Samuel Adams; son of liberty, father of revolution; [by] Benjamin H. Irvin. Oxford Univ. Press 2002 176p il (Oxford portraits) $28 (7 and up)   **92**

1. United States—History—1775-1783, Revolution
ISBN 0-19-513225-4   LC 2002-4283

Contents: The elusive Samuel Adams; Samuel Adams's Boston; Raised for rebellion; Tis not in mortals to command success; Sam the publican and the Stamp Act Riots; Mobs and massacre; To save the country; The Coercive Acts and the Continental Congress; Is not America already independent; The storm is now over

Examines the life of Samuel Adams, a hero of the American Revolution who is credited by some with having fired the first shot at Lexington Green, the "shot heard 'round the world"

"Irvin's account of events is exciting and written in a compelling narrative style. He presents an unbiased assessment of Adams's actions and character." SLJ

Includes bibliographical references

Addams, Jane, 1860-1935
Harvey, Bonnie C. Jane Addams; Nobel Prize winner and founder of Hull House; {by} Bonnie Carman Harvey. Enslow Pubs. 1999 128p il (Historical American biographies) lib bdg $26.60
92
1. Hull House (Chicago, Ill.) 2. Chicago (Ill.)—Social conditions
ISBN 0-7660-1094-5   LC 98-35589
This is "a good, basic introductory biography of the author, social reformer, and humanitarian. . . . Black-and-white photographs, maps, and quotes enliven the presentation." SLJ
Includes bibliographical references

Aguirre, Hank, 1932-1994
Copley, Bob. The tall Mexican: the life of Hank Aguirre, all-star pitcher, businessman, humanitarian; with a foreword by Jose F. Niño. Piñata Bks. 1998 159p il pa $9.95 hardcover o.p. (7 and up)   **92**
1. Baseball—Biography 2. Businessmen
ISBN 1-55885-294-8   LC 98-3185
A biography of the All-Star major-league pitcher whose commitment to his Hispanic heritage led him to found Mexican Industries to help provide economic opportunities to the inner-city Detroit community
"Myriad reminiscences from friends, family, employees, colleagues, and fellow athletes provide readers with the sense of true admiration felt for the subject." SLJ

Ailey, Alvin
Cruz, Bárbara. Alvin Ailey; celebrating African-American culture in dance; [by] Bárbara C. Cruz. Enslow Pub. 2004 112p il lib bdg $26.60
92
1. African American dancers 2. Choreographers
ISBN 0-7660-2293-5
Profiles the life of one of the most popular and acclaimed dancers and choreographers in the world.
"A solid addition to any biography collection." SLJ

Albright, Madeleine Korbel, 1937-
Hasday, Judy L. Madeleine Albright. Chelsea House 1999 134p il (Women of achievement) lib bdg $23.95; pa $9.95   **92**
1. Women politicians 2. Cabinet officers
ISBN 0-7910-4708-3 (lib bdg); 0-7910-4709-1 (pa)
LC 98-14110
Focuses on the accomplishments of the former United States ambassador to the United Nations who became the first woman to serve as Secretary of State
"Good for assignments year-round, and especially valuable for women's history month." SLJ
Includes bibliographical references

Howard, Megan. Madeleine Albright. Lerner Pubs. 1998 128p il (A & E biography) $25.26
92
1. Women politicians 2. Cabinet officers
ISBN 0-8225-4935-2   LC 97-27450

This biography traces the life and career of the first woman appointed U.S. Secretary of State, from her childhood in Czechoslovakia to her role in the Middle East peace talks
Includes bibliographical references

Alcott, Louisa May, 1832-1888
Meigs, Cornelia Lynde. Invincible Louisa; the story of the author of Little Women; with a new introduction by the author. Little, Brown 1968 195p il hardcover o.p. paperback available $5.95
92
1. Authors, American 2. Women authors
ISBN 0-316-56594-6 (pa)
Awarded the Newbery Medal, 1934
"Alcott Centennial edition"
First published 1933
This biography "is to be praised still for its straightforward account of a life of struggle and success. . . . If you want to know about Louisa's external life, and trace there the events which gave rise to the internal urges and passions that produced 'Little Women,' this book will serve well." N Y Times Book Rev

Ruth, Amy. Louisa May Alcott. Lerner Publs. 1999 128p il (A & E biography) $27.93
92
1. Authors, American 2. Women authors
ISBN 0-8225-4938-7   LC 97-47283
Discusses the life of the popular nineteenth-century author of "Little Women"
This is a "well-written, highly readable biography. . . . Both Alcott's personal life and writing career are effectively explored. Like the TV biographies, this is a lucid and inspirational production." SLJ
Includes bibliographical references

Ali, Muhammad, 1942-
Myers, Walter Dean. The greatest: Muhammad Ali. Scholastic 2001 172p il $16.95; pa $4.99 (7 and up)   **92**
1. Boxing—Biography 2. African American athletes
ISBN 0-590-54342-3; 0-590-54343-1 (pa)
In this biography Myers combines "reportage of Ali's major fights (especially against Sonny Liston, Joe Frazier, and George Foreman) with his own reflections about the sport's destructiveness and about Ali's unpopular views." Horn Book
"Readers will enjoy the fast-paced action, crisp writing, photographs of significant events and personalities, and the vivid fight scenes." Voice Youth Advocates

Tessitore, John. Muhammed Ali; the world's champion. Watts 1998 143p il (Impact biography) lib bdg $20; pa $9.95 (7 and up)   **92**
1. Boxing—Biography 2. African American athletes
ISBN 0-531-11437-6 (lib bdg); 0-531-15927-2 (pa)
LC 97-31204
A biography of the only boxer crowned Heavyweight Champion of the World three times
"In this well-documented biography, Tessitore details not only the fights Ali faced in the ring, but the battles fought throughout his life. The comprehensive account

Ali, Muhammad, 1942-—_Continued_
covers Ali's controversial involvement in boxing, the civil rights movement, Vietnam protests, the Islamic faith,
and international humanitarian efforts. Black-and-white
photographs accompany the informative text." Horn
Book Guide
Includes bibliographical references

Anderson, Marian, 1897-1993
Freedman, Russell. The voice that challenged a
nation; Marian Anderson and the struggle for
equal rights. Clarion Books 2004 114p il $18 (5
and up)   **92**
1. African American singers 2. African American
women 3. African Americans—Civil rights
ISBN 0-618-15976-2   LC 2003-19558
A Newbery Medal honor book, 2005
Contents: Easter Sunday, April 9, 1939; Twenty-five
cents a song; A voice in a thousand four: Marian fever;
Banned by the DAR; Singing to the nation; Breaking
barriers; "What I had was singing."
In the mid-1930s, Marian Anderson was a famed vo-
calist who had been applauded by European royalty and
welcomed at the White House. But, because of her race,
she was denied the right to sing at Constitution Hall in
Washington, D.C. This is the story of her resulting involvement in the civil rights movement of the time.
"In his signature prose, plain yet eloquent, Freedman
tells Anderson's triumphant story, with numerous black-
and-white photos and prints that convey her personal
struggle, professional artistry, and landmark civil rights
role." Booklist
Includes bibliographical references

Andreessen, Marc
Ehrenhaft, Daniel. Marc Andreessen; Web
warrior. 21st Cent. Bks. (Brookfield) 2001 77p il
(Techies) lib bdg $23.90   **92**
1. Netscape Communications Corporation 2. Internet
3. Businessmen
ISBN 0-7613-1964-6   LC 00-57710
The author "introduces the man who coauthored the
early Web-browsing software Mosaic, co-founded the
firm Netscape, and was a multimillionaire at the age of
24." Booklist
This offers "a breezy style, short length, large font,
numerous photographs, and attractive page design."
Voice Youth Advocates
Includes bibliographical references

Andrews, Roy Chapman, 1884-1960
Bausum, Ann. Dragon bones and dinosaur eggs:
a photobiography of Roy Chapman Andrews.
National Geographic Soc. 2000 64p il map $17.95
(5 and up)   **92**
1. Fossils 2. Dinosaurs 3. Naturalists
ISBN 0-7922-7123-8   LC 99-38363
A biography of the great explorer-adventurer, who discovered huge finds of dinosaur bones in Mongolia, pio-
neered modern paleontology field research, and became
the director of the American Museum of Natural History
"Bausum's account reads smoothly, and a layout

dense with captioned sepia photographs and quotes from
Andrews provides plenty of oases for readers as they fol-
low him through the desert." Bull Cent Child Books
Includes bibliographical references

Marrin, Albert. Secrets from the rocks: dinosaur
hunting with Roy Chapman Andrews. Dutton
Children's Bks. 2002 64p il map $18.99 (4 and
up)   **92**
1. Fossils 2. Dinosaurs 3. Naturalists
ISBN 0-525-46743-2   LC 2001-47084
A biography of the scientist-adventurer, Roy Chapman
Andrews, focusing on the expeditions he led for New
York's American Museum of Natural History to the Gobi
Desert in Mongolia in an effort to uncover dinosaur fos-
sils
This "is a colorful portrait that offers thought-
provoking insight into the constantly shifting nature of
scientific discovery." Booklist
Includes bibliographical references

Angelou, Maya
Cuffie, Terrasita A. Maya Angelou. Lucent Bks.
1999 80p il (Importance of) $28.70 (7 and up)
      92
1. African American authors 2. Women authors
ISBN 1-56006-532-X   LC 99-20045
Discusses the life and work of the well-known writer,
entertainer, and political activist
"Referenced quotes and sidebars paint an inspirational
picture of a woman who has succeeded in so many areas.
. . . This volume will work best for those who need an
overview of how {Angelou} began her career and why
she is important." SLJ
Includes bibliographical references

Harper, Judith E. Maya Angelou. Child's World
1999 39p il (Journey to freedom) lib bdg $28.50
      92
1. African American authors 2. Women authors
ISBN 1-56766-570-5   LC 98-45559
Examines the life and accomplishments of the African
American writer, performer, and teacher, as well as her
impact on literature and black culture
This biography is "attractively formatted with lots of
white space, print size that is easy on the eyes, and one
or two clear sepia-toned or full-color photographs or reproductions per spread. Boxed captions for each picture
add to the information found in the text." SLJ
Includes bibliographical references

Kite, L. Patricia. Maya Angelou. Lerner Publs.
1999 112p il (A & E biography) $27.93
      92
1. African American authors 2. Women authors
ISBN 0-8225-4944-1   LC 98-15763
A biography of the multi-faceted African-American
woman, Maya Angelou, tracing her life from her childhood in the segregated South to her prominence as a
well-known writer
Includes bibliographical references

Anning, Mary, 1799-1847

Goodhue, Thomas W. Curious bones: Mary Anning and the birth of paleontology. Morgan Reynolds 2002 112p il lib bdg $21.95   **92**

1. Fossils
ISBN 1-88384-693-5   LC 2002-8540
Contents: The girl on the cliff; A new vocation; The fish lizard; The monster on the beach; The old fossil depot; The flying dragon and the winged fish; The lioness of Lyme Regis; Praise; Through the storm
Recounts the life and work of Mary Anning, who collected fossils throughout her life and made major discoveries in paleontology when that branch of science was first emerging
This "accessible biography gives readers not only insight into Anning's life but also the time in which she lived. The documentation is excellent." Booklist
Includes glossary and bibliographical references

Anthony, Susan B., 1820-1906

Weisberg, Barbara. Susan B. Anthony. Chelsea House 1988 111p il (American women of achievement) lib bdg $23.95; pa $9.95   **92**

1. Feminism 2. Women—Suffrage
ISBN 1-55546-639-7 (lib bdg); 0-7910-0408-2 (pa)
                                    LC 87-35528
A biography of an early leader in the campaign for women's rights, particularly in getting women the right to vote
Includes bibliographical references

Arafat, Yasir, 1929-2004

Headlam, George. Yasser Arafat; by George Headlam. Lerner Publications 2004 112p il map (A & E biography) lib bdg $27.93; pa $7.95
                                    92

1. Palestinian Arabs
ISBN 0-8225-5004-0 (lib bdg); 0-8225-9902-3 (pa)
                                    LC 2002-13957
Contents: The father of Palestine; Watching and learning; The making of a revolutionary; Fame and notoriety; Appearing on the world stage; On the road to nowhere; One step forward, two steps back
A biography of the Palestinian leader
The "author maintains a high level of objectivity given the sensitive and controversial subject matter. Personal anecdotes and psychological insights are woven into the story." SLJ
Includes bibliographical references

Arden, Elizabeth, 1878-1966

Shuker, Nancy. Elizabeth Arden; beauty empire builder. Blackbirch Press 2001 112p il (Giants of American industry) lib bdg $28.70 (7 and up)
                                    92

1. Businesswomen 2. Cosmetics
ISBN 1-56711-510-1   LC 00-53000
First published 1989 by Silver Burdett
This biography relates how "Elizabeth Arden rose from a life of poverty as the daughter of a farmer to become one of the best-known names in the world of beauty." Booklist

This is "filled with pertinent historical information. The pictures and captions give the reader a sense of the time period. . . . A good addition to collections that need biographical material for reports and papers." Book Rep
Includes bibliographical references

Aristotle, 384-322 B.C.

Anderson, Margaret Jean. Aristotle; philosopher and scientist; {by} Margaret J. Anderson and Karen F. Stephenson. Enslow Publishers 2004 112p il map (Great minds of science) $26.60 (5 and up)   **92**

1. Philosophers 2. Scientists
ISBN 0-7660-2096-7   LC 2003-2270
Contents: Living in interesting times; Aristotle's childhood; Athens, the City of Wonder; The Academy; A new direction; The Father of Zoology; Alexander; The Lyceum; "A Desire for Knowledge"; The end of the road; His writings live on; Aristotle's influence
"After opening with an overview of the time during which Aristotle lived, the authors discuss his childhood, his student days at the Academy in Athens, his tutoring of Alexander, and his founding of the Lyceum. The bulk of the text focuses on Aristotle's contributions to philosophy and science. . . . The text is clear and concise. . . . This easy-to-understand offering will prove useful for reports." SLJ
Includes bibliographical references

Armstrong, Lance

Stewart, Mark. Sweet victory: Lance Armstrong's incredible journey; the amazing story of the greatest comeback in sports. Millbrook Press 2000 64p il lib bdg $24.90; pa $8.95 (5 and up)   **92**

1. Bicycle racing
ISBN 0-7613-1861-5 (lib bdg); 0-7613-1387-7 (pa)
                                    LC 99-53173
The story of the bicyclist who, having won the battle against cancer, went on to win the world's most grueling bicycle race, the Tour de France
"This easy-to-read title is as inspirational as it is informational." SLJ

Armstrong, Louis, 1900-1971

Old, Wendie. Louis Armstrong; king of jazz. Enslow Pubs. 1998 128p il (African-American biographies) lib bdg $26.60   **92**

1. Jazz musicians 2. African American musicians
ISBN 0-89490-997-5   LC 97-35860
Explores the life and career of the renowned trumpeter and bandleader of the jazz era
This book is "eye-catching and highly readable." SLJ
Includes bibliographical references

Armstrong, Neil, 1930-

Bredeson, Carmen. Neil Armstrong; a space biography. Enslow Pubs. 1998 48p il (Countdown to space) lib bdg $23.93   **92**

1. Astronauts
ISBN 0-89490-973-8   LC 97-25449

Armstrong, Neil, 1930-—*Continued*
A biography of the first man on the moon, covering his youth, his career as an astronaut, and his life after NASA
"The clear, concise {text is} enhanced by full-color and black-and-white photos throughout. The information is well organized and the rigors of training and space flight are clearly explained." SLJ
Includes bibliographical references

Arnold, Benedict, 1741-1801
Fritz, Jean. Traitor: the case of Benedict Arnold. Putnam 1981 191p il $16.95; pa $5.99   **92**
1. Generals 2. United States—History—1775-1783, Revolution
ISBN 0-399-20834-8; 0-698-11553-8 (pa)
    LC 81-10584
"The writing is smooth, the material carefully organized and used in the best of biographical style—that is, Arnold is presented accurately and the reader is left to judge the strength and weaknesses of his character rather than being told by the author." Bull Cent Child Books
Includes bibliographical references

King, David C. Benedict Arnold and the American Revolution. Blackbirch Press 1999 80p il (Notorious Americans and their times) lib bdg $19.95   **92**
1. Generals 2. United States—History—1775-1783, Revolution
ISBN 1-56711-221-8   LC 98-11580
"A humanized portrayal of Arnold emerges from the pages. Interesting details about Arnold in his youth will keep students reading." Book Rep
Includes glossary and bibliographical references

Attila, King of the Huns, d. 453
Ingram, Scott. Attila the Hun. Blackbirch Press 2003 c2002 112p il maps (History's villains) lib bdg $23.95   **92**
1. Rome—History
ISBN 1-56711-628-0   LC 2002-3378
Discusses the Roman Empire, its collapse at the hands of barbarian hordes led by Attila the Hun, and Attila's legacy
"This title accurately reflects what is known about the man and the battles he fought. . . . Good-quality, black-and-white reproductions, photos, and maps appear throughout." SLJ
Includes glossary and bibliographical references

Augustus, Emperor of Rome, 63 B.C.-14 A.D.
Forsyth, Fiona. Augustus: the first emperor. Rosen Pub. Group 2003 110p il maps (Leaders of ancient Rome) $23.95   **92**
1. Emperors—Rome
ISBN 0-8239-3588-4   LC 2001-6261
A biography of the emperor of Rome who lived from 63 B.C. to 14 A.D.
"Written in a conversational tone, with large type and plentiful illustrations, [this] user-friendly [title] will draw readers into the history and intrigues of ancient Rome." Libr Media Connect
Includes glossary and bibliographical references

Aung San Suu Kyi
Stewart, Whitney. Aung San Suu Kyi; fearless voice of Burma. Lerner Publs. 1997 128p il lib bdg $27.93 (7 and up)   **92**
1. Myanmar—Politics and government
ISBN 0-8225-4931-X   LC 96-41812
A biography of the Burmese leader who won the Nobel Peace Prize in 1991 while under house arrest
"A thorough, well-documented effort." Booklist
Includes bibliographical references

Austen, Jane, 1775-1817
Ruth, Amy. Jane Austen. Lerner Publs. 2001 112p il (A & E biography) lib bdg $27.93
    92
1. Women authors 2. Authors, English
ISBN 0-8225-4992-1   LC 00-9315
A biography of the English author of Pride and prejudice and other novels
"Easy to understand, this short biography is attractive in format and filled with illustrations, excerpts from letters, and black-and-white portraits. . . . This is a good source for students." SLJ
Includes bibliographical references

Wagner, Heather Lehr. Jane Austen. Chelsea House 2003 c2004 (Who wrote that?) $23.95
    92
1. Authors, English 2. Women authors
ISBN 0-7910-7623-7   LC 2003-14409
Describes the life and novels of the nineteenth century British author, Jane Austen.
"This clearly written, short biography contains descriptions of Austen's family life, her early education, writing career, and influences. Illustrations and photographs of movie adaptations, the family home, engravings from original publications, and places familiar to the writer help to familiarize students with aspects of her writing and her life." SLJ
Includes bibliographical references

Babbage, Charles, 1791-1871
Collier, Bruce. Charles Babbage and the engines of perfection; {by} Bruce Collier and James MacLachlan. Oxford Univ. Press 1998 123p il (Oxford portraits in science) $28 (7 and up)
    92
1. Mathematicians 2. Computers—History
ISBN 0-19-508997-9   LC 98-17054
Traces the life and work of the man whose nineteenth century inventions led to the development of the computer
"This is a fascinating portrait of Charles Babbage. . . . Generous b&w illustrations enliven the work." Book Rep
Includes bibliographical references

Bailey, Anne Hennis, 1742-1825
Furbee, Mary R. Anne Bailey; frontier scout. Morgan Reynolds 2002 112p il (Women of the frontier) lib bdg $21.95   **92**
1. Frontier and pioneer life
ISBN 1-88384-670-6   LC 00-54904

Bailey, Anne Hennis, 1742-1825—*Continued*
A biography of Anne Bailey, who came to America in 1761 as an endentured servant and eventually became a scout for the American revolutionary army
"Furbee's straightforward retelling of Bailey's life makes for brisk, engaging reading." Booklist
Includes bibliographical references

Balboa, Vasco Núñez de, 1475-1519
Otfinoski, Steven. Vasco Nuñez de Balboa; explorer of the Pacific; by Steven Otfinoski. Benchmark Books 2005 79p il map (Great explorations) lib bdg $29.93 (5 and up)
92
1. Explorers 2. America—Exploration
ISBN 0-7614-1609-9   LC 2003-14927
Contents: A daring youth; To the New World; From stowaway to governor; The first conquistador; To the South Sea; Discoverer of the Pacific; A new rival; Last adventure; The final treachery
Describes the life of Vasco Nuñez de Balboa, the Spanish explorer who was the first European to see the Pacific Ocean and who conceived the idea of a canal connecting the Atlantic and Pacific.
Includes bibliographical references

Banneker, Benjamin, 1731-1806
Hinman, Bonnie. Benjamin Banneker; American mathematician and astronomer; Arthur M. Schlesinger, senior consulting editor. Chelsea House 2000 79p il (Colonial leaders) lib bdg $21.85; pa $8.95 (5 and up)
92
1. Astronomers 2. African Americans—Biography
ISBN 0-7910-5348-2 (lib bdg); 0-7910-5691-0 (pa)
LC 99-24118
A biography of the eighteenth-century African American who taught himself mathematics and astronomy and helped survey what would become Washington, D.C
Banneker's "life, efforts, and achievements are described in a most engaging manner." Sci Books Films
Includes bibliographical references

Litwin, Laura Baskes. Benjamin Banneker; astronomer and mathematician. Enslow Pubs. 1999 112p il (African-American biographies) lib bdg $26.60
92
1. Astronomers 2. African Americans—Biography
ISBN 0-7660-1208-5   LC 98-34913
A biography of the eighteenth-century African-American who taught himself mathematics and astronomy and helped survey what would become Washington, D.C
Includes bibliographical references

Barton, Clara, 1821-1912
Whitelaw, Nancy. Clara Barton; Civil War nurse. Enslow Pubs. 1997 128p il maps (Historical American biographies) lib bdg $26.60   92
1. Nurses
ISBN 0-89490-778-6   LC 97-7270

Traces the life of the Civil War nurse who cared for wounded soldiers and earned the title, "Angel of the Battlefield"
"Whitelaw makes use of her subject's original diaries from the Library of Congress, along with her published work. The chapters consist of easy, short sentences, lots of footnotes, and some direct quotes. Occasionally a box offers interesting incidental information." SLJ
Includes glossary and bibliographical references

Baryshnikov, Mikhail, 1948-
Glassman, Bruce. Mikhail Baryshnikov; dance genius. Blackbirch Press 2001 128p il (Giants of art and culture) lib bdg $27.45   92
1. Ballet dancers
ISBN 1-56711-507-1   LC 00-53004
First published 1990 by Silver Burdett
.
"Glassman covers his subject's childhood, his emergence as a star in Leningrad's Kirov Ballet Company, his defection to the West, and his dazzling career with the American Ballet Theatre as well as other creative endeavors. . . . This is a readable and balanced portrait of Baryshnikov." SLJ
Includes glossary and bibliographical references

Bates, Daisy
Fradin, Judith Bloom. The power of one; Daisy Bates and the Little Rock Nine; by Judith Bloom Fradin & Dennis Brindell Fradin. Clarion Books 2004 178p il $19 (7 and up)   92
1. Central High School (Little Rock, Ark.) 2. School integration 3. Arkansas—Race relations
ISBN 0-618-31556-X   LC 2004-4618
This is a biography of Daisy Bates. Born in a small town in rural Arkansas, Bates was a journalist and activist. In 1957 she mentored the nine black students who were integrated into Central High School in Little Rock, Arkansas
"This compelling biography clearly demonstrates that one person can indeed make a difference." SLJ
Includes bibliographical references

Polakow, Amy. Daisy Bates; civil rights crusader. Linnet Bks. 2003 108p il $25 (7 and up)
92
1. Central High School (Little Rock, Ark.) 2. School integration 3. Arkansas—Race relations
ISBN 0-208-02513-8   LC 2002-31276
A biography of the civil rights activist who led the fight to integrate schools in Little Rock, Arkansas, during the 1950s
"This is a respectful introduction to an important woman and her husband and an overview of their contributions to civil rights for African Americans." SLJ
Includes bibliographical references

Bauer, Marion Dane, 1938-
Bauer, Marion Dane. A writer's story; from life to fiction. Clarion Bks. 1995 134p $14.95; pa $6.95 (7 and up)   92
1. Authors, American 2. Women authors
ISBN 0-395-72094-X; 0-395-75053-9 (pa)
LC 94-48800

Bauer, Marion Dane, 1938——*Continued*

"Drawing on her own experiences, the novelist examines the origins of inspiration and the subconscious drives that compel authors to write. She points out that many components of fiction—characters, settings, plot details—need not be autobiographical, yet the text does suggest that a story's meaning is directly linked to the unique experiences of its creator. . . . Bauer provides invaluable information for both writers and readers of fiction." Publ Wkly

Bearden, Romare, 1914-1988

Greenberg, Jan. Romare Bearden; collage of memories. Abrams 2003 52p il $17.95 (4 and up)
         92

1. African American artists
ISBN 0-8109-4589-4   LC 2002-153715
Recounts the life of the twentieth-century African-American collage artist who used his southern childhood, New York City, jazz, and Paris to influence his art

"This beautiful, large-size volume with exquisite reproductions of [Bearden's] art is both a biography and an exciting accessible introduction to his amazing work." Booklist
Includes bibliographical references

Bell, Alexander Graham, 1847-1922

Matthews, Tom L. Always inventing: a photobiography of Alexander Graham Bell. National Geographic Soc. 1999 64p il $17.95 (4 and up)
         92

1. Inventors
ISBN 0-7922-7391-5   LC 98-27209
A biography, with photographs and quotes from Bell himself, which follows this well known inventor from his childhood in Scotland through his life-long efforts to come up with ideas that would improve people's lives

"Succinct, lively, and readable, the text is illustrated with many well-captioned period photographs of Bell, his family, his associate, and his inventions as well as a host of diagrams." Booklist
Includes bibliographical references

Bell, Cool Papa, 1903-1991

McCormack, Shaun. Cool Papa Bell. Rosen Pub. Group 2002 112p il (Baseball Hall of Famers of the Negro leagues) lib bdg $29.25   **92**

1. Baseball—Biography 2. African American athletes
ISBN 0-8239-3474-8   LC 2001-3121
This is a biography of the African American who played in the Negro Leagues and was elected to the Baseball Hall of Fame in 1974

This "title presents an unvarnished picture of the racism in this country and how it impacted amateur and professional baseball from 1868 onward. . . . The layout . . . is attractive, the style . . . is engaging, and the b&w photographs enhance the narrative." Book Rep
Includes glossary and bibliographical references

Berlin, Irving, 1888-1989

Furstinger, Nancy. Say it with music: the story of Irving Berlin. Morgan Reynolds 2003 128p il (Masters of music) lib bdg $21.95   **92**

1. Composers—United States
ISBN 1-931798-12-5   LC 2003-6039
Contents: On the bum; Making the country hum; The hit maker; New music for new action; A crack of insecurity; God bless America; Show business; Counting his blessings; Out of tune; The melody lingers

A biography of the Russian immigrant who came to America as a boy and became one of the most successful composers of popular songs, including "White Christmas" and "God Bless America"

"Written in a lively style, the text is clearly documented with source notes, and well-placed, black-and-white photographs appear throughout." SLJ
Includes bibliographical references

Bernstein, Leonard, 1918-1990

Blashfield, Jean F. Leonard Bernstein; conductor and composer. Ferguson, J.G. 2000 127p il (Ferguson's career biographies) lib bdg $21.95 (7 and up)   **92**

1. Musicians—United States
ISBN 0-89434-337-8   LC 00-37580
This illustrated biography looks at the life, career, and influence of the prominent composer/conductor

"A comprehensive time line of Bernstein's life and information about becoming a conductor or a composer are appended. There are three lists of further reading that give books, Web sites, and related places to contact or visit." SLJ

Bethune, Mary Jane McLeod, 1875-1955

Meltzer, Milton. Mary McLeod Bethune; voice of black hope; illustrated by Stephen Marchesi. Viking Kestrel 1987 58p il (Women of our time) hardcover o.p. paperback available $4.99
         92

1. African American educators 2. African American women
ISBN 0-14-032219-1   LC 86-15923
This profile of the African American educator describes "not only her accomplishments but also the context in which those achievements occurred." Booklist

"The book offers a well-researched, non-fictionalized account that's not hard to read and offers an introduction to more multi-dimensional coverage." Bull Cent Child Books

Bezos, Jeffrey

Garty, Judy. Jeff Bezos; business genius of Amazon.com. Enslow Pubs. 2003 48p il (Internet biographies) lib bdg $18.95   **92**

1. Amazon.com Inc. 2. Entrepreneurs
ISBN 0-7660-1972-1   LC 2002-153174
Contents: The visionary; The explorer; The mastermind; The pioneer; The hurricane's eye

Explores the life and career of the creator of the online bookstore Amazon.com, discussing his early interest in computers, business philosophy, and plans for the

Bezos, Jeffrey—_Continued_
future

"Brief but thorough. . . . _Jeff Bezos_ is written in approachable, descriptive language. . . . The accompanying photographs are not to be missed." Booklist

Includes bibliographical references

Bitton-Jackson, Livia
Bitton-Jackson, Livia. My bridges of hope; searching for life and love after Auschwitz. Simon & Schuster Bks. for Young Readers 1999 258p pa $4.99 hardcover o.p. (7 and up) **92**

1. Holocaust survivors
ISBN 0-689-84898-6 LC 98-8046
Sequel to: I have lived a thousand years
In 1945, after surviving a harrowing year in Auschwitz, fourteen-year-old Elli returns, along with her mother and brother, to the family home, now part of Slovakia, where they try to find a way to rebuild their shattered lives

The author's "story is utterly involving, and adds an important chapter to the ongoing attempt to understand the Holocaust and its consequences." Publ Wkly

Includes glossary

Blume, Judy
Ludwig, Elisa. Judy Blume. Chelsea House Publishers 2004 102p il (Who wrote that?) $23.95 **92**

1. Authors, American 2. Women authors
ISBN 0-7910-7619-9 LC 2003-19352
.
A biography of Judy Blume, author of a number of popular and controversial books for young people

Bly, Nellie, 1864-1922
Davidson, Sue. Getting the real story: Nellic Bly and Ida B. Wells. Seal Press 1992 152p il (Women who dared series) pa $8.95 **92**

1. Wells-Barnett, Ida B., 1862-1931 2. Women journalists
ISBN 1-87806-716-8 LC 91-38041
Parallel biographies of two women who used their journalistic skills to fight against unjust treatment based on sex and race in late nineteenth- and early twentieth-century America

"The readable and interesting stories focus on their personal and professional failures and achievements. . . . Davidson's work, although a good blending of fact and fiction, will be most useful as a smooth-flowing introduction to the lives of these two 19th-century crusaders." SLJ

Bohr, Niels Henrik David, 1885-1962
Pasachoff, Naomi E. Niels Bohr; physicist and humanitarian; {by} Naomi Pasachoff. Enslow Publishers 2003 128p il (Great minds of science) lib bdg $26.60 **92**

1. Scientists
ISBN 0-7660-1997-7 LC 2002-3887
Contents: A secret message; Growing up in Denmark; Postdoctoral work in England; Groundbreaking work; A world-class institute; The winds of war; An open world

A biography of the Danish physicist who won a Nobel Prize for his discoveries about the nature of the atom, saved thousands of Jews from the Nazis, and, after helping to develop the atomic bomb, campaigned for peaceful uses of atomic energy

The author "successfully describes both the science and the scientist in admirably clear language that explains both basic concepts and advanced theories, often illustrated with diagrams. . . . {This is} a useful volume that will support a variety of curricular studies." Booklist

Includes bibliographical references

Bonetta, Sarah Forbes, b. 1843?
Myers, Walter Dean. At her majesty's request; an African princess in Victorian England. Scholastic Press 1999 146p il maps $17.95 (5 and up) **92**

ISBN 0-590-48669-1 LC 98-7217
Biography of the African princess saved from execution and taken to England where Queen Victoria oversaw her upbringing and where she lived for a time before marrying an African missionary

"Myers tells an extraordinary tale which will intrigue young readers. . . . A fascinating narrative of a little-known facet of Victorian history, this book is rich with illustrations, including photographs, sketches, portraits, and maps." ALAN

Includes bibliographical references

Boone, Blind, 1864-1927
Harrah, Madge. Blind Boone; piano prodigy; by Madge Harrah. Carolrhoda Books 2004 120p il (Trailblazer biography) lib bdg $27.93 (5 and up) **92**

1. African American musicians
ISBN 1-575-05057-9 LC 2002-153294
Contents: Growing up blind; Adventures in St. Louis; Kidnapped!; New horizons; The challenge; The early years; A concert career; Ragtime and Jim Crow; The final years

"John William 'Blind' Boone, born to a runaway slave in 1864, lost his sight at the age of six months. . . . Boone became a concert pianist, composing and performing everything from ragtime to classical music, everywhere from local churches to international concert halls. . . . [This is] an interesting biography of a remarkable man. . . . Period photos, prints, and drawings illustrate the book." Booklist

Includes bibliographical references

Boone, Daniel, 1734-1820
Calvert, Patricia. Daniel Boone; beyond the mountains. Benchmark Bks. 2002 79p il (Great explorations) lib bdg $23.90 **92**

1. West (U.S.)—Biography 2. Frontier and pioneer life—West (U.S.)
ISBN 0-7614-1243-3 LC 00-51902
A biography of the Western pioneer
This "well-researched {book} . . . will be useful to students writing reports." Horn Book Guide
Includes bibliographical references

Booth, Edwin, 1833-1893
Giblin, James. Good brother, bad brother. See entry under Booth, John Wilkes, 1838-1865

Booth, John Wilkes, 1838-1865
Giblin, James. Good brother, bad brother; the story of Edwin Booth and John Wilkes Booth. Clarion Books 2005 244p il $22 (5 and up)
92
1. Booth, Edwin, 1833-1893 2. Lincoln, Abraham, 1809-1865—Assassination 3. Actors 4. United States—History—1861-1865, Civil War 5. Brothers
ISBN 0-618-09642-6   LC 2004-21260
Giblin "frames the intertwined tale of two brothers with accounts of their families, friends, the Civil War, and nineteenth-century theater. . . . Alcoholism and depression afflicted the family, but Giblin is brilliant at showing that darkness was only one part of a life. . . . Giblin's book will engross readers until the very last footnote." Booklist
Includes bibliographical references

Otfinoski, Steven. John Wilkes Booth and the Civil War; by Steve Otfinoski. Blackbirch Press 1999 80p il (Notorious Americans and their times) lib bdg $19.95   92
1. Lincoln, Abraham, 1809-1865—Assassination 2. United States—History—1861-1865, Civil War
ISBN 1-56711-222-6   LC 98-11571
Sets the life story of the man who assassinated Abraham Lincoln against the backdrop of the Civil War
Includes glossary and bibliographical references

Bosch, Hieronymus, d. 1516
Schwartz, Gary. Hieronymus Bosch. Abrams 1997 92p il (First impressions) $19.95 (7 and up)
92
1. Artists, Dutch 2. Middle Ages
ISBN 0-8109-3138-9   LC 95-34369
Discusses the life of the fifteenth-century Dutch artist and explores his complex works
"Although little is known of the artist's life, Schwartz does a good job of communicating how his society differed from the present and what scholars know and surmise about him based on historical records and the work he left behind. The full-color reproductions of Bosch's paintings give readers many opportunities to view the faces of his beautifully painted yet frequently disturbing visions." Booklist

Bourgeois, Louise
Greenberg, Jan. Runaway girl: the artist Louise Bourgeois; [by] Jan Greenberg and Sandra Jordan. Abrams 2003 80p il $19.95 (7 and up)
92
1. Artists—United States
ISBN 0-8109-4237-2   LC 2002-11922
Contents: Family tapestry; Family secrets; A young artist in Paris ; Runaway girl; The New York art scene; The great decade; Spider, spider burning bright

Introduces the life of renowned modern artist Louise Bourgeois, who is known primarily for her sculptures
"In clear, elegant prose, bolstered with numerous quotes from the artist, the authors seamlessly juxtapose stories of Bourgeois' life with relevant artworks. . . . Beautifully reproduced photographs, printed on well-designed pages, offer an excellent mix of the artist's personal life and her art." Booklist
Includes bibliographical references

Bourke-White, Margaret, 1904-1971
Rubin, Susan Goldman. Margaret Bourke-White; her pictures were her life; photographs by Margaret Bourke-White. Abrams 1999 96p il $19.95   92
1. Women photographers
ISBN 0-8109-4381-6   LC 98-53967
"Rubin traces the celebrated photographer's life." SLJ
"Filled with Bourke-White's marvelous photographs, this stellar biography seamlessly blends the personal and the professional." Booklist
Includes bibliographical references

Welch, Catherine A. Margaret Bourke-White; racing with a dream. Carolrhoda Bks. 1998 104p il $27.93   92
1. Women photographers
ISBN 1-57505-049-8   LC 97-37939
Examines the personal life and photographic career of the woman who served as a photojournalist for the magazine "Life" during World War II and the Korean War
"While Welch presents the drama of Bourke-White's assignments . . . she does not gloss over the personal tradeoffs resulting from her career choices, including her battle with Parkinson's disease. Crisp black-and-white photographs capture the progression of both her vision and visage." SLJ
Includes bibliographical references

Wooten, Sara McIntosh. Margaret Bourke-White; daring photographer. Enslow Pubs. 2002 112p il (People to know) lib bdg $26.60
92
1. Women photographers
ISBN 0-7660-1534-3   LC 2001-7285
This is a "biography of the well-known photojournalist. . . . This book will appeal to students looking for research material and those simply interested in innovative people." SLJ
Includes bibliographical references

Bowie, James, 1799?-1836
Edmondson, J. R. Jim Bowie; frontier legend, Alamo hero. PowerPlus Bks. 2003 112p il maps (Library of American lives and times) lib bdg $31.95   92
1. West (U.S.) 2. Frontier and pioneer life—West (U.S.)
ISBN 0-8239-5734-9   LC 2001-4954
Describes the tumultuous times in early Texas history that formed the character of Jim Bowie, who is known both for inventing the Bowie knife and for fighting and dying at the Alamo

Bowie, James, 1799?-1836—*Continued*
"This is a captivating, exciting biography. . . . Students will use this attractive book for reports and general reading." SLJ
Includes glossary and bibliographical references

Bradford, William, 1588-1657
Doherty, Kieran. William Bradford; rock of Plymouth. 21st Cent. Bks. (Brookfield) 1999 192p il lib bdg $24.90 **92**
1. Pilgrims (New England colonists) 2. Massachusetts—History—1600-1775, Colonial period
ISBN 0-7613-1304-4 LC 99-10631
A biography of one of the founders of the Plymouth Colony in Massachusetts and a history of the Pilgrims' difficult times during their early years in the New World

Brady, Mathew B., ca. 1823-1896
Pflueger, Lynda. Mathew Brady; photographer of the Civil War. Enslow Pubs. 2001 128p il (Historical American biographies) lib bdg $26.60 **92**
1. Photographers 2. United States—History—1861-1865, Civil War
ISBN 0-7660-1444-4 LC 00 10732
A biography of "the preeminent photographer in the 1850s who zealously recorded the Civil War in photographs yet died a poor man." Voice Youth Advocates
This "book is interesting to read, well researched, and well documented." SLJ
Includes glossary and bibliographical references

Brahe, Tycho, 1546-1601
Boerst, William J. Tycho Brahe; mapping the heavens. Morgan Reynolds 2003 144p il maps (Renaissance scientists) lib bdg $23.95 (7 and up) **92**
1. Astronomers
ISBN 1-88384-697-8 LC 2002-153640
Contents: Noble genius; Student days; Stargazer gets an offer; His Lordship of Uraniborg; Life at Hven; The star with a tail; Calamity; Starting over; Enter Kepler; Rebirth
Presents the life and work of the famous sixteenth-century Danish astronomer
"Boerst provides a clearly written account of Brahe's education, background, personality, and career. Full-color illustrations, including many reproductions of period portraits and other artwork, appear throughout the book." Booklist
Includes bibliographical references

Gow, Mary. Tycho Brahe: astronomer. Enslow Pubs. 2002 128p il (Great minds of science) lib bdg $26.60 **92**
1. Astronomers
ISBN 0-7660-1757-5 LC 2001-3269
Presents the life and work of the famous sixteenth-century Danish astronomer
"In simple, accessible language, Gow tells Brahe's story in a sympathetic fashion." SLJ
Includes glossary and bibliographical references

Braille, Louis, 1809-1852
Freedman, Russell. Out of darkness: the story of Louis Braille; illustrated by Kate Kiesler. Clarion Bks. 1997 81p il $16.95; pa $7.95 (4 and up) **92**
1. Blind
ISBN 0-395-77516-7; 0-395-96888-7 (pa)
LC 95-52353
This biography "tells about Braille's life and the development of his alphabet system for the blind." SLJ
"Without melodrama, Freedman tells the momentous story in quiet chapters in his best plain style, making the facts immediate and personal. . . . A diagram explains how the Braille alphabet works, and Kate Kessler's full-page shaded pencil illustrations are part of the understated poignant drama." Booklist

Brave Bird, Mary
Brave Bird, Mary. Lakota woman; by Mary Crow Dog and Richard Erdoes. Grove Weidenfeld 1990 263p il o.p. HarperCollins Pubs. paperback available $13 **92**
1. Dakota Indians
ISBN 0-06-097389-7 (pa) LC 89-24862
"Born in 1955 and raised in poverty on the Rosebud Reservation, Mary Crow Dog escaped an oppressive Catholic boarding school but fell into a marginal life of urban shoplifting and barhopping. A 1971 encounter with AIM (the American Indian Movement), participation in the 1972 Trail of Broken Treaties march on Washington, and giving birth to her first child while under fire at the 1973 siege of Wounded Knee radicalized her." Libr J
"The story of Mary Crow Dog's coming of age in the Indian civil rights movement is simply told—and, at times, simply horrifying." N Y Times Book Rev

Breckinridge, Mary, 1881-1965
Wells, Rosemary. Mary on horseback; three mountain stories; pictures by Peter McCarty. Dial Bks. for Young Readers 1998 53p il $16.99; pa $4.99 (4 and up) **92**
1. Nurses
ISBN 0-670-88923-7; 0-14-130815-x (pa)
LC 97-43409
Tells the stories of three families who were helped by the work of Mary Breckinridge, the first nurse to go into the Appalachian Mountains and give medical care to the isolated inhabitants. Includes an afterword with facts about Breckinridge and the Frontier Nursing Service she founded
"These beautifully written stories will remain with the reader long after the book is closed." Booklist

Brooks, Gwendolyn
Rhynes, Martha E. Gwendolyn Brooks; poet from Chicago. Morgan Reynolds 2003 112p il (World writers) lib bdg $21.95 (7 and up) **92**
1. Poets, American 2. African American authors 3. Women poets
ISBN 1-931798-05-2 LC 2002-151122

Brooks, Gwendolyn—*Continued*

Presents a biography of the African American poet who has received the National Book Award and the Pulitzer Prize

"The writing is clear, lively, and detailed." SLJ

Includes bibliographical references

Brown, Molly, 1867-1932

Landau, Elaine. Heroine of the Titanic: the real unsinkable Molly Brown. Clarion Bks. 2001 132p il $18 (5 and up)   92

ISBN 0-395-93912-7   LC 00-57015

This is a biography of the survivor of the Titanic who supported such causes as worker's rights and feminism

"A realistic biography of an independent and strong-willed woman. . . . Black-and-white archival illustrations and photos highlight her life as well as greater relevant aspects of the period in which she lived." SLJ

Includes bibliographical references

Bruchac, Joseph, 1942-

Bruchac, Joseph. Bowman's store; a journey to myself. Dial Bks. 1997 311p il o.p. Lee & Low Bks. paperback available $6.95   92

1. Abnaki Indians 2. Authors, American

ISBN 1-58430-027-2 (pa)   LC 96-33708

"Combining Native American stories with personal memories and dreams, Bruchac crafts a memoir of his childhood growing up with his grandparents in upstate New York." Horn Book Guide

"Each episode is constructed with a true storyteller's attention to language and plot development. Students of modern Native American cultures will find plenty of food for thought." Booklist

Bunche, Ralph J. (Ralph Johnson), 1904-1971

Schraff, Anne E. Ralph Bunche; winner of the Nobel Peace Prize; {by} Anne Schraff. Enslow Pubs. 1999 128p il (African-American biographies) lib bdg $26.60   92

1. African Americans—Biography

ISBN 0-7660-1203-4   LC 98-26886

Discusses the personal and professional life of the statesman and diplomat who was one of the founders of the United Nations and who received the Nobel Prize for his peacemaking efforts

"A solid introduction to a man who devoted his career to fighting war and intolerance." SLJ

Includes bibliographical references

Burns, Anthony, 1834-1862

Hamilton, Virginia. Anthony Burns: the defeat and triumph of a fugitive slave. Knopf 1988 193p pa $5.50 hardcover o.p. (5 and up)   92

1. Slavery—United States 2. African Americans—Biography

ISBN 0-679-83997-6   LC 87-38063

A biography of the slave who escaped to Boston in 1854, was arrested at the instigation of his owner, and whose trial caused a furor between abolitionists and those determined to enforce the Fugitive Slave Act

"This book does exactly what good biography for children ought to do: takes readers directly into the life of the subject and makes them feel what it was like to be that person in those times." Horn Book

Includes bibliographical references

Burroughs, John, 1837-1921

Wadsworth, Ginger. John Burroughs; the sage of Slabsides. Clarion Bks. 1997 95p il $16.95 (5 and up)   92

1. Naturalists

ISBN 0-395-77830-1   LC 95-48400

A photobiography of the naturalist, ornithologist, author, poet, teacher, and pioneer of the conservation movement who lived and worked in his rustic cabin in the Catskill Mountains

"The pictures are mostly informal and candid, taken from personal collections, with a few studio portraits interspersed. Written with a familiar, almost intimate tone, the text is liberally sprinkled with quotes from Burroughs's publications." SLJ

Includes bibliographical references

Bush, Barbara, 1925-

Greenberg, Judith E. Barbara Pierce Bush, 1925-. Children's Press 1999 110p il (Encyclopedia of first ladies) $34.50   92

1. Presidents' spouses—United States

ISBN 0-516-20475-0   LC 98-45255

A biography of the wife of the forty-first president, describing her childhood, marriage, family life, political activities, and volunteer work for such causes as literacy and AIDS

Includes bibliographical references

Bush, George W.

Kachurek, Sandra J. George W. Bush. Enslow Publishers 2004 128p il (United States presidents) lib bdg $26.60 (4 and up)   92

1. Presidents—United States

ISBN 0-7660-2040-1   LC 2003-19539

Discusses the life and political career of George W. Bush, up through the events of September 11, 2001, and the subsequent War on Terror.

"This biography is a solid introduction to the forty-third president. . . . The writing is involving, and Kachurek's coverage is evenhanded. . . . Studding the text are crisply reproduced, black-and-white photos." Booklist

Includes bibliographical references

McNeese, Tim. George W. Bush; first president of the new century. Morgan Reynolds 2002 112p il lib bdg $21.95 (7 and up)   92

1. Presidents—United States

ISBN 1-88384-685-4   LC 2001-40202

A biography of the former Texas governor who was elected President in the much-contested presidential race in 2000

"This biography gives a well-rounded look at a man with strong traditional values. . . . Teens interested in American history or current events will find this book absorbing and informative." Voice Youth Advocates

Includes bibliographical references

Byars, Betsy Cromer, 1928-

Byars, Betsy Cromer. The moon and I; {by} Betsy Byars. Messner 1991 96p il o.p. Beech Tree Bks. paperback available $4.95 (4 and up)

92

1. Authors, American 2. Women authors

ISBN 0-688-13704-0 (pa)   LC 91-15000

A "personal narrative that gives readers some info about snakes, a fair amount of insight into how writers do what they do, and the unmistakable impression that autobiographies are great entertainment. Byars's genuine, humorous outlook on life shines through on every page." SLJ

Cammarano, Rita. Betsy Byars. Chelsea House 2002 106p il (Who wrote that?) $22.95 (4 and up)

92

1. Authors, American 2. Women authors

ISBN 0-7910-6720-3   LC 2001-8337

Contents: Planes, people and pets; Miss Harriet, Bubba, and the zoo; Books, a river, and a fox; Swan time; Wings and things; From swimming to soaring; Golly blossom bingo; Reaching for the moon; A well that never goes dry

Describes the personal life and successful writing career of the Newbery Award-winning author, whose memorable characters include Bingo Brown, Herculeah Jones, and the Golly sisters

"An excellent resource for author studies and creative writing classes." Book Rep

Includes bibliographical references

Caesar, Julius, 100-44 B.C.

Bruns, Roger. Julius Caesar. Chelsea House 1987 112p il (World leaders past & present) lib bdg $21.95   **92**

1. Emperors—Rome 2. Rome—History

ISBN 0-87754-514-6   LC 87-6339

"Drawing in part upon writings of the Greek historian Plutarch, the Roman historian Suetonius, and Shakespeare, {the author} tells the story of Caesar. . . . Bruns' well-paced analytical text points out the many facets of this complex man." Booklist

Includes bibliographical references

Julius Caesar; Don Nardo, book editor. Greenhaven Press 2002 186p il (People who made history) lib bdg $34.95; pa $23.70   **92**

1. Emperors—Rome 2. Rome—History

ISBN 0-7377-0665-1 (lib bdg); 0-7377-0664-3 (pa)

LC 2001-23902

This profiles the life of the Roman emperor and includes essays and primary source documents

Includes bibliographical references

Calamity Jane, 1852-1903

Faber, Doris. Calamity Jane; her life and her legend. Houghton Mifflin 1992 62p il $16; pa $6.95 (5 and up)   **92**

1. Cowhands

ISBN 0-395-56396-8; 0-395-86539-5 (pa)

LC 91-40050

Examines the life of the Wild West heroine, born Mary Jane Cannary, who was transformed into a legendary figure in the public mind

"With little reliable fact to go on, Faber's portrait of Cannary remains elusive, but the legend of Calamity Jane comes through strong and clear. . . . The book is spaciously and cleanly designed, with reproductions of old photos and dime novel covers . . . that further the evidence of both life and myth." Bull Cent Child Books

Includes bibliographical references

Sanford, William R. Calamity Jane: frontier original; [by] William R. Sanford & Carl R. Green. Enslow Pubs. 1996 48p il (Legendary heroes of the Wild West) lib bdg $15.95

92

1. Cowhands

ISBN 0-89490-647-X   LC 95-41420

"*Calamity Jane* focuses on uncovering the truth about this unusual woman who dressed like a man, could do a man's job, and could outshoot, outdrink, and outcuss most men. . . . The authors have done a fine job of sorting fact from fiction, giving a well-rounded picture of this woman's life." SLJ

Capone, Al, 1899-1947

King, David C. Al Capone and the roaring twenties. Blackbirch Press 1999 80p il (Notorious Americans and their times) lib bdg $19.95

92

1. Criminals

ISBN 1-56711-218-8   LC 98-14591

The life of one of America's most infamous and powerful gangsters set in 1920s Chicago during the Prohibition

"Important information is here, supplemented by black-and-white photographs and some particularly interesting Web-site references. . . . The introduction to organized crime makes this a worthy addition to most collections." SLJ

Includes bibliographical references

Yancey, Diane. Al Capone. Lucent Bks. 2003 112p il (Heroes and villains) lib bdg $21.96

92

1. Criminals 2. Organized crime

ISBN 1-56006-949-X   LC 2002-3285

In this biography the Chicago gangster "is characterized through his actions and primary-source information. . . . The black-and-white photographs add dimension to the text. . . . This is an accessible, concise book on a complex man." SLJ

Includes bibliographical references

Carnegie, Andrew, 1835-1919

Kent, Zachary. Andrew Carnegie; steel king and friend to libraries. Enslow Pubs. 1999 128p il maps (Historical American biographies) lib bdg $26.60   **92**

1. Capitalists and financiers 2. Philanthropists

ISBN 0-7660-1212-3   LC 98-3160

A biography of the Scottish immigrant who made a fortune in the steel industry and used much of it for philanthropic causes

Includes glossary and bibliographical references

Carroll, Lewis, 1832-1898

Carpenter, Angelica Shirley. Lewis Carroll; through the looking glass. Lerner Publs. 2003 128p il map (Lerner biography) lib bdg $27.93 (7 and up)   **92**

1. Authors, English
ISBN 0-8225-0073-6   LC 2002-3266
A biography of the mathematician, teacher, photographer, and author who wrote "Alice in Wonderland"
"An accessible, well-documented portrait." SLJ
Includes bibliographical references

Carvalho, Solomon Nunes, 1815-1897

Hirschfelder, Arlene B. Photo odyssey: Solomon Carvalho's remarkable Western adventure, 1853-54. Clarion Bks. 2000 118p il $18   **92**

1. Photographers 2. West (U.S.)—Exploration
ISBN 0-395-89123-X   LC 99-42201
Describes the life of Carvalho, a Jewish photographer who accompanied John Charles Fremont on his last expedition to the West
"Through the author's historically accurate, vivid descriptions of the various stages of this journey, the reader gains incredible insight into the rigors endured by those who explored the vastness of our country during the 19th century." Book Rep
Includes bibliographical references

Carver, George Washington, 1864?-1943

Adair, Gene. George Washington Carver. Chelsea House 1989 110p il (Black Americans of achievement) lib bdg $23.95; pa $9.95   **92**

1. Scientists 2. African Americans—Biography
ISBN 1-55546-577-3 (lib bdg); 0-7910-0234-9 (pa)
LC 89-770
A biography of the African American whose scientific research revolutionized the economy of the South
"Carver's great accomplishments, as this book demonstrates, lay less in his inventions than in his teaching and in his efforts to help the poorest black and white farmers manage on what little they had." Sci Books Films
Includes bibliographical references

Castro, Fidel, 1926-

Platt, Richard. Fidel Castro. Raintree Steck-Vaughn 2003 112p il map (Twentieth-century history makers) lib bdg $32.85
92

1. Cuba—Politics and government
ISBN 0-7398-6141-7   LC 2002-15089
Contents: Old Cuba; Schoolboy and student; Lawyer and rebel leader; Rebels in waiting; Che and Fidel fight for freedom; Viva la revolución!; Freedom fighter to politician; Cuba goes red; The Bay of Pigs; The Missile Crisis; Building a people's paradise; Making friends abroad; The lone red flag; Hero or monster?
"Platt chronicles Castro's childhood, education, political activities, incarceration, rise to power in the late 1950s, and rule since that time. . . . Good-quality archival and full-color photographs and maps extend the text, and insets explain the significance of individuals and

ideas. A clear and well-organized offering that is well suited for research." SLJ
Includes bibliographical references

Press, Petra. Fidel Castro; an unauthorized biography. Heinemann Lib. 2000 56p il (Heinemann profiles) lib bdg $20.45   **92**

1. Cuba—Politics and government
ISBN 1-57572-497-9   LC 99-51675
A biography of the president of Cuba, Fidel Castro, discussing his childhood, family, revolutionary activities, and role as leader of his country since 1959
"This volume will entice readers to learn more about this enduring, charismatic leader." SLJ
Includes bibliographical references

Woog, Adam. Fidel Castro. Lucent Bks. 2003 112p (Importance of) lib bdg $27.45   **92**

1. Cuba—Politics and government
ISBN 1-59018-231-6   LC 2002-14363
A biography of the Cuban leader
This is a "well-researched account . . . . Black-and-white photos enhance the text. . . . A good choice for research where needed." SLJ
Includes bibliographical references

Chagall, Marc, 1887-1985

Pozzi, Gianni. Chagall; illustrated by Claudia Saraceni, L.R. Galante. Bedrick Bks. 1997 64p il (Masters of art) $22.50   **92**

1. Artists, Russian
ISBN 0-87226-527-7   LC 97-7330
A "look at Chagall's life, art, and times. Not a standard biography, this visually stunning, oversized volume looks at where the artist came from; the influences in his life; and the people, places, and artistic and cultural developments that took place during his 97 years. . . . A visual gallery complemented by an intelligent and far-ranging text." SLJ

Chaka, Zulu Chief, 1787?-1828

Stanley, Diane. Shaka, king of the Zulus; [by] Diane Stanley and Peter Vennema; illustrated by Diane Stanley. Morrow Junior Bks. 1988 unp il hardcover o.p. paperback available $5.95 (4 and up)   **92**

1. Zulu (African people)
ISBN 0-688-13114-X (pa)   LC 87-27376
A biography of the nineteenth-century military genius and Zulu chief
"Diane Stanley and Peter Vennema have culled the massive amount of historical material that exists about this strange and fascinating figure. Their text is lucid; the incidents are tactfully within the scope and decorum of a children's book but representative and true to the facts. . . . The rhythm of the illustrations . . . makes each page not only a realistic representation but also an artistic composition." N Y Times Book Rev
Includes bibliographical references

Champlain, Samuel de, 1567-1635

Faber, Harold. Samuel de Champlain; explorer of Canada; Harold Faber. Benchmark Books 2005 80p il map (Great explorations) lib bdg $29.93 (5 and up) **92**

1. Explorers 2. America—Exploration

ISBN 0-7614-1608-0   LC 2003-974

Contents: Growing up; First voyage to Canada; The fur trade; Founding of Quebec; The battle of Lake Champlain; More voyages to Canada; Disappointments; Governor of New France

"Faber draws on Champlain's own accounts to trace his exploration of and dogged determination to colonize Canada. . . . Illustrated with beautiful reproductions of period illustrations, paintings, and maps. . . . Well-written." SLJ

Includes bibliographical references

Sonneborn, Liz. Samuel de Champlain. Watts 2001 63p il $24; pa $8.95 **92**

1. Explorers 2. America—Exploration

ISBN 0-531-11978-5; 0-531-16580-9 (pa)

LC 00-43782

"Watts library"

A biography of the French explorer of the St. Lawrence River

This book not only has "appealing color pictures throughout but also provide{s} interesting reading with plenty of useful related information." Book Rep

Includes glossary and bibliographical references

Charles, Ray

Turk, Ruth. Ray Charles: soul man. Lerner Publs. 1996 112p il (Newsmakers) lib bdg $25.26 **92**

1. African American singers

ISBN 0-8225-4928-X   LC 95-20953

A biography of the African American popular singer, who became blind as a young boy

"The material about Charles's childhood is compelling. Turk includes the unpleasant aspects of his subject's life—his failed marriages and drug addiction." SLJ

Includes discography and bibliographical references

Chavez, Cesar, 1927-1993

Cesar Chavez; Michelle Houle, book editor. Greenhaven Press 2003 186p (People who made history) lib bdg $33.70; pa $22.45 (7 and up) **92**

1. Migrant labor 2. Mexican Americans

ISBN 0-7377-1298-8 (lib bdg); 0-7377-1299-6 (pa)

LC 2002-27152

"Chavez is the subject of 17 essays excerpted from various biographies, social histories, and magazine articles. . . . A conflation of opinions and personal observations about the nonviolent reformer, the book is also a piecemeal history of a social movement and its imperfect leader. Excellent for reports." SLJ

Includes bibliographical references

Collins, David R. Farmworker's friend: the story of Cesar Chavez. Carolrhoda Bks. 1996 80p il (Trailblazers) lib bdg $22.60 **92**

1. Migrant labor 2. Mexican Americans

ISBN 0-87614-982-4   LC 95-42759

Examines the life and accomplishments of the Mexican American labor activist who helped organize migrant farm workers and establish a union to fight for their rights

"Set against the backdrop of turbulent times aspects of Chavez' personal life are smoothly blended with his continued struggles to improve the plight of his fellow man. The book is enriched by black-and-white photographs and authenticated by the inclusion of a notes section providing additional information on incidents mentioned in the text." Booklist

Includes bibliographical references

Chen, Da, 1962-

Chen, Da. China's son; growing up in the Cultural Revolution. Delacorte Press 2001 213p $15.95; pa $8.95 (7 and up) **92**

1. China

ISBN 0-385-72929-4; 0-385-73050-0 (pa)

LC 00-47588

Adapted from the author's Colors of the mountain, published 1999 by Random House

"Because his grandfather was once a landlord, Chen's formerly privileged family were considered outcasts during China's Cultural Revolution. Chen recalls his mistreatment by neighbors and teachers, his gang experiences, and his determination to attend college." Horn Book Guide

This offers "an engaging writing style that pulls readers right into the story. . . . This is highly readable and very personal." Booklist

Child, Lydia Maria Francis, 1802-1880

Kenschaft, Lori. Lydia Maria Child; the quest for racial justice. Oxford Univ. Press 2002 126p il (Oxford portraits) lib bdg $24 (7 and up) **92**

1. Women authors 2. Abolitionists 3. Authors, American

ISBN 0-19-513257-2   LC 2001-52339

A biography of the popular writer who, in the mid-nineteenth century, gave up her literary success to fight for the abolition of slavery, for women's rights, and for the fair treatment of American Indians

"This well-done book will give young people an opportunity to learn more about one woman and the ideals for which she stood." SLJ

Includes bibliographical references

Churchill, Sir Winston, 1874-1965

Macdonald, Fiona. Winston Churchill. World Almanac 2003 48p il (Trailblazers of the modern world) lib bdg $26.60 **92**

1. Great Britain—Politics and government—20th century

ISBN 0-8368-5082-3   LC 2002-38044

Examines the childhood, war years, political career, and personal life of the twentieth-century British statesman, soldier, and historian

"A fascinating peek into British society, the army, and Parliament. . . . Suitable as a first purchase." SLJ

Includes bibliographical references

Churchill, Sir Winston, 1874-1965—*Continued*

Severance, John B. Winston Churchill; soldier, statesman, artist. Clarion Bks. 1996 144p il map $17.95 (5 and up)   **92**
1. Great Britain—Politics and government—20th century
ISBN 0-395-69853-7   LC 94-25129
This "biography presents an affectionate portrait of Britain's renowned Prime Minister. Although Severance focuses on Churchill's contributions during World War II, he also describes the statesman's boyhood, Boer War adventures, and political ascendancy." SLJ
"This fair, balanced, and duly appreciative biography is handsomely produced and illustrated with a fine collection of photographs." Horn Book Guide
Includes bibliographical references

Wrigley, Chris. Winston Churchill: a biographical companion. ABC-CLIO 2002 xxvi, 367p il (ABC-CLIO biographical companion) $55 (7 and up)   **92**
1. Great Britain—Politics and government—20th century
ISBN 0-87436-990-8   LC 2002-2178
"This book is an A-Z compilation of events, people, issues, laws, places, and groups having some historical association with Churchill. Easy to use, it presents material in readable topics with B&W photos, related entries, and suggestions for further reading. . . . This book is a valuable resource for browsing or for research on specific people, places, or events connected to Churchill." Libr Media Connect
Includes bibliographical references

Cisneros, Sandra

Mirriam-Goldberg, Caryn. Sandra Cisneros; Latina writer and activist. Enslow Pubs. 1998 112p il maps (Hispanic biographies) lib bdg $26.60   **92**
1. Authors, American 2. Mexican Americans 3. Women authors
ISBN 0-7660-1045-7   LC 98-20828
Surveys the life and work of this award-winning Latina author
"An inspirational portrait of a Latina woman who showed perseverance and grit, overcoming poverty and cultural biases to become a noted writer and activist. . . . A valuable title, especially where the writer's books are studied." SLJ
Includes bibliographical references

Clark, Eugenie

Ross, Michael Elsohn. Fish watching with Eugenie Clark; illustrations by Wendy Smith. Carolrhoda Bks. 2000 48p il (Naturalist's apprentice) $19.93 (4 and up)   **92**
1. Women scientists 2. Fishes
ISBN 1-575-05384-5   LC 99-19963
Describes the life and career of ichthyologist Eugenie Clark, who began her research observing fresh-water aquarium fishes and moved on to the underwater study of sharks and other marine animals. Includes observation tips and and related activities

"Ross presents a bright, readable, up-to-the-minute biography. . . . The well-organized text is illustrated with a number of somewhat unpretentious black-and-white and full-color photos, but they are almost eclipsed by Smith's colorful drawings of a wide variety of fish mentioned in Clark's studies." SLJ
Includes bibliographical references

Cleary, Beverly

Cleary, Beverly. A girl from Yamhill: a memoir. Morrow 1988 279p il $21.99 (6 and up)   **92**
1. Authors, American 2. Women authors
ISBN 0-688-07800-1   LC 87-31554
Also available in paperback from Avon Camelot Bks.
Follows the popular children's author from her childhood years in Oregon through high school and into young adulthood, highlighting her family life and her growing interest in writing
"The author sees her child self with the same clarity and objectivity as she has seen her fictional characters, and her reminiscences have a resultant integrity and candor." Bull Cent Child Books

Cleary, Beverly. My own two feet. Morrow Junior Bks. 1995 261p il $15   **92**
1. Authors, American 2. Women authors
ISBN 0-688-14267-2   LC 95-1764
Also available in paperback from Avon Bks.
"This second installment of the Newbery Medalist's autobiography (after A Girl from Yamhill) begins during the '30s, with the young Cleary leaving her home state of Oregon to attend junior college in California. The volume ends in 1949, with Morrow's acceptance of Cleary's first novel, the now-classic *Henry Huggins.*" Publ Wkly
"Cleary recalls the past with humor, affection, and insight. Those who have always admired her books will, after reading this memoir, have an even greater admiration for the author." Horn Book

Cleopatra, Queen of Egypt, d. 30 B.C.

Brooks, Polly Schoyer. Cleopatra; goddess of Egypt, enemy of Rome. HarperCollins Pubs. 1995 151p il maps lib bdg $16.89 hardcover o.p. (7 and up)   **92**
1. Queens 2. Egypt—History
ISBN 0-06-023608-6   LC 95-10688
The "portrait that emerges here of the last Ptolomeic ruler of Egypt is an admiring one: she is charming and erudite, multilingual, a brave warrior, a savvy politician and, above all, a beloved queen dedicated to maintaining Egypt's independence from Rome. Her relationship with Julius Caesar is portrayed as motivated by personal attraction, not political expediency; with Mark Antony, mutual need is said to have led to affection. Avoiding the temptation to tell too much, Brooks demonstrates a keen eye for recognizing the essential components of a compelling narrative." Publ Wkly
Includes bibliographical references

Cleopatra, Queen of Egypt, d. 30 B.C.—*Continued*

Cleopatra; Don Nardo, book editor. Greenhaven Press 2000 173p il (People who made history) $34.95; pa $23.70 (7 and up)   **92**

    1. Queens 2. Egypt—History

    ISBN 0-7377-0322-9; 0-7377-0321-0 (pa)

                              LC 99-85743

"A collection of essays that focuses on specific aspects in the life of an intriguing woman. Introductory biographical information is followed by excerpts from the writings of noted contemporary and ancient historians and biographers and literary critics. In three sections, the book discusses the relationships of Cleopatra and Julius Caesar; Cleopatra and Mark Antony; and the queen's portrayal in the works of various playwrights and novelists, poets, and dramatists. . . . This useful resource has a wealth of information and will be fascinating reading for students interested in this 'most queenly queen.'" SLJ

Includes bibliographical references

Morgan, Julian. Cleopatra; ruling in the shadow of Rome. Rosen Pub. Group 2003 112p il (Leaders of ancient Egypt) lib bdg $31.95   **92**

    1. Queens 2. Egypt—History

    ISBN 0-8239-3591-4   LC 2002-1214

"This title focuses on Cleopatra VII and her volatile relationship with Rome. A brief history of the Ptolemies and their rule in Egypt provides readers with essential background information. Vivid descriptions of Cleopatra's relationships with Julius Caesar and Mark Antony include possible motives for the alliances she formed. Clear discussions of the intricate politics, fragile unions, and the possibility of foreign invasions and internal rebellion are also provided. . . . Full-color photographs of the art, architecture, and artifacts of this time period enhance understanding." SLJ

Includes bibliographical references

Stanley, Diane. Cleopatra; {by} Diane Stanley, Peter Vennema; illustrated by Diane Stanley. Morrow Junior Bks. 1994 unp il maps $16.95; lib bdg $17.89; pa $6.99 (4 and up)   **92**

    1. Queens 2. Egypt—History

    ISBN 0-688-10413-4; 0-688-10414-2 (lib bdg);
    0-688-15480-8 (pa)   LC 93-27032

This is a biography of the ancient Egyptian queen

"Lucid writing combines with carefully selected anecdotes, often attributed to the Greek historian Plutarch to create an engaging narrative. . . . Stanley's stunning, full-color gouache artwork is arresting in its large, well-composed images executed in flat Greek style." SLJ

Includes bibliographical references

Cochise, Apache Chief, d. 1874

Schwarz, Melissa. Cochise, Apache chief. Chelsea House 1992 119p il maps (North American Indians of achievement) lib bdg $19.95   **92**

    1. Apache Indians

    ISBN 0-7910-1706-0   LC 91-23495

Examines the life and career of the noted Apache warrior chief

"This sympathetic profile of a strong native American leader, illustrated with many black-and-white museum maps, reproductions, and photographs, would be best read along with a book on Apache history." SLJ

Includes bibliographical references

Coleman, Bessie, 1896?-1926

Hart, Philip S. Up in the air: the story of Bessie Coleman. Carolrhoda Bks. 1996 80p il (Trailblazers) pa $8.95 hardcover o.p.   **92**

    1. Women air pilots 2. African American pilots

    ISBN 0-87614-978-6   LC 95-32906

Presents the story of Bessie Coleman, an American, who in 1920 traveled to France to become the first black woman to earn a pilot's license

This "will be useful for research and recreational reading." SLJ

Includes bibliographical references

Collins, Michael, 1930-

Schyffert, Bea Uusma. The man who went to the far side of the moon: the story of Apollo 11 astronaut Michael Collins. Chronicle 2003 77p il $14.95 (5 and up)   **92**

    1. Astronauts 2. Space flight

    ISBN 0-8118-4007-7

A biography of the astronaut, Michael Collins, who circled the moon in the Apollo 12 space capsule while his colleagues Neil Armstrong and Buzz Aldrin landed the lunar module and walked on the moon.

"This excellent book—illustrated scrapbook-style with a cleverly presented mix of photographs, illustrations, and charts—communicates the excitement of space travel." Booklist

Coltrane, John, 1926-1967

Barron, Rachel. John Coltrane; jazz revolutionary; {by} Rachel Stiffler Barron. Morgan Reynolds 2001 112p il (Masters of music) lib bdg $21.95 (7 and up)   **92**

    1. Jazz musicians

    ISBN 1-88384-657-9   LC 2001-40195

Traces the life of the innovative jazz saxophonist and the evolution of his music

"The coverage of Coltrane's life is well balanced by thoughtful analysis of his music." Horn Book Guide

Includes discography and bibliographical references

Columbus, Christopher

Meltzer, Milton. Columbus and the world around him. Watts 1990 192p il maps lib bdg $20   **92**

    1. Explorers 2. America—Exploration

    ISBN 0-531-10899-6   LC 89-24764

"Meltzer excels in a candid and graphic exposé of the Spaniards' behaviors and attitudes, including enormous cruelty and greed. . . . This thought-provoking book includes handsome and profuse reproductions of historical maps, artwork, manuscripts, and letters." Booklist

Includes bibliographical references

Confucius

Freedman, Russell. Confucius; the golden rule; illustrated by Frédéric Clément. Levine Bks. 2002 48p il $15.95 (4 and up) **92**

1. Philosophers
ISBN 0-439-13957-0   LC 2001-29372

This is a "biography of the 5th-century B.C. philosopher Confucius, whose teachings have influenced the development of modern government and education in both China and the West." Publ Wkly

"The fascinating narrative seamlessly intersperses stories from the *Analects* with Chinese history and biographical information about Confucius. . . . Clement's muted, elegant paintings of towns, temples, and the bucktoothed Confucius himself have a suitably ancient feel with jagged borders and fading colors." Booklist

Cook, James, 1728-1779

Meltzer, Milton. Captain James Cook; three times around the world. Benchmark Bks. 2001 80p il maps (Great explorations) lib bdg $19.95 **92**

1. Explorers 2. Voyages around the world
ISBN 0-7614-1240-9   LC 00-51899

This "well-researched {book} . . . will be useful to students writing reports. Maps and archival reproductions in both black and white and color extend the text." Horn Book Guide

Includes bibliographical references

Copernicus, Nicolaus, 1473-1543

Andronik, Catherine M. Copernicus; founder of modern astronomy. Enslow Pubs. 2002 112p il (Great minds of science) lib bdg $26.60 **92**

1. Astronomers
ISBN 0-7660-1755-9   LC 2001-1815

This "covers Copernicus' life and the development of his theory of the universe." Book Rep

"This is a highly readable book that presents a good balance between the biographical information needed to understand Copernicus as a man and the scientific explanations necessary to understand his work." SLJ

Includes glossary and bibliographical references

Goble, Todd. Nicholas Copernicus and the founding of modern astronomy. Morgan Reynolds 2004 144p il (Renaissance scientists) lib bdg $23.95 (7 and up) **92**

1. Astronomers
ISBN 1-88384-699-4   LC 2003-4659

Contents: Born at the right time; From Koppernigk to Copernicus; The perks of the office; The return to Italy; The wages of nepotism; The duties of the canon; The astronomer emerges; On revolutions; An elder canon; Publication; The retreat of the stars

Presents the life and work of the famous sixteenth-century Polish astronomer

"This methodical biography places the astronomer within the turbulent political and religious events of his times and the concurrent intellectual riptides that marked the shift from medieval to modern science." SLJ

Cormier, Robert

Thomson, Sarah L. Robert Cormier. Rosen Central 2003 112p il (Library of author biographies) $26.50 **92**

1. Authors, American
ISBN 0-8239-3776-3   LC 2002-7954

A biography of the popular author for young adults. This "will capture readers' attention. Quality information delivered in a well-organized manner." SLJ

Includes bibliographical references

Cortés, Hernán, 1485-1547

Calvert, Patricia. Hernando Cortés; fortune favored the bold. Benchmark Bks. 2003 80p il maps (Great explorations) lib bdg $19.95 **92**

1. Explorers 2. Mexico—History
ISBN 0-7614-1482-7   LC 2002-18462

Describes the life of Hernando Cortés, the Spanish explorer who discovered Baja California and explored the Pacific coast of Mexico, but who is best remembered for conquering the Aztec Empire

Includes bibliographical references

Crane, Stephen, 1871-1900

Lukes, Bonnie L. Soldier's courage: the story of Stephen Crane. Morgan Reynolds 2002 144p il lib bdg $21.95 (7 and up) **92**

1. Authors, American
ISBN 1-88384-694-3   LC 2002-5095

A biography of the 19th century American author of The Red Badge of Courage, who died at the age of 28

"Lukes's gift for storytelling and her stirring prose result in a thoroughly readable and informative volume." SLJ

Includes bibliographical references

Crazy Horse, Sioux Chief, ca. 1842-1877

Freedman, Russell. The life and death of Crazy Horse; drawings by Amos Bad Heart Bull. Holiday House 1996 166p il maps $22.95 (5 and up) **92**

1. Oglala Indians
ISBN 0-8234-1219-9   LC 95-33303

A biography of the Oglala Indian leader who relentlessly resisted the white man's attempt to take over Indian lands

This is "a compelling biography that is based on primary source documents and illustrated with pictographs by a Sioux band historian." Voice Youth Advocates

Includes bibliographical references

Crick, Francis, 1916-2004

Edelson, Edward. James Watson and Francis Crick and the building blocks of life. See entry under Watson, James D., 1928-

Cromwell, Oliver, 1599-1658

Aronson, Marc. John Winthrop, Oliver Cromwell, and the Land of Promise. See entry under Winthrop, John, 1588-1649

Crutcher, Chris, 1946-

Crutcher, Chris. King of the mild frontier: an ill-advised autobiography. Greenwillow Bks. 2003 260p il $16.99; lib bdg $17.89 **92**

1. Authors, American

ISBN 0-06-050249-5; 0-06-050250-9 (lib bdg)

LC 2002-11224

Chris Crutcher, author of young adult novels such as "Ironman" and "Whale Talk," as well as short stories, tells of growing up in Cascade, Idaho, and becoming a writer

"Like his novels, Crutcher's autobiography is full of heartbreak, poignancy, and hilarity. . . . This honest, insightful, revealing autobiography is a joy to read." Booklist

Curie, Marie, 1867-1934

Birch, Beverley. Marie Curie; courageous pioneer in the study of radioactivity. Blackbirch Press 2000 64p il (Giants of science) lib bdg $24.95 **92**

1. Chemists 2. Women scientists

ISBN 1-56711-333-8 LC 00-8806

First published 1992 in Great Britain

Presents the life and accomplishments of the Polish-born chemist, discussing her methods of scientific research, discovery of radium, and its use as a treatment for cancer

"The illustrations, many in color, include period photographs, drawings, and paintings, as well as artifacts and documents." Booklist

Lassieur, Allison. Marie Curie; a scientific pioneer; Allison Lassieur. F. Watts 2003 111p il (Great life stories) $30.50 **92**

1. Women scientists 2. Chemists

ISBN 0-531-12270-0 LC 2003-953

Contents: Early years in Poland; Launching a dream; A student in Paris; A new life; The great discovery; The Nobel Prize, fame, and strange ailments; The dark years; New successes, new ordeals; World War I and the later years

A biography of the Nobel Prize-winning scientist who discovered radium.

This "is elegantly written and flows smoothly, creating a balanced portrayal of the scientist's life." SLJ

Includes bibliographical references

MacLeod, Elizabeth. Marie Curie; a brilliant life; written by Elizabeth MacLeod. Kids Can Press 2004 32p il $14.95; pa $6.95 (5 and up) **92**

1. Chemists 2. Women scientists

ISBN 1-55337-570-x; 1-55337-571-8 (pa)

"The drive and self-sacrifice that enabled Marie Curie to win two Nobel Prizes and become the most acclaimed female scientist to date are explored in this accessible biography, which covers Curie's personal and professional lives. Illustrated with well-chosen archival photos." Horn Book Guide

Pasachoff, Naomi E. Marie Curie and the science of radioactivity; {by} Naomi Pasachoff. Oxford Univ. Press 1996 109p il (Oxford portraits in science) lib bdg $28; pa $11.95 **92**

1. Chemists 2. Women scientists

ISBN 0-19-509214-7 (lib bdg); 0-19-512011-6 (pa)

LC 95-13639

"The book discusses the lack of recognition accorded the Curies by the French scientific community, the personal attacks Curie experienced because of her friendship with Paul Langevin, and professional criticisms of her work. Boxed sections provide related information on such topics as radioactivity, radon, and Mendeleyev's organization of the periodic table." Booklist

"This is a thorough biography, particularly useful for reports." SLJ

Includes bibliographical references

Poynter, Margaret. Marie Curie: discoverer of radium. Enslow Pubs. 1994 128p il maps (Great minds of science) lib bdg $26.60; pa $10.95 (4 and up) **92**

1. Chemists 2. Women scientists

ISBN 0-89490-477-9 (lib bdg); 0-7660-1875-X (pa)

LC 93-21224

This "biography emphasizes Marie Curie's early life of poverty, desire to study, and contributions to the fields of chemistry, physics, and medicine." Horn Book Guide

"The writing style is straightforward, with a combination of personal detail and scientific explanation. . . . Sure to be in demand for those middle-grade biography and science assignments." Booklist

Includes glossary and bibliographical references

Dahl, Roald

Dahl, Roald. Boy: tales of childhood. Farrar, Straus & Giroux 1984 160p il o.p. Puffin Bks. paperback available $6.99 **92**

1. Authors, English

ISBN 0-14-130305-0 (pa) LC 84-48462

"In these memoirs, Dahl reminisces about growing up in a large Norwegian family living in Wales during the 1920s and 1930s. The text is illustrated with sketches, old photographs and excerpts of letters he wrote as a boy." SLJ

"This should be of particular interest to Dahl's fans, but it should also appeal to anyone who likes writing that is direct, candid, and free-flowing." Bull Cent Child Books

Dalai Lama XIV, 1935-

Demi. The Dalai Lama; a biography of the Tibetan spiritual and political leader. Holt & Co. 1998 unp il $18.95 (3-6) **92**

1. Buddhism 2. Tibet (China)

ISBN 0-8050-5443-X LC 97-30654

In this biography of the Buddhist spiritual leader, Demi "uses straightforward prose and fluid, eastern-influenced art—small pen-and-ink and watercolor images with fine, intricate detail. . . . Told with respect and devotion, this is an inspirational picture-book biography." Horn Book

D'Angelo, Pascal, 1894-1932
Murphy, Jim. Pick & shovel poet: the journeys of Pascal D'Angelo. Clarion Bks. 2000 162p il $20   **92**
1. Italian Americans
ISBN 0-395-77610-4   LC 00-22573
"Murphy has written an inspiring biography of a truly remarkable man. Through words and moving archival photographs, he has given readers a glimpse of the difficult life that many immigrants led in the early twentieth century." Book Rep
Includes bibliographical references

Darwin, Charles, 1809-1882
Patent, Dorothy Hinshaw. Charles Darwin; the life of a revolutionary thinker. Holiday House 2001 144p il map $22.95 (7 and up)   **92**
1. Naturalists 2. Evolution
ISBN 0-8234-1494-9   LC 00-37034
This "biography presents the life and theories of one of history's most innovative and influential scientists. Patent . . . excels when dissecting Darwin's experiments and thought processes, and her analysis is clear and passionate." Publ Wkly
Includes glossary and bibliographical references

Stefoff, Rebecca. Charles Darwin and the evolution revolution. Oxford Univ. Press 1996 126p il (Oxford portraits in science) $28 (7 and up)   **92**
1. Naturalists 2. Evolution
ISBN 0-19-508996-0   LC 95-35802
Examines the personality as well as the thought process which led this naturalist to his discoveries which have helped shape our understanding of the natural world
"Extensive photos of Darwin and his family, friends, and colleagues, as well as reproductions of public notices and cartoons, are handsome additions to the nicely laid-out text. . . . It offers generally thorough, clear explanations of Darwin's scientific theories and sheds light on his personality." Booklist
Includes glossary and bibliographical references

Dickens, Charles, 1812-1870
Stanley, Diane. Charles Dickens; the man who had great expectations; {by} Diane Stanley & Peter Vennema; illustrated by Diane Stanley. Morrow Junior Bks. 1993 unp il $15; lib bdg $14.93 (4 and up)   **92**
1. Authors, English
ISBN 0-688-09110-5; 0-688-09111-3 (lib bdg)
                                           LC 91-41552
"This picture-book biography of the great English novelist is attractive and appealing. Stanley's full-color, full-page gouache paintings are expressive and inviting; the abbreviated text covers all of the major events in Dickens's life." SLJ
Includes bibliographical references

Dickinson, Emily, 1830-1886
Dommermuth-Costa, Carol. Emily Dickinson; singular poet. Lerner Publs. 1998 112p il $27.93
                                           92
1. Poets, American 2. Women poets
ISBN 0-8225-4958-1   LC 97-40081
Examines the life, work, and significance of the visionary poet from Amherst, Massachusetts
"Extensive quotations from poems and letters help bring the major figures to life and offer a period flavor as well. A solid addition to biography collections." Booklist
Includes bibliographical references

Domingo, Placido
Stefoff, Rebecca. Plácido Domingo. Chelsea House 1992 111p il (Hispanics of achievement) lib bdg $19.95; pa $8.95   **92**
1. Singers
ISBN 0-7910-1563-7 (lib bdg); 0-7910-1692-7 (pa)
                                           LC 91-32358
Profiles the life and career of the Spanish opera singer who is also known in the world of popular music
Includes discography and videography

Douglas, Marjory Stoneman
Doherty, Kieran. Marjory Stoneman Douglas; guardian of the 'glades. 21st Cent. Bks. (Brookfield) 2002 143p il map lib bdg $24.90 (7 and up)   **92**
1. Conservationists 2. Everglades (Fla.)
ISBN 0-7613-2371-6   LC 2002-4977
A biography of the Florida environmental activist whose efforts on behalf of the Everglades have resulted in the protection and revitalization of that area
"Ten chapters chronicle Douglas's life in a readable, well-organized style that utilizes quotes, documented in the endnotes." SLJ
Includes bibliographical references

Douglass, Frederick, 1817?-1895
Douglass, Frederick. Escape from slavery; the boyhood of Frederick Douglass in his own words; edited and illustrated by Michael McCurdy; foreword by Coretta Scott King. Knopf 1994 63p il pa $6.99 hardcover o.p.   **92**
1. Abolitionists 2. African Americans—Biography
ISBN 0-679-84651-4 (pa)   LC 93-19239
"McCurdy has done a splendid job of bringing the *Narrative of the Life of Frederick Douglass* to middle-grade readers. There are brief introductory notes about what's been left out in each chapter; otherwise, the voice is Douglass' own, in all its simplicity, lyricism, and fury." Booklist
Includes bibliographical references

Yancey, Diane. Frederick Douglass. Lucent Bks. 2003 112p il (Heroes and villains) lib bdg $27.45
                                           92
1. Abolitionists 2. African Americans—Biography
ISBN 1-56006-950-3   LC 2002-9462
Contents: Dreams of freedom; "Cut out for a hero"; "I live a new life"; The North Star; Jubilee Day; "Give him equality"; Cedar Hill; A place in history

Douglass, Frederick, 1817?-1895—*Continued*

This traces the life of the African American abolitionist, editor, writer, and orator

Includes bibliographical references

Doyle, Sir Arthur Conan, 1859-1930

Pascal, Janet B. Arthur Conan Doyle; beyond Baker Street. Oxford Univ. Press 1999 158p il (Oxford portraits) $28 (7 and up) **92**

1. Authors, Scottish

ISBN 0-19-512262-3   LC 99-36643

In this biography of the creator of Sherlock Holmes the author examines the "events and people in his life that later showed up in his books, . . . paints him as a decent, likable fellow with a talent for forceful, vivid writing and unwavering enthusiasm for new ideas and enterprises." Booklist

"Pascal does a fine job of conveying the era in which her object lived." SLJ

Includes bibliographical references

Drake, Sir Francis, 1540?-1596

Rice, Earle. Sir Francis Drake, navigator and pirate; by Earle Rice, Jr. Benchmark Bks. 2003 76p il maps (Great explorations) lib bdg $19.95 **92**

1. Explorers

ISBN 0-7614-1483-5   LC 2002-3523

Contents: The making of a sea dog; Drake's war; Plundering the Spanish Main; Circling the globe; El Draque returns; Philip's Grand Armada

"Students will find the time lines and further-research sections valuable." SLJ

Drew, Charles

Schraff, Anne E. Dr. Charles Drew; blood bank innovator; {by} Anne Schraff. Enslow Publishers 2003 112p il (African-American biographies) $26.60 **92**

1. Surgeons 2. African Americans—Biography

ISBN 0-7660-2117-3 (lib bdg)   LC 2002-10402

Contents: Blood for Britain; Foggy Bottom beginnings; The calling; North to Canada; Howard and Freedmen's, a new era; Meeting Minnie Lenore Robbins; Blood for life; "My greatest contribution"

A biography of the pioneering African American doctor famous for his work with blood plasma.

Includes bibliographical references

Du Bois, W. E. B. (William Edward Burghardt), 1868-1963

Troy, Don. W.E.B. DuBois. Child's World 1999 39p il (Journey to freedom) lib bdg $28.50 **92**

1. African Americans—Biography

ISBN 1-56766-555-1   LC 98-4328

A brief biography of the African American educator and activist who helped found the NAACP and worked much of his life to gain equitable treatment for his people

"Attractive and clearly written. . . . The large, beautifully reproduced sepia-toned photographs on almost every page help personalize the text." SLJ

Includes glossary and bibliographical references

Dunbar, Paul Laurence, 1872-1906

Reef, Catherine. Paul Laurence Dunbar; portrait of a poet. Enslow Pubs. 2000 128p il (African-American biographies) lib bdg $26.60 **92**

1. Poets, American 2. African American authors

ISBN 0-7660-1350-2   LC 99-16456

A biography of the poet who faced racism and devoted himself to depicting the black experience in America

"Excerpts from select poems and numerous quotes by and about the subject, cited in the lengthy source notes, enliven the text. Black-and-white photographs and reproductions appear throughout." SLJ

Includes bibliographical references

Duncan, Isadora, 1878-1927

O'Connor, Barbara. Barefoot dancer: the story of Isadora Duncan. Carolrhoda Bks. 1994 95p il (Trailblazers) lib bdg $27.93; pa $8.95 **92**

1. Dancers

ISBN 0-87614-807-0 (lib bdg); 0-87614-911-5 (pa)   LC 93-14312

Describes the life of the modern dancer who created a spontaneous, free-form dance style accompanied by literary readings and non-dance music

This is "a competent and easy-reading survey of a glamorous life." Bull Cent Child Books

Includes bibliographical references

Edelman, Marian Wright, 1939-

Old, Wendie. Marian Wright Edelman; fighting for children's rights. Enslow Pubs. 1995 128p il (People to know) lib bdg $26.60 (7 and up) **92**

1. African American women

ISBN 0-89490-623-2   LC 95-7508

A biography of the African American lawyer and social reformer who is known for her work on behalf of children's rights

Includes bibliographical references

Edison, Thomas A. (Thomas Alva), 1847-1931

Delano, Marfe Ferguson. Inventing the future: a photobiography of Thomas Alva Edison. National Geographic Soc. 2002 64p il $18.95 **92**

1. Inventors

ISBN 0-7922-6721-4   LC 2001-7357

Presents a biography of the tireless Thomas Edison, illustrated with many photos of his life and inventions

"Well-written and -illustrated. . . . This biography would inspire young people who are interested in experimenting with new ideas and methods." Libr Media Connect

Includes bibliographical references

Edison, Thomas A. (Thomas Alva), 1847-1931—
Continued

Mason, Paul. Thomas A. Edison. Raintree Steck-Vaughn Pubs. 2002 48p il (Scientists who made history) lib bdg $29.93   **92**
1. Inventors
ISBN 0-7398-4414-8   LC 2001-19510
The author portrays "Edison as an outstanding businessman/inventor whose creative period was largely over after the turn of the century." SLJ
This is "fun to read, chock full of interesting, surprising information—both personal and scientific—and will jump from the shelves into the hands of readers and researchers." Book Rep
Includes glossary and bibliographical references

Sproule, Anna. Thomas A. Edison; the world's greatest inventor; by Anna Sproule. 1st U.S. ed. Blackbirch Press 2000 64p il (Giants of science) $24.95   **92**
1. Inventors
ISBN 1-567-11331-1   LC 00-8072
First published 1991 in the United Kingdom
Details the life and work of Thomas Edison, who developed the electric light bulb and patents for numerous other inventions and innovations
"Clear, relevant, black-and-white and full-color photographs and reproductions with captions provide additional information." SLJ
Includes bibliographical references and index

Tagliaferro, Linda. Thomas Edison; inventor of the age of electricity. Lerner Publs. 2003 128p il (Lerner biography) lib bdg $25.26 (7 and up)   **92**
1. Inventors
ISBN 0-8225-4689-2   LC 2002-7603
A biography of Thomas Alva Edison, the inventor of the electric lighting system and the phonograph
"The life of this remarkable inventor and scientific genius is explored in lively and accessible detail. . . . In this clearly written and thoroughly researched volume, the information flows smoothly and logically." SLJ
Includes bibliographical references

Einstein, Albert, 1879-1955

Albert Einstein; Clarice Swisher, book editor. Greenhaven Press 2002 224p il (People who made history) lib bdg $34.95; pa $23.70   **92**
1. Physicists
ISBN 0-7377-0893-X (lib bdg); 0-7377-0892-1 (pa)
    LC 2001-28925
This profiles Einstein's life and work and includes essays and primary source documents
Includes bibliographical references

Bernstein, Jeremy. Albert Einstein and the frontiers of physics. Oxford Univ. Press 1996 189p il (Oxford portraits in science) lib bdg $24; pa $12.95 (7 and up)   **92**
1. Physicists
ISBN 0-19-509275-9 (lib bdg); 0-19-512029-9 (pa)
    LC 95-37500

"Bernstein devotes considerable space in this . . . biography to explanations of relativity, quantum mechanics, gravitation, and the relevant mathematical formulas, and to the various scientists whose theories influenced Einstein in some way." SLJ
"Einstein's personal life, his political and religious beliefs, and his work for control of nuclear arms are well covered. . . . Recommended for those who want to know as much about Einstein's science as about his life." Voice Youth Advocates
Includes bibliographical references

Delano, Marfe Ferguson. Genius; a photobiography of Albert Einstein. National Geographic 2005 63p il $17.95; lib bdg $27.90 (5 and up)   **92**
1. Scientists
ISBN 0-7922-9544-7; 0-7922-9545-5 (lib bdg)
    LC 2004-15001
A biography of the German American physicist.
This "combines a solid text with a particularly attractive format. . . . Delano offers just enough information about Einstein's theories to give a sense of his work. . . . Oversize and filled with well-selected photographs, the book is very handsome." Booklist

Macdonald, Fiona. Albert Einstein; genius behind the theory of relativity. Blackbirch Press 2000 64p il $24.95   **92**
1. Physicists
ISBN 1-56711-330-3
First published 1992 in the United Kingdom
This biography "describes the physicist's childhood, education, revolutionary theories, personal life, political outlook, and international awards." Booklist
Includes glossary and bibliographical references

MacLeod, Elizabeth. Albert Einstein; a life of genius; written by Elizabeth MacLeod. Kids Can Press 2003 32p il $14.95; pa $6.95 (4 and up)   **92**
1. Physicists
ISBN 1-55337-396-0; 1-55337-397-9 (pa)
A brief introduction to the life and work of the physicist
"It looks like a scrapbook, with information offered in small bites accompanied by lots of small photos and illustrations, but this introduction to the life of Einstein is as informative as it is appealing. . . . This is concise, but there's still plenty here for students and browsers alike." Booklist

Sullivan, Anne Marie. Albert Einstein. Mason Crest Publs. 2003 unp il $19.95 (4 and up)   **92**
1. Physicists
ISBN 1-59084-140-9   LC 2003-6034
This is a brief introduction to the life and work of the physicist
"Einstein comes alive in this delightful, entertaining, well-written, and beautifully illustrated biography." Libr Media Connect

Eisenhower, Dwight D. (Dwight David), 1890-1969

Young, Jeff C. Dwight D. Eisenhower; soldier and president. Morgan Reynolds 2002 128p il (Notable Americans) lib bdg $21.95   **92**
1. Presidents—United States 2. Generals
ISBN 1-88384-676-5   LC 2001-30822
A biography of the World War II commander general who became the thirty-fourth President of the United States

"Young reveals Ike's story with a flair that makes both the man's questionable and admirable traits interesting. . . . There is enough drama here to make the story of the thirty-fourth president a surprisingly dynamic tale." Booklist

Includes bibliographical references

Elizabeth I, Queen of England, 1533-1603

Stanley, Diane. Good Queen Bess: the story of Elizabeth I of England; by Diane Stanley and Peter Vennema; illustrated by Diane Stanley. HarperCollins Pubs. 2001 c1990 unp il $16.99 (4 and up)   **92**
1. Queens 2. Great Britain—Kings and rulers 3. Great Britain History—1485-1603, Tudors
ISBN 0-688-17961-4   LC 00-47267

Follows the life of the strong-willed queen who ruled England in the time of Shakespeare and the defeat of the Spanish Armada

"The handsome illustrations . . . are worthy of their subject. Although the format suggests a picture-book audience, this biography needs to be introduced to older readers who have the background to appreciate and understand this woman who dominated and named an age." SLJ

Includes bibliographical references

Thomas, Jane Resh. Behind the mask: the life of Queen Elizabeth I. Clarion Bks. 1998 196p il maps $20 (7 and up)   **92**
1. Queens 2. Great Britain—Kings and rulers 3. Great Britain—History—1485-1603, Tudors
ISBN 0-395-69120-6   LC 94-31975
This biography "begins with Elizabeth's father, King Henry VIII. . . . Thomas then covers the Tudor queen's life from her negotiation of pre-accession pitfalls to the major aspects of her tenure, both political and personal." Bull Cent Child Books

This is a "vital and intelligent biography. Throughout, Thomas has a good story to tell—one full of intrigue, passion, and larger-than-life characters—and her documentation backs it up. This handsome book, filled with black-and-white photographs, contains a stunning eight-page color insert of the queen's life in portraits." Horn Book Guide

Includes bibliographical references

Ellington, Duke, 1899-1974

Brown, Gene. Duke Ellington: jazz master. Blackbirch Press 2001 128p il (Giants of art and culture) lib bdg $27.45 (7 and up)   **92**
1. Jazz musicians
ISBN 1-56711-505-5   LC 00-52993

First published 1990 by Silver Burdett
A biography of the jazz musician and composer
This is "solidly grounded in the times. . . . Numerous historical photographs add interest." Booklist

Includes glossary and bibliographical references

Old, Wendie. Duke Ellington: giant of jazz; {by} Wendie C. Old. Enslow Pubs. 1996 128p il (African-American biographies) lib bdg $26.60   **92**
1. Jazz musicians 2. African American musicians
ISBN 0-89490-691-7   LC 96-3279
Examines the life and career of the talented jazz composer, bandleader, and pianist, from his childhood in Washington, D.C., through his battle against racism, to his influence on the world of jazz

"This biography will send young jazz enthusiasts back to their CD players or even to the piano to find out for themselves just what was that great Ellington sound." BAYA Book Rev

Includes bibliographical references

Ellison, Lawrence J., 1944-

Ehrenhaft, Daniel. Larry Ellison; sheer nerve. 21st Cent. Bks. (Brookfield) 2001 80p il (Techies) lib bdg $23.93   **92**
1. Oracle Corp. 2. Computer software industry 3. Businessmen
ISBN 0-7613-1962-X   LC 2001-27167
This is a profile of the computer software executive who founded the Oracle Corporation
This "will appeal not only to report writers, but also to recreational readers." SLJ

Includes bibliographical references

Equiano, Olaudah, b. 1745

Cameron, Ann. The kidnapped prince: the life of Olaudah Equiano; by Olaudah Equiano; adapted by Ann Cameron; with an introduction by Henry Louis Gates, Jr. Knopf 1995 133p il hardcover o.p. paperback available $4.99 (4 and up)   **92**
1. Slavery 2. Blacks—Biography
ISBN 0-375-80346-7 (pa)   LC 93-29914
Adaptation of The interesting narrative of the life of Olaudah Equiano
This is an "adaptation of an influential slave narrative by an African prince who was kidnapped as a child and later freed from slavery; first published in 1789." N Y Times Book Rev

"The inspired simplicity of Cameron's adaptation quickly allows Equiano's gifted voice to establish a compelling relationship between himself and young readers. Well sculpted with detail." SLJ

Includes glossary and bibliographical references

Estefan, Gloria

Gonzales, Doreen. Gloria Estefan; singer and entertainer. Enslow Pubs. 1998 128p il maps (Hispanic biographies) lib bdg $26.60   **92**
1. Singers 2. Hispanic Americans
ISBN 0-89490-890-1   LC 97-42787

Estefan, Gloria—*Continued*
"Estefan is presented as a talented teenager who was able to achieve more than she could have dreamed despite tragic setbacks in her career. It shows what can be accomplished with a will to persevere. Estefan is portrayed as more than an entertainer. She is devoted to family, social and political concerns. . . . This book highlights the integrity of a positive role model for youth today." Book Rep
Includes discography and bibliographical references

Evers, Medgar Wiley, 1925-1963
Ribeiro, Myra. The assassination of Medgar Evers. Rosen Pub. Group 2002 64p il (Library of political assassinations) $26.50   **92**
1. African Americans—Civil rights
ISBN 0-8239-3544-2   LC 2001-2389
This is the story of the life and untimely death of a leader "on the forefront in the important fight for civil rights in the South." Book Rep
The author "does a good job of introducing the inspiring leader and the cause he fought for." Booklist
Includes glossary and bibliographical references

Farnsworth, Philo T., 1906-1971
McPherson, Stephanie Sammartino. TV's forgotten hero: the story of Philo Farnsworth. Carolrhoda Bks. 1996 96p il (Trailblazers) $27.93
                                                     92
1. Inventors 2. Television
ISBN 1-57505-017-X   LC 95-26383
A biography of the persistent experimenter whose interest in electricity led him to develop an electronic television system in the 1920s
This is a "well-researched and accurate biography. . . . There is enough drama and suspense to stimulate readers' interest. Good, clear diagrams explain concepts and theory." SLJ
Includes bibliographical references

Farrakhan, Louis, 1933-
De Angelis, Therese. Louis Farrakhan. Chelsea House 1998 112p il (Black Americans of achievement) $23.95   **92**
1. Black Muslims
ISBN 0-7910-4688-5   LC 98-6101
"De Angelis recounts the life of the . . . leader of the Nation of Islam. . . . The author reveals some pertinent facts about Farrakhan, clearly explains the evolution of his leadership, and clarifies the reasons for the controversy that surrounds him." SLJ
Includes bibliographical references

Fermi, Enrico, 1901-1954
Cooper, Dan. Enrico Fermi and the revolutions in modern physics. Oxford Univ. Press 1999 117p il (Oxford portraits in science) lib bdg $28 (7 and up)   **92**
1. Physicists
ISBN 0-19-511762-X   LC 98-34471

A biography of the Nobel Prize-winning physicist whose work led to the discovery of nuclear fission, the basis of nuclear power and the atom bomb
"This book will be useful for reports. . . . The extensive list for further reading includes biographies of Fermi, books on both scientific and political aspects of the atomic-bomb project, and information on tours of laboratories involved in nuclear research today." SLJ

Filipovic, Zlata
Filipovic, Zlata. Zlata's diary; a child's life in Sarajevo; with an introduction by Janine Di Giovanni; translated with notes by Christina Pribichevich-Zoric. Viking 1994 200p il hardcover o.p. paperback available $8.95   **92**
1. Sarajevo (Bosnia and Hercegovina)
ISBN 0-14-024205-8 (pa)
"In September 1991, at the beginning of a new school year and while war was already as close as Croatia, Filipovic, a ten-year-old girl in Sarajevo began keeping a diary about her school friends, her classes, and her after-school activities. The following spring that childhood world disappeared when the war moved to Sarajevo." Libr J
"Filipovic's diary personalizes the tragedy in war-torn Sarajevo." Booklist

Filo, David
Sherman, Josepha. Jerry Yang and David Filo. See entry under Yang, Jerry, 1968-

Fitzgerald, F. Scott (Francis Scott), 1896-1940
Lazo, Caroline Evensen. F. Scott Fitzgerald; voice of the Jazz Age; [by] Caroline Lazo. Lerner Pubs. 2003 128p il (Lerner long biographies) lib bdg $25.26   **92**
1. Authors, American
ISBN 0-8225-0074-4   LC 2001-7210
Traces the troubled life of writer F. Scott Fitzgerald, from his spoiled, yet insecure childhood through his difficult marriage and writing career to his early death
"This well-documented book offers a fascinating glimpse into the acclaimed author's early years, unremarkable academic record, extravagant lifestyle, and work." SLJ
Includes bibliographical references

Fleischman, Sid, 1920-
Fleischman, Sid. The abracadabra kid; a writer's life. Greenwillow Bks. 1996 198p il $16.99; pa $4.95 (5 and up)   **92**
1. Authors, American
ISBN 0-688-14859-X; 0-688-15855-2 (pa)
                                          LC 95-47382
This autobiography, "turns real life into a story complete with cliffhangers. And it's a classic *boy's* story, from card tricks and traveling magic shows to World War II naval experiences and screen-writing gigs for John Wayne movies. En route, we learn how Fleischman learned the craft of writing." Bull Cent Child Books
Includes bibliographical references

Fleischman, Sid, 1920—— *Continued*

Freedman, Jeri. Sid Fleischman; Jeri Freedman. 1st ed. Rosen Pub. Group 2004 112p (Library of author biographies) $26.50 (5 and up) **92**

1. Authors, American 2. Authorship

ISBN 0-8239-4019-5   LC 2003-5203

Discusses the life and work of this popular author, including his writing process and methods, inspirations, a critical discussion of his books, biographical timeline, and awards.

"Libraries looking to expand their biography section will be well served by [this] informative [title]." SLJ

Includes bibliographical references

Fleming, Alexander, 1881-1955

Birch, Beverley. Alexander Fleming; pioneer with antibiotics. Blackbirch Press 2002 64p il (Giants of science) lib bdg $21.96 **92**

1. Bacteriologists 2. Penicillin

ISBN 1-56711-656-6   LC 2002-3242

Recounts the life story of Alexander Fleming, his study of medicine and bacteriology, and his discovery of penicillin

"Short and richly illustrated with drawings and full-color and black-and-white photographs. The writing will appeal to middle-school science fans." SLJ

Includes glossary and bibliographical references

Hantula, Richard. Alexander Fleming. World Almanac 2003 48p il (Trailblazers of the modern world) lib bdg $26.60 **92**

1. Bacteriologists 2. Penicillin

ISBN 0-8368-5083-1   LC 2002-33124

Recounts the life story of Alexander Fleming, his study of medicine and bacteriology, and his discovery of penicillin

"Plenty of anecdotal information is provided to pique readers' interest. Also, Hantula does a good job of explaining the importance of his subject's discoveries. . . . The book's colorful layout will appeal to students." SLJ

Includes bibliographical references

Ford, Henry, 1863-1947

Bankston, John. Henry Ford and the assembly line. Mitchell Lane Pubs. 2004 48p il (Unlocking the secrets of science) lib bdg $17.95 **92**

1. Automobile industry

ISBN 1-58415-173-0   LC 2002-8324

Examines the life and accomplishments of Henry Ford who, among other things, is credited with inventing the assembly line, which changed not only the automotive industry but all industries

The "text provides smooth flowing readability without glorifying a genius whose warts, including overt anti-Semitism, made him a less than totally admirable human being. . . . [This] will enrich biography sections." SLJ

Includes glossary and bibliographical references

Tilton, Rafael. Henry Ford. Lucent Bks. 2002 112p il (Importance of) $21.96 (7 and up)

92

1. Automobile industry

ISBN 1-56006-846-9   LC 2001-6212

Discusses the early life of Henry Ford, including his moving to the big city and his success as an inventor, engineer, and pioneer of the automobile

Includes bibliographical references

Fortune, Amos, 1709 or 10-1801

Yates, Elizabeth. Amos Fortune, free man; illustrations by Nora S. Unwin. Dutton 1950 181p il $16.99; pa $5.99 **92**

1. African Americans—Biography 2. Slavery—United States

ISBN 0-525-25570-2; 0-14-034158-7 (pa)

Awarded the Newbery Medal, 1951

"Born free in Africa, Amos Fortune was sold into slavery in America in 1725. After more than 40 years of servitude Amos was able to purchase his freedom and, in time, that of several others. He died a tanner of enviable reputation, a landowner, and a respected citizen of his community. Based on fact, this is a . . . story of a life dedicated to the fight for freedom and service to others." Booklist

Fossey, Dian

Gogerly, Liz. Dian Fossey. Raintree Steck-Vaughn Pubs. 2003 48p il map (Scientists who made history) $29.93 **92**

1. Women scientists 2. Gorillas

ISBN 0-7398-5225-6   LC 2001-58913

Profiles the life of the scientist who studied mountain gorillas in central Africa and worked to ensure their survival

"Even readers who are not interested in the political aspects of Fossey's life will find themselves gripped by the story of her work." Booklist

Includes bibliographical references

Matthews, Tom L. Light shining through the mist: a photobiography of Dian Fossey. National Geographic Soc. 1998 64p il $17.95 (4 and up)

92

1. Gorillas 2. Women scientists

ISBN 0-7922-7300-1   LC 97-34084

Traces the adventurous life of the American woman who worked as a zoologist among the mountain gorillas of the Virunga area of central Africa

"Gorgeous color photographs will be the main draw to this biography of the controversial primatologist, but Matthews's text also does a fine job." Horn Book

Includes bibliographical references

Nicholson, Lois. Dian Fossey; primatologist; [by] Lois P. Nicholson. Chelsea House 2002 120p il map (Women in science) lib bdg $22.95 (7 and up) **92**

1. Gorillas 2. Women scientists

ISBN 0-7910-6907-9   LC 2002-15592

Profiles the life of the scientist who studied mountain gorillas in central Africa and worked to ensure their survival

"The writing is clear and engaging, enhanced by well-captioned, color photographs." SLJ

Includes bibliographical references

Frank, Anne, 1929-1945

Frank, Anne. The diary of a young girl; translated from the Dutch by B. M. Mooyaart-Doubleday (6 and up)   **92**
1. World War, 1939-1945—Jews 2. Netherlands—History—1940-1945, German occupation 3. Jews—Netherlands 4. Holocaust, 1933-1945
Various editions available
This is the diary of a "German-Jewish girl who hid from the Nazis with her parents, their friends, and some other fugitives in an Amsterdam warehouse from 1942 to 1944. Her diary, covering the years of hiding, was found by friends and published as Het achterhu*s (1947); it* was later published in English as The Diary of *a Young Girl (1952).* . . . Written with humor as well as insight, it shows a growing girl with all the preoccupations of adolescence and first love. The diary ends three days before the Franks and their group were discovered by the Nazis." Reader's Ency. 4th edition

Frank, Anne. The diary of a young girl: the definitive edition; edited by Otto H. Frank and Mirjam Pressler; translated by Susan Massotty. Doubleday 1995 340p $27.50; pa $12.95 (6 and up)   **92**
1. World War, 1939-1945—Jews 2. Netherlands—History—1940-1945, German occupation 3. Jews—Netherlands 4. Holocaust, 1933-1945
ISBN 0-385-47378-8; 0-385-42360-8 (pa)
LC 94-41379
"This new translation of Frank's famous diary includes material about her emerging sexuality and her relationship with her mother that was originally excised by Frank's father, the only family member to survive the Holocaust." Libr J

Gold, Alison Leslie. Memories of Anne Frank; reflections of a childhood friend. Scholastic 1997 135p il hardcover o.p. paperback available $5.99 (5 and up)   **92**
1. Pick-Goslar, Hannah 2. Jews—Netherlands 3. Holocaust, 1933-1945
ISBN 0-590-90723-9 (pa)   LC 96-41185
This "story of Anne Frank's neighbor and friend, Hannah Elizabeth Pick-Goslar, recounts the tragedy of World War II through a young girl's eyes. . . . The account traces the childhood friendship of the two girls from the time Anne disappeared to the removal of Hannah and her family to concentration camps. The narrative also tells of the brief meeting between Anne and Hannah at Bergen-Belsen shortly before Anne's death." SLJ
"Gold uses carefully chosen details and specific incidents to communicate the horrors of the Holocaust. . . . Readers drawn to Anne Frank's diary will be grateful for the fuller picture rendered here." Publ Wkly

Müller, Melissa. Anne Frank; the biography; translated by Rita and Robert Kimber. Holt & Co. 1998 330p $23; pa $14 (7 and up)   **92**
1. World War, 1939-1945—Jews 2. Netherlands—History—1940-1945, German occupation 3. Jews—Netherlands 4. Holocaust, 1933-1945
ISBN 0-8050-5996-2; 0-8050-5997-0 (pa)
LC 98-22923

This biography covers Anne Frank's life from her childhood to her last days in Bergen-Belsen concentration camp
"Müller includes a family tree; a family history; and considerable insight into the character, personality, and quality of life of Anne's parents, relatives, and friends. Interviews with many of these surviving people give a clearer idea of the situation and Anne's reactions to it." SLJ

Pressler, Mirjam. Anne Frank: a hidden life; foreword by Rabbi Hugo Gryn; translated by Anthea Bell; with a note from Eva Schloss. Dutton Children's Bks. 2000 176p il hardcover o.p. paperback available $7.99   **92**
1. Holocaust, 1933-1945
ISBN 0-14-131226-2 (pa)   LC 99-89604
Also available in paperback from Puffin Bks.
Original German edition, 1992
"Rather than highlighting Anne's idealism, the author examines the tensions in her diary, performing a critical reading of Anne's description of herself and others, and analyzing how Anne reworked her diary in hopes of postwar publication. Pressler's work could serve as a model for how to read a subjective narrative." Publ Wkly
Includes bibliographical references

Rol, Ruud van der. Anne Frank, beyond the diary; a photographic remembrance; by Ruud van der Rol and Rian Verhoeven; in association with the Anne Frank House; translated by Tony Langham and Plym Peters; with an introduction by Anna Quindlen. Viking 1993 113p il maps $17; pa $10.99 (5 and up)   **92**
1. Jews—Netherlands 2. Holocaust, 1933-1945
ISBN 0-670-84932-4; 0-14-036926-0 (pa)
LC 92-41528
Original Dutch edition, 1992
Photographs, illustrations, and maps accompany historical essays, diary excerpts, and interviews, providing an insight to Anne Frank and the massive upheaval which tore apart her world
"Readers will become absorbed in the richness of the detail and careful explanation which revisit and expand the familiar, well-loved story." Horn Book

Sawyer, Kem Knapp. Anne Frank. DK Pub 2004 127p il (DK biography) $14.99 (5 and up)   **92**
1. Jews—Netherlands 2. Holocaust, 1933-1945
ISBN 0-7566-0341-2   LC 2004-8450
For this biography "Sawyer drew extensively on several sources, including the diary in its various versions and accounts by Anne's father and their rescuer Miep Gies. Her clear history makes this a good place to start research." Booklist
Includes bibliographical references

Wukovits, John F. Anne Frank. Lucent Bks. 1999 96p il maps (Importance of) $28.70 (7 and up)   **92**
1. Jews—Netherlands 2. Holocaust, 1933-1945
ISBN 1-56006-353-X   LC 98-4327

Frank, Anne, 1929-1945—*Continued*
Discusses the life of Anne Frank, focusing on the years she and her family spent in hiding and the impact of her story upon the world
"Do we need yet another book about Anne Frank? The answer is yes, if junior-high and high-school readers want a context for the diary. . . . This combines biography, history, and commentary, in a highly readable format, with photos and boxed quotes from the diary and from other sources." Booklist
Includes bibliographical references

Franklin, Benjamin, 1706-1790
Adler, David A. B. Franklin, printer. Holiday House 2001 126p il lib bdg $19.95 (4 and up)
92
ISBN 0-8234-1675-5   LC 2001-24535
This "surveys Benjamin Franklin's life as a printer, a scientist, an inventor, a writer, and a statesman. . . . Throughout the book, details, anecdotes, and quotations bring the man's portrait into clearer focus, while period illustrations . . . help readers envision the background of his times." Booklist
Includes bibliographical references

Benjamin Franklin; Tanja Lee, book editor. Greenhaven Press 2002 252p il (People who made history) lib bdg $34.95; pa $23.70 (7 and up)
92
1. Statesmen—United States
ISBN 0-7377-0899-9 (lib bdg); 0-7377-0898-0 (pa)
LC 2001-33795
This profiles the American statesman and scientist and includes essays and primary source documents
Includes bibliographical references

Fleming, Candace. Ben Franklin's almanac; being a true account of the good gentleman's life. Atheneum Bks. for Young Readers 2003 120p il $19.95 (5 and up)
92
ISBN 0-689-83549-3   LC 2002-6136
"An Anne Schwartz book"
Brings together eighteenth century etchings, artifacts, and quotations to create the effect of a scrapbook of the life of Benjamin Franklin
"An authoritative work of depth, humor, and interest, presenting Franklin in all his complexity, ranging from the heroic to the vulgar, the saintly to the callous." SLJ

Franklin, Rosalind, 1920-1958
Senker, Cath. Rosalind Franklin. Raintree Steck-Vaughn Pubs. 2003 48p il (Scientists who made history) lib bdg $27.12 (5 and up)
92
1. Women scientists 2. DNA
ISBN 0-7398-5226-4   LC 2001-48961
Describes the life and career of Rosalind Franklin, a British molecular biologist who played a vital role in the discovery of the structure of DNA
This book has "ample full-color and black-and-white photos, reproductions, and maps to supplement the accessible {text}." SLJ
Includes glossary and bibliographical references

Frémont, John Charles, 1813-1890
Faber, Harold. John Charles Frémont; pathfinder to the West. Benchmark Bks. 2002 c2003 79p il maps (Great explorations) lib bdg $19.95
92
1. Explorers 2. West (U.S.)—Exploration
ISBN 0-7614-1481-9   LC 2002-18461
A biography of the nineteenth-century soldier, politician, and explorer whose many expeditions helped open up the American West to settlers
"Maps and full-color and black-and-white reproductions appear throughout, and shaded information boxes provide points of reference and explain topics mentioned in the text. . . . Useful." SLJ
Includes bibliographical references

Freud, Sigmund, 1856-1939
Muckenhoupt, Margaret. Sigmund Freud; explorer of the unconscious. Oxford Univ. Press 1997 157p il (Oxford portraits in science) lib bdg $28 (7 and up)
92
1. Psychiatrists
ISBN 0-19-509933-8   LC 95-42340
The author discusses "Freud's groundbreaking work in psychoanalysis and includes examples of some of his actual cases to illustrate his theories. His personal life, from his struggle with his Jewish identity to family relationships is explored and related to developments in his work. . . . The writing is clear and concise; terms of psychoanalysis are defined and explained." SLJ
Includes bibliographical references

Reef, Catherine. Sigmund Freud: pioneer of the mind. Clarion Bks. 2001 152p il $19 (7 and up)
92
1. Psychiatrists
ISBN 0-618-01762-3   LC 00-43008
"Reef weaves the developing theories of the first psychoanalyst into a chronological report of his eventful life, setting both in the political and social currents of his era." Horn Book
"Effective use of personal details that reveal Freud's intellect, emotions, and personality, plus photos of his family, friends, and professional life, make this book rich and visually appealing." Voice Youth Advocates
Includes bibliographical references

Fritz, Jean
Fritz, Jean. Homesick: my own story; illustrated with drawings by Margot Tomes and photographs. Putnam 1982 163p il $15.95; pa $5.99 (5 and up)
92
1. China
ISBN 0-399-20933-6; 0-698-11782-4 (pa)
LC 82-7646
A Newbery Medal honor book, 1983
Companion volume to China homecoming
This is a somewhat fictionalized memoir of the author's childhood in China. "Born in Hankow, where her father was director of the YMCA, Jean loved the city. . . . But she knew she 'belonged on the other side of the world'—in Pennsylvania with her grandmother and her other relations." Horn Book

Fritz, Jean—*Continued*

"The descriptions of places and the times are vivid in a book that brings to the reader, with sharp clarity and candor, the yearnings and fears and ambivalent loyalties of a young girl." Bull Cent Child Books

Fulton, Robert, 1765-1815

Kroll, Steven. Robert Fulton; from submarine to steamboat; illustrated by Bill Farnsworth. Holiday House 1999 unp il $16.95   **92**
1. Inventors 2. Steamboats
ISBN 0-8234-1433-7   LC 98-29944
Describes the life and work of the inventor who developed the steamboat and made it a commercial success
"Report writers will find most of what they need to know about Fulton's early career as a painter of miniatures and panoramas, his later business ventures into marine engineering, and his eventual perfection of the commercially viable steamship which plied the Hudson River." Bull Cent Child Books

Pierce, Morris A. Robert Fulton and the development of the steamboat. PowerPlus Books 2003 112p il map (Library of American lives and times) lib bdg $31.95   **92**
1. Inventors 2. Steamboats
ISBN 0-8239-5737-3   LC 2001-5541
Contents: Childhood, 1765-1780; Apprentice, 1780-1787; Artist, 1787-1793; Canal engineer, 1793-1797; Submarines, 1797-1802; Steamboats, 1802-1804; Torpedoes, 1804-1806; Pioneer, 1806-1807; Entrepreneur, 1807-1815
"The life and times of this complex and creative man are captured in this attractive presentation replete with maps and full-color reproductions of building sketches and period paintings." SLJ
Includes glossary and bibliographical references

Galilei, Galileo, 1564-1642

White, Michael. Galileo Galilei; inventor, astronomer and rebel. Blackbirch Press 1999 64p il (Giants of science) $24.95   **92**
1. Astronomers
ISBN 1-56711-325-7   LC 98-49141
Describes the life and work of the scientist who was persecuted by the Inquisition for his views of the universe
"White does an excellent job of explaining the background of the conflict between the scientists of the time and the Catholic Church." SLJ
Includes bibliographical references

Gama, Vasco da, 1469-1524

Calvert, Patricia. Vasco da Gama; so strong a spirit; Patricia Calvert. Benchmark Books 2005 96p il map (Great explorations) lib bdg $29.93 (5 and up)   **92**
1. Explorers
ISBN 0-7614-1611-0   LC 2003-22946
Recounts the voyages undertaken by fifteenth-century Portuguese explorer Vasco da Gama to strengthen his nation's power by establishing a sea trade route to India.
Includes bibliographical references

Goodman, Joan E. A long and uncertain journey: the 27,000 mile voyage of Vasco da Gama; by Joan Elizabeth Goodman; illustrated by Tom McNeely. Mikaya Press 2001 47p il map (Great explorers book) $19.95 (4 and up)   **92**
1. Explorers
ISBN 0-9650493-7-X   LC 00-63795
"Goodman reviews the accomplishments of 15th century Portuguese explorer Vasco da Gama and his role in the rise of the Portuguese Empire." Book Rep
"McNeely's full-page illustrations, which vibrate with life and action, lighten the format, and quotations from the diary of an anonymous sailor on the voyage add fascinating detail and vivid description. . . . A good resource for reports, but the book is also intelligently written and exciting." Booklist

Gandhi, Mahatma, 1869-1948

Adams, Simon. Mahatma Gandhi. Raintree Steck-Vaughn Pubs. 2003 112p il maps (20th-century history makers) lib bdg $32.82 (7 and up)   **92**
1. India—Politics and government 2. Passive resistance
ISBN 0-7398-5255-8   LC 2002-15706
A biography of Mahatma Gandhi, the Indian political and spiritual leader who led his country to freedom from British rule through his policy of nonviolent resistance
This biography is "insightful . . . detailed and well researched." SLJ
Includes glossary and bibliographical references

Hatt, Christine. Mahatma Ghandhi; by Christine Hatt. World Almanac Library 2004 64p il (Judge for yourself) lib bdg $30   **92**
1. India—Politics and government 2. Passive resistance
ISBN 0-8368-5561-2   LC 2003-60993
First published 2002 in the United Kingdom
This traces "Gandhi's story from his humble beginnings, through his awakening as a reformer in South Africa, to his historic fasts and the achievement of India's independence from Britain. Then [it looks] . . . at some of the issues surrounding Gandhi's career and [examines] evidence from opposing perspectives as to whether his methods were successful and his goals were achieved." Publisher's note
"The suggestion that students think beyond the facts makes [this book] stand out from other biographies." SLJ

Severance, John B. Gandhi, great soul. Clarion Bks. 1997 143p il map $18 (5 and up)   **92**
1. India—Politics and government 2. Passive resistance
ISBN 0-395-77179-X   LC 95-20887
Severance "begins with an introduction to Gandhi's message and gives a brief overview of the mahatma's personal evolution as well as India's external and internal struggles. He then chronicles Gandhi's life. . . . Severance details Gandhi's philosophy of *satyagraha,* or peaceful resistance." Booklist
"It is not only Gandhi who comes alive in this consid-

Gandhi, Mahatma, 1869-1948—*Continued*
ered, well-documented biography but the multifarious
personalities and politics of his world." Horn Book
Guide

Includes bibliographical references

Gantos, Jack
Gantos, Jack. Hole in my life. Farrar, Straus &
Giroux 2002 199p il $16; pa $8 (7 and up)
92

1. Authors, American
ISBN 0-374-39988-3; 0-374-43089-6 (pa)
LC 2001-40957

The author relates how, as a young adult, he became
a drug user and smuggler, was arrested, did time in prison, and eventually got out and went to college, all the
while hoping to become a writer

"Gantos' spare narrative style and straightforward revelation of the truth have, together, a cumulative power
that will capture not only a reader's attention but also
empathy and imagination." Booklist

Garvey, Marcus, 1887-1940
Lawler, Mary. Marcus Garvey. Chelsea House
1988 110p il (Black Americans of achievement)
lib bdg $23.95; pa $9.95
92
1. Universal Negro Improvement Association
2. African Americans—Biography
ISBN 1-55546-587-0 (lib bdg); 0-7910-0203-9 (pa)
LC 87-14593

The author "traces Garvey's life from his birth in Jamaica to his founding of the Universal Negro Improvement Association (UNIA) and his lifelong efforts to secure an independent African homeland for all the world's
blacks." Booklist

Includes bibliographical references

Gauguin, Paul, 1848-1903
Greenfeld, Howard. Paul Gauguin. Abrams 1993
92p il (First impressions) $19.95 (7 and up)
92

1. Artists, French
ISBN 0-8109-3376-4
LC 93-9454

Examines the life and work of the nineteenth-century
post-Impressionist painter known for his use of bright
colors and his depiction of South Seas scenes

This is "written in a conversational tone that will hold
readers' interest. . . . The format is an open and inviting
one, and the numerous full-color reproductions are of excellent quality. Engaging and informative." SLJ

Genghis Khan, 1162-1227
Humphrey, Judy. Genghis Khan. Chelsea House
1987 111p il (World leaders past & present) lib
bdg $21.95
92
1. Kings and rulers
ISBN 0-87754-527-8
LC 87-5194

Traces the life of the chief of a small Mongol tribe
who established a vast empire from Peking to the Black
Sea in the twelfth century

"The author succeeds admirably in presenting 800-
year-old history in a powerful present tense. An era that
will be unfamiliar to many, Humphrey's view of the culture and time is well balanced." Booklist

Includes bibliographical references

Lange, Brenda. Genghis Khan. Chelsea House
2003 100p il map (Ancient world leaders) lib bdg
$23.95; pa $9.95 (7 and up)
92
1. Mongols
ISBN 0-7910-7222-3 (lib bdg); 0-7910-7496-X (pa)
LC 2002-152057

Traces the life of the chief of a small Mongol tribe
who established a vast empire from Peking to the Black
Sea in the twelfth century.

Includes bibliographical references

George III, King of Great Britain, 1738-1820
Ingram, Scott. King George III; Scott Ingram.
Blackbirch Press 2004 104p il map (Triangle
histories, Revolutionary War) $27.45
92
1. United States—History—1775-1783, Revolution
ISBN 1-567-11779-1
LC 2003-2622

"The book reads well as biography or history, with
lots of black-and-white and full-color pictures, reproductions, and sidebars to break up the text. A solid, well-
organized choice." SLJ

Includes bibliographical references

George, Jean Craighead, 1919-
George, Jean Craighead. A tarantula in my
purse; and 172 other wild pets; written and
illustrated by Jean Craighead George.
HarperCollins Pubs. 1996 134p il $15.99; pa $4.99
(4-6)
92
1. Women authors 2. Authors, American
3. Naturalists 4. Pets
ISBN 0-06-023626-4; 0-06-446201-3 (pa)
LC 95-54151

"George tells of the many wild pets that lived with
her family, particularly while her children were growing
up. Each chapter describes a different animal or incident." Booklist

"Told in a casual and thoroughly engaging manner,
the stories will enchant all animal lovers and even those
who aren't." SLJ

Geronimo, Apache Chief, 1829-1909
Schwarz, Melissa. Geronimo, Apache warrior.
Chelsea House 1992 127p il maps (North
American Indians of achievement) pa $9.95
hardcover o.p.
92
1. Apache Indians
ISBN 0-7910-1691-9
LC 91-12691

Examines the life and career of the Apache warrior
chief

"This is an eye-opening account." SLJ

Includes bibliographical references

Getty, J. Paul, 1892-1976

Glassman, Bruce. John Paul Getty; billionaire oilman; by Bruce S. Glassman. Blackbirch Press 2001 112p il (Giants of American industry) lib bdg $28.70 (7 and up)   **92**

1. Businessmen 2. Petroleum industry

ISBN 1-56711-513-6   LC 00-53001

First published 1989 by Silver Burdett

A biography of the rich and powerful businessman in the petroleum industry

This book is "filled with pertinent historical information. The pictures and captions give the reader a sense of the time period. . . . A good addition to collections that need biographical material for reports and papers." Book Rep

Includes bibliographical references

Gibson, Josh, 1911-1947

Twemlow, Nick. Josh Gibson. Rosen Pub. Group 2002 112p il (Baseball Hall of Famers of the Negro leagues) lib bdg $29.25   **92**

1. Baseball—Biography 2. African American athletes

ISBN 0-8239-3475-6   LC 2001-4143

Presents a biography of the powerful home run hitter and chronicles the history of African American participation in organized baseball, the formation of the Negro leagues, and racial politics in America

Includes glossary and bibliographical references

Giff, Patricia Reilly

Giff, Patricia Reilly. Don't tell the girls; a family memoir; by Patricia Reilly Giff. 1st ed. Holiday House 2005 131p il $16.95 (4 and up)   **92**

1. Women authors 2. Authors, American

ISBN 0-8234-1813-8   LC 2004-47452

"Giff reflects on her childhood and her family, going back through several generations. Spotlighting her two grandmothers, she lovingly relates remembered conversations and incidents involving the one she knew well before turning to the other grandmother, whom she never met. . . . This little book has much to offer thoughtful children. . . . With . . . sharply reproduced family photos and documents, this handsome book's small format reflects its intimate, conversational style." Booklist

Goeppert-Mayer, Maria, 1906-1972

Ferry, Joseph. Maria Goeppert Mayer, physicist; [by] Joseph P. Ferry. Chelsea House 2003 110p il (Women in science) lib bdg $22.95 (7 and up)   **92**

1. Physicists 2. Women scientists

ISBN 0-7910-7247-9   LC 2002-15580

A biography of Maria Goeppert-Mayer, a physicist who contributed to the development of the atomic bomb and who, in 1963, was cowinner of the Nobel Prize in Physics for her work on the nuclear shell model theory

This is "well written and well organized." SLJ

Includes bibliographical references

Gogh, Vincent van, 1853-1890

Bassil, Andrea. Vincent van Gogh; by Andrea Bassil. {New ed}. World Almanac Library 2004 48p il (Lives of the artists) lib bdg $30; pa $11 (4 and up)   **92**

1. Artists, Dutch

ISBN 0-8368-5602-3 (lib bdg); 0-8368-5607-4 (pa)

     LC 2003-67236

Original Italian edition 2003

This is a biography of the Dutch painter.

This is "concise and straightforward, and there's no sensationalizing: Van Gogh's famous ear injury is only mentioned in a brief, matter-of-fact note. The interesting mix of photos and art is the biggest attraction." Booklist

Greenberg, Jan. Vincent Van Gogh; portrait of an artist; {by} Jan Greenberg and Sandra Jordan. Delacorte Press 2001 132p il $14.95; lib bdg $18.99   **92**

1. Artists, Dutch

ISBN 0-385-32803-6; 0-385-90005-8 (lib bdg)

     LC 00-31850

This "book begins with van Gogh's boyhood and traces the various career paths (art dealer, missionary) he pursued before dedicating himself to painting. The authors draw on the artist's voluminous correspondence with his brother Theo to elicit his thoughts and feelings. . . . This outstanding, well-researched biography is fascinating reading." SLJ

Includes glossary and bibliographical references

Goh, Chan Hon, 1969-

Goh, Chan Hon. Beyond the dance; a ballerina's life; [by] Chan Hon Goh with Cary Fagan. Tundra Bks. 2002 151p lib bdg $15.95   **92**

1. Ballet

ISBN 0-88776-596-3   LC 2002-101724

This "autobiography introduces a prima ballerina with the National Ballet of Canada. Goh was born in Beijing but raised in Vancouver by her dancer parents. She discusses the events in her homeland that led her family to emigrate, their adjustment to life in Vancouver, and her parents' struggles to build the Goh Ballet Company. . . . The book is lavishly illustrated with black-and-white photographs, and balletomanes will enjoy poring over every detail." SLJ

Goodall, Jane, 1934-

Kozleski, Lisa. Jane Goodall. Chelsea House 2003 116p il (Women in science) lib bdg $22.95 (7 and up)   **92**

1. Chimpanzees 2. Women scientists

ISBN 0-7910-6905-2   LC 2002-15591

A biography of the zoologist, discussing her personal life as well as her work with chimpanzees at the Gombe Stream Reserve in Tanzania

"The writing is clear and engaging, enhanced by well-captioned, color photographs." SLJ

Includes bibliographical references

Gordeeva, Ekaterina

Shea, Pegi Deitz. Ekaterina Gordeeva. Chelsea House 1999 64p il $16.95   **92**
1. Ice skating—Biography 2. Women athletes
ISBN 0-7910-5027-0   LC 98-25571
A biography of skating star Ekaterina Gordeeva who, with her husband Sergei Grinkov, won two Olympic gold medals, and who, since his untimely death in 1995, skates alone
Gordeeva's "story offers readers hope that although tragic things happen, life goes on. Skating terminology used in the text is explained in the glossary. The black-and-white photographs depict both happy and sad times in the skaters' lives." SLJ
Includes bibliographical references

Graham, Martha

Freedman, Russell. Martha Graham, a dancer's life. Clarion Bks. 1998 175p il $18 (7 and up)
92
1. Dancers 2. Choreographers 3. Modern dance
ISBN 0-395-74655-8   LC 97-15832
A photo-biography of the American dancer, teacher, and choreographer who was born in Pittsburgh in 1895 and who became a leading figure in the world of modern dance
"A showstopping biography that captures its dynamic subject's personality, vision, and artistry." SLJ
Includes bibliographical references

Gretzky, Wayne

Santella, Andrew. Wayne Gretzky; the great one. Watts 1998 112p il (Book report biography) $22; pa $6.95   **92**
1. Hockey—Biography
ISBN 0-531-11567-4; 0-531-15954-X (pa)
LC 98-17976
Describes the personal life and hockey career of one of the greatest players in the NHL
Includes bibliographical references

Grimké, Angelina Emily, 1805-1879

Todras, Ellen H. Angelina Grimké; voice of abolition. Linnet Bks. 1999 178p il $25 (7 and up)
92
1. Abolitionists 2. Feminism
ISBN 0-208-02485-9   LC 98-42931
This "illustrated biography of the Quaker abolitionist includes the famous 1838 address, delivered in Philadelphia, that made her the first Southern woman to speak publicly against slavery. A helpful chronology places her life against other events in American history." N Y Times Book Rev
Includes bibliographical references

Gunther, John, 1929-1947

Gunther, John. Death be not proud; a memoir. Harper & Row 1949 261p il hardcover o.p. paperback available $11.95 (7 and up)   **92**
ISBN 0-06-092989-8 (pa)
Also available in hardcover from Buccaneer Bks.

A memoir of John Gunther's seventeen-year-old son, who died after a series of operations for a brain tumor. Not only a tribute to a remarkable boy but an account of a brave fight against disease

Guthrie, Woody, 1912-1967

Neimark, Anne E. There ain't nobody that can sing like me: the life of Woody Guthrie. Atheneum Bks. for Young Readers 2002 122p il $17.95 (5 and up)   **92**
1. Singers
ISBN 0-689-83369-5   LC 00-56933
The author "chronicles the tragedy-and triumph-laced life of folksinger and activist Woody Guthrie." Publ Wkly
The author's "ideas are cohesive and well developed, yet she writes with an energy reflective of young Woody hurrying to get words on paper as his thoughts seemingly spilled off his pencil. She doesn't ignore Woody's imperfections. . . . And his political leanings and influence are given their due. But with quotes from *Bound for Glory* and plentiful reproduction of his song lyrics, it is Woody's own voice that takes center stage here." Horn Book
Includes bibliographical references

Partridge, Elizabeth. This land was made for you and me: the life and songs of Woody Guthrie. Viking 2002 217p il $21.99 (7 and up)
92
1. Singers
ISBN 0-670-03535-1   LC 2001-46770
A biography of Woody Guthrie, a singer who wrote over 3,000 folk songs and ballads as he traveled around the United States, including "This Land is Your Land" and "So Long It's Been Good to Know Yuh"
This "presents an unflinchingly accurate portrait of a rambling and unpredictable man. . . . In addition to a panoply of archival photographs, which add realism to this engrossing story of a life, the book includes carefully selected quotes from songs, acquaintances, and documents to punctuate the story with authenticating detail without detracting from the momentum of the narrative." Bull Cent Child Books
Includes bibliographical references

Hamilton, Alexander, 1757-1804

Rosenburg, John M. Alexander Hamilton; America's bold lion; {by} John Rosenburg. 21st Cent. Bks. (Brookfield) 2000 192p il lib bdg $24.90   **92**
1. United States—Politics and government—1783-1809
ISBN 0-7613-1617-5   LC 99-57292
A biography of Alexander Hamilton, the first Secretary of the Treasury of the United States, discussing his accomplishments as well as the controversy and scandal that marked his career
"Frequent quotes and segments of letters and speeches are included." SLJ
Includes bibliographical references

Handel, George Frideric, 1685-1759

Anderson, M. T. Handel, who knew what he liked; illustrated by Kevin Hawkes. Candlewick Press 2001 unp $16.99; pa $6.99 (4-6)   **92**
1. Composers
ISBN 0-7636-1046-1; 0-7636-2562-0 (pa)
LC 00-57210
In this biography Handel, who would later compose some of the world's most beautiful music, is shown as a stubborn little boy with a mind of his own
The author "infuses the composer's story with warmth and color, humor and humanity. . . . Relating pithy stories with plain words and short sentences, Anderson never forgets his audience in his enthusiasm for his subject." Booklist

Harrison, John, 1693-1776

Dash, Joan. The longitude prize; pictures by Dučsan Petrički'c. Foster Bks. 1999 200p il $16 (5 and up)   **92**
1. Longitude
ISBN 0-374-34636-4   LC 97-44257
The story of John Harrison, inventor of watches and clocks, who spent forty years working on a time-machine which could be used to accurately determine longitude at sea
"Students looking for new subjects for reports will discover . . . an excellent resource on a topic seldom addressed in a book for youth. Charming ink drawings by Dusan Petricic illustrate. A glossary, an afterword, a time line, and a bibliography conclude." Booklist

Haskell, Katharine Wright, 1874-1929

Maurer, Richard. The Wright sister; Katharine Wright and her famous brothers. Millbrook Press 2003 127p il $18.95; lib bdg $25.90 (5 and up)   **92**
1. Wright, Wilbur, 1867-1912 2. Wright, Orville, 1871-1948 3. Air pilots
ISBN 0-7613-1546-2; 0-7613-2564-6 (lib bdg)
LC 2002-151080
"Maurer chronicles the events surrounding Wilbur and Orville, while all along filling in the details of their younger sister's life and the relationship among the three." SLJ
"Quotations from diaries and letters bring the close-knit Wright family to life. . . . The layout is spacious, and the many well chosen, black-and-white photos help visualize the Wrights and their times." Booklist

Hautzig, Esther Rudomin, 1930-

Hautzig, Esther Rudomin. The endless steppe: growing up in Siberia; by Esther Hautzig. Crowell 1968 243p pa $5.99 hardcover o.p.   **92**
1. World War, 1939-1945—Personal narratives
2. Siberia (Russia)
ISBN 0-06-447027-X
"When the Russians invaded Poland in 1941, Esther, her parents and grandmother were exiled to Siberia. In her very personal narrative about this little-known aspect of World War II, the author recalls four years of hardship, challenge and, miraculously, survival of the fami-

ly." Cincinnati Public Libr
"This is a magnificent book. Amazingly free of bitterness and hate, it radiates the optimism, the resilience of the human spirit as typified in its vital young author." Book World

Hawking, S. W. (Stephen W.)

Bankston, John. Stephen Hawking; breaking the boundaries of time and space; John Bankston. Enslow Publishers 2005 128p il (Great minds of science) $26.60   **92**
1. Physicists 2. Physically handicapped
ISBN 0-7660-2281-1   LC 2004-9193
Contents: A lucky man; Controversy; A lazy student?; Cosmic eggs and big bangs; The beginning of time; The big and the small of it; Black holes and white dwarfs; A new beginning; The brief history
This biography of the English physicist, who suffers from amyotrophic lateral sclerosis, includes explanations of his theories and experiments.
"This excellent book features large font size and double spacing that makes it easy for any one to read. . . . The activities part of the book is outstanding." Sci Books Films
Includes glossary and bibliographical references

Hayden, Lewis, 1815-1889

Strangis, Joel. Lewis Hayden and the war against slavery. Linnet Bks. 1999 167p il $25   **92**
1. African Americans—Biography 2. Abolitionists
ISBN 0-208-02430-1   LC 98-29406
A biography of a former slave who was active in the anti-slavery movement, as a fugitive in Canada, a "stationmaster" on the Underground Railroad, a supporter of John Brown, and a recruiter for "black regiments"
"Strangis acknowledges the difficulties involved in conveying this man's life, as there were few written records about him. The book is well researched and has a detailed bibliographical essay." SLJ
Includes bibliographical references

Hemingway, Ernest, 1899-1961

Yannuzzi, Della A. Ernest Hemingway; writer and adventurer. Enslow Pubs. 1998 112p il (People to know) lib bdg $26.60   **92**
1. Authors, American
ISBN 0-89490-979-7   LC 97-33351
Describes the life and career of the Pulitzer and Nobel prize winner whose accounts of his adventures and new style of writing brought him worldwide recognition
"After reading this biography, even those unfamiliar with Hemingway will discover how his vivid and adventurous life impacted his writing." SLJ
Includes bibliographical references

Hickam, Homer H., 1943-

Hickam, Homer H. The Coalwood way; by Homer H. Hickam, Jr. Delacorte Press 2000 318p hardcover o.p. paperback available $6.99 (7 and up)   **92**
ISBN 0-440-23716-5 (pa)   LC 00-35884

Hickam, Homer H., 1943-—*Continued*
This sequel to Rocket boys "continues the author's life story with his senior year in high school, 1959, in the declining West Virginia mining town of Coalwood. The rocket club, featured in the last book, is pushed to the periphery, and the focus shifts to Hickam's teenage problems, which include his parents, girls, and a sadness whose cause he cannot divine." Booklist

Hickam, Homer H. Rocket boys; a memoir; [by] Homer H. Hickam, Jr. Delacorte Press 1998 368p $25.95; pa $14 (7 and up)   **92**
ISBN 0-385-33320-X; 0-385-33321-8 (pa)
                                             LC 98-19304
"Raised in Appalachian coal country, Homer H. Hickam, Jr., might well have followed his father and grandfather into the mine. But when he was 14, his life was changed by a space launch on the other side of the world. Hickam's story of how a teenage boy's handmade rockets lifted the hopes of a hardscrabble town is told in his [memoir]." Smithsonian
"Even if Hickam stretched the strict truth to metamorphose his memories into Stand By Me-like material for Hollywood . . . the embellishing only converts what is a good story into an absorbing, rapidly readable one that is unsentimental but artful about adolescence, high school, and family life." Booklist

Hillary, Sir Edmund
Brennan, Kristine. Sir Edmund Hillary, modern day explorer. Chelsea House 2001 63p il (Explorers of new worlds) lib bdg $21.85; pa $8.95 (4 and up)   **92**
1. Mount Everest (China and Nepal)
2. Mountaineering
ISBN 0-7910-5953-7 (lib bdg); 0-7910-6163-9 (pa)
                                             LC 00-43077
A biography of the New Zealander who, with his Sherpa climbing partner Tenzing Norgay, first reached the Summit of Mount Everest in 1953
"Accessible and well organized. . . . Fresh, appealing, and well written." SLJ
Includes glossary and bibliographical references

Hinton, S. E.
Wilson, Antoine. S.E. Hinton. Rosen Central 2003 112p il (Library of author biographies) lib bdg $26.50   **92**
1. Authors, American
ISBN 0-8239-3778-X   LC 2002-7905
Discusses the life, novels, and writing habits of S.E. Hinton, author of such popular books as "The Outsiders" and "That Was Then, This Is Now."
"This is an informative and interesting resource." SLJ
Includes bibliographical references

Hitler, Adolf, 1889-1945
Giblin, James. The life and death of Adolf Hitler; by James Cross Giblin. Clarion Bks. 2002 246p il maps $20 (7 and up)   **92**
1. Dictators 2. Germany—History—1918-1933
3. Germany—History—1933-1945 4. National socialism
ISBN 0-395-90371-8   LC 2001-47091

The author "presents the rise and fall of 'the most dangerous—and ultimately the most destructive—twentieth-century dictator.'" Publ Wkly
"The most complete and successful biography of the Führer available for this audience. . . . The historical perspective is superb. . . . Good-quality photos, political cartoons, and reproductions augment the text." SLJ
Includes glossary and bibliographical references

Nardo, Don. Adolf Hitler. Lucent Bks. 2003 112p il maps (Heroes and villains) lib bdg $21.96
                                             92
1. Dictators 2. Germany—History—1933-1945
3. Germany—History—1918-1933 4. National socialism
ISBN 1-56006-951-1   LC 2002-3812
A biography of the struggling Austrian artist who rose from obscurity to power as the leader of the Nazi party and, later, the German nation and whose ambitions led the world to war
"Quotes from Hitler's speeches and contemporary witnesses help readers learn about his lies to the German people, his hatred of Jews . . . and his absolute lack of human compassion." Booklist
Includes bibliographical references

Holiday, Billie, 1915-1959
Kliment, Bud. Billie Holiday. Chelsea House 1990 111p il (Black Americans of achievement) lib bdg $23.95   **92**
1. African American singers 2. African American women
ISBN 1-55546-592-7   LC 89-30450
"Neither sentimental nor exploitative, {the author} describes Holiday's life of bitter struggle—against poverty, prostitution, prejudice, heroin, prison—and shows how her art grew from and transcended her pain. He places her blues-inspired jazz singing in the black music tradition." Booklist
Includes discography and bibliographical references

Hoover, Herbert, 1874-1964
Holford, David M. Herbert Hoover. Enslow Pubs. 1999 128p il (United States presidents) lib bdg $26.60   **92**
1. Presidents—United States
ISBN 0-7660-1035-X   LC 98-11688
A biography of Herbert Hoover, thirty-first president of the United States, describing his career as mining engineer, businessman, and president during the Great Depression
"This biography is insightful. . . . The writing is lucid, and the information is not overwhelming." SLJ
Includes bibliographical references

Hoover, J. Edgar (John Edgar), 1895-1972
Streissguth, Thomas. J. Edgar Hoover: powerful FBI Director. Enslow Pubs. 2002 128p il map (Historical American biographies) lib bdg $26.60
                                             92
1. United States. Federal Bureau of Investigation
ISBN 0-7660-1623-4   LC 2001-3143

Hoover, J. Edgar (John Edgar), 1895-1972—
Continued
Discusses the life and controversy of J. Edgar Hoover, former chief of the Federal Bureau of Investigation
This "is informative, important, and interesting." SLJ
Includes glossary and bibliographical references

Horne, Lena
Palmer, Leslie. Lena Horne. Chelsea House 1989 127p il (Black Americans of achievement) lib bdg $22.95 **92**
1. African American singers 2. African American women
ISBN 1-55546-594-3   LC 88-30248
A look at the black singer's successful musical career and her active participation in the civil rights movement

Houston, Samuel, 1793-1863
Fritz, Jean. Make way for Sam Houston; illustrations by Elise Primavera. Putnam 1986 109p il map $15.99; pa $5.99 (4 and up)
92
ISBN 0-399-21303-1; 0-698-11646-1 (pa)
LC 85-25601
This is a biography of the "lawyer, governor of Tennessee, general in the wars against Santa Anna, president of the Republic of Texas, and finally U.S. senator and governor of the state of Texas." Horn Book
"Artfully weaving the threads of fact, Fritz creates a biography that is both interesting and informative. Developing Houston as a human character that readers can identify with as well as admire, and drawing him against the scene of America's own political turmoil, Fritz gives us a book to be read and to be felt." Voice Youth Advocates
Includes bibliographical references

Hubble, Edwin Powell, 1889-1953
Datnow, Claire L. Edwin Hubble; discoverer of galaxies. Enslow Pubs. 1997 128p il (Great minds of science) lib bdg $26.60; pa $10.95 **92**
1. Astronomers
ISBN 0-89490-934-7; 0-7660-1869-5 (pa)
LC 96-37095
Traces the life and work of the man whose study of galaxies led to a new understanding of the universe
"There is a good balance between the presentation of the scientist's personal life . . . and his achievements. Good-quality black-and-white photos appear throughout. A highly readable biography." SLJ
Includes bibliographical references

Hudson, Henry, d. 1611
Edwards, Judith. Henry Hudson and his voyages of exploration in world history. Enslow Pubs. 2002 128p il maps (In world history) lib bdg $26.60 (7 and up) **92**
1. Explorers 2. America—Exploration
ISBN 0-7660-1885-7   LC 2001-4119
Examines the life and career of Henry Hudson, tracing his voyages in the Arctic and North America and his dis-

covery of the Hudson River and other bodies of water during his unsuccessful search for a Northwest Passage to Asia
Includes bibliographical references

Santella, Andrew. Henry Hudson. Watts 2001 64p il lib bdg $24.50; pa $8.95 **92**
1. Explorers
ISBN 0-531-11968-8 (lib bdg); 0-531-16577-9 (pa)
LC 00-43781
"Watts library"
This is a biography of the English explorer of North America
This book not only has "appealing color pictures throughout but also provide{s} interesting reading with plenty of useful related information." Book Rep
Includes bibliographical references

Hughes, Langston, 1902-1967
Hill, Christine M. Langston Hughes; poet of the Harlem Renaissance. Enslow Pubs. 1997 128p il (African-American biographies) lib bdg $26.60
92
1. Poets, American 2. African American authors
ISBN 0-89490-815-4   LC 97-10991
Surveys the private life and literary accomplishments of the writer whose varied works reflect the traditions, feelings, and experiences of African Americans
"The text flows smoothly and is written in an engaging style that will hold students' interest." SLJ
Includes bibliographical references

Hunter, Clementine, 1886?-1988
Hunter, Clementine. Talking with Tebé: Clementine Hunter, memory artist; edited by Mary Lyons. Houghton Mifflin 1998 48p il $17 (4-6)
92
1. African American artists 2. Women artists
ISBN 0-395-72031-1   LC 97-42253
"Clementine Hunter was an African-American primitive painter who lived all of her 101 years in Louisiana as a manual laborer. . . . The story of her life and art is fascinating, and Lyons has let Tebé, as she was called, tell it in her own words. . . . Hunter's bright, colorful, childlike paintings and a handful of black-and-white photographs decorate the book and illuminate her words." SLJ
Includes bibliographical references

Hurston, Zora Neale, 1891-1960
Lyons, Mary E. Sorrow's kitchen: the life and folklore of Zora Neale Hurston. Scribner 1990 144p il hardcover o.p. paperback available $7.99
92
1. African American authors 2. African American women
ISBN 0-02-044445-1 (pa)   LC 90-8058
This biography details "Hurston's migration from Florida to Baltimore, Washington, D.C., and finally Harlem as well as her travels through the West Indies to collect folklore. The text contains eleven excerpts from Hurston's books. . . . Lyons has created a prime example of

Hurston, Zora Neale, 1891-1960—*Continued*
biography—fascinating, enlightening, stimulating, and satisfying." Horn Book
Includes bibliographical references

Hussein, Ṣaddām
Anderson, Dale. Saddam Hussein; by Dale Anderson. Lerner Publications 2004 112p il map (A & E biography) lib bdg $27.93; pa $7.95
92
1. Iraq—Politics and government
ISBN 0-8225-5005-9 (lib bdg); 0-8225-9901-5 (pa)
LC 2002-13956
Contents: The ace of spades; The fight for independence; Growing power; The Ba'ath at the helm; President Hussein; War again; On top of the rubble
A biography of the powerful president of Iraq, Saddam Hussein, whose rule began in 1979 with a coup and the assassination of sixty-six men who were allegedly conspiring against him.
The "author maintains a high level of objectivity given the sensitive and controversial subject matter. Personal anecdotes and psychological insights are woven into the story." SLJ
Includes bibliographical references

Huynh, Quang Nhuong
Huynh, Quang Nhuong. The land I lost: adventures of a boy in Vietnam; with pictures by Vo-Dinh Mai. Harper & Row 1982 115p il pa $4.99 hardcover o.p. (5 and up) **92**
1. Vietnam—Social life and customs
ISBN 0-06-440183-9 LC 80-8437
"Each chapter in this book of reminiscence about the author's boyhood in a hamlet in the Vietnamese highlands, is a separate episode, although the same characters appear in many of the episodes. . . . The writing has an ingenuous quality that adds to the appeal of the strong sense of familial and communal ties that pervades the story." Bull Cent Child Books

Jackson, Andrew, 1767-1845
Marrin, Albert. Old Hickory; Andrew Jackson and the American people; by Albert Marrin. 1st ed. Dutton Children's Books 2004 262p il $30 (7 and up) **92**
1. Presidents—United States
ISBN 0-525-47293-2 LC 2003-28299
"More than a biography, this fine study of our seventh president is also a history and analysis of the times in which he lived. . . . Marrin discusses the changes to society brought about by the Industrial Revolution, the railroads, and the rise of the market economy. Written in an engaging style and with a wealth of detail, the book is enhanced by numerous black-and-white illustrations." SLJ
Includes bibliographical references

Jackson, Mahalia, 1911-1972
Orgill, Roxane. Mahalia; a life in gospel music. Candlewick Press 2002 132p il $19.99 (5 and up)
92
1. Gospel music 2. African American singers 3. African American women
ISBN 0-7636-1011-9 LC 00-48669
This is a "portrait of a passionately religious woman devoted to bringing the gospel to audiences around the world through her music. . . . Rhythmic sentences, sometimes fragments, capture the beat of gospel music and incorporate vernacular African-American speech patterns from the 1920s to the early 1970s. Events in the singer's personal life and musical career are skillfully blended with material about the social climate of the times." SLJ

Jackson, Stonewall, 1824-1863
Fritz, Jean. Stonewall; with drawings by Stephen Gammell. Putnam 1979 152p il map $16.99; pa $5.99 (4 and up) **92**
1. Generals 2. United States—History—1861-1865, Civil War
ISBN 0-399-20698-1; 0-698-11552-X (pa)
LC 79-12506
A biography of the brilliant southern general who gained the nickname Stonewall by his stand at Bull Run during the Civil War
"Fritz's trenchant, compassionate life of General Thomas Jonathan Jackson grips the reader and makes one understand why Stonewall is an honored legend in American history. . . . The tragic irony of his death at age 39 is movingly described." Publ Wkly
Includes bibliographical references

Pflueger, Lynda. Stonewall Jackson; Confederate general. Enslow Pubs. 1997 128p il (Historical American biographies) lib bdg $26.60 **92**
1. Confederate States of America. Army—Biography—Juvenile literature 2. Generals 3. United States—History—1861-1865, Civil War
ISBN 0-89490-781-6 LC 96-8827
A biography of the Confederate general who gained the nickname Stonewall for his stand at the first battle of Bull Run during the Civil War
"The content is thorough and includes valuable historical background." Horn Book Guide
Includes glossary and bibliographical references

Robertson, James I., Jr. Standing like a stone wall: the life of General Thomas J. Jackson; by James I. Robertson, Jr. Atheneum Bks. for Young Readers 2001 185p il maps $22 (7 and up)
92
1. Generals 2. United States—History—1861-1865, Civil War
ISBN 0-689-82419-X LC 00-36253
This is a biography of the Confederate general who fell at the battle of Chancellorsville
"Robertson finds a good balance between Jackson's life before [the Civil War] and his experiences in the campaigns that made him famous. . . . The many illustrations include reproductions of period photographs and prints as well as several maps and photos of artifacts.

Jackson, Stonewall, 1824-1863—*Continued*
Robertson's extensive source notes and a bibliography
are appended. A good choice for biography collections."
Booklist

James, Jesse, 1847-1882
Bruns, Roger. Jesse James; legendary outlaw.
Enslow Pubs. 1998 128p il maps (Historical
American biographies) lib bdg $26.60   92
1. Thieves
ISBN 0-7660-1055-4   LC 97-24615
Traces the life of the renowned bandit, from his child-
hood in Missouri, through his years as guerilla fighter
and outlaw, exploring the development of his legend and
the romanticization of his illegal deeds
"The book is heavily footnoted, thus providing not
only avenues for further research, but also a more authoritative tone than many biographies for this age group.
Even so, the scholarship does not impede the flow of the
narrative or the clear analysis of events." SLJ
Includes bibliographical references

Jefferson, Thomas, 1743-1826
Severance, John B. Thomas Jefferson; architect
of democracy. Clarion Bks. 1998 192p il maps
$18 (7 and up)   92
1. Presidents—United States
ISBN 0-395-84513-0   LC 97-31010
Explores the life of the third president, from his childhood in Virginia, through his involvement in the Revolutionary War, to his years in office
"In this respectful, literate, and handsomely illustrated
biography, Severance focuses equally on Jefferson's remarkable accomplishments and the beliefs behind them."
Booklist
Includes bibliographical references

Whitelaw, Nancy. Thomas Jefferson;
philosopher and president. Morgan Reynolds 2002
144p il $21.95 (7 and up)   92
1. Presidents—United States
ISBN 1-88384-681-1   LC 2001-44960
An account of Jefferson's life highlighting his many
accomplishments as governor, architect, gardener, inventor, and president
"A clear, crisp biography. . . . A solid and practical
book for reports." SLJ
Includes bibliographical references

Jemison, Mae C.
Alagna, Magdalena. Mae Jemison; the first
African American woman in space; by Magdalena
Alagna. 1st ed. Rosen Pub. Group 2004 112p il
(Women hall of famers in mathematics and
science) lib bdg $29.25 (4 and up)   92
1. Astronauts 2. African American women
ISBN 0-8239-3878-6   LC 2002-11132
Provides insights into the life of Mae Jemison, the
first female African American astronaut, including some
of the steps she took to reach her goals.
This "well-written [volume has an] interesting [story],
well-documented facts, well-chosen photographs, and an
easy and enjoyable writing style." SLJ
Includes bibliographical references

Jemison, Mae C. Find where the wind goes;
moments from my life; {by} Mae Jemison.
Scholastic Press 2001 196p il $16.95; pa $4.99 (5
and up)   92
1. Astronauts 2. African American women
ISBN 0-439-13195-2; 0-439-13196-0 (pa)
                                  LC 00-41008
"Dr. Jemison, the first woman of color to travel in
space, shares her life story in this autobiographical selection." Book Rep
"Jemison's vitality, intelligence, and humor shine
through the book, and she has a fascinating and inspiring
life story to tell." Booklist

Yannuzzi, Della A. Mae Jemison; a space
biography. Enslow Pubs. 1998 48p il (Countdown
to space) lib bdg $23.93   92
1. Women astronauts 2. African American women
ISBN 0-89490-813-8   LC 97-34159
Traces the life of the first African-American woman
to go into space, from her childhood in Chicago through
her astronaut training and first spaceflight to life after
working with NASA
The text is "readable and interesting. . . . Many colorful photographs illustrate the {book}." Booklist
Includes glossary and bibliographical references

Joan, of Arc, Saint, 1412-1431
Stanley, Diane. Joan of Arc. Morrow Junior
Bks. 1998 unp il $16 (4 and up)   92
1. Christian saints 2. France—History—1328-1589,
House of Valois
ISBN 0-688-14329-6   LC 97-45652
A biography of the fifteenth-century peasant girl who
led a French army to victory against the English and was
burned at the stake for witchcraft
Stanley "orchestrates the complexities of history into
a gripping, unusually challenging story in this exemplary
biography. . . . Judiciously chosen details build atmosphere in both the text and the artwork—painstakingly
wrought, gilded paintings modeled after the illuminated
manuscripts of Joan's day." Publ Wkly
Includes bibliographical references

Johnson, Isaac, 1844-1905
Marston, Hope Irvin. Isaac Johnson; from slave
to stonecutter; illustrated by Maria Magdalena
Brown. Cobblehill Bks. 1995 80p il $14.99
                                      92
1. Slavery—United States 2. African Americans—Biography
ISBN 0-525-65165-9   LC 94-32671
"Based on Johnson's own *Slavery Days in Old Kentucky,* this readable biography begins in 1851 when seven-year-old Isaac was sold into slavery by his white father. It briefly recounts his 10 years of labor as a slave
and how he ran away to join the Union Army. Marston's
account of Johnson's life after the war is documented
and enlivened by primary-source material. She avoids
sensationalism, but depicts slavery and her subject's con-
sequent career as a stonecutter and stonemason in Ontario and in New York in a spare and poignant manner."
SLJ
Includes bibliographical references

Johnson, Mamie, 1935-
Green, Michelle Y. A strong right arm: the story of Mamie "Peanut" Johnson; introduction by Mamie Johnson. Dial Bks. for Young Readers 2002 111p il $15.99; pa $5.99 (4 and up)
92
1. Baseball—Biography 2. Women athletes 3. African American athletes
ISBN 0-8037-2661-9; 0-14-240072-6 (pa)
LC 2001-28616
"Johnson was a pitcher with the Negro Leagues' Indianapolis Clowns from 1953 to 1955. In the introduction, Johnson speaks directly and movingly to the reader about her meeting with author Green, who then lets the famous ballplayer tell her own story in a lively first-person narrative. Johnson's ebullient personality and determination fairly leap off the page." Booklist
Includes bibliographical references

Jones, Mother, 1830-1930
Josephson, Judith Pinkerton. Mother Jones; fierce fighter for workers' rights. Lerner Publs. 1997 144p il lib bdg $27.93
92
1. Reformers
ISBN 0-8225-4924-7
LC 96-11802
A biography of Mary Harris Jones, the union organizer who worked tirelessly for the rights of workers
"Josephson brings this remarkable woman to life through well-documented sources and photographs of Jones and the environs in which she worked." SLJ
Includes bibliographical references

Joplin, Scott, 1868-1917
Preston, Katherine K. Scott Joplin; {by} Katherine Preston. Chelsea House 1988 110p il (Black Americans of achievement) lib bdg $22.95
92
1. Composers—United States 2. African American musicians
ISBN 1-55546-598-6
LC 87-21218
The author "describes the musician's Texas upbringing and his development as a talented composer of ragtime. Woven through the account is a social history of the time that underscores the racial prejudice that hindered Joplin in pursuing his livelihood." Booklist
Includes bibliographical references

Joseph, Nez Percé Chief, 1840-1904
Scott, Robert Alan. Chief Joseph and the Nez Percés; {by} Robert A. Scott. Facts on File 1993 134p il maps (Makers of America) lib bdg $25
92
1. Nez Percé Indians
ISBN 0-8160-2475-8
LC 92-15885
A biography of the nineteenth-century Nez Percé chief, concentrating on his unending struggle to win peace and equality for his people
Includes bibliographical references

Taylor, M. W. (Marian W.). Chief Joseph; Nez Perce leader; {by} Marian W. Taylor. Chelsea House 1993 110p il (North American Indians of achievement) lib bdg $19.95
92
1. Nez Percé Indians
ISBN 0-7910-1708-7
LC 92-31311
Presents the life and times of the Nez Percé Indian chief who led his people on a great trek to escape the injustices of the American government
Includes bibliographical references

Kahlo, Frida, 1907-1954
Laidlaw, Jill A. Frida Kahlo. Watts 2003 46p il (Artists in their time) lib bdg $22.50; pa $6.95 (5 and up)
92
1. Women artists 2. Artists, Mexican
ISBN 0-531-12236-0 (lib bdg); 0-531-16642-2 (pa)
LC 2003-535333
A biography of the Mexican artist and Communist activist
"The text is clear, concise, and written with vigor. . . . The large, full-color reproductions of [Kahlo's] paintings are excellent, and numerous archival photographs and quotes add a personal and immediate connection to the artist's life." SLJ

Kaiulani, Princess of Hawaii, 1875-1899
Linnea, Sharon. Princess Ka'iulani; hope of a nation, heart of a people. Eerdmans Bks. for Young Readers 1999 234p il $18; pa $12
92
1. Princesses 2. Hawaii—History
ISBN 0-8028-5145-2; 0-8028-5088-X (pa)
LC 97-14260
"This biography describes the life of Hawaiian crown princess Ka'iulani. Born in 1875, Ka'iulani was raised in Hawaii, educated in England, and remained in Europe until the overthrow of her aunt Queen Lili'uokalani in 1893 when she traveled to America." Booklist
"Linnéa presents a thorough and detailed account of her subject's life. . . . This is an interesting, accessible book about an intriguing individual. Black-and-white photos and reproductions add visual interest." SLJ
Includes bibliographical references

Keller, Helen, 1880-1968
Dash, Joan. The world at her fingertips: the story of Helen Keller. Scholastic Press 2001 235p $15.95; pa $4.99 (5 and up)
92
1. Blind 2. Deaf
ISBN 0-590-90715-8; 0-590-90716-6 (pa)
LC 00-34502
In this "biography, Dash recaps the life of an extraordinary woman. The popularly known events of Helen Keller's early years—the arrival of teacher Annie Sullivan and her efforts to break through to Helen—are encapsulated in the first few chapters, after which the text turns to Keller's continuing education, her years at Radcliffe, and her growing autonomy." Bull Cent Child Books
"A smooth, readable narrative. . . . The use of primary-source material . . . brings the subject's vibrant personality, intelligence, and sensitivity to life." SLJ
Includes bibliographical references

Keller, Helen, 1880-1968—*Continued*

Garrett, Leslie. Helen Keller. DK Publishing 2004 127p il (DK biography) $14.99; pa $4.99 (5 and up)   **92**
1. Blind 2. Deaf
ISBN 0-7566-0488-5; 0-7566-0339-0 (pa)
LC 2004-8451
This is a "first look at the . . . woman, blind and deaf since childhood, who . . . learned to read and speak and traveled the world as an inspiring public speaker and political activist. The . . . illustration-rich page design works well . . . and the smooth [narrative is] broken up on every page with boxed facts and quotes as well as well-chosen, small color photos." Booklist
Includes bibliographical references

Keller, Helen. The story of my life; edited and with a preface by James Berger. The restored ed. Modern Library 2003 xlvi, 343p il $19.95; pa $9.95   **92**
1. Blind 2. Deaf
ISBN 0-679-64287-0; 0-8129-6886-7 (pa)
LC 2002-40971
This biography of the inspirational Keller contains accounts of her home life and her relationship with her devoted teacher Anne Sullivan
Includes bibliographical references

Lawlor, Laurie. Helen Keller: rebellious spirit. Holiday House 2001 168p il $22.95 (5 and up)
92
1. Blind 2. Deaf
ISBN 0-8234-1588-0   LC 00-36950
A "biography of the most famous deaf and blind person in history. Drawing on social and scientific studies of deafness and blindness as well as on American history texts, Lawlor puts Keller's experiences in context. . . . At the same time, readers get a strong feel for Keller's personality and for the personalities of Annie Sullivan, Alexander Graham Bell, and other major figures in her life. Aided by numerous well-chosen photographs and excerpts from Keller's writings." Horn Book
Includes bibliographical references

Kennedy, John F. (John Fitzgerald), 1917-1963
Burgan, Michael. John F. Kennedy. World Almanac 2001 48p il (Trailblazers of the modern world) lib bdg $30   **92**
1. Presidents—United States
ISBN 0-8368-5065-3   LC 2001-34178
A biography of the thirty-fifth president of the United States, who served from 1961 until his assassination in 1963
"Students will enjoy reading . . . {this book} for both pleasure and research." Book Rep
Includes glossary and bibliographical references

Cooper, Ilene. Jack: the early years of John F. Kennedy. Dutton Children's Bks. 2003 168p il $22.99   **92**
1. Presidents—United States
ISBN 0-525-46923-0   LC 2002-75912

A description of the childhood and youth of John Fitzgerald Kennedy, the thirty-fifth president of the United States
"Intelligent design and numerous fabulous, well-placed, and well-captioned black-and-white photographs enrich Cooper's clear prose. . . . This sensitive, well-researched biography will enhance any collection." Voice Youth Advocates
Includes bibliographical references

Uschan, Michael V. John F. Kennedy. Lucent Bks. 1999 120p il (Importance of) lib bdg $27.45 (7 and up)   **92**
1. Presidents—United States
ISBN 1-56006-482-X   LC 98-36402
A biography of the thirty-fifth president of the United States who served from 1961 until his assassination in 1963
"Objective, well-chosen primary-source material includes many quotes from Kennedy's speeches and books. Chapter endnotes and familiar black-and-white archival photos and maps contribute to the title's usefulness for reports." SLJ
Includes bibliographical references

Kepler, Johannes, 1571-1630
Boerst, William J. Johannes Kepler; discovering the laws of celestial motion. Morgan Reynolds 2003 144p il maps (Renaissance scientists) lib bdg $23.95   **92**
1. Astronomers
ISBN 1-88384-698-6   LC 2003-708
A biography of Johannes Kepler, the seventeenth-century German astronomer and mathematician who formulated the three laws of planetary motion
"Boerst not only offers a good portrait of the astronomer and his work but also shows the effects of the contentious political and religious forces that created upheaval in his society and made scholarship anything but a safe haven. The well-designed pages feature excellent color illustrations." Booklist
Includes bibliographical references

Voelkel, James R. Johannes Kepler and the new astronomy. Oxford Univ. Press 1999 141p il (Oxford portraits in science) lib bdg $28; pa $11.95 (7 and up)   **92**
1. Astronomers
ISBN 0-19-511680-1 (lib bdg); 0-19-515021-X (pa)
LC 99-23844
A biography of the German astronomer who discovered three laws of planetary motion
"This book is enhanced with fascinating and informative reproductions, including facsimiles of Kepler's writings. Overall, an enjoyable introduction to a complex scientific life." SLJ
Includes bibliographical references

Kherdian, Veron, 1907-

Kherdian, David. The road from home; the story of an Armenian girl. Greenwillow Bks. 1979 238p il map lib. bdg $16.89; pa $5.99 (6 and up) **92**
1. Armenians—Turkey 2. Armenian massacres, 1915-1923
ISBN 0-688-84205-4 (lib bdg); 0-688-14425-X (pa)
LC 78-72511
A Newbery Medal honor book, 1980
The author presents a "biography of his mother's early life as a young Armenian girl. Veron Dumehjian was part of a prosperous Armenian family in Turkey, but the Armenian minority undergoes a holocaust when the Turkish government persecutes its Christian minorities. In 1915 Veron and her family are deported and, as refugees, live through hardships of disease, starvation, bombing, and fire until, at sixteen, Veron is able to go to America as a 'mail-order' bride." Babbling Bookworm

King, B. B.

Shirley, David. Everyday I sing the blues: the story of B.B. King. Watts 1995 127p il (Impact biography) lib bdg $20 (7 and up) **92**
1. African American musicians 2. Blues music
ISBN 0-531-11229-2 LC 95-16151
Traces the life of the influential African American blues musician, from his birth in the Mississippi Delta in 1925 to the present
Includes bibliographical references

King, Coretta Scott, 1927-

Klingel, Cynthia Fitterer. Coretta Scott King; by Cynthia Klingel. Child's World 1999 39p il (Journey to freedom) lib bdg $28.50 **92**
1. King, Martin Luther, 1929-1968 2. African American women 3. African Americans—Civil rights
ISBN 1-56766-567-5 LC 98-27012
A brief biography of the wife of the Reverend Martin Luther King, Jr., who shared his dedication to working peaceably to achieve equality for all Americans
"The clean, uncluttered book design features framed photographs meant to look like snapshots, with handsomely boxed captions. Heartbreaking, difficult subjects such as segregation, lynching (including photographs), the Ku Klux Klan, and assassination are lucidly explained." Booklist
Includes bibliographical references

Rhodes, Lisa Renee. Coretta Scott King. Chelsea House 1997 143p il (Black Americans of achievement) lib bdg $22.95; pa $9.95 **92**
1. King, Martin Luther, 1929-1968 2. African American women 3. African Americans—Civil rights
ISBN 0-7910-4690-7 (lib bdg); 0-7910-4691-5 (pa)
LC 97-36364
Biography of Martin Luther King's widow, from her childhood in rural Alabama to her crusade to keep her husband's message of peace and equality alive after his murder in 1968
"The chapters are well organized and the clear, well-chosen black-and-white photographs are attractively presented." SLJ
Includes bibliographical references

King, Martin Luther, 1929-1968

Haskins, James. The life and death of Martin Luther King, Jr. Lothrop, Lee & Shepard Bks. 1977 176p il hardcover o.p. paperback available $5.95 (5 and up) **92**
1. African Americans—Biography 2. African Americans—Civil rights
ISBN 0-688-11690-6 LC 77-3157
The author "writes about the civil rights leader in a simple, readable manner. Part one describes the development of the civil rights movement; part two describes the assassination, and an inordinate amount of space is given to James Earl Ray and the theory of a conspiracy behind the murder." Horn Book

Hatt, Christine. Martin Luther King, Jr; Christine Hatt. World Almanac Library 2004 64p il map (Judge for yourself) lib bdg $30
92
1. African Americans—Biography 2. African Americans—Civil rights
ISBN 0-8368-5562-0 LC 2003-60945
First published 2002 in the United Kingdom
This traces King's life "from the birth of his commitment to the fight against racism, through the triumphs in Montgomery and Birmingham, to his tragic assassination. Then [the book explores] some of the issues raised during King's career and [examines] evidence from opposing perspectives as to whether his methods were successful and his goals met." Publisher's note
"The suggestion that students think beyond the facts makes [this book] stand out from other biographies." SLJ

Klingel, Cynthia Fitterer. Coretta Scott King. See entry under King, Coretta Scott, 1927-

Manheimer, Ann S. Martin Luther King Jr; dreaming of equality; by Ann S. Manheimer. Carolrhoda Books 2005 112p (Trailblazer biography) lib bdg $27.93 (5 and up) **92**
1. African Americans—Biography 2. African Americans—Civil rights
ISBN 1-575-05627-5 LC 2004-2155
Contents: Childhood: remember the seeds; Early years: called to serve; The Montgomery bus boycott: something big; The new leader of Black America: standing up without fear; Sit-ins, freedom rides, and Albany: going to jail to help people; From Birmingham to Oslo: with audacious faith; Selma: we shall overcome; Northern protests: the flame of hope; Vietnam and Memphis: I may not get there with you; Afterword-legacy: to love and serve humanity
"Beginning with King's birth in 1929, Manheimer dedicates several chapters to his youth, early education, and decision to enter the ministry. The majority of the book focuses on his involvement with the civil rights movement." SLJ
"This biography is a solid introduction to the civil rights leader." Horn Book Guide
Includes bibliographical references

Rhodes, Lisa Renee. Coretta Scott King. See entry under King, Coretta Scott, 1927-

King, Stephen, 1947-
Wilson, Suzan. Stephen King: king of thrillers and horror. Enslow Pubs. 2000 128p il (People to know) lib bdg $26.60   **92**
1. Authors, American
ISBN 0-7660-1233-6   LC 99-33545
Traces the life of a popular novelist, from his childhood as an avid reader to his current success as a creator of horror fiction
"Fans will delight in the background stories that Wilson provides about a variety of King's works. . . . Black-and-white photographs and illustrations enhance the accompanying text." SLJ
Includes bibliographical references

Wukovits, John F. Stephen King. Lucent Bks. 1999 96p il (People in the news) $28.70 (7 and up)   **92**
1. Authors, American
ISBN 1-56006-562-1   LC 99-20085
Discusses the life, career, and influence of the popular horror writer Stephen King
"Librarians and teachers may not be thrilled with King's books, but middle-school and high-school students certainly are. They will read this biography for pleasure and use it for the 'read a biography or autobiography' assignment, if they can. Black-and-white photos are scattered throughout, as are boxed insets and numerous quotes from the author, his friends, associates, and rivals." Booklist
Includes bibliographical references

King-Smith, Dick, 1922-
King-Smith, Dick. Chewing the cud; illustrated by Harry Horse. Knopf 2002 c2001 196p il $16.95; lib bdg $18.99 (5 and up)   **92**
1. Authors, English
ISBN 0-375-81459-0; 0-375-91459-5 (lib bdg)
       LC 2002-67128
First published 2001 in the United Kingdom
Dick King-Smith recounts his life from soldier to farmer to salesman to factory worker to teacher to, finally, author
This is a "warm and witty memoir. . . . These pages reveal a gifted writer with an affection for animals and a simple country life, a passion for his work, and sheer goodness of heart." Publ Wkly

La Salle, Robert Cavelier, sieur de, 1643-1687
Faber, Harold. La Salle; down the Mississippi. Benchmark Bks. 2002 80p il maps (Great explorations) lib bdg $29.93   **92**
1. Explorers 2. Mississippi River valley
ISBN 0-7614-1239-5   LC 00-51901
A biography of the 17th century French explorer of North America
This "well-researched {book} . . . will be useful to students writing reports. Maps and archival reproductions in both black and white and color extend the text." Horn Book Guide
Includes bibliographical references

Goodman, Joan E. Despite all obstacles: La Salle and the conquest of the Mississippi; by Joan Elizabeth Goodman; illustrated by Tom McNeely. Mikaya Press 2001 47p il maps (Great explorers book) $19.95 (4 and up)   **92**
1. Explorers 2. Mississippi River valley
ISBN 1-931414-01-7   LC 2001-31732
A biography of the man who explored the St. Lawrence, Ohio, Illinois, and Mississippi rivers, and who claimed America's heartland for King Louis XIV and France
"Vivid color illustrations and Goodman's exciting writing style will attract both researchers and pleasure readers." Voice Youth Advocates

Lafayette, Marie Joseph Paul Yves Roch Gilbert du Motier, marquis de, 1757-1834
Fritz, Jean. Why not, Lafayette? illustrated by Ronald Himler. Putnam 1999 87p il $16.99; pa $5.99 (5 and up)   **92**
1. United States—History—1775-1783, Revolution
ISBN 0-399-23411-X; 0-698-11882-0 (pa)
       LC 98-31417
Traces the life of the French nobleman who fought for democracy in revolutions in both the United States and France
This biography is "chock-full of quotes, anecdotes, and wry humor." Booklist
Includes bibliographical references

Lange, Dorothea, 1895-1965
Partridge, Elizabeth. Restless spirit: the life and work of Dorothea Lange. Viking 1998 122p il $19.99; pa $10.99 (6 and up)   **92**
1. Women photographers
ISBN 0-670-87888-X; 0-14-230024-1 (pa)
       LC 98-9807
A biography of Dorothea Lange, whose photographs of migrant workers, Japanese American internees, and rural poverty helped bring about important social reforms
"Generously placed throughout this accessibly written biography are the photographic images that make Lange a pre-eminent artist of the century. The book is elegantly designed and the photographic reproductions are excellent." Bull Cent Child Books

Lawrence, Jacob, 1917-2000
Duggleby, John. Story painter: the life of Jacob Lawrence. Chronicle Bks. 1998 55p il $16.95 (4 and up)   **92**
1. African American artists
ISBN 0-8118-2082-3   LC 98-4513
A biography of the African American artist who grew up in the midst of the Harlem Renaissance and became one of the most renowned painters of the life of his people
"Lawrence's expressionistic, stark paintings, in excellent full-page color reproduction . . . nicely complement Duggleby's measured account of a materially poor but culturally rich childhood and Lawrence's subsequent struggles and successes." Publ Wkly
Includes bibliographical references

Leakey, Louis Seymour Bazett, 1903-1972

Poynter, Margaret. The Leakeys; uncovering the origins of humankind. Enslow Pubs. 1997 128p il maps (Great minds of science) lib bdg $26.60

92

1. Leakey, Mary D., 1913-1996 2. Anthropologists 3. Human origins

ISBN 0-89490-788-3   LC 96-40899

Profiles the lives of Louis and Mary Leakey and their dedication to the study of human evolution

Includes bibliographical references

Leakey, Mary D., 1913-1996

Poynter, Margaret. The Leakeys. See entry under Leakey, Louis Seymour Bazett, 1903-1972

Leeuwenhoek, Antoni van, 1632-1723

Yount, Lisa. Antoni van Leeuwenhoek; first to see microscopic life. Enslow Pubs. 1996 128p il (Great minds of science) lib bdg $26.60; pa $13.26

92

1. Biologists 2. Microscopes

ISBN 0-89490-680-1 (lib bdg); 0-7660-1866-0 (pa)
          LC 96-6057

A biography of the cloth merchant-turned-scientist who made many discoveries examining microsopic life

"The book ends with experiments the reader can do, a chronology of van Leeuwenhoek's life, and chapter notes. These are useful additions for a reader or teacher who wants to delve more deeply into the science aspects of the book." Sci Books Films

Includes bibliographical references

Lemieux, Mario

Stewart, Mark. Mario Lemieux; own the ice. Millbrook Press 2002 64p il lib bdg $24.90; pa $8.95

92

1. Hockey—Biography

ISBN 0-7613-2555-7 (lib bdg); 0-7613-1687-6 (pa)
          LC 2001-7006

A biography of the hockey superstar who overcame injury, disease, and even aging to return to the rink

"The accessible text moves beyond the typical athlete's chronology by describing Lemieux's drive and attitude toward the game and giving readers a sense of what it takes to succeed at that level. There are plenty of nicely reproduced photos and quotes." Booklist

Lennon, John, 1940-1980

Rappaport, Doreen. John's secret dreams; the life of John Lennon; written by Doreen Rappaport; illustrated by Bryan Collier. Hyperion Books for Children 2004 unp il $16.99 (4 and up)

92

1. Rock musicians

ISBN 0-7868-0817-9   LC 2003-57116

"Using a combination of simple prose, song lyrics, and illustration, this heartfelt picture-book biography traces Lennon's life from his childhood to his death. Striking in both its simplicity and complexity, it captures this enigmatic singer, artist, songwriter, and folk hero in a way that will move and fascinate those too young to remember the man but are surrounded by his music and myth." SLJ

Leonard, Buck, 1907-1997

Payment, Simone. Buck Leonard. Rosen Pub. Group 2002 112p il (Baseball Hall of Famers of the Negro leagues) lib bdg $29.25   **92**

1. Baseball—Biography 2. African American athletes

ISBN 0-8239-3473-X   LC 2001-3151

A biography of first-baseman who played in the Negro Leagues and was inducted into the Baseball Hall of Fame in 1972

This "title presents an unvarnished picture of the racism in this country and how it impacted amateur and professional baseball from 1868 onward. . . . The layout . . . is attractive, the style . . . is engaging." Book Rep

Includes glossary and bibliographical references

Leonardo, da Vinci, 1452-1519

Herbert, Janis. Leonardo da Vinci for kids; his life and ideas: 21 activities. Chicago Review Press 1998 90p il $16.95 (4 and up)   **92**

1. Artists, Italian

ISBN 1-55652-298-3   LC 98-25690

Presents a biography of this prolific artist and inventor through projects in cartography, animal art, bird observation, and mask making

"Herbert describes Leonardo's life while also providing a good deal of historical information about Italy and background about art. . . . The high-quality reproductions of the artist's sketches and paintings coupled with an interesting text give readers a full picture of this truly amazing man." SLJ

Includes bibliographical references

O'Connor, Barbara. Leonardo da Vinci; Renaissance genius. Carolrhoda Bks. 2003 112p il (Trailblazer biography) lib bdg $27.93 (5 and up)

92

1. Artists, Italian

ISBN 0-87614-467-9   LC 2001-6470

A biography of the notable Italian Renaissance artist, scientist, and inventor

"Outstanding writing and design result in a compelling and accessible portrait of this master artist." SLJ

Includes bibliographical references

Lewis, C. S. (Clive Staples), 1898-1963

Davenport, John. C.S. Lewis. Chelsea House 2004 119p il (Who wrote that?) $22.95

92

1. Authors, English

ISBN 0-7910-7620-2   LC 2003-12281

Contents: France, 191; The little end room; School days; War and peace; The kilns and Christian revival; *Screwtape* and success; Narnia; Surprised by love; Living and dying with joy; A life remembered

Describes the personal life and successful writing career of the author famed both for explaining the Christian faith to adults and for introducing young readers to

Lewis, C. S. (Clive Staples), 1898-1963—*Continued*
Narnia
This is "readable and visually appealing. . . . [A] useful [resource] for reports and fun and [a] fast [read] for fans." Voice Youth Advocates
Includes bibliographical references

Gormley, Beatrice. C.S. Lewis; Christian and storyteller. Eerdmans Bks. for Young Readers 1998 182p il hardcover o.p. paperback available $8 **92**
1. Authors, English
ISBN 0-8028-5069-3 (pa)   LC 97-7860
This "is a clearly written, solidly researched, and insightful picture of the popular author. Gormley weaves human texture into the book by layering the threads of Lewis' life whether trivial, tragic, literary, or spiritual into a highly readable exposition of a warm, amiable, and brilliant man." Bull Cent Child Books
Includes index

Lewis, John, 1940-
Hill, Christine M. John Lewis; from freedom rider to Congressman. Enslow Pubs. 2002 128p il (African-American biographies) lib bdg $20.95 **92**
1. Politicians—United States 2. African Americans—Civil rights
ISBN 0-7660-1768-0   LC 2001-6718
Chronicles the life of the man whose politics took him from civil rights worker in the South to serving as a United States Congressman
Includes bibliographical references

Lincoln, Abraham, 1809-1865
Freedman, Russell. Lincoln: a photobiography. Clarion Bks. 1987 149p il $18; pa $7.95 (5 and up) **92**
1. Presidents—United States 2. United States—History—1861-1865, Civil War
ISBN 0-89919-380-3; 0-395-51848-2 (pa)
LC 86-33379
Awarded the Newbery Medal, 1988
The author "begins by contrasting the Lincoln of legend to the Lincoln of fact. His childhood, self-education, early business ventures, and entry into politics comprise the first half of the book, with the rest of the text covering his presidency and assassination." SLJ
This is "a balanced work, elegantly designed and enhanced by dozens of period photographs and drawings, some familiar, some refreshingly unfamiliar." Publ Wkly
Includes bibliographical references

Lincoln, Abraham. Abraham Lincoln the writer; a treasury of his greatest speeches and letters; compiled and edited by Harold Holzer. Boyds Mills Press 2000 106p il lib bdg $15.95 (7 and up) **92**
1. Presidents—United States 2. United States—History—1861-1865, Civil War
ISBN 1-56397-772-9   LC 99-66551

"Lincoln's writings include personal letters, notes on the law, excerpts from speeches, debates, and inaugural addresses, letters to parents of fallen soldiers, and telegrams to his family. Reproductions of period photos, portraits, and documents illustrate the text effectively. . . . Highly interesting and a fine resource for students seeking quotations or for those wanting to meet Lincoln through his own words." Booklist

Sullivan, George. Abraham Lincoln. Scholastic Ref. 2000 128p il (In their own words) $12.95 (4 and up) **92**
1. Presidents—United States 2. United States—History—1861-1865, Civil War
ISBN 0-439-09554-9   LC 99-33387
Presents a biography, including excerpts from his speeches, letters, and other writings, of the man who was President during the Civil War
This book features "black-and-white photos and reproductions, a useful index, a short bibliography of primary and secondary sources, and a short list of further readings, along with places to contact for further information." SLJ
Includes bibliographical references

Sullivan, George. Picturing Lincoln; famous photographs that popularized the president. Clarion Bks. 2000 88p il $16 **92**
1. Presidents—United States 2. United States—History—1861-1865, Civil War
ISBN 0-395-91682-8   LC 00-27576
Examines some of the famous photographs taken of President Abraham Lincoln, discussing the circumstances under which they were taken and how these images were used
"This unique and sharply focused volume offers an introductory exploration of photographic processes and photographers while tracing the political fortunes of our 16th president." SLJ
Includes bibliographical references

Lindbergh, Charles, 1902-1974
Giblin, James. Charles A. Lindbergh; a human hero; {by} James Cross Giblin. Clarion Bks. 1997 212p il $22 **92**
1. Air pilots
ISBN 0-395-63389-3   LC 96-9501
A biography of the pilot whose life was full of controversy and tragedy, but also fulfilling achievements
"This sympathetic and informed account (beautifully illustrated with contemporary photographs) is an excellent introduction to Lindbergh and also to the early years of the celebrity society in which we live now." N Y Times Book Rev
Includes bibliographical references

Koopmans, Andy. Charles Lindbergh. Lucent Bks. 2003 112p il maps (Importance of) lib bdg $27.45 **92**
1. Air pilots
ISBN 1-59018-245-6   LC 2002-9882
Profiles the childhood, education, interest in aviation, fame, tragedy, and controversy surrounding the first man to fly solo across the Atlantic Ocean

Lindbergh, Charles, 1902-1974—*Continued*
"This well-written book gives insight into a shy but purposeful man. . . . Framed inserts from primary sources and many high-quality, black-and-white photographs are well placed within the text." SLJ
Includes bibliographical references

Linné, Carl von, 1707-1778
Anderson, Margaret Jean. Carl Linnaeus; father of classification. Enslow Pubs. 1997 128p il maps (Great minds of science) lib bdg $26.60

92

1. Naturalists
ISBN 0-89490-786-7   LC 96-48900
Profiles the life of the eighteenth-century Swedish naturalist whose scientific naming of plants and animals provided an international language of nature
"Well organized and clearly written. . . . This sound chronological study provides useful report material." SLJ
Includes bibliographical references

Lobel, Anita, 1934-
Lobel, Anita. No pretty pictures; a child of war. Greenwillow Bks. 1998 193p il $16 (7 and up)

92

1. Jews—Poland 2. Holocaust, 1933-1945—Personal narratives 3. Holocaust survivors
ISBN 0-688-15935-4   LC 97-48392
Also available in paperback from Avon Camelot Bks.
The author, known as an illustrator of children's books, describes her experiences as a Polish Jew during World War II and for years in Sweden afterwards
"Lobel brings to these dramatic experiences an artist's sensibility for the telling detail, a seemingly unvarnished memory and heartstopping candor." Publ Wkly

London, Jack, 1876-1916
Dyer, Daniel. Jack London; a biography. Scholastic 1997 221p il $17.95 (7 and up)

92

1. Authors, American
ISBN 0-590-22216-3   LC 96-29910
Biography of the colorful American writer who had been an oyster pirate, a seal hunter, a mill worker, a hobo, and a political activist before becoming a popular author at the age of twenty-nine
"This is a superior biography that is likely to inspire YAs to read London's novels and stories." SLJ
Includes bibliographical references

Stefoff, Rebecca. Jack London; an American original. Oxford Univ. Press 2002 127p il maps (Oxford portraits) lib bdg $28 (7 and up)

92

1. Authors, American
ISBN 0-19-512223-2   LC 2001-53087
Examines the life, beliefs, adventures, and works of Jack London, American author best known for his tales of hardship and survival set in the Yukon Territory
"This volume does an excellent job of illuminating London's extraordinary life and career. The narrative is exciting and accessible. . . . The text is supplemented by

interesting and informative illustrations, and includes excerpts from primary-source material." SLJ
Includes bibliographical references

Streissguth, Thomas. Jack London; {by} Tom Streissguth. Lerner Publs. 2001 112p il (Biography) lib bdg $27.93   **92**
1. Authors, American
ISBN 0-8225-4987-5   LC 99-50988
Describes the life of well-known author, Jack London, including his childhood, his writing, his belief in Socialism, and his worldwide adventures
"Streissguth effectively conveys the writer's restlessness and personal struggles through the occasional use of quotations. . . . Both succinct and honest, this biography will more than suffice for reports and may encourage young people to seek out some of London's classics." SLJ
Includes bibliographical references

Lowry, Lois
Lowry, Lois. Looking back; a book of memories. Houghton Mifflin 1998 181p il $17 (5 and up)   **92**
1. Authors, American 2. Women authors
ISBN 0-395-89543 X   LC 98-11376
Also available in paperback from Delacorte Press
"A Walter Lorraine book"
Using family photographs and quotes from her books, the author provides glimpses into her life
"A compelling and inspirational portrait of the author emerges from these vivid snapshots of life's joyful, sad and surprising moments." Publ Wkly

Lucid, Shannon
Bredeson, Carmen. Shannon Lucid; space ambassador. Millbrook Press 1998 48p il (Gateway biography) lib bdg $23.90; pa $8.95   **92**
1. Women astronauts
ISBN 0-7613-0406-1 (lib bdg); 0-7613-1375-3 (pa)
                    LC 97-47147
Chronicles the life of the astronaut from her childhood in Oklahoma through her various space shuttle missions to her six months aboard the Mir space station
"Full-color photographs are a bonus, as are fun facts about life in space. A chronology and a bibliography are also included." Booklist

Lyons, Maritcha Rémond, 1848-1929
Bolden, Tonya. Maritcha; a nineteenth-century American girl. Abrams 2005 47p il $17.95 (4 and up)   **92**
1. African American women 2. New York (N.Y.)—Race relations 3. African Americans—New York (N.Y.)
ISBN 0-8109-5045-6   LC 2004-05849
This is a "life history of Maritcha Rémond Lyons, born a free black in 1848 in lower Manhattan. The author draws her biographical sketch primarily from Lyons's unpublished memoir, dated one year before her death in 1929. . . . One of the . . . sections of the book documents the Draft Riots . . . of July 1868, and the im-

Lyons, Maritcha Rémond, 1848-1929—*Continued*

pact of them on Maritcha and other citizens." Publ Wkly
"The high quality of writing and the excellent documentation make this a first choice for all collections."
SLJ

Ma, Yo-Yo, 1955-

Chippendale, Lisa A. Yo-Yo Ma; a cello superstar brings music to the world. Enslow Publishers 2004 112p il (People to know) lib bdg $26.60   **92**

1. Violoncellists 2. Chinese Americans
ISBN 0-7660-2286-2   LC 2003-14972

Contents: Inspired by Bach; Choosing a "big instrument"; From high school to Harvard; An emerging star; Yo-yo Ma branches out; Seeking new musical forms; Traveling the Silk Road (1997-1999); When strangers meet

Tracks the life and career of violoncellist Yo-Yo Ma, a child prodigy who grew to become world famous for his playing ability, as well as for experimenting with different kinds of music and performance.

"The author does a commendable job of presenting Ma in a professional light as well as a personal one."
SLJ

Includes bibliographical references

MacArthur, Douglas, 1880-1964

Feinberg, Barbara Silberdick. Douglas MacArthur; an American hero. Watts 1999 128p il (Book report biography) lib bdg $22   **92**

1. Generals
ISBN 0-531-11562-3   LC 98-29755

Examines the childhood, training, and career of the man known for his military leadership during World War II, the administration of occupied Japan after the war, and the Korean War

"The exciting and controversial life of this famous general is told in easy-to-read prose, with plenty of black-and-white photos. Readers get a feel for MacArthur's flair and style and a sense of his personal life."
SLJ

Includes bibliographical references

Madison, James, 1751-1836

Fritz, Jean. The great little Madison. Putnam 1989 159p il $16.99; pa $5.99 (5 and up)
    92

1. Presidents—United States
ISBN 0-399-21768-1; 0-698-11621-6 (pa)
     LC 88-31584

"Small, soft-spoken, and by nature diffident, James Madison found it difficult to speak in the midst of controversy, but his zeal and his convictions in the struggle between Republicans and Federalists gave him confidence, and his successes brought him to the presidency. Fritz has given a vivid picture of the man and an equally vivid picture of the problems—especially the internal dissension—that faced the leaders of the new nation. . . . Notes by the author and a bibliography are appended."
Bull Cent Child Books

Malone, Mary. James Madison. Enslow Pubs. 1997 128p il (United States presidents) lib bdg $26.60   **92**

1. Presidents—United States
ISBN 0-89490-834-0   LC 96-39133

Chronicles the life and career of the fourth President with emphasis on his many contributions to the government of the United States including his role in writing the Constitution and the Bill of Rights

This "is a well-researched, smoothly written biography." Booklist

Includes bibliographical references

Magellan, Ferdinand, 1480?-1521

Levinson, Nancy Smiler. Magellan and the first voyage around the world. Clarion Bks. 2001 132p il maps $19 (5 and up)   **92**

1. Explorers 2. Voyages around the world
ISBN 0-395-98773-3   LC 00-52350

This "biography of the great explorer, navigator, and adventurer presents him as a man of action who overcame political, social, and financial obstacles to sail around the globe." Horn Book Guide

"This clearly written book shows through involving narrative and vivid detail what a monumental achievement the journey was. . . . A well-designed volume, useful for research and interesting as biography." Booklist

Includes bibliographical references

Meltzer, Milton. Ferdinand Magellan; first to sail around the world. Benchmark Bks. 2002 80p il (Great explorations) lib bdg $29.93   **92**

1. Explorers 2. Voyages around the world
ISBN 0-7614-1238-7   LC 00-64374

"Meltzer's wry comments make history anything but dry. . . . The colorful and sometimes quite beautiful illustrations include paintings, drawings, and prints, as well as a few photographs of sites and artifacts." Booklist

Includes bibliographical references

Mah, Adeline Yen, 1937-

Mah, Adeline Yen. Chinese Cinderella. Delacorte Press 1999 205p hardcover o.p. paperback available $5.99   **92**

1. China—Social life and customs
ISBN 0-440-22865-4 (pa)   LC 99-11007

An adaptation for young readers of the author's Falling leaves (1998)

The author, blamed for her mother's death shortly after childbirth, recalls "her sad and lonely childhood in China during the 1940s and 1950s. Wu Mei, whose English name is Adeline, faces the anger and cruelty of her family; only an aunt and frail grandfather are supportive. Shunted off to boarding schools, left out of family activities, Adeline nevertheless thrives academically and hopes desperately (and futily) to please her father." Booklist

Malcolm X, 1925-1965

Draper, Allison Stark. The assassination of Malcolm X. Rosen Pub. Group 2002 64p il (Library of political assassinations) lib bdg $26.50
92

1. African Americans—Biography 2. Black Muslims

ISBN 0-8239-3542-6   LC 2001-3323

Contents: The assassination; The making of Malcolm X; Minister Malcolm X; The death of Malcolm X; The assassination revisited

This "book begins with an introduction, followed by a . . . description of the assassination, and account of the subject's earlier life, and a concluding chapter on his impact on America." Book Rep

"Draper confronts the important issues with exceptional candor and clarity, including the ongoing controversy of who ordered the murder." Booklist

Includes glossary and bibliographical references

Mandela, Nelson

Finlayson, Reggie. Nelson Mandela. Lerner Publs. 1999 112p il (A & E biography) $27.93
92

1. South Africa—Race relations 2. South Africa—Politics and government

ISBN 0-8225-4936-0   LC 97-50167

"This overview concentrates on Mandela's childhood in the Xhosa nation, his training as a lawyer, and his rise through the ranks of the ANC, and includes ample black-and-white and full-color photographs. His actual imprisonment, release, and election to the presidency of South Africa are confined to the last 15 pages. His divorce from Winnie Mandela and marriage to Graca Machel are not mentioned." SLJ

Includes bibliographical references

Kramer, Ann. Nelson Mandela. Raintree Pubs. 2003 112p il (Twentieth-century history makers) lib bdg $32.85 (7 and up)   **92**

1. South Africa—Race relations 2. South Africa—Politics and government

ISBN 0-7398-5258-2   LC 2002-15933

Contents: Early years; Johannesburg; European dominance; From union to apartheid; Defiance; Treason; Underground; Rivonia trial; Robben Island struggle continues; Mandela freed; Mr. President

This biography of the South African leader is "accurate and eloquent about the man and the political struggle, and it has dramatic, well-chosen news photos of both." Booklist

Includes glossary and bibliographical references

Mao Zedong, 1893-1976

Slavicek, Louise Chipley. Mao Zedong. Chelsea House 2004 116p il (Great military leaders of the 20th century) lib bdg $23.95   **92**

1. Heads of state 2. China—History—1949-1976

ISBN 0-7910-7407-2   LC 2003-6929

Contents: From the barrel of a gun: October 1, 1949; Finding a road: the early years: 1893-1921; Mao and the young Chinese communist movement: 1921-1930; The encirclement campaigns and the long march: 1930-1935; Fighting the Japanese and the Nationalists: 1936-1949; Confronting challenges at home and abroad: 1949-1959; An era of turmoil: 1960-1976

A biography of Chinese leader Mao Zedong, discussing the battles that helped shape him and reasons behind his popularity among his countrymen

"Slavicek blends personal, philosophical, and historical information to trace Mao's journey to power. Clear accounts of the communist movement, the Long March, and the eventual battle with the Nationalists and Japanese are included." SLJ

Includes bibliographical references

Marconi, Guglielmo, 1874-1937

Birch, Beverley. Guglielmo Marconi; radio pioneer. Blackbirch Press 2001 64p il (Giants of science) lib bdg $24.95   **92**

1. Inventors 2. Radio—History

ISBN 1-56711-337-0   LC 01-35463

First published 1990 in the United Kingdom

Describes the life and work of the Italian inventor, who was a pioneer in the development of the radio

This "delivers vital biographical information while focusing on scientific principles and applications. . . . The illustrations are outstanding. Photographs, drawings, and other illustrations were well documented with short narrative explanations." Book Rep

Includes glossary and bibliographical references

Marley, Bob

Dolan, Sean. Bob Marley. Chelsea House 1997 119p il (Black Americans of achievement) lib bdg $23.95   **92**

1. Singers 2. Reggae music 3. Blacks—Biography

ISBN 0-7910-2041-X   LC 95-35932

Traces the life of the Jamaican musician who helped popularize reggae before his untimely death

"The book is fascinating reading: it brings its subject alive, and inspires readers to listen to Marley's music. The text is filled with details that keep readers' interest." SLJ

Includes bibliographical references

Marshall, Thurgood, 1908-1993

Kent, Deborah. Thurgood Marshall and the Supreme Court. Children's Press 1997 30p il (Cornerstones of freedom) lib bdg $21; pa $5.95
92

1. United States. Supreme Court 2. Judges 3. African Americans—Biography

ISBN 0-516-20297-9 (lib bdg); 0-516-26139-8 (pa)
LC 96-9865

"Kent's clear and simple text adequately covers the noted Justice. . . . Color and black-and-white photographs and a time line are included." Horn Book Guide

Includes glossary

Rowh, Mark. Thurgood Marshall; civil rights attorney and Supreme Court justice. Enslow Pubs. 2002 112p il (African-American biographies) lib bdg $26.60   **92**

1. United States. Supreme Court 2. Judges 3. African Americans—Biography

ISBN 0-7660-1547-5   LC 2001-3141

Marshall, Thurgood, 1908-1993—*Continued*
"This well-written and accessible title is ideal for research and a valuable supplement to biography collections." SLJ
Includes bibliographical references

Martínez, María Montoya, 1887-1980
Morris, Juddi. Tending the fire: the story of Maria Martinez. Rising Moon Bks. for Young Readers 1997 113p map $12.95; pa $6.95 (4 and up) **92**
1. Pueblo Indians 2. Women artists
ISBN 0-87358-665-4; 0-87358-654-9 (pa)
LC 97-12009
A biography of the Tewa Indian woman who revived the dying art of her people, ceramic pottery, and shared her knowledge of pottery-making with others
"Maria Martinez . . . is given her due in this straightforward, chronological biography. . . . A welcome book about a little-known American artist." Booklist
Includes glossary and bibliographical references

Martinez, Pedro, 1971-
Gallagher, Jim. Pedro Martinez. Mitchell Lane Pubs. 1999 64p il (Latinos in baseball) $18.95 **92**

1. Baseball—Biography
ISBN 1-883845-85-8
LC 98-48047
Presents a biography of the professional baseball pitcher from the Dominican Republic who won the National League's Cy Young Award in 1997 and currently pitches for the Boston Red Sox
Includes bibliographical references

Matisse, Henri
Welton, Jude. Henri Matisse. Watts 2002 46p il (Artists in their time) $22; pa $6.95 **92**
1. Artists, French
ISBN 0-531-12228-X; 0-531-16621-X (pa)
LC 2002-69106
Discusses the life and career of this French artist, describing and giving examples of his work
This offers a "clear and lively {text}. . . . Captioned, full-color and black-and-white photographs and art reproductions are liberally scattered throughout." SLJ

Mawson, Sir Douglas, 1882-1958
Bredeson, Carmen. After the last dog died; the true-life, hair-raising adventure of Douglas Mawson and his 1912 Antarctic Expedition. National Geographic 2003 63p il map $18.95 **92**

1. Antarctica—Exploration
ISBN 0-7922-6140-2
LC 2003-0756
Describes the life and career of the Australian explorer, Sir Douglas Mawson, focusing on his 1912 scientific expedition to Antarctica.
"Bredson's compelling story of courage and survival draws heavily on quotes from Mawson and other primary source documents; there are also charts, maps, and many photographs." Booklist

McAuliffe, Christa
Jeffrey, Laura S. Christa McAuliffe; a space biography. Enslow Pubs. 1998 48p il (Countdown to space) lib bdg $23.93 **92**
1. Challenger (Space shuttle) 2. Women astronauts
ISBN 0-89490-976-2
LC 97-22114
A biography of the school teacher turned astronaut whose life was tragically ended when the space shuttle Challenger exploded just after liftoff
"An accurate, well-researched . . . biography." SLJ
Includes glossary and bibliographical references

McCaffrey, Anne
Trachtenberg, Martha P. Anne McCaffrey; science fiction storyteller. Enslow Pubs. 2001 112p il (People to know) lib bdg $26.60 **92**
1. Authors, American 2. Women authors
ISBN 0-7660-1151-8
LC 00-10952
"Trachtenberg begins with McCaffrey's 1968 Hugo Award, a first for a woman, then backtracks to reveal the author's childhood, work in music and theater, marriage and divorce, move to Ireland, and prolific writing career." SLJ
Includes bibliographical references

McCarthy, Joseph, 1908-1957
Sherrow, Victoria. Joseph McCarthy and the Cold War. Blackbirch Press 1998 80p il (Notorious Americans and their times) lib bdg $27.45; pa $8.95 **92**
1. United States—Politics and government—1945-1953 2. United States—Politics and government—1953-1961
ISBN 1-56711-219-6 (lib bdg); 1-56711-457-1 (pa)
LC 98-15559
A biography of the unknown first-term senator from Wisconsin who gained notoriety by stirring up anti-Communist fears in the years after World War II
"Interesting sidebars introduce some of McCarthy's contemporaries such as 'The Hollywood Ten,' Alger Hiss, and Robert Oppenheimer. . . . As many history books at this level contain surprisingly scant information about the father of McCarthyism, this title is a worthwhile addition for most libraries." SLJ
Includes bibliographical references

McClintock, Barbara
Cullen, J. Heather. Barbara McClintock, geneticist. Chelsea House 2003 122p il (Women in science) lib bdg $22.95 (7 and up) **92**
1. Women scientists 2. Genetics
ISBN 0-7910-7248-7
LC 2002-15549
Presents the life and career of the geneticist who in 1983 was awarded the Nobel Prize for her study of maize cells
This is "well written and well organized." SLJ
Includes bibliographical references

Fine, Edith Hope. Barbara McClintock; Nobel Prize geneticist. Enslow Pubs. 1998 128p il (People to know) lib bdg $26.60 (7 and up) **92**

1. Women scientists 2. Genetics
ISBN 0-89490-983-5
LC 97-43754

McClintock, Barbara—*Continued*

Presents the life and career of the geneticist who spent many years studying the cells of maize and in 1983 was awarded the Nobel Prize in Physiology or Medicine

"This book is what every good biography should be. . . . Throughout the narrative, McClintock's lively personality and dedication to her work shine through." SLJ

Includes glossary and bibliographical references

Mead, Margaret, 1901-1978

Mark, Joan T. Margaret Mead; coming of age in America; {by} Joan Mark. Oxford Univ. Press 1998 110p il (Oxford portraits in science) $28 (7 and up)   **92**

1. Anthropologists

ISBN 0-19-511679-8   LC 98-18604

An "account of the life and works of the influential, pioneering anthropologist. . . . Mark does a fine job of abstracting Mead's research and published works and showing why they were both critically acclaimed and criticized. The reader-friendly prose is peppered with fascinating anecdotes and photos. Mead herself is presented as a complex, intriguing figure, with fascinating, often contradictory, public and private lives." Booklist

Includes bibliographical references

Pollard, Michael. Margaret Mead; bringing world cultures together. Blackbirch Press 1999 64p il (Giants of science) lib bdg $24.95   **92**

1. Anthropologists

ISBN 1-56711-327-3   LC 98-47864

"Pollard explains how Mead's lifework of studying the cultures of the South Pacific informed and eventually defined our ideas of culture, diversity, and anthropology in the 20th century. Some criticism of her work is included and her nonconformist lifestyle is noted." SLJ

Includes bibliographical references

Meitner, Lise, 1878-1968

Hamilton, Janet. Lise Meitner; pioneer of nuclear fission. Enslow Pubs. 2002 128p il maps (Great minds of science) lib bdg $26.60

92

1. Physicists 2. Women scientists 3. Nuclear physics

ISBN 0-7660-1756-7   LC 2001-2119

A biography of the German physicist who discovered nuclear fission in 1938

"Hamilton does a fine job of outlining the political climate of the time, which helps place the events of Meitner's life in historical context." SLJ

Includes glossary and bibliographical references

Meltzer, Milton, 1915-

Meltzer, Milton. Milton Meltzer; writing matters; by Milton Meltzer. Franklin Watts 2004 160p il lib bdg $29 (7 and up)   **92**

1. Authors, American

ISBN 0-531-12257-3   LC 2004-2947

Meltzer "writes about his own life through the prism of his craft. He tells about his growing up in Worcester, Massachusetts, the child of immigrants from the Austro-Hungarian empire, and his coming-of-age during the De-

pression. After his student days at Columbia, he worked at the Works Progress Administration and as an air traffic controller in World War II. But the focus here is on his writing, how he started, why it was important to him, and how long it took him to be able to work full-time as a writer." Booklist

"The author includes clear, interesting explanations about the American historical and economic events that influenced his life. While this book is a pleasure to read for general interest, it would also supplement units on American history." SLJ

Includes bibliographical references

Mendel, Gregor, 1822-1884

Edelson, Edward. Gregor Mendel, and the roots of genetics. Oxford Univ. Press 1999 105p il (Oxford portraits in science) lib bdg $28; pa $11.95 (7 and up)   **92**

1. Genetics

ISBN 0-19-512226-7 (lib bdg); 0-19-515020-1 (pa)

LC 98-37541

"This biography provides details of the scientist's life and his experiments as well as the political and social context of his times. . . . A two-page chronology tracks important events in his life and the vital contributions he made to the study of genetics. Black-and-white photographs, reproductions of artwork, and pages from the scientist's notebooks and manuscripts accompany the text." SLJ

Includes bibliographical references

Klare, Roger. Gregor Mendel; father of genetics. Enslow Pubs. 1997 128p il (Great minds of science) lib bdg $26.60   **92**

1. Genetics

ISBN 0-89490-789-1   LC 96-35791

Examines the life and work of the nineteenth-century Austrian monk who discovered the laws of genetics

"Easy-to-understand explanations of groundbreaking discoveries. . . . An activity section encourages readers to try their hands at the techniques and principles under discussion. Black-and-white photos, reproductions, and diagrams enhance the [presentation]. Useful . . . especially for reports." SLJ

Includes bibliographical references

Michelangelo Buonarroti, 1475-1564

Stanley, Diane. Michelangelo. HarperCollins Pubs. 2000 unp il $16.99; lib bdg $17.89; pa $7.99   **92**

1. Artists, Italian

ISBN 0-688-15085-3; 0-688-15086-1 (lib bdg); 0-06-052113-9 (pa)

A biography of the Renaissance sculptor, painter, architect, and poet, well known for his work on the Sistine Chapel in Rome's St. Peter's Cathedral

This is "as readable as it is useful. . . . Integrating Michelangelo's art with Stanley's watercolor, gouache, and colored-pencil figures and settings has the desired effect: readers will be dazzled with the master's ability, while at the same time pulled into his daily life and struggles." SLJ

Includes bibliographical references

Mitchell, Maria, 1818-1889

Anderson, Dale. Maria Mitchell, astronomer. Chelsea House 2003 110p il (Women in science) $22.95 (7 and up)   **92**

1. Women astronomers

ISBN 0-7910-7249-5   LC 2002-13738

Contents: Watching the sun disappear ; A child of Nantucket : 1818-1835; Teaching and learning: 1835-1847; Earning a medal: 1847-1855; Expanding the horizon: 1855-1861; Mitchell as professor: 1862-1869; Carrying the torch for women: 1869-1876; The force of personal character

Profiles a Vassar professor who was one of the most famous astronomers in the United States at the end of the nineteenth century and whose central message to her students was never cease to wonder

"Color prints or photographs with brief descriptions are interspersed throughout and add considerably to the [text]." Libr Media Connect

Includes bibliographical references

Gormley, Beatrice. Maria Mitchell; the soul of an astronomer. Eerdmans 1995 123p il hardcover o.p. paperback available $8 (7 and up)   **92**

1. Women astronomers

ISBN 0-8028-5099-5 (pa)   LC 95-21980

A biography of the first female science professor at Vassar College and the first American woman astronomer

"With a smoothly flowing and lively style, this biography introduces readers to the 19th-century astronomer. Well-chosen, primary-source quotations and quality black-and-white photos add authenticity to the text, and contribute greatly to the author's objective and comprehensive description of Mitchell's accomplishments." SLJ

Includes bibliographical references

Morrison, Toni, 1931-

Haskins, James. Toni Morrison; the magic of words; [by] Jim Haskins. Millbrook Press 2001 48p il (Gateway biography) lib bdg $23.90 (4 and up)   **92**

1. Authors, American 2. African American authors 3. Women authors

ISBN 0-7613-1806-2   LC 00-32868

Haskins discusses Morrison's "childhood, her career as an editor . . . and he gives a very brief outline of each of her books and its critical reception, from *The Bluest Eye* to *Beloved.*" Booklist

"This introductory biography is well organized, attractive, and inspiring." SLJ

Includes bibliographical references

Mowat, Farley

Mowat, Farley. Born naked. Houghton Mifflin 1994 c1993 256p il maps hardcover o.p. paperback available $13 (7 and up)   **92**

ISBN 0-395-73528-9 (pa)   LC 93-23702

"A Peter Davison book"

First published 1993 in Canada

The "renowned naturalist and writer gives us a glimpse of his parents, his growing up in Canada, and

the roots of his love for animals." Booklist

"There are no dull pages here; every man, woman, child, and animal mentioned even casually makes an impression. . . . Highly recommended to all those who like good writing." Libr J

Muir, John, 1838-1914

Naden, Corinne J. John Muir; saving the wilderness; [by] Corinne J. Naden and Rose Blue. Millbrook Press 1992 48p il (Gateway biography) lib bdg $23.90; pa $9.95   **92**

1. Naturalists 2. Nature conservation

ISBN 1-56294-110-0 (lib); 1-56294-797-4 (pa)

     LC 91-18106

This book profiles the life and times of naturalist John Muir

"Attractively designed with clear framed text and lots of photographs. . . . Kids will be intrigued by Muir's work for conservation, especially his role in founding the national parks." Booklist

Includes bibliographical references

Warrick, Karen Clemens. John Muir: crusader for the wilderness. Enslow Pubs. 2002 128p il map (Historical American biographies) lib bdg $26.60   **92**

1. Nature conservation 2. Naturalists

ISBN 0-7660-1622-6   LC 2001-3000

Describes the life of the naturalist who became a founder of the Sierra Club and a proponent of the establishment of national parks in America

"Thorough and interesting, this is a good choice for most collections." SLJ

Includes glossary and bibliographical references

Myers, Walter Dean, 1937-

Myers, Walter Dean. Bad boy; a memoir. HarperCollins Pubs. 2001 214p $15.95; lib bdg $16.89; pa $6.99 (7 and up)   **92**

1. Authors, American 2. African American authors

ISBN 0-06-029523-6; 0-06-029524-4 (lib bdg); 0-06-447288-4 (pa)   LC 00-52978

In this memoir "young adult author Walter Dean Myers recalls the life path that lead him to a career in writing. . . . His personal account allows the reader to get a glimpse of Myers, the man, touching on the issues of racism, adoption, self-identity, alcoholism, gang violence, and a speech impediment that almost altered Myers's path to the written word." Voice Youth Advocates

This "is a story full of funny anecdotes, lofty ideals, and tender moments." SLJ

Nakahama, Manjirō, 1827-1898

Blumberg, Rhoda. Shipwrecked!: the true adventures of a Japanese boy. HarperCollins Pubs. 2000 80p il map $16.95; pa $7.99 (5 and up)   **92**

1. Japan—History

ISBN 0-688-17484-1; 0-688-17485-X (pa)

     LC 99-86664

In 1841, rescued by an American whaler after a terrible shipwreck leaves him and his four companions cast-

Nakahama, Manjirō, 1827-1898—*Continued*
aways on a remote island, fourteen-year-old Manjiro learns new laws and customs as he becomes the first Japanese person to set foot in the United States
"Exemplary in both her research and writing, Blumberg hooks readers with anecdotes that astonish without sensationalizing, and she uses language that's elegant and challenging, yet always clear. Particularly notable is the well-chosen reproductions of original artwork." Booklist
Includes bibliographical references

Napoleon I, Emperor of the French, 1769-1821
Napoleon Bonaparte; Raymond Obstfeld and Loretta Obstfeld, book editors. Greenhaven Press 2001 202p il (People who made history) pa $23.70 hardcover o.p. **92**
1. France—Kings and rulers
ISBN 0-7377-0422-5   LC 00-58689
A collection of essays with primary source documents about the Emperor of the French
Includes bibliographical references

Nation, Carry Amelia Moore, 1846-1911
Harvey, Bonnie C. Carry A. Nation: saloon smasher and prohibitionist; {by} Bonnie Carman Harvey. Enslow Pubs. 2002 128p il (Historical American biographies) lib bdg $26.60   **92**
1. Woman's Christian Temperance Union
2. Prohibition
ISBN 0-7660-1907-1   LC 2001-7431
Contents: Saloon smashing; Childhood; Blushing bride at twenty-one; Life with an alcoholic; Marriage to David Nation; The making of a crusader; The prize of Wichita; Fearless crusader; Carry Nation gains national fame; Lasting accomplishments; Carry Nation's legacy
Examines the life of Carry Nation, whose destruction of saloons and other businesses that sold liquor in the late nineteenth and early twentieth century won her both praise and criticism from fellow prohibitionists and temperance workers
"A solid resource and a good starting place for readers interested in learning more about this woman." SLJ
Includes glossary and bibliographical references

Newton, Sir Isaac, 1642-1727
Anderson, Margaret Jean. Isaac Newton; the greatest scientist of all time; {by} Margaret J. Anderson. Enslow Pubs. 1996 128p il (Great minds of science) lib bdg $26.60 (4 and up)
92
1. Scientists
ISBN 0-89490-681-X   LC 96-4958
"The life, work, and goals of the brilliant scientist Isaac Newton are described in this very readable book about perhaps 'the greatest scientist of all time.' A descriptive chapter of experiments on color, paddle wheels, and gravity motivates children to think and explore, as Newton did." Sci Child
Includes glossary and bibliographical references

Boerst, William J. Isaac Newton; organizing the universe. Morgan Reynolds Pub. 2004 144p il (Renaissance scientists) lib bdg $23.95 (7 and up)
92
1. Scientists
ISBN 1-931798-01-X   LC 2003-14571
"Boerst describes Newton's life from his premature birth through an isolated adulthood dominated by study and experimentation to his death at the age of 84. The author deftly explores his subject's accomplishments in relation to the scientific community and notable historical events of the time and includes information concerning his religious views. . . . This well-written book makes an excellent choice for teens exploring scientists or just looking for a good biography." SLJ
Includes bibliographical references

Christianson, Gale E. Isaac Newton and the scientific revolution. Oxford Univ. Press 1996 155p il (Oxford portraits in science) lib bdg $28 paperback o.p. (7 and up)   **92**
1. Scientists
ISBN 0-19-509224-4 (lib bdg)   LC 96-13179
Explores the life and scientific contributions of the famed English mathematician and natural philosopher
This book "reads easily and with a pleasant and comfortable flow. Structured around pivotal moments in Newton's life, the book is an excellent reference for biographical data on the great English scientist; in addition, it affords a fine historical perspective of the scientific revolution." Sci Books Films
Includes bibliographical references

White, Michael. Isaac Newton; discovering laws that govern the universe. Blackbirch Press 1999 64p il (Giants of science) lib bdg $24.95
92
1. Scientists
ISBN 1-56711-326-5   LC 98-49142
Describes the life and scientific contributions of the famed English mathematician who changed our perception of the universe
Includes bibliographical references

Nixon, Joan Lowery, 1927-2003
Nixon, Joan Lowery. The making of a writer. Delacorte Press 2002 97p il $14.95; lib bdg $16.99; pa $4.99   **92**
1. Authors, American 2. Women authors
ISBN 0-385-73000-4; 0-385-90046-5 (lib bdg); 0-440-41905-0 (pa)   LC 2001-53909
The author recalls events from her childhood and adolescence before and during World War II that contributed to her development as a writer
"This will be of tremendous value to adults who teach writing to children, but it will also appeal to Nixon's legion of fans, including those who have no desire to write a word of their own; it's a delightful look back at a time and a life." Booklist

Nixon, Richard M. (Richard Milhous), 1913-1994

Barron, Rachel. Richard Nixon; American politician. Morgan Reynolds 1998 112p il (Notable Americans) $21.95 (7 and up) **92**

1. Presidents—United States

ISBN 1-88384-633-1 LC 98-29836

"A comprehensive portrait of the statesman's political career and personal life. . . . Barron is objective about her subject, giving him credit for his considerable successes and holding him responsible for his failures." SLJ

Includes bibliographical references

Goldman, Martin S. Richard M. Nixon; a complex legacy. Facts on File 1998 146p il (Makers of America) $25 (7 and up) **92**

1. Presidents—United States

ISBN 0-8160-3397-8 LC 97-19928

A biography of the controversial president which covers his early life and political career, the presidential elections of 1960 and 1968, his roles in the Vietnam War and Watergate scandal, and his retirement

Includes bibliographical references

Oakley, Annie, 1860-1926

Macy, Sue. Bulls-eye: a photobiography of Annie Oakley. National Geographic Soc. 2001 64p il $17.95 (4 and up) **92**

ISBN 0-7922-7008-8 LC 2001-125

A biography of the woman born Phoebe Ann Moses, who, under the name Annie Oakley, became a famous sharpshooter touring with Buffalo Bill's Wild West Show

"This book is exemplary nonfiction: well documented, lots of period photos with credits, a resource list, and a chronology. Equally important is its engaging and well crafted account of this famous woman of the West." SLJ

Orwell, George, 1903-1950

Boerst, William J. Generous anger: the story of George Orwell. Morgan Reynolds 2001 112p il lib bdg $21.95 (7 and up) **92**

1. Authors, English

ISBN 1-88384-674-9 LC 2001-30877

"Beginning with school days and family life, this biography . . . describes George Orwell, author of 1984 and Animal Farm." Book Rep

This "biography will be a helpful resource for readers studying Orwell's writings. Drawing on primary sources such as letters and essays, Boerst has compiled a readable and enjoyable glimpse into the man's life and the influences that inspired his work." SLJ

Includes glossary and bibliographical references

Osama bin Laden

Landau, Elaine. Osama bin Laden; a war against the West. 21st Cent. Bks. (Brookfield) 2002 144p il lib bdg $23.90 (7 and up) **92**

1. Terrorism

ISBN 0-7613-1709-0 LC 2001-41465

Presents biographical information about militant Islamic leader Osama bin Laden, including his role in international terrorism and the beliefs that fuel his actions

"Landau's book is a comprehensive, well-researched, and in-depth look at arguably the most hated man in the country." Voice Youth Advocates

Includes bibliographical references

Loehfelm, Bill. Osama bin Laden. Blackbirch Press 2004 112p il (History's villains) lib bdg $27.45 **92**

1. Terrorism

ISBN 1-56711-760-0 LC 2003-8046

First published 2003 in Heroes and villains series

.

Contents: The sheik; Empires in the desert; Lessons of a changing world; The first jihad; Path to exile; The business of terrorism; Declaration of war; War comes to America

A biography of Osama bin Laden, radical leader of al-Queda, the international terrorist organization, including his involvement in the September 11, 2001 terrorist attacks on the United States

"This book is a coherent study of bin Laden's career, methods, and stated beliefs." SLJ

Includes bibliographical references

Parker, Charlie, 1920-1955

Frankl, Ron. Charlie Parker, musician. Chelsea House 1992 127p il (Black Americans of achievement) lib bdg $22.95 **92**

1. Jazz musicians 2. African American musicians

ISBN 0-7910-1134-8 LC 92-12126

Introduces the life and times of the noted jazz musician Charlie Parker

"In this brief, authoritative, and well-written biography of the greatest saxophonist in jazz history, Frankl conveys both the brilliance of Bird's music and the tragedy of his short life." SLJ

Includes discography and bibliographical references

Parks, Rosa, 1913-

Parks, Rosa. Rosa Parks: my story; by Rosa Parks with Jim Haskins. Dial Bks. 1992 192p il $17.99; pa $6.99 (5 and up) **92**

1. African American women 2. African Americans—Civil rights

ISBN 0-8037-0673-1; 0-14-130120-7 (pa)

LC 89-1124

Rosa Parks describes her early life and experiences with race discrimination, and her participation in the Montgomery bus boycott and the civil rights movement

"A remarkable story, a record of quiet bravery and modesty, a document of social significance, a taut drama told with candor." Bull Cent Child Books

Pasteur, Louis, 1822-1895

Ackerman, Jane. Louis Pasteur and the founding of microbiology. Morgan Reynolds Pub. 2003 144p il (Renaissance scientists) lib bdg $23.95 (7 and up) **92**

1. Scientists

ISBN 1-931798-13-3 LC 2003-17655

Follows the life and career of the French scientist who proved the existence of germs and their connection with

Pasteur, Louis, 1822-1895—*Continued*
diseases
"Students interested in science, biography, or medicine will find this an interesting account." SLJ
Includes bibliographical references

Robbins, Louise E. Louis Pasteur; and the hidden world of microbes. Oxford Univ. Press 2001 140p il (Oxford portraits in science) lib bdg $28 (7 and up)   **92**
1. Scientists
ISBN 0-19-512227-5   LC 2001-31405
This provides a "view of one of microbiology's best-known scientists, from his childhood in France as a tanner's son to his death 73 years later. The inviting format is easy to read and includes many well-captioned, black and white photographs. . . . The chronology will be especially helpful for reports. This is a valuable research tool for any library." SLJ
Includes glossary and bibliographical references

Smith, Linda Wasmer. Louis Pasteur; disease fighter. Enslow Pubs. 1997 128p il (Great minds of science) lib bdg $26.60   **92**
1. Scientists
ISBN 0-89490-790-5   LC 96-38082
A biography of the noted French scientist whose discoveries, including a rabies vaccine and the process of pasteurization, had important practical applications in both medicine and industry
"This well-rounded biography gives enough information about Pasteur's childhood and private life to be interesting but devotes most of the pages to the world-altering discoveries that put Pasteur solidly at the forefront of scientists in history." Booklist
Includes glossary and bibliographical references

Pauling, Linus C., 1901-1994
Hager, Thomas. Linus Pauling and the chemistry of life. Oxford Univ. Press 1998 142p il (Oxford portraits in science) $28 (7 and up)   **92**
1. Chemists
ISBN 0-19-510853-1   LC 97-43403
Profiles the Nobel Prize-winning chemist who described the nature of chemical bonds, made important discoveries in the fields of quantum mechanics, immunology, and evolution, and used his scientific fame to help advance political causes
"Students with a strong science background will get the most out of this biography, but even young people who don't like science will be able to identify with a man whose scientific curiosity and political principles led him to try to change the world. Chronology and recommended readings." Booklist

Paulsen, Gary
Fine, Edith Hope. Gary Paulsen; author and wilderness adventurer. Enslow Pubs. 2000 128p il (People to know) lib bdg $26.50 (5 and up)
                    92
1. Authors, American
ISBN 0-7660-1146-1   LC 99-37950

A biography of the outdoor adventurer and author, whose writing includes adventure stories, historical novels, sports books, and nature stories
"Those who have read Paulsen's books are sure to enjoy this biography, and those who have not will definitely be inspired to look for them." SLJ
Includes bibliographical references

Paulsen, Gary. Caught by the sea; my life on boats. Delacorte Press 2001 103p maps $15.95; pa $5.50 (5 and up)   **92**
1. Authors, American 2. Boats and boating 3. Ocean travel
ISBN 0-385-32645-9; 0-440-40716-8 (pa)
                    LC 2001-17336
"Paulsen traces his life at sea, from buying his first sailboat to getting lost in the Pacific to encountering sharks. . . . His sometimes comic, sometimes near-fatal sea-going errors make for absorbing, captivating reading." Booklist

Paulsen, Gary. Guts; the true stories behind Hatchet and the Brian books. Delacorte Press 2001 148p $16.95; pa $5.50   **92**
1. Authors, American
ISBN 0-385-32650-5; 0-440-40712-5 (pa)
                    LC 00-34061
Paulsen offers an autobiographical "collection of wilderness survival/hunting essays that concentrates on drawing parallels between his own life and the fictional adventures and misadventures of Brian Robeson in *Hatchet* . . . and its sequels." SLJ
"Readers squeamish about hunting or the death of animals will find many of the stories disturbing . . . but those who embrace the sport or have enjoyed the novels will see in Paulsen a responsible role model a man who respects life and death as equal partners." Booklist

Paulsen, Gary. How Angel Peterson got his name; and other outrageous tales about extreme sports. Wendy Lamb Bks. 2003 111p $12.95; lib bdg $14.99 (5 and up)   **92**
1. Authors, American
ISBN 0-385-72949-9; 0-385-90090-2 (lib bdg)
                    LC 2002-7668
Author Gary Paulsen relates tales from his youth in a small town in northwestern Minnesota in the late 1940s and early 1950s, such as skiing behind a souped-up car and imitating daredevil Evel Knievel
"Writing with humor and sensitivity, Paulsen shows boys moving into adolescence believing they can do anything. . . . None of them dies (amazingly), and even if Paulsen exaggerates the teensiest bit, his tales are side-splittingly funny and more than a little frightening." Booklist

Paulsen, Gary. My life in dog years; with drawings by Ruth Wright Paulsen. Delacorte Press 1998 137p il $15.95; pa $5.99 (4 and up)
                    92
1. Authors, American 2. Dogs
ISBN 0-385-32570-3; 0-440-41471-7 (pa)
                    LC 97-40254
Also available Thorndike Press large print edition

Paulsen, Gary—*Continued*

The author describes some of the dogs that have had special places in his life, including his first dog, Snowball, in the Philippines; Dirk, who protected him from bullies; and Cookie, who saved his life

"Paulsen differentiates his canine friends beautifully, as only a keen observer and lover of dogs can. At the same time, he presents an intimate glimpse of himself, a lonely child of alcoholic parents, who drew strength and solace from his four-legged companions and a love of the great outdoors. Poignant but never saccharine, honest, and open." Booklist

Peary, Robert Edwin, 1856-1920

Calvert, Patricia. Robert E. Peary; to the top of the world. Benchmark Bks. 2002 80p il maps (Great explorations) lib bdg $29.93   **92**

1. Explorers 2. North Pole

ISBN 0-7614-1242-5   LC 00-51900

A biography of Admiral Robert Peary whose expedition reached the North Pole in 1909

"The well-researched {book} . . . will be useful to students writing reports. Maps and archival reproductions in both black and white and color extend the text." Horn Book Guide

Includes bibliographical references

Peet, Bill

Peet, Bill. Bill Peet: an autobiography. Houghton Mifflin 1989 190p il $22; pa $15 (4 and up)   **92**

1. Walt Disney Productions 2. Authors, American 3. Illustrators

ISBN 0-395-50932-7; 0-395-68982-1 (pa)

LC 88-37067

A Caldecott Medal honor book, 1990

This memoir "describes the life of the well-known children's book author who worked as an illustrator for Walt Disney from the making of 'Dumbo' until 'Mary Poppins.'" N Y Times Book Rev

"Every page of this oversized book is illustrated with Peet's unmistakable black-and-white drawings of himself and the people, places, and events described in the text. Familiar characters from his books and movies appear often." SLJ

Pembroke, William Marshal, Earl of, 1144?-1219

Weatherly, Myra. William Marshal, medieval England's greatest knight. Morgan Reynolds 2001 112p il maps lib bdg $21.95   **92**

1. Knights and knighthood 2. Great Britain—History—1154-1399, Plantagenets

ISBN 1-88384-648-X   LC 00-48751

This is the "saga of William Marshal (1147-1219), who became a knight, fought in tournaments and wars, traveled to the Holy Land, negotiated and witnessed the Magna Carta, and served as Regent of England when Henry III was crowned king at the age of nine. . . . {The author's} account of Marshal's life is lively, informative, and full of action that pauses for a discussion of some aspect of the times." Booklist

Includes glossary and bibliographical references

Picasso, Pablo, 1881-1973

Beardsley, John. Pablo Picasso. Abrams 1991 92p il (First impressions) $19.95 (7 and up)

92

1. Artists, French

ISBN 0-8109-3713-1   LC 91-7741

Examines the life and work of Picasso, discussing how and why his art looks the way it does and how it relates to the artist

This is a "readable and informative study. . . . This book is as much a series of marvelous lessons in 'reading' art as it is a tribute to a unique artist." Horn Book

Hodge, Susie. Pablo Picasso; by Susie Hodge. {New ed}. World Almanac Library 2004 48p il (Lives of the artists) lib bdg $30; pa $11 (4 and up)   **92**

1. Artists, French

ISBN 0-8368-5601-5 (lib bdg); 0-8368-5606-6 (pa)

LC 2003-67238

Original Italian edition 2003

This discusses the life and work of the twentieth century artist

This is "concise and straightforward. . . . [It] includes remarkably accomplished sketches and paintings from the artist's childhood and adolescence." Booklist

Includes bibliographical references

Loria, Stephano. Pablo Picasso; illustrated by Simone Boni, L.R. Galante. Bedrick Bks. 1995 64p il (Masters of art) $22.50   **92**

1. Artists, French

ISBN 0-87226-318-5   LC 95-31830

The author examines periods of the artists work through full-color reproductions of major paintings. Picasso's political views, friendships, and relationships with women are discussed

MacDonald, Patricia A. Pablo Picasso; greatest artist of the 20th century. Blackbirch Press 2001 128p il (Giants of art and culture) lib bdg $27.45 (7 and up)   **92**

1. Artists, French

ISBN 1-56711-504-7   LC 00-53003

First published 1990 by Silver Burdett

In this biography of Picasso "the vibrant colors of an innovative artist come alive. . . . Numerous historical photographs add interest." Booklist

Includes glossary and bibliographical references

Scarborough, Kate. Pablo Picasso. Watts 2002 46p il map (Artists in their time) lib bdg $22; pa $6.95 (5 and up)   **92**

1. Artists, French

ISBN 0-531-12229-8; 0-531-16622-8 (pa)

LC 2002-27017

Discusses the life, art, and legacy of the artist Pablo Picasso. Includes a timeline linking the events in his life with world events

This offers a "clear and lively {text}. . . . Captioned, full-color and black-and-white photographs and art reproductions are liberally scattered throughout." SLJ

Includes glossary

Pick-Goslar, Hannah
Gold, Alison Leslie. Memories of Anne Frank.
See entry under Frank, Anne, 1929-1945

Pickett, Bill, ca. 1860-1932
Sanford, William R. Bill Pickett:
African-American rodeo star; {by} William R.
Sanford & Carl R. Green. Enslow Pubs. 1997 48p
il (Legendary heroes of the Wild West) lib bdg
$21.26   **92**
   1. Cowhands 2. African Americans—Biography
   ISBN 0-89490-676-3   LC 96-1891
   Describes the life and accomplishments of the son of
a former slave whose unusual bulldogging style made
him a rodeo star
   Includes glossary and bibliographical references

Pike, Zebulon Montgomery, 1779-1813
Calvert, Patricia. Zebulon Pike; lost in the
Rockies; by Patricia Calvert. Benchmark Books
2005 96p il map (Great explorations) lib bdg
$29.93 (5 and up)   **92**
   1. Explorers 2. West (U.S.)—Exploration
   ISBN 0-7614-1612-9   LC 2003-17583
   This "discusses the explorer's military service, relationship with the corrupt general James Wilkinson, the
historical speculation about his motives for his meandering expedition to the Spanish west, and his failure to
climb the mountain named for him. . . . Illustrated with
beautiful reproductions of period illustrations, paintings,
and maps. . . . Well-written." SLJ
   Includes bibliographical references

Pizarro, Francisco, ca. 1475-1541
Meltzer, Milton. Francisco Pizarro; the conquest
of Peru; by Milton Meltzer. Benchmark Books
2005 80p il map (Great explorations) lib bdg
$29.93 (5 and up)   **92**
   1. Explorers 2. America—Exploration
   ISBN 0-7614-1607-2   LC 2002-156000
   Contents: Where Pizarro came from; The Spanish conquistadores; The business of conquest; A glimpse of
gold; The Inca empire; Epidemics and civil wars; The
decisive day; Turning an empire into a colony
   Introduces the life of the explorer who was sent to
Peru in the sixteenth century by the king of Spain to
conquer the Incas and claim their land and wealth for the
Spanish crown.
   Includes bibliographical references

Poe, Edgar Allan, 1809-1849
Kent, Zachary. Edgar Allan Poe; tragic poet and
master of mystery. Enslow Pubs. 2001 128p il
(Historical American biographies) lib bdg $26.60
                              92
   1. Authors, American
   ISBN 0-7660-1600-5   LC 00-10994
   "The stranger-than-fiction story of the rise and fall of
one of America's most important literary figures. . . .
The biography includes material gleaned from primary-

source documents and reference works with snippets
from Poe's stories and poems. The writing is clear and
interesting, with moments of colorful prose to captivate
readers." SLJ
   Includes glossary and bibliographical references

Meltzer, Milton. Edgar Allan Poe: a biography.
Twenty-First Century Books 2003 144p $31.90 (7
and up)   **92**
   1. Authors, American
   ISBN 0-7613-2910-2   LC 2002-155802
   Contents: Theater in the blood; A quick and clever
boy; The teenager; Soldier and poet; In West Point, and
out; Satire and science fiction; Editor, novelist, husband;
Hoaxes and horrors; The first ever detective story; A
popular lecturer; New York : the rich and the poor; "The
raven" and fame; Death of the beloved; The last years;
Chronology of Poe's life
   "More than most other biographers for young people,
Meltzer places his subject within the framework of his
society. Readers will come away not only with greater
knowledge of Poe's life and accomplishments but also a
clearer picture of American life in the first half of the
nineteenth century." Booklist
   Includes bibliographical references

Polo, Marco, 1254-1323?
Otfinoski, Steven. Marco Polo; to China and
back. Benchmark Bks. 2003 77p il maps (Great
explorations) lib bdg $19.95   **92**
   1. Voyages and travels 2. Explorers 3. China—Description and travel
   ISBN 0-7614-1480-0   LC 2002-68
   Contents: A distant world; A father's journey; Marco
joins the adventure; Mountain and desert; In the court of
Kublai Khan; A most trusted aide; Escort for a princess;
Strange homecoming; A prisoner of war; Marco millions
   This describes the life of the medieval explorer and
his travels through Asia
   "Maps, contemporary drawings and paintings, and diary excerpts reveal not only the complexities of Polo's
groundbreaking adventures but also the awe and exhilara-
tion they brought him." SLJ
   Includes bibliographical references

Worth, Richard. The great empire of China and
Marco Polo in world history. Enslow Pubs. 2003
112p il map (In world history) lib bdg $26.60
                              92
   1. Voyages and travels 2. Explorers 3. China—Description and travel
   ISBN 0-7660-1939-X   LC 2002-152264
   "This book puts the explorer's travels in the context
of the Middle Ages. It begins with the history of Venice
as a center for trade and of the Polo family's position as
merchants within this society. Students are introduced to
the beliefs and customs of a number of powerful
societies of the time including the Huns and the Mongols. Interspersed are quotes from period documents.
. . . . Worth's title is a thoroughly researched account of
Polo's travels and his influence on later explorers, and
will be helpful to students writing reports." SLJ
   Includes bibliographical references

Ponce de Leon, Juan, 1460?-1521
Otfinoski, Steven. Juan Ponce de Leon; discoverer of Florida; by Steven Otfinoski. Benchmark Books 2005 77p il map (Great explorations) lib bdg $29.93 (5 and up)
          92
1. Explorers 2. America—Exploration
ISBN 0-7614-1610-2   LC 2003-17582
Contents: The soldier's way; Westward with Columbus; The Governor of Higuey; Father of Puerto Rico; The Fountain of Youth; An island called Florida; The King's favorite; At war with the Carib; To die in Florida
A biography of the Spanish explorer who was called the Father of Puerto Rico and who discovered Florida in his search for the Fountain of Youth.
Includes bibbliographical references

Powell, Colin L., 1937-
Finlayson, Reggie. Colin Powell; by Reggie Finlayson. Lerner Publications Co. 2004 112p il map (A & E biography) lib bdg $27.93; pa $7.95
          92
1. Generals 2. Statesmen—United States 3. African Americans—Biography
ISBN 0-8225-4966-2 (lib bdg); 0-8225-9698-9 (pa)
           LC 2002-156556
Contents: Ordinary or extraordinary?; The streets of New York; Soldiering on; Over where?; The home front; Lessons in leadership; Stepping stones to power; Center of the storm; Powell, peace, and war
A biography covering the childhood and military and political careers of General Colin Powell.
Includes bibliographical references

Presley, Elvis, 1935-1977
Denenberg, Barry. All shook up: the life and death of Elvis Presley. Scholastic Press 2001 176p il pa $5.99 hardcover o.p. (5 and up)   **92**
1. Rock musicians
ISBN 0-439-52811-9   LC 00-68780
This "biography of the man who swayed his hips and ushered in the age of rock 'n' roll chronicles not only the turbulent life of Elvis but the sweeping shifts he brought to popular culture. . . . The author effectively portrays the psychological motivation, professional compromises and seedy characters that contributed to Elvis's downward spiral." Publ Wkly
Includes discography, filmography, and bibliographical references

Raleigh, Sir Walter, 1552?-1618
Aronson, Marc. Sir Walter Ralegh and the quest for El Dorado. Clarion Bks. 2000 222p il map $20 (7 and up)   **92**
1. Explorers
ISBN 0-395-84827-X   LC 99-43096
In this biographical portrait "Ralegh—warrior, champion of North American colonialism, court favorite of Queen Elizabeth I, adventurer and writer—is placed in the center of a broad canvas depicting life in sixteenth-century England and beyond." Horn Book
"Incorporating critical examinations of period art and

poetry as well as standard historical documentary evidence and pausing frequently to review and explicitly support its thesis, this title is at once lively, accessible, and challenging. Period illustrations, an index, and fastidiously annotated endnotes and bibliography are included." Bull Cent Child Books

Randolph, Asa Philip, 1889-1979
Miller, Calvin Craig. A. Philip Randolph and the African American labor movement. Morgan Reynolds Pub. 2005 160p il (Portraits of Black Americans) $24.95   **92**
1. African Americans—Biography 2. African Americans—Civil rights 3. Labor unions
ISBN 1-931798-50-8
A biography of the African American leader
"Miller lucidly traces Randolph's spectacular career while presenting a case study in the effective use of hard-nosed rhetoric and nonviolent tactics to achieve breakthroughs in the fight against segregation. Profusely illustrated with photographs, sometimes in color, and capped by resource lists." Booklist
Includes bibliographical references

Rawlings, Marjorie Kinnan, 1896-1953
Cook, Judy. Natural writer: a story about Marjorie Kinnan Rawlings; by Judy Cook and Laura Lee Smith; illustrated by Laurie Harden. Carolrhoda Bks. 2001 64p il (Creative minds biography) lib bdg $21.27   **92**
1. Authors, American 2. Women authors 3. Frontier and pioneer life
ISBN 1-57505-468-X   LC 00-9657
"This biography begins with Rawling's childhood in the early 1900s and shows her development as a writer through her death. . . . This easy-to-read biography has an attractive cover and a full-page charcoal illustration in each chapter." SLJ
Includes bibliographical references

Reeve, Christopher, 1952-2004
Howard, Megan. Christopher Reeve. Lerner Pubs. 1999 128p il (A & E biography) $25.26
          92
1. Actors 2. Physically handicapped
ISBN 0-8225-4945-X   LC 98-8200
"In friendly, accessible prose, Howard offers an intimate portrait of the actor. . . . Readers may find the detailed description of Reeve's accident and physical repercussions painful to read, but will gain perspective on the daily challenges facing quadriplegics." Booklist
Includes bibliographical references

Reiss, Johanna
Reiss, Johanna. The journey back. Crowell 1976 212p hardcover o.p. paperback available $4.95
          92
1. Jews—Netherlands
ISBN 0-06-447042-3 (pa)
Sequel to The upstairs room

Reiss, Johanna—*Continued*
"The journey is the return home in the spring of 1945 for thirteen-year-old Annie and her older sister Sini. . . . The background of the early years is recapitulated. . . . The book offers an intensely provocative story, recalling many personal crises and tests of human nature cruelly beset by the dangers and deprivations of war." Horn Book

Reiss, Johanna. The upstairs room. Crowell 1972 273p $16.99; pa $5.99 (5 and up)
                                                        92
1. World War, 1939-1945—Jews 2. Netherlands—History—1940-1945, German occupation 3. Jews—Netherlands 4. Holocaust, 1933-1945—Personal narratives
ISBN 0-690-85127-8; 0-06-440370-X (pa)
Also available Spanish language edition
A NewberyMedal honor book, 1973
"In a vital, moving account the author recalls her experiences as a Jewish child hiding from the Germans occupying her native Holland during World War II. . . . Ten-year-old Annie and her twenty-year-old sister Sini, . . . are taken in by a Dutch farmer, his wife, and mother who hide the girls in an upstairs room of the farm house. Written from the perspective of a child the story affords a child's-eye-view of the war." Booklist
Followed by The journey back

Rembert, Winfred
Rembert, Winfred. Don't hold me back; my life and art; with Charles and Rosalie Baker. Cricket Books 2003 40p il $19.95 (4 and up)   **92**
1. African Americans—Biography 2. African American artists
ISBN 0-8126-2703-2   LC 2003-9980
"A Marcato book"
Through words and paintings, an artist tells about growing up on a cotton plantation in Cuthbert, Georgia, serving time in prison for his actions during a civil rights demonstration, and finding a purpose and direction in life.
"Rembert's unusual pictures are classified as 'outsider art.' . . . Each one is a piece of leather that has been carved, tooled, and dyed with rich colors. . . . This beautifully designed, very accessible book offers a vivid impression of an African American man's experiences in the mid-twentieth-century South." Booklist
Includes bibliographical references

Renoir, Auguste, 1841-1919
Rayfield, Susan. Pierre-Auguste Renoir. Abrams 1998 92p il (First impressions) $19.95 (7 and up)
                                                        92
1. Artists, French
ISBN 0-8109-3795-6   LC 98-12988
Examines the life and work of this French impressionist painter and sculptor whose work reflects his joy in life
"The author writes in a clear, informative, easy-to-read, well-organized style. The collection of 55 illustrations, 37 in full color, celebrates Renoir's artistic development." Book Rep

Revere, Paul, 1735-1818
Sullivan, George. Paul Revere. Scholastic Ref. 1999 128p il map (In their own words) $12.95; pa $4.99   **92**
1. United States—History—1775-1783, Revolution
ISBN 0-439-14748-4; 0-439-09552-2 (pa)
                                      LC 99-17381
A biography of the man made famous by a poem about the American Revolution, placing his life and work in its real historical context
Includes bibliographical references

Rizal, José, 1861-1896
Arruda, Suzanne Middendorf. Freedom's martyr; the story of Jose Rizal, national hero of the Phillipines; Suzanne Middendorf Arruda. Avisson Press 2003 106p il (Avisson young adult series) pa $19.95   **92**
1. Philippines
ISBN 1-88810-555-0   LC 2003-45320
"Born in the Philippines on June 19, 1861, Rizal was executed by the Spanish for treason on December 30, 1896. . . . Rizal wanted representation for native peoples in the Spanish government and wrote three novels and several poems detailing their plight. . . . This well-written, readable biography will prove useful for reports and background information on the history of the Philippines." SLJ
Includes bibliographical references

Robeson, Paul, 1898-1976
Wright, David K. Paul Robeson; actor, singer, political activist. Enslow Pubs. 1998 128p il (African-American biographies) $26.60   **92**
1. African Americans—Biography
ISBN 0-89490-944-4   LC 97-34194
"This book chronicles the life of 'actor, singer, political activist' Paul Robeson, and the times and country that shaped him. While style and format are targeted at young YAs, older teens doing reports will find much of value here. In addition to the index, further reading and notes on each chapter, there is also a discography, filmography and chronology of Robeson's life." BAYA Book Rev

Robinson, Jackie, 1919-1972
Robinson, Sharon. Promises to keep: how Jackie Robinson changed America. Scholastic 2004 64p il $16.95 (4 and up)   **92**
1. Baseball—Biography 2. African American athletes
ISBN 0-439-42592-1   LC 2003-42709
"Robinson's daughter, Sharon, describes her father's youth, his rise to become major-league baseball's first African American player, and his involvement in the civil rights movement. . . . Her private view of her father's accomplishments, placed within the context of American sports and social history, makes for absorbing reading. An excellent selection of family and team photographs and other materials . . . illustrate this fine tribute." Booklist

Rockefeller, John D. (John Davison), 1839-1937

Segall, Grant. John D. Rockefeller; anointed with oil. Oxford Univ. Press 2000 125p il (Oxford portraits) $28 **92**

1. Capitalists and financiers 2. Philanthropists

ISBN 0-19-512147-3 LC 00-44616

This biography presents a "view of the man, his business and personal interests, and his philanthropic legacy." Booklist

"Included in the biography are some primary documents, such as letters, photos, and cartoons, as well as references to some of the other giants of industry, such as Flagler, Carnegie, and Gould." Book Rep

Includes bibliographical references

Rockwell, Norman, 1894-1978

Gherman, Beverly. Norman Rockwell; storyteller with a brush. Atheneum Bks. for Young Readers 2000 57p il $19.95 (4 and up)

92

1. Artists—United States

ISBN 0-689-82001-1 LC 98-36546

Describes the life and work of the popular American artist who depicted both traditional and contemporary subjects, including children, family scenes, astronauts, and the poor

"The format of the biography is appealing and attractive. The pages are replete with color reproductions of Rockwell's paintings as well as photographs of the man and his family. The text is well researched and authentic; the writing style is free-flowing and the words capture the naturalness of Rockwell's paintings." SLJ

Includes bibliographical references

Roosevelt, Eleanor, 1884-1962

Freedman, Russell. Eleanor Roosevelt; a life of discovery. Clarion Bks. 1993 198p il $17.95; pa $10.95 (5 and up) **92**

1. Presidents' spouses—United States

ISBN 0-89919-862-7; 0-395-84520-3 (pa)

LC 92-25024

"Readers are made privy to the telling details of a full life through numerous quotes from Roosevelt and her wide inner circle in this frank, well-documented portrait of the 'First Lady of the World.' A superlative biography." SLJ

Includes bibliographical references

Roosevelt, Franklin D. (Franklin Delano), 1882-1945

Freedman, Russell. Franklin Delano Roosevelt. Clarion Bks. 1990 200p il $20; pa $9.95 (5 and up) **92**

1. Presidents—United States 2. United States—Politics and government—1933-1945

ISBN 0-89919-379-X; 0-395-62978-0 (pa)

LC 89-34986

The author "traces the personal and public events in a life that led to the formation of one of the most influential and magnetic leaders of the twentieth century." Horn Book

"The carefully researched, highly readable text and ex-

tremely effective coordination of black-and-white photographs chronicle Roosevelt's priviledged youth, his early influences, and his maturation. . . . Even students with little or no background in American history will find this an intriguing and inspirational human portrait." SLJ

Includes bibliographical references

Gilbert, Adrian. Franklin D. Roosevelt. Raintree Steck-Vaughn Pubs. 2003 112p il (Twentieth-century history makers) lib bdg $32.82 (7 and up) **92**

1. Presidents—United States 2. United States—Politics and government—1933-1945

ISBN 0-7398-5260-4 LC 2002-36733

Contents: A privileged upbringing; Harvard and marriage; A career in politics; War and political defeat; Disaster strikes; From New York to the White House; The first New Deal; Life in the White House; The second New Deal; The road to war; The commander-in-chief; F.D.R. and the home front; The Roosevelt legacy

A biography of the thirty-second president of the United States, who led the country during the years of World War II

This "insightful [biography is] . . . detailed and well researched." SLJ

Includes glossary and bibliographical references

Roosevelt, Theodore, 1858-1919

Donnelly, Matt. Theodore Roosevelt: larger than life. Linnet Bks. 2003 184p il lib bdg $27.50 (7 and up) **92**

1. Presidents—United States

ISBN 0-208-02510-3 LC 2002-73061

"In this biographical account of the twenty-sixth president, Donnelly offers a sense of what he calls 'Roosevelt's high-octane personality' as well as his childhood, youth, goals, careers, and achievements. . . . The illustrations include period photographs and political cartoons. Livelier than most presidential biographies, this is engaging as well as informative." Booklist

Includes bibliographical references

Fritz, Jean. Bully for you, Teddy Roosevelt! illustrations by Mike Wimmer. Putnam 1991 127p il $16.99; pa $5.99 (5 and up) **92**

1. Presidents—United States

ISBN 0-399-21769-X; 0-698-11609-7 (pa)

LC 90-8142

Follows the life of the twenty-sixth president, discussing his conservation work, hunting expeditions, family life, and political career

"Jean Fritz gives a rounded picture of her subject and deftly blends the story of a person and a picture of an era." Bull Cent Child Books

Includes bibliographical references

Kraft, Betsy Harvey. Theodore Roosevelt; champion of the American spirit. Clarion Bks. 2003 180p il $19 (5 and up) **92**

1. Presidents—United States

ISBN 0-618-14264-9 LC 2002-152825

Contents: The strenuous life; The sweetness of home; Darling wifie; The wild west; My literary work; We stirred things up; Man's work; Immense fun; A great his-

Roosevelt, Theodore, 1858-1919—*Continued*
torical expedition; New York politics; A most honorable
office; I felt at once that he had bad news; A household
of children; No easy job; A coal famine; Roosevelt's cor-
ollary; In the interest of the United States; If elected...;
A square deal; The bride at every wedding; Carry a big
stick; Good-bye, Mr. President; My hat is in the ring;
The rights of the people; My last chance to be a boy
   A biography of the energetic New Yorker who became the twenty-sixth president of the United States and
who once exclaimed "No one has ever enjoyed life more
than I have"
   "Interwoven with the well-told story of Roosevelt's
public activities is Kraft's vivid portrayal of his personal
life, laced with anecdotes and quotations (mainly from
letters) that help bring the famous figure to life. The spacious layout and the many black-and-white reproductions
of photos, drawings, and prints add to the book's appeal." Booklist
   Includes bibliographical references

Rowling, J. K.
   Chippendale, Lisa A. Triumph of the
imagination; the story of writer J.K. Rowling;
introduction by James Scott Brady. Chelsea House
2002 112p il (Overcoming adversity) lib bdg
$22.95 (5 and up)   **92**
   1. Authors, English 2. Women authors
   ISBN 0-7910-6312-7   LC 2001-47604
   "This title blends biographical data, literary review,
and the effects of the 'Harry Potter' books on the world,
written at a reading level that is accessible to many of
Rowling's fans." SLJ
   Includes bibliographical references

Runyon, Brent
   Runyon, Brent. The burn journals. Alfred A.
Knopf 2004 373p $17.95; lib bdg $18.99 (7 and
up)   **92**
   1. Burns and scalds 2. Suicide
   ISBN 0-375-82621-1; 0-375-92621-6 (lib bdg)
     LC 2004-5643
   "One February day in 1991, Runyon came home from
eighth grade . . . and set himself on fire. . . . The dialogue between Runyon and his nurses, parents, and especially his hapless psychotherapists is natural and believable, and his inner dialogue is flip, often funny, and
sometimes raw. . . . The authentically adolescent voice
of the journals will engage even those reluctant to read
such a dark story." SLJ

Rustin, Bayard, 1910-1987
   Miller, Calvin Craig. No easy answers; Bayard
Rustin and the civil rights movement; Calvin Craig
Miller. Morgan Reynolds Pub 2005 160p il lib bdg
$24.95 (7 and up)   **92**
   1. African Americans—Civil rights
   ISBN 1-931798-43-5   LC 2004-18518
   "Miller combines the life story of a great social activ-
ist with the history of the struggle for civil rights in the
U.S. The politics are exciting, with details of the radical
campaigns in the 1940s and 1950s, Rustin's impassioned

call for nonviolent protest, and his role in organizing
both the Montgomery Bus Boycott and the 1963 March
on Washington." Booklist
   Includes bibliographical references

Sacagawea, b. 1786
   St. George, Judith. Sacagawea. Putnam 1997
115p maps $16.99 (4-6)   **92**
   1. Lewis and Clark Expedition (1804-1806)
   2. Shoshoni Indians
   ISBN 0-399-23161-7   LC 96-49311
   Tells the story of the Shoshoni Indian girl who served
as interpreter, peacemaker, and guide for the Lewis and
Clark Expedition to the Northwest in 1805-1806
   "In a well-written and well-researched account, St.
George humanizes her subject. . . . Adventure lovers
will find much to like in the book." Booklist
   Includes bibliographical references

Sachar, Louis, 1954-
   Greene, Meg. Louis Sachar. Rosen Pub. Group
2004 112p il (Library of author biographies) lib
bdg $26.50 (5 and up)   **92**
   1. Authors, American
   ISBN 0-8239-4017-9   LC 2002-154252
   Contents: Meet Louis Sachar; "Louis the yard teacher"; Success; From middle school to grade school; Holes;
How does he do it?; Interview with Louis Sachar;
Timeline
   Discusses life and work of the popular children's author, including his writing process and methods, inspirations, a critical discussion of his books, biographical
timeline, and awards
   A "solid {introduction}. . . . Libraries looking to expand their biography section will be well served by
{this} informative {title}." SLJ

Saladin, Sultan of Egypt and Syria, 1137-1193
   Stanley, Diane. Saladin: noble prince of Islam.
HarperCollins Pubs. 2002 unp il $16.99; lib bdg
$18.89 (4 and up)   **92**
   1. Crusades 2. Kings and rulers
   ISBN 0-688-17135-4; 0-688-17136-2 (lib bdg)
     LC 2001-24636
   A biography of the Islamic leader who defended his
people during the Crusades
   The author demonstrates "her trademark ability to research and then distill complex topics in terms accessible
to middle-graders. . . . Stanley's precise, detailed artwork pays homage to period architecture. She evokes the
colors of Persian miniatures (and medieval stained glass)
as her paintings incorporate the complex patterning associated with Islamic art." Publ Wkly
   Includes glossary and bibliographical references

Salk, Jonas, 1914-1995
   Tocci, Salvatore. Jonas Salk; creator of the polio
vaccine. Enslow Pubs. 2003 128p il (Great minds
of science) lib bdg $20.95   **92**
   1. Scientists 2. Poliomyelitis vaccine
   ISBN 0-7660-2097-5   LC 2002-3888

Salk, Jonas, 1914-1995—*Continued*

Contents: Innocent victims; Survival and success; A change of plans; Relationships; His own project; His next project; The polio vaccine; The polio pioneers; An American hero

A biography of the American doctor and medical researcher who helped to develop successful influenza and polio vaccines, then turned his attention to vaccines for cancer and AIDS prevention

This is an "effective volume. . . . Tocci does a good job of showing how the fear of polio affected the public during the 1950s." Booklist

Includes glossary and bibliographical references

Schindler, Oskar, 1908-1974

Wukovits, John F. Oskar Schindler. Lucent Bks. 2003 112p il maps (Heroes and villains) lib bdg $21.96   **92**

1. Holocaust, 1933-1945

ISBN 1-56006-952-X   LC 2002-2221

A biography of the profit-hungry businessman who became a protector and savior of the Jews during the Nazi holocaust

"Well-placed black-and-white photos accompany a thorough, well-written text." SLJ

Includes bibliographical references

Schulke, Flip

Schulke, Flip. Witness to our times; my life as a photojournalist; {by} Flip Schulke; in association with Matt Schudel. Cricket Books 2003 112p il $19.95   **92**

1. Photographers

ISBN 0-8126-2682-6   LC 2002-151457

"A Marcato book"

Contents: Early years; The divine seed of discontent; The hardest pictures I ever took; The greatest man I ever met; Views of a troubled age; The space race and beyond; A life in pictures

An autobiography of a man whose documentary photographs in American magazines helped to shape public opinion on such issues as the civil rights movement and the space race.

"Photojournalist Schulke shot some of the most important photographs of the twentieth century, and the passion, concentration, and sensitivity that characterize his photos come across as powerfully in his prose. . . . His black-and-white photos make up most of the book, and they express such strong emotion that readers will feel the depth of his passion even on pages without a word of text." Booklist

Includes bibliographical references

Schumann, Clara, 1819-1896

Reich, Susanna. Clara Schumann; piano virtuoso. Clarion Bks. 1999 118p il $18; pa $9.95 (5 and up)   **92**

1. Pianists 2. Women composers

ISBN 0-395-89119-1; 0-618-55160-3 (pa)

     LC 98-24510

Describes the life of the German pianist and composer who made her professional debut at age nine and who

devoted her life to music and to her family

"This thoroughly researched book draws on primary sources, both Clara's own diaries and her voluminous correspondence with her husband. . . . Reich's lucid, quietly passionate biography is liberally illustrated with photographs and reproductions." Horn Book Guide

Sequoyah, 1770?-1843

Klausner, Janet. Sequoyah's gift; a portrait of the Cherokee leader; with an afterword by Duane H. King. HarperCollins Pubs. 1993 111p il lib bdg $15.89 (4 and up)   **92**

1. Cherokee Indians

ISBN 0-06-021236-5   LC 92-24939

"Sequoyah is best remembered for his remarkable feat of creating a Cherokee syllabary that allowed his people to read and write their own language. Klausner's detailed account includes discussion of Sequoyah's role during the Trail of Tears journey, the forced removal in 1838 of the Cherokee nation from Georgia to what became Oklahoma. . . . This is a solid work with many applications for study." Booklist

Includes bibliographical references

Serra, Junípero, 1713-1784

Dolan, Sean. Junípero Serra. Chelsea House 1991 111p il (Hispanics of achievement) pa $9.95 hardcover o.p.   **92**

1. Explorers 2. Christian missionaries

ISBN 0-7910-1282-4   LC 91-6863

Focuses on the achievements of the eighteenth-century Spanish missionary who was one of the early explorers of California

"Clearly written and objective, the text presents an intriguing picture of the man's life." SLJ

Includes bibliographical references

Seuss, Dr.

Dean, Tanya. Theodor Geisel. Chelsea House 2002 112p il (Who wrote that?) $22.95 (4 and up)   **92**

1. Authors, American 2. Illustrators

ISBN 0-7910-6724-6   LC 2002-166

Describes the life and career of the author and illustrator known as Dr. Seuss who created such popular children's picture books as The cat in the hat, How the Grinch stole Christmas, and Horton hears a Who

"Well organized and clearly written." Booklist

Includes bibliographical references

Shackleton, Sir Ernest Henry, 1874-1922

Calvert, Patricia. Sir Ernest Shackleton; by endurance we conquer. Benchmark Bks. 2003 80p il maps (Great explorations) lib bdg $19.95   **92**

1. Endurance (Ship) 2. Imperial Trans-Antarctic Expedition (1914-1917) 3. Antarctica 4. Explorers

ISBN 0-7614-1485-1   LC 2002-3784

Contents: A pig-headed, obstinate boy; Afraid of nothing; Don't expect a feather bed; No eagles in the barnyard; An old dog for the hard road; The long road home; He never spares himself; A lone star above the bay

Shackleton, Sir Ernest Henry, 1874-1922—*Continued*

Presents the life and Arctic explorations of Sir Ernest Shackleton

"This concise and straightforward account is enhanced by archival photos, reproductions, and maps." SLJ

Includes bibliographical references

Johnson, Rebecca L. Ernest Shackleton; gripped by the Antarctic. Carolrhoda Bks. 2003 112p il maps (Trailblazer biography) lib bdg $25.26 **92**

1. Endurance (Ship) 2. Imperial Trans-Antarctic Expedition (1914-1917) 3. Antarctica 4. Explorers

ISBN 0-87614-920-4 LC 2002-6816

A biography of Sir Ernest Shackleton, the daring, charismatic Antarctic explorer who fell short of his goal of crossing Antarctica, but accomplished a far greater feat by bringing every member of his crew back alive

"The writing is lively and clear and the story is compelling. A useful title for reports and recreational reading." SLJ

Includes bibliographical references

Siegal, Aranka

Siegal, Aranka. Upon the head of the goat: a childhood in Hungary, 1939-1944. Farrar, Straus & Giroux 1981 213p $16; pa $5.95 **92**

1. World War, 1939-1945—Jews 2. Jews—Hungary 3. Holocaust, 1933-1945—Personal narratives

ISBN 0-374-38059-7; 0-374-48079-6 (pa)

LC 81-12642

Also available in paperback from Viking

The author "recalls her childhood in Hungary at the time of Hitler's rise to power. As the book opens, she is nine years old and is trapped in the Ukraine at her grandmother's as the border is temporarily closed. When she returns to Hungary, she begins to feel more acutely the impact of the war on her life. . . . As the story ends the author and her family are boarded on a train for Auschwitz." Voice Youth Advocates

"The story is familiar . . . but a few pages into Aranka Siegal's fine memoir . . . you feel the power and interest of her particular experience and remember that this story cannot be told too often." Newsweek

Simmons, Philip

Lyons, Mary E. Catching the fire: Philip Simmons, blacksmith; with photographs by Mannie Garcia. Houghton Mifflin 1997 47p il $17 (4 and up) **92**

1. African American artists

ISBN 0-395-72033-8 LC 96-38643

Tells the story of this African American artist, the great-grandson of slaves, who has achieved fame and admiration for his ornamental wrought-iron creations

"The narrative, based on Simmons' memories and words, involves readers through its lively presentation of an intriguing subject. . . . Photographs appear on every spread, with black-and-white pictures of Simmons' early days and beautifully lit and composed color shots of the man today." Booklist

Includes bibliographical references

Smith, John, 1580-1631

Doherty, Kieran. To conquer is to live: the life of Captain John Smith of Jamestown. 21st Cent. Bks. (Brookfield) 2001 144p il lib bdg $23.90 **92**

1. United States—History—1600-1775, Colonial period 2. Jamestown (Va.)—History

ISBN 0-7613-1820-8 LC 00-44309

A biography of the English soldier and adventurer who helped establish the colony of Jamestown, Virginia

A "well-written, appealing biography. . . . This book reads much like a swashbuckling adventure and most likely will inspire further interest in the man." SLJ

Includes bibliographical references

Spielberg, Steven, 1947-

Rubin, Susan Goldman. Steven Spielberg; crazy for movies. Abrams 2001 94p il $19.95 **92**

1. Motion picture producers and directors

ISBN 0-8109-4492-8 LC 00-69973

"This overview of Spielberg's life and career is of particular interest because of its insights into the director's childhood and his youthful interest in moviemaking. Illustrated with family photos and film stills, the clearly written volume explains how each of Spielberg's major movies came to be made." Horn Book Guide

Includes glossary and bibliographical references

Spinelli, Jerry, 1941-

Spinelli, Jerry. Knots in my yo-yo string; the autobiography of a kid. Knopf 1998 148p il lib bdg $16.99; pa $10.95 (4 and up) **92**

1. Authors, American

ISBN 0-679-98791-6 (lib bdg); 0-679-88791-1 (pa)

LC 97-30827

Also available Thorndike Press large print edition

This Italian-American Newbery Medalist presents a humorous account of his childhood and youth in Norristown, Pennsylvania

"There is an 'everyboy' universality to Spinelli's experiences, but his keen powers of observation and recall turn the story into a richly rewarding personal history." Horn Book Guide

Stalin, Joseph, 1879-1953

Ingram, Scott. Joseph Stalin. Blackbirch Press 2003 112p il maps (History's villains) $23.95 **92**

1. Dictators 2. Soviet Union—History

ISBN 1-56711-626-4 LC 2002-8427

Chronicles the youth, rise to power, and dictatorial reign of the Soviet Union's Joseph Stalin

"This text intrigues the reader immediately. . . . The information is interesting and sometimes gossipy, which may draw readers in." Libr Media Connect

Includes glossary and bibliographical references

Stanton, Elizabeth Cady, 1815-1902

Sigerman, Harriet. Elizabeth Cady Stanton; the right is ours. Oxford Univ. Press 2001 143p il (Oxford portraits) $28 (7 and up) **92**

1. Feminism
ISBN 0-19-511969-X   LC 2001-31404

A biography of one of the first leaders of the women's rights movement, whose work led to women's right to vote

"This inspiring biography . . . is both interestingly written and easy to follow. . . . Black-and-white photographs and original documents add greatly to the appeal of this resource." SLJ

Includes bibliographical references

Steinbeck, John, 1902-1968

Reef, Catherine. John Steinbeck. Clarion Bks. 1996 163p il $17.95; pa $8.95 (7 and up) **92**

1. Authors, American
ISBN 0-395-71278-5; 0-618-43244-2 (pa)
LC 95-11500

"The book traces Steinbeck's life from his childhood in California, to his burgeoning writing career and his passion for social justice, to his worldwide recognition. Reef does an excellent job of synthesizing Steinbeck's work, his private life, and his politics and philosophy." Bull Cent Child Books

Includes bibliographical references

Tessitore, John. John Steinbeck, a writer's life. Watts 2001 143p il $26 (7 and up) **92**

1. Authors, American
ISBN 0-531-11707-3   LC 00-38200

After tracing "Steinbeck's early life, the text moves quickly to his adulthood and his life as a writer. Subsequent chapters chronicle his uneven journey to literary acclaim, his lifelong search for issues and voice, and his pursuit of excellence in his craft. Quotations from Steinbeck's work preface each chapter. This well-documented book will be appreciated by students for its wealth of information, conciseness, and readability." SLJ

Includes bibliographical references

Steinem, Gloria

Lazo, Caroline Evensen. Gloria Steinem; feminist extraordinaire. Lerner Publs. 1998 128p il $27.93 (7 and up) **92**

1. Feminism
ISBN 0-8225-4934-4   LC 97-16831

"Looking at Steinem's difficult childhood, her experiences in India, her career as a journalist, and her role as an advocate for women's rights and a cofounder of *Ms.* magazine, this biography presents a thorough picture of an influential leader of the modern women's movement." Horn Book Guide

Includes bibliographical references

Steiner, Matt

Warren, Andrea. Escape from Saigon; how a Vietnam War orphan became an American boy. Farrar, Straus and Giroux 2004 110p il map $17 **92**

1. Vietnamese Americans 2. Vietnam War, 1961-1975 3. Interracial adoption
ISBN 0-374-32224-4   LC 2003-60672

"Melanie Kroupa books"

Chronicles the experiences of an orphaned Amerasian boy from his birth and early childhood in Saigon through his departure from Vietnam in the 1975 Operation Babylift and his subsequent life as the adopted son of an American family in Ohio.

"The child-at-war story and the facts about the Operation Babylift rescue are tense and exciting. Just as gripping is the boy's personal conflict." Booklist

Stevenson, Robert Louis, 1850-1894

Murphy, Jim. Across America on an emigrant train. Clarion Bks. 1993 150p il $18; pa $9.95 (5 and up) **92**

1. Authors, Scottish 2. Railroads—History 3. United States—Description and travel
ISBN 0-395-63390-7; 0-395-76483-1 (pa)
LC 92-38650

"Murphy presents a forthright and thoroughly engrossing history of the transcontinental railway, with entries from Robert Louis Stevenson's 1879 journal as he rode cross country. It's also an inviting introduction to Stevenson, with a romance in the bargain." SLJ

Includes bibliographical references

Stiles, Jackie, 1978-

Stewart, Mark. Jackie Stiles; gym dandy. Millbrook Press 2002 48p il (Basketball's new wave) lib bdg $22.90 (4 and up) **92**

1. Basketball 2. Women athletes
ISBN 0-7613-2614-6   LC 2002-2670

A biography of WNBA star Jackie Stiles, a guard for the Portland Fire who was named Rookie of the Year in 2001

This title is distinguished by "a breezy, narrative style and well-selected color photos. . . . [This is a] solid, well-presented [volume]." Booklist

Still, Peter, b. 1801

Fradin, Dennis B. My family shall be free!: the life of Peter Still; {by} Dennis Brindell Fradin. HarperCollins Pubs. 2001 190p il $16.99; lib bdg $17.89 **92**

1. Slavery—United States 2. African Americans—Biography
ISBN 0-06-029595-3; 0-06-029328-4 (lib bdg)
LC 00-44862

"Fradin tells the story of Peter Still's life in slavery, buying his freedom at age fifty, reuniting with his long-lost mother and siblings in the North, and returning to rescue his wife and children still in the South." Horn Book Guide

This "book is an engrossing saga that is both sweeping and intensely personal." Booklist

Includes bibliographical references

Stone, Miriam

Stone, Miriam. At the end of words; a daughter's memoirs. Candlewick Press 2003 55p $14 (7 and up) **92**

1. Stone, Martha Kaufman, 1949-1999 2. Cancer 3. Death 4. Mother-daughter relationship

ISBN 0-7636-1854-3   LC 2002-73703

The author records her feelings and experiences as she realizes that her mother is dying of cancer

"What moves the book beyond message is the raw, simple, personal imagery. . . . The prose is as rhythmic and poetic as the verse. . . . Anyone who mourns a loved one will relate to this." Booklist

Stowe, Harriet Beecher, 1811-1896

Fritz, Jean. Harriet Beecher Stowe and the Beecher preachers. Putnam 1994 144p il $15.99; pa $5.99 (5 and up) **92**

1. Beecher family 2. Women authors 3. Authors, American 4. Abolitionists

ISBN 0-399-22666-4; 0-698-11660-7 (pa)

LC 93-6408

This is a biography of the abolitionist author of "Uncle Tom's Cabin," with an emphasis on the influence of her preacher father and her family on her life and work

"Written with vivacity and insight, this readable and engrossing biography is an important contribution to women's history as well as to the history of American letters." Horn Book

Includes bibliographical references

Tan, Amy

Shields, Charles J. Amy Tan. Chelsea House 2002 116p il (Women of achievement) lib bdg $22.95; pa $9.95 **92**

1. Authors, American 2. Women authors 3. Chinese Americans—Biography

ISBN 0-7910-5889-1 (lib bdg); 0-7910-5890-5 (pa)

LC 01-47334

Explores the life and career of Amy Tan, from her childhood in California, through her struggle to accept her Chinese heritage, to her career as a writer

This offers a "lively, well-organized text. . . . An absorbing read, whether for pleasure or a classroom assignment." SLJ

Includes bibliographical references

Teresa, Mother, 1910-1997

Ruth, Amy. Mother Teresa. Lerner Publs. 1999 112p il (A & E biography) $27.93 **92**

1. Missionaries of Charity 2. Nuns

ISBN 0-8225-4943-3   LC 98-23315

A biography of the nun who founded the order known as the Missionaries of Charity to work with the sick and destitute in Calcutta and other places and who was awarded the Nobel Peace Prize in 1979

Includes bibliographical references

Terrell, Mary Church, 1863-1954

Fradin, Dennis B. Fight on!: Mary Church Terrell's battle for integration; [by] Dennis Brindell Fradin & Judith Bloom Fradin. Clarion Bks. 2003 181p il $17 **92**

1. African American women 2. African Americans—Civil rights

ISBN 0-618-13349-6   LC 2002-151356

Contents: Mary Church Terrell's family tree; Who was Mary Church Terrell?; A bowl of soup; Bob Church's daughter; "Hold high the banner of my race"; "I am a colored girl"; "The welfare of my race"; Mr. Terrell "goes to Church"; "Lifting as we climb"; "I have done so little"; A "meddler"; "I intend never to grow old"; "Your indomitable spirit"; "Fight on"; "Your long and valiant struggle"

Profiles the first black Washington D.C. Board of Education member, who helped to found the NAACP and organized pickets and boycotts that led to the 1953 Supreme Court decision to integrate D.C. area restaurants

"In this carefully researched, fascinating biography, the life of the feisty, courageous, and determined woman . . . vividly unfolds." SLJ

Includes bibliographical references

Lommel, Cookie. Mary Church Terrell; speaking out for civil rights. Enslow Pubs. 2003 112p il (African-American biographics) $20.95 **92**

1. African American women 2. African Americans—Civil rights

ISBN 0-7660-2116-5   LC 2002-10401

Contents: Lost laws; A child of privilege; Education was her life; A born activist; The turning point; The lecture circuit; Women's rights; Serving education; The NAACP calls; An author of note; The tireless organizer

Traces the life and achievements of the black civil rights worker whose greatest accomplishment, the integration of restaurants in Washington, D.C., came when she was nearly ninety years old

"With its open format and interesting accounts of events in Terrell's life, this well-documented biography will satisfy general readers as well as students writing reports." SLJ

Includes bibliographical references

Thoreau, Henry David, 1817-1862

Thoreau, Henry David. New suns will arise; from the diaries of Henry David Thoreau; photography by John Dugdale; text edited by Frank Crocitto. Hyperion Bks. for Children 2000 76p il $24.99 **92**

1. Authors, American 2. Naturalists

ISBN 0-7868-0539-0   LC 00-29601

Selections from Thoreau's journals spanning the whole of his writing career. John Dugdale's cyanotypes were developed using an early photographic process

Tillage, Leon, 1936-

Tillage, Leon. Leon's story; {by} Leon Walter Tillage; collage art by Susan L. Roth. Farrar, Straus & Giroux 1997 107p il $15; pa $4.95 (4 and up)   **92**

1. African Americans—Biography 2. North Carolina—Race relations

ISBN 0-374-34379-9; 0-374-44330-0 (pa)

LC 96-43544

The son of a North Carolina sharecropper recalls the hard times faced by his family and other African Americans in the first half of the twentieth century and the changes that the civil rights movement helped bring about

The author's "voice is direct, the words are simple. There is no rhetoric, no commentary, no bitterness. . . . This quiet drama will move readers of all ages . . . and may encourage them to record their own family stories." Booklist

Tiulana, Paul, 1921-1994

Tiulana, Paul. Wise words of Paul Tiulana; an Inupiat Alaskan's life; {edited} by Vivian Senungetuk. Watts 1998 80p il maps (In their own voices) $24   **92**

1. Inuit

ISBN 0-531-11448-1   LC 97-51859

"An earlier version of this book was published as A place for winter: Paul Tiulana's story, by the CIRI Foundation in 1987." Verso of title page

Presents the life of an Alaskan hunter, storyteller, craftsman, and traditional leader who grew up on King Island, Alaska, in the 1920s

"The text is taken from interviews with Tiulana in 1987 and has been updated since his death in 1994. Added are a note about the Jesuit whose contemporary photos illustrate the story, and a brief outline of how one might go about writing the stories of one's own elders." Booklist

Includes bibliographical references

Tolkien, J. R. R. (John Ronald Reuel), 1892-1973

Lynch, Doris. J.R.R. Tolkien; creator of languages and legends. Franklin Watts 2003 127p il (Great life stories) $29.50   **92**

1. Authors, English

ISBN 0-531-12253-0   LC 2003-958

Contents: An ocean voyage; A home in Hobbitland; Animalic, Nevbosh, and Naffarin; Tea clubs and poetry; From Quenya to secret codes; In the shadow of war; From hospital elves to forest muses; Walrus to Leeds; Oxford again; On hobbits and fairy stories; Hobbits and beyond; Birth of a trilogy; The Shire lives on

"Lynch explains how the beloved hobbit came to be created by a man whose fascination with dead languages led him to write fantasy stories, as well as to create and study language throughout his lifetime. Tolkien's fans will meet the man behind the tales. . . . Readers will be touched and inspired by this carefully crafted portrait." SLJ

Includes bibliographical references

Willett, Edward. J.R.R. Tolkien; master of imaginary worlds. Enslow Publishers 2004 128p il (Authors teens love) lib bdg $26.60   **92**

1. Authors, English

ISBN 0-7660-2246-3   LC 2003-15657

Examines the personal life and literary career of the author of the Lord of the Rings trilogy

This "clearly goes a step beyond the typical series book, offering a more perceptive and more detailed, satisfying portrayal of its subject. . . . [The] volume includes a great deal of back matter: a time line, a list of selected works, a glossary, detailed chapter notes, and lists of recommended books and Internet sites." Booklist

Includes bibliographical references

Truth, Sojourner, d. 1883

Brezina, Corona. Sojourner Truth's "Ain't I a woman?" speech; a primary source investigation; Corona Brezina. 1st ed. RosenCentral Primary Source 2005 64p il (Great historic debates and speeches) $29.25   **92**

1. African American women 2. Feminism 3. Abolitionists

ISBN 1-4042-0154-8   LC 2004-1443

"Brezina faces an unusual challenge in this volume. . . . Because Sojourner Truth could neither read nor write, there is no authoritative version of the speech under discussion. The book does a good job with the topic, though, by providing clearly written biographical information about Truth, offering a straightforward account of the versions of the speech that were reported, discussing their relative merits, and including two texts in an appendix." Booklist

Butler, Mary G. Sojourner Truth; from slave to activist for freedom. PowerPlus Bks. 2003 112p il map (Library of American lives and times) lib bdg $31.95 (5 and up)   **92**

1. Abolitionists 2. African American women 3. Feminism

ISBN 0-8239-5736-5   LC 2001-6169

Contents: Slavery in America; The slave Isabella; Living free; The sojourn begins; The Northampton Association ; On the lecture circuit; The Battle Creek years; The legend grows; The nation divided; The last crusade

A biography of the former slave who became an abolitionist and advocate for women's rights

"The text is well documented, and the numerous illustrations, photos, and reproductions, both in color and in black and white, are authoritative and informative." SLJ

Includes glossary and bibliographical references

Krass, Peter. Sojourner Truth. Chelsea House 1988 110p il (Black Americans of achievement) lib bdg $23.95; pa $9.95   **92**

1. African American women 2. Abolitionists 3. Feminism

ISBN 1-55546-611-7 (lib bdg); 0-7910-0215-2 (pa)

LC 88-6107

Traces the life of the former slave who could neither read nor write, yet earned a reputation as one of the most articulate and outspoken antislavery and women's rights activists in the United States

Includes bibliographical references

Tubman, Harriet, 1815?-1913

Schraff, Anne E. Harriet Tubman; Moses of the Underground Railroad. Enslow Pub 2001 128p il map (African-American biographies) lib bdg $26.60 **92**

1. African American women 2. Underground railroad

ISBN 0-7660-1548-3 LC 00-10953

This biography describes Tubman's "life from her birth into slavery on a Maryland plantation around 1820 . . . until her death in 1913. In discussing Tubman's life as a slave, Schraff does not gloss over the harsh treatment her subject received. The book also mentions Tubman's service to the Union during the Civil War, working as a nurse, scout, and spy." SLJ

Includes bibliographical references

Taylor, M. W. (Marian W.). Harriet Tubman. Chelsea House 1991 111p il (Black Americans of achievement) lib bdg $23.95; pa $9.95 **92**

1. African American women 2. Underground railroad

ISBN 1-55546-612-5 (lib bdg); 0-7910-0249-7 (pa) LC 89-77281

"Beginning with her tough and often brutal treatment as a young child in slavery, Taylor traces the development of an unconventional and heroic woman. . . . A good, solid biography." SLJ

Includes bibliographical references

Turner, Nat, 1800?-1831

Bisson, Terry. Nat Turner. Chelsea House 1988 111p il (Black Americans of achievement) pa $9.95 hardcover o.p. **92**

1. African Americans—Biography 2. Slavery—United States

ISBN 0-7910-0214-4 (pa) LC 87-37559

A biography of the slave and preacher who, believing that God wanted him to free the slaves, led a major revolt in 1831

"A well-written, sympathetic biography. . . . Bisson creates an excellent background to Turner's life, describing not only the daily life of a slave, but also how it felt to have no control over one's destiny. The violence of Turner's revolt is toned down a bit for the younger audience, without losing the chaotic emotions behind it." SLJ

Includes bibliographical references

Twain, Mark, 1835-1910

Lasky, Kathryn. A brilliant streak: the making of Mark Twain; illustrated by Barry Moser. Harcourt Brace & Co. 1998 41p il $18 (4 and up) **92**

1. Authors, American

ISBN 0-15-252110-0 LC 95-18479

An illustrated biography of young Samuel Clemens, who grew up to be the writer known as Mark Twain

"An obvious delight in her subject makes Lasky's biography an appealing choice, and a similar enthusiasm invests Moser's illustrations." Horn Book Guide

Includes bibliographical references

Mark Twain; Todd Howard, book editor. Greenhaven Press 2002 190p il (People who made history) lib bdg $34.95; pa $23.70 **92**

1. Authors, American

ISBN 0-7377-0897-2 (lib bdg); 0-7377-0896-4 (pa) LC 2001-28923

A collection of essays about the American author and humorist with primary source documents

Includes bibliographical references

Meltzer, Milton. Mark Twain himself; produced by Milton Meltzer. Wings Bks. 1993 303p il map $12.99 **92**

1. Authors, American

ISBN 0-517-01248-0 LC 92-42530

A reissue of the title first published 1960 by Crowell

This pictorial biography combines photographs, drawings, cartoons and other illustrations with selections from Twain's autobiography, letters, notebooks, fiction and other writings

Includes bibliographical references

Vázquez de Coronado, Francisco, 1510-1549

Otfinoski, Steven. Francisco Coronado; in search of the seven cities of gold. Benchmark Bks. 2003 76p il maps (Great explorations) lib bdg $19.95 **92**

1. Explorers

ISBN 0-7614-1484-3 LC 2002-3935

Contents: A gentleman of Spain; A new life in the New World; The grandest expedition; The battle of Cibola; Lands of wonders; Trouble at Tiguex; The sea of grass; End of the rainbow; A conquistador's fall

This describes Coronado's life and his explorations in the Southwestern United States in the 1540s

Includes bibliographical references

Verne, Jules, 1828-1905

Schoell, William. Remarkable journeys: the story of Jules Verne. Morgan Reynolds 2002 112p il (World writers) lib bdg $21.95 **92**

1. Authors, French

ISBN 1-88384-692-7 LC 2002-2016

A biography of the nineteenth-century Frenchman whose childhood love of literature, science, and adventure, along with his vivid imagination, led him to become a highly successful science fiction author

"Thanks to Schoell's smooth, crisp writing, this fascinating, approachable biography, which lends insight into Verne's eccentric characters and relatives, proves nearly as exciting as the writer's best stories." Booklist

Includes bibliographical references

Ward, Nancy, 1738?-1822

Furbee, Mary R. Wild Rose: Nancy Ward and the Cherokee Nation. Morgan Reynolds 2002 112p il maps lib bdg $21.95 **92**

1. Cherokee Indians

ISBN 1-88384-671-4 LC 00-54884

This is a biography of the leader of the Cherokee Indians

"The style is lively, engaging, and accessible, and the story is fascinating." SLJ

Includes bibliographical references

Warhol, Andy, 1928?-1987
Greenberg, Jan. Andy Warhol; prince of pop;
[by] Jan Greenberg & Sandra Jordan. Delacorte
Press 2004 193p il $16.95 (7 and up)   **92**
1. Artists—United States 2. Pop art
ISBN 0-385-73056-X   LC 2003-24102
A biography of the 20th century American artist famous for his Pop art images of Campbell's soup cans
and Marilyn Monroe.
"Greenberg and Jordan offer a riveting biography that
humanizes their controversial subject without making
judgments or sensationalizing." Booklist
Includes glossary and bibliographical references

Washington, Booker T., 1856-1915
Washington, Booker T. Up from slavery; an
autobiography   **92**
1. Tuskegee Institute
Hardcover and paperback editions available from vari-
ous publishers
First published 1901
"The classic autobiography of the man who, though
born in slavery, educated himself and went on to found
Tuskegee Institute." N Y Public Libr

Washington, Denzel
Hill, Anne E. Denzel Washington. Chelsea
House 1999 96p il (Black Americans of
achievement) $23.95 (7 and up)   **92**
1. African American actors
ISBN 0-7910-4692-3   LC 98-15401
"Hill traces the meteoric rise of this media star
through stage and television roles to feature films. In his
career, Washington has avoided typecasting; instead, he
has exhibited chameleonlike versatility in playing a variety of figures. . . . Stock black-and-white photographs,
mostly of the actor in his various roles, appear throughout." SLJ
Includes filmography and bibliographical references

Washington, George, 1732-1799
Adler, David A. George Washington; an
illustrated biography; by David A. Adler. 1st ed.
Holiday House 2004 274p il map $24.95 (5 and
up)   **92**
1. Presidents—United States
ISBN 0-8234-1838-3   LC 2003-67606
This "look at America's premier founding father literally spans his lifetime and attempts to focus . . . on how
Washington's early character formation impacted his decisions as a military officer and later as president. . . .
The illustrations are largely engravings from the late 19th
century. . . . The writing style is accessible without ever
falling prey to oversimplification." SLJ

Allen, Thomas B. George Washington,
spymaster; how America outspied the British and
won the Revolutionary War; featuring illustrations
by Cheryl Harness. National Geographic 2004
184p il $16.95   **92**
1. United States—History—1775-1783, Revolution
2. Spies 3. Presidents—United States
ISBN 0-7922-5126-1   LC 2003-6019

Contents: Birth of a spymaster; Spy against spy; A
spy must die; George Washington, Agent 711; Tools of
the spymaster; Franklin's French friends; Spymaster at
work; The General is a spy; Victory in the spy war
A biography of Revolutionary War general and first
President of the United States, George Washington, focusing on his use of spies to gather intelligence that
helped the colonies win the war.
"Allen presents the facts with a gleeful edge, clearly
enjoying his subject and writing with vigor. . . . Set in
an antique typeface, {the book} is well illustrated with
black-and-white reproductions of archival art and Harness's charming pen-and-ink sketches." SLJ
Includes glossary and bibliographical references

Rosenburg, John M. First in peace: George
Washington, the Constitution, and the presidency;
{by} John Rosenburg. Millbrook Press 1998 256p
il lib bdg $25.90 (7 and up)   **92**
1. Presidents—United States
ISBN 0-7613-0422-3   LC 98-18631
First volume in the author's biographical trilogy begun
with: First in war (1998) and Young George Washington
(1997)
"Rosenburg opens the book with Washington's resig-
nation as commander in chief of the Continental Army
and goes on to outline significant events such as the
Constitutional Convention, the Whiskey Rebellion, and
debates concerning controversial issuses like slavery and
taxation. The author's straightforward, factual narrative
contains a painstaking amount of detail sprinkled with dialogue and primary-source material." SLJ

Washington, Martha, 1731-1802
McPherson, Stephanie Sammartino. Martha
Washington; first lady. Enslow Pubs. 1998 128p il
(Historical American biographies) lib bdg $26.60
           92
1. Presidents' spouses—United States
ISBN 0-7660-1017-1   LC 97-23478
Traces the life of the wife of the first president of the
United States, from her childhood in Virginia through
her marriage to George Washington to her role in the
American Revolution and the early years of the new
country's history
"The author describes the historical events of the time
to set the scene, but does not let George Washington
overshadow Martha's story. The facts are accurate and
sidebars add anecdotal information about this period in
American history." SLJ
Includes bibliographical references

Watson, James D., 1928-
Edelson, Edward. James Watson and Francis
Crick and the building blocks of life. Oxford Univ.
Press 1998 110p il (Oxford portraits in science)
$28 (7 and up)   **92**
1. Crick, Francis, 1916-2004 2. Scientists 3. Genetics
ISBN 0-19-511451-5   LC 97-42791
Describes the collaboration of Watson and Crick in
the effort to discover DNA
This dual biography is "also a history of the develop-
ment of modern molecular biology. . . . The science is
well presented and quite current." Sci Books Films
Includes bibliographical references

Watson, James D., 1928——*Continued*

Hamilton, Janet. James Watson; solving the mystery of DNA. Enslow Publishers 2004 104p il (Nobel Prize-winning scientists) lib bdg $26.60
92

1. Scientists 2. Genetics
ISBN 0-7660-2258-7 LC 2003-22972

A biography of James Watson, one of the scientists who helped discover the structure of DNA, the carrier of heredity in higher organisms.

This "makes science exciting for young readers. . . . Black-and-white portraits, photographs, and diagrams add to the text. . . . This solidly researched title fills a gap and is entertainingly written." Sci Books Films

Includes glossary and bibliographical references

Watt, James, 1736-1819

Sproule, Anna. James Watt; master of the steam engine. Blackbirch Press 2001 64p il (Giants of science) lib bdg $24.95
92

1. Inventors
ISBN 1-56711-338-9 LC 01-35462

A biography of the eighteenth-century Scottish inventor and engineer whose improved designs of the steam engine made its wide use possible

This "delivers vital biographical information while focusing on scientific principles and applications. . . . The illustrations are outstanding." Book Rep

Includes glossary and bibliographical references

Weber, EdNah New Rider

Weber, EdNah New Rider. Rattlesnake Mesa; stories from a native American childhood; by EdNah New Rider Weber; photographs by Richela Renkun. 1st ed. Lee & Low Books 2004 132p il (4 and up)
92

1. Native Americans
ISBN 1-58430-231-3 LC 2004-2385

"Weber grew up in the early twentieth century on the Crown Point Navajo Reservation . . . and she attended a government boarding school for Native American children. She recounts childhood experiences in both places." Booklist

"Weber describes her experiences with warmth and affection in this unusually compelling memoir. Striking black-and-white photos . . . add to the book's appeal." Horn Book Guide

Webster, Daniel, 1782-1852

Harvey, Bonnie C. Daniel Webster; "Liberty and union, now and forever"; {by} Bonnie Carman Harvey. Enslow Pubs. 2001 112p il maps (Historical American biographies) lib bdg $26.60
92

ISBN 0-7660-1392-8 LC 00-9662

"Harvey's chronological account covers Webster's life from his birth in 1782 to his death in 1852. The author includes information about the statesman's childhood, education, and years in politics as well as his oratory skills and personal life. . . . Readers will find *Webster* sufficiently detailed without being overwhelming." SLJ

Includes glossary and bibliographical references

Wells-Barnett, Ida B., 1862-1931

Davidson, Sue. Getting the real story: Nellie Bly and Ida B. Wells. See entry under Bly, Nellie, 1864-1922

Lisandrelli, Elaine Slivinski. Ida B. Wells-Barnett; crusader against lynching. Enslow Pubs. 1998 128p il (African-American biographies) lib bdg $26.60 (7 and up)
92

1. African American women 2. African Americans—Civil rights
ISBN 0-89490-947-9 LC 97-34253

Traces the life and career of the African American journalist and social activist who spoke out against the lynching of blacks in the South

"Students looking for material on this well-known crusader will appreciate this clearly written biography." SLJ

Includes bibliographical references

Wheatley, Phillis, 1753-1784

Richmond, M. A. (Merle A.). Phillis Wheatley; {by} Merle Richmond. Chelsea House 1987 111p il (American women of achievement) lib bdg $23.95; pa $9.95
92

1. Poets, American 2. African American authors 3. Women poets
ISBN 1-55546-683-4 (lib bdg); 0-7910-0218-7 (pa) LC 87-6626

Traces the life of the black American poet who was born in Africa, brought over to New England as a slave, and published her first poem while still a teenager

"The biographer indulges in much drumbeating and grandiose foreshadowing . . . and provides no footnotes, but she is careful to distinguish fact from surmise, making this a readable introduction to a remarkable woman." Booklist

Includes bibliographical references

Salisbury, Cynthia. Phillis Wheatley; legendary African-American poet. Enslow Pubs. 2001 112p il map (Historical American biographies) lib bdg $26.60
92

1. Poets, American 2. African American authors 3. Women poets
ISBN 0-7660-1394-4 LC 00-8882

Follows the life of one of America's first black poets from her sale as a child slave on the Boston auction block to her death as an impoverished freedwoman in 1784

"A practical, well-documented introduction to the life and work of the poet. . . . The main events of Wheatley's life are related in a clear fashion; the text is organized into interesting subheadings and accompanied by period maps and reproductions." SLJ

Includes glossary and bibliographical references

Whistler, James McNeill, 1834-1903

Berman, Avis. James McNeill Whistler. Abrams 1993 92p il (First impressions) $19.95 (7 and up)
92

1. Artists—United States
ISBN 0-8109-3968-1 LC 93-9453

Whistler, James McNeill, 1834-1903—*Continued*
A biography of the nineteenth-century American artist who spent most of his life in Europe and is known for his flamboyant personality, as well as his innovative painting and printmaking techniques and famous portrait of his mother

This book is "filled with attractive black-and-white and color reproductions. . . . Berman's text . . . is chatty and readable, fleshing out the character of Whistler as well as describing in clear and concise terms his techniques and philosophies." Bull Cent Child Books

Whitman, Walt, 1819-1892
Kerley, Barbara. Walt Whitman; words for America; illustrated by Brian Selznick. Scholastic Press 2004 unp il $16.95 (4 and up)   **92**
1. Poets, American
ISBN 0-439-35791-8   LC 2003-20085
A biography of the American poet whose compassion led him to nurse soldiers during the Civil War, to give voice to the nation's grief at Lincoln's assassination, and to capture the true American spirit in verse

"Delightfully old-fashioned in design, {the book's} oversized pages are replete with graceful illustrations and snippets of poetry. The brilliantly inventive paintings add vibrant testimonial to the nuanced text." SLJ

Meltzer, Milton. Walt Whitman; a biography. 21st Cent. Bks. (Brookfield) 2002 160p il lib bdg $31.90 (7 and up)   **92**
1. Poets, American
ISBN 0-7613-2272-8   LC 2001-27798
"The book honestly explores Whitman's character and actions, including his racial prejudice and his tendency to write anonymous (and effective) praises of his own writing. Ultimately, this has a definite edge and relevance that gives it more resonance than blander overviews of the poet. . . . Photographs of Whitman and his family, images of his work, and reproductions of period illustrations . . . liven up the formatting." Bull Cent Child Books
Includes bibliographical references

Reef, Catherine. Walt Whitman. Clarion Bks. 1995 148p il $16.95; pa $7.95 (7 and up)
              92
1. Poets, American
ISBN 0-395-68705-5; 0-618-24616-9 (pa)
              LC 94-7405
"Here is a biography of Whitman that presents the life of the subject, the world in which he lived, and representative passages from his writings." Voice Youth Advocates
"This is not a biography for pleasure reading, but it could be a source for those interested in historical events of 19th century America. It also would be a good resource for students doing a critique of Whitman's work for an American literature course." Book Rep
Includes bibliographical references

Wilder, Laura Ingalls, 1867-1957
Anderson, William T. Laura Ingalls Wilder; a biography; by William Anderson. HarperCollins Pubs. 1992 240p il pa $6.99 hardcover o.p. (4 and up)   **92**
1. Authors, American 2. Frontier and pioneer life 3. Women authors
ISBN 0-06-446103-3   LC 91-33805
A biography of the writer whose pioneer life on the American prairie became the basis for her "Little House" books
"A readable biography that is easily accessible to middle grade children who are likely to read the Little House books. Particularly interesting are the sections that fill in the gaps in Wilder's stories." Booklist

Williams, Roger, 1604?-1683
Gaustad, Edwin Scott. Roger Williams; prophet of liberty; {by} Edwin S. Gaustad. Oxford Univ. Press 2000 139p il maps (Oxford portraits) $28 (7 and up)   **92**
1. Puritans 2. United States—History—1600-1775, Colonial period
ISBN 0-19-513000-6   LC 00-56675
"Gaustad recounts Williams's life and identifies his contribution to the concept of religious liberty. His lively prose never transgresses scholarly limits, but makes the most of the few biographical details available. . . . The author makes excellent use of primary-source excerpts." SLJ
Includes bibliographical references

Williams, Serena, 1981-
Williams, Venus. Venus & Serena. See entry under Williams, Venus, 1980-

Williams, Venus, 1980-
Williams, Venus. Venus & Serena; serving from the hip, ten rules for living, loving, and winning; [by] Venus and Serena Williams with Hilary Beard. Houghton Mifflin 2005 133p il pa $14 (7 and up)   **92**
1. Williams, Serena, 1981- 2. Tennis 3. African American athletes 4. Women athletes
ISBN 0-618-44913-2   LC 2004-13204
"The sisters and tennis players . . . give teens advice on everyday living, showing them how to aim high and reach their goals. The 10 rules for success include building a 'dream team' (people who support your goals), doing well in school, learning self-respect, valuing friendships, taking care of yourself emotionally and physically, obtaining financial security, and overcoming setbacks. The final chapter discusses the virtues of volunteerism and charity. . . . Never preachy and always practical, this is a welcome addition to most collections." SLJ

Wilson, Edith Bolling Galt, 1872-1961
Flanagan, Alice K. Edith Bolling Galt Wilson, 1872-1961. Children's Press 1998 111p il (Encyclopedia of first ladies) $34.50   **92**
1. Presidents' spouses—United States
ISBN 0-516-20596-X   LC 98-7893

Wilson, Edith Bolling Galt, 1872-1961—*Continued*

Presents a biography of the wife of the twenty-eighth president of the United States, a woman who helped her husband manage the affairs of his office after he suffered a stroke

Includes bibliographical references

Winthrop, John, 1588-1649

Aronson, Marc. John Winthrop, Oliver Cromwell, and the Land of Promise. Clarion Books 2004 205p il map $20 (7 and up) 92

1. Cromwell, Oliver, 1599-1658 2. Puritans 3. Massachusetts—History—1600-1775, Colonial period 4. Great Britain—History—1603-1714, Stuarts
ISBN 0-618-18177-6 LC 2003-16418

Looks at how the lives of John Winthrop, governor of Massachusetts, and Oliver Cromwell, Lord Protector of the Puritan Commonwealth in England, were intertwined at a time of conflict between church and state and between Native and European Americans

"The accessible text is accompanied by excerpts from primary source documents and vivid illustrations. The author's passion for the period comes across in his writing. Aronson provides an excellent source for historical and biographical data." Voice Youth Advocates

Includes bibliographical references

Wollstonecraft, Mary, 1759-1797

Miller, Calvin Craig. Mary Wollstonecraft and the rights of women. Morgan Reynolds 1999 112p il (World writers) $21.95 (7 and up) 92

1. Authors, English 2. Women authors 3. Feminism
ISBN 1-88384-641-2 LC 99-13519

A "anecdotal portrait of a founding member of the women's rights movement. Victimized by a father whose 'bad habits' eroded family finances, and exposed to the gender inequities of 18th-century British society, Wollstonecraft sought independence through work as a lady's companion, a school teacher, and a governess. . . . She found her voice at last, however, in writing and published several works, including *Thoughts on the Education of Daughters* (1786) and *A Vindication of the Rights of Woman* (1792)." SLJ

"Miller's lively biography of this most interesting woman makes an excellent resource for students studying the women's movement or modern history." Booklist

Includes bibliographical references

Woodson, Carter Godwin, 1875-1950

Durden, Robert Franklin. Carter G. Woodson; father of African-American history. Enslow Pubs. 1998 128p il (African-American biographies) lib bdg $26.60 (7 and up) 92

1. Historians 2. African Americans—Biography
ISBN 0-89490-946-0 LC 97-30243

A biography of the son of former slaves who received a Ph.D. in history from Harvard and devoted his life to bringing the achievements of his race to the world's attention

"This balanced and documented account focuses on the historian's successes and failures (his prickly personality alienated many would-be supporters). Black-and-white photographs appear throughout." SLJ

Includes bibliographical references

Wright, Frank Lloyd, 1867-1959

Rubin, Susan Goldman. Frank Lloyd Wright. Abrams 1994 92p il (First impressions) $19.95 (7 and up) 92

1. Architects
ISBN 0-8109-3974-6 LC 93-48523

"Rubin integrates Wright's life story with a detailed focus on his development as an architect and on his wide and lasting influence." Booklist

"Lots of photographs and illustrations, many in full color, provide a look at many interesting projects, including the only dog house Wright ever designed." SLJ

Wright, David K. Frank Lloyd Wright; visionary architect. Enslow Pubs. 1999 128p il (People to know) lib bdg $26.60 92

1. Architects
ISBN 0-7660-1032-5 LC 97-29056

Examines the life and career of the American architect, detailing the evolution of his innovative design and the structures which won him fame around the world

Includes bibliographical references

Wright, Orville, 1871-1948

Collins, Mary. Airborne: a photobiography of Wilbur and Orville Wright. National Geographic Soc. 2003 63p il maps $18.95 (4 and up) 92

1. Wright, Wilbur, 1867-1912 2. Aeronautics—History
ISBN 0-7922-6957-8 LC 2002-5279

Examines the lives of the Wright brothers and discusses their experiments and triumphs in the field of flight

"The well-chosen photos give readers a feel for Kitty Hawk—windy, sandy, solitary. This is an exceptionally well-informed picture of the Wright brothers and what their 100-year-old achievement really meant." SLJ

Freedman, Russell. The Wright brothers: how they invented the airplane; with original photographs by Wilbur and Orville Wright. Holiday House 1991 129p il hardcover o.p. paperback available $12.95 92

1. Wright, Wilbur, 1867-1912 2. Aeronautics—History
ISBN 0-8234-1082-X (pa) LC 90-48440

A Newbery Medal honor book, 1992

In this "combination of photography and text, Freedman reveals the frustrating, exciting, and ultimately successful journey of these two brothers from their bicycle shop in Dayton, Ohio, to their Kitty Hawk flights and beyond. . . . An essential purchase for younger YAs." Voice Youth Advocates

Includes bibliographical references

Wright, Orville, 1871-1948—*Continued*

Sproule, Anna. The Wright brothers; the birth of modern aviation. Blackbirch Press 1999 64p il (Giants of science) lib bdg $24.95; pa $9.95
92
1. Wright, Wilbur, 1867-1912 2. Aeronautics—History
ISBN 1-56711-328-1; 1-41030-507-4 (pa)
LC 98-49139
A biography of the brothers who made the world's first flight in a power-driven, heavier-than-air machine at Kitty Hawk, North Carolina, in 1903
"Sproule does a good job of explaining the science behind the Wright brothers' flight and the progression and enormity of their efforts at Kitty Hawk to worldwide air travel." SLJ
Includes bibliographical references

Wright, Richard, 1908-1960

Hart, Joyce. Native son: the story of Richard Wright. Morgan Reynolds 2002 128p il (World writers) lib bdg $21.95 (7 and up) **92**
1. Authors, American 2. African American authors
ISBN 1-931798-06-0   LC 2002-13686
Contents: A troubling beginning; Memphis; Finding a voice; Exploring the Communist Party; First book; Reaching the masses; Controversy; Black boy; Expatriate
Traces the life and achievements of the twentieth-century African American novelist, whose early life was shaped by a strict grandmother who had been a slave, an illiterate father, and a mother educated as a schoolteacher
"The writing is accessible and flows smoothly." SLJ
Includes bibliographical references

Wright, Wilbur, 1867-1912

Collins, Mary. Airborne: a photobiography of Wilbur and Orville Wright. See entry under Wright, Orville, 1871-1948
Freedman, Russell. The Wright brothers: how they invented the airplane. See entry under Wright, Orville, 1871-1948
Sproule, Anna. The Wright brothers. See entry under Wright, Orville, 1871-1948

Wyeth, Andrew, 1917-

Meryman, Richard. Andrew Wyeth. Abrams 1991 92p il (First impressions) $19.95 (7 and up)
92
1. Artists—United States
ISBN 0-8109-3956-8   LC 90-47605
The author "provides in-depth coverage of the painter's formative years. . . . The book contains a number of black-and-white photographs and 28 full-color plates that complement the text nicely. Although the book presents paintings created as recently as 1988, the biography ends in the late 1940s. . . . This is a beautiful, powerful book that stresses the significance of childhood." SLJ

Yang, Jerry, 1968-

Sherman, Josepha. Jerry Yang and David Filo; chief yahoos of Yahoo! 21st Cent. Bks. (Brookfield) 2001 80p il (Techies) lib bdg $23.90
92
1. Filo, David 2. Yahoo! Inc. 3. Computer software industry 4. Businessmen
ISBN 0-7613-1961-1   LC 00-66790
This is a dual biography of the executives who founded the Yahoo! internet search engine
"Fairly short and definitely accessible, the {book} will appeal not only to report writers, but also to recreational readers." SLJ
Includes bibliographical references

Yep, Laurence

Yep, Laurence. The lost garden. Messner 1991 117p il (In my own words) o.p. HarperCollins Pubs. paperback available $4.95 (5 and up)
92
1. Authors, American 2. Chinese Americans
ISBN 0-688-13701-6 (pa)   LC 90-40647
The author describes how he grew up as a Chinese American in San Francisco and how he came to use his writing to celebrate his family and his ethnic heritage
"The writing is warm, wry, and humorous. . . . *The Lost Garden* will be welcomed as a literary autobiography for children and, more, a thoughtful probing into what it means to be an American." SLJ

Zaharias, Babe Didrikson, 1911-1956

Freedman, Russell. Babe Didrikson Zaharias; the making of a champion. Clarion Bks. 1999 192p il $18 (5 and up) **92**
1. Women athletes
ISBN 0-395-63367-2   LC 98-50208
A biography of Babe Didrikson, who broke records in golf, track and field, and other sports, at a time when there were few opportunities for female athletes
"Freedman's measured yet lively style captures the spirit of the great athlete. . . . Plenty of black-and-white photos capture Babe's spirit and dashing good looks; the documentation . . . is impeccable." Horn Book
Includes bibliographical references

Zenatti, Valérie, 1970-

Zenatti, Valérie. When I was a soldier; a memoir; translated by Adriana Hunter. Bloomsbury Children's Books 2005 235p $16.95 (7 and up)
92
1. Women soldiers 2. Israel
ISBN 1-58234-978-9
In this "memoir, Zenatti, first among her group of friends to be called for compulsory military service, chronicles two years of growing up in the Israeli army between 1988 and 1990." SLJ
A "fast, wry, present-tense memoir. . . . Readers on all sides of the war-peace continuum, here and there, will find much to talk about." Booklist

929 Genealogy, names, insignia

Douglas, Ann, 1942-
The family tree detective; cracking the case of your family's story; illustrated by Stephen MacEachern. Owl Bks. (Toronto); distributed by Firefly Bks. (Buffalo) 1999 48p il pa $9.95 hardcover o.p. **929**
1. Genealogy
ISBN 1-895688-89-2 (pa)
"In 16 brief chapters, a . . . method for conducting genealogical research is outlined. General background predominates in the first four sections, which cover rationale, basic Mendelian genetics, and degrees of relatedness. The rest of the book introduces various interviewing techniques, data collection and storage, and ways to present the story of a family once it is together. . . . MacEachern's cartoon illustrations are bright and energetic enough to carry readers through the more nuts-and-bolts portions. A brief glossary and short but accurate index round out this useful resource." SLJ

Perl, Lila
The great ancestor hunt; the fun of finding out who you are; drawings by Erika Weihs; illustrated with photographs. Clarion Bks. 1989 104p il pa $8.95 hardcover o.p. (5 and up) **929**
1. Genealogy
ISBN 0-395-54790-3 (pa)   LC 88-36211
The author "weaves the how-to of genealogy with a historical perspective on immigration. All the basics are covered: drawing an ancestry chart, conducting interviews with relatives, finding family memorabilia, and, for those who wish to continue their quest, writing away for documentation. The format is also a plus. Interesting black-and-white photos alternate with charts, diagrams, and a few (softly executed) drawings by Erika Weihs." Booklist
Includes bibliographical references

Taylor, Maureen, 1955-
Through the eyes of your ancestors. Houghton Mifflin 1999 86p il $17; pa $8.95 (4 and up) **929**
1. Genealogy
ISBN 0-395-86980-3; 0-395-86982-X (pa)
LC 98-8776
Discusses genealogy, the study of one's family, examining how such an interest develops, how to get started, how to use family stories and keepsakes, where to get help, and the positive effects of such study
"Motivated young researchers with adult help will find the book a good starting place." SLJ
Includes bibliographical references

Wolfman, Ira
Climbing your family tree; online and offline genealogy for kids: the official Ellis Island handbook; foreword by Alex Haley; illustrations by Michael Klein. Workman 2002 228p il pa $13.95 **929**
1. Genealogy
ISBN 0-7611-2539-6   LC 2002-16797

A revised edition of Do people grow on family trees? published 1990
A guide to finding out one's own family history using web sites, libraries, archives and other public records
This "is so fascinating that one becomes motivated to start a genealogical search. . . . Throughout the book, photographs and special boxed portions add to the text to make it interesting. Bibliographies and Web sites are included throughout the chapters." Libr Media Connect

929.9 Flags

Bateman, Teresa
Red, white, blue, and Uncle who? the stories behind some of America's patriotic symbols; illustrated by John O'Brien. Holiday House 2001 64p il $16.95; pa $6.95 (4 and up) **929.9**
1. National emblems 2. National monuments
ISBN 0-8234-1285-7; 0-8234-1784-0 (pa)
LC 00-57258
This "volume presents 17 'patriotic symbols,' an umbrella term that encompasses everything from the flag to Uncle Sam, from Mount Rushmore to the Korean War Memorial. Bateman finds plenty of interesting information to share about each symbol or site, and browsers will be entertained by the many stories of origination, construction, and history." Booklist
Includes bibliographical references

Flags of the world. Grolier Educ. 1997 9v il maps set $289 (4 and up) **929.9**
1. Flags
ISBN 0-7172-9159-6   LC 97-24204
Depicts the flags of every independent nation, as well as the flags of the U.S. states and territories and those of Canadian provinces and territories
"Arrangement is attractive and accessible. . . . *Flags of the World* is an impressive, comprehensive, and useful compilation, bound to receive heavy use in school and public library environments." Booklist

Shearer, Benjamin F.
State names, seals, flags, and symbols; a historical guide. 3rd ed, rev and expanded. Greenwood Press 2001 495p il $73.95 **929.9**
1. Geographic names—United States 2. Seals (Numismatics) 3. Flags—United States
ISBN 0-313-31534-5   LC 2001-23525
First published 1987
"Chapters on mottoes, flowers, trees, birds, songs, holidays, and license plates are just a sampling of what is covered, and the format is such that the concisely written material can be found as expeditiously as possible. Even though the book is touted predominantly as a reference tool, the information provided makes fascinating and enlightening reading." Libr J {review of 1994 edition}
Includes bibliographical references

Smith, Whitney
Flag lore of all nations. Millbrook Press 2001
112p il map $29.90; pa $12.95 (4 and up)
929.9
1. Flags
ISBN 0-7613-1753-8; 0-7613-1899-2 (pa)
LC 00-48973
"Arranged alphabetically, each country's flag is illustrated, with an accompanying text covering its history,
symbolism, and lore, if appropriate. . . . With two countries per page, readers can easily locate the material.
Flags and any images on them are crisply and cleanly
displayed, with colors remaining true." SLJ
Includes glossary and bibliographical references

930   History of ancient world to
ca.499

Ancient civilizations. Grolier Educ. 2000 10v il
maps $369 (5 and up)   **930**
1.   Ancient   civilization—Encyclopedias
2. Archeology—Encyclopedias
ISBN 0-7172-9471-4   LC 99-28387
This encyclopedia incorporates "three types of alphabetical entries. The first describes in selective detail an
ancient civilization or people. The second chronicles the
discovery of noteworthy and unique archeological sites
and examines the evidence that provides solid clues as to
their former inhabitants. The third type of entry is a discussion of specific subjects such as medicine and surgery
and their role in various cultures. . . . The profuse illustrations include clearly captioned color photos and drawings and lucid maps."
Includes bibliographical references

Exploring ancient civilizations. Marshall
Cavendish 2004 11v il map set $471.36
930
1. Ancient civilization—Encyclopedias
ISBN 0-7614-7456-0   LC 2003-41224
Contents: v1 Aboriginal culture-Aryans; v2 Ashoka-
Chang'an; v3 Chavin-Dong Son culture; v4 Drama-Great
Wall of China; v5 Greece-Indian philosophy; v6 Indus
Valley-Marduk; v7 Marriage-Nero; v8 Nineveh-Religion;
v9 Roads-Sports and entertainment; v10 Stonehenge-
Zoroastrianism; v11 Index
"Containing 249 cross-referenced articles, this alpha-
betically organized encyclopedia . . . covers the time period between 6,500 B.C.E and 500 C.E., the span begin-
ning with the development of writing and agriculture and
concluding with the fall of the Roman Empire. . . .
Clearly reproduced color photos, reproductions, and maps
enhance the readable text. {This set is} accessible, attractive, informative, and recommended." Booklist
Includes bibliographical references

Knight, Judson
Ancient civilizations: almanac; Stacy A.
McConnell and Lawrence W. Baker, editors.
U.X.L 1999 2v set $110 (7 and up)   **930**
1. Ancient civilization
ISBN 0-7876-3982-6   LC 99-46791

Provides historical information and interpretation on
ancient civilizations in Egypt, Mesopotamia, Asia Minor,
China, Africa, Israel, and elsewhere
Includes bibliographical references

Pickels, Dwayne E.
Egyptian kings and queens and classical deities.
Chelsea House 1997 64p il (Looking into the past:
people, places, and customs) lib bdg $20.95
930
1.   Kings   and   rulers   2.   Egypt—Civilization
3. Classical mythology
ISBN 0-7910-4677-X   LC 97-25504
Introduces a dozen kings and queens of ancient Egypt
and relates the often amazing exploits of other figures
from the classical age of Greek and Roman mythology
Includes bibliographical references

Service, Pamela F.
300 B.C. Benchmark Bks. 2003 96p il maps
(Around the world in—) lib bdg $28.50
930
1. Ancient history
ISBN 0-7614-1080-5   LC 00-36026
Surveys important occurrences in Europe, Africa,
Asia, and the Americas 2300 years ago
"Well written, informative, attractively designed and
illustrated, and logically organized." Libr Media Connect
Includes glossary and bibliographical references

930.1   Archaeology

Barnes, Trevor
Archaeology; foreword by Tony Robinson.
Kingfisher 2004 63p il map (Kingfisher
knowledge) $11.95 (5 and up)   **930.1**
1. Archeology
ISBN 0-7534-5768-7
Explores the science of excavating and examining the
debris of centuries of human life, from the Iron Age to
recent history
Includes glossary and bibliographical references

Deem, James M.
Bodies from the bog. Houghton Mifflin 1998
42p il $16; pa $5.95 (4 and up)   **930.1**
1. Mummies 2. Prehistoric peoples 3. Archeology
ISBN 0-395-85784-8; 0-618-35402-6 (pa)
LC 97-12010
Describes the discovery of bog bodies in northern Europe and the evidence which their remains reveal about
themselves and the civilizations in which they lived
"The text is engaging and accessible, and the starkly
dramatic photos are given dignity by the spacious and
understated page design." Horn Book Guide

Getz, David, 1957-

Frozen man; illustrated by Peter McCarty. Holt & Co. 1994 68p il maps $14.95; pa $8.95 (5 and up)   **930.1**

1. Mummies 2. Prehistoric peoples 3. Archeology

ISBN 0-8050-3261-4; 0-8050-4645-3 (pa)

LC 94-9109

"A Redfeather book"

"This is an account of the mummified stone-age corpse who was found in Austria in 1991. . . . Getz's generally well-organized information and smooth exposition makes the effort to understand the Iceman, as this book calls him, into an intriguing detective story. This could well stimulate the interest of kids who didn't think they liked science or archeology. Black-and-white drawings include useful maps and diagrams." Bull Cent Child Books

Includes glossary and bibliographical references

Macdonald, Fiona

The Stone Age news. Candlewick Press 1998 32p il maps $16.99; pa $6.99   **930.1**

1. Stone Age 2. Prehistoric peoples

ISBN 0-7636-0451-8; 0-7636-1291-X (pa)

LC 97-41255

Uses a newspaper format to present the inventions, lifestyles, climate changes, and progress in hunting and farming of the Stone Age

"The layout is impressive, yielding copious amounts of information while remaining easy on the eye. . . . Enjoyable and useful in the classroom, with endless possibilities for discussion and tie-in projects." Booklist

McGowen, Tom

Giant stones and earth mounds. Millbrook Press 2000 80p il lib bdg $25.90   **930.1**

1. Megalithic monuments 2. Mounds and mound builders 3. Stone Age

ISBN 0-7613-1372-9

LC 00-25687

Describes the mysterious standing stones and earth mounds which were built by Stone Age peoples and explores how and why they may have been built

"Attractive, full-color photographs dramatically show mysterious hills and stone giants from around the world, including a mound in West Virginia and animal-shaped formations in Ohio and Wisconsin." Booklist

Includes bibliographical references

McIntosh, Jane

Archeology; written by Jane McIntosh. Knopf 1994 63p il (Eyewitness books) (4 and up)

930.1

1. Archeology

LC 94-9378

Available DK Pub. edition $15.99; lib bdg $19.99 (ISBN 0-7894-5864-0; 0-7894-6605-8)

"A Dorling Kindersley book"

This volume "touches on aspects of archaeology in many locations around the world. Each double-page spread examines one or two concepts: preservation and decay, excavation, clues to the past, human remains, fakes and forgeries, etc. . . . Readers are not likely to use this book for research, but will want to make repeated short visits." SLJ

Moloney, N. (Norah)

The young Oxford book of archaeology; {by} Norah Moloney. Oxford Univ. Press 1997 160p il maps pa $18.95 hardcover o.p. (7 and up)

930.1

1. Archeology 2. Antiquities

ISBN 0-19-910100-0 (pa)

LC 97-16096

Defines archaeology, examines how archaeologists work, surveys excavation methods, and visits archaeology sites—from Olduvai Gorge in Tanzania to the Garbage Project in America

"For anyone looking for report topics covering the most significant finds of the 19th and 20th centuries, this will be the place to start. . . . The stunning full-color photographs and illustrations found on every page will entice browsers of a wide age group, but the text is sophisticated." SLJ

Includes glossary

Patent, Dorothy Hinshaw

Secrets of the ice man. Benchmark Bks. 1999 72p il (Frozen in time) $28.50 (5 and up)

930.1

1. Mummies 2. Prehistoric peoples 3. Archeology

ISBN 0-7614-0782-0

LC 97-49512

Describes the examination of the Ice Man, his clothing and equipment, found in the Alps near the Austrian-Italian border in September 1991 and thought to be more than 4000 years old

This book is "well researched." Book Rep

Includes glossary and bibliographical references

Reinhard, Johan

Discovering the Inca Ice Maiden; my adventures on Ampato. National Geographic Soc. 1998 48p il $17.95 (5 and up)   **930.1**

1. Mummies 2. Peru—Antiquities 3. Incas 4. Archeology

ISBN 0-7922-7142-4

LC 97-31291

"Vibrant color photographs of the mummy and Incan artifacts found on the expedition illustrate the engrossing text." Horn Book Guide

Includes glossary

Smith, KC

Exploring for shipwrecks. Watts 2000 63p $24.50; pa $8.95   **930.1**

1. Underwater exploration 2. Shipwrecks 3. Excavations (Archeology)

ISBN 0-531-20377-8; 0-531-16471-3 (pa)

LC 99-40537

"Watts library"

Introduces the discipline of underwater archaeology and the techniques used to find and study submerged ships. Ancient ships such as the Cheops vessel from Egypt and the Ulubrurn wreck of the Bronze Age are highlighted

Includes bibliographical references

931   China to 420 A.D.

Cotterell, Arthur
Ancient China; written by Arthur Cotterell; photographed by Alan Hills & Geoff Brightling. Knopf 1994 63p il maps (Eyewitness books) (4 and up)   **931**
1. China—Civilization
LC 94-9319
Available DK Pub. edition $15.99; lib bdg $19.99 (ISBN 0-7894-5866-7; 0-7894-6604-X)
"A Dorling Kindersley book"
"This volume touches upon such topics as Chinese history, the first emperor, inventions, health and medicine, waterways, food and drink, clothing, the Silk Road, and arts and crafts. . . . The book will . . . be popular for browsing." SLJ

DuTemple, Lesley A., 1952-
The Great Wall of China. Lerner Publs. 2003 80p il maps (Great building feats) lib bdg $27.93 (5 and up)   **931**
1. Great Wall of China
ISBN 0-8225-0377-8   LC 2001-3271
A history of the building of the various pieces of the Great Wall of China, with details of how the walls were built through the ages
"A well-researched and engaging account of one of humankind's most fascinating engineering feats. . . . Full-color photos, diagrams, as well as reproductions of ancient illustrations are plentiful and enliven the presentation." SLJ
Includes bibliographical references

Immell, Myra
The Han dynasty. Lucent Bks. 2003 96p il maps (Lost civilizations) lib bdg $21.96   **931**
1. China—History
ISBN 1-59018-096-8   LC 2002-3816
A "look at China's fifth dynasty (206 B.C.E. to C.E. 220). . . . Immell first puts this period into the context of what came before. After describing the history of the dynasty, she looks at various aspects of the era: the belief systems, the role of the emperor, the development and training of the bureaucracy, and the agricultural system. Written in an easily understandable, though sophisticated, style, the book contains a wealth of well-organized information." SLJ
Includes bibliographical references

O'Connor, Jane, 1947-
The emperor's silent army; terracotta warriors of Ancient China. Viking 2002 48p il $17.99 (4 and up)   **931**
1. Ch'in Shih-huang, Emperor of China, 259-210 B.C.—Tomb 2. China—Antiquities
ISBN 0-670-03512-2   LC 2001-46900
Describes the archaeological discovery of thousands of life-sized terracotta warrior statues in northern China in 1974, and discusses the emperor who had them created and placed near his tomb

"This intriguing book is enhanced by beautiful illustrations—pictures of stone engravings, colorful paintings, drawings, and maps—while numerous photographs show the clay soldiers from different perspectives. . . . The author's writing style is entertaining, yet informative." Book Rep
Includes bibliographical references

Schomp, Virginia, 1953-
The ancient Chinese; written by Virginia Schomp. Franklin Watts 2004 112p il map (People of the ancient world) $29.50; pa $9.95 (5 and up)   **931**
1. China—Civilization
ISBN 0-531-11817-7; 0-531-16737-2 (pa)
LC 2004-2174
Contents: At the center of the world; Kings and emperors; Civil servants and nobles; Philosophers and holy men; Peasant farmers and soldiers; Artisans and silk makers; Merchants and traders; Inventors, scientists, and healers; Writers and artists; The legacy of ancient China
"Focusing mainly on the Shang, Zhou, Qin, and Han dynasties, this book explores ancient China through its social structure. It takes a look at its people and details the duties of an emperor, the activities of a merchant, and . . . more. It also describes some of the discoveries and writings that have led to our present-day understanding of this . . . civilization." Publisher's note
"Crisp reproductions of visuals, along with impressive ancilliary content. . . . help make [this title] among the best available on ancient [China]." Booklist
Includes bibliographical references

932   Egypt to 640 A.D.

Baker, Rosalie F.
Ancient Egyptians; people of the pyramids; {by} Rosalie F. and Charles F. Baker. Oxford Univ. Press 2001 189p il maps (Oxford profiles) $50 (7 and up)   **932**
1. Egypt—Civilization 2. Egypt—Biography
ISBN 0-19-512221-6   LC 2001-21209
"Divided into five periods from the Old Kingdom, about 2686 B.C., to the declining New Kingdom, about 245 B.C., this book profiles some 30 Egyptian leaders, devoting a three- to seven-page chapter to each one. . . . The entries are well written and researched. . . . A useful addition for report writers and subject enthusiasts." SLJ
Includes glossary and bibliographical references

Berger, Melvin, 1927-
Mummies of the pharaohs; exploring the Valley of the Kings; [by] Melvin Berger & Gilda Berger. National Geographic Soc. 2001 64p il $17.95   **932**
1. Egypt—Antiquities 2. Mummies
ISBN 0-7922-7223-4   LC 00-55411
"Beginning with the . . . discovery of King Tut's tomb, . . . the book continues through other . . . finds, introducing a few of the major rulers and their relation-

Berger, Melvin, 1927-—*Continued*
ships, as well as speculation on the political scandals that surrounded some burials." SLJ

This offers "stunning photographs and clear, compelling text. . . . A fascinating historical resource that kids will read straight through for pleasure and also find useful for report writing." Booklist

Giblin, James, 1933-
Secrets of the Sphinx; by James Cross Giblin; illustrated by Bagram Ibatoulline. Scholastic Press 2004 47p il map $17.95 (4 and up)   **932**
   1. Egypt—Antiquities 2. Egypt—Civilization
   ISBN 0-590-09847-0   LC 2003-19666
Discusses some of Egypt's most famous artifacts and monuments, including the pyramids, the Rosetta Stone, and, especially, the Great Sphinx, presenting research and speculation about their origins and their future

"In his signature plain style the . . . author presents a wealth of scholarship. . . . He vividly conveys the drama of recent discoveries. . . . The photorealistic gouache and watercolor illustrations are beautiful." Booklist
Includes bibliographical references

Green, Robert, 1969-
Tutankhamun. Watts 1996 64p il map pa $6.95 hardcover o.p.   **932**
   1. Tutankhamen, King of Egypt 2. Egypt—Antiquities
   ISBN 0-531-15802-0 (pa)   LC 95-46150
"A First book"
Tells the story of the discovery of Tutankhamen's tomb by Howard Carter and Lord Carnarvon and the supposed curse connected with it, as well as information on the life and dynasty of the pharaoh

"This account nicely intermingles details of what is known about the pharaoh and his reign with Howard Carter's amazing rediscovery. . . . Full-color and black-and-white photographs show objects described in the text, and a timeline and list of Internet sites provide backup information." SLJ
Includes bibliographical references

Harris, Geraldine
Ancient Egypt; Geraldine Harris. rev ed. Facts on File 2003 96p il map (Cultural atlas for young people) $35 (5 and up)   **932**
   1. Egypt—Civilization 2. Egypt—Antiquities
   ISBN 0-8160-5148-8   LC 2003-40869
First published 1990
Maps, charts, illustrations, and text explore the history and culture of ancient Egypt

This "is replete with enough colorful maps, time lines, photographs, and illustrations to satisfy even the most finicky student." Voice Youth Advocates
Includes glossary and bibliographical references

Hart, George, 1945-
Ancient Egypt; written by George Hart. Knopf 1990 63p il (Eyewitness books) $13.95; lib bdg $14.99 (4 and up)   **932**
   1. Egypt—Civilization 2. Egypt—Antiquities
   ISBN 0-679-80742-X; 0-679-90742-4 (lib bdg)
                    LC 90-4106

Avaliable from DK Pub. $15.99; lib bdg $19.99 (0-7566-0646-2; 0-7566-0652-7)

A photo essay on ancient Egypt and the people who lived there, documented through the mummies, pottery, weapons, and other objects they left behind. Describes their society, religion, obsession with the afterlife, and methods of mummification

"Dazzles the eye with hundreds of color photographs and illustrations. Each two-page spread treats one particular aspect of the civilization. . . . All items pictured are identified with brief captions and clear definitions." SLJ

Hawass, Zahi A.
Curse of the pharaohs; my adventures with mummies. National Geographic Society 2004 144p il $19.95; lib bdg $29.90 (5 and up)   **932**
   1. Egypt—Antiquities 2. Archeology
   ISBN 0-7922-6963-2; 0-7922-6665-X (lib bdg)
                    LC 2003-18813
"Hawass delineates and attempts to debunk the alleged curses attached to the entering of the pharaohs' tombs." Publ Wkly

"Hawass' writing is passionate, informative, and kid friendly. . . . Even so, what will probably most attract aspiring archeologists are the National Geographic-quality photographs, which lend tantalizing immediacy to real-life tales from the crypt." Booklist
Includes glossary and bibliographical references

Haynes, Joyce
Egyptian dynasties. Watts 1998 64p il (African civilizations) lib bdg $23   **932**
   1. Egypt—Civilization
   ISBN 0-531-20280-1   LC 97-29390
"A First book"
A survey of the history and culture of the North African Egyptian dynasties

This book is "clearly written. . . . Captioned color photographs . . . archival portraits, maps, and time lines are included." Horn Book
Includes glossary and bibliographical references

Malam, John, 1957-
Ancient Egyptian jobs. Heinemann Lib. 2003 48p il map (People in the past) $29.93; pa $8.50 (5 and up)   **932**
   1. Egypt—Civilization
   ISBN 1-4034-0311-2; 1-4034-0515-8 (pa)
                    LC 2002-12595
Contents: Egypt: gift of the Nile; Who worked in ancient Egypt?; Organizing the workforce; Professions of ancient Egypt; Priest; Doctor; Merchant; Dancer; Farmer; Fisher; Hunter; Baker; Carpenter; Spinner and weaver; Jeweler; Who built the tombs of ancient Egypt?; Pyramid builder; Artist; Embalmer; How do we know?

This "volume begins with a brief introduction that offers geographical and historical background. [It] covers an assortment of workers including scribe, priest, dancer, baker, hunter, pyramid builder, and embalmer. Training, daily routines, and other pertinent information is included. . . . Color photographs of sites and artifacts and maps enhance the [presentation]. Insets provide additional tidbits of information." SLJ
Includes bibliographical references

Meltzer, Milton, 1915-
In the days of the pharoahs; a look at ancient
Egypt. Watts 2001 159p il lib bdg $33.50 (7 and
up)   **932**
1. Egypt—Civilization
ISBN 0-531-11791-X   LC 00-49985
"Meltzer presents what we know about ancient Egypt
and how we know it. . . . The author touches upon such
popular subjects as war, pharaohs, pyramids, making
mummies, hieroglyphics, and family life. Meltzer also
conveys how these ancient discoveries have contributed
to contemporary knowledge. . . . The writing is concise
and easy to read. . . . Sixteen pages of color plates
make the book more visually exciting. A worthwhile, informative addition." SLJ
Includes bibliographical references

Nardo, Don, 1947-
Ancient Alexandria. Lucent Bks. 2003 112p il
maps (Travel guide to) $21.96 (7 and up)
                                               932
1. Alexandria (Egypt) 2. Egypt—Civilization
ISBN 1-59018-142-5   LC 2002-6599
A historical look at ancient Alexandria and its people,
education, weather, transportation, hotels, shopping, festivals, sporting events, banks, government, and sightseeing
"This well-written, easy-to-understand text will be a
useful addition." SLJ
Includes bibliographical references

Ancient Egypt. Lucent Bks. 2003 111p il maps
(History of weapons and warfare) $27.45 (7 and
up)   **932**
1. Military art and science 2. Egypt—Civilization
ISBN 1-59018-066-6   LC 2002-447
Contents: Early Egyptian weapons and warfare; The
new kingdom and chariot warfare; Military service and
organization; Borders, fortifications, and sieges; Egypt's
military zenith, The battle of Kadesh; Warships and the
defeat of the sea peoples; Epilogue, Decline of the Egyptian military
Discusses the weapons used by the ancient Egyptians
and their different means of warfare
Includes glossary and bibliographical references

Netzley, Patricia D.
The Greenhaven encyclopedia of ancient Egypt.
Greenhaven Press 2003 336p (A to Z
encyclopedias) $74.95   **932**
1. Egypt—Antiquities—Encyclopedias
ISBN 0-7377-1150-7   LC 2002-6965
"Alphabetical entries range from prehistory to the time
of Greco-Roman domination and are generally between
a paragraph and a page in length. Coverage includes individual pharaohs, places, practices, trades, beliefs, artwork, and aspects of daily and family life with entries
such as 'furniture,' 'children,' and 'entertaining guests.'
Important individuals such as archaeologist Howard Carter are also included." SLJ
Includes bibliographical references

Perl, Lila
The ancient Egyptians; written by Lila Perl.
Franklin Watts 2004 112p il map (People of the
ancient world) $29.50; pa $9.95 (5 and up)
                                               932
1. Egypt—Civilization
ISBN 0-531-12345-6; 0531-16738-0 (pa)
                                      LC 2004-1940
Contents: How we know about ancient Egypt; Farmers, bakers, and brewers; Priests and scribes; Kings,
queens, and pharaohs; Builders in stone; Quarrymen and
craft workers; Warriors and captives; Mummy makers;
The legacy of ancient Egypt
"Crisp reproductions of visuals, along with impressive
ancillary content. . . . help make [this title] among the
best available on ancient [Egypt]." Booklist
Includes bibliographical references

Smith, Stuart Tyson
Valley of the Kings; {by} Stuart Tyson Smith
and Nancy Stone Bernard. Oxford Univ. Press
2002 47p il map (Digging for the past) $19.95 (4
and up)   **932**
1. Egypt—Antiquities
ISBN 0-19-514770-7   LC 2002-4288
Contents: Tourists and plunderers; Explorers, observ-
ers, and patrons; Sensation of the century; The last lost
tomb?; Where did all the mummies go?; Interview with
Stuart Tyson Smith
Explores Egypt's Valley of the Kings, a vast burial
ground containing more than seventy tombs, and discusses archaeologists' findings and challenges during
nearly two hundred years of excavation
"The easy-to-read text is enhanced by good-quality,
color photographs of artifacts, period photographs, reproductions of artwork, and maps." SLJ
Includes glossary and bibliographical references

Steedman, Scott
The Egyptian news; consultant, James Putnam.
Candlewick Press 1997 32p il maps $15.99
                                               932
1. Egypt—Civilization
ISBN 1-56402-873-9   LC 96-30842
Uses a newspaper format to present articles about the
history, politics, fashion, food, daily life, and afterlife of
the ancient Egyptians
This book brings "readers a wealth of information in
colorful pictures, short articles, and witty 'ads.'" SLJ

933 Palestine to 70 A.D.

Sherman, Josepha
Your travel guide to ancient Israel. Lerner
Publications 2004 80p il map (Passport to history)
lib bdg $26.60   **933**
1. Palestine—Civilization
ISBN 0-8225-3072-4   LC 2003-5622
Takes readers on a journey back in time in order to
experience life in Israel at the time of King Solomon, describing clothing, accommodations, foods, local customs,

Sherman, Josepha—*Continued*
transportation, a few notable personalities, and more.

"Written in a lively conversational style, [this] book contains boxed trivia and informative photos, reproductions, drawings, and maps. Useful for reports or just browsing." SLJ

Waldman, Neil, 1947-
Masada; written and illustrated by Neil Waldman. Boyds Mills Press 2003 c1998 64p il map $18.95 (4 and up)   **933**
1. Jews—History 2. Excavations (Archeology) 3. Masada Site (Israel)
ISBN 1-59078-063-9
A reissue of the title first published 1998 by Morrow Junior Bks.

Discusses the history of Masada, from the building of Herod's Temple through its use by Zealots as a refuge from the Romans to its rediscovery in the mid-20th century

"Dramatic illustrations and two large maps, all in charcoal shades of acrylic and India ink, show realistic scenes, many of them painted from photos, relief sculptures, and artifacts found during the excavation of Masada." SLJ
Includes glossary and bibliographical references

935   Mesopotamia and Iranian Plateau to 637 A.D.

Chrisp, Peter
Mesopotamia; Iraq in ancient times. Enchanted Lion 2004 32p il (Picturing the past) $15.95 (5 and up)   **935**
1. Iraq—Civilization
ISBN 1-59270-024-1
This introduction to Mesopotamia "covers such topics as farming, writing, craft, trade, domestic life, religion, warfare, burial, kingship and law. [It includes descriptions of] artifacts, . . . geographical sites, and archaeological evidence." Publisher's note

"Brief but substantive, [this] attractive [title] will spark students' curiosity about the specifics of ancient life and the importance of archaeology." Booklist
Includes glossary and bibliographical references

Schomp, Virginia, 1953-
Ancient Mesopotamia; the Sumerians, Babylonians, and Assyrians; written by Virginia Schomp. Franklin Watts 2004 112p il map (People of the ancient world) $29.50; pa $9.95 (5 and up)   **935**
1. Iraq—Civilization
ISBN 0-531-11818-5; 0-531-16741-0 (pa)
LC 2004-1947
Contents: Cradle of civilization; The warrior-kings; Nobles, government officials, and priests; Merchants and traders; Artisans and artists; Peasant farmers; Soldiers and slaves; Doctors and scientists; Scribes and poets; The legacy of ancient Mesopotamia

"This book explores the cultures of ancient Mesopotamia through their social structure. It takes a look at the people and details the duties of a king, the activities of a peasant farmer, and . . . more. It also describes some of the discoveries and writings that have led to our present-day understanding of this . . . civilization." Publisher's note

"Crisp reproductions of visuals, along with impressive ancillary content . . . help make [this title] among the best available on ancient [Mesopotamia]." Booklist
Includes bibliographical references

Whitcraft, Melissa
The Tigris and Euphrates Rivers. Watts 1999 63p il map lib bdg $24.50; pa $8.95   **935**
1. Tigris River 2. Euphrates River
ISBN 0-531-11741-3; 0-531-16432-2 (pa)
LC 99-24120
Traces the course of the Tigris and Euphrates Rivers, emphasizes their effects on human settlements and civilization, and indicates their contributions to the development of Turkey, Iraq, and Syria

"The concise and timely facts will be useful for reports." SLJ
Includes bibliographical references

936   Europe north and west of Italian peninsula to ca. 499 A.D.

Millard, Anne
A street through time; written by Anne Millard; illustrated by Steve Noon. DK Pub. 1998 32p col il $17.99   **936**
1. Cities and towns
ISBN 0-7894-3426-1
LC 98-3226
Traces the development of one street from the Stone Age to the present day, from dirt track to the rebuilding of inns as wine bars, showing how people lived and what they did all day

"The time-line construct is a useful demonstration for children, and the busy vistas would make a fine springboard for encouraging students to create scenes of local history." Horn Book Guide
Includes glossary

936.2   England to 410 A.D.

Malone, Caroline
Stonehenge; {by} Caroline Malone and Nancy Stone Bernard. Oxford Univ. Press 2002 47p il maps (Digging for the past) $21.95   **936.2**
1. Stonehenge (England) 2. Great Britain—Antiquities
ISBN 0-19-514314-0
LC 2001-7113
Contents: Imaginary tales and early depictions; The people behind the stones; Moving tons of stones; Years and years of building; Abandoned but not forgotten; Interview with Caroline Malone

Examines the site of the huge stone monument known as Stonehenge, discussing who built it, as well as theories on when, how, and why it was constructed

Malone, Caroline—*Continued*

"This book will make a useful addition to the study of archaeology as part of the curriculum or just for pleasure." Libr Media Connect

Includes glossary and bibliographical references

937   Roman Empire

Biesty, Stephen

Rome: in spectacular cross section; text by Andrew Solway. Scholastic Nonfiction 2003 29p il $18.95 (4 and up)   **937**

1. Rome—Civilization 2. Rome—Social life and customs

ISBN 0-439-45546-4   LC 2002-70694

Detailed illustrations with explanatory captions and narrative text survey some sites in ancient Rome, including the house of a wealthy family, the Colosseum, the Baths of Trajan, and the Temple of Jupiter

This "is a visually intriguing, reader-friendly introduction to ancient Rome." Booklist

Includes glossary

Blacklock, Dyan

The Roman Army; the legendary soldiers who created an empire; illustrations by David Kennett. Walker & Company 2004 48p il map $17.95; lib bdg $18.85 (4 and up)   **937**

1. Rome—Military history

ISBN 0-8027-8896-3; 0-8027-8897-1 (lib bdg)

    LC 2003-57574

An illustrated history of the Roman Army, including information about its composition, organization, training, methods, weapons, and campaigns.

"Blacklock's writing is clear and lively and the book, packed with dramatic cartoon illustrations, will captivate readers." SLJ

Includes bibliographical references

Connolly, Peter, 1935-

Pompeii; written and illustrated by Peter Connolly. Oxford Univ. Press 1990 77p il maps hardcover o.p. paperback available $12.95

    937

1. Pompeii (Extinct city) 2. Excavations (Archeology)—Italy

ISBN 0-19-917158-0 (pa)

Presents archeological information about Pompeii through text, photographs, and reconstructive drawings

"This is as complete and thorough a documentation of the story of Pompeii as any that can currently be found in children's collections." SLJ

Includes glossary

Corbishley, Mike

Ancient Rome. rev ed. Facts on File 2003 96p il map (Cultural atlas for young people) $35 (5 and up)   **937**

1. Rome—History 2. Rome—Civilization

ISBN 0-8160-5147-X   LC 2003-40258

First published 1989

Text, maps, illustrations, charts, tables, and chronologies depict the history, society, and political life of ancient Rome and its vast empire

This is "valuable for research and for a brief overview of the history of {this civilization.}" SLJ

Includes glossary and bibliographical references

Hinds, Kathryn, 1962-

The city. Benchmark Books 2004 c2005 87p il (Life in the Roman Empire) lib bdg $20.95

    937

1. Rome—Civilization 2. City and town life

ISBN 0-7614-1655-2   LC 2004-8255

Contents: An empire of cities; Public places and private spaces; Working for a living; Roman men : from high to low; City women; An urban childhood; Rest and recreation; Surviving in the city

This considers city life in the Roman empire, describing public and private spaces, work, roles of men and women, childhood, and recreation.

Includes glossary and bibliographical references

The countryside. Benchmark Books 2004 c2005 72p il (Life in the Roman Empire) lib bdg $20.95

    937

1. Rome—Civilization 2. Country life

ISBN 0-7614-1656-0   LC 2004-9496

Contents: The empire's support system; Country communities Country homes; Working the land; Men of the soil; Rural women; Growing up in the countryside; Hard times and holidays

This examines country life during the Roman Empire, describing the economy, homes, labor, roles of men and women, childhood, and holidays.

Includes glossary and bibliographical references

The Patricians. Benchmark Books 2004 c2005 72p il (Life in the Roman Empire) $20.95

    937

1. Rome—Civilization 2. Social classes

ISBN 0-7614-1654-4   LC 2004-3080

Contents: The man at the top; Monuments to power; The imperial court; A man's world; Imperial women; Children of the empire; Privileges and peril

This considers life of the ruling class during the Roman empire, describing the Senate, the emperors, the imperial court, the roles of men and women, children, and the perils of priviledge.

Includes glossary and bibliographical references

James, Simon, 1957-

Ancient Rome; written by Simon James. Knopf 1990 62p il (Eyewitness books) $13.95; lib bdg $14.99 (4 and up)   **937**

1. Rome—Civilization 2. Rome—Antiquities

ISBN 0-679-80741-1; 0-679-90741-6 (lib bdg)

    LC 90-4111

Avaliable from DK Pub. edition $15.99; lib bdg $19.99 (0-7566-0651-9; 0-7894-6573-6)

A photo essay documenting ancient Rome and the people who lived there as revealed through the many artifacts they left behind, including shields, swords, tools, toys, cosmetics, and jewelry

Langley, Andrew

The Roman news; {by} Andrew Langley & Philip De Souza. Candlewick Press 1996 32p il maps pa $6.99 hardcover o.p. **937**

1. Rome—Civilization

ISBN 0-7636-0341-4 (pa)   LC 96-3584

Uses a newspaper format to present Roman history, politics, religion, fashion, food, and daily life, spanning the years of the Roman Empire from 753 B.C. to 476 A.D

"Each page presents readable articles complete with headlines, boldface, column breaks, illustrations, and, often classifieds. . . . The facts . . . are accurate." SLJ

Lassieur, Allison

The ancient Romans; written by Allison Lassieur. Franklin Watts 2004 112p il map (People of the ancient world) lib bdg $29.50; pa $9.95 (5 and up) **937**

1. Rome—Civilization

ISBN 0-531-12338-3 (lib bdg); 0-531-16742-9 (pa)
    LC 2004-1955

Contents: The rulers of Rome; Power and influence of the Roman senate; People of the Roman government; Scholars and writers; Soldiers and the Roman army; The lives of Roman women; Priests and the Roman religion; Architects and engineers; Working-class Romans; Slaves and slavery; Legacy of the Roman empire

"This attractive, thorough, and comprehensible book . . . offers a stellar introduction to life in ancient Rome." Booklist

Includes bibliographical references

Mann, Elizabeth, 1948-

The Roman Colosseum; with illustrations by Michael Racz. Mikaya Press 1998 45p (Wonders of the world book) $19.95 **937**

1. Colosseum (Rome, Italy) 2. Rome—Antiquities

ISBN 0-9650493-3-7   LC 98-20060

This offers "a clear, well-written text and full-color drawings and paintings." SLJ

Includes glossary

Mellor, Ronald

The ancient Roman world; [by] Ronald J. Mellor & Marni McGee. Oxford University Press 2004 190p il map (World in ancient times) $32.95 (7 and up) **937**

1. Rome—History 2. Rome—Civilization

ISBN 0-19-515380-4   LC 2003-17799

Introduces the history, culture, and people of ancient Rome and examines its many contributions to the development of Western society.

This volume is "somewhat more inclusive than many other works for this audience. What makes this book accessible is the lively writing. . . . The numerous illustrations include full-color photographs and reproductions of sites, artifacts, period artwork, and an occasional movie still." SLJ

Includes bibliographical references

Nardo, Don, 1947-

The ancient Romans. Lucent Bks. 2001 128p il maps (Lost civilizations) lib bdg $27.45 (7 and up) **937**

1. Rome—Civilization

ISBN 1-56006-706-3   LC 00-8650

Discusses the civilization of ancient Rome, including its founding and early centuries, its high point, social classes and institutions, aspects of daily life, its eventual decline and fall, and the enduring legacy of Rome

"The use of quotations from primary and secondary scholarly sources provides a firsthand glimpse into the period and personal views on a number of topics. . . . A well-written, solidly researched study." SLJ

Includes bibliographical references

Ancient Rome. KidHaven Press 2002 48p il maps (Daily life) $23.70 **937**

1. Rome—Civilization

ISBN 0-7377-0612-0   LC 2001-2248

In this introduction to life in ancient Rome "Nardo covers family life and homes; work, workers, and education; public baths; and worship. Throughout, he examines the different roles played by men and women, adults and children, slaves and free men, and rich and poor. . . . The author presents his information clearly without fictionalizing, and offers some first-person accounts by period writers. . . . The layout is clear and logical. An informative introduction." SLJ

Includes bibliographical references

Ancient Rome. Lucent Bks. 2003 128p il maps (History of weapons and warfare) $27.45 (7 and up) **937**

1. Military art and science 2. Rome—Civilization

ISBN 1-59018-067-4   LC 2002-6601

Contents: The early Roman army; The development of manipular tactics; The professional Imperial military forces; Fortifications and siege warfare; Naval weapons and tactics

Discusses the weapons used by the ancient Romans and their different means of warfare

Includes glossary and bibliographical references

Arts, leisure, and entertainment; life of the ancient Romans. Lucent Books 2004 128p il (The Lucent library of historical eras, Ancient Rome) $27.45 **937**

1. Rome—Civilization

ISBN 1-59018-317-7   LC 2003-7625

An overview of Rome's leisure pursuits, dinners, the theater, literature, games and sports, and chariot races and battles.

This is "an excellent overview of the history and culture of the civilization and {includes} numerous quotations from ancient sources." SLJ

Includes bibliographical references

The fall of the Roman Empire; Don Nardo. Lucent Books 2004 112p il map (History's great defeats) $28.70 (7 and up) **937**

1. Rome—History

ISBN 1-590-18427-0   LC 2003-27422

Contents: The giant shadow of Rome's fall; Barbarians overrun the Roman realm; Loss of economic stabili-

Nardo, Don, 1947-—*Continued*
ty and security; Increasing political and social disunity;
Christianity weakens the Roman spirit; Fatal deterioration
of the Roman Army

Discusses some of the causes that may have led to the
end of the Roman Empire, including changes in population, economic decay, class and religious divisions, and
military conquest.

Includes bibliographical references

From founding to fall: a history of Rome.
Lucent Books 2003 128p il map (Lucent library of
historical eras: Ancient Rome) $27.45　　**937**
1. Rome—History
ISBN 1-59018-254-5

Explores the Roman Empire from its mythical founding by Romulus, through development and expansion to
decline after the barbarian invasions of the fourth and
fifth centuries.

This offers "an excellent overview of the history and
culture of the civilization and {includes} numerous quotations from ancient sources." SLJ

The Roman army; an instrument of power.
Lucent Books 2004 112p il map (The Lucent
library of historical eras, Ancient Rome) $27.45
937
1. Rome—Military history 2. Rome—Civilization
ISBN 1-59018-316-9　　　　　　　　LC 2003-5757

Contents: Rome's early enemies and expansion; Un-
disputed masters of Italy; Rome against Carthage: round
one; Rome against Carthage: round two; Roman armies
overrun Greece; Julius Caesar conquers Gaul; Rome's
early imperial conquests; Epilogue: the Roman army's
decline

This "covers the rise of Roman military prowess and
includes a clear description of a Roman legion and a discussion of how it differed and was superior to other military systems such as the Greek phalanx. Nardo also considers the social and political forces that gave the Romans great advantages over many of their foes. The diagrams of many famous battles are helpful in understanding ancient military tactics." SLJ

Women of ancient Rome. Lucent Bks. 2003
128p il map (Women in history) lib bdg $27.45 (7
and up)　　　　　　　　　　　　　　**937**
1. Women—Rome 2. Rome—Civilization
ISBN 1-59018-169-7　　　　　　　　LC 2002-1392

"Nardo examines the lives of women in Rome—aristocrat and slave, Christian and worshippers of the gods.
He discusses their roles as wives, mothers, and women
with lives outside the home. The book is also open (but
not sensationalistic) about how sexuality affected Roman
civilization." Booklist

"A well-researched and clearly written book." SLJ

Includes bibliographical references

Words of the ancient Romans; primary sources;
Don Nardo, editor. Lucent Books 2003 128p il
(The Lucent library of historical eras, Ancient
Rome) $27.45　　　　　　　　　　　**937**
ISBN 1-590-18318-5　　　　　　　　LC 2003-1645

Contents: Rome's founding and early expansion; Julius Caesar's exploits and conquests; Reign of Augustus,

the first emperor; The home and family life; Entertainment and leisure activities; Gods and religious worship;
Chronology of ancient Rome

"Excerpts from historians such as Plutarch, Livy, and
Suetonius, as well as the satires of Juvenal and poetry of
Ovid, are included in this history of ancient Rome as
told through the words of those who lived at the time.
Various chapters cover the founding of the city, Julius
Caesar's life, the reign of Augustus, home and family
life, entertainment, leisure, and religion. . . . Each chapter . . . [begins] with an introduction that helps to put
the subject in perspective for modern readers." SLJ

938　Greece to 323 A.D.

Ancient Greece and Rome; an encyclopedia for
students; Carroll Moulton, editor in chief.
Scribner 1998 4v il maps set $415　　　**938**
1. Classical civilization—Encyclopedias
ISBN 0-684-80507-3　　　　　　　　LC 98-13728

Presents a history of ancient Greece and Rome as well
as information about the literature and daily life of these
early civilizations

"The articles are readable and direct, and topics include those that students typically investigate such as
food, alphabets, burial customs, festivals, and weapons.
. . . Articles are of an appropriate length for the importance of each topic, with long entries about historic
events, famous individuals, religion, and the arts. Some
articles about Greece are followed by a similar article
about Rome." Voice Youth Advocates

Baker, Rosalie F.
Ancient Greeks; creating the classical tradition;
{by} Rosalie F. Baker and Charles F. Baker.
Oxford Univ. Press 1997 254p il maps (Oxford
profiles) $50 (7 and up)　　　　　　　**938**
1. Greece—Biography 2. Greece—Civilization
ISBN 0-19-509940-0　　　　　　　　LC 95-26637

"The influence of ancient Greek civilization is chronicled in concise biographies of over 37 Greek statesmen,
playwrights, artists, mathematicians, philosophers, and
military leaders." Book Rep

"Students looking for biographical or historical information on ancient Greece will find it valuable, as will
teachers seeking to integrate the classics into other disciplines." Booklist

Includes glossary and bibliographical references

Hart, Avery
Ancient Greece! 40 hands-on activities to
experience this wondrous age; {by} Avery Hart &
Paul Mantell; illustrations by Michael Kline.
Williamson 1999 104p il pa $12.95 (4 and up)
938
1. Greece—Civilization 2. Handicraft
ISBN 1-885593-25-2　　　　　　　　LC 98-35762

"A Kaleidoscope Kids book"

Introduces the places, people, historical events, myths,
culture, and philosophy of ancient Greece. Includes forty
hands-on activities, such as making an early Greek theater, building an Ionic temple, and pressing olives for oil

Hart, Avery—*Continued*
This is "a clever title that encourages learning and creativity." SLJ
Includes bibliographical references

Lassieur, Allison
The ancient Greeks; written by Allison Lassieur. Franklin Watts 2004 112p il map (People of the ancient world) $29.50 (5 and up)   **938**
1. Greece—Civilization
ISBN 0-531-12339-1   LC 2004-1942
Contents: The people of the government; Scientists of Greece; Greek athletes and sport; Philosophers and thinkers; Priests, priestesses, and the Greek religion; Poets and playwrights; Artists and architects; Warriors; Slaves and workers; Legacy of the ancient Greeks
This title offers "useful information that would help report writers and would also engage interested readers." SLJ
Includes bibliographical references

Malam, John, 1957-
Ancient Greece. Enchanted Lion 2004 32p il map (Picturing the past) $15.95 (5 and up)
938
1. Greece—Civilization 2. Greece—Antiquities
ISBN 1-59270-022-5
This "touches on such topics as ancient Greek religion, sport, theater, and government, each one introduced with an accompanying image of painted pottery, a statue, or photos of the present-day ruins of ancient structures. . . . .Brief but substantive,[this] attractive [title] will spark students' curiosity about the specifics of ancient life and the importance of archaeology." Booklist
Includes bibliographical references

Greek town; written by John Malam; illustrated by David Antram; created and designed by David Salariya. Watts 1999 45p il (Metropolis) hardcover o.p. paperback available $8.95   **938**
1. Greece—Civilization
ISBN 0-531-15379-7   LC 98-41945
Presents life in a town in ancient Greece, covering the temple, town square, a family home, an open-air theatre, games, the cemetery, the port, and more

Nardo, Don, 1947-
Ancient Athens. Lucent Bks. 2003 112p il maps (Travel guide to) $27.45 (7 and up)   **938**
1. Greece—Civilization 2. Athens (Greece)
ISBN 1-59018-016-X   LC 2002-4893
A historical look at ancient Athens and its people, education, weather, transportation, hotels, shopping, festivals, sporting events, banks, government, and sightseeing
"The detailed descriptions of this illustrious city-state should be a welcome addition to any collection." SLJ
Includes bibliographical references

Ancient Greece. Lucent Bks. 2003 112p il maps (History of weapons and warfare) $27.45 (7 and up)   **938**
1. Military art and science 2. Greece—Civilization
ISBN 1-59018-004-6   LC 2002-4894

Discusses the weapons used by the ancient Greeks and their different means of warfare
"A useful resource." SLJ
Includes glossary and bibliographical references

The ancient Greeks. Lucent Bks. 2001 128p il maps (Lost civilizations) lib bdg $27.45 (7 and up)
938
1. Greece—Civilization
ISBN 1-56006-705-5   LC 00-8760
Describes the rise to power of ancient Greece, its empire, its civilization, and its eventual decline
The text is "quite readable and authoritative. Well-researched, well-organized, enlightening." Booklist
Includes bibliographical references

Powell, Anton
Ancient Greece; updated by Sean Sheehan. rev ed. Facts on File 2003 96p il map (Cultural atlas for young people) $35 (5 and up)   **938**
1. Greece—History—0-323 2. Greece—Civilization
ISBN 0-8160-5146-1   LC 2003-40864
First published 1989
Maps, charts, illustrations, and text trace the history and culture of ancient Greece
This is "valuable for research and for a brief overview of the history of [this civilization.]" SLJ
Includes glossary and bibliographical references

The Greek news; {by} Anton Powell & Philip Steele. Candlewick Press 1996 32p il maps lib bdg $15.99; pa $6.99   **938**
1. Greece—Civilization
ISBN 1-56402-874-7 (lib bdg); 0-7636-0340-6 (pa)
LC 95-48489
Uses an newspaper format to present Greek civilization from the years 1500 to 146 B.C. and contains articles about history, politics, feasts, fashions, theater, gods, and wars
This book is "entertaining {and} deftly organized." Publ Wkly

Stefoff, Rebecca, 1951-
The ancient Mediterranean. Benchmark Books 2004 c2005 48p il map (World historical atlases) lib bdg $18.95 (5 and up)   **938**
1. Mediterranean region—History 2. Greece—History—0-323 3. Rome—Civilization 4. Greece—Civilization
ISBN 0-7614-1641-2   LC 2003-12027
Contents: Greece: Bronze Age ancestors; The Dark Age; Greek civilization is born; The Persian wars; Athens against Sparta; Alexander's empire: Macedonian might; To rule the world; The Hellenistic age; Conquest by Rome; Rome: The Kingdom; The Republic; Conquest and war; The birth of an empire; East and West; An empire falls
Text plus historical and contemporary maps provide a look at the history of cultures that flourished along the Mediterranean Sea
The text is "clearly written and well organized. The [book includes] large, full-color photographs and illustrations reproduced from original pieces of art found in di-

Stefoff, Rebecca, 1951-—*Continued*
verse national museums. Maps placed throughout clearly show the boundaries and areas of the empires. [This volume makes an] excellent [supplement] to history lessons and [a] good starting [point] for research." SLJ

939 Other parts of ancient world to ca. 640

Caselli, Giovanni
In search of Troy; one man's quest for Homer's fabled city; written and illustrated by Giovanni Caselli. Bedrick Bks. 1999 44p il lib bdg $18.95 (4 and up)   **939**
1. Schliemann, Heinrich, 1822-1890 2. Troy (Extinct city)
ISBN 0-87226-542-0   LC 98-42579
Discusses the efforts of Heinrich Schliemann to uncover the ancient city of Troy and what his archeological finds revealed about life in this legendary location
"Each spread features a well-written paragraph or two on the topic, supported by nicely drawn artwork, with captions giving extra information." Booklist
Includes glossary

Hunter, Erica C. D.
First civilizations; updated by Mike Corbishley. rev ed. Facts on File 2003 96p il map (Cultural atlas for young people) $35 (5 and up)
939
1. Middle East—History 2. Middle East—Antiquities
ISBN 0-8160-5149-6   LC 2003-40261
"An Andromeda book"
First published 1994
Text, maps, illustrations, charts, tables, and chronologies depict the history, society, and political life of the first civilizations, from Mesopotamia to Persia and Assyria
"Each spread contains several colorful photographs, drawings, diagrams, and/or maps that will help readers visualize the places and cultures discussed. . . . {This book} will aid students with their assignments." SLJ
Includes glossary and bibliographical references

Marston, Elsa
The Phoenicians. Benchmark Bks. 2001 80p il (Cultures of the past) lib bdg $29.93   **939**
1. Phoenicians
ISBN 0-7614-0309-4   LC 00-41452
This describes the civilization of the ancient Phoenicians, including history, culture, beliefs, and their modern legacy
This offers "balanced, thoughtfully interpreted material. . . . Reinforcing the text are a number of extensions, including illustrations, color photos of artifacts, a map, time line, and brief samples of literature." Horn Book Guide
Includes glossary and bibliographical references

Russmann, Edna R.
Nubian kingdoms. Watts 1998 64p il (African civilizations) lib bdg $23   **939**
1. Nubia
ISBN 0-531-20283-6   LC 97-29389
"A First book"
A survey of the history and culture of the North African Nubian kingdoms first settled by humans about 6,000 B.C
Includes bibliographical references

Stefoff, Rebecca, 1951-
The ancient Near East; Rebecca Stefoff. Benchmark Books 2004 c2005 48p il map (World historical atlases) lib bdg $27.07 (5 and up)
939
1. Middle East—History 2. Middle East—Civilization
ISBN 0-7614-1639-0   LC 2003-12030
Contents: Mesopotamia - Empires and invasions: Beginnings; The rise of city-states; Sumer and Akkad; Babylonia and Assyria; The Persian conquest; Anatolia - Cultures of the crossroads: Where three worlds meet; Early Anatolian states; Trade and war; The Hittite empire; Phrygia and Lydia; Egypt - Land of the river: Before the pharaohs; The old kingdom; The middle kingdom; The new kingdom; Foreign rulers
Text plus historical and contemporary maps provide a look at the history of the Ancient Near East
This is "clearly written and well organized. The [book includes] large, full-color photographs and illustrations reproduced from original pieces of art found in diverse national museums. . . . [This volume makes an] excellent [supplement] to history lessons and [a] good starting [point] for research." SLJ
Includes bibliographical references

940 History of Europe

Peoples of Europe. Marshall Cavendish 2002 c2003 11v il map set $329.95 (5 and up)
940
1. Europe—Encyclopedias
ISBN 0-7614-7378-5   LC 2002-19490
Contents: v1 Albania-Belgium; v2 Bosnia and Herzegovina—Czech Republic; v3 Denmark-France; v4 Germany-Hungary; v5 Iceland-Liechtenstein; v6 Lithuania-Netherlands; v7 Norway-Romania; v8 Russia-Slovakia; v9 Slovenia-Switzerland; v10 Ukraine-Yugoslavia; v11 Index volume
This "set 'uses geography and national identity to organize information' on 44 countries. Entries are arranged alphabetically by country. Each contains a short introduction to the country, including its landscape, climate, and history. . . . All of the following areas are treated: religion, housing, clothing, language, health and education, food and drink, family and social life, and art and music. Political upheavals, economic turmoil and hardship, war, and ethnic disputes are covered with commendable frankness and clarity. . . . Given the wealth of information, excellent indexing, and attractive format, this is a recommended purchase for middle-school, high-school, and public libraries." Booklist
Includes bibliographical references

940.1 Europe--Early history to 1453

Chrisp, Peter
Town and country life; by Peter Chrisp. Lucent Books 2004 48p il (Medieval realms) $28.70 (5 and up) **940.1**
1. Medieval civilization
ISBN 1-59018-536-6   LC 2003-24516
This briefly describes life in Europe in the Middle Ages for landholders, peasants, monks and nuns, on manors and in churches and villages.
Includes glossary and bibliographical references

Corbishley, Mike
The Middle Ages. rev ed. Facts on File 2003 96p il map (Cultural atlas for young people) $35 (5 and up) **940.1**
1. Medieval civilization 2. Middle Ages
ISBN 0-8160-5150-X   LC 2003-40260
First published 1989
Maps, charts, illustrations, and text explore the history and culture of the Middle Ages
This "is replete with enough colorful maps, time lines, photographs, and illustrations to satisfy even the most finicky student." Voice Youth Advocates
Includes glossary and bibliographical references

Dean, Ruth, 1947-
Women of the Middle Ages; [by] Ruth Dean and Melissa Thomson. Lucent Bks. 2003 128p il maps (Women in history) lib bdg $27.45 (7 and up) **940.1**
1. Women—History 2. Women—Employment 3. Medieval civilization
ISBN 1-59018-171-9   LC 2002-11838
Contents: Introduction: Vital contributions to medieval society; Women in the countryside: peasants working at home and in the fields; Women in the towns and cities: skilled workers and business owners; Women in the professions; Women estate administrators; Women in power; Women in religion; Women writers and artists
"Chapters cover women as peasants, skilled workers, artists, in professions, in religion, and with positions of power. In each category, education, family, economics, and lifestyle are discussed, and anecdotal sidebars add excerpts from primary sources. . . . The strength of the book is that the format—with almost one illustration per page, large print, and accessible language—should hold [young readers'] interest." SLJ
Includes bibliographical references

Gravett, Christopher
Knight; written by Christopher Gravett; photographed by Geoff Dann. rev ed. DK Pub. 2004 72p il (DK eyewitness books) $15.99; lib bdg $19.99 (4 and up) **940.1**
1. Knights and knighthood 2. Medieval civilization
ISBN 0-7566-0696-9; 0-7566-0695-0 (lib bdg)
First published 1993 by Knopf
Discusses the age of knighthood, covering such aspects as arms, armor, training, ceremonies, tournaments, the code of chivalry, and the Crusades

Hart, Avery
Knights & castles; 50 hands-on activities to experience the Middle Ages; {by} Avery Hart & Paul Mantell. Williamson 1998 96p il pa $10.95 (4 and up) **940.1**
1. Medieval civilization 2. Middle Ages 3. Knights and knighthood 4. Handicraft
ISBN 1-885593-17-1   LC 97-32863
"A Kaleidoscope Kids book"
Introduces the Middle Ages, including activities and crafts that are representative of medieval life, for example creating an hour glass, a catapult, a coat of arms, and a code of honor
"The text is written in a breezy tone and illustrated with a combination of line drawings and blue-or-purple-ink reproductions of medieval art and woodcuts." SLJ
Includes bibliographical references

Howarth, Sarah
The Middle Ages. Viking 1993 48p il maps (See through history) $14.99 **940.1**
1. Middle Ages 2. Medieval civilization
ISBN 0-670-85098-5   LC 92-56930
This volume "includes information on family organization, clothing, and food, with the differences in the status and lifestyle of peasant, noble, and cleric clearly depicted . . . . Each topic is briefly presented in its own two-page spread, extensively illustrated with paintings, charts, examples of objects from the period, and original artwork." Booklist
Includes glossary

Langley, Andrew
Medieval life; written by Andrew Langley; photographed by Geoff Brightling. rev ed. DK Pub. 2004 72p il (DK eyewitness books) $15.99; lib bdg $19.99 (4 and up) **940.1**
1. Medieval civilization
ISBN 0-7566-0705-1; 0-7566-0704-3 (lib bdg)
First published 1996 by Knopf
An illustrated look at various aspects of life in medieval Europe, covering everyday life, religion, royalty, and more.

Martin, Alex, 1953-
Knights & castles; exploring history through art; Alex Martin. Two-Can Pub 2005 64p il (Picture that!) $19.95 (5 and up) **940.1**
1. Knights and knighthood 2. Castles 3. Medieval civilization 4. Medieval art
ISBN 1-58728-441-3   LC 2004-14902
This "introduces readers to the . . . world of the medieval knight and his entourage. Including works by Paolo Uccello, Lucas Cranach, Pietr Brueghel the Younger, and Hieronymous Bosch, the book [also examines] . . . a section of the Bayeux tapestry and . . . [the] illuminated manuscript, *Les Tres Riches Heures du Duc de Berry*." Publisher's note
"Art and history meld with entertaining and successful results. . . . [This] unique, well-thought-out [title is] good for reports, and browsers would enjoy [it] too." SLJ
Includes glossary and bibliographical references

Nardo, Don, 1947-
The medieval castle. Lucent Bks. 1998 96p il
(Building history series) lib bdg $28.70 (7 and up)
940.1
1. Castles 2. Medieval civilization
ISBN 1-56006-430-7   LC 97-34638
Describes how medieval castles were built and examines the daily lives of those inhabiting them
"A well-written, thorough study. . . . Black-and-white diagrams, drawings, and reproductions are effectively used to further inform readers about castle life." SLJ
Includes bibliographical references

The Middle Ages. Lucent Bks. 2003 111p il
(History of weapons and warfare) $27.95 (7 and up)
940.1
1. Military art and science 2. Medieval civilization
3. Knights and knighthood 4. Castles
ISBN 1-59018-069-0   LC 2002-6253
Discusses the weapons, tactics, gunpowder, castles, fortifications, cannons, handheld guns, ships and other weapons used in the Middle Ages warfare
Includes glossary and bibliographical references

Nicolle, David, 1944-
Medieval knights. Viking 1997 48p il maps (See through history) $19.99   **940.1**
1. Knights and knighthood 2. Medieval civilization
ISBN 0-670-87463-9   LC 96-61599
This introduction to knights and medieval civilization covers such topics as "myths and legends, the feudal system, the tournament, the Crusades, and the decline of the knight. . . . A welcome addition." SLJ

Ross, Stewart
Monarchs; Stewart Ross. Lucent 2004 48p il map (Medieval realms) $28.70 (5 and up)
940.1
1. Kings and rulers 2. Medieval civilization
ISBN 1-590-18535-8   LC 2003-60387
This describes medieval kings and queens of Europe and their governments, courts, succession, relationships to the church, wars, the Crusades, and the beginnings of nations.
This is "attractive, informative. . . . Well reproduced and mostly colorful, the illustrations include a great many reproductions of period paintings and prints, along with maps and a few photos." Booklist
Includes glossary and bibliographical references

Woolf, Alex
Education; by Alex Woolf. Lucent Books 2004 48p il map (Medieval realms) $28.70 (5 and up)
940.1
1. Medieval civilization 2. Education—History
ISBN 1-590-18532-3   LC 2003-18309
Contents: Education in 1000 AD; Education during the Dark Ages; Charlemagne; The role of the Church; Beliefs and ideas in education; Who went to school?; What did children learn at school?; Song schools; Grammar schools; Monastic schools; School life; Teachers; Chivalric education; Apprenticeship; The education of girls;

The rise of universities; The university curriculum; University life; The great universities of Europe; The rise of humanism; The spread of humanism
Discusses the development of formal education during the Middle Ages, describing various methods of education, types of schools, curricula, who went to school, the rise of higher education, and more.
"Clear, well-organized {text} along with full-color reproductions of art and artifacts and photos of period structures immerse readers in . . . medieval life and offer sufficient information for reports." SLJ
Includes glossary and bibliographical references

Zohorsky, Janet R., 1958-
Medieval knights and warriors. Lucent Bks. 2003 112p il maps (History makers) lib bdg $21.96   **940.1**
1. Knights and knighthood 2. Middle Ages
3. Medieval civilization
ISBN 1-56006-954-6   LC 2002-7175
A "chronicle of the lives of six men who personified the characteristics of a virtuous warrior. In addition to outlining the long and difficult path to knighthood, the author provides historical background on the code and conduct of chivalry. Separate chapters cover William Marshal, Richard the Lionheart, Saladin, Don Pero Nino, Bertrand du Guesclin, and Sir John de Hawkwood." SLJ
Includes bibliographical references

940.2   Europe--1453-

Dunn, John M., 1949-
The Enlightenment. Lucent Bks. 1999 108p il
(World history series) lib bdg $27.45 (7 and up)
940.2
1. Enlightenment 2. World history—18th century
ISBN 1-56006-242-8   LC 98-8373
Discusses various aspects of the Enlightenment including its roots, philosophies, attacks on Christianity, revolt against reason, campaigns to reform society, and legacy
Includes bibliographical references

Hinds, Kathryn, 1962-
The city. Benchmark Bks. 2003 c2004 95p il
(Life in the Renaissance) lib bdg $20.95
940.2
1. Renaissance 2. City and town life 3. Europe—Civilization
ISBN 0-7614-1678-1   LC 2003-1477
Describes the social and economic structure of city life during the Renaissance, from about 1400 to 1600, explaining how cities varied in government, commerce, population, and culture, and how they influenced the shaping of European civilization
"Report writers will be richly rewarded. . . . Interesting sidebars feature recipes, games, and stories. Black-and-white and full-color reproductions of artwork taken from libraries and museums appear throughout." SLJ
Includes glossary and bibliographical references

Hinds, Kathryn, 1962-—_Continued_

The countryside. Benchmark Bks. 2004 93p il (Life in the Renaissance) lib bdg $20.95

940.2

1. Renaissance 2. Country life 3. Europe—Civilization
ISBN 0-7614-1677-3   LC 2003-1449

Describes the social and economic structure of country life during the Renaissance, from about 1400-1600, and the role of the peasants, villagers, and landowners in the shaping of European civilization

"Report writers will be richly rewarded. . . . Interesting sidebars feature recipes, games, and stories. Black-and-white and full-color reproductions of artwork taken from libraries and museums appear throughout." SLJ

Includes glossary and bibliographical references

The court. Benchmark Bks. 2004 80p il (Life in the Renaissance) lib bdg $20.95   **940.2**

1. Renaissance 2. Courts and courtiers 3. Kings and rulers 4. Europe—Civilization
ISBN 0-7614-1676-5   LC 2003-1126

Describes court life during the Renaissance, from about 1400 to 1600, explaining how various rulers governed and help shape European civilization

This features "well-written [text] and excellent color illustrations in a format that is unusually attractive. . . . Most impressive are the beautiful reproductions of period paintings and prints." Booklist

Includes glossary and bibliographical references

Netzley, Patricia D.

Life during the Renaissance. Lucent Bks. 1998 96p il maps (Way people live) lib bdg $28.70 (7 and up)   **940.2**

1. Renaissance
ISBN 1-56006-375-0   LC 97-39781

Describes the history, culture, and life of people living during the Renaissance addressing such topics as the distribution of wealth and the rise of the middle class, education and humanism, religious reforms and conflicts, exploration and conquest as sources of wealth, and the arts and sciences

Includes bibliographical references

Renaissance. Grolier Educ. 2002 10v il maps set $345 (7 and up)   **940.2**

1. Renaissance
ISBN 0-7172-5673-1   LC 2002-2477

"More than 220 entries are arranged alphabetically by subject and cover the innovative and tumultuous time period from 1375 to 1575. . . . The set covers a broad variety of topics among them adventurers and scholars, architecture, geographic regions, religion, and the sciences. . . . Pages are illustrated with paintings, photographs, drawings, and maps, including many reproductions of world-famous art from the period. Each of the pictures is nicely annotated. . . . The arrangement and layout are appealing, and coverage is thorough. Students seeking a direct route to specific topics from the Renaissance will be well served by this set." Booklist

The **Renaissance**; Jeff Hay, book editor. Greenhaven Press 2002 255p il maps (World history by era) lib bdg $44.95; pa $28.70

940.2

1. Renaissance
ISBN 0-7377-0765-8 (lib bdg); 0-7377-0764-X (pa)
            LC 2001-23842

This collection of primary and secondary source articles examines the Renaissance in Europe, Africa and the Americas, the Ottoman Turkish Empire and the Mughal Empire in India

Includes bibliographical references

Renaissance & Reformation: almanac; Peggy Saari & Aaron Saari, editors; Julie Carnagie, project editor. U.X.L 2002 2v il set $105

940.2

1. Renaissance 2. Reformation
ISBN 0-7876-5467-1   LC 2002-6152

This "is organized into topical chapters that include sidebars with additional information and more than 100 black-and-white illustrations. Volume 1 begins with a time line of important events. Following the time line are a 17-page vocabulary list and a research and activity guide. Chapters . . . deal with topics such as the rise of European monarchies, the Protestant and Catholic Reformations, the scientific revolution, the status of women, and daily life. A concluding bibliography lists books, Web sites, and video recordings and DVDs." Booklist

Renaissance & Reformation: primary sources; Peggy Saari & Aaron Saari, editors; Julie Carnagie, project editor. U.X.L 2002 201p il $58   **940.2**

1. Renaissance 2. Reformation
ISBN 0-7876-5473-6   LC 2002-3928

Contents: On the equal or unequal sin of Eve and Adam, by I. Nogarola; The Prince, by N. Machiavelli; The Muqaddimah, by I. Khaldûn; Notebooks, by L. da Vinci; The Starry messenger, "A grand revolution" (box) by G. Galilie; Merchant of Venice, William Shakespeare (box) by W. Shakespeare; Heptaméron, by Margaret of Navarre; Don Quixote, by M. Cervantes; "Of cannibals", by M. de Montaigne; The description of the new world called the blazing world, by M. Cavendish; "The ninety-five theses or disputation on the power and efficacy of indulgences", by M. Luther; "The sixty-seven articles of Ulrich Zwingli", by H. Zwingli; Ecclesiastical ordinances, Institutes of the Christian religion, by J. Calvin; "Elizabeth, a dutch anabaptist martyr: a letter", by Elizabeth; Spiritual exercises, by Ignatius of Loyola; Centuries, by Nostradamus; The life of Teresa of Jesus, by Teresa de Avila; "Profession of the Tridentine faith", by The Roman Catholic Church; Malleus maleficarum, by H. Kramer and J. Sprenger

This "provides selected specific writings of the time. Introductory information about the original author begins each section, and sidebars list definitions of obscure or antiquated words. Following each document piece is a discussion of the historical effects of the piece along with additional readings." Booklist

Includes bibliographical references

Thomson, Melissa
Women of the Renaissance; [by] Melissa Thomson and Ruth Dean. Lucent Books 2004 128p il map (Women in history) $28.70
940.2
1. Renaissance 2. Women—History
ISBN 1-59018-473-4   LC 2004-10849
Contents: Introduction: worlds of the Renaissance; Wives, mothers, and caregivers; Women at work; Women in religious life; Women who filled the role of queen; Political leaders, rebels, and pirates; Women scholars and scientists; Women writers; Women artists
This is discusses the roles of women in the Renaissance, as wives, mothers, workers, religious figures, queens, politicians, pirates, scholars and scientists, writers, and artists
"A concise, accessible account of life during this period and the issues specific to women. . . . The index is comprehensive, the endnotes are extensive, and the full-color reproductions and a few maps are well placed. This attractive title will serve report writers and general readers." SLJ
Includes bibliographical references

Wood, Tim
The Renaissance. Viking 1993 48p il maps (See through history) $19.99 (4 and up)   **940.2**
1. Renaissance
ISBN 0-670-85149-3   LC 93-60028
Drawings, photographs, and text describe 15th and 16th century European civilization. Four see-through acetate pages lift to reveal the inner structures of three buildings and Columbus' ship, the Santa Maria
Includes glossary

940.3   World War I, 1914-1918

Adams, Simon
World War I; written by Simon Adams; photographed by Andy Crawford. rev ed. DK Pub. 2004 72p il (DK eyewitness books) $15.99; lib bdg $19.99 (4 and up)   **940.3**
1. World War, 1914-1918
ISBN 0-7566-0740-X; 0-7566-0741-8 (lib bdg)
First published 2001
This study covers how and why the First World War started, equipment used, and what it was like in trenches and at home

Bosco, Peter I.
World War I; revised by Antoinette Bosco. updated ed. Facts on File 2003 162p il map (America at war) $35 (7 and up)   **940.3**
1. World War, 1914-1918—United States
ISBN 0-8160-4940-8   LC 2002-5106
First published 1991
In words and pictures this "illustrates the military strategies and tactics of combatants involved as well as the national mindsets of the nations and soldiers who fought in World War I. . . . [It is] a must-read volume for both adults and younger readers. . . . Highly recommended for both public and school libraries." Am Ref Books Annu, 2004
Includes bibliographical references

Coetzee, Frans, 1955-
World War I: a history in documents; [by] Frans Coetzee and Marilyn Shevin-Coetzee. Oxford Univ. Press 2002 174p il maps (Pages from history) lib bdg $36.95 (7 and up)   **940.3**
1. World War, 1914-1918—Sources
ISBN 0-19-513746-9   LC 2001-36605
"Introductory essays define 'document' and then point out strategies for analyzing and evaluating one so that it can be of value to students. Personal letters, posters, song lyrics, and poems are among the documents included. The book has extensive citations and sidebar quotes with dates, speaker, position held, and the context." SLJ
Includes bibliographical references

Feldman, Ruth Tenzer
World War I; Ruth Tenzer Feldman. Lerner 2004 88p il map (Chronicle of America's wars) lib bdg $27.93   **940.3**
1. World War, 1914-1918
ISBN 0-8225-0148-1   LC 2003-18806
Contents: Entanglements; Widening war; Turning points; Over there; Over the top; Pershing's Army; Uneasy peace; Epilogue
"Feldman provides a thorough background of the complicated alliances and disagreements of countries prior to World War I. Discussions of propaganda, the draft, and fear as a result of the Sedition Act help readers understand how ordinary Americans were affected by the conflict." SLJ
Includes bibliographical references

Gay, Kathlyn, 1930-
World War I; {by} Kathlyn Gay, Martin Gay. 21st Cent. Bks. (NY) 1995 64p il maps (Voices from the past) lib bdg $25.90 (5 and up)
940.3
1. World War, 1914-1918
ISBN 0-8050-2848-X   LC 95-12300
An illustrated look at America's role in World War I on the battlefield and on the home front. Includes excerpts from letters, diaries and newspaper accounts
Includes bibliographical references

Hatt, Christine
World War I, 1914-18. Watts 2001 62p il maps (Documenting history) lib bdg $23.50 (7 and up)
940.3
1. World War, 1914-1918
ISBN 0-531-14611-1   LC 00-51354
First published 2000 in the United Kingdom
This "discusses the causes of the conflict and offers a chronological recounting of major campaigns. . . . Sources, which range from diaries, interviews, and advertisements to government documents and works of literature, are identified and put into context." Booklist
Includes glossary

History of World War I. Marshall Cavendish 2001
3v il maps set $399.92   **940.3**
1. World War, 1914-1918
ISBN 0-7614-7231-2   LC 2001-17413
Contents: v1 War and response, 1914-1916; v2 Victory and defeat, 1917-1918; v3 Home fronts. Technologies of war
Chronicles World War I, "the war to end all wars," including its historical, social, political, and military significance

Kirchberger, Joe H.
The First World War; an eyewitness history.
Facts on File 1992 402p il maps (Eyewitness history series) $75 (7 and up)   **940.3**
1. World War, 1914-1918—Personal narratives
ISBN 0-8160-2552-5   LC 91-19970
The author bases this narrative history of World War I on eyewitness accounts from personalitites such as Rudyard Kipling, Theodore Roosevelt, Alexandra Feodorovna and Austrian empress Zita
Includes bibliographical references

Pendergast, Tom, 1964-
World War I almanac; [by] Tom Pendergast, Sara Pendergast; edited by Christine Slovey.
U.X.L 2001 xl, 210p $60 (7 and up)
                                        940.3
1. World War, 1914-1918
ISBN 0-7876-5476-0   LC 2001-53012
This "contains 12 chapters covering major topics related to the period, including the roots of the war; causes of U.S. involvement; the Espionage Act and Sedition Act; weapons of mass destruction; and more. Other features include maps, a detailed chronology of events, sidebars featuring related information, a glossary of 'Words to Know,' research and activity ideas, and a list of further reading sources." Publisher's note
Includes bibliographical references

World War I primary sources; [by] Tom Pendergast, Sara Pendergast; Christine Slovey, editor. U.X.L 2001 xxxlx, 215p $60 (7 and up)
                                        940.3
1. World War, 1914-1918
ISBN 0-7876-5478-7   LC 2001-53163
Provides approximately thirty full or excerpted speeches, diary entries, novels, poems, correspondence, and artwork related to World War I, with information placing each in context
Includes bibliographical references

Ross, Stewart
The technology of World War I. Raintree Steck-Vaughn 2003 64p il map (World Wars) $32.79   **940.3**
1. World War, 1914-1918 2. Technology
ISBN 0-7398-5482-8   LC 2002-69812
Contents: A new kind of war; Stalemate: defensive technology on land; Breakthrough: offensive technology on land; War at sea: ships of steel; War in the air: the third dimension; Behind the lines; Conclusion: total war

Describes the new military technology used during World War I on land, sea, and in the air
Includes bibliographical references

Ruggiero, Adriane
World War I. Benchmark Bks. 2002 c2003 117p il maps (American voices from—) lib bdg $32.79
                                        940.3
1. World War, 1914-1918
ISBN 0-7614-1203-4   LC 2001-8747
Presents the history of the United States's involvement in World War I through excerpts taken from letters, newspaper articles, speeches and songs dating from the period
"Period photos and posters (many in full color) with informative captions give readers a better understanding of the [conflict]." SLJ
Includes glossary and bibliographical references

World War I; Donald J. Murphy, book editor.
Greenhaven Press 2002 289p il (Turning points in world history) lib bdg $34.95; pa $23.70 (7 and up)   **940.3**
1. World War, 1914-1918
ISBN 0-7377-0933-2 (lib bdg); 0-7377-0932-4 (pa)
                                        LC 2001-33513
This is a collection of essays about World War I, with an introduction placing the essays in context and summaries of each one
Includes bibliographical references

Zeinert, Karen, 1942-2002
Those extraordinary women of World War I.
Millbrook Press 2001 96p il lib bdg $29.90
                                        940.3
1. World War, 1914-1918—Women
ISBN 0-7613-1913-1   LC 00-68371
"This volume explores women's roles in WWI as nurses, journalists, telephone operators, and industrial workers. Particular attention is paid to ways the war affected women's status." Horn Book Guide
"This solid offering will be a real boon to history report writers." Bull Cent Child Books
Includes bibliographical references

940.4 World War I, 1914-1918 (Military conduct of the war)

Preston, Diana
Remember the Lusitania. Walker & Co. 2003 102p il maps $22.95; lib bdg $23.85 (5 and up)
                                        940.4
1. Lusitania (Steamship) 2. World War, 1914-1918—Naval operations
ISBN 0-8027-8846-7; 0-8027-8847-5 (lib bdg)
                                        LC 2002-27444
An account of the World War I German torpedo attack on and sinking of the passenger liner, the Lusitania, describing the experiences of some of those involved
"Most material is derived from a broad spectrum of primary sources . . . and this adherence to firsthand ac-

Preston, Diana—*Continued*
counts pays off in the riveting immediacy of Preston's
prose. Plentiful illustrations (including historical photographs, documents, and maps) help bring the presentation
well within the grasp of able younger readers." Bull Cent
Child Books

940.53 World War II, 1939-1945

Adams, Simon
World War II; written by Simon Adams;
photographed by Andy Crawford. rev ed. DK Pub.
2004 il (DK eyewitness books) $15.99; lib bdg
$19.99 (4 and up)   **940.53**
1. World War, 1939-1945
ISBN 0-7566-0742-6; 0-7566-0743-4 (lib bdg)
First published 2000
In photographs and text this introduces the events of
World War II, briefly covering such topics as bombing
raids, the role of women, the atomic bomb, the American
home front, the Holocaust, the D-Day invasion and propaganda.

Adler, David A., 1947-
We remember the Holocaust. Holt & Co. 1989
147p il hardcover o.p. paperback available $14
                                               940.53
1. Holocaust, 1933-1945—Personal narratives
2. World War, 1939-1945—Jews
ISBN 0-8050-3715-2 (pa)   LC 87-21139
"Survivors of the Holocaust share their unique stories
in an informative, moving account that serves to remind
readers of the terrible effects of hatred." Soc Educ
Includes glossary and bibliographical references

Altman, Linda Jacobs, 1943-
Crimes and criminals of the Holocaust. Enslow
Publishers 2004 104p il map (Holocaust in history)
lib bdg $26.60   **940.53**
1. Holocaust, 1933-1945 2. Nuremberg Trial of Major
German War Criminals, 1945-1946
ISBN 0-7660-1995-0   LC 2003-19759
Describes the atrocities committed against Jews, Gyp-
sies, the handicapped, and other minorities in the German
concentration camps, and the many trials which brought
to justice some of those who were responsible.
This covers the "facts without sensationalism and
[raises] important issues about evil and human rights for
class discussion. . . . The documentation is excellent."
Booklist
Includes bibliographical references

The forgotten victims of the Holocaust. Enslow
Pubs. 2003 104p il map (Holocaust in history) lib
bdg $20.95   **940.53**
1. Holocaust, 1933-1945
ISBN 0-7660-1993-4   LC 2002-151085
Contents: Building the "Master Race"; The Polish vic-
tims; The Russian Campaign; The Gypsies of Europe;
The race criminals

This focuses on the non-Jewish victims of the Holocaust, including Poles, Russians, Slavs, gypsies, homosexuals, and the disabled
This "will fill a gap even in large Holocaust collections, with statistics and searing eyewitness accounts."
Booklist
Includes glossary and bibliographical references

Impact of the Holocaust. Enslow Publishers
2004 104p il map (Holocaust in history) lib bdg
$20.95   **940.53**
1. Holocaust, 1933-1945
ISBN 0-7660-1996-9   LC 2003-21118
Contents: Introduction: World War II and the Holocaust; "Never again!" ; Interrupted lives; Childhood lost;
The taint of evil; History and memory; Legacy of the
Holocaust
Discusses the effects and legacy of the Holocaust,
including the experiences of survivors, the urgency to establish a Jewish homeland in Palestine, the need for a
worldwide human rights policy, and the need to examine
the terrible cost of racism and hatred.
This covers "the facts without sensationalism and
{raises} important issues about evil and human rights.
. . . The documentation is excellent." Booklist
Includes bibliographical references

The Jewish victims of the Holocaust. Enslow
Pubs. 2003 104p il maps (Holocaust in history) lib
bdg $20.95   **940.53**
1. Holocaust, 1933-1945 2. Jews—Europe
ISBN 0-7660-1992-6   LC 2002-151084
Contents: A people dispossessed; The ghettos of Eastern Europe; Organizing murder; Living and dying in the
camps; Marching to nowhere
This is an introduction to the Holocaust and its Jewish
victims in the ghettos of Eastern Europe, in the concentration camps and their liberation at the end of World
War II
This is "well organized and accurate, and the writing
is sound." SLJ
Includes glossary and bibliographical references

Ambrose, Stephen E.
The good fight; how World War II was won.
Atheneum Bks. for Young Readers 2001 96p il
maps $19.95 (5 and up)   **940.53**
1. World War, 1939-1945
ISBN 0-689-84361-5   LC 00-49600
"A Byron Preiss Visual Publications Inc. book"
"Beginning with an explanation of the origin of the
war in Europe and Asia, the text moves on to Pearl Harbor through the major battles to the war-crimes trials and
the Marshall Program." SLJ
"An excellent balance between the big picture and the
humanizing details, well supported by fact boxes, tinted
photographs, and battlefield maps that are both simple
and clear. . . . Ambrose's style is authoritative and
warm." Booklist
Includes glossary and bibliographical references

Ayer, Eleanor H.
A firestorm unleashed; January 1942—June 1943. Blackbirch Press 1998 80p il map (Holocaust) lib bdg $19.45   **940.53**
1. Holocaust, 1933-1945 2. Genocide
ISBN 1-567-11204-8   LC 96-44430
This explores the unique aspects and events in the period of the Holocaust between January 1942 and June 1943, blending historical narrative and primary sources
This "is impeccably researched and well presented. . . . [It] records the full fury of the Holocaust as Germany implemented the genocide of the Jews." SLJ
Includes glossary and bibliographical references

In the ghettos; teens who survived the ghettos of the Holocaust. Rosen Pub. Group 1998 64p il map (Teen witnesses to the Holocaust) $26.50 (7 and up)   **940.53**
1. Holocaust, 1933-1945—Personal narratives
ISBN 0-8239-2845-4   LC 98-43859
Chronicles the deportation of Jews into ghettos during Hitler's Third Reich and presents the narratives of three individuals who, as teenagers, lived in the ghettos of Lodz, Theresienstadt, and Warsaw and survived physical deprivations, abuse, and deportation to the death camps
Includes bibliographical references

Inferno; June 1943—May 1945. Blackbirch Press 1998 80p il maps (Holocaust) lib bdg $19.45   **940.53**
1. Holocaust, 1933-1945 2. Holocaust survivors
ISBN 1-56711-205-6   LC 96-48528
This title in the Blackbirch Press Holocaust series "chronicles the last battles, resistance, rescue, and liberation. It includes a discussion of the plight of the Displaced Persons (DPs) and of U.S. President Harry Truman's efforts on their behalf." SLJ
Includes glossary and bibliographical references

Barr, Gary, 1951-
World War II home front; [by] Gary E. Barr. Heinemann Library 2004 56p il (Witness to history) lib bdg $31.36; pa $8.95   **940.53**
1. World War, 1939-1945—United States
ISBN 1-403-44571-0 (lib bdg); 1-403-44579-6 (pa)
          LC 2003-18146
This "covers America's efforts to mobilize for war by inviting readers to think about what it is like to be involved in civil defense, volunteer for military service, buy war bonds, and use ration coupons; photos and first-person accounts are included. The segregation of and discrimination against African Americans, Japanese Americans, and women are discussed along with the change in the roles of women and families as a result of the war." SLJ
Includes bibliographical references

Bitton-Jackson, Livia
I have lived a thousand years; growing up in the Holocaust; by Livia E. Bitton-Jackson. Simon & Schuster Bks. for Young Readers 1997 224p pa $4.99 hardcover o.p. (7 and up)   **940.53**
1. Holocaust, 1933-1945—Personal narratives
2. Jews—Hungary
ISBN 0-689-82395-9 (pa)   LC 96-19971

Based on the author's book for adults, Elli: coming of age in the Holocaust (1980)
"This memoir covers the last fourteen months of World War II, during which thirteen-year-old Elli Friedmann (as the author was then named) and members of her family are deported from their home . . . to two ghettos and several camps, including Auschwitz." Bull Cent Child Books
"This is a memorable addition to the searing accounts of Holocaust survivors." Horn Book
Includes glossary

Boas, Jacob
We are witnesses; five diaries of teenagers who died in the Holocaust. Holt & Co. 1995 196p (7 and up)   **940.53**
1. Holocaust, 1933-1945—Personal narratives
2. World War, 1939-1945—Jews 3. Jews—Europe
          LC 94-43889
Available in paperback from Scholastic
"Narrative accounts of five young Jews, including Anne Frank, whose diaries hold their observations and emotions, give immediacy to the horrors of the Holocaust. The text provides historical information and compares the experiences of the diarists, quoting liberally from the teenagers' writings. Although these condensed versions lack the impact of a complete diary, the cumulative effect of the five journals is overwhelming." Horn Book Guide
Includes bibliographical references

Byers, Ann
The Holocaust overview. Enslow Pubs. 1998 128p il maps (Holocaust remembered series) lib bdg $26.60 (7 and up)   **940.53**
1. Holocaust, 1933-1945 2. Germany—Politics and government—1933-1945
ISBN 0-7660-1062-7   LC 97-37637
Examines Hitler's treatment of the Jews, before and during World War II, from their early exclusion from German society to the later policy of extermination
"Life in the concentration camps, liberation, and subsequent war-crimes trials are vividly described. This is a thorough and accurate book." SLJ
Includes glossary and bibliographical references

Chicoine, Stephen
From the ashes; June 1945 and after; by Stephen D. Chicoine and Eleanor H. Ayer. Blackbirch Press 1998 80p il map (Holocaust) lib bdg $19.45   **940.53**
1. Holocaust survivors 2. Jews—Europe
ISBN 1-56711-206-4   LC 96-47707
This title in the Blackbirch Press Holocaust series discusses the fate of those Jews who survived annihilation by the Nazis: their further persecution, search for a homeland in Palestine, and hunt for war criminals. Also examines other cases of genocide in Bosnia, Rwanda, and elsewhere
Includes glossary and bibliographical references

Collier, Christopher, 1930-
The United States in World War II: 1941-1945;
{by} Christopher Collier, James Lincoln Collier.
Benchmark Bks. 2001 95p il maps (Drama of
American history) lib bdg $31.36   **940.53**
1. World War, 1939-1945—United States
ISBN 0-7614-1316-2   LC 00-51874
This "provides a brief survey of America's role in
{World War II} . . . and the impact the conflict had on
life in the United States. Illustrations are plentiful, uniformly well chosen, and include photographs, paintings,
posters, and . . . maps. . . . Young readers will find this
survey of their cultural past to be easy to read and informative." Book Rep
Includes bibliographical references

The **Complete** history of the Holocaust; Mitchell
G. Bard, book editor. Greenhaven Press 2001
567p il (Complete history of) lib bdg $123.75 (7
and up)   **940.53**
1. Holocaust, 1933-1945
ISBN 0-7377-0373-3   LC 00-56046
This is a compilation of primary and secondary
sources about the Holocaust
"An excellent collection of seminal accounts and com-
mentaries by some of the leading writers in the field."
Booklist
Includes bibliographical references

Cooper, Michael L., 1950-
Fighting for honor; Japanese Americans and
World War II. Clarion Bks. 2000 118p il map $16
(6 and up)   **940.53**
1. Japanese Americans—Evacuation and relocation,
1942-1945 2. World War, 1939-1945—United States
ISBN 0-395-91375-6   LC 00-26855
Examines the history of Japanese in the United States,
focusing on their treatment during World War II, includ-
ing the mass relocation to internment camps and the dis-
tinguished service of Japanese Americans in the
American military
The author's "description of life in the camps is vivid,
and the battlefield accounts are graphic and dramatic.
Both are enlivened with first-person testimony." Booklist
Includes bibliographical references

Remembering Manzanar; life in a Japanese
relocation camp; by Michael Cooper. Clarion Bks.
2002 68p il $15   **940.53**
1. Manzanar War Relocation Center 2. Japanese
Americans—Evacuation and relocation, 1942-1945
3. World War, 1939-1945—United States
ISBN 0-618-06778-7   LC 2002-2745
Uses firsthand accounts, oral histories, and essays
from school newspapers and yearbooks to tell the story
of the Japanese Americans who were sent to live in gov-
ernment-run internment camps during World War II
"On nearly every double-page spread are haunting
photos from the time by Dorothea Lange, Ansel Adams,
and others that document what happened. . . . Cooper
tells it quietly, drawing on the records of Manzanar's
daily newspaper, and, most movingly, on primary archival sources." Booklist
Includes bibliographical references

Feldman, George
Understanding the Holocaust. U.X.L 1998 2v il
maps set $110   **940.53**
1. Holocaust, 1933-1945 2. Germany—Politics and
government—1933-1945 3. Germany—History—1933-
1945
ISBN 0-7876-1740-7   LC 97-26864
"This overview describes the Holocaust, the events
that led up to it, and how the Nazis attempted to eradicate an entire people while fighting a war on two fronts.
Sidebars provide information on related individuals,
events, and policies. Black-and-white photographs help
clarify the text." SLJ
Includes bibliographical references

World War II: almanac; edited by Christine
Slovey. U.X.L 2000 2v il set $110
    940.53
1. World War, 1939-1945
ISBN 0-7876-3830-7   LC 99-36179
This volume "covers the buildup to the war, major
turning points, the defeat of Germany and Japan, and the
aftermath of the war and its impact on civilians. The
many sidebars help keep the text lively. The topical arrangement might initially throw students but the thorough
index will quickly allay misgivings about finding what is
needed." SLJ
Includes bibliographical references

Finkelstein, Norman H., 1941-
Remember not to forget; a memory of the
Holocaust; illustrations by Lois and Lars
Hokanson. Watts 1985 31p il lib bdg o.p. (4 and
up)   **940.53**
1. Holocaust, 1933-1945
ISBN 0-531-04892-6   LC 84-17315
Available in paperback from Jewish Publication Socie-
ty $9.95 (ISBN 0-827-60770-9)
"This spare, starkly illustrated book explains what the
Holocaust was and how it is remembered on Yom
Hashoa, Holocaust Remembrance Day. The explanation
reaches back to the explusion of the Jews from Jerusalem
in A.D. 70 and describes how Jews, strangers in many
lands became targets of anti-Semitism, which culminated
in the systematic murder of six million by the Nazis in
World War II. The tone is straightforward and matter-of-
fact. Black-and-white woodcuts accompany the text with
somber scenes reflective of the narrative. A useful explanation for younger readers, especially the non-Jews
among them." Booklist

Fox, Anne L., 1926-
Ten thousand children; true stories told by
children who escaped the Holocaust on the
Kindertransport; by Anne L. Fox and Eva
Abraham-Podietz. Behrman House 1998 128p il pa
$11.75 (5 and up)   **940.53**
1. Holocaust, 1933-1945—Personal narratives
2. Jewish refugees
ISBN 0-87441-648-5   LC 98-33600
Accompanied by Teaching guide for Ten thousand
children

Fox, Anne L., 1926- —*Continued*

Tells the true stories of children who escaped Nazi Germany on the Kindertransport, a rescue mission led by concerned British to save Jewish children from the Holocaust

"The design is like an open scrapbook, with different size typefaces, snapshots, news photos, and marginal notes; and the combination of the general overview with personal memories will bring readers, from middle grades through adult, close to the experience." Booklist

Friedman, Ina R.

The other victims; first-person stories of non-Jews persecuted by the Nazis. Houghton Mifflin 1990 214p hardcover o.p. paperback available $6.95 **940.53**

1. Holocaust, 1933-1945—Personal narratives 2. Holocaust survivors

ISBN 0-395-74515-2 (pa) LC 89-27036

Personal narratives of Christians, Gypsies, deaf people, homosexuals, and blacks who suffered at the hands of the Nazis before and during World War II

"Well organized and edited, the tales are harrowing, though they all end happily, often with escape or immigration to America and highly successful careers. Friedman points out that these were the lucky ones, and her book serves as a much-needed reminder that the Nazi nightmare extended far beyond Europe's Jewish population." Bull Cent Child Books

Includes bibliographical references

Goldstein, Margaret J.

World War II, Europe; by Margaret J. Goldstein: . Lerner Publications Co 2004 96p il map (Chronicle of America's wars) lib bdg $27.93 (5 and up) **940.53**

1. World War, 1939-1945

ISBN 0-8225-0139-2 LC 2003-12846

A chronicle of the United States and Allied forces' involvement in World War II Europe, including the political and social motivations for entering the war as well as major air, land, and sea campaigns

Includes glossary and bibliographical references

Gottfried, Ted, 1928-

Children of the slaughter; young people of the Holocaust; illustrations by Stephen Alcorn. 21st Cent. Bks. (Brookfield) 2001 112p il (Holocaust) lib bdg $29.90 (7 and up) **940.53**

1. Hitler-Jugend 2. Holocaust, 1933-1945 3. World War, 1939-1945—Children

ISBN 0-7613-1716-3 LC 00-30222

This discusses "the effect of the Holocaust not only on the Jewish children but also on the German youngsters who were forced to join the Hitler youth and on the offspring of Holocaust survivors." Voice Youth Advocates

"With clear, direct prose and a very spacious, readable design {this volume presents} the history without rhetoric or exploitation. There is much here for classroom discussion. . . . Stephen Alcorn's illustrations at the start of each chapter are jagged and dramatic; even more moving

are the occasional black-and-white archival photos." Booklist

Includes glossary and bibliographical references

Deniers of the Holocaust; who they are, what they do, why they do it; illustrations by Stephen Alcorn. 21st Cent. Bks. (Brookfield) 2001 112p il (Holocaust) lib bdg $29.90 (7 and up) **940.53**

1. Holocaust, 1933-1945

ISBN 0-7613-1950-6 LC 00-51221

This takes a "look at the people and organizations that claim the Holocaust never happened. This book looks at the rise of Nazi-affiliated groups, explores the techniques of moral relativism, and examines the current use of the Internet by the ring of deniers." Voice Youth Advocates

The book is "rich with topics for discussion, and the documentation is meticulous. . . . The spacious design, with lots of subheads, photos, and dramatic woodcuts at the start of each chapter, makes the {book} very readable." Booklist

Includes glossary and bibliographical references

Displaced persons; the liberation and abuse of Holocaust survivors. 21st Cent. Bks. (Brookfield) 2001 127p il maps (Holocaust) lib bdg $29.90 (7 and up) **940.53**

1. Jewish refugees 2. Holocaust survivors

ISBN 0-7613-1924-7 LC 00-51225

This book "looks at the suffering of survivors immediately following {World War II} when many people returned 'home' to face racism, displacement, even massacre, and when countries, including the U.S., denied shelter to most refugees. . . . {This volume is} rich with topics for discussion, and the documentation is meticulous." Booklist

Includes glossary and bibliographical references

Heroes of the Holocaust; illustrations by Stephen Alcorn. 21st Cent. Bks. (Brookfield) 2001 112p il (Holocaust) lib bdg $29.90 (7 and up) **940.53**

1. Holocaust, 1933-1945 2. World War, 1939-1945—Jews—Rescue 3. World War, 1939-1945—Underground movements

ISBN 0-7613-1717-1 LC 00-32571

This book "focuses on the Jews and Gentiles who risked their lives to save others." Horn Book Guide

This offers "clear, direct prose and a very spacious, readable design. . . . There is much here for classroom discussion." Booklist

Includes bibliographical references

Nazi Germany; the face of tyranny; illustrations by Stephen Alcorn. 21st Cent. Bks. (Brookfield) 2000 128p il map (Holocaust) lib bdg $29.90 (7 and up) **940.53**

1. Hitler, Adolf, 1889-1945 2. Holocaust, 1933-1945 3. National socialism

ISBN 0-7613-1714-7 LC 99-57589

Describes the Nazis' rise to power in Germany and their efforts to conquer Europe, as well as their full-scale war against Jews and others

Includes bibliographical references

Greenfeld, Howard

After the Holocaust. Greenwillow Bks. 2001 146p il maps $18.95; lib bdg $19.89 (6 and up)
                             940.53

1. Holocaust survivors 2. Holocaust, 1933-1945
3. Jewish refugees

ISBN 0-688-17752-2; 0-06-029420-5 (lib bdg)
                             LC 00-52798

"Eight Jewish survivors (five women, three men) share their personal experiences of what happened after the defeat of Hitler." SLJ

"The readable, slightly oversize design features lots of black-and-white photographs, news photos, and family snapshots. . . . The truth of the individual voices gives the history immediacy." Booklist

Includes bibliographical references

Hatt, Christine

World War II, 1939-45. Watts 2001 62p il maps (Documenting history) lib bdg $23.50 (7 and up)
                             940.53

1. World War, 1939-1945

ISBN 0-531-14612-X   LC 00-53587

First published 2000 in the United Kingdom

"Two-page treatments address such topics as the wars' origins, noteworthy battles, major offensive movements, and related aspects such as propaganda, women at war, and the home fronts. On each spread, less than a page of narrative is accompanied by snippets of various primary-source documents . . . as well as by black-and-white and full-color photographs, maps, and reproductions." SLJ

This "may encourage browsing and will be especially useful to students looking for information in a brief, inviting format, as well as for those who want a topic review or introduction." Book Rep

Includes glossary

Hillman, Laura, 1923-

I will plant you a lilac tree; a memoir of a Schindler's list survivor; Laura Hillman. 1st ed. Atheneum Books for Young Readers 2004 243p il map $16.95 (7 and up)   **940.53**

1. Jews—Germany 2. Holocaust, 1933-1945—Personal narratives

ISBN 0-689-86980-0   LC 2004-10534

"In 1942 Berlin, Hannelore, 16, bravely volunteers to be deported with her mother and two younger brothers to Poland. . . . They are soon separated, and during the next three years Hannelore is moved through eight concentration camps. In clipped, first-person narrative, she remembers the worst. . . . She tells it as she endured it, quietly relaying the facts without sensationalism or sentimentality." Booklist

The **Holocaust**; editor, Geoffrey Wigoder. Grolier 1997 4v il map set $219   **940.53**

1. Holocaust, 1933-1945—Encyclopedias

ISBN 0-7172-7637-6   LC 96-9566

Contents: v1 Abwehr to extermination camps; v2 Family camps to Lvov; v3 Macedonia to Szenes; v4 Tehran children to Zyklon B

Articles identify and describe individuals and events connected with the persecution of Jews and others across Europe in the 1930s and 1940s

"Essential for middle-school libraries and useful wherever a basic guide on the Holocaust is required." Libr J

Includes bibliographical references

Holocaust memories; speaking the truth in their own words; {compiled} by Elaine Landau. Watts 2001 95p il (In their own voices) lib bdg $24 (5 and up)   **940.53**

1. Holocaust, 1933-1945—Personal narratives

ISBN 0-531-11742-1   LC 00-32511

These personal narratives of the Holocaust include "accounts of *Kristallnacht,* the Warsaw Ghetto rebellion against the Nazi army, the Nazi medical mutilations of Jews, and the Allied liberation of the death camps. . . . The easy-to-read, very revealing, and unsparingly honest text is accompanied by black-and-white maps and some remarkable photos depicting the horrors of the Nazi genocide." SLJ

Includes bibliographical references

Houston, Jeanne Wakatsuki, 1933-

Farewell to Manzanar; a true story of Japanese American experience during and after the World War II internment; {by} Jeanne Wakatsuki Houston and James D. Houston. Houghton Mifflin 2002 c1973 188p $15 (7 and up)   **940.53**

1. Manzanar War Relocation Center 2. Japanese Americans—Evacuation and relocation, 1942-1945
3. World War, 1939-1945—United States

ISBN 0-618-21620-0   LC 2002-727748

Also available in paperback from Bantam Bks.

A reissue with a new afterword of the title first published 1973

"The author tells of the three years she and her family spent at Manzanar, a Japanese internment camp. . . . The last part of the book deals with her postwar adolescence and reentry into American life." Libr J

" A spare, powerful memoir." Rochman. Against borders

Isserman, Maurice

World War II. Updated ed. Facts on File 2003 226p il map (America at war) $35 (7 and up)
                             940.53

1. World War, 1939-1945—United States 2. United States—History—1933-1945

ISBN 0-8160-4938-6   LC 2002-5504

First published 1991

This describes and interprets the role of the United States in World War II

The "emphasis on personalities enhances the narration of the actual events and issues, thus keeping the text both lively and absorbing. . . . [This] will prove to be a valuable tool for students doing research." Am Ref Books Annu, 2004

Includes glossary and bibliographical references

Japanese American internment camps; William Dudley, book editor. Greenhaven Press 2002 144p il (At issue in history) lib bdg $29.95 (7 and up) **940.53**
1. Japanese Americans—Evacuation and relocation, 1942-1945
ISBN 0-7377-0821-2   LC 2001-33804
"This collection of articles includes primary source documents and historical studies examining the decision to intern Japanese Americans and its lasting ramifications for American constitutional law and the Japanese-American community." Publisher's note
Includes bibliographical references

Kustanowitz, Esther
The hidden children of the Holocaust; teens who hid from the Nazis. Rosen Pub. Group 1998 64p il map (Teen witnesses to the Holocaust) $26.50 **940.53**
1. Holocaust, 1933-1945—Personal narratives 2. World War, 1939-1945—Jews—Rescue
ISBN 0-8239-2562-5   LC 98-32072
In their own words, details the experiences of Jewish teenagers hiding from the Nazis
Includes bibliographical references

Leapman, Michael, 1938-
Witnesses to war; eight true-life stories of Nazi persecution. Viking 1998 127p il maps (5 and up) **940.53**
1. Holocaust, 1933-1945 2. World War, 1939-1945—Children
ISBN 0-670-87386-1, 0-14-130841-9 (pa)
LC 98-208868
Facsimiles on end-papers
The author "suggests the far reaches of Nazi terror by focusing on the experiences of eight children, each victimized during WWII." Publ Wkly
"Leapman presents an authoritative, informative, and attractive work. . . . The narrative is riveting." Voice Youth Advocates

Lee, Carol Ann
A friend called Anne; one girl's story of war, peace, and a unique friendship with Anne Frank; by Jacqueline van Maarsen; retold for children by Carol Ann Lee. Viking Children's Books 2005 163p il $15.99 (4 and up) **940.53**
1. Frank, Anne, 1929-1945 2. Jews—Netherlands 3. Holocaust, 1933-1945
ISBN 0-670-05958-7   LC 2004-21418
Contents: The Road to war; Anne; Getting to know each other; Separation; Removing the yellow star; Last goodbyes; The hunger winter; Liberation; The Diary of Anne Frank; Fame
"Jacqueline van Maarsen met Anne Frank in 1941, and the two girls quickly became best friends. A Friend Called Anne details their relationship. . . . The book also shares Jacqueline's own chilling experience of narrowly escaping Nazi deportation thanks to her Catholic mother. " Publisher's note
"This is a clearly written, demonstrative memoir. . . .

Black-and-white photos of family and school settings, letters, poems, and a time line of events in wartime Netherlands are included." SLJ

Levine, Ellen
Darkness over Denmark; the Danish resistance and the rescue of the Jews. Holiday House 2000 164p $22.95; pa $14.95 **940.53**
1. Holocaust, 1933-1945 2. Jews—Denmark 3. World War, 1939-1945—Jews—Rescue 4. Denmark—History
ISBN 0-8234-1447-7; 0-8234-1755-7 (pa)
LC 99-25607
This "narrative history, which weaves together events of the Nazi occupation of Denmark with eyewitness testimonies, is based on personal interviews with more than 20 Danish survivors, rescuers, and Resistance fighters, many of whom helped Jews hide and escape." Booklist
Includes bibliographical references

Levy, Patricia Marjorie, 1951-
The home front in World War II; [by] Pat Levy. Raintree 2004 64p il (World wars) lib bdg $32.79 (7 and up) **940.53**
1. World War, 1939-1945
ISBN 0-7398-6065-8   LC 2003-993
Contents: Home fronts across the world; Bombing civilians; Occupation and resistance; The war effort at home; Hardships; Foreigners; Changed lives
Explores life in various countries during World War II for the ordinary citizens who contributed to war efforts in factories and other venues and who, in some cases, experienced the horrors of war firsthand.
This is "brief but effective. . . .[It includes] high-quality photos and illustrations." SLJ
Includes glossary and bibliographical references

McGowen, Tom
World War II. Watts 1993 64p il maps pa $6.95 hardcover o.p. (4 and up) **940.53**
1. World War, 1939-1945
ISBN 0-531-15661-3 (pa)   LC 92-28328
"A First book"
Provides an overview of the military battles and political changes that occurred during World War II
Includes bibliographical references

Meltzer, Milton, 1915-
Never to forget: the Jews of the Holocaust. Harper & Row 1976 217p maps hardcover o.p. paperback available $7.95 (6 and up)
940.53
1. Holocaust, 1933-1945
ISBN 0-06-446118-1
"The mass murder of six million Jews by the Nazis during World War II is the subject of this compelling history. Interweaving background information, chilling statistics, individual accounts and newspaper reports, it provides an excellent introduction to its subject." Interracial Books Child Bull
Includes bibliographical references

Meltzer, Milton, 1915-—*Continued*

Rescue: the story of how Gentiles saved Jews in the Holocaust. Harper & Row 1988 168p maps pa $7.99 hardcover o.p. (6 and up)   **940.53**

1. Holocaust, 1933-1945 2. World War, 1939-1945—Jews—Rescue

ISBN 0-06-446117-3 (pa)   LC 87-47816

A recounting drawn from historic source material of the many individual acts of heroism performed by righteous gentiles who sought to thwart the extermination of the Jews during the holocaust

"This is an excellent portrayal of a difficult topic. Meltzer manages to both explain without accusing, and to laud without glorifying. . . . The discussion of the complicated relations between countries are clear, but not simplistic. An impressive aspect of this book is its lack of didacticism." Voice Youth Advocates

Includes bibliographical references

Ng, Wendy L.

Japanese American internment during World War II; a history and reference guide; [by] Wendy Ng. Greenwood Press 2002 xxvi, 204p $45   **940.53**

1. Japanese Americans—Evacuation and relocation, 1942-1945

ISBN 0-313-31375-X   LC 00-69128

Contents: Chronology of events in Japanese American history: the Japanese in America before World War II; Evacuation; Life within barbed wire; The question of loyalty: Japanese Americans in the military and draft resisters; Legal challenges to the evacuation and internment; After the war: resettlement and redress; Photographic essay

"The combination of historical facts as presented in the essays and the ideas and sentiments expressed in the primary documents gives readers a vivid sense of this period in history. This readable book would be a solid addition to high school, public, and academic libraries." Voice Youth Advocates

Includes bibliographical references

O'Neill, William L.

World War II: a student companion. Oxford Univ. Press 1999 384p il (Oxford student companions to American history) lib bdg $60 (7 and up)   **940.53**

1. World War, 1939-1945

ISBN 0-19-510800-0   LC 98-54918

This volume includes "entries on individuals, battles, military organizations, theaters, origins, weapon systems, and countries. . . . Articles vary in length from two or three paragraphs to several pages. . . . *Literature* and *motion pictures* have brief lists of classic World War II novels and films, respectively. A chronology, a list of museums and historic sites, and a general bibliography that includes Web sites give students additional tools to expand their original search." Booklist

"A readable, concise, and informative book." SLJ

Opdyke, Irene Gut, 1921-

In my hands; memories of a Holocaust rescuer; {by} Irene Gut Opdyke with Jennifer Armstrong. Knopf 1999 276p il $18; pa $12 (7 and up)   **940.53**

1. World War, 1939-1945—Jews—Rescue 2. World War, 1939-1945—Personal narratives 3. Holocaust, 1933-1945—Personal narratives 4. World War, 1939-1945—Poland

ISBN 0-679-89181-1; 0-385-72032-7 (pa)

LC 98-54095

Recounts the experiences of the author who, as a young Polish girl, hid and saved Jews during the Holocaust

"No matter how many Holocaust stories one has read, this one is a must, for its impact is so powerful. . . . Opdyke's remarkable story is simply told, with clarity and feeling." SLJ

Perl, Lila

Behind barbed wire; the story of Japanese-American internment during World War II. Benchmark Bks. 2002 112p il (Great journeys) lib bdg $32.79   **940.53**

1. Japanese Americans—Evacuation and relocation, 1942-1945 2. World War, 1939-1945—United States

ISBN 0-7614-1321-9   LC 2001-43337

Discusses the forced internment of Japanese-Americans in camps following the attack on Pearl Harbor and the entry of the United States into World War II

Includes bibliographical references

Four perfect pebbles; a Holocaust story; by Lila Perl and Marion Blumenthal Lazan. Greenwillow Bks. 1996 130p il $16.99; pa $5.99 (6 and up)   **940.53**

1. Holocaust, 1933-1945—Personal narratives 2. Jews—Germany

ISBN 0-688-14294-X; 0-380-73188-6 (pa)

LC 95-9752

"Starting with a description of one of the days that Marion Blumenthal Lazan survived in Bergen-Belsen, this chronicle of her experiences during the Holocaust then goes further back for a look at her family's secure prewar life in Germany." Bull Cent Child Books

"This book warrants attention both for the uncommon experiences it records and for the fullness of that record. . . . Quotes from Lazan's 87-year-old mother are invaluable—her memories of the family's experiences afford Marion's story a precision and wholeness rarely available to child survivors." Publ Wkly

Includes bibliographical references

Rescue and resistance: portraits of the Holocaust. Macmillan Lib. Ref. USA 1999 399p il $80   **940.53**

1. Holocaust, 1933-1945 2. Holocaust survivors 3. World War, 1939-1945—Jews—Rescue

ISBN 0-02-865362-9   LC 98-56458

This volume includes biographies of 166 people who fought to save Jews during World War II. Soldiers, partisans, ghetto leaders, diplomats, writers, and ordinary citizens are profiled. Each entry includes quotations, definitions and an individual time line

Includes glossary and bibliographical references

Rogasky, Barbara, 1933-
Smoke and ashes; the story of the Holocaust.
rev and expanded ed. Holiday House 2002 256p il
maps $27.50; pa $14.95   **940.53**
1. Holocaust, 1933-1945
ISBN 0-8234-1612-7; 0-8234-1677-1 (pa)
LC 2001-16797
First published 1988
The author "details the dark horror of Nazism—from
the beginning pogroms the Nazis organized against German Jews to the setting up of concentration camps and
death factories. . . . In clear and simple prose, she relates how the Jews lived and died in the camps . . . and
how a small number of non-Jews helped them in their
struggle. She concludes with an account of the
Nuremburg Trials and the many instances of contemporary anti-Semitism that have outlived Hitler." SLJ [re-
view of 1988 edition]
Includes bibliographical references

Rosenberg, Maxine B., 1939-
Hiding to survive; stories of Jewish children
rescued from the Holocaust. Clarion Bks. 1994
166p il (5 and up)   **940.53**
1. Holocaust, 1933-1945—Personal narratives
2. Jews—Europe
ISBN 0-395-65014-3; 0-395-90020-4 (pa)
LC 93-28328
First person accounts of fourteen Holocaust survivors
who as children were hidden from the Nazis by non-Jews
"Told in the plain, unvarnished language of childhood
memories, these harrowing first-person accounts are particularly moving in their straightforward simplicity, and
all are accompanied by photos of the survivors as children and as they are today." Voice Youth Advocates
Includes glossary and bibliographical references

Ruggiero, Adriane
World War II. Benchmark Bks. 2002 c2003
117p il (American voices from—) lib bdg $22.95
940.53
1. World War, 1939-1945
ISBN 0-7614-1206-9   LC 2002-3247
Presents the history of the United States participation
in World War II, including the role of women and
African Americans and the internment of Japanese Americans
"News articles, first-person accounts, diary and journal
entries, and more offer insights from combatants, civilians, writers, and poets, and provide a wide variety of
viewpoints. . . . Period photos and posters (many in full
color) with informative captions give readers a better understanding of the [conflict]." SLJ
Includes bibliographical references

Sender, Ruth Minsky, 1926-
The cage. Macmillan 1986 245p pa $5.99
hardcover o.p. (7 and up)   **940.53**
1. Holocaust, 1933-1945—Personal narratives
2. Jews—Poland
ISBN 0-689-81321-X (pa)   LC 86-8562

This "Holocaust memoir presents a series of brief
scenes from 1939, when the author was 12 and Hitler invaded Poland, through the Russian liberation of the
Mitelsteine labor camp in 1945. . . . Older students with
previous knowledge of the subject will find Sender's narrative moving and thought provoking." SLJ

Sherrow, Victoria
The blaze engulfs; January 1939—December
1941. Blackbirch Press 1998 80p il map
(Holocaust) lib bdg $26.20   **940.53**
1. Holocaust, 1933-1945
ISBN 1-56711-202-1   LC 96-37216
Book 3 in the series "begins with Germany's invasion
of Poland and Czechoslovakia, and ends with the forming of the Axis partners. . . . Those who helped the
Jews are not neglected, nor are the complex relations between Poles and Jews. The presence of little known information and quotes throughout reveal the depth of the
author's research." SLJ
Includes glossary and bibliographical references

Smoke to flame; September 1935 - December
1938. Blackbirch Press 1998 80p il maps
(Holocaust) lib bdg $26.20   **940.53**
1. Holocaust, 1933-1945 2. Jews—Persecutions
ISBN 1-56711-201-3   LC 96-52206
Book 2 in the Holocaust series. This volume provides
"a description of and commentary on the increasing anti-
Semitism and restrictions upon the Jews, first in Germany and then in other countries as conditions deteriorat-
ed and panic escalated throughout Europe." SLJ
Includes glossary and bibliographical references

Shuter, Jane, 1955-
The camp system. Heinemann Lib. 2003 56p il
map (Holocaust) lib bdg $28.50 (7 and up)
940.53
1. Holocaust, 1933-1945 2. Concentration camps
ISBN 1-40340-809-2   LC 002-6754
Contents: Camps and the Holocaust; Types of camps;
Prisoners; How camps were used ; Running the camps;
Camp discipline; Efficient camps; Processing arrivals at
Auschwitz; The main camps
This is an "account of the carefully planned concentra-
tion camp network where millions suffered and died.
. . . {The book combines} a good historical overview
with moving personal accounts. " Booklist
Includes glossary and bibliographical references

Soumerai, Eve Nussbaum
A voice from the Holocaust; [by] Eve
Nussbaum Soumerai and Carol D. Schulz.
Greenwood Press 2003 xxvii, 128p il (Voices of
twentieth century conflict) $35   **940.53**
1. Holocaust, 1933-1945—Personal narratives
2. Germany—History—1933-1945
ISBN 0-313-32358-5   LC 2003-45528
"Eve Soumerai recounts her childhood as a Jewish girl
growing up in Nazi Berlin, as a teenaged refugee in the
United Kingdom, and later as a young adult searching
for answers in postwar Germany." Publisher's note

Soumerai, Eve Nussbaum—*Continued*

"Readers will get to know Soumerai's family through photos and vivid personal anecdotes. . . . Personal postscripts and extensive discussion questions and endnotes round out this memorable title." SLJ

Includes bibliographical references

Spiegelman, Art

Maus; a survivor's tale. Pantheon Bks. 1996 2v in 1 il $35 (7 and up)   **940.53**

1. Spiegelman, Vladek 2. Holocaust, 1933-1945

ISBN 0-679-40641-7   LC 96-32796

Also available CD-ROM version, The complete Maus; available paperback boxed set edition $28 (ISBN 0-679-74840-7)

A combined edition of Maus (1986) and Maus II (1991)

Contents: My father bleeds history; And here my troubles began

In this work "Spiegelman takes the comic book to a new level of seriousness, portraying Jews as mice and Nazis as cats. Depicting himself being told about the Holocaust by his Polish survivor father, Spiegelman not only explores the concentration-camp experience, but also the guilt, love, and anger between father and son." Rochman. Against borders

Talbott, Hudson

Forging freedom; a true story of heroism during the Holocaust. Putnam 2000 64p il $15.99 (4 and up)   **940.53**

1. Penraat, Jaap 2. World War, 1939-1945—Jews—Rescue 3. Holocaust, 1933-1945

ISBN 0-399-23434-9   LC 99-52551

"Talbott tells the story of his friend Jaap Penraat, who, as a young architectural student in Amsterdam under the Nazi occupation, saved hundreds of Jews from arrest, first by forging their ID cards, and then by devising an elaborate escape plan to smuggle them over the border to freedom." Booklist

Tunnell, Michael O.

The children of Topaz; the story of a Japanese-American internment camp; based on a classroom diary; by Michael O. Tunnell and George W. Chilcoat. Holiday House 1996 74p il $19.95 (5 and up)   **940.53**

1. Central Utah Relocation Center 2. Japanese Americans—Evacuation and relocation, 1942-1945 3. World War, 1939-1945—Children

ISBN 0-8234-1239-3   LC 95-49360

"Interned behind barbed wire in a desert relocation camp in Topaz, Utah, Japanese American teacher Lillian 'Anne' Yamauchi Hori kept a classroom diary with her third-grade class from May to August 1943. . . . Twenty of the small diary entries appear in this book, together with several black-and-white archival photos of the camps. Tunnell and Chilcoat provide a long historical introduction and then detailed commentary that puts each diary entry in the context of what was happening in the camp and in the country at war. . . . The primary sources have a stark authority; it's the very ordinariness of the children's concerns that grabs you." Booklist

Includes bibliographical references

Voices and visions; a collection of primary sources; compiled by William L. Shulman. Blackbirch Press 1998 80p il (Holocaust) lib bdg $26.20   **940.53**

1. Holocaust, 1933-1945—Personal narratives 2. Holocaust survivors

ISBN 1-56711-207-2   LC 97-2578

Book 7 in the series is a compilation of personal narratives of people who survived the Holocaust

This "is especially well designed for classroom and group discussion as well as for personal reading." Booklist

Includes glossary and bibliographical references

Warren, Andrea

Surviving Hitler; a boy in the Nazi death camps. HarperCollins Pubs. 2001 146p il $16.99; lib bdg $17.89; pa $6.99 (5 and up)   **940.53**

1. Mandelbaum, Jack 2. Holocaust, 1933-1945

ISBN 0-688-17497-3; 0-06-029218-0 (lib bdg); 0-06-000767-2 (pa)   LC 00-38899

"Jack Mandelbaum, a Polish Jew, had a happy family life until 1939, when Germany invaded Poland, beginning World War II. Fifteen-year-old Jack is sent to Nazi concentration camps. Despite fear, starvation, and other horrors, he survives." Voice Youth Advocates

"Simply told, Warren's powerful story blends the personal testimony of Holocaust survivor Jack Mandelbaum with the history of his time, documented by stirring photos from the archives of the U.S. Holocaust Memorial Museum. . . . An excellent introduction for readers who don't know much about the history." Booklist

Includes bibliographical references

World War II: primary sources; [compiled by] Barbara C. Bigelow; Christine Slovey, editor. U.X.L 1999 xxxix, 222p il $60   **940.53**

1. World War, 1939-1945—Sources

ISBN 0-7876-3896-X   LC 99-27170

Presents fifteen excerpts from primary sources related to World War II, including speeches, diary entries, newspaper accounts, novels, poems, and memoirs

The "documents are accompanied by clearly written introductory and background material. Notes in the side margins explain terms and expressions." SLJ

Includes bibliographical references

World War II; Myra Immell, book editor. Greenhaven Press 2001 283p il maps (Turning points in world history) lib bdg $34.95; pa $23.70 (7 and up)   **940.53**

1. World War, 1939-1945

ISBN 0-7377-0699-6 (lib bdg); 0-7377-0698-8 (pa)   LC 2001-16033

This is a collection of essays about World War II, with an introduction placing the essays in context and summaries of each one

Includes bibliographical references

Yancey, Diane
The internment of the Japanese. Lucent Bks. 2001 112p il (World history series) lib bdg $27.45
940.53
1. Japanese Americans—Evacuation and relocation, 1942-1945 2. World War, 1939-1945—United States
ISBN 1-59018-013-5   LC 2001-6270
This is a history of the internment of Japanese Americans during World War II
"Well designed for research and reports, this account includes primary- and secondary-source quotations. . . . The numerous black-and-white photos set the tone and enhance the information. . . . This informative, approachable text will be useful in most collections." SLJ
Includes bibliographical references

940.54   World War II, 1939-1945 (Military conduct of the war)

Aaseng, Nathan, 1953-
Navajo code talkers. Walker & Co. 1992 114p il map pa $8.95 hardcover o.p.   **940.54**
1. World War, 1939-1945 2. Navajo Indians 3. Cryptography
ISBN 0-8027-7589-6 (pa)   LC 92-11408
Describes how the American military in World War II used a group of Navajo Indians to create an indecipherable code based on their native language
"A good choice for an offbeat 'war book,' this would also make an unusual complement for both history and language arts classes. Historical photos of the code-talkers in action are included." Bull Cent Child Books
Includes bibliographical references

Allen, Thomas B., 1929-
Remember Pearl Harbor; American and Japanese survivors tell their stories; foreword by Robert D. Ballard. National Geographic Soc. 2001 57p il maps $17.95 (5 and up)   **940.54**
1. Pearl Harbor (Oahu, Hawaii), Attack on, 1941 2. World War, 1939-1945—Personal narratives
ISBN 0-7922-6690-0   LC 2001-796
Personal accounts of the Japanese attack on Pearl Harbor, with background information
"Eyewitness testimony of Japanese and American men and women from various backgrounds enriches this balanced treatment of World War II. . . . The first-person voices along with dozens of black-and-white photos and several full-color maps make this a draw for both browsers and World War II buffs." Booklist
Includes bibliographical references

Anderson, Madelyn Klein
So proudly they served; American military women in World War II. Watts 1995 63p il lib bdg $23   **940.54**
1. Women in the armed forces 2. World War, 1939-1945—Women
ISBN 0-531-20197-X   LC 94-39907
"A First book"

This outlines the role of women in the armed forces during World War II, and traces the history of discrimination against women in the military from the American Revolution to the present
Includes bibliographical references

Barr, Gary, 1951-
Pearl Harbor; [by] Gary E. Barr. Heinemann Library 2004 56p il map (Witness to history) $31.36; pa $8.95   **940.54**
1. Pearl Harbor (Oahu, Hawaii), Attack on, 1941
ISBN 1-403-44569-9; 1-403-44577-X (pa)
LC 2003-18147
Contents: Learning about the past; Geography of the Pacific; Japan: 1853-1930; Why Fascism?; Expansionist Japan: 1930-1941; Japanese military strategy; U.S. military leaders; Japanese military leaders; The countdown to war begins: November 25, 1941; Japanese movements: December 1-2, 1941; Final preparations: December 3-6, 1941; Attack! December 7, 1941; With the Japanese forces; Battleships under attack; Onboard the USS Arizona; Two hours of destruction; Medical personnel; Aftermath; The United States reacts; Fighting back and the Japanese surrender; Japanese Americans after Pearl Harbor; What happened to the leaders?; What have we learned from Pearl Harbor?; Timeline
Uses primary source materials to study what led to the Japanese attack on Pearl Harbor and the repercussions of this event.
"Barr presents clear and easy-to-read background accounts of the motives and views of the leaders of the U.S., Japan, and Germany prior to the attack." SLJ
Includes bibliographical references

Bradley, James
Flags of our fathers; heroes of Iwo Jima; {by} James Bradley with Ron Powers; adapted for young people by Michael French. Delacorte Press 2001 211p il $15.95; pa $8.95 (7 and up)
940.54
1. Rosenthal, Joe, 1911- 2. United States. Marine Corps 3. Iwo Jima, Battle of, 1945
ISBN 0-385-72932-4; 0-385-73064-0 (pa)
LC 00-50914
"A journalistic, accessible adaptation of the earlier book for adult readers, this account by a survivor's son centers on {Rosenthal's} famous photo of six Marines raising a U.S. flag on Iwo Jima. The accurate, engaging text provides the men's pre-war backgrounds, their war service to that time, what they actually did on the island and afterward, and the consequences of the famous photo." Horn Book Guide
Includes bibliographical references

Cartlidge, Cherese
Life of a Nazi soldier; by Cherese Cartlidge and Charles Clark. Lucent Bks. 2001 96p il (Way people live) lib bdg $27.45 (7 and up)
940.54
1. National socialism 2. Germany—History—1933-1945
ISBN 1-56006-484-6   LC 00-9559

Cartlidge, Cherese—*Continued*

"This examination of a German soldier's experience begins by describing the rise of the country's militarized culture under Hitler and his requirements of universal military service. The authors then describe the army's rigorous training and devote chapters to Germany's major campaigns in Poland, France, Russia, and Africa, as well as its final defense of its homeland at the end of the war. . . . {This helps} readers see beyond the leaders and the larger strategic picture to the human face of the young men who carried out orders. A strong choice for history collections." SLJ

Includes bibliographical references

Drez, Ronald J.

Remember D-day; the plan, the invasion, survivor stories. National Geographic Books 2004 61p il map $17.95 (5 and up)   **940.54**
1. World War, 1939-1945—Campaigns—France
ISBN 0-7922-6666-8   LC 2003-17733
Discusses the events and personalities involved in the momentous Allied invasion of France on June 6, 1944.

"This well-organized, clearly written account provides a solid overview for readers unfamiliar with the subject. A first-rate purchase." SLJ

Includes bibliographical references

Durrett, Deanne, 1940-

Unsung heroes of World War II; the story of the Navajo code talkers. Facts on File 1998 122p il (Library of American Indian history) $25 (7 and up)   **940.54**
1. World War, 1939-1945 2. Navajo Indians 3. Cryptography
ISBN 0-8160-3603-9   LC 97-50083
Describes the role of a select group of Navajo Marines who developed a code based on their own native language that provided a means for secure communications among American forces in the Pacific during World War II

"Astounding facts, as well as stirring personal accounts of battle, make for fascinating, educational reading." Booklist

Includes bibliographical references

George, Linda

The Tuskegee Airmen; [by] Linda and Charles George. Children's Press 2001 30p il maps (Cornerstones of freedom) lib bdg $21; pa $5.95   **940.54**
1. World War, 1939-1945—Aerial operations 2. African American pilots
ISBN 0-516-21602-3 (lib bdg); 0-516-27280-2 (pa)   LC 00-24020
This is an account of the African American air pilots of World War II

Includes glossary and bibliographical references

Grant, R. G. (Reg G.)

Hiroshima and Nagasaki. Raintree Steck-Vaughn Pubs. 1998 64p il (New perspectives) lib bdg $28.54 (7 and up)   **940.54**
1. Atomic bomb 2. Hiroshima (Japan)—Bombardment, 1945 3. Nagasaki (Japan)—Bombardment, 1945
ISBN 0-8172-5013-1   LC 97-3250
Describes the causes and horrible effects of the 1945 bombing of Hiroshima and Nagasaki

This combines "a clear historical perspective, vivid personal accounts, and contemporary viewpoints from all sides. The writing is direct and detailed." Booklist

Includes glossary and bibliographical references

Kuhn, Betsy

Angels of mercy; the Army nurses of World War II. Atheneum Bks. for Young Readers 1999 114p il map $18 (5 and up)   **940.54**
1. United States. Army Nurse Corps 2. World War, 1939-1945—Women 3. Women in the armed forces
ISBN 0-689-82044-5   LC 98-36610
Relates the experiences of World War II Army nurses, who brought medical skills, courage, and cheer to hospitals throughout Europe, North Africa, and the Pacific

"Excellent reproductions, maps and a time line accompany the clear, well-written text." SLJ

Includes bibliographical references

Lawton, Clive

Hiroshima; the story of the first atom bomb; [by] Clive A. Lawton. 1st U.S. ed. Candlewick Press 2004 48p il map $18.99 (5 and up)   **940.54**
1. Hiroshima (Japan)—Bombardment, 1945 2. Atomic bomb 3. World War, 1939-1945
ISBN 0-7636-2271-0   LC 2004-45166
The author "explores the politics and the science behind the military decision that began the nuclear arms race. . . . He investigates the events that led up to the disaster at Hiroshima in 1945 and discusses the consequences that we are still living with today." Publisher's note

"Engaging text and powerful photographs are intricately woven together to make a long-lasting impact on readers." Libr Media Connect

Maruki, Toshi, 1912-

Hiroshima no pika; words and pictures by Toshi Maruki. Lothrop, Lee & Shepard Bks. 1982 c1980 unp il $17.99   **940.54**
1. Hiroshima (Japan)—Bombardment, 1945 2. World War, 1939-1945—Japan
ISBN 0-688-01297-3   LC 82-15365
First published 1980 in Japan
Focusing on the experiences of a real family "the horrifying story of the atomic bombing or 'flash' of Hiroshima is told here with a remarkable eloquence, including many poignant details. The story is terribly disturbing and painful to read, but the narrative is at the same time so spare and compelling one must go on. . . . Young people twelve and over, as well as adults, should know this terrible story. This superb book can begin to tell it to them." Appraisal

McGowen, Tom

Air raid; bombing campaigns of World War II. 21st Cent. Bks. (Brookfield) 2001 64p il (Military might) lib bdg $26.90   **940.54**
1. World War, 1939-1945—Aerial operations
2. Military airplanes
ISBN 0-7613-1810-0   LC 00-41806
This describes the history of military aircraft and how they became formidable weapons in World War II, with a discussion of bombing campaigns

Assault from the sky; airborne infantry of World War II. 21st Cent. Bks. (Brookfield) 2002 64p il (Military might) lib bdg $26.90   **940.54**
1. World War, 1939-1945—Aerial operations
2. Parachute troops
ISBN 0-7613-1809-7   LC 00-47934
A history of parachute troops operations during World War II
Includes bibliographical references

Carrier war; aircraft carriers in World War II. 21st Cent. Bks. (Brookfield) 2001 64p il (Military might) lib bdg $26.90   **940.54**
1. Aircraft carriers 2. World War, 1939-1945—Naval operations 3. World War, 1939-1945—Aerial operations
ISBN 0-7613-1808-9   LC 00-42303
This begins with a "history of the evolution of aircraft carriers, followed by a discussion of the world situation in 1941 and the importance of the U.S. military bases at Pearl Harbor. Another chapter tells briefly of the Japanese attack on Pearl Harbor. The remainder of the text describes the major battles in the Pacific and the shift in the role of battleships as carriers became more important. . . . A good introduction for readers who are becoming familiar with this period of history." SLJ

Germany's lightning war; Panzer divisions of World War II. 21st Cent. Bks. (Brookfield) 1999 64p il (Military might) lib bdg $26.90 (5 and up)   **940.54**
1. World War, 1939-1945—Germany 2. Military tanks
ISBN 0-7613-1511-X   LC 98-44009
Discusses the development and actions of German tank units in World War II, covering specific battles and the changes that tanks brought to warfare in general
This book "should inspire youngsters to pursue their interest in the subject." SLJ

Sink the Bismarck; Germany's super-battleship of World War II. 21st Cent. Bks. (Brookfield) 1999 64p il (Military might) lib bdg $26.90 (5 and up)   **940.54**
1. Bismarck (Battleship) 2. World War, 1939-1945—Naval operations
ISBN 0-7613-1510-1   LC 98-48500
Describes the actions of the German battleship "Bismarck" during World War II and the operations of the British navy to destroy this ship
The presentation is "straightforward, simple. . . . The writing is . . . easy to follow." SLJ

Nathan, Amy

Yankee doodle gals; women pilots of World War II; foreword by Eileen Collins. National Geographic Soc. 2001 86p il maps $21
   940.54
1. Women air pilots 2. World War, 1939-1945—Aerial operations
ISBN 0-7922-8216-7   LC 2001-560
This describes the Women's Air Force Service Pilots of World War II
"There's plenty of action to involve readers, and the women's perseverance in the face of obstacles is inspiring. Wonderful black-and-white photos extend the text." Booklist

Nelson, Pete

Left for dead; a young man's search for justice for the USS Indianapolis; {by} Peter Nelson; with a preface by Hunter Scott. Delacorte Press 2002 xx, 201p il $15.95; lib bdg $17.99; pa $8.95 (7 and up)   **940.54**
1. McVay, Charles Butler, III 2. Scott, Hunter 3. Indianapolis (Cruiser) 4. World War, 1939-1945—Naval operations
ISBN 0-385-72959-6; 0-385-90033-3 (lib bdg); 0-385-73091-8 (pa)   LC 2001-53774
Recalls the sinking of the U.S.S. Indianapolis at the end of World War II, the navy cover-up and unfair court martial of the ship's captain, and how a young boy helped the survivors set the record straight fifty-five years later
"Written in simple chronological order, it tells a powerful story." Book Rep
Includes bibliographical references

Sheehan, Sean, 1951-

The technology of World War II. Raintree Steck-Vaughn Pubs. 2003 64p il map (World wars) $32.79   **940.54**
1. World War, 1939-1945 2. Technology
ISBN 0-7398-6064-X   LC 2002-151935
Contents: Victories and defeats; Technology and people; Improving the tools of war; The secret war; Inventions and discoveries; Did technology win the war?
Describes the new military technology used during World War II on land, at sea, and in the air
"The vintage photos are of good quality and not heavily duplicated in other sources." SLJ
Includes bibliographical references

Stein, R. Conrad, 1937-

World War II in Europe; "America goes to war". Enslow Pubs. 1994 128p il maps (American war series) lib bdg $26.60; pa $13.26
   940.54
1. World War, 1939-1945—Campaigns
ISBN 0-89490-525-2 (lib bdg); 0-7660-1733-8 (pa)
    LC 93-47396
"Stein commences with a reprise of the opening shots on the Polish frontier in 1939 and takes a quick look at Nazi Germany's origins and subsequent 'lightning war' across Europe. Coverage moves quickly onward to the

Stein, R. Conrad, 1937-—*Continued*
attack on Pearl Harbor, Germany's declaration of war on America, through V-E Day and the conclusion of hostilities with Japan. . . . {This offers} the interest-holding and informative prose befitting such an introductory title. Furthermore, Stein has appended a useful chronology, detailed chapter notes, a short list of books for further reading, and a helpful index; these features add greatly to the book's value." SLJ

World War II in the Pacific; "remember Pearl Harbor". Enslow Pubs. 1994 128p il maps (American war series) lib bdg $26.60; pa $13.26
940.54
1. World War, 1939-1945—Campaigns—Pacific Ocean
ISBN 0-89490-524-4 (lib bdg); 0-7660-1734-6 (pa)
LC 93-33623
This is an "overview of U.S. participation in the Pacific war. . . . Stein packs a great deal of information into this slim volume and manages to do so without oversimplification. The narrative is arranged in basic chronological order . . . and is enlivened by direct, nononsense prose, the prudent use of quotations, black-and-white archival photographs, and helpful maps." SLJ
Includes bibliographical references

Tanaka, Shelley
Attack on Pearl Harbor; the true story of the day America entered World War II; text by Shelley Tanaka; paintings by David Craig; maps by Jack McMaster; historical consultation by John Lundstrom. Hyperion Bks. for Children 2001 64p il $19.99 (4 and up)
940.54
1. Pearl Harbor (Oahu, Hawaii), Attack on, 1941
2. World War, 1939-1945
ISBN 0-7868-0736-9
LC 2001-16634
"An I was there book; A Hyperion/Madison Press book"
.
"Tanaka reconstructs key events of the attack on Pearl Harbor, based on the harrowing, real-life experiences of four young men. . . . The account is riveting. She includes plenty of sensory details and writes in a clipped, concise manner that clearly conveys the danger and frenzied pace of the events. . . . Dramatic, full-color paintings, black-and-white photos, maps, and diagrams contribute much to the readers' understanding of the events." Booklist
Includes glossary and bibliographical references

Uschan, Michael V., 1948-
The bombing of Pearl Harbor. World Almanac Library 2003 48p il map (Landmark events in American history) lib bdg $29.27; pa $14.60
940.54
1. Pearl Harbor (Oahu, Hawaii), Attack on, 1941
ISBN 0-8368-5373-3 (lib bdg); 0-8368-5401-2 (pa)
LC 2002-36022
Contents: World War II; The United States in the Pacific; The attack on Pearl Harbor; After the attack; The United States in World War II

This describes the 1941 attack on Pearl Harbor and its effects
The book is "heavily illustrated with well-chosen and carefully placed archival photographs. . . . [It] will be useful for reports." SLJ
Includes glossary and bibliographical references

Williams, Barbara
World War II, Pacific; by Barbara Williams: . Lerner Publications 2005 96p il map (Chronicle of America's wars) lib bdg $27.93 (5 and up)
940.54
1. World War, 1939-1945
ISBN 0-8225-0138-4
LC 2004-3371
This chronicles World War II in the Pacific focusing on the war's impact on America and its people.
"A precise, well-documented chronology of the major battles in the Pacific theater. Though the narration is brief, it is informative and avoids misconceptions." SLJ
Includes glossary and bibliographical references

World War II battles and leaders; Aaron R. Murray, editor. DK Pub 2004 96p il map (Battles and leaders) $16.99; pa $9.99
940.54
1. World War, 1939-1945—Campaigns
ISBN 0-7566-0259-9; 0-7566-0260-2 (pa)
LC 2003-27382
This begins with an overview of the causes of the war, and continues year-by-year looking at the major battles and their results.
"The clear open design and succinctly presented facts make finding information a snap while the spot art, vintage photos, maps and pull-out quotes bring history up close." Booklist

940.55   Europe--1945-

Blohm, Craig E., 1948-
An uneasy peace, 1945-1980. Lucent Bks. 2003 128p il map (American war library, Cold War) $27.45
940.55
1. Cold war
ISBN 1-59018-201-4
LC 2002-434
Discusses the Cold War, its origins and the resulting conflicts, including the arms race, The Korean War, the Cuban missile crisis, and the Vietnam War
Includes bibliographical references

941.081   British Isles--Reign of Victoria, 1837-1901

Ashby, Ruth
Victorian England. Benchmark Bks. 2002 c2003 80p il map (Cultures of the past) lib bdg $29.93
941.081
1. Great Britain—History—19th century 2. Great Britain—Civilization
ISBN 0-7614-1493-2
LC 2002-2184
Contents: A time of change; A popular art; Faith and doubt; Social order, social change; A lasting memory

Ashby, Ruth—*Continued*
Describes English society in the years of Queen Victoria's reign (1837-1901), with attention to class structure, gender roles, artistic and scientific achievements
This is "sure to draw report writers and history buffs alike. . . . Copiously illustrated with period reproductions and modern-day photos." Horn Book Guide
Includes glossary and bibliographical references

Price-Groff, Claire
Queen Victoria and nineteenth-century England. Benchmark Bks. 2002 c2003 96p il map (Rulers and their times) lib bdg $29.93 **941.081**
1. Victoria, Queen of Great Britain, 1819-1901 2. Great Britain—History—19th century 3. Great Britain—Social life and customs 4. Great Britain—Kings and rulers 5. Queens
ISBN 0-7614-1488-6   LC 2002-1095
Provides an overview of Queen Victoria's life and reign and of the daily lives of the people of nineteenth-century England, and includes excerpts from letters, newspaper articles, and books of the time
"Color reproductions of art and manuscripts accompany the text, which is spaciously designed with plenty of white space." Horn Book Guide
Includes glossary and bibliographical references

941.1 Scotland

Levy, Patricia Marjorie, 1951-
Scotland. Marshall Cavendish 2001 128p il map (Cultures of the world) lib bdg $37.07 (5 and up) **941.1**
1. Scotland
ISBN 0-7614-1159-3   LC 00-39831
An illustrated look at the geography, history, government, politics, people, religion, language, food and culture of Scotland
Includes glossary and bibliographical references

941.5 Ireland

Bartoletti, Susan Campbell, 1958-
Black potatoes; the story of the great Irish famine, 1845-1850. Houghton Mifflin 2001 184p il $18; pa $9.95 (7 and up) **941.5**
1. Famines 2. Ireland—History
ISBN 0-618-00271-5; 0-618-54883-1 (pa)
LC 2001-24156
The author "examines the causes of the famine, considering the roles of both the potato blight and of social conditions in mid-nineteenth century Ireland." Voice Youth Advocates
"The bibliography (also narrative) provides some of the most fascinating historical reading in the book. Overall, a useful addition to collections, for both personal and research uses." SLJ
Includes bibliographical references and index

Dolan, Edward F., 1924-
The Irish potato famine; the story of Irish-American immigration. Benchmark Bks. 2003 109p il map (Great journeys) lib bdg $32.79
941.5
1. Ireland—History 2. Famines 3. Irish Americans 4. United States—Immigration and emigration
ISBN 0-7614-1323-5   LC 2001-6237
Discusses the potato famine that devastated Ireland in the nineteenth century and led to a widespread immigration to the United States
Includes bibliographical references

Feed the children first; Irish memories of the Great Hunger; edited by Mary E. Lyons. Atheneum Bks. for Young Readers 2002 43p il $17 **941.5**
1. Ireland—History 2. Famines
ISBN 0-689-84226-0   LC 00-49606
Lyons "compiles quotations from Irish citizens on the devastating effects of the potato famine that ravaged Ireland between 1845 and 1852." Publ Wkly
"This brief book is a powerful introduction to Ireland's history and to the human devastation of a country in extreme poverty." Horn Book
Includes bibliographical references

Levy, Patricia Marjorie, 1951-
Ireland. 2nd ed. Benchmark Books 2004 144p il map (Cultures of the world) lib bdg $29.95 (5 and up) **941.5**
1. Ireland
ISBN 0-7614-1784-2   LC 2004-12902
First published 1994
This describes the geography, history, government, economy, environment, lifestyle, religion, and culture of Ireland.
Includes glossary and bibliographical references

941.6 Ulster. Northern Ireland

Wagner, Heather Lehr
The IRA and England. Chelsea House 2002 111p il maps (People at odds) lib bdg $22.95 (7 and up) **941.6**
1. Irish Republican Army 2. Northern Ireland 3. Terrorism 4. Ireland—History
ISBN 0-7910-6706-8   LC 2001-7938
Contents: The lines are drawn; The war years; A return to arms; Streets full of sorrow; The political front; The peace process
Discusses the background and development of the conflict between the Irish Republican Army fighting for the Catholics in Ireland and the British government forces supporting the Irish Protestants
"Wagner has done an admirable job of attempting to explain this conflict without oversimplifying the issues." SLJ
Includes bibliographical references

942   England and Wales

Lace, William W.
England. Lucent Bks. 1997 128p il maps (Modern nations of the world) lib bdg $28.70 (7 and up)   **942**
1. England
ISBN 1-56006-194-4   LC 96-40121
Examines the land, people, and history of England and discusses its state of affairs and place in the world today
This "is full of reliable facts packaged in a compact and easily accessible format." SLJ
Includes bibliographical references

Lister, Maree
England; {written by Maree Lister and Marti Sevier}. Stevens, G. 1998 96p il (Countries of the world) lib bdg $30   **942**
1. England
ISBN 0-8368-2125-4   LC 98-13067
Introduces the geography, history, economy, government, culture, food, and people of England
This book "will provide students with a solid introduction." SLJ
Includes glossary and bibliographical references

942.01   England--Early history to 1066

Crossley-Holland, Kevin
The world of King Arthur and his court; people, places, legend, and lore; illustrated by Peter Malone. Dutton Children's Bks. 1999 c1998 125p il hardcover o.p. paperback available $14.95 (5 and up)   **942.01**
1. Arthur, King 2. Great Britain—History—0-1066 3. Middle Ages
ISBN 0-525-47321-1 (pa)   LC 98-37698
First published 1998 in the United Kingdom
Surveys the known history of King Arthur, the legends and lore surrounding him, his treatment in literature, and the possible historical background of his associates and stories
An "eminently browsable, stylishly written trove of Arthuriana. . . . Lavishly detailed, both the full-spread paintings and spot illustrations are ripe with mystery and romance." Publ Wkly

Nardo, Don, 1947-
King Arthur. Lucent Bks. 2003 96p il (Heroes and villains) lib bdg $24.45   **942.01**
1. Arthur, King 2. Great Britain—History—0-1066
ISBN 1-56006-948-1   LC 2001-8668
Contents: Arthur in history, legend, and literature; The coming of Arthur; The order of the Round Table; The coming of Lancelot; The treachery of Mordred; The passing of Arthur
Surveys the known history of King Arthur, the legends and lore surrounding him, his treatment in literature, and the possible historical background of his associates and stories
"Nardo does a nice job of mixing the exciting stories with historical background of first-millennium England." Booklist
Includes bibliographical references

942.03   England--Period of House of Plantagenet, 1154-1399

Hinds, Kathryn, 1962-
Medieval England. Benchmark Bks. 2002 79p il maps (Cultures of the past) lib bdg $29.93
    942.03
1. Great Britain—Social life and customs 2. Medieval civilization
ISBN 0-7614-0308-6   LC 00-46769
This introduction to medieval England is divided into five sections: history, cultural history, belief system; beliefs and society, the legacy of the medieval England
This offers "balanced, thoughtfully interpreted material. . . . Reinforcing the text are a number of extensions, including illustrations, color photos of artifacts, a map, time line, and brief samples of literature." Horn Book Guide
Includes glossary and bibliographical references

Tanaka, Shelley
In the time of knights; the real-life history of history's greatest knight; illustrations by Greg Ruhl. Hyperion 2000 48p il $16.99 (4 and up)
    942.03
1. Pembroke, William Marshal, Earl of, 1144?-1219 2. Knights and knighthood 3. Great Britain—History—1154-1399, Plantagenets
ISBN 0-7868-0651-6   LC 00-29552
"An I was there book"
This "tells the life story of William Marshal, one of the most successful knights of the twelfth century and regent to Henry, the son of Eleanor of Aquitaine." Horn Book Guide
"Tanaka weaves a fascinating tale filled with plenty of historical detail. . . . She draws on documents, maps, period reproductions, and other primary sources. Clear, colorful photos of sites and artifacts and original art complement the story line. Excellent organization is an added plus." SLJ
Includes glossary and bibliographical references

942.05   England--Tudor period, 1485-1603

Ashby, Ruth
Elizabethan England. Benchmark Bks. (Tarrytown) 1999 80p il (Cultures of the past) lib bdg $29.93   **942.05**
1. Great Britain—History—1485-1603, Tudors 2. World history—16th century 3. England—Social life and customs
ISBN 0-7614-0269-1   LC 96-43868

Ashby, Ruth—*Continued*
This is "an effective presentation, enhanced by colorful illustrations and graphics." SLJ
Includes glossary and bibliographical references

Greenblatt, Miriam
Elizabeth I and Tudor England. Benchmark Bks. 2002 88p il maps (Rulers and their times) lib bdg $29.93   **942.05**
1. Elizabeth I, Queen of England, 1533-1603 2. Queens 3. Great Britain—Kings and rulers 4. Great Britain—History—1485-1603, Tudors
ISBN 0-7614-1028-7   LC 00-57209
Examines the reign of Elizabeth I, including information about her personal life and accomplishments and everyday life in Tudor England, plus contemporary writings which characterize the Elizabethan Age
"Interesting facts about society, clothing, housing, food, cosmetics, sports, and other daily activities are brought to life. . . . Illustrated with plentiful archival art." Horn Book Guide
Includes glossary and bibliographical references

Lace, William W.
Elizabeth I and her court. Lucent Bks. 2003 112p il maps (Lucent library of historical eras, Elizabethan England) $27.45   **942.05**
1. Elizabeth I, Queen of England, 1533-1603 2. Great Britain—History—1485-1603, Tudors
ISBN 1-59018-098-4   LC 2002-8119
Contents: Introduction: The One Sun; Gloriana; The queen's majesty; All the queen's men; All the queen's women; The court at home; The court on the move; The court at play; The court on display; Epilogue: Faded but not forgotten
A biography of England's Queen Elizabeth I, looking as well as the members of her court and how they served her
This is a combination "of solid research and fascinating history." SLJ
Includes bibliographical references

Primary sources; Clarice Swisher, editor. Lucent Bks. 2003 96p il maps (Lucent library of historical eras. Elizabethan England) lib bdg $27.45   **942.05**
1. Elizabeth I, Queen of England, 1533-1603 2. Great Britain—History—1485-1603, Tudors 3. England—Social life and customs
ISBN 1-59018-097-6   LC 2002-13080
Contents: The reign of Elizabeth I; Political and social issues; Entertainment and literature; English life
"An insight into Elizabethan England is provided in this text by primary sources such as correspondence, speeches, poetry, and excerpts from books written by Elizabeth I's contemporaries. . . . Black and white captioned illustrations, portraits, drawings, and maps are found throughout the text. Students doing research on Elizabethan England will find this a very useful resource." Libr Media Connect
Includes bibliographical references

Stewart, Gail, 1949-
Life in Elizabethan London; [by] Gail B. Stewart. Lucent Bks. 2003 112p il map (Lucent library of historical eras, Elizabethan England) lib bdg $27.45   **942.05**
1. London (England)—Social life and customs 2. Great Britain—History—1485-1603, Tudors
ISBN 1-59018-100-X   LC 2002-11292
Contents: Introduction: Elizabeth's London; An infinite order; Marriage and family; A London home; Elizabethan fashion; At the table; "Lord, have mercy upon London"; Crime in Elizabethan London; Pleasure and sport
Looks at the daily life of those living in London, England, during the reign of Elizabeth I, including a glimpse of what a first-time visitor might have noticed
This is a combination "of solid research and fascinating history." SLJ
Includes bibliographical references

942.06 England--Stuart and Commonwealth periods, 1603-1714

Barter, James, 1946-
Shakespeare's London. Lucent Bks. 2003 112p il maps (Travel guide to) lib bdg $27.45 (7 and up)   **942.06**
1. London (England)—History 2. Great Britain—History—1603-1714, Stuarts
ISBN 1-59018-146-8   LC 2002-3286
A visitors' guide to London in 1604, including what to see, where to stay, and where to eat, with sidebars on such topics as proper etiquette, famous residents, and student life at Oxford
"This is a very enjoyable approach to history and definitely succeeds in transporting students to another place and time." SLJ
Includes bibliographical references

942.1 London

Stacey, Gill
London; by Gill Stacey. World Almanac Library 2004 48p il map (Great cities of the world) lib bdg $30; pa $11.95 (4 and up)   **942.1**
1. London (England)
ISBN 0-8368-5022-X (lib bdg); 0-8368-5182-X (pa)
LC 2003-49693
Contents: Introduction; History of London; People of London; Living in London; London at work; London at play; Looking forward
This "up-to-date, attractively formatted [title contains an] interesting, informative [text] set in an easy-to-read font. Well-chosen, excellent-quality color photos, quotations, and sidebars appear throughout." SLJ
Includes bibliographical references

942.9   Wales

Hestler, Anna
Wales. Marshall Cavendish 2001 128p il maps
(Cultures of the world) lib bdg $37.07
942.9
1. Wales
ISBN 0-7614-1195-X   LC 00-47426
This title provides "information on the geography, history, government, lifestyles, religion, festivals, arts, and
contemporary life in {Wales}. . . . The concise writing
offers enough material for report writers without overwhelming them." SLJ
Includes glossary and bibliographical references

943   Central Europe. Germany

Allan, Tony, 1946-
The Rhine. World Almanac 2003 48p il maps
(Great rivers of the world) lib bdg $26.60 (4 and
up)   **943**
1. Rhine River
ISBN 0-8368-5446-2   LC 2002-34318
Contents: The course of the Rhine; The Rhine in his-
tory; Cities and settlements; Economic activity; Animals
and plants; Environmental issues; Recreation and leisure;
The future
The Rhine river's "flow, history, ecological concerns,
tourism, flora and fauna, etc., are explained. . . . Clear
and colorful photos appear on every page." SLJ
Includes glossary and bibliographical references

Ayer, Eleanor H.
Germany. Lucent Bks. 1999 112p il maps
(Modern nations of the world) lib bdg $28.70 (7
and up)   **943**
1. Germany
ISBN 1-56006-355-6   LC 98-15471
Examines the land, people, and history of Germany
and discusses its state of affairs and place in the world
today
"A volume that stands on its own as a fine little history book. . . . Rich in sharp, interesting details. . . . Interspersed throughout each section are well-chosen black-
and-white illustrations." Booklist
Includes bibliographical references

Fuller, Barbara, 1961-
Germany; [by] Barbara Fuller, Gabriele
Vossmeyer. 2nd ed. Benchmark Bks. 2003 c2004
144p il maps (Cultures of the world) lib bdg
$37.07 (5 and up)   **943**
1. Germany
ISBN 0-7614-1667-6   LC 2003-8186
First published 1993
Explores the geography, history, government, econo-
my, people, and culture of Germany
Includes glossary and bibliographical references

Kallen, Stuart A., 1955-
The Rhine. Lucent Bks. 2003 112p il maps
(Rivers of the world) lib bdg $27.45   **943**
1. Rhine River
ISBN 1-59018-062-3   LC 2002-11051
Describes the Rhine River from ancient times to the
present, and discusses what must be done to protect and
preserve this river
This is "good for serious report writers looking for
solid information." SLJ
Includes bibliographical references

Kort, Michael
The handbook of the new Eastern Europe; [by]
Michael G. Kort. 21st Cent. Bks. (Brookfield)
2001 256p il maps lib bdg $39.90 (7 and up)
943
1. Eastern Europe 2. Central Europe
ISBN 0-7613-1362-1   LC 00-57708
This handbook begins with a "overview of the region.
Economic and historical profiles are given for seven nations plus those in the former Yugoslavia, with an emphasis on post-1989 events after the fall of Communism.
. . . Other reference material includes flags of each nation, a chronology of events since 1989, and an encyclopedia. The latter emphasizes names and places, with a
few general topics such as environmental pollution."
Voice Youth Advocates
"The book will be useful for serious students needing
research materials." Horn Book Guide
Includes bibliographical references

943.086   Germany--Period of Third Reich, 1933-1945

Altman, Linda Jacobs, 1943-
Hitler's rise to power and the Holocaust. Enslow
Pubs. 2003 104p il map (Holocaust in history) lib
bdg $20.95   **943.086**
1. Hitler, Adolf, 1889-1945 2. National socialism
3. Germany—History—1933-1945 4. Holocaust, 1933-
1945
ISBN 0-7660-1991-8   LC 2002-151083
Explores events in Germany that led up to World War
II including Hitler's rise to power and the creation of the
Third Reich
Includes glossary and bibliographical references

Bartoletti, Susan Campbell
Hitler Youth; growing up in Hitler's shadow; by
Susan Campbell Bartoletti. Scholastic Nonfiction
2005 176p il maps $19.95 (7 and up)
943.086
1. National socialism 2. Germany—History—1933-
1945 3. Holocaust, 1933-1945
ISBN 0-439-35379-3   LC 2004-51040
The author "explores how Hitler gained the loyalty,
trust, and passion of so many of Germany's young people." Publisher's note
"Bartoletti draws on oral histories, diaries, letters, and
her own extensive interviews with Holocaust survivors,

Bartoletti, Susan Campbell—*Continued*

Hitler Youth, resisters, and bystanders to tell the history from the viewpoints of people who were there. . . . The stirring photos tell more of the story. . . . The extensive back matter is a part of the gripping narrative." Booklist

Includes bibliographical references

Damon, Duane

Mein Kampf; Hitler's blueprint for aryan supremacy. Lucent Bks. 2003 112p il map (Words that changed history) lib bdg $27.45 (7 and up)
943.086

1. Hitler, Adolf, 1889-1945 2. National socialism 3. Germany—History—1933-1945

ISBN 1-56006-800-0   LC 2002-11028

Profiles the conditions that led to the rise of Adolf Hitler and his philosophy, ultimately leading to Germany's defeat during World War II

"The writing is clear, lively, and well suited to literate teenage readers. Excerpts from primary-source documents and good-quality, black-and-white photos and reproductions appear throughout." SLJ

Includes bibliographical references

Living in Nazi Germany; Elaine Halleck, book editor. Greenhaven Press 2004 158p il map (Exploring cultural history) $29.95; pa $21.20 (7 and up)
943.086

1. Germany—Politics and government—1933-1945 2. National socialism

ISBN 0-7377-1731-9; 0-7377-1732-7 (pa)
LC 2003-57961

This includes "eyewitness accounts from victims of Hitler's brutality as well as from those who found places in the Nazi machine. . . . Most of the accounts are from less well known sources, and many are compelling. Excerpts from a few familiar volumes, such as Albert Speer's memoirs and the wartime diaries of Joseph Goebbels, also appear. . . . An effective, insightful look at aspects of the Nazi system." Booklist

Includes bibliographical references

The **Rise** of Nazi Germany; Don Nardo, book editor. Greenhaven Press 1999 240p (Turning points in world history) lib bdg $34.95; pa $23.70 (7 and up)
943.086

1. Hitler, Adolf, 1889-1945 2. National socialism 3. Germany—Politics and government—1933-1945

ISBN 1-56510-965-1 (lib bdg); 1-56510-964-3 (pa)
LC 98-8404

"This book contains well-chosen excerpts of essays and books written by historians. They describe Hitler's roots, his rise to power, why Germany succumbed to the dictator's diabolical politics, how he remade German society, how and why Hitler so easily conquered established European countries, and, finally, what led to the fall of the Nazi empire. . . . An appendix with excerpts of primary documents written by Hitler and his supporters and opponents further illuminate the issues addressed in the main body of the book. A useful overview and cogent analysis." SLJ

Includes bibliographical references

Shuter, Jane, 1955-

Resistance to the Nazis. Heinemann Lib. 2003 56p il map (Holocaust) lib bdg $28.50; pa $8.95
943.086

1. Holocaust, 1933-1945 2. World War, 1939-1945—Underground movements 3. Germany—History—1933-1945

ISBN 1-4034-0814-9 (lib bdg); 1-4034-3206-6 (pa)
LC 2002-6853

This is "an excellent blend of overview and personal stories." SLJ

Includes glossary and bibliographical references

943.6   Austria and Liechtenstein

Sheehan, Sean, 1951-

Austria. 2nd ed. Benchmark Bks. 2003 144p il map (Cultures of the world) lib bdg $25.95 (5 and up)
943.6

1. Austria

ISBN 0-7614-1497-5   LC 2002-11623

First published 1993

Presents the geography, history, economy, and social life and customs of Austria, the birthplace of such people as Kurt Waldheim, Wolfgang Amadeus Mozart, Sigmund Freud, and Arnold Schwarzenegger

Includes glossary and bibliographical references

943.7   Czech Republic and Slovakia

Gottfried, Ted, 1928-

Slovakia; by Ted Gottfried. Benchmark Books 2005 144p il map (Cultures of the world) lib bdg $37.07 (5 and up)
943.7

1. Slovakia

ISBN 0-7614-1856-3   LC 2004-22241

Contents: Geography; History; Government; Economy; Environment; Slovakians; Lifestyle; Religion; Language; Arts; Leisure; Festivals; Food

Includes glossary and bibliographical references

Sioras, Efstathia

Czech Republic. Marshall Cavendish 1999 128p il maps (Cultures of the world) lib bdg $37.07 (5 and up)
943.7

1. Czech Republic

ISBN 0-7614-0870-3   LC 98-30290

Describes the geography, history, government, economy, people, lifestyle, religion, language, arts, leisure, festivals, and food of the Czech Republic

Includes glossary and bibliographical references

943.8   Poland

Hintz, Martin, 1945-

Poland. Children's Press 1998 144p il (Enchantment of the world, second series) lib bdg $35 (4 and up)
943.8

1. Poland

ISBN 0-516-20605-2   LC 97-25559

Hintz, Martin, 1945--—*Continued*
Describes the history, geography, economy, plants and animals, language, religion, sports, arts, and people of this central European country which has ties to both East and West
Includes bibliographical references

943.9 Hungary

Ake, Anne, 1943-
Hungary. Lucent Books 2003 112p il map (Modern nations of the world) $27.45 (7 and up)
943.9
1. Hungary
ISBN 1-560-06970-8   LC 2001-5699
Discusses the diversity of Hungary and the struggle between the East and West for control of it
Includes bibliographical references

944 France and Monaco

Gofen, Ethel, 1937-
France; [by] Ethel Caro Gofen, Blandine Pengili Reymann. 2nd ed. Benchmark Bks. 2002 144p il maps (Cultures of the world) lib bdg $37.07
944
1. France
ISBN 0-7614-1498-3   LC 2002-11624
First published 1992 under the authorship of Ethel Caro Gofen
Introduces the geography, history, economy, cultures, and people of France
Includes glossary and bibliographical references

NgCheong-Lum, Roseline, 1962-
France. Stevens, G. 1999 96p il (Countries of the world) lib bdg $30 (4 and up)   **944**
1. France
ISBN 0-8368-2260-9   LC 98-33770
An overview of France, discussing its history, geography, government, economy, culture, and relations with North America
"The full-color photos on every page are outstanding and the style of writing is graceful." SLJ
Includes glossary and bibliographical references

Plain, Nancy
Louis XVI, Marie Antoinette, and the French Revolution. Benchmark Bks. 2002 88p il maps (Rulers and their times) lib bdg $29.93
944
1. Louis XVI, King of France, 1754-1793 2. Marie Antoinette, Queen, consort of Louis XVI, King of France, 1755-1793 3. France—History—1789-1799, Revolution
ISBN 0-7614-1029-5   LC 00-57152
This covers the lives of King Louis XVI of France and his queen Marie Antoinette "as well as everyday life and the literature of the times. Interesting facts about so-

ciety, clothing, housing, food, cosmetics, sports, and other daily activities are brought to life. . . . Illustrated with plentiful archival art." Horn Book Guide
Includes glossary and bibliographical references

944.04 France--Revolutionary period, 1789-1804

The **French** Revolution; Don Nardo, book editor. Greenhaven Press 1999 223p (Turning points in world history) lib bdg $34.95 paperback o.p. (7 and up)   **944.04**
1. France—History—1789-1799, Revolution
ISBN 1-56510-934-1 (lib bdg)   LC 98-16604
"After a historical summary, 19 essays are presented in four sections, covering causes, significant events, social and cultural aspects, and the impact and legacy of the Revolution. An appendix contains excerpts from 26 original documents relevant to the topic. . . . The book is thorough and thought-provoking." SLJ
Includes bibliographical references

945 Italian Peninsula and adjacent islands. Italy

Barter, James, 1946-
Renaissance Florence. Lucent Bks. 2003 112p il maps (Travel guide to) lib bdg $21.96
945
1. Florence (Italy)—History 2. Renaissance
ISBN 1-59018-145-X   LC 2001-6816
Examines the history, people, educational system, scientific and artistic discoveries, social structure, shopping, festivals, and famous artists of Florence
"A Renaissance traveler would have greatly benefited from this guide, and modern students should likewise enjoy this vibrant look at Florence in the early 1500s. Presented in the format and tone of today's travel guides, the present-tense text is engaging and friendly." SLJ
Includes bibliographical references

Behnke, Alison
Italy in pictures. Lerner Publs. 2003 80p il maps (Visual geography series) lib bdg $27.93 (5 and up)
945
1. Italy
ISBN 0-8225-0368-9   LC 2001-5483
A historical and current look at Italy, discussing the land, the government, the people, and the economy
Includes glossary and bibliographical references

Cohen, Elizabeth Storr, 1946-
Daily life in Renaissance Italy; [by] Elizabeth S. Cohen and Thomas V. Cohen. Greenwood Press 2001 316p il maps (Daily life through history) $49.95 (7 and up)   **945**
1. Renaissance 2. Italy—Civilization
ISBN 0-313-30426-2   LC 00-69150

Cohen, Elizabeth Storr, 1946-—*Continued*
"A brief historical background precedes chapters covering society, families, morality, schooling, marriage, disease, and death, as well as many aspects of rural and city life. . . . The documented information is ideal for student reports and reference questions." Voice Youth Advocates
Includes bibliographical references

Foster, Leila Merrell
Italy. Lucent Bks. 1999 112p il (Modern nations of the world) lib bdg $28.70 (7 and up)

945

1. Italy
ISBN 1-56006-481-1   LC 98-36878
Examines the land, people, and history of Italy and discusses its state of affairs and place in the world today
"Collapsing several millennia into a survey that is both succinct and readable is a daunting task, but Foster succeeds admirably." SLJ
Includes bibliographical references

Greenblatt, Miriam
Lorenzo de' Medici and Renaissance Italy. Benchmark Bks. 2002 c2003 80p il map (Rulers and their times) lib bdg $29.93   **945**
1. Medici, Lorenzo de', 1449-1492 2. Renaissance 3. Florence (Italy)—History
ISBN 0-7614-1490-8   LC 2002-1975
Contents: A Renaissance man; Everyday life in Renaissance Italy; Renaissance Italians in their own words
Provides an overview of the lives of Lorenzo de Medici and his subjects in late fourteenth-century Florence, a Renaissance-era city-state, and includes excerpts from poems, laws, and sermons of the time
"Color reproductions of art and manuscripts accompany the text, which is spaciously designed with plenty of white space." Horn Book Guide
Includes glossary and bibliographical references

Hinds, Kathryn, 1962-
Venice and its merchant empire. Benchmark Bks. 2002 80p il maps (Cultures of the past) lib bdg $29.93   **945**
1. Venice (Italy)—History
ISBN 0-7614-0305-1   LC 97-50353
Examines the history, culture, religion, society, and achievements of the Italian city of Venice, from its founding to its surrender to Napoleon at the end of the eighteenth century
This offers a "good, balanced {overview}. . . . Clearly written, the discussion wisely does not presume prior knowledge of subjects, such as the beliefs of Catholics. . . . Greatly enhanced by many richly colored and beautifully reproduced works of art and by photographs of artifacts and historical sites." Booklist
Includes glossary and bibliographical references

Lace, William W.
The Vatican; by William W. Lace. Lucent Books 2004 128p il (Building history series) $28.70   **945**
1. Vatican City
ISBN 1-560-06843-4   LC 2003-11218
History of the buildings, occupants, and uses of the Vatican in Rome.
This is written "in accessible, straightforward language. . . . Quotes from Michelangelo and others, fascinating details, and intriguing mysteries . . . will draw readers easily into the text. . . . . Black-and-white reproductions of maps, etchings, and portraits mix with a central section of glossy color photographs that showcase some of the Vatican's artistic treasures." Booklist
Includes bibliographical references

Schomp, Virginia, 1953-
The Italian Renaissance. Benchmark Bks. 2002 c2003 80p il map (Cultures of the past) lib bdg $29.93   **945**
1. Renaissance 2. Italy—Civilization
ISBN 0-7614-1492-4   LC 2002-1971
Contents: Birthplace of the Renaissance; A new age; The power of the church; The impact of Humanism; Our Renaissance world
Discusses how and why the Renaissance began in Italy, the cultural and intellectual achievements of the Italian Renaissance, and the lasting effects of these achievements on Western civilization
This is "sure to draw report writers and history buffs alike. . . . Copiously illustrated with period reproductions and modern-day photos." Horn Book Guide
Includes glossary and bibliographical references

Sheehan, Sean, 1951-
Malta. Marshall Cavendish 2000 128p il map (Cultures of the world) lib bdg $37.07 (5 and up)   **945**
1. Malta
ISBN 0-7614-0993-9   LC 99-53436
The text covers Malta's "government, economy, people, lifestyles, religion, language, arts and leisure, festivals, and food. . . . Copious colorful photographs and reproductions complement and reinforce the facts presented." SLJ
Includes glossary and bibliographical references

Winter, Jane Kohen, 1959-
Italy; {by} Jane Kohen Winter, Leslie Jermyn. 2nd ed. Benchmark Bks. 2003 144p il maps (Cultures of the world) lib bdg $37.07 (5 and up)   **945**
1. Italy
ISBN 0-7614-1500-9   LC 2002-11628
First published 1995
Describes the geography, history, government, economy, and culture of Italy
"Colorful photographs with informative captions decorate almost every page of [this book]." SLJ
Includes glossary and bibliographical references

946   Iberian Peninsula and adjacent islands. Spain

Mann, Kenny, 1946-
Isabel, Ferdinand and fifteenth-century Spain. Benchmark Bks. 2002 80p il maps (Rulers and their times) lib bdg $29.93   **946**
1. Ferdinand V, King of Spain, 1452-1516 2. Isabella I, Queen of Spain, 1451-1504 3. Spain—History
ISBN 0-7614-1030-9   LC 00-41450
This covers the lives of King Ferdinand and Queen Isabella of Spain "as well as everyday life and the literature of the times. Interesting facts about society, clothing, housing, food, cosmetics, sports, and other daily activities are brought to life. . . . Illustrated with plentiful archival art." Horn Book Guide
Includes glossary and bibliographical references

Millar, Heather, 1963-
Spain in the age of exploration. Benchmark Bks. (Tarrytown) 1999 80p il map (Cultures of the past) $28.70   **946**
1. Spain—History
ISBN 0-7614-0303-5   LC 97-2090
Surveys the important events in the history of Spain between the voyages of Columbus and the defeat of the Spanish Armada and examines the role of the arts and religion during these two centuries
Includes bibliographical references

947   Eastern Europe. Russia

Bachrach, Deborah, 1943-
The Crimean War. Lucent Bks. 1998 112p il maps (World history series) lib bdg $28.70 (7 and up)   **947**
1. Crimean War, 1853-1856
ISBN 1-56006-315-7   LC 97-34045
A historical overview of the events leading up to, during, and after the Crimean War
"The prose is lean and engaging. The author's writing and the well-chosen quotes, maps, and black-and-white photographs and illustrations bring the story to life." SLJ
Includes bibliographical references

Gottfried, Ted, 1928-
The road to Communism; illustrated by Melanie Reim. 21st Cent. Bks. (Brookfield) 2002 144p il lib bdg $28.90   **947**
1. Soviet Union—History—1917-1921, Revolution
ISBN 0-7613-2557-3   LC 2001-52252
Chronicles the Czarist Russian Empire in the 1800s, the birth of Bolshevism, events leading to the Russian Revolution of 1917, and the development of new political structures in its aftermath
"Gottfried writes with clarity and distance even as he narrates the dramatic details of the political conflict and the emotion of the 'dream that failed.'" Booklist
Includes glossary and bibliographical references

Kort, Michael
Russia. 3rd ed. Facts on File 2004 228p il map (Nations in transition) $40 (7 and up)   **947**
1. Russia (Federation)
ISBN 0-8160-5075-9
First published 1995
Examines the people, religion, environmental problems, politics, culture, history, and geography of Russia, emphasizing its transition, since 1991, from a communist to a free nation
Includes bibliographical references

947.084   Russia (Soviet Union)-- 1917-1991

Gottfried, Ted, 1928-
The Stalinist empire; illustrated by Melanie Reim. 21st Cent. Bks. (Brookfield) 2002 127p il lib bdg $28.90   **947.084**
1. Stalin, Joseph, 1879-1953 2. Soviet Union—History
ISBN 0-7613-2558-1   LC 2001-52251
Chronicles the years of Joseph Stalin's iron-fisted reign in the Soviet Union, from the time of Lenin's death to the dawn of World War II
"The book treats the subject matter frankly, in a straightforward and readable fashion." Voice Youth Advocates
Includes glossary and bibliographical references

The **Rise** of the Soviet Union; Tom Streissguth, book editor. Greenhaven Press 2002 256p (Turning points in world history) lib bdg $34.95; pa $23.70 (7 and up)   **947.084**
1. Soviet Union—History
ISBN 0-7377-0929-4 (lib bdg); 0-7377-0928-6 (pa)
                        LC 2001-40866
A collection of essays concerning the social, economic and political issues in the history of the Soviet Union
Includes bibliographical references

947.085   Russia (Soviet Union)-- 1953-1991

The **Collapse** of the Soviet Union; Paul A. Winters, book editor. Greenhaven Press 1999 288p (Turning points in world history) lib bdg $34.95 (7 and up)   **947.085**
1. Soviet Union—Politics and government 2. Russia (Federation)—Politics and government
ISBN 1-56510-997-X (lib bdg)   LC 98-17506
"A chapter summarizing the history of the Soviet Union from the end of the Brezhnev era to the collapse of the government introduces a compilation of excerpts from articles organized into five topical chapters. . . . The compendium includes short questions about each essay; excerpts from reports, speeches, and interviews; a chronology; suggestions for further research." SLJ
"Sophisticated reading, the book will nicely support a modern history curriculum." Booklist
Includes glossary and bibliographical references

947.086 Russia--1991-

Russia today: opposing viewpoints; William Dudley, book editor. Greenhaven Press 2000 203p il lib bdg $34.95; pa $23.70 (7 and up)
947.086
1. Russia (Federation)—Politics and government
ISBN 0-7377-0522-1 (lib bdg); 0-7377-0521-3 (pa)
LC 99-86133
"Opposing viewpoints series"
"Articles or excerpts written between 1996 and 1999 are divided into four chapters dealing with sources of Russia's domestic problems, prospects for democracy, Russia as a threat to the rest of the world, and U.S. foreign policy toward that country. Each article has a short introduction that includes three questions to consider, and each section concludes with a periodical bibliography." SLJ

947.5 Caucasus

Dhilawala, Sakina, 1964-
Armenia. Benchmark Bks. 1997 128p il maps (Cultures of the world) lib bdg $37.07 (5 and up)
947.5
1. Armenia
ISBN 0-7614-0683-2
LC 96-30046
Discusses the geography, history, government, economy, culture, and religion of the republic atop the Armenian Plateau in the Caucausus Mountains
Includes glossary and bibliographical references

Spilling, Michael
Georgia. Benchmark Bks. 1998 128p il maps (Cultures of the world) lib bdg $37.07 (5 and up)
947.5
1. Georgia (Republic)
ISBN 0-7614-0691-3
LC 97-16570
Describes the geography, history, government, economy, people, lifestyle, religion, language, arts, leisure, festivals, and food of a Caucasian republic with a turbulent past
Includes glossary and bibliographical references

947.6 Moldova

Sheehan, Patricia, 1954-
Moldova. Marshall Cavendish 2000 128p il map (Cultures of the world) lib bdg $37.07 (5 and up)
947.6
1. Moldova
ISBN 0-7614-0997-1
LC 99-53433
An illustrated look at the history and culture of the small landlocked country between Russia and the Ukraine that proclaimed its independence in August, 1991
Includes glossary and bibliographical references

947.7 Ukraine

Bassis, Volodymyr
Ukraine. Marshall Cavendish 1997 128p il maps (Cultures of the world) lib bdg $35.64 (5 and up)
947.7
1. Ukraine
ISBN 0-7614-0684-0
LC 96-40207
Examines the geography, history, government, economy, and customs of Ukraine, formerly part of the Union of Soviet Socialist Republics
Includes glossary and bibliographical references

Kummer, Patricia K.
Ukraine. Children's Press 2001 144p il (Enchantment of the world, Second series) lib bdg $35 (4 and up)
947.7
1. Ukraine
ISBN 0-516-21101-3
LC 00-57040
Describes the geography, history, culture, and people of Ukraine
The chapters "are clearly written and have the details needed for reports, but many of the sidebars set off within the chapters are more engaging. . . . Excellent-quality, full-color photos and reproductions enhance the presentation." SLJ
Includes bibliographical references

Otfinoski, Steven, 1949-
Ukraine. Second ed. Facts on File 2004 139p il map (Nations in transition) $40 (7 and up)
947.7
1. Ukraine
ISBN 0-8160-5115-1
LC 2004-43241
First published 1999
Gives a historical and cultural overview of the country of Ukraine with particular emphasis on changes that have occurred since the collapse of the Soviet Union
Includes bibliographical references

947.8 Belarus

Levy, Patricia Marjorie, 1951-
Belarus. Benchmark Bks. 1998 128p il maps (Cultures of the world) lib bdg $37.07 (5 and up)
947.8
1. Belarus
ISBN 0-7614-0811-8
LC 97-48562
This describes the geography, history, government, economy, people, lifestyle, religion, language, arts, leisure, festivals, and food of Belarus
Includes glossary and bibliographical references

947.9   Lithuania, Latvia, Estonia

Barlas, Robert
Latvia. Marshall Cavendish 2000 128p il map
(Cultures of the world) lib bdg $37.07 (5 and up)
947.9
1. Latvia
ISBN 0-7614-0977-7   LC 99-30168
Describes the geography, history, government, economy, people, religion, language, arts, leisure, festivals, and food of Latvia
Includes glossary and bibliographical references

Kagda, Sakina, 1939-
Lithuania. Benchmark Bks. 1997 128p il maps
(Cultures of the world) lib bdg $37.07 (5 and up)
947.9
1. Lithuania
ISBN 0-7614-0681-6   LC 96-29460
Examines the geography, history, government, economy, and customs of the Baltic state
"Kagda manages to tell an interesting story in Lithuania, by writing gracefully and eschewing the use of too much detail." SLJ
Includes glossary and bibliographical references

Spilling, Michael
Estonia. Benchmark Bks. 1999 128p il maps
(Cultures of the world) lib bdg $37.07 (5 and up)
947.9
1. Estonia
ISBN 0-7614-0951-3   LC 98-43682
Introduces the geography, history, government, economy, culture, and people of Estonia, the northernmost and least populated of the three Baltic states
Includes glossary and bibliographical references

948   Scandinavia

Margeson, Susan M.
Viking; written by Susan M. Margeson; photographed by Peter Anderson. rev ed. DK Pub. 2005 72p il map (DK eyewitness books) $15.99; lib bdg $19.99 (4 and up)   **948**
1. Vikings
ISBN 0-7566-1095-8; 0-7566-1096-6 (lib bdg)
First published 1994 by Knopf
Presents an illustrated look at the Vikings - their ships and weapons, heroes and myths, and great adventures in war and exploration.

Morley, Jacqueline
Viking town; written by Jacqueline Morley; illustrated by Mark Bergin; created and designed by David Salariya. Watts 1999 45p (Metropolis) pa $8.95   **948**
1. Vikings
ISBN 0-531-15380-0   LC 98-52918
Takes the reader through a typical Viking town in the ninth or tenth century, describing the different areas, major buildings, and the daily occupations of the people

Robinson, Deborah B.
The Sami of Northern Europe. Lerner Publs. 2002 48p il map (First peoples) lib bdg $23.93
948
1. Sami (European people)
ISBN 0-8225-4175-0   LC 2001-4237
Describes the history, modern and traditional cultural practices and economies, geographic background, and ongoing oppression and struggles of the Sami
"Each topic is discussed on a spread that features colorful, engaging, and well-selected photographs. The text is primarily written in simple, declarative sentences." SLJ
Includes glossary and bibliographical references

Trent, Lynda
The Viking longship. Lucent Bks. 1999 112p il maps (Building history series) lib bdg $28.70 (7 and up)   **948**
1. Vikings 2. Ships
ISBN 1-56006-443-9   LC 98-30360
Describes the history and culture of the Vikings and attributes much of their exploring and raiding success to the well-designed longship
Includes glossary and bibliographical references

Wright, Rachel
The Viking news; consultant, Richard Hall. Candlewick Press 1998 32p il maps   **948**
1. Vikings
ISBN 0-7636-0450-X; 0-7636-1292-8 (pa)
LC 97-35634
Uses a newspaper format to present information about the explorations, heroes, battles, and traditions of the Vikings
"Colorful pages with informative articles, advertising, and heavy use of illustrations result in a wonderful way to introduce readers to Viking . . . life, as well as to interest students in journalism. {This text is} easy to understand, light, and breezy." SLJ

948.5   Sweden

Gan, Delice, 1954-
Sweden; {by} Delice Gan, Leslie Jermyn. 2nd ed. Benchmark Bks. 2003 144p il maps (Cultures of the world) lib bdg $37.07 (5 and up)
948.5
1. Sweden
ISBN 0-7614-1502-5   LC 2002-152559
First published 1993 under the authorship of Delice Gan
Introduces the geography, history, economy, culture, and people of the fourth largest country in Europe
Includes glossary and bibliographical references

949.3 Southern Low Countries. Belgium

Pateman, Robert, 1954-
Belgium. Benchmark Bks. 1995 128p il maps (Cultures of the world) lib bdg $37.07 (5 and up) **949.3**
1. Belgium
ISBN 0-7614-0176-8   LC 95-14900
Introduces the geography, history, government, economy, culture, and people of the small European country of Belgium
"Organization is clear and user friendly. Fine-quality, full-color photographs and reproductions draw readers in and help to hold their interest." SLJ
Includes glossary and bibliographical references

949.35 Luxembourg

Sheehan, Patricia, 1954-
Luxembourg. Marshall Cavendish 1997 128p il maps (Cultures of the world) lib bdg $37.07 (5 and up) **949.35**
1. Luxembourg
ISBN 0-7614-0685-9   LC 96-53367
Discusses the geography, history, government, economy, and customs of the smallest of the Benelux countries
This is "lucidly written. . . . Informative chapters include discussion about body language, religion, education, and women." Horn Book Guide
Includes glossary and bibliographical references

949.5 Greece

DuBois, Jill, 1952-
Greece; [by] Jill Dubois, Xenia Skoura, Olga Gratsaniti. 2nd ed. Benchmark Bks. 2003 143p il maps (Cultures of the world) lib bdg $37.07 (5 and up) **949.5**
1. Greece
ISBN 0-7614-1499-1   LC 2002-11625
First published 1992 under the authorship of Jill DuBois
Introduces the geography, history, economics, culture, and people of the Mediterranean country of Greece
"An attractive, lively, and perceptive look at Greece." SLJ
Includes glossary and bibliographical references

Marston, Elsa
The Byzantine Empire. Benchmark Bks. 2003 80p il maps (Cultures of the past) lib bdg $28.50 **949.5**
1. Byzantine Empire
ISBN 0-7614-1495-9   LC 2002-3222
Traces the history, society, culture, and lasting influences of the Byzantine Empire, which grew from the decaying Roman empire and ruled from Constantinople from the fourth to the end of the fifteenth century
"Copiously illustrated with period reproductions as well as modern-day photos, this book provides a well-rounded history of the Byzantines." Horn Book Guide
Includes glossary and bibliographical references

949.7 Serbia and Montenegro, Croatia, Slovenia, Bosnia and Hercegovina, Macedonia

Andryszewski, Tricia, 1956-
Kosovo; the splintering of Yugoslavia. Millbrook Press 2000 64p il map (Headliners) lib bdg $25.90 **949.7**
1. Kosovo (Serbia) 2. Yugoslavia—History
ISBN 0-7613-1750-3   LC 99-48933
"In the first chapter, a history of important milestones and movements of people in the Balkans is laid out in an easy-to-understand manner. The sections that follow discuss the breakup of Yugoslavia, the Dayton peace accord, and the involvement of NATO forces. . . . Black-and-white and full-color photographs show the plight of refugees and the results of bombing without being too graphic. A useful addition for collections needing background information on current events." SLJ
Includes bibliographical references

Cooper, Robert, 1945-
Croatia. Marshall Cavendish 2001 128p il map (Cultures of the world) lib bdg $37.07 (5 and up) **949.7**
1. Croatia
ISBN 0-7614-1156-9   LC 00-29510
"The initial chapters go over basic geography, history, and government, while the bulk of the book examines Croatia's culture and contemporary life. The short chapters are divided into highlighted segments of a page or two. This format allows easy access to information." SLJ
Includes glossary and bibliographical references

Gottfried, Ted, 1928-
Slovenia; by Ted Gottfried. Benchmark Books 2005 144p il map (Cultures of the world) lib bdg $37.07 (5 and up) **949.7**
1. Slovenia
ISBN 0-7614-1857-1   LC 2004-22240
Contents: Geography; History; Government; Economy; Environment Slovenes; Lifestyle; Religion; Language; Arts; Leisure; Festivals; Food
Includes glossary and bibliographical references

King, David C., 1933-
Bosnia and Herzegovina; David C. King. 1st ed. Benchmark Books 2005 144p il map (Cultures of the world) lib bdg $37.07 (5 and up) **949.7**
1. Bosnia and Hercegovina
ISBN 0-7614-1853-9   LC 2004-21120
Contents: Geography; History; Government; Economy; Environment; Bosnians; Lifestyle; Religion; Language; Arts; Leisure; Festivals; Food

King, David C., 1933-—*Continued*
Explores the geography, history, government, economy, people, and culture of Bosnia and Herzegovina
Includes glossary and bibliographical references

Milivojevic, JoAnn
Bosnia and Herzegovina. Children's Press 2004
144p il map (Enchantment of the world, Second series) lib bdg $35 (5 and up) **949.7**
1. Bosnia and Hercegovina
ISBN 0-516-24247-4   LC 2002-15581
Contents: Wrapped; Land of forests and mountains; What lives high and low; Bosnia through the centuries; Forming a new country; Economy past, present, future; One country, three ethnic groups; Three faiths; Artistic expressions; Enjoying life
Describes the history, geography, economy, and culture of Bosnia and Herzegovina
This offers "lucid commentary, digestible quantities of facts and statistics, eye-catching color photos, and eminently useful back matter." Booklist
Includes bibliographical references

Serbia. rev ed. Children's Press 2003 144p il map (Enchantment of the world, Second series) lib bdg $35 (5 and up) **949.7**
1. Serbia
ISBN 0-516-22695-9   LC 2002-8262
First published 1999
Contents: Crossroads; From the mountains to the Valleys; Where the wild things grow; When Serbia began; Citizens revolt, a new president leads; Money, money, money; Who lives in Serbia?; Traditions, faith, and folklore; Pictures, words, and music; At home, school, and play
An introduction to the geography, history, economy, government, and culture of Serbia
Includes bibliographical references

O'Grady, Scott F.
Basher five-two; the true story of F-16 fighter pilot Captain Scott O'Grady; {by} Scott O'Grady with Michael French. Doubleday 1997 133p il map pa $4.99 hardcover o.p. (5 and up) **949.7**
1. Yugoslav War, 1991-1995
ISBN 0-440-41313-3 (pa)   LC 96-51181
"O'Grady writes about being shot down, escaping capture, and surviving in enemy territory in Bosnia in 1995." Book Rep
This account "is smartly paced, with care taken over the particulars young readers will want to know. An insert of photos is included." Horn Book Guide

Orr, Tamra
Slovenia; by Tamra Orr. Children's Press 2004
144p il map (Enchantment of the world, Second series) lib bdg $35 (5 and up) **949.7**
1. Slovenia
ISBN 0-516-24249-0   LC 2003-15253
Contents: A small but mighty country; Frigid Alps to underground caverns; Animal and plant life; From instability to independence; A new independence; Economic stability and strength; Proud Slovenes; Faith and tradition; The arts and sports; Daily life

Discusses the geography and climate, history, wildlife, economy, government, people, religion, and culture of Slovenia.
This "basically well-written [book] should engage a wide range of readers with varied interests. . . . The excellent quality of the photos contributes to the attractiveness of [this volume.]" SLJ
Includes bibliographical references

War-torn Bosnia; Helen Cothran, book editor. Greenhaven Press 2002 192p il maps (History firsthand) lib bdg $34.95; pa $23.70 (7 and up)
949.7
1. Yugoslav War, 1991-1995 2. Bosnia and Hercegovina
ISBN 0-7377-0889-1 (lib bdg); 0-7377-0888-3 (pa)
LC 2001-40608
This is a compilation of eyewitness accounts of war in Bosnia from a variety of perspectives
Includes bibliographical references

949.9   Bulgaria

Otfinoski, Steven, 1949-
Bulgaria. 2nd ed. Facts on File 2004 144p il map (Nations in transition) $35 (7 and up)
949.9
1. Bulgaria
ISBN 0-8160-5116-X   LC 2004-43274
First published 1998
Examines the people, religion, daily life, politics, culture, history, and geography of Bulgaria, including the return of former king Simeon II, who became prime minister in June 2001 as head of the newly formed National Movement party.

950   Asia. Orient. Far East

Greenblatt, Miriam
Genghis Khan and the Mongol Empire. Benchmark Bks. 2002 80p il maps (Rulers and their times) lib bdg $29.93 **950**
1. Genghis Khan, 1162-1227 2. Mongols
ISBN 0-7614-1027-9   LC 99-86634
"This book covers the life of the infamous Genghis Khan, as well as everyday life and literature of the twelveth- and thirteenth-century Mongolian Empire. Illustrated with plentiful archival art, the facts about society, sports, housing, food, clothing, cosmetics, and other topics are brought to life." Horn Book Guide
Includes glossary and bibliographical references

LoBaido, Anthony C.
The Kurds of Asia; {by} Anthony C. LoBaido, Yumi Ng, and Paul A. Rozario. Lerner Publs. 2003 48p il map (First peoples) lib bdg $23.93
950
1. Kurds
ISBN 0-8225-0664-5   LC 2002-6471

LoBaido, Anthony C.—*Continued*

Describes the history, modern and traditional cultural practices and economies, geographic background, and on-going oppression and struggles of the Kurds

This book "positively glow{s} with brilliant photographs of the countryside and the people. The text . . . is clear and to the point." Voice Youth Advocates

Includes bibliographical references

Major, John S., 1942-

The Silk Route; 7,000 miles of history; illustrated by Stephen Fieser. HarperCollins Pubs. 1995 32p il maps hardcover o.p. paperback available $5.95   **950**

1. Trade routes 2. China—History

ISBN 0-06-443468-0 (pa)   LC 92-38169

"Major traces the journey of a caravan as it leaves Chang'an, China, in A.D.700, travels along the established silk traders' route, and finally arrives at its destination in Byzantium several months later. The 7,000-mile trek crosses cities, deserts, mountains, and the Mediterranean Sea." SLJ

"The pictures and short segments make the book a teaching tool as well as a resource when learning about China and its silk industry." Child Book Rev Serv

Pascoe, Elaine

The Pacific rim; East Asia at the dawn of a new century. 21st Cent. Bks. (Brookfield) 1999 128p il lib bdg $25.90 (7 and up)   **950**

1. Pacific rim

ISBN 0-7613-3015-1   LC 98-28556

Examines the history and current economic and political importance of Japan, China, Taiwan, the Koreas, Southeast Asia, Indonesia, and Malaysia

"Teenagers investigating the current economic crisis in the Pacific Rim will benefit from the encapsulated histories and the relative currency of the text." Booklist

Includes bibliographical references

Peoples of Eastern Asia. Marshall Cavendish 2004 11v p. cmp il map set $329.95 (5 and up)   **950**

1. Asia

ISBN 0-7614-7547-8   LC 2003-69645

Contents: v1 Bangladesh-Brunei; v2 Cambodia-China; v3 China-East Timor; v4 India; v5 Indonesia; v6 Japan-Korea, North; v7 Korea, South-Malaysia; v8 Mongolia-Nepal; v 9 Philippines-Sri Lanka; v10 Taiwan-Vietnam; v11 Index

This "alphabetically arranged set covers the countries ranging from India in the West to the island nations of the western Pacific, and from Mongolia southward through Indonesia. . . . The entries open with a brief geographical introduction and map, a facts and figures box, and information on the nation's history with a time line running along the bottom of the page. The text then discusses the people, minority populations, lifestyles, religion, jobs, foods . . ., transportation, health, education, architecture, the performing and visual arts, literature, recreation, and festivals. . . . Numerous full-color and archival black-and-white photographs lend appeal. . . . This useful set is reliable." SLJ

Includes bibliographical references

Stefoff, Rebecca, 1951-

The Asian empires; by Rebecca Stefoff. Benchmark Books 2004 c2005 48p il map (World historical atlases) lib bdg $27.07 (5 and up)   **950**

1. China—History 2. China—Civilization 3. India 4. Turkey

ISBN 0-7614-1643-9   LC 2004-8703

This introduces the empires of Imperial China, early India, and Ottoman Turkey

This is "clearly written and well organized. The [book includes] large, full-color photographs and illustrations reproduced from original pieces of art found in diverse national museums. . . . [This volume makes an] excellent [supplement] to history lessons and [a] good starting [point] for research." SLJ

Includes bibliographical references

The **Wilson** chronology of Asia and the Pacific; edited by David M. Brownstone and Irene M. Franck. Wilson, H.W. 1999 442p $105   **950**

1. Asia—History 2. Pacific region—History

ISBN 0-8242-0950-8   LC 99-29402

"This volume features events in politics, government, and law; war; religion; education; economic life; arts and entertainment; science and technology; and medicine. A subject index is included." Publisher's note

Includes bibliographical references

951   China and adjacent areas

Behnke, Alison

China in pictures. rev and expanded. Lerner Publs. 2003 80p il maps (Visual geography series) lib bdg $27.93   **951**

1. China

ISBN 0-8225-0370-0   LC 2001-7217

First published 1989

Text and illustrations present detailed information on the geography, history and government, economy, people, cultural life and society of traditional and modern China, home to over one-fifth of the earth's population

This "entices readers with its handsome open format, clear maps, informative sidebars, and well-chosen illustrations." SLJ

Includes glossary and bibliographical references

Ferroa, Peggy Grace

China; {by} Peggy Ferroa, Elaine Chan. 2nd ed. Benchmark Bks. 2002 144p il maps (Cultures of the world) lib bdg $37.07 (5 and up)   **951**

1. China

ISBN 0-7614-1474-6   LC 2002-19209

First published 1991

Describes the geography, history, government, economy, environment, people, and culture of China

Includes glossary and bibliographical references

Kummer, Patricia K.

Tibet; Patricia K. Kummer. Children's Press 2003 144p il map (Enchantment of the world, second series) lib bdg $35 (5 and up)

951

1. Tibet (China)

ISBN 0-516-22693-2   LC 2002-156704

Introduces Tibet, including its geography and climate, history, government, economy, people, culture, religion, language, and activities of daily life

Includes bibliographical references

Sís, Peter, 1949-

Tibet; through the red box. Farrar, Straus & Giroux 1998 unp il maps $25   **951**

1. Tibet (China)

ISBN 0-374-37552-6   LC 97-50175

A Caldecott Medal honor book, 1999

"Frances Foster books"

"When Sis opens the red lacquered box that has sat on his father's table for decades, he finds the diary his father kept when he was lost in Tibet in the mid-1950s. The text replicates the diary's spidery handwriting, while the illustrations depict elaborate mazes and mandalas, along with dreamlike spreads that are filled with fragmented details of the father's and son's lives. . . . Impeccably designed and beautifully made, the book has a dreamlike quality that will keep readers of many ages coming back to find more in its pages." Booklist

951.05   China--Period of People's Republic, 1949-

Fritz, Jean

China homecoming; with photographs by Michael Fritz. Putnam 1985 143p il $19.99 (6 and up)   **951.05**

1. China

ISBN 0-399-21182-9   LC 84-24775

Companion volume to Homesick: my own story

This account of the author's return to Hankow after four decades "is intended for a slightly older readership than 'Homesick' . . . as it is not only an autobiography, but also a glimpse of Chinese history and a social commentary. It is, however, a book to be read and reread." SLJ

Includes bibliographical references

Jiang, Ji-li

Red scarf girl; a memoir of the Cultural Revolution; foreword by David Henry Hwang. HarperCollins Pubs. 1997 285p $16.99; pa $6.99 (6 and up)   **951.05**

1. China—History—1949-1976—Personal narratives

ISBN 0-06-027585-5; 0-06-446208-0 (pa)

LC 97-5089

"This is an autobiographical account of growing up during Mao's Cultural Revolution in China in 1966. . . . Jiang describes in terrifying detail the ordeals of her family and those like them, including unauthorized search and seizure, persecution, arrest and torture, hunger, and

public humiliation. . . . Her voice is that of an intelligent, confused adolescent, and her focus on the effects of the revolution on herself, her family, and her friends provides an emotional focal point for the book, and will allow even those with limited knowledge of Chinese history to access the text." Bull Cent Child Books

The **Tiananmen** Square massacre; Kelly Barth, book editor. Greenhaven Press 2003 124p map (At issue in history) $28.70; pa $19.95 (7 and up)   **951.05**

1. Tiananmen Square Incident, Beijing (China), 1989

ISBN 0-7377-1176-0; 0-7377-1175-2 (pa)

LC 2001-8517

A collection of articles using primary and secondary sources analyzes the Tiananmen Square incident and "discusses communism, the divided leadership of the Chinese, the citizens' protest in the square, how the protests were handled, the imposition of martial law, the crackdown, and the aftermath of the crackdown." Libr Media Connect

Includes bibliographical references

Zhang, Ange

Red land, yellow river; a story from the Cultural Revolution. Douglas & McIntyre 2004 55p il $16.95 (5 and up)   **951.05**

1. China—History—1949-1976—Personal narratives

ISBN 0-88899-489-3

"A Groundwood book"

"Zhang was a teen living in Beijing when Mao Zedong began the Cultural Revolution. In a youthful voice he records his experiences in the early years of that turbulent decade that began in 1966. . . . This moving account of a youngster swept up in the revolutionary fervor and then beginning to question its goals is accompanied by attractive, digitally rendered illustrations." SLJ

951.2   Taiwan, Hong Kong, Macau

Waterlow, Julia

The Yangtze. World Almanac Lib. 2003 48p il maps (Great rivers of the world) lib bdg $26.60; pa $14.60 (4 and up)   **951.2**

1. Yangtze River valley (China)

ISBN 0-8368-5447-0 (lib bdg); 0-8368-5454-3 (pa)

LC 2002-33134

Contents: The course of the Yangtze; The Yangtze in history; Cities and settlements; Farming, transportation and industry; Animals and plants; Environmental issues; Recreation and leisure; The future

This covers the Yangtze River's "geography, wildlife, and history . . . and its impact on nearby peoples. The presentation is exceptionally clear and lively. . . . Exquisite, full-color photos and maps." SLJ

Includes glossary and bibliographical references

951.25 Hong Kong

Kagda, Falaq
Hong Kong. reference ed. Benchmark Bks. 1998 128p il maps (Cultures of the world) lib bdg $37.07 (5 and up)   **951.25**
1. Hong Kong (China)
ISBN 0-7614-0692-1   LC 97-15885
Surveys the geography, history, government, economy, and culture of this territory on China's southeastern coast, made up of a section of the mainland and 235 islands of various sizes
Includes glossary and bibliographical references

951.7 Mongolia

Pang, Guek-Cheng, 1950-
Mongolia. Benchmark Bks. 1999 128p il maps (Cultures of the world) lib bdg $37.07 (5 and up)   **951.7**
1. Mongolia
ISBN 0-7614-0954-8   LC 98-31897
Describes the geography, history, government, economy, people, lifestyle, religion, language, arts, leisure, festivals, and food of Mongolia
"High-quality, full-color photography combines with clearly written text and meaningful sidebars." SLJ
Includes glossary and bibliographical references

951.9 Korea

Ashabranner, Brent K., 1921-
Remembering Korea; the Korean War Veterans Memorial; {by} Brent Ashabranner; photographs by Jennifer Ashabranner. 21st Cent. Bks. (Brookfield) 2001 64p il (Great American memorials) lib bdg $25.90 (4 and up)
                     951.9
1. Korean War Veterans Memorial (Washington, D.C.)
2. Korean War, 1950-1953
ISBN 0-7613-2156-X   LC 00-68282
This "book begins at the memorial's dedication ceremony and gives an account of the planning, funding, site choice and the controversy surrounding the design. There is also an account of the Korean War. . . . Throughout, the writing is crisp and informative; excellent photographs, including evocative, black-and-white photos from the war and color photos of the dedication ceremony, and the memorial expand the text." Booklist
Includes bibliographical references

Benson, Sonia
Korean War: almanac and primary sources; {by} Sonia G. Benson; Gerda-Ann Raffaelle, editor. U.X.L 2002 xxxiv, 318p il maps $60 (7 and up)
                     951.9
1. Korean War, 1950-1953
ISBN 0-7876-5691-7   LC 2001-44242

An overview of the Korean War, including biographies and full or excerpted memoirs, speeches, and other source documents
"An excellent starting point for researching the events . . . of the Korean War." Booklist
Includes glossary and bibliographical references

Dolan, Edward F., 1924-
America in the Korean War. Millbrook Press 1998 112p il maps lib bdg $30.90 (7 and up)
                     951.9
1. Korean War, 1950-1953
ISBN 0-7613-0361-8   LC 97-50460
In this history of the Korean War the author concentrates "on the military action of the conflict itself and describing the campaigns and the strategies behind them. . . . He also profiles many of the commanders and discusses the Truman-MacArthur confrontation." SLJ
"Readers interested in battlefield strategies will relish this account. . . . The book will provide good curriculum support for history classes, but it will need to be supplemented by other books." Booklist
Includes bibliographical references

DuBois, Jill, 1952-
Korea. 2nd ed. Benchmark Books 2004 144p il map (Cultures of the world) lib bdg $25.95 (5 and up)   **951.9**
1. Korea
ISBN 0-7614-1786-9   LC 2004-7678
First published 1994
Describes the geography, history, government, economy, environment, people, and culture of Korea
Includes glossary and bibliographical references

Feldman, Ruth Tenzer
The Korean War; by Ruth Tenzer Feldman. Lerner Publications Co 2004 88p il map (Chronicle of America's wars) lib bdg $27.93 (5 and up)   **951.9**
1. Korean War, 1950-1953
ISBN 0-8225-4716-3   LC 2002-156557
Contents: Korea sometime in January 1951; Drawing the line; Storm!; Saving the South; North to the Yalu almost; "An entirely new war"; Setting limits; The talking war; Epilogue; Timeline
This "begins briefly with the events that led to Korea's division before focusing in greater detail on North Korea's invasion of South Korea. The author offers good overviews of the roles of the major players, and she outlines the significant battles and campaigns, and the lengthy negotiations that resulted in armistice. . . . [This is] abundantly illustrated with color and black-and-white photographs as well as maps." Booklist
Includes glossary and bibliographical references

Granfield, Linda
I remember Korea; veterans tell their stories of the Korean War, 1950-53. Clarion Books 2003 136p il $16   **951.9**
1. Korean War, 1950-1953—Personal narratives
ISBN 0-618-17740-X   LC 2003-5397

Granfield, Linda—*Continued*

Personal accounts of more than thirty men and women who served with the American and Canadian forces in Korea during the years 1950-1953

This title "has much to recommend it. . . . The text is timely, given both the renewed U.S.-North Korean tension and the increasing age of the veterans of the conflict. . . . The stories range from short anecdotes to more developed reminiscences; none are more than a few pages. Many are moving, some are surprisingly funny, and all offer insight into life at war from an insider's perspective." Quill & Quire

Includes bibliographical references

Isserman, Maurice

Korean war. updated ed. Facts on File 2003 146p il map (America at war) lib bdg $35 (7 and up)   **951.9**

1. Korean War, 1950-1953

ISBN 0-8160-4939-4   LC 2002-7916

First published 1992

Contents: Task force Smith; Background to war; Defeat and retreat; Pusan and Inchon; Disaster in the north; Ridgway takes command; Long road to peace; Lessons from a forgotten war

Examines the political climate and military situation that led to the Korean War and discusses the key people and events involved in the conflict itself.

This volume provides "a great deal of information." Libr J

951.93   North Korea (People's Democratic Republic of Korea)

North Korea; Debra A. Miller, book editor. Greenhaven Press 2004 127p il map (World's hot spots) $28.70; pa $19.95   **951.93**

1. Korea (North)

ISBN 0-7377-2294-0; 0-7377-2295-9 (pa)
LC 2003-59903

"A collection of essays and periodical excerpts that discusses the situation within the country and its relationships within the world community. The book expounds on the reasons that North Korea is so often in the news. The introduction outlines the nation's history and its relationships with South Korea, the United States, and the Soviet Union. . . . The majority of the selections lean toward a United States bias and a post-9/11 mentality, but perspectives that are critical of the United States are still evident, which results in a well-rounded, interesting collection of views. . . . A useful tool for debate and discussion." SLJ

Includes bibliographical references

951.95   South Korea (Republic of Korea)

Williams, Jean Kinney

South Korea. Lucent Bks. 1999 111p il maps (Modern nations of the world) lib bdg $27.45 (7 and up)   **951.95**

1. Korea (South)

ISBN 1-56006-446-3   LC 98-34605

Discusses the history, geography, culture, and current state of South Korea, a land of both tradition and modern development

Includes bibliographical references

952   Japan

Behnke, Alison

Japan in pictures. Lerner Publs. 2003 79p il maps (Visual geography series) lib bdg $27.93 (5 and up)   **952**

1. Japan

ISBN 0-8225-1956-9   LC 2001-2955

First published 1989, catalogued under title

This describes Japan's "land, history and government, people, cultural life, and economy. Other information includes a timeline, fast facts, currency, flag, national anthem, famous people, sights to see . . . and Web sites. The [book is] visually appealing with photos and sidebars that complement the text." Libr Media Connect

Includes glossary and bibliographical references

Blumberg, Rhoda, 1917-

Commodore Perry in the land of the Shogun. Lothrop, Lee & Shepard Bks. 1985 144p il map $18.95; pa $7.95 (5 and up)   **952**

1. Perry, Matthew Calbraith, 1794-1858 2. United States Naval Expedition to Japan (1852-1854) 3. United States—Foreign relations—Japan 4. Japan—Foreign relations—United States

ISBN 0-688-03723-2; 0-06-008625-4 (pa)
LC 84-21800

A Newbery Medal honor book, 1986

"The diplomatic expeditions of Commodore Matthew C. Perry to secure a treaty to provide for U.S. trade with Japan are described. The black-and-white period illustrations and informative text provide an in-depth and intimate view of nineteenth century Japan, Japanese and U.S. values and attitudes, and treaty negotiations." Soc Educ

Includes bibliographical references

Heinrichs, Ann

Japan. Children's Press 1998 143p il (Enchantment of the world, second series) lib bdg $35 (4 and up)   **952**

1. Japan

ISBN 0-516-20649-4   LC 97-38771

Describes the history, geography, plants and animals, economy, language, people and culture of the island nation of Japan

"The writing is clear . . . the topics covered are broad in scope and will be suitable for assignments. Good-quality, full-color photographs, reproductions, and maps are interspersed throughout." SLJ

Includes bibliographical references

Roberson, John R., 1930-

Japan meets the world; the birth of a super power. Millbrook Press 1998 208p il maps $24.90 (7 and up)   **952**

1. Japan—History

ISBN 0-7613-0407-X   LC 98-6071

Roberson, John R., 1930——*Continued*
First published 1985 with title: Japan from Shogun to Sony, 1543-1984
Examines the history of Japan through various stages of progress and isolationism, including its rise to world power, up to the present day and the current Asian economic crisis
"This is an accessible, must-have resource for students needing detailed information about the history and current status of Japan. Glossary; bibliography; well-chosen but average-quality black-and white-photos." Booklist

Schomp, Virginia, 1953-
Japan in the days of the samurai. Benchmark Bks. 2002 80p il maps (Cultures of the past) lib bdg $19.95   **952**
1. Japan—Civilization
ISBN 0-7614-0304-3   LC 98-12228
Describes the Japanese way of life during the samurai eras through information about the politics, military, culture, and the belief system; also indicates the legacy of the period
"Offering balanced, thoughtfully interpreted material, this book effectively introduces Japan's early culture." Horn Book Guide
Includes glossary and bibliographical references

Shelley, Rex, 1930-
Japan; by Rex Shelley, Teo Chuu Yong, and Russell Mok. 2nd ed. Benchmark Bks. 2002 144p il maps (Cultures of the world) lib bdg $37.07
                    952
1. Japan
ISBN 0-7614-1356-1   LC 2001-28609
First published 1990
This discusses the geography, history, government, economy, and culture of Japan
This book "will be helpful to report-writing. . . . The color photographs are well reproduced." Horn Book Guide
Includes glossary and bibliographical references

953 Arabian Peninsula and adjacent areas

Augustin, Byron
United Arab Emirates. Children's Press 2002 144p il maps (Enchantment of the world, Second series) lib bdg $35 (4 and up)   **953**
1. United Arab Emirates
ISBN 0-516-20473-4   LC 00-65958
Describes the geography, history, culture, economy, and people of the United Arab Emirates
"This attractive title enhanced with full-color photographs provides everything that most students need for a basic understanding of the country." SLJ
Includes bibliographical references

953.3 Yemen

Hestler, Anna
Yemen. Benchmark Bks. 1999 128p il maps (Cultures of the world) lib bdg $37.07 (5 and up)
                    953.3
1. Yemen
ISBN 0-7614-0956-4   LC 98-53993
Presents information about the geography, history, government, and economy of this country located on the southwestern tip of the Arabian Peninsula and describes many aspects of the lifestyle of its people
Includes glossary and bibliographical references

953.6 Persian Gulf States

Cooper, Robert, 1945-
Bahrain. Marshall Cavendish 2000 128p il map (Cultures of the world) lib bdg $37.07
                    953.6
1. Bahrain
ISBN 0-7614-1161-5   LC 00-43116
"Cooper covers aspects of Bahraini society and daily life from the history, religion, government, and economy to the people, the arts, dress, and food. A particularly interesting chapter addresses the ancient findings of the prehistoric era. Good-quality, full-color photographs are well-matched to the text." SLJ
Includes glossary and bibliographical references

953.67 Kuwait

Foster, Leila Merrell
Kuwait. Children's Press 1998 143p il (Enchantment of the world, second series) lib bdg $35 (4 and up)   **953.67**
1. Kuwait
ISBN 0-516-20604-4   LC 97-23845
Describes the history, geography, economy, language, religion, sports, arts, and people of this oil-rich country located on the northwestern shore of the Persian Gulf
Includes bibliographical references

Marcovitz, Hal
Kuwait. Mason Crest Publs. 2003 112p il maps (Modern Middle East nations and their strategic place in the world) lib bdg $24.95   **953.67**
1. Kuwait
ISBN 1-59084-510-2   LC 2002-13002
Discusses the geography, history, economy, government, religion, people, foreign relations, and major cities of Kuwait
This volume is "clearly written and accurate." SLJ
Includes glossary and bibliographical references

O'Shea, Maria
Kuwait. Benchmark Bks. 1999 128p il maps
(Cultures of the world) lib bdg $37.07 (5 and up)
953.67
1. Kuwait
ISBN 0-7614-0871-1   LC 98-25833
Introduces the geography, history, religious beliefs,
government, and people of Kuwait, a small country on
the Persian Gulf
Includes glossary and bibliographical references

953.8   Saudi Arabia

Broberg, Catherine
Saudi Arabia in pictures. rev & expanded.
Lerner Publs. 2003 80p il maps (Visual geography
series) lib bdg $27.93   953.8
1. Saudi Arabia
ISBN 0-8225-1958-5   LC 2001-2967
First published 1979 by Sterling under the authorship
of Eugene Gordon
This describes the geography, people, culture, and
economy of Saudi Arabia
This "is an exemplary starting point for student researchers. . . . A page of specifically chosen Web sites
will link kids to other information about the Arabic language, interpretation of political events, Islamic prayer,
and much more." Booklist
Includes bibliographical references

Janin, Hunt, 1940-
Saudi Arabia; [by] Hunt Janin, Margaret
Besheer. 2nd ed. Benchmark Bks. 2003 144p il
maps (Cultures of the world) lib bdg $37.07
953.8
1. Saudi Arabia
ISBN 0-7614-1666-8   LC 2003-6931
First published 1993
Contents: Geography; History; Government; Economy;
Environment; Saudi Arabians; Lifestyle; Religion; Lan-
guage; Arts; Leisure; Festivals; Food; Map of Saudi Ara-
bia; About the economy; About the culture; Time line
Includes glossary and bibliographical references

954   South Asia. India

Barter, James, 1946-
The Ganges. Lucent Bks. 2003 112p il maps
(Rivers of the world) $27.45 (7 and up)
954
1. Ganges River (India and Bangladesh) 2. Ganges
River valley (India and Bangladesh)
ISBN 1-59018-060-7   LC 2002-5163
Discusses the source, course, and tributaries of the
Ganges River, its spiritual significance, its use for agri-
culture and industry, and its problems with pollution
Includes bibliographical references

Downing, David, 1946-
Conflict: India vs. Pakistan. Raintree 2004 64p
il map (Troubled world) lib bdg $28.56
954
1. India 2. Pakistan
ISBN 1-4109-0181-5
Takes an in-depth look at the ongoing conflict and
troubles between the countries of India and Pakistan.
"Information presented here provides valuable background material even in view of rapidly changing
events." SLJ

Engfer, Lee, 1963-
India in pictures. Lerner Publs. 2003 80p il map
(Visual geography series) lib bdg $27.93 (5 and
up)   954
1. India
ISBN 0-8225-0371-9   LC 2002-950
Contents: The land; History and government; The peo-
ple; Cultural life; The economy
Text and illustrations present detailed information on
the geography, history and government, economy, people,
cultural life and society of traditional and modern India
The book is "visually appealing with photos and
sidebars that complement the text." Libr Media Connect
Includes bibliographical references

Srinivasan, Radhika
India; {by} Radhika Srinivasan, Leslie Jermyn.
2nd ed. Benchmark Bks. 2002 144p il maps
(Cultures of the world) $37.07 (5 and up)
954
1. India
ISBN 0-7614-1354-5   LC 2001-28608
First published 1990
This describes the geography, history, government,
economy, environment, people, and culture of India
Includes glossary and bibliographical references

954.9   Jurisdictions of South Asia other than India

Cooper, Robert, 1945-
Bhutan. Benchmark Bks. 2001 128p il maps
(Cultures of the world) lib bdg $37.07
954.9
1. Bhutan
ISBN 0-7614-1191-7   LC 00-47435
Describes the geography, history, government, econo-
my, and culture of Bhutan
Includes glossary and bibliographical references

954.91   Pakistan

Sheehan, Sean, 1951-
Pakistan; by Sean Sheehan. 2nd ed. Benchmark
Books 2004 144p il map (Cultures of the world)
lib bdg $37.07 (5 and up)   954.91
ISBN 0-7614-1787-7   LC 2004-7677

Sheehan, Sean, 1951----_Continued_
First published 1994
Contents: Geography; History; Government; Economy; Environment; Pakistanis; Lifestyle; Religion; Language; Arts; Leisure; Festivals; Food
An introduction to the geography, history, government, and culture of Pakistan
"Excellent-quality, full-color photographs and sidebars highlight special information and make this book accessible and appealing. . . . A gold mine of information for reports." SLJ
Includes glossary and bibliographical references

954.92 Bangladesh

Whyte, Mariam
Bangladesh. Benchmark Bks. 1999 128p il maps (Cultures of the world) lib bdg $37.07 (5 and up)
954.92
1. Bangladesh
ISBN 0-7614-0869-X   LC 98-22428
Describes the geography, history, government, economy, people, religion, language, arts, leisure, festivals, and food of Bangladesh
Includes glossary and bibliographical references

954.93 Sri Lanka

Wanasundera, Nanda P.
Sri Lanka; {by} Nanda Pethiyagoda Wanasundera. 2nd ed. Benchmark Bks. 2002 144p il maps (Cultures of the world) lib bdg $37.07
954.93
1. Sri Lanka
ISBN 0-7614-1477-0   LC 2002-25980
First published 1990
Describes the geography, history, government, economy, social life and customs, religion, culture, and more of this island country in the Indian Ocean
Includes glossary and bibliographical references

954.96 Nepal

Burbank, Jon
Nepal. 2nd ed. Benchmark Bks. 2002 144p il maps (Cultures of the world) lib bdg $37.07 (5 and up)
954.96
1. Nepal
ISBN 0-7614-1476-2   LC 2002-25994
First published 1991
Describes the geography, history, government, economy, people, religion, language, and culture of Nepal, a predominantly Hindu country located north of India. Includes several recipes
Includes glossary and bibliographical references

955 Iran

Rajendra, Vijeya, 1936-
Iran; (by) Vijeya Rajendra, Gisela Kaplan, Rudi Rajendra. 2nd ed. Benchmark Bks. 2003 c2004 144p il maps (Cultures of the world) lib bdg $37.07 (5 and up)
955
1. Iran
ISBN 0-7614-1665-X   LC 2003-8257
First published 1993
Contents: Geography; History; Government; Economy; Environment; Iranians; Lifestyle; Religion; Language; Arts; Leisure; Festivals; Food
Explores the geography, history, government, economy, people, and culture of Iran
Includes glossary and bibliographical references

Ramen, Fred
A historical atlas of Iran. Rosen Pub. Group 2003 il map (Historical atlases of South Asia, Central Asia, and the Middle East) lib bdg $30.60
955
1. Iran
ISBN 0-8239-3864-6   LC 2002-31031
This focuses on the political history of Iran "as determined by geography and religion. . . . Brief descriptions of the art and architecture of {the} country testify to the richness of {this culture}. . . . {This} well-organized and ambitious {book provides} needed information." SLJ

956 Middle East

Crompton, Samuel
The Third Crusade; Richard the Lionhearted vs. Saladin; {by} Samuel Willard Crompton. Chelsea House 2003 114p il map (Great battles through the ages) $22.95 (7 and up)
956
1. Richard I, King of England, 1157-1199 2. Saladin, Sultan of Egypt and Syria, 1137-1193 3. Crusades
ISBN 0-7910-7437-4   LC 2003-4593
"In 1187 King Richard I sought control of the Holy Land. This text details the Third Crusade in which the king of England lead an army of Christians to sieze the Holy Land from the Muslims." Publisher's note
"The value of this book is not so much its depictions of battles, but rather of the men who came to symbolize the reasons for the struggle. . . . Some excellent color and black-and-white illustrations are included." SLJ
Includes bibliographical references

Kort, Michael
The handbook of the Middle East; {by} Michael G. Kort. 21st Cent. Bks. (Brookfield) 2002 303p il maps $39.90 (7 and up)
956
1. Middle East
ISBN 0-7613-1611-6   LC 2001-37330
Examines the past, present, and future of all the countries in the Middle East, discussing their history and culture

Kort, Michael—*Continued*
"The writing is clear, concise, lively, and full of fascinating details that will motivate readers to do more than just browse for facts. . . . This outstanding and timely resource should be purchased for all middle and high school libraries." Voice Youth Advocates
Includes glossary and bibliographical references

The **Middle** East. Greenwood Press 2004 5v il map (Discovering world cultures) set $200

        956

1. Middle East
ISBN 0-313-32922-2
"A Creative Media Applications, Inc. production"
Contents: v1 Bahrain, Cyprus, Egypt; v2 Iran, Iraq, Israel; v3 Jordan, Kuwait, Lebanon, Oman; v4 Qatar, Saudi-Arabia, Syria; v5 Turkey, United Arab Emirates, Yemen
This "set profiles the 16 countries that lie in the geographic region between the Mediterranean Sea and India. . . . Each country . . . is covered in a multipage chapter providing detailed information on ethnic groups, land and resources, history, economy, religion, everyday life, holidays, and the arts. . . . Readers in need of a source of solid, unbiased information will be well served by this resource." Booklist

The **Middle** East: opposing viewpoints; Mary E. Williams, book editor. Greenhaven Press 2000 224p il map lib bdg $33.70 (7 and up)

        956

1. Middle East—Politics and government
ISBN 0-7377-0133-1   LC 99-10881
"Opposing viewpoints series"
Replaces the edition published 1992 under the editorship of William Dudley
This collection of essays about the Middle East "debates the causes of conflict in the area, the role of religion, how to advance peace, and what role the U.S. should play. . . . There are lists of organizations to contact and bibliographies of books and periodicals." Booklist

956.04   Middle East--1945-1980

The **Arab-Israeli** conflict; Mark Rackers, book editor. Greenhaven Press 2004 234p (Great speeches in history) $34.95 (7 and up)

        956.04

1. Israel-Arab conflicts 2. Speeches
ISBN 0-7377-1649-5
"This book offers 20 speeches by major players in the history of this turmoil, beginning with David Ben-Gurion's 1946 address to the Anglo-American Committee that would decide the fate of the future state of Israel and ending with Ariel Sharon's 2002 plea for peace. An excellent introductory essay sets the stage for the modern conflict. . . . This volume is a core resource for Middle East collections." SLJ

The **Palestinians** and the disputed territories; Neil Alger, book editor. Greenhaven Press 2004 144p il map (World's hot spots) lib bdg $28.70; pa $19.95 (7 and up)   **956.04**
1. Israel-Arab conflicts
ISBN 0-7377-1489-1 (lib bdg); 0-7377-1490-5 (pa)
         LC 2003-48327
This "collection of essays, articles, and analyses traces the history of strife in the region and looks at the current situation from a variety of perspectives. The writers discuss the complex issues with attention toward readers who may be unfamiliar with the circumstances of the Middle Eastern conflict. The selections expound on the importance of Jerusalem and the groups, both the religious and political, that wish to control the city. International influences and involvement by the U.S., Britain, and Russia are also addressed." SLJ
Includes bibliographical references

956.1   Turkey

Eboch, Chris
Turkey. Lucent Bks. 2003 112p il maps (Modern nations of the world) lib bdg $27.45 (7 and up)   **956.1**
1. Turkey
ISBN 1-59018-122-0   LC 2002-11052
Contents: Where continents collide; The passing of empires; The republic; Daily life; Art and entertainment; Today's challenges
This is an "overview of Turkey 's history and geography as well as the challenges the nation faces in today's world. . . . The book is well written." SLJ
Includes bibliographical references

Greenblatt, Miriam
Süleyman the Magnificent and the Ottoman Empire. Benchmark Bks. 2002 80p il (Rulers and their times) lib bdg $28.50   **956.1**
1. Süleyman I, Sultan of the Turks, 1495-1566
2. Turkey—History
ISBN 0-7614-1489-4   LC 2002-1974
Provides an overview of the lives of Suleyman I and his subjects in the Ottoman Empire of the late sixteenth century, and includes excerpts from poems, letters, and stories of the time
This "uses primary documents to illustrate sixteenth-century Ottoman thought. Color reproductions of art and manuscripts illustrate the text, which is spaciously designed with plenty of white space." Horn Book Guide
Includes glossary and bibliographical references

Orr, Tamra
Turkey. Children's Press 2003 144p il maps (Enchantment of the world, Second series) lib bdg $34 (4 and up)   **956.1**
1. Turkey
ISBN 0-516-22679-7   LC 2002-1590
Contents: Traveling through time; A unique meeting point; The flora and the fauna; A 3,000 year history; The new face of the government; Shifting the economy; The

Orr, Tamra—*Continued*
richness of the people; The ways of a spiritual life; The expanding world of Turkish culture; Daily life in Turkey; Timeline; Fast facts

This describes the history, culture, flora and fauna, government, and economy of Turkey

"Good-quality graphics and lively . . . [text makes this title] readable and visually enticing." SLJ

Includes bibliographical references

Ruggiero, Adriane
The Ottoman Empire. Benchmark Bks. 2003 80p il maps (Cultures of the past) lib bdg $28.50
956.1
1. Turkey—History
ISBN 0-7614-1494-0   LC 2002-2264
Contents: History: From nomads to sultans; Cultural history: The age of Suleyman the Magnificent; Belief system: The Turks and Islam; Beliefs and society: Shaping the empire; The legacy of the Ottomans: The Ottoman influence lives on

This "volume covers the history, belief system, cultural history and legacy of [the Ottoman Empire]. . . . Students of world history will find this . . . useful for basic information and research." Libr Media Connect

Includes glossary and bibliographical references

Sheehan, Sean, 1951-
Turkey. 2nd ed. Benchmark Bks. 2004 144p il map (Cultures of the world) lib bdg $25.95 (5 and up)
956.1
1. Turkey
ISBN 0-7614-1705-2   LC 2003-20885
First published 1993
Contents: Geography; History; Government; Economy; Environment; The Turks; Lifestyle; Religion; Language; Arts; Leisure; Festivals; Food

Examines the geography, history, government, economy, people, and culture of Turkey

Includes glossary and bibliographical references

956.7 Iraq

Al-Windawi, Thura
Thura's diary; my life in wartime Iraq; translated by Robin Bray. Viking 2004 131p il map $15.99 (7 and up)
956.7
1. Iraq War, 2003
ISBN 0-670-05886-6   LC 2004-44031
"The author, now a scholarship student at an American university, writes of her daily life in war-besieged Baghdad. She describes the events just prior to the U.S. and Britain's 'shock & awe' attack on Iraq. . . . Political sentiments occasionally poke through, but the focus is on explicitly and calmly exposing the ravages of war on the vulnerable members of society." SLJ

Campbell, Geoffrey A.
Life of an American soldier. Lucent Bks. 2001 128p il (American war library, Persian Gulf War) lib bdg $27.45
956.7
1. Persian Gulf War, 1991
ISBN 1-56006-713-6   LC 00-10677

"A foreword explains why it is important to look at America as a country defined by the wars it chose to wage while an introduction seeks to explain why the United States chose to wage this particular war. Campbell has clearly done his research as evidenced by the numerous interviews (both personal and culled from sources) with veterans of the Persian Gulf War that enrich this history. . . . Clear, concise, and user-friendly, it is tailor-made for reports but will still attract browsers." SLJ

Includes glossary and bibliographical references

Gay, Kathlyn, 1930-
Persian Gulf War; {by} Kathlyn Gay and Martin Gay. 21st Cent. Bks. (NY) 1996 63p il map (Voices from the past) lib bdg $25.90 (5 and up)
956.7
1. Persian Gulf War, 1991
ISBN 0-8050-4102-8   LC 96-15579
Describes the circumstances leading up to Iran's invasion of Kuwait and the political and military events of the Persian Gulf War

"A clearly written, objective overview. . . . First-person quotes from television reporters, journalists, political leaders, military correspondents, pilots, and ground soldiers add immediacy to the text. A map of the conflict and small full-color and black-and-white photos further enhance the presentation." SLJ

Includes bibliographical references

Hassig, Susan M., 1969-
Iraq; (by) Susan M. Hassig, Laith Muhmood Al Adely. 2nd ed. Benchmark Bks. 2003 144p il maps (Cultures of the world) lib bdg $37.07 (5 and up)
956.7
1. Iraq
ISBN 0-7614-1668-4   LC 2003-10082
First published 1993
Explores the geography, history, government, economy, people, and culture of Iraq

McArthur, Debra
Desert storm--the first Persian Gulf War in American history; Debra McArthur. Enslow Publishers 2004 128p il map (In American history) lib bdg $26.60
956.7
1. Persian Gulf War, 1991
ISBN 0-7660-2149-1   LC 2003-13460
Contents: Baghdad blasted; Rumors of war; Preparing for war; Raising the shield; Ready...set...wait; War from the air; One hundred hours to victory; Incomplete victory?

Recounts the 1991 military action of the United States and its allies against the forces of Iraqi President Saddam Hussein, relating historical reasons for the war and reactions of combatants.

Schaffer, David
The Iran-Iraq War. Lucent Bks. 2003 128p il
maps (World history series) lib bdg $27.45 (7 and
up) **956.7**
1. Hussein, Ṣaddām 2. Khomeini, Ruhollah
3. Iran-Iraq War, 1980-1988
ISBN 1-59018-184-0   LC 2002-6299
Contents: The Persian Gulf, global hot spot; Conflict
evolves and emerges; Militants take power: war breaks
out; Settling into stalemate; Boldness and backlash: the
world takes sides; War frontiers expand; Iran and the
United States face-to-face; War's last gasps and an uneasy peace
This discussion of the Iran-Iraq war begins "with an
overview of the historical tensions between Persian, Shi'a
Iran and Arab, Sunni Iraq, Schaffer moves on to the
Iraqi invasion of the Shatt al Arab. . . . Focusing on the
personal war between Saddam Hussein and Ayatollah
Khomeni, Schaffer quotes extensively from primary and
secondary sources to give readers a solid introduction to
both leaders. . . . Kids looking for background into contemporary Middle East conflicts will do well to start
here." Booklist
Includes glossary and bibliographical references

956.92   Lebanon

Hutchison, Linda
Lebanon. Lucent Bks. 2003 128p il maps
(Modern nations of the world) lib bdg $24.95 (7
and up) **956.92**
1. Lebanon
ISBN 1-59018-116-6   LC 2002-11024
Contents: Bigger than its borders; The diverse people
of Lebanon; A link between empires; In search of a
modern identity; The shifting patterns of daily life; Cele-
brating life with arts and entertainment; Rebuilding for
the twenty-first century
Presents information on the history, geography, peo-
ple, culture, and contemporary issues of the country of
Lebanon
This offers "solid information." Booklist
Includes glossary and bibliographical references

Sheehan, Sean, 1951-
Lebanon. Benchmark Bks. 1997 128p il maps
(Cultures of the world) lib bdg $37.07 (5 and up)
956.92
1. Lebanon
ISBN 0-7614-0283-7   LC 96-22480
This describes the geography, history, government,
economy and culture of Lebanon
Includes glossary and bibliographical references

956.93   Cyprus

Spilling, Michael
Cyprus. Benchmark Bks. 2000 128p il map
(Cultures of the world) lib bdg $37.07 (5 and up)
956.93
1. Cyprus
ISBN 0-7614-0978-5   LC 99-31942

Discusses the geography, history, government, economy, people, and culture of Cyprus
Includes glossary and bibliographical references

956.94   Palestine. Israel

Altman, Linda Jacobs, 1943-
The creation of Israel. Lucent Bks. 1998 112p
il maps (World history series) $27.45 (7 and up)
956.94
1. Zionism 2. Israel—History
ISBN 1-56006-288-6   LC 97-46033
Provides a historical overview of the treatment of
Jews and discusses the role of various individuals and
specific events in leading to the creation of the state of
Israel in 1948
Includes bibliographical references

Blumberg, Arnold, 1925-
The history of Israel. Greenwood Press 1998
218p (Greenwood histories of the modern nations)
$45 (7 and up) **956.94**
1. Israel—History 2. Zionism
ISBN 0-313-30224-3   LC 97-45659
"Starting with a description of life in modern Israel,
Blumberg . . . quickly covers Israel's early history, from
3,500 years ago to World War I. . . . The battles leading
to independence, the isolation of Israel, conflicts within
Israel, the Suez Crisis and subsequent wars, the Intifada,
the development of the PLO, and the Peace Process are
described in a manner that enables readers to have a
much better understanding of the events happening in Israel now." Voice Youth Advocates
Includes bibliographical references

Corona, Laurel, 1949-
Israel. Lucent Bks. 2003 112p il maps (Modern
nations of the world) lib bdg $27.45 (7 and up)
956.94
1. Israel
ISBN 1-59018-115-8   LC 2002-10428
Discusses the vision of a Jewish homeland, the founding of Israel, and the struggles and dangers of daily life
in Israel
"This title is well researched and solidly written." SLJ
Includes glossary and bibliographical references

DuBois, Jill, 1952-
Israel; by Jill DuBois, Mair Rosh. 2nd ed.
Benchmark Bks. 2003 c2004 144p il maps
(Cultures of the world) lib bdg $37.07 (5 and up)
956.94
1. Israel
ISBN 0-7614-1669-2   LC 2003-10083
First published 1993
Explores the geography, history, government, econo-
my, people, and culture of Israel
Includes glossary and bibliographical references

Ellis, Deborah, 1960-

Three wishes; Palestinian and Israeli children speak. Groundwood Bks. 2004 110p il map $16.95 (5 and up) **956.94**

1. Israel-Arab conflicts 2. Palestinian Arabs

ISBN 0-88899-608-X

"Growing up separate and apart in a world of bombs, bullets, removals, checkpoints, and curfews, 20 Israeli and Palestinian young people talk about how the war has affected them." Booklist

"An excellent presentation of a confusing historic struggle, told within a palpable, perceptive and empathetic format." SLJ

Includes bibliographical references

Frank, Mitch

Understanding the Holy Land; answering questions about the Israeli-Palestinian Conflict; by Mitch Frank. Viking 2004 152p il map $17.99 (7 and up) **956.94**

1. Israel-Arab conflicts

ISBN 0-670-06032-1   LC 2004-14973

This offers a history of the Arab-Israeli conflict, and discusses the issues involved.

The author "tackles the complex subject of the Israeli-Palestinian conflict, making it comprehensible, if not any less horrific. . . . Evenhanded and honest." Booklist

Includes glossary and bibliographical references

Israel: opposing viewpoints; John Woodward, book editor. Greenhaven Press 2005 203p il lib bdg $34.95; pa $23.70 **956.94**

1. Israel 2. Zionism 3. Palestinian Arabs

ISBN 0-7377-2589-3 (lib bdg); 0-7377-2590-7 (pa)
          LC 2004-60586

"Opposing viewpoints series"

"The authors in this book explore the founding of Israel, potential solutions to the Arab-Israeli dispute, America's relationship with the Jewish state, and the question of its right to exist." Publisher's note

Includes bibliographical references

Rosaler, Maxine

Hamas: Palestinian terrorists. Rosen Pub. Group 2003 64p il map (Inside the world's most infamous terrorist organizations) lib bdg $26.50

956.94

1. Hamas 2. Terrorism 3. Israel-Arab conflicts 4. Palestinian Arabs

ISBN 0-8239-3820-4   LC 2002-7769

Contents: A land divided; Inside Hamas; The suicide bombers; The cycle of violence

Discusses the origins, philosophy, and most notorious attacks of the Hamas terrorist group, including their present activities, possible plans, and counter-terrorism efforts directed against them

"With color photos that aren't too shocking and long reading lists updated by links gathered on a dedicated Web site [this] will be useful for school reports." Booklist

Includes bibliographical references

Schroeter, Daniel J.

Israel; an illustrated history. Oxford Univ. Press 1998 157p il maps (Illustrated histories) $29.95 (7 and up) **956.94**

1. Israel—History 2. Zionism

ISBN 0-19-510885-X   LC 98-15915

Presents information on ancient Israel while focusing on the modern nation with both religious and secular history including the roles of Romans, Muslims, and Palestinians as well as Jews

The author's "insights into modern Israeli life are abundant and honestly address the social and economic tensions and the pressing security concerns of the culturally diverse nation." Booklist

Includes bibliographical references

958.1   Afghanistan

Behnke, Alison

Afghanistan in pictures. rev and expanded. Lerner Publs. 2003 80p il map (Visual geography series) lib bdg $27.93 (5 and up) **958.1**

1. Afghanistan

ISBN 0-8225-4683-3   LC 2002-13613

First published 1989

An introduction to the geography, history, government, people, and economy of this landlocked country with a long history of warfare and conquest

Includes glossary and bibliographical references

Corona, Laurel, 1949-

Afghanistan. Lucent Bks. 2002 112p il (Modern nations of the world) lib bdg $27.45

958.1

1. Afghanistan

ISBN 1-59018-217-0   LC 2002-3615

Contents: Introduction: Afghanistan at the crossroads; The shape of a nation: land and people; Cradle to colony: Afghanistan from prehistory to the nineteenth century; In the crossfire of world history: the nineteenth and twentieth centuries; The rise and fall of the Taliban; Life in today's Afghanistan; The crossroads of art and culture; Facing the future: contemporary challenges

Discusses the people, land, culture, history, and future of the nation of Afghanistan

The author provides "well-selected details and {a} generally balanced treatment." Booklist

Includes bibliographical references

Greenblatt, Miriam

Afghanistan; Miriam Greenblatt. Children's Press 2003 144p il map (Enchantment of the world, Second series) lib bdg $35 (5 and up)

958.1

1. Afghanistan

ISBN 0-516-22696-7   LC 2002-156471

Contents: A troubled land; A difficult environment; Forests, flowers, animals, and plants; A turbulent history; A transitional government; Earning a living; A varied population; Religious beliefs; An active culture; Lifestyles; Timeline; Fast facts

An introduction to the geography, history, economy, government, and culture of Afghanistan

Kazem, Halima
Afghanistan. Stevens, G. 2003 96p il map
(Countries of the world) lib bdg $29.26 (4 and up)
958.1

1. Afghanistan
ISBN 0-8368-2357-5   LC 2002-75787
Discusses the geography, history, government, economy, people, politics, and culture of Afghanistan
"A well-organized title that fills the need for an up-to-date book on this country. Clearly written information . . . is illustrated with vibrant color photographs on almost every page." SLJ
Includes glossary and bibliographical references

Otfinoski, Steven, 1949-
Afghanistan. Facts on File 2004 130p il map
(Nations in transition) $35   **958.1**
1. Afghanistan
ISBN 0-8160-5056-2   LC 2003-49030
This volume provides an "examination of Afghanistan's long history and the traditions, religions, and cultural heritage of its many ethnic groups. It examines the different factions vying for power in Afghanistan today, as well as the difficulties Afghan people encounter in their daily life, and it outlines the staggering problems that the country faces in the future." Publisher's note
This is "informative, thought-provoking, and well-organized . . . well-researched . . . include{s} interesting and pertinent sidebars . . . the in-depth presentations provide solid and balanced overviews." SLJ
Includes bibliographical references

Romano, Amy, 1978-
A historical atlas of Afghanistan. Rosen Pub.
Group 2003 64p il map (Historical atlases of
South Asia, Central Asia, and the Middle East) lib
bdg $30.60   **958.1**
1. Afghanistan
ISBN 0-8239-3863-8   LC 2002-31034
Maps and text chronicle the history of Afghanistan, from the Aryan invasion in 1500 B.C. to the rise of the Taliban
This "well-organized and ambitious {book provides} needed information." SLJ
Includes glossary and bibliographical references

Stewart, Gail, 1949-
Life under the Taliban; by Gail B. Stewart.
Lucent Books 2005 112p il map (Way people live)
lib bdg $27.45   **958.1**
1. Afghanistan
ISBN 1-590-18291-X   LC 2004-10378
Contents: The land of The Great Game; The coming of the Taliban; Life under the Sharia; Women under the Taliban; A life of grinding poverty; A training ground for terrorism; Resistance to the Taliban
Discusses the history of Afghanistan, the rise and fall of the Taliban, and daily life under the regime.
"Quotes from residents, journalists, aid workers, and U.N. officials enliven the clearly presented, accurate material. . . . An excellent resource for reports." SLJ
Includes bibliographical references

959.1   Myanmar

Yin, Saw Myat
Myanmar. 2nd ed. Benchmark Bks. 2002 144p
il maps (Cultures of the world) lib bdg $37.07 (5
and up)   **959.1**
1. Myanmar
ISBN 0-7614-1353-7   LC 2001-25412
First published 1990
This describes the geography, history, government, economy, environment, people, and culture of Myanmar
Includes glossary and bibliographical references

959.3   Thailand

Goodman, Jim
Thailand. 2nd ed. Benchmark Bks. 2003 144p il
maps (Cultures of the world) lib bdg $37.07 (5
and up)   **959.3**
1. Thailand
ISBN 0-7614-1478-9   LC 2002-25979
First published 1990
Describes the geography, history, government, economy, people, religion, language, and culture of Thailand, a predominantly Buddhist country located in Southeast Asia. Includes several recipes
Includes glossary and bibliographical references

McNair, Sylvia, 1924-
Thailand. Children's Press 1998 144p
(Enchantment of the world, second series) $35 (4
and up)   **959.3**
1. Thailand
ISBN 0-516-21100-5   LC 98-16319
Explores the geography, history, arts, religion, and everyday life of Thailand
Includes bibliographical references

959.4   Laos

Mansfield, Stephen
Laos. Benchmark Bks. 1998 128p il maps
(Cultures of the world) lib bdg $35.64 (5 and up)
959.4
1. Laos
ISBN 0-7614-0689-1   LC 97-16568
Introduces the geography, history, religious beliefs, government, and people of Laos
Includes glossary and bibliographical references

Zickgraf, Ralph
Laos. Chelsea House 1999 110p il (Major world
nations) $23.95   **959.4**
1. Laos
ISBN 0-7910-4743-1
First published 1990 in the Places and peoples of the world series
This examines the land, plant and animal life, people, history, and future of Laos

959.5 Commonwealth of Nations territories. Malaysia

Munan, Heidi
Malaysia; {by} Heidi Munan, Foo Yuk Yee. 2nd ed. Benchmark Bks. 2002 144p il maps (Cultures of the world) lib bdg $37.07 (5 and up)
959.5
1. Malaysia
ISBN 0-7614-1351-0   LC 2001-25302
First published 1990
This describes the geography, history, government, economy, environment, people and culture of Malaysia
Includes glossary and bibliographical references

959.57 Singapore

Layton, Lesley
Singapore; {by} Lesley Layton, Pang Guek Cheng. 2nd ed. Benchmark Bks. 2002 144p il maps (Cultures of the world) lib bdg $37.07 (5 and up)
959.57
1. Singapore
ISBN 0-7614-1352-9   LC 2001-25413
First published 1990
This describes the geography, history, government, economy, environment, people, and culture of Singapore
Includes glossary and bibliographical references

959.6 Cambodia

Green, Robert, 1969-
Cambodia. Lucent Bks. 2003 112p il maps (Modern nations of the world) lib bdg $27.45 (7 and up)
959.6
1. Cambodia
ISBN 1-59018-109-3   LC 2002-11294
This describes the geography, history, culture, religions, people and government of Cambodia
"A well-written and well-organized overview. . . . A useful resource for reports." SLJ
Includes bibliographical references

959.7 Vietnam

Dramer, Kim
The Mekong River. Watts 2001 63p il maps lib bdg $24.50; pa $8.95
959.7
1. Mekong River
ISBN 0-531-11854-1 (lib bdg); 0-531-13985-9 (pa)
LC 00-31918
"Watts library"
This presents "a multifaceted look at one particular river's impact on the area's landforms, industry, and history. The {text is} sprightly and packed with facts. The focused chapters seem especially well reasoned, which enhances their readability and usefulness for research. Fine full-color photos, maps, and historical photos appear throughout." SLJ
Includes glossary and bibliographical references

959.704 Vietnam--1949-

Hillstrom, Kevin
Vietnam War: almanac; {by} Kevin Hillstrom and Laurie Collier Hillstrom; Diane Sawinski, editor. U.X.L 2001 293p il $60 (7 and up)
959.704
1. Vietnam War, 1961-1975
ISBN 0-7876-4883-3   LC 00-56379
This "combines early history from the colonial period, U.S. involvement, and the war years and continues through the reestablishment of diplomacy and trade in recent years. Arranged chronologically, each of the 17 chapters includes 'Words to Know' and 'People to Know.' . . . Highly recommended for the junior- and senior-high-school libraries and public libraries." Booklist
Includes bibliographical references

Vietnam War: primary sources; {by} Kevin Hillstrom and Laurie Collier Hillstrom; Diane Sawinski, editor. U.X.L 2001 various paging $60 (7 and up)
959.704
1. Vietnam War, 1961-1975
ISBN 0-7876-4887-6   LC 00-56377
This "presents 13 full or excerpted speeches and writings 'that reflect the painfully diversified points of view on the war.' . . . Each excerpt includes background material to provide context. Unfamiliar terms and their definitions fill sidebars, along with other relevant information and photographs. The numerous sidebars, photographs, and maps enhance the text." Booklist
Includes bibliographical references

Levy, Debbie
The Vietnam War; by Debbie Levy. Lerner Publications 2004 88p il map (Chronicle of America's wars) lib bdg $27.93 (5 and up)
959.704
1. Vietnam War, 1961-1975
ISBN 0-8225-0421-9   LC 2002-156558
Contents: A history of struggle; Deadly dominoes; From Cold War to hot war; Americans at war; Turning point; The end begins; America lets go
This describes the events of the Vietnam War, focusing on the impact the war had on America and its people.
Includes glossary and bibliographical references

Seah, Audrey, 1958-
Vietnam; [by] Audrey Seah, Charissa M. Nair. 2nd ed. Benchmark Books 2004 144p il map (Cultures of the world) lib bdg $37.07 (5 and up)
959.704
1. Vietnam
ISBN 0-7614-1789-3   LC 2004-12903
First published 1994
Contents: Geography; History; Government; Economy; Environment; Vietnamese; Lifestyle; Religion; Language; Arts; Leisure; Festivals; Food
This describes the geography, history, government, economy environment, and culture of Vietnam
Includes glossary and bibliographical references

The **Vietnam** War; Ryn Shane-Armstrong and Lynn Armstrong, book editors. Greenhaven Press 2003 237p il map (Great speeches in history series) lib bdg $25.96; pa $16.96 (7 and up)   **959.704**
1. Vietnam War, 1961-1975 2. Speeches
ISBN 0-7377-1433-6 (lib bdg); 0-7377-1434-4 (pa)
                                          LC 2002-27890
This collection of speeches relating to the Vietnam War includes the words of such speakers as Ho Chi Minh, Barry Goldwater, Martin Luther King, and Bill Clinton
This "provides insight into the lengthy conflict." SLJ
Includes bibliographical references

Yancey, Diane
Life of an American soldier. Lucent Bks. 2001 128p il (American war library, Vietnam War) lib bdg $27.45   **959.704**
1. Vietnam War, 1961-1975
ISBN 1-56006-676-8   LC 00-8386
Describes the men and women who fought in the Vietnam War, the kind of war they fought, and the distress and difficulty they suffered on their return to the United States
This is "liberally illustrated with good-quality, black-and-white captioned photos. Vocabulary is appropriate while at the same time describing the situation without softening the impact or tempering the language in the soldiers' statements." SLJ
Includes glossary and bibliographical references

Young, Marilyn Blatt
The Vietnam War: a history in documents; [by] Marilyn B. Young, John J. Fitzgerald, A. Tom Grunfeld. Oxford Univ. Press 2002 175p il maps (Pages from history) lib bdg $32.95 (7 and up)
                                          959.704
1. Vietnam War, 1961-1975
ISBN 0-19-512278-X   LC 2001-52338
This is a "collection of original documents and photographs that detail the war in Vietnam. The text includes speeches, cartoons, news articles, and parallel events occurring in the United States and in Asia." Soc Educ
"The documents are skillfully tied together by brief text that gives good background information. . . . The book is well balanced in showing both sides. . . . Good-quality, black-and-white photos and illustrations are plentiful and informative." SLJ
Includes glossary and bibliographical references

959.8   Indonesia and East Timor

Lyle, Garry
Indonesia. Chelsea House 1999 104p il (Major world nations) lib bdg $23.95   **959.8**
1. Indonesia
ISBN 0-7910-4987-6   LC 98-15072
Published 1984 by Burke with title: Let's visit Indonesia
Describes the geography, history, government, culture, and daily life of the country that is comprised of 13,000 islands

Mirpuri, Gouri, 1960-
Indonesia; by Gouri Mirpuri, Robert Cooper. 2nd ed. Benchmark Bks. 2002 144p il maps (Cultures of the world) lib bdg $37.07
                                          959.8
1. Indonesia
ISBN 0-7614-1355-3   LC 2001-28607
First published 1990
This describes the geography, history, government, economy, environment and culture of Indonesia
"The pictures are lush, with captions in tiny print offering much additional information. The text is written smoothly and readably, and it contains a substantial amount of information." Booklist
Includes glossary and bibliographical references

959.9   Philippines

Tope, Lily Rose R.
Philippines; {by} Lily R. Tope, Detch P. Nonan-Mercado. 2nd ed. Benchmark Bks. 2002 144p il maps (Cultures of the world) lib bdg $37.07 (5 and up)   **959.9**
1. Philippines
ISBN 0-7614-1475-4   LC 2002-19725
First published 1990
Discusses the geography, history, government, economy, people, and culture of the Philippines, an archipelago of many islands in the Western Pacific
Includes glossary and bibliographical references

Wee, Jessie
The Philippines. Chelsea House 1998 104p il (Major world nations) lib bdg $23.95
                                          959.9
1. Philippines
ISBN 0-7910-4984-1   LC 98-4314
First published 1988
Explores the people, history, culture, land, climate, and economy of the Philippines, the only Christian nation in Asia

960   Africa

Africa: an encyclopedia for students; John Middleton, editor. Scribner 2002 4v il maps set $395 (7 and up)   **960**
1. Africa—Encyclopedias
ISBN 0-684-80650-9   LC 2001-49348
A comprehensive look at the continent of Africa and the countries that comprise it, including peoples and cultures, the land and its history, art and architecture, and daily life

Africa: opposing viewpoints; Laura K. Egendorf, book editor. Greenhaven Press 2005 208p il $34.95; pa $23.70   **960**
1. Africa
ISBN 0-7377-2218-5; 0-7377-2219-3 (pa)
                                          LC 2004-42432
"Opposing viewpoints series"

Africa: opposing viewpoints—*Continued*

"The authors in this book debate the issues facing modern Africa in the following chapters: What Problems Does Africa Face? How Can the Spread of AIDS in Africa Be Reduced? What Policies Will Best Help Africa? How Can Africa's Wild Lands Be Preserved?" Publisher's note

Includes bibliographical references

African history on file. rev ed. Facts on File 2003 various paging il maps loose-leaf $185
960
1. Africa—History
ISBN 0-8160-5139-9   LC 2002-192848
Also available CD-ROM version
First published 1994
More than 500 "reproducible maps, charts, timelines, and drawings visually detail the broad range of human experience in Africa, from prehistory to the present." Publisher's note
Includes bibliographical references

Downing, David, 1946-
Africa; postcolonial conflict; David Downing. Raintree 2004 64p il map (Troubled world) pa $32.79   **960**
1. Africa—Politics and government 2. African Americans—Social conditions
ISBN 1-410-90183-1   LC 2003-2154
Contents: Troubled continent; Turning point : independence; The Muslim-Christian divide; Victims of the Cold War : the Horn of Africa; Victims of the Cold War : Angola; Thieves and murderers; Turning point : 1970's - oil price rise; West African civil wars; Turning point: genocide in Rwanda; Africa's "great war"; Independence : 40 years later; Three leaders; The Western media and Africa; Turning point: 2002 - year of peace?; Prospects

Describes political, economic, religious, and other problems which plague the entire continent of Africa today, and their sources in European colonial rule in the nineteenth and twentieth centuries.

"Information presented here provides valuable background material even in view of rapidly changing events." SLJ

Encyclopedia of African nations and civilizations; {edited by} Keith Lye and The Diagram Group. Facts on File 2002 400p il maps (Facts on File library of world history) $75 (7 and up)
960
1. Africa—Encyclopedias
ISBN 0-8160-4568-2   LC 2001-40283
.
This "covers the major historic civilizations and the fifty-two nations of Africa in an . . . A-to-Z format. Each nation's entry narrates the history of the region from the early development of its peoples to the political, cultural, and economic circumstances that characterize the area today. The volume includes a . . . list of rulers and presidents, the history and culture of its indigenous peoples, and brief biographic details on major political and cultural personalities." Publisher's note
.

Haskins, James, 1941-2005
African beginnings; {by} James Haskins & Kathleen Benson; paintings by Floyd Cooper. Lothrop, Lee & Shepard Bks. 1998 48p il map $17.99; lib bdg $17.89 (4 and up)   **960**
1. Africa—History
ISBN 0-688-10256-5; 0-688-10257-3 (lib bdg)
LC 94-9848
This is an "overview of the great African kingdoms between 3800 B.C. and A.D. 1800. Sections on the kingdoms of Nubia, Egypt, Jenne-Jeno, Ghana, Mao, Songhay, etc., briefly discuss trade, education, art, agriculture, and other practices." Bull Cent Child Books
Cooper "fills in the geographical and cultural details with soft-edged, luminous oil paintings." Publ Wkly
Includes bibliographical references

Peoples of Africa. Marshall Cavendish 2000 11v il map set $471.36   **960**
1. Ethnology—Africa 2. Africa
ISBN 0-7614-7158-8   LC 99-88550
"Arranged alphabetically by country, this set chronicles the history and migration of African peoples from ancient civilizations and kingdoms to the present day." SLJ
"With the coverage of fashion, sports, music, art, and recipes, this set offers information difficult to find elsewhere and has excellent potential for cross-curricular use." Book Rep
Includes bibliographical references

961.1 Tunisia

Brown, Roslind Varghese
Tunisia. Benchmark Bks. 1998 128p il maps (Cultures of the world) lib bdg $37.07 (5 and up)
961.1
1. Tunisia
ISBN 0-7614-0690-5   LC 97-15883
Examines the history, economy, people, lifestyles, and culture of this Arab country in northern Africa
Includes glossary and bibliographical references

961.2 Libya

Malcolm, Peter, 1937-
Libya; [by] Peter Malcolm, Elie Losleben. 2nd ed. Benchmark Bks. 2004 144p il map (Cultures of the world) lib bdg $37.07 (5 and up)
961.2
1. Libya
ISBN 0-7614-1702-8   LC 2003-20887
First published 1993
Contents: Geography; History; Government; Economy; Environment; Libyans minority; Lifestyle; Religion; Language; Arts; Leisure; Festivals; Food
Examines the geography, history, government, economy, people, and culture of Libya
Includes glossary and bibliographical references

962   Egypt and Sudan

Barter, James, 1946-
The Nile. Lucent Bks. 2003 112p il maps
(Rivers of the world) lib bdg $21.96   **962**
1. Nile River 2. Nile River valley
ISBN 1-56006-935-X   LC 2001-7679
Describes the Nile River from ancient times to the
present, and discusses what must be done to protect and
preserve this river
"Detailed and informative . . .[this is] well organized
and [has] good-quality, black-and-white photos, reproductions, and maps that provide valuable points of reference
and visual appeal." SLJ
Includes bibliographical references

Bowden, Rob
The Nile; Rob Bowden. Raintree Steck-Vaughn
Publishers 2004 48p il map (River journey) lib
bdg $29.93 (5 and up)   **962**
1. Nile River 2. Nile River valley
ISBN 0-7398-6072-0   LC 2002-155378
Contents: The source of the Nile; Calming the Nile;
The rivers meet; The Nile cataracts; The Nile Valley;
The Nile Delta
The author presents information about the Nile River
"as though readers are taking a trip from the river's
source to where it meets the sea. This approach works
surprisingly well at drawing youngsters in. . . . The author presents an integrated view of the geological, economic, and cultural aspects of {The Nile}, and does not
shy away from realities, such as how thousands of people lose their homes when dams are built, or the pollution that threatens wildlife. Full-color photographs appear
throughout." SLJ

Cumming, David, 1953-
The Nile. World Almanac Lib. 2003 48p il
maps (Great rivers of the world) lib bdg $26.60 (4
and up)   **962**
1. Nile River 2. Nile River valley
ISBN 0-8368-5445-4   LC 2002-33139
Contents: The course of the river; The Nile in history;
Cities and settlements; Farming, trade, and industry; Animals and plants; Environmental issues; Recreation and
leisure; The future
This describes the geography, wildlife, and history of
the Nile River and its impact on people of the Nile River
valley
"The presentation is exceptionally clear and lively.
. . . Exquisite, full-color photos and maps show the
beauty and dangers of the [river]. . . . Useful for reports
and enjoyable as recreational reading." SLJ
Includes glossary and bibliographical references

Kallen, Stuart A., 1955-
Egypt. Lucent Bks. 1999 111p il maps (Modern
nations of the world) lib bdg $28.70 (7 and up)
          962
1. Egypt
ISBN 1-56006-535-4   LC 98-43851

Discusses the history, geography, people, and culture
of Egypt and its significance in the world today
"The strength of this volume is its carefully developed
history of Egypt from ancient times to the present." SLJ
Includes bibliographical references

Pateman, Robert, 1954-
Egypt; [by] Robert Pateman, Salwa
El-Hamamsy. 2nd ed. Benchmark Bks. 2003 144p
il maps (Cultures of the world) lib bdg $37.07 (5
and up)   **962**
1. Egypt
ISBN 0-7614-1670-6   LC 2003-9859
First published 1993
Contents: Geography; History; Government; Economy;
Environment; Egyptians; Lifestyle; Religion; Language;
Arts; Leisure; Festivals; Food; Map of Egypt; About the
economy; About the culture
Explores the geography, history, government, econo-
my, people, and culture of Egypt
Includes glossary and bibliographical references

Wilkens, Frances
Egypt. Chelsea House 1998 104p il (Major
world nations) lib bdg $23.95   **962**
1. Egypt
ISBN 0-7910-4989-2   LC 98-15075
Describes the history, geography, economy, culture,
and people of the North African nation of Egypt

Zuehlke, Jeffrey
Egypt in pictures. Lerner Publs. 2003 80p il
map (Visual geography series) lib bdg $27.93 (5
and up)   **962**
1. Egypt
ISBN 0-8225-0367-0   LC 2001-6613
Contents: The land, the Nile River and Delta, deserts,
the Aswan High Dam, climate, Flora and Fauna, natural
resources, Cairo, ports, secondary cities; History and
government, the age of the pyramids, the middle kingdom, the new kingdom, Greek and Roman rule, early
Arab rulers, the Fatimids, the Mamluks, the Ottoman
Empire, Muhammad Ali Pasha, European intervention,
independence, the revolution of 1952, the Suez war,
union with Syria, the Six-Day war, Anwar el-Sadat,
peace with Israel, Hosni Mubarak government; The People, ethnic groups, way of life, health, education,
langauge; Cultural life, religion, architecture, literature,
marriage, social life and customs, festivals and food,
sports and recreation; The Economy, agriculture, industry, transportation, trade, tourism, the future
Discusses the physical features, history, government,
people, culture, and economy of Egypt
Includes bibliographical references

962.4   Sudan

Levy, Patricia Marjorie, 1951-
Sudan. Benchmark Bks. 1997 128p il maps
(Cultures of the world) $37.07 (5 and up)
          962.4
1. Sudan
ISBN 0-7614-0284-5   LC 96-20493

Levy, Patricia Marjorie, 1951-—*Continued*
Examines the geography, history, government, economy, and culture of the war-torn country where the African and Arab worlds mingle
Includes glossary and bibliographical references

963.5 Eritrea

NgCheong-Lum, Roseline, 1962-
Eritrea. Benchmark Bks. 2001 128p il maps (Cultures of the world) lib bdg $37.07
963.5
1. Eritrea
ISBN 0-7614-1192-5   LC 00-50834
This describes the geography, history, government, economy, environment and culture of Eritrea
"Strong visuals and a comprehensive text give readers a vivid picture of one of the newest nations in Africa." Horn Book Guide
Includes glossary and bibliographical references

964 Northwest African coast and offshore islands. Morocco

Blauer, Ettagale
Morocco; by Ettagale Blauer and Jason Lauré. Children's Press 1999 144p il maps (Enchantment of the world, second series) lib bdg $35
964
1. Morocco
ISBN 0-516-20961-2   LC 98-17644
Describes the geography, plants and animals, history, economy, language, religions, culture, and people of Morocco, a unique northern African nation surrounded by both water and desert
Includes bibliographical references

965 Algeria

Kagda, Falaq
Algeria. Benchmark Bks. 1997 128p il maps (Cultures of the world) lib bdg $37.07 (5 and up)
965
1. Algeria
ISBN 0-7614-0680-8   LC 96-40373
Examines the geography, history, government, economy, people, and culture of Algeria
Includes glossary and bibliographical references

966.1 Mauritania

Green, Rebecca L.
The empire of Ghana. Watts 1998 64p il (African civilizations) $23
966.1
1. Ghana Empire
ISBN 0-531-20276-3   LC 97-37574
"A First book"

A survey of the history and culture of the West African Empire of Ghana that, flourishing from about 750 until 1076, is not related to modern Ghana
Includes glossary and bibliographical references

966.2 Mali, Burkina Faso, Niger

Conrad, David C.
The Songhay Empire; {by} David Conrad. Watts 1998 64p il maps (African civilizations) $23
966.2
1. Songhai Empire
ISBN 0-531-20284-4   LC 97-31288
"A First book"
A survey of the history and culture of the West African Songhai Empire that flourished from the 1460s until the 1590s, when it was conquered by Morocco
Includes glossary and bibliographical references

McKissack, Patricia C., 1944-
The royal kingdoms of Ghana, Mali, and Songhay; life in medieval Africa; {by} Patricia and Fredrick McKissack. Holt & Co. 1993 142p il maps hardcover o.p. paperback available $8.95 (5 and up)
966.2
1. Ghana Empire 2. Songhai Empire 3. Mali—History
ISBN 0-8050-4259-8 (pa)   LC 93-4838
Examines the civilizations of the Western Sudan which flourished from 700 to 1700 A.D., acquiring such vast wealth that they became centers of trade and culture for a continent
"The McKissacks are careful to distinguish what is known from what is surmised; they draw on the oral tradition, eyewitness accounts, and contemporary scholarship; and chapter source notes discuss various conflicting views of events." Booklist
Includes bibliographical references

966.3 Senegal

Berg, Elizabeth, 1953-
Senegal; {by} Elizabeth L. Berg. Benchmark Bks. 1999 128p il maps (Cultures of the world) lib bdg $37.07 (5 and up)
966.3
1. Senegal
ISBN 0-7614-0872-X   LC 98-7790
Describes the geography, history, economy, lifestyle, and religion of Senegal, as well as its people, languages, and festivals
Includes glossary and bibliographical references

966.62 Liberia

Levy, Patricia Marjorie, 1951-
Liberia; {by} Patricia Levy. Benchmark Bks. 1998 128p il maps (Cultures of the world) lib bdg $37.07 (5 and up)
966.62
1. Liberia
ISBN 0-7614-0810-X   LC 97-43613

Levy, Patricia Marjorie, 1951-—*Continued*
Describes the geography, history, government, economy, people, lifestyle, religion, language, arts, leisure, festivals, and food of the West African nation of Liberia
Includes glossary and bibliographical references

Reef, Catherine
This our dark country; the American settlers of Liberia. Clarion Bks. 2002 136p il maps $17
966.62
1. American Colonization Society 2. African Americans—History 3. Liberia—History 4. Slavery—United States
ISBN 0-618-14785-3   LC 2002-3966
Contents: "These Free, Sunny Shores"; "Beyond the Reach of Mixture"; Divine providence; Americans; Life upriver; Progress; "Some Fertile Country"; "The Beclouded Sun"; Epilogue: Liberia, troubled land
Explores the history of the colony, later the independent nation of Liberia, which was established on the west coast of Africa in 1822 as a haven for free African Americans
"This photo-essay is a grim, disturbing history of Liberia. . . . Reef tells it in clear, plain style, always showing the connections between the two homelands. The handsome, very spacious design . . . makes the hard facts accessible. . . . A must for history collections." Booklist
Includes bibliographical references

966.68 Ivory Coast

Sheehan, Patricia, 1954-
Côte d'Ivoire. Benchmark Bks. 2000 128p il map (Cultures of the world) lib bdg $37.07 (5 and up)
966.68
1. Ivory Coast
ISBN 0-7614-0980-7   LC 99-27250
Surveys the geography, history, government, economy, and culture of Côte d'Ivoire, formerly known as the Ivory Coast
Includes glossary and bibliographical references

966.7 Ghana

Levy, Patricia Marjorie, 1951-
Ghana. Benchmark Bks. 1999 128p il maps (Cultures of the world) lib bdg $37.07 (5 and up)
966.7
1. Ghana
ISBN 0-7614-0952-1   LC 98-49004
Describes the geography, history, government, economy, people, lifestyle, religion, language, arts, festivals, and food of Ghana
This offers "a readable text along with plenty of clear color photos." Horn Book Guide
Includes glossary and bibliographical references

966.9 Nigeria

Levy, Patricia Marjorie, 1951-
Nigeria. 2nd ed. Benchmark Bks. 2004 144p il map (Cultures of the world) lib bdg $25.95 (5 and up)
966.9
1. Nigeria
ISBN 0-7614-1703-6   LC 2003-20886
First published 1993
Contents: Geography; History; Government; Economy; Environment; Nigerians; Lifestyle; Religion; Language; Arts; Leisure; Festivals; Food
Examines the geography, history, government, economy, people, and culture of Nigeria
Includes glossary and bibliographical references

Nnoromele, Salome, 1967-
Life among the Ibo women of Nigeria. Lucent Bks. 1998 96p il maps (Way people live) lib bdg $28.70 (7 and up)
966.9
1. Igbo (African people) 2. Nigeria—Social life and customs 3. Women—Nigeria
ISBN 1-56006-344-0   LC 97-45172
Examines the traditional role of Ibo women as equal participants in the social, economic, religious, and political lives of their communities and how this role has been influenced and changed by centuries of colonization and the pressures of modern society
"Nnoromele's clear language will make research a pleasure and understanding a given." Booklist
Includes bibliographical references

967.51 Democratic Republic of the Congo

Heale, Jay
Democratic Republic of the Congo. Benchmark Bks. 1999 128p il maps (Cultures of the world) lib bdg $37.07 (5 and up)
967.51
1. Congo (Republic)
ISBN 0-7614-0874-6   LC 98-28538
Describes the geography, history, government, economy, people, lifestyle, religion, languages, arts, leisure, festivals, and food of the third largest country in Africa, a former colony of Belgium
Includes glossary and bibliographical references

Willis, Terri
Democratic Republic of the Congo. Children's Press 2004 143p il map (Enchantment of the world, Second series) lib bdg $34.50 (5 and up)
967.51
1. Congo (Republic)
ISBN 0-516-24250-4   LC 2003-504
Contents: Collapsing under its weight; The country and the river; Congo's bountiful diversity; Kingdoms, colonies, and corruption; Moving toward freedom; Poverty amidst plenty; People of the Congo; Overlapping faiths; Expression through the arts; Life in Congo; Timeline; Fast facts

Willis, Terri—*Continued*
Discusses the geography and climate, history, wildlife, economy, government, people, religion, and culture of the Congo.
This offers "lucid commentary, digestible quantities of facts and statistics, eye-catching color photos, and eminently useful back matter." Booklist
Includes bibliographical references

967.6 Uganda and Kenya

Barlas, Robert
Uganda. Benchmark Bks. 2000 128p il map (Cultures of the world) lib bdg $37.07 (5 and up)
967.6
1. Uganda
ISBN 0-7614-0981-5   LC 99-27577
Discusses the geography, history, government, economy, people, and culture of the African nation of Uganda
Includes glossary and bibliographical references

Wilson, Thomas H.
City states of the Swahili coast. Watts 1998 64p il maps (African civilizations) $23   **967.6**
1. East Africa—History
ISBN 0-531-20281-X   LC 97-37569
"A First book"
Discusses the history and culture of the Swahili peoples living along the eastern coast of Africa, from present-day Somalia to Mozambique
Includes glossary and bibliographical references

967.62 Kenya

Bowden, Rob
Kenya. Facts on File 2003 61p il map (Countries of the world) $30   **967.62**
1. Kenya
ISBN 0-8160-5384-7
This covers Kenya's "physical geography, resources, ethnic populations, tourism, and commerce. . . . It includes a detailed overview of the tensions between commercial development in an impoverished nation and the need to protect natural resources and wildlife. . . . {This title offers} a wealth of nearly up-to-date information and a realistic introduction to {its subject}. . . . {It also features} good-quality color photos of urban and rural homes and buildings and traditional and western lifestyles." Booklist
Includes bibliographical references

Broberg, Catherine
Kenya in pictures. rev and expanded. Lerner Publs. 2003 80p il map (Visual geography series) lib bdg $27.93 (5 and up)   **967.62**
1. Kenya
ISBN 0-8225-1957-7   LC 2001-3829
First published 1988 under the authorship of Joel Reuben

A brief overview of Kenya's land, history, government, people, and culture
The book is "visually appealing with photos and sidebars that complement the text." Libr Media Connect
Includes bibliographical references

Lekuton, Joseph
Facing the lion; growing up Maasai on the African savanna; by Joseph Lekuton with Herman Viola. National Geographic Soc. 2003 127p il map $15.95   **967.62**
1. Masai (African people) 2. Kenya
ISBN 0-7922-5125-3   LC 2003-750
Contents: A lion hunt; The proud one; Cows; The pinching man; School; Herdsman; Initiation; Kabarak; Soccer; America; A warrior in two worlds
A member of the Masai people describes his life as he grew up in a northern Kenya village, travelled to America to attend college, and became an elementary school teacher in Virginia
"Lekuton's story touches a universal chord, and shows readers the beauty of another culture from the inside. Simple and direct enough for reluctant readers, and written in a conversational and occasionally wryly humorous style, this book will be enjoyed by a wide range of readers." SLJ

Pateman, Robert, 1954-
Kenya; by Robert Pateman. 2nd ed. Benchmark Bks. 2004 144p il map (Cultures of the world) lib bdg $37.07 (5 and up)   **967.62**
1. Kenya
ISBN 0-7614-1701-X   LC 2003-20921
First published 1993
Contents: Geography; History; Government; Economy; Environment; Kenyans; Lifestyle; Religion; Language; Arts; Leisure; Festivals; Foods
Examines the geography, history, government, economy, people, and culture of Kenya
Includes glossary and bibliographical references

967.73 Somalia

Hassig, Susan M., 1969-
Somalia. Benchmark Bks. 1997 128p il maps (Cultures of the world) lib bdg $37.07 (5 and up)
967.73
1. Somalia
ISBN 0-7614-0288-8   LC 96-20492
Discusses the geography, history, government, economy, people, and culture of this peninsular African nation on the Indian Ocean
Includes glossary and bibliographical references

967.8 Tanzania

Heale, Jay
Tanzania. Benchmark Bks. 1998 128p il maps (Cultures of the world) lib bdg $37.07 (5 and up)
967.8
1. Tanzania
ISBN 0-7614-0809-6   LC 97-42180

Heale, Jay—*Continued*

Describes the geography, history, government, economy, ethnic groups, lifestyle, religion, language, arts, leisure, festivals, and food of this Eastern African nation

This offers "a clear and informative text {and} . . . captioned color photographs." Horn Book Guide

Includes glossary and bibliographical references

McCulla, Patricia E.

Tanzania. Chelsea House 1999 112p il map (Major world nations) lib bdg $23.95

967.8

1. Tanzania

ISBN 0-7910-4768-7

First published 1989 in the Places and peoples of the world series

Discusses the history, geography, industry, culture and people of Tanzania

Includes glossary

967.9   Mozambique

James, R. S.

Mozambique. Chelsea House 1999 103p il (Major world nations) lib bdg $23.95 (7 and up)

967.9

1. Mozambique

ISBN 0-7910-4744-X

First published 1988 in the Places and peoples of the world series

Surveys the history, topography, people, and culture of Mozambique

Includes glossary

968   Southern Africa. Republic of South Africa

Blauer, Ettagale

South Africa; by Ettagale Blauer and Jason Lauré. Children's Press 1998 144p il (Enchantment of the world, second series) lib bdg $35 (4 and up)

968

1. South Africa

ISBN 0-516-20606-0   LC 97-26014

Describes the geography, plants, animals, history, economy, languages, religions, sports, arts, and people of a country that shares land borders with six nations and surrounds one of them

Includes bibliographical references

Downing, David, 1946-

Apartheid in South Africa; David Downing. Heinemann Library 2004 56p il (Witness to history) $31.36   968

1. Apartheid 2. South Africa—Race relations

ISBN 1-403-44870-1   LC 2003-18235

Contents: How do we know?; South Africa in 1910; Discrimination; Early opposition to white rule; South Af-

rica adopts apartheid; How apartheid worked; For Europeans only; Resistance grows; Sharpeville; A change of tactics; South Africa isolated; Life for whites; Life for nonwhites; The Bantustans; Soweto; The terrorist state; Pressure from inside; Pressure from outside; First cracks; The end of apartheid; Reconciliation; Today and the future; What have we learned from apartheid?

Examines the historical forces that led to the development of the system of apartheid, what life was like under the system for both blacks and whites, and the efforts that caused the end of this system.

"This dense volume is an excellent narrative overview of the apartheid struggle, drawing extensively on primary sources that provide depth, detail, drama, and authenticity." Booklist

Rosmarin, Ike, 1915-

South Africa; {by} Ike Rosmarin, Dee Rissik. 2nd ed. Benchmark Bks. 2004 144p il map (Cultures of the world) lib bdg $37.07 (5 and up)

968

1. South Africa

ISBN 0-7614-1704-4   LC 2003-20923

First published 1993

Contents: Geography; History; Government; Economy; Environment; South Africans; Lifestyle; Religion; Language; Arts; Leisure; Festivals; Food

Examines the geography, history, government, economy, people, and culture of South Africa

Includes glossary and bibliographical references

968.06   Period as Republic, 1961-

Beecroft, Simon

The release of Nelson Mandela; by Simon Beecroft. World Almanac Library 2004 48p il (Days that changed the world) lib bdg $30; pa $11.95   968.06

1. Mandela, Nelson 2. South Africa—Politics and government 3. Apartheid

ISBN 0-8368-5571-X (lib bdg); 0-8368-5578-7 (pa)

LC 2003-65807

First published 2003 in the United Kingdom with title: The freeing of Nelson Mandela

.

A biography of the black South African leader who became a civil rights activist, political prisoner, and president of South Africa, told in the context of the history of his country.

This does "a fine job of combining a closeup view of an earth-shattering event with what led up to the drama and a sense of the event's impact on the future. . . . The . . . design is ideal for browsing." Booklist

Includes bibliographical references

Canesso, Claudia

South Africa. Chelsea House 1999 120p il (Major world nations) $22.95   968.06

1. South Africa

ISBN 0-7910-4766-0   LC 87-18273

Surveys the history, topography, people, and culture of South Africa, with emphasis on its current economy, in-

Canesso, Claudia—*Continued*
dustry, and place in the political world
This is "readable, informative, current, and fair, with
lots of good photos and up-to-date maps." Booklist
Includes glossary

968.91 Zimbabwe

Sheehan, Sean, 1951-
Zimbabwe. 2nd ed. Benchmark Bks. 2004 144p
il map (Cultures of the world) lib bdg $37.07 (5
and up) **968.91**
1. Zimbabwe
ISBN 0-7614-1706-0   LC 2003-20883
Contents: Geography; History; Government; Economy;
Environment; Zimbabweans; Lifestyle; Religion; Lan-
guage; Arts; Leisure; Festivals; Foods
Examines the geography, history, govenment, econo-
my, people, and culture of Zimbabwe
Includes glossary and bibliographical references

968.94 Zambia

Holmes, Timothy
Zambia. Benchmark Bks. 1998 128p il maps
(Cultures of the world) lib bdg $37.07 (5 and up)
968.94
1. Zambia
ISBN 0-7614-0694-8   LC 97-22298
Describes the geography, history, government, economy, people, lifestyle, religion, language, arts, leisure, festivals, and food of this high plateau country in the interi-
or of Africa
Includes glossary and bibliographical references

969.1 Madagascar

Heale, Jay
Madagascar. Benchmark Bks. 1998 128p il
maps (Cultures of the world) lib bdg $37.07 (5
and up) **969.1**
1. Madagascar
ISBN 0-7614-0693-X   LC 97-16569
Introduces the geography, history, religious beliefs,
government, and people of Madagascar
This offers a "lucidly written text. . . . Informative
chapters include discussion about ethnic groups, rites of
passage, family life, sports, etiquette, and human rights."
Horn Book Guide
Includes glossary and bibliographical references

Stevens, Rita
Madagascar. Chelsea House 1999 111p il map
(Major world nations) $21.95 **969.1**
1. Madagascar
ISBN 0-7910-4762-8
First published 1988 in the Places and peoples of the
world series
Surveys the history, topography, people, and culture of
Madagascar
Includes glossary

970 North America

Peoples of the Americas. Marshall Cavendish
1999 11v set $471.36 **970**
1. Ethnology—America
ISBN 0-7614-7050-6   LC 98-2801
Contents: v1 Anguilla-Belize; v2 Bermuda-Brazil; v3
Canada-Cayman Islands; v4 Chile-Costa Rica; v5 Cuba-
French Guiana; v6 Greenland-Jamaica; v7 Martinique-
Paraguay; v8 Peru-Turks and Caicos Islands; v9 United
States of America; v10 United States of America-Virgin
Islands
"The 50 entries, arranged alphabetically by country,
vary in length from 2 to 74 pages and focus on native,
ethnic, and immigrant groups in these nations. Discussions center on their way of life; on their contributions,
both cultural and political; and often, on their struggle
for survival." SLJ
"The amount of information, logical organization,
multiple access points, and attractive layout combine to
create a reference tool that most school and public libraries will want in their collections." Booklist

970.004 North American native peoples

Anderson, Madelyn Klein
North American Indian games. Watts 2000 63p
il $24.50; pa $8.95 **970.004**
1. Native Americans—Games
ISBN 0-531-20403-0; 0-531-16474-8 (pa)
LC 99-30240
Examines the origins, nature, and significance of
games played by North American Indians, including
shinny and other ball games, dice games, and guessing
games
"The layout and photographs in this series are attractive to browsers as well as researchers." Book Rep
Includes glossary and bibliographical references

Bial, Raymond
Lifeways [series] Benchmark Books 1999-2003
24v il map lib bdg each group set of four volumes
$136.86 **970.004**
1. Native Americans
ISBN 0-614-0800-2 (Group 1); 0-7614-0860-6 (Group
2); 0-7614-0936-X (Group 3); 0-7614-1208-5 (Group
4); 0-7614-1412-6 (Group 5); 0-7614-1680-3 (Group
6)
Also available as separate volumes each $34.21
Contents: Group 1: The Cherokee; The Iroquois; The
Navajo; The Sioux; Group 2: The Comanche; The
Ojibwe; The Pueblo; The Seminole; Group 3: The
Apache; The Cheyenne; The Haida; The Huron; Group
4: The Inuit; The Nez Perce; The Powhatan; The Shoshone; Group 5: The Blackfeet; The Choctaw; The
Mandan; The Tlingit; Group 6: The Arapaho; The
Chumash; The Shawnee; The Wampanoag
"Prefaced by the creation story, each book looks at the
original lifeways of a tribe. Daily life, religious beliefs
and sacred rituals are . . . explored, as well as a tribe's
social systems, rules of warfare and their sense of them-

Bial, Raymond—*Continued*
selves within the natural universe. In addition, the cycle
of life—from birth to marriage to death—is [described]."
Publisher's note
"It's the comprehensive content, the attractive presentation, and the varied and well-chosen illustrations that
make these books worthy of consideration." SLJ

The Long Walk; the story of Navajo captivity.
Benchmark Bks. 2003 94p il map (Great journeys)
lib bdg $31.36   **970.004**
1. Carson, Kit, 1809-1868 2. Barboncito, Navajo
Chief, 1820?-1871 3. Navajo Indians
ISBN 0-7614-1322-7   LC 2001-43969
"The book is illustrated with informative black-and-
white photographs and reproductions." SLJ
Includes bibliographical references

Brown, Dee Alexander
Bury my heart at Wounded Knee; an Indian
history of the American West; [by] Dee Brown.
Thirtieth anniversary ed. Holt & Co. 2001 487p il
$35; pa $16   **970.004**
1. Native Americans—West (U.S.) 2. Native Ameri-
cans—Wars 3. West (U.S.)—History
ISBN 0-8050-6634-9; 0-8050-6669-1 (pa)
     LC 00-40958
First published 1970
This is an account of the experience of the American
Indian during the white man's expansion westward
Includes bibliographical references

Bruchac, Joseph, 1942-
Lasting echoes; an oral history of native
American people. Harcourt Brace & Co. 1997 xx,
148p il $16 (7 and up)   **970.004**
1. Native Americans
ISBN 0-15-201327-X   LC 97-11884
Also available in paperback from HarperCollins Pubs.
"Bruchac uses the words of American Indians (including songs and poetry) from a wide variety of tribes and
sources to bring the history and plight of American Indians after their initial encounter with European explorers
to life. . . . This is a well-constructed, involving presentation of an integral part of American history." Bull Cent
Child Books

Collier, Christopher, 1930-
Clash of cultures, prehistory-1638; {by}
Christopher Collier, James Lincoln Collier.
Benchmark Bks. (Tarrytown) 1998 95p il maps
(Drama of American history) lib bdg $31.36
     970.004
1. Native Americans 2. United States—History—1600-
1775, Colonial period 3. Culture conflict
ISBN 0-7614-0436-8   LC 96-31859
This volume "examines the civilizations on both sides
of the Atlantic in the years before and during European
settlement in North America. . . . While consistently
presenting the big picture, the Colliers paint their
American portrait 'warts and all,' caring less about ideal-
izing our history than increasing understanding of it."
Booklist
Includes bibliographical references

Cooper, Michael L., 1950-
Indian school; teaching the white man's way.
Clarion Bks. 1999 103p il $16   **970.004**
1. Native Americans—Education
ISBN 0-395-92084-1   LC 98-43640
"In the late 19th century, government-supported board-
ing schools were created to educate and assimilate Native
American children into the overriding white culture.
Cooper examines the Carlisle Indian School in Pennsyl-
vania . . . and some of its former students." SLJ
"This moving photo-essay is simply told and focused
on the personal. . . . The list of Web sites will encour-
age those who want to read more about this savage ex-
periment that failed." Booklist
Includes glossary and bibliographical references

Dolan, Edward F., 1924-
The American Indian wars; Edward F. Dolan.
Millbrook Press 2003 112p il map lib bdg $29.90
     970.004
1. Native Americans—Wars
ISBN 0-7613-1968-9   LC 2002-153012
Contents: Warpaths; The first battles; Deep into the
West; Two Apache warriors; The Battle of the Little
Bighorn; The magnificent march; Death at Wounded
Knee
Examines the battles and treaties between native peo-
ples and early European settlers of what was to become
the United States, as conflicts arose primarily over land,
but also over food and other issues.
"Period drawings, paintings, and photographs effec-
tively illustrate a text packed with history." Booklist
Includes bibliographical references

Ehrlich, Amy, 1942-
Wounded Knee: an Indian history of the
American West; adapted for young readers by
Amy Ehrlich from Dee Brown's Bury my heart at
Wounded Knee. Holt & Co. 1974 202p il maps
hardcover o.p. paperback available $13.95 (6 and
up)   **970.004**
1. Native Americans—West (U.S.) 2. Native Americans—Wars 3. West (U.S.)—History
ISBN 0-8050-2700-9 (pa)
This book traces the plight of the Navaho, Apache,
Cheyenne and Sioux Indians in their struggles against the
white man in the West between 1860 and 1890. It recounts battles and their causes, participants, and consequences during this era
"Some chapters {of the original} have been deleted,
others condensed, and in some instances sentence structure and language have been simplified. The editing is
good, and this version is interesting, readable, and
smooth. " SLJ
Includes bibliographical references

Elish, Dan, 1960-
The Trail of Tears; the story of the Cherokee
removal. Benchmark Bks. 2002 96p il maps (Great
journeys) lib bdg $32.79   **970.004**
1. Cherokee Indians
ISBN 0-7614-1228-X   LC 00-52902

Elish, Dan, 1960-—*Continued*
This "begins with the Cherokees' encounter with European explorers, discusses their experiences with the American government, and gives information on their forced removal from Georgia to locations West." SLJ
This "is particularly moving. Elish does a fine job introducing the Cherokee nation. . . . Filled with crisp, well-selected photographs and historical illustrations." Booklist
Includes bibliographical references

The **Encyclopedia** of North American Indians; general editor, D.L. Birchfield. Marshall Cavendish 1997 11v il maps set $657.07
970.004
1. Native Americans—Encyclopedias
ISBN 0-7614-0227-6   LC 96-7700
A comprehensive reference work on the culture and history of Native Americans
This "is a lavishly illustrated encyclopedia providing a multicultural perspective that will enhance the juvenile or general reference collections of any library." Libr J

The **Gale** encyclopedia of Native American tribes; edited by Sharon Malinowski {et al.}. Gale Res. 1998 4v il maps set $465   **970.004**
1. Native Americans—Encyclopedias
ISBN 0-7876-1085-2   LC 97-36848
Contents: v1 Northeast, Southeast Caribbean; v2 Great Basin, Southwest Middle America; v3 Arctic, Subarctic, Great Plains, Plateau; v4 California, Pacific Northwest, Pacific Islands
This set provides historical, cultural and current information on Native American tribes

Hirschfelder, Arlene B.
Native American; {by} Arlene Hirschfelder. DK Pub. 2000 192p il $24.95 (7 and up)
970.004
1. Native Americans
ISBN 0-7894-5162-X   LC 99-49061
This "heavily pictorial book resembles a stop-frame documentary film. Historic photos crowd its pages, showing American Indian life from ancestral times to the present. Excerpts from Indian autobiographies offer the voices of Black Elk, Tecumseh, Louis Riel, Sarah Winnemucca, and others, and Hirschfelder's own text is concise and comprehensive." Booklist
Includes bibliographical references

Indians of North America series. Heritage edition. Chelsea House 2005 6v il map set $137.70; pa set $59.70   **970.004**
1. Native Americans
ISBN 0-7910-8417-5; 0-7910-8399-3 (pa)
Separate volumes available ea $22.95, pa $9.95; some titles from original series available; for full information contact publisher
Series first published 1987-1997 in 67 volumes
Contents: The Cherokees by T. Perdue; The Choctaw by J. O. McKee; The Hopi by N. Bonvillian; The Iroquois by B. Graymont; The Mohawk by N. Bonvillian; The Teton Sioux by N. Bonvillian
These books cover Native American tribes describing their histories, life styles, religions, relationships with European explorers and settlers, and present situations.

Lassieur, Allison
Before the storm; American Indians before the Europeans. Facts on File 1998 150p il maps (Library of American Indian history) $25 (7 and up)   **970.004**
1. Native Americans
ISBN 0-8160-3651-9   LC 97-50072
A narrative history about the various Indian people of North America and their way of life before contact with Europeans
"Archaeological evidence and the science of ethnographic and historical research are utilized throughout the book. Numerous side-bars enliven the text. . . . A well-researched account." SLJ
Includes bibliographical references

Lavender, David Sievert, 1910-2003
Mother Earth, Father Sky; Pueblo Indians of the American Southwest; {by} David Lavender. Holiday House 1998 117p il $16.95
970.004
1. Pueblo Indians 2. Southwestern States—Antiquities
ISBN 0-8234-1365-9   LC 97-38119
"Lavender has combined a study of the Anasazi with a general overview of recorded Pueblo Indian history and culture. . . . This is a lively, intriguing exploration into the archaeological study of the Anasazi culture. . . . The last three chapters sum up Pueblo peoples from the Spanish invaders to education efforts today." SLJ
Includes glossary and bibliographical references

Murdoch, David Hamilton, 1937-
North American Indian; written by David Murdoch; chief consultant, Stanley A. Freed; photographed by Lynton Gardiner. rev ed. 2005 72p il (DK eyewitness books) $15.99; lib bdg $19.99 (4 and up)   **970.004**
1. Native Americans
ISBN 0-7566-1082-6; 0-7566-1082-6 (lib bdg)
First published 1995 by Knopf
Published in association with the American Museum of Natural History
This is a guide to the civilizations of North American Indians including full-color photographs of artifacts and descriptions ceremonies and customs.

Nardo, Don, 1947-
The Native Americans. Lucent Bks. 2003 112p il maps (History of weapons and warfare) $27.45 (7 and up)   **970.004**
1. Military art and science 2. Native Americans—Wars
ISBN 1-59018-070-4   LC 2002-8589
Contents: Two very different concepts of warfare; Precontact offensive weapons; Weapons borrowed from the whites; Defensive weapons and tactics; Horses transform warfare on the plains; When Indians fought Indians; The struggle between Indians and whites; Faith as a weapon: the ghost dance
Discusses the weapons used by Native Americans and their different means of warfare
Includes glossary and bibliographical references

Native Americans: opposing viewpoints; William Dudley, book editor. Greenhaven Press 1998 320p il (American history series) lib bdg $34.95; pa $22.45 (7 and up) **970.004**

1. Native Americans—History

ISBN 1-56510-705-5 (lib bdg); 1-56510-704-7 (pa)

LC 97-38334

A collection of primary sources documenting the history of European-Indian relations. Culture conflict, land tenure, forced removal, and assimilation are among the topics debated

Includes bibliographical references

The **Native** North American almanac; a reference work on Native North Americans in the United States and Canada; Duane Champagne, editor. 2nd ed. Gale Group 2001 xxvii, 1472p il maps $160 **970.004**

1. Native Americans

ISBN 0-7876-1655-9

First published 1994

"This source covers the civilization and culture of the indigenous peoples of the U.S. and Canada—both historic and contemporary. Included are signed essays, annotated directories, excerpts and biographies. Each chapter contains a subject-specific bibliography, photographs, maps and charts." Publisher's note

Includes bibliographical references

North American Indians today [series] Mason Crest 2003 15v il map set $344.25

970.004

1. Native Americans

ISBN 1-59084-663-X

Volumes also available separately each $22.95

Contents: Apache by K. McIntosh; Cherokee by P. Stewart; Cheyenne by K. McIntosh; Comanche by J. Libal; Creek by A. Libal; Crow by K. McIntosh; Huron by A. Libal; Iroquois by K. McIntosh; Navajo by K. McIntosh; Ojibwa by G. L. Cronell; Osage by P. Stewart; Powtawotami by E. Sanna; Pueblo by K. McIntosh; Seminole by J. Libal; Sioux by K. Lonehill

"Although each book gives some cultural and historical background for a Native American tribal group, its main focus is the struggles and accomplishments of the featured tribe in modern times. . . . These informative, accessible titles will be useful for reports." Horn Book Guide

Pritzker, Barry

Native Americans; an encyclopedia of history, culture, and peoples; {by} Barry M. Pritzker. ABC-CLIO 1998 2v il maps set $175

970.004

1. Native Americans—Encyclopedias

ISBN 0-87436-836-7　　　　LC 98-21718

"Organized geographically, each section begins with an introduction to the area and its original inhabitants. Tribal entries follow, with some smaller related groups discussed together. Each article includes sections on location, population, language, history, religion, government, customs, dwellings, diet, key technology, trade, notable arts, transportation, dress, and war/weapons. A contempo-

rary section follows, with information on government/reservations, economy, legal status, and daily life." Libr J

Includes bibliographical references

Student almanac of Native American history; Media Projects, Inc. Greenwood Press 2003 2v v cmp il map (Middle school reference) set $80

970.004

1. Native Americans—History

ISBN 0-313-32599-5　　　　LC 2002-35215

Contents: v1 From prehistoric times to the Trail of Tears, 35,000 BCE-1838; v2 From the Trail of Tears to the present, 1839-today

Presents an overview of the history of Native Americans from before European contact up to the present day, including historical documents, legislation, statistics, court cases, and timelines

"This attractive almanac provides information on topics of interest to users in middle school and up. . . . [This] will be a welcome addition to school and public libraries where there is a need for additional information about Native Americans." Booklist

Includes bibliographical references

Terry, Michael Bad Hand

Daily life in a Plains Indian village, 1868. Clarion Bks. 1999 48p il map $20; pa $9.95 (4 and up) **970.004**

1. Native Americans—Great Plains

ISBN 0-395-94542-9; 0-395-97499-2 (pa)

LC 98-32382

Depicts the historical background, social organization, and daily life of a Plains Indian village in 1868, presenting interiors, landscapes, clothing, and everyday objects

"The author presents short paragraphs of fascinating information accompanied by visuals that explain even more than the text." SLJ

Includes glossary

U·X·L encyclopedia of Native American tribes; Sharon Malinowski, Anna Sheets, & Linda Schmittroth, editors. Gale Group 1999 4v il map set $215 **970.004**

1. Native Americans—Encyclopedias

ISBN 0-7876-2838-7　　　　LC 98-54353

Contents: v1 The Northeast and Southeast; v2 The Great Basin and Southwest; v3 The Arctic, Subarctic, Great Plains, and Plateau; v4 California and the Pacific Northwest

"Eighty tribes are described and arranged alphabetically within each volume. . . . Each region is introduced with a signed, six-to-eight-page article describing the area's geography, history, and cultural interrelationships. Chapters on individual tribes range from 8 to 22 pages, enhanced with black-and-white photos and drawings. . . . Middle-schoolers will find the clearly organized information useful for research." Booklist

Waldman, Carl
Encyclopedia of Native American tribes; illustrations by Molly Braun. rev ed. Facts on File 1999 xxiii, 312p il maps $71.50; pa $19.95
970.004
1. Native Americans—Encyclopedias
ISBN 0-8160-3963-1; 0-8160-3964-X (pa)
LC 98-50263
"Facts on File library of American history"
First published 1988
This "gives an overview of the history and culture of tribes and peoples from Abenaki to Zuni. Focus is on U.S. North American tribes, but there is also coverage of cultural groupings in Canada and Central America. The volume is notable for its ease of use, its wonderful illustrations, and the great starting point it provides." Booklist
Includes bibliographical references

Wolfson, Evelyn
From Abenaki to Zuni; a dictionary of native American tribes; illustrated by William Sauts Bock. Walker & Co. 1988 215p il maps (4 and up)
970.004
1. Native Americans—Dictionaries
ISBN 0-8027-6790-7; 0-8027-7445-8 (pa)
LC 87-27875
An alphabetical identification of sixty-eight of the larger North American Indian tribes, describing their habitats, social life and customs, food, means of travel, and modern descendants
"Although, as the author notes, the book is not exhaustive in terms of tribes covered, Wolfson has provided help for researchers by pulling together data on so many native peoples in such a handy format. Students will be pleased with the concise summaries of information needed for school reports." Booklist
Includes bibliographical references

Yue, Charlotte
The wigwam and the longhouse; {by} Charlotte and David Yue. Houghton Mifflin 2000 118p il $15
970.004
1. Woodland Indians
ISBN 0-395-84169-0
LC 98-28971
Describes the history, customs, religion, government, homes, and present-day status of the various native peoples that inhabited the eastern woodlands since before the coming of the Europeans
Includes bibliographical references

970.01 North America--Early history to 1599

Lauber, Patricia, 1924-
Who came first; new clues to prehistoric Americans. National Geographic Soc. 2003 64p il maps $18.95 (5 and up)
970.01
1. Native Americans—Origin 2. America—Antiquities
ISBN 0-7922-8228-0
LC 2002-5278
Contents: A surprising discovery; The mystery; Searching for South American settlers; A second look at North America; Skulls, languages, and genetics; The search goes on

Presents recent archaeological findings about the first people to settle the Americas, how they got here, and from what continent they came
"In a lively narrative that draws readers right into crucial research going on now, Lauber weaves together geology, archaeology, genetics, anthropology [and] language. . . . The inviting, spacious, magazine-style design, with lots of paintings, maps, photos, and screened insets, makes the complex information accessible." Booklist
Includes bibliographical references

Wood, Marion
Ancient America; updated by Brian Williams. rev ed. Facts on File 2003 96p il map (Cultural atlas for young people) $35 (5 and up)
970.01
1. Native Americans—Antiquities 2. America—Antiquities
ISBN 0-8160-5145-3
LC 2003-40863
First published 1990
Maps and text offer information on the cultures and histories of native groups in both North and South America
This offers "facts, figures, and plenty of visuals that young researchers will find useful. . . . Each spread contains several colorful photographs, drawings, diagrams, and/or maps that will help readers visualize the places and cultures discussed." SLJ
Includes glossary and bibliographical references

971 Canada

Braun, Eric
Canada in pictures. Lerner Publs. 2003 80p il maps (Visual geography series) lib bdg $27.93 (5 and up)
971
1. Canada
ISBN 0-8225-4679-5
LC 2002-8107
First published 1989, catalogued under title
A historical and current look at Canada, discussing the land, the government, the culture, the people, and the economy
"An excellent introduction . . . . [This offers] easy-to-read and informative text, maps, charts, and full-color photographs." SLJ
Includes glossary and bibliographical references

Exploring Canada. Lucent Bks. 2003 10v il maps lib bdg ea $29.45
971
1. Canada
Contents: Alberta, by G. D. Laws & L. M. Laws; British Columbia, by B. J. Palana; Manitoba, by G. D. Laws & L. M. Laws; Maritime Provinces, by G. D. Laws & L. M. Laws; Newfoundland, by M. Mayell; Northwest Territory, by G. D. Laws & L. M. Laws; Ontario, by S. Ferry; Quebec, by S. Ferry; Saskatchewan, by M. Mayell; Yukon Territory, by S. Ferry, B. Harris, & L. Szynkowski
"These volumes provide overviews of the geography, history, and culture of each province or territory, along with an idea of how it fits into Canada as a whole. The maps are clear and well labeled. 'Facts About' sections

Exploring Canada—*Continued*
provide ready-reference information. Interesting and well-produced black-and-white photographs appear throughout.
. . . The strength of these titles is in their organization and the amount of information they provide." SLJ

Harris, Tim
The Mackenzie River; by Tim Harris. Gareth Stevens Pub 2003 32p il map (Rivers of North America) lib bdg $24.67 (5 and up)   **971**
1. Mackenzie River (N.W.T.)
ISBN 0-8368-3756-8   LC 2003-42741
Contents: River of the North; From source to mouth; The life of the river; Northern people; Land of black gold; Places to visit
This describes the longest river in Canada, which runs from its source east of the Rocky Mountains in the Northwest Territories to its mouth at the Arctic Ocean.
This "clearly describes [the Mackenzie River's], colorful history, and strong impact on the development of towns found along its banks. In well-organized fashion, the [author delves] into wild life, environmental issues facing [this region], and the people who live there. The color photographs enhance the [text] nicely to enrich readers' understanding." SLJ
Includes bibliographical references

Junior Worldmark encyclopedia of the Canadian provinces; {Timothy L. Gall and Susan Bevan Gall, editors}. 4th ed. UXL 2004 276p il map $60   **971**
1. Canada
ISBN 0-7876-9196-8   LC 2004-8308
First published 1997
Contents: Reader's guide; Guide to articles; Alberta; British Columbia; Manitoba; New Brunswick; Newfoundland and Labrador; Northwest Territories; Nova Scotia; Nunavut; Ontario; Prince Edward Island; Quebec; Saskatchewan; Yukon Territory; Canada; Glossary; Abbreviations & acronyms
This "includes profiles of the 10 provinces and 3 territories, plus a general article on Canada. Each chapter is about 20 pages long and provides data on the province name and meaning, nickname, motto, flag, and time zone plus 40 numbered sections covering size, climate, plants and animals, population, history, government, industry, health, the arts, education, libraries, tourism, famous people, and more." Booklist
Includes bibliographical references

Pang, Guek-Cheng
Canada. 2nd ed. Benchmark Books 2004 144p il map (Cultures of the world) lib bdg $37.07 (5 and up)   **971**
1. Canada
ISBN 0-7614-1788-5   LC 2004-8584
First published 1994
This describes the geography, history, government, economy, environment, and culture of Canada.
"There is excellent coverage of Canadian arts. . . . Full-color photos appear throughout, and the maps are current and easy to read." SLJ
Includes glossary and bibliographical references

971.9   Northern territories of Canada

Walsh Shepherd, Donna, 1948-
The Klondike gold rush. Watts 1998 64p il maps pa $6.95 hardcover o.p. (4 and up)   **971.9**
1. Klondike River valley (Yukon)—Gold discoveries
ISBN 0-531-15909-4 (pa)   LC 97-38340
"A First book"
Describes the adventures of those who flocked to the Klondike after gold was discovered there in 1896
"Short enough to appeal to reluctant researchers and long enough to provide a basic grasp of the events, the book succeeds admirably." SLJ
Includes bibliographical references

972   Middle America. Mexico

Hamilton, Janice
Mexico in pictures. Lerner Publs. 2003 80p il map (Visual geography series) lib bdg $27.93 (5 and up)   **972**
1. Mexico
ISBN 0-8225-1960-7   LC 2001-4238
First published 1987, catalogued under title
A historical and current look at Mexico, discussing the land, the government, the people, and the economy
The book is "visually appealing with photos and sidebars that complement the text." Libr Media Connect
Includes glossary and bibliographical references

Junior Worldmark encyclopedia of the Mexican states; {Timothy L. Gall and Susan Bevan Gall, editors}. 1st ed. UXL 2004 xxviii, 336p $60   **972**
1. Mexico
ISBN 0-7876-9161-5   LC 2004-8307
"Each profile opens with some fast facts and a full-page state map, followed by 27 consistent, coherent topical subsections (location, history, economy, government, public services, media, the arts, etc.) that make comparison among regions easy. . . . [This is] well-written and timely. . . . This unique book will be enlightening." SLJ

Reilly, Mary-Jo
Mexico; by Mary Jo Reilly, Leslie Jermyn. 2nd ed. Benchmark Bks. 2002 144p il maps (Cultures of the world) lib bdg $37.07 (5 and up)   **972**
1. Mexico
ISBN 0-7614-1363-4   LC 2001-47760
First published 1991
Presents the history, geography, economy, people, and social life and customs of Mexico
Includes glossary and bibliographical references

Steele, Philip
The Aztec news; consultants: Penny Bateman & Norma Rosso. Candlewick Press 1997 32p il pa $6.99 hardcover o.p. **972**
1. Aztecs
ISBN 0-7636-0427-5 (pa)   LC 96-31655
Uses a newspaper format to present articles about Aztec history, politics, religion, trading and farming, sports, the military and other aspects of daily life
"An alternative way of writing nonfiction that will attract those who are turned off by traditional nonfiction or are looking for something fresh." Booklist

Stein, R. Conrad, 1937-
Mexico. Children's Press 1998 144p il maps (Enchantment of the world, second series) lib bdg $35 (4 and up) **972**
1. Mexico
ISBN 0-516-20650-8   LC 97-40708
This describes the geography, history, government, economy and culture of Mexico
"For the most part, the writing and presentation of information are of high quality." SLJ
Includes bibliographical references

Tanaka, Shelley
Lost temple of the Aztecs; what it was like when the Spaniards invaded Mexico; illustrations by Greg Ruhl; diagrams and maps by Jack McMaster; historical consultation by Eduardo Matos Moctezuma. Hyperion Bks. for Children 1998 48p il maps (I was there books) $16.95; pa $7.99 (4 and up) **972**
1. Aztecs 2. Mexico—History
ISBN 0-7868-0441-6; 0-7868-1542-6 (pa)
          LC 98-10986
"A Hyperion/Madison Press book"
Uses the discovery of the temple in Mexico City, what was the Aztec city of Tenochtitlan, to introduce the story of the Spanish conquest of Moctezuma and his empire in the sixteenth century
"Lavishly illustrated with full-color photos, period artwork, and dramatic full-page paintings, the book is handsome and eye-catching." SLJ
Includes glossary and bibliographical references

972.81   Guatemala

Sheehan, Sean, 1951-
Guatemala. Benchmark Bks. 1998 128p il maps (Cultures of the world) lib bdg $37.07 (5 and up) **972.81**
1. Guatemala
ISBN 0-7614-0812-6   LC 97-44619
Introduces the geography, history, religion, government, economy, and culture of one of the poorest countries in the western hemisphere
"A good-quality full-color photograph, reproduction, or map appears on most pages. This {is a} solid volume." SLJ
Includes glossary and bibliographical references

972.82   Belize

Jermyn, Leslie
Belize. Reference ed. Benchmark Bks. 2001 128p il map (Cultures of the world) lib bdg $37.07 (5 and up) **972.82**
1. Belize
ISBN 0-7614-1190-9   LC 00-65699
This offers "information on the geography, history, government, lifestyles, religion, festivals, arts, and contemporary life in {Belize}. . . . The concise writing offers enough material for report writers without overwhelming them." SLJ
Includes glossary and bibliographical references

Shields, Charles J., 1951-
Belize. Mason Crest Pubs. 2003 63p il map (Discovering Central America) lib bdg $19.95 (4 and up) **972.82**
1. Belize
ISBN 1-59084-092-5   LC 2002-8937
Contents: A warm, sultry land cooled by sea breezes; A history different from the rest of Central America; Careful land use strengthens the economy; A mosaic of backgrounds and languages; Communities and cultures clustered by districts; A calendar of Belizean festivals; Recipes
This describes the history, geography, and culture of Belize
"Tailored for the quick research needs of students, the . . . [title presents its] information smoothly and in well-organized fashion." Booklist
Includes glossary and bibliographical references

972.83   Honduras

McGaffey, Leta
Honduras. Benchmark Bks. 1999 128p il maps (Cultures of the world) lib bdg $37.07 (5 and up) **972.83**
1. Honduras
ISBN 0-7614-0955-6   LC 98-54908
This is a look at the Central American nation. "Following introductory chapters on the geography, history, and government, the clearly written book focuses on contemporary life. The economy, population, religion, leisure activities, holidays, indigenous and ethnic groups, and rural and urban lifestyles are all covered. . . . A quality, full-color photograph appears on almost every page." SLJ
Includes glossary and bibliographical references

Shields, Charles J., 1951-
Honduras. Mason Crest Pubs. 2003 63p il map (Discovering Central America) lib bdg $19.95 (4 and up) **972.83**
1. Honduras
ISBN 1-59084-096-8   LC 2002-9089
Contents: Honduras, the knee of Central America; Honduras becomes the "Banana Republic"; A fragile economy; The people of Honduras; Language, religion, and home life; A calendar of Honduran festivals; Recipes

Shields, Charles J., 1951-—*Continued*
This describes the history, geography, and culture of Honduras
This is "jam-packed with useful information. . . . [It contains] straightforward writing, clearly titled chapters, high quality color, and well-captioned photographs and graphics." Libr Media Connect
Includes glossary and bibliographical references

972.86   Costa Rica

Foley, Erin, 1967-
Costa Rica. Benchmark Bks. 1997 128p il maps (Cultures of the world) lib bdg $37.07 (5 and up)
972.86
1. Costa Rica
ISBN 0-7614-0285-3   LC 96-17309
Surveys the geography, history, government, and culture of the oldest democracy in Latin America
Includes glossary and bibliographical references

Morrison, Marion
Costa Rica. Children's Press 1998 144p il maps (Enchantment of the world, second series) lib bdg $35 (4 and up)
972.86
1. Costa Rica
ISBN 0-516-20469-6   LC 97-40665
Describes the geography, history, culture, religion, and people of the small Central American nation of Costa Rica
Includes bibliographical references

972.87   Panama

DuTemple, Lesley A., 1952-
The Panama Canal. Lerner Publs. 2003 96p il maps (Great building feats) lib bdg $27.93
972.87
1. Panama Canal
ISBN 0-8225-0079-5   LC 2001-4656
Contents: The path between two oceans; The United States and Panama; One canal, three engineers; Culebra cut; Taming the Chagres; Sculpting bays and building locks; The Panama Canal
A history of the building of the Panama Canal, with emphasis on the difficulties of digging a canal where some engineers said it could not be done
"The text is peppered with quotes from letters, speeches, and diaries of those involved in the project. . . . Sidebars present interesting asides. . . . A fascinating and well-documented blend of history and engineering." SLJ
Includes bibliographical references

Winkelman, Barbara Gaines
The Panama Canal. Children's Press 1999 30p il (Cornerstones of freedom) lib bdg $21; pa $5.95
972.87
1. Panama Canal
ISBN 0-516-21142-0 (lib bdg); 0-516-26460-5 (pa)
LC 98-3493

Relates the history of how the Panama Canal was built and studies the economic and political consequences of its construction
This title "is straightforward and well organized. . . . Relevant photographs, two excellent if simple maps, and a time line add to readers' understanding as well as to the attractiveness of this package." SLJ
Includes glossary and bibliographical references

972.9   West Indies and Bermuda

Anthony, Suzanne
West Indies. Chelsea House 1999 127p il maps (Major world nations) $23.95
972.9
1. West Indies
ISBN 0-7910-4772-5   LC 88-30434
An overview of the history, geography, economy, government, people, and culture of the West Indies
Includes glossary

972.91   Cuba

Castro's Cuba; Charles W. Carey Jr., book editor. Greenhaven Press 2004 205p il (History firsthand) $37.95; pa $23.70 (7 and up)
972.91
1. Castro, Fidel, 1926- 2. Cuba
ISBN 0-7377-1654-1; 0-7377-1655-X (pa)
LC 2003-47286
"Through the use of interviews, articles, and first-person narratives, this book focuses on the significance of the 1959 revolution and its aftermath. An extensive introduction explaining events precipitating the rise of Fidel Castro, the revolution, and the current situation in Cuba provides readers with a necessary overview to understand the succeeding chapters." SLJ
Includes bibliographical references

972.92   Jamaica and Cayman Islands

Sheehan, Sean, 1951-
Jamaica; [by] Sean Sheehan & Angela Black. 2nd ed. Benchmark Books 2004 144p il map (Cultures of the world) lib bdg $37.07 (5 and up)
972.92
1. Jamaica
ISBN 0-7614-1785-0   LC 2004-7676
First published 1996
Explores the geography, history, government, economy, and culture of Jamaica.
"An informative book with captivating pictures, a visually attractive layout, and flowing text. . . .A well-balanced and interesting look at one country's culture." SLJ
Includes glossary and bibliographical references

972.96 Bahama Islands

Barlas, Robert
Bahamas. Benchmark Bks. 2000 128p il map
(Cultures of the world) lib bdg $37.07 (5 and up)
972.96
1. Bahamas
ISBN 0-7614-0992-0   LC 99-88028
Introduces the geography, history, government, economy, religion, language, arts, leisure activities, festivals, food, and people of this archipelago lying in the Atlantic Ocean off the coast of Florida
Includes bibliographical references

972.98 Windward and other southern islands

Elias, Marie Louise
Barbados. Benchmark Bks. 2000 128p il map
(Cultures of the world) lib bdg $37.07 (5 and up)
972.98
1. Barbados
ISBN 0-7614-0976-9   LC 99-27594
Discusses the geography, history, government, economy, people, and culture of Barbados, a small island nation in the Caribbean
Includes glossary and bibliographical references

Pang, Guek-Cheng, 1950-
Grenada. Benchmark Bks. 2001 128p il map
(Cultures of the world) lib bdg $37.07 (5 and up)
972.98
1. Grenada
ISBN 0-7614-1160-7   LC 00-47583
Discusses the geography, history, government, economy, and culture of this Caribbean island country
Includes glossary and bibliographical references

972.983 Trinidad and Tobago

Sheehan, Sean, 1951-
Trinidad & Tobago. Benchmark Bks. 2001 128p il maps (Cultures of the world) lib bdg $37.07 (5 and up)
972.983
1. Trinidad and Tobago
ISBN 0-7614-1194-1   LC 00-47457
This describes the geography, history, economy, government, environment, and culture of Trinidad and Tobago
"The exuberance of the many different ethnic groups shines out of the photographs." Horn Book Guide
Includes glossary and bibliographical references

973 United States

America the beautiful, second series. Children's Press 1998-2001 53v il map ea $32 lib bdg ea $35 (5 and up)
973
1. United States
Also available online version
Replaces titles in the original series published 1987-1992
Contents: Alabama, by L. Davis; Alaska, by D. Walsh Shepherd; Arizona by J. F. Blashfield; Arkansas by S. McNair; California, by A. Heinrichs; Colorado, by J. F. Blashfield; Connecticut, by S. McNair; Delaware by J. F. Blashfield; Florida, by A. Heinrichs; Georgia, by N. Robinson Masters; Hawaii, by M. Hintz; Idaho by L. & C. George; Illinois, by A. Santella; Indiana, by A. Heinrichs; Iowa, by M. Hintz; Kansas, by N. Robinson Masters; Kentucky, by R. C. Stein; Louisiana, by M. Hintz; Maine, by D. Kent; Maryland by M. Burgan; Massachusetts, by S. McNair; Michigan, by M. Hintz; Minnesota, by M. Hintz; Mississippi, by C. George; Missouri, by M. Hintz; Nebraska, by S. McNair; Nevada, by R. C. Stein; New Hampshire by R. Stein; New Jersey, by R. C. Stein; New Mexico, by D. Kent; New York, by A. Heinrichs; North Carolina, by M. Hintz; North Dakota by M. Hintz; Ohio, by A. Heinrichs; Oklahoma, by J. Reedy; Oregon, by S. Ingram; Pennsylvania by A. Heinrichs; Puerto Rico, by L. Davis; Rhode Island, by S. McNair; South Carolina, by R. C. Stein; Tennessee by D. Kent; Texas, by A. Heinrichs; U. S. Territories by S. McNair; Utah by D. Kent; Vermont by A. Heinrichs; Virginia, by J. F. Blashfield; Washington by J. F. Blashfield; Washington, D.C., by R. C. Stein; Wisconsin, by J. F. Blashfield; Wyoming by D. Kent
"Several chapters on the history of the state begin each book; sections on geography, government and politics, the economy, diversity of the population, education, arts and leisure, famous citizens, and museums and historical sites follow." SLJ
These books "are solid purchases for many libraries. They feature clear, lively writing with considerable amounts of information. . . , Maps are a particularly strong feature." Booklist

American history on file; George Ochoa and Melinda Corey, editors. Facts on File 2002 2v unp il set $297
973
1. United States—History
ISBN 0-8160-4661-1   LC 2002-1673
Also available CD-ROM version
This includes maps, timelines, illustrations and text divided into ten eras of United States history, which may be reproduced for classroom use.
Includes bibliographical references

The **American** scene: events. Grolier Educ. 1999 9v il set $299
973
1. United States—History
ISBN 0-7172-9448-X   LC 98-44206
v1 Before independence, to 1775; v2 A new nation emerges, 1776-1828; v3 Growth and conflicts, 1829-1862; v4 Civil War and its aftermath, 1863-1890; v5 Rise to world power, 1891-1917; v6 World War I and the Depression, 1918-1941; v7 World War II and the Cold War, 1942-1958; v8 Superpower, 1959-1982; v9 America today, 1983-
"This set features chronologically arranged one-page entries that focus on a single event, year, person, or group in American history. . . . Each page includes a fact box providing who, what, when, and where information; two-to-three paragraphs of text; a full-color or

The American scene: events—*Continued*
black-and-white photo, reproduction, or drawing; a small, captioned map; and a 'Did you know . . .' fun fact. Information is accurate and objective and minorities and women are well represented." SLJ

The **Blackbirch** kid's visual reference of the United States; by the editors of Blackbirch Press; maps, charts, and graphs by Bob Italiano. Blackbirch Press 2003 336p il maps $49.94 (4 and up) **973**
1. United States
ISBN 1-56711-659-0   LC 2002-4239
An alphabetical presentation of brief statistics and pictorial information about each of the United States, as well as U.S. territories and possessions
"This colorful, fact-filled work will be an ideal addition to elementary and middle school libraries as well as children's reference collections in public libraries." Am Ref Books Annu, 2003

Bornstein, Jerry
An American chronology. Neal-Schuman 2000 303p pa $75 **973**
1. United States—Civilization—Chronology
ISBN 1-55570-369-0   LC 99-56396
"Some 119 lists are arranged in several parts, covering key events in national and state history, politics, and the military, as well as major disasters. The final section, "Notably American," details award winners, Miss Americas, sports championships, and other claims to fame. Depending upon the list, a typical entry can be from one sentence to a paragraph in length. . . . Bornstein's book has some unique features, including the chronologies of the history of each state, and is recommended for libraries wanting to add another year-by-year outline of aspects of American life." Booklist
Includes bibliographical references

Brownstone, David M.
The young nation: America 1787-1861; [by] David M. Brownstone, Irene M. Franck. Grolier Educ. 2002 10v il maps set $339 **973**
1. United States—History—1783-1865
ISBN 0-7172-5645-6   LC 2002-20047
Contents: v1 A new nation; v2 The early years; v3 The way West; v4 Beyond the Mississippi; v5 Slavery and the coming storm; v6 The new Americans; v7 Women's lives, women's rights; v8 Science, technology, and everyday life; v9 The arts, literature, religion, and education; v10 A growing nation
This "set covers American history during the period beginning with the Constitution and ending with the Civil War. . . . A handsome layout and many excellent pictures, most in full color, give the books an inviting look. The illustrations include many period paintings and engravings as well as maps, documents, and photos of historic sites and reenactments of events." Booklist

Celebrate the states. Benchmark Bks. 1996-2001 52v il maps music lib bdg ea $37.07 (5 and up) **973**

1. United States
Contents: Alabama, by D. Shirley; Alaska, by R. Stefoff; Arkansas, by L. Altman; Arizona, by M. McDaniel; California, by L. Altman; Colorado, by E. H. Ayer; Connecticut, by V. Sherrow; Delaware, by M. Schuman; Florida, by P. Chang; Georgia, by S. Otfinoski; Hawaii, by J. Goldberg; Idaho, by R. Steffof; Illinois, by M. T. Brill; Indiana, by M. T. Brill; Iowa, by P. Morice; Kansas, by R. Bjorkland; Kentucky, by T. Barrett; Louisiana, by S. LeVert; Maine, by M. Dornfeld; Maryland, by L. Pietrzyk; Massachusetts, by S. LeVert; Michigan, by M. T. Brill; Minnesota, by M. Schwabacher; Mississippi, by D. Shirley; Missouri, by M. Bennett; Montana by G. Bennett; Nebraska by R. Bjorklund; Nevada by R. Stefoff; New Hampshire, by S. Otfinoski; New Jersey, by W. Moragne; New Mexico, by M. McDaniel; New York, by V. Schomp; North Carolina, by D. Shirley; North Dakota by M. McDaniel; Ohio, by V. Sherrow; Oklahoma, by G. Baldwin; Oregon, by R. Stefoff; Pennsylvania, by S. Peters; Puerto Rico by M. Schwabacher; Rhode Island, by T. Klein; South Carolina, by N. Hoffman; South Dakota, by M. McDaniel; Tennessee, by T. Barrett; Texas, by C. Bredeson; Utah, by R. Steffof; Vermont, by D. Elish; Virginia, by T. Barrett; Washington, by R. Steffof; Washington, D.C., by D. Elish; West Virginia, by N. Hoffman; Wisconsin, by K. Zeinert; Wyoming by G. Baldwin
"These books each contain six chapters devoted to the state's geography, history, government and economy, people, achievements, and landmarks. A section of reference facts and figures is also included. Competently written, the books serve as attractive and accessible introductions to the . . . states." Horn Book Guide

Facts about the states; editors, Joseph Nathan Kane, Janet Podell, Steven Anzovin. 2nd ed. Wilson, H.W. 1994 c1993 624p il $100
973
1. United States—Local history 2. State governments
ISBN 0-8242-0849-8   LC 93-30328
First published 1989
Provides geographic, demographic, economic, political, and cultural facts about the fifty states, Puerto Rico, and the District of Columbia. Part I presents state entries in alphabetical order. Part II provides comparative tables that rank states in categories such as population, geography, education, and finance

Greenberg, Judith E.
Young people's letters to the president. Watts 1998 96p il (In their own voices) $24
973
1. Presidents—United States 2. Children—United States 3. United States—Politics and government—20th century
ISBN 0-531-11435-X   LC 97-51202
A selection of letters written to United States presidents by young people is accompanied by information providing historical context for the writers' concerns and ideas
"This is a worthwhile purchase for those interested in a look at letters to presidents over time." SLJ
Includes bibliographical references

Hakim, Joy
A history of US. 3rd ed. Oxford University Press 2003 11v il map set $219.45; pa $175.45 (5 and up) **973**
1. United States—History
ISBN 0-19-515256-8; 0-19-515259-X (pa)
LC 2002-25169
First published 1993-1995
Contents: bk 1 The first Americans; bk 2 Making thirteen colonies; bk 3 From colonies to country; bk 4 The new nation; bk 5 Liberty for all?; bk 6 War, terrible war; bk 7 Reconstructing America; bk 8 An age of extremes; bk 9 War, peace, and all that jazz; bk 10 All the people; bk 11 Sourcebook and index
Presents the history of America from the earliest times of the Native Americans to the administration of George W. Bush
Includes bibliographical references

Hoose, Phillip M., 1947-
We were there, too! young people in U.S. history; {by} Phillip Hoose. Farrar, Straus & Giroux 2001 264p il $28 (5 and up) **973**
1. United States—History 2. Children 3. Youth
ISBN 0-374 38252-2
LC 99-89052
"Melanie Kroupa books"
Biographies of dozens of young people who made a mark in American history, including explorers, planters, spies, cowpunchers, sweatshop workers, and civil rights workers
"A treasure chest of history come to life, this is an inspired collection. . . . Because the book is packed with historical documents, evocatively illustrated . . . and full of eyewitness quotations, it should prove valuable to young historians and researchers." SLJ
Includes bibliographical references

Johnston, Robert D. (Robert Dougall)
The making of America; the history of the United States from 1492 to the present; with a foreword by Laura Bush. National Geographic Soc. 2002 240p il maps $29.95 (5 and up) **973**
1. United States—History
ISBN 0-7922-6944-6
LC 2002-4825
Contents: A new world from many old worlds: beginnings to 1763; A revolutionary age: 1763-1789; The new republic: 1789-1848; A new birth of freedom: Civil War and Reconstruction, 1848-1877; Industry and empire: 1876-1900; Progressivism and the New Deal, 1900-1941; War, prosperity, and social change: 1941-1968; The age of conservatism: 1969-present
This is a "narrative of American history from Columbus through the terrorist attacks on Sept. 11, 2001." Libr Media Connect
"Johnston takes on an enormous, complex topic and presents an excellent overview for young people. . . . This well-written book does a particularly good job of balancing political and social history." Booklist
Includes bibliographical references

Junior state maps on file. Facts on File 2002 unp il loose-leaf $185 (4 and up) **973**

1. United States—Maps
ISBN 0-8160-4752-9
Also available CD-ROM version
"This title offers more than 400 reproducible state maps and fact sheets in a looseleaf, three-ring binder format. . . . After a general section on the United States and its regions, the maps are arranged by geographic region. . . . Five maps and a fact sheet are provided for each state: major cities, outline map, physical features, industry, agriculture and state facts and flag. . . . This is an excellent U.S. geography resource for school and public libraries that do not subscribe to the online version." Am Ref Books Annu, 2003

Leacock, Elspeth, 1946-
Journeys in time; a new atlas of American history; {by} Elspeth Leacock and Susan Buckley; illustrations by Rodica Prato. Houghton Mifflin 2001 48p il maps $15; pa $6.95 (4 and up) **973**
1. United States—History 2. United States—Historical geography
ISBN 0-395-97956-0; 0-618-31114-9 (pa)
LC 00-40803
Each double-page spread of this book "takes an individual who was part of a historic movement (such as the Underground Railroad or immigration) and gives a brief narrative outlining his or her circumstances. Added to the text are sequential numbers that indicate major events in each of the twenty journeys. A double-page location map traces the routes each took, using illustrative vignettes marked with corresponding numbers that reference the text." Horn Book

Monuments and historic places of America. Macmillan Lib. Ref. USA 2000 513p (Macmillan profiles) $95 **973**
1. Historic sites 2. National monuments 3. United States—Local history
ISBN 0-02-865374-2
LC 99-51559
More than ninety articles describe monuments and memorials that commemorate people and events from our nation's history as well as battlefields, forts, factories, homes, churches, cemeteries, and laboratories
"This work is timely and well thought out and should be a welcome addition to any school or public library." Booklist

Moss, Joyce, 1951-
Profiles in American history; significant events and the people who shaped them; {by} Joyce Moss and George Wilson. U.X.L 1994 8v il maps set $390 **973**
1. United States—History 2. United States—Biography
ISBN 0-8103-9207-0
Contents: v1 Exploration to Revolution; v2 Constitutional convention to the War of 1812; v3 Indian removal to the antislavery movement; v4 Westward movement to the Civil War; v5 Reconstruction to the Spanish-American War; v6 Immigration to women's rights and roles; v7 Great Depression to the Cuban Missile Crisis; v8 Civil rights movement to the present

Moss, Joyce, 1951——_Continued_

"Each volume encompasses a specific time period, focusing on 5 to 7 events and 20 people who helped shape those events. . . . While biographical information on most of the subjects is available elsewhere, the vocabulary, simple explanation of events, and obvious interrelation of people and events make this a good source for middle-school libraries or high schools needing material for lower-level students." Booklist

Our country's founders; a book of advice for young people; edited with commentary by William J. Bennett. Simon & Schuster 1998 314p il pa $10 hardcover o.p. (7 and up)
                                                                    973
1. United States—History—Sources 2. Social ethics
ISBN 0-689-84469-7 (pa)   LC 98-6592
Based on: Our sacred honor (1997)
A book of advice from our nation's founders on how to be a good citizen and a worthy member of civil society
Bennett "draws on a wide variety of primary, secondary, and tertiary sources, ranging from the love letters of John and Abigail Adams to Mason Weems' apocryphal tale of George Washington and the cherry tree. Few young adults are likely to pick this up on their own, but teachers will find it a valuable resource." Booklist
Includes bibliographical references

Sandler, Martin W.

America's great disasters; by Martin W. Sandler. HarperCollins Pubs. 2003 95p il $17.99; lib bdg $18.89   **973**
1. Disasters 2. United States—History
ISBN 0-06-029107-9; 0-06-029108-7 (lib bdg)
                                           LC 2001-39218
Examines the causes and effects of such American disasters as the sinking of the steamboat Sultana in 1871, the Johnstown Flood, the Dust Bowl, the influenza epidemic of 1918-1919, and the Exxon Valdez oil spill
"Dramatic material, archival photographs, and an accessible text combine to create an appealing title." SLJ
Includes bibliographical references

Vaqueros; America's first cowmen. Holt & Co. 2001 117p il map $17.95   **973**
1. Mexican Americans 2. Cowhands
ISBN 0-8050-6019-7   LC 00-24285
"Sandler details the vaqueros' responsibilities and retells some of the stories they told. He also discusses the beginning of cowboy lore. A final chapter covers cowboy and ranch life today, focusing on Hispanics. A lively narrative, fascinating information, solid research, and black-and-white historic prints and contemporary photographs combine to make this both enjoyable reading and a good source of fact." Booklist
Includes glossary and bibliographical references

973.03   United States--History-- Encyclopedias and dictionaries

The **American** Heritage encyclopedia of American history; general editor, John Mack Faragher. Holt & Co. 1998 1106p il $45   **973.03**
1. United States—History—Encyclopedias
ISBN 0-8050-4438-8   LC 97-19097
Covering American history from pre-Columbian times to the 1990s this reference comprises some 3000 entries each averaging "about a paragraph, with broader topics covered in several paragraphs. Most entries have See references, and larger subjects conclude with a bibliography. State entries have a chronology detailing their exploration and development." Libr J
Includes bibliographical references

English, June, 1955-
Scholastic encyclopedia of the United States at war; {by} June A. English, Thomas D. Jones. Scholastic Ref. 1998 188p il maps $18.95; pa $8.95   **973.03**
1. United States—Military history—Encyclopedias
ISBN 0-590-59959-3; 0-439-59229-1 (pa)
                                           LC 97-46492
Discusses all of the major wars in which the United States has participated beginning with the American Revolution and concluding with the Gulf War of 1991
"The use of color throughout the book is especially effective in keeping readers focused on the different areas under discussion. This would be a good choice for middle school students." Book Rep

Junior Worldmark encyclopedia of the states; {Timothy L. Gall and Susan Bevan Gall, editors}. 4th ed. UXL 2004 4v .p il map set $195   **973.03**
1. United States—Encyclopedias
ISBN 0-7876-9197-6   LC 2004-8306
First published 1996
Contents: v1 Alabama to Illinois; v2 Indiana to Nebraska; v3 Nevada to South Dakota; v4 Tennessee to Wyoming, Washington D.C., Puerto Rico, U.S. Pacific and Caribbean dependencies, and U.S. overview, cumulative index
"Each entry begins with an introductory section of about 20 quick facts such as origin of the name, nickname(s), capital, motto, description of the flag, and title of the state song. There are also small black-and-white line drawings of the seal and flag. . . . Following this introduction is the profile containing 40 numbered subsections with information on topics such as location, topography, population, ethnic groups, religion, arts, communications, and famous people. . . . The entries have been thoughtfully arranged to make them easy to use. The introductory section contains all those quick facts that students need for reports, and the arrangement of the meatier profile sections facilitates comparison between different states." Booklist
Includes bibliographical references

King, David C., 1933-
Children's encyclopedia of American history.
DK Pub. 2003 304p il map $29.99

973.03

1. United States—History—Encyclopedias
ISBN 0-7894-8330-0   LC 2002-73388
Full-color maps, photographs, and paintings illustrate
a comprehensive reference guide to American history
"A visually enticing and textually fascinating survey."
SLJ

Worldmark encyclopedia of the states. Gale Res.
maps set $180   **973.03**
1. United States—Encyclopedias
ISBN 0-7876-7338-2
First published 1981 by Harper & Row (6th edition
2003) Periodically revised
"Comprehensive examination of each state within the
framework of 50 standard subject headings. Includes economic policy, energy and power, resources, education,
the press, famous persons, etc." N Y Public Libr. Ref
Books for Child Collect. 2d edition

973.2   United States--Colonial
period, 1607-1775

Burgan, Michael
Colonial and revolutionary times; a Watts guide;
historical consultant, W. Guthrie Sayen. Watts
2003 144p il map lib bdg $40 (5 and up)

973.2

1. United States—History—1600-1775, Colonial period 2. United States—History—1775-1783, Revolution
ISBN 0-531-15453-X   LC 2002-27029
A guide to the major people, places, ideas, and events
of colonial and revolutionary times
"Sidebars highlight interesting anecdotes and personalities, and offer other supplements to the readable text.
Excellent-quality, color photos, diagrams, and reproductions of period prints and documents add to the presentation." SLJ
Includes glossary and bibliographical references

Collier, Christopher, 1930-
The French and Indian War, 1660-1763; {by}
Christopher Collier, James Lincoln Collier.
Benchmark Bks. (Tarrytown) 1998 94p il maps
(Drama of American history) lib bdg $31.36

973.2

1. United States—History—1755-1763, French and Indian War 2. United States—History—1600-1775, Colonial period
ISBN 0-7614-0439-2   LC 96-44063
This volume "explains what was happening in Europe
as well as in North America during the conflict, giving
the broad perspective necessary for understanding the
events." Booklist
Includes bibliographical references

Colonial America. Grolier Educ. 1998 10v il set
$359 (4 and up)   **973.2**
1. United States—History—1600-1775, Colonial period
ISBN 0-7172-9193-6   LC 97-44595

Contents: v1 Arcadia-Byrd II, William; v2 Cabot-
Detroit; v3 Disease-Games and sports; v4 George III-
Indentured servants; v5 Indigo-Marquette, Jacques; v6
Marriage-Navigation acts; v7 New France-Pennsylvania;
v8 Philadelphia-Revere; v9 Rhode Island-Stamp Act; v10
Stono Rebellion-Zenger
"Topics and items related to Colonial America are ar-
ranged alphabetically throughout this set. . . . The more
than 250 entries are generally one to six pages long. . . .
The numerous illustrations include photographs, draw-
ings, diagrams, and maps—all fully captioned, many in
color." Booklist
"An accessible, eye-catching, and valuable resource."
SLJ
Includes bibliographical references

Gray, Edward G., 1964-
Colonial America: a history in documents.
Oxford Univ. Press 2003 191p il maps (Pages
from history) lib bdg $36.95 (7 and up)

973.2

1. United States—History—1600-1775, Colonial period
ISBN 0-19-513747-7   LC 2002-4285
Contents: England expands; New lands, new lives;
Colonists confront first nations; Who built the colonies?;
Ties that bind; A spiritual people; Gentle women and
gentle men, A world of things
This title "presents excerpts from printed and pictorial
primary sources that together form a compact portrait of
the Colonial era in America from the late 15th century
through 1763. . . . Each chapter begins with concise introductory remarks that create a clear context for the
lists, letters, drawings, maps, portraits, ads, diagrams,
news stories, diary entries, poems, and other documentation that follow. . . . A fine source for reports about this
period." SLJ
Includes bibliographical references

Howarth, Sarah
Colonial places. Millbrook Press 1994 46p il
(People and places) lib bdg $22.90 (4 and up)

973.2

1. United States—Social life and customs—1600-1775,
Colonial period
ISBN 1-56294-513-0   LC 94-25754
This "describes several sites around which life in early
America revolved, including the governor's house, the
meetinghouse, the tobacco field, the church, the post office, the harbor, and the fort. . . . Topics {are} presented
in short, well-outlined chapters. Large print and numerous photographic reproductions and drawings (some in
color) add to the . . . appeal. Chapters also include quotations from period writings." Booklist
Includes glossary and bibliographical references

Saari, Peggy
Colonial America: almanac. U.X.L 2000 2v set
$110   **973.2**
1. Almanacs 2. United States—History—1600-1775,
Colonial period
ISBN 0-7876-3763-7   LC 99-39081

Saari, Peggy—*Continued*
Examines the colonial period in America, discussing both the Native American culture before the arrival of Europeans and the exploration and settlement of different parts of the New World

Colonial America: primary sources; Julie Carnagie, editor. U.X.L 1999 297p il $60
973.2
1. United States—History—1600-1775, Colonial period
ISBN 0-7876-3766-1   LC 99-34460
Presents the historical events and social issues of colonial America through twenty-four primary documents, including diary entries, poems, and personal narratives
"Each chapter adds helpful material before and after the excerpt to explain its importance. Illustrations and sidebars are used in this volume also, and difficult words are defined." Booklist

Sakurai, Gail, 1952-
The Thirteen Colonies. Children's Press 2000 30p il map (Cornerstones of freedom) lib bdg $21; pa $5.95
973.2
1. United States—History—1600-1775, Colonial period
ISBN 0-516-21603-1 (lib bdg); 0-516-27091-5 (pa)
LC 99-53533
Includes index
Describes the history of the thirteen original English colonies in America, including their early exploration, settlement, and regional differences

Stefoff, Rebecca, 1951-
Colonial life. Benchmark Bks. 2003 119p il maps (American voices from—) lib bdg $32.79
973.2
1. United States—History—1600-1775, Colonial period
ISBN 0-7614-1205-0   LC 2002-3223
Presents the history of the British colonies in North America, beginning with the Jamestown settlement, through excerpts from letters, pamphlets, journal entries, and other documents of the time
Includes glossary and bibliographical references

973.3   United States--Periods of Revolution and Confederation, 1775-1789

American Revolution: battles and leaders; Aaron R. Murray, editor. DK Pub. 2004 96p il map $19.99; pa $12.99
973.3
1. United States—History—1775-1783, Revolution
ISBN 0-7894-9888-x; 0-7894-9889-8 (pa)
LC 2004-298941
This "shows and tells readers where the key battles took place, what happened during the clashes, and who the main figures were in the struggle for independence from England." Publisher's note
This is "filled with great information and statistics that are not always immediately available. . . . Attractively placed color spot art, thumbnail-sized portraits, small maps showing troop movements, vintage photos, and helpful pull-quotes comprise half of each well-designed spread." Booklist

American Revolution: primary sources; {compiled by} Linda Schmittroth; Lawrence W. Baker and Stacy A. McConnell, editors. U.X.L 2000 xxxiii, 264p il lib bdg $60 (5 and up)
973.3
1. United States—History—1775-1783, Revolution
ISBN 0-7876-3790-4   LC 99-46940
This volume "presents 32 excerpted documents, beginning with the 1765 Stamp Act and ending with Washington's farewell address to the Continental Army in 1783. Each entry has helpful material to give the context for the document. The adjoining margins contain definitions of terms that may be unfamiliar. . . . {This volume} is attractive and easy to use." Booklist
Includes bibliographical references

The **American** revolutionaries: a history in their own words, 1750-1800; edited by Milton Meltzer. Crowell 1987 210p il hardcover o.p. paperback available $6.95 (6 and up)
973.3
1. United States—History—1775-1783, Revolution
2. United States—History—1755-1763, French and Indian War
ISBN 0-06-446145-9   LC 86-47846
"Meltzer has assembled a collage of eyewitness accounts, speech and diary excerpts, letters, and other documents for a chronological account of the half century that included the American Revolution. . . . The voices of women who accompanied the troops and of blacks who fought with the army are both represented." Bull Cent Child Books

Beller, Susan Provost, 1949-
The Revolutionary War. Benchmark Bks. 2002 c2003 104p il maps (American voices from—) lib bdg $32.79
973.3
1. United States—History—1775-1783, Revolution
ISBN 0-7614-1202-6   LC 2001-8741
Contents: The road to independence: the British and loyalists speak; The road to independence: the colonists speak; To be a soldier; On the battlefield; Women on the home front: sacrifice and service; On the world stage; To pay the price; Victory and defeat
Presents the history of the American Revolution through excerpts from letters, newspaper articles, journal entries, and laws of the time
Includes glossary and bibliographical references

Bigelow, Barbara Carlisle
American Revolution: almanac; {by} Barbara Bigelow and Linda Schmittroth; Stacy A. McConnell, editor. U.X.L 2000 xxxiii, 188, xxxv-xlip il map lib bdg $60 (5 and up)
973.3
1. Almanacs 2. United States—History—1775-1783, Revolution
ISBN 0-7876-3795-5   LC 99-46939

Bigelow, Barbara Carlisle—*Continued*

Provides in-depth background and interpretation of the American Revolution, with short biographies of people relevant to the topics discussed in each chapter

"Illustrations, sidebars, a time line, glossary, and activity ideas enhance the value of the volume." Booklist

Includes bibliographical references and index

Bobrick, Benson, 1947-

Fight for freedom; the American Revolutionary War. Atheneum Books for Young Readers 2004 96p il map $22.95 (5 and up)   **973.3**

1. United States—History—1775-1783, Revolution

ISBN 0-689-86422-1   LC 2003-25548

"This large-format volume profiles significant individuals and discusses the progress of the Revolutionary War. . . . Printed in color, most of the illustrations are period paintings and prints. . . . Students will find the book a well-organized and clearly written introduction to the war." Booklist

Includes glossary and bibliographical references

Bohannon, Lisa Frederiksen

The American Revolution; Lisa Fredcriksen Bohannon. Lerner Publications Co 2004 88p il (Chronicle of America's wars) lib bdg $27.23 (5 and up)   **973.3**

1. United States—History—1775-1783, Revolution

ISBN 0-8225-4717-1   LC 2002-10036

Chronicles the American Revolution, including the causes, strategies, and characters of the war, both famous and lesser-known.

"The clear, well-written text is enhanced with black-and-white and sepia reproductions and woodcuts, eyewitness quotes, and sidebars." SLJ

Includes bibliographical references

Brenner, Barbara, 1925-

If you were there in 1776. Bradbury Press 1994 136p il $17.95 (4 and up)   **973.3**

1. United States. Declaration of Independence 2. United States—Social life and customs

ISBN 0-02-712322-7   LC 93-24060

Demonstrates how the concepts and principles expressed in the Declaration of Independence were drawn from the experiences of living in America in the late eighteenth century, with emphasis given to how children lived on a New England farm, a Southern plantation, and the frontier

"The author's inclusion of details of how peoples' lives began to change as a result of the Revolution and her accessible style are the selling points here. Both budding historians and report writers will find this title worth their time." SLJ

Includes bibliographical references

Collier, Christopher, 1930-

The American Revolution, 1763-1783; {by} Christopher Collier, James Lincoln Collier. Benchmark Bks. (Tarrytown) 1998 95p il maps (Drama of American history) lib bdg $31.36   **973.3**

1. United States—History—1775-1783, Revolution

ISBN 0-7614-0440-6   LC 96-45440

Examines the people and events involved in the significant war by which the thirteen original colonies broke away from England

Includes bibliographical references

Cox, Clinton

Come all you brave soldiers; blacks in the Revolutionary War. Scholastic 1999 182p il $15.95; pa $4.99 (6 and up)   **973.3**

1. African American soldiers 2. United States—History—1775-1783, Revolution

ISBN 0-590-47576-2; 0-590-47577-0 (pa)

LC 97-44198

"An interesting and informative survey. . . . Black-and-white reproductions of period prints, documents, and paintings are included." SLJ

Includes bibliographical references

Ferrie, Richard

The world turned upside down; George Washington and the Battle of Yorktown. Holiday House 1999 168p il map $18.95 (5 and up)   **973.3**

1. Washington, George, 1732-1799 2. Yorktown (Va.)—History—Siege, 1781

ISBN 0-8234-1402-7   LC 98-19574

This examination of the events surrounding the pivotal Revolutionary War battle that led to the defeat of the British forces at Yorktown, Virginia, focuses on the central role of General George Washington

An "exemplary and readable history. . . . The text is engrossing, the format inviting, the facts accurate, and the illustrative material—maps, photographs, and reproductions—informative." Horn Book

Includes bibliographical references

The **Founding** of America; Leora Maltz, book editor. Greenhaven Press 2002 236p il (Great speeches in history series) lib bdg $34.95; pa $23.70   **973.3**

1. American speeches 2. United States—Politics and government

ISBN 0-7377-0871-9 (lib bdg); 0-7377-0870-0 (pa)

LC 2001-40736

This collection of American speeches from the late 18th and early 19th centuries includes an introductory essay, introductions to each speech and an appendix of biographical sketches

Includes bibliographical references

Freedman, Russell
Give me liberty! the story of the Declaration of Independence. Holiday House 2000 90p il $24.95; pa $12.95 (5 and up)   **973.3**
1. United States. Declaration of Independence 2. United States—Politics and government—1775-1783, Revolution
ISBN 0-8234-1448-5; 0-8234-1753-0 (pa)
LC 99-57513
Describes the events leading up to the Declaration of Independence as well as the personalities and politics behind its framing
"Handsomely designed with a generous and thoughtful selection of period art, the book is dramatic and inspiring." Horn Book
Includes bibliographical references

Hull, Mary
The Boston Tea Party in American history. Enslow Pubs. 1999 128p il lib bdg $26.60
    973.3
1. Boston Tea Party, 1773 2. United States—History—1775-1783, Revolution
ISBN 0-7660-1139-9   LC 98-5798
Presents the people and events connected with the dynamic episode called the Boston Tea Party, which helped to spawn the American Revolution
Includes bibliographical references

Jaffe, Steven H.
Who were the founding fathers? two hundred years of reinventing American history. Holt & Co. 1996 227p il $21.95 (7 and up)   **973.3**
1. United States—History—1775-1783, Revolution 2. Historiography
ISBN 0-8050-3102-2   LC 95-42581
"Beginning with the Founding Fathers as seen in their own time, by contemporary reporters and historians, Jaffe shows how we have reinterpreted our early leaders with each new historical era." Book Rep
"The text clips along at a lively pace, accompanied by interesting, seldom-seen archival cartoons and reproductions that illustrate the points. A fine way to encourage critical thinking and get young people to examine the societal values that we all take so much for granted." SLJ
Includes bibliographical references

Lukes, Bonnie L.
The Boston Massacre. Lucent Bks. 1998 111p il (Famous trials) lib bdg $28.70 (7 and up)
    973.3
1. Boston Massacre, 1770
ISBN 1-56006-467-6   LC 97-27445
"This book describes the Boston Massacre of March 5, 1770, as well as the laws, events, and public sentiments leading up to it, and the trials of the British soldiers accused of killing civilians that evening." Booklist
"A well-researched, readable book. Lukes presents a fair and detailed look at the many facets of the Boston Massacre." SLJ
Includes bibliographical references

Miller, Brandon Marie
Growing up in revolution and the new nation, 1775 to 1800. Lerner Publs. 2003 59p il map (Our America) $26.60 (5 and up)   **973.3**
1. United States—History—1775-1783, Revolution 2. United States—Social life and customs 3. Children—United States
ISBN 0-8225-0078-7   LC 2001-4654
Presents details of daily life of American children during the period from 1775 to 1800
The author "does a good job presenting this information by using quotes from primary sources, historical photographs, and artwork from this time period." Libr Media Connect
Includes bibliographical references

Morton, Joseph C.
The American Revolution; Joseph C. Morton. Greenwood Press 2003 218p il map (Greenwood guides to historic events, 1500-1900) $45 (7 and up)   **973.3**
1. United States—History—1775-1783, Revolution
ISBN 0-313-31792-5   LC 2003-40836
This "reference guide includes an overview essay that traces the course of the Revolution and five essays on various aspects of the conflict. Also included are biographical sketches of 19 important historical figures and a selection of primary documents with introductions by the author." Publisher's note
This is a "well-written, concise resource." SLJ
Includes bibliographical references

Murphy, Jim, 1947-
A young patriot; the American Revolution as experienced by one boy. Clarion Bks. 1996 101p il maps $16; pa $7.95 (5 and up)   **973.3**
1. Martin, Joseph Plumb, 1760-1850 2. United States—History—1775-1783, Revolution
ISBN 0-395-60523-7; 0-395-90019-0 (pa)
LC 93-38789
"Using Joseph Plumb Martin's first person account of his participation in the Revolutionary War as primary source material, Murphy intertwines this story of one teenager's life as a soldier with broader information about the Revolution, to put Martin's story in context. The handsome, informative, and fascinating look at American history is illustrated with many period reproductions." Horn Book Guide
Includes bibliographical references

Nardo, Don, 1947-
Weapons of war. Lucent Bks. 2003 128p il maps (American war library, American Revolution) lib bdg $21.96   **973.3**
1. Military weapons 2. United States—History—1775-1783, Revolution
ISBN 1-59018-226-X   LC 2002-7293
"Nardo looks at the various weapons used in the Revolutionary War: muskets, rifles, bayonets, swords, and other types of knives. Later chapters deal with both American and British battle tactics, artillery, ships and naval warfare, spies, and military intelligence. . . . Lib-

Nardo, Don, 1947-—*Continued*
erally illustrated with black-and-white lithographs, a few maps, and some photos of reenactments. Primary-source materials appear in shaded boxes. . . . Thorough, but not overwhelming." SLJ
Includes glossary and bibliographical references

Nash, Gary B.
Landmarks of the American Revolution. Oxford Univ. Press 2003 158p il map (American landmarks) lib bdg $30   **973.3**
1. Historic sites 2. United States—History—1775-1783, Revolution
ISBN 0-19-512849-4   LC 2002-14152
"Published in association with the National Register of Historic Places, National Park Service, and the National Parks Foundation"
Contents: Lexington Green; Independence Hall, Independence National; Valley Forge National Historic Park; Marblehead Historic District; Faneuil Hall; Peyton Randolph House; John and Abigail Adams House, Adams; Johnson Hall; Old Saint Mary's Episcopal Church; Old South Meeting House; Francis Hopkinson House ; Yorktown Battlefield, Colonial National Historic Park
"Written with the idea that historic sites can be considered primary sources, this book skillfully demonstrates the 'power of places.' Traditional documents, such as excerpts from letters, broadsides, and maps, as well as well-placed quotes, are incorporated into the text. The places include churches, halls, homes, and battlefields, covering the many facets of the Revolution: political, religious, and actual battles. . . .This well-organized book includes clear, full-color photographs or reproductions and a small inset map for each site." SLJ
Includes bibliographical references

The **Revolutionary** War. Grolier Educ. 2002 10v il maps set $309   **973.3**
1. United States—History—1775-1783, Revolution
ISBN 0-7172-5553-0   LC 2001-18998
Contents: v1 The road to rebellion; v2 The shot heard around the world; v3 Taking up arms; v4 The spirit of 1776; v5 1777, year of decision; v6 The road to Valley Forge; v7 War of attrition; v8 The American cause in peril; v9 The turn of the tide; v10 An independent nation
This "set provides broad coverage of the American Revolution. Each volume chronicles a specific period, beginning with the causes; moving through the political and military events of the conflict; and ending with the adoption of the Constitution, Washington's presidency, and Westward expansion after the war. The books offer considerable background material and objectively discuss how civilian, governmental, diplomatic, and military actions influenced the course of events. . . . These books provide enough detail to serve researchers, but they are also interesting enough to appeal to general readers." SLJ
Includes bibliographical references

Ross, Stewart
The American Revolution. Watts 2001 62p il maps (Documenting history) $23.50 (7 and up)
                    973.3
1. United States—History—1775-1783, Revolution
ISBN 0-531-14613-8   LC 2001-17575
Includes index

This focuses on the American Revolution through primary source documents including "letters, biographies, autobiographies, speeches, newspapers, and excerpts from government documents and political commentaries. . . . This attractive {book} may encourage browsing and will be especially useful to students looking for information in a brief, inviting format, as well as for those who want a topic review or introduction." Book Rep

Slavicek, Louise Chipley, 1956-
Women of the American Revolution. Lucent Bks. 2003 128p il map (Women in history) lib bdg $27.45 (7 and up)   **973.3**
1. Women—United States—History 2. United States—History—1775-1783, Revolution
ISBN 1-59018-172-7   LC 2002-456
"Well-organized and well written. . . . The print is a good size, and there are lovely, well-chosen black-and-white photographs and lithographs." Booklist
Includes bibliographical references

Stewart, Gail, 1949-
Life of a soldier in Washington's army; by Gail B. Stewart. Lucent Bks. 2003 112p il map (American war library, American Revolution) lib bdg $21.96   **973.3**
1. Soldiers—United States 2. United States—History—1775-1783, Revolution
ISBN 1-59018-215-4   LC 2002-6602
Discusses the training, organization, diversity, fighting and survival skills, daily routine, diseases, fears, and morale of the first army of the United States
This volume is "thorough, but not overwhelming." SLJ
Includes bibliographical references

Whitelaw, Nancy
The shot heard round the world; the battles of Lexington and Concord. Morgan Reynolds 2001 112p il (First battles) lib bdg $21.95
                    973.3
1. Lexington (Mass.), Battle of, 1775 2. Concord (Mass.), Battle of, 1775 3. United States—History—1775-1783, Revolution
ISBN 1-88384-675-7   LC 00-67567
This "overview starts with the Boston Massacre and includes an account of the Tea Party. In addition to describing famous individuals associated with the two battles, a final chapter recounts the experiences of an @ordinary' man connected with the historic events." Horn Book Guide
"This is a clear, well-organized discussion of events in Boston leading up to the American Revolution." Booklist
Includes glossary and bibliographical references

Zeinert, Karen, 1942-2002
Those remarkable women of the revolution. Millbrook Press 1996 96p il lib bdg $30.60 (7 and up)   **973.3**
1. Women—United States—History 2. United States—History—1775-1783, Revolution
ISBN 1-5629-4657-9   LC 95-47609

Zeinert, Karen, 1942-2002—_Continued_

"Zeinert chronicles the many contributions made by women during the Revolutionary War. She describes the role of both patriots and loyalists; black and Indian women; Northern women as well as those on Southern plantations, showing how the war forced them to assume nontraditional roles." SLJ

Students "will be well-served by Zeinert's work. . . . The bibliography, index, and further reading sections make this a helpful resource for students doing more indepth research on a particular woman or event." Voice Youth Advocates

973.4   United States--Constitutional period, 1789-1809

Blumberg, Rhoda, 1917-

What's the deal? Jefferson, Napoleon and the Louisiana Purchase. National Geographic Soc. 1998 144p il maps $18.95 (7 and up)

973.4

1. Napoleon I, Emperor of the French, 1769-1821 2. Jefferson, Thomas, 1743-1826 3. Louisiana Purchase 4. United States—History—1783-1809

ISBN 0-7922-7013-4   LC 97-43679

Discusses the Louisiana Purchase of 1803 and the political maneuverings of Napoleon and Jefferson that made it possible. Includes information on the people involved

"This is a straightforward, well-researched, and smoothly written book of political history." SLJ

Includes bibliographical references

Collier, Christopher, 1930-

Building a new nation; the Federalist era, 1789-1801; {by} Christopher Collier, James Lincoln Collier. Benchmark Bks. 1999 95p il (Drama of American history) $31.36

973.4

1. United States—Politics and government—1783-1809 2. United States—History—1783-1809

ISBN 0-7614-0777-4   LC 97-26491

.

Examines the events and personalities involved in the political development of the United States in the period following the creation of the Constitution

Includes bibliographical references

The Jeffersonian Republicans, 1800-1823; the Louisian Purchase and the War of 1812; {by} Christopher Collier, James Lincoln Collier. Benchmark Bks. (Tarrytown) 1999 93p il map (Drama of American history) $31.36

973.4

1. Republican Party (U.S.)—History 2. United States—Politics and government—1783-1865 3. War of 1812

ISBN 0-7614-0778-2   LC 97-35909

Discusses the events and personalities that shaped this country, from the hotly contested election of 1800 which brought Thomas Jefferson into office through the westward expansion to the War of 1812 and James Madison's presidency

Includes bibliographical references

Corrick, James A.

The Louisiana Purchase. Lucent Bks. 2001 108p il maps (World history series) lib bdg $27.45 (7 and up)

973.4

1. Louisiana Purchase

ISBN 1-56006-637-7   LC 00-9156

Examines the Louisiana Purchase, discussing the negotiation of the treaty with France, the formation of Louisiana, taking possession of the land, and the exploration, growth, and settlement of the territory

This overview is "well-written . . . {and} thought-provoking." SLJ

Includes bibliographical references

Stefoff, Rebecca, 1951-

American voices from the new republic, 1783-1830; by Rebecca Stefoff. Benchmark Books 2004 c2005 xxiii, 116p il (American voices from--) lib bdg $34.21

973.4

1. United States—History—1783-1865

ISBN 0-7614-1695-1   LC 2004-11391

Contents: Birth of a nation; Forming a new government; Presidents and parties; International affairs; American affairs; African Americans and slavery; Arts and sciences; The age of new possibilities

Describes, through excerpts from diaries, speeches, newspaper articles, and other documents of the time, United States history from 1783 to 1830. Includes review questions.

973.5   United States--1809-1845

Childress, Diana

The War of 1812; Diana Childress. Lerner Publications Co 2004 80p il map (Chronicle of America's wars) lib bdg $27.93 (5 and up)

973.5

1. War of 1812

ISBN 0-8225-0800-1   LC 2003-18805

Contents: The road to war; Losses on land, victories at sea; The pattern changes; A new front and a victory in the Northwest; The Creek vanquished, the last invasion; The British counterattack; A dramatic end

This describes the events of the War of 1812 and focusing on the impact the war had on America and its people.

Includes glossary and bibliographical references

Collier, Christopher, 1930-

Andrew Jackson's America, 1824-1850; {by} Christopher Collier, James Lincoln Collier. Benchmark Bks. 1999 95p il map (Drama of American history) $31.36   **973.5**

1. Jackson, Andrew, 1767-1845 2. United States—History—1815-1861 3. United States—Politics and government—1815-1861

ISBN 0-7614-0779-0   LC 97-30546

Examines the events and personalities, particularly President Andrew Jackson, that shaped the development of the United States during the first half of the nineteenth century

Includes bibliographical references

Goodman, Susan, 1952-
Ultimate field trip 4: a week in the 1800s; by
Susan E. Goodman; photographs by Michael J.
Doolittle. Atheneum Bks. for Young Readers 2000
50p il hardcover o.p. paperback available $6.99 (5
and up) **973.5**
1. Kings Landing Historical Settlement (N.B.)
2. United States—Social life and customs
ISBN 0-689-84260-0 (pa) LC 99-19156
Describes the experiences of a group of middle school
students who spend a week at Kings Landing Historical
Settlement, learning what life was like for young people
in the nineteenth century
"Well written and beautifully photographed, this book
offers a vicarious experience that teachers may want to
share with their classes." Booklist
Includes bibliographical references

Greenblatt, Miriam
War of 1812; John S. Bowman, general editor.
Updated ed. Facts on File 2003 166p il maps
(America at war) lib bdg $35 (7 and up)
973.5
1. War of 1812
ISBN 0-8160-4933-5 LC 2002 9555
First published 1994
Contents: "The darkest day"; "Free trade and sailors'
rights"; Warriors and war hawks; The United States on
the eve of war; "Go march to Canada"; The naval war;
"O'er the land of the free"; The war in the South; Ghent,
Hartford, and peace
An account of the events surrounding the War of 1812
between the newly established United States and Great
Britain
This offers "high quality writing . . . [a] wealth of in-
formation and good organization." SLJ
Includes glossary and bibliographical references

Howes, Kelly King
War of 1812; Julie L. Carnagie, editor. U.X.L
2002 xxvi, 318p $60 (7 and up) **973.5**
1. War of 1812
ISBN 0-7876-5574-0 LC 2001-44240
Preliminary pagnation continues after p.318
A chronological overview of the events of the War of
1812, accompanied by fifteen biographies of individuals
associated with the war
Includes glossary and bibliographical references

Marker, Sherry, 1941-
Plains Indian wars; John S. Bowman, general
editor. Updated ed. Facts on File 2003 164p il
maps (America at war) lib bdg $35 (7 and up)
973.5
1. Native Americans—Wars 2. Native Americans—
Great Plains
ISBN 0-8160-4931-9 LC 2002-9556
First published 1996
This is an account of the wars between Plains Indians
and white settlers in the American West in the 19th
century
"Marker does an excellent job of detailing the cultural

and social complexity of the many tribes of the Great
Plains while offering both a political and social picture
of the U.S. Army at this time. The work concludes with
an excellent chapter on the history of the stereotypes of
the Plains Indians." SLJ
Includes glossary and bibliographical references

Marquette, Scott
War of 1812. Rourke Pub. 2002 48p il map
(America at war) lib bdg $29.93; pa $6.95 (4 and
up) **973.5**
1. War of 1812
ISBN 1-58952-389-X (lib bdg); 1-58952-475-6 (pa)
LC 2002-1239
Contents: Introduction: The strangest war; Map of the
U.S., 1812-1815; Timeline; Sea battles and Indian wars;
Victory at sea, defeat on land; "We have met the enemy"; America in Flames; The mistaken victory; "Don't
give up the ship"
Discusses the events connected with the conflict between the United States and England during the early
years of the nineteenth century
This "works very well in terms of both design and information. Large print on glossy pages, plenty of color
photographs, and clear, simple text invite readers into
{the book}. Marquette writes simply but supplies children with facts set firmly into context." Booklist
Includes glossary and bibliographical references

Warrick, Karen Clemens
The War of 1812; "We have met the enemy and
they are ours". Enslow Pubs. 2002 128p il maps
(American war series) lib bdg $26.60
973.5
1. War of 1812
ISBN 0-7660-1854-7 LC 2001-4120
Traces the history of the War of 1812, examining the
maritime and boundary issues that caused it and highlighting the roles of famous personalities, including Oliver Hazard Perry, Andrew Jackson, and Dolley Madison
"With a text that is less dry than many history books,
this title will earn its keep as a circulating resource for
assignments. . . . {This book has} numerous black-and-
white illustrations, a time line, solid footnotes, and chapters that begin with relevant quotes." SLJ
Includes bibliographical references

973.6 United States--1845-1861

Bardhan-Quallen, Sudipta
The Mexican-American War; by Sudipta
Bardhan-Quallen. Blackbirch Press 2005 48p il
map (People at the center of) $23.70 (5 and up)
973.6
1. Mexican War, 1846-1848
ISBN 1-56711-927-1 LC 2004-13973
This offers biographical profiles of 15 people prominent in the Mexican War of 1846-1848.
This is a "unique and easily accessible [presentation]
of biographical and historical information. . . . Maps,
photos, drawings, . . . add to the appeal. . . . Great for
reports." SLJ
Includes bibliographical references

Carey, Charles W.
The Mexican War; "Mr. Polk's war"; {by} Charles W. Carey, Jr. Enslow Pubs. 2002 128p il (American war series) lib bdg $26.60

973.6

1. Mexican War, 1846-1848
ISBN 0-7660-1853-9   LC 2001-817
This "account of the 1846-1848 war addresses the origins, strategies, battles, and people involved in the conflict. The ramifications of the war for each country are discussed in separate chapters. . . . {This volume has} numerous black-and-white illustrations, a time line, solid footnotes, and chapters that begin with relevant quotes." SLJ
Includes bibliographical references

Collier, Christopher, 1930-
Hispanic America, Texas, and the Mexican War, 1835-1850; {by} Christopher Collier, James Lincoln Collier. Benchmark Bks. (Tarrytown) 1999 94p il col il col maps (Drama of American history) $31.36   **973.6**

1. Mexican War, 1846-1848 2. Southwestern States—History
ISBN 0-7614-0780-4   LC 97-34962
Examines the settlement of the area that became the southwestern portion of the United States, detailing how it evolved from land settled by Native Americans, to Spanish territory, to states that were pawns between the North and South prior to the Civil War
Includes bibliographical references

Slavery and the coming of the Civil War, 1831-1861; {by} Christopher Collier, James Lincoln Collier. Benchmark Bks. (Tarrytown) 2000 93p il map (Drama of American history) lib bdg $31.36   **973.6**

1. Slavery—United States 2. United States—History—1815-1861 3. United States—History—1861-1865, Civil War
ISBN 0-7614-0817-7   LC 98-2620
Discusses attitudes and events that led up to the Civil War, particularly the institution of slavery
This title is "clearly written. . . . Includes many maps and full color as well as black-and-white photos and reproductions." SLJ
Includes bibliographical references

Feldman, Ruth Tenzer
The Mexican-American War; Ruth Tenzer Feldman. Lerner Publications Co 2004 88p il map (Chronicle of America's wars) lib bdg $27.93 (5 and up)   **973.6**

1. Mexican War, 1846-1848
ISBN 0-8225-0831-1   LC 2003-23395
Contents: Bordering on war; Manifest destiny; Rough and ready; Continuing conflict; Conquering peace; March to Mexico City; The struggle for peace; Two nations, one border
This chronicles the events of the Mexican War of 1846-1848 focusing the impact the war had on America and its people.
Includes glossary and bibliographical references

Nardo, Don, 1947-
The Mexican-American War. Lucent Bks. 1999 112p il maps (World history series) lib bdg $28.70

973.6

1. Mexican War, 1846-1848
ISBN 1-56006-495-1   LC 99-14263
Examines the Mexican-American War, discussing American expansion, the fall of Mexico City, the conclusion of the war, the peace treaty, and the legacy of a "dirty" war
This "title should be a boon to high school collections." SLJ
Includes bibliographical references

973.7   United States--Administration of Abraham Lincoln, 1861-1865. Civil War

Altman, Linda Jacobs, 1943-
Slavery and abolition in American history. Enslow Pubs. 1999 128p il maps (In American history) lib bdg $26.60   **973.7**

1. Slavery—United States 2. Abolitionists
ISBN 0-7660-1124-0   LC 99-19885
Traces the history of slavery in the United States, focusing on the abolition movement and the final steps that freed an enslaved people
Includes bibliographical references

Armstrong, Jennifer, 1961-
Photo by Brady; a picture of the Civil War; . Atheneum Books For Young Readers 2005 147p il $18.95   **973.7**

1. Brady, Mathew B., ca. 1823-1896 2. United States—History—1861-1865, Civil War 3. Photography—History
ISBN 0-689-85785-3   LC 2004-8967
"Armstrong chronicles the Civil War from Lincoln's election to his death with both a storylike narrative of events and a photo-essay. . . . This book is also a look at early photographic techniques and offers a description of {Mathew} Brady's rare collection. . . . When readers remember that the pictures are more than 100 years old, they should recognize their exquisiteness, grandeur, and genius." SLJ
Includes bibliographical references

Barney, William L.
The Civil War and Reconstruction; a student companion. Oxford Univ. Press 2001 368p il maps (Oxford student companions to American history) $60 (7 and up)   **973.7**

1. Reconstruction (1865-1876) 2. United States—History—1861-1865, Civil War
ISBN 0-19-511559-7   LC 00-57444
This reference guide includes "articles on the military, political, social, economic, and cultural aspects of the war and its aftermath, as well as biographical sketches of major figures." SLJ
"The book is encyclopedic in format, with many use-

Barney, William L.—*Continued*
ful access points, and bibliographic information is located both at the ends of the articles and in several appendixes that suggest books, historic sites and addresses, and Web sites." Voice Youth Advocates
Includes bibliographical references

Beller, Susan Provost, 1949-
Billy Yank & Johnny Reb; soldiering in the Civil War. 21st Cent. Bks. (Brookfield) 2000 96p il lib bdg $26.90 (5 and up)   **973.7**
1. United States—History—1861-1865, Civil War
2. Soldiers—United States
ISBN 0-7613-1869-0   LC 99-462169
Describes military life for the average soldier in the Civil War, including camp life, diseases, and conditions for the wounded and prisoners of war. Includes excerpts from first-person accounts, letters, and diaries
The author "presents a good deal of solid information in an interesting manner. . . . Good black-and-white reproductions, mainly of photographs from the 1860s, appear throughout the book." Booklist
Includes bibliographical references

The Civil War. Benchmark Bks. 2002 c2003 103p il (American voices from—) lib bdg $32.79
                   973.7
1. United States—History—1861-1865, Civil War
ISBN 0-7614-1204-2   LC 2002-3224
Presents the history of the American Civil War through excerpts from letters, newspaper articles, journal entries, and other primary source documents
Includes glossary and bibliographical references

Confederate ladies of Richmond. 21st Cent. Bks. (Brookfield) 1999 96p il lib bdg $26.90
                   973.7
1. United States—History—1861-1865, Civil War
2. Richmond (Va.)—History
ISBN 0-7613-1470-9   LC 98-42412
Tells stories of several Confederate women who supported the secession of the southern states during the Civil War, with particular emphasis on the siege of Richmond
"Illustrated with many period photographs and engravings and well documented with source notes, this book offers an unusual focus on the war." Booklist
Includes bibliographical references

Bolotin, Norm, 1951-
Civil War A to Z; a young readers' guide to over 100 people, places, and points of importance; [by] Norman Bolotin. Dutton Children's Bks. 2002 148p il maps $19.99 (4 and up)   **973.7**
1. United States—History—1861-1865, Civil War
ISBN 0-525-46268-6   LC 2001-33370
Alphabetically arranged articles present over 100 people, places, and points of importance of the Civil War
"Bolotin has a good eye for what students need to understand about the war and provides a great deal of information, skillfully whittled down to its most salient points. . . . The format is attractive, with numerous photographs." Booklist
Includes glossary and bibliographical references

The **Civil** War. Grolier 2004 10v il map set $309 (5 and up)   **973.7**
1. United States—History—1861-1865, Civil War
ISBN 0-7172-5883-1   LC 2003-49315
Contents: v1 Abolition-Camp followers; v2 Camp life-Custer, George A.; v3 Daily life-Flags; v4 Florida-Hill, Ambrose P.; v5 Home Front, Confederacy-Legacy of the Civil War; v6 Lincoln, Abraham-Mobile Bay, Battle of ; v7 Money and banking-Politics, Confederate; v8 Politics, Union-Shenandoah Valley; v9 Sheridan, Philip H.-Trade; v10 Training-Zouaves
This set "features detailed multipage articles that address significant individuals, battles, events, and conditions of the American Civil War." Booklist
"The variety of topics addressed in this set will give students a wide perspective on the conflict. . . . The clearly written, objective entries, ranging in length from one to six pages, all offer basic analysis." SLJ

Civil War: battles and leaders; Aaron R. Murray, editor. DK Pub. 2004 $19.99; pa $12.99
                   973.7
1. United States—History—1861-1865, Civil War
ISBN 0-7894-9890-1; 0-7894-9891-x (pa)
                   LC 2004-298417
This is a guide to the battles and leading figures of the Civil War
This is "filled with great information and statistics that are not always immediately available. . . . Attractively placed color spot art, thumbnail-sized portraits, small maps showing troop movements, vintage photos, and helpful pull-quotes comprise half of each well-designed spread." Booklist

Collier, Christopher, 1930-
The Civil War, 1860-1865; {by} Christopher Collier, James Lincoln Collier. Benchmark Bks. (Tarrytown) 1998 95p il map (Drama of American history) lib bdg $31.36   **973.7**
1. United States—History—1861-1865, Civil War
ISBN 0-7614-0818-5   LC 97-49178
Examines the people and events involved in the bloody war that pitted the Northern states against those that seceded to form the Confederacy
Includes bibliographical references

Dolan, Edward F., 1924-
The American Civil War; a house divided. Millbrook Press 1997 96p il maps lib bdg $30.60
                   973.7
1. United States—History—1861-1865, Civil War
ISBN 0-7613-0255-7   LC 97-6995
An account of the Civil War from its causes to its final battles including discussions of dominant figures of the era, strategies of major battles, and brutal sieges which marked this conflict
"This is a good acquisition for libraries that need a simple introduction to this oft-confusing episode in American history." SLJ
Includes bibliographical references

The **election** of 1860 and the administration of Abraham Lincoln; editor, Arthur M. Schlesinger, Jr. ; associate editors, Fred L. Israel, David J. Frent. Mason Crest Publishers 2003 128p il map (Major presidential elections and the administrations that followed) $24.95 (7 and up)

973.7

1. Lincoln, Abraham, 1809-1865 2. Presidents—United States—Election 3. United States—Politics and government—1861-1865

ISBN 1-590-84355-X   LC 2002-11261

Contents: The election of 1860 \ William E. Gienapp; Facts at a glance; 1858 "House divided" speech; Republican Party platform of 1860; Democratic Party platforms; Constitutional union platform; The Crittenden compromise; Lincoln's first inaugural address; Message to Congress, July 4, 1861; The Homestead Act of 1862; The Pacific Railway Act; Letter to Horace Greeley; The Emancipation Proclamation; The Gettysburg Address; Lincoln's plan for reconstruction; Lincoln's veto of the Wade-Davis Bill; The Wade-Davis Manifesto; Lincoln's second inaugural address

Provides an overview of the election of 1860 and the administration of President Abraham Lincoln, using a variety of source materials.

This is "well-organized. . . . There is much that report writers will appreciate in [this] thorough and attractive [volume]." SLJ

Includes bibliographical references

Fraser, Mary Ann

Vicksburg—the battle that won the Civil War. Holt & Co. 1999 104p il map $17.95 (4 and up)

973.7

1. Vicksburg (Miss.)—Siege, 1863

ISBN 0-8050-6106-1   LC 99-19701

Describes the events preceding and during the key Civil War battle of Vicksburg, its significance, and its aftermath

"Bringing the history to life, quotations from diaries, memoirs, and other sources give voices to the participants. Illustrations . . . include black-and-white photographs, maps, and engravings. Source notes, a glossary, and lists of books and Internet sites are appended." Booklist

Golay, Michael, 1951-

Civil War. Updated ed. Facts on File 2003 xxi, 234p il map (America at war) $35   **973.7**

1. United States—History—1861-1865, Civil War

ISBN 0-8160-4934-3   LC 2002-6371

First published 1992

Contents: Irrepressible conflict; Purged with blood; On to Richmond; The river war; The uses of sea power;America's bloodiest day; The war at home; Jubilee; Battles lost and won; Long remember : Gettysburg; Siege at Vicksburg; In the charnel house; The battle for Chattanooga; Tecumseh the Great; Grant and Lee; Epilogue : touched with fire

This includes "not only the military history of the American Civil War, but also the politics on both sides, the homefronts, the prologue, and the aftermath. . . . The battle maps are unusually clear. . . . The text

throughout the book is precise and yet interesting and even colorful. The author has used many contemporary accounts and quotations." Am Ref Books Annu, 2004

Includes glossary and bibliographical references

Hansen, Joyce

Freedom roads: searching for the Underground Railroad; [by] Joyce Hansen and Gary McGowan. Cricket Bks. 2003 164p il maps $18.95 (5 and up)

973.7

1. Underground railroad 2. Slavery—United States

ISBN 0-8126-2673-7   LC 2002-13711

Contents: Running South: artifacts from Fort Mose; Land of the free: History on a ship's log; A more perfect Union: learning from the law; Running: The WPA slave narratives; Steal away: the enslaved speak through spirituals; I will be heard: archaeology meets an oral tradition; Midnight seekers after liberty: anecdotes and memories uncover the past; The last stop: outrunning the fugitive slave laws; A mystery: when history keeps a secret; The search continues

The authors "explore the ways historians have traced the path of the enslaved as they traveled northward to freedom. . . . The authors demonstrate how the study of artifacts, laws, slave narratives and more contribute to an understanding of how this crucial chapter of American history evolved. Reproductions of period photographs and documents extend the value of this well-researched volume." Publ Wkly

Includes bibliographical references

Haugen, David, 1969-

The Civil War; {by} David M. Haugen and Lori Shein. Greenhaven Press 1999 141p il maps (Opposing viewpoints digests) pa $17.45 hardcover o.p. (7 and up)   **973.7**

1. United States—History—1861-1865, Civil War

ISBN 1-56510-886-8 (pa)   LC 98-46105

Offers opposing viewpoints on issues associated with the Civil War including secession, slavery, the Emancipation Proclamation, and the President's right to suspend civil liberties

Includes bibliographical references

Hillstrom, Kevin

American Civil War: almanac; {by} Kevin Hillstrom and Laurie Collier Hillstrom; Lawrence W. Baker, editor. U.X.L 2000 xlvi, 251, xlvii-lxip il $60   **973.7**

1. Almanacs 2. United States—History—1861-1865, Civil War

ISBN 0-7876-3823-4   LC 99-46918

Describes and interprets the era of the Civil War, its events, and topics with viewpoints, definitions, report topics, chronologies, sidebars, and statistics

"Added features such as 'Words to Know' and 'People to Know' sidebars in each chapter and research and activity ideas help make the volume a good jumping-off point for research on Civil War-era events." Booklist

Includes bibliographical references

Hillstrom, Kevin—*Continued*

American Civil War: primary sources; {by} Kevin Hillstrom and Laurie Collier Hillstrom; Lawrence W. Baker, editor. U.X.L 2000 xxxi, 176, xxxiii-xliiip il $60   **973.7**
1. United States—History—1861-1865, Civil War—Sources
ISBN 0-7876-3824-2   LC 99-46919
This volume "offers 14 full or excerpted speeches and written works. Each entry provides context, telling students what to keep in mind while reading the sources, as well as 'what happened next.' The speeches and writings come from Frederick Douglass, Abraham Lincoln, William Tecumseh Sherman, and Harriet Beecher Stowe, among others." Booklist

Experiencing the American Civil War; {by} Kevin Hillstrom and Laurie Collier Hillstrom; Lawrence W. Baker, editor. U.X.L 2002 2v il maps lib bdg set $105   **973.7**
1. United States—History—1861-1865, Civil War
ISBN 0-7876-5585-6
Contents: v1 Novels; nonfiction books; v2 Short stories; poems; plays; films; songs
"Discussing 25 original works . . . this set serves as an introduction for young adults to the wide range of creative treatments of the Civil War." Booklist
"Although most useful as a supplementary source for classroom study, this reference tool has sufficient visual and textual appeal to arouse browers' curiosity about the materials discussed." SLJ

Holzer, Harold

The president is shot! the assassination of Abraham Lincoln. Boyds Mills Press 2004 181p il $17.95 (5 and up)   **973.7**
1. Lincoln, Abraham, 1809-1865—Assassination
ISBN 1-56397-985-3
This is a "description of the violent end to Lincoln's life. Holzer provides the Civil War context of the event and then details April 14 and 15, 1865." SLJ
"A page-turner of a text, a fascinating array of photos and archival illustrations, and an event that changed the course of history: all these elements combine in this strong, highly readable book." Booklist
Includes bibliographical references

Hughes, Chris

The Battle of Antietam. Blackbirch Press 2001 32p il maps (Civil War) $22.45   **973.7**
1. Antietam (Md.), Battle of, 1862
ISBN 1-56711-551-9   LC 01-1572
"Triangle histories"
Describes the 1862 battle in Maryland
This offers "a readable text that makes judicious use of quotes from participants. . . . Supplemental information about notable figures, locations, and incidents is included in sidebars, while historical reproductions and occasional photographs add further accessibility." Horn Book Guide
Includes glossary and bibliographical references

January, Brendan, 1972-

The assassination of Abraham Lincoln. Children's Press 1998 30p il (Cornerstones of freedom) $21; pa $5.95   **973.7**
1. Lincoln, Abraham, 1809-1865—Assassination
ISBN 0-516-20947-7; 0-516-26394-3 (pa)
     LC 97-34997
Chronicles the events leading to the murder of President Lincoln by John Wilkes Booth in April 1865

John Brown's raid on Harpers Ferry. Children's Press 2000 30p il (Cornerstones of freedom) $21; pa $5.95 (4 and up)   **973.7**
1. Brown, John, 1800-1859 2. Abolitionists 3. Harpers Ferry (W. Va.)—History—John Brown's Raid, 1859
ISBN 0-516-21144-7; 0-516-27037-0 (pa)
     LC 99-14965
Recounts the story of John Brown's rebellion in Harpers Ferry in 1859, intended to start a massive slave uprising in the South and the establishment of a state in the Allegheny Mountains for freed slaves

The Lincoln-Douglas debates. Children's Press 1998 30p il maps (Cornerstones of freedom) pa $5.95 hardcover o.p.   **973.7**
1. Lincoln, Abraham, 1809-1865 2. Douglas, Stephen Arnold, 1813-1861 3. Lincoln-Douglas debates, 1858
ISBN 0-516-26335-8 (pa)   LC 97-9302
Describes the seven debates held from August to October 1858 between Stephen Douglas and Abraham Lincoln who were campaigning for election as Illinois Senator

King, David C., 1933-

The Battle of Gettysburg. Blackbirch Press 2001 32p il maps (Civil War) $22.45   **973.7**
1. Gettysburg (Pa.), Battle of, 1863
ISBN 1-56711-550-0   LC 2001-2569
"Triangle histories"
Discusses the strategy, tactics, actual fighting, aftermath, and key figures involved in one of the Civil War's pivotal battles at Gettysburg, Pennsylvania
This offers "a readable text that makes judicious use of quotes from participants. . . . Supplemental information about notable figures, locations, and incidents is included in sidebars, while historical reproductions and occasional photographs add further accessibility." Horn Book Guide
Includes glossary and bibliographical references

The Battle of Vicksburg. Blackbirch Press 2001 32p il maps (Civil War) $22.45   **973.7**
1. Vicksburg (Miss.)—Siege, 1863
ISBN 1-56711-552-7   LC 2001-724
"Triangle histories"
This describes the siege of Vicksburg, Mississippi in 1863
This offers "a readable text that makes judicious use of quotes from participants. . . . Supplemental information about notable figures, locations, and incidents is included in sidebars, while historical reproductions and occasional photographs add further accessibility." Horn Book Guide
Includes glossary and bibliographical references

Kirchberger, Joe H.
The Civil War and Reconstruction; an eyewitness history; {by} Joe Kirchberger. Facts on File 1991 389p il maps (Eyewitness history series) $75 (7 and up)   **973.7**
1. United States—History—1861-1865, Civil War—Sources 2. Reconstruction (1865-1876)
ISBN 0-8160-2171-6   LC 90-40852
This work contains "quotations from eyewitnesses' memoirs, letters, diaries, newspapers, and official documents. Those quoted come from all walks of life. . . . Thirty-three documents are excerpted. Four appendixes contain valuable primary-source and reference materials. . . . Interspersed throughout are political cartoons, photographs, and paintings. . . . An excellent reference tool." SLJ
Includes bibliographical references

Kops, Deborah
The Battle of Bull Run. Blackbirch Press 2001 32p il maps (Civil War) $22.45   **973.7**
1. Bull Run, 1st Battle of, 1861
ISBN 1-56711-553-5   LC 2001-2570
"Triangle histories"
Presents the events leading up to the first major battle in the Civil War, at Bull Run in 1861, and describes that clash and its aftermath
This offers "a readable text that makes judicious use of quotes from participants. . . . Supplemental information about notable figures, locations, and incidents is included in sidebars, while historical reproductions and occasional photographs add further accessibility." Horn Book Guide
Includes glossary and bibliographical references

Marrin, Albert, 1936-
Commander in Chief Abraham Lincoln and the Civil War. Dutton Children's Bks. 1997 246p il maps pa $14.99 hardcover o.p. (7 and up)
    973.7
1. Lincoln, Abraham, 1809-1865 2. United States—History—1861-1865, Civil War
ISBN 0-525-47069-7 (pa)   LC 97-8518
The author places Lincoln in the context of his own personal background and the larger circumstances of the Civil War
"The narrative is skillfully constructed and expressed in a strong, compelling style." SLJ
Includes bibliographical references

Matthews, Tom L., 1949-
Grierson's raid; a daring cavalry strike through the heart of the Confederacy; [by] Tom Lalicki; original maps by David Cain. Farrar Straus Giroux 2004 200p il map $18 (7 and up)   **973.7**
1. United States—History—1861-1865, Civil War—Campaigns
ISBN 0-374-32787-4   LC 2003-49253
Describes Colonel Benjamin H. Grierson's sixteen-day raid through central Mississippi in the spring of 1863, which distracted Confederate attention while Union troops moved on Vicksburg.

"The use of firsthand accounts brings the events vividly to life in a way that makes the book read more like an adventure story than a history text. . . . Accessibly written and scrupulously researched." Booklist
Includes glossary and bibliographical references

McKissack, Patricia C., 1944-
Days of Jubilee; the end of slavery in the United States; [by] Patricia C. & Fredrick L. McKissack. Scholastic Press 2003 134p il $18.95 (5 and up)   **973.7**
1. Slavery—United States 2. African Americans—History 3. United States—History—1861-1865, Civil War
ISBN 0-590-10764-X   LC 2001-57568
Uses slave narratives, letters, diaries, military orders, and other documents to chronicle the various stages leading to the emancipation of slaves in the United States
"The balanced perspective, vivid telling, and well-chosen details give this book an immediacy that many history books lack." Booklist

McPherson, James M.
Fields of fury; the American Civil War. Atheneum Bks. for Young Readers 2002 96p il maps $22.95 (5 and up)   **973.7**
1. United States—History—1861-1865, Civil War
ISBN 0-689-84833-1   LC 2001-46048
"A Byron Preiss Visual Publications, Inc. book"
Examines the events and effects of the American Civil War
"Mcpherson writes with authority, offering a broad overview as well as many details and anecdotes that give his account a human dimension. . . . The many fine illustrations include period photographs, paintings, prints, some excellent maps." Booklist
Includes glossary and bibliographical references

Murphy, Jim, 1947-
The boys' war; Confederate and Union soldiers talk about the Civil War. Clarion Bks. 1990 110p il $18; pa $8.95 (5 and up)   **973.7**
1. United States—History—1861-1865, Civil War
ISBN 0-89919-893-7; 0-395-66412-8 (pa)
     LC 89-23959
This book includes diary entries, personal letters, and archival photographs to describe the experiences of boys, sixteen years old or younger, who fought in the Civil War
"An excellent selection of more than 45 sepia-toned contemporary photographs augment the text of this informative, moving work." SLJ
Includes bibliographical references

The long road to Gettysburg. Clarion Bks. 1992 116p il maps $17; pa $7.95 (5 and up)
    973.7
1. Gettysburg (Pa.), Battle of, 1863
ISBN 0-395-55965-0; 0-618-05157-0 (pa)
     LC 90-21881
Describes the events of the Battle of Gettysburg in 1863 as seen through the eyes of two actual participants, nineteen-year-old Confederate lieutenant John Dooley

Murphy, Jim, 1947-—*Continued*
and seventeen-year-old Union soldier Thomas Galway.
Also discusses Lincoln's famous speech delivered at the
dedication of the National Cemetery at Gettysburg

The author "uses all of his fine skills as an information writer—clarity of detail, conciseness, understanding
of his age group, and ability to find the drama appealing
to readers—to frame a well-crafted account of a single
battle in the war." Horn Book

Includes bibliographical references

Nardo, Don, 1947-
The Civil War. Lucent Bks. 2003 109p il maps
(History of weapons and warfare) $27.45 (7 and
up)   **973.7**
1. Military art and science 2. United States—History—1861-1865, Civil War
ISBN 1-59018-068-2   LC 2002-11032
Contents: Muskets and rifles; Artillery guns and batteries; Infantry units and tactics; Cavalry units and tactics; Ships and naval warfare; Espionage and experimental weapons

Discusses the weapons of American Civil War soldiers
and different means of warfare used during that conflict
Includes glossary and bibliographical references

Netzley, Patricia D.
Civil War. Greenhaven Press 2004 336p il
(Greenhaven encyclopedias) lib bdg $74.95
                                                973.7
1. United States—History—1861-1865, Civil War—
Encyclopedias
ISBN 0-7377-0438-1   LC 2003-11808
An alphabetical presentation of definitions and de-
scriptions of terms, people, and events of the Civil War
"Basic, accurate information about many aspects of
the war. . . . The well-written, objective entries are
cross-referenced. . . . Netzley's solid volume will be
helpful to students needing introductory research material." SLJ
Includes bibliographical references

Ray, Delia
Behind the Blue and Gray; the soldier's life in
the Civil War. Lodestar Bks. 1991 102p il (Young
readers' history of the Civil War) $17.99; pa $9.95
(5 and up)   **973.7**
1. United States—History—1861-1865, Civil War
ISBN 0-525-67333-4; 0-14-038304-2 (pa)
                                    LC 90-46412
This book traces the events of the Civil War from the
first battle to the surrender with emphasis on the experiences of the individual soldier

The author "has chosen many informative, perceptive
personal accounts upon which to base her work. The
fears, horrors, boredom, and simple, transitory pleasures
of these young men are brought into sharp focus by the
many first-person writings. . . . Black-and-white historical photographs and reproductions flesh out this highly
readable volume." SLJ
Includes glossary and bibliographical references

A nation torn; the story of how the Civil War
began. Lodestar Bks. 1990 102p il maps (Young
readers' history of the Civil War) $18; pa $9.99 (5
and up)   **973.7**
1. United States—History—1861-1865, Civil War
2. United States—Politics and government—1815-
1861
ISBN 0-525-67308-3; 0-14-038105-8 (pa)
                                    LC 90-5533
The author "probes the causes of the Civil War, tracing key movements and events that culminated in the
Confederate attack on Fort Sumter." Booklist
"Ms. Ray provides a superb introduction to the events
that plunged this country into the Civil War. . . . Interesting drawings, cartoons and photos enhance the readable text." Child Book Rev Serv
Includes glossary and bibliographical references

Seidman, Rachel Filene
The Civil war: a history in documents. Oxford
Univ. Press 2001 206p il map (Pages from history)
$36.95   **973.7**
1. United States—History—1861-1865, Civil War—
Sources
ISBN 0-19-511558-9   LC 00-37523
"Seidman's documents bookend the Civil War with
the territorial expansion that preceded the conflict and
with the Reconstruction that followed it. In this structure
the documents, under the guidance of Seidman's linking
narrative, all make a powerful impression of immediacy
about ordinary people's experience of, and condemnation
or defense of, slavery." Booklist
Includes bibliographical references

Stanchak, John E.
The visual dictionary of the Civil War; written
by John Stanchak. DK Pub. 2000 64p il (Dorling
Kindersley visual dictionaries) $18.99
                                                973.7
1. United States—History—1861-1865, Civil War
ISBN 0-7894-5166-2   LC 99-55516
"A Dorling Kindersley book"
Text and illustrations present information about various aspects of the Civil War, including the infantry, artil-
lerymen, horse soldiers, sailors, weapons, medical treatment, armored ships, leaders, communications, transportation, and more

Stein, R. Conrad, 1937-
John Brown's Raid on Harpers Ferry in
American history. Enslow Pubs. 1999 128p il (In
American history) lib bdg $26.60   **973.7**
1. Brown, John, 1800-1859 2. Harpers Ferry (W.
Va.)—History—John Brown's Raid, 1859
3. Abolitionists
ISBN 0-7660-1123-2   LC 98-35950
Explores the people and events connected with John
Brown's attempted slave uprising in Harpers Ferry in
1859
Includes bibliographical references

Sullivan, George, 1933-
The Civil War at sea. 21st Cent. Bks.
(Brookfield) 2001 80p il lib bdg $27.90
973.7
1. United States—History—1861-1865, Civil War—
Naval operations
ISBN 0-7613-1553-5   LC 00-41805
"Sullivan tells of the struggle between the Union and
Confederate forces at sea and in America's bays, rivers,
and harbors. He describes the two rival navies and their
most famous ships, most significant battles, and most
memorable commanders. He also looks at the lives of or-
dinary sailors." Booklist
"The illustrations and reproductions included here and
the lively text will appeal to every Civil War buff, and
will be an excellent source of information for reports."
SLJ
Includes bibliographical references

Tackach, James, 1954-
The Emancipation Proclamation; abolishing
slavery in the South. Lucent Bks. 1999 112p il
(Words that changed history) lib bdg $27.45 (7
and up)   **973.7**
1. United States. President (1861-1865: Lincoln). .
Emancipation Proclamation 2. Slavery—United States
ISBN 1-56006-370-X   LC 98-49678
Discusses slavery as a cause of the American Civil
War and examines the events surrounding Lincoln's
Emancipation Proclamation and the impact of this decla-
ration on the course of the war and the institution of
slavery
This is "presented in a well-organized and readable
style. Frequent sidebars feature excerpts from the original
sources and present supplemental information." SLJ
Includes bibliographical references

Taylor, Susie King, 1848-1912
The diary of Susie King Taylor, Civil War
nurse; edited by Margaret Gay Malone;
illustrations by Laszlo Kubinyi. Marshall
Cavendish 2003 80p il (In my own words) $18.95
(5 and up)   **973.7**
1. Taylor, Susie King, 1848-1912 2. United States—
History—1861-1865, Civil War
ISBN 0-7614-1648-X   LC 2003-7088
Excerpts from the diary of a woman who served as
nurse to a regiment of black soldiers fighting for the
Union during the Civil War, including her observations
on the treatment of "coloreds" after the war
"The past comes strikingly to light in {this} first-
person {account}. . . . {This} woman emerges as strong
and extraordinary as she becomes the hero of her own
story." SLJ
Includes glossary and bibliographical references

Trudeau, Noah Andre, 1949-
Like men of war; black troops in the Civil War,
1862-1865. Little, Brown 1998 xxii, 548p il maps
$29; pa $18 (7 and up)   **973.7**
1. African American soldiers 2. United States—History—1861-1865, Civil War
ISBN 0-316-85325-9; 0-316-85344-5 (pa)
LC 97-15380

A "study of the battlefield experiences of black Union
regiments. Some 60 maps help the reader make sense of
famous engagements (Fort Wagner and the Crater) and
notorious incidents (Fort Pillow) in which black soldiers
fought, as well as scores of lesser-known clashes. Rich
archival research is integrated into a lively narrative that
places the raising and deployment of black regiments in
broader contexts. This book will become a basic source
of information on the subject." Libr J
Includes bibliographical references

Uschan, Michael V., 1948-
The cavalry during the Civil War. Lucent Bks.
2003 112p il maps (Working life) $27.45
973.7
1. United States—History—1861-1865, Civil War
2. Soldiers—United States
ISBN 1-59018-175-1   LC 2002-11840
Contents: Recruiting and training the cavalry; Life in
the saddle: the varied duties of the cavalry trooper; Cavalry raiders and guerillas; Cavalry soldiers in combat;
Noncombat life of the cavalry
This examines the life of cavalry soldiers during the
civil war
This is "well written and the authors draw on and
quote from many primary sources." Libr Media Connect
Includes bibliographical references

Walker, Sally M.
Secrets of a Civil War submarine; solving the
mysteries of the H.L. Hunley. Carolrhoda Books
2005 112p il lib bdg $17.95 (7 and up)
973.7
1. Hunley (Submarine) 2. United States—History—
1861-1865, Civil War—Naval operations
3. Shipwrecks 4. Underwater exploration
5. Submarines
ISBN 1-575-05830-8   LC 2004-19646
Contents: Prologue : a lost treasure; A seafaring
stealth weapon; Climb aboard; Disaster; Lieutenant Dixon's mission; A stunning discovery; The Hunley talks;
Buried treasures; In touch with the past; Forensic tales
This discusses "the Confederate submarine H. L.
Hunley. . . . Walker begins with the history of the
Hunley's design and construction as well as its place in
Civil War and naval history. She really hits her stride,
though, in explaining the complex techniques and loving
care used in raising the craft, recovering its contents, and
even reconstructing models of the crewmembers' bodies.
. . . Thoroughly researched, nicely designed, and well il-
lustrated with clear, color photos." Booklist
Includes glossary and bibliographical references

Watkins, Samuel R., 1839-1901
The diary of Sam Watkins, a confederate
soldier; .; edited by Ruth Ashby; illustrations by
Laszlo Kubinyi. Benchmark Bks. 2004 95p il (In
my own words) lib bdg $18.95 (5 and up)
973.7
1. Watkins, Samuel R., 1839-1901 2. United States—
History—1861-1865, Civil War
ISBN 0-7614-1646-3   LC 2003-1478

Watkins, Samuel R., 1839-1901—_Continued_
Excerpts from the diary of a Confederate soldier from Tennessee, describing the battles he fought in during the Civil War
This offers "an engaging history lesson." Horn Book Guide
Includes bibliographical references

Wisler, G. Clifton, 1950-
When Johnny went marching; young Americans fight the Civil War. HarperCollins Pubs. 2001 116p il $18.95; lib bdg $18.89 (5 and up) **973.7**
1. United States—History—1861-1865, Civil War
ISBN 0-688-16537-0; 0-06-029242-3 (lib bdg)
LC 00-53617
The author "tells the personal stories of the youngest soldiers to fight in the Civil War." Horn Book
"Spaciously laid out and well designed, the book is illustrated mainly with period photographs. The stories themselves are varied and interesting. . . . This solid yet personal approach to history will complement more traditional books on the War between the States." Booklist
Includes glossary and bibliographical references

Zeinert, Karen, 1942-2002
Those courageous women of the Civil War. Millbrook Press 1998 96p il map lib bdg $30.60 (7 and up) **973.7**
1. Women—United States—History 2. United States—History—1861-1865, Civil War
ISBN 0-7613-0212-3 LC 97-21485
Examines the important contributions of various women, Northern, Southern, and slave, to the American Civil War, on the battlefield, in print, on the home front, and in other areas where they challenged traditional female roles
"A solid work that is sure to open the eyes of many readers and add a different dimension to studies about this era." SLJ
Includes bibliographical references

973.8 United States--Reconstruction period, 1865-1901

Collier, Christopher, 1930-
Reconstruction and the rise of Jim Crow, 1864-1896; by Christopher Collier, James Lincoln Collier. Benchmark Bks. (Tarrytown) 2000 93p il (Drama of American history) lib bdg $31.95
973.8
1. Reconstruction (1865-1876) 2. African Americans—History 3. United States—Race relations
ISBN 0-7614-0819-3 LC 98-8821
Describes the struggles following the Civil War to decide how to deal with the newly freed slaves, through the years of Reconstruction, Jim Crow, sharecropping, and segregation
Includes bibliographical references

The rise of industry, 1860-1900; {by} Christopher Collier, James Lincoln Collier. Benchmark Bks. (Tarrytown) 2000 94p il (Drama of American history) lib bdg $31.36
973.8
1. Industries 2. United States—Economic conditions—1865-1918
ISBN 0-7614-0820-7 LC 98-38528
"By focusing on broad themes, the Colliers are able to show cause and effect over several decades and to make the sweep of time 'bite-sized' and intelligible. The frequent full-color and black-and-white period photographs and engravings effectively supplement and enrich the text." SLJ
Includes bibliographical references

The United States enters the world stage: from the Alaska Purchase through World War I, 1867-1919; {by} Christopher Collier, James Lincoln Collier. Benchmark Bks. (Tarrytown) 2001 94p il map (Drama of American history) lib bdg $31.36 **973.8**
1. United States—History—1865-1898 2. United States—History—1898-1919 3. United States—Foreign relations 4. World War, 1914-1918 5. Spanish-American War, 1898
ISBN 0-7614-1053-8 LC 00-29483
This discusses topics in United States history and politics including Westward expansion, imperialism, the Spanish-American War, the Panama Canal, and World War I
Includes bibliographical references

Custer, Elizabeth Bacon, 1842-1933
The diary of Elizabeth Bacon Custer; on the plains with General Custer; edited by Nancy Plain; illustrations and map by Laszlo Kubinyi. Benchmark Bks. 2004 95p il map (In my own words) lib bdg $18.95 (5 and up) **973.8**
1. Custer, George Armstrong, 1839-1876 2. Native Americans—Wars
ISBN 0-7614-1647-1 LC 2003-1432
Presents the diary of the wife of General George Armstrong Custer, focusing on their life on the Great Plains from 1873 to 1876, when Custer and his Seventh Cavalry were clearing the way for the Northern Pacific Railroad and battling Native Americans
This offers "an engaging history lesson." Horn Book Guide
Includes glossary and bibliographical references

Custer's last stand; Thomas Streissguth, book editor. Greenhaven Press 2003 142p il maps (At issue in history) lib bdg $21.96; pa $14.96 (7 and up) **973.8**
1. Custer, George Armstrong, 1839-1876 2. Little Bighorn, Battle of the, 1876
ISBN 0-7377-1358-5 (lib bdg); 0-7377-1359-3 (pa)
LC 2002-27875
"Using primary and secondary sources, this volume examines the controversial history of the Battle at the Little Bighorn in June, 1876. . . . Each of the 11 entries is preceded by a summary of the author's main points

Custer's last stand—*Continued*
and conclusions. This excellent volume helps students
understand the 'what' and 'why' of history." SLJ
Includes bibliographical references

Dolan, Edward F., 1924-
The Spanish-American War. Millbrook Press
2001 112p il lib bdg $28.90   **973.8**
1. Spanish-American War, 1898
ISBN 0-7613-1453-9   LC 2001-18677
Beginning with a "recounting of the U.S.S. *Maine's*
explosion off the coast of Cuba, which killed 260 U.S.
soldiers, Dolan traces the history of the Spanish
American War. Additional details about other contributing factors . . . broaden the historical scope. Statistics-
rich battle scenes are made more memorable with descriptions of such key military leaders as Teddy
Roosevelt and . . . Major General William Shafter. . . .
Throughout, drawings, maps, and authentic photographs
provide worthwhile support to the chronological descriptions." Booklist
Includes bibliographical references

Ferrell, Nancy Warren
The Battle of the Little Bighorn in American
history. Enslow Pubs. 1996 128p il maps lib bdg
$18.95   **973.8**
1. Little Bighorn, Battle of the, 1876
ISBN 0-89490-768-9   LC 96-11592
Describes the Battle of Little Bighorn and the events
that led up to it
Includes bibliographical references

The **Gilded** Age: a history in documents;
{compiled by} Janette Thomas Greenwood.
Oxford Univ. Press 2000 191p il map (Pages
from history) hardcover o.p. paperback available
$19.95 (7 and up)   **973.8**
1. United States—History—1865-1898
ISBN 0-19-516638-8 (pa)   LC 99-98194
Uses a wide variety of documents to show how Americans dealt with an age of extremes from 1887 to 1900,
including rapid industrialization, unemployment, unprece-
dented wealth, and immigration
"There's plenty to absorb and much to capture the
imagination. . . . Greenwood presents the history as a
seamless tapestry sewn by the people who lived it."
Booklist
Includes bibliographical references

Hansen, Joyce
Bury me not in a land of slaves;
African-Americans in the time of Reconstruction.
Watts 2000 160p il lib bdg $23; pa $8.95 (7 and
up)   **973.8**
1. African Americans—History 2. Reconstruction
(1865-1876) 3. United States—Race relations
ISBN 0-531-11539-9 (lib bdg); 0-531-16463-2 (pa)
LC 99-30040
An account of African-American life in the period of
Reconstruction following the Civil War, based on first-
person narratives, contemporary documents, and other

historical sources
"Readers of this balanced, well-written account will
come away with a solid understanding of the period's
events and how they contributed to the twentieth
century's segregation and prejudice." Booklist
Includes bibliographical references

January, Brendan, 1972-
Reconstruction. Children's Press 1999 30p il
maps (Cornerstones of freedom) lib bdg $21; pa
$5.95   **973.8**
1. Reconstruction (1865-1876) 2. United States—Poli-
tics and government—1865-1898
ISBN 0-516-21143-9 (lib bdg); 0-516-26461-3 (pa)
LC 98-3492
A history of Reconstruction, the period after the Civil
War during which programs were implemented to bring
the Confederate States back to the Union
"The design is attractive, with clear type, photographs
or prints on every page (some in color)." Booklist
Includes glossary

McGowen, Tom
The Spanish-American War and Teddy
Roosevelt in American history. Enslow Pubs. 2003
128p il (In American history) lib bdg $26.60
973.8
1.   Roosevelt,   Theodore,   1858-1919
2. Spanish-American War, 1898
ISBN 0-7660-1987-X   LC 2002-152065
Details the pivotal role that Teddy Roosevelt played
during the Spanish-American War and the consequences
of his involvement
Includes bibliographical references

McNeese, Tim
Remember the Maine! the Spanish-American
War begins. Morgan Reynolds 2002 112p il (First
battles) lib bdg $21.95   **973.8**
1. Maine (Battleship) 2. Spanish-American War, 1898
ISBN 1-88384-679-X   LC 2001-40203
"This book chronicles the events . . . that led to the
destruction of the *Maine* and the aftermath. McNeese's
fluid writing and thorough research is especially notice-
able in his description of the actual explosion." Horn
Book Guide
Includes bibliographical references

Somerlott, Robert, 1928-
The Spanish-American War; "Remember the
Maine!"; [by] Bob Somerlott. Enslow Pubs. 2002
128p il maps (American war series) lib bdg $26.60
973.8
1. Spanish-American War, 1898
ISBN 0-7660-1855-5   LC 2001-4118
Contents: Explosion in Havana; "Remember the
Maine"; America's most popular war; The Rough Riders;
The struggle for Cuba; The naval battle of Santiago de
Cuba; Americans on the Spanish islands; The new
American empire

Somerlott, Robert, 1928-—_Continued_
"This gripping overview of the 114-day Spanish-American War combines general information and specific details in straightforward prose." Booklist
Includes bibliographical references

Uschan, Michael V., 1948-
The Battle of the Little Bighorn. World Almanac 2002 48p il map (Landmark events in American history) lib bdg $26.60 (5 and up)
973.8
1. Custer, George Armstrong, 1839-1876 2. Little Bighorn, Battle of the, 1876
ISBN 0-8368-5338-5   LC 2002-24632
Describes the causes, events, and aftermath of the fateful encounter at the Little Bighorn River on June 25, 1876, between the Seventh Cavalry troops commanded by Lieutenant Colonel Custer and the Cheyenne and Lakota Sioux led by Chiefs Sitting Bull and Crazy Horse
The "design is attractive, with drawings, maps, paintings, and photos; primary sources, such as excerpts from diaries, letters, and newspapers, support and enhance the {text}." Booklist
Includes glossary and bibliographical references

Viola, Herman J., 1938-
It is a good day to die; Indian eyewitnesses tell the story of the Battle of the Little Bighorn. Crown 1998 101p il maps (5 and up)
973.8
1. Custer, George Armstrong, 1839-1876 2. Little Bighorn, Battle of the, 1876 3. Dakota Indians—Wars 4. Cheyenne Indians
ISBN 0-517-70913-9   LC 98-16477
Also available in paperback from University of Neb. Press
A series of eyewitness accounts of the 1876 Battle of Little Bighorn and the defeat of General Custer as told by Native American participants in the war
"This is a thought-provoking, accessible compilation that will give new insight to the study of American history." Bull Cent Child Books
Includes bibliographical references

973.9   United States--1901-

America in the 20th century. 2nd ed, rev and expanded with primary sources. Marshall Cavendish 2003 13v il maps set $399.95
973.9
1. United States—Civilization 2. United States—History—20th century
ISBN 0-7614-7364-5   LC 2001-52949
First published 1995 in eleven volumes
Authors of individual volumes include Ann Angel, Janet McDonnell, Carolyn Kott Washburne, Kelli Peduzzi, and David Wright
Contents: v1 1900-1909; v2 1910-1919; v3 1920-1929; v4 1930-1939; v5 1940-1949; v6 1950-1959; v7 1960-1969; v8 1970-1979; v9 1980-1989; v10 1990-1999; v11 Primary sources, 1900-1949; v12 Primary sources, 1950-1999; [v13] Index volume

"Examines America's progress and setbacks, decade by decade, throughout the twentieth century including important people and trends in American politics, social policy and civil rights, foreign policy, economy and trade, literature and arts, and the environment." Publisher's note
"This compendium offers a solid, in-depth approach to its subject and would be a useful reference tool in school libraries and YA collections in public libraries." Libr J [review of 1995 edition]
Includes bibliographical references

America's decades. Greenhaven Press 2000 10v ea lib bdg $44.95; pa $28.70   **973.9**
1. United States—Civilization 2. United States—History—20th century
The set is divided as follows: The 1900s (ISBN 0-7377-0294-X; pa 0-7377-0293-1); The 1910s (ISBN 0-7377-0296-6; pa 0-7377-0295-8); The 1920s (ISBN 0-7377-0298-2; pa 0-7377-0297-4); The 1930s (ISBN 0-7377-0300-8; pa 0-7377-0299-0); The 1940s (ISBN 0-7377-0302-4; pa 0-7377-0301-6); The 1950s (ISBN 0-7377-0304-0; pa o.p.); The 1960s (ISBN 0-7377-0306-7; pa 0-7377-0305-9); The 1970s (ISBN 0-7377-0308-3; pa 0-7377-0307-5); The 1980s (ISBN 0-7377-0310-5; pa 0-7377-0309-1); The 1990s (ISBN 0-7377-0312-1; pa 0-7377-0311-3)
"Excerpts from monographs, periodical articles, and electronic publications focus on the political, economic, and social conditions that illuminate the America of each decade. . . . Each volume has a comprehensive introduction, an annotated table of contents, a thorough index, and a detailed chronology of events and inventions." SLJ

Brown, Gene
Conflict in Europe and the Great Depression; World War I (1914-1940). 21st Cent. Bks. (NY) 1994 c1993 64p il (First person America) $20.90
973.9
1. United States—History—20th century 2. World War, 1914-1918—United States
ISBN 0-8050-2585-5   LC 93-24998
First published 1993 in Canada
Primary source materials present such topics as U.S. involvement in World War I, the Great Depression, Prohibition, the growth of mass media, and the New Deal
"The writing is clear, the full-color and black-and-white photographs are plentiful, and the limited information is sound." SLJ
Includes bibliographical references

The **Century** that was; reflections on the last one hundred years; edited and with an introduction by James Cross Giblin. Atheneum Bks. for Young Readers 2000 166p il $19.95 (7 and up)
973.9
1. United States—History—20th century
ISBN 0-689-82281-2   LC 99-27011
A collection of essays by well-known authors for young people, reflecting on various aspects of life in twentieth-century America, including politics, the environment, sports, fashion, and civil rights
"The 11 essays show tremendous range in voice and scope. . . . What unites these perspectives are a sharp

The Century that was—*Continued*
analysis of history, fine writing and, for the most part, an optimistic sense of progress to lead us into the next 100 years." Publ Wkly
Includes bibliographical references

973.91   United States--1901-1953

Burg, David F.
The Great Depression; an eyewitness history. Facts on File 1996 390p il (Eyewitness history series) $75 (7 and up)   **973.91**
1. United States—Economic conditions—1933-1945
2. United States—Economic conditions—1919-1933
3. Great Depression, 1929-1939
ISBN 0-8160-3095-2   LC 95-15830
The author "delivers a narrative summary and chronology of major events in the United States and throughout the world during the Depression. He offers seven chapters, each covering one or more years; brief contemporary quotations from politicians, journalists, authors, and advertisements; and 80 black-and-white photographs. The appendixes contain a selection of primary sources, mainly New Deal statutes and other documents, and capsule biographies." Libr J

Collier, Christopher, 1930-
Progressivism, the Great Depression, and the New Deal, 1901 to 1941; by Christopher Collier, James Lincoln Collier. Benchmark Bks. (Tarrytown) 2001 95p il map (Drama of American history) lib bdg $31.36   **973.91**
1. United States—History—20th century 2. Great Depression, 1929-1939 3. United States—Economic conditions—1933-1945
ISBN 0-7614-1054-6   LC 00-29481
This "follows events and movements during the first four decades of the twentieth century, including the growing involvement of government in reforming business practices, the impact of the Great Depression, and the social policies of Franklin D. Roosevelt's New Deal. . . . Illustrations, many in color, include period photographs and engravings as well as maps and charts. . . . Highly readable and informative." Booklist
Includes bibliographical references

The **Great** Depression; Don Nardo, book editor. Greenhaven Press 2000 223p (Turning points in world history) lib bdg $33.70 (7 and up)
                                       973.91
1. Great Depression, 1929-1939 2. United States—Economic conditions—1933-1945
ISBN 0-7377-0231-1   LC 99-28801
"A collection of essays by noted scholars that looks at varying issues surrounding the era, including 'Rural Poverty, Drought, and Migration'; 'The Struggles of American Blacks'; 'Depression-era Cinema Reflected Social Values'; and 'Social Security Protects the Elderly and Infirm.' The standard subjects such as origins of the Depression, the Crash of 1929, and the initiatives of the New Deal are covered as well." SLJ
Includes bibliographical references

Living through the Great Depression; Tracy Brown Collins, book editor. Greenhaven Press 2004 160p il (Exploring cultural history) $29.95 (7 and up)   **973.91**
1. Great Depression, 1929-1939 2. United States—Social conditions
ISBN 0-7377-2096-4   LC 2003-56833
"Beginning with the stock market crash of 1929 and continuing throughout the 1930s, the Great Depression was a time of economic crisis and social and political change in America. This book explores everyday life for those who lived through this difficult period." Publisher's note
Includes bibliographical references

McElvaine, Robert S.
The Depression and New Deal; a history in documents. Oxford Univ. Press 2000 192p il (Pages from history) lib bdg $36.95 (7 and up)
                                       973.91
1. Great Depression, 1929-1939 2. United States—Economic conditions—1933-1945
ISBN 0-19-510493-5   LC 99-36644
"A vast assortment of diary entries, newspaper articles, campaign memos and speeches, political cartoons, songs, poetry, art, advertisements, photographs, and personal letters provide students with a political, economic, and social picture of this nation during the Depression. . . . {This} provides a balanced, inclusive picture of the period through the senses of the people who lived it." SLJ
Includes bibliographical references

973.917   United States-- Administration of Franklin D. Roosevelt, 1933-1945

Cooper, Michael L., 1950-
Dust to eat; drought and depression in the 1930's. Clarion Books 2004 81p il map $15 (4 and up)   **973.917**
1. Great Depression, 1929-1939 2. Migrant labor 3. Droughts
ISBN 0-618-15449-3   LC 2003-17807
Contents: The "Okie" problem; The dirty thirties; "Dust to eat, dust to breathe, dust to drink"; California-bound; Harvest gypsies; Crisis in the valley; World War II ends the Depression
This is a history of the Great Depression and the Dust Bowl drought of the 1930s that drove desperate families to California in search of work.
This includes "lots of stunning black-and-white archival photos and a clear, spacious text that draws on eloquent eyewitness reports - including comments from John Steinbeck and Woody Guthrie. . . . This is an excellent historical account." Booklist
Includes bibliographical references

Grant, R. G. (Reg G.)
The Great Depression. Barron's Educational Series 2003 c2002 64p il map (Lives in crisis) $14.95   **973.917**

Grant, R. G. (Reg G.)—*Continued*
1. Great Depression, 1929-1939
ISBN 0-7641-5601-2
First published 2002 in the United Kingdom
Discusses the economic chaos that follows the 1929 stock market crash, including accounts of the Roosevelt Administration's social programs and the social disorder in Europe that fuels the rise of fascism.
"This book strikes a good balance between human interest and factual information." SLJ
Includes bibliographical references

973.92 United States--1953-2001

Anderson, Dale, 1953-
The Cold War years. Raintree Steck-Vaughn Pubs. 2001 96p il (Making of America) lib bdg $35.64 **973.92**
1. Cold war 2. United States—History—1945- 3. United States—Social conditions
ISBN 0-8172-5711-X LC 00-62827
This discusses factors that led to the Cold War and the formation of alliances in reaction to it, as well as domestic issues such as the demand for equality for women and African Americans
"Written in a clear and concise fashion [this book provides] . . . enough details to give a taste for the era without overwhelming students." SLJ
Includes bibliographical references

Campbell, Geoffrey A.
The home front. Lucent Bks. 2003 112p il map (American war library, Cold War) $27.45 **973.92**
1. Cold war 2. United States—Social conditions 3. United States—History—1945-
ISBN 1-59018-213-8 LC 2002-663
Examines how the Cold War period in America, lasting roughly fifty years following World War II, was a contradictory time of prosperity and optimism coupled with concerns over Soviet espionage infiltrating American institutions and fear of nuclear apocalypse
Includes bibliographical references

Collier, Christopher, 1930-
The changing face of American society: 1945-2000; {by} Christopher Collier, James Lincoln Collier. Benchmark Bks. 2002 94p il (Drama of American history) lib bdg $31.36 **973.92**
1. United States—History—1945- 2. United States—Social conditions 3. United States—Social life and customs
ISBN 0-7614-1319-7 LC 2001-25963
This outlines American social conditions from 1945 to 2000, including greater prosperity, the movements for African American civil rights and women's rights, the 1960s counterculture, the Vietnam War, scientific advancements and social changes
"Illustrations are plentiful, uniformly well chosen, and include photographs, paintings, posters, and in some ti-

tles, maps. . . . [This title is] easy to read and informative." Book Rep
Includes bibliographical references

The middle road: American politics, 1945-2000; {by} Christopher Collier, James Lincoln Collier. Benchmark Bks. 2002 95p il maps (Drama of American history) lib bdg $31.36 **973.92**
1. United States—Politics and government—1945-
ISBN 0-7614-1318-9 LC 2001-25615
This outlines the course of American politics from the end of World War II, through McCarthyism, the 1960s, President Nixon and the Watergate scandal, and Presidents Carter, Reagan, Bush, and Clinton
"Illustrations are plentiful, uniformly well chosen, and include photographs, paintings, posters, and in some titles, maps. . . . {This title is} easy to read and informative." Book Rep
Includes bibliographical references

Kronenwetter, Michael
America in the 1960s. Lucent Bks. 1998 112p il maps (World history series) lib bdg $28.70 (7 and up) **973.92**
1. United States—History—1961-1974
ISBN 1-56006-294-0 LC 97-34055
Discusses a decade of enormous change and conflict in all areas of life including science, civil rights, social welfare, national defense, politics, and the arts
"Kronenwetter has synthesized solid research with considerable skill to create a panoramic picture of the stormy decade that literally changed America. His prose is taut and straightforward but readable and scrupulously objective." SLJ
Includes bibliographical references

973.921 United States-- Administration of Dwight D. Eisenhower, 1953-1961

Lindop, Edmund
America in the 1950s. 21st Cent. Bks. (Brookfield) 2002 128p il lib bdg $25.90 (7 and up) **973.921**
1. United States—Civilization 2. United States—History—1945-1953 3. United States—History—1953-1961
ISBN 0-7613-2551-4 LC 2001-52254
Contents: The Korean War; A Red scare haunts Americans; "I Like Ike" and "I'm Madly for Adlai"; African Americans seek racial justice; The Cold War escalates; Big changes come to the United States; Television takes center stage; More entertainment; A golden age of sports
Outlines life in the United States in the 1950s, including the development of suburbia, advances in technology and entertainment, politics, the space race, and the Cold War
"Lindop's book offers a solid, serious discussion in a relatively appealing package." SLJ
Includes bibliographical references

The **McCarthy** hearings; Jesse G. Cunningham, book editor; Laura K. Egendorf, assistant book editor. Greenhaven Press 2003 144p (At issue in history) lib bdg $21.96; pa $14.96 (7 and up)
973.921
1. McCarthy, Joseph, 1908-1957 2. United States—Politics and government—1945-1953 3. United States—Politics and government—1953-1961
ISBN 0-7377-1346-1 (lib bdg); 0-7377-1347-X (pa)
LC 2002-69323
"This anthology focuses on the hearings that resulted from McCarthy's famous efforts to expose communists in government positions and his use of dubious tactics such as smearing and guilt by association." Publisher's note
"Because of the evenhanded presentation, the title makes a strong and lasting impression. The writings are well chosen." SLJ
Includes bibliographical references

973.922 United States-- Administration of John F. Kennedy, 1961-1963

Hampton, Wilborn
Kennedy assassinated! the world mourns: a reporter's story. Candlewick Press 1997 96p il $17.99; pa $8.99 (5 and up)   **973.922**
1. Kennedy, John F. (John Fitzgerald), 1917-1963—Assassination 2. Journalism
ISBN 1-56402-811-9; 0-7636-1564-1 (pa)
LC 96-25801
This is the author's "account of November 22, 1963, when, as a cub reporter for UPI in Dallas, he was drafted to cover JFK's assassination. His personal response to the tragedy is fluidly juxtaposed with the nuts and bolts of scooping the story in this insider's view of one of the most pivotal events of our nation's recent history." Publ Wkly
Includes bibliographical references

973.923 United States-- Administration of Lyndon B. Johnson, 1963-1969

Schomp, Virginia, 1953-
American voices from the Vietnam era; by Virginia Schomp. Benchmark Books 2004 c2005 xxiii, 134p il (American voices from--) lib bdg $34.21   **973.923**
1. Vietnam War, 1961-1975 2. United States—History—1961-1974
ISBN 0-7614-1693-5   LC 2003-1475
Contents: A television war; The unseen enemy; The war at home: "doves" for peace; The war at home: "hawks" for war; American youth and the counterculture; The battle for civil rights; The women's liberation movement; The credibility gap; Coming home
Describes, through excerpts from diaries, speeches, newspaper articles, and other documents of the time, the

Vietnam War and related events that occurred in the United States during the 1960's, including the women's movement, the struggle for civil rights, and the generation gap. Includes review questions.
Includes bibliographical references

973.929 United States-- Administration of Bill Clinton, 1993-2001

Cohen, Daniel, 1936-
The impeachment of William Jefferson Clinton. 21st Cent. Bks. (Brookfield) 2000 112p il lib bdg $23.90 (7 and up)   **973.929**
1. Clinton, Bill, 1946-—Impeachment 2. United States—Politics and government—1989-
ISBN 0-7613-1711-2   LC 99-56179
Examines the events leading to the impeachment of President Bill Clinton, including the Whitewater investigation, the media coverage, the grand jury proceedings, impeachment by the Senate, and the legacy of this scandal
"The chronology of events is smoothly presented, and issues of national importance which became part of the public debate . . . are clearly explained." Bull Cent Child Books
Includes bibliographical references

973.931 United States-- Administration of George W. Bush, 2001-

America under attack: primary sources; Tamara Roleff, book editor. Lucent Bks. 2002 96p il map (Lucent terrorism library) $27.45 (7 and up)   **973.931**
1. September 11 terrorist attacks, 2001 2. Terrorism
ISBN 1-59018-216-2   LC 2002-1816
Contents: On the scene; America's response; Response from abroad; Who is to blame?; War on terrorism
Looks at the September 11, 2001 terrorist attack on the World Trade Center and Pentagon, U.S. response, world reaction, and the war on terrorism
"Roleff's useful compendium offers thematically arranged perspectives from witnesses in New York and Washington, DC, U.S. and world leaders, the blamed and the accusers, and war proponents and opponents. . . . This will be a sought-after research tool." SLJ
Includes bibliographical references

Frank, Mitch
Understanding September 11th; answering questions about the attacks on America. Viking 2002 136p il maps $16.99; pa $8.99 (7 and up)
973.931
1. September 11 terrorist attacks, 2001 2. Terrorism
ISBN 0-670-03582-3; 0-670-03587-4 (pa)
LC 2002-1725
Explains the historical and religious issues that sparked terrorists to attack America on September 11,

Frank, Mitch—*Continued*
2001, including information on Islam, Osama bin Laden, and the Middle East

This is written "in remarkably simple, accessible language. . . . Direct, unflinching, intelligent, and humane, this is an invaluable resource." Booklist

Includes glossary and bibliographical references

Gow, Mary
Attack on America; the day the Twin Towers collapsed. Enslow Pubs. 2002 64p il (American disasters) lib bdg $23.93   **973.931**
1. September 11 terrorist attacks, 2001 2. Terrorism
ISBN 0-7660-2118-1   LC 2001-7613

An account of events surrounding the terrorist attacks that took place at the World Trade Center in New York City, at the Pentagon near Washington, D.C., and in rural western Pennsylvania on September 11, 2001

"Gow's book relies heavily on survivor and eyewitness quotes, and the results are a terrifying overview of the day. . . . This offers a good place to begin sharing and debate." Booklist

Hampton, Wilborn
September 11, 2001; attack on New York City. Candlewick Press 2003 145p il $17.99
                                                973.931
1. September 11 terrorist attacks, 2001 2. Terrorism
ISBN 0-7636-1949-3   LC 2002-41204

Describes the September 11 attacks in the United States and presents several personal stories of tragedy told by New Yorkers who lived through the collapse of the World Trade Center

"Hampton re-creates the terrible events of that day clearly. . . . There are many . . . books about 9/11 written for young people, but this is one of the best." Booklist

Includes bibliographical references

Lalley, Pat
9.11.01: terrorists attack the U.S.; by Patrick Lalley. Raintree Steck-Vaughn Pubs. 2002 48p il $29.93; pa $8.50 (4 and up)   **973.931**
1. September 11 terrorist attacks, 2001 2. Terrorism
ISBN 0-7398-6021-6; 0-7398-6356-8 (pa)
                                    LC 2002-277397

"Lalley covers the events of September 11th and provides brief background on the World Trade Center, Islamic extremism, and Osama bin Laden. He also comments on the impact the terrorists' attacks have had both here and abroad." SLJ

"This compact book does an excellent job of explaining the terrorist attacks on September 11, but equally important is its presentation of the background that led to the events." Booklist

Margulies, Phillip
Al Qaeda: Osama bin Laden's army of terrorists. Rosen Pub. Group 2003 64p il (Inside the world's most infamous terrorist organizations) lib bdg $26.50   **973.931**
1. Al Qaeda (Organization) 2. Terrorism 3. September 11 terrorist attacks, 2001
ISBN 0-8239-3817-4   LC 2002-7526

Contents: Mujahedeen; Inside al-Qaeda; September 11; The investigation; Conclusion

Discusses the Islamic organization known as Al-Qaeda, focusing on its presumed role in the September 11 terrorist attacks in the United States

"With color photos that aren't too shocking and long reading lists updated by links gathered on a dedicated Web site. {This} will be useful for school reports." Booklist

Includes bibliographical references

Marquette, Scott
America under attack. Rourke Pub. 2003 48p il (America at war) lib bdg $29.93; pa $6.95 (4 and up)   **973.931**
1. September 11 terrorist attacks, 2001 2. Terrorism 3. United States—Foreign relations—Middle East
ISBN 1-58952-386-5 (lib bdg); 1-58952-471-3 (pa)
                                    LC 2002-1215

Contents: Introduction: "A War to Save Civilization"; Map of Middle East/Central Asia, 2001; Timeline; Roots of terror; "An Act of War"; A war of many fronts; "The New Normal"; America changed forever

The author "begins with 9/11 and then presents a chronology of prior events of terrorism against the U.S. He goes on to describe the war in Afghanistan and changes in American life. Even within the limits of 48 pages, he is able to point out some of the dissent in American policy concerning the Patriot Act." Booklist

Includes glossary and bibliographical references

A **Nation** challenged; a visual history of 9/11 and its aftermath; {by} The New York Times; introduction by Howell Raines; photographs edited by Nancy Lee and Lonnie Schlein; text edited by Mitchel Levitas. Young reader's ed. Scholastic 2002 96p il map $18.95 (4 and up)
                                                973.931
1. September 11 terrorist attacks, 2001—Pictorial works 2. Terrorism
ISBN 0-439-48803-6   LC 2002-26879

Contents: September 11, 2001; The days after; Meeting the challenge abroad; Meeting the challenge at home

In this Young Reader's edition of the title published for adults by the New York Times and Calloway, text, photographs, and illustrations from the New York Times section, "A Nation Challenged," record how the world was changed due to the September 11, 2001, terrorist attacks on the United States and their aftermath

This "is beautifully designed with unforgettable images on every page. . . . The book is an excellent resource for every library desiring a sweeping visual account of this momentous time in America's history." Libr Media Connect

Includes glossary and bibliographical references

Stewart, Gail, 1949-
America under attack; September 11, 2001; [by] Gail B. Stewart. Lucent Bks. 2002 96p il (Terrorism library) lib bdg $27.45 (7 and up)
973.931
1. September 11 terrorist attacks, 2001 2. Terrorism
ISBN 1-59018-208-1   LC 2001-7506
Contents: "The mouth of hell"; Two new targets; A nation reacts; Looking for answers; Taking stock
Discusses the events surrounding the attacks on the World Trade Center and the Pentagon on September 11, 2001, and describes the experiences of those involved and the impact of these attacks
"An excellent resource that demonstrates thorough research and opens up issues for discussion." Booklist
Includes bibliographical references

Wheeler, Jill C.
September 11, 2001: the day that changed America. Abdo & Daughters 2002 64p il (War on terrorism) lib bdg $25.65   **973.931**
1. September 11 terrorist attacks, 2001 2. Terrorism
ISBN 1-57765-656-3   LC 2001-53930
Describes the events and immediate aftermath of the September 11, 2001 terrorist attacks on the United States, in which planes were crashed into the Twin Towers buildings in New York City as well as into the Pentagon building near Washington, D.C
"The tone of the writing is matter-of-fact, and the color photos illustrate the text effectively." Booklist
Includes glossary

974   Northeastern United States

Johnson, Claudia D.
Daily life in colonial New England; {by} Claudia Durst Johnson. Greenwood Press 2002 xxvii, 215p (Daily life through history) $49.95 (7 and up)   **974**
1. New England—History 2. United States—Social life and customs—1600-1775, Colonial period
ISBN 0-313-31458-6   LC 00-61721
This description of colonial life in New England covers such topics as the clergy and the church, crime and punishment, government and law, labor, shelter and attire, food and health, marriage and sex, arts and amusements, and Native Americans and Africans in New England
"In this excellent volume, Johnson draws a remarkably clear and complete picture of the day-to-day existence of the first European settlers in New England." Voice Youth Advocates
Includes bibliographical references

Rylant, Cynthia
Appalachia; the voices of sleeping birds; illustrated by Barry Moser. Harcourt Brace Jovanovich 1991 21p il $17; pa $6   **974**
1. Appalachian region
ISBN 0-15-201605-8; 0-15-201893-X (pa)
LC 90-36798

"This is a running narrative description of the dogs, people, houses, seasons, and lifestyles of Appalachia." Bull Cent Child Books
"Taking her subtitle from a passage by James Agee, the author conveys with a marvelous economy of words the essence of the very special part of America where she was raised. A poetic text projects emotion as well as information. . . . Moser's watercolors capture the scene perfectly. . . . The book is a treasure—simply a beautiful combination of text and art." Horn Book

974.4   Massachusetts

Bowen, Gary
Stranded at Plimoth Plantation, 1626; words and woodcuts by Gary Bowen; introduction by David Freeman Hawke. HarperCollins Pubs. 1994 81p il map pa $12.95 hardcover o.p. (4 and up)
974.4
1. Pilgrims (New England colonists) 2. Massachusetts—History—1600-1775, Colonial period
ISBN 0-06-440719-5 (pa)   LC 93-31016
The author "gives an account of the year 1626 at the by-then-well-established Pilgrim colony, rendered in the form of a journal kept by an orphaned 13-year-old. Shipwrecked on the way to Jamestown, taken in by the settlers at Plimoth, Christopher Sears observes their customs, planting, harvesting, home tutoring, the eight-hour Sabbath meeting, court day, the use of the stocks, etc." Publ Wkly
"The youthful voice and observations, in language that is a remarkable blend of clarity and period flavor, provide a more intimate and involving picture of the period than more straightforward factual accounts." SLJ

Collier, Christopher, 1930-
Pilgrims and Puritans, 1620-1676; {by} Christopher Collier, James Lincoln Collier. Benchmark Bks. (Tarrytown) 1998 94p il maps (Drama of American history) lib bdg $31.36
974.4
1. Pilgrims (New England colonists) 2. Puritans 3. Massachusetts—History—1600-1775, Colonial period
ISBN 0-7614-0438-4   LC 96-49382
Recounts the religious, political, and social history of the Massachusetts Bay Colony, and its influence on our lives today
Includes bibliographical references

Edwards, Judith
The Plymouth Colony and the Pilgrim adventure in American history. Enslow Pubs. 2003 128p il map (In American history) lib bdg $26.60 (7 and up)   **974.4**
1. Pilgrims (New England colonists) 2. Massachusetts—History—1600-1775, Colonial period
ISBN 0-7660-1989-6   LC 2002-12809

Edwards, Judith—*Continued*

Contents: Landahoy!; In search of religious freedom; The first emigration; Setting out for America; The Mayflower Compact; The howling of wolves; Betrayal and the threat of war; Hunger, treachery and pirates; Daily life at Plymouth; Expansion and legacy

Traces the dangers and adventures surrounding the history of the Pilgrim settlement at Plymouth, Massachusetts, highlighting the roles played by William Brewster, Miles Standish, and other individuals

Includes bibliographical references

Erickson, Paul, 1976-

Daily life in the Pilgrim colony, 1636. Clarion Bks. 2001 48p il map $20; pa $9.95

974.4

1. Pilgrims (New England colonists) 2. Massachusetts—History—1600-1775, Colonial period

ISBN 0-618-05846-X; 0-395-98841-1 (pa)

LC 2001-17203
.

This "describes the day-to-day activities of the Prentiss family, owners of a small farm just outside the colony of Plymouth. Full-color photographs, maps, line drawings, and detailed illustrations accompany engaging present-tense text to provide insight into Pilgrim society as a whole, and into the lives of specific family members as well." Book Rep

Pilgrim voices; our first year in the New World; edited by Connie and Peter Roop; illustrations by Shelley Pritchett. Walker & Co. 1995 48p il pa $7.95 hardcover o.p. **974.4**

1. Pilgrims (New England colonists) 2. Massachusetts—History—1600-1775, Colonial period

ISBN 0-8027-7530-6 (pa)

LC 95-10114

Drawing on diaries and journals, the editors "use the Pilgrims' own words to describe the voyage on the Mayflower; *explo*ring the land and meeting the Indians; the hardships, illnesses, and hunger during the first winter; and the harvest festival. The diary format and first-person voice contribute authenticity and vitality to the text, with colorful paintings by Shelley Pritchett adding interest." Booklist

Includes bibliographical references

974.6 Connecticut

Fradin, Dennis B.

The Connecticut colony; by Dennis Brindell Fradin. Children's Press 1990 159p il maps lib bdg $33.50 **974.6**

1. Connecticut—History—1600-1775, Colonial period

ISBN 0-516-00393-3

LC 89-29205

Surveys the history of the colony of Connecticut from its early days up through the American Revolution. Includes biographical sketches of prominent individuals

"Thorough and appealing with large print. . . . Despite a huge amount of factual information, Fradin injects a degree of drama, especially with regard to the politics of the times." Booklist

974.7 New York

Bial, Raymond

Tenement; immigrant life on the Lower East Side. Houghton Mifflin 2002 48p il $16 (4 and up) **974.7**

1. Poor 2. Immigrants—United States 3. Lower East Side (New York, N.Y.)

ISBN 0-618-13849-8

LC 2002-00407

Presents a view of New York City's tenements during the peak years of foreign immigration, discussing living conditions, laws pertaining to tenements, and the occupations of their residents

"The writing is particularly clear and sharp. Calling upon and quoting the writing of reformer Jacob Riis (and featuring his compelling photographs), Bial explains simply, yet engagingly, what tenement life was like. . . . Along with Riis' photographs, Bial provides some of his own, taken at the Lower East Side Tenement Museum in New York City." Booklist

Includes bibliographical references

Hansen, Joyce

Breaking ground, breaking silence; the story of New York's African burial ground; by Joyce Hansen and Gary McGowan. Holt & Co. 1998 130p il maps $19.95 **974.7**

1. African Americans—History 2. Cemeteries 3. Excavations (Archeology) 4. New York (N.Y.)—Antiquities

ISBN 0-8050-5012-4

LC 97-19105

Describes the discovery and study of the African burial site found in Manhattan in 1991, while excavating for a new building, and what it reveals about the lives of black people in Colonial times

"This book is well written and attractively designed, and readers should have access to it in social studies classrooms as well as in libraries. It will generate lots of class discussion and writing projects." Voice Youth Advocates

Hopkinson, Deborah

Shutting out the sky; life in the tenements of New York, 1880-1924. Orchard Bks. 2003 134p il $17.95 (5 and up) **974.7**

1. Poor 2. Immigrants—United States 3. Lower East Side (New York, N.Y.)

ISBN 0-439-37590-8

LC 2002-44781

Contents: Coming to the golden land; Tenements; shutting out the sky; Settling in: greenhorns and boarders; Everyone worked on; On the streets: pushcarts, pickles and play; A new language, a new life; Looking to the future: will it ever be different?

Photographs and text document the experiences of five individuals who came to live in the Lower East Side of New York City as children or young adults from Belarus, Italy, Lithuania, and Romania at the turn of the twentieth century

"The text is supported by numerous tinted archival photos of living and working conditions. Although this book will appeal to students looking for material for projects, the writing lends immediacy and vivid images make it simply a fascinating read." SLJ

Includes bibliographical references

Houle, Michelle M.
Triangle Shirtwaist Factory fire; flames of labor reform. Enslow Pubs. 2002 48p il (American disasters) lib bdg $23.93   **974.7**
1. Triangle Shirtwaist Company, Inc. 2. Factories 3. Clothing industry
ISBN 0-7660-1785-0   LC 2001-7667
Discusses the 1911 fire that killed 146 New York garment factory workers, the conditions that led up to it, and some of the legislation that came about to prevent the occurrence of similar disasters
"The short chapters are enlivened with period photographs, including a horrific view of the bodies of women who had leaped to their deaths to escape the flames. Although the text is easy to read, the horror is not sugarcoated." SLJ
Includes bibliographical references

Levy, Janey
The Erie Canal; a primary source history of the canal that changed America. Rosen Central Primary Source 2003 64p il maps (Primary sources in American history) lib bdg $29.25
      974.7
1. Erie Canal (N.Y.)
ISBN 0-8239-3680-5   LC 2002-5608
Contents: An idea is born; Timeline; The big ditch; An engineering marvel; The canal age; Competition from the railroad; The end of an era
Uses primary source documents, narrative, and illustrations to recount how construction of the Erie Canal changed America by vastly improving the movement of goods to settlers in the newly purchased Louisiana Territory
This "will be extremely effective when introducing students to primary source material." Libr Media Connect
Includes glossary and bibliographical references

Lieurance, Suzanne
The Triangle Shirtwaist fire and sweatshop reform in American history. Enslow Pubs. 2003 128p il (In American history) $20.95 (7 and up)
      974.7
1. Triangle Shirtwaist Company, Inc. 2. Clothing industry 3. Factories
ISBN 0-7660-1839-3   LC 2002-8761
Contents: Fire in the factory; A general strike is declared; A city mourns; Investigations and a trial; Steps to improve working conditions
Explores the people and events connected with the 1911 fire in a New York City sewing factory that killed 146 people and led to reforms in legislation regarding workplace safety
This is written "in a clear, moving yet meticulously documented style. . . . Period photographs and judicious use of personal stories add a human face to the tragedy." Libr Media Connect
Includes bibliographical references

Matsen, Bradford
Go wild in New York City; [by] Brad Matsen; illustrations by Paul Corio; scientific illustration by Kate Lake. National Geographic 2005 79p il map $16.95 (4 and up)   **974.7**
1. Natural history 2. New York (N.Y.)
ISBN 0-7922-7982-4
This is a "picture-book tour through New York City's 'true wildness,' with chapters that cover the area's water, rocks, air, plants, and animals as well as a closing section about food production and waste removal. . . . Packed with color photographs, cartoons, diagrams, and numerous sidebars. . . . There's an impressive array of basic science here, described mostly in accessible, enthusiastic text. Students will find enough to support reports, and the open format will attract browsers. " Booklist

Murphy, Jim, 1947-
Blizzard!: the storm that changed America. Scholastic Press 2000 136p il map $18.95
      974.7
1. Blizzards 2. New York (N.Y.)—History
ISBN 0-590-67309-2   LC 99-24894
"This is an example of stellar nonfiction. The haunting jacket illustration grabs attention, and the dramatic power of the splendid narrative . . . will keep the pages turning." Booklist
Includes bibliographical references

Pellowski, Michael, 1949-
The terrorist trial of the 1993 bombing of the World Trade Center; a headline court case. Enslow Pubs. 2003 112p il (Headline court cases) lib bdg $26.60   **974.7**
1. Trials 2. World Trade Center Bombing, New York, N.Y., 1993 3. Terrorism
ISBN 0-7660-2045-2   LC 2002-156033
Contents: Smoke, terror, and death; A plot unravels; Islam and Terrorism: a history; Tracking the terrorists; Terror on trial; A worldwide manhunt; Justice revisited; The terrorism continues
Examines the trials of Mahmoud Abouhalima, Ramzi Yousef, Mohammad Salameh, Sheik Omar Abdel-Rahman, and others for their roles in the 1993 bombing of the World Trade Center
"A well-balanced look at the events leading up to, during, and after the 1993 bombing. . . . The text is clear and succinct." SLJ
Includes glossary and bibliographical references

Whitcraft, Melissa
The Hudson River. Watts 1999 63p il lib bdg $24.50; pa $8.95   **974.7**
1. Hudson River (N.Y. and N.J.)
ISBN 0-531-11739-1; 0-531-16425-X (pa)
      LC 99-28585
Examines the history, uses, changing nature, and ecological aspects of the Hudson River
The text is "well researched and thoughtful, making sure both the geographic concepts and the history are understandable. The spacious layout includes large color photographs on every spread, with sidebars adding further information. . . . Lists of further readings, organizations, Internet sites, and a glossary are appended." Booklist
Includes bibliographical references

975 Southeastern United States. Southern States

975.5 Virginia

Erickson, Paul, 1976-
Daily life on a Southern plantation, 1853. Lodestar Bks. 1998 c1997 48p il pa $7.99 hardcover o.p. (4 and up)   **975**
1. Plantation life 2. Slavery—United States
ISBN 0-14-056668-6 (pa)   LC 97-22540
First published 1997 in the United Kingdom
Recreates a southern plantation of 1853 and describes the daily lives of its owners and of the slaves who worked there
"Erickson uses a family to make the information in the text accessible. This book follows two families . . . one living in the 'Big House' and the other a slave family, through a typical day—a technique that provides a personal, well-informed view of slavery." Horn Book Guide
Includes glossary

975.3 District of Columbia (Washington)

Ashabranner, Brent K., 1921-
No better hope; what the Lincoln Memorial means to America; {by} Brent Ashabranner; photographs by Jennifer Ashabranner. 21st Cent. Bks. (Brookfield) 2001 64p il (Great American memorials) lib bdg $25.90 (4 and up)
                    975.3
1. Lincoln, Abraham, 1809-1865 2. Lincoln Memorial (Washington, D.C.)
ISBN 0-7613-1523-3   LC 00-61546
"Seven brief chapters review Lincoln's presidency, discuss preliminary plans for a permanent memorial, describe the processes by which architect Henry Bacon and sculptor Daniel French developed and executed their creation, and suggest how the site has 'become a symbol of the "patient confidence" that Lincoln had in the wisdom and courage of the common people.'" Bull Cent Child Books
A "well-designed volume. . . . Excellent color photographs by Jennifer Ashabranner appear throughout the book." Booklist
Includes bibliographical references

Feinberg, Barbara Silberdick, 1938-
The changing White House. Children's Press 2000 30p il (Cornerstones of freedom) lib bdg $21; pa $5.95   **975.3**
1. White House (Washington, D.C.) 2. Presidents—United States
ISBN 0-516-21651-1; 0-516-27164-4 (pa)
                    LC 99-52353
Describes the White House through the years and the changes made by its different inhabitants

Collier, Christopher, 1930-
The paradox of Jamestown, 1585-1700; {by} Christopher Collier, James Lincoln Collier. Benchmark Bks. (Tarrytown) 1998 93p il maps (Drama of American history) lib bdg $31.36
                    975.5
1. Powhatan, ca. 1550-1618 2. Slavery—United States 3. Jamestown (Va.)—History 4. United States—History—1600-1775, Colonial period
ISBN 0-7614-0437-6   LC 96-34998
Discusses the circumstances surrounding English colonization of Virginia and the evolution of slavery in that colony
Includes bibliographical references

Edwards, Judith
Jamestown, John Smith, and Pocahontas in American history. Enslow Pubs. 2002 128p il maps (In American history) $26.60 (7 and up)
                    975.5
1. Smith, John, 1580-1631 2. Pocahontas, d. 1617 3. Jamestown (Va.)—History 4. United States—History—1600-1775, Colonial period
ISBN 0-7660-1842-3   LC 2001-3002
Traces the dangers and adventures surrounding the history of the first permanent British settlement in America, highlighting the roles played by John Smith, Pocahontas, and other individuals
"Edwards has collected an amazing amount of information about a century of American history that is usually covered in a few pages. . . . The wealth of details about personalities of the time is what makes this book worth buying." Book Rep
Includes bibliographical references

Kent, Zachary
The mysterious disappearance of Roanoke Colony in American history. Enslow Pubs. 2004 128p il map (In American history) lib bdg $26.60 (7 and up)   **975.6/175**
1. Roanoke Island (N.C.)—History
ISBN 0-7660-2147-5   LC 2003-11108
Contents: Croatoan; The New World; Amadas and Barlowe set sail; Sir Richard Grenville's expedition; Ralph Lane in command; Sir Francis Drake; Return to Roanoke; John White's adventures; Solving a mystery
Traces the dangers and adventures surrounding the short history of the first British colony in America, highlighting the roles played by Sir Walter Raleigh, Roanoke chief Wingina, and other individuals
"With its lively writing style and multiple illustrations, this book will be a good addition to history collections and provide support for school assignments." SLJ
Includes bibliographical references and index

976.4 Texas

977 North Central United States. Lake states

Levy, Janey
The Alamo; a primary source history of the legendary Texas mission. Rosen Central Primary Source 2003 64p il maps (Primary sources in American history) lib bdg $29.25   **976.4**
1. Alamo (San Antonio, Tex.) 2. Texas—History
ISBN 0-8239-3681-3   LC 2002-2368
Contents: The first settlers and explorers; Timeline; Life on Mexico's northern frontier; The gathering clouds of war; The Alamo's defenders; The siege and battle of the Alamo; After the Alamo; The legend of the Alamo
A collection of primary source materials highlights the story behind the Alamo and its place in the history of San Antonio, Texas
This "will be extremely effective when introducing students to primary source material." Libr Media Connect
Includes bibliographical references

McNeese, Tim
The Alamo. Chelsea House 2003 136p il map (Sieges that changed the world) lib bdg $22.95
          976.4
1. Alamo (San Antonio, Tex.) 2. Texas—History
ISBN 0-7910-7101-4   LC 2002-12914
Contents: The lands of Tejas; Gone to Texas; A land of revolution; The Texans defend themselves; The siege begins; Victory or death; The Mexicans are coming; Will you come to the bower?
Describes the historical background, events, and aftermath of the 1836 attack on the Alamo, in which Jim Bowie and Davy Crockett were among the many Texans killed or captured by Santa Ana's troops
The author presents "an excellent overview of Texas history in the first half of the book and details the two-week siege in the second. . . . A well-written, well-researched chronicle." SLJ
Includes bibliographical references

Murphy, Jim, 1947-
Inside the Alamo. Delacorte Press 2003 121p il map $16.95; lib bdg $18.99 (5 and up)
          976.4
1. Alamo (San Antonio, Tex.) 2. Texas—History
ISBN 0-385-32574-6; 0-385-90092-9 (lib bdg)
          LC 2002-24029
An overview of the struggle between the Texan settlers and Mexico's General Santa Anna for control of Texas, with a detailed description of the 1836 siege of the Alamo. Includes biographical sketches and quotations of some of those involved
This is "an absorbing, interpretive, highly readable account. . . . Murphy has done an admirable job of separating prejudicial speculation (by survivors on both sides) from documentation." SLJ
Includes bibliographical references

Currie, Stephen, 1960-
The Mississippi. Lucent Bks. 2003 112p il maps (Rivers of the world) lib bdg $27.45   **977**
1. Mississippi River 2. Mississippi River valley
ISBN 1-59018-061-5   LC 2002-13088
Contents: The Big Muddy; The river as highway; Resources and livelihoods; Floods; Ecological damage and restoration
Discusses the importance of the Mississippi River, its role in the agricultural and industrial development of the United States, floods and their impact, and various threats to the river
This is "good for serious report writers looking for solid information." SLJ
Includes bibliographical references

Walsh, Kieran
The Mississippi. World Almanac 2003 48p il maps (Great rivers of the world) lib bdg $26.60; pa $14.60 (4 and up)   **977**
1. Mississippi River 2. Mississippi River valley
ISBN 0-8368-5444-6 (lib bdg); 0-8368-5451-9 (pa)
          LC 2002-34315
Contents: The course of the Mississippi; The Mississippi in history; Cities and settlements; Trade, transportation, and industry; Animals and plants; Environmental issues; Recreation and leisure; The future
This explains the Mississippi River's "flow, history, ecological concerns, tourism, flora and fauna, etc. . . . Clear and colorful photos appear on every page." SLJ
Includes glossary and bibliographical references

977.3 Illinois

Murphy, Jim, 1947-
The great fire. Scholastic 1995 144p il maps $16.95 (5 and up)   **977.3**
1. Fires—Chicago (Ill.)
ISBN 0-590-47267-4   LC 94-9963
Newbery honor book, 1996
"Firsthand descriptions by persons who lived through the 1871 Chicago fire are woven into a gripping account of this famous disaster. Murphy also examines the origins of the fire, the errors of judgment that delayed the effective response, the organizational problems of the city's firefighters, and the postfire efforts to rebuild the city. Newspaper lithographs and a few historical photographs convey the magnitude of human suffering and confusion." Horn Book Guide
Includes bibliographical references

978 Western United States

Alter, Judy
The Santa Fe Trail. Children's Press 1998 30p
il maps (Cornerstones of freedom) $21; pa $5.95
978
1. Santa Fe Trail
ISBN 0-516-21145-5; 0-516-26396-X (pa)
LC 97-32710
Presents a history of the trail that became an important commercial route to the southwestern United States during the 1800s

The **American** frontier; James D. Torr, book
editor. Greenhaven Press 2002 240p il (Turning
points in world history) lib bdg $34.95; pa
$23.70 (7 and up) **978**
1. Frontier and pioneer life—West (U.S.) 2. United
States—Territorial expansion 3. West (U.S.)—History
ISBN 0-7377-0786-0 (lib bdg); 0-7377-0785-2 (pa)
LC 2001-33514
This is a collection of essays about the American
frontier, with an introduction and summaries
Includes bibliographical references

Blumberg, Rhoda, 1917-
The incredible journey of Lewis and Clark.
Lothrop, Lee & Shepard Bks. 1987 143p il maps
pa $12.99 (5 and up) **978**
1. Lewis, Meriwether, 1774-1809 2. Clark, William,
1770-1838 3. Lewis and Clark Expedition (1804-1806)
4. West (U.S.)—Exploration
ISBN 0-688-14421-7 (pa) LC 87-4235
Also available in hardcover from Smith, P.
Describes the expedition led by Lewis and Clark to
explore the unknown western regions of America at the
beginning of the nineteenth century
"Blumberg's writing is dignified but never dry, and
her sense of narrative makes familiar history an exciting
story." Bull Cent Child Books
Includes bibliographical references

York's adventures with Lewis and Clark; an
African-American's part in the great expedition.
HarperCollins 2004 88p il map $17.99; lib bdg
$18.89 (5 and up) **978**
1. York, ca. 1775-ca. 1815 2. Lewis and Clark Expedition (1804-1806) 3. West (U.S.)—Exploration
4. African Americans—Biography
ISBN 0-06-009111-8; 0-06-009112-6 (lib bdg)
LC 2003-9425
Relates the adventures of York, a slave and "body servant" to William Clark, who journeyed west with the
Lewis and Clark Expedition of 1804-1806
"This well-researched selection helps to round out the
study of an amazing event in our country's history. . . .
Meticulously documented and illustrated with black-and-
white photos and reproductions, this is a solid purchase
for all collections." SLJ
Includes bibliographical references

Calabro, Marian
The perilous journey of the Donner Party.
Clarion Bks. 1999 192p il maps $20 (5 and up)
978
1. Donner party 2. Frontier and pioneer life—West
(U.S.) 3. Overland journeys to the Pacific
ISBN 0-395-86610-3 LC 98-29610
Uses materials from letters and diaries written by survivors of the Donner Party to relate the experiences of
that ill-fated group as they endured horrific circumstances on their way to California in 1846-47
"Calabro's offering is a fine addition to the Donner
Party canon and particularly well suited to its young audience, for whom the story of hardship and survival will
be nothing short of riveting. . . . From the haunting cover with its lonely campfire to the recounting of a survivors' reunion, this is a page-turner." Booklist
Includes bibliographical references

Clark, William, 1770-1838
Off the map; the journals of Lewis and Clark;
edited by Peter and Connie Roop; illustrations by
Tim Tanner. Walker & Co. 1993 40p il pa $8.95
hardcover o.p. **978**
1. Lewis and Clark Expedition (1804-1806) 2. West
(U.S.) Exploration
ISBN 0-8027-7546-2 (pa) LC 92-18340
A compilation of entries and excerpts from the journals of William Clark and Meriwether Lewis, describing
their historic expedition
"The full-color illustrations, mainly in warm earth
tones, give the pages an attractive look, but the most vivid pictures come from the journals themselves. . . . This
vivid source material would be a welcome part of any
classroom study of the subject." Booklist

Collier, Christopher, 1930-
Indians, cowboys, and farmers and the battle for
the Great Plains, 1865-1910; {by} Christopher
Collier, James Lincoln Collier. Benchmark Bks.
(Tarrytown) 2001 95p il map (Drama of American
history) lib bdg $31.36 **978**
1. Great Plains—History 2. Native Americans—Great
Plains
ISBN 0-7614-1052-X LC 00-21103
Discusses the settling of the area between the Missouri
River and the Rocky Mountains and the conflicting interests of the different groups involved--the Indians, cowboys, farmers, sheepherders, and railroad barons
Includes bibliographical references

Cox, Clinton
The forgotten heroes; the story of the Buffalo
Soldiers. Scholastic 1993 174p il hardcover o.p.
paperback available $4.50 **978**
1. African American soldiers 2. West (U.S.)—History
ISBN 0-590-45122-7 (pa) LC 92-36622
"'Buffalo Soldiers' was the name Native Americans
gave to the African-American soldiers posted in the
American West in the years following the Civil War.
. . . Their job: to clear the way for settlement of the
West." Voice Youth Advocates

Cox, Clinton—*Continued*
"A thoroughly researched, well-written account. . . . The narrative is enlivened by dialogue taken from primary sources." SLJ
Includes bibliographical references

DeAngelis, Gina
The black cowboys. Chelsea House 1997 104p il maps (African-American achievers) $33.50
978
1. Cowhands 2. African Americans—History 3. West (U.S.)—History
ISBN 0-7910-2589-6   LC 97-24823
An account of the adventurous African Americans whose exploits contributed to the legends of the Wild West
This "will be useful for young report writers." Booklist
Includes bibliographical references

Faber, Harold
Lewis and Clark; from ocean to ocean. Benchmark Bks. 2002 80p il maps (Great explorations) lib bdg $29.93   **978**
1. Lewis, Meriwether, 1774-1809 2. Clark, William, 1770-1838 3. Lewis and Clark Expedition (1804-1806) 4. West (U.S.)—Exploration
ISBN 0-7614-1241-7   LC 00-51898
This "discusses the 1804 expedition that set out to explore the American continent. . . . Supplementing Faber's account are journal quotations that offer firsthand reportage of events, conditions, and reflections about the journey. The last chapter tells what happened to significant members of the expedition and includes information on the Lewis and Clark Trail. . . . The colorful and sometimes quite beautiful illustrations include paintings, drawings, and prints, as well as a few photographs of sites and artifacts." Booklist
Includes bibliographical references

Galford, Ellen
The trail West; exploring history through art; Ellen Galford. Two-Can Pub 2005 64p il (Picture that!) $19.95 (5 and up)   **978**
1. West (U.S.)—History 2. West (U.S.) in art
ISBN 1-587-28442-1   LC 2004-8334
Contents: Heading West; The travellers' rest : Benjamin Franklin Reinhart; Fur-trapping trip : George Caleb Bingham; Hunting buffalo : George Catlin; Trouble on the trail : Charles Ferdinand Wimar; At home in the wilderness : Cornelius Krieghoff; Home by the fireside : Eastman Johnson; A Mandan village : George Catlin; A sacred festival : Silver Horn; The shooting match : George Caleb Bingham; Schooldays : Winslow Homer; At the trading post : Alfred Jacob Miller; Life in the saddle : Frederic Remington; Gold rush : Charles Christian Nahl; End of the line : O.E. Berninghaus
This examines pioneer life in the American West through the works of such artists as Wislow Homer, Eastman Johnson, George Catlin, and George Caleb Bingham
"Art and history meld with entertaining and successful results. . . .[This] unique, well-thought-out [title is] good for reports, and browsers would enjoy [it], too." SLJ

Josephson, Judith Pinkerton
Growing up in pioneer America, 1800 to 1890. Lerner Publs. 2003 64p il map (Our America) lib bdg $26.60   **978**
1. Frontier and pioneer life—West (U.S.) 2. West (U.S.)—History
ISBN 0-8225-0659-9   LC 2001-6825
Describes what life was like for young people moving to and living on the western frontier
"Primary-source materials including selections from letters and diaries join numerous reproductions and archival photos to deliver a clear picture of the varied experiences of children living in the U.S. during the 1800s. Accessible, attractive, and useful." SLJ
Includes bibliographical references

Katz, William Loren
Black women of the Old West. Atheneum Bks. for Young Readers 1995 84p il $19.95 (5 and up)
978
1. African American women 2. Frontier and pioneer life—West (U.S.) 3. West (U.S.)—History
ISBN 0-689-31944-4   LC 95-9969
This work contains "vignettes and photographs of dozens of women, some famous, others unknown outside their own family circles, who lived across the West in the 19th and early 20th centuries." N Y Times Book Rev
"Katz succeeds in establishing that women of color were an important, if unsung, presence on the westward-shifting frontier." Bull Cent Child Books

Kimmel, Elizabeth Cody
As far as the eye can reach; Lewis and Clark's westward quest. Random House 2003 119p il maps $14.95; lib bdg $16.99 (4 and up)
978
1. Lewis, Meriwether, 1774-1809 2. Clark, William, 1770-1838 3. Lewis and Clark Expedition (1804-1806) 4. West (U.S.)—Exploration
ISBN 0-375-81348-9; 0-375-91348-3 (lib bdg)
LC 2002-31621
"Landmark books"
An account of the journey across the unexplored territory west of the Mississippi River undertaken by Meriwether Lewis and William Clark in the early eighteen hundreds by order of President Jefferson
"Chock-full of historical detail, Kimmel's account of Lewis and Clark's expedition is an eye-opener. . . . A book such as this can excite young readers to delve further into U.S. history." SLJ
Includes bibliographical references

Lavender, David Sievert, 1910-2003
Snowbound; the tragic story of the Donner Party; by David Lavender. Holiday House 1996 87p il maps $22.95 (4 and up)   **978**
1. Donner party 2. Frontier and pioneer life—West (U.S.) 3. Overland journeys to the Pacific
ISBN 0-8234-1231-8   LC 95-41266
Relates the ordeals faced by a group of pioneers on their journey from Illinois to California in 1846
The author "draws on authentic primary documents,

Lavender, David Sievert, 1910-2003—*Continued*
combining a vivid narrative with his analysis of what
happened and why. His handsomely designed, slightly
oversize volume has lots of photos of the places and
people." Booklist
Includes bibliographical references

Lawlor, Laurie
Window on the West; the frontier photography
of William Henry Jackson. Holiday House 1999
132p il $18.95 (7 and up)   **978**
1. Jackson, William Henry, 1843-1942 2. West
(U.S.)—History
ISBN 0-8234-1380-2   LC 98-56083
Presents the photographs taken by William Henry
Jackson from 1869 to 1893, discussing his life and how
his work captured and introduced the American West to
the public
"Jackson's images are balanced by Lawlor's eloquent
text, which folds in details about everything from the
wonder of Yellowstone's geysers to the debasement of
the Native Americans. . . . A memorable, bittersweet
valentine to the Old West." Booklist
Includes glossary and bibliographical references

McArthur, Debra
The dust bowl and the Depression in American
history. Enslow Pubs. 2002 128p il maps (In
American history) lib bdg $26.60 (7 and up)
                                                  978
1. Great Plains—History 2. Dust storms 3. Great Depression, 1929-1939
ISBN 0-7660-1838-5   LC 2001-1377
"McArthur provides information on government programs instituted during the Depression, correlates the effects of the drought and the Depression on American
farm families, and describes various soil conservation
methods attempted. He also briefly mentions the droughts
and dustbowls of the 1950's and the 1970's, visual and
performing arts programs of the New Deal, and writers
whose accomplishments reflected the attitudes and problems of Americans during this period." Book Rep
Includes bibliographical references

McGowen, Tom
African-Americans in the Old West. Children's
Press 1998 30p il map (Cornerstones of freedom)
$21; pa $5.95   **978**
1. African Americans—History 2. Frontier and pioneer
life—West (U.S.) 3. West (U.S.)—History
ISBN 0-516-20835-7; 0-516-26348-X (pa)
                                      LC 97-26583
Describes the important role of freed slaves and other
African-Americans in the settlement of the West

Meltzer, Milton, 1915-
Driven from the land; the story of the Dust
Bowl. Benchmark Bks. 2000 111p il (Great
journeys) lib bdg $32.79 (4 and up)   **978**
1. Great Plains—History 2. Dust storms 3. Great Depression, 1929-1939
ISBN 0-7614-0968-8   LC 98-47501

"Well-reproduced photographs by Dorothea Lange and
others of the time greatly enhance the text." Booklist
Includes bibliographical references

Murdoch, David Hamilton, 1937-
Cowboy; written by David H. Murdoch;
photographed by Geoff Brightling. Dorling
Kindersley 2000 63p il map (DK eyewitness
books) $19.99 (4 and up)   **978**
1. Cowhands
ISBN 0-789-46594-9
First published 1993
Text and photographs trace the history and lore of
cowboys around the globe.

Patent, Dorothy Hinshaw
Animals on the trail with Lewis and Clark;
photographs by William Muñoz. Clarion Bks. 2002
118p il maps $18 (4 and up)   **978**
1. Lewis and Clark Expedition (1804-1806)
2. Animals—United States 3. West (U.S.)—Exploration
ISBN 0-395-91415-9   LC 2001-42200
Retraces the Lewis and Clark journey and blends their
observations of previously unknown animals with modern information about those same animals
"The spacious page layouts, beautiful illustrations, and
well-written text help ensure that this historically significant story will be read and enjoyed." Booklist
Includes bibliographical references

Homesteading; settling America's heartland;
photographs by William Muñoz. Walker & Co.
1998 32p il maps $16.95 (4 and up)   **978**
1. Frontier and pioneer life—West (U.S.) 2. West
(U.S.)—Social life and customs
ISBN 0-8027-8664-2   LC 98-12463
"An attractive, informative, and well-written guide."
Booklist

The Lewis and Clark trail; then and now;
photographs by William Muñoz. Dutton Children's
Bks. 2002 60p il maps $19.99 (4 and up)
                                                  978
1. Lewis and Clark Expedition (1804-1806) 2. West
(U.S.)—Exploration
ISBN 0-525-46912-5   LC 2002-70857
Patent provides a "narrative account of the Lewis and
Clark Expedition, beginning with a realistically harsh,
you-are-there introduction to life with the Corps of Discovery. Among the many books on the subject appearing
in time for the bicentennial of that event . . . this one
distinguishes itself by incorporating information about
how the land, rivers, vegetation, wildlife and trails today
differ from what Lewis and Clark saw 200 years ago.
. . . A well-written presentation of the topic." Booklist
Includes bibliographical references

Plants on the trail with Lewis and Clark;
photographs by William Muñoz. Clarion Bks. 2003
104p il map $18 (4 and up)   **978**
1. Lewis and Clark Expedition (1804-1806)
2. Plants—United States 3. West (U.S.)—Exploration
ISBN 0-618-06776-0   LC 2002-10383

Patent, Dorothy Hinshaw—*Continued*

Contents: Jefferson, Lewis, and plants; The importance of trees; Plants as food; Wildflowers and their uses; The fate of Lewis's specimens

Describes the journey of Lewis and Clark through the western United States, focusing on the plants they cataloged, their uses for food and medicine, and the plant lore of Native American people

"Good-quality, full-color photos and reproductions clearly extend the text. . . . The author's knowledge of and keen interest in her subject matter is very evident in this fascinating account." SLJ

Includes bibliographical references

Pendergast, Tom, 1964-

Westward expansion: almanac; {by} Tom Pendergast and Sara Pendergast; Christine Slovey, editor. U.X.L 2000 xlvi, 254p il $60   **978**

1. Frontier and pioneer life—West (U.S.) 2. West (U.S.)—History

ISBN 0-7876-4862-0   LC 00-36375

This almanac "documents the chronological events that created a romantic national mythology around the pioneers who blazed trails through the wilderness." Publisher's note

Includes bibliographical references

Westward expansion: primary sources; {by} Tom Pendergast and Sara Pendergast; Christine Slovey, editor. U.X.L 2001 xxix, 260p $60 (7 and up)   **978**

1. United States—Territorial expansion 2. West (U.S.)—History

ISBN 0-7876-4864-7   LC 00-107861

This volume provides "full text or excerpts from diaries, books, letters and many other documents." Publisher's note

Includes bibliographical references

Sakurai, Gail, 1952-

Asian-Americans in the old West. Children's Press 2000 30p il (Cornerstones of freedom) $21; pa $5.95 (4 and up)   **978**

1. West (U.S.)—History 2. Asian Americans

ISBN 0-516-21152-8; 0-516-27035-4 (pa)

     LC 99-24463

Includes index

Describes the important role of the Chinese, Japanese, and other Asians in the settlement of the American West

Schlissel, Lillian

Black frontiers; a history of African American heroes in the Old West. Simon & Schuster Bks. for Young Readers 1995 80p il pa $7.99 hardcover o.p.   **978**

1. African Americans—History 2. Frontier and pioneer life—West (U.S.) 3. West (U.S.)—History

ISBN 0-689-83315-6 (pa)   LC 92-120

Focuses on the experiences of blacks as mountain men, soldiers, homesteaders, and scouts on the frontiers of the American West

"Good-quality period photos and black-and-white reproductions appear on nearly every page, adding human interest and realism to the text. An excellent addition to black history or westward movement units." Booklist

Includes bibliographical references

Sonneborn, Liz

The American West: an illustrated history. Scholastic 2002 144p il $19.95 (7 and up)

     978

1. West (U.S.)—History

ISBN 0-439-21970-1   LC 2001-20938

"A Fair Street book"

This "book looks at the American West as a physical place, with magnificent vistas and extremes in weather, and also as an idea, a land of promise and new beginnings. It traces the different people who inhabited or crossed through this area west of the Mississippi River to make their dreams come true. . . . A first-rate, engaging offering." SLJ

Includes bibliographical references

Stefoff, Rebecca, 1951-

The opening of the West. Benchmark Bks. 2002 c2003 105p il maps (American voices from—) lib bdg $32.79   **978**

1. Frontier and pioneer life—West (U.S.) 2. West (U.S.)—History

ISBN 0-7614-1201-8   LC 2001-8681

Contents: The frontier; The explorers; Mountain men and miners; The Overland Trails; Women and children in the West; Living and working on the land; Building the new West; The fate of the Native Americans

Presents the history of the westward expansion of the United States in the eighteenth and nineteenth centuries through excerpts from letters, newspaper articles, journal entries, and laws of the time

Includes glossary and bibliographical references

Stovall, TaRessa

The Buffalo Soldiers. Chelsea House 1997 104p il (African-American achievers) $23.95; pa $9.95

     978

1. African American soldiers 2. West (U.S.)—History

ISBN 0-7910-2595-0; 0-7910-2596-9 (pa)

     LC 97-14568

An account of the achievements of the Afro-American Army regiments that distinguished themselves during numerous campaigns and played a vital role in the settlement of the American West

"A well-written, eye-opening account of a shamefully obscure aspect of African American and U.S. armed forces history." Booklist

Includes bibliographical references

Tunis, Edwin, 1897-1973

Frontier living; written and illustrated by Edwin Tunis. Crowell 1976 c1961 165p il maps o.p. Lyons Press paperback available $18.95 (5 and up)

     978

Tunis, Edwin, 1897-1973—*Continued*
1. Frontier and pioneer life—West (U.S.) 2. West (U.S.)—History
ISBN 1-58574-137-X (pa)
Companion volume to Colonial living (1976)
A reprint of the title first published 1961 by World Publishing Company
This volume "portrays the manners and customs of the frontiersman and his family from the beginning of the westward movement through the 19th century in . . . text and more than 200 drawings." Wis Libr Bull

Vivian, R. Gwinn
Chaco Canyon; [by] R. Gwinn Vivian and Margaret Anderson. Oxford Univ. Press 2002 47p il maps (Digging for the past) $19.95　　**978**
1. Pueblo Indians 2. Cliff dwellers and cliff dwellings 3. Chaco Culture National Historical Park (N.M.) 4. Archeology
ISBN 0-19-514280-2　　LC 2001-54855
Relates the nineteenth-century discovery of cliff dwellings in the Chaco Canyon of northwest New Mexico, the excavations of the ancient ruins, and what the artifacts reveal about the civilization of the ancient Pueblo Indians
This "brings young readers up close to the field of archaeology. . . . Sharp color photos show the sites, artifacts, and the scientists at work." Booklist
Includes glossary and bibliographical references

Westward expansion; James D. Torr, book editor. Greenhaven Press 2003 208p map (Interpreting primary documents) $33.70; pa $22.45 (7 and up)　　**978**
1. Frontier and pioneer life—West (U.S.) 2. West (U.S.)—History
ISBN 0-7377-1134-5; 0-7377-1133-7 (pa)
　　LC 2002-499
Contents: The lure of the west; Conquest of native America; Manifest Destiny; The Western railroads
Uses primary source materials, including letters and magazine articles of the time, to examine the exploration and conquest of the American West by explorers and settlers of European descent
"Students will welcome the summary provided at the beginning of each document and the questions for consideration. A good choice for those who are eager to understand arguments and attitudes that shaped the history of the West." SLJ
Includes bibliographical references

Westward expansion; an eyewitness history; [edited by] Sanford Wexler. Facts on File 1991 418p il maps (Eyewitness history series) $75
　　978
1. Frontier and pioneer life—West (U.S.) 2. West (U.S.)—History 3. United States—Territorial expansion
ISBN 0-8160-2407-3　　LC 90-42599
This work "includes primary-source material from various points of view, arranged chronologically from the French and Indian War through the settlement of the Great Plains. It presents stories of exploration, Indian-white relations, war and diplomacy, and settlers' experiences." Booklist

The accounts "are well chosen to portray the promises and realities of the frontier. Strongly recommended as a good introduction to source material." Libr J
Includes bibliographical references

978.1　Kansas

McArthur, Debra
The Kansas-Nebraska Act and "Bleeding Kansas" in American history. Enslow Pubs. 2003 128p il map (In American history) lib bdg $26.60
　　978.1
1. Abolitionists 2. Slavery—United States 3. Kansas—History
ISBN 0-7660-1988-8　　LC 2002-152064
Describes the violent period of Kansas Territory history, prior to statehood and the Civil War, when abolitionists and pro-slavery factions openly murdered in defense of their cause
Includes bibliographical references

Zeinert, Karen, 1942-2002
Tragic prelude: bleeding Kansas. Linnet Bks. 2001 105p il lib bdg $25 (7 and up)
　　978.1
1. Abolitionists 2. Slavery—United States 3. Kansas—History
ISBN 0-208-02446-8　　LC 00-69435
"Zeinert offers a historical account of the violence of Bleeding Kansas, the unofficial battle over slavery in the territory of Kansas during the 1850s." Voice Youth Advocates
"With its primary sources and readable format, this title would be a valuable addition to library collections." Book Rep
Includes bibliographical references

979.1　Arizona

Rawlins, Carol
The Colorado River; {by} Carol B. Rawlins. Watts 1999 63p il (Watts library) lib bdg $24.50; pa $8.95　　**979.1**
1. Colorado River (Colo.-Mexico)
ISBN 0-531-11738-3; 0-531-16421-7 (pa)
　　LC 98-52125
This title discusses "the course of the river and its related landforms, including the Grand Canyon. There is also an extensive section on dams and their ability to produce hydroelectric power, as well as on the many irrigation canals and ditches built along the river. The ancient peoples of the area are described, as are Spanish and American explorers." SLJ
Includes glossary and bibliographical references

979.4   California

Goldsmith, Connie, 1945-
Lost in Death Valley; the true story of four families in California's gold rush. 21st Cent. Bks. (Brookfield) 2001 144p il lib bdg $24.90
979.4
1. California—Gold discoveries 2. Frontier and pioneer life—California
ISBN 0-7613-1915-8   LC 00-57774
"Based on journals, letters, and other primary documents, the book follows the stories of four families as they traveled from Salt Lake City to California in 1849, some of them fatefully taking a false shortcut through Death Valley." Horn Book Guide
"The suffering is not sensationalized. . . . The impartial narrative allows readers to form their own opinions about the participants. . . . A useful addition." SLJ
Includes bibliographical references

O'Donnell, Kerri, 1972-
The gold rush; a primary source history of the search for gold in California. Rosen Central Primary Source 2003 64p il maps (Primary sources in American history) lib bdg $29.25 (4 and up)
979.4
1. California—Gold discoveries 2. Frontier and pioneer life—California
ISBN 0-8239-3682-1   LC 2002-1367
Contents: El Dorado; Timeline; The great discovery; Gold fever; To California by sea; The Overlanders; Life in the mines; The lawless West
Uses primary source documents, narrative, and illustrations to recount how the mid-nineteenth century California gold rush affected Americans and immigrants and how it shaped history
This "will be extremely effective when introducing students to primary source material." Libr Media Connect
Includes glossary and bibliographical references

Tanaka, Shelley
Earthquake! on a peaceful spring morning disaster strikes San Francisco; text by Shelley Tanaka ; paintings by David Craig ; historical consultation by Gladys Hansen. 1st U.S. ed. Hyperion Books for Children 2004 48p il map (Day that changed America) $16.99 (4 and up)
979.4
1. San Francisco (Calif.)—History 2. Earthquakes
ISBN 0-7868-1882-4   LC 2004-44457
"A Hyperion\Madison Press book"
"Using dramatic material culled from the adult recollections of four survivors . . . Tanaka recreates a series of events during and following the great San Francisco earthquake of April 18, 1906." SLJ
"Attractively illustrated and designed, this book offers a good story as well as solid information." Booklist
Includes glossary and bibliographical references

979.5   Oregon. Pacific Northwest

Blackwood, Gary L.
Life on the Oregon Trail. Lucent Bks. 1999 111p il maps (Way people live) lib bdg $28.70 (7 and up)
979.5
1. Oregon Trail 2. Overland journeys to the Pacific 3. Frontier and pioneer life—West (U.S.)
ISBN 1-56006-540-0   LC 98-48958
Describes how people traveling on the Oregon Trail lived, discussing their reasons for going west, modes of transportation, interaction with the Indians, and activities on the Trail
"Inserts, maps, and black-and-white reproductions effectively augment the narrative. Well organized and extremely informative, this book is well suited for reports." SLJ
Includes bibliographical references

Fisher, Leonard Everett, 1924-
The Oregon Trail. Holiday House 1990 64p il maps $18.95 (4 and up)
979.5
1. Oregon Trail 2. Overland journeys to the Pacific 3. Frontier and pioneer life—West (U.S.)
ISBN 0-8234-0833-7   LC 90-55103
Charts the journey of those who followed the Oregon Trail in the first half of the nineteenth century
"Fisher brings this migration to life with a clear, readable text that makes generous use of the emigrants' own journal entries. . . . The illustrations are many and varied, including maps, photographs, drawings, documents, and paintings." Booklist

980   South America. Latin America

Latin America, history and culture; an encyclopedia for students; Barbara A. Tenenbaum, editor in chief. Scribner 1999 4v il set $415
980
1. Latin America—Encyclopedias
ISBN 0-684-80576-6   LC 99-23057
Based on Encyclopedia of Latin American history and culture (1996)
"Articles cover topics in history, social studies, literature, government, geography, humanities {and} current events." Publisher's note
"This encyclopedia contains a plethora of information. . . . This reference set will be useful for research projects." Voice Youth Advocates

981   Brazil

Barter, James, 1946-
The Amazon. Lucent Bks. 2003 112p il maps (Rivers of the world) lib bdg $21.96
981
1. Amazon River valley 2. Amazon River
ISBN 1-56006-934-1   LC 2002-1091
The "*Amazon* gives coverage to the habitat this mighty river provides for the world's most diverse collection of wildlife and to the changes that have occurred due to

Barter, James, 1946-—_Continued_
modern technology, progress, commercialism, and man's efforts to repair the ecosystems. The information is well documented through photographs, maps, and authoritative sources." Libr Media Connect

Dicks, Brian
Brazil; Brian Dicks. Facts on File 2003 61p il map (Countries of the world) $30 **981**
1. Brazil
ISBN 0-8160-5382-0
Discusses the geography, history, government, economy, people, politics, and culture of Brazil
This is "is frank about the country's racial frictions and economic inequality. . . . {This title offers} a wealth of nearly up-to-date information and a realistic introduction to {Brazil.} . . . {It also features} good-quality color photos of urban and rural homes and buildings and traditional and western lifestyles." Booklist

Richard, Christopher, 1959-
Brazil; {by} Christopher Richard, Leslie Jermyn. 2nd ed. Benchmark Bks. 2002 144p il maps (Cultures of the world) lib bdg $37.07 (5 and up) **981**
1. Brazil
ISBN 0-7614-1359-6   LC 2001-47263
First published 1991
Presents the geography, history, government, economy, and social life and customs of the South American country of Brazil
Includes glossary and bibliographical references

Streissguth, Thomas
Brazil in pictures; by Tom Streissguth. rev and expanded. Lerner Publs. 2003 80p il map (Visual geography series) lib bdg $21.27 (5 and up) **981**
1. Brazil
ISBN 0-8225-1959-3   LC 2001-3275
Replaces the edition published 1987 prepared by Nathan A. Haverstock
An introduction to Brazil, discussing its history, government, economy, people, and culture
Includes bibliographical references

982   Argentina

Gofen, Ethel, 1937-
Argentina; by Ethel Caro Gofen, Leslie Jermyn. 2nd ed. Benchmark Bks. 2002 144p il maps (Cultures of the world) lib bdg $37.07 (5 and up) **982**
1. Argentina
ISBN 0-7614-1358-8   LC 2001-47759
First published 1991
Presents the history, geography, government, economy, people, and social life and customs of Argentina
Includes glossary and bibliographical references

Hintz, Martin, 1945-
Argentina. Children's Press 1998 144p il (Enchantment of the world, second series) $35 (4 and up) **982**
1. Argentina
ISBN 0-516-20647-8   LC 97-40666
Describes the geography, history, culture, religion, and people of the environmentally diverse South American country of Argentina
Includes bibliographical references

983   Chile

Dwyer, Christopher
Chile. Chelsea House 1999 128p il map (Major world nations) lib bdg $22.95 **983**
1. Chile
ISBN 0-7910-4734-2
First published 1990 in Places and peoples of the world series
An introduction to the geography, history, government, economy, people, and culture of Chile

Winter, Jane Kohen, 1959-
Chile; by Jane Kohen Winter, Susan Roraff. 2nd ed. Benchmark Bks. 2002 144p il map (Cultures of the world) lib bdg $37.07 (5 and up) **983**
1. Chile
ISBN 0-7614-1360-X   LC 2001-47827
First published 1991
Introduces the history, geography, culture, and lifestyles of Chile
Includes glossary and bibliographical references

985   Peru

Calvert, Patricia, 1931-
The ancient Inca; written by Patricia Calvert. Franklin Watts 2004 128p il (People of the ancient world) lib bdg $29.50; pa $9.95 (5 and up) **985**
1. Incas
ISBN 0-531-12358-8 (lib bdg); 0-531-16740-2 (pa)
LC 2004-1956
Contents: The science of the past : why it matters; Before the Inca; Children of the sun; Life in a highland family; Growing up among the Inca; Medicine, magic, and death; The top of the Inca pyramid; Warriors, war, and keeping the peace; Buildings, bridges, and roads; The war of two brothers; Suncasapa, the bearded one; The aftermath of conquest
This "well-written, attractive [title has] extensive collections of quality color photographs of ruins and artifacts." SLJ
Includes bibliographical references

Hinds, Kathryn, 1962-
The Incas. Benchmark Bks. (Tarrytown) 1998
80p il map (Cultures of the past) lib bdg $29.93
985

1. Incas
ISBN 0-7614-0270-5   LC 96-30799
Examines the history, culture, religion, and social
structure of the ancient Incas
Includes glossary and bibliographical references

986.1 Colombia

DuBois, Jill, 1952-
Colombia; by Jill DuBois, Leslie Jermyn. 2nd
ed. Benchmark Bks. 2002 144p il maps (Cultures
of the world) lib bdg $37.07 (5 and up)
986.1

1. Colombia
ISBN 0-7614-1361-8   LC 2001-47264
First published 1991
Presents the geography, history, government, economy,
and social life and customs of the country of Colombia
Includes glossary and bibliographical references

Haynes, Tricia
Colombia. Chelsea House 1999 102p il maps
(Major world nations) $22.95   **986.1**
1. Colombia
ISBN 0-7910-4969-8   LC 98-17466
Examines the history, people, geography, economy,
climate, and culture of the South American nation of Co-
lombia
Includes glossary

987 Venezuela

Winter, Jane Kohen, 1959-
Venezuela; [by] Jane Kohen Winter, Kitt
Baguley. 2nd ed. Benchmark Bks. 2002 144p il
maps (Cultures of the world) lib bdg $37.07
987

1. Venezuela
ISBN 0-7614-1362-6   LC 2001-53877
First published 1990
Presents the geography, history, economy, and social
life and customs of Venezuela
Includes glossary and bibliographical references

988.1 Guyana

Jermyn, Leslie
Guyana. Benchmark Bks. 2000 128p il map
(Cultures of the world) lib bdg $37.07 (5 and up)
988.1
1. Guyana
ISBN 0-7614-0994-7   LC 99-55063
Examines the geography, history, government, econo-
my, people, and culture of Guyana
Includes glossary and bibliographical references

Morrison, Marion
Guyana. Children's Press 2003 144p il maps
(Enchantment of the world, Second series) lib bdg
$34.50 (4 and up)   **988.1**
1. Guyana
ISBN 0-516-22377-1   LC 2001-6915
Describes the geography, history, culture, religion, and
people of Guyana
Includes bibliographical references

989.2 Paraguay

Jermyn, Leslie
Paraguay. Benchmark Bks. 2000 128p il map
(Cultures of the world) lib bdg $37.07 (5 and up)
989.2
1. Paraguay
ISBN 0-7614-0979-3   LC 99-27257
Describes the geography, history, government, econo-
my, people, lifestyle, religion, language, arts, leisure, fes-
tivals, and food of Paraguay
Includes glossary and bibliographical references

989.5 Uruguay

Jermyn, Leslie
Uruguay. Benchmark Bks. (Tarrytown) 1999
128p il maps (Cultures of the world) lib bdg
$37.07 (5 and up)   **989.5**
1. Uruguay
ISBN 0-7614-0873-8   LC 98-27375
Describes the geography, history, government, economy, people, lifestyle, religion, language, arts, leisure, festivals, and food of the smallest country in South America
Includes glossary and bibliographical references

993 New Zealand

Smelt, Roselynn
New Zealand. Benchmark Bks. (Tarrytown)
1998 128p il maps (Cultures of the world) lib bdg
$37.07 (5 and up)   **993**
1. New Zealand
ISBN 0-7614-0808-8   LC 97-42179
Introduces the geography, history, religion, government, economy, and culture of a Pacific-island country
first populated by the Maori, to whom it was the "Land
of the Long White Cloud"
Includes glossary and bibliographical references

Theunissen, Steve
The Maori of New Zealand. Lerner Publs. 2003
48p il (First peoples) lib bdg $23.93   **993**
1. Maoris
ISBN 0-8225-0665-3   LC 2002-5525
An introduction to the history, modern and traditional
cultural practices, and economy of the Maori people of
New Zealand

Theunissen, Steve—*Continued*
The book "positively glow{s} with brilliant photographs of the countryside and the people. The text . . . is clear and to the point." Voice Youth Advocates
Includes glossary and bibliographical references

994 Australia

Arnold, Caroline, 1944-
Uluru, Australia's Aboriginal heart; photographs by Arthur Arnold. Clarion Books 2003 64p il $16 (5 and up)   **994**
1. Aboriginal Australians 2. Australia 3. Uluru-Kata Tjuta National Park (Australia)
ISBN 0-618-18181-4   LC 2002-15542
Describes Uluru, formerly known as Ayers Rock, in Australia's Uluru-Kata Tjuta National Park, its plant and animal life, and the country's Aboriginal people for whom the site is sacred
"The book's greatest accomplishment . . . is to give readers a sense of the ongoing spiritual importance of Uluru to the Anangu, who have lived around it for 10,000 years. Clear, colorful photos of Uluru and its surroundings appear on nearly every page, illustrating the text with beauty and finesse." Booklist

Einfeld, Jann
Life in the Australian Outback. Lucent Bks. 2003 112p il map (Way people live) lib bdg $21.96   **994**
1. Australia
ISBN 1-59018-014-3   LC 2001-7504
Contents: An ancient people; Cattle mustering and sheep shearing; At home on the station; School by air; Opal fever; Outback town life
"An in-depth look at a unique culture that exists in Australia's remote interior. Well detailed and meticulously documented, this book does an excellent job of illustrating the diversity of the outback population as well as the challenges faced by its inhabitants." SLJ
Includes glossary and bibliographical references

Grabowski, John F.
Australia. Lucent Bks. 2002 112p il (Modern nations of the world) $29.95 (7 and up)
                                          994
1. Australia
ISBN 1-560-06566-4   LC 2001-6626
Discusses Australia's history, geography, government, people, and culture
"The strength of the work is . . . its readability. The author . . . uses his writing skills to present basic facts about Australian history and culture in an entertaining manner." Am Ref Books Annu, 2003
Includes bibliographical references

Heinrichs, Ann
Australia. Children's Press 1998 144p il (Enchantment of the world, second series) $35 (4 and up)   **994**
1. Australia
ISBN 0-516-20648-6   LC 98-15780

Explores the geography, history, arts, religions, and everyday life of the Land Down Under, also called the Lucky Country
Includes bibliographical references

Rajendra, Vijeya, 1936-
Australia; [by] Vijeya & Sundran Rajendra. 2nd ed. Benchmark Bks. 2002 143p il maps (Cultures of the world) lib bdg $37.07 (5 and up)
                                          994
1. Australia
ISBN 0-7614-1473-8   LC 2002-19206
First published 1990
Presents the history, geography, government, economy, environment, religion, people, and social life and customs of the island continent of Australia
Includes glossary and bibliographical references

Sharp, Anne Wallace
Australia. Lucent Bks. 2003 112p il map (Indigenous peoples of the world) $27.45
                                          994
1. Australian aborigines
ISBN 1-59018-091-7   LC 2002-457
Contents: Who are the indigenous people of Australia?; The land and its resources; The dreamtime; Family and community life; A clash of cultures; A white Australia; Aboriginal life in modern Australia; Hope for the future
Discusses the historical origins, beliefs, arts, family life, cultural clashes with whites, and future hopes of the aboriginal people of Australia
"A well-researched, thorough look at the Aborigines' way of life. . . . Black-and-white captioned photographs, reproductions, and maps enhance the presentation." SLJ
Includes bibliographical references

995.3 Papua New Guinea. New Guinea region

Gascoigne, Ingrid
Papua New Guinea. Benchmark Bks. (Tarrytown) 1998 128p il maps (Cultures of the world) lib bdg $37.07 (5 and up)   **995.3**
1. Papua New Guinea
ISBN 0-7614-0813-4   LC 97-43611
Discusses the geography, history, economy, government, varied culture and peoples of the country made up of more than 600 islands and archipelagos
Includes glossary and bibliographical references

996 Polynesia and Micronesia

Arnold, Caroline, 1944-
Easter Island; giant stone statues tell of a rich and tragic past; text and photographs by Caroline Arnold. Clarion Bks. 2000 48p il map $15; pa $5.95 (5 and up)   **996**
1. Easter Island
ISBN 0-395-87609-5; 0-618-48605-4 (pa)
                              LC 99-27189

Arnold, Caroline, 1944—*Continued*

Describes the formation, geography, ecology, and inhabitants of the isolated Easter Island in the Pacific Ocean

This is a "straightforward account of what archaeologists have determined about the history of the Rapanui people and their monuments. The clearly written text is accompanied by breathtaking color photographs that show the beauty of the island and its rich collection of archaeological features." Horn Book

Includes bibliographical references

NgCheong-Lum, Roseline, 1962-

Fiji. Benchmark Bks. 2000 128p il map (Cultures of the world) lib bdg $37.07 (5 and up)

996

1. Fiji

ISBN 0-7614-0996-3   LC 99-54120

Describes the geography, history, government, economy, people, lifestyle, religion, language, arts, leisure, festivals, and food of the South Pacific island of Fiji

Includes glossary and bibliographical references

Tahiti. Benchmark Bks. (Tarrytown) 1997 128p il maps (Cultures of the world) $37.07 (5 and up)

996

1. Tahiti (French Polynesia)

ISBN 0-7614-0682-4   LC 96-40213

Discusses the geography, history, government, economy, people, and culture of the largest island in French Polynesia

This offers "lucidly written text. . . . Chapters include discussion of nuclear testing in the Pacific, the Tahitian language, and nationalism in the French territory. Maps and a page of basic facts about Tahiti round out the useful book." Horn Book Guide

Includes glossary and bibliographical references

Pelta, Kathy

Rediscovering Easter Island. Lerner Publs. 2000 112p il maps (How history is invented) lib bdg $23.93   **996**

1. Easter Island

ISBN 0-8225-4890-9   LC 00-9163

Discusses the many visits made by explorers, missionaries, businessmen, scientists, and others to Easter Island since the late 1600s and what they revealed about life on this remote Pacific island

"Coverage is serious, generally evenhanded, and smoothly presented, making this a fine foundation for readers who enjoy digging up the past." Bull Cent Child Books

Includes bibliographical references

998 Arctic islands and Antarctica

Beattie, Owen

Buried in ice; by Owen Beattie and John Geiger with Shelley Tanaka. Scholastic 1992 64p il maps (Time quest book) hardcover o.p. paperback available $6.95 (4 and up)   **998**

1. Franklin, Sir John, 1786-1847 2. Arctic regions

ISBN 0-590-43849-2 (pa)   LC 91-23897

"A Scholastic/Madison Press book"

Probes the tragic and mysterious fate of Sir John Franklin's failed expedition to the Arctic to find the Northwest Passage in 1845

"The narrative is interspersed with an imaginative section that relates the story of the expedition from the point of view of 19-year-old Luke, a member of the crew. While the text is exciting, the book's greatest strength is its superb illustrations: drawings, paintings, and historic and present day photographs are used to enrich each page." SLJ

Includes glossary and bibliographical references

Dewey, Jennifer

Antarctic journal; four months at the bottom of the world. HarperCollins Pubs. 2001 64p il $16.99; lib bdg $17.89 (4 and up)   **998**

1. Antarctica

ISBN 0-06-028586-9; 0-06-028587-7 (lib bdg)

      LC 99-89065

"Dewey relates the experience of her four-month trip to the Antarctic peninsula in diary entries, letters, sketches, and photographs." Bull Cent Child Books

A "well-written, eye-opening book. . . . This is a remarkable read." Booklist

Includes bibliographical references

Kimmel, Elizabeth Cody

Ice story; Shackleton's lost expedition. Clarion Bks. 1999 120p il maps $18 (4 and up)   **998**

1. Shackleton, Sir Ernest Henry, 1874-1922 2. Endurance (Ship) 3. Imperial Trans-Antarctic Expedition (1914-1917) 4. Antarctica—Exploration

ISBN 0-395-91524-4   LC 98-29956

Describes the events of the 1914 Shackleton Antarctic expedition, when the ship the Endurance was crushed in a frozen sea and the men made the perilous journey across ice and stormy seas to reach inhabited land

"The amazing story is well served in this account, which includes photos by expedition photographer Frank Hurley." Horn Book Guide

Includes bibliographical references

Myers, Walter Dean, 1937-

Antarctica; journeys to the South Pole. Scholastic Press 2004 134p il maps $18.95

      998

1. Antarctica

ISBN 0-439-22001-7   LC 2004-2501

This is an "overview of the discovery and exploration of Antarctica. . . . What drives the narrative is the personal adventures of those who raced to reach the South Pole first, especially the fierce rivalry between Norwegian explorer Roald Amundsen . . . and Britain's Robert Scott."

This is "a lucid, well-written text." SLJ

Includes bibliographical references

Fic FICTION

A number of subject headings have been added to the books in this section to aid in curriculum work. It is not necessarily recommended that these subjects be used in the library catalog.

Abelove, Joan

Go and come back; a novel. DK Ink 1998 176p (7 and up)   **Fic**
1.   Anthropologists—Fiction   2.   Peru—Fiction   3. Native Americans—Fiction
ISBN 0-7894-2476-2; 0-14-130694-7 (pa)
                                                         LC 97-36070
"A Richard Jackson book"

Alicia, a young tribeswoman living in a Amazonian village in the Andes, tells about the two American women anthropologists who arrive to study the way of life of her people

"By juxtaposing two radically different cultures (with attitudes toward sexuality prominent), Abelove provides humorous yet respectful insight into both." Horn Book

Saying it out loud; a novel. DK Pub. 1999 136p o.p. Puffin Bks. paperback available $5.99 (7 and up)   **Fic**
1.   Mother-daughter   relationship—Fiction   2. Father-daughter relationship—Fiction 3. Death—Fiction
ISBN 0-14-131227-0 (pa)   LC 98-33265
"A Richard Jackson book"

"In a series of journal entries beginning November 4, 1961, and ending just over a month later, 16-year-old Mindy describes the process of losing her mother to brain cancer. Abelove lifts Mindy's feelings of isolation and grief to a metaphoric level in the novel, making it a story about leaving childhood behind." Publ Wkly

Abrahams, Peter, 1947-

Down the rabbit hole; an Echo Falls mystery; by Peter Abrahams. 1st ed. Laura Geringer Books 2005 375p $15.99; lib bdg $16.89 (7 and up)
                                                            Fic
1. Mystery fiction
ISBN 0-06-073701-8; 0-06-073702-6 (lib bdg)
                                               LC 2004-14778
Also available audiobook edition

"Ingrid Levin-Hill . . . has just been cast as the lead in Alice in Wonderland when she finds herself in a different role - murder detective. The corpse is that of 'Cracked-Up Katie,' whom Ingrid encountered when she attempted to get from her orthodontist to soccer practice." Publ Wkly

Ingrid "and the other main characters are all solidly drawn. . . . Deft use of literary allusions and ironic humor add further touches of class to a topnotch mystery." SLJ

Adams, Douglas, 1952-2001

The Hitchhiker's Guide to the Galaxy. Harmony Bks. 1980 215p $15 (7 and up)   **Fic**
1. Science fiction
ISBN 0-517-54209-9   LC 80-14572
Also available in paperback from Ballantine Bks.

"Based on a BBC radio series, . . . this is the episodic story of Arthur Dent, a contemporary Englishman who discovers first that his unpretentious house is about to be demolished to make way for a bypass, and second that a good friend is actually an alien galactic hitchhiker who announces that Earth itself will soon be demolished to make way for an intergalactic speedway. A suitably bewildered Dent soon finds himself hitching . . . rides throughout space, aided by a . . . reference book, The Hitchhiker's Guide to the Galaxy, a compendium of 'facts,' philosophies, and wild advice." Libr J

Other titles featuring Arthur Dent are:
Life, the universe and everything (1982)
Mostly harmless (1992)
The restaurant at the end of the universe (1981)
So long, and thanks for all the fish (1984)

Adams, Richard, 1920-

Watership Down. Scribner Classics 1974 c1972 429p $27.50 (6 and up)   **Fic**
1. Rabbits—Fiction 2. Allegories
ISBN 0-684-83605-4
Available in paperback from Avon Bks. and Audiobook version

First published 1972 in the United Kingdom; first United States edition 1974 by Macmillian

"Faced with the annihilation of its warren, a small group of male rabbits sets out across the English downs in search of a new home. Internal struggles for power surface in this intricately woven, realistically told adult adventure when the protagonists must coordinate tactics in order to defeat an enemy rabbit fortress. It is clear that the author has done research on rabbit behavior, for this tale is truly authentic." Shapiro. Fic for Youth. 3d edition

Adler, C. S. (Carole S.), 1932-

One unhappy horse. Clarion Bks. 2000 156p $15   **Fic**
1. Horses—Fiction 2. Friendship—Fiction
ISBN 0-618-04912-6   LC 00-25907
Things are difficult for twelve-year-old Jan and her mother after her father's death, and when it turns out that her beloved horse needs an operation, Jan reluctantly gets money from an elderly woman whom she has befriended

"A well-paced story with interesting and mostly sympathetic characters." SLJ

Winning. Clarion Bks. 1999 156p $15
                                                            Fic
1. Tennis—Fiction
ISBN 0-395-65017-8   LC 98-51935
Vicky is thrilled to be on the eighth-grade tennis team, until she realizes that her new playing partner Brenda is ruthless about winning and will even cheat to do so

"The treatment of Vicky's developing athletic prowess is particularly authentic and engaging. . . . Many youngsters will see themselves here, and they'll appreciate the literary support." Bull Cent Child Books

Adlington, L. J., 1970-
The diary of Pelly D; by L.J. Adlington. 1st
U.S. ed. Greenwillow Books 2005 282p $15; lib
bdg $16.89 (7 and up)   **Fic**
1. Science fiction
ISBN 0-06-076615-8; 0-06-076616-6 (lib bdg)
    LC 2004-52258
When Toni V, a construction worker on a futuristic
colony, finds the diary of a teenage girl whose life has
been turned upside-down by holocaust-like events, he begins to question his own beliefs.
"Adlington has crafted an original and disturbing
dystopian fantasy told in a smart and sympathetic teen
voice." Booklist

Aiken, Joan, 1924-2004
The wolves of Willoughby Chase; illustrated by
Pat Marriott. Delacorte Press 2000 c1962 181p
$16.95; pa $5.99 (5 and up)   **Fic**
1. Great Britain—Fiction
ISBN 0-385-32790-0; 0-440-49603-9 (pa)
First published 1962 in the United Kingdom; first
United States edition 1963 by Doubleday
"In this burlesque of a Victorian melodrama, two Lon-
don children are sent to a country estate while their par-
ents are away. Here they outwit a wicked governess, es-
cape from packs of hungry wolves, and restore the estate
to its rightful owner." Hodges. Books for Elem Sch Libr
"Plot, characterization, and background blend perfectly
into an amazing whole. . . . Highly recommended." SLJ
Other titles in this series are:
Black hearts in Battersea (1964)
Cold Shoulder Road (1996)
The cuckoo tree (1971)
Dangerous games (1999)
Is underground (1993)
Midwinter nightingale (2003)
The stolen lake (1981)
The witch of Clatteringshaws (2005)

Alder, Elizabeth
Crossing the panther's path. Farrar, Straus &
Giroux 2002 229p $18   **Fic**
1. Caldwell, Billy, 1780-1841—Fiction 2. Tecumseh,
Shawnee Chief, 1768-1813—Fiction 3. Native Americans—Fiction 4. War of 1812—Fiction
ISBN 0-374-31662-7   LC 2001-54483
Sixteen-year-old Billy Caldwell, son of a British soldier and a Mohawk woman, leaves school to join Tecumseh in his efforts to prevent the Americans from taking any more land from the Indians in the Northwest
Territory.
"Alder's novel goes a long way toward explaining the
issues and events of the War of 1812. . . . Readers will
identify with Tecumseh's plight and come to understand,
if not agree with, the British and American points of
view." Booklist

The king's shadow. Farrar, Straus & Giroux
1995 259p (7 and up)   **Fic**
1. Harold, King of England, 1022?-1066—Fiction
2. Orphans—Fiction 3. Great Britain—History—0-
1066—Fiction
ISBN 0-374-34182-6   LC 93-34159
Available in paperback from Doubleday

After he is orphaned and has his tongue cut out in a
clash with the bullying sons of a Welsh noble, Evyn is
sold as a slave and serves many masters, from the gracious Lady Swan Neck to the valiant Harold Godwinson,
England's last Saxon king
"Readers will get their history almost without noticing
it, but will come to understand the complex society and
world within which these individuals functioned easily.
Evyn is easy to identify with as both a victim and an
outcast." Voice Youth Advocates

Alexander, Lloyd
The Arkadians. Dutton Children's Bks. 1995
272p $17.99; pa $6.99 (5 and up)   **Fic**
1. Fantasy fiction
ISBN 0-525-45415-2; 0-14-038073-6 (pa)
    LC 94-35025
Also available Audiobook version
To escape the wrath of the king and his wicked sooth-
sayers, Lucian joins with Fronto, a poet-turned-jackass,
and Joy-in-the-Dance, a young girl with mystical powers,
on a series of epic adventures
"On one level, this is a rousing adventure complete
with cliffhangers and do-or-die situations. On another,
readers familiar with Greek mythology will find clever
hints at the myths' purpose and genesis." SLJ

The book of three. rev ed. Holt & Co. 1999
190p (Chronicles of Prydain) $19.95 (5 and up)
    Fic
1. Fantasy fiction
ISBN 0-8050-6132-0   LC 98-40901
Also available in paperback from Yealing Bks
First published 1964
"The first of five books about the mythical land of
Prydain finds Taran, an assistant pig keeper, fighting
with Prince Gwydion against the evil which theatens the
kingdom." Hodges. Books for Elem Sch Libr
"Related in a simple, direct style, this fast-paced tale
of high adventure has a well-balanced blend of fantasy,
realism, and humor." SLJ
Other titles about the mythical land of Prydain are:
The black cauldron (1965)
The castle of Llyr (1966)
The foundling and other tales of Prydain (1999)
The high king (1968)
Taran Wanderer (1967)

Gypsy Rizka. Dutton Children's Bks. 1999 195p
$16.99; pa $5.99 (5 and up)   **Fic**
1. Gypsies—Fiction 2. Fantasy fiction
ISBN 0-525-46121-3; 0-14-130980-6 (pa)
    LC 98-41399
Living alone in her wagon on the outskirts of a Greater Dunitsa while waiting for her father's return, Rizka,
a Gypsy and a trickster, exposes the ridiculous foibles of
some of the townspeople
"Scenes of broad slapstick effervesce with mind-
tickling repartee in this book that is . . . lively, satirical,
and with a core of pure gold." Horn Book Guide

The high king. Holt & Co. 1999 c1968 253p rev
ed (Chronicles of Prydain) $18.95 (5 and up)
    Fic
1. Fantasy fiction
ISBN 0-8050-6135-5   LC 98-40900

Alexander, Lloyd—_Continued_

Also available in paperback from Yearling Bks.

Awarded The Newbery Medal, 1969

Concluding title in the chronicles of Prydain which include: The book of three, The black cauldron, The castle of Llyr, and Taran Wanderer

First published 1968

This edition includes a pronunciation guide

In this final volume Taran, the assistant pig-keeper "becomes High King of Prydain, Princess Eilonwy becomes his queen, the predictions of Taran's wizard guardian Dallben are fulfilled, and the forces of black magic led by Arawn, Lord of Annuvin, Land of the Dead, are vanquished forever." SLJ

"The fantasy has the depth and richness of a medieval tapestry, infinitely detailed and imaginative." Saturday Rev

The Illyrian adventure. Dutton 1986 132p hardcover o.p. paperback available $5.99 (5 and up) **Fic**

1. Adventure fiction

ISBN 0-14-130313-1 (pa)   LC 85-30762

"Sixteen-year-old Vesper Holly drags her long-suffering guardian, Brinnie, off to Illyria to vindicate her late father's reputation as a scholar. With humor, beguiling charm, and intelligence she manages to find a treasure, thwart a conspiracy to murder Illyria's King Osman, and guide two rival factions to the peace table." Wilson Libr Bull

"Alexander's archeological mystery has intricate plotting and witty wording." Bull Cent Child Books

Other adventure titles featuring Vesper Holly are:

The Drackenberg adventure (1988)

The El Dorado adventure (1987)

The Jedera adventure (1989)

The Philadelphia adventure (1990)

The Xanadu adventure (2005)

The iron ring. Dutton Children's Bks. 1997 283p (5 and up) **Fic**

1. Adventure fiction 2. India—Fiction

ISBN 0-525-45597-3; 0-14-130348-4 (pa)

LC 96-29730

"Young Tamar, ruler of a small Indian kingdom, wagers with a visiting king and loses his kingdom and his freedom. Traveling to the king's land to make good on his debt, he collects quite an entourage and eventually overcomes his enemies with his friends' help. This tale offers delightful characters, a philosophical interest in the meaning of life, a thoughtful look at the caste system, and a clever use of Indian animal folktales." Horn Book Guide

The remarkable journey of Prince Jen. Dutton Children's Bks. 1991 273p (5 and up) **Fic**

1. Adventure fiction 2. China—Fiction

ISBN 0-525-44826-8; 0-14-240225-7 (pa)

LC 91-13720

Also available in paperback from Dell

Bearing six unusual gifts, young Prince Jen in Tang Dynasty China embarks on a perilous quest and emerges triumphantly into manhood

"Alexander satisfies the taste for excitement, but his vivid characters and the food for thought he offers will nourish long after the last page is turned." SLJ

Westmark. Dutton 1981 184p hardcover o.p. Laurel-Leaf Bks. paperback available $4.50 (5 and up) **Fic**

1. Adventure fiction

ISBN 0-440-99731-3 (pa)

A boy fleeing from criminal charges falls in with a charlatan, his dwarf attendant, and an urchin girl, travels with them about the kingdom of Westmark, and ultimately arrives at the palace where the king is grieving over the loss of his daughter

The author "peoples his tale with a marvelous cast of individuals, and weaves an intricate story of high adventure that climaxes in a superbly conceived conclusion, which, though predictable, is reached through carefully built tension and subtly added comic relief." Booklist

Other titles in this series are:

The Beggar Queen (1984)

The Kestrel (1982)

Allende, Isabel

City of the beasts; translated from the Spanish by Margaret Sayers Peden. HarperCollins Pubs. 2002 406p $19.99; lib bdg $21.89; pa $7.99 (7 and up) **Fic**

1. Adventure fiction 2. Supernatural—Fiction

ISBN 0-06-050918-X; 0-06-050917-1 (lib bdg); 0-06-051032-3 (pa)   LC 2002-22338

Also available Spanish language edition

When fifteen-year-old Alexander Cold accompanies his individualistic grandmother on an expedition to find a humanoid Beast in the Amazon, he experiences ancient wonders and a supernatural world as he tries to avert disaster for the Indians

"The story is a struggle between good and evil, filled with surprises and adventure. . . . It is a real page-turner." SLJ

Other titles in this series are:

Forest of the Pygmies (2005)

Kingdom of the Golden Dragon (2004)

Almond, David, 1951-

Counting stars. Delacorte Press 2002 c2000 205p lib bdg $18.99; pa $5.99 (7 and up) **Fic**

1. City and town life—Fiction 2. Family life—Fiction 3. Great Britain—Fiction

ISBN 0-385-90034-1; 0-440-41826-7 (pa)

LC 2001-32498

First published 2000 in the United Kingdom

In a series of interconnected stories, a boy describes his life growing up in the English urban district of Felling

"Almond writes with lyrical simplicity." Booklist

The fire-eaters. Delacorte Press 2004 c2003 218p $15.95 **Fic**

1. Great Britain—Fiction

ISBN 0-385-73170-1   LC 2003-55709

First published 2003 in the United Kingdom

Almond, David, 1951-—*Continued*

In 1962 England, despite observing his father's illness and the suffering of the fire-eating Mr. McNulty, as well as enduring abuse at school and the stress of the Cuban Missile Crisis, Bobby Burns and his family and friends still find reasons to rejoice in their lives and to have hope for the future.

"The author's trademark themes - courage in resisting evil; the importance of love among friends and family, especially in the face of crisis; suffering and death amidst peace and beauty; and the fragility of life - are here in full, and resonate long after the last page is turned." SLJ

Kit's wilderness. Delacorte Press 1999 229p $15.95; pa $5.99 (5 and up)   **Fic**
1. Coal mines and mining—Fiction 2. Ghost stories 3. Great Britain—Fiction
ISBN 0-385-32665-3; 0-440-41605-1 (pa)
LC 99-34332
Also available Thorndike Press large print edition
Thirteen-year-old Kit goes to live with his grandfather in the decaying coal mining town of Stoneygate, England, and finds both the old man and the town haunted by ghosts of the past

The author "explores the power of friendship and family, the importance of memory, and the role of magic in our lives. This is a highly satisfying literary experience." SLJ

Skellig. Delacorte Press 1999 c1998 182p $16.95; pa $5.50 (5 and up)   **Fic**
1. Fantasy fiction
ISBN 0-385-32653-X; 0-440-41602-7 (pa)
LC 98-23121
Also available Thorndike Press large print edition and Audiobook version
First published 1998 in the United Kingdom
Unhappy about his baby sister's illness and the chaos of moving into a dilapidated old house, Michael retreats to the garage and finds a mysterious stranger who is something like a bird and something like an angel

"The plot is beautifully paced and the characters are drawn with a graceful, careful hand. . . . A lovingly done, thought-provoking novel." SLJ

Alton, Steve

The Malifex. Carolrhoda Bks. 2003 181p lib bdg $14.95   **Fic**
1. Fantasy fiction
ISBN 0-8225-0959-8   LC 2001-8651
First published 2001 in the United Kingdom
In the Dorset, England, countryside on a family vacation, a video game fanatic reluctantly embarks on a quest to battle an ancient evil, aided by the daughter of a Wiccan and a man once apprenticed to Merlin

"This novel is a splendid read that will enchant fans of fantasy literature." Voice Youth Advocates

Alvarez, Julia, 1950-

Before we were free. Knopf 2002 167p $15.95; lib bdg $17.99; pa $5.99 (7 and up)   **Fic**
1. Trujillo Molina, Rafael Leónidas, 1891-1961—Fiction 2. Dominican Republic—Fiction 3. Family life—Fiction
ISBN 0-375-81544-9; 0-375-91544-3 (lib bdg); 0-440-23784-X (pa)   LC 2001-50520
In the early 1960s in the Dominican Republic, twelve-year-old Anita learns that her family is involved in the underground movement to end the bloody rule of the dictator, General Trujillo

This "is a realistic and compelling account of a girl growing up too quickly while coming to terms with the cost of freedom." Horn Book

Finding miracles; Julia Alvarez. Knopf 2004 264p $15.95; lib bdg $17.99   **Fic**
1. Adoption—Fiction 2. School stories
ISBN 0-375-82760-9; 0-375-92760-3 (lib bdg)
LC 2003-25127
Fifteen-year-old Milly Kaufman is an average American teenager until Pablo, a new student at her school, inspires her to search for her birth family in his native country

"Complex multicultural characters and skillful depiction of Latino culture raises this well-written, readable novel, which is a school story, a family story, and a love story, to far above average." Voice Youth Advocates

How Tia Lola came to visit/stay. Knopf 2001 147p $15.95; lib bdg $17.99; pa $5.50 (4 and up)
Fic
1. Aunts—Fiction 2. Dominican Americans—Fiction 3. Vermont—Fiction
ISBN 0-375-80215-0; 0-375-90215-5 (lib bdg); 0-440-41870-4 (pa)   LC 00-62932
On title page "visit" is crossed out
Although ten-year-old Miguel is at first embarrassed by his colorful aunt, Tia Lola, when she comes to Vermont from the Dominican Republic to stay with his mother, his sister, and him after his parents' divorce, he learns to love her

"Readers will enjoy the funny situations, identify with the developing relationships and conflicting feelings of the characters, and will get a spicy taste of Caribbean culture in the bargain." SLJ

Anderson, Janet, 1946-

The last treasure; {by} Janet S. Anderson. Dutton 2003 257p il $17.99 (5 and up)
Fic
1. Family life—Fiction 2. Buried treasure—Fiction
ISBN 0-525-46919-2   LC 2002-74143
Thirteen-year-old Ellsworth leaves his father to visit the relatives he has never met and eventually joins forces with Jess, his distant cousin, to uncover family secrets and search for their ancestor's hidden treasure

"Anderson has conjured up a fascinating read for puzzle lovers while sandwiching in an important message about intergenerational relationships." SLJ

Anderson, Laurie Halse

Fever, 1793. Simon & Schuster Bks. for Young Readers 2000 251p hardcover o.p. paperback available $5.99 (5 and up) **Fic**

1. Yellow fever—Fiction

ISBN 0-689-84891-9 (pa) LC 00-32238

In 1793 Philadelphia, sixteen-year-old Matilda Cook, separated from her sick mother, learns about perseverance and self-reliance when she is forced to cope with the horrors of a yellow fever epidemic

"A vivid work, rich with well-drawn and believable characters. Unexpected events pepper the top-flight novel that combines accurate historical detail with a spellbinding story line." Voice Youth Advocates

Speak. Farrar, Straus & Giroux 1999 197p $16 (7 and up) **Fic**

1. Rape—Fiction 2. School stories

ISBN 0-374-37152-0 LC 98-31933

Also available in paperback from Puffin Bks.

"Having broken up an end-of-summer party by calling the police, high school freshman Melinda Sordino begins the school year as a social outcast. She's the only person who knows the real reason behind her call: she was raped at the party by Andy Evans, a popular senior at her school" Booklist

The novel is "keenly aware of the corrosive details of outsiderhood and the gap between home and daily life at high school; kids whose exclusion may have less concrete cause than Melinda's will nonetheless find the picture recognizable. This is a gripping account of personal wounding and recovery." Bull Cent Child Books

Anderson, M. T., 1968-

The Game of Sunken Places; M.T. Anderson. Scholastic Press 2004 260p $16.95; pa $5.99 (5 and up) **Fic**

1. Games—Fiction 2. Vermont—Fiction

ISBN 0-439-41660-4; 0-439-41661-2 (pa)

LC 2003-20055

When two boys stay with an eccentric relative at his mansion in rural Vermont, they discover an old-fashioned board game that draws them into a mysterious adventure.

"Deliciously scary, often funny, and crowned by a pair of deeply satisfying surprises, this tour de force leaves one marveling at Anderson's ability to slip between genres as fluidly as his middle-grade heroes straddle worlds." Booklist

Armstrong, Jennifer, 1961-

The kindling; Fire-us trilogy: book 1; {by} Jennifer Armstrong and Nancy Butcher. HarperCollins Pubs. 2002 224p $15.95; lib bdg $15.89; pa $5.99 (7 and up) **Fic**

1. Science fiction

ISBN 0-06-008048-5; 0-06-029411-6 (lib bdg); 0-06-447273-6 (pa) LC 2001-39679

In 2007, a small band of children have joined together in a Florida town, trying to survive in a world where it seems that all the adults have been killed off by a catastrophic virus

"Armstrong and Butcher's grim, well-written tale moves swiftly and packs an emotional wallop." Voice Youth Advocates

Other titles in this series are:

The keepers of the flame [book 2] (2003)

The kiln [book 3] (2003)

Steal away. Orchard Bks. 1992 206p o.p. Scholastic paperback available $3.99 (5 and up) **Fic**

1. Slavery—Fiction 2. African Americans—Fiction 3. Underground railroad—Fiction

ISBN 0-590-46921-5 (pa) LC 91-18504

"A Richard Jackson book"

In 1855 two thirteen-year-old girls, one white and one black, run away from a southern farm and make the difficult journey north to freedom, living to recount their story forty-one years later to two similar young girls

"Armstrong's novel has pace and suspense, characterization that is solid and consistent, and a crescendo that builds to a logical yet dramatic climax." Bull Cent Child Books

Armstrong, William Howard, 1914-1999

Sounder; {by} William H. Armstrong; illustrations by James Barkley. Harper & Row 1969 116p il $15.99; pa $5.99 (5 and up) **Fic**

1. Dogs—Fiction 2. African Americans—Fiction 3. Family life—Fiction

ISBN 0-06-020143-6; 0-06-440020-4 (pa)

Awarded the Newbery Medal, 1970

"Set in the South in the era of sharecropping and segregation, this succinctly told tale poignantly describes the courage of a father who steals a ham in order to feed his undernourished family; the determination of the eldest son, who searches for his father despite the apathy of prison authorities; and the devotion of a coon dog named Sounder." Shapiro. Fic for Youth. 3d edition

Arrington, Frances

Bluestem. Philomel Bks. 2000 140p $16.99 (4-6) **Fic**

1. Sisters—Fiction 2. Frontier and pioneer life—Fiction

ISBN 0-399-23564-7 LC 99-53726

With their father away and their mother traumatized by some unknown event, eleven-year-old Polly and her younger sister are left to take care of themselves and their prairie homestead

"Arrington uses poetic language and deep description to provide her audience with a clear vision of the open prairie. Her characters are realistic and their struggle evident." ALAN

Prairie whispers. Philomel Bks. 2003 184p $17.99 (5 and up) **Fic**

1. Frontier and pioneer life—Fiction 2. Family life—Fiction 3. South Dakota—Fiction

ISBN 0-399-23975-8 LC 2002-6698

Only twelve-year-old Colleen knows that her baby sister died just after she was born and that Colleen put another baby in her place, until the baby's father shows up and makes trouble for her and her family on the South Dakota prairie in the 1860s

Arrington, Frances—*Continued*
"The story is rich in atmosphere, both literal and emotional. . . . This is a suspenseful and well-told tale."
Horn Book

Ashby, John
Sea gift. Clarion Bks. 2003 202p $15
                                                                    Fic
1. Buried treasure—Fiction 2. Nova Scotia—Fiction
ISBN 0-395-77603-1   LC 2003-2476
While working on the lobster boats in his Nova Scotia town, thirteen-year-old Lauchie hauls up an old crock which hides a letter that sends him on a quest for treasure that was hidden long ago
"Middle-school readers will enjoy the personal stories and rich setting just as much as the basic adventure." Booklist

Atinsky, Steve
Tyler on prime time. Delacorte Press 2002 168p $14.95 (5 and up)   **Fic**
1. Television—Fiction
ISBN 0-385-72917-0   LC 2001-32468
While visiting his uncle, a writer on the most popular show on television, twelve-year-old Tyler auditions for a part on the show
"Written with a light touch, the novel features likable characters and a well-detailed setting. . . . The vagaries of show business . . . are convincingly portrayed." Horn Book Guide

Atkins, Catherine
Alt ed. Putnam 2003 198p $17.99 (7 and up)
                                                                    Fic
1. School stories
ISBN 0-399-23854-9   LC 2002-16942
Participating in a special after-school counseling class with other troubled students, including a sensitive gay classmate, helps Susan, an overweight tenth grader, develop a better sense of herself
"Most of the characters . . . come to life in new and interesting ways, and Susan's story is strong, because she is reinventing family relationships as well as trying to communicate with her peers." Booklist

Auch, Mary Jane
Ashes of roses. Holt & Co. 2002 250p $16.95 (7 and up)   **Fic**
1. Triangle Shirtwaist Company, Inc. —Fiction
2. Immigrants—Fiction 3. Irish Americans—Fiction
4. New York (N.Y.)—Fiction
ISBN 0-8050-6686-1   LC 2001-51896
Sixteen-year-old Margaret Rose Nolan, newly arrived from Ireland, finds work at New York City's Triangle Shirtwaist Factory shortly before the 1911 fire in which 146 employees died
"Fast-paced, populated by distinctive characters, and anchored in Auch's convincing sense of time and place, this title is a good choice for readers who like historical fiction." SLJ

Journey to nowhere. Holt & Co. 1997 202p
                                                                    Fic
1. Frontier and pioneer life—Fiction 2. New York (State)—Fiction
ISBN 0-8050-4922-3; 0-440-41491-1 (pa)
                            LC 96-42249
Also available in paperback from Bantam Bks.
This is the first title in the Genesee trilogy. In 1815, while traveling by covered wagon to settle in the wilderness of western New York, eleven-year-old Mem experiences a flood and separation from her family
"A well-written, realistic, and thoroughly researched novel." Booklist
Other titles in the Genesee trilogy are;
Frozen summer (1998)
The road to home (2000)

Wing nut; [by] MJ Auch. 1st ed. Henry Holt 2005 231p $16.95 (5 and up)   **Fic**
1. Moving—Fiction 2. Birds—Fiction 3. Old age—Fiction
ISBN 0-8050-7531-3   LC 2004-54046
When twelve-year-old Grady and his mother relocate yet again, they find work taking care of an elderly man, who teaches Grady about cars, birds, and what it means to have a home
"Auch's story . . . is engaging. . . . What will attract readers . . . is the author's careful integration of bird lore and the unusual challenges of creating and maintaining a purple martin colony." Booklist

Avi, 1937-
The barn. Orchard Bks. 1994 106p $14.95; lib bdg $15.99 (4 and up)   **Fic**
1. Farm life—Fiction 2. Frontier and pioneer life—Fiction 3. Father-son relationship—Fiction
ISBN 0-531-06861-7; 0-531-08711-5 (lib bdg)
                            LC 94-6920
Also available in paperback from Avon Bks.
"A Richard Jackson book"
In an effort to fulfill their dying father's last request, nine-year-old Ben and his brother and sister construct a barn on their land in the Oregon Territory in the 1850s
"While focusing mainly on his characters, Avi presents a vivid picture of the time and place, including fairly involved details about how the barn is constructed. This novel . . . is a thought-provoking and engaging piece of historical fiction." SLJ

Beyond the western sea. Orchard Bks. 1996 2v ea $18.95; lib bdg $19.99   **Fic**
1. Immigrants—Fiction 2. Siblings—Fiction
                            LC 95-36058
"A Richard Jackson book"
Contents: bk 1 The escape from home $18.95, pa $6.99 (ISBN 0-531-09513-4; pa 0-531-08863-4); bk 2 Lord Kirkle's money $18.95, pa $6.99 (ISBN 0-531-09520-7; pa 0-531-08870-7)
Driven from their impoverished Irish village, fifteen-year-old Maura and her younger brother meet their landlord's runaway son in Liverpool while all three wait for a ship to America; their fates continue to intertwine on board ship and in the New World
"Beyond the Western Sea offers readers a terrific ad-

Avi, 1937-—*Continued*

venture tale, patterned on serialized Victorian novels. Avi creates vivid characters and an engrossing story." Christ Sci Monit

The Book Without Words; a fable of medieval magic. Hyperion Books for Children 2005 203p $15.99 (5 and up)   **Fic**
1. Supernatural—Fiction 2. Magic—Fiction 3. Middle Ages—Fiction 4. Great Britain—History—0-1066—Fiction
ISBN 0-7868-0829-2

"At the dawning of the Middle Ages, Thorston, an old alchemist, works feverishly to create gold and to dose himself with a concoction that will enable him to live forever. The key to his success lies in a mysterious book with blank pages that can only be read by desperate, green-eyed people. . . . Avi's compelling language creates a dreary foreboding. . . . Clearly this is a story with a message, a true fable. Thoughtful readers will devour its absorbing plot and humorous elements, and learn a 'useful truth' along the way." SLJ

The Christmas rat. Simon & Schuster 2000 135p $16; pa $4.99   **Fic**
1. Rats—Fiction 2. Christmas—Fiction
ISBN 0-689-83842-5; 0-689-83843-3 (pa)
                                            LC 99-87429
"A Richard Jackson book"

Alone in his apartment during Christmas vacation, eleven-year-old Eric finds himself caught in a battle between a strange exterminator and the rat he wants to kill

"The mood is dark, intensified by the determined cheer of the season, and the writing is punchy and suspenseful." Horn Book Guide

Crispin; the cross of lead. Hyperion Bks. for Children 2002 262p $15.99; lib bdg $16.49; pa $6.99   **Fic**
1. Orphans—Fiction
ISBN 0-7868-0828-4; 0-7868-2647-9 (lib bdg); 0-7868-1658-9 (pa)   LC 2001-51829

Falsely accused of theft and murder, an orphaned peasant boy in fourteenth-century England flees his village and meets a larger-than-life juggler who holds a dangerous secret

"Avi has done an excellent job of integrating background and historical information, of pacing the plot so that the book is a page-turner from beginning to end, and of creating characters for whom readers will have great empathy. The result is a meticulously crafted story, full of adventure, mystery, and action." SLJ

Don't you know there's a war on? HarperCollins Pubs. 2001 200p $15.95; pa $5.99 (4 and up)   **Fic**
1. World War, 1939-1945—Fiction 2. Teachers—Fiction 3. Brooklyn (New York, N.Y.)—Fiction
ISBN 0-380-97863-6; 0-380-81544-3 (pa)
                                            LC 00-46102

In wartime Brooklyn in 1943, eleven-year-old Howie Crispers mounts a campaign to save his favorite teacher from being fired

"The 1943 Brooklyn setting is well evoked in Howie's lively, slang-spangled narration. The novel's uncomplicated, compact structure invites reading aloud." Horn Book Guide

The fighting ground. Lippincott 1984 157p hardcover o.p. paperback available $4.95 (5 and up)   **Fic**
1. United States—History—1775-1783, Revolution—Fiction
ISBN 0-06-440185-5   LC 82-47719

"It's April 1776, and the fighting ground is both the farm country of Pennsylvania and the heart of a boy which is 'wonderful ripe for war.' Twenty-four hours transform Jonathan from a cocky 13-year-old, eager to take on the British, into a young man who now knows the horror, the pathos, the ambiguities of war." Voice Youth Advocates

The author "has written a taut, fast-paced novel that builds to a shattering climax. His protagonist's painful, inner struggle to understand the intense and conflicting emotions brought on by a war that spares no one is central to this finely crafted novel." ALAN

The man who was Poe; a novel. Orchard Bks. 1989 208p hardcover o.p. Avon Bks. paperback available $4.99   **Fic**
1. Poe, Edgar Allan, 1809-1849—Fiction 2. Mystery fiction
ISBN 0-380-73022-7 (pa)   LC 89-42537
"A Richard Jackson book"

In Providence, R.I., in 1848, Edgar Allan Poe reluctantly investigates the problems of eleven-year-old Edmund, whose family has mysteriously disappeared and whose story suggests a new Poe tale with a ghastly final twist

Avi blends "drama, history, and mystery without a hint of pastiche or calculation. And, as in the best mystery stories, readers will be left in the end with both the comfort of puzzles solved and the unease of mysteries remaining." Bull Cent Child Books

Midnight magic. Scholastic Press 1999 249p $15.95; pa $5.99 (5 and up)   **Fic**
1. Magicians—Fiction 2. Renaissance—Fiction 3. Italy—Fiction
ISBN 0-590-36035-3; 0-439-24219-3 (pa)
                                            LC 98-50192

In Italy in 1491, Mangus the magician and his apprentice are summoned to the castle of Duke Claudio to determine if his daughter is indeed being haunted by a ghost.

An "entertaining tale of mystery and intrigue." SLJ

Never mind! a twin novel; {by} Avi and Rachel Vail. HarperCollins 2004 200p $15.99; lib bdg $16.89 (5 and up)   **Fic**
1. Twins—Fiction 2. New York (N.Y.)—Fiction
ISBN 0-06-054314-0; 0-06-054315-9 (lib bdg)
                                            LC 2003-21439

Twelve-year-old New York City twins Meg and Edward have nothing in common, so they are just as shocked as everyone else when Meg's hopes for popularity and Edward's mischievous schemes coincidentally collide in a hilarious showdown.

"The dialogue is great, especially the conversations that reveal how hard it is to listen and to say what you mean. . . . The wit and slapstick carry the story, which has moments of sadness that raise serious issues everyone will recognize. Best of all is the message: laugh at yourself." Booklist

Avi, 1937——*Continued*

Nothing but the truth; a documentary novel. Orchard Bks. 1991 177p $16.95 (6 and up)

Fic

1. School stories
ISBN 0-531-05959-6   LC 91-9200
Also in paperback from Avon Bks.
"A Richard Jackson book"

A ninth-grader's suspension for singing "The Star-Spangled Banner" during homeroom becomes a national news story

"The book is effectively set entirely in monologue or dialogue; conversations, memos, letters, diary entries, talk-radio transcripts, and newspaper articles are all interwoven to present an uninterrupted plot. The construction is nearly flawless; the characters seem painfully human and typically ordinary. . . . A powerful, explosive novel that involves the reader from start to finish." Horn Book

The secret school. Harcourt 2001 153p $16; pa $5.95 (4 and up)   **Fic**

1. School stories 2. Colorado—Fiction
ISBN 0-15-216375-1; 0-15-204699-2 (pa)
LC 2001-629

In 1925, fourteen-year-old Ida Bidson secretly takes over as the teacher when the one-room schoolhouse in her remote Colorado area closes unexpectedly

"This carefully plotted, enjoyable, old-fashioned tale of children taking control of a bad situation is a welcome addition to the literature of empowerment." SLJ

The true confessions of Charlotte Doyle; decorations by Ruth E. Murray. Orchard Bks. 1990 215p $16.95; pa $5.99 (6 and up)   **Fic**

1. Sea stories
ISBN 0-531-05893-X; 0-380-72885-0 (pa)
LC 90-30624

A Newbery Medal honor book, 1991
"A Richard Jackson book"

This is a "seafaring adventure, set in 1832. Charlotte Doyle, 13, returning from school in England to join her family in Rhode Island, is deposited on a seedy ship with a ruthless, mad captain and a mutinous crew. Refusing to heed warnings about Captain Jaggery's brutality, Charlotte seeks his guidance and approval only to become his victim, a pariah to the entire crew, and a convicted felon for the murder of the first mate." SLJ

The author has "fashioned an intriguing, suspenseful, carefully crafted tale, with nonstop action on the high seas." Booklist

Wolf rider; a tale of terror. Bradbury Press 1986 202p $17; pa $4.99   **Fic**

1. Mystery fiction
ISBN 0-689-84159-0; 0-02-041513-3 (pa)
LC 86-13607

"Fifteen-year-old Andrew Zadinsky receives a call from a mysterious man names Zeke, who says he has just killed a woman named Nina. Everyone Andy talks to, including his father, the school counselor, the police, his friends, and even the girl herself (once Andy finds her alive) believes the call is a crank, but Andy is convinced the caller is a dangerous psychotic and becomes obsessed with identifying and exposing him . . . Perhaps just a touch too cold and calculating, this is a nevertheless a gripping and above-average YA thriller." Bull Cent Child Books

Ayres, Katherine

Macaroni boy. Delacorte Press 2003 182p $15.95; lib bdg $17.99 (5 and up)   **Fic**

1. School stories 2. Great Depression, 1929-1939—Fiction
ISBN 0-385-73016-0; 0-385-90085-6 (lib bdg)
LC 2002-6768

In Pittsburgh in 1933, sixth-grader Mike Costa notices a connection between several strange occurrences, but the only way he can find out the truth about what's happening is to be nice to the class bully. Includes historical facts

"Actual places and events are interwoven with a heartwarming story of a close-knit family facing difficult times." Voice Youth Advocates

North by night; a story of the Underground Railroad. Delacorte Press 1998 176p (6 and up)

Fic

1. Underground railroad—Fiction 2. Slavery—Fiction
ISBN 0-385-32564-9; 0-440-22747-x (pa)
LC 98-10039

Companion volume to: Stealing south

Presents the journal of Lucinda, a sixteen-year-old girl whose family operates a stop on the Underground Railroad

This "is an absorbing tale. Ayres slips in a lot of evocative detail about the hard work of running a farm and a household before the Civil War, as well as some rather charming musing about kissing and its myriad effects on the psyche." Booklist

Bagdasarian, Adam

First French kiss and other traumas. Farrar, Straus & Giroux 2002 134p $16 (7 and up)

Fic

ISBN 0-374-32338-0   LC 2001-50510
"Melanie Kroupa books"

This is a collection of fictionalized autobiographical episodes on such topics as "hypochondria, schoolyard fights, and illusion-bursting make-out sessions in Beverly Hills. . . . The mix of comic situations . . . with intelligent reflection gives each reminiscence a larger relevance." Horn Book

Forgotten fire. DK Pub. 2000 273p $19.99 (7 and up)   **Fic**

1. Armenian massacres, 1915-1923—Fiction
2. Turkey—Fiction
ISBN 0-7894-2627-7   LC 99-46465
Also available in paperback from Laurel Leaf

"Based on a true story, this . . . historical novel tells about the Turkish genocide of the Armenians. Vahan Kenderian, age 12 when his home is torn apart, sees many of his family and friends butchered before his eyes." Booklist

"Bagdasarian has created a story that is a tribute to the human ability to endure. Because of the sexual and physical violence, this book is recommended for mature readers." Book Rep

Baker, Julie
Up Molasses Mountain. Wendy Lamb Bks. 2002
209p lib bdg $17.99; pa $5.50   **Fic**
　　1. Coal mines and mining—Fiction
　　ISBN 0-385-90048-1 (lib bdg); 0-440-22903-0 (pa)
　　　　　　　　　　　　　　　　LC 2001-50692
When union members arrive to organize their West
Virginia coal mining town, fourteen-year-old Clarence
Henderson, shunned for his cleft lip, and his neighbor
Elizabeth Braxton narrate the changes in their own lives
and in the lives of everyone in their community
"Baker does an excellent job of presenting both sides
of the issues. . . . Baker also offers a deeply moving
psychological portrait of a tormented boy who finds a
way outside himself." Booklist

Baldwin, James, 1924-1987
Go tell it on the mountain. Knopf 1953 303p
$15.95; pa $6.99 (7 and up)   **Fic**
　　1. African Americans—Fiction 2. Harlem (New York,
　　N.Y.)—Fiction
　　ISBN 0-679-60154-6; 0-440-33007-6 (pa)
Also available in paperback from Laurel-Leaf Bks.
This novel is an "autobiographical story of a Harlem
child's relationship with his father against the background of his being saved in the pentecostal church." Benet's Reader's Ency of Am Lit

Banks, Kate, 1960-
Walk softly, Rachel. Farrar, Straus & Giroux
2003 149p $16 (7 and up)   **Fic**
　　1. Family life—Fiction 2. Death—Fiction
　　ISBN 0-374-38230-1   LC 2002-26503
　　"Frances Foster books"
When fourteen-year-old Rachel reads the journal of
her brother, who died when she was seven, she learns secrets that help her understand her parents and herself
"While Banks's poetic prose may consist of simple
words, its effect on the ear and heart is remarkable." SLJ

Banks, Lynne Reid, 1929-
Alice-by-accident. HarperCollins Pubs. 2000
140p hardcover o.p. paperback available $5.95
　　　　　　　　　　　　　　　　　　　Fic
　　1. Single parent family—Fiction 2. School stories
　　3. Great Britain—Fiction
　　ISBN 0-380-81560-5 (pa)   LC 99-47641
Nine-year-old Alice must write about herself for an
assignment in her London school, and in doing so, she
sorts out her feelings about her somewhat prickly single
mother, the father she has never met, her flamboyant paternal grandmother, and the rest of her sometimes confusing life
"Alice's upbeat, albeit naive account comes off refreshing and funny." Booklist

Maura's angel. Avon Bks. 1998 150p $14; pa
$4.99   **Fic**
　　1. Angels—Fiction 2. Belfast (Northern Ireland)—Fic-
　　tion
　　ISBN 0-380-97590-4; 0-380-79514-0 (pa)
　　　　　　　　　　　　　　　　LC 97-50350

Just when her home life and the circumstances in vio-
lence-plagued Belfast seem more than she can bear, eleven-year-old Maura encounters an unusual person whose
name, Angela, gives a clue to her real identity
"The author's skillful balancing of the magical elements and often grim reality that life holds will ring true
for many young readers." Publ Wkly

Banks, Sara H., 1942-
Abraham's battle; a novel of Gettysburg; {by}
Sara Harrell Banks. Atheneum Bks. for Young
Readers 1999 88p $15.95; pa $4.99   **Fic**
　　1. Gettysburg (Pa.), Battle of, 1863—Fiction
　　2. United States—History—1861-1865, Civil War—
　　Fiction 3. African Americans—Fiction
　　ISBN 0-689-81779-7; 0-689-84046-2 (pa)
　　　　　　　　　　　　　　　　LC 98-21108
"An Anne Schwartz book"
"This very personal account, well-written and filled
with Southern expressions and historical details, focuses
on the common humanity that survives despite political
differences and the horrors of war." Booklist

Barker, Clive
Abarat. Joanna Cotler Bks. 2002 388, xxvp il
$24.99; pa $6.99 (7 and up)   **Fic**
　　1. Fantasy fiction
　　ISBN 0-06-028092-1; 0-06-059637-6 (pa)
　　　　　　　　　　　　　　　　LC 2002-1299
Candy Quackenbush of Chickentown, Minnesota,
"finds herself transported to the Abarat, a magical realm
composed of 25 islands, each representing one hour of
the day, with the mysterious Twenty-Fifth designated for
Time Outside of Time." SLJ
"The first of a planned four-book series, Barker imbues the traditional conventions of fantasy with a whimsical Wonderland quality, providing a host of bizarre
characters, a fabulous landscape, and a coherent underlying mythology." Booklist
Another title in this series is:
Days of magic, nights of war (2004)

Barrett, Tracy, 1955-
Anna of Byzantium. Delacorte Press 1999 209p
map   **Fic**
　　1. Comnena, Anna, 1083-1148—Fiction 2. Middle
　　Ages—Fiction 3. Sex role—Fiction
　　ISBN 0-385-32626-2; 0-440-41536-5 (pa)
　　　　　　　　　　　　　　　　LC 98-47457
Based on The Alexiad by Anna Comnena
In the eleventh century the teenage princess Anna
Comnena fights for her birthright, the throne to the Byz-
antine Empire, which she fears will be taken from her by
her younger brother John because he is a boy
"The book is a fascinating mix of history, mystery,
and intrigue." Horn Book Guide

Cold in summer. Holt & Co. 2003 203p $16.95
(5 and up)   **Fic**
　　1. Ghost stories 2. Tennessee—Fiction
　　ISBN 0-8050-7052-4   LC 2002-67888
At the beginning of seventh grade, Ariadne moves to
a Tennessee town near a former farming community sub-

Barrett, Tracy, 1955—*Continued*
merged under a man-made lake and meets the ghost of
a girl from the past
"This is a straightforward ghost tale with a doughty
main character, a strong sense of history, and solid secondary players." Bull Cent Child Books

Barron, T. A.
The lost years of Merlin. Philomel Bks. 1996
326p $19.99 (6 and up)   **Fic**
1. Merlin (Legendary character)—Fiction 2. Fantasy
fiction
ISBN 0-399-23018-1   LC 96-33920
Also available in paperback from Ace Bks.
"A boy, hurled on the rocks by the sea, regains consciousness unable to remember anything—not his parents, not his own name. He is sure that the secretive
Branwen is not his mother, despite her claims, and that
Emrys is not his real name. The two soon find them-
selves feared because of Branwen's healing abilities and
Emrys' growing powers. . . . Barron has created not
only a magical land populated by remarkable beings but
also a completely magical tale, filled with ancient Celtic
and Druidic lore, that will enchant readers." Booklist
Other titles in this series are:
The fires of Merlin (1998)
The mirror of Merlin (1999)
The seven songs of Merlin (1997)
The wings of Merlin (2000)

The Merlin effect. Philomel Bks. 1994 254p
$19.99; pa $6.99   **Fic**
1. Merlin (Legendary character)—Fiction 2. Buried
treasure—Fiction 3. Fantasy fiction
ISBN 0-399-22689-3; 0-441-01222-1 (pa)
                                       LC 93-36234
Also available in paperback from TOR Bks.
When she joins her father and several others investigating a strange whirlpool and possible sunken treasure
ship off the coast of Baja California, thirteen-year-old
Kate, featured in Heartlight (1990) and The Ancient One
(1992), is drawn into a centuries-old conflict between
Merlin and the evil Vagar
The author "blends a wealth of sea lore with ancient
myth and fast-paced adventure." Libr J

Barry, Dave
Peter and the starcatchers; by Dave Barry and
Ridley Pearson. Hyperion 2004 451p il $17.99 (5
and up)   **Fic**
1. Fairy tales 2. Pirates—Fiction
ISBN 0-7868-5445-6   LC 2004-55275
Soon after Peter, an orphan, sets sail from England on
the ship Never Land, he befriends and assists Molly, a
young Starcatcher, whose mission is to guard a trunk of
magical stardust from a greedy pirate and the native inhabitants of a remote island.
"The authors plait multiple story lines together in
short, fast-moving chapters. . . . Capitalizing on familiar
material, this adventure is carefully crafted to set the
stage for Peter's later exploits. This smoothly written
page-turner just might send readers back to the original."
SLJ

Bartoletti, Susan Campbell, 1958-
A coal miner's bride; the diary of Anetka
Kaminska. Scholastic 2000 219p il (Dear America)
$10.95; lib bdg $12.95 (4 and up)   **Fic**
1. Polish Americans—Fiction 2. Immigrants—Fiction
3. Coal mines and mining—Fiction
ISBN 0-439-05386-2; 0-439-55510-8 (lib bdg)
                                       LC 99-29864
A diary account of thirteen-year-old Anetka's life in
Poland in 1896, immigration to America, marriage to a
coal miner, widowhood, and happiness in finally finding
her true love
"Bartoletti paints an accessible and evocative picture
of life in a harsh era." SLJ

The journal of Finn Reardon; a newsie.
Scholastic 2003 156p il (My name is America)
$10.95 (4 and up)   **Fic**
1. Irish Americans—Fiction 2. New York (N.Y.)—
Fiction 3. Newspaper carriers—Fiction
ISBN 0-439-18894-6   LC 2002-30874
Finn Reardon, a thirteen-year-old Irish-American
newspaper carrier who hopes to be a journalist someday,
keeps a journal of his experiences living in New York
City in 1899. Includes historical notes
This "is a standout in the series. . . . It's entertaining
and the characters leap off the pages." SLJ

No man's land; a young soldier's story. Blue
Sky Press (NY) 1999 168p $16.95 (5 and up)
                                                 Fic
1. Father-son relationship—Fiction 2. United States—
History—1861-1865, Civil War—Fiction
ISBN 0-590-38371-X   LC 98-24714
"Bartoletti grounds her story in careful historical re-
search, and in an afterword she talks about her union of
fact and imagination." Booklist

Baskin, Nora Raleigh, 1961-
Almost home; a novel. Little, Brown 2003 173p
$16.95   **Fic**
1. Family life—Fiction 2. Stepmothers—Fiction
3. Friendship—Fiction
ISBN 0-316-09313-0   LC 2002-28297
After years of being shuffled from town to town and
back and forth between her divorced parents, twelve-
year-old Leah, now living permanently with her father
and stepmother, finds it difficult to adjust to her new situation and the circumstances that made it possible
"This is a respectful and affecting portrait of a girl
discovering family strengths as well as family weaknesses." Bull Cent Child Books

What every girl (except me) knows; a novel.
Little, Brown 2001 213p $16.95; pa $4.99 (4 and
up)   **Fic**
1. Mothers—Fiction 2. Friendship—Fiction 3. Death—
Fiction
ISBN 0-316-07021-1; 0-440-41852-6 (pa)
                                       LC 00-40557
"Twelve-year-old Gabby feels like she's speeding into
womanhood without a map, since her mother died when
she was small. . . . She's convinced that girls with
mothers have knowledge to which she's not privy, and

Baskin, Nora Raleigh, 1961-—*Continued*
one of the benefits of her friendship with new girl Taylor
is a helpful dose of female camaraderie. . . . The book's
depiction of Gabby's family dynamics . . . is perceptive
and sympathetic." Bull Cent Child Books

Bat-Ami, Miriam, 1950-
Two suns in the sky. Front St./Cricket Bks.
1999 223p $17.95; pa $6.99 (7 and up)
Fic
1. Jewish refugees—Fiction 2. World War, 1939-
1945—Fiction 3. New York (State)—Fiction
ISBN 0-8126-2900-0; 0-14-230036-5 (pa)
LC 98-88522
"Chris Cook is a Catholic American teenager who
feels stuck in her hometown of Oswego, New York, in
1944. Adam Bornstein is a young, Jewish Holocaust survivor from Yugoslavia living in the fenced-off Emergency Refugee Camp in Oswego. Their passionate love story
is woven into a docunovel that gives a strong sense of
the times." Booklist

Bath, K. P.
The secret of Castle Cant; being an account of
the remarkable adventures of Lucy Wickwright,
maidservant and spy; with artistic embellishments
by David Christiana. Little, Brown 2004 291p il
$16.99 (5 and up)
Fic
1. Orphans—Fiction 2. Fantasy fiction
ISBN 0-316-10848-0
LC 2004-03643
When twelve-toed orphan Lucy Wickwright is brought
to Castle Cant to be serving girl to the Baron's daughter,
the Adorable & Honorable Pauline, she becomes involved with revolutionaries and uncovers surprising palace intrigues.
"Bath deals with a familiar fairy-tale theme: the discovery of noble lineage in a maidservant. His treatment,
however, is quirky, funny, and rife with social satire; his
style, full of puns, similes, alliteration, and just the right
tone of tongue-in-cheek pomposity, is delightful." SLJ

Bauer, Joan
Backwater. Putnam 1999 185p $16.99; pa $6.99
(7 and up)
Fic
1. Genealogy—Fiction 2. Aunts—Fiction
3. Adirondack Mountains (N.Y.)—Fiction
ISBN 0-399-23141-2; 0-698-11865-0 (pa)
LC 98-50729
While compiling a genealogy of her family of successful attorneys, sixteen-year-old history buff Ivy Breedlove
treks into the mountain wilderness to interview a reclusive aunt with whom she identifies and who in turn helps
her to truly know herself and her family
"This warm, funny, patchwork quilt of a book offers
a sturdy heroine, vivid characters, a touch of romance,
and a final survival adventure that will keep readers turning the pages to the last." Booklist

Hope was here. Putnam 2000 186p $16.99; pa
$7.99 (7 and up)
Fic
1. Aunts—Fiction 2. Restaurants—Fiction
3. Wisconsin—Fiction
ISBN 0-399-23142-0; 0-14-240424-1 (pa)
LC 00-38232

A Newbery Medal honor book, 2001
When sixteen-year-old Hope and the aunt who has
raised her move from Brooklyn to Mulhoney, Wisconsin,
to work as waitress and cook in the Welcome Stairways
diner, they become involved with the diner owner's political campaign to oust the town's corrupt mayor
"Bauer manages to fill her heartfelt novel with gentle
humor, quirky but appealing characters, and an engaging
plot." Book Rep

Rules of the road. Putnam 1998 201p $16.99; pa
$6.99 (7 and up)
Fic
1. Old age—Fiction
ISBN 0-399-23140-4; 0-698-11828-6 (pa)
LC 97-32198
Sixteen-year-old Jenna gets a job driving the elderly
owner of a chain of successful shoe stores from Chicago
to Texas to confront the son who is trying to force her
to retire, and along the way Jenna hones her talents as
a saleswoman and finds the strength to face her alcoholic
father
"The author creates some fabulous and sometimes
flamboyant characters, witty dialogue, and memorable
scenes." SLJ

Squashed; Joan Bauer. 1st G.P. Putnam's Sons
ed. Puffin Books 2001 c1992 194p $16.99; pa
$7.99
Fic
1. Country life—Fiction 2. Iowa—Fiction
ISBN 0-399-23750-X; 0-14-240426-8 (pa)
LC 2001-18595
A reissue of the title first published 1992 by Delacorte
Press
As sixteen-year-old Ellie pursues her two goals -
growing the biggest pumpkin in Iowa and losing twenty
pounds herself - she strengthens her relationship with her
father and meets a young man with interests similar to
her own.
"Skillful plot development and strong characterization
are real stengths here. Ellie's perspective, intelligent, and
funny narrative keeps the story lively right up to its satisfying conclusion." SLJ

Stand tall. Putnam 2002 182p $16.99; pa $6.99
Fic
1. Divorce—Fiction 2. Grandfathers—Fiction
ISBN 0-399-23473-X; 0-14-240148-X (pa)
LC 2002-23876
Tree, a six-foot-three-inch twelve-year-old, copes with
his parents' recent divorce and his failure as an athlete
by helping his grandfather, a Vietnam vet and recent amputee, and Sophie, a new girl at school
The "swiftly paced story artfully blends poignant and
outright funny moments, resulting in a triumphant tale
that will resonate with many young readers." Publ Wkly

Bauer, Marion Dane, 1938-
An early winter. Clarion Bks. 1999 120p $15;
pa $4.50
Fic
1. Grandfathers—Fiction 2. Grandfathers—Fiction
3. Fishing—Fiction
ISBN 0-395-90372-6; 0-440-41694-9 (pa)
LC 98-54975

Bauer, Marion Dane, 1938——*Continued*

When eleven-year-old Tim's beloved grandfather develops Alzheimer's Disease, Tim tries to restore and save him by taking him out for a fishing adventure at the pond, but the outing turns into a disaster

"The book presents a realistic portrayal of the early stages of Alzheimer's." Horn Book

Land of the buffalo bones; the diary of Mary Ann Elizabeth Rodgers, an English girl in Minnesota. Scholastic 2003 221p il (Dear America) $12.95   **Fic**

1. Frontier and pioneer life—Fiction 2. British Americans—Fiction

ISBN 0-439-22027-0   LC 2002-73344

Fourteen-year-old Polly Rodgers keeps a diary of her 1873 journey from England to Minnesota as part of a colony of eighty people seeking religious freedom, and of their first year struggling to make a life there, led by her father, a Baptist minister

"This Dear America book is unusual in that it is based on real people and events in 1873. . . . This is an engrossing look at the hardships faced by many pioneers." Booklist

On my honor. Clarion Bks. 1986 90p $15 (4 and up)   **Fic**

1. Accidents—Fiction

ISBN 0-89919-439-7   LC 86-2679

Also available in paperback from Dell and Audiobook version

A Newbery Medal honor book, 1987

When his best friend drowns while they are both swimming in a treacherous river that they had promised never to go near, Joel is devastated and terrified at having to tell both sets of parents the terrible consequences of their disobedience

"Bauer's association of Joel's guilt with the smell of the polluted river on his skin is particularly noteworthy. Its miasma almost rises off the pages. Descriptions are vivid, characterization and dialogue natural, and the style taut but unforced. A powerful, moving book." SLJ

Bawden, Nina, 1925-

Granny the Pag. Clarion Bks. 1996 184p $15 (4 and up)   **Fic**

1. Grandmothers—Fiction 2. Parent-child relationship—Fiction

ISBN 0-395-77604-X   LC 95-38191

Also available in paperback from Puffin Bks.

First published 1995 in the United Kingdom

Originally abandoned by her actor parents who later attempt to gain custody, Cat wages a spirited campaign to decide her own fate and remain with her grandmother

"Bawden has created some enormously appealing characters in this funny and very touching novel." SLJ

Off the road. Clarion Bks. 1998 192p $16; pa 5.99   **Fic**

1. Grandfathers—Fiction 2. Science fiction

ISBN 0-395-91321-7; 0-14-131100-2 (pa)

    LC 97-42576

Large print available from Galaxy (2001)

In 2040, eleven-year-old Tom follows his grandfather through the Wall and into the forbidden Wild, where they seek to find his grandfather's boyhood home

"The characters will make readers think about ideas. . . . The great surprise ending shouts for a sequel." Booklist

Beale, Fleur

I am not Esther. Hyperion 2002 250p $15.99; pa $6.99 (7 and up)   **Fic**

1. Cults—Fiction

ISBN 0-7868-0845-4; 0-7868-1673-2 (pa)

    LC 2002-27256

After her mother unexpectedly leaves her with her uncle's family, members of a fanatical Christian cult, Kirby tries to learn what has become of her mother and struggles to cope with the repressiveness of her new surroundings and to maintain her own identity

"The author builds tension well, introducing layers of conflict, revealing elements of the plot realistically and plausibly." SLJ

Beatty, Patricia, 1922-1991

Jayhawker. Morrow Junior Bks. 1991 214p hardcover o.p. paperback available $5.95 (5 and up)   **Fic**

1. United States—History—1861-1865, Civil War—Fiction 2. Underground railroad—Fiction 3. Spies—Fiction

ISBN 0-688-14422-5   LC 91-17890

In the early years of the Civil War, teenage Kansan farm boy Lije Tulley becomes a Jayhawker, an abolitionist raider freeing slaves from the neighboring state of Missouri, and then goes undercover there as a spy

"Peppered with fascinating historical figures, vivid with drama and action, Beatty's story has an accuracy and a realism that are both addictive and illuminating." Booklist

Bell, Hilari, 1958-

Flame; The book of Sorahb, volume one. Simon & Schuster Bks. for Young Readers 2003 344p $16.95   **Fic**

1. Fantasy fiction

ISBN 0-689-85413-7   LC 2003-114815

Available in paperback with title: Fall of a Kingdom (Farsala trilogy) $5.99 (ISBN 0-689-85414-5)

"The story is set in Farsala, a peaceful land now targeted for invasion by the Hrum, who have already conquered 28 other countries. As the enemy advances, routing the overconfident Farsalan army, three young people caught up in the fray move inexorably toward new futures in which they will play leading roles in the outcome and aftermath of the war. They are Soraya, the spoiled daughter of the Farsalan army's high commander; Jiaan, the high commander's peasant-born bastard son; and Kavi, an itinerant peddler and sometime con artist." Booklist

"The crisp dialogue, finely tuned characterizations, and vivid descriptions make the people and landscape seem as real as those in any grand historical epic." SLJ

Another title in this series is:

Rise of a hero (2005)

Bell, Hilari, 1958— *Continued*

The Goblin Wood. Eos/HarperCollins Pubs. 2003 294p $16.99; lib bdg $17.89 **Fic**
1. Fantasy fiction
ISBN 0-06-051371-3; 0-06-051372-1 (lib bdg)
LC 2002-15281
"Leavened by humor and a dollop of romance, this well-crafted fantasy adventure demonstrates Bell's talent for creating enduring characters and worlds." Booklist

A matter of profit. HarperCollins Pubs. 2001 281p lib bdg $17.89; pa $6.99 (7 and up)
Fic
1. Science fiction 2. Mystery fiction
ISBN 0-06-029514-7 (lib bdg); 0-06-447300-7 (pa)
LC 00-50555
"This is well-written, thought-provoking, and exciting science fiction." SLJ

Bellairs, John
The curse of the blue figurine. Dial Bks. for Young Readers 1983 200p hardcover o.p. paperback available $4.99 (5 and up) **Fic**
1. Mystery fiction
ISBN 0-14-038005-1 (pa)
LC 82-73217
Also available Brad Strickland's titles based on John Bellairs characters; Hardcover available from P. Smith
"The terror for young Johnny Dixon begins when cranky eccentric Professor Childermass tells him that St. Michael's Church is haunted by Father Baart, an evil sorcerer who mysteriously disappeared years ago. When Johnny finds a blue Egyptian figurine hidden in the church basement, he takes it home in spite of the warning note from Father Baart threatening harm to anyone who removes it from the church." SLJ
The author "intertwines real concerns with sorcery in a seamless fashion, bringing dimension to his characters and events with expert timing and sharply honed atmosphere." Booklist
Other titles about Johnny Dixon and Professor Childermass are:
The chessmen of doom (1989)
The eyes of the killer robot (1986)
The mummy, the will and the crypt (1983)
The revenge of the wizard's ghost (1985)
The secret of the underground room (1990)
The spell of the sorcerer's skull (1984)
The trolley to yesterday (1989)

Bennett, Cherie
Life in the fat lane. Delacorte Press 1998 260p (7 and up) **Fic**
1. Obesity—Fiction
ISBN 0-385-32274-7; 0-440-22029-7 (pa)
LC 97-24072
Also available Thorndike Press large print edition
Sixteen-year-old Lara, winner of beauty pageants and Homecoming Queen, is distressed and bewildered when she starts gaining weight and becomes a fat girl
"A fast-paced story about compelling teen issues." Child Book Rev Serv

Zink. Delacorte Press 1999 243p il hardcover o.p. paperback available $4.99 **Fic**
1. Leukemia—Fiction
ISBN 0-440-22810-7 (pa)
LC 99-18165
With the help of a fantasy zebra named Zink, sixth-grader Becky faces her battle with leukemia, her family's fears for her, her competition with a hypocritical classmate, and the possibility that she might die
"Inspired by an actual child's life and writings, recast from Bennett's award-winning play of the same title, this tale . . . will elicit both tears and laughter." Booklist

Bennett, Jay, 1912-
Coverup; a novel. Watts 1991 144p (7 and up)
Fic
1. Mystery fiction
ISBN 0-531-15224-3; 0-449-70409-2 (pa)
LC 91-18506
Teenage Brad is tormented by confused memories of a drunken ride with his best friend Alden, during which they may have hit and killed a man
"Bennett has created another suspenseful mystery that is sure to please his confirmed fans and attract new ones." Booklist

Sing me a death song; a novel. Watts 1990 160p hardcover o.p. Fawcett Bks. paperback available $4.50 (7 and up) **Fic**
1. Mystery fiction 2. Mother-son relationship—Fiction
ISBN 0-449-70369-X (pa)
LC 89-24812
Jason risks his life to find evidence that his mother, a convicted murderer facing execution, was framed
"Taut, spare, poignant, this mystery offers both a gripping plot and a convincing argument against capital punishment." Voice Youth Advocates

Berry, James
Ajeemah and his son. Perlman Bks. 1992 c1991 83p hardcover o.p. paperback available $4.95
Fic
1. Slavery—Fiction 2. Jamaica—Fiction
ISBN 0-06-440523-0 (pa)
LC 92-6615
First published 1991 in the United Kingdom in a collection entitled The Future-telling lady
"Ajeemah and his son Atu are kidnapped and sold in West Africa, never to see home or family again. After the bitter journey to Jamaica, they are separated forever, sold off to plantations 20 miles apart. . . . The son's rebellion ends in heartbreak, flogging, suicide. The father is betrayed, but he survives to marry, sire a daughter, and celebrate when freedom comes." Booklist
"The power of Berry's writing places us in the story, confronted by the feelings of Ajeemah and Atu—and the author keeps us there until the last word." Horn Book

Billingsley, Franny
The Folk Keeper. Atheneum Bks. for Young Readers 1999 162p $16; pa $4.99 (5 and up)
Fic
ISBN 0-689-82876-4; 0-689-84461-1 (pa)
LC 98-48778
"A Jean Karl book"

Billingsley, Franny—*Continued*

Orphan Corinna disguises herself as a boy to pose as a Folk Keeper, one who keeps the Evil Folk at bay, and discovers her heritage as a seal maiden when she is taken to live with a wealthy family in their manor by the sea

"The intricate plot, vibrant characters, dangerous intrigue, and fantastical elements combine into a truly remarkable novel steeped in atmosphere." Horn Book

Blacker, Terence

The angel factory. Simon & Schuster Bks. for Young Readers 2002 c2001 216p $16.95; pa $4.99
Fic

1. Adoption—Fiction 2. Extraterrestrial beings—Fiction 3. London (England)—Fiction
ISBN 0-689-85171-5; 0-689-86413-2 (pa)

LC 2002-1262

First published 2001 in the United Kingdom

Spurred on by his best friend, twelve-year-old Thomas uncovers two major family secrets: that he was adopted, and that his perfect-seeming family is part of an otherworldly organization

The author "masterfully constructs an intriguing world of remarkable possibilities and chilling consequences that bears an eerie resemblance to the here and now. . . . This complex novel raises some thought-provoking questions." Publ Wkly

Blackwood, Gary L.

Moonshine. Marshall Cavendish 1999 158p $14.95
Fic

1. Great Depression, 1929-1939—Fiction
ISBN 0-7614-5056-4   LC 99-10756

During the Depression, in the Ozarks of Missouri, thirteen-year-old Thad has adventures selling moonshine and fishing with a rich visitor

"The story jumps off to a quick start, and . . . the pace never slackens. . . . All characters, even the bootlegger, are sympathetically presented." Booklist

The Shakespeare stealer; {by} Gary Blackwood. Dutton Children's Bks. 1998 216p $15.99; pa $5.99 (5 and up)
Fic

1. Shakespeare, William, 1564-1616—Fiction 2. Theater—Fiction 3. Orphans—Fiction 4. Great Britain—History—1485-1603, Tudors—Fiction
ISBN 0-525-45863-8; 0-14-130595-9 (pa)

LC 97-42987

A young orphan boy is ordered by his master to infiltrate Shakespeare's acting troupe in order to steal the script of "Hamlet," but he discovers instead the meaning of friendship and loyalty

"Wry humor, cliffhanger chapter endings, and a plucky protagonist make this a fitting introduction to Shakespeare's world." Horn Book

Other titles in this series are:
Shakespeare's scribe (2000)
Shakespeare's spy (2003)

The year of the hangman; [by] Gary Blackwood. Dutton Children's Bks. 2002 261p $16.99; pa $5.99
Fic

1. United States—History—1775-1783, Revolution—Fiction
ISBN 0-525-46921-4; 0-14-240078-5 (pa)

LC 2002-67498

In 1777, having been kidnapped and taken forcibly from England to the American colonies, fifteen-year-old Creighton becomes part of developments in the political unrest there that may spell defeat for the patriots and change the course of history

"Packed with action, convincing historical speculation, and compelling portrayals of real-life and fictional characters, this page-turner will appeal to fans of both history and fantasy." SLJ

Blakeslee, Ann R.

A different kind of hero. Marshall Cavendish 1997 143p $14.95; pa $5.95
Fic

1. Frontier and pioneer life—Fiction 2. Prejudices—Fiction 3. West (U.S.)—Fiction
ISBN 0-7614-5000-9; 0-7614-5147-1 (pa)

LC 96-32786

In 1881 twelve-year-old Renny, who resists his father's efforts to turn him into a rough, tough, brawling boy, earns the disapproval of the entire mining camp when he befriends a newly arrived Chinese boy

"This story of friendship, hardship, and many forms of prejudice has a well-drawn main character and realistic conflict rooted in historic detail." SLJ

Bloor, Edward, 1950-

Crusader. Harcourt Brace & Co. 1999 390p $17 (7 and up)
Fic

1. Courage—Fiction 2. Virtual reality—Fiction
ISBN 0-15-201944-8   LC 99-6293

Also available in paperback from Scholastic

After a violent virtual-reality game arrives at the mall arcade where she works, fifteen-year-old Roberta finds the courage to search out the person who murdered her mother

This is a "disturbing, complex novel. . . . Bloor knows there are no easy answers, and he refuses to do anything except ask the questions. This is a stretch book in the truest sense; it will challenge young adults—and you." Booklist

Story time. Harcourt 2004 424p $17
Fic

1. School stories 2. Ghost stories
ISBN 0-15-204670-4   LC 2002-151503

George and Kate are promised the best education but instead face obsessed administrators, endless tests, and evil spirits when they are transferred to Whittaker Magnet School.

"Bloor successfully combines humor, mystery, and fantasy in this satire about the pitfalls of education." Voice Youth Advocates

Tangerine. Harcourt Brace & Co. 1997 294p $17 (7 and up)
Fic

1. Soccer—Fiction 2. Brothers—Fiction 3. Florida—Fiction
ISBN 0-15-201246-X   LC 96-34182

Bloor, Edward, 1950-—*Continued*

Also available in paperback from Scholastic

Twelve-year-old Paul, who lives in the shadow of his football hero brother Erik, fights for the right to play soccer despite his near blindness and slowly begins to remember the incident that damaged his eyesight

"Readers will cheer for this bright, funny, decent kid." Horn Book Guide

Blume, Judy

Are you there God? it's me, Margaret. Twentieth anniversary ed. Bradbury Press 1990 c1970 149p $17.95; pa $5.99 (5 and up)   **Fic**

1. Religion—Fiction
ISBN 0-689-84158-2; 0-440-40419-3 (pa)
LC 90-44484

Also available in paperback from Dell

First published 1970

"A perceptive story about the emotional, physical, and spiritual ups and downs experienced by 12-year-old Margaret, child of a Jewish-Protestant union." Natl Counc of Teach of Engl. Adventuring with Books. 2d edition

"The writing style is lively, the concerns natural, and the problems are treated with both humor and sympathy, but the story is intense in its emphasis on the four girls' absorption in, and discussions of, menstruation and brassieres." Bull Cent Child Books

Here's to you, Rachel Robinson. Orchard Bks. 1993 196p (5 and up)   **Fic**

1. Siblings—Fiction 2. Gifted children—Fiction
3. Friendship—Fiction
ISBN 0-531-06801-3; 0-440-21974-4 (pa)
LC 93-9631

Expelled from boarding school, Charles' presence at home proves disruptive, especially for sister Rachel, a gifted seventh grader juggling friendships and school activities

"Blume once again demonstrates her ability to shape multidimensional characters and to explore—often through very convincing dialogue—the tangled interactions of believable, complex people." Publ Wkly

Tiger eyes; a novel. Bradbury Press 1981 206p $16.95 (7 and up)   **Fic**

1. Death—Fiction
ISBN 0-689-85872-8
LC 81-6152

Also available paperback from Laurel Leaf

Resettled in the "Bomb City" with her mother and brother, Davey Wexler recovers from the shock of her father's death during a holdup of his 7-Eleven store in Atlantic City

"The plot is strong, interesting and believable. . . . The story though intense and complicated flows smoothly and easily." Voice Youth Advocates

Boling, Katharine

January 1905. Harcourt 2004 170p $16 (5 and up)   **Fic**

1. Twins—Fiction 2. Sisters—Fiction 3. Child labor—Fiction
ISBN 0-15-205119-8
LC 2003-24470

In a 1905 mill town, eleven-year-old twin sisters, Pauline, who goes to work with the rest of the family, and Arlene, whose crippled foot keeps her home doing the cooking, cleaning, and washing, are convinced that the other sister has an easier life until a series of incidents helps them see each other in a new light.

"This vivid account will draw readers into the period." Horn Book Guide

Booth, Teena

Falling from fire. Wendy Lamb Bks. 2002 201p $15.95; lib bdg $17.99 (7 and up)   **Fic**

1. Fires—Fiction
ISBN 0-385-72978-2; 0-385-90047-3 (lib bdg)
LC 2001-50694

Fourteen-year-old Teri is trying to find out where she fits in, both at home and at school, and when her house burns down in a fire, she thinks she may get a fresh start

"Booth provides a satisfying wrap-up to a story rich in life lessons, tenderness, and humor." Voice Youth Advocates

Borland, Hal, 1900-1978

When the legends die. Lippincott 1963 288p pa $6.50 hardcover o.p.   **Fic**

1. Ute Indians—Fiction
ISBN 0-553-25738-2

"Thomas Black Bull, a Ute Indian, is being reared in the traditional Native American way when his parents are forced to flee from the world of the white man. After the death of his parents Tom is returned to the white world, where he suffers the disintegration of his native heritage and traditions as he experiences school, sheep herding, and rodeo life. Following a serious accident at a rodeo he returns to the mountains and is drawn back into his past." Shapiro. Fic for Youth 3rd edition

Bornstein, Ruth Lercher, 1927-

Butterflies and lizards, Beryl and me. Marshall Cavendish 2002 144p $14.95 (4 and up)   **Fic**

1. Great Depression, 1929-1939—Fiction
ISBN 0-7614-5114-5
LC 2001-47473

In 1934, eleven-year-old Charlotte and her mother move to tiny Valley Junction, Missouri, where Charlotte befriends an eccentric old woman in spite of her mother's and others' warnings

"The characters are drawn with aching truth." Booklist

Bowler, Tim, 1953-

Firmament. Margaret K. McElderry Books 2004 306p $16.95 (7 and up)   **Fic**

1. Death—Fiction 2. Music—Fiction
ISBN 0-689-86161-3
LC 2003-44157

While struggling to cope with the death of his father, a gifted musician, fourteen-year-old Luke must deal with a dangerous bully, a lonely old woman, a blind young girl, his mother's romantic involvement, and his own musical talent.

"The author's lyrical writing will enthrall readers and draw them into a heartfelt story that resonates just like great music." SLJ

Bowler, Tim, 1953——_Continued_

River boy. Margaret K. McElderry Bks. 2000
c1997 155p $16; pa $4.99   **Fic**
1. Grandfathers—Fiction 2. Death—Fiction
3. Artists—Fiction
ISBN 0-689-82908-6; 0-689-84804-8 (pa)
                                  LC 99-20418
First published 1997 in the United Kingdom
Knowing that he is dying, Jess's grandfather insists on
returning to the river he had known as a boy to finish
a special painting and fulfill a life-long dream
"Bowler's story is steeped in magic realism. . . .
Anyone who grieves for a lost relative or friend will recognize Jess' intense feeling and her search for 'something more enduring than human life.' There's poetry in
the simple, elemental words and the space between
them." Booklist

Storm catchers. Margaret K. McElderry Bks.
2003 c2001 200p $16.95 (7 and up)   **Fic**
1. Kidnapping—Fiction
ISBN 0-689-84573-1   LC 2001-55750
First published 2001 in the United Kingdom
Filled with guilt over his younger sister's kidnapping,
teenaged Fin tries to rescue her and in the process learns
about a dark family secret
"Bowler's plot is tightly scripted, with good pacing
and steadily building tension. The complex themes of
guilt and betrayal enhance the suspense." SLJ

Bradbury, Ray, 1920-
The Halloween tree; illustrated by Joseph
Mugnaini. Knopf 1988 c1972 145p   **Fic**
1. Halloween—Fiction 2. Fantasy fiction
ISBN 0-394-82409-1; 0-375-80301-7 (pa)
A reissue of the title first published 1972
A group of boys meet a spirit-being and are carried
back in time to the origins of Halloween celebrations
This is "fast-moving, genuinely eerie" Booklist

Something wicked this way comes. Avon Bks.
1999 293p $15.99; pa $6.99 (7 and up)
                                  Fic
ISBN 0-380-97727-3; 0-380-72940-7 (pa)
A reissue of the title first published 1962 by Simon
and Schuster
"We read here of the loss of innocence, the recognition of evil, the bond between generations, and the purely fantastic. These forces enter Green Town, Illinois, on
the wheels of Cooger and Dark's Pandemonium Shadow
Show. Will Halloway and Jim Nightshade, two 13-year-
olds, explore the sinister carnival for excitement, which
becomes desperation as the forces of the dark threaten to
engulf them. Bradbury's gentle humanism and lyric style
serve this fantasy well." Shapiro. Fic for Youth. 3d edition

Bradley, Kimberly Brubaker
For freedom; the story of a French spy.
Delacorte Press 2003 181p $15.95; lib bdg $17.99
                                  Fic
1. World War, 1939-1945—Fiction 2. France—History—1940-1945, German occupation—Fiction
ISBN 0-385-72961-8; 0-385-90087-2 (lib bdg)
                                  LC 2002-13057
Despite the horrors of World War II, a French
teenager pursues her dream of becoming an opera singer,
which takes her to places where she gains information
about what the Nazis are doing—information that the
French Resistance needs
"This taut, engrossing World War II novel instantly
immerses readers in the horrors faced by everyday citizens during the Nazi Occupation. The real focus, however, is the skin-crawling suspense story about one of
France's youngest spies." Booklist

Halfway to the sky. Delacorte Press 2002 166p
$15.95; pa $4.99   **Fic**
1. Hiking—Fiction
ISBN 0-385-72960-X; 0-440-41830-5 (pa)
                                  LC 2001-37246
After her brother dies and her parents get a divorce,
twelve-year-old Katahdin sets out to hike the whole Appalachian Trail from Georgia to Maine on her own
"The story is remarkably affecting. As it unfolds,
Bradley allows her gutsy heroine to manage extreme
physical and emotional stresses in a way that's both believable and reassuring." Booklist

Weaver's daughter. Delacorte Press 2000 166p
$14.95 (5 and up)   **Fic**
1. Asthma—Fiction 2. Frontier and pioneer life—Fiction 3. Tennessee—Fiction
ISBN 0-385-32769-2   LC 00-26193
Also available Thorndike Press large print edition
"Lizzy's a sympathetic heroine who faces uncertainty
with aplomb. This well-developed story also offers insight into early medical practices." Horn Book Guide

Brenaman, Miriam
Evvy's Civil War. Putnam 2002 209p $18.99;
pa $6.99   **Fic**
1. Sex role—Fiction 2. United States—History—1861-
1865, Civil War—Fiction 3. Virginia—Fiction
ISBN 0-399-23713-5; 0-14-240039-4 (pa)
                                  LC 2001-18353
In Virginia in 1860, on the verge of the Civil War,
fourteen-year-old Evvy chafes at the restrictions that her
society places on both women and slaves
"More complex and better researched than most Civil
War fiction for young people, the novel has strong characterizations, an involving story, and timeless reflections
on a woman's need to find her place in life." Booklist

Breslin, Theresa
Remembrance. Delacorte Press 2002 296p
$16.95; lib bdg $18.99; pa $6.50 (7 and up)
                                  Fic
1. World War, 1914-1918—Fiction
ISBN 0-385-73015-2; 0-385-90067-8 (lib bdg);
0-440-23778-5 (pa)   LC 2002-1629

Breslin, Theresa—*Continued*

The destinies of two Scottish families, one of shop-keepers and one of wealth and power, become entwined through their involvement in World War I, social causes, and love

"The chaos and waste of World War I battlefields is clearly depicted here. . . . This thought-provoking examination of the nature of that war and that world results in splendid historical fiction." SLJ

Brittain, Bill

Shape-changer. HarperCollins Pubs. 1994 108p hardcover o.p. paperback available $4.95 (5 and up) **Fic**

1. Science fiction 2. Extraterrestrial beings—Fiction
ISBN 0-06-440514-1 (pa)   LC 93-27268

Two seventh-grade friends help a shape-changing policeman from the planet Rodinam as he tries to recapture an alien master criminal who can also change form

"Funny scenes abound in the fast-paced, enthralling adventure." Horn Book Guide

The wish giver; three tales of Coven Tree; drawings by Andrew Glass. Harper & Row 1983 181p il $16.89 hardcover o.p.; pa $5.99 hardcover o.p.   **Fic**

1. Wishes—Fiction 2. Magic—Fiction
ISBN 0-06-020687-X; 0-06-440168-5 (pa)
     LC 82-48264

A Newbery Medal honor book, 1984

"Witchy and devilish things happen in Coven Tree, New England, and their chronicler is Stew Meat, proprietor of the Coven Tree store. . . . Stew relates the King Midas luck that came to three young people, each of whom had a wish fulfilled, and each of whom rued that fulfillment." SLJ

"Captivating, fresh, and infused with homespun humor." Horn Book

Other titles about Coven Tree are:

Dr. Dredd's wagon of wonders (1987)
Professor Popkin's prodigious polish (1990)

Brokaw, Nancy Steele

Leaving Emma. Clarion Bks. 1999 137p $15
     Fic

1. Friendship—Fiction 2. Aunts—Fiction
ISBN 0-395-90699-7   LC 98-22688

Fifth-grader Emma faces many unpleasant changes as her best friend prepares to move away, her father goes to Turkey for five months, and her mother starts college, but with the help of her great-aunt Grace, Emma becomes a lot more independent and self-reliant

"A sympathetic heroine, Emma experiences personal growth that is believable and satisfying." Horn Book Guide

Brooke, Peggy

Jake's orphan. DK Ink 2000 261p $16.99
     Fic

1. Orphans—Fiction 2. Brothers—Fiction 3. Farm life—Fiction
ISBN 0-7894-2628-5   LC 99-46466

Also available in paperback from Aladdin Bks.

When taken from an orphanage to work on a farm in North Dakota in 1926, twelve-year-old Tree searches for a home not only for himself but also for his irrepressible younger brother

"This is a poignant, action-filled story about farm life and the meaning of family." Booklist

Brooks, Bruce, 1950-

All that remains. Atheneum Bks. for Young Readers 2001 168p $16; pa $6.99 (7 and up)
     Fic

1. Death—Fiction
ISBN 0-689-83351-2; 0-689-83442-X (pa)
     LC 00-56912

Three novellas explore the effects of death on young lives. "In the title story, two cousins become caught in a scheme to cremate their Aunt Judith's remains. State law forbids her cremation because Judith died of AIDS. . . . The second story, *Playing the Creeps*, is about another set of cousins, Hank and Bobby. . . . When Bobby tries out for the hockey team, Hank is torn between a deathbed promise to Bobby's father to 'help' Bobby, and his embarrassment over Bobby's effeminate nature. . . . The final story, *Teeing Up*, takes place on a golf course. Three guys form a reluctant foursome with a girl who never removes her backpack. The backpack, the boys eventually discover, contains her father's cremated remains." Voice Youth Advocates

"All three offerings feature believable dialogue and attitudes true to the emotions of their young characters as well as intriguingly offbeat events." Horn Book Guide

Midnight hour encores. Harper & Row 1986 263p pa $6.99 hardcover o.p. (7 and up)
     Fic

1. Musicians—Fiction 2. Father-daughter relationship—Fiction 3. Mother-daughter relationship—Fiction
ISBN 0-06-020709-4   LC 86-45035

"A cello prodigy and her father take both a literal cross-country journey to meet the mother who gave her up at birth and a figurative trip through the 1960s to understand the woman." SLJ

"This is a rich and delightful book." Wilson Libr Bull

The moves make the man; a novel. HarperCollins Pubs. 1984 280p   **Fic**

1. African Americans—Fiction 2. Friendship—Fiction
ISBN 0-06-020679-9; 0-06-020698-5 (lib bdg); 0-06-447022-9 (pa)

"Jerome Foxworthy's consuming passion is @hoops', and he gets excited when he sees a shortstop who has the same kind of love for baseball. 'Jayfox', 13, is the first and only black kid to integrate the junior high in Wilmington, N.C. His mother has a terrible accident, and in order to cook for his older brothers, he takes home economics, and finds that the only other male is that shortstop, Bix. Bix's mother is in a mental institution, and his stepfather will not allow Bix to visit her. Bix's problem becomes Jerome's with all sorts of consequences." BAYA Book Rev

This is an "excellent novel about values and the way people relate to one another." N Y Times Book Rev

Brooks, Bruce, 1950-—*Continued*

Throwing smoke. HarperCollins Pubs. 2000
136p lib bdg $15.89; pa $5.95   **Fic**
1. Baseball—Fiction 2. Supernatural—Fiction
ISBN 0-06-028320-3 (lib bdg); 0-06-440774-8 (pa)
LC 99-59555
"A Laura Geringer book"
When his teammates on the Breadhurst Newts baseball
team continue their losing ways, Whiz uses an unusual
printing press to create several star players in hopes of
winning a game
"Readers will be drawn in by the witty, edgy prose;
great dialogue; dimensional, diverse characters; and
abundant baseball lingo and plays. But this sports-fantasy
novel is also thought-provoking." Booklist

Vanishing. HarperCollins Pubs. 1999 103p
$14.95; lib bdg $14.89; pa $6.95   **Fic**
1. Death—Fiction 2. Hospitals—Fiction
ISBN 0-06-028236-3; 0-06-028237-1 (lib bdg);
0-06-447234-5 (pa)   LC 99-11743
"A Laura Geringer book"
"Hospitalized with bronchitis and not wanting to go
home to her self-absorbed mother and racist stepfather,
Alice goes on a hunger strike that keeps her in the hospi-
tal, where she shares space with Rex, who has cancer."
Horn Book Guide
"This is a deeply felt, unusual, and absorbing story."
SLJ

Brooks, Kevin, 1959-

Lucas. Chicken House/Scholastic 2003 423p
$16.95 (7 and up)   **Fic**
1. Prejudices—Fiction 2. Great Britain—Fiction
ISBN 0-439-45698-3   LC 2002-29189
On an isolated English island, fifteen-year-old Caitlin
McCann makes the painful journey from adolescence to
adulthood through her experiences with a mysterious
boy, whose presence has an unsettling effect on the island's inhabitants
"This beautifully written allegorical tale . . . stays
with readers long after it ends. . . . All of the characters
are sharply defined. Lucas, with his mixture of real and
unearthly qualities, is unique and unforgettable. This is
a powerful book to be savored by all who appreciate fine
writing and a gripping read." SLJ

Martyn Pig; a novel. Scholastic 2002 230p
$16.95; pa $6.99 (7 and up)   **Fic**
1. Death—Fiction 2. Alcoholism—Fiction
ISBN 0-439-29595-5; 0-439-50752-9 (pa)
LC 2001-49414
"The Chicken House"
.
Faced with the possibility of living with a dreadful
aunt, fifteen-year-old Martyn Pig decides not to tell authorities when his alcoholic father dies accidentally, instead asking a friend for her help in disposing of the
body
Readers "will be fascinated with the gripping plot
twists and turns, and fully engaged by Martyn's distinctive voice. . . . The bleakness is tempered by some
tongue-in-cheek and zany humor." SLJ

Brooks, Martha, 1944-

Being with Henry. Dorling Kindersley 2000
c1999 216p $17.99   **Fic**
ISBN 0-7894-2588-2   LC 99-46464
"Melanie Kroupa book"
First published 1999 in Canada
An expanded version of the author's story Kindness of
strangers from Traveling on into the light and other stories
Forced out of his home by a disagreeable and bullying
stepfather, sixteen-year-old Laker moves to another town
and strikes up an unexpected friendship with a frail but
determined old man
"The characters here are poignant and believable, and
the writing is poetic and moving." Voice Youth Advocates

True confessions of a heartless girl. Farrar,
Straus & Giroux 2003 181p $16 (7 and up)
Fic
1. Canada—Fiction 2. City and town life—Fiction
ISBN 0-374-37806-1   LC 2002-72461
"Melanie Kroupa books"
A confused seventeen-year-old girl, a single mother
and her young son, two elderly women, and a sad and
lonely man, with their own individual tragedies to bear,
come together in a small Manitoba town and find a way
to a better future
"The writing is plain, with a flatness about it that mirrors the Canadian prairie where the story is set. The style
also suits the novel's bleak mood; even the most horrific
events seem somehow expected. The characterizations
are bare-to-the-bones as well, but the people are so
expertly revealed that their pain is palpable." Booklist

Brown, Don, 1949-

Our time on the river. Houghton Mifflin 2003
135p $15   **Fic**
1. Brothers—Fiction 2. Canoes and canoeing—Fiction
ISBN 0-618-31116-5   LC 2002-15325
Two brothers take a river trip by canoe in advance of
the elder brother being shipped out to Vietnam
"This is a satisfying read, with the river journey offering a microcosm of society at that time." Booklist

Bruchac, Joseph, 1942-

Code talker; a novel about the Navajo Marines
of World War Two. Dial 2005 240p $16.99
Fic
1. Navajo Indians—Fiction 2. World War, 1939-
1945—Fiction
ISBN 0-8037-2921-9
After being taught in a boarding school run by whites
that Navajo is a useless language, Ned Begay and other
Navajo men are recruited by the Marines to become
Code Talkers, sending messages during World War II in
their native tongue.
"Bruchac's gentle prose presents a clear historical picture of young men in wartime. . . . Nonsensational and
accurate, Bruchac's tale is quietly inspiring." SLJ
Includes bibliographical references

Bruchac, Joseph, 1942——*Continued*
The heart of a chief; a novel. Dial Bks. for
Young Readers 1998 153p $16.99; pa $5.99
Fic
1. Native Americans—Fiction 2. Alcoholism—Fiction
ISBN 0-8037-2276-1; 0-14-131236-X (pa)
LC 97-49248

Chris, an eleven-year-old Penacook Indian boy living
on a reservation faces his father's alcoholism, a controversy surrounding plans for a casino on a tribal island,
and insensitivity toward Native Americans in his school
and nearby town
"The story's themes are universal and Chris's compelling voyage of self-discovery is grounded in everyday
events that middle-graders will recognize." Publ Wkly

Hidden roots; by Joseph Bruchac. 1st ed.
Scholastic 2004 136p $16.95 **Fic**
1. Family life—Fiction 2. Native Americans—Fiction
3. Prejudices—Fiction 4. New York (State)—Fiction
ISBN 0-439-35358-0 LC 2003-50396

Although he is uncertain why his father is so angry
and what secret his mother is keeping from him, eleven-
year-old Sonny knows that he is different from his classmates in their small New York town.
"Bruchac's story takes its roots in the 1930s Native
American sterilization program known as the Vermont
Eugenics Program. . . . This purposeful but discerning
book will prompt discussion and further research into the
plight of the Native people from the Green Mountain
State." SLJ

Pocahontas. Silver Whistle 2003 173p $17 (7
and up) **Fic**
1. Pocahontas, d. 1617—Fiction 2. Smith, John, 1580-
1631—Fiction 3. Powhatan Indians—Fiction
ISBN 0-15-216737-4 LC 2002-7214

Told from the viewpoints of Pocahontas and John
Smith, describes their lives in the context of the encounter between the Powhatan Indians and the English colonists of 17th century Jamestown, Virginia
This is a "vivid, detailed historical novel. . . . The author goes to great lengths to present a historically accurate depiction . . . and he succeeds admirably." Booklist
Includes glossary and bibliographical references

Sacajawea; the story of Bird Woman and the
Lewis and Clark Expedition. Silver Whistle Bks.
2000 199p o.p. Scholastic paperback available
$4.99 (6 and up) **Fic**
1. Sacagawea, b. 1786—Fiction 2. Clark, William,
1770-1838—Fiction 3. Lewis and Clark Expedition
(1804-1806)—Fiction 4. Native Americans—Fiction
ISBN 0-439-28068-0 (pa) LC 99-47653

Sacajawea, a Shoshoni Indian interpreter, peacemaker,
and guide, and William Clark alternate in describing
their experiences on the Lewis and Clark Expedition to
the Northwest
This is an "intelligent, elegantly written novel." SLJ
Includes bibliographical references

Skeleton man. HarperCollins Pubs. 2001 114p il
$15.99; lib bdg $16.89; pa $4.99 (4 and up)
Fic
1. Kidnapping—Fiction 2. Mohawk Indians—Fiction
ISBN 0-06-029075-7; 0-06-029076-5 (lib bdg);
0-06-440888-4 (pa) LC 00-54345

After her parents disappear and she is turned over to
the care of a strange "great-uncle," Molly must rely on
her dreams about an old Mohawk story for her safety
and maybe even for her life
"The mix of traditional and contemporary cultural references adds to the story's haunting appeal, and the
quick pace and suspense . . . will likely hold the interest
of young readers." Publ Wkly

The winter people. Dial Bks. 2002 168p $16.99;
pa $5.99 (5 and up) **Fic**
1. Abnaki Indians—Fiction
ISBN 0-8037-2694-5; 0-14-240229-X (pa)
LC 2002-338

As the French and Indian War rages in October of
1759, Saxso, a fourteen-year-old Abenaki boy, pursues
the English rangers who have attacked his village and
taken his mother and sisters hostage
"The narrative itself is thrilling, its spiritual aspects
enlightening." Booklist

Bryant, Sharon, 1954-
The earth kitchen. HarperCollins Pubs. 2002
148p $15.95 **Fic**
1. Mentally ill—Fiction
ISBN 0-06-029605-4 LC 2001-24357

In 1963, twelve-year-old Gwen tries to find the path
to recovery in a mental ward
"The carefully rendered narrative reveals that what
threw Gwen into this merciless 'hospital' was a traumatic
concatenation of the Cold War's relentless air raid drills
with memories of the car accident that killed her parents.
A haunting, quietly compassionate novel." Horn Book
Guide

Bunting, Eve, 1928-
Blackwater. HarperCollins Pubs. 1999 146p lib
bdg $15.89; pa $5.99 (5 and up) **Fic**
1. Death—Fiction
ISBN 0-06-027843-9 (lib bdg); 0-06-440890-6 (pa)
LC 99-24895

"Joanna Cotler books"
When a boy and girl are drowned in the Blackwater
River, thirteen-year-old Brodie must decide whether to
confess that he may have caused the accident
"Bunting's thought-provoking theme, solid characterization and skillful juggling of suspense and pathos make
this a top-notch choice." Publ Wkly

Doll baby; illustrated by Catherine Stock.
Clarion Bks. 2000 47p il $15 **Fic**
1. Unmarried mothers—Fiction 2. Pregnancy—Fiction
3. Infants—Fiction
ISBN 0-395-93094-4 LC 99-57808

A fifteen-year-old girl who is pregnant decides she
wants to keep her baby, not realizing how much harder
it will be than caring for her beloved Daisy Doll
"The message is direct but not belabored, and Ellie's
somber voice rings true. Realistic watercolor-and-pencil
pictures reflect her emotional conflict and sense of isolation. . . . The simple, direct narrative and attractive format make it particularly accessible for reluctant readers
and ESL students." Booklist

Bunting, Eve, 1928- —*Continued*
The hideout. Harcourt Brace Jovanovich 1991
133p pa $6 hardcover o.p. (5 and up)   **Fic**
1. Runaway children—Fiction 2. Kidnapping—Fiction
3. Parent-child relationship—Fiction
ISBN 0-15-233991-4 (pa)   LC 90-45515
Feeling unloved by his mother and new stepfather,
Andy hides out in a luxurious San Francisco hotel and
stages his own kidnapping in order to obtain ransom
money to pay for a trip to England to see his father
"The involving first-person narrative and the mounting
tension offset the unlikely events. Andy's character . . .
is vividly portrayed." SLJ

The Presence. Clarion Bks. 2003 195p $15
    Fic
1. Ghost stories
ISBN 0-618-26919-3   LC 2003-4034
While visiting her grandmother in California, seventeen-year-old Catherine comes in contact with a mysterious stranger who says he can help her contact a friend
who died in a car crash for which Catherine feels responsible
"Crisp writing and questions that remain unanswered
till tale's end will likely keep fans of ghost stories engaged." Publ Wkly

Someone is hiding on Alcatraz Island. Clarion
Bks. 1984 136p pa $4.99 hardcover o.p.
    Fic
1. Alcatraz Island (Calif.)—Fiction 2. Gangs—Fiction
ISBN 0-425-10294-7 (pa)   LC 84-5019
"The Outlaws, the toughest gang in school, follow
Danny Sullivan to Alcatraz Island after he unintentionally thwarts one member's attempt to mug an old woman.
There he is trapped as they plot their revenge." Publ
Wkly
The authors "builds suspense and sustains it with brisk
dialogue and taut scenes. Characters aren't given much
depth, and the ending is fairly predictable, but the swiftly
unfolding events are sure to keep kids turning pages. The
story's content, simple style, and fast pace also target
this as a good selection for reluctant readers." Booklist

SOS Titanic. Harcourt Brace & Co. 1996 240p
$13; pa $6 (7 and up)   **Fic**
1. Titanic (Steamship)—Fiction 2. Shipwrecks—Fiction
ISBN 0-15-200271-5; 0-15-201305-9 (pa)
    LC 95-10712
Fifteen-year-old Barry O'Neill, traveling from Ireland
to America on the maiden voyage of the Titanic, finds
his life endangered when the ship hits an iceberg and begins to sink
"Bunting accurately and dramatically describes the
ship's sinking and, at the same time, immerses readers in
the many human tragedies. . . . This fast-paced story
will satisfy readers looking for the human element in the
Titanic's history." Booklist

Spying on Miss Müller. Clarion Bks. 1995 179p
$15 (5 and up)   **Fic**
1. World War, 1939-1945—Fiction 2. School stories
3. Ireland—Fiction
ISBN 0-395-69172-9   LC 94-15003
Also available in paperback from Batnam Bks.

At Alveara boarding school in Belfast at the start of
World War II, thirteen-year-old Jessie must deal with her
suspicions about a teacher whose father was German and
with her worries about her own father's drinking problem
"A thoughtful, moving coming-of-age novel. Jessie
and her world . . . are portrayed with page-turning immediacy." Horn Book

The summer of Riley. HarperCollins Pubs. 2001
170p $15.95; lib bdg $16.89; pa $5.99
    Fic
1. Dogs—Fiction 2. Divorce—Fiction
ISBN 0-06-029141-9; 0-06-029142-7 (lib bdg);
0-06-440927-9 (pa)   LC 00-63203
"Joanna Cotler books"
"William is still adjusting to his parents' separation
and his father's engagement when his beloved grandfather dies. He knows his mother is letting him adopt a
dog so he'll start feeling better, and Riley appears to be
a perfect pet. . . . But when Riley violates a state law
by chasing a neighbor's horse, William has to convince
the county commissioners not to destroy his friend. . . .
Bunting's story will have strong appeal for middle-
graders who will relish the bittersweet but satisfying resolution." Booklist

Burks, Brian
Soldier boy. Harcourt Brace & Co. 1997 151p
$12; pa $6   **Fic**
1. Custer, George Armstrong, 1839-1876—Fiction
2. Frontier and pioneer life—Fiction
ISBN 0-15-201218-4; 0-15-201219-2 (pa)
    LC 96-30289
A boy who grew up in the slums of late nineteenth-
century Chicago runs away, joins the cavalry, and fights
with General Custer in the battle of Little Big Horn
"Burks can write gripping, thoroughly researched historical fiction. Here, he mixes humor with the day-to-day
detail of a soldier's life in a fort, and he shows his character maturing into a thoughtful man." Booklist

Walks Alone. Harcourt Brace & Co. 1998 115p
$16; pa $6   **Fic**
1. Apache Indians—Fiction
ISBN 0-15-201612-0; 0-15-202472-7 (pa)
    LC 97-14738
After a surprise attack leaves many of her people
dead, fifteen-year-old Walks Alone, an Apache girl
wounded in the massacre, struggles to survive and rejoin
the refugee band
"Fascinating details of Apache life are woven into a
novel that remains powerful even through a fatalistic
conclusion." Horn Book Guide

Byalick, Marcia
Quit it. Delacorte Press 2002 171p $15.95; lib
bdg $17.99; pa $5.50   **Fic**
1. Tourette syndrome—Fiction 2. New York (N.Y.)—
Fiction
ISBN 0-385-72997-9; 0-385-90061-9 (lib bdg);
0-440-41865-8 (pa)   LC 2002-1324
Diagnosed with a neurological disorder that causes uncontrollable tics, such as coughing and head jerking,
sixth-grader Carrie must cope with the embarrassment

Byalick, Marcia—*Continued*
and strain of various reactions from family, friends, and strangers

"Carrie is an engaging character, whose descriptive, first-person narrative balances a matter-of-fact tone with wry observations and lively commentary." Booklist

Byars, Betsy Cromer, 1928-
The burning questions of Bingo Brown; [by] Betsy Byars. Viking 1988 166p hardcover o.p. paperback available $4.99 (4 and up)   **Fic**
1. School stories
ISBN 0-14-032479-8 (pa)   LC 87-21022
Also available Spanish language edition
A boy is puzzled by the comic and confusing questions of youth and worried by disturbing insights into adult conflicts

"A fully worked out novel. . . . Readers will recognize the pitfalls, agonies, and joys of elementary school life in this book. . . . The short chapters and comic style are designed to appeal to young readers and to move them right into other books." Christ Sci Monit
Other titles about Bingo Brown are:
Bingo Brown and the language of love (1989)
Bingo Brown, gypsy lover (1990)
Bingo Brown's guide to romance (1992)

Cracker Jackson; [by] Betsy Byars. Viking Kestrel 1985 147p pa $5.99 hardcover o.p. (5 and up)   **Fic**
1. Wife abuse—Fiction 2. Child abuse—Fiction
ISBN 0-14-031881-X (pa)   LC 84-24684
"Young Jackson discovers that his ex-baby sitter has been beaten by her husband; and, spurred by affection for her, the boy enlists his friend Goat to help drive her to a home for battered women. The pathetic story of Alma, with her adored baby, tidy home, and treasured collection of Barbie dolls, is relieved by flashbacks to the two boys' antics at school and by their hilarious, if potentially lethal, attempt to drive her to safety." Horn Book

"Suspense, danger, near-tragedy, heartbreak and tension-relieving, unwittingly comic efforts at seriously heroic action mark this as the best of middle-grade fiction to highlight the problems of wife-battering and child abuse." SLJ

The dark stairs; a Herculeah Jones mystery; by Betsy Byars. Viking 1994 130p $14.99; pa $5.99 (4 and up)   **Fic**
1. Mystery fiction
ISBN 0-670-85487-5; 0-14-036996-1 (pa)
          LC 94-14012
The intrepid Herculeah Jones helps her mother, a private investigator, solve a puzzling and frightening case

"There is plenty to laugh at in this book, including classic chapter headings guaranteed to cause shivers for the uninitiated; practiced mystery readers may feel that they are in on a bit of a joke and appreciate the hint of parody. This is a page-turner that is sure to entice the most reluctant readers." SLJ
Other titles about Herculeah Jones series are:
Dead letter (1996)
Death's door (1997)
Disappearing acts (1998)
Tarot says beware (1995)

The keeper of the doves; by Betsy Byars. Viking 2002 121p $14.99; pa $5.99 (4 and up)   **Fic**
1. Sisters—Fiction 2. Family life—Fiction 3. Kentucky—Fiction
ISBN 0-670-03576-9; 0-14-240063-7 (pa)
          LC 2002-9283
In the late 1800s in Kentucky, Amie McBee and her four sisters both fear and torment the reclusive and seemingly sinister Mr. Tominski, but their father continues to provide for his needs

"This is Byars at her best—witty, appealing, thought-provoking." Horn Book

The pinballs; [by] Betsy Byars. Harper & Row 1977 136p lib bdg $16.89; pa $5.99 (5 and up)   **Fic**
1. Foster home care—Fiction 2. Friendship—Fiction
ISBN 0-06-020918-6 (lib bdg); 0-06-440198-7 (pa)
Also available Audiobook version
"Pinballs go where they're pushed—and life's 'tilts' have thrown together three misfits. Suddenly finding themselves in a warm, loving foster home are Thomas J., eight, who is homeless now that his octogenarian twin guardians are hospitalized; Harvey, 13, whose mother ran off to a commune and whose hard-drinking father ran over him in a car; and Carlie, 15, who cannot get along with a succession of stepfathers—or the rest of the world, for that matter." SLJ

"A deceptively simple, eloquent story, its pain and acrimony constantly mitigated by the author's light, off-hand style and by Carlie's wryly comic view of life." Horn Book

The summer of the swans; [by] Betsy Byars; illustrated by Ted CoConis. Viking 1970 142p il $15.99; pa $5.99 (5 and up)   **Fic**
1. Mentally handicapped children—Fiction 2. Siblings—Fiction
ISBN 0-670-68190-3; 0-14-031420-2 (pa)
Also available Audiobook version
Awarded the Newbery Medal, 1971
"The thoughts and feelings of a young girl troubled by a sense of inner discontent which she cannot explain are tellingly portrayed in the story of two summer days in the life of fourteen-year-old Sara Godfrey. Sara is jolted out of her self-pitying absorption with her own inadequacies by the disappearance of her ten-year-old retarded brother who gets lost while trying to find the swans he had previously seen on a nearby lake. Her agonizing, albeit ultimately successful, search for Charlie and the reactions of others to this traumatic event help Sara gain a new perspective on herself and life." Booklist

Cabot, Meg, 1967-
All-American girl. HarperCollins Pubs. 2002 247p $15.99; lib bdg $17.89 (7 and up)   **Fic**
1. Presidents—Fiction
ISBN 0-06-029469-8; 0-06-029470-1 (lib bdg)
          LC 2002-19049
Samantha stops a presidential assassination attempt, is appointed Teen Ambassador to the United Nations, and catches the eye of the very cute First Son

Cabot, Meg, 1967-—*Continued*

There's "surprising depth in the characters and plenty of authenticity in the cultural details and the teenage voices—particularly in Sam's poignant, laugh-out-loud narration." Booklist

The princess diaries. Avon Bks. 2000 238p $15.95; lib bdg $15.89; pa $6.99 **Fic**
1. Princesses—Fiction 2. New York (N.Y.)—Fiction
ISBN 0-380-97848-2; 0-06-029210-5 (lib bdg); 0-380-81402-1 (pa) LC 99-46479

Fourteen-year-old Mia, who is trying to lead a normal life as a teenage girl in New York City, is shocked to learn that her father is the Prince of Genovia, a small European principality, and that she is a princess and the heir to the throne

"Readers will relate to Mia's bubbly, chatty voice and enjoy the humor of this unlikely fairy tale." SLJ

other titles about Princess Mia are:

Princess in pink (2004)
Princess in the spotlight (2001)
Princess in training (2005)
Princess in waiting (2003)
The princess present (2004)

Cadnum, Michael

Blood gold. Viking 2004 210p $16.99 (7 and up) **Fic**
1. California—Gold discoveries—Fiction
ISBN 0-670-05884-X LC 2003-22362

After an arduous journey, Will Dwinelle and his friend Ben finally reach California in 1849 intending to bring home the man who betrayed the honor of a girl back home in Philadelphia, but find themselves tempted by the riches of the Gold Rush

"Cadnum's painstaking attention to historical detail brings the setting vividly to life and skillfully captures both the obvious and obscure nuances of life in the era. Complementing the historical insight is an expertly crafted, fast-paced, engrossing adventure story full of fascinating characters." Booklist

The book of the Lion. Viking 2000 204p $15.99; pa $5.99 (7 and up) **Fic**
1. Knights and knighthood—Fiction 2. Crusades—Fiction 3. Middle Ages—Fiction
ISBN 0-670-88386-7; 0-14-230034-9 (pa) LC 99-39370

In twelfth-century England, after his master, a maker of coins for the king, is brutally punished for alleged cheating, seventeen-year-old Edmund finds himself traveling to the Holy Land as squire to a knight crusader on his way to join the forces of Richard Lionheart

"Cadnum brilliantly captures both the grisly horror and the taut, sinewy excitement of hard travel and battle readiness. . . . There's bawdy and violent talk, but religion as part of the heart and bone of life is present, too." Booklist

Followed by The leopard sword

Daughter of the wind; a novel. Orchard Books 2003 266p $17.95 (7 and up) **Fic**
1. Vikings—Fiction
ISBN 0-439-35224-X LC 2002-72286

In medieval times as various groups of Vikings fight for supremacy of the northern lands and waters, Hallgerd, Gauk, and Hego, three young people from the quiet coastal village of Spjothof, find their fates intertwined as a series of events take them into danger far from home.

"The story is ... gripping, and full of graphic scenes of violence, which may be unpleasant reading for some. Yet it is Cadnum's glimpses of everyday life and the stirring sagas that bring the inner world of these Northern people to life." SLJ

Edge. Viking 1997 215p (7 and up) **Fic**
1. Violence—Fiction 2. Crime—Fiction 3. California—Fiction
ISBN 0-670-87335-7; 0-14-038714-5 (pa) LC 96-44561

Zachary, living with his divorced mother in California, finds violence gradually invading his life and making significant changes in his day-to-day existence

"Cadnum tells a thought-provoking story full of rich, well-developed characters. He immediately engages readers' attention and brilliantly maintains pacing." SLJ

Forbidden forest; the story of Little John and Robin Hood. Orchard Bks. 2002 218p $17.95 (7 and up) **Fic**
1. Robin Hood (Legendary character)—Fiction 2. Great Britain—History—1154-1399, Plantagenets—Fiction 3. Middle Ages—Fiction
ISBN 0-439-31774-6 LC 2001-32932

Profiles Little John, from his quiet life before joining Robin Hood through his adventures protecting a beautiful lady when she is wrongfully accused of murdering her husband

"The book is fast paced and exciting yet does not sugarcoat the grim realities of medieval life. Cadnum gives the familiar tale of Robin Hood a fresh look by making minor characters the focus of the story." Voice Youth Advocates

In a dark wood. Orchard Bks. 1998 246p $17.95; pa $6.99 **Fic**
1. Robin Hood (Legendary character)—Fiction 2. Great Britain—History—1154-1399, Plantagenets—Fiction 3. Middle Ages—Fiction
ISBN 0-531-30071-4; 0-14-130638-6 (pa) LC 97-24780

Also available in paperback from Penguin Bks.

On orders from the King, the Sheriff of Nottingham seeks to capture the outlaw Robin Hood, but he finds him to be a tricky and elusive foe

"This complex, many-layered novel, which does not shirk in its descriptions of filth, violence, and sexual desire, offers an unusually subtle character study and a plot full of surprises." Horn Book Guide

The leopard sword. Viking 2002 195p $15.99 (7 and up) **Fic**
1. Knights and knighthood—Fiction 2. Crusades—Fiction 3. Middle Ages—Fiction
ISBN 0-670-89908-9 LC 2002-18933

Sequel to The book of the Lion

A knight's squire, exhausted from the Crusades, must use his sword to fight attacking infidels during the return

Cadnum, Michael—*Continued*
voyage to England
"This action-packed novel includes several well-rounded characters and some unusual settings. . . . Like its predecessor, this novel does not shy away from the brutality of combat, though the narrative is often reflective, as well." Booklist

Raven of the waves. Orchard Bks. 2001 200p $17.95; pa $5.99 (7 and up)   **Fic**
1. Vikings—Fiction 2. Anglo-Saxons—Fiction
ISBN 0-531-30334-9; 0-439-62661-7 (pa)
LC 00-64986
On his first Viking raid, seventeen-year-old Lidsmod sails on the ship Raven, joining his comrades as they destroy and plunder villages in medieval England and take an Anglo-Saxon boy as captive
"Hard to read because of the gruesome scenes and hard to put down, this book provokes strong emotions and raises many fascinating questions." SLJ

Rundown. Viking 1999 168p pa $6.99 hardcover o.p. (7 and up)   **Fic**
1. Truthfulness and falsehood—Fiction 2. Rape—Fiction
ISBN 0-14-131087-1 (pa)   LC 98-49554
As a game, sixteen-year-old Jennifer pretends that she has been attacked by a serial rapist, but then she finds herself getting more attention than she wanted, from the police and her parents
"Deft characterization and adroit descriptions of setting and motivation raise Cadnum's writing above the commonplace." SLJ

Ship of fire. Viking 2003 197p $16.99 (7 and up)   **Fic**
1. Drake, Sir Francis, 1540?-1596—Fiction 2. Apprentices—Fiction
ISBN 0-670-89907-0   LC 2003-5832
In 1587, sailing to Spain on board Sir Francis Drake's ship "Elizabeth Bonaventure," seventeen-year-old surgeon's apprentice Thomas Spyre finds that, with the sudden death of his master, he must take over as ship's surgeon and prove his skill not only as a doctor but also as a fighter when he is enlisted by Drake to face battle
"Brimming with historical detail and ambience, this fast-paced maritime adventure will surely please devotees of the genre." SLJ

Calhoun, Dia, 1959-
White midnight. Farrar, Straus, and Giroux 2003 289p $18 (7 and up)   **Fic**
1. Toleration—Fiction 2. Handicapped—Fiction 3. Social classes—Fiction
ISBN 0-374-38389-8   LC 2002-35939
Prequel to Firegold (1999)
While barbarians threaten the land, mysterious visions help guide fifteen-year-old Rose when she is given the chance to free her family from servitude, if only she will provide a wicked old man an heir fathered by his deformed grandson, "the Thing" locked in the attic.
"Brooding and atmospheric, sensual but not sexually graphic, this gripping fantasy questions the nature of such cultural components as family, race, and war, without sacrificing the story." Booklist

Calvert, Patricia, 1931-
Bigger. Scribner 1994 137p pa $4.99 hardcover o.p. (5 and up)   **Fic**
1. Frontier and pioneer life—Fiction 2. Father-son relationship—Fiction 3. Dogs—Fiction
ISBN 0-689-86003-X (pa)   LC 93-14415
When his father disappears near the Mexican border at the end of the Civil War, twelve-year-old Tyler decides to go after him and bring him home, acquiring on the journey a strange dog which he names Bigger
"Calvert's story has many tantalizing elements: Tyler is likable and realistically portrayed, the book raises some provocative issues, and the ending is sad but satisfying. . . . This is an entertaining story even reluctant readers will relish." Booklist
Other titles in this series are:
Betrayed! (2002)
Sooner (1998)

Cameron, Ann, 1943-
Colibri. Farrar, Straus & Giroux 2003 227p $17 (5 and up)   **Fic**
1. Kidnapping—Fiction 2. Mayas—Fiction
ISBN 0-374-31519-1   LC 2002-192542
"Frances Foster books"
Kidnapped when she was very young by an unscrupulous man who has forced her to lie and beg to get money, a twelve-year-old Mayan girl endures an abusive life, always wishing she could return to the parents she can hardly remember
"The taut, chilling suspense and search for riches will keep readers flying through the pages. But it's Cameron's beautiful language and Rosa's larger identity quest that make this novel extraordinary." Booklist

Campbell, Eric
The Shark Callers. Harcourt Brace & Co. 1994 232p $10.95; pa $6.00 (7 and up)   **Fic**
1. Sharks—Fiction 2. Volcanoes—Fiction 3. New Guinea—Fiction 4. Adventure fiction
ISBN 0-15-200007-0; 0-15-200010-0 (pa)
LC 93-44881
First published 1993 in the United Kingdom
Two teenage boys, one on a shark hunt and the other traveling with his family, face the challenge of their lives when a volcano erupts, causing a massive tidal wave in the South Seas
"Campbell does a fine job of building suspense, skillfully describing violent and intense moments, and neatly integrates background information about geology and sailing into the story." SLJ

Cannon, A. E.
Charlotte's Rose. Wendy Lamb Bks. 2002 246p $15.95; pa $5.50 (5 and up)   **Fic**
1. Infants—Fiction 2. Frontier and pioneer life—Fiction 3. Immigrants—Fiction 4. Mormons—Fiction
ISBN 0-385-72966-9; 0-440-41840-2 (pa)
LC 2002-427
As Charlotte, twelve-year-old Welsh immigrant, carries a motherless baby along the Mormon Trail in 1856, she comes to love the baby as her own and fear the day the baby's father will reclaim her

Cannon, A. E.—*Continued*

"Based on historical fact, the book offers a genuine headstrong girl in hardscrabble circumstances with a lightness of heart and a strong will to do right." SLJ

Carbone, Elisa Lynn, 1954-

Stealing freedom; {by} Elisa Carbone. Knopf 1998 258p   **Fic**
1. Weems, Anne-Marie—Fiction 2. Slavery—Fiction 3. Underground railroad—Fiction 4. African Americans—Fiction
ISBN 0-679-89307-5; 0-440-41707-4 (pa)
           LC 98-36929
A novel based on the events in the life of Anne-Marie Weems, a young slave girl from Maryland who endures all kinds of mistreatment and cruelty, including being separated from her family, but who eventually escapes to freedom in Canada
"This is a fine piece of historical fiction with a strong, appealing heroine." SLJ

Card, Orson Scott

Ender's game. TOR Bks. 1991 c1985 xxi, 226p $24.95; pa $6.99 (7 and up)   **Fic**
1. Science fiction
ISBN 0-312-93208-1; 0-812-55070-6 (pa)
"A Tom Doherty Associates book"
A reissue of the title first published 1985
"Chosen as a six-year-old for his potential military genius, Ender Wiggin spends his childhood in outer space at the Battle School of the Belt. Severed from his family, isolated from his peers, and rigorously tested and trained, Ender pours all his talent into the war games that will one day repel the coming alien invasion." Libr J
"The key, of course, is Ender Wiggin himself. Mr. Card never makes the mistake of patronizing or sentimentalizing his hero. Alternately likable and insufferable, he is a convincing little Napoleon in short pants." N Y Times Book Rev
 Other titles in the author's distant future series about
  Ender Wiggin are:
Speaker for the dead (1986)
Xenocide (1991)
Children of the mind (1996)
Ender's shadow (1999)
Shadow of the Hegemon (2001)
Shadow puppets (2002)
Shadow of the giant (2005)

Carter, Alden R.

Crescent Moon. Holiday House 1999 153p $16.95   **Fic**
1. Wood carving—Fiction 2. Wisconsin—Fiction 3. Ojibwa Indians—Fiction 4. Uncles—Fiction
ISBN 0-8234-1521-X   LC 99-24654
Living in the logging area of northern Wisconsin during the early 1900s, twelve-year-old Jeremy helps his uncle carve a statue of a Chippewa maiden as a tribute to the vanishing culture of her people
"The story has a comfortable tone that appropriately supports its reverent tribute to a simpler era." Booklist

Carvell, Marlene

Who will tell my brother? Hyperion Bks. for Children 2002 150p $15.99; pa $5.99 (7 and up)
              Fic
1. Mohawk Indians—Fiction 2. School stories
ISBN 0-7868-0827-6; 0-7868-1657-0 (pa)
           LC 2001-51759
During his lonely crusade to remove offensive mascots from his high school, Evan, part-Mohawk Indian, learns more about his heritage, his ancestors, and his place in the world
"The blank verse format will be appealing, especially to reluctant readers. . . . {A} lovely, heart-wrenching and profound little book." Voice Youth Advocates

Casanova, Mary

When eagles fall. Hyperion Bks. for Children 2002 152p $15.99; lib bdg $16.49; pa $5.99
              Fic
1. Eagles—Fiction
ISBN 0-7868-0665-6; 0-7868-2557-X (lib bdg); 0-7868-1491-8 (pa)   LC 2001-51830
Still coping with her brother's death and her parents' subsequent divorce, thirteen-year-old Alex finds herself stranded on a small, deserted island in Minnesota with an injured eaglet
This is "an obviously well-researched survival novel with lots of local color and a teenage heroine who turns out to have plenty of grit." Booklist

Caseley, Judith, 1951-

Losing Louisa. Foster Bks. 1999 235p $17 (7 and up)   **Fic**
1. Divorce—Fiction 2. Family life—Fiction 3. Pregnancy—Fiction
ISBN 0-374-34665-8   LC 98-19501
.
Sixteen-year-old Lacey worries about the effect of her parents' divorce on her family, especially her mother, and about her older sister's sexual activity, which may have made her pregnant
"Never maudlin or didactic, Caseley's novel is a story of love, family, and the resilience of the spirit." SLJ

Castellucci, Cecil, 1969-

Boy proof; Cecil Castellucci. 1st U.S. ed. Candlewick Press 2005 203p $15.99 (7 and up)
              Fic
1. Motion pictures—Fiction 2. Los Angeles (Calif.)—Fiction
ISBN 0-7636-2333-4   LC 2004-50256
Feeling alienated from everyone around her, Los Angeles high school senior and cinephile Victoria Denton hides behind the identity of a favorite movie character until an interesting new boy arrives at school and helps her realize that there is more to life than just the movies.
This "novel's clipped, funny, first-person, present-tense narrative will grab teens . . . with its romance and the screwball special effects, and with the story of an outsider's struggle both to belong and to be true to herself." Booklist

Catran, Ken, 1944-

Voyage with Jason. Lothian; distributed by Star Bright 2003 c2000 208p pa $6.95   **Fic**
1. Jason (Greek mythology)—Fiction
ISBN 0-7344-0151-5
"Catran provides a new focus to the well-known story of Jason and the Argonauts, emphasizing the characters rather than the quest itself. Pylos, an apprentice shipbuilder, is rescued by Hercules from his cruel master, Thegus, and accompanies the Argonauts as the ship's boy. He narrates the events during this three-year quest. . . . The superstitions, religion, and battles at sea are just some examples of the cultural elements woven into this fascinating, well-written story." SLJ

Chabon, Michael

Summerland. Hyperion Bks. for Children 2002 500p $22.95; pa $8.95 (5 and up)   **Fic**
1. Fantasy fiction 2. Baseball—Fiction 3. Magic—Fiction
ISBN 0-7868-0877-2; 0-7868-1615-5 (pa)
LC 2002-27497
Ethan Feld, the worst baseball player in the history of the game, finds himself recruited by a 100-year-old scout to help a band of fairies triumph over an ancient enemy
"Much of the prose is beautifully descriptive as Chabon navigates vividly imagined other worlds and offers up some timeless themes." Horn Book

Chan, Gillian

A foreign field. Kids Can Press 2002 184p $16.95; pa $5.95 (7 and up)   **Fic**
1. World War, 1939-1945—Fiction 2. Love stories
ISBN 1-55337-349-9; 1-55337-350-2 (pa)
"Fourteen-year-old Ellen, who lives near a Canadian air base that the Royal Air Force is using for training during WWII, has what she considers a tedious job as her war work: looking after her disobedient, airplane-mad younger brother, Colin. Colin introduces her to Stephen, a very young RAF trainee. . . . They find common ground and their friendship grows and deepens into love. . . . Chan beautifully captures the particular tensions and intensity of wartime relationships in this quiet, absorbing novel." Booklist

Cheaney, J. B.

The playmaker. Knopf 2000 307p $15.95; pa $5.99   **Fic**
1. Theater—Fiction 2. Great Britain—History—1485-1603, Tudors—Fiction 3. Mystery fiction 4. London (England)—Fiction
ISBN 0-375-80577-X; 0-440-41710-4 (pa)
LC 00-30193
While working as an apprentice in a London theater company in 1597, fourteen-year-old Richard uncovers a mystery involving the disappearance of his father and a traitorous plot to overthow Queen Elizabeth
"Although there is plenty of breathless action, the mystery of Richard's father reveals itself subtly. . . . Most compelling are the highly detailed theater scenes. . . . {A} challenging, well-researched coming-of-age tale." Booklist

The true Prince. Knopf 2002 340p $15.95; lib bdg $17.99; pa $5.99   **Fic**
1. Theater—Fiction 2. Mystery fiction 3. Great Britain—History—1485-1603, Tudors—Fiction 4. London (England)—Fiction
ISBN 0-375-81433-7; 0-375-91433-1 (lib bdg); 0-440-41940-9 (pa)   LC 2002-72972
Newly apprenticed to Shakespeare's theater company, Richard and Kit are drawn into a series of crimes involving the members of Queen Elizabeth's court
"Returning to the milieu and characters of *The Playmaker* . . . Cheaney offers another historical thriller. . . . Turbulent action, engaging characters, vivid period details, and a gripping denouement make this a worthy successor to the first book." SLJ

Cheng, Andrea, 1957-

The lace dowry; . . Front Street 2005 113p $16.95 (4 and up)   **Fic**
1. Friendship—Fiction 2. Sex role—Fiction 3. Hungary—Fiction
ISBN 1-932425-20-9   LC 2004-21186
In Hungary in 1933, a twelve-year-old from Budapest befriends the Halas village family of lacemakers hired to stitch her dowry.
"Cheng tells a familiar story of children discovering empathy across class and cultural divides, enriching the theme with a vivid historical setting and Juli's strong narration, which is written in spare language and a believable voice." Booklist

Childress, Alice, 1920-1994

Rainbow Jordan. Coward, McCann & Geoghegan 1981 142p pa $4.99 hardcover o.p. (7 and up)   **Fic**
1. Foster home care—Fiction 2. Mother-daughter relationship—Fiction 3. African Americans—Fiction
ISBN 0-38058974-5 (pa)   LC 81-596
The author "examines the relationships among three women—Rainbow, a teenage child becoming a woman, her errant mother Kathie and Josephine, the foster mother who provides an anchor for Rainbow and when Kathie can't or won't keep her stuff together. The reader also gets a few glimpses of Mayola, the Black social worker, who works conscientiously on Rainbow's behalf." Interacial Books Child Bull
"The handling of sex is tasteful, and positive social values are gently presented without moralizing. Race relations, crimes, aging, and drugs are also well handled." Voice Youth Advocates

Choi, Sook Nyul

Year of impossible goodbyes. Houghton Mifflin 1991 171p $16 (5 and up)   **Fic**
1. Korea—Fiction
ISBN 0-395-57419-6   LC 91-10502
Also available in paperback from Dell
Sookan, a young Korean girl survives the oppressive Japanese and Russian occupation of North Korea during the 1940s, to later escape to freedom in South Korea
"Tragedies are not masked here, but neither are they overdramatized. . . . The observations are honest, the details authentic, the characterizations vividly developed." Bull Cent Child Books

Choi, Sook Nyul—*Continued*
Other titles about Sookan are:
Echoes of the white giraffe (1993)
Gathering of pearls (1994)

Choldenko, Gennifer, 1957-
Al Capone does my shirts. G.P. Putnam's Sons
2004 225p il $15.99 (5 and up)   **Fic**
1. Alcatraz Island (Calif.)—Fiction 2. Autism—Fiction
3. Siblings—Fiction
ISBN 0-399-23861-1   LC 2002-31766
A Newbery Medal honor book, 2005
A twelve-year-old boy named Moose moves to Alcatraz Island in 1935 when guards' families were housed
there, and has to contend with his extraordinary new environment in addition to life with his autistic sister.
"With its unique setting and well-developed characters, this warm, engaging coming-of-age story has plenty
of appeal, and Choldenko offers some fascinating historical background on Alcatraz Island in an afterword."
Booklist

Notes from a liar and her dog. Putnam 2001
216p $16.99; pa $5.99 (5 and up)   **Fic**
1. Family life—Fiction 2. Truthfulness and falsehood—Fiction
ISBN 0-399-23591-4; 0-14-250068-2 (pa)
     LC 00-55354
Eleven-year-old Ant, stuck in a family that she does
not like, copes by pretending that her "real" parents are
coming to rescue her, by loving her dog Pistachio, by
volunteering at the zoo, and by bending the truth and
telling lies
"Choldenko's writing is snappy and tender, depicting
both Ant's bravado and her isolation with sympathy."
Bull Cent Child Books

Chotjewitz, David
Daniel half human; and the good Nazi;
translated by Doris Orgel. 1st ed. Atheneum Books
for Young Readers 2004 298p $17.95 (7 and up)
     Fic
1. Jews—Fiction 2. Germany—Fiction 3. National socialism—Fiction
ISBN 0-689-85747-0   LC 2003-25554
"A Richard Jackson Book."
In 1933, best friends Daniel and Armin admire Hitler,
but as anti-Semitism buoys Hitler to power, Daniel learns
he is half Jewish, threatening the friendship even as life
in their beloved Hamburg, Germany, is becoming night-
marish. Also details Daniel and Armin's reunion in 1945
in interspersed chapters
"Orgel's translation reads smoothly and movingly. An
outstanding addition to the large body of World War
II/Holocaust fiction." SLJ

Christie, Agatha, 1890-1976
The mirror crack'd. Dodd, Mead 1962 246p o.p.
HarperCollins Pubs. paperback available $4.99 (7
and up)   **Fic**
1. Mystery fiction
ISBN 0-06-100285-2 (pa)
First published 1962 in the United Kingdom with title:
The mirror crack'd from side to side

Miss Jane Marple, whose house in St. Mary Mead is
close to the scene of the crime "gives Scotland Yard her
gracious cooperation in solving a poisoning that takes
place at a village reception where the hostess is a lovely
film star. The murder puzzle is a good one, the village
people and their gossip are acute and interesting." Publ
Wkly

Christopher, John, 1922-
The White Mountains. 35th anniversary ed.
Simon & Schuster Bks. for Young Readers 2003
c1967 164p $16.95   **Fic**
1. Science fiction
ISBN 0-689-85504-4   LC 2002-70808
A reissue of the title first published 1967 by Macmil-
lan
Young Will Parker and his companions make a peril-
ous journey toward an outpost of freedom where they
hope to escape from the ruling Tripods, who capture ma-
ture human beings and make them docile, obedient ser-
vants
This "remarkable story . . . belongs to the school of
science-fiction which puts philosophy before technology
and is not afraid of telling an exciting story." Times Lit
Suppl
Other available titles about the Tripods are:
The city of gold and lead (2003 c1967)
The pool of fire (2003 c1968)
When the Tripods came (2003 c1988)

Cisneros, Sandra
The house on Mango Street. Knopf 1994 134p
$24; pa $9.95 (7 and up)   **Fic**
1. Chicago (Ill.)—Fiction 2. Mexican Americans—Fiction
ISBN 0-679-43335-X; 0-679-73477-5 (pa)
     LC 93-43564
"Originally published by Arte Público Press in 1984."
Verso of title page
Composed of a series of interconnected vignettes, this
"is the story of Esperanza Cordero, a young girl growing
up in the Hispanic quarter of Chicago. For Esperanza,
Mango Street is a desolate landscape of concrete and
run-down tenements, where she discovers the hard realities of life—the fetters of class and gender, the specter
of racial enmity, the mysteries of sexuality, and more."
Publisher's note
This is "a composite of evocative snapshots that manages to passionately recreate the milieu of the poor quarters of Chicago." Commonweal

Clapp, Patricia, 1912-
The tamarack tree; a novel of the Siege of
Vicksburg. Lothrop, Lee & Shepard Bks. 1986
214p $16.99 (7 and up)   **Fic**
1. Vicksburg (Miss.)—Siege, 1863—Fiction
2. United States—History—1861-1865, Civil War—
Fiction
ISBN 0-688-02852-7   LC 86-108
"There is a romantic element, but this is primarily a
record of the long siege of the city and it gives, through
its British narrator, a good perspective of the tragic division and of the conflicting viewpoints of North and
South." Bull Cent Child Books

Clark, Clara Gillow, 1951-
Hill Hawk Hattie. Candlewick Press 2003 159p
$15.99 (5 and up)   **Fic**
1. Father-daughter relationship—Fiction 2. Death—
Fiction 3. Sex role—Fiction
ISBN 0-7636-1963-9   LC 2002-73740
"With beautiful rhythmic sentences, the simple first-
person narrative captures {Hattie's} rustic innocence, the
thrilling rafting adventure, and the heartfelt struggle of a
tough girl who feels useful to her father only in the role
of a boy." Booklist
Another available title about Hattie is:
Hattie on her way (2005)

Clarke, Arthur C., 1917-
2001: a space odyssey. New Am. Lib. 1968
221p (7 and up)   **Fic**
1. Science fiction
Available in paperback from ROC
"Based on a screenplay by Stanley Kubrick and Arthur C. Clarke." Title page
Astronauts of the spaceship Discovery, aided by their
computer, HAL, blast off in search of proof that extraterrestrial beings had a part in the development of intelligent life forms on Earth millions of years ago.
"By standing the universe on its head, the author
makes us see the ordinary universe in a different light.
. . . [This novel becomes] a complex allegory about the
history of the world." New Yorker
Followed by 2010: odyssey two (1982); 2061: odyssey
three (1987); and 3001: the final odyssey (1997)

Clarke, Judith, 1943-
Kalpana's dream. Front Street 2004 164p $16.95
                                                      Fic
1. School stories 2. Australia—Fiction 3. East Indians—Fiction
ISBN 1-932425-22-5   LC 2004-21005
While an English class of 7B students at Wentworth
High in Australia struggle with a six-week essay assignment answering, "Who am I?," one child's great-
grandmother arrives unexpectedly from India to follow
her dream.
"Clarke is brilliant at making gossamer connections
between her characters. The interweavings can be common or unexpected, but they are always meticulously
rendered." Booklist

Starry nights. Front St. 2003 148p $15.95
                                                      Fic
1. Ghost stories 2. Death—Fiction
ISBN 1-88691-082-0   LC 2002-192884
Guilty over their older brother's drowning and their
mother's subsequent breakdown, fourteen-year-old Vida
ventures into the occult but it is ten-year-old Jess who
meets the ghost who is trying to help them
"This tantalizing ghost story . . . will keep readers on
the edge of their seats. . . . A spine-tingler with staying
power." Publ Wkly

Wolf on the fold. Front St. 2002 169p $16.95 (7
and up)   **Fic**
1. Family life—Fiction
ISBN 1-886910-79-0   LC 2001-59750
First published 2000 in Australia

"In this novel, six loosely connected short stories that
may be read independently follow four Australian generations through their few ups and many downs. The first
story takes place during the Great Depression, when 14-
year-old Kenny's father has died and the teen drops out
of school to support his family. The fifth is set in 1991,
in war-stressed Israel." SLJ
"These are powerful and truthful depictions of the
complexity of human, especially familial, relationships."
Bull Cent Child Books

Cleary, Beverly
Dear Mr. Henshaw; illustrated by Paul O.
Zelinsky. Morrow 1983 133p il $15.99; lib bdg
$16.89 (4 and up)   **Fic**
1. Divorce—Fiction 2. Parent-child relationship—Fic-
tion 3. School stories
ISBN 0-688-02405-X; 0-688-02406-8 (lib bdg)
                                  LC 83-5372
Also available in paperback from Avon Bks.; Spanish
language edition also available
Awarded the Newbery Medal, 1984
"Leigh Botts started writing letters to his favorite author, Boyd Henshaw, in the second grade. Now, Leigh is
in the sixth grade, in a new school, and his parents are
recently divorced. This year he writes many letters to
Mr. Henshaw, and also keeps a journal. Through these
the reader learns how Leigh adjusts to new situations,
and of his triumphs." Child Book Rev Serv
"The story is by no means one of unrelieved gloom,
for there are deft touches of humor in the sentient, subtly
wrought account of the small triumphs and tragedies in
the life of an ordinary boy." Horn Book
Followed by Strider

Strider; illustrated by Paul O. Zelinsky. Morrow
Junior Bks. 1991 179p il $15.95; lib bdg $16.89
(4 and up)   **Fic**
1. Dogs—Fiction 2. Divorce—Fiction
ISBN 0-688-09900-9; 0-688-09901-7 (lib bdg)
                                  LC 90-6608
Also available in paperback from Avon Bks.; Spanish
language edition also available
Sequel to Dear Mr. Henshaw
In a series of diary entries, Leigh Botts, now fourteen
and beginning high school, tells how he comes to terms
with his parents' divorce, acquires joint custody of an
abandoned dog, and joins the track team at school
"The development of the narrative is vintage Beverly
Cleary, an inimitable blend of comic and poignant moments." Horn Book

Cleaver, Vera
Where the lillies bloom; [by] Vera & Bill
Cleaver; illustrated by Jim Spanfeller. Lippincott
1969 174p il $15.95; pa $5.99 (5 and up)
                                                      Fic
1. Orphans—Fiction 2. Siblings—Fiction
3. Appalachian region—Fiction
ISBN 0-397-31117-7; 0-064-47005-9 (pa)
Mary Call Luther is "fourteen years old and made of
granite. When her sharecropper father dies, Mary Call
becomes head of the household, responsible for a boy of

Cleaver, Vera—*Continued*

ten and a retarded, gentle older sister. Mary and her brother secretly bury their father so they can retain their home {in the Appalachian hills}; tenaciously she fights to keep the family afloat by selling medicinal plants and to keep them together by fending off {Kiser Pease, their landlord}, who wants to marry her sister." Saturday Rev

"The setting is fascinating, the characterization good, and the style of the first-person story distinctive." Bull Cent Child Books

Followed by Trial Valley (1977)

Clement-Davies, David

Fire bringer. Dutton 2000 c1999 498p $19.95; pa $6.99 (7 and up) **Fic**

1. Fantasy fiction

ISBN 0-525-46492-1; 0-14-230060-8 (pa)

First published 1999 in the United Kingdom

This "animal epic follows the fawn Rannoch and his friends through many years on the run from their herd's harsh dictator. Although the animals think and speak, they otherwise have the characteristics of wild deer. Rannoch's trials are monumental; his character is complex; and his enemies are truly vile. Set in Scotland during the thirteenth century, the novel refers to some historical events that give the story additional depth." Horn Book Guide

Clements, Andrew, 1949-

The school story; illustrated by Brian Selznick. Simon & Schuster Bks. for Young Readers 2001 196p il $16; pa $5.99 (5 and up) **Fic**

1. Authorship—Fiction 2. Publishers and publishing—Fiction

ISBN 0-689-82594-3; 0-689-85186-3 (pa)

LC 00-49683

After twelve-year-old Natalie writes a wonderful novel, her friend Zoe helps her devise a scheme to get it accepted at the publishing house where Natalie's mother works as an editor

"The girls are believable characters. . . . Selznick's black-and-white illustrations add humorous details. A comic novel that's a sure winner." SLJ

Things not seen. Philomel Bks. 2002 251p $15.99; pa $5.99 (7 and up) **Fic**

1. Blind—Fiction 2. Science fiction

ISBN 0-399-23626-0; 0-14-240076-9 (pa)

LC 00-69900

When fifteen-year-old Bobby wakes up and finds himself invisible, he and his parents and his new blind friend Alicia try to find out what caused his condition and how to reverse it

"The author spins a convincing and affecting story." Publ Wkly

Clements, Bruce

A chapel of thieves. Farrar, Straus & Giroux 2002 209p $16 **Fic**

1. Brothers—Fiction 2. Voyages and travels—Fiction 3. Paris (France)—Fiction

ISBN 0-374-37701-4 LC 2001-46030

Sequel to I tell a lie every so often (1974)

In 1849, Henry, a resourceful young man, sets off from Missouri to Paris in hopes of saving his older brother, a self-styled preacher, from the clutches of a clever charlatan

"Clement's characters are larger than life and very funny in a deadpan sort of way, and danger, intrigue, and dastardly villains pop up on nearly every page." Booklist

Clinton, Cathryn

A stone in my hand. Candlewick Press 2002 191p $15.99; pa $5.99 **Fic**

1. Palestinian Arabs—Fiction 2. Family life—Fiction

ISBN 0-7636-1388-6; 0-7636-2561-2 (pa)

LC 2001-58423

Eleven-year-old Malaak and her family are touched by the violence in Gaza between Jews and Palestinians when first her father disappears and then her older brother is drawn to the Islamic Jihad

"With a sharp eye for nuances of culture and the political situation in the Middle East, Clinton has created a rich, colorful cast of characters and created an emotionally charged novel." SLJ

Cochran, Thomas, 1955-

Roughnecks. Harcourt Brace & Co. 1997 248p $15; pa $6 (7 and up) **Fic**

1. Football—Fiction

ISBN 0-15-201433-0; 0-15-202200-7 (pa)

LC 96-43939

"Gulliver books"

Travis Cody prepares for the final game of his high school football career, a rematch with his school's chief rival

"Travis is an appealing, positive character. . . . Football descriptions are authentic, intense, even lyrical at times." Booklist

Cohn, Rachel

The Steps. Simon & Schuster Bks. for Young Readers 2003 137p $15.95 (4 and up) **Fic**

1. Stepfamilies—Fiction 2. Family life—Fiction 3. Australia—Fiction

ISBN 0-689-84549-9 LC 2001-57566

Over Christmas vacation, Annabel goes from her home in Manhattan to visit her father, his new wife, and her half- and step-siblings in Sydney, Australia

"Packed with humorous incident, life lessons learned, Australian travel tidbits, and a litany of preteen-girl touchstones." Horn Book

Cole, Brock, 1938-

Celine. Farrar, Straus & Giroux 1989 216p hardcover o.p. paperback available $3.95 **Fic**

1. Divorce—Fiction 2. Remarriage—Fiction

ISBN 0-374-41083-6 (pa) LC 89-45614

"Before Celine, a sixteen-year-old artist, can take a promised trip to Europe, she must show a little maturity, finish an overdue term paper and support her seven-year-old neighbor during his parent's separation." Publisher's note

This is "a fine story about an unforgettable character." N Y Times Book Rev

Cole, Brock, 1938——*Continued*

The facts speak for themselves. Front St. 1997 184p $16.95 (7 and up) **Fic**
1. Rape—Fiction
ISBN 1-88691-014-6 LC 97-4250
Also available in paperback from Puffin Bks.

At the request of her social worker, thirteen-year-old Linda gradually reveals how her life with her unstable mother and her younger brother led to her rape and the murder she witnessed

"A complex character of great emotional subtlety, Linda is caught up in the uncontrollable facts of her life, powerless yet capable, battered yet loving, and disturbingly unforgettable." Bull Cent Child Books

The goats; written and illustrated by Brock Cole. Farrar, Straus & Giroux 1987 184p il pa $5.99 hardcover o.p. **Fic**
1. Camps—Fiction 2. Friendship—Fiction
ISBN 0-374-42575-2 (pa) LC 87-45362
"A boy and the girl have been chosen as 'the goats' at summer camp. Stripped naked, they are marooned on Goat Island, as part of an annual prank played on campers who don't fit in. But the goats have much more spirit than their fellow campers expect, and they decide to disappear completely." Publ Wkly

"This is an unflinching book, and there is a quality of raw emotion that may score some discomfort among adults. Such a first novel restores faith in the cultivation of children's literature." Bull Cent Child Books

Colfer, Eoin, 1965-

Artemis Fowl. Hyperion Bks. for Children 2001 277p $16.95; pa $7.99 **Fic**
1. Fairies—Fiction 2. Fantasy fiction
ISBN 0-7868-0801-2; 0-7868-1707-0 (pa)
LC 2001-16632
When a twelve-year-old evil genius tries to restore his family fortune by capturing a fairy and demanding a ransom in gold, the fairies fight back with magic, technology, and a particularly nasty troll

"Colfer's antihero, techno fantasy is cleverly written and filled to the brim with action, suspense, and humor." SLJ
Other titles in this series are:
Artemis Fowl: the Arctic incident (2002)
Artemis Fowl: the Eternity code (2003)
Artemis Fowl: the Opal deception (2005)

Collier, James Lincoln, 1928-

The bloody country; by James Lincoln Collier and Christopher Collier. Four Winds Press 1976 183p hardcover o.p. Scholastic paperback available $4.50 **Fic**
1. Pennsylvania—Fiction
ISBN 0-590-43126-9 (pa) LC 75-34461
"An engrossing story which is based on historical facts of a Connecticut man, Daniel Buck and his family, who settled near the banks of the Susquehanna in Wyoming Valley [Pennsylvania] in the 1750's, survived the Wyoming Massacre, suffered disastrous losses in a flood, and struggled against the injustice of the Penamites' legal maneuvers to wrest their land from them. Told by young Ben, . . . he is first seen as a youngster of seven though we share his thoughts and actions as he matures to a boy of fifteen." Child Book Rev Serv

"The story is dramatic and convincing, the characters drawn with depth and vigor." Bull Cent Child Books

Jump ship to freedom; [by] James Lincoln Collier, Christopher Collier. Delacorte Press 1981 198p hardcover o.p. paperback available $5.99 (6 and up) **Fic**
1. United States—History—1783-1809—Fiction 2. Slavery—Fiction 3. African Americans—Fiction
ISBN 0-440-44323-7 (pa) LC 81-65492
Companion volume to War comes to Willie Freeman and Who is Carrie?

In 1787 Dan Arabus, a fourteen-year-old slave, anxious to buy freedom for himself and his mother, escapes from his dishonest master and tries to find help in cashing the soldier's notes received by his father, Jack Arabus, for fighting in the Revolution

"The period seems well researched, and the speech has an authentic ring without trying to imitate a dialect." SLJ

Me and Billy; James Lincoln Collier. 1st ed. Marshall Cavendish 2004 185p $15.95 (5 and up) **Fic**
1. Swindlers and swindling—Fiction 2. Orphans—Fiction 3. Friendship—Fiction
ISBN 0-7614-5174-9 LC 2003-26865
After escaping the orphanage where they have spent their lives together, two boys become assistants to a con artist, and while Possum objects to the lying, stealing, and cheating, Billy only cares about making money and taking life easy.

"A small gem. . . . The book's momentum is sustained by the author's wonderful use of vernacular and the friendship/tension between the boys." SLJ

My brother Sam is dead; by James Lincoln Collier and Christopher Collier. Four Winds Press 1985 c1974 216p $17.95 (6 and up) **Fic**
1. United States—History—1775-1783, Revolution—Fiction
ISBN 0-02-722980-7 LC 84-28787
Also available in paperback from Scholastic and Audiobook version
A reissue of the title first published 1974

"In 1775 the Meeker family lived in Redding, Connecticut, a Tory community. Sam, the eldest son, allied himself with the Patriots. The youngest son, Tim, watched a rift in the family grow because of his brother's decision. Before the war was over the Meeker family had suffered at the hands of both the British and the Patriots." Shapiro. Fic for Youth. 3d edition

War comes to Willy Freeman; [by] James Lincoln Collier, Christopher Collier. Delacorte Press 1983 178p hardcover o.p. paperback available $4.99 (6 and up) **Fic**
1. United States—History—1775-1783, Revolution—Fiction 2. African Americans—Fiction 3. Slavery—Fiction
ISBN 0-440-49504-0 LC 82-70317

Collier, James Lincoln, 1928-—*Continued*

This deals with events prior to those in Jump ship to freedom, and involves members of the same family. "Willy is thirteen when she begins her story, which takes place during the last two years of the Revolutionary War; her father, a free man, has been killed fighting against the British, her mother has disappeared. Willy makes her danger-fraught way to Fraunces Tavern in New York, her uncle, Jack Arabus, having told her that Mr. Fraunces may be able to help her. She works at the tavern until the war is over, goes to the Arabus home to find her mother dying, and participates in the trial (historically accurate save for the fictional addition of Willy) in which her uncle sues for his freedom and wins." Bull Cent Child Books

Who is Carrie? {by} James Lincoln Collier {and} Christopher Collier. Delacorte Press 1984 158p pa $12 hardcover o.p. **Fic**
1. United States—History—1783-1809—Fiction
2. Slavery—Fiction 3. African Americans—Fiction
ISBN 0-375-89503-5 (pa) LC 83-23947

Companion volume to Jump ship to freedom, and War comes to Willy Freeman

Carrie "is a kitchen slave in Samuel Fraunces Tavern. . . . She keeps in touch with her special friend, Dan Arabus, and he enlists Carrie's help in finding out if the new government will honor the notes with which Dan hopes to purchase his mother's freedom. In so doing, Carrie finds out the truth about herself." Child Book Rev Serv

"This is historical fiction at its best. The Collier's familiar 'How Much of This Book is True' addendum fills readers in on the essentials concerning fictional and factual elements of the plot, as well as the research involved in its composition." SLJ

With every drop of blood; [by] James Lincoln Collier, Christopher Collier. Delacorte Press 1994 235p maps (5 and up) **Fic**
1. United States—History—1861-1865, Civil War—Fiction 2. Race relations—Fiction 3. African Americans—Fiction
ISBN 0-385-32028-0; 0-440-21983-3 (pa)
LC 93-37655

This is a "docu-novel of the Civil War. Johnny, 14, a young, white rebel soldier, is captured by a black Union soldier, Cush, a runaway slave. As they get to know each other in the mess and slaughter of battle and retreat, the two boys gradually lose their mutual distrust, and each risks his life to save the other." Booklist

"The relationship of Cush and Johnny and the convincingly conversational tone of Johnny's voice make this book an effectively immediate evocation of a distant and sometimes difficult-to-understand time." Horn Book

Collier, Kristi

Jericho walls. Holt & Co. 2002 213p $16.95 (7 and up) **Fic**
1. Segregation—Fiction 2. Race relations—Fiction 3. African Americans—Fiction 4. Friendship—Fiction
ISBN 0-8050-6521-0 LC 2001-39931

In 1957, when her preacher father accepts a post in Jericho, Alabama, Jo wants to fit in but her growing friendship with a black boy forces her to confront the racism of the South and to reconsider her own values

"Jo's eventual rejection of the weight of racism, rather than the initial fact of it, creates a realistic, but seldom articulated, Southern setting of fifty years ago." Horn Book Guide

Collins, Suzanne

Gregor the Overlander. Scholastic Press 2003 311p $16.95; pa $5.99 (4 and up) **Fic**
1. Fantasy fiction
ISBN 0-439-43536-6; 0-439-67813-7 (pa)
LC 2002-155865

When eleven-year-old Gregor and his two-year-old sister are pulled into a strange underground world, they trigger an epic battle involving men, bats, rats, cockroaches, and spiders while on a quest foretold by ancient prophecy

"Collins creates a fascinating, vivid, highly original world and a superb story to go along with it." Booklist

Other titles in this series are:
Gregor and the curse of the warmbloods (2005)
Gregor and the prophecy of Bane (2004)

Coman, Carolyn

What Jamie saw. Front St. 1995 $13.95 (5 and up) **Fic**
1. Child abuse—Fiction
ISBN 1-886910-02-2 LC 95-23545

Having fled to a family friend's hillside trailer after his mother's boyfriend tried to throw his baby sister against a wall, nine-year-old Jamie finds himself living an existence full of uncertainty and fear

"Shocking in its simple narration and child's-eye view, *What Jamie Saw* is a bittersweet miracle in understated language and forthright hopelessness." SLJ

Conly, Jane Leslie

Crazy lady! HarperCollins Pubs. 1993 180p lib bdg $16.89; pa $5.99 (5 and up) **Fic**
1. Prejudices—Fiction 2. Death—Fiction 3. Alcoholism—Fiction 4. Mentally handicapped—Fiction
ISBN 0-06-021360-4 (lib bdg); 0-06-440571-0 (pa)
LC 92-18348

Also available Audiobook version
A Newbery Medal honor book, 1994
"A Laura Geringer book"

As he tries to come to terms with his mother's death, Vernon finds solace in his growing relationship with the neighborhood outcasts, an alcoholic and her retarded son

The narration "is fast and blunt, and the conversations are lively and true." Bull Cent Child Books

Racso and the rats of NIMH; illustrations by Leonard Lubin. Harper & Row 1986 278p il lib bdg $17.89; pa $5.99 (4 and up) **Fic**
1. Mice—Fiction 2. Rats—Fiction
ISBN 0-06-021362-0 (lib bdg); 0-06-440245-2 (pa)
LC 85-42634

Sequel to Mrs. Frisby and the rats of NIMH by Robert C. O'Brien

Conly, Jane Leslie—*Continued*

This book "continues the NIMH saga with a focus on the second rodent generation: Timothy, Mrs. Frisby's son, and Racso, son of the rebel rat Jenner. On his way to classes at Thorn Valley, Timothy saves Racso's life but is himself severely injured. Both reach the Utopian colony only to discover that the valley and surrounding farms are to be turned into a tourist lake and camp-grounds." SLJ

"The book is cleverly and gracefully built upon both the philosophy of self-sufficiency and the details of the plot of its predecessor." Horn Book

Another title about the rats of NIMH is:

RT, Margaret, and the rats of NIMH (1990)

Trout summer. Holt & Co. 1995 234p $15.95 (5 and up) **Fic**
1. Siblings—Fiction 2. Canoes and canoeing—Fiction 3. Summer—Fiction
ISBN 0-8050-3933-3 LC 95-16381
Also available in paperback from Scholastic

"When their father leaves them, Shana, 13, and Cody, 12, move with their mother to Maryland. . . . The kids convince Mama that they should stay in an abandoned cabin along the Leanna River for the summer. There they meet Henry, an irascible old man who professes to be a ranger. Ill and difficult but an excellent canoeist, he teaches Cody his skills. . . , Shana's fast-paced, first-person narrative is enhanced by Henry's quirky character and revealing dialogue." SLJ

What happened on Planet Kid. Holt & Co. 2000 216p $16.95 **Fic**
1. Friendship—Fiction 2. Farm life—Fiction 3. Domestic violence—Fiction
ISBN 0-8050-6065-0 LC 99-16655
Also available in paperback from HarperCollins

To help her deal with her separation from her family, worry about her mother's serious operation, and suspicions about a new friend's abusive father, twelve-year-old Dawn creates an imaginary world while spending the summer of 1958 with her great-aunt and uncle on their Virginia farm

"Conly vividly yet subtly evokes era and place; and Dawn is entirely believable as a child who loses her innocence while grappling on her own with adult issues." Horn Book Guide

While no one was watching. Holt & Co. 1998 233p $16.95 (5 and up) **Fic**
1. Poverty—Fiction
ISBN 0-8050-3934-1 LC 97-48718
Also available in paperback from HarperCollins and Audiobook version

This "story is told from the point of view of five characters: siblings Earl, Frankie, and Angela (on their own after their aunt disappears on a drinking binge) and, from a very different part of the city, Maynard and Addie (whose pet rabbit has been stolen by affection-starved, seven-year-old Frankie). Conly writes convincingly and unsentimentally about the working class poor in an urban setting." Horn Book Guide

Connelly, Neil O.

St. Michael's scales; {by} Neil Connelly. Levine Bks. 2002 309p $16.95; pa $6.99 (7 and up) **Fic**
1. Suicide—Fiction 2. School stories
ISBN 0-439-19445-8; 0-439-49171-1 (pa)
LC 00-46367

Keegan Flannery, feeling responsible for his twin brother's death and his mother's mental illness, believes he must atone by committing suicide before his sixteenth birthday, but he gains new insights when he joins his school's wrestling team

"Connelly's complex coming-of-age novel delves deeply into the human psyche and the soul. . . . This is a dark story but one that is ultimately hopeful." SLJ

Conrad, Pam, 1947-1996

My Daniel. Harper & Row 1989 137p lib bdg $16.89; pa $5.99 (5 and up) **Fic**
1. Siblings—Fiction 2. Nebraska—Fiction
ISBN 0-06-021314-0 (lib bdg); 0-06-440309-2 (pa)
LC 88-19850

"When she's 80 years old, Julia Summerwaithe decides to visit her grandchildren, Ellie and Stevie, in New York City, for the first time. She has something important to show them; in the Natural History Museum is the dinosaur she and her brother discovered on their farm in Nebraska when they were young. But even more important to Julia than seeing the dinosaur is sharing her memories of the discovery and excavation with her grandchildren." SLJ

"Rendering scenes from both the past and the present with equal skill, Conrad is at the peak of her storytelling powers." Publ Wkly

Prairie songs; illustrations by Darryl S. Zudeck. Harper & Row 1985 167p il $5.99 hardcover o.p. (5 and up) **Fic**
1. Frontier and pioneer life—Fiction 2. Nebraska—Fiction
ISBN 0-06-440206-1 (pa) LC 85-42633

"The deterioration of the frail, young wife of a doctor who is unable to adapt to the harshness of prairie life is made more vivid because the reader views it through the eyes of an adolescent girl who lives nearby. Set in Nebraska at the turn of the century, this story is rich with detail about the beauty and hardships of pioneer life in the American West." Soc Educ

Stonewords; a ghost story. Harper & Row 1990 130p hardcover o.p. paperback available $4.95 (5 and up) **Fic**
1. Ghost stories 2. Space and time—Fiction
ISBN 0-06-440354-8 (pa) LC 89-36382

Zoe discovers that her house is occupied by the ghost of an eleven-year-old girl, who carries her back to the day of her death in 1870 to try to alter that tragic event

"The supernatural and time-travel elements of the book are viscerally convincing, and the desperate neediness of both girls is fierce and real. The disquieting ending is in the richest gothic tradition, resolving only one mystery only to reveal another even more frightening. This is a very scary book." Bull Cent Child Books

Constable, Kate

The singer of all songs. Arthur A. Levine Books 2004 c2002 297p $16.95 (7 and up)   **Fic**

1. Fantasy fiction 2. Magic—Fiction

ISBN 0-439-55478-0   LC 2003-9034

First published 2002 in Australia

Calwyn, a young priestess of ice magic, or chantment, joins with other chanters who have different magical skills to fight a sorcerer who wants to claim all powers for his own.

"An impressive debut by an author who clearly has much to contribute to the fantasy genre." Booklist

Cooney, Caroline B., 1947-

Burning up. Delacorte Press 1999 230p pa $5.99 hardcover o.p. (7 and up)   **Fic**

1. Race relations—Fiction

ISBN 0-440-22687-2 (pa)   LC 98-19343

When a girl she had met at an innercity church is murdered, fifteen-year-old Macey channels her grief into a school project that leads her to uncover prejudice she had not imagined in her grandparents and their wealthy Connecticut community

"The plot moves along and stays right on track in this complex and thought-provoking novel." Voice Youth Advocates

The face on the milk carton. Bantam Bks. 1990 184p o.p. Delacorte Press reissue available $15.95; pa $5.50 (7 and up)   **Fic**

1. Kidnapping—Fiction

ISBN 0-385-32328-X; pa 0-440-22065-3

             LC 89-18311

"Up to her fifteenth year, the most Jane Johnson had to worry about was her boring name. . . . Then the picture of a missing child on a school milk carton triggers flashbacks to long-buried memories of Jane as a child—the milk carton child, in fact. Is she the missing Jennie Spring, snatched from her family years before? Or is she simply Jane, who doesn't like her name?" Booklist

"Cooney again demonstrates an excellent ear for dialogue and a gift for portraying responsible middle-class teenagers trying to come to terms with very real concerns." SLJ

Other available titles in this series are:

The voice on the radio (1996)

What Janie found (2000)

Whatever happened to Janie? (1993)

Followed by Whatever happened to Janie?

Flight #116 is down. Scholastic 1992 201p hardcover o.p. paperback available $4.99

             Fic

1. Aircraft accidents—Fiction

ISBN 0-590-44479-4 (pa)   LC 91-9796

Teenager Heidi Landseth helps rescue people from a plane crash on her family's property, and the experience changes her life forever

"Using her trademark lightning pace, Cooney depicts the drama and human interest inherent in disaster. . . . This story will keep even the least bookish readers glued to their seats." Publ Wkly

Goddess of yesterday. Delacorte Press 2002 263p $15.95; pa $6.50 (7 and up)   **Fic**

1. Helen of Troy (Legendary character)—Fiction

ISBN 0-385-72945-6; 0-440-22930-8 (pa)

             LC 2002-73447

Taken from her home on a Aegean island as a six-year-old girl, Anaxndra calls on the protection of her goddess while she poses as two different princesses over the next six years, before ending up as a servant in the company of Helen and Paris as they make their way to Troy

"Cooney's trademark staccato narrative style gives the proceedings a breathless urgency. . . . Her gift for adopting the voices of adolescent girls results in a compulsively readable story and may well lead readers to other Greek myths." Publ Wkly

The ransom of Mercy Carter. Delacorte Press 2001 249p $15.95; pa $5.99   **Fic**

1. Mohawk Indians—Fiction 2. Massachusetts—Fiction

ISBN 0-385-32615-7; 0-440-22775-5 (pa)

             LC 00-31545

In 1704, in the English settlement of Deerfield, Massachusetts, eleven-year-old Mercy and her family and neighbors are captured by Mohawk Indians and their French allies, and forced to march through bitter cold to French Canada, where some adapt to new lives and some still hope to be ransomed

"As Mercy wavers between her birth culture and her adopted one, she raises excellent questions about notions of 'savagery' that will make this vivid, dramatic novel an excellent discussion book." Booklist

What child is this? a Christmas story. Delacorte Press 1997 150p $14.95; pa $5.50   **Fic**

1. Christmas—Fiction 2. Foster home care—Fiction

ISBN 0-385-32317-4; 0-440-22684-8 (pa)

             LC 96-54891

When seventeen-year-old Matt tries to find a family for an eight-year-old foster child, his attempt backfires and both of them need a Christmas miracle

"Cooney weaves the threads of these young and fragile lives together in an involving, emotionally moving novel." Bull Cent Child Books

Cooper, Susan, 1935-

The Boggart. Margaret K. McElderry Bks. 1993 196p $15.95; pa $5.99 (4 and up)   **Fic**

1. Supernatural—Fiction 2. Scotland—Fiction 3. Canada—Fiction

ISBN 0-689-50576-0; 0-689-86930-4 (pa)

             LC 92-15527

After visiting the castle in Scotland which her family has inherited and returning home to Canada, twelve-year-old Emily finds that she has accidentally brought back with her a boggart, an invisible and mischievous spirit with a fondness for practical jokes

"Using both electronics and theater as metaphors for magic, Cooper has extended the world of high fantasy into contemporary children's lives through scenes superimposing the ordinary and the extraordinary." Bull Cent Child Books

Another available title about the Boggart is:

The Boggart and the monster (1997)

Cooper, Susan, 1935——*Continued*

Over sea, under stone; illustrated by Margery Gill. Harcourt Brace Jovanovich 1966 c1965 252p il $18; pa $4.99 (5 and up)   **Fic**

1. Fantasy fiction 2. Good and evil—Fiction 3. Great Britain—Fiction

ISBN 0-15-259034-X; 0-689-84035-7 (pa)

Also available in paperback from Macmillan

First published 1965 in the United Kingdom

In this series about the "conflict between the good of the Servants of Light and the evil of the Powers of Dark, Cooper has created an intricate fantasy. Ancient lore and mythology are believably interwoven into a modern setting. Ostensibly, the three Drew children, on a holiday in Cornwall, find an old map and, aided by their uncle, they begin a search for an ancient treasure linked with King Arthur. With each book, more reliance is placed on folklore and legend. There is much action and excitement included in the carefully wrought stories." Roman. Sequences

Other available titles in The dark is rising series are:

The dark is rising (1973)

Greenwitch (1974)

The grey king (1975)

Silver on the tree (1977)

Corbet, Robert

Fifteen love. Walker & Co. 2003 186p $16.95 (7 and up)   **Fic**

1. Musicians—Fiction   2.   Tennis—Fiction 3. Australia—Fiction

ISBN 0-8027-8851-3   LC 2002-31146

First published 2001 in Australia

Mia, a violinist, and Will, a tennis player, each relate their feelings about each other, school, friends, and family troubles as they struggle to understand the opposite sex and to survive being fifteen

"The story is witty and fresh. . . . The novel is appealing on many levels—it is funny, quirky, and satisfyingly romantic." SLJ

Corbett, Sue

12 again. Dutton Children's Bks. 2002 227p $16.99   **Fic**

1. Mother-son relationship—Fiction

ISBN 0-525-46899-4   LC 2002-512627

This "story is told from the alternating perspectives of its two protagonists—12-year-old Patrick and his mother, Bernadette, who becomes 12 again through wishful thinking and by drinking a potion." Booklist

"Interesting, suspenseful, and unique, this well-written supernatural story will keep younger teen readers turning pages." Voice Youth Advocates

Cormier, Robert

After the first death. Pantheon Bks. 1979 233p pa $6.50 hardcover o.p.   **Fic**

1. Terrorism—Fiction

ISBN 0-440-20835-1 (pa)   LC 78-11770

Also available in paperback from Dell, and in

"A busload of children is hijacked by a band of terrorists whose demands include the exposure of a military brainwashing project. The narrative line moves from the teenage terrorist Milo to Kate the bus driver and the involvement of Ben, whose father is the head of the military operation, in this confrontation. The conclusion has a shocking twist." Shapiro. Fic for Youth. 2d edition

The bumblebee flies anyway. Pantheon Bks. 1983 241p pa $5.99 hardcover o.p. (7 and up)   **Fic**

1. Death—Fiction 2. Terminal care—Fiction 3. Friendship—Fiction

ISBN 0-440-90871-X (pa)   LC 83-2458

Sixteen-year-old Barney has only fleeting memories about his past but, as a voluntary patient at the institute for experimental medicine, he knows he is different from the terminally ill patients surrounding him. His involvement with the bitter, slowly dying, Mazzo brings Barney hope, pain, and a moment of heroic glory

"In a story that is as trenchant as it is poignant, Cormier shows the courage and desperation of adolescents who know that their deaths are imminent. . . . Although it is tragic, [it is] a stunning book." Bull Cent Child Books

The chocolate war; a novel. Pantheon Bks. 1974 253p $19.95 (7 and up)   **Fic**

1. School stories

ISBN 0-394-82805-4

Also available in paperback from Random House Children's Bks.

"In the Trinity School for Boys the environment is completely dominated by an underground gang, the Vigils. During a chocolate candy sale Brother Leon, the acting headmaster of the school, defers to the Vigils, who reign with terror in the school. Jerry Renault is first a pawn for the Vigils' evil deeds and finally their victim." Shapiro. Fic for Youth. 3d edition

Followed by Beyond the chocolate war (1985)

Frenchtown summer. Delacorte Press 1999 113p $16.95; pa $5.99 (7 and up)   **Fic**

ISBN 0-385-32704-8; 0-440-22854-9 (pa)

LC 99-12244

A verse novel set 1938 in the Frenchtown section of fictional Monument, Massachusetts. "Narrator Eugene recalls the summer of his twelfth birthday, with its grim legends of suicide and murder and muffled rattling of family skeletons in their closets." Bull Cent Child Books

"Every observation implies mystery and hidden drama; while the short verse chapters seem less plot-driven than Cormier fans may expect, they subtly convey the shadows in Frenchtown and the action those shadows conceal." Publ Wkly

Heroes; a novel. Delacorte Press 1998 135p pa $5.99 hardcover o.p. (7 and up)   **Fic**

1. World War, 1939-1945—Fiction 2. Veterans—Fiction

ISBN 0-440-22769-0 (pa)   LC 97-40326

After joining the army at fifteen and having his face blown away by a grenade in a battle in France, Francis returns home to Frenchtown hoping to find—and kill—the former childhood hero he feels betrayed him

"This lean, compelling read . . . is a powerful and thought-provoking study." SLJ

Cormier, Robert—*Continued*

In the middle of the night. Delacorte Press 1995 182p pa $5.99 hardcover o.p. (7 and up)

                                           Fic

1. Father-son relationship—Fiction 2. Guilt—Fiction

ISBN 0-440-22686-4 (pa)   LC 94-38894

"In three narrative threads that twist into each other, a woman nurses her rage over a childhood accident that 'killed' her many years ago, a man still wrestles with his guilt over that tragic event, and his son Denny finds himself drawn into the pain of them both." Bull Cent Child Books

"Cormier's chilling tale of revenge and remorse is told by several narrators: the tormenter as well as the tormented father and son. Suspense and horror build as the harassment worsens for the family. This psychological thriller draws the reader deeper in to discover the truth." Book Rep

The rag and bone shop; a novel. Delacorte Press 2001 154p $15.95; lib bdg $17.99; pa $5.99 (7 and up)   **Fic**

1. Homicide—Fiction 2. Police—Fiction

ISBN 0-385-72962-6; 0-385-90027-9 (lib bdg); 0-440-22971-5 (pa)   LC 2001-28540

Trent, an ace interrogator from Vermont, works to procure a confession from an introverted twelve-year-old accused of murdering his seven-year-old friend in Monument, Massachusetts

"Terse and terrifying, this final book from Cormier will leave a lasting impression. . . . The book's horrifying, surprising conclusion will engender discussion." Booklist

Tunes for bears to dance to. Delacorte Press 1992 101p hardcover o.p. paperback available $4.50 (7 and up)   **Fic**

1. Prejudices—Fiction 2. Jews—Fiction

ISBN 0-440-21903-5 (pa)   LC 92-2734

Eleven-year-old Henry escapes his family's problems by watching the woodcarving of Mr. Levine, an elderly Holocaust survivor, but when Henry is manipulated by his employer, Mr. Hairston, into betraying his friend he comes to know true evil

"A powerful book for discussion with readers of all ages. Henry's loss of innocence is a dramatic event, but how he reacts to this event is thought-provoking." Voice Youth Advocates

We all fall down. Delacorte Press 1991 193p $5.50 hardcover o.p.   **Fic**

1. Juvenile delinquency—Fiction

ISBN 0-440-21556-0 (pa)   LC 91-12190

"Four teen vandals trash a home. Into the melee steps the unsuspecting fourteen-year-old Karen Jerome. Forty-nine minutes later the invaders depart, leaving a battered Karen sprawled at the foot of the basement steps. The Jerome family is changed forever, especially Karen's sister, Jane. She falls in love with Buddy, never dreaming that he was one of the trashers." Child Book Rev Serv

"Signature Cormier, with calculated impact, sinister implications, and inevitable appeal." Bull Cent Child Books

Cottrell Boyce, Frank

Millions. HarperCollins 2004 247p $15.99; lib bdg $16.89 (5 and up)   **Fic**

1. Money—Fiction 2. Great Britain—Fiction

ISBN 0-06-073330-6; 0-06-073331-4 (lib bdg)

After their mother dies, two brothers find a huge amount of money which they must spend quickly before England switches to the new European currency, but they disagree on what to do with it.

"The humor, the strong family story, and Damian's narrative voice make this satisfying novel succeed on several levels." SLJ

Couloumbis, Audrey

Getting near to baby. Putnam 1999 211p $17.99; pa $5.99 (5 and up)   **Fic**

1. Sisters—Fiction 2. Death—Fiction 3. Aunts—Fiction

ISBN 0-399-23389-X; 0-698-11892-8 (pa)

                                   LC 99-18191

Also available Thorndike Press large print edition

A Newbery Medal honor book, 2000

Although thirteen-year-old Willa Jo and her Aunt Patty seem to be constantly at odds, staying with her and Uncle Hob helps Willa Jo and her younger sister come to terms with the death of their family's baby

"Couloumbis's writing is strong; she captures wonderfully the Southern voices of her characters and conveys with great depth powerful emotions. . . . A compelling novel." SLJ

Say yes. Putnam 2002 200p $16.99; pa $5.99

                                       Fic

1. Stepmothers—Fiction 2. New York (N.Y.)—Fiction

ISBN 0-399-23390-3; 0-14-250186-7 (pa)

                                   LC 2001-48126

In her efforts to hang on following the disappearance of her stepmother, twelve-year-old Casey resorts to anything including robbery

"Throughout the novel, skillfully crafted dialogue adds depth and humor to both story and characters. . . . The hopeful conclusion will please readers who have come to know and like the young protagonists through Couloumbis's gripping, tension-filled story." Horn Book

Coville, Bruce

Aliens ate my homework; illustrated by Katherine Coville. Pocket Bks. 1993 179p il $4.99 hardcover o.p.   **Fic**

1. Science fiction 2. Extraterrestrial beings—Fiction

ISBN 0-671-72712-5 (pa)   LC 93-3945

A Minstrel book.

Rod is surprised when a miniature spaceship lands in his school science project and reveals five tiny aliens, who ask his help in apprehending an interstellar criminal

"A funny and suspenseful romp, with appealing illustrations throughout." Horn Book Guide

Other titles in this series are:

Aliens stole my body (1998)

I left my sneakers in Dimension X (1994)

The search for Snout (1995)

Coville, Bruce—*Continued*

Juliet Dove, Queen of Love; a magic shop book. Harcourt 2003 190p $17 (4-6)   **Fic**
1. Magic—Fiction 2. Classical mythology—Fiction
ISBN 0-15-204561-9   LC 2003-11846

A shy twelve-year-old girl must solve a puzzle involving characters from Greek mythology to free herself from a spell which makes her irresistible to boys

"Although humorous, the story has surprising depth. . . . Coville capably interweaves mythological characters with realistic modern ones, keeping readers truly absorbed." SLJ

The monsters of Morley Manor. Harcourt 2001 224p $16; pa $5.95   **Fic**
1. Monsters—Fiction 2. Extraterrestrial beings—Fiction
ISBN 0-15-216382-4; 0-15-204705-0 (pa)
LC 00-12912

Anthony and his younger sister discover that the monster figures he got in an unusual box at an estate sale are alive, but they have no way of knowing that the "monsters" will lead them on fantastical adventures to other worlds in an effort to try to save Earth

"Coville's rollicking tale has an unbelievable plot and exaggerated characters, but this is exactly what makes it so entertaining." Horn Book Guide

The skull of truth; a magic shop book; illustrated by Gary A. Lippincott. Harcourt Brace & Co. 1997 195p il $17 (4 and up)   **Fic**
1. Truthfulness and falsehood—Fiction 2. Fantasy fiction
ISBN 0-15-275457-1   LC 97-9264

Also available in paperback from Pocket Bks.

Charlie, a sixth-grader with a compulsion to tell lies, acquires a mysterious skull that forces its owner to tell only the truth, causing some awkward moments before he understands its power

"Coville has structured the story very carefully, with a great deal of sensitivity to children's thought processes and emotions. The mood shifts from scary to funny to serious are fused with understandable language and sentence structures." SLJ

Crane, Stephen, 1871-1900

The red badge of courage (7 and up)
    Fic
1. Chancellorsville (Va.), Battle of, 1863—Fiction
Available from various publishers
First published 1895

"A young Union soldier, Henry Fleming, tells of his feelings when he is under fire for the first time during the battle of Chancellorsville. He is overcome by fear and runs from the field. Later he returns to lead a charge that re-establishes his own reputation as well as that of his company. One of the great novels of the Civil War." Cincinnati Public Libr

Craven, Margaret

I heard the owl call my name. Doubleday 1973 166p hardcover o.p. Dell paperback available $6.50 (7 and up)   **Fic**

1. Native Americans—Fiction 2. Clergy—Fiction 3. Death—Fiction
ISBN 0-89966-854-2 (pa)

Also available in hardcover from Buccaneer Bks.

Not knowing that he has a fatal illness, a young Anglican priest is assigned to serve a parish of Kwakiutl Indians in the seacoast wilds of British Columbia. Among these vanishing Indians, Mark Brian learns enough of the meaning of life not to fear death

The author's "writing glows with delicate, fleeting images and a sense of peace. Her characters' hearts are bared by a few words—or by the fact that nothing is said at all." Christ Sci Monit

Creech, Sharon

Absolutely normal chaos. HarperCollins Pubs. 1995 c1990 230p $16.99; lib bdg $16.89; pa $5.99 (5 and up)   **Fic**
1. Family life—Fiction
ISBN 0-06-026989-8; 0-06-026992-8 (lib bdg); 0-06-440632-6 (pa)   LC 95-22448

First published 1990 in the United Kingdom

"Mary Lou Finney's summer journal describes family life in a high-spirited household in Ohio that includes five children." N Y Times Book Rev

"Those in search of a light, humorous read will find it; those in search of something a little deeper will also be rewarded." SLJ

Bloomability. HarperCollins Pubs. 1998 273p $16.99; pa $5.99 (5 and up)   **Fic**
1. School stories 2. Switzerland—Fiction
ISBN 0-06-026993-6; 0-06-440823-X (pa)
LC 98-14601

"Joanna Cotler books"

When her aunt and uncle take her from New Mexico to Lugano, Switzerland, to attend an international school, thirteen-year-old Dinnie discovers her world expanding

"As if fresh, smart characters in a picturesque setting weren't engaging enough, Creech also poses an array of knotty questions, both personal and philosophical. . . . A story to stimulate both head and heart." Booklist

Chasing Redbird. HarperCollins Pubs. 1997 261p $16.99; pa $5.99 (5 and up)   **Fic**
1. Family life—Fiction 2. Kentucky—Fiction
ISBN 0-06-026987-1; 0-06-440696-2 (pa)
LC 96-44128

"Joanna Cotler books"

Thirteen-year-old Zinnia Taylor uncovers family secrets and self truths while clearing a mysterious settler trail that begins on her family's farm in Kentucky

"With frequent flashbacks, the narrative makes clear the complexities of the story, while the unsolved puzzles lead the reader on to the end. The writing is laced with figurative language and folksy comments that intensify both atmosphere and emotion." Horn Book Guide

Love that dog. HarperCollins Pubs. 2001 86p $15.99; lib bdg $14.89; pa $5.99 (4 and up)
    Fic
1. Poetry—Fiction 2. School stories
ISBN 0-06-029287-3; 0-06-029289-X (lib bdg); 0-06-440959-7 (pa)   LC 00-54233

"Joanna Cotler books"

Creech, Sharon—*Continued*

"Jack's free-verse journal charts his evolution from doubt to delight in poetry. His teacher, Miss Stretchberry, introduces him to poetry, serves as an advocate for his writing, and flatters him into believing he's a poet." Horn Book

"Creech has created a poignant, funny picture of a child's encounter with the power of poetry. . . . This book is a tiny treasure." SLJ

Ruby Holler. HarperCollins Pubs. 2002 310p $16.99; lib bdg $16.89; pa $5.99 (4 and up)   **Fic**

1. Orphans—Fiction 2. Twins—Fiction 3. Country life—Fiction

ISBN 0-06-027732-7; 0-06-027733-5 (lib bdg); 0-06-056015-0 (pa)   LC 00-66371

"Joanna Cotler books"

Thirteen-year-old fraternal twins Dallas and Florida have grown up in a terrible orphanage but their lives change forever when an eccentric but sweet older couple invites them each on an adventure, beginning in an almost magical place called Ruby Holler

"This poignant story evokes a feeling as welcoming as fresh-baked bread. . . . The novel celebrates the healing effects of love and compassion." Publ Wkly

Walk two moons. HarperCollins Pubs. 1994 280p $16.99; lib bdg $17.89; pa $6.99 (6 and up)   **Fic**

1. Death—Fiction 2. Grandparents—Fiction 3. Family life—Fiction 4. Friendship—Fiction

ISBN 0-06-023334-6; 0-06-023337-0 (lib bdg); 0-06-440517-6 (pa)   LC 93-31277

Also available Audiobook version

Awarded the Newbery Medal, 1995

After her mother leaves home suddenly, thirteen-year-old Sal and her grandparents take a car trip retracing her mother's route. Along the way, Sal recounts the story of her friend Phoebe, whose mother also left

"An engaging story of love and loss, told with humor and suspense. . . . A richly layered novel about real and metaphorical journeys." SLJ

Crew, Gary, 1947-

Troy Thompson's excellent peotry book. Kane/Miller 2003 unp il $14.95 (4 and up)   **Fic**

1. Poetry—Fiction 2. Authorship—Fiction

ISBN 1-929132-52-2

Troy Thompson, a grade six student at Daggaburra State School, writes poems in order to win contest prize.

"This colorful book resembles a student's notebook. . . . The poems are typewritten, handwritten, or printed from a computer and 'pasted' into his book. This title is complete with silliness and serious topics." SLJ

Crew, Linda

Brides of Eden; a true story imagined. HarperCollins Pubs. 2001 223p $15.95; pa $6.99 (7 and up)   **Fic**

1. Cults—Fiction 2. Fanaticism—Fiction 3. Christian life—Fiction

ISBN 0-06-028750-0; 0-06-447217-5 (pa)   LC 00-40904

In this story based on true events, sixteen-year-old Eva and her female friends become obsessed with a charismatic young man who comes to Corvallis, Oregon, in 1904, claiming to be a Christian prophet

"Crew deftly explores religious fanaticism, group thought, and the psychology of victimization, at the same time weaving a strong tale." Booklist

Children of the river. Delacorte Press 1989 213p $5.99 hardcover o.p. (7 and up)   **Fic**

1. Asian Americans—Fiction 2. Refugees—Fiction

ISBN 0-440-21022-4 (pa)   LC 88-20401

Having fled Cambodia four years earlier to escape the Khmer Rouge army, seventeen-year-old Sundara is torn between remaining faithful to her own people and enjoying life in her Oregon high school as a "regular" American

"Crew's characterization is excellent. . . . The plot is well-structured, allowing profound concepts to be simply and beautifully presented. . . . Crew entertains without trivializing and instructs without sermonizing." SLJ

Fire on the wind. Delacorte Press 1995 198p maps $12 hardcover o.p.   **Fic**

1. Forest fires—Fiction 2. Oregon—Fiction 3. Lumber and lumbering—Fiction

ISBN 0-375-89512-4 (pa)   LC 95-7092

The summer before her fourteenth birthday, a fierce forest fire rages throughout northwestern Oregon and threatens the logging camp where Storie and her family live

"An enlightening, quick read that infuses an interesting coming-of-age subplot into a larger tale of disaster and herosim."

Crichton, Michael, 1942-

Jurassic Park; a novel. Knopf 1990 399p $28.95 (7 and up)   **Fic**

1. Science fiction 2. Dinosaurs—Fiction 3. Genetic engineering—Fiction

ISBN 0-394-58816-9   LC 90-52960

Also available in paperback from Ballantine Bks.

This novel "tells of a modern-day scientist bringing to life a horde of prehistoric animals." N Y Times Book Rev

"Crichton is a master at blending technology with fiction. . . . Suspense, excitement, and good adventure pervade this book." SLJ

Followed by The lost world (1995)

Crisp, Marty, 1947-

Private Captain; a story of Gettysburg. Philomel Bks. 2001 293p $18.99; pa $6.99   **Fic**

1. Gettysburg (Pa.), Battle of, 1863—Fiction 2. United States—History—1861-1865, Civil War—Fiction 3. Dogs—Fiction

ISBN 0-399-23577-9; 0-689-11969-X (pa)   LC 00-25570

"The brutality of war is characterized through vivid descriptions of the battlefield site. . . . Crisp's extensive research is obvious, and her ability to capture the sights and emotions of the time make this novel a satisfying read." Voice Youth Advocates

Crist-Evans, Craig

Amaryllis. Candlewick Press 2003 184p $15.99 (7 and up)   **Fic**

1. Brothers—Fiction 2. Father-son relationship—Fiction 3. Vietnamese Conflict, 1961-1975—Fiction 4. Florida—Fiction

ISBN 0-7636-1863-2   LC 2002-34997

Jimmy and his older brother Frank share a love of surfing and their problems with a drunken father, until Frank turns eighteen and goes to Vietnam

"Crist-Evans has written an interesting, although somber, account of a troubled family in emotional turmoil. Both teens are believable and likable characters with whom many young adults will identify. . . . This is a crisply written and a worthwhile addition to fiction collections." SLJ

Crocker, Carter

The tale of the swamp rat; illustrated by the author. Philomel Bks. 2003 232p il $16.99 (4 and up)   **Fic**

1. Rats—Fiction 2. Florida—Fiction

ISBN 0-399-23964-2   LC 2003-429

Guided by an ancient alligator, a silent young rat learns to find his own way in the drought-stricken swamp, despite having been orphaned under circumstances that sometimes cause other animals to reject him

"All the characters are well drawn. . . . But the swamp itself is the star of this story, and Crocker evokes its complex ecology with clever phrasing and a laid-back southern storytelling style. . . . The writing is uncommonly evocative, and this is the kind of folkloric fiction that kids can treasure." Booklist

Cross, Gillian, 1945-

The dark ground; book one in the Dark ground trilogy. Dutton Children's Books 2004 264p (Dark ground trilogy, Bk1) $15.99   **Fic**

1. Science fiction

ISBN 0-525-47350-5

"Robert wakes up naked and alone in a thick jungle. The last thing he remembers is being in a plane with his family, but there is no sign of a crash or survivors. . . . He is in the park near his house, but his familiar world has been transformed into an alien landscape. When he finds others in the same position, he enlists their help in getting back home." Publisher's note

"This is a fast-moving, suspenseful science-fiction adventure. The ending is surprising and satisfying." SLJ

The great American elephant chase. Holiday House 1993 193p $17.95   **Fic**

1. Elephants—Fiction 2. Adventure fiction

ISBN 0-8234-1016-1   LC 92-54492

Engl. title: The great elephant chase

"Pursed by the villainous Hannibal Jackson, Tad and Cissie trek from Pennsylvania to Nebraska to bring Khush, a prized Indian elephant, to safety." Horn Book Guide

"The chase is thrilling, the landscape brilliant and sprawling, the characters thoughtfully drawn; these elements alone provide uncommonly thrilling reading. But this novel offers more than mere adventure; along with rescuing the great elephant, Tad saves something just as important-his sense of self." Publ Wkly

Phoning a dead man. Holiday House 2002 252p $16.95 (7 and up)   **Fic**

1. Organized crime—Fiction

ISBN 0-8234-1685-2   LC 2001-24158

First published 2001 in the United Kingdom with title: Calling a dead man

When John, a British demolitions expert, is supposedly killed blowing up a building in Siberia, his fiancée Annie insists on investigating, despite being in a wheelchair, and John's teenage sister Hayley goes along and finds that the Russian Mafia is involved

"The narrative . . . moves along at a good pace. Filled with a variety of colorful characters and a suspenseful plot, it will keep even reluctant readers turning the pages." SLJ

Tightrope. Holiday House 1999 216p $16.95 (7 and up)   **Fic**

1. Mystery fiction 2. Gangs—Fiction

ISBN 0-8234-1512-0   LC 98-55149

Also available in paperback from HarperCollins

When she begins receiving bizarre threatening messages from someone who seems to know her every move, teenage Ashley, after seeking help from the neighborhood tough guy, comes to realize that she alone can end the stalker's reign of terror

"Impeccable plotting, a brisk narrative and complex characterizations make this . . . a novel to read in a single sitting." Publ Wkly

Crossley-Holland, Kevin

The seeing stone; Arthur trilogy book one. Levine Bks. 2001 c2000 342p $17.95; pa $6.99   **Fic**

1. Arthur, King—Fiction 2. Magic—Fiction 3. Middle Ages—Fiction 4. Great Britain—History—1154-1399, Plantagenets—Fiction

ISBN 0-439-26326-3; 0-439-43524-2 (pa)

          LC 00-61883

First published 2000 in the United Kingdom

In late twelfth-century England, a thirteen-year-old boy named Arthur recounts how Merlin gives him a magical seeing stone which shows him images of the legendary King Arthur, the events of whose life seem to have many parallels to his own

"The novel unfolds in short, lucid chapters, vividly describing events, personalities, and life on a medieval manor." Booklist

Other titles in the Arthur trilogy are:
At the crossing-places [book two] (2002)
King of the Middle March [book three] (2004)

Crowe, Chris

Mississippi trial, 1955. Penguin Putnam 2002 231p $17.99; pa $5.99 (7 and up)   **Fic**

1. Till, Emmett—Fiction 2. Grandfathers—Fiction 3. Racism—Fiction

ISBN 0-8037-2745-3; 0-14-250192-1 (pa)

          LC 2001-40221

"Phyllis Fogelman books"

In Mississippi in 1955, a sixteen-year-old finds himself at odds with his grandfather over issues surrounding

Crowe, Chris—*Continued*
the kidnapping and murder of a fourteen-year-old African
American from Chicago named Emmett Till
"By combining real events with their impact upon a
single fictional character, Crowe makes the issues in this
novel hard-hitting and personal. The characters are complex." Voice Youth Advocates

Crum, Shutta
Spitting image. Clarion Bks. 2003 218p $15
                                               Fic
1. Family life—Fiction
ISBN 0-618-23477-2   LC 2002-15912
In the small town of Baylor, Kentucky, twelve-year-
old Jessie K. Bovey and her friends confront some of
life's questions during their summer vacation in the late
1960s
"Truly memorable characters abound, and
moonshining, snake handling, a rape 13 years earlier, and
racial discord are knitted together in an absorbing plot
with an uplifting ending. A remarkable first novel." SLJ

Crutcher, Chris, 1946-
Ironman; a novel. Greenwillow Bks. 1995 181p
$16.99   **Fic**
1. Father-son relationship—Fiction 2. School stories
3. Triathlon—Fiction
ISBN 0-688-13503-X   LC 94-1657
Also available in paperback from Greenwillow Bks.
While training for a triathlon, seventeen-year-old Bo
attends Mr. Nak's anger management group at school
which leads him to examine his relationship with his father
"Through Crutcher's masterful character development,
readers will believe in Bo, empathize with the other
members of the anger-management group, absorb the
wisdom of Mr. Nak and despise, yet at times pity, the
boy's father. This is not a light read, as many serious issues surface, though the author's trademark dark humor
(and colorful use of street language) is abundant." SLJ

Running loose. Greenwillow Bks. 1983 190p
$18.99 (7 and up)   **Fic**
1. School stories
ISBN 0-688-02002-X   LC 82-20935
Also available in paperback from Laurel-Leaf Bks.
"Louie Banks tells what happened to him in his senior
year in a small town Idaho high school. Besides falling
in love with Becky and losing her in a senseless accident, Louie takes a stand against the coach when he sets
the team up to injure a black player on an opposing
team, and learns that you can't be honorable with dis-
honorable men." Voice Youth Advocates
"This is a story of honor and principles, messages that
are achieved without preaching. An unusually fine first
novel." Bull Cent Child Books

Staying fat for Sarah Byrnes. Greenwillow Bks.
1993 216p $17.99   **Fic**
1. Obesity—Fiction 2. Child abuse—Fiction
3. Friendship—Fiction 4. Swimming—Fiction
ISBN 0-688-11552-7   LC 91-40097
Also available in paperback from Greenwillow Bks.

"An obese boy and a disfigured girl suffer the emotional scars of years of mockery at the hands of their
peers. They share a hard-boiled view of the world until
events in their senior year hurl them in very different directions. A story about a friendship with staying power,
written with pathos and pointed humor." SLJ

Stotan! Greenwillow Bks. 1986 183p $17.99 (7
and up)   **Fic**
1. Swimming—Fiction
ISBN 0-688-05715-2   LC 85-12712
A high school coach invites members of his swimming team to a memorable week of rigorous training that
tests their moral fiber as well as their physical stamina
"A subplot involving the boys' fight against local
Neo-Nazi activists provides some immediate action,
while the various characters' conflicts tighten the middle
and ending. The pace lags through the story's introduction; nevertheless, this is a searching sports novel, with
a tone varying from macho-tough to sensitive." Bull Cent
Child Books

Whale talk. Greenwillow Bks. 2001 220p
$15.99; lib bdg $16.89; pa $5.99 (7 and up)
                                             Fic
1. Swimming—Fiction 2. School stories 3. Racially
mixed people—Fiction
ISBN 0-688-18019-1; 0-06-029369-1 (lib bdg);
0-440-22938-3 (pa)   LC 00-59292
Intellectually and athletically gifted, TJ, a multiracial,
adopted teenager, shuns organized sports and the gung-ho
athletes at his high school until he agrees to form a
swimming team and recruits some of the school's less
popular students
"This remarkable novel is vintage Crutcher: heart-
pounding athletic competitions, raw emotion, an insufferable high school atmosphere that allows bullying and re-
veres athletes, and a larger-than-life teen hero who champions the underdog while skewering both racists and
abusers with his rapier-sharp wit." Book Rep

Cummings, Priscilla, 1951-
A face first. Dutton Children's Bks. 2001 197p
$16.99; pa $6.99   **Fic**
1. Burns and scalds—Fiction
ISBN 0-525-46522-7; 0-14-230247-3 (pa)
                                           LC 00-44240
Twelve-year-old Kelley decides to cut off contact with
her friends and classmates after suffering third-degree
burns to her face and body in a car accident near her
home on Maryland's Kent Island
"A thoughtful read that will encourage empathy."
Booklist

Red kayak; Priscilla Cummings. 1st ed. Dutton
Children's Books 2004 209p $15.99 (7 and up)
                                             Fic
1. Friendship—Fiction 2. Death—Fiction
3. Maryland—Fiction
ISBN 0-525-47317-3   LC 2003-63532
Living near the water on Maryland's Eastern Shore,
thirteen-year-old Brady and his best friends J.T. and Dig-
ger become entangled in a tragedy which tests their
friendship and their ideas about right and wrong.
"This well-crafted story will have broad appeal." SLJ

Cummings, Priscilla, 1951-—*Continued*

Saving Grace. Dutton Children's Bks. 2003 240p $16.99 (5 and up) **Fic**
1. Family life—Fiction 2. Great Depression, 1929-1939—Fiction 3. Washington (D.C.)—Fiction 4. Family life—Fiction
ISBN 0-525-47123-5 LC 2002-31539
When Grace's family is evicted from their Washington, D.C., apartment just before Christmas 1932, and she and her younger brothers are sent to the Mission, Grace wonders what will become of her sick older brother, her pregnant mother, and her out-of-work father
"The realistic historical detail is an integral part of the family drama, but the class differences and adoption conflicts are universal." Booklist

Currier, Katrina Saltonstall, 1969-

Kai's journey to Gold Mountain; an Angel Island story; illustrated by Gabhor Utomo. Angel Island Association 2005 39p il $16.95 (4 and up) **Fic**
1. Chinese Americans—Fiction 2. Immigrants—Fiction 3. Los Angeles (Calif.)—Fiction
ISBN 0-9667352-4-2 LC 2004-14821
In 1934, twelve-year-old Kai leaves China to join his father in America, but first he must take a long sea voyage, then endure weeks of crowded conditions and harsh examinations on Angel Island, fearing that he or his new friend will be sent home.
"The character Kai is based on a real person, whose photos, then and now, are part of the historical notes at the back of the book. Opposite each page of the intensely moving, detailed text are beautiful full-page watercolor-and-pencil illustrations that capture the crowded holding place, and, in unforgettable closeups, the characters' heartbreak and strength." Booklist

Curry, Jane Louise, 1932-

The Black Canary. Margaret K. McElderry Books 2005 279p $16.95 (5 and up) **Fic**
1. Essex, Robert Devereux, 2nd Earl of, 1566-1601—Fiction 2. Racially mixed people—Fiction 3. Singers—Fiction 4. London (England)—Fiction 5. Great Britain—History—1485-1603, Tudors—Fiction
ISBN 0-689-86478-7 LC 2003-26150
As the child of two musicians, twelve-year-old James has no interest in music until he discovers a portal to seventeenth-century London in his uncle's basement, and finds himself in a situation where his beautiful voice and the fact that he is biracial might serve him well.
"A genuinely good story that conveys a sense of darkness and mystery in the textured backdrop of a storied time and place." Booklist

Curtis, Christopher Paul

Bucking the Sarge. Wendy Lamb Books 2004 259p $15.95; lib bdg $17.99 (5 and up) **Fic**

1. Mothers—Fiction 2. Fraud—Fiction 3. African Americans—Fiction
ISBN 0-385-32307-7; 0-385-90159-3 (lib bdg)
Deeply involved in his cold and manipulative mother's shady business dealings in Flint, Michigan, fourteen-year-old Luther keeps a sense of humor while running the Happy Neighbor Group Home For Men, all the while dreaming of going to college and becoming a philosopher.
This is a "hilarious, anguished novel. . . .There are some real surprises in plot and character. . . .The farce and the failure tell the truth in this gripping story." Booklist

Bud, not Buddy. Delacorte Press 1999 245p $16.95 (4 and up) **Fic**
1. Orphans—Fiction 2. African Americans—Fiction 3. Great Depression, 1929-1939—Fiction
ISBN 0-385-32306-9 LC 99-10614
Also available Thorndike Press large print edition and Audiobook version
Awarded the Newbery Medal, 2000; Coretta Scott King Award for text, 2000
Ten-year-old Bud, a motherless boy living in Flint, Michigan, during the Great Depression, escapes a bad foster home and sets out in search of the man he believes to be his father—the renowned bandleader, H. E. Calloway of Grand Rapids
"Curtis says in a afterword that some of the characters are based on real people, including his own grandfathers, so it's not surprising that the rich blend of tall tale, slapstick, sorrow, and sweetness has the wry, teasing warmth of family folklore." Booklist

The Watsons go to Birmingham—1963; a novel. Delacorte Press 1995 210p $16.95; pa $6.50 (4 and up) **Fic**
1. African Americans—Fiction 2. Family life—Fiction 3. Prejudices—Fiction
ISBN 0-385-32175-9; 0-440-41412-1 (pa)
LC 95-7091
A Newbery Medal honor book, 1996
The ordinary interactions and everyday routines of the Watsons, an African American family living in Flint, Michigan, are drastically changed after they go to visit Grandma in Alabama in the summer of 1963
"Curtis's ability to switch from fun and funky to pinpoint-accurate psychological imagery works unusually well. . . . Ribald humor, sly sibling digs, and a totally believable child's view of the world will make this book an instant hit." SLJ

Cushman, Karen, 1941-

The ballad of Lucy Whipple. Clarion Bks. 1996 195p $15 (5 and up) **Fic**
1. Frontier and pioneer life—Fiction 2. Family life—Fiction 3. California—Gold discoveries—Fiction
ISBN 0-395-72806-1 LC 95-45257
Also available in paperback from HarperCollins
In 1849, twelve-year-old California Morning Whipple, who renames herself Lucy, is distraught when her mother moves the family from Massachusetts to a rough California mining town
"Cushman's heroine is a delightful character, and the historical setting is authentically portrayed." SLJ

Cushman, Karen, 1941-—*Continued*

Catherine, called Birdy. Clarion Bks. 1994 169p
$16 (6 and up)   **Fic**
1. Middle Ages—Fiction 2. Great Britain—Fiction
ISBN 0-395-68186-3   LC 93-23333
Also available in paperback from HarperCollins
A Newbery Medal honor book, 1995
The fourteen-year-old daughter of an English country
knight keeps a journal in which she records the events
of her life, particularly her longing for adventures beyond the usual role of women and her efforts to avoid
being married off
"In the process of telling the routines of her young
life, Birdy lays before readers a feast of details about
medieval England. . . . Superb historical fiction." SLJ

Matilda Bone. Clarion Bks. 2000 167p $15; pa
$5.99 (5 and up)   **Fic**
1. Physicians—Fiction 2. Middle Ages—Fiction
3. Great Britain—Fiction
ISBN 0-395-88156-0; 0-440-41822-4 (pa)
                                          LC 00-24032
Fourteen-year-old Matilda, an apprentice bonesetter
and practitioner of medicine in a village in medieval
England, tries to reconcile the various aspects of her life,
both spiritual and practical
"A fascinating glimpse into the colorful life and times
of the 14th century. . . . Cushman's character descriptions are spare, with each word carefully chosen to paint
wonderful pictures." SLJ
Includes bibliographical references

The midwife's apprentice. Clarion Bks. 1995
122p $12 (6 and up)   **Fic**
1. Middle Ages—Fiction 2. Midwives—Fiction
3. Great Britain—Fiction
ISBN 0-395-69229-6   LC 94-13792
Also available in paperback from HarperCollins
Awarded the Newbery Medal, 1996
In medieval England, a nameless, homeless girl is tak-
en in by a sharp-tempered midwife, and in spite of obstacles and hardship, eventually gains the three things she
most wants: a full belly, a contented heart, and a place
in this world
"Earthy humor, the foibles of humans both high and
low, and a fascinating mix of superstition and genuinely
helpful herbal remedies attached to childbirth make this
a truly delightful introduction to a world seldom seen in
children's literature." SLJ

Rodzina. Clarion Bks. 2003 215p $16 (5 and
up)   **Fic**
1. Polish Americans—Fiction 2. Orphans—Fiction
ISBN 0-618-13351-8   LC 2002-15976
A twelve-year-old Polish American girl is boarded
onto an orphan train in Chicago with fears about traveling to the West and a life of unpaid slavery
"The story features engaging characters, a vivid setting, and a prickly but endearing heroine. . . . Rodzina's
musings and observations provide poignancy, humor, and
a keen sense of the human and topographical landscape."
SLJ

D'Adamo, Francesco

Iqbal; a novel; written by Francesco D'Adamo;
translated by Ann Leonori. Atheneum Bks. for
Young Readers 2003 120p $15.95 (5 and up)
                                                   Fic
1. Masih, Iqbal, d. 1995—Fiction 2. Child labor—Fiction 3. Pakistan—Fiction
ISBN 0-689-85445-5   LC 2002-153498
Original Italian edition, 2001
A fictionalized account of the Pakistani child who escaped from bondage in a carpet factory and went on to
help liberate other children like him before being gunned
down at the age of thirteen
"The situation and setting are made clear in this novel.
Readers cannot help but be moved by the plight of these
youngsters. . . . This readable book will certainly add
breadth to most collections." SLJ

Danticat, Edwidge

Behind the mountains. Orchard Bks. 2002 166p
(First person fiction) $16.95; pa $6.99   **Fic**
1. Haitian Americans—Fiction 2. Immigrants—Fiction
3. Brooklyn (New York, N.Y.)—Fiction
ISBN 0-439-37299-2; 0-439-37300-X (pa)
                                          LC 2001-58768
Writing in the notebook which her teacher gave her,
thirteen-year-old Celiane describes life with her mother
and brother in Haiti as well as her experiences in Brooklyn after the family finally immigrates there to be reunited with her father
"The short journal entries make for a readable, immediate narrative." Booklist

Danziger, Paula, 1944-2004

The cat ate my gymsuit. Delacorte Press 1974
147p o.p. Putnam Pub. Group paperback available
$3.99   **Fic**
1. School stories 2. Teachers—Fiction
ISBN 0-698-11684-4 (pa)
Also available Thorndike Press large print edition
Marcy Lewis is bored by school and tyrannized by her
father. With the help of an unconventional teacher, she
conquers many of her feelings of insecurity and, in turn,
rallies the student body in support of the teacher who
was fired because of her behavior
"A sad-funny novel. . . . Ms. Danziger has an attractive style; her prose sparkles with wit and originality."
Publ Wkly
Followed by There's a bat in bunk five

The Divorce Express. Delacorte Press 1982
148p il o.p. Putnam Pub. Group paperback
available $5.99   **Fic**
1. Divorce—Fiction 2. Parent-child relationship—Fiction
ISBN 0-698-11685-2 (pa)   LC 82-70318
The protagonist, fourteen year old Phoebe, shuttles
"back and forth between her father's home in Woodstock
and her mother's apartment in Manhattan via the bus she
calls 'The Divorce Express' because there are so many
children like her who ride it. She has not become adjust-
ed to the man her mother is planning to marry, and feels
more and more at home in Woodstock, especially when

Danziger, Paula, 1944-2004—*Continued*
she makes a new friend, Rosie, whose parents . . . are
also divorced." Bull Cent Child Books
This is "a warm, tender book for adolescents who
must deal with the complexities of growing up." Child
Book Rev Serv

P.S. Longer letter later; {by} Paula Danziger &
Ann M. Martin. Scholastic 1998 234p $15.95; pa
$4.99 (5 and up)   **Fic**
1. Friendship—Fiction 2. Letters—Fiction
ISBN 0-590-21310-5; 0-590-21311-3 (pa)
LC 97-19120
Companion volume to Snail mail no more
Twelve-year-old best friends Elizabeth and Tara-Starr
continue their friendship through letter-writing after Tara-
Starr's family moves to another state
"The authenticity of the well-drawn characters gives
life and vitality to the story. . . . Readers will thorough-
ly enjoy this fast-paced read." SLJ

The pistachio prescription; a novel. Delacorte
Press 1978 154p o.p. Putnam Pub. Group
paperback available $5.99   **Fic**
1. Family life—Fiction 2. School stories
ISBN 0-698-11690-9 (pa)   LC 77-86330
"Thirteen-year-old Cassie, who tells the story, has
asthma, is a hypochondriac, and eats pistachio nuts compulsively when anything goes wrong. And almost everything does, she thinks. But Cassie's elected president of
the freshman class, she acquires Bernie, she has the stalwart support of her friend Vickie, who won't let Cassie
retreat into coddling fears, and she manages to cope with
a nagging mother, parental quarrels, and a hostile, competitive sister. . . . The characterization and dialogue are
strong, the relationships depicted with perception, and the
writing style vigorous." Bull Cent Child Books

Snail mail no more; {by} Paula Danziger &
Ann M. Martin. Scholastic Press 2000 307p
$16.95; pa $5.99 (5 and up)   **Fic**
1. Friendship—Fiction 2. Letters—Fiction
ISBN 0-439-06335-3; 0-439-06336-1 (pa)
LC 99-33593
Also available Audiobook version
Companion volume to P.S. Longer letter later
Now that they live in different cities, thirteen-year-old
Tara and Elizabeth use e-mail to "talk" about everything
that is occurring in their lives and to try to maintain their
closeness as they face big changes
"A funny, thought-provoking page-turner that will de-
light readers and leave them ready for more messages."
Booklist

There's a bat in bunk five. Delacorte Press 1980
150p il o.p. Putnam Pub. Group paperback
available $5.99   **Fic**
1. Camps—Fiction
ISBN 0-698-11689-5 (pa)   LC 80-15581
"A thinner Marcy than appeared in 'The Cat Ate My
Gymsuit' here eagerly accepts an invitation from Ms.
Finney, her favorite teacher, to work as a counselor-in-
training at a summer camp. Though wanting to do a
good job, particularly in reaching the abrasive and unco-
operative Ginger, Marcy also indulges in a romance with

fellow camper Ted and spends time sorting out her own
inner conflicts." Booklist
"In some ways this is the usual camping story of
pranks, bunkmates, adjustment to separation from parents, etc. This doesn't, however, follow a formula plot;
it has depth in the relationships and characterizations;
and it's written with vigor and humor." Bull Cent Child
Books

United Tates of America; a novel with
scrapbook art. Scholastic Press 2002 123p il
$17.95; pa $5.99 (4 and up)   **Fic**
1. School stories 2. Friendship—Fiction 3. Death—
Fiction
ISBN 0-590-69221-6; 0-590-69222-4 (pa)
LC 2001-42019
Eleven-year-old Skate Tate experiences many changes
when she enters middle school, finds her best friend
drifting away from her, and loses her beloved Great Uncle Mort, or GUM
"Young scrapbook artists, in particular, will take delight in this book's unique artwork. . . . The pictures
(collages of photos, stickers, cut-outs and humorous captions) synchronize perfectly with Danziger's . . . sparkling narrative." Publ Wkly

Davies, Jacqueline
Where the ground meets the sky. Marshall
Cavendish 2002 224p $14.95; pa $5.95
     Fic
1. Manhattan Project—Fiction 2. World War, 1939-
1945—Fiction 3. New Mexico—Fiction
ISBN 0-7614-5105-6; 0-7614-5187-0 (pa)
LC 2001-32519
During World War II, a twelve-year-old girl is uprooted from her quiet, East coast life and moved to a secluded army post in the New Mexico desert where her father
and other scientists are working on a top secret project
"The story is told in Hazel's lively, if self-conscious
voice. . . . Davies skillfully describes the secrecy and intensity of the work and how it affected every aspect of
the researchers' and their families' lives." Booklist

De Guzman, Michael
Beekman's big deal; Michael de Guzman. 1st
ed. Farrar Straus Giroux 2004 213p $16 (5 and
up)   **Fic**
1. New York (N.Y.)—Fiction 2. Moving—Fiction
ISBN 0-374-30672-9   LC 2003-60773
Tired of the frequent moves that he and his father
must make, twelve-year-old Beekman begins to make
connections with neighbors and classmates after settling
in a small, unusual New York City neighborhood
"Featuring interesting, well-developed characters and
sprinkled with gentle humor, this novel strikes a pleasing
balance between heart-wrenching and heartwarming moments." SLJ

Melonhead. Farrar, Straus & Giroux 2002 213p
$17   **Fic**
1. Birth defects—Fiction 2. Runaway children—Fiction
ISBN 0-374-34944-4   LC 2002-20863

De Guzman, Michael—Continued

Tired of living with his uncaring, divorced parents, Sidney, a twelve-year-old boy with an unusually large head, takes a bus trip across the United States which becomes a journey of self-discovery

"At times emotionally wrenching, the story is also entertaining and ultimately satisfying." SLJ

De la Cruz, Melissa, 1971-

Fresh off the boat; by Melissa de la Cruz. 1st ed. HarperCollins Pub. 2005 243p $15; lib bdg $16.89 (7 and up)   **Fic**

1. Filipino Americans—Fiction 2. Immigrants—Fiction 3. School stories

ISBN 0-06-054540-2; 0-06-054541-0 (lib bdg)

LC 2004-15513

When her family emigrates from the Philippines to San Francisco, California, fourteen-year-old Vicenza Arambullo struggles to fit in at her exclusive, all-girl private school.

"This well-written, heartfelt novel is a worthy addition to most YA collections, but especially where there are strong immigrant populations." SLJ

De Lint, Charles, 1951-

The blue girl; Charles de Lint. Viking 2004 368p $17.99 (7 and up)   **Fic**

1. Fairies—Fiction 2. Ghost stories 3. School stories

ISBN 0-670-05924-2   LC 2004-19051

New at her high school, Imogene enlists the help of her introverted friend Maxine and the ghost of a boy who haunts the school after receiving warnings through her-dreams that soul-eaters are threatening her life

"The book combines the turmoil of high school intertwined with rich, detailed imagery drawn from traditional folklore and complex characters with realistic relationships. . . . This book is not just another ghost story, but a novel infused with the true sense of wonder and magic that is De Lint at his best. It is strongly recommended." Voice Youth Advocates

Dean, Carolee

Comfort. Houghton Mifflin 2002 230p $15; pa $6.99 (7 and up)   **Fic**

1. Poetry—Fiction

ISBN 0-618-13846-3; 0-618-43912-9 (pa)

LC 2001-39250

Fourteen-year-old Kenny Roy Willson fantasizes about escape from his hometown of Comfort, Texas, following his alcoholic father's release from prison

"The small-town setting . . . is depicted effectively, characters are complex and believable, and the concept of comfort weaves through this outstanding, realistic, and hopeful first novel." Voice Youth Advocates

Deans, Sis Boulos, 1955-

Every day and all the time; {by} Sis Deans. Holt & Co. 2003 234p $16.95 (5 and up)

    Fic

1. Bereavement—Fiction 2. Ballet—Fiction

ISBN 0-8050-7337-X   LC 2002-38893

Eleven-year-old Emily, still reeling from the car accident that took her older brother's life and badly injured her, uses psychotherapy and ballet dancing to cope with her parents' decision to sell their house—the only place she can still feel and talk to her brother

"In the hands of a lesser author this could have been maudlin, but Deans wisely adds a humorous subplot involving the naive realtor that lightens the goings-on just enough. She also realistically shepherds her characters through their grief, before permitting the closure that allows them to move forward." Booklist

Deaver, Julie Reece

Say goodnight, Gracie. Harper & Row 1988 214p $15; pa $5.99 (7 and up)   **Fic**

1. Death—Fiction 2. Friendship—Fiction 3. Actors—Fiction 4. Chicago (Ill.)—Fiction

ISBN 0-06-021418-X; 0-06-447007-5 (pa)

LC 87-45278

"A Charlotte Zolotow book"

When a car accident kills her best friend Jimmy, with whom she has shared everything from childhood escapades to breaking into the professional theater scene in Chicago, seventeen-year-old Morgan must find her own way of coping with his death

"This is impressive in style (particularly dialogue) and narrative flow; while the pace is uneven and the focus narrow, the characters are strongly drawn and the protagonist is convincing and sympathetic." Bull Cent Child Books

DeClements, Barthe, 1920-

6th grade can really kill you. Viking Kestrel 1985 146p pa $5.99 hardcover o.p. (5 and up)

    Fic

1. Learning disabilities—Fiction

ISBN 0-14-037130-3   LC 85-40382

"Helen dreads the first day in sixth grade. Good in math and gifted on the pitcher's mound, she is a non-reader diagnosed as a behavior problem. Against the slice-of-life background of a skating party, pierced ears and overnights at friend Louise's, Helen loses the battle with the printed word." SLJ

This is "a story that amply compensates for its uneven pace by the natural quality of the relationships and the dialogue in the classroom environment and by the insight gained through the first person treatment of a learning disability." Bull Cent Child Books

DeFelice, Cynthia C.

The apprenticeship of Lucas Whitaker; {by} Cynthia DeFelice. Farrar, Straus & Giroux 1996 151p $16 (5 and up)   **Fic**

1. Apprentices—Fiction 2. Orphans—Fiction

ISBN 0-374-34669-0   LC 95-26728

Also available in paperback from Avon Bks.

"Orphaned Lucas Whitaker has lost all his family to consumption, the scourge of the mid-nineteenth century. His grief leads him away from the family's marginal hill farm, and he stumbles into an apprenticeship with Doc Beecher, a rare college-trained physician. The pace of this fine piece of historical fiction is brisk in spite of a wealth of detail that not only establishes the setting but exposes beliefs and attitudes of the day regarding health, hygiene, and witchcraft." Horn Book

DeFelice, Cynthia C.—*Continued*

Death at Devil's Bridge; {by} Cynthia DeFelice. Farrar, Straus & Giroux 2000 181p $16 (5 and up) **Fic**

1. Drug traffic—Fiction 2. Fishing—Fiction 3. Martha's Vineyard (Mass.)—Fiction

ISBN 0-374-31723-2 LC 99-56097

Also available in paperback from HarperCollins

Sequel to Devil's Bridge (1992)

Despite a great summer job as first mate on a fishing boat out of Martha's Vineyard, thirteen-year-old Ben gets caught up with illegal drugs and possible murder

"The lively prose style, a plot that keeps readers wondering, and generally fleshed-out characters create a selection that will hook its target audience to the end." SLJ

The ghost and Mrs. Hobbs; {by} Cynthia DeFelice. Farrar, Straus & Giroux 2001 180p $16; pa $5.99 (4-6) **Fic**

1. Ghost stories

ISBN 0-374-38046-5; 0-06-001172-6 (pa)

LC 00-52827

Also available Thorndike Press large print edition

Hindered by a fight with her friend Dub and a series of mysterious fires, eleven-year-old Allie investigates the fire seventeen years earlier which claimed the lives of the husband and infant son of a school cafeteria worker, as well as the handsome young man whose ghost asks Allie for help

"This is a diverting and suspenseful ghost story offering a likable protagonist and a thrilling romantic spark." Horn Book

The ghost of Fossil Glen; {by} Cynthia DeFelice. Farrar, Straus & Giroux 1998 167p $16 (4-6) **Fic**

1. Ghost stories

ISBN 0-374-31787-9 LC 97-33230

Also available in paperback from Avon Bks. and Thorndike Press large print edition

"Sixth-grader Allie Nichols encounters the ghost of Lucy Stiles and becomes involved with Lucy's unsolved death, eventually finding proof that Lucy was murdered." Horn Book Guide

"A supernatural cliff-hanger with breathless chases and riveting suspense." SLJ

Nowhere to call home; {by} Cynthia DeFelice. Farrar, Straus & Giroux 1999 199p $16

Fic

1. Great Depression, 1929-1939—Fiction 2. Orphans—Fiction 3. Tramps—Fiction

ISBN 0-374-35552-5 LC 98-36602

Also available in paperback from HarperTrophy

When her father kills himself after losing his money in the stock market crash, twelve-year-old Frances, now a penniless orphan, decides to hop aboard a freight train and live the life of a hobo

"The dialogue rings true, and the fast pace of the narrative will keep readers turning pages until the poignant resolution." Voice Youth Advocates

Defoe, Daniel, 1661?-1731

Robinson Crusoe (7 and up) **Fic**

1. Survival after airplane accidents, shipwrecks, etc.—Fiction

Hardcover and paperback editions available from various publishers

First published 1719

"A minutely circumstantial account of the hero's shipwreck and escape to an uninhabited island, and the methodical industry whereby he makes himself a comfortable home. The story is founded on the actual experiences of Alexander Selkirk, who spent four years on the island of Juan Fernandez in the early 18th century." Lenrow. Reader's Guide to Prose Fic

Del Vecchio, Gene, 1955-

The Pearl of Anton; by Gene Del Vecchio. Pelican Pub. Co 2004 256p $16.95 (7 and up) **Fic**

1. Fantasy fiction

ISBN 1-589-80172-5 LC 2003-20930

Jason Del struggles to master himself and the Pearl of Anton in order to defend humanity in the Final Contest

"Del Vecchio has created a richly detailed world. . . . The climactic battle is catastrophic and convincing, and the suspense leading up to it is almost overwhelming." Booklist

Denenberg, Barry

Early Sunday morning; the Pearl Harbor diary of Amber Billows. Scholastic 2001 156p il (Dear America) $10.95; lib bdg $12.95 **Fic**

1. Pearl Harbor (Oahu, Hawaii), Attack on, 1941—Fiction 2. World War, 1939-1945—Fiction 3. Hawaii—Fiction

ISBN 0-439-32874-8; 0-439-55513-2 (lib bdg)

LC 2001-42616

In her diary, twelve-year-old Amber describes moving to Hawaii in 1941 and experiencing the horror of the bombing of Pearl Harbor

Elisabeth: the princess bride. Scholastic 2003 151p il (Royal diaries) $10.95 **Fic**

1. Elisabeth, Empress, consort of Franz Joseph I, Emperor of Austria, 1837-1898—Fiction 2. Austria—History—Fiction

ISBN 0-439-26644-0 LC 2002-70818

The diary of Princess Elisabeth, written in 1853-1854, describing her engagement and marriage to her cousin Franz Joseph I, Emperor of Austria. Includes historical notes concerning her life as Empress

"Elisabeth is a charming figure from the past, and this book should prove to be an enjoyable read for historical fiction and diary fans." SLJ

The journal of Ben Uchida, citizen #13559, Mirror Lake internment camp. Scholastic 1999 156p (My name is America) $10.95 **Fic**

1. Japanese Americans—Evacuation and relocation, 1942-1945—Fiction 2. World War, 1939-1945—Fiction

ISBN 0-590-48531-8 LC 98-40956

Twelve-year-old Ben Uchida keeps a journal of his experiences as a prisoner in a Japanese internment camp in Mirror Lake, California, during World War II

Denenberg, Barry—*Continued*

Ben "comes across as a real kid, coping with anger, resentment, confusion, and fear. Historical notes put the World War II internment in the context of a long history of prejudice against Japanese Americans." Booklist

When will this cruel war be over? the Civil War diary of Emma Simpson. Scholastic 1996 156p il maps (Dear America) $10.95; lib bdg $12.95   **Fic**

1. United States—History—1861-1865, Civil War—Fiction

ISBN 0-590-22862-5; 0-439-55517-5 (lib bdg)

LC 95-25540

"The book is filled with kindling for class discussion. . . . It is both informative and a good read." Voice Youth Advocates

Includes bibliographical references

Derby, Pat

Away to the goldfields! Pat Derby. 1st ed. Farrar Straus Giroux 2004 248p $18   **Fic**

1. California—Gold discoveries—Fiction 2. Voyages and travels—Fiction

ISBN 0-374-39961-1   LC 2003-64217

Yearning for adventure and tired of farm life in New Hampshire, sixteen-year-old Mary Margaret Malarkey journeys to California in 1848 to find her father who arrived earlier to make his fortune in the goldfields.

"This is an engrossing adventure with an attractive heroine." SLJ

Desai Hidier, Tanuja

Born confused. Scholastic Press 2002 413p $16.95; pa $7.99 (7 and up)   **Fic**

1. East Indians—United States—Fiction 2. Friendship—Fiction

ISBN 0-439-35762-4; 0-439-51011-2 (pa)

LC 2002-4515

Seventeen-year-old Dimple, whose family is from India, discovers that she is not Indian enough for the Indians and not American enough for the Americans, as she sees her hypnotically beautiful, manipulative best friend taking possession of both her heritage and the boy she likes

"This involving story . . . will reward its readers. The family background and richness in cultural information add a new level to the familiar girl-meets-boy story." SLJ

Dessen, Sarah, 1970-

Dreamland; a novel. Viking 2000 250p $15.99; pa $7.99 (7 and up)   **Fic**

1. Violence—Fiction

ISBN 0-670-89122-3; 0-14-240175-7 (pa)

LC 99-44102

Also available in paperback from Puffin Bks.

After her older sister runs away, sixteen-year-old Caitlin decides that she needs to make a major change in her own life and begins an abusive relationship with a boy who is mysterious, brilliant, and dangerous

"Dessen writes with utter realism as she describes Caitlin's descent, first into drugs, then into sex, and finally into a relationship that turns violent. . . . It's not only the plot that's vivid; the characters are also intensely real." Booklist

Someone like you. Viking 1998 281p $16.99; pa $7.99 (7 and up)   **Fic**

1. Pregnancy—Fiction 2. Unmarried mothers—Fiction 3. Friendship—Fiction

ISBN 0-670-87778-6; 0-14-240177-3 (pa)

LC 97-36437

Halley's junior year of high school includes the death of her best friend Scarlett's boyfriend, the discovery that Scarlett is pregnant, and Halley's own first serious relationship

"Sparkling dialogue and incisive characterization illuminate this special novel." SLJ

This lullaby; a novel. Viking 2002 345p $16.99; pa $7.99 (7 and up)   **Fic**

1. Dating (Social customs)—Fiction 2. Musicians—Fiction

ISBN 0-670-03530-0; 0-14-250155-7 (pa)

LC 2001-55917

Raised by a mother who's had five husbands, eighteen-year-old Remy believes in short-term, no-commitment relationships until she meets Dexter, a rock band musician

"As the plot suggests, this is at its heart a classic romance . . . and Dessen plays the dynamics of the traditional story effectively." Bull Cent Child Books

The truth about forever. Viking 2004 382p lib bdg $16.99 (7 and up)   **Fic**

1. Death—Fiction 2. Catering—Fiction

ISBN 0-670-03639-0   LC 2003-28298

The summer following her father's death, Macy plans to work at the library and wait for her brainy boyfriend to return from camp, but instead she goes to work at a catering business where she makes new friends and finally faces her grief.

"All of Dessen's characters ... are fully and beautifully drawn. Their dialogue is natural and believable, and their care for one another is palpable...Dessen charts Macy's navigation of grief in such an honest way it will touch every reader who meets her. " SLJ

Deuker, Carl, 1950-

High heat. Houghton Mifflin 2003 277p $16 (7 and up)   **Fic**

1. Fathers—Fiction 2. School stories

ISBN 0-618-31117-3   LC 2002-15324

When high school sophomore Shane Hunter's father is arrested for money laundering at his Lexus dealership, the star pitcher's life of affluence and private school begins to fall apart

This is "a story that delivers baseball action along with a rich psychological portrait, told through a compelling first-person narration." SLJ

Night hoops. Houghton Mifflin 2000 212p $15 (7 and up)   **Fic**

1. Basketball—Fiction 2. Friendship—Fiction

ISBN 0-395-97936-6   LC 99-47882

Also available in paperback from HarperCollins Pubs.

Deuker, Carl, 1950-—*Continued*

While trying to prove that he is good enough to be on his high school's varsity basketball team, Nick must also deal with his parents' divorce and erratic behavior of a troubled classmate who lives across the street

"The descriptions of the games are well written and accurate. Best of all, the complexities of basketball are contrasted with the complexities of life." SLJ

On the Devil's court. Little, Brown 1988 252p o.p. Avon Bks. paperback available $5.99 (7 and up)   **Fic**
1. Basketball—Fiction
ISBN 0-380-70879-5 (pa)   LC 88-13432
Also available in hardcover from Smith, P.
"Joy Street books"
Struggling with his feelings of inadequacy and his failure to make the basketball team in his new school, seventeen-year-old Joe Faust finds himself willing to trade his soul for one perfect season of basketball
"This is a rare sports novel, with complex plot and characterization as well as gripping game play." Bull Cent Child Books

Painting the black. Houghton Mifflin 1997 248p $14.95; pa $5.99 (7 and up)   **Fic**
1. Baseball—Fiction 2. School stories
ISBN 0-395-82848-1; 0 380 73104 5 (pa)
LC 96-23763
Also available in paperback from Avon Camelot Bks.
"After a disastrous fall from a tree, senior Ryan Ward wrote off baseball. But he is swept back into the game when cocky, charismatic Josh Daniels—a star quarterback with the perfect spiral pass as well as a pitcher with a mean slider—moves into the neighborhood. . . . The well-written sports scenes—baseball and football—will draw reluctant readers, but it is Ryan's moral courage that will linger when the reading is done." Booklist

DiCamillo, Kate, 1964-

Because of Winn-Dixie. Candlewick Press 2000 182p $15.99; pa $5.99 (4 and up)   **Fic**
1. Dogs—Fiction 2. Florida—Fiction
ISBN 0-7636-0776-2; 0-7636-1605-2 (pa)
LC 99-34260
A Newbery honor book, 2001
Ten-year-old India Opal Buloni describes her first summer in the town of Naomi, Florida, and all the good things that happen to her because of her big ugly dog Winn-Dixie
"This well-crafted, realistic, and heartwarming story will be read and reread as a new favorite deserving a long-term place on library shelves." SLJ

The tiger rising. Candlewick Press 2001 116p $15.99; pa $5.99   **Fic**
1. Tigers—Fiction 2. Death—Fiction 3. Friendship—Fiction
ISBN 0-7636-0911-0; 0-7636-1898-5 (ps)
LC 99-88635
"Rob Horton has 'a way of not-thinking about things,' including his mother's recent death. His life changes when he discovers a caged tiger in the woods and meets an emotionally volatile new classmate." Horn Book

Guide
"This slender story is lush with haunting characters and spare descriptions, conjuring up vivid images." SLJ

Dickinson, Peter, 1927-

A bone from a dry sea. Delacorte Press 1993 199p pa $5.50 hardcover o.p.   **Fic**
1. Fossil hominids—Fiction 2. Fossils—Fiction
ISBN 0-440-21928-0   LC 92-20491
First published 1992 in the United Kingdom
"Li, a female child in a tribe of 'sea-apes' living some four million years ago, and Vinny, teenage daughter of a modern-day paleontologist, are the protagonists of alternating third-person stories, one extrapolating what life might have been like for an intelligent youngster in prehistoric times and the other demonstrating the difficulty of interpreting ancient shards." Booklist
"Basing his account of Li's people on an intriguing recent theory that we evolved from a semi-aquatic, apelike mammal, the author brilliantly suggests how we might have started along the road to what we are today." SLJ

Eva. Delacorte Press 1989 219p hardcover o.p. Bantam Bks. paperback available $5.50 (7 and up)
Fic
1. Chimpanzees—Fiction 2. Science fiction
ISBN 0-440-20766-5 (pa)   LC 88-29435
"Eva wakes up from a deep coma that was the result of a terrible car accident and finds herself drastically altered. The accident leaves her so badly injured that her parents consent to a radical experiment to transplant her brain and memory into the body of a research chimpanzee. With the aid of a computer for communication, Eva slowly adjusts to her new existence while scientists monitor her progress, feelings, and insight into the animal world." Voice Youth Advocates
"Raising ethical and moral questions, Dickinson creates a vision both profound and chilling." SLJ

The kin; illustrations by Ian Andrew. Putnam 2003 c1998 628p $24.99   **Fic**
1. Prehistoric peoples
ISBN 0-399-24022-5   LC 2002-13350
This omnibus volume replaces the four titles published separately by Grosset & Dunlop in 1998
Contents: Suth's story; Noli's story; Po's story; Mana's story
"It is Africa, 200,000 years ago. Suth and five other children may be all that's left of their Kin—the Moonhawks. They are alone in the desert, and they must set out on a dangerous journey in search of new Good Places." Publisher's note

Tears of the salamander. Wendy Lamb Bks. 2003 197p $16.95; lib bdg $18.99   **Fic**
1. Magic—Fiction 2. Volcanoes—Fiction 3. Italy—Fiction
ISBN 0-385-73098-5; 0-385-90125-9 (lib bdg)
LC 2003-584
When Alfredo, a twelve-year-old choir boy in eighteenth-century Italy, loses his family in a fire, he goes to live with Uncle Giorgio, who he discovers is a sorcerer in control of the fires of Mt. Etna with sinister plans for his nephew

Dickinson, Peter, 1927— —*Continued*
"Pitch-perfect, unobtrusive storytelling gracefully
cedes center stage to the story's near-mythic elements.
Thoughtful readers will find much to ponder." Publ
Wkly

Divakaruni, Chitra Banerjee, 1956-
The conch bearer. Roaring Brook Press 2003
265p $16.95; lib bdg $23.90 (5 and up)
Fic
1. Magic—Fiction 2. India—Fiction
ISBN 0-7613-1935-2; 0-7613-2793-2 (lib bdg)
LC 2003-8578
"A Neal Porter book"
In India, a healer invites twelve-year-old Anand to
join him on a quest to return a magical conch to its safe
and rightful home, high in the Himalayan mountains
"Divakaruni keeps her tale fresh and riveting." Publ
Wkly

Doherty, Berlie
Holly Starcross. Greenwillow Bks. 2002 c2001
186p $15.99; lib bdg $17.89 (7 and up)
Fic
1. Divorce—Fiction
ISBN 0-06-001341-9; 0-06-001342-7 (lib bdg)
LC 2001-54808
First published 2001 in the United Kingdom
When fourteen-year-old Holly Starcross meets her father for the first time in eight years, the experience
changes the way she thinks about him, her mother, and
even herself
"Doherty writes with urgency and intimate detail
about family love and distance, and tension builds to the
very last chapter." Booklist

Dorris, Michael
Guests. Hyperion Bks. for Children 1994 119p
Fic
1. Algonquian Indians—Fiction 2. America—Explora-
tion—Fiction
ISBN 0-7868-0047-X; 0-7868-1356-3
LC 94-26057
"Dorris's writing is elegant, full of evocative images
and lush metaphors. He develops his intriguing characters
in a leisurely way." SLJ

Morning Girl. Hyperion Bks. for Children 1992
74p hardcover o.p. paperback available $4.99 (4
and up)
Fic
1. Taino Indians—Fiction 2. Siblings—Fiction
3. America—Exploration—Fiction
ISBN 0-78681-358-X LC 92-52989
Also available Spanish language edition
Twelve year old Morning Girl, a Taino Indian who
loves the day, and her younger brother Star Boy, who
loves the night, take turns describing their life on a Ba-
hamian island in 1492; in Morning Girl's last narrative,
she witnesses the arrival of the first Europeans to her
world
"The author uses a lyrical, yet easy-to-follow, style to
place these compelling characters in historical context.

. . . Dorris does a superb job of showing that family dynamics are complicated, regardless of time and place.
. . . A touching glimpse into the humanity that connects
us all." Horn Book

Sees Behind Trees. Hyperion Bks. for Children
1996 104p pa $4.99 hardcover o.p. (4 and up)
Fic
1. Native Americans—Fiction 2. Vision disorders—
Fiction
ISBN 0-7868-1357-1 LC 96-15859
"For the partially sighted Walnut, it is impossible to
prove his right to a grown-up name by hitting a target
with his bow and arrow. With his highly developed
senses, however, he demonstrates that he can do something even better: he can see 'what cannot be seen'
which earns him the name Sees Behind Trees. . . . Set
in sixteenth-century America, this richly imagined and
gorgeously written rite-of-passage story has the gravity
of legend. Moreover, it has buoyant humor and the immediacy of a compelling story that is peopled with multidimensional characters." Booklist

Dowell, Frances O'Roark
Chicken boy. Atheneum Books for Young
Readers 2005 201p $15.95 (4 and up) **Fic**
1. Chickens—Fiction 2. Friendship—Fiction
3. Family life—Fiction
ISBN 0-689-85816-7 LC 2004-10928
Since the death of his mother, Tobin's family life and
school life have been in disarray, but after he starts raising chickens with his seventh-grade classmate, Henry,
everything starts to fall into place.
"There is no glib resolution, here. But the strong narration and the child's struggle with forgiveness make for
poignant, aching drama." Booklist

Dovey Coe. Atheneum Bks. for Young Readers
2000 181p $16; pa $4.99 (5 and up) **Fic**
1. Mountain life—Fiction 2. North Carolina—Fiction
ISBN 0-689-83174-9; 0-689-84667-3 (pa)
LC 99-46870
When accused of murder in her North Carolina mountain town in 1928, Dovey Coe, a stronged-willed twelve-
year-old girl, comes to a new understanding of others,
including her deaf brother
"Dowell has created a memorable character in Dovey,
quick-witted and honest to a fault. . . . This is a delightful book, thoughtful and full of substance." Booklist

The secret language of girls. Atheneum Books
for Young Readers 2004 247p $15.95 (5 and up)
Fic
1. Friendship—Fiction 2. School stories
ISBN 0-689-84421-2 LC 2003-12026
Marylin and Kate have been friends since nursery
school, but when Marylin becomes a middle school
cheerleader and Kate begins to develop other interests,
their relationship is put to the test.
"Excellent characterization, an accurate portrayal of
the painful and often cruel machinations of preteens, and
evocative dialogue will make this tale resonate with most
readers." SLJ

Dowell, Frances O'Roark—*Continued*

Where I'd like to be. Atheneum Bks. for Young Readers 2003 232p $15.95 (4 and up)   **Fic**

1. Foster home care—Fiction 2. Tennessee—Fiction 3. Friendship—Fiction

ISBN 0-689-84420-4   LC 2002-2183

"When a new girl moves into the East Tennessee Children's Home, her charisma has an immediate effect on Maddie, the story's narrator. Maddie's scrapbooks filled with pictures of the houses she dreams of living in serve as a catalyst for Murphy, as she gathers a fledgling group of unlikely friends around her. . . . The foster children's backgrounds are believable, diverse, and engaging, and readers familiar with eastern Tennessee will appreciate the references to real towns and cities that are sprinkled throughout the text." SLJ

Downer, Ann, 1960-

Hatching magic. Atheneum Bks. for Young Readers 2003 242p $16.95 (4 and up)   **Fic**

1. Dragons—Fiction 2. Magic—Fiction

ISBN 0-689-83400-4   LC 00-56570

When a thirteenth-century wizard confronts twenty-first century Boston while seeking his pet dragon, he is followed by a rival wizard and a very unhappy demon, but eleven-year-old Theodora Oglethorpe may hold the secret to setting everything right

"With likable characters, and laced with plenty of humor and adventure, Downer's fantasy will have solid appeal for young genre fans." Booklist

Doyle, Brian

Boy O'Boy. Douglas & McIntyre 2003 161p $15.95; pa $12.95   **Fic**

1. Child sexual abuse—Fiction 2. Canada—Fiction

ISBN 0-88899-588-1; 0-88899-590-3 (pa)

"A Groundwood book"

Living in Ottawa in 1945, Martin O'Boy must deal with a drunken father, an overburdened mother, a disabled twin brother, and a sexual predator at his church.

"Martin O'Boy is an expert observer and narrator. . . . Martin's world is believably real. Even the description of the sexual encounter seems like what a confused 11 or 12-year-old might say. " SLJ

Doyle, Eugenie F.

Stray voltage; {by} Eugenie Doyle. Front St. 2002 133p $16.95   **Fic**

1. Farm life—Fiction 2. Vermont—Fiction

ISBN 1-88691-086-3   LC 2002-69252

After his mother leaves to start a new life elsewhere, eleven-year-old Ian sees changes in his father and in their failing Vermont farm, changes that cannot be ignored

This is a "distinguished first novel. . . . The raw language is appropriate, given the anger and desperation of the characters. The author's obvious understanding of the young adolescent mind makes this a fine choice for reluctant readers." SLJ

Doyle, Malachy

Who is Jesse Flood? Bloomsbury Children's Bks. 2002 172p $14.95; pa $6.95   **Fic**

1. Northern Ireland—Fiction

ISBN 1-58234-776-X; 1-58234-922-3 (pa)

          LC 2002-19065

Striving to cope with the arguments of his parents and his feelings of not belonging, fourteen-year-old Jesse Flood struggles to find his place in a small town in Northern Ireland

"Jesse's voice comes through with poignant tellings of embarrassing situations and with a wonderful sense of humor, as well as with an honest exploration of painful emotions." SLJ

Draanen, Wendelin van

Flipped. Knopf 2001 212p $14.95; lib bdg $16.99; pa $8.95 (6 and up)   **Fic**

ISBN 0-375-81174-5; 0-375-91174-X (lib bdg); 0-375-82544-4 (pa)   LC 2001-29238

In alternating chapters, eighth-graders Juli and Bryce, describe how their feelings about themselves, each other, and their families have changed over the years

"There's lots of laugh-out-loud egg puns and humor in this novel. There's also, however, a substantial amount of serious social commentary woven in, as well as an exploration of the importance of perspective in relationships." SLJ

Sammy Keyes and the hotel thief. Knopf 1998 163p il pa $4.99 hardcover o.p. (4 and up)   **Fic**

1. Mystery fiction

ISBN 0-679-89264-8   LC 97-40776

Thirteen-year-old Sammy's penchant for speaking her mind gets her in trouble when she involves herself in the investigation of a robbery at the "seedy" hotel across the street from the seniors' building where she is living with her grandmother

"This is a breezy novel with vivid characters." Bull Cent Child Books

Other available titles about Sammy Keyes are:

Sammy Keyes and the art of deception (2003)

Sammy Keyes and the curse of Moustache Mary (2000)

Sammy Keyes and the Hollywood mummy (2001)

Sammy Keyes and the psycho Kitty Queen (2004)

Sammy Keyes and the runaway elf (1999)

Sammy Keyes and the search for snake eyes (2002)

Sammy Keyes and the Sisters of Mercy (1999)

Sammy Keyes and the skeleton man (1998)

Draper, Sharon M., 1950-

The Battle of Jericho. Atheneum Books for Young Readers 2003 297p $16.95 (7 and up)   **Fic**

1. Clubs—Fiction 2. School stories 3. Cousins—Fiction 4. Death—Fiction

ISBN 0-689-84232-5   LC 2002-8612

"The Warriors of Distinction has been the school's most exclusive club for 50 years, so when 16-year-old Jericho is asked to pledge, he's excited—and intimidated. . . . When the ceremony turns cruel—with the one girl pledge being singled out for abuse—Jericho begins to

Draper, Sharon M., 1950-—*Continued*
have second thoughts. Then the affair turns deadly."
Booklist
"This title is a compelling read that drives home important lessons about making choices." SLJ

Double Dutch. Atheneum Bks. for Young
Readers 2002 183p $16; pa $4.99   **Fic**
1. Rope skipping—Fiction 2. Friendship—Fiction
3. African Americans—Fiction
ISBN 0-689-84230-9; 0-689-84231-7 (pa)
     LC 00-50247
Three eighth-grade friends, preparing for the International Double Dutch Championship jump rope competition in their home town of Cincinnati, Ohio, cope with Randy's missing father, Delia's inability to read, and Yo Yo's encounter with the class bullies
"Teens will like the high-spirited, authentic dialogue . . . the honest look at tough issues, and the team workout scenes that show how sports can transform young lives." Booklist

Forged by fire. Atheneum Bks. for Young
Readers 1997 151p $16.95; pa $4.99 (7 and up)
     Fic
1. Child abuse—Fiction 2. Siblings—Fiction
3. African Americans—Fiction
ISBN 0-689-80699-X; 0-689-81851-3 (pa)
     LC 96-2763
Companion volume to Tears of a tiger
Teenage Gerald, who has spent years protecting his fragile half-sister from their abusive father, faces the prospect of one final confrontation before the problem can be solved
"What started out as an award-winning short story in Ebony magazine was expanded into this sad but inspirational story. . . . With non-stop excitement, this is well-written, easy to read, and possibly an inspiration for anyone trapped in family situations involving child abuse or domestic violence." Voice Youth Advocates

Tears of a tiger. Atheneum Pubs. 1994 162p
$16.95; pa $5.99 (7 and up)   **Fic**
1. Death—Fiction 2. African Americans—Fiction
3. Suicide—Fiction
ISBN 0-689-31878-2; 0-689-80698-1 (pa)
     LC 94-10278
The death of African American high school basketball star Rob Washington in a drunk driving accident leads to the suicide of his friend Andy, who was driving the car
"The story emerges through newspaper articles, journal entries, homework assignments, letters, and conversations that give the book immediacy; the teenage conversational idiom is contemporary and well written. Andy's perceptions of the racism directed toward young black males . . . will be recognized by African American YAs." Booklist

Dreyer, Ann L.
After Elaine. Front St./Cricket Bks. 2002 129p
$16.95   **Fic**
1. Sisters—Fiction 2. Death—Fiction 3. School stories
ISBN 0-8126-2651-6   LC 2002-593
Gina relives events that preceeded her angry, hostile, older sister Elaine's senseless death, as her family struggles with their grief and Gina faces the added pressures of starting middle school
"Readers will understand and empathize with Gina's intense feelings, and they'll pass on the book to their friends." Booklist

Dumas, Alexandre, 1802-1870
The three musketeers (7 and up)   **Fic**
1. France—History—1589-1789, Bourbons—Fiction
Hardcover and paperback editions available from various publishers
Original French edition, 1844
"D'Artagnan arrives in Paris one day in 1625 and manages to be involved in three duels with three musketeers . . . Athos, Porthos and Aramis. They become d'Artagnan's best friends. The account of their adventures from 1625 on develops against the rich historical background of the reign of Louis XIII and the early part of that of Louis XIV, the main plot being furnished by the antagonism between Cardinal de Richelieu and Queen Anne d'Autriche." Haydn. Thesaurus of Book Dig

Duncan, Lois, 1934-
Don't look behind you. Delacorte Press 1989
180p pa $5.50 hardcover o.p.   **Fic**
1. Mystery fiction
ISBN 0-440-20729-0   LC 88-30045
Seventeen-year-old April finds her comfortable life changed forever when death threats to her father, a witness in a federal case, force her family to go into hiding under assumed names and flee the pursuit of a hired killer
"Though April's petulance may grate, her behavior rings true enough, and teens who relish the trappings of thrillers can immerse themselves in FBI agents, murder, and secrets galore." Booklist

I know what you did last summer. Little, Brown
1973 199p o.p. Dell paperback available pa $5.50
     Fic
1. Mystery fiction
ISBN 0-440-22844-1 (pa)
"Julie, Barry, Helen, and Ray have almost made themselves forget the terrible night when their joyriding had ended in tragedy. Barry hit and killed a young cyclist on the road and kept on going; they all swear to keep the accident a secret. A year passes and they all believe they are safe, but one day Julie gets a note in the mail which says, 'I know what you did last summer.' Barry is shot and lying paralyzed in the hospital when Helen is attacked and their silent menace goes about completing his scheme to exact revenge." Publ Wkly
This book "has vivid characterization, good balance, and the boding sense of impending danger that adds excitement to the best mystery stories." Bull Cent Child Books

Killing Mr. Griffin. Little, Brown 1978 243p
o.p. Dell paperback available pa $5.50 (7 and up)
     Fic
1. School stories 2. Kidnapping—Fiction
ISBN 0-440-94515-1 (pa)   LC 77-27658
"Mr. Griffin, the stern high-school English teacher, is loathed by those who should appreciate his determination

Duncan, Lois, 1934-—*Continued*
to educate them. Mark, a student, uses his cool glamour and cleverness to mesmerize classmates Jeff, David, Betsy and Sue, persuading them to kidnap Mr. Griffin, with the idea of scaring the teacher into handing out high grades for inferior work. They leave the man trussed and gagged in a remote spot, where he dies. Sue wants to go to the police with a confession, but Mark masterminds a frantic coverup." Publ Wkly

The author's "skillful plotting builds layers of tension that draws readers into the eye of the conflict. The ending is nicely handled in a manner which provides relief without removing any of the chilling implications." SLJ

Locked in time. Little, Brown 1985 210p o.p. Dell paperback available pa $5.50 (7 and up)
Fic
1. Mystery fiction 2. Louisiana—Fiction
ISBN 0-440-94942-4 (pa)   LC 85-23

"Shortly after arriving at her strangely youthful stepmother's isolated Louisiana mansion, Nore realizes that Lisette and her two children—handsome, 17-year-old Gabe and moody 13-year-old Josie—hide a sinister, century-old secret, a secret that threatens the lives of Nore and her infatuated father." Booklist

"The writing style is smooth, the characters strongly developed, and the plot, which has excellent pace and momentum, is an adroit blending of fantasy and realism." Bull Cent Child Books

Stranger with my face. Little, Brown 1981 250p pa $8.95 hardcover o.p. (7 and up)   **Fic**
1. Supernatural—Fiction 2. Twins—Fiction
ISBN 0-440-98356-8   LC 81-8299

"There are small things, at first—a face in the mirror, a presence in an empty room, a beckoning figure on treacherous rocks—that portend 17-year-old Laurie's confrontation with the astral projection of her previously unknown, malevolent identical twin. . . . The jealous twin, Lia, pursues her, prodding her to explore astral projection so that Lia may enter Laurie's body." SLJ

"The ghostly Lia is deliciously evil; the idea of astral projection—Lia's method of travel—is novel; the island setting is vivid; and the relationships among the young people are realistic in the smoothly written supernatural tale." Horn Book

Dunkle, Clare B.
The hollow kingdom; Clare B. Dunkle. 1st ed. Henry Holt 2003 230p $16.95   **Fic**
1. Fantasy fiction
ISBN 0-8050-7390-6   LC 2002-38899

In nineteenth-century England, a powerful sorcerer and King of the Goblins chooses Kate, the elder of two orphan girls recently arrived at their ancestral home, Hallow Hill, to be his bride and queen.

"This is a fresh, powerful twist on the Beauty-and-the-Beast theme, and the impact of Dunkle's evocative storytelling lingers long after the final page." Booklist
Another title in this series is:
Close kin (2004)

DuPrau, Jeanne, 1944-
The city of Ember. Random House 2003 270p $15.95; lib bdg $17.99 (5 and up)   **Fic**
1. Science fiction
ISBN 0-375-82273-9; 0-375-92274-1 (lib bdg)
LC 2002-10239

"More than 200 years after an unspecified holocaust, the residents of Ember have lost all knowledge of anything beyond the area illuminated by the floodlamps on their buildings. . . . Food and other supplies are running low, and the power failures that plunge the town into impenetrable darkness are becoming longer and more frequent. Then Lina, a young foot messenger, discovers a damaged document from the mysterious Builders that hints at a way out." SLJ

"The writing and storytelling are agreeably spare and remarkably suspenseful." Horn Book
Followed by The people of Sparks

The people of Sparks. Random House 2004 338p $15.95; lib bdg $17.99 (5 and up)
Fic
1. Science fiction
ISBN 0-375-82824-9; 0-375-92824-3 (lib bdg)
LC 2003-20760

Sequel to The City of Ember

"DuPrau continues the adventures of Lina and Doon, who have led the 400 residents from the underground city of Ember to the unfamiliar world above. The refugees are tentatively welcomed, housed, and fed by the people of Sparks, located near the wasteland left by the long-ago Disaster that destroyed most of civilization. Conflicts arise between the two groups. . . . DuPrau clearly explores themes of nonviolence and when to stand up for oneself. The text smoothly involves new readers and fans of the first story, creating a range of three dimensional characters." Booklist

Durbin, William, 1951-
Blackwater Ben. Wendy Lamb Bks. 2003 199p $15.95; lib bdg $17.99 (5 and up)   **Fic**
1. Lumber and lumbering—Fiction 2. Father-son relationship—Fiction 3. Frontier and pioneer life—Fiction
ISBN 0-385-72928-6; 0-385-90149-6 (lib bdg)
LC 2002-155586

In the winter of 1898, a seventh-grade boy drops out of school to work with his father, the cook at Blackwater Logging Camp in Minnesota

"Lively details about logging add depth to this warm, colorful historical novel." Booklist

The broken blade. Delacorte Press 1997 163p pa $5.50 hardcover o.p.   **Fic**
1. Fur trade—Fiction 2. Canada—Fiction
ISBN 0-440-41184-X   LC 96-22114

When an injury prevents his father from going into northern Canada with fur traders, thirteen-year-old Pierre decides to take his father's place as a voyageur

"This look at the early nineteenth-century Canadian fur trade should appeal to reluctant readers as well as adventure buffs, and it may be a welcome suggestion for middle-school historical fiction reports." Bull Cent Child Books

Durbin, William, 1951---*Continued*

The journal of C.J. Jackson: a Dust Bowl migrant. Scholastic 2002 169p il (My name is America) $10.95 (4 and up)   **Fic**
1. Great Depression, 1929-1939—Fiction 2. Migrant labor—Fiction
ISBN 0-439-15306-9   LC 2001-41150
Thirteen-year-old C.J. records in a journal the conditions of the Dust Bowl that cause the Jackson family to leave their farm in Oklahoma and make the difficult journey to California, where they find a harsh life as migrant workers
"C.J. is an authentic and likable protagonist. Durbin effectively conveys the plight of Dust Bowl families." SLJ

The journal of Otto Peltonen, a Finnish immigrant. Scholastic 2000 171p (My name is America) $10.95   **Fic**
1. Immigrants—Fiction 2. Finnish Americans—Fiction 3. Miners—Fiction 4. Minnesota—Fiction
ISBN 0-439-09254-X   LC 00-21919
"Otto Peltonen is a fictional character created by the author and his journal and its epilogue are works of fiction"--Copyright page
In 1905 fifteen-year-old Otto describes in his journal how he travels from Finland to America, joining his father in a dreary iron mining community in Minnesota and becoming involved in a union fight for better working conditions
"Otto's journal entries are short and riveting. . . . Well written, fast paced, and historically accurate." Voice Youth Advocates

The journal of Sean Sullivan; a Transcontinental Railroad worker. Scholastic 1999 188p il (My name is America) $10.95 (5 and up)   **Fic**
1. West (U.S.)—Fiction 2. Railroads—Fiction
ISBN 0-439-04994-6   LC 98-47705
In 1867, fifteen-year-old Sean experiences both hardships and rewards when he joins his father in working on the building of the Transcontinental Railroad
This "focuses on historic details to bring the Old West vibrantly alive. . . . Durbin expertly handles racial issues and also does a good job of being authentic to the time and place, yet sensitive to modern sensibilities." Booklist

Wintering. Delacorte Press 1999 191p pa $4.99 hardcover o.p.   **Fic**
1. Fur trade—Fiction
ISBN 0-440-22759-3   LC 98-25546
Companion to The broken blade
In 1801, fourteen-year-old Pierre returns to work for the North West Fur Company and makes the long and difficult journey to a winter camp, where he learns from both the other voyageurs and from the Ojibwa Indians whose land they share
This offers "adventure, surprises, humor, and a touching conclusion." Booklist

Durrant, Lynda, 1956-

The beaded moccasins; the story of Mary Campbell. Clarion Bks. 1998 183p $15; pa $5.50 (5 and up)   **Fic**
1. Campbell, Mary, fl. 1764—Fiction 2. Delaware Indians—Fiction
ISBN 0-395-85398-2; 0-440-41591-8 (pa)
     LC 97-16288
Also available in paperback from Dell
After being captured by a group of Delaware Indians and given to their leader as a replacement for his dead granddaughter, twelve-year-old Mary Campbell is forced to travel west with them to Ohio
"Based on a 1759 historical incident. . . . Thoughtful characterizations, a strong sense of place, and an involving present tense narration make this a solid historical novel." Horn Book Guide

Echohawk. Clarion Bks. 1996 181p $16
     Fic
1. Mohegan Indians—Fiction 2. Brothers—Fiction
ISBN 0-395-74430-X   LC 96-2113
Also available in paperback from Dell
A twelve-year-old white boy, adopted and raised by Mohicans in the Hudson River Valley during the 1730's, is sent with his younger brother to an English settlement for schooling
"Durrant presents rich history, vast cultural information, and a story that will trigger discussion. An extensive bibliography demonstrates the author's depth of research." SLJ

Turtle clan journey. Clarion Bks. 1999 180p $15
     Fic
1. Mohegan Indians—Fiction
ISBN 0-395-90369-6   LC 98-22710
Sequel to Echohawk
As the captive white boy Echohawk and his Mohican father and brother make a perilous journey from the Hudson River Valley to a settlement on the Ohio River, Echohawk feels the conflicting pulls of his dual heritage
"In this well-researched novel, the author gives life to the prejudices and fears of the time while offering a look into the culture and traditions of the Mohicans and the conflict resulting from the colonists' usurping of Native American lands." SLJ

Dygard, Thomas J., 1931-1996

River danger. Morrow 1998 151p $15.99 (7 and up)   **Fic**
1. Brothers—Fiction 2. Canoes and canoeing—Fiction
ISBN 0-688-14852-2   LC 97-36362
Although he reluctantly agrees to accompany his little brother on a canoe trip, eighteen-year-old Eric finally gains new respect for this younger sibling whose ingenuity rescues him
"Several unexpected plot twists keep the reader engaged. . . . Dygard proves once again that appealing, believable characters in any context are the strength of good fiction." Booklist

Second stringer. Morrow Junior Bks. 1998 174p $15.99 (7 and up)   **Fic**
1. Football—Fiction
ISBN 0-688-15981-8   LC 98-11361

Dygard, Thomas J., 1931-1996—_Continued_

When Kevin replaces the quarterback and football hero who suffers a knee injury, the second stringer needs to prove that he can do the job and is not just a substitute

"Dygard offers just enough conflict and character development to add texture to the fast-paced plot." Booklist

Easton, Kelly, 1960-

The life history of a star. Margaret K. McElderry Bks. 2001 200p $16; pa $6.99 (7 and up) **Fic**

1. Siblings—Fiction 2. Vietnam War, 1961-1975—Fiction

ISBN 0-689-83134-X; 0-689-085270-3 (pa)

LC 99-46910

Also available Thorndike Press large print edition

For more than a year, fourteen-year-old Kristin uses her diary to record her confused thoughts about the physical changes brought on by adolescence and the emotional strain on her family of living with the "ghost" of her beloved older brother who was physically and mentally destroyed while serving in Vietnam

"Passages of dialogue, appearing within the entries like the script of a play, reflect the characters' random, unsettling pain, and readers will connect with Kristin's sharp humor." Booklist

Eberhardt, Thom

Rat boys; a dating experiment. Hyperion Bks. for Children 2001 154p $15.99 **Fic**

1. Dating (Social customs)—Fiction

ISBN 0-7868-0696-6   LC 2001-16630

Fourteen-year-olds Marci and Summer use a magic ring to turn two rats into cute boys so that they can have dates for the Spring Fling

This "is an extremely funny social satire. Fast moving and easy to read, this novel would be a particularly good pick for reluctant readers." Voice Youth Advocates

Efaw, Amy

Battle dress. HarperCollins Pubs. 2000 291p lib bdg $16.89; pa $6.99 (7 and up) **Fic**

1. United States Military Academy—Fiction 2. Military education—Fiction 3. Women in the armed forces—Fiction

ISBN 0-06-028411-0 (lib bdg); 0-06-053520-2 (pa)

LC 99-34516

As a newly arrived freshman at West Point, seventeen-year-old Andi finds herself gaining both confidence and self esteem as she struggles to get through the grueling six weeks of new cadet training known as the Beast

"This book by a West Point graduate is a gripping, hard-to-put-down look at a young woman's struggle to succeed in a traditionally all-male environment." Voice Youth Advocates

Ehrlich, Gretel

A blizzard year; Timmy's almanac of the seasons; illustrations by Kate Kiesler. Hyperion Bks. for Children 1999 122p hardcover o.p. paperback available $5.99 **Fic**

1. Ranch life—Fiction 2. Seasons—Fiction 3. Nature—Fiction 4. Wyoming—Fiction

ISBN 0-7868-1245-1 (pa)   LC 98-43730

For one year, thirteen-year-old Timmy records in her journal the changes she sees in the natural world and her family's activities on their Wyoming ranch as they fight to save it from financial ruin

"The vivid depictions of rural life make this a great read." SLJ

Elish, Dan, 1960-

Born too short; the confessions of an eighth-grade basket case. Atheneum Bks. for Young Readers 2002 152p $16; pa $4.99 (7 and up) **Fic**

1. Friendship—Fiction 2. New York (N.Y.)—Fiction

ISBN 0-689-84386-0; 0-689-86213-X (pa)

LC 2001-22987

"A Richard Jackson book"

Thirteen-year-old Matt is so envious of his best friend Keith that he wishes things would go badly for him, and when Keith's fortune changes while at the same time Matt finds his first true girlfriend, Matt is overcome with guilt

"This manages to treat adolescent guyhood with authentic, rueful comedy while steering clear of all-too-common descent into sitcom shallowness." Bull Cent Child Books

Elliott, Laura

Under a war-torn sky; {by} L.M. Elliott. Hyperion Bks. for Children 2001 284p $15.99; pa $5.99 (7 and up) **Fic**

1. World War, 1939-1945—Fiction 2. France—Fiction

ISBN 0-7868-0755-5; 0-7868-1753-4 (pa)

LC 2001-16633

After his plane is shot down by Hitler's Luftwaffe, nineteen-year-old Henry Forester of Richmond, Virginia, strives to walk across occupied France, with the help of the French Resistance, in hopes of rejoining his unit

"It's packed with action, intrigue, and suspense, but this novel celebrates acts of kindness and heroism without glorifying war." Booklist

Engdahl, Sylvia Louise

The far side of evil. Walker & Co. 2003 324p $18.95 **Fic**

1. Science fiction

ISBN 0-8027-8848-3   LC 2002-71386

Sequel to Enchantress from the stars

A reissue of the title first published 1971 by Atheneum Pubs.

"Elana, newly graduated from the Federation Anthropological Service Academy, is sent immediately into danger on the planet Toris—a Youngling world poised on the brink of nuclear war. This assignment is far more

Engdahl, Sylvia Louise—*Continued*
challenging than anything she has ever done. She is ordered to merely observe, and must not reveal her alien
origin or interfere with the planet's natural course of
evolution. But how can she stand by and watch as an entire world drives itself to nuclear annihilation?" Publisher's note

Engdahl, Sylvia Louise, 1933-
Enchantress from the stars; foreword by Lois
Lowry; illustrations by Leo and Diane Dillon.
Walker & Co. 2001 288p il $18.95   **Fic**
1. Science fiction
ISBN 0-8027-8764-9   LC 00-65853
A reissue of the title first published 1970 by
Atheneum Pubs.
When young Elana unexpectedly joins the team leaving the spaceship to study the planet Andrecia, she becomes an integral part of an adventure involving three
very different civilizations, each one centered on the
third planet from the star in its own solar system
"Emphasis is on the intricate pattern of events rather
than on characterization, and readers will find fascinating
symbolism—and philosophical parallels to what they
may have observed or thought. The book is completely
absorbing and should have a wider appeal than much science fiction." Horn Book
Followed by The far side of evil

English, Karen
Francie. Farrar, Straus & Giroux 1999 199p
$17; pa $5.95 (5 and up)   **Fic**
1. African Americans—Fiction 2. Race relations—Fiction 3. Alabama—Fiction
ISBN 0-374-32456-5; 0-374-42459-4 (pa)
       LC 98-53047
Also availableThorndike Press large print edition
Coretta Scott King honor book for text, 2000
"The best student in her small, all-black school in
preintegration Alabama, 12-year-old Francie hopes for a
better life. . . . When Jessie, an older school friend who
is without family, is forced on the run by a racist employer, Francie leaves her mother's labeled canned food
for him in the woods. Only when the sheriff begins
searching their woods . . . does she realize the depth of
the danger she may have brought to her family. Francie's
smooth-flowing, well-paced narration is gently assisted
by just the right touch of the vernacular. Characterization
is evenhanded and believable, while place and time en-
velop readers." SLJ

Erdrich, Louise
The birchbark house. Hyperion Bks. for
Children 1999 244p il $17.99; pa $6.99 (5 and up)
    Fic
1. Ojibwa Indians—Fiction
ISBN 0-7868-0300-2; 0-7868-1454-3 (pa)
       LC 98-46366
Also available Thorndike Press large print edition
Omakayas, a seven-year-old Native American girl of
the Ojibwa tribe, lives through the joys of summer and
the perils of winter on an island in Lake Superior in
1847

"Erdrich crafts images of tender beauty while weaving
Ojibwa words seamlessly into the text. Her gentle spot
art throughout complements this first of several projected
stories that will 'attempt to retrace {her} own family's
history.'" Horn Book Guide

The game of silence; Louise Erdrich. 1st ed.
HarperCollins 2004 256p $15.99; lib bdg $16.89
(5 and up)   **Fic**
1. Ojibwa Indians—Fiction
ISBN 0-06-029789-1; 0-06-029790-5 (lib bdg)
       LC 2004-6018
Sequel to The birchbark house
Nine-year-old Omakayas, of the Ojibwa tribe, moves
west with her family in 1849.
"Erdrich's captivating tale of four seasons portrays a
deep appreciation of our environment, our history, and
our Native American sisters and brothers." SLJ

Esckilsen, Erik E.
The last mall rat. Houghton Mifflin 2003 182p
$15 (7 and up)   **Fic**
1. Shopping centers and malls—Fiction
ISBN 0-618-23417-9   LC 2002-14436
"Walter Lorraine books"
Too young to get a job at the Onion River Mall, fif-
teen-year-old Mitch earns money from salesclerks to
harrass rude shoppers
"Realistic dialogue and a keen sense of what matters
to teens will draw them to this quick read." Booklist

Farmer, Nancy, 1941-
The Ear, the Eye, and the Arm; a novel.
Orchard Bks. 1994 311p $9.95 (6 and up)
    Fic
1. Science fiction 2. Zimbabwe—Fiction
ISBN 0-439-53064-4   LC 93-11814
Also available in paperback from Puffin Bks. and
Thorndike Press large print edition
A Newbery Medal honor book, 1995
"A Richard Jackson book"
In 2194 in Zimbabwe, General Matsika's three chil-
dren Tendai, Rita, and Kuda, are kidnapped and put to
work in a plastic mine, while three mutant detectives
named The Ear, the Eye and the Arm use their special
powers to search for them
"Throughout the story, it's the thrilling adventure that
will grab readers, who will also like the comic, tender
characterizations." Booklist

A girl named Disaster. Orchard Bks. 1996 309p
$19.95 (6 and up)   **Fic**
1. Supernatural—Fiction 2. Adventure fiction
3. Mozambique—Fiction 4. Zimbabwe—Fiction
ISBN 0-531-09539-8   LC 96-15141
Also available in paperback from Penguin Bks.
A Newbery Medal honor book, 1997
"A Richard Jackson book"
While journeying from Mozambique to Zimbabwe to
escape an arranged marriage, eleven-year-old Nhamo
struggles to escape drowning and starvation and in so doing comes close to the luminous world of the African
spirits
"This story is humorous and heartwrenching, complex
and multilayered." SLJ

Farmer, Nancy, 1941-—*Continued*

The house of the scorpion. Atheneum Bks. for Young Readers 2002 380p $17.95; pa $7.99 (7 and up)　　　　　　　　　　　　　**Fic**
1. Cloning—Fiction 2. Science fiction
ISBN 0-689-85222-3; 0-689-85223-1 (pa)
　　　　　　　　　　　　　LC 2001-56594
"This is a powerful, ultimately hopeful, story that builds on today's sociopolitical, ethical, and scientific issues and prognosticates a compelling picture of what the future could bring." Booklist

The Sea of Trolls. Atheneum Books for Young Readers 2004 459p $17.95 (5 and up)　　**Fic**
1. Norse mythology—Fiction 2. Druids and Druidism—Fiction 3. Vikings—Fiction 4. Fantasy fiction
ISBN 0-689-86744-1　　　　　LC 2003-19091
"A Richard Jackson book"
After Jack becomes apprenticed to a Druid bard, he and his little sister Lucy are captured by Viking Berserkers and taken to the home of King Ivar the Boneless and his half-troll queen, leading Jack to undertake a vital quest to Jotunheim, home of the trolls.
"This exciting and original fantasy will capture the hearts and imaginations of readers." SLJ
Includes bibliographical references

Farrell, Mame

And sometimes why. Farrar, Straus & Giroux 2001 165p $16　　　　　　　　　　　**Fic**
1. Friendship—Fiction
ISBN 0-374-32289-9　　　　　　LC 00-49045
Eighth grader Jack is confused when he finds his relationship changing with his best friend, an athletic girl named Chris who has suddenly become attractive
"A funny, intelligent story of friendship, cleverly disguised as a romantic comedy." Horn Book Guide

Fast, Howard, 1914-2003

April morning; a novel. Crown 1961 184p hardcover o.p. Bantam Bks. paperback available $7.50 (7 and up)　　　　　　　　　　**Fic**
1. United States—History—1775-1783, Revolution—Fiction 2. Lexington (Mass.), Battle of, 1775—Fiction
ISBN 0-553-27322-1　　　　　　LC 61-10306
"The spirit of the Revolutionary War, a country coming of age, and the life of a boy passing into manhood are captured in this historical novel. Fast focuses on one day in the life of Adam Cooper as his family and the community of Lexington rise to the events of April 19, 1775. Adam at first is caught up in the excitement, but by the end of the first skirmish the death of his father has brought home the horror and reality of war." Shapiro. Fic for Youth. 3d edition

Feiffer, Jules

The man in the ceiling; entirely written and illustrated by Jules Feiffer. HarperCollins Pubs. 1993 185p il lib bdg $14.89; pa $7.99 (4 and up)　　　　　　　　　　　　　　**Fic**
1. Artists—Fiction
ISBN 0-06-205036-2 (lib bdg); 0-06-205907-6 (pa)
　　　　　　　　　　　　　LC 92-59953

"Michael di Capua books"
"With his quest to invent the best-ever superhero, 10-year-old cartoonist Jimmy Jiggett bids for immortality—or at least some attention from his type-A father." Publ Wkly
"Feiffer's deft depiction of moments of family dysfunction are wickedly funny. His rough-drawn, signature cartoon illustrations are charged with an energy that matches the briskly paced text." Booklist

Fenner, Carol

The king of dragons. Margaret K. McElderry Bks. 1998 216p $17; pa $4.99 (5 and up)
　　　　　　　　　　　　　　　　Fic
1. Homeless persons—Fiction
ISBN 0-689-82217-0; 0-689-83540-X (pa)
　　　　　　　　　　　　　LC 98-15434
Also available Audiobook version
Having lost access to the old railroad station where they had been staying, homeless Ian and his father move into an unused city courthouse and try to avoid being discovered by the authorities
"The characters are sharply etched, and the narrative moves swiftly, with moments of poignancy and suspense." Horn Book Guide

Randall's wall. Margaret K. McElderry Bks. 1991 85p $15　　　　　　　　　　　　**Fic**
1. Poverty—Fiction 2. School stories
ISBN 0-689-50518-3　　　　　　LC 90-46490
Also available in paperback from Dell Bks.
"Fifth grader Randall Lord is filthy. He smells. No one in his small Midwest school sits near him. . . . There's no water in his rundown shack. His abusive father hasn't been around for months; his mother is crumpled with suffering, both physically and mentally ill. . . . Behind his wall Randall keeps secret the fact that he loves to draw, and no one knows that he has a shining artistic gift. Then his feeling for Jean, a cheerful, bold girl in his class, makes him reach out." Booklist
"Fenner presents a disturbing yet believable story. . . . The serious and sometimes tragic tone is tempered by some touches of real humor. A well-written, compassionate story." SLJ

Yolonda's genius. Margaret K. McElderry Bks. 1995 211p hardcover o.p. paperback available $5.99 (4-6)　　　　　　　　　　　　**Fic**
1. Siblings—Fiction 2. Musicians—Fiction 3. African Americans—Fiction
ISBN 0-689-81327-9 (pa)　　　　LC 94-46962
A Newbery Medal honor book, 1996
After moving from Chicago to Grand River, Michigan, fifth grader Yolonda, big and strong for her age, determines to prove that her younger brother is not a slow learner but a true musical genius
"In this brisk and appealing narrative, readers are introduced to a close-knit, middle-class African-American family. . . . {This novel} is suffused with humor and spirit." Horn Book

Ferris, Jean, 1939-
Eight seconds. Harcourt 2000 186p $17 (7 and up)   **Fic**
1. Homosexuality—Fiction 2. Prejudices—Fiction 3. Rodeos—Fiction
ISBN 0-15-202367-4   LC 99-48796
Also available in paperback from Puffin Bks.
Eighteen-year-old John must confront his own sexuality when he goes to rodeo school and finds himself strangely attracted to Kit, an older boy who is smart, tough, complicated, gorgeous, and gay
"Ferris burrows her story firmly, and very authentically, in the heart of her characters. Through John's thoughts, Kit's dialogue, and a wealth of raging emotions that pack dramatic punch, she compassionately shares the challenges of gay teens." Booklist

Love among the walnuts. Harcourt Brace & Co. 1998 216p $16 (7 and up)   **Fic**
1. Crime—Fiction 2. Wealth—Fiction 3. Uncles—Fiction
ISBN 0-15-201590-6   LC 97-50291
Born and raised in isolation in a wealthy, eccentric family, Sandy is shocked when he, his parents, and their servants become victims of a vicious plot by his greedy uncles to incapacitate them and take their money
"This book is intentionally melodramatic, coincidental, improbable, and hilarious. The restrained, tongue-in-cheek tone heightens the humor of this spoof." SLJ

Of sound mind. Farrar, Straus & Giroux 2001 215p $16; pa $6.95 (7 and up)   **Fic**
1. Deaf—Fiction 2. Friendship—Fiction
ISBN 0-374-35580-0; 0-374-45584-8 (pa)
LC 00-68123
Also available Thorndike Press large print edition
Tired of interpreting for his deaf family and resentful of their reliance on him, high school senior Theo finds support and understanding from Ivy, a new student who also has a deaf parent
"Both a thought-provoking study of just when being deaf matters and when it does not, and an unusually rich coming-of-age story that explores universal issues of family responsibility, emotional maturation, love, and loss." Booklist

Once upon a Marigold. Harcourt 2002 266p $17; pa $5.95   **Fic**
1. Fairy tales 2. Princesses—Fiction
ISBN 0-15-216791-9; 0-15-205084-1 (pa)
LC 2002-311
Christian, a young man with a mysterious past and a penchant for inventing things, leaves the troll who raised him, meets an unhappy princess he has loved from afar, and discovers a plot against her and her father
"This complex, fast-paced plot, a mixture of fantasy, romance, comedy, and coming-of-age novel, succeeds because these characters are compelling, well developed, and sympathetic." SLJ

Fine, Anne
Flour babies. Little, Brown 1994 c1992 178p o.p. Dell paperback available $5.50 (6 and up)
Fic
1. School stories
ISBN 0-440-21941-8 (pa)   LC 93-35698

First published 1992 in the United Kingdom
When his class of underachievers is assigned to spend three torturous weeks taking care of their own "babies" in the form of bags of flour, Simon makes amazing discoveries about himself while coming to terms with his long-absent father
"There's no mistaking Fine's underlying theme (she's not a bit subtle), but it's couched in such splendid, trenchant humor—spiffy one-liners, funny, well-devised characters, and hilarious situations—that the story simply flies along." Booklist

The true story of Christmas. Delacorte Press 2003 133p $15.95; lib bdg $17.99 (4 and up)
Fic
1. Christmas—Fiction 2. Family life—Fiction
ISBN 0-385-73130-2; 0-385-90156-9 (lib bdg)
LC 2003-5166
"Banished to his room on Christmas Day, Ralph recounts the disasters that occur when his highly eccentric relatives come together to celebrate the holiday. Funny dialogue . . . unique characters, from a demonic preschooler to a daft great-aunt; and hilarious but believable situations make this book a great read-aloud." SLJ

Up on cloud nine. Delacorte Press 2002 151p $15.95; lib bdg $17.99; pa $4.99 (5 and up)
Fic
1. Friendship—Fiction 2. Suicide—Fiction
ISBN 0-385-73009-8; 0-385-90058-9 (lib bdg); 0-440-41916-6 (pa)   LC 2001-53937
While Stolly struggles to regain consciousness in a hospital bed after falling, or possibly jumping, from a third story window, Ian recalls some of their best and worst times together
"It's rare for such a serious subject to be accessibly addressed for readers of this age group, and it's even rarer for it to be addressed in an easygoing yet thoughtful story of friendship." Bull Cent Child Books

Fisher, Catherine
The oracle betrayed; book one of The Oracle Prophecies; by Catherine Fisher. 1st American ed. Greenwillow Books 2004 341p $16.99; lib bdg $17.89; pa $6.99   **Fic**
1. Fantasy fiction
ISBN 0-06-057157-8; 0-06-057158-6 (lib bdg); 0-06-057159-4 (pa)   LC 2003-48498
After she is chosen to be "Bearer-of-the-god," Mirany questions the established order and sets out, along with a musician and a scribe, to find the legitimate heir of the religious leader known as the Archon.
"The first book in a planned trilogy. . . . This [is] a well-developed world with its own culture, some sharply realized settings, and several strong, distinctive characters." Booklist
Another title in this series is:
The Sphere of Secrets (2005)

Fisk, Pauline
Midnight blue. Bloomsbury Press 2003 217p $16.95   **Fic**
1. Fantasy fiction
ISBN 1-58234-829-4   LC 2003-51862

Fisk, Pauline—*Continued*

First published 1990 in the United Kingdom

Bonnie's newfound happiness in a world beyond the sky is threatened by the cruel Grandbag, and although she is offered help by the ancient, elusive lord and lady of the hill, she alone must meet the challenge in the end

"An enjoyable fantasy that offers food for thought." SLJ

The secret of Sabrina Fludde. Bloomsbury Children's Bks. 2002 256p $15.95   **Fic**

1. Amnesia—Fiction

ISBN 1-58234-754-9   LC 2001-43983

First published 2001 in the United Kingdom with title: Sabrina Fludde

"The first installment of a planned trilogy, Fisk's . . . tale centers on the ethereal and mysterious Abren, introduced as her body floats slowly down a river to the town of Pengwern. Lacking memory, the thin girl wanders the streets, 'looking for clues to who she was and where she'd come from.'" Publ Wkly

The author "creates a wonderful sense of place in the town of Pengwern, and the twisting plot will keep readers intrigued to the very end of this atmospheric mystery." Booklist

Flake, Sharon G.

Money hungry. Jump at the Sun 2001 187p $15.99; pa $5.99   **Fic**

1. Poor—Fiction 2. African Americans—Fiction

ISBN 0-7868-0548-X; 0-7868-1503-X (pa)

      LC 00-63387

All thirteen-year-old Raspberry can think of is making money so that she and her mother never have to worry about living on the streets again

"The razor-sharp dialogue and unerring details evoke characters, rooms, and neighborhoods with economy and precision, creating a story that's immediate, vivid, and unsensationalized." Booklist

Another title about Raspberry is:

Begging for change (2003)

The skin I'm in. Jump at the Sun 1998 171p $14.95; pa $5.99   **Fic**

1. African Americans—Fiction 2. Teachers—Fiction 3. School stories

ISBN 0-7868-0444-0; 0-7868-1307-5 (pa)

      LC 98-19615

Thirteen-year-old Maleeka, uncomfortable because her skin is extremely dark, meets a new teacher with a birthmark on her face and makes some discoveries about how to love who she is and what she looks like

This "novel is fast-paced and realistic." Horn Book Guide

Fleischman, Paul

The borning room. HarperCollins Pubs. 1991 101p hardcover o.p. paperback available $4.95 (6 and up)   **Fic**

1. Frontier and pioneer life—Fiction 2. Ohio—Fiction

ISBN 0-06-447099-7 (pa)   LC 91-4432

"A Charlotte Zolotow book"

Lying at the end of her life in the room where she was born in 1851, Georgina remembers what it was like to grow up on the Ohio frontier

"Fleischman successfully tackles many important themes and once again gifts readers with writing lush with similes, metaphors, and allusions, so subtly woven into the mesh of the narrative that they enrich without distracting. A memorable novel, rich and resonant in familial love and the strength of connection and tradition." SLJ

Breakout. Cricket Bks. 2003 124p il $16.95 (7 and up)   **Fic**

1. Runaway teenagers—Fiction 2. Los Angeles (Calif.)—Fiction

ISBN 0-8126-2696-6   LC 2003-12264

A young woman presents a play based on her life as a seventeen-year-old runaway whose escape from her foster home in Los Angeles is thwarted by an all-day traffic jam, an event which provides time for her to explore her free-floating identity, hunger for her unknown mother, and yearning for human connection

"Fleischman's artful structure, distinctive voices, and carefully chosen details make this a splendid choice for teens on the verge of a breakout of their own." SLJ

Bull Run; woodcuts by David Frampton. HarperCollins Pubs. 1993 104p il lib bdg $16.89; pa $4.99 (6 and up)   **Fic**

1. Bull Run, 1st Battle of, 1861—Fiction 2. United States—History—1861-1865, Civil War—Fiction

ISBN 0-06-021447-3 (lib bdg); 0-06-440588-5 (pa)

      LC 92-14745

"A Laura Geringer book"

"In a sequence of sixty one- to two-page narratives, fifteen fictional characters (and one real general) recount their experiences during the Civil War. A few encounter each other, most meet unawares or not at all, but they have in common a battle, Bull Run, that affects—and sometimes ends—their lives." Bull Cent Child Books

"Abandoning the conventions of narrative fiction, Fleischman tells a vivid, many-sided story in this original and moving book. An excellent choice for readers' theater in the classroom or on stage." Booklist

A fate totally worse than death. Candlewick Press 1995 124p pa $5.99 hardcover o.p. (7 and up)   **Fic**

1. School stories

ISBN 0-7636-2189-7   LC 94-48433

In this horror novel parody, three self-centered members of Cliffside High School's ruling clique, who are beginning to age rapidly, become convinced that the beautiful new exchange student is the ghost of the girl whose death they caused the year before

"The fun is in the vapid thinking of the girls, the trendy teen scenes, and the parody of YA actions and dialogue. This hilarious farce should have teen-horror fans screaming with laughter." SLJ

Mind's eye. Holt & Co. 1999 108p $15.95 (7 and up)   **Fic**

1. Physically handicapped—Fiction 2. Old age—Fiction

ISBN 0-8050-6314-5   LC 99-20844

Also available in paperback from Laurel-Leaf Bks.

Fleischman, Paul—*Continued*

A novel in play form in which sixteen-year-old Courtney, paralyzed in an accident, learns about the power of the mind from an elderly blind woman who takes Courtney on an imaginary journey to Italy using a 1910 guidebook

"Fleischman's gift for language and dialogue vividly brings to life the distinctive characters and drama." Booklist

Saturnalia. Harper & Row 1990 113p hardcover o.p. paperback available $4.95 (6 and up) **Fic**

1. Narraganset Indians—Fiction 2. Apprentices—Fiction 3. Prejudices—Fiction 4. Boston (Mass.)—Fiction

ISBN 0-06-447089-X　　LC 89-36380

"A Charlotte Zolotow book"

This novel is set in Boston in 1681. Fourteen-year-old William, a Narraganset Indian captured six years earlier in a raid, is apprenticed to Mr. Currie, a printer. "William's accomplishments enrage Mr. Baggot, the tithingman whose grandsons were killed by Indians. . . . William often wanders the streets after curfew playing an Indian melody on a small bone flute in the hope of finding his lost brother. One night, the melody does bring him to an uncle and young cousin, now servants of a cruel eyeglass maker. When the eyeglass maker is found murdered, . . . {Mr. Baggot} accuses William of the crime." Horn Book

"While William is the main focus of the story, there are several bubbling subplots that illuminate the texture of Puritan colonial life. . . . Especially welcome as a support for history units, this absorbing story exemplifies Fleischman's graceful, finely honed use of the English language." Booklist

Seedfolks; illustrations by Judy Pedersen. HarperCollins Pubs. 1997 69p $14.99; lib bdg $15.89; pa $4.99 (4 and up) **Fic**

1. Gardens—Fiction 2. City and town life—Fiction

ISBN 0-06-027471-9; 0-06-027472-7 (lib bdg); 0-06-447207-8 (pa)　　LC 96-26696

"Joanna Cotler books"

This "novel tells about an urban garden started by a child and nurtured by people of all ages and ethnic and economic backgrounds. Each of the thirteen chapters is narrated by a different character, allowing the reader to watch as a community develops out of disconnected lives and prior suspicions." Horn Book Guide

"The characters' vitality and the sharply delineated details of the neighborhood make this not merely an exercise in craftsmanship or morality but an engaging, entertaining novel as well." Booklist

Seek. Front St./Cricket Bks. 2001 167p $16.95 (7 and up) **Fic**

1. Fathers—Fiction 2. Radio—Fiction

ISBN 0-8126-4900-1　　LC 2001-28869

"Using a script format, Rob relates his experiences growing up listening to local and distant radio stations, searching for the disk jockey father who abandoned him before birth." Horn Book Guide

"Fleischman has orchestrated a symphony that is both joyful and poignant with this book designed for reader's theatre." Voice Youth Advocates

Whirligig. Holt & Co. 1998 133p $16.95 (7 and up) **Fic**

1. Guilt—Fiction

ISBN 0-8050-5582-7　　LC 97-24429

Also available in paperback from Laurel-Leaf Bks.

"Humiliated at a party, Brent tries to commit suicide while driving home but instead kills a seventeen-year-old girl. Desperate to atone, Brent agrees to the victim's mother's request that he build four whirligigs and set them up in the four corners of the United States as monuments to her daughter." Horn Book Guide

"Mystical, powerful, and transcendent." SLJ

Fleischman, Sid, 1920-

Bandit's moon; illustrations by Jos. A. Smith. Greenwillow Bks. 1998 136p $15.99; pa $4.99 (4-6) **Fic**

1. Murieta, Joaquín, d. 1853—Fiction 2. Thieves—Fiction 3. California—Gold discoveries—Fiction 4. Adventure fiction

ISBN 0-688-15830-7; 0-440-41586-1 (pa)

　　　　LC 97-36197

Twelve-year-old Annyrose relates her adventures with Joaquin Murieta and his band of outlaws in the California gold-mining region during the mid-1800s

"A quick read, with lots of twists, wonderful phrasing, historical integrity, and a bit of the tall tale thrown in." SLJ

Bo & Mzzz Mad. Greenwillow Bks. 2001 103p $14.99; lib bdg $15.89; pa $4.99 (5 and up) **Fic**

1. Family life—Fiction 2. Gold mines and mining—Fiction 3. Orphans—Fiction

ISBN 0-06-029397-7; 0-06-029398-5 (lib bdg); 0-06-440972-4 (pa)　　LC 00-56198

When his father dies, Bo Gamage warily moves to the Mojave Desert home of his distant and estranged relatives, the Martinkas, and finds that "Mad" lives up to her name, PawPaw despises him, and Aunt Juna hopes he'll help search for the gold mine that started a family feud

"Fleischman does a first-rate job, using some clever twists and snappy repartee. . . . Add to that a shot of genuine suspense, and you have a quick, enjoyable read that will fly off the shelves." Booklist

The whipping boy; illustrations by Peter Sís. Greenwillow Bks. 1986 90p il $16.99 (5 and up) **Fic**

1. Thieves—Fiction 2. Adventure fiction

ISBN 0-688-06216-4　　LC 85-17555

Also available in paperback from HarperTrophy

Awarded the Newbery Medal, 1987

"A round tale of adventure and humor, this follows the fortunes of Prince Roland (better known as Prince Brat) and his whipping boy, Jemmy, who has received all the hard knocks for the prince's mischief. . . . There's not a moment's lag in pace, and the stock characters, from Hold-Your-Nose Billy to Betsy's dancing bear Petunia, have enough inventive twists to project a lively air to it all." Bull Cent Child Books

Fletcher, Ralph, 1953-
Flying solo. Clarion Bks. 1998 138p $15; pa
$5.50 (5 and up)   **Fic**
1. School stories 2. Death—Fiction
ISBN 0-395-87323-1; 0-440-41601-9
LC 98-10775
Also available in paperback from Dell
Rachel, having chosen to be mute following the sudden death of a classmate, shares responsibility with the
other sixth-graders who decide not to report that the substitute teacher failed to show up
"Fletcher expertly balances a wide variety of emotions, giving readers a story that is by turns sad, poignant, and funny." Booklist

Spider Boy. Clarion Bks. 1997 180p $15
Fic
1. Moving—Fiction 2. Honesty—Fiction 3. Spiders—
Fiction
ISBN 0-395-77606-6   LC 96-31464
Also available in paperback from Dell
After moving to another state, seventh grader Bobby
deals with the change by telling people at school made-
up stories and then retreating into his world of pet spiders and books about spiders
"A sensitively written novel. . . . While accessible
and fast-moving, the book is not lightweight; it deals
head on with problems such as the bully who deliberately kills one of Bobby's pet tarantulas." Horn Book Guide

Fletcher, Susan, 1951-
Dragon's milk. Atheneum Pubs. 1989 242p pa
$4.99 hardcover o.p. (7 and up)   **Fic**
1. Dragons—Fiction 2. Fantasy fiction
ISBN 0-689-71623-0   LC 88-35059
"A Jean Karl book"
Kaeldra, an outsider adopted by an Elythian family as
a baby, possesses the power to understand dragons and
uses this power to try to save her younger sister who
needs dragon's milk to recover from an illness
"High-fantasy fans will delight in the clash of swords,
the flash of magic, the many escape-and-rescue scenes."
Booklist
Other titles in this series are:
Flight of the Dragon Kyn (1993)
Sign of the dove (1996)

Shadow spinner. Atheneum Bks. for Young
Readers 1998 219p $17; pa $4.99 (6 and up)
Fic
1. Storytelling—Fiction 2. Physically handicapped—
Fiction 3. Iran—Fiction
ISBN 0-689-81852-1; 0-689-83051-3 (pa)
LC 97-37346
"A Jean Karl book"
When Marjan, a thirteen-year-old crippled girl, joins
the Sultan's harem in ancient Persia, she gathers for
Shahrazad the stories which will save the queen's life
"An elegantly written novel that will delight and en-
tertain even as it teaches." SLJ

Walk across the sea. Atheneum Bks. for Young
Readers 2001 214p $16; pa $4.99   **Fic**
1. Chinese Americans—Fiction 2. Prejudices—Fiction
ISBN 0-689-84133-7; 0-689-85707-1 (pa)
LC 00-50246

Also available Thorndike Press large print edition
In late nineteenth-century California, when Chinese
immigrants are being driven out or even killed for fear
they will take jobs from whites, fifteen-year-old Eliza
Jane McCully defies the townspeople and her lighthouse-
keeper father to help a Chinese boy who has been kind
to her
"This is a gripping and complex story, and Fletcher's
lyrical depiction of 19th-century life, her exceptionally
well-drawn protagonist, and her deft analysis of racial
discrimination make the book even more powerful." SLJ

Flinn, Alex
Breaking   point;   {by}   Alex   Flinn.
HarperTempest 2002 241p $15.95; lib bdg $16.89;
pa $6.99 (7 and up)   **Fic**
1. Friendship—Fiction 2. School stories
ISBN 0-06-623847-1; 0-06-623848-X (lib bdg);
0-06-447371-6 (pa)   LC 2001-39504
"Gate-Brickell Christian is a toney private school attended by the rich and privileged—and a few despised
offspring of the staff, like Paul Richmond. . . . Charlie,
the magnetic class ringleader, becomes the center of
Paul's world. . . . Paul's loyalty to Charlie takes him
from vandalism (battering mailboxes) to cheating . . . to,
finally, leaving a Charlie-made bomb in a classroom."
Bull Cent Child Books
"In this intense story of peer pressure and the need to
be accepted, the characters are realistically drawn and reflect the nature of high school relationships." SLJ

Fogelin, Adrian, 1951-
Sister spider knows all; Adrian Fogelin. 1st ed.
Peachtree Publishers 2003 209p $14.95 (5 and up)
Fic
1. Poor—Fiction 2. Family life—Fiction
ISBN 1-56145-290-4   LC 2003-4875
Twelve-year-old Rox and her grandmother Mimi sell
at a flea market every weekend to supplement the family's only income, that of construction worker and college
student, cousin John Martin.
"Delivered in a wry voice that swings from laugh-out-
loud funny to wrenching sadness, Rox's narrative is neither sentimental nor condescending." Booklist

Foster, Alan Dean, 1946-
The Hand of Dinotopia; illustrations by James
Gurney. HarperCollins Pubs. 1999 407p il $22.99
Fic
1. Dinosaurs—Fiction 2. Fantasy fiction
ISBN 0-06-028005-0   LC 98-27814
Based on the Dinotopia books by James Gurney
Will and Sylvia search for the mysterious Hand of
Dinotopia, which will supposedly lead to a safe sea route
to and from the hidden island where people and dino-
saurs live together peacefully
"A smoothly crafted tale with an entertainingly
contentious supporting cast, grandly formal language . . .
and replete with jawbreaking dinosaur nomenclature and
a plot urged along at a steady, if deliberate, pace." SLJ
Another available title about Dinotopia by this author
is:
Dinotopia lost (1996)

Fox, Paula

One-eyed cat; a novel. Bradbury Press 1984
216p hardcover o.p. paperback available $4.99 (5
and up)   **Fic**
1. Firearms—Fiction 2. Cats—Fiction
ISBN 0-689-83970-7 (pa)   LC 84-10964
A Newbery Medal honor book, 1985
"Told by his father that he's too young for the air rifle
an uncle gives him as a birthday present, Ned sneaks the
gun out one night and takes a shot at a shadowy creature. He is subsequently smitten with guilt when he sees
a one-eyed feral cat, and the knowledge that he may
have been responsible as well as {having disobeyed} his
father colors all his days." Bull Cent Child Books
The author's "writing is sure. Her characterization is
outstanding, and she creates a strong sense of place and
mood." SLJ

The slave dancer; a novel; with illustrations by
Eros Keith. Bradbury Press 1973 176p il $16.95 (5
and up)   **Fic**
1. Slave trade—Fiction 2. Sea stories
ISBN 0-02-735560-8   LC 73-80642
Also available in paperback from Dell; Audiobook
version also available
Awarded the Newbery Medal, 1974
"Thirteen-year-old Jessie Bollier is kidnapped from
New Orleans and taken aboard a slave ship. Cruelly tyrannized by the ship's captain, Jessie is made to play his
fife for the slaves during the exercise period into which
they are forced in order to keep them fit for sale. When
a hurricane destroys the ship, Jessie and Ras, a young
slave, survive. They are helped by an old black man who
finds them, spirits Ras north to freedom, and assists Jessie to return to his family." Shapiro. Fic for Youth. 3d
edition

Frank, E. R.

Friction; a novel. Atheneum Bks. for Young
Readers 2003 197p $16.95 (7 and up)   **Fic**
1. Teachers—Fiction 2. Child sexual abuse—Fiction
ISBN 0-689-85384-X   LC 2002-8040
"A Richard Jackson book"
When a new girl at the private school Alex attends
starts rumors about Alex's favorite teacher, Alex and her
eighth-grade classmates are not sure how to act around
him or with each other
"Frank tells a riveting story of abuse and peer pressure in Alex's pitch-perfect voice that's just on the cusp
of adolescence." Booklist

Life is funny; a novel. DK Ink 2000 263p
$19.99 (7 and up)   **Fic**
1. Brooklyn (New York, N.Y.)—Fiction
ISBN 0-7894-2634-X   LC 99-23452
Also available in paperback from Puffin Bks.
"A Richard Jackson book"
The lives of eleven young people of different races,
economic backgrounds, and family situations living in
Brooklyn, New York, become intertwined over a seven
year period
"The voices ring true, and the talk is painful, vulgar,
rough, sexy, funny, fearful, furious, gentle." Booklist

Frank, Lucy K.

Oy, Joy! DK Pub. 1999 277p o.p. Simon Pulse
paperback available $4.99   **Fic**
1. Uncles—Fiction 2. Family life—Fiction
3. Friendship—Fiction
ISBN 0-689-84318-6 (pa)   LC 98-54299
Although her ailing uncle creates problems for her
whole family when he moves in with them, Joy survives
his bungling attempts at matchmaking even as she plays
the game herself
"Frank, who has a real gift for characterization, has
written a funny, downright joyful story about first love,
family feelings, and the surprises and rewards of cross-
generational friendship." Booklist

Franklin, Kristine L., 1958-

Dove song. Candlewick Press 1999 190p $16.99
    Fic
1. Mental illness—Fiction 2. Siblings—Fiction
3. Vietnam War, 1961-1975—Fiction
ISBN 0-7636-0409-7   LC 98-37621
When eleven-year-old Bobbie Lynn's father is reported missing in action in Vietnam, she and her thirteen-
year-old brother must learn to cope with their own despair, as well as their mother's breakdown
"This is both a sensitive story of friendship and family
problems and solid historical fiction." SLJ

Grape thief. Candlewick Press 2003 290p il
$16.99 (5 and up)   **Fic**
1. Croatian Americans—Fiction
ISBN 0-7636-1325-8   LC 2002-23774
In 1925, in a small Washington State community
made up of families from different ethnic backgrounds,
twelve-year-old Cuss tries to stay in school as he watches those around him struggle with various financial difficulties
"Franklin has drawn on her Croatian father's stories to
create a strong sense of the multiethnic community in
that time and place. . . . Cuss' fast, first-person narrative
rings true." Booklist

Frederick, Heather Vogel

The voyage of Patience Goodspeed. Simon &
Schuster Bks. for Young Readers 2002 219p
$16.95; pa $4.99 (5 and up)   **Fic**
1. Seafaring life—Fiction
ISBN 0-689-84851-X; 0-689-84869-2 (pa)
    LC 2001-49039
Following their mother's death in Nantucket, Captain
Goodspeed brings twelve-year-old Patience and six-year-
old Tad aboard his whaling ship, where a new crew
member incites a mutiny and Patience puts her mathe-
matical ability to good use
"This is an exciting voyage of peril and self-
discovery." N Y Times Book Rev
Another title about Patience is:
The education of Patience Goodspeed (2004)

Fredericks, Mariah

Head games; . . Atheneum Books for Young
Readers 2004 260p $15.95 (7 and up)   **Fic**
1. Dating (Social customs)—Fiction 2. School stories
ISBN 0-689-85532-X   LC 2003-17012

Fredericks, Mariah—*Continued*
"A Richard Jackson book"
Two teenagers connect online in a roleplaying game which leads them into their own face-to-face, half-acknowledged courtship.
"This novel realistically portrays young adults trying to find themselves, fit in, and resist the labels put on them." SLJ

The true meaning of cleavage. Atheneum Bks. for Young Readers 2003 211p $15.95 (7 and up) **Fic**
1. Friendship—Fiction 2. School stories
ISBN 0-689-85092-1 LC 2002-6809
"A Richard Jackson book"
When Jess and Sari, best friends since seventh grade, begin their freshman year of high school and Sari becomes obsessed with a senior boy and has secret sexual encounters with him, Jess wonders if their friendship will survive
This is a "must-read for every middle and junior high school girl. With Jess as the narrator, the message is clear, but it is not told in sexually graphic terms." Voice Youth Advocates

French, Jackie, 1950-
Hitler's daughter. HarperCollins Pubs. 2003 c1999 121p $15.99; lib bdg $16.89 **Fic**
1. Hitler, Adolf, 1889-1945—Fiction 2. Storytelling—Fiction 3. Australia—Fiction
ISBN 0-06-008652-1; 0-06-008653-X (lib bdg) LC 2002-14459
First published 1999 in Australia
After hearing a fictional tale about Hitler's daughter, Mark, an Australian boy, wonders what it would be like if someone he loved and trusted turned out to be evil
"French's style is precise and effective. Her descriptions vividly profile even secondary characters." Bull Cent Child Books

French, Simon, 1957-
Where in the world. Peachtree Publishers 2003 174p $14.95 (5 and up) **Fic**
1. Musicians—Fiction 2. Australia—Fiction 3. Immigrants—Fiction 4. Grandfathers—Fiction
ISBN 1-561-45292-0 LC 2003-43867
First published 2002 in Australia
When Ari and his mother leave their home in Germany for a new life and family in Australia, he parts from the grandfather who taught him to play violin, but finds that his music and memories are intertwined.
"The lyrical writing style suits the theme of musical improvisation in a story that's poignant without being overly sentimental." Booklist

Freymann-Weyr, Garret, 1965-
The kings are already here. Houghton Mifflin 2003 149p $15 (7 and up) **Fic**
1. Ballet—Fiction 2. Chess—Fiction
ISBN 0-618-26363-2 LC 2002-10819
Phebe, obsessed with the world of ballet, and Nikolai, obsessed with the world of chess, join together in a quest

across Europe and begin to learn not only how to connect with other people, but why
"An entertaining read for all young adults, but especially for those seeking answers to life's complex questions." SLJ

My heartbeat. Houghton Mifflin 2002 154p $15 (7 and up) **Fic**
1. Siblings—Fiction 2. Homosexuality—Fiction
ISBN 0-618-14181-2 LC 2001-47059
Also available in paperback from Puffin Bks.
As she tries to understand the closeness between her older brother and his best friend, fourteen-year-old Ellen finds her relationship with each of them changing
"This beautiful novel tells a frank, upbeat story of teen bisexual love in all its uncertainty, pain, and joy. . . . The fast, clipped dialogue will sweep teens into the story, as will Ellen's immediate first-person, present-tense narrative." Booklist

When I was older. Houghton Mifflin 2000 167p $15 (7 and up) **Fic**
1. Death—Fiction
ISBN 0-618-05545-2 LC 00-27601
Also available in paperback from Puffin Bks.
A new friendship with a boy who is both attractive and intelligent helps fifteen-year-old Sophie sort out her feelings about her younger brother Erhard, who died three years earlier, her self-centered older sister, and her distant father
"Fast-paced, light, yet introspective, this novel of transition, love, and loss explores emotion while telling a fine story." SLJ

Friesen, Gayle
Losing forever. Kids Can Press 2002 247p $16.95; pa $6.95 (7 and up) **Fic**
1. Divorce—Fiction
ISBN 1-55337-031-7; 1-55337-032-5 (pa)
"Ninth-grader Jes Miner-Cooper knows that she isn't responsible for her parents' divorce; their marriage started to fail after her little sister, Alberta, died. What bothers is the perception that her folks are hiding something from her. . . . Then along comes beautiful Pamela, the daughter of Jes' mother's intended." Booklist
This "is a sympathetic and emotional account of a girl's adjustment to the complexities of her family as well as to change." Bull Cent Child Books

Fritz, April Young
Waiting to disappear. Hyperion 2002 316p $15.99; pa $5.99 (7 and up) **Fic**
1. Mothers—Fiction 2. Depression (Psychology)—Fiction
ISBN 0-7868-0790-3; 0-7868-1608-02 (pa)
"Just before Buddy enters high school, Mom descends into a debilitating depression, and when she enters a psychiatric hospital, Buddy feels lost and angry at being abandoned. . . . Events unfold believably and hopefully in this moving story." Booklist

Frost, Helen, 1949-

Keesha's house. Frances Foster Bks./Farrar, Straus & Giroux 2003 116p $16 (7 and up)

Fic

1. Home—Fiction

ISBN 0-374-34064-1   LC 2002-22698

Seven teens facing such problems as pregnancy, closeted homosexuality, and abuse each describe in poetic forms what caused them to leave home and where they found home again

"Spare, eloquent, and elegantly concise. . . . Public, private, or correctional educators and librarians should put this must-read on their shelves." Voice Youth Advocates

Funke, Cornelia Caroline

Dragon rider; [by] Cornelia Funke; translated by Anthea Bell. Scholastic 2004 523p il $12.95 (5 and up)

Fic

1. Dragons—Fiction 2. Fantasy fiction

ISBN 0-439-45695-9   LC 2004-45419

Original German edition 1997

"Funke proves she knows how to tickle the imaginations of younger readers. . . .This is a good, old-fashioned ensemble-cast quest." Booklist

Inkheart; [by] Cornelia Funke; translated from the German by Anthea Bell. Scholastic 2003 534p $19.95

Fic

1. Books and reading—Fiction 2. Fantasy fiction

ISBN 0-439-53164-0   LC 2003-45844

"The Chicken House"

The author "proves the power of her imagination; readers will be captivated by the chilling and thrilling world she has created here." Publ Wkly

The Thief Lord; [by] Cornelia Funke. Scholastic 2002 c2001 349p $16.95; pa $6.99

Fic

1. Orphans—Fiction 2. Thieves—Fiction 3. Brothers—Fiction 4. Venice (Italy)—Fiction

ISBN 0-439-40437-1; 0-0439-42089-X (pa)

LC 2002-21037

Original German edition, 2000

"After their mother dies, 12-year-old Prosper and his brother, Bo, five, flee from Hamburg to Venice. . . . They live in an abandoned movie theater with several other street children under the care of the Thief Lord, a cocky youth who claims to rob 'the city's most elegant houses.' " Publ Wkly

This is "a compelling tale, rich in ingenious twists, with a setting and cast that will linger in readers' memories." SLJ

Fuqua, Jonathon Scott

Darby. Candlewick Press 2002 242p $16.99 (4 and up)

Fic

1. Race relations—Fiction 2. African Americans—Fiction 3. South Carolina—Fiction

ISBN 0-7636-1417-3   LC 2001-35061

In 1926, nine-year-old Darby Carmichael stirs up trouble in Marlboro County, South Carolina, when she writes a story for the local newspaper promoting racial equality

"Darby's voice, rich with Southern idiom, rings true." Horn Book Guide

The Willoughby Spit wonder. Candlewick 2004 145p $15.99

Fic

1. Sick—Fiction 2. Father-son relationship—Fiction 3. Virginia—Fiction

ISBN 0-7636-1776-8   LC 2002-41141

In 1950s Norfolk, Virginia, as Carter and his sister watch their dying father struggle to remain cheerful, Carter decides to emulate Prince Namor, comic superhero, in order to inspire his father to stay alive.

"Carter . . . is a compelling character, and his growing understanding and acceptance of the world is shown quietly through an array of accurately observed details. A subtle, engaging novel." Booklist

Fusco, Kimberly Newton

Tending to Grace. Knopf 2004 167p $14.95; lib bdg $16.99 (7 and up)

Fic

1. Speech disorders—Fiction 2. Mothers—Fiction 3. Aunts—Fiction

ISBN 0-375-82862-1; 0-375-92862-6 (lib bdg)

LC 2003-60406

When Cornelia's mother runs off with a boyfriend, leaving her with an eccentric aunt, Cornelia must finally confront the truth about herself and her mother.

"This quiet, beautiful first novel makes the search for home a searing drama." Booklist

Gaeddert, LouAnn Bigge

Friends and enemies; {by} LouAnn Gaeddert. Atheneum Bks. for Young Readers 1999 177p $16

Fic

1. World War, 1939-1945—Fiction 2. Friendship—Fiction 3. Mennonites—Fiction 4. Kansas—Fiction

ISBN 0-689-82822-5   LC 99-19143

"A Jean Karl book"

In 1941 in Kansas, as America enters World War II, fourteen-year-old William finds himself alienated from his friend Jim, a Mennonite who does not believe in fighting for any reason, as they argue about the war

"With its strong plot, believable dialogue, and realistic characterizations, 'Friends and Enemies' deserves a role in classroom discussions about discrimination or the struggles of friendship." Voice Youth Advocates

Gaiman, Neil

Coraline; {by} Neil Gaiman; with illustrations by Dave McKean. HarperCollins Pubs. 2002 162p il $15.99; lib bdg $17.89; pa $5.99 (5 and up)

Fic

1. Supernatural—Fiction

ISBN 0-380-97778-8; 0-06-623744-0 (lib bdg); 0-380-80734-3 (pa)   LC 2002-18937

Looking for excitement, Coraline ventures through a mysterious door into a world that is similar, yet disturbingly different from her own, where she must challenge a gruesome entity in order to save herself, her parents, and the souls of three others

"Gaiman twines his taut tale with a menacing tone and crisp prose fraught with memorable imagery . . . yet keeps the narrative just this side of terrifying." Publ Wkly

Gaines, Ernest J., 1933-

The autobiography of Miss Jane Pittman. Dial Press (NY) 1971 245p o.p. Bantam Bks. paperback available $6.99 (7 and up)   **Fic**
1. African Americans—Fiction 2. Louisiana—Fiction
ISBN 0-553-26357-9 (pa)   LC 77-144380
"In the epic of Miss Jane Pittman, a 110-year-old ex-slave, the action begins at the time she is a small child watching both Union and Confederate troops come into the plantation on which she lives. It closes with the demonstrations of the sixties and the freedom walk she decides to make. This is a log of trials, heartaches, joys, love—but mostly of endurance." Shapiro. Fic for Youth. 3d edition

Gantos, Jack

Jack on the tracks; four seasons of fifth grade. Farrar, Straus & Giroux 1999 182p il $16; pa $5.95 (5 and up)   **Fic**
1. School stories 2. Family life—Fiction 3. Miami (Fla.)—Fiction
ISBN 0-374-33665-2; 0-374-43717-3 (pa)
LC 99-27897
Also available Thorndike Press large print edition
Moving with his unbearable sister to Miami, Florida, Jack tries to break some of his bad habits but finds himself irresistibly drawn to things disgusting, gross, and weird
"Jack is a likable and appealing fifth grader. His first-person preadolescent musings and worries are poignant, funny, and real." SLJ
Other available titles in this series are:
Heads or tails (1994)
Jack's black book (1997)
Jack's new power (1995)

Joey Pigza swallowed the key. Farrar, Straus & Giroux 1998 153p $16 (5 and up)   **Fic**
1. Attention deficit disorder—Fiction 2. School stories
ISBN 0-374-33664-4   LC 98-24264
Also available in paperback from HarperCollins and Audiobook version
To the constant disappointment of his mother and his teachers, Joey has trouble paying attention or controlling his mood swings when his prescription meds wear off and he starts getting worked up and acting wired
This "frenetic narrative pulls at heartstrings and tickles funny bones." SLJ
Other titles about Joey Pigza are:
Joey Pigza loses control (2000)
What would Joey do? (2002)

Garden, Nancy

The year they burned the books. Farrar, Straus & Giroux 1999 247p $17 (7 and up)   **Fic**
1. School stories 2. Homosexuality—Fiction 3. Censorship—Fiction
ISBN 0-374-38667-6   LC 98-43483
While trying to come to terms with her own lesbian feelings, Jamie, a high-school senior and editor of the school newspaper, finds herself in the middle of a battle with a group of townspeople over the new health education curriculum

"Garden's occasional attempts to add some nuanced viewpoint never really succeed, leaving the ethical deck heavily stacked; the good characters' earnest high-mindedness and sensitive longings are also rather heavily hammered home. The crusade and anti-crusade dynamic still makes for energizing reading, however, and the book wisely avoids tying things up too neatly." Bull Cent Child Books

Garland, Sherry, 1948-

In the shadow of the Alamo. Harcourt 2001 282p $17   **Fic**
1. Santa Anna, Antonio López de, 1794?-1876—Fiction 2. Mexico—Fiction 3. Soldiers—Fiction
ISBN 0-15-201744-5   LC 2001-695
"Gulliver books"
Conscripted into the Mexican Army, fifteen-year-old Lorenzo Bonifacio makes some unexpected alliances and learns some harsh truths about General Santa Anna as the troops move toward the Battle of the Alamo
"Garland paints superb word pictures, portraying unspeakable living conditions and horrible scenes of death and war. The best part of the book is the characterization." ALAN

Shadow of the dragon. Harcourt Brace & Co. 1993 314p pa $6 hardcover o.p.   **Fic**
1. Vietnamese Americans—Fiction 2. Family life—Fiction
ISBN 0-15-273532-1 (pa)   LC 93-17258
"Danny Vo's attempts to meld his responsibilities as the oldest son in a traditional Vietnamese family and his desire to be part of the mainstream of American life are complicated by a runaway younger sister; a newly arrived cousin who becomes involved with a dangerous gang; and Tiffany, the girl he loves. Rich characterization and an earthy view of the Vietnamese immigrant experience distinguish the coming-of-age novel." Horn Book Guide

The silent storm. Harcourt Brace Jovanovich 1993 240p $15; pa $6   **Fic**
1. Orphans—Fiction 2. Grandfathers—Fiction 3. Hurricanes—Fiction
ISBN 0-15-274170-4; 0-15-200016-X (pa)
LC 92-33690
Thirteen-year-old Alyssa has not spoken since seeing her parents die in a hurricane, and now, three years later, another storm threatens the home she shares with her grandfather on Galveston Island
"Garland writes evocatively of her coastal setting, developing a solid sense of place. . . . The characterizations of family members made fearful by previous losses are well developed. . . . This book will have appeal for lovers of the outdoors as well as anyone who appreciates an exciting, atmospheric story." SLJ

Song of the buffalo boy. Harcourt Brace Jovanovich 1992 249p pa $6 hardcover o.p.
Fic
1. Amerasians—Fiction 2. Vietnam—Fiction
ISBN 0-15-200098-4 (pa)   LC 91-31872
Shunned and mistreated because of her mixed heritage and determined to avoid an arranged marriage, seventeen-year-old Loi runs away to Ho Chi Minh City with

Garland, Sherry, 1948-—*Continued*

the hope that she and the boy she loves will be able to go to the United States to find her American father

"This is a poignant and illuminating story drawn from a sorrowful chapter in American history. . . . Without becoming preachy or overbearing, this is a quietly effective story." Voice Youth Advocates

Valley of the Moon; the diary of Maria Rosalia de Milagros. Scholastic 2001 217p (Dear America) $10.95   **Fic**
1. California—Fiction
ISBN 0-439-08820-8   LC 00-55620

The 1845-1846 diary of thirteen-year-old Maria, servant to the wealthy Spanish family which took her in when her Indian mother died. Includes a historical note about the settlement and early history of California

"Garland has cast Maria as a sturdy heroine, whose love for Alta California infuses her story with a strong sense of place, and the historical details are both accurate and interestingly woven into the story." Booklist

Garner, Alan, 1934-

The owl service. Walck, H. Z. 1968 c1967 202p o.p. Magic Carpet Bks. paperback available $6
                                                     Fic
1. Wales—Fiction
ISBN 0-15-201798-4 (pa)
First published 1967 in the United Kingdom

"The discovery of a strangely patterned set of plates in the attic loft of an old Welsh house where Alison, daughter of the deceased owner of the house, her stepbrother Roger, and the housekeeper's son Gwyn are spending the summer marks the beginning of ominous events which embitter relationships among the three and endanger the life of Alison." Booklist

"It is hard to write with restraint about Alan Garner's talent, so deftly does he build his story with laminations of bright fantasy and somber Welsh legend, of romantic adventure and acid realism." N Y Times Book Rev

Gauthier, Gail, 1953-

The hero of Ticonderoga. Putnam 2001 231p $16.99; pa $6.99   **Fic**
1. Allen, Ethan, 1738-1789—Fiction 2. School stories 3. Vermont—Fiction
ISBN 0-399-23559-0; 0-698-11968-1 (pa)
                                            LC 00-39018

When sixth-grader Thérèse is chosen to do the coveted oral report on Ethan Allen, she learns a great deal about the Vermont hero and also discovers what pleasure she gets from writing and presenting the report

"The author addresses important issues with humor and sensitivity: school and community prejudices, alienation, and peer acceptance." SLJ

Saving the planet & stuff. Putnam 2003 232p $17.99   **Fic**
1. Summer employment—Fiction
ISBN 0-399-23761-5   LC 2002-67954

After losing his summer job with his uncle, sixteen-year-old Michael agrees to go to work for an environmentalist magazine in Vermont run by friends of

his grandparents

"This is a funny look at what it's like being an intern at a small business where office politics are rife and everyone knows everyone else's business. . . . The frequent references to pop culture, mass consumerism, and ecological issues will have lots of teen appeal." SLJ

Gavin, Jamila, 1941-

Coram boy. Farrar, Straus & Giroux 2001 c2000 327p $19; pa $7.95 (7 and up)   **Fic**
1. Adventure fiction 2. Great Britain—Fiction
ISBN 0-374-31544-2; 0-374-41374-6 (pa)
                                            LC 00-67200
First published 2000 in the United Kingdom

In the mid-eighteenth century, an unsavory character and his simpleton son become involved in the lives of a wealthy English family when that family's eldest son is disinherited because of his love of music

"Gavin provides a chilling, terrifying, and painful portrayal of life in this era. . . . Gavin's rich prose will entice any devotee of historical fiction as well as any reader intrigued by graceful language or a solid adventure." Voice Youth Advocates

George, Jean Craighead, 1919-

Charlie's raven; written and illustrated by Jean Craighead George. Dutton Children's Books 2004 190p il $15.99 (5 and up)   **Fic**
1. Ravens—Fiction 2. Grandfathers—Fiction 3. Naturalists—Fiction
ISBN 0-525-47219-3

Charlie's friend, Singing Bird, a Teton Sioux, tells him that ravens have curing powers, so Charlie steals a baby bird from its nest, hoping to heal his ailing Granddad, a retired naturalist.

"The story is technically accurate and offers a vivid sense of place and a window into Native American beliefs through storytelling." SLJ

Julie; illustrated by Wendell Minor. HarperCollins Pubs. 1994 226p il pa $5.99 hardcover o.p. (6 and up)   **Fic**
1. Inuit—Fiction 2. Arctic regions—Fiction 3. Wolves—Fiction
ISBN 0-06-440573-7   LC 93-27738

This sequel to Julie of the wolves "details Julie's adjustment to family and modernization after returning home. Her father's musk oxen enterprise depicts the problems inherent to environment-versus-economics issues as Julie struggles to save her wolf friends." Sci Child

Followed by Julie's wolf pack

Julie of the wolves; pictures by John Schoenherr. Harper & Row 1972 170p il $15.99; lib bdg $16.89; pa $5.99 (6 and up)   **Fic**
1. Inuit—Fiction 2. Arctic regions—Fiction 3. Wilderness survival—Fiction
ISBN 0-06-021943-2; 0-06-021944-0 (lib bdg); 0-06-440058-1 (pa)
Awarded the Newbery Medal, 1973

"Lost in the Alaskan wilderness, thirteen-year old Miyax {Julie in English}, an Eskimo girl, is gradually

George, Jean Craighead, 1919-—*Continued*
accepted by a pack of Arctic wolves that she comes to love." Booklist

"The superb narration includes authentic descriptions and details of the Eskimo way-of-life and of Eskimo rituals. . . . The whole book has a rare, intense reality which the artist enhances beautifully with animated drawings." Horn Book

Followed by Julie

The talking earth. Harper & Row 1983 151p lib bdg $16.89 hardcover o.p.; pa $5.99 hardcover o.p. **Fic**
1. Seminole Indians—Fiction 2. Everglades (Fla.)—Fiction 3. Wilderness survival—Fiction
ISBN 0-06-021976-9 (lib bdg); 0-06-440212-6 (pa)
LC 82-48850

"Billie Wind, a Seminole girl, has been going to school at the Kennedy Space Center and has lost faith in her people's legends. For not believing in talking animals and earth, she is sent into the Everglades to find her roots. What was to be several days becomes months as fire and other events force her to survive with only the animals and earth to help her." Child Book Rev Serv

This story, "imbued with Seminole lore, is appealing because of the pitting of one human being against the elements, and is . . . convincing in its plot development and impressive in its descriptions of natural phenomena." Bull Cent Child Books

Water sky. Harper & Row 1987 208p pa $5.99 hardcover o.p. (5 and up) **Fic**
1. Inuit—Fiction 2. Whaling—Fiction 3. Alaska—Fiction
ISBN 0-06-440202-9   LC 86-45496

"Because his father had so enjoyed his own stay, when young, with an Eskimo family, he has sent Lincoln to Alaska. Caught up in the beauty of Eskimo culture, the excitement of whale hunting (Eskimo style) and a first shy love affair, Lincoln almost forgets that he is determined to find the beloved uncle who had disappeared in the vicinity. The characters are strong, the plot is smoothly developed, and the setting vividly drawn in a novel imbued with understanding and respect for the rich traditions of Eskimo life." Bull Cent Child Books

Geras, Adèle
Troy. Harcourt 2001 340p $17; pa $6.95 (7 and up) **Fic**
1. Trojan War—Fiction
ISBN 0-15-216492-8; 0-15-204570-8 (pa)
LC 00-57262

Homer's "tales of Paris and Helen, Achilles and Hector, and Odysseus and the Trojan horse are recast in the form of a modern novel, using the heroes' fates as background and focus for the real subjects: the women of Troy." Horn Book Guide

"Mythology buffs will savor the author's ability to embellish stories of old without diminishing their original flavor, while the uninitiated will find this a captivating introduction to a pivotal event in classic Greek literature." Publ Wkly

Giff, Patricia Reilly
All the way home. Delacorte Press 2001 169p $15.95; pa $5.99 (4 and up) **Fic**
1. Poliomyelitis—Fiction 2. Friendship—Fiction 3. Brooklyn (New York, N.Y.)—Fiction
ISBN 0-385-32209-7; 0-440-41182-3 (pa)
LC 2001-28174

In 1941, circumstances bring together Brick, a boy from New York's apple country, and Mariel, a young girl made shy by her bout with polio, and the two make a journey from Brooklyn back to help Brick's elderly neighbors save their apple crop and to help Mariel learn about her past

"A compelling story of two unforgettable youngsters, their strength, and their friendship." SLJ

A house of tailors. Wendy Lamb Books 2004 148p $15.95; lib bdg $17.99 (5 and up) **Fic**
1. Immigrants—Fiction 2. German Americans—Fiction 3. Brooklyn (New York, N.Y.)—Fiction
ISBN 0-385-73066-7; 0-385-90879-2 (lib bdg)
LC 2003-26103

When thirteen-year-old Dina emigrates from Germany to America in 1871, her only wish is to return home as soon as she can, but as the months pass and she survives a multitude of hardships living with her uncle and his young wife and baby, she finds herself thinking of Brooklyn as her home.

"This novel is rich with believable, endearing characters as well as excitement and emotion." SLJ

Lily's crossing. Delacorte Press 1997 180p $15.95; pa $5.99 (4 and up) **Fic**
1. World War, 1939-1945—Fiction 2. Friendship—Fiction
ISBN 0-385-32142-2; 0-440-41453-9 (pa)
LC 96-23021

.Also available Thorndike Press large print edition
A Newbery honor book, 1998

During a summer spent at Rockaway Beach in 1944, Lily's friendship with a young Hungarian refugee causes her to see the war and her own world differently

"Gentle elements of danger and suspense . . . keep the plot moving forward, while the delicate balance of characters and setting gently coalesces into an emotional whole that is fully satisfying." Bull Cent Child Books

Nory Ryan's song. Delacorte Press 2000 148p $15.95; pa $5.99 (5 and up) **Fic**
1. Ireland—Fiction 2. Famines—Fiction
ISBN 0-385-32141-4; 0-440-41829-1 (pa)
LC 00-27690

When a terrible blight attacks Ireland's potato crop in 1845, twelve-year-old Nory Ryan's courage and ingenuity help her family and neighbors survive

"Giff brings the landscape and the cultural particulars of the era vividly to life and creates in Nory a heroine to cheer for. A beautiful, heart-wrenching novel that makes a devastating event understandable." Booklist

Another title about Nory is:

Maggie's door (2003)

Giff, Patricia Reilly—*Continued*

Pictures of Hollis Woods. Wendy Lamb Bks. 2002 166p $15.95; lib bdg $17.99; pa $6.50 (5 and up)   **Fic**
1. Artists—Fiction 2. Foster home care—Fiction 3. Old age—Fiction
ISBN 0-385-32655-6; 0-385-90070-8 (lib bdg); 0-440-41578-0 (pa)   LC 2002-426
A Newbery Medal honor book, 2003
"She was named for the place where she was found as an abandoned baby. Twelve-year-old Hollis Woods has been through many foster homes—and she runs away, every time. In her latest placement, with an artist named Josie, the tightly wound Hollis begins to relax ever so slightly. . . . But Josie is slowly slipping into dementia, and Hollis knows that she'll be taken away from her if Josie is found out. . . . Giff has a sure hand with language, and the narrative is taut and absorbing." Booklist

Gilbert, Barbara Snow, 1954-

Stone water. Front St. 1996 169p pa $7.95 hardcover o.p. (7 and up)   **Fic**
1. Grandfathers—Fiction 2. Death—Fiction 3. Euthanasia—Fiction
ISBN 1-886910-12-X   LC 95-50378
Fifteen-year-old Grant confronts the difficult decision of whether or not to cooperate with his grandfather's wish that he not be placed on life-support systems
"The handling of this difficult subject is thoughtful, poignant, respectful, and honest." SLJ

Giles, Gail

Shattering Glass. Roaring Brook Press 2002 152p $15.95; lib bdg $22.90 (7 and up)

    Fic
1. School stories 2. Violence—Fiction
ISBN 0-7613-1581-0; 0-7613-2601-4 (lib bdg)
    LC 2001-41713
When Rob, the charismatic leader of the senior class, turns Simon Glass, the school nerd, into Prince Charming, his actions lead to unexpected violence
"Tricky, surprising, and disquieting, this tension-filled story is a psychological thriller as well as a book about finding oneself and taking responsibility." Booklist

Gilmore, Kate

The exchange student. Houghton Mifflin 1999 216p $15 (7 and up)   **Fic**
1. Science fiction 2. Extraterrestrial beings—Fiction
ISBN 0-395-57511-7   LC 97-47162
When her mother arranges to host one of the young people coming to Earth from Chela, Daria is both pleased and intrigued by the keen interest shown by the Chelan in her work breeding endangered species
"Gilmore makes a farfetched premise seem more reasonable with everyday details of life in the twenty-first century, sympathetic characters, and logical consequences. . . . A story that will appeal to readers on many levels." Booklist

Gilmore, Rachna, 1953-

A group of one. Holt & Co. 2001 184p $16.95
    Fic
1. East Indians—Fiction 2. Grandmothers—Fiction 3. Canada—Fiction
ISBN 0-8050-6475-3   LC 00-47278
Learning from her grandmother that her family was active in the Quit India movement of 1942, a rebellion against nearly two centuries of British occupation, gives fifteen-year-old Tara new pride in her heritage, but she still objects when her teacher implies she is not a "regular Canadian"
"Slang and sarcasm make the narration realistic-sounding in this well-written novel about identity and prejudice." Horn Book Guide

Gilson, Jamie, 1933-

Stink Alley. HarperCollins Pubs. 2002 183p $15.95; lib bdg $15.89 (4 and up)   **Fic**
1. Puritans—Fiction 2. Artists—Fiction
ISBN 0-688-17864-2; 0-06-029217-2 (lib bdg)
    LC 2001-39515
Living in Holland in 1614 with the harsh Puritan leader, William Brewster, and working for the family of a mischievous Dutch boy named Rembrandt, Lizzie, a spirited twelve-year-old orphan girl struggles to do what is right
"Gilson adds information about the real-life characters . . . in a historical note, but the story will first of all resound with young readers as a coming-of-age tale. It's a deftly woven mix of adventure, youthful ingenuity, and overcoming the odds." Horn Book

Gipson, Frederick Benjamin, 1903-1973

Old Yeller; {by} Fred Gipson; drawings by Carl Burger. Harper & Row 1956 158p il $23; pa $5.99 (6 and up)   **Fic**
1. Dogs—Fiction 2. Texas—Fiction 3. Frontier and pioneer life—Fiction
ISBN 0-06-011545-9; 0-06-440382-3 (pa)
    LC 56-8780
A Newbery Medal honor book, 1957
"Travis at fourteen was the man of the family during the hard summer of 1860 when his father drove his herd of cattle from Texas to the Kansas market. It was the summer when an old yellow dog attached himself to the family and won Travis' reluctant friendship. Before the summer was over, Old Yeller proved more than a match for thieving raccoons, fighting bulls, grizzly bears, and mad wolves. This is a skillful tale of a boy's love for a dog as well as a description of a pioneer boyhood and it can't miss with any dog lover." Horn Book

Going, K. L.

Fat kid rules the world. Putnam 2003 187p $17.99 (7 and up)   **Fic**
1. Obesity—Fiction 2. Musicians—Fiction 3. Friendship—Fiction
ISBN 0-399-23990-1   LC 2002-67956
Seventeen-year-old Troy, depressed, suicidal, and weighing nearly 300 pounds, gets a new perspective on life when a homeless teenager who is a genius on guitar wants Troy to be the drummer in his rock band

Going, K. L.—*Continued*
"Going has put together an amazing assortment of characters. . . . This is an impressive debut that offers hope for all kids." Booklist

Golding, Theresa Martin
The secret within. Boyds Mills Press 2002 240p $16.95   **Fic**
1. Fathers—Fiction 2. Child abuse—Fiction
ISBN 1-56397-995-0   LC 2001-93641
"Thirteen-year-old Carly Chambers keeps secrets. Her peers can't breech her armor of silence. No one in the resort community of Oceanside knows that her father causes the bruises she wears. . . . When a tall stranger follows her, and she discovers that the @candy' deliveries her father forces her to make aren't candy, and the house of cards crumbles." ALAN
"The atmosphere and a bit of a love story keep this solid, well-paced tale moving along." SLJ

Golding, William, 1911-1993
Lord of the Flies; introduction by E. M. Forster. Coward, McCann & Geoghegan 1962 243p il $22.95; pa $13   **Fic**
1. Allegories 2. Boys—Fiction 3. Survival after airplane accidents, shipwrecks, etc.—Fiction
ISBN 0-399-52920-9; 1-57322-612-2 (pa)
First published 1954 in the United Kingdom; first United States edition, 1955
"Stranded on an island, a group of English schoolboys leave innocence behind in a struggle for survival. A political structure modeled after English government is set up and a hierarchy develops, but forces of anarchy and aggression surface. The boys' existence begins to degenerate into a savage one. They are rescued from their microcosmic society to return to an adult, stylized milieu filled with the same psychological tensions and moral voids. Adventure and allegory are brilliantly combined in this novel." Shapiro. Fic for Youth. 3d edition

Goobie, Beth, 1959-
Before wings; a novel. Orca Bk. Pubs. 2001 203p $16.95; pa $7.95 (7 and up)   **Fic**
1. Death—Fiction 2. Camps—Fiction
ISBN 1-55143-161-0; 1-55143-163-7 (pa)
     LC 00-105582
"Since surviving a brain aneurysm, fifteen-year-old Adrian has been seeing spirits. Working at her aunt's summer camp, Adrian meets a boy who is also clouded by visions of his own death, then discovers that the spirits she sees are connected to the dark mystery surrounding her aunt." Horn Book Guide
"Full of magic realism and beautifully written, this is a story of good triumphing over evil, life triumphing over death, the power of love, friendship, and the hope for an afterlife." Booklist

Goodman, Alison, 1966-
Singing the Dogstar blues. Viking 2003 c1998 261p $16.99 (7 and up)   **Fic**
1. Australia—Fiction 2. Science fiction
ISBN 0-670-03610-2   LC 2002-12161

First published 1998 in Australia
In a future Australia, the saucy eighteen-year-old daughter of a famous newscaster and a sperm donor teams up with a hermaphrodite from the planet Choria in a time travel adventure that may significantly change both of their lives
"This wildly entertaining novel successfully mixes adventure, humor, mystery, and sf into a fast-paced, thrilling story that will appeal to a wide audience." Booklist

Goodman, Joan E., 1950-
Paradise; based on a true story of survival; [by] Joan Elizabeth Goodman. Houghton Mifflin 2002 209p $16 (7 and up)   **Fic**
1. Canada—History—0-1763 (New France)—Fiction
ISBN 0-618-11450-5   LC 2001-51918
In 1542, eager to escape the French Huguenot household of her harsh father, sixteen-year-old Marguerite de la Rocque sails with her equally stern uncle, the Sieur de Roberval, to the New World, where she is left alone on an island with only her young Catholic lover and her chaperone to help her survive
"Goodman's superb characterization echoes realistically in the dialogue and actions of Marguerite and Pierre. . . . The intensity and honesty of the survival story make this book a real page-turner." SLJ

Gordon, Amy, 1949-
The Gorillas of Gill Park. Holiday House 2003 247p il $16.95 (4 and up)   **Fic**
1. Parks—Fiction 2. Friendship—Fiction 3. Aunts—Fiction
ISBN 0-8234-1751-4   LC 2002-69092
While spending the summer before seventh grade with his aunt, Willy Wilson finds his first friends ever in the colorful characters who all love the neighborhood park owned by an eccentric old man
"The protagonist's first-person narration is both humorous and insightful. . . . An action-filled bildungsroman with quirky, unforgettable characters." SLJ

Graham, Rosemary
My not-so-terrible time at Hippie Hotel. Viking 2003 214p $16.99   **Fic**
1. Divorce—Fiction 2. Friendship—Fiction
ISBN 0-670-03611-0   LC 2002-15753
Forced to go with her father to a house on Cape Cod where divorced parents spend "Together Time" with their kids, teenaged Tracy finds the experience bearable after meeting a local boy named Kevin
"Readers will immediately recognize themselves in Graham's spot-on dialogue and her subtle portrayal of family dynamics. A tender, funny debut." Booklist

Grant, K. M.
Blood red horse. Walker & Co. 2005 c2004 277p $16.95   **Fic**
1. Crusades—Fiction 2. Horses—Fiction 3. Middle Ages—Fiction
ISBN 0-8027-8960-9
First published 2004 in the United Kingdom

Grant, K. M.—*Continued*

A special horse named Hosanna changes the lives of two English brothers and those around them as they fight with King Richard I against Saladin's armies during the Third Crusades.

This "story . . . transcends boundaries of gender and genre, with something to offer fans of equestrian fare, historical fiction, and battlefield drama alike." Booklist

Gray, Dianne E.

Together apart. Houghton Mifflin 2002 193p $16 (7 and up) **Fic**

1. Sex role—Fiction 2. Blizzards—Fiction

ISBN 0-618-18721-9 LC 2002-408

In 1888 in Prairie Hill, Nebraska, a few months after barely surviving a deadly blizzard that has killed two of her brothers, fourteen-year-old Hannah goes to work at the home of a wealthy widow with progressive social ideas, where she finds Isaac, who is also trying to make a new life for himself. Told from alternating points of view of Hannah and Isaac

"The blossoming love story will keep readers involved, and Gray's memorable characters reveal the late 19th-century society's attitudes toward women's rights and class consciousness." Publ Wkly

Greene, Bette, 1934-

Summer of my German soldier. Dial Bks. for Young Readers 1973 230p hardcover o.p. paperback available $5.99 (6 and up) **Fic**

1. World War, 1939-1945—Fiction 2. German prisoners of war—Fiction 3. Arkansas—Fiction

ISBN 0-14-130636-X (pa)

"Patty knows the pain of loneliness, rejection, and beatings in a family where she is the ugly duckling, unable to gain her parents' love. This is in contrast to the affection shown to her beautiful and submissive sister. Anton Reiker is a German prisoner-of-war in a camp outside of Jenkinsville, Arkansas, and when he escapes, Patty helps him. Because her family is Jewish, she pays dearly for this intervention." Shapiro. Fic for Youth. 3d edition

Followed by Morning is a long time coming (1978)

Gregory, Kristiana

Eleanor: crown jewel of Aquitaine. Scholastic 2002 187p il (Royal diaries) $10.95 **Fic**

1. Eleanor, of Aquitaine, Queen, consort of Henry II, King of England, 1122?-1204—Fiction 2. France—History—0-1328—Fiction

ISBN 0-439-16484-2 LC 2001-57628

The diary of Eleanor, first daughter of the duke of Aquitaine, from 1136 until 1137, when at age fifteen she becomes queen of France. Includes historical notes on her later life

"With attention focused on the small details of life and her youthful dreams, Eleanor comes to life. . . . An epilogue, historical note, family tree, photographs, and glossary of characters round out the book." SLJ

Orphan runaways. Scholastic Press 1998 151p pa $7.95 hardcover o.p. **Fic**

1. Brothers—Fiction 2. Orphans—Fiction 3. Gold mines and mining—Fiction

ISBN 0-590-60367-1 LC 97-4345

Harrowing adventures accompany twelve-year-old Danny and his younger brother Judd when they run away from a San Francisco orphanage and search for their uncle in a gold rush boom town

"The adventures of two boys will intrigue reluctant readers of historical fiction. . . . Gregory strikes a balance between fine character development, action, and adventure." Book Rep

Seeds of hope; the gold rush diary of Susanna Fairchild. Scholastic 2001 182p il map (Dear America) $10.95; lib bdg $12.95 **Fic**

1. California—Gold discoveries—Fiction 2. Frontier and pioneer life—Fiction

ISBN 0-590-51157-2; 0-439-55509-4 (lib bdg)

LC 00-63725

A diary account of fourteen-year-old Susanna Fairchild's life in 1849, when her father succumbs to gold fever on the way to establish his medical practice in Oregon after losing his wife and money on their steamship journey from New York. Includes a historical note

"A gripping, realistic fictional glimpse of history." Booklist

The winter of red snow; the Revolutionary War diary of Abigail Jane Stewart. Scholastic 1996 173p il maps (Dear America) $12.95; pa $9.95

Fic

1. United States—History—1775-1783, Revolution—Fiction

ISBN 0-439-55507-8; 0-590-22653-3 (pa)

LC 95-44052

At head of title: Dear America

"*The Winter of Red Snow* gives readers an interesting and realistic look at the Revolutionary War." SLJ

Griffin, Adele

Amandine. Hyperion Bks. for Children 2001 220p $15.99; pa $6.99 (7 and up) **Fic**

1. School stories 2. Friendship—Fiction

ISBN 0-7868-0618-4; 0-7868-1441-1 (pa)

LC 00-54010

Her first week at a new high school, shy, plain Delia befriends Amandine, not anticipating the dangerous turns their friendship would take

"Griffin offers this cautionary message to readers in a riveting, richly layered, and emotionally honest story." Voice Youth Advocates

Hannah, divided. Hyperion Bks. for Children 2002 264p $15.99; pa $5.99 (4 and up)

Fic

1. Mathematics—Fiction

ISBN 0-7868-0879-9; 0-7868-1727-5 (pa)

LC 2002-68929

In 1934, a thirteen-year-old with a gift for numbers is offered the chance to leave her family's dairy farm to spend one term at an exclusive Philadelphia girls' school preparing for a scholarship exam

"Griffin does a marvelous job of presenting a girl who is very different and letting readers peek inside her head. She also touches characters and situations with a freshness that sets her writing apart." Booklist

Griffin, Adele—*Continued*

The other Shepards. Hyperion Bks. for Children 1998 218p $14.95; pa $5.99 (6 and up)

Fic

1. Sisters—Fiction 2. New York (N.Y.)—Fiction
ISBN 0-7868-0423-8; 0-7868-1333-4 (pa)

LC 98-12609

Also available Thorndike Press large print edition

Teenage Holland and her younger sister Geneva, having always lived under the shadow of siblings who died before they were born, struggle to establish separate identities and escape from the oppressive weight of their parents' continuing grief

"This is a stunning, quietly moving novel." SLJ

Overnight. Putnam 2003 151p $15.99

Fic

1. Kidnapping—Fiction
ISBN 0-399-23782-8   LC 2002-69778

Gray hopes that going to a slumber party with the "Lucky Seven" at her private school will take her mind off her mother's cancer, but when she is taken from the party by a deranged woman, both she and the other girls discover things about themselves and each other

"Griffin's characterizations of girls walking the thin line between childhood and adolescence are brilliant. . . . This unsettling memorable middle-grade novel will have readers riveted." Voice Youth Advocates

Sons of liberty. Hyperion Bks. for Children 1997 230p $14.95; pa $4.95   **Fic**

1. Runaway teenagers—Fiction 2. Father-son relationship—Fiction
ISBN 0-7868-0351-7; 0-7868-1300-8 (pa)

LC 97-2729

When thirteen-year-old Rock helps his friend Liza run away from home, he wonders whether escaping from his own troubled family would be an act of patriotism or of treason

The author's "pointedly jarring dialogue and keen ear for adolescent jargon have a magnetic quality few readers will be able to resist." Publ Wkly

Where I want to be; by Adele Griffin. G.P. Putnam's Sons 2005 150p $15.99 (7 and up)

Fic

1. Sisters—Fiction 2. Mental illness—Fiction
3. Death—Fiction 4. Rhode Island—Fiction
ISBN 0-399-23783-6   LC 2004-1887

Two teenaged sisters, separated by death but still connected, work through their feelings of loss over the closeness they shared as children that was later destroyed by one's mental illness, and finally make peace with each other

"Thoughtful, unique, and ultimately life-affirming, this is a fascinating take on the literary device of a main character speaking after death." SLJ

Griffin, Peni R.

The ghost sitter. Dutton Children's Bks. 2001 131p $14.99; pa $5.99 (4 and up)   **Fic**

1. Ghost stories
ISBN 0-525-46676-2; 0-14-230216-3 (pa)

LC 00-65859

When she realizes that her new house is haunted by the ghost of a ten-year-old girl who used to live there, Charlotte tries to help her find peace

"Griffin's book has several strong appeals: new best friends solving a mystery together, a just-scary-enough ghost girl, and a deathless bond between sisters that provides the book with its resoundingly satisfying conclusion and bang-up last sentence." Horn Book

Griffis, Molly Levite

The Feester filibuster. Eakin Press 2002 236p il $18.95; pa $8.95 (4 and up)   **Fic**

1. World War, 1939-1945—Fiction 2. School stories
3. Oklahoma—Fiction
ISBN 1-57168-693-2; 1-57168-694-0 (pa)

LC 2002-8188

Sequel to The Rachel resistance (2001)

The war declared by President Roosevelt after the bombing of Pearl Harbor in December, 1941, seems remote to fifth-grader John Allan until he finds out that his classmate Rachel thinks he is a spy for the Japanese and wants him deported to another country

"This is a compelling book, filled with humor, emotion, and well-drawn characters." SLJ

Grimes, Nikki

Bronx masquerade. Dial Bks. 2002 167p $16.99; pa $5.99 (7 and up)   **Fic**

1. School stories 2. African Americans—Fiction
3. Bronx (New York, N.Y.)—Fiction
ISBN 0-8037-2569-8; 0-14-250189-1 (pa)

LC 00-31701

While studying the Harlem Renaissance, students at a Bronx high school read aloud poems they've written, revealing their innermost thoughts and fears to their formerly clueless classmates

"Funny and painful, awkward and abstract, the poems talk about race, abuse, parental love, neglect, death, and body image. . . . Readers will enjoy the lively, smart voices that talk bravely about real issues and secret fears. A fantastic choice for readers' theater." Booklist

Jazmin's notebook. Dial Bks. 1998 102p $15.99

Fic

1. African Americans—Fiction 2. Authorship—Fiction
3. Harlem (New York, N.Y.)—Fiction
ISBN 0-8037-2224-9   LC 97-5850

Also available in paperback from Puffin Bks.

A Coretta Scott King honor book for text, 1999

Jazmin, an Afro-American fourteen-year-old who lives with her older sister in a small Harlem apartment in the 1960s, finds strength in writing poetry and keeping a record of the events in her sometimes difficult life

"An articulate, admirable heroine, Jazmin leaps over life's hurdles with agility and integrity." Publ Wkly

Grove, Vicki, 1948-

Destiny. Putnam 2000 169p hardcover o.p. paperback available $5.99 (5 and up)   **Fic**

1. Family life—Fiction 2. Artists—Fiction
ISBN 0-698-11912-6   LC 99-27778

Grove, Vicki, 1948——_Continued_

Twelve-year-old Destiny tries to find meaning in her art in a life complicated by three younger siblings, a mother who dreams of winning the lottery, and her mother's unscrupulous boyfriend

"The vivid details and snappy dialogue in each of the characters' interactions keep this story grounded and valuable." Publ Wkly

Reaching Dustin. Putnam 1998 199p pa $5.99 hardcover o.p. (5 and up)   **Fic**

1. School stories
ISBN 0-698-11839-1   LC 97-8181

"An interview assignment forces Carly to get to know Dustin Groat, the most unpopular member of her sixth-grade class. Dustin's unsociable behavior began at school in third grade, just after his mother died, and Carly and her friends have looked down upon him ever since. . . . Carly's inner development is convincingly painful as she realizes the part she played in creating Dustin's problems." SLJ

The starplace. Putnam 1999 214p pa $5.99 hardcover o.p.   **Fic**

1. Prejudices—Fiction 2. African Americans—Fiction 3. Oklahoma—Fiction
ISBN 0-698-11868-5 (pa)   LC 98-40894

Thirteen-year-old Frannie learns hard lessons about prejudice and segregation when she becomes friends with Celeste, a young black girl who moves into her small Oklahoma town in 1961.

"The characterizations, particularly of Frannie and Celeste, are strong and memorable. . . . A wonderful, well-written, multilayered novel with lots of appeal." SLJ

Gruber, Michael

The witch's boy. HarperTempest 2005 377p $17.89 (7 and up)   **Fic**

1. Witches—Fiction 2. Fairy tales
ISBN 0-06-076165-2   LC 2004-20845

A grotesque foundling turns against the witch who sacrificed almost everything to raise him when he becomes consumed by the desire for money and revenge against those who have hurt him, but he eventually finds his true heart's desire

"Gruber cleverly weaves elements from familiar fairy tales into a saga that moves across forest, earth, and sea." Booklist

Grunwell, Jeanne Marie

Mind games. Houghton Mifflin 2003 133p $15
Fic

1. School stories 2. Extrasensory perception—Fiction
ISBN 0-618-17672-1   LC 2002-10820

Each of the six members of Mr. Ennis's Mad Science Club presents a report of his or her experiences working on a science fair project to investigate ESP, which resulted in their winning the Maryland lottery

"A fast-paced and fascinating read." SLJ

Gündisch, Karin, 1948-

How I became an American; translated from German by James Skofield. Cricket Publs. 2001 120p $15.95 (4 and up)   **Fic**

1. German Americans—Fiction 2. Immigrants—Fiction
ISBN 0-8126-4875-7   LC 01-37223
Original German edition, 2000

In 1902, ten-year-old Johann and his family, Germans who had been living in Austria-Hungary, board a ship to immigrate to Youngstown, Ohio, where they make a new life as Americans

"This upbeat, often humorous, realistic narrative incorporates songs used to encourage or discourage potential emigrants and even neatly ties in the story of the Pied Piper of Hamlin." SLJ

Gurney, James, 1958-

Dinotopia; a land apart from time; written and illustrated by James Gurney. HarperCollins Pubs. 1998 159p il $35; pa $19.99   **Fic**

1. Fantasy fiction 2. Dinosaurs—Fiction
ISBN 0-06-028003-4; 0-06-053064-2 (pa)
LC 98-10961

Also available in hardcover from HarperTrophy

A reissue of the title first published 1992 by Turner Pub.

Other titles about Dinotopia entered under Alan Dean Foster

In 1862, after being shipwrecked in uncharted seas, Professor Arthur Denison and his twelve-year-old son Will find themselves washed up on a strange island where people and dinosaurs live together peacefully

"This fairytale will capture the interests of older fantasy readers. . . . Younger readers, too, will be enticed by the dramatic, full-color illustrations." SLJ

Other available titles about Dinotopia by James Gurney are:

Dinotopia: first flight (1999)
Dinotopia: the world beneath (1995)

Gutman, Dan

The million dollar shot. Hyperion Bks. for Children 1997 114p $15.99; pa $4.99   **Fic**

1. Basketball—Fiction 2. Contests—Fiction
ISBN 0-7868-0334-7; 0-7868-1220-6 (pa)
LC 97-6461

Eleven-year-old Eddie gets a chance to win a million dollars by sinking a foul shot at the National Basketball Association finals

This "will appeal to both sports readers and general audiences. Gutman's subtle humor, exciting sports action, and excruciating suspense make this title an outstanding choice for reluctant readers." SLJ

Shoeless Joe & me; a baseball card adventure. HarperCollins Pubs. 2002 163p $15.95 (4 and up)
Fic

1. Jackson, Joe, 1887 or 8-1951—Fiction 2. Baseball—Fiction
ISBN 0-06-029253-9   LC 2001-24638

Joe Stoshack travels back to 1919, where he meets Shoeless Joe Jackson and tries to prevent the fixing of the World Series in which Jackson was wrongly impli-

Gutman, Dan—*Continued*
cated

"A not-quite-believable, but still highly enjoyable time-travel adventure." Booklist

Other titles in the Baseball card adventures series are:
Abner & me (2005)
Babe & me (2000)
Honus & me (1997)
Jackie & me (1999)
Mickey & me (2003)

Virtually perfect. Hyperion Bks. for Children 1998 123p $15.99; pa $4.99   Fic
1. Computers—Fiction 2. Science fiction
ISBN 0-7868-0394-0; 0-7868-1316-4 (pa)
LC 97-34849

When twelve-year-old Yip uses his father's new software to make a computer simulation of a boy his age, the creation breaks out of cyberspace into the real world and begins to complicate Yip's life

"Gutman has created an amusing and thoughtful novel." SLJ

Guy, Rosa
The disappearance. Delacorte Press 1979 246p o.p. Bantam Bks. paperback available $4.99
Fic
1. Foster home care—Fiction 2. Mystery fiction 3. African Americans—Fiction
ISBN 0-440-92064-7 (pa)   LC 79-50672

The disappearance of the seven-year-old daughter of a Brooklyn family casts suspicion on a juvenile offender from Harlem who has recently come to live with them

"Some readers might have difficulty with the Black and West Indian speech; others may not appreciate the 'down' ending. But, by story's close, each character has touched us and the fine delineation of all of them stands out as Guy's greatest strength." SLJ

Followed by New guys around the block (1983)

Haas, Jessie
Shaper. Greenwillow Bks. 2002 186p $16.99; lib bdg $16.89   Fic
1. Dogs—Fiction
ISBN 0-06-000170-4; 0-06-000171-2 (lib bdg)
LC 2001-33368

While recovering from the loss of his dog Shep, fourteen-year-old Chad tries to learn how to control the family dog Queenie with the help of a friendly new neighbor, an animal trainer

The author "uses well-chosen details to create living, breathing characters." Horn Book Guide

Unbroken. Greenwillow Bks. 1999 185p pa $5.95 hardcover o.p. (5 and up)   Fic
1. Death—Fiction 2. Orphans—Fiction 3. Horses—Fiction
ISBN 0-380-73313-7   LC 98-10485

Also available Thorndike Press large print edition

Following her mother's death in the early 1900s, thirteen-year-old Harry lives on Aunt Sarah's farm where an accident with her spirited colt leaves her a changed young woman

"The quiet novel moves quickly and is enriched by genuine dialogue, realistic portrayals of grief, and careful observations in the first-person narrative." Horn Book Guide

Will you, won't you? Greenwillow Bks. 2000 167p $15.95   Fic
1. Grandmothers—Fiction 2. Dance—Fiction
ISBN 0-06-029196-6   LC 00-25382

Spending the summer with her strong-willed politician grandmother, fourteen-year-old Mad achieves breakthroughs in both her horseback riding and her Scottish dancing and begins to develop the self-confidence she has always lacked

"The author has created memorable characters, a descriptive plot, and an honest portrayal of the emotional struggles of a young girl." Voice Youth Advocates

Haddix, Margaret Peterson, 1964-
Among the hidden. Simon & Schuster Bks. for Young Readers 1998 153p $16.95; pa $5.99
Fic
1. Science fiction
ISBN 0-689-81700-2; 0-689-82475-0 (pa)
LC 97-33052

In a future where the Population Police enforce the law limiting a family to only two children, Luke has lived all his twelve years in isolation and fear on his family's farm, until another 'third' convinces him that the government is wrong

"The fully realized setting, honest characters, and fast paced plot combine for a suspenseful tale." ALAN

Other titles in this series are:
Among the Barons (2003)
Among the betrayed (2002)
Among the brave (2004)
Among the enemy (2005)
Among the impostors (2001)

Escape from memory. Simon & Schuster Bks. for Young Readers 2003 220p $16.95   Fic
1. Memory—Fiction 2. Mothers—Fiction 3. Kidnapping—Fiction
ISBN 0-689-85421-8   LC 2002-8487

Allowing herself to be hynotized, fifteen-year-old Kira reveals memories of another time and place that may eventually cost her and her mother their lives

"Haddix nimbly balances a fascinating examination of the significance of memory with an exciting, fantastical adventure story." Booklist

Just Ella. Simon & Schuster Bks. for Young Readers 1999 185p $17; pa $5.99 (7 and up)
Fic
1. Princesses—Fiction 2. Sex role—Fiction
ISBN 0-689-82186-7; 0-689-83128-5 (pa)
LC 98-8384

In this continuation of the Cinderella story, fifteen-year-old Ella finds that accepting Prince Charming's proposal ensnares her in a suffocating tangle of palace rules and royal etiquette, so she plots to escape

"In lively prose, with well-developed characters, creative plot twists, wit, and drama, Haddix transforms the Cinderella tale into an insightful coming-of-age story." Booklist

Haddix, Margaret Peterson, 1964-—*Continued*

Leaving Fishers. Simon & Schuster Bks. for Young Readers 1997 211p pa $5.99 hardcover o.p. (7 and up)   **Fic**
1. Cults—Fiction
ISBN 0-689-86793-X   LC 96-47857

After joining her new friends in the religious group called Fishers of Men, Dorry finds herself immersed in a cult from which she must struggle to extricate herself

"The novel does a credible job of showing the effect of a cult on a vulnerable person, without disavowing strong religious beliefs." Child Book Rev Serv

Running out of time. Simon & Schuster Bks. for Young Readers 1995 184p $16.95; pa $4.99
                                                Fic
1. Diphtheria—Fiction 2. Space and time—Fiction
ISBN 0-689-80084-3; 0-689-81236-1 (pa)
                                        LC 95-8459

When a diphtheria epidemic hits her 1840 village, thirteen-year-old Jessie discovers it is actually a 1995 tourist site under unseen observation by heartless scientists, and it's up to Jessie to escape the village and save the lives of the dying children

"This absorbing novel develops an unusual premise into the gripping story. . . . This book will appeal to fans of time-travel or historical novels as well as those who prefer realistic contemporary fiction." SLJ

Takeoffs and landings. Simon & Schuster Bks. for Young Readers 2001 201p $16; pa $4.99
                                                Fic
1. Mothers—Fiction 2. Siblings—Fiction 3. Death—Fiction
ISBN 0-689-83299-0; 0-689-85543-5 (pa)
                                        LC 00-52222

An overweight, timid fifteen-year-old boy and his popular fourteen-year-old sister begin to overcome their guilt over their father's death and reconnect with each other and their emotionally-distant mother when they accompany her on a two-week speaking tour

"This family's healing journey is convincingly portrayed from varying perspectives." Horn Book Guide

Turnabout. Simon & Schuster 2000 223p $17; pa $5.99 (7 and up)   **Fic**
1. Science fiction
ISBN 0-689-82178-5; 0-689-84037-3 (pa)
                                        LC 99-86677

After secretly receiving injections at the age of 100 that are meant to reverse the aging process, Melly and Anny Beth grow younger until, as teenagers, they try to find a guardian to take care of them as they return to infancy

"Haddix has crafted a thought-provoking tale that raises medical ethics questions while deftly weaving together an unforgettable story." Voice Youth Advocates

Hahn, Mary Downing, 1937-

Daphne's book. Clarion Bks. 1983 177p $15; pa $5.99 (5 and up)   **Fic**
1. School stories 2. Friendship—Fiction 3. Authorship—Fiction 4. Family life—Fiction
ISBN 0-89919-183-5; 0-380-72355-7 (pa)
                                        LC 83-7348

Also available in paperback from Avon Bks.

As author Jessica and artist Daphne collaborate on a picture book for a seventh-grade English class contest, Jessica becomes aware of conditions in Daphne's home life that seem to threaten her health and safety

"The story is compelling in its portrayal of peer group cruelty and the disturbing dilemma Daphne faces. Jessica's own conflict about how long to shield Daphne will provoke its share of thought too. Characterizations are strong and the situations pressing." Booklist

Following my own footsteps. Clarion Bks. 1996 186p $16 (5 and up)   **Fic**
1. Domestic violence—Fiction 2. Grandmothers—Fiction 3. World War, 1939-1945—Fiction
ISBN 0-395-76477-7   LC 95-50144

In 1945, Gordy's grandmother takes him and his family into her North Carolina home after his abusive father is arrested, and he just begins to respond to his grandmother's loving discipline when his father returns

"Hahn gets us inside her character so quickly and skillfully that she maintains our sympathy for William without ever resorting to the sentimental. . . . Sometimes heartrending, sometimes funny, Gordy Smith will prove memorable to all who meet him." Booklist

Followed by As ever, Gordy

Hear the wind blow. Clarion Bks. 2003 212p $15 (5 and up)   **Fic**
1. United States—History—1861-1865, Civil War—Fiction 2. Siblings—Fiction
ISBN 0-618-18190-3   LC 2002-15977

With their mother dead and their home burned, a thirteen-year-old boy and his little sister set out across Virginia in search of relatives during the final days of the Civil War

The author "gives readers an entertaining and thought-provoking combination: a strong adventure inextricably bound to a specific time and place, but one that resonates with universal themes." Horn Book

Promises to the dead. Clarion Bks. 2000 202p $15; pa $5.95 (5 and up)   **Fic**
1. Slavery—Fiction 2. United States—History—1861-1865, Civil War—Fiction 3. Maryland—Fiction
ISBN 0-395-96394-X; 0-06-440982-1 (pa)
                                        LC 99-48525

"Hahn skillfully blends the language and customs of the Civil War era with an exciting plot." Voice Youth Advocates

Stepping on the cracks. Clarion Bks. 1991 216p $16; pa $5.99 (5 and up)   **Fic**
1. World War, 1939-1945—Fiction
ISBN 0-395-58507-4; 0-380-71900-2   LC 91-7706

Also available in paperback from Avon Bks.

In 1944, while her brother is overseas fighting in World War II, eleven-year-old Margaret gets a new view of the school bully Gordy when she finds him hiding his own brother, an army deserter, and decides to help him

"Well-drawn characters and a satisfying plot. . . . There is plenty of action and page-turning suspense to please those who want a quick read, but there is much to ponder and reflect on as well." SLJ

Hale, Marian

The truth about sparrows; Marian Hale. 1st ed. H. Holt 2004 260p $16.95 (5 and up)   **Fic**

1. Friendship—Fiction 2. Moving—Fiction 3. Great Depression, 1929-1939—Fiction

ISBN 0-8050-7584-4   LC 2003-56981

Twelve-year-old Sadie promises that she will always be Wilma's best friend when their families leave drought-stricken Missouri in 1933, but once in Texas, Sadie learns that she must try to make a new home—and new friends, too

"Rich with social history, this first novel is informative, enjoyable, and evocative." SLJ

Hale, Shannon

The Goose girl. Bloomsbury Children's Books 2003 383p $17.95   **Fic**

1. Fairy tales 2. Princesses—Fiction

ISBN 1-58234-843-X   LC 2002-28336

On her way to marry a prince she's never met, Princess Anidori is betrayed by her guards and her lady-in-waiting and must become a goose girl to survive until she can reveal her true identity and reclaim the crown that is rightfully hers

"A fine adventure tale full of danger, suspense, surprising twists, and a satisfying conclusion." Booklist

Another title about Princess Anidori is:

Enna burning (2004)

Hamilton, Virginia, 1936-2002

Bluish; a novel. Blue Sky Press (NY) 1999 127p $16.95; pa $4.99   **Fic**

1. Leukemia—Fiction 2. School stories 3. Friendship—Fiction 4. New York (N.Y.)—Fiction

ISBN 0-590-28879-2; 0-439-36786-7 (pa)

                                    LC 99-25971

Ten-year-old Dreenie feels both intrigued and frightened when she thinks about the girl nicknamed Bluish, whose leukemia is making her pale and causing her to use a wheelchair

"The compelling writing and themes of friendship, compassion, and understanding make this title a must." Voice Youth Advocates

Cousins. Philomel Bks. 1990 125p (5 and up)   **Fic**

1. Death—Fiction 2. Cousins—Fiction 3. Grandmothers—Fiction 4. African Americans—Fiction

ISBN 0-399-22164-6   LC 90-31451

Available in paperback from Scholastic $4.99 (ISBN 0-590-45436-6)

Concerned that her grandmother may die, Cammy is unprepared for the accidental death of her cousin Patty Ann

"The book deals essentially with emotions and sensations, and the writing reverberates with honesty and truth. Virginia Hamilton encases the story in family tradition, which offsets the instabilities of contemporary life, and she beautifully counterposes superstition and rationality, separation and reconciliation, love and death." Horn Book

Followed by Second Cousins (1998)

The house of Dies Drear; illustrated by Eros Keith. Macmillan 1968 246p il $18.95; pa $5.99 (5 and up)   **Fic**

1. African Americans—Fiction 2. Mystery fiction

ISBN 0-02-742500-2; 0-02-043520-7 (pa)

"A hundred years ago, Dies Drear and two slaves he was hiding in his house, an Underground Railroad station in Ohio, had been murdered. The house, huge and isolated, was fascinating, Thomas thought, but he wasn't sure he was glad Papa had bought it—funny things kept happening, frightening things." Bull Cent Child Books

"The answer to the mystery comes in a startling dramatic dénouement that is pure theater. This is gifted writing; the characterization is unforgettable, the plot imbued with mounting tension." Saturday Rev

Followed by The mystery of Drear House (1987)

Plain City. Blue Sky Press (NY) 1993 194p pa $5.99 hardcover o.p. (5 and up)   **Fic**

1. Racially mixed people—Fiction 2. African Americans—Fiction

ISBN 0-590-47365-4   LC 93-19910

Twelve-year-old Buhlaire, a "mixed" child who feels out of place in her community, struggles to unearth her past and her family history as she gradually discovers more and more about her long-missing father

"Richly textured with a cast of unforgettable characters, this extraordinary novel offers a rare glimpse of unconditional love, family loyalty and compassion." Publ Wkly

The planet of Junior Brown. Macmillan 1971 210p (6 and up)   **Fic**

1. Friendship—Fiction 2. African Americans—Fiction

ISBN 0-02-742510-X; 0-02-043540-1

"This is the story of a crucial week in the lives of two black, eighth-grade dropouts who have been spending their time with the school janitor. Each boy is presented as a distinct individual. Jr. is a three-hundred pound musical prodigy as neurotic as his overprotective mother. Buddy has learned to live by his wits in a world of homeless children. Buddy becomes Jr. Brown's protector and says to the other boys, 'We are together because we have to learn to live for each other.'" Read Ladders for Hum Relat. 6th edition

Time pieces; the book of times. Blue Sky Press (NY) 2002 199p $16.95; pa $5 (5 and up)   **Fic**

1. Family life—Fiction 2. African Americans—Fiction 3. Ohio—Fiction

ISBN 0-590-28881-4; 0-439-51714-1 (pa)

                                    LC 2001-43608

Valena, her family, and dog live in rural Ohio, where she and her cousin Melinda share experiences that include seeing the aurora borealis, surviving a tornado, and going to an amazing circus

"The simplicity and directness of the language serve the subject matter beautifully." SLJ

Hansen, Joyce

One true friend. Clarion Bks. 2001 154p $14   **Fic**

1. Friendship—Fiction 2. African Americans—Fiction

ISBN 0-395-84983-7   LC 2001-28483

Hansen, Joyce—*Continued*

Other titles about Amir and Doris are The gift-giver (1980), and Yellow Bird and me (1985)

Fourteen-year-old orphan Amir, living in Syracuse, exchanges letters with his friend Doris, still living in their old Bronx neighborhood, in which they share their lives and give each other advice on friendship, family, foster care, and making decisions

"Both sad and hopeful, this story dramatizes the struggle for survival, the primal pull of family, and the gift of 'one true friend.'" Booklist

Which way freedom? Walker & Co. 1986 120p o.p. $4.99; o.p. Avon Bks. paperback available (5 and up)   **Fic**

1. African Americans—Fiction 2. United States—History—1861-1865, Civil War—Fiction

ISBN 0-380-71408-6   LC 85-29547

"Walker's American history series for young readers"

The author "describes the way in which one young black man, Obi, struggles over a period of three years (1861-1864) politically and ideologically toward the goal of being a free man. . . . [He] eventually joins a Union regiment and is one of the few to escape from the bloody battle at Fort Pillow, Tennessee." Bull Cent Child Books

"There is sufficient action to sustain readers' interest, but it is in the book's characterization that the chief strength lies. . . . A sensitive, thought-provoking historical novel." SLJ

Followed by Out from this place (1988)

Haptie, Charlotte

Otto and the flying twins; the first book of the Karmidee; Charlotte Haptie. 1st ed. Holiday House 2004 304p il $17.95 (4 and up)   **Fic**

1. Fantasy fiction 2. Magic—Fiction

ISBN 0-8234-1826-X   LC 2003-57135

First published 2002 in the United Kingdom

Young Otto comes to the rescue when he discovers that his family and city are the last remnants of an ancient magical world now under threat from the Normal Police.

"The amazing oddities and quirks of this world and its residents are described with delicious nonchalance. . . . The characters are equally surprising and unpredictable. . . .The writing is as fresh and invigorating as the setting." SLJ

Harlow, Joan Hiatt

Joshua's song. Margaret K. McElderry Bks. 2001 176p $16; pa $4.99 (4 and up)   **Fic**

1. Newspaper carriers—Fiction 2. Disasters—Fiction 3. Boston (Mass.)—Fiction

ISBN 0-689-84119-1; 0-689-85542-7 (pa)

LC 00-52537

Needing to earn money after his father's death during the influenza epidemic of 1918, thirteen-year-old Joshua works as a newspaper boy in Boston, one day finding himself in the vicinity of an explosion that sends tons of molasses coursing through the streets.

"Even readers who don't usually like historical fiction will enjoy Harlow's vivid depiction of early-twentieth-

century working-class life and conditions. They will also like the fast-paced story, which revolves around an actual incident." Booklist

Hartnett, Sonya, 1968-

Thursday's child. Candlewick Press 2002 261p $15.99; pa $7.99 (7 and up)   **Fic**

1. Poverty—Fiction 2. Family life—Fiction 3. Farm life—Fiction 4. Australia—Fiction

ISBN 0-7636-1620-6; 0-7636-2203-6 (pa)

LC 2001-25223

Harper Flute recounts her Australian farm family's poverty during the Depression, her father's cowardice, and her younger brother Tin's obsession for digging tunnels and living underground

"This coming-of-age story with allegorical overtones will burrow into young people's deepest hopes and fears, shining light in the darkest inner rooms." Booklist

What the birds see. Candlewick Press 2003 196p $15.99 (7 and up)   **Fic**

1. Missing children—Fiction

ISBN 0-7636-2092-0   LC 2002-73717

While the residents of his town concern themselves with the disappearance of three children, a lonely, rejected nine-year-old boy worries that he may inherit his mother's insanity

"Tightly composed and ripe with symbolism, this complex book will offer opportunities for rich discussion." SLJ

Haseley, Dennis

The amazing thinking machine. Dial Bks. 2002 117p $17.99 (4 and up)   **Fic**

1. Great Depression, 1929-1939—Fiction 2. Poverty—Fiction

ISBN 0-8037-2609-0   LC 00-63860

During the Great Depression, while their father is away looking for work, eight-year-old Patrick and thirteen-year-old Roy create a machine to help their mother make ends meet, even as she is helping tramps

"Thoughtfully written, the novel is alternately poignant and humorous, with a satisfying resolution." Horn Book Guide

Hausman, Gerald

Escape from Botany Bay; the true story of Mary Bryant; [by] Gerald & Loretta Hausman. Orchard Bks. 2003 220p $16.95 (7 and up)   **Fic**

1. Bryant, Mary, b. 1765—Fiction 2. Prisoners—Fiction

ISBN 0-439-40327-8   LC 2002-35594

In 1791, after being transported to Australia in the first shipment of convicts, Mary Bryant, her husband, two children, and seven other convicts, unable to endure the terrible conditions of the penal colony, organize a daring escape in an open boat

"The Hausmans use a vivid first-person narrative to unfold Mary's incredible story, and although their character's occasional eloquence is inconsistent with her illiteracy, she's still a fascinating, credible protagonist that readers will like and remember." Booklist

Hautman, Pete, 1952-

Godless. Simon & Schuster Books for Young Readers 2004 208p $15.95 (7 and up) **Fic**

1. Religion—Fiction

ISBN 0-689-86278-4 LC 2003-10468

When sixteen-year-old Jason Bock and his friends create their own religion to worship the town's water tower, what started out as a joke begins to take on a power of its own

"The witty text and provocative subject will make this a supremely enjoyable discussion-starter as well as pleasurable read." Bull Cent Child Books

Hole in the sky. Simon & Schuster Bks. for Young Readers 2001 179p $16 (7 and up)

Fic

1. Science fiction 2. Grand Canyon (Ariz.)—Fiction

ISBN 0-689-83118-8 LC 00-58324

In a future world ravaged by a mutant virus, sixteen-year-old Ceej and three other teenagers seek to save the Grand Canyon from being flooded, while trying to avoid capture by a band of renegade Survivors

"Readers will appreciate the novel's intense action and fascinating premise." Horn Book Guide

Invisible. Simon & Schuster Books for Young Readers 2005 149p $15.95 (7 and up) **Fic**

1. Mental illness—Fiction 2. Friendship—Fiction

ISBN 0-689-86800-6 LC 2004-2484

Doug and Andy are unlikely best friends—one a loner obsessed by his model trains, the other a popular student involved in football and theater—who grew up together and share a bond that nothing can sever

"With its excellent plot development and unforgettable, heartbreaking protagonist, this is a compelling novel of mental illness." SLJ

Sweetblood. Simon & Schuster Bks. for Young Readers 2003 180p $16.95 (7 and up) **Fic**

1. Diabetes—Fiction

ISBN 0-689-85048-4 LC 2002-11179

"Lucy Szabo has been an insulin-dependent diabetic since she was 6, and now, at age 16, she has developed an interesting theory that links vampirism with diabetic ketoacidosis." SLJ

"Hautman does an outstanding job of making Lucy's theory and her struggle to accept herself credible. . . . Lucy's clever, self-deprecating voice is endlessly original." Booklist

Havill, Juanita

Eyes like Willy's. HarperCollins 2004 135p $15.99; lib bdg $16.89 **Fic**

1. World War, 1914-1918—Fiction

ISBN 0-688-13672-9; 0-688-13673-7 (lib bdg)

LC 2003-14954

While vacationing over the course of several summers in Austria, French siblings Guy and Sarah Masson become best friends with a German boy, until the outbreak of World War I puts them on opposing sides.

"This spare, thoughtful story does a superb job of personalizing the pain of this brutal, futile war." Booklist

Hawes, Louise, 1943-

Waiting for Christopher; a novel. Candlewick Press 2002 224p $15.99 (7 and up) **Fic**

1. Child abuse—Fiction 2. Friendship—Fiction
3. Books and reading—Fiction

ISBN 0-7636-1371-1 LC 2001-43476

Shortly after moving with her mother to Florida, a lonely, fourteen-year-old bibliophile is reminded of her infant brother who died and decides to care for an abused, abandoned child with help from a new friend

"Hawes's writing is distinctive, with many wonderful turns of phrase and beautiful images. Her main characters are memorable and well developed." SLJ

Hayes, Daniel, 1952-

No effect. Godine 1993 212p o.p. Avon Bks. paperback available $3.99 **Fic**

1. School stories 2. Wrestling—Fiction

ISBN 0-380-72392-1 (pa) LC 93-29329

This novel about Tyler and Lyme "has the eighth-grade boys trying out for the varsity wrestling team. Tyler's desire to be a wrestler stems less from any intrinsic interest in the sport than from his belief that it will attract girls. . . . When a pretty young instructor takes over their science classes after Mrs. Waverly is overcome by a fatal stroke, Tyler is helplessly smitten." Horn Book

"The dialogue rings true to the age group, and Tyler's feelings, which range from euphoria to depression, are thoughtfully drawn." SLJ

Heneghan, James

Flood. Foster Bks. 2002 182p $16 **Fic**

1. Fathers—Fiction 2. Aunts—Fiction 3. Irish—Fiction
4. Canada—Fiction

ISBN 0-374-35057-4 LC 2001-23218

After his mother and stepfather die in a Vancouver mudslide, eleven-year-old Andy Flynn, having been saved by leprechauns, is taken by his stern aunt to Halifax, Nova Scotia, where he meets the charming father he thought was dead, and where he must decide what place to call home

"Heneghan treats all his characters with kindness, and Andy's bruised sorrow and battered hope will engage readers to the last page." Booklist

The grave. Farrar, Straus & Giroux 2000 245p $17; pa $5.50 **Fic**

1. Ireland—Fiction 2. Famines—Fiction

ISBN 0-374-32765-3; 0-440-22948-0 (pa)

LC 99-27599

Thirteen-year-old Tom, an unhappy foster child in Liverpool, falls into a massive open grave and is transported to Ireland in 1847, where he finds himself in the midst of the deadly potato famine

This novel "is sure to appeal to readers who appreciate hints of the supernatural . . . combined with adventure, mystery, and historical context." Voice Youth Advocates

Henkes, Kevin, 1960-
The birthday room. Greenwillow Bks. 1999
152p $15.99; pa $5.99 (5 and up)   **Fic**
1. Family life—Fiction 2. Uncles—Fiction
ISBN 0-688-16733-0; 0-06-443828-7 (pa)
LC 98-39887
Also available in paperback from Puffin Bks. and
Audiobook version
"For his twelfth birthday, Ben Hunter receives a room
that he can use as an art studio and a letter from his uncle—the one responsible for the loss of Ben's little finger
when Ben was a toddler. . . . Mrs. Hunter, who has
been angry at her brother since the accident, reluctantly
agrees to go to Oregon with Ben." Booklist
"Told in spare, unobtrusive prose, a story that helps us
see our own chances for benefiting from mutual tolerance, creative conflict resolution, and other forms of
good will." Horn Book

Olive's ocean. Greenwillow Bks. 2003 217p
$15.99; lib bdg $16.89 (5 and up)   **Fic**
1. Grandmothers—Fiction 2. Family life—Fiction
ISBN 0-06-053543-1; 0-06-053544-X (lib bdg)
LC 2002-29782
A Newbery Medal honor book, 2004
On a summer visit to her grandmother's cottage by
the ocean, twelve-year-old Martha gains perspective on
the death of a classmate, on her relationship with her
grandmother, on her feelings for an older boy, and on
her plans to be a writer.
"Rich characterizations move this compelling novel to
its satisfying and emotionally authentic conclusion." SLJ

Protecting Marie. Greenwillow Bks. 1995 195p
$16.99 (5 and up)   **Fic**
1. Father-daughter relationship—Fiction 2. Dogs—Fiction
ISBN 0-688-13958-2   LC 94-16387
Also available in paperback from Puffin Bks.
Relates twelve-year-old Fanny's love-hate relationship
with her father, a temperamental artist, who has given
Fanny a new dog
"The characters ring heartbreakingly true in this quiet,
wise story; they are complex and difficult—like all of
us—and worthy of our attention." Horn Book

Sun & Spoon. Greenwillow Bks. 1997 135p
$14.95 (4 and up)   **Fic**
1. Grandmothers—Fiction 2. Death—Fiction
ISBN 0-688-15232-5   LC 96-46259
Also available in paperback from Puffin Bks.
"Spoon, 10, spends his summer trying to reconfigure
his world, which seems strangely out of kilter since his
grandmother's death." SLJ
"Sensitively placed metaphors enrich the narrative,
embuing its perceptive depictions of grief with a powerful message of affirmation." Publ Wkly

Hentoff, Nat
The day they came to arrest the book; a novel.
Delacorte Press 1982 169p pa $5.99 o.p. (7 and
up)   **Fic**
1. Censorship—Fiction 2. School stories
ISBN 0-440-91814-6   LC 82-71100

"Barney Roth, editor of the high school newspaper,
believes he must take a stand when a group of students
and parents decide that 'The Adventures of Huckleberry
Finn' should be removed from the school library. The
group finds the book offensive to blacks and insists that
it be omitted from school reading lists. The question is,
where does censorship end? What stops the next group
from finding another book offensive to someone else's
sensibilities?" Books for You

Hermes, Patricia, 1936-
Summer secrets. Marshall Cavendish 2004 141p
$15.95 (5 and up)   **Fic**
1. Mental illness—Fiction 2. Race relations—Fiction
3. Mississippi—Fiction
ISBN 0-7614-5074-2   LC 2003-17669
Twelve-year-old Missy tries to learn more about her
mother's odd behavior as she and her two friends share
some secrets during a long, hot summer in Mississippi
toward the end of World War II
"Hermes's child's-eye view of a small southern town
is on target. . . . An evocative and satisfying coming-of-
age story." SLJ

Hesse, Karen
Letters from Rifka. Holt & Co. 1992 148p
$16.95 (5 and up)   **Fic**
1. Immigrants—Fiction 2. Jews—Fiction 3. Letters—
Fiction
ISBN 0-8050-1964-2   LC 91-48007
Also available in paperback from Puffin Bks.
In letters to her cousin, Rifka, a young Jewish girl,
chronicles her family's flight from Russia in 1919 and
her own experiences when she must be left in Belgium
for a while when the others emigrate to America
"Based on the true story of the author's great-aunt, the
moving account of a brave young girl's story brings to
life the day-to-day trials and horrors experienced by
many immigrants as well as the resourcefulness and
strength they found within themselves." Horn Book

A light in the storm; the Civil War diary of
Amelia Martin. Scholastic 1999 169p (Dear
America) $10.95 (5 and up)   **Fic**
1. United States—History—1861-1865, Civil War—
Fiction 2. Delaware—Fiction
ISBN 0-590-56733-0   LC 98-49204
In 1860 and 1861, while working in her father's light-
house on an island off the coast of Delaware, fifteen-
year-old Amelia records in her diary how the Civil War
is beginning to devastate her divided state
"This well-paced story features a seamless combina-
tion of history, sociology, drama, and romance." Horn
Book

Out of the dust. Scholastic 1997 227p $15.95;
pa $5.99 (5 and up)   **Fic**
1. Dust storms—Fiction 2. Farm life—Fiction
3. Great Depression, 1929-1939—Fiction
4. Oklahoma—Fiction
ISBN 0-590-36080-9; 0-590-37125-8 (pa)
LC 96-40344
Also available Spanish language edition
Awarded the Newbery Medal, 1998

Hesse, Karen—*Continued*

"After facing loss after loss during the Oklahoma Dust Bowl, Billie Jo begins to reconstruct her life." SLJ

"Hesse's writing transcends the gloom and transforms it into a powerfully compelling tale of a girl with enormous strength, courage, and love. The entire novel is written in very readable blank verse." Booklist

Phoenix rising. Holt & Co. 1994 182p $17.95
      Fic

1. Nuclear power plants—Fiction 2. Death—Fiction
3. Friendship—Fiction
ISBN 0-8050-3108-1   LC 93-47301

Also available in paperback from Penguin Bks.

Thirteen-year-old Nyle learns about relationships and death when fifteen-year-old Ezra, who was exposed to radiation leaked from a nearby nuclear plant, comes to stay at her grandmother's Vermont farmhouse

"The author's under-stated approach heightens the emotional impact of her searching and memorable tale." Publ Wkly

Stowaway; with drawings by Robert Andrew Parker. Margaret K. McElderry Bks. 2000 319p il $17.95; pa $6.99 (5 and up)   **Fic**

1. Cook, James, 1728-1779 Fiction 2. Voyages around the world—Fiction 3. Sea stories
ISBN 0-689-83987-1; 0-689-83989-8 (pa)
      LC 00-56976

A fictional journal relates the experiences of Nicholas, a young stowaway, from 1768 to 1771 aboard the Endeavor which sailed around the world under Captain James Cook

"Hesse is a master storyteller who gives Nicholas an authentic voice. . . . The author's subtle yet thorough attention to detail creates a memorable tale that is a virtual encyclopedia of life in the days when England ruled the seas." SLJ

Witness. Scholastic Press 2001 161p $16.95; pa $5.99 (6 and up)   **Fic**

1. Ku Klux Klan—Fiction 2. Prejudices—Fiction
3. Vermont—Fiction
ISBN 0-439-27199-1; 0-439-27200-9 (pa)
      LC 00-54139

A series of poems express the views of eleven people in a small Vermont town, including a young black girl and a young Jewish girl, during the early 1920s when the Ku Klux Klan is trying to infiltrate the town

"The story is divided into five acts, and would lend itself beautifully to performance. The plot unfolds smoothly, and the author creates multidimensional characters." SLJ

Hesser, Terry Spencer

Kissing doorknobs. Delacorte Press 1998 149p (7 and up)   **Fic**

1. Obsessive-compulsive disorder—Fiction
ISBN 0-385-32329-8; 0-440-41314-1
      LC 97-26937

Fourteen-year-old Tara describes how her increasingly strange compulsions begin to take over her life and affect her relationships with her family and friends

"An honest, fresh, and multilayered story to which readers will instantly relate. . . . The prose is forthright, economical, and peppered with wry humor." SLJ

Heuston, Kimberley Burton

The Shakeress; {by} Kimberley Heuston. Front St. 2002 207p $16.95 (7 and up)   **Fic**

1. Shakers—Fiction 2. Orphans—Fiction
ISBN 1-88691-056-1   LC 2001-40298

While searching for her true self and for the way to meet the needs of her personal sense of spirituality, an orphaned teenaged girl joins a Shaker community in mid-nineteenth century New England and learns about a new religion called Mormonism

"This is an introspective story that will attract readers seeking their own spiritual path." Booklist

Hewett, Lorri

Dancer. Dutton Children's Bks. 1999 214p $15.99 (7 and up)   **Fic**

1. Ballet—Fiction 2. African Americans—Fiction
ISBN 0-525-45968-5   LC 98-55501

"Sixteen-year-old Stephanie works hard toward her goal of becoming a professional ballerina, but there are complications. Her father feels that her career choice is unrealistic, particularly for an African American girl. . . . Readers familiar with ballet will find the dance background vivid and convincing, but the strength of the book comes from the carefully drawn characters and relationships." Booklist

Hiaasen, Carl

Hoot. Knopf 2002 292p $15.95; lib bdg $17.99; pa $8.95 (5 and up)   **Fic**

1. Owls—Fiction 2. Florida Fiction
ISBN 0-375-82181-3; 0-375-92181-8 (lib bdg); 0-375-82916-4 (pa)   LC 2002-25478

Roy, who is new to his small Florida community, becomes involved in another boy's attempt to save a colony of burrowing owls from a proposed construction site

"The story is full of offbeat humor, buffoonish yet charming supporting characters, and genuinely touching scenes of children enjoying the wildness of nature." Booklist

Hickman, Janet

Ravine. Greenwillow Bks. 2002 215p $15.95
      Fic

1. Space and time—Fiction 2. Dogs—Fiction
ISBN 0-688-17952-5   LC 2001-42493

As Ulf searches for a friend to ease his difficult life in the castle keep of a cruel king and queen and, in a very different time and place, Jeremy looks for adventure in the war games he plays with his best friend, the two boys are brought together by Jeremy's dog

"Young readers will empathize with the youthful protagonists of both time periods and find themselves caught up in the adventure." SLJ

Hill, Kirkpatrick, 1938-

Minuk; ashes in the pathway. Pleasant Co. Publs. 2002 198p (Girls of many lands) hardcover o.p. paperback available $7.95 (5 and up)
      Fic

1. Inuit—Fiction 2. Alaska—Fiction
ISBN 1-58485-520-7   LC 2002-3216

Hill, Kirkpatrick, 1938-—*Continued*

Twelve-year-old Minuk's traditional Eskimo way of life is changed forever in 1892 with the arrival of Christian missionaries

"Minuk's story, and the skillful, involving manner in which it is told, should knock the socks off habitual readers of series historical fiction. Back matter includes an essay on Yup'ik customs and history, a glossary, and an author's note." Horn Book

Hinton, S. E.

The outsiders. Viking 1967 188p $16.99; pa $6.99 (7 and up)   **Fic**

1. Juvenile delinquency—Fiction

ISBN 0-670-53257-6; 0-14-038572-X (pa)

Also available in paperback from Prentice-Hall

"From the perspective of Ponyboy Curtis, the author relates the story of the Greasers, who are from the lower class, and their conflict with the Socs, who are their middle-class opposite number. For the Greasers, the gang comprises their street family, all the family that some of them have. In the collision between the two social factions, two buddies die, one as a hood, the other, a hero." Shapiro. Fic for Youth. 3d edition

"This remarkable novel by a seventeen-year-old girl gives a moving, credible view of the outsiders from the inside—their loyalty to each other, their sensitivity under tough crusts, their understanding of self and society." Horn Book

Rumble fish. Delacorte Press 1975 132p pa $5.99 hardcover o.p. (7 and up)   **Fic**

1. Brothers—Fiction 2. Juvenile delinquency—Fiction

ISBN 0-440-07534-4

"Young Rusty-James rapidly loses everything meaningful to him—his girl, his 'rep' as number one tough guy, and, most important, his idolized older brother—a James Dean look- and act-alike known only as the Motorcycle Boy. And, although it is the Motorcycle Boy who is gunned down at the end after breaking into a pet store, it is Rusty-James, emotionally burnt out at 14, who is the ultimate victim." SLJ

"Believable, written convincingly in first person, the story line is less a plot than a picture of personality disintegration. Memorable, but with no relief from depression, no note of hope." Bull Cent Child Books

Taming the Star Runner. Delacorte Press 1988 181p pa $5.99 hardcover o.p.   **Fic**

1. Authorship—Fiction 2. Horses—Fiction

ISBN 0-440-20479-8 (pa)   LC 88-7065

Sent to live with his uncle after a violent confrontation with his stepfather, sixteen-year-old Travis, an aspiring writer, finds life in a small Oklahoma town confining until he meets an eighteen-year-old horse trainer named Casey.

"This is far from a formula horse story; it has depth, pattern, perception, and a communicable empathy for its protagonist." Bull Cent Child Books

Tex. Delacorte Press 1979 194p o.p. Laurel-Leaf Bks. paperback available $5.99 (7 and up)

    Fic

1. Brothers—Fiction

ISBN 0-440-97850-5 (pa)   LC 78-50448

"Fourteen-year-old Tex lives with his 17-year-old brother Mason in a rural area. Their father hasn't been home in five months, and the relationship between the two boys is tense. Each has his own problems, fears, and growing pains which keep him alienated from his brother, until a dramatic and terrifying experience forces them to seek comfort and support from each other." SLJ

"Many teens will empathize with Tex and his friends in their problems with parents, money, drugs, sex, and the law." Child Book Rev Serv

That was then, this is now. Viking 1971 159p $15.99; pa $6.99 (7 and up)   **Fic**

1. Drug abuse—Fiction 2. Juvenile delinquency—Fiction

ISBN 0-670-69798-2; 0-14-038966-0 (pa)

"Mark had lived with Byron's family since he was nine (his parents had shot each other) and the two boys were like brothers. Now they are adolescent, skirmishing on the edge of delinquency. Bryon, who tells the story, is in love with a girl whose younger brother is a gentle, candid thirteen-year-old; when he and Cathy find that the boy has taken drugs and is on a bad trip, Bryon is deeply upset. Then he finds a cache of pills in Mark's room and realizes that Mark is a pusher. . . . The book has a bitter realism . . . it is distinguished by percipience in characterization, natural dialogue, and a sensitivity toward the complexity of human relationships." Sutherland. The Best in Child Books

Hite, Sid, 1954-

A hole in the world. Scholastic Press 2001 204p $16.95; pa $5.99 (7 and up)   **Fic**

1. Farm life—Fiction

ISBN 0-439-09830-0; 0-439-09831-9 (pa)

    LC 00-53149

Fifteen-year-old Paul Shackleford experiences an eye-opening and transformative summer living and working on the central Virginia farm belonging to a distant relative, where everyone seems to be haunted by the death of a much-loved and admired farmhand the year before

"Leavened with a healthy dose of humor, a dash of tender and respectful romance, and tantalizing bits of supernatural intrigue." Bull Cent Child Books

Those darn Dithers. Holt & Co. 1996 184p $15.95   **Fic**

1. Family life—Fiction 2. Country life—Fiction 3. Virginia—Fiction

ISBN 0-8050-3838-8   LC 96-22400

Also available in paperback from Dell

In this book about the eccentric Dither family of rural Virginia "nine-year-old Archibald Dither helps former government operative and parapsychologist Aunt Bean build an astral projector, a vaudeville show features Porcellina the dancing pig, and a trip to the beach ends when elderly eccentric Leopold Hillacre falls asleep on a rubber raft and drifts out into the shipping lanes. . . . The pace is as leisurely as a stroll on a hot summer day, and the story is really character driven, with Hite managing to breathe life into a host of major and minor players." Booklist

Another available title about the Dither family is:

Dither farm (1992)

Hobbs, Valerie, 1941-

Charlie's run. Farrar, Straus & Giroux 2000 165p $16 **Fic**

1. Runaway children—Fiction 2. Divorce—Fiction 3. California—Fiction

ISBN 0-374-34994-0 LC 99-22376

Also available in paperback from Puffin Bks.

"Frances Foster books"

Hoping to stop his parents' impending separation and keep them from getting a divorce, eleven-year-old Charlie runs away from their house in the California countryside and finds a ride to the coast

"Compellingly told. . . . This is an engaging novel about accepting fallibility in those we love—and in ourselves." Horn Book Guide

Sonny's war. Farrar, Straus & Giroux 2002 215p $16 (7 and up) **Fic**

1. Vietnam War, 1961-1975—Fiction

ISBN 0-374-37136-9 LC 2002-23891

"Frances Foster books"

In the late 1960s, fourteen-year-old Cory's life is greatly changed by the sudden death of her father and her brother's tour of duty in Vietnam

"Hobbs writes like a dream . . . but the Cory she conjures up for us is as real as real, completely believable in all her teenage vulnerability and sharp-eyed observation." Horn Book

Tender. Foster Bks. 2001 245p $18; pa $6.99 (7 and up) **Fic**

1. Father-daughter relationship—Fiction 2. California—Fiction

ISBN 0-374-37397-3; 0-14-240075-0 (pa)

LC 00-49513

After her beloved Gran dies, fifteen-year-old Liv goes to California to live with the father she has never known and must adjust to his gruff ways and his life as an abalone diver, so different from her life in New York City

"Hobbs gives readers a strong and personable protagonist caught in a complex series of events. . . . Hobbs's storytelling pace is quick without feeling rushed, drawing readers in immediately and inextricably." SLJ

Hobbs, Will

Bearstone. Atheneum Pubs. 1989 154p pa $4.99 hardcover o.p. (7 and up) **Fic**

1. Ute Indians—Fiction

ISBN 0-689-87071-X (pa) LC 89-6641

"Rebellious at being forced to abandon his family and his Ute Indian heritage to attend high school, Cloyd is sent to spend a summer with a lonely old rancher in Colorado. Upon arriving, Cloyd accidentally finds a turquoise bear totem in an Anasazi grave site, which serves as a touchstone between his cultural roots and his feelings. As time goes by, he also develops a mutual respect and friendship for the old man." ALAN

"The growth and maturity that Cloyd acquires as the summer progresses is juxtaposed poetically against the majestic Colorado landscape. Hobbs has creatively blended myth and reality as Cloyd forges a new identity for himself." Voice Youth Advocates

Followed by Beardance (1993)

The Big Wander. Atheneum Pubs. 1992 181p $17 (7 and up) **Fic**

1. Uncles—Fiction 2. Navajo Indians—Fiction 3. Horses—Fiction

ISBN 0-689-31767-0 LC 92-825

Also available in paperback from Aladdin Bks.

As he searches for his uncle through the rugged Southwest canyon country, fourteen-year-old Clay becomes involved with a group of Navajo Indians who are trying to save some of the last wild mustangs

"Hobbs skillfullly blends action scenes (flash flood, quicksand, and wild chases) with moments of humor and insight." SLJ

Downriver. Atheneum Pubs. 1991 204p $13.95 (7 and up) **Fic**

1. White-water canoeing—Fiction

ISBN 0-689-31690-9 LC 90-1044

Fifteen-year-old Jessie and the other rebellious teenage members of a wilderness survival school team abandon their adult leader, hijack his boats, and try to run the dangerous white water at the bottom of the Grand Canyon

Far North. Morrow Junior Bks. 1996 226p $16.99 (7 and up) **Fic**

1. Wilderness survival—Fiction 2. Northwest Territories—Fiction

ISBN 0-688-14192-7 LC 95-42686

Also available in paperback from HarperTrophy

This "delivers breathless action and an inspiring sense of Canada's vast landscape." Publ Wkly

Ghost canoe. Morrow Junior Bks. 1997 195p $16.99 **Fic**

1. Buried treasure—Fiction 2. Adventure fiction 3. Pacific Northwest—Fiction

ISBN 0-688-14193-5 LC 96-34417

Also available in paperback from HarperTrophy

Fourteen-year-old Nathan, fishing with the Makah in the Pacific Northwest, finds himself holding a vital clue when a mysterious stranger comes to town looking for Spanish treasure

"Hobbs blends together a number of elements to create an exciting adventure set in 1874. . . . A winning tale that artfully combines history, nature, and suspense." SLJ

Jackie's Wild Seattle. HarperCollins Pubs. 2003 200p $15.99; lib bdg $16.89 (5 and up)

Fic

1. Uncles—Fiction

ISBN 0-688-17474-4; 0-06-051631-3 (lib bdg)

LC 2002-13386

Fourteen-year-old Shannon and her little brother, Cody, spend the summer with their uncle, helping at a wildlife rescue center named Jackie's Wild Seattle

"This story is packed with action. Each character has a storm to weather, which is ultimately confronted in a way that seems a natural part of the overall plot." Booklist

Hobbs, Will—*Continued*

Jason's gold. Morrow Junior Bks. 1999 221p
$16.99; pa $5.99 (5 and up) **Fic**
1. Klondike River Valley (Yukon)—Gold discoveries—Fiction 2. Voyages and travels—Fiction
3. Orphans—Fiction
ISBN 0-688-15093-4; 0-380-72914-8 (pa)
LC 99-17973
Also available Audiobook version
When news of the discovery of gold in Canada's Yukon Territory in 1897 reaches fifteen-year-old Jason, he
embarks on a 10,000-mile journey to strike it rich
"The successful presentation of a fascinating era, coupled with plenty of action, makes this a good historical
fiction choice." SLJ
Followed by Down the Yukon (2001)

Leaving Protection. HarperCollins 2004 178p il
map $15.99; lib bdg $16.89 (7 and up)
Fic
1. Fishing—Fiction 2. Buried treasure—Fiction
3. Alaska—Fiction
ISBN 0-688-17475-2; 0-06-051632-1 (lib bdg)
LC 2003-15545
Sixteen-year-old Robbie Daniels, happy to get a job
aboard a troller fishing for king salmon off southeastern
Alaska, finds himself in danger when he discovers that
his mysterious captain is searching for long-buried Russian plaques that lay claim to Alaska and the Northwest
This "nautical thriller brims with detail about the fishing life and weaves in historical facts as well. . . .
Robbie's doubts build to a climactic finale involving a
dramatic and fateful storm at sea, grippingly rendered.
Fans of maritime tales will relish the atmosphere and the
bursts of action." Publ Wkly

The maze. Morrow Junior Bks. 1998 198p
$15.99 (7 and up) **Fic**
1. Runaway teenagers—Fiction 2. Condors—Fiction
ISBN 0-688-15092-6 LC 98-10791
Also available in paperback from HarperTrophy
Rick, a fourteen-year-old foster child, escapes from a
juvenile detention facility near Las Vegas and travels to
Canyonlands National Park in Utah where he meets a
bird biologist working on a project to reintroduce condors to the wild
"Hobbs spins an engrossing yarn, blending adventure
with a strong theme, advocating the need for developing
personal values." Horn Book Guide

Wild Man Island. HarperCollins Pubs. 2002
184p $15.99; lib bdg $16.89; pa $5.99
Fic
1. Wilderness survival—Fiction 2. Alaska—Fiction
ISBN 0-688-17473-6; 0-06-029810-3 (lib bdg);
0-380-73310-2 (pa) LC 2001-39818
After fourteen-year-old Andy slips away from his kayaking group to visit the wilderness site of his archaeologist father's death, a storm strands him on Admiralty Island, Alaska, where he manages to survive, encounters
unexpected animal and human inhabitants, and looks for
traces of the earliest prehistoric immigrants to America
"A well-paced adventure, this novel combines survival
saga, mystery, and archaeological expedition." Voice
Youth Advocates

Hoeye, Michael, 1947-

Time stops for no mouse; a Hermux Tantamoq
adventure. Putnam 2002 250p $14.99; pa $7.99 (5
and up) **Fic**
1. Mice—Fiction 2. Animals—Fiction 3. Mystery fiction
ISBN 0-399-23878-6; 0-698-11991-6 (pa)
LC 2001-48486
Also available in paperback from Terfle Bks.

First published 2000 by Terfle Bks.
When Linka Perflinger, a jaunty mouse, brings a
watch into his shop to be repaired and then disappears,
Hermux Tantamoq is caught up in a world of dangerous
search for eternal youth as he tries to find out what happened to her
"The snappy, sophisticated writing makes this adventure a delight from start to finish. The city of Pinchester
comes alive brilliantly with its multispecies population of
rats, mice, gophers, and other small furry folk. . . . A
delightful romp for imaginative readers and fantasy
fans." Voice Youth Advocates
Other titles in this series are:
No time like show time (2004)
The sands of time (2002)

Hoffman, Alice

Green angel. Scholastic Press 2003 116p $16.95
(7 and up) **Fic**
1. Gardening—Fiction
ISBN 0-439-44384-9 LC 2002-6980
Haunted by grief and by her past after losing her family in a fire, fifteen-year-old Green retreats into her ruined garden as she struggles to survive emotionally and
physically on her own
"A powerfully written and thought-provoking selection." SLJ

Hoffman, Mary

Stravaganza: city of masks; city of masks.
Bloomsbury Children's Bks. 2002 344p $17.95; pa
$7.95 (7 and up) **Fic**
1. Space and time—Fiction
ISBN 1-58234-791-3; 1-58234-917-7 (pa)
LC 2001-56464

While sick in bed with cancer, Lucien begins making
journeys to a place in a parallel world that resembles
Venice, Italy, and he becomes caught up in the political
intrigues surrounding the Duchessa who rules the city
"Utterly fascinating, this rich, rip-roaring adventure—
the first in a series—will no doubt whet readers' appetites for Italian history and culture as well as the next installment." Booklist
Other available titles in this series are:
Stravaganza: city of flowers (2005)
Stravaganza: city of stars (2003)

Hoffman, Nina Kiriki

A stir of bones. Viking 2003 211p $15.99 (7
and up) **Fic**
1. Ghost stories 2. Wife abuse—Fiction
ISBN 0-670-03551-3 LC 2003-5029

Hoffman, Nina Kiriki—*Continued*

Prequel to the author's adult novels, A red heart of memories (1999) and Past the size of dreaming (2000)

Fourteen-year-old Susan Blackstrom "begins the painful process of breaking away from her abusive father, with help from allies both human and supernatural. A chance encounter with three classmates leads Susan to an abandoned house that . . . harbors an uncommonly substantial ghost named Nathan. . . . Richly endowed with complex relationships, a strange and subtle brand of magic, evocative language, and suspenseful storytelling, this will draw readers into a world less safe and simple than it seems at first glance." Booklist

Holland, Isabelle

The man without a face. Harper & Row 1987 c1972 159p hardcover o.p. paperback available $4.50   **Fic**

1. Homosexuality—Fiction

ISBN 0-06-447028-8 (pa)   LC 88-140924

Reissue of the title first published 1972

"From his tutor, the badly scarred recluse Justice McLeod, 14-year-old Charles Norstadt learns much more than the meaning of homosexuality." Booklist

"The author handles the homosexual experience with taste and discretion; the act of love between Justin and Charles is a necessary emotional catharsis for the boy within the context of his story, and is developed with perception and restraint. . . . A highly moral book, powerfully and sensitively written; a book that never loses sight of the humor and pain inherent in the human condition." Horn Book

Holm, Jennifer L.

Boston Jane: an adventure. HarperCollins Pubs. 2001 273p $16.95; lib bdg $17.89; pa $6.99   **Fic**

1. Chinook Indians—Fiction 2. Frontier and pioneer life—Fiction 3. Washington (State)—Fiction

ISBN 0-06-028738-1; 0-06-028739-X (lib bdg); 0-06-440849-3 (pa)   LC 2001-16753

Schooled in the lessons of etiquette for young ladies of 1854, Miss Jane Peck of Philadelphia finds little use for manners during her long sea voyage to the Pacific Northwest and while living among the American traders and Chinook Indians of Washington Territory

"Strong characterizations, meticulous attention to historical details . . . and a perceptive understanding of human nature make this a first-rate story not to be missed." Booklist

Other available titles about Boston Jane are:

Boston Jane: the claim (2004)

Boston Jane: wilderness days (2002)

Our only May Amelia. HarperCollins Pubs. 1999 253p il $15.95; lib bdg $15.89 (5 and up)   **Fic**

1. Frontier and pioneer life—Fiction 2. Family life—Fiction 3. Finnish Americans—Fiction

ISBN 0-06-027822-6; 0-06-028354-8 (lib bdg)   LC 98-47504

Also available audiobook version

A Newbery Medal honor book, 2000

As the only girl in a Finnish American family of seven brothers, May Amelia Jackson resents being expected to act like a lady while growing up in Washington State in 1899

"The voice of the colloquial first-person narrative rings true and provides a vivid picture of frontier and pioneer life. . . . An afterword discusses Holm's research into her own family's history and that of other Finnish immigrants." Horn Book Guide

Holman, Felice

Real. Atheneum Bks. for Young Readers 1997 176p $16   **Fic**

1. Space and time—Fiction 2. Native Americans—Fiction 3. California—Fiction

ISBN 0-689-80772-4   LC 96-47457

In 1932, while exploring the California desert, Colly finds a Cahuilla Indian boy and his grandmother, who are trapped in a Forever Day that they are constantly repeating from their lives in 1774

"Holman does a nice job of combining a supernatural story with early Hollywood movie history, Cahuilla Indian traditions, and Indian heritage preservation. This is an easy read and will keep most middle schoolers interested." Voice Youth Advocates

Slake's limbo. Scribner 1974 117p hardcover o.p. paperback available $4.99 (6 and up)   **Fic**

1. Runaway children—Fiction 2. Subways—Fiction 3. New York (N.Y.)—Fiction

ISBN 0-689-71066-6 (pa)

Aremis Slake, at the age of thirteen, takes to the New York City subways as a refuge from an abusive home life and oppressive school system

"The economically told chronicle of Slake's adventures is more than a survival saga: it is also an eloquent study of poverty, of fear, and finally of hope." Horn Book

Holmes, Barbara Ware

Following Fake Man; illustrations by Sarah Hokanson. Knopf 2001 228p il pa $5.99 hardcover o.p.   **Fic**

1. Fathers—Fiction 2. Artists—Fiction 3. Maine—Fiction

ISBN 0-440-41855-0 (pa)   LC 00-51461

During his summer in Maine, twelve-year-old Homer, together with his new friend Roger, is determined to find the truth about himself, his long-dead father, and a mysterious costumed man

"The strength of this book lies in the characters. . . . A genuinely satisfying book about friendship and family." SLJ

Holt, Kimberly Willis

Dancing in Cadillac light. Putnam 2001 167p $16.99; pa $5.99 (5 and up)   **Fic**

1. Grandfathers—Fiction 2. Old age—Fiction 3. Texas—Fiction

ISBN 0-399-23402-0; 0-698-11970-3 (pa)   LC 00-40267

Also available Thorndike Press large print edition

Holt, Kimberly Willis—*Continued*

In 1968, eleven-year-old Jaynell's life in the town of Moon, Texas, is enlivened when her eccentric Grandpap comes to live with her family

"This nostalgic parable about loss and redemption is at once gritty and poetic, stark and sentimental, howlingly funny and depressingly sad, but it is a solid page-turner." SLJ

Keeper of the night. Holt & Co. 2003 308p $16.95 (7 and up)   **Fic**
1. Suicide—Fiction 2. Death—Fiction 3. Guam—Fiction
ISBN 0-8050-6361-7   LC 2002-27553
Isabel, a thirteen-year-old girl living on the island of Guam, and her family try to cope with the death of Isabel's mother who committed suicide

"A beautifully written description of sorrow and recovery that should appeal to a wide audience." SLJ

My Louisiana sky. Holt & Co. 1998 200p $16.95; pa $5.99 (6 and up)   **Fic**
1. Mentally handicapped—Fiction 2. Louisiana—Fiction
ISBN 0-8050-5251-8; 0-440-41570-5 (pa)
                                      LC 98-12345
Also available in paperback from Dell and Audiobook version

Growing up in Saitter, Louisiana, in the 1950s, twelve-year-old Tiger Ann struggles with her feelings about her stern, but loving grandmother, her mentally slow parents, and her good friend and neighbor, Jesse

"Holt never resorts to over-dramatization or sentimentality in developing her uncannily credible characters." Horn Book Guide

When Zachary Beaver came to town. Holt & Co. 1999 227p $16.95   **Fic**
1. Obesity—Fiction 2. Friendship—Fiction 3. Texas—Fiction
ISBN 0-8050-6116-9   LC 99-27998
Also available in paperback from Dell

During the summer of 1971 in a small Texas town, thirteen-year-old Toby and his best friend Cal meet the star of a sideshow act, 600-pound Zachary, the fattest boy in the world

"Holt writes with a subtle sense of humor and sensitivity, and reading her work is a delightful experience." Voice Youth Advocates

Honey, Elizabeth

Remote man. Knopf 2002 c2000 260p $15.95; pa $4.99   **Fic**
1. Smuggling—Fiction
ISBN 0-375-81413-2; 0-440-41901-8 (pa)
                                      LC 2001-37697
First published 2000 in Australia

Thirteen-year-old Ned and his depressed mother leave Australia for a rest in America, but he is soon on the trail of international smugglers of exotic animals, with help from his Internet friends

"The originality; careening pace; intelligent, quirky characters; and wordplay will pull readers effortlessly along." Booklist

Hoobler, Dorothy

The ghost in the Tokaido Inn; [by] Dorothy and Thomas Hoobler. Philomel Bks. 1999 214p $17.99; pa $6.99   **Fic**
1. Japan—Fiction 2. Mystery fiction
ISBN 0-399-23330-X; 0-698-11879-0 (pa)
                                      LC 98-14089
Sequel: Demon in the teahouse

While attempting to solve the mystery of a stolen jewel, Seikei, a merchant's son who longs to be a samurai, joins a group of kabuki actors in eighteenth-century Japan

"Precise characterization, suspenseful plot twists, and a pace defined by swift and sometimes violent action make this a lively period thriller." Bull Cent Child Books
Other titles about Seikei are:
The demon in the teahouse (2001)
In darkess, death (2004)

Hooper, Mary

At the sign of the Sugared Plum. Bloomsbury Children's Bks. 2003 169p $16.95   **Fic**
1. Sisters—Fiction 2. Plague—Fiction 3. London (England)—Fiction
ISBN 1-582-34849-9   LC 2003-51863
In June 1665, excited at the prospect of coming to London to work at her sister Sarah's candy shop, teenaged Hannah is unconcerned about rumors of Plague until, as the hot summer advances and increasing numbers of people succumb to the disease, she and Sarah find themselves trapped in the city with no means of escape

"The story moves quickly and the tension builds at a rapid pace and will hold readers' interest. . . . A captivating entry in the historical fiction genre." SLJ
Includes bibliographical references

Horowitz, Anthony, 1955-

The Devil and his boy. Philomel Bks. 2000 c1998 182p $16.99; pa $5.99 (5 and up)   **Fic**
1. Theater—Fiction 2. Adventure fiction 3. London (England)—Fiction
ISBN 0-399-23432-2; 0-698-11913-4 (pa)
                                      LC 99-39791
First published 1998 in the United Kingdom

In 1593, thirteen-year-old Tom travels through the English countryside to London, where he falls in with a troupe of actors and finds himself in great danger from several sources

"In this delightful and inventive mixture of historical fact and grand storytelling, Horowitz has conjured a fabulous, fast-paced tale of humor, intrigue, magic, and adventure." Voice Youth Advocates

Public enemy number two; a Diamond brothers mystery; Anthony Horowitz. 1st American ed. Philomel Books 2004 c1997 190p $16.99; pa $5.99   **Fic**
1. Mystery fiction
ISBN 0-399-24154-X; 0-14-240218-4 (pa)
                                      LC 2004-10418

Horowitz, Anthony, 1955——*Continued*

When thirteen-year-old Nick is framed for a jewel robbery, he and his brother, the bumbling detective Tim Diamond, attempt to clear his name by capturing the master criminal known as the Fence.

"Horowitz has a knack for puns and humor, and he successfully combines it with a nonstop action mystery that has everything from hydraulically controlled buses to secret caverns. A readable and exciting adventure." SLJ

Other available titles in the Diamond Brothers Mystery series are:

The falcon's Maltester (2004)

Three of Diamonds (2005)

Raven's gate; book one of the Gatekeepers; Anthony Horowitz. 1st ed. Scholastic Press 2005 254p $17.95 (7 and up) **Fic**
1. Witchcraft—Fiction 2. Supernatural—Fiction 3. Great Britain—Fiction
ISBN 0-439-67995-8 LC 2004-21512

Sent to live in a foster home in a remote Yorkshire village, Matt, a troubled fourteen-year-old English boy, uncovers an evil plot involving witchcraft and the site of an ancient stone circle.

"The creepy activities and the overall atmosphere of fear are well defined, and once the action starts, it doesn't let up. . . . This powerful struggle between good and evil is a real page-turner." SLJ

Stormbreaker. Philomel Bks. 2001 c2000 192p $17.99; pa $5.99 **Fic**
1. Spies—Fiction 2. Terrorism—Fiction 3. Orphans—Fiction 4. Great Britain—Fiction
ISBN 0-399-23620-1; 0-14-240165-X (pa)
LC 00-63683
First published 2000 in the United Kingdom

After the death of the uncle who had been his guardian, fourteen-year-old Alex Rider is coerced to continue his uncle's dangerous work for Britain's intelligence agency, MI6

"Horowitz thoughtfully balances Alex's super-spy finesse with typical teen insecurities to create a likable hero living a fantasy come true. An entertaining, nicely layered novel." Booklist

Other titles about Alex Rider are:

Eagle strike (2004)

Point blank (2002)

Scorpia (2005)

Skeleton key (2003)

Horvath, Polly

The canning season. Farrar, Straus & Giroux 2003 195p $16 **Fic**
1. Aunts—Fiction
ISBN 0-374-39956-5 LC 2002-66296

Thirteen-year-old Ratchet spends a summer in Maine with her eccentric great-aunts Tilly and Penpen, hearing strange stories from the past and encountering a variety of unusual and colorful characters

"Offbeat, slapstick humor is mitigated by poignancy in Horvath's distinctive rollicking style. There is occasional use of strong language, and the family stories are woven with death, often gruesomely described. . . . Readers are in for a wise and wacky ride when they open this novel." SLJ

Everything on a waffle. Farrar, Straus & Giroux 2001 149p $16; pa $5.95 (4 and up) **Fic**
1. Uncles—Fiction 2. British Columbia—Fiction
ISBN 0-374-32236-8; 0-374-42208-7 (pa)
LC 00-35399

A Newbery Award honor book, 2002

Eleven-year-old Primrose living in a small fishing village in British Columbia recounts her experiences and all that she learns about human nature and the unpredictability of life in the months after her parents are lost at sea

"The story is full of subtle humor and wisdom, presented through the eyes of a uniquely appealing young protagonist." SLJ

Hotze, Sollace

A circle unbroken. Clarion Bks. 1988 202p hardcover o.p. paperback available $5.95
Fic
1. Dakota Indians—Fiction 2. Native Americans—Fiction
ISBN 0-395-59702-1 (pa) LC 88-2569

Captured by a roving band of Sioux Indians and brought up as the chief's daughter, Rachel is recaptured by her white family and finds it difficult to adjust, as she longs to return to the tribe

"Rachel-Kata Wi is an extremely likable heroine. Her story moves quickly, filled more with people and their relationship than great detail of place or time, and is always grounded in her own growth and feelings. Involving historical fiction, with powerful emotional impact." SLJ

Houston, Gloria

Bright Freedom's song; a story of the Underground Railroad. Harcourt Brace & Co. 1998 145p $16 **Fic**
1. Underground railroad—Fiction 2. Slavery—Fiction 3. African Americans—Fiction
ISBN 0-15-201812-3 LC 98-13756

In the years before the Civil War, Bright discovers that her parents are providing a safehouse for the Underground Railroad and helps to save a runaway slave named Marcus

"Readable and well-researched historical fiction." SLJ

Includes bibliographical references (p.143-145)

Houston, James A., 1921-2005

Frozen fire; a tale of courage; by James Houston; drawings by the author. Atheneum Pubs. 1977 149p il pa $4.95 hardcover o.p. (6 and up)
Fic
1. Wilderness survival—Fiction 2. Arctic regions—Fiction 3. Inuit—Fiction
ISBN 0-689-71612-5 (pa) LC 77-6366

"A Margaret K. McElderry book"

"Based on the true and dramatic ordeal of an Eskimo boy in the 1960's, this adventure story is set . . . in the far north. Kayak, a classmate of Matthew Morgan's in their Baffin Island school, suggests to his new friend Mattoosie (Matthew) that they take a snowmobile and go to the rescue of Mattoosie's father when the latter, a

Houston, James A., 1921-2005—*Continued*
prospector, disappears. The spare can of gasoline leaks,
and the two boys face a homeward trek through seventy-
five miles of whirling snow and bitter cold." Bull Cent
Child Books

"Convincing dialogue, good pace, and lean style mark
this as first-class adventure with a partial basis in fact."
SLJ

Followed by Black diamonds (1982)

Howe, James, 1946-
The misfits. Atheneum Bks. for Young Readers
2001 274p $16; pa $5.99   **Fic**
1. School stories 2. Elections—Fiction 3. Friendship—
Fiction
ISBN 0-689-83955-3; 0-689-83956-1 (pa)
LC 00-66390
Four students who do not fit in at their small-town
middle school decide to create a third party for the stu-
dent council elections to represent all students who have
ever been called names
This is a "timely, sensitive, laugh-out-loud must-read
for all middle school students and teachers." Voice
Youth Advocates

The watcher. Atheneum Bks. for Young Readers
1997 167p $16; pa $8 (7 and up)   **Fic**
1. Child abuse—Fiction 2. Beaches—Fiction
ISBN 0-689-80186-6; 0-689-82662-1 (pa)
LC 96-43045
"Margaret thinks that the families she observes on her
summer vacation at the beach are happier than her own,
but Howe slowly and skillfully reveals the truth—about
those Margaret observes and about Margaret herself.
While the book provides some small hope that Margaret—a victim of child abuse—will find a better life, the
overall outlook is bleak. Somber but honest." Horn Book
Guide

Howe, Norma
The adventures of Blue Avenger. Holt & Co.
1999 230p $15.95 (7 and up)   **Fic**
ISBN 0-8050-6062-6   LC 98-29788
Also available in paperback from HarperCollins
On his sixteenth birthday, still trying to cope with the
unexpected death of his father, David Schumacher de-
cides--or does he--to change his name to Blue Avenger,
hoping to find a way to make a difference in his Oak-
land neighborhood and in the world
"This is at once ingeniously plotted and howlingly
funny." Bull Cent Child Books
Other available titles about Blue Avenger are:
Blue Avenger and the theory of everything (2002)
Blue Avenger cracks the code (2000)

Howland, Ethan, 1963-
The lobster war. Front St./Cricket Bks. 2001
146p $15.95   **Fic**
1. Brothers—Fiction 2. Lobsters—Fiction
ISBN 0-8126-2800-4   LC 00-47619
Although he fears being in the water, sixteen-year-old
Dain is determined to be a professional lobsterman, de-
spite pressure from his older brother and widowed moth-

er that he attend college instead, and despite the fact that
someone is sabotaging his lobster traps
"Howland is a sensitive observer of relationships, and
untangling the multiple motives from which his characters often act will keep readers involved in the story."
Booklist

Hughes, Dean, 1943-
Soldier boys. Atheneum Bks. for Young Readers
2001 162p $16.95; pa $5.99   **Fic**
1. World War, 1939-1945—Fiction 2. Ardennes, Battle of the, 1944-1945—Fiction 3. Soldiers—Fiction
ISBN 0-689-81748-7; 0-689-86021-8 (pa)
LC 00-46920
"This World War II novel tells the parallel stories of
two young soldiers fighting on opposite sides of the conflict—a paratrooper from Utah and a Hitler Youth who
joins the German army. Spence and Dieter's paths cross
briefly on a snow-covered Belgian hill in a scene both
compassionate and tragic. Hughes tells their tales in as-
sured prose that's harrowing without being exploitive."
Horn Book Guide

Hughes, Mark Peter
I am the wallpaper; .; . Delacorte Press 2005
228p $15.95; lib bdg $17.99   **Fic**
ISBN 0-385-73241-4; 0-385-90265-4 (lib bdg)
LC 2004-10163
Thirteen-year-old Floey Packer, jealous of her attractive and popular older sister, shares her home with two
younger cousins and experiences a summer vacation
filled with embarrassing events, with herself as the star.
"Humorous incidents abound, character growth is convincing, and the plot moves irresistibly forward." SLJ

Hughes, Monica
Invitation to the game. Simon & Schuster Bks.
for Young Readers 1991 183p pa $4.99 hardcover
o.p. (7 and up)   **Fic**
1. Science fiction
ISBN 0-671-86692-3   LC 90-22832
"The graduates of 2154 find a bleak and dangerous
world with no jobs. Home for Lisse and friends is an
abandoned warehouse, and they must scrounge for neces-
sities. To their delight, they are asked to join The Game,
which transports them to a paradise. Is this beautiful
world real—or a computer simulation?" Publisher's note
"This bold and incisive parable for the future will by
turns terrify and enchant both science fiction enthusiasts
and readers concerned about the earth's fate." Publ Wkly

Hughes, Pat, 1933-
The breaker boys. Farrar Straus Giroux 2004
247p $18   **Fic**
1. Coal mines and mining—Fiction 2. Immigrants—
Fiction   3.   Labor   movement—Fiction
4. Pennsylvania—Fiction
ISBN 0-374-30956-6   LC 2003-49433
In 1897, Nate Tanner, the hot-tempered twelve-year-
old son of wealthy Pennsylvania mine owners, goes
against his father's wishes by befriending some of the

Hughes, Pat, 1933—— *Continued*
boys who work in the mines and gets caught up in a disasterous clash between mine workers and the law.
"Hughes has created a complex protagonist who's likable even when acting 'ugly.' The author doesn't provide pat answers, but offers the hope that the questions Nate faces will be resolved." SLJ

Guerrilla season. Farrar, Straus & Giroux 2003 328p $18 (7 and up) **Fic**
1. Quantrill, William Clarke, 1837-1865—Fiction 2. United States—History—1861-1865, Civil War—Fiction 3. Guerrillas—Fiction
ISBN 0-374-32811-0　　　　LC 2002-32208
Two fifteen-year-old boys in Missouri in 1863 find friendship and family loyalty tested by Quantrell's raiders, a Rebel guerrilla band who roamed under the black flag of "no quarter to be given by Union troops"
"Delivering lifelike characters and a stimulating plot, this novel is a good exploration of the turmoil surrounding war-torn Missouri." SLJ

Hunter, Erin
Into the wild; warriors #1. HarperCollins Pubs. 2003 272p $15.99; lib bdg $16.89; pa $5.99 **Fic**
1. Cats—Fiction 2. Fantasy fiction
ISBN 0-06-000002-3; 0-06-052548-7 (lib bdg); 0-06-052550-9 (pa)
For generations, four clans of wild cats have shared the forest. When their warrior code is threatened by mysterious deaths, a house cat named Rusty may turn out to be the bravest warrior of all.
"The author has created an intriguing world with an intricate structure and mythology, and an engaging young hero." SLJ
Other titles in the Warriors series are:
A dangerous path (2004)
The darkest hour (2004)
Fire and ice (2003)
Forest of secrets (2003)
Midnight (2005)
Rising storm (2004)

Hurst, Carol Otis
Through the lock. Houghton Mifflin 2001 160p $15 **Fic**
1.　Orphans—Fiction　2.　Canals—Fiction 3. Connecticut—Fiction
ISBN 0-618-03036-0　　　　LC 99-28510
"Walter Lorraine books"
Etta, a twelve-year-old orphan in nineteenth-century Connecticut, meets Walter, a boy living in an abandoned cabin on the New Haven and Northampton Canal and has adventures with him while trying to be reunited with her siblings
"Etta and Walter's terse conversations, anguished and funny, are the best part of the book, and the history is fascinating." Booklist

Huxley, Aldous, 1894-1963
Brave new world. Harper & Row 1946 xx, 311p hardcover o.p. paperback available $16 (7 and up) **Fic**

1. Utopias—Fiction 2. Technology and civilization—Fiction
ISBN 0-06-090101-2 (pa)
Also available in hardcover from Buccaneer Bks.
First published 1932 by Doubleday, Doran & Company
"The ironic title, which Huxley has taken from Shakespeare's 'The Tempest,' describes a world in which science has taken control over morality and humaneness. In this utopia humans emerge from test tubes, families are obsolete, and even pleasure is regulated. When a so-called savage who believes in spirituality is found and is imported to the community, he cannot accomodate himself to this world and ends his life." Shapiro. Fic for Youth. 3d edition

Ibbotson, Eva
Island of the aunts; illustrated by Kevin Hawkes. Dutton Children's Bks. 2000 c1999 281p il $15.99; pa $5.99 (5 and up) **Fic**
1. Fantasy fiction
ISBN 0-526-46484-0; 0-14-230049-7 (pa)
　　　　　　　　　　　　　LC 00-41703
First published 1999 in the United Kingdom
As they get older, several sisters decide that they must kidnap children and bring them to their secluded island home to help with the work of caring for an assortment of unusual sea creatures
"At once funny and poignant, the story is a fascinating tapestry comprising vivid human characters, powerfully imagined magical creatures, and an engrossing plot." Booklist

Journey to the river sea; illustrated by Kevin Hawkes. Dutton Children's Bks. 2002 298p il $17.99; pa $5.99 (5 and up) **Fic**
1. Orphans—Fiction 2. Amazon River valley—Fiction 3. Brazil—Fiction
ISBN 0-525-46739-4; 0-14-250184-0 (pa)
　　　　　　　　　　　　　LC 2001-28733
Sent with her governess to live with the dreadful Carter family in exotic Brazil in 1910, Maia endures many hardships before fulfilling her dream of exploring the Amazon River
"The unconventional cast of characters is highly appealing, and Ibbotson does a wonderful job of turning genre themes topsy-turvy in delightfully humorous style, at the same time adding fine details that expand and enrich the traditional orphan-adventure plot." Booklist

The star of Kazan; illustrated by Kevin Hawkes. Dutton 2004 405p il $16.99 (5 and up) **Fic**
1. Vienna (Austria)—Fiction 2. Germany—Fiction 3. Mystery fiction
ISBN 0-525-47347-5　　　　LC 2004-45455
After twelve-year-old Annika, a foundling living in late nineteenth-century Vienna, inherits a trunk of costume jewelry, a woman claiming to be her aristocratic mother arrives and takes her to live in a strangely decrepit mansion in Germany
"This is a rich saga . . . full of stalwart friends, sly villains, a brave heroine, and good triumphing over evil. . . . An intensely satisfying read." SLJ

Ingold, Jeanette

The Big Burn. Harcourt 2002 295p $17; pa
$6.95 (7 and up)   **Fic**
1. Forest fires—Fiction
ISBN 0-15-216470-7; 0-15-204924-X (pa)
                                    LC 2001-5667
Three teenagers battle the flames of the Big Burn of
1910, one of the century's biggest wildfires
"A solid adventure story with a well-realized setting."
Booklist

Hitch; Jeanette Ingold. Harcourt, Inc 2005 272p
$17 (7 and up)   **Fic**
1. Civilian Conservation Corps (U.S.)—Fiction
2. Great Depression, 1929-1939—Fiction
3. Montana—Fiction
ISBN 0-15-204747-6   LC 2004-19447
To help his family during the Depression and avoid
becoming a drunk like his father, Moss Trawnley joins
the Civilian Conservation Corps, helps build a new camp
near Monroe, Montana, and leads the other men in making the camp a success.
This is "a credible, involving story. . . . Both [the author's] writing style and her 1930s setting feels totally
true to the time." Booklist

Mountain solo. Harcourt 2003 309p $17 (7 and
up)   **Fic**
1. Violinists—Fiction 2. Family life—Fiction
ISBN 0-15-202670-3   LC 2003-42326
Back at her childhood home in Missoula, Montana, after a disastrous concert in Germany, a teenage violin
prodigy contemplates giving up life with her mother in
New York City and her music as she, her father, stepmother, and stepsister hike to a pioneer homesite where
another violinist once faced difficult decisions of his own
"Mountain Solo is a good read for anyone fascinated
by the power of music and its effects on individuals'
lives." SLJ

Irwin, Hadley

The original Freddie Ackerman. Margaret K.
McElderry Bks. 1992 183p (5 and up)
                                                Fic
1. Aunts—Fiction 2. Islands—Fiction 3. Maine—Fiction
ISBN 0-689-50562-0; 0-689-80389-3
                                      LC 91-43145
Twelve-year-old Trevor Frederick Ackerman refuses to
spend another summer with his extended family of divorced parents, step-parents, and step-brothers and stepsisters, so he is sent up to Maine to stay with two eccentric great aunts and there gets involved in a series of adventures
"This is a beautiful coming-of-age story with wonderful characterizations. Trevor's loneliness and low self-
esteem are palpable as he escapes painful realities
through a series of fantasies of himself as a war hero.
. . . A fine book with a winning combination of humor
and poignancy." SLJ

Isaacs, Anne

Torn thread. Scholastic 2000 188p $15.95 (7
and up)   **Fic**
1. World War, 1939-1945—Fiction 2. Holocaust,
1933-1945—Fiction 3. Jews—Fiction
ISBN 0-590-60363-9   LC 95-31655
Also available Thorndike Press large print edition and
in paperback from New American Library
In an attempt to save his daughter's life, Eva's father
sends her from Poland to a labor camp in Czechoslovakia where she and her sister survive the war
"Given its precise detail and sensitivity to unimagin-
able suffering, this gripping novel reads like the strongest
of Holocaust memoirs." Publ Wkly

Jacobsson, Anders, 1963-

In Ned's head; by Anders Jacobsson & Sören
Olsson; translated by Kevin Read. Atheneum Bks.
for Young Readers 2001 133p $16; pa $4.99
                                                Fic
1. Diaries—Fiction
ISBN 0-689-83870-0; 0-689-87355-7 (pa)
                                       LC 99-86169
Eleven-year-old Ned, who prefers the name Treb, uses
his diary to record his wild thoughts about romance,
school, and the rest of his eventful life
The "journal entries are witty and insightful, yet full
of insecurity and irrational thoughts." SLJ

Jacques, Brian

Castaways of the Flying Dutchman; illustrated
by Ian Schoenherr. Philomel Bks. 2001 327p il
$22.95; pa $7.99   **Fic**
1. Fantasy fiction
ISBN 0-399-23601-5; 0-14-250118-2 (pa)
                                       LC 00-59822
In 1620, a boy and his dog are rescued from the
doomed ship, Flying Dutchman, by an angel who guides
them in travelling the world, eternally helping those in
great need
"The swashbuckling language brims with color and
melodrama; the villains are dastardly and stupid; and
buried treasure, mysterious clues, and luscious culinary
descriptions . . . keep the pages turning." Booklist
Followed by The angel's command (2003)

Redwall; illustrated by Gary Chalk. Philomel
Bks. 1986 351p il $23.99; pa $7.99 (6 and up)
                                                Fic
1. Mice—Fiction 2. Animals—Fiction 3. Fantasy fiction
ISBN 0-399-21424-0; 0-14-230237-6 (pa)
                                       LC 86-25467
"Only the lost sword of Martin the Warrior can save
Redwall Abbey from the evil rat Cluny and his greedy
horde. The young mouse Matthias (formerly Redwall's
most awkward novice) vows to recover the legendary
weapon." Publ Wkly
"Thoroughly engrossing, this novel captivates despite
its length. . . . The theme will linger long after the story
is finished." Booklist
Other available titles about Redwall Abbey are:

Jacques, Brian—*Continued*
The Bellmaker (1995)
The legend of Luke (2000)
Loamhedge (2003)
The long patrol (1998)
Lord Brocktree (2000)
Mariel of Redwall (1992)
Marlfox (1998)
Martin the Warrior (1994)
Mattimeo (1990)
Mossflower (1998)
The outcast of Redwall (1996)
Pearls of Lutra (1997)
Rakkety Tam (2004)
Salamandastron (1993)
Taggerung (2001)
Triss (2002)

Janeczko, Paul B., 1945-
Worlds afire. Candlewick Press 2004 92p
$15.99   **Fic**
1. Fires—Fiction 2. Circus—Fiction 3. Connecticut—
Fiction
ISBN 0-7636-2235-4   LC 2003-55337
"In a collection of narrative poems, Janeczko describes
a circus fire that took place on July 6, 1944 in Hartford,
CT, from the viewpoints of those who were there." SLJ
"Janeczko never sensationalizes the horror, but the
combination of a thrilling circus and true catastrophe will
grab middle-schoolers, especially for readers' theater."
Booklist

Janke, Katelan
Survival in the storm; the dust bowl diary of
Grace Edwards. Scholastic 2002 189p il (Dear
America) $10.95   **Fic**
1. Great Depression, 1929-1939—Fiction 2. Family
life—Fiction
ISBN 0-439-21599-4   LC 2002-18992
A twelve-year-old girl keeps a journal of her family's
and friends' difficult experiences in the Texas panhandle,
part of the "Dust Bowl," during the Great Depression.
Includes a historical note about life in America in 1935
"The 15-year-old author interviewed several people
who lived through the Dust Bowl. . . . As an example
of what a teen can achieve when she explores her neighborhood and nations past, *Survival* succeeds." SLJ

Jarvis, Robin
The alchemist's cat; book one of the Deptford
histories. Seastar Books 2004 304p $17.95 (5 and
up)   **Fic**
1. Witchcraft—Fiction 2. Horror fiction 3. London
(England)—Fiction
ISBN 1-58717-257-7
Prequel to the Deptford mice trilogy that includes The
dark portal, The crystal prison, and The final reckoning
First published 1989 in the United Kingdom
When Will Godwin, assistant to a wicked alchemist in
1664 London, takes in a mother cat and her kittens, a
story of villainy unfolds which reveals how Jupiter, Lord
of Darkness, became so evil and powerful.
"Jarvis delivers a vivid tale of treachery, cruelty, and
sorcery, leavened only by Will's innate goodness. It's
also a real page-turner." Booklist

The dark portal; book one of the Deptford mice
trilogy. SeaStar Bks. 2000 243p il $17.95; pa
$6.95 (5 and up)   **Fic**
1. Mice—Fiction 2. Rats—Fiction 3. Fantasy fiction
ISBN 1-58717-021-3; 1-58717-112-0 (pa)
                                  LC 00-26517
"Books of wonder"
First published 1989 in the United Kingdom
.
While on a rescue mission, a few daring mice journey
below to the sewers to an evil world populated by rats
who peel mice before eating them and worship the Dark
Lord
This "is a spooky and enthralling animal fantasy. . . .
Jarvis provides counterpoint to the heart-racing adventure
with scenes of haunting beauty." Publ Wkly
Other titles in the Deptford mice trilogy are:
The crystal prison (2001)
The final reckoning (2002)

Thorn ogres of Hagwood; the Hagwood trilogy,
book one. Silver Whistle Bks. 2002 c1999 244p
$16; pa $5.95   **Fic**
1. Fantasy fiction
ISBN 0-15-216752-8; 0-15-205122-8 (pa)
                                  LC 2001-57606
First published 1999 in the United Kingdom
The werlings, a peaceful group of forgotten forest
creatures whose only magic is the ability to change
shapes, are unwittingly drawn into the search for a valuable item stolen from an evil queen many years before
"An assortment of odd and humorous characters
quickens the pace of this plot-driven tale. Highly imaginative, ornately descriptive, and vividly gory." ALAN

Jeapes, Ben
The new world order. Fickling 2005 435p
$15.95; lib bdg $17.99 (7 and up)   **Fic**
1. Charles I, King of Great Britain, 1600-1649—Fiction 2. Cromwell, Oliver, 1599-1658—Fiction
3. Space and time—Fiction
ISBN 0-385-75013-7; 0-385-75015-3 (lib bdg)
                                  LC 2004-3402
Having ended England's Civil War between the
Roundheads and the Royalists in 1645, the Overlord of
the Holekhor, a race from another world, and his half-
English son question the decision to colonize the island
and convert their beloved English to a faith characterised
by witches and myriad gods
"The riveting story has enough twists and turns, battles and bloodshed to intrigue even hardcore sf fans, but
readers will also get a painless lesson in English history." Booklist

The xenocide mission. Random House 2002
387p $15.95; pa $6.50   **Fic**
1. Extraterrestrial beings—Fiction 2. Science fiction
ISBN 0-385-75007-2; 0-440-23785-8 (pa)
                                  LC 2002-20666
"David Fickling books"
In a far-distant solar system, Lieutenant Joel Gilmore
and his space observation team are suddenly attacked by
the very aliens they were sent to watch

Jeapes, Ben—*Continued*
"The action is convincing and so fast paced that the result is a real thriller of a story." Booklist

Jenkins, A. M. (Amanda McRaney)
Out of order. HarperCollins Pubs. 2003 247p $15.99; lib bdg $16.89 (7 and up)   **Fic**
1. School stories
ISBN 0-06-623968-0; 0-06-623969-9 (lib bdg)
LC 2002-15621
Sophomore Colt Trammel loves baseball and his girlfriend Grace, but he hates the rest of high school and maintains a tough facade to hide his feelings of inferiority
"The best part of this novel is the portrait of Colt. Every part rings true, from his rough language and obsession with sex to his need to act cool at all costs. It's also a very funny portrait, without ever lapsing into stereotypes or becoming too broad. Readers looking for a dead-on look at high school will enjoy this novel." SLJ

Jennings, Patrick, 1962-
The wolving time. Scholastic Press 2003 197p $15.95   **Fic**
1. Werewolves—Fiction 2. France—Fiction
ISBN 0-439-39555-0   LC 2002-151865
In France during a time of witch-hunts, in a village with a corrupt priest, thirteen-year-old Laszlo longs to be able to turn into a wolf as his parents can, but also desires the friendship of a village girl
"One of the pleasures of reading this cleanly written fantasy is how natural it seems when Laszlo's parents transform from human to wolf. Another is how gracefully the story folds this element of fantasy into a work of historical fiction." Booklist

Jennings, Richard W., 1945-
The great whale of Kansas. Houghton Mifflin 2001 150p $15   **Fic**
1. Fossils—Fiction 2. Whales—Fiction 3. Kansas—Fiction
ISBN 0-618-10228-0   LC 00-56737
"Walter Lorraine books"
While digging a hole in his back yard, an eleven-year-old Kansas boy finds the fossilized remains of a gigantic prehistoric animal, a discovery that brings both fame and controversy
"Fast paced and well written." Book Rep

My life of crime. Houghton Mifflin 2002 145p $15 (5 and up)   **Fic**
1. Parrots—Fiction 2. School stories
ISBN 0-618-21433-X   LC 2002-1183
"Walter Lorraine books"
A sixth grader's discovery of a bedraggled classroom pet parrot sets him on an adventure with real ethical and legal implications
This is a "buoyant, briskly paced novel." Publ Wkly

Orwell's luck; {by} Richard Jennings. Houghton Mifflin 2000 146p $15 (5 and up)   **Fic**
1. Rabbits—Fiction 2. Magic—Fiction
ISBN 0-618-03628-8   LC 99-33501

"Walter Lorraine books"
While caring for an injured rabbit which becomes her confidant, horoscope writer, and source of good luck, a thoughtful seventh grade girl learns to see things in more than one way
"This absolutely captivating tale is about everyday magic . . . filled with quiet humor and seamless invention. The characters . . . are the sort that readers fall in love with." Booklist

Jiménez, Francisco, 1943-
Breaking through. Houghton Mifflin 2001 195p il $15; pa $6.95 (5 and up)   **Fic**
1. Mexican Americans—Fiction 2. Migrant labor—Fiction
ISBN 0-618-01173-0; 0-618-34248-6 (pa)
LC 2001-16941
Sequel to The circuit
Having come from Mexico to California ten years ago, fourteen-year-old Francisco is still working in the fields but fighting to improve his life and complete his education
"For all its recounting of deprivation, this is a hopeful book, told with rectitude and dignity." Horn Book

Jinks, Catherine, 1963-
Pagan's crusade. Candlewick Press 2003 c1993 246p maps (Pagan chronicles) $15.99 (7 and up)   **Fic**
1. Crusades—Fiction 2. Knights and knighthood—Fiction 3. Orphans—Fiction 4. Middle Ages—Fiction
ISBN 0-7636-2019-X   LC 2002-42883
First published 1993 in Australia
In twelfth-century Jerusalem, orphaned sixteen-year-old Pagan is assigned to work for Lord Roland, a Templar knight, as Saladin's armies close in on the Holy City
"With characters as lively and engaging as Pagan and Lord Roland, readers will be glad to see there are three books of their adventures yet to come." Horn Book
Other available titles in the Pagan Chronicles series are:
Pagan in exile (2004)
Pagan's vows (2004)

Jocelyn, Marthe, 1956-
Mable Riley; a reliable record of humdrum, peril, and romance. Candlewick Press 2004 279p $15.99 (5 and up)   **Fic**
1. Teachers—Fiction 2. Women's rights—Fiction 3. Canada—Fiction
ISBN 0-7636-2120-X   LC 2003-55322
In 1901, fourteen-year-old Mable Riley dreams of being a writer and having adventures while stuck in Perth County, Ontario, assisting her sister in teaching school and secretly becoming friends with a neighbor who holds scandalous opinions on women's rights.
"This book is a funny and inspiring tale of a young girl finding her voice and the courage to make it heard." Voice Youth Advocates

Johnson, Angela, 1961-

Bird. Dial Books 2004 133p $15.99 (5 and up)
Fic

1. Runaway teenagers—Fiction 2. Stepfathers—Fiction
3. African Americans—Fiction 4. Alabama—Fiction
ISBN 0-8037-2847-6   LC 2003-22793

Devastated by the loss of a second father, thirteen-year-old Bird follows her stepfather from Cleveland to Alabama in hopes of convincing him to come home, and along the way helps two boys cope with their difficulties

"Johnson writes with a poet's knowledge of rhythm and knows how to use the space between words. . . . Johnson also creates a visceral sense of each character's search for love and connection." Booklist

A cool moonlight. Dial Bks. 2003 133p $14.99
(5 and up)   **Fic**

1. Skin—Diseases—Fiction
ISBN 0-8037-2846-8   LC 2002-31521

Nine-year-old Lila, born with xeroderma pigmentosum, a skin disease that make her sensitive to sunlight, makes secret plans to feel the sun's rays on her tenth birthday

"The book's real magic resides in the spell cast by Johnson's spare, lucid, lyrical prose. Using simple words and vivid sensory images, she creates Lila's inner world as a place of quiet intensity." Booklist

The first part last. Simon & Schuster Bks for Young Readers 2003 131p $15.95 (7 and up)
Fic

1. Teenage fathers—Fiction 2. Infants—Fiction
3. African Americans—Fiction
ISBN 0-689-84922-2   LC 2002-36512

Prequel to Heaven (1998)

Bobby's carefree teenage life changes forever when he becomes a father and must care for his adored baby daughter

"Brief, poetic, and absolutely riveting." SLJ

Heaven. Simon & Schuster Bks. for Young Readers 1998 138p $16.95; pa $5.99 (6 and up)
Fic

1. Adoption—Fiction 2. African Americans—Fiction
ISBN 0-689-82229-4; 0-689-82290-1 (pa)
LC 98-3291

Coretta Scott King Award for text, 1999

Fourteen-year-old Marley's seemingly perfect life in the small town of Heaven is disrupted when she discovers that her father and mother are not her real parents

"In spare, often poetic prose . . . Johnson relates Marley's insightful quest into what makes a family." SLJ

Looking for Red. Simon & Schuster Bks. for Young Readers 2002 116p $15.95; pa $4.99
Fic

1. Siblings—Fiction 2. Missing persons—Fiction
3. African Americans—Fiction
ISBN 0-689-83253-2; 0-689-86388-8 (pa)
LC 2001-42846

A thirteen-year-old girl struggles to cope with the loss of Red, her beloved older brother, who disappeared four months earlier off the coast of Cape Cod

"In beautiful prose, the narrative moves fluidly from flashbacks to the present, and the stages of grief are represented in startling but realistic ways." Booklist

Songs of faith. Orchard Bks. 1998 103p $16.99
(5 and up)   **Fic**

1. Divorce—Fiction 2. African Americans—Fiction
ISBN 0-531-30023-4   LC 97-40216

Also available in paperback from Knopf

Living in a small town in Ohio in 1975 and desperately missing her divorced father, thirteen-year-old Doreen comes to terms with disturbing changes in her family life

"Johnson has set attractive and realistic African-American characters in situations in which race is not the focus. This short, sensitive book will appeal most to reflective readers." SLJ

Toning the sweep. Orchard Bks. 1993 103p hardcover o.p. paperback available $5.99
Fic

1. Grandmothers—Fiction 2. Family life—Fiction
3. Death—Fiction 4. African Americans—Fiction
ISBN 0-590-48142-8 (pa)   LC 92-34062

Coretta Scott King award for text, 1994

"A Richard Jackson book"

On a visit to her grandmother Ola, who is dying of cancer in her house in the desert, fourteen-year-old Emmie hears many stories about the past and her family history and comes to a better understanding of relatives both dead and living

"Full of subtle nuance, the novel is overlaid with meaning about the connections of family and the power of friendship." SLJ

Johnson, Maureen

The key to the golden Firebird; a novel. HarperCollins 2004 297p $15.99; lib bdg $16.89 (7 and up)   **Fic**

1. Bereavement—Fiction 2. Sisters—Fiction
ISBN 0-06054138-5; 0-06-054139-3 (lib bdg)

As three teenaged sisters struggle to cope with their father's sudden death, they find they must reexamine friendships, lifelong dreams, and their relationships with each other and their father

"Poignant and laced with wry humor. . . . This is a wonderfully moving and entertaining novel full of authentic characters and emotions." SLJ

Johnston, Julie

Adam and Eve and Pinch-me. Little, Brown 1994 180p (7 and up)   **Fic**

1. Foster home care—Fiction
ISBN 0-316-46990-4   LC 93-21023

Available in paperback from Tundra Bks. $9.95 (ISBN 0-8877-6648-X)

Fifteen-year-old Sara Moone, abandonded at birth and shunted from one foster home to another, finds that she cannot remain aloof from her latest family

"Sara is a frequently unlikable but completely real character that young adult readers will understand, respect, and ultimately admire. . . . Other characters are equally unique and credible in this well-written novel." Voice Youth Advocates

In spite of killer bees. Tundra Bks. 2001 253p hardcover o.p. paperback available $9.95 (7 and up)   **Fic**

Johnston, Julie—*Continued*

1. Sisters—Fiction

ISBN 0-88776-601-3 (pa)

"Fourteen-year-old Agatha and her two older sisters, Jeannie and Helen, have been eking out their existence since the death of their father and the departure of their mother, but all that's going to change now that their wealthy grandfather has died, leaving them his heirs. Or so they think." Bull Cent Child Books

"Johnston's descriptive, present-tense narrative is compelling, fluctuating between distance, edginess, and heartfelt intimacy." Booklist

Johnston, Tim, 1962-

Never so green. Farrar, Straus & Giroux 2002
227p $18 (7 and up)   **Fic**

1. Baseball—Fiction 2. Stepfamilies—Fiction

ISBN 0-374-35509-6   LC 2001-51119

In Iowa in the 1970s, twelve-year-old Tex overcomes his self-consciousness about his deformed right hand to take baseball lessons from his stepfather and his tomboy stepsister, who harbors a dark secret

"This powerful novel approaches tough themes, and doesn't give away any easy answers." SLJ

Johnston, Tony

Any small goodness; a novel of the barrio; illustrations by Raúl Colón. Blue Sky Press (NY) 2001 128p il $16.95; pa $4.99 (4 and up)

    Fic

1. Mexican Americans—Fiction

ISBN 0-439-18936-5; 0-439-23384-4 (pa)

    LC 99-59877

Arturo and his family and friends share all kinds of experiences living in the barrio of East Los Angeles—reclaiming their names, playing basketball, championing the school librarian, and even starting their own gang

"The characters are likable and warm. . . . The message is positive and the episodes, while occasionally serious, are more often humorous and gratifying." SLJ

Jones, Diana Wynne

Cart and cwidder. Greenwillow Bks. 1995 214p
pa $6.95 hardcover o.p. (7 and up)   **Fic**

1. Fantasy fiction

ISBN 0-06-447313-9   LC 94-1512

First published 1975 in the United Kingdom; first United States edition, 1977 by Atheneum

"Accompanying their gregarious father, Clennen the Singer, on panhorns and cwidders (a lute-like instrument) and traversing the earldoms of Dalemark in their gaily decorated cart make up the only life 11-year-old Moril and his brother and sister have ever known. . . . When his father is suddenly killed, Moril becomes heir to the large, ancient cwidder supposedly owned once by an old bard and having mystical powers. . . . Jones strikes a note of timelessness and universality in her forest setting and her theme of the struggle against oppressive forces, developing her characters in depth." Booklist

Followed by Drowned Ammet (1995)

Castle in the air. Greenwillow Bks. 1991 199p
pa $6.99 hardcover o.p. (6 and up)   **Fic**

1. Fantasy fiction

ISBN 0-06-447345-7   LC 90-30266

In this "follow-up to *Howl's Moving Castle* . . . the protagonist is a young carpet merchant called Abdullah, who spends much of his time creating a richly developed daydream in which he is the long-lost son of a great prince, kidnapped as a child by a villainous bandit. . . . Feisty Sophie and the Wizard Howl (from *Howl's Moving Castle*) do not become apparent till late in the story, but their fortunes do link up with those of Abdullah and his love. Jones maintains both suspense and wit throughout, demonstrating once again that frequently nothing is what it seems to be." Booklist

Charmed life. Greenwillow Bks. 2000 272p
$15.95; pa $5.99   **Fic**

1. Witches—Fiction 2. Magic—Fiction

ISBN 0-06-029876-6; 0-688-15546-4 (pa)

The first four titles in this series also available in 2 volume compilation, The chronicles of Chrestomanci

A reissue of the title first published 1977

Gwendolen Chant and her brother Cat find the Chrestomanci Castle family's magic powers difficult to counter with the inferior powers of the Coven Street witches.

"The concept is ingenious." Horn Book

Other titles in this series are:

Conrad's fate (2005)

The lives of Christoper Chant (1988)

The magicians of Caprona (1980)

Witch week (1982)

Howl's moving castle. Greenwillow Bks. 1986
212p (6 and up)   **Fic**

1. Fantasy fiction

ISBN 0-688-06233-4   LC 85-21981

Available in paperback from HarperTrophy $6.99 (ISBN 0-06-441034-X)

"When the wicked Witch of the Waste turns Sophie Hatter into an ugly crone, the girl seeks refuge in Wizard Howl's moving castle. To her surprise and dismay, she finds herself embroiled in a contest between the witch and the wizard, in the tangled love affairs of the wizard, and in a perplexing mystery." Child Book Rev Serv

"Satisfyingly, Sophie meets a fate far exceeding her dreary expectations. This novel is an exciting, multi-faceted puzzle, peopled with vibrant, captivating characters. A generous sprinkling of humor adds potency to this skillful author's spell." Voice Youth Advocates

Jordan, Sherryl, 1949-

The hunting of the last dragon. HarperCollins Pubs. 2002 186p $15.99; lib bdg $15.89; pa $5.99

    Fic

1. Dragons—Fiction 2. Fantasy fiction

ISBN 0-06-028902-3; 0-06-028903-1 (lib bdg); 0-06-447231-0 (pa)   LC 2001-39375

In England in 1356, as a monk records his every word, a young peasant tells of his journey with a young Chinese noblewoman to St. Alfric's Cove and the lair of a dragon

"Appropriate to the telling, the writing is mannered yet lyrical as the rich tale spins out into a lovely combination of fantasy, historical fiction, and romance." Booklist

Jordan, Sherryl, 1949-—*Continued*

The raging quiet. Simon & Schuster Bks. for Young Readers 1999 266p $17; pa $5.99 (7 and up)   **Fic**

1. Prejudices—Fiction 2. Deaf—Fiction 3. Middle Ages—Fiction

ISBN 0-689-82140-9; 0-689-87004-3 (pa)

LC 98-23283

Suspicious of sixteen-year-old Marnie, a newcomer to their medieval village, the residents accuse her of witchcraft when she discovers that the village madman is not crazy but deaf and she begins to communicate with him through hand gestures

"Eloquent, descriptive prose draws readers into the period, and through memorable, well-defined characters, Jordan effectively illustrates the timeless dangers of targeting individuals for being different." Booklist

Secret sacrament. HarperCollins Pubs. 2001 338p il $15.99; lib bdg $17.89; pa $6.99 (7 and up)   **Fic**

1. Fantasy fiction

ISBN 0-06-028904-X; 0-06-028905-8 (lib bdg); 0-06-447230-2 (pa)   LC 00-38838

"Eighteen-year-old Gabriel is not only a gifted healer, but, unbeknownst to him, he is destined to break through the corruption rotting the Empire and to save the Shinali, a native people under oppression." Horn Book Guide

"Gabriel is a memorable character who is both mystically powerful and engagingly human, and young adult fantasy fans will be transfixed by this mythic tale of an injustice that is slowly but surely overcome." Bull Cent Child Books

Joseph, Lynn

The color of my words. HarperCollins Pubs. 2000 138p $14.99; lib bdg $15.89 (5 and up)   **Fic**

1. Family life—Fiction 2. Siblings—Fiction 3. Dominican Republic—Fiction

ISBN 0-06-028232-0; 0-06-028233-9 (lib bdg)

LC 00-22440

"Joanna Cotler books"

When life gets difficult for Ana Rosa, a twelve-year-old would-be writer living in a small village in the Dominican Republic, she can depend on her older brother to make her feel better—until the life-changing events on her thirteenth birthday

"A finely crafted novel, lovely and lyrical." SLJ

Juby, Susan, 1969-

Alice, I think. HarperTempest 2003 290p $15.99; lib bdg $16.89 (7 and up)   **Fic**

1. Family life—Fiction 2. Psychotherapy—Fiction

ISBN 0-06-051543-0; 0-06-051544-9 (lib bdg)

LC 2002-27360

"A very different form of this book was previously published in 2000 in Canada." Verso of title page

Fifteen-year-old Alice keeps a diary as she struggles to cope with the embarrassments and trials of family, dating, school, work, small town life, and a serious case of "outcastitis"

"While Juby's novel stands out more for her narrator's voice than for its plot, her dark wit virtually glitters on every page." Publ Wkly

Another title about Alice is:

Alice Macleod, reAlist at last (2005)

Jung, Reinhardt

Dreaming in black and white; translated by Anthea Bell. Phyllis Fogelman Books 2003 112p $15.99 (5 and up)   **Fic**

1. Handicapped—Fiction 2. Germany—Fiction 3. Holocaust, 1933-1945—Fiction

ISBN 0-8037-2811-5   LC 2002-19918

Original German edition, 1996

A boy dreams that he is a student during the period of the Nazi Third Reich in Germany, where he is persecuted for being physically handicapped

"This spare, deeply felt novel adds a new dimension to Holocaust literature." Horn Book Guide

Kaaberbol, Lene

The Shamer's daughter. Henry Holt 2004 235p $16.95   **Fic**

1. Fantasy fiction

ISBN 0-8050-7541-0   LC 2003-56580

After her mother, a Shamer, is summoned to Dunark for a mission, ten-year-old Dina is forced to use her own special powers as she is caught up in an adventure of political intrigue and survival

"Classic adventure fantasy, with the right combination of personalities, power, intrigue, and dragons. . . . It will prove to be a sure hit." Voice Youth Advocates

Another title about Dina is:

The Shamer's signet (2005)

Kadohata, Cynthia

Kira-Kira. Atheneum Bks. for Young Readers 2004 244p $15.95 (5 and up)   **Fic**

1. Sisters—Fiction 2. Japanese Americans—Fiction 3. Death—Fiction 4. Georgia—Fiction

ISBN 0-689-85639-3

Awarded the Newbery Medal, 2005

"This beautifully written story tells of a girl struggling to find her own way in a family torn by illness and horrendous work conditions. . . . All of the characters are believable and well developed." SLJ

Kantor, Melissa

Confessions of a not it girl. Hyperion 2004 247p $15.99 (7 and up)   **Fic**

1. School stories

ISBN 0-7868-1837-9

"Jan Miller is a . . . teen seeking her first romance during her senior year in high school. . . . Jan obsesses about the college applications she has not yet begun; the size of her butt; and Josh. . . .Lots of fun, lots of truth, very satisfying." SLJ

Karr, Kathleen

The boxer. Farrar, Straus & Giroux 2000 169p $16; pa $5.99 (7 and up)   **Fic**

1. Boxing—Fiction 2. New York (N.Y.)—Fiction

ISBN 0-374-30921-3; 0-374-40886-6 (pa)

LC 99-54794

Karr, Kathleen—*Continued*

Having learned how to box while in prison, fifteen-year-old Johnny sets out to discover if he can make a decent living as a fighter in late nineteenth-century New York City

"A wonderful blend of fascinating history and compelling drama." SLJ

Gilbert and Sullivan set me free. Hyperion Bks. for Children 2003 226p $15.99   **Fic**
1. Prisons—Fiction 2. Theater—Fiction 3. Orphans—Fiction 4. Massachusetts—Fiction
ISBN 0-7868-1916-2   LC 2002-32801

During the early 1900s, a teenaged inmate's dreary life at Massachusetts's Sherborn Prison for Women changes for the better after she becomes a member of the prison choir and participates in the production of the operetta "The Pirates of Penzance"

The author "bases this vivid historical novel on an actual performance of Gilbert and Sullivan's *Pirates of Penzance* in a women's prison in 1914. . . . Wittily illuminating the issues of another era, this novel both stimulates and entertains." Publ Wkly

The great turkey walk. Farrar, Straus & Giroux 1998 197p $17; pa $5.95 (5 and up)   **Fic**
1. Turkeys—Fiction 2. West (U.S.)—Fiction
ISBN 0-374-32773-4; 0-374-42798-4 (pa)
LC 97-38859

Also available Audiobook version

In 1860, a somewhat simple-minded fifteen-year-old boy attempts to herd one thousand turkeys from Missouri to Denver, Colorado, in hopes of selling them at a profit

"Based on an actual event, this is a lively and entertaining story." Horn Book Guide

Skullduggery. Hyperion Bks. for Children 2000 227p hardcover o.p. paperback available $5.99 (5 and up)   **Fic**
1. Phrenology—Fiction 2. Orphans—Fiction 3. Adventure fiction
ISBN 0-7868-1698-8 (pa)   LC 99-39426

In 1839, twelve-year-old Matthew's job as assistant to the phrenologist Dr. Cornwall takes him up and down the Eastern Seaboard and to Europe, as they rob graves and try to find out who is following them and why

"The narrative's somewhat formal style contains glints of dark humor and quietly reveals the characters of the smart, deferential boy and his imperfect but sincere partner." Horn Book Guide

Kass, Pnina

Real time; by Pnina Moed Kass. Clarion Books 2004 186p $15 (7 and up)   **Fic**
1. Israel—Fiction 2. Germans—Israel—Fiction 3. Terrorism—Fiction
ISBN 0-618-44203-0   LC 2004-8481

Sixteen-year-old Tomas Wanninger persuades his mother to let him leave Germany to volunteer at a kibbutz in Israel, where he experiences a violent political attack and finds answers about his own past

This "volume is an exhausting but illuminating read that will provide much-needed insight into life in modern Israel. . . . The characters are deeply developed and painfully sympathetic." SLJ

Keehn, Sally M., 1947-

Anna Sunday. Philomel Bks. 2002 266p $18.99; pa $6.99   **Fic**
1. United States—History—1861-1865, Civil War—Fiction 2. Sex role—Fiction
ISBN 0-399-23875-1; 0-14-240026-2 (pa)
LC 2001-50081

In 1863 twelve-year-old Anna, disguised as a boy and accompanied by her younger brother Jed, leaves their Pennsylvania home and makes the difficult journey to join their wounded father in Winchester, Virginia, where they find themselves in danger from Confederate troops.

"Keehn creates a number of vivid settings and original, believable characters, whose idiosyncrasies add texture and occasional humor to the story." Booklist

Gnat Stokes and the Foggy Bottom Swamp Queen; Sally M. Keehn. Philomel Books 2005 152p il $16.99 (5 and up)   **Fic**
1. Magic—Fiction 2. Tennessee—Fiction
ISBN 0-399-24287-2   LC 2003-26635

In Mary's Cove, Tennessee, in 1869, twelve-year-old Gnat Stokes decides to prove she's not just a trouble maker by rescuing a boy who was spirited away seven years earlier by the evil Swamp Queen of Foggy Bottom.

"Keehn's tale is by turns, creepy, laugh-aloud funny, touching, and utterly satisfying. Her voice is sassy and straight out of the Tennessee hills." Booklist

I am Regina. Philomel Bks. 1991 240p $17.99; pa $6.99   **Fic**
1. Native Americans—Fiction
ISBN 0-399-21797-5; 0-440-40754-0 (pa)
LC 90-20098

In 1755, as the French and Indian War begins, ten-year-old Regina is kidnapped by Indians in western Pennsylvania, and she must struggle to hold onto memories of her earlier life as she grows up under the name of Tskinnak and starts to become Indian herself

"A first-person narrative based on [a] true story . . . related with all the impact of a hard-hitting documentary." SLJ

Kehret, Peg, 1936-

Abduction! Peg Kehret. 1st ed. Dutton Children's Books 2004 215p $16.99 (5 and up)
Fic
1. Kidnapping—Fiction
ISBN 0-525-47294-0   LC 2003-63531

Thirteen-year-old Bonnie has a feeling of foreboding on the very day that her six-year-old brother Matt and their dog Pookie are abducted, and she becomes involved in a major search effort as well as a frightening adventure

"This novel has enough suspense to keep children interested, and it will also appeal to reluctant readers." SLJ

Cages. Cobblehill Bks. 1991 150p o.p. Pocket Bks. paperback available $4.99   **Fic**
1. Shoplifting—Fiction 2. Animal welfare—Fiction
ISBN 0-671-75879-9 (pa)   LC 90-21230

After losing an acting role and fighting with her alcoholic stepfather, Kit is arrested for shoplifting and ordered to work, as part of her sentence, at an animal shel-

Kehret, Peg, 1936——_Continued_

ter

"Kit is a bit too good to be true, but readers will relate to her anguish and her spirit and courage. Though the outcome is neat and positive, the journey, which is laced with humor as well as heartache, offers grist for thought." Booklist

Don't tell anyone. Dutton Children's Bks. 2000 137p $15.99; pa $5.99 (5 and up)   **Fic**
1. Cats—Fiction 2. Criminals—Fiction
ISBN 0-525-46388-7; 0-14-230031-4 (pa)
                                        LC 99-89605
Twelve-year-old Megan does not realize that feeding a group of feral cats living in a field near her house will involve her as a witness to a traffic accident and in the dangerous plan of an unstable criminal
"There are subplots galore in this quick read . . . but they all hang together, and thanks to Kehret's even tone, the scary aspects won't frighten younger readers." Booklist

I'm not who you think I am. Dutton Children's Bks. 1999 154p pa $5.99 hardcover o.p.
                                              Fic
1. Mentally ill—Fiction 2. Mother-daughter relationship—Fiction
ISBN 0-14-131237-8   LC 98-33879
Ginger "is being stalked by a mentally ill woman who believes that the 13-year-old is her daughter. Meanwhile, Ginger's favorite teacher, Mr. Wren, is being harassed by Mrs. Vaughn, an irate and influential parent who doesn't like the way he is coaching the girls' basketball team. . . . When the two plots converge in the final scenes, everything is resolved satisfactorily. This enjoyable novel will draw readers' interest and keep them turning pages." SLJ

Searching for Candlestick Park. Cobblehill Bks. 1997 149p $14.99   **Fic**
1. Runaway children—Fiction 2. Cats—Fiction
3. Father-son relationship—Fiction
ISBN 0-525-65256-6   LC 97-11222
Determined to find his father and relive their good times, twelve-year-old Spencer takes his cat, slips away from home in Seattle, and sets out for San Francisco's Candlestick Park
This is "a fast-paced, exciting adventure. A good choice for reading aloud as well as starting class discussion." Booklist

The secret journey. Pocket Bks. 1999 135p $16; pa $4.99   **Fic**
1. Adventure fiction 2. Survival after airplane accidents, shipwrecks, etc.—Fiction
ISBN 0-671-03416-2; 0-671-03417-0 (pa)
                                        LC 99-42222
"A Minstrel hardcover"
In 1834 when a storm at sea destroys the slave ship on which she is a stowaway, twelve-year-old Emma musters all her resourcefulness to survive in the African jungle
"A fast-paced adventure, with superb backdrop details." Booklist

Keith, Harold, 1903-1998

Rifles for Watie. Crowell 1957 332p $16.89; pa $5.99   **Fic**
1. Watie, Stand, 1806-1871—Fiction 2. United States—History—1861-1865, Civil War—Fiction
ISBN 0-690-04907-2; 0-06-447030-X (pa)
Awarded the Newbery Medal, 1958
"Young Jeff Bussey longs for the life of a Union soldier during the Civil War, but before long he realizes the cruelty and savagery of some men in the army situation. The war loses its glamor as he sees his very young friends die. When he is made a scout, his duties take him into the ranks of Stand Watie, leader of the rebel troops of the Cherokee Indian Nation, as a spy. He makes good friends among the enemy troops and falls in love with Lucy Washbourne, beautiful part-Cherokee girl and rebel sympathizer." Stensland. Lit By & About the Am Indian
"An exceptionally well-written story of the Civil War as it was fought in the western states." Bull Cent Child Books

Keizer, Garret

God of beer. HarperCollins Pubs. 2002 242p $15.95; lib bdg $15.89; pa $6.99 (7 and up)
                                              Fic
1. Friendship—Fiction 2. School stories
ISBN 0-06-029456-6; 0-06-029457-4 (lib bdg); 0-06-447276-0 (pa)   LC 2001-24598
To complete a class assignment at his high school in rural Vermont, Kyle and his friends Quake and Diana do a social protest project involving alcohol
"Keizer provides much food for thought about alcohol use. . . . His facility with setting and dialogue, as well as his reluctance to oversimplify a complex topic, make him a novelist to watch." Horn Book

Kerr, M. E., 1927-

Night kites. Harper & Row 1986 216p pa $5.99 hardcover o.p. (7 and up)   **Fic**
1. Homosexuality—Fiction 2. Brothers—Fiction
3. AIDS (Disease)—Fiction
ISBN 0-06-447035-0   LC 85-45386
"A Charlotte Zolotow book"
"Seventeen-year-old Erick suddenly learns that his older brother, Pete, whom he admires and tries to emulate, is gay and sick with AIDS. He also struggles with his feelings for his best friend's girl, Nicki, a nonconformist with a 'fast' reputation. Pete and Nicki are the 'night kites' of the title—they dare to be different." BAYA Book Rev
"Pete and his methods of coping with his disease and its effects on himself, his friends, his family, and ultimately, his community, are sensitively and nonsentimentally drawn, and seem to be portrayed accurately. This is sure to be a popular title, and will be a natural for booktalks." Voice Youth Advocates

Slap your sides; a novel. HarperCollins Pubs. 2001 198p $15.95; lib bdg $16.89; pa $5.99 (7 and up)   **Fic**
1. World War, 1939-1945—Fiction 2. Brothers—Fiction 3. Conscientious objectors—Fiction 4. Society of Friends—Fiction
ISBN 0-06-029481-7; 0-06-029482-5 (lib bdg); 0-06-447274-4 (pa)   LC 00-54037

Kerr, M. E., 1927—*Continued*

Life in their Pennsylvania hometown changes for Jubal Shoemaker and his family when his older brother witnesses to his Quaker beliefs by becoming a conscientious objector during World War II

"The ideas are gripping, not only because Kerr is fair to all sides but also because the characters are complicated." Booklist

Kessler, Cristina

Our secret, Siri Aang. Philomel Books 2004 218p $16.99 (7 and up)   **Fic**
1. Masai (African people)—Fiction 2. Kenya—Fiction 3. Sex role—Fiction 4. Rhinoceros—Fiction
ISBN 0-399-23985-5   LC 2003-24075
Namelok, a Masai girl, tries to persuade her traditionalist father to delay her initiation and marriage because they will restrict her freedom and keep her from the black rhino mother and baby she is protecting from poachers.

"Because of the wealth of descriptive detail, readers will easily envision the Kenyan landscape and be caught up in the suspense of this intriguing survival story. The cultural dilemmas of the Maasai should stimulate discussion." SLJ

Kimmel, Elizabeth Cody

In the stone circle. Scholastic 1998 225p pa $4.50 hardcover o.p. (5 and up)   **Fic**
1. Ghost stories 2. Wales—Fiction
ISBN 0-439-06259-4   LC 97-14737
While spending the summer in an old stone house in Wales, fourteen-year-old Cristyn comes to terms with the death of her mother while satisfying the request of a thirteenth-century princess

"Kimmel handles the history and the ghost of the girl Carwen with a deft naturalness that keeps both vivid, and the resolution of all the plots strands is satisfying without being overly pat." Booklist

Lily B. on the brink of cool. HarperCollins Pubs. 2003 245p $15.99; lib bdg $16.89
    Fic
1. Authorship—Fiction 2. Family life—Fiction
ISBN 0-06-000586-6; 0-06-000587-4 (lib bdg)
     LC 2002-13385
"The eventually internationally recognized writer Lily Blennerhassett" spends her thirteenth summer missing her best friend and keeping a journal of her boring life at home and exciting newly-discovered relatives

"The pacing of the book is fast and smooth." SLJ

Visiting Miss Caples. Dial Bks. 2000 168p $17.99 (6 and up)   **Fic**
1. Old age—Fiction 2. Friendship—Fiction
ISBN 0-8037-2502-7   LC 99-27899
The elderly shut-in she visits once a week becomes an unexpected source of friendship and strength for thirteen-year-old Jenna, and they help each other face and overcome painful aspects of their lives

"Young readers coping with difficult changes at school and at home will respond to this thoughtful story." Booklist

Kincaid, Jamaica

Annie John. Farrar, Straus & Giroux 1985 148p hardcover o.p. paperback available $10
    Fic
1. Antigua and Barbuda—Fiction
ISBN 0-374-52510-2 (pa)
"Episodes from the young life of Annie John, aged 10 to 17, as she grows up on the Caribbean island of Antigua. This is a magical coming-of-age tale, ripe with the special ambience of its tropical setting and sustained by Annie's far from naive awareness of the world around her. Death, illness, and poverty intrude on the narrator's perceptive sensibility from time to time, but even these experiences instruct her and expand her understanding of life and its shifting reality. . . . A poetic and intensely moving work." Booklist

Kindl, Patrice, 1951-

Goose chase; a novel. Houghton Mifflin 2001 214p $15   **Fic**
1. Fairy tales 2. Geese—Fiction
ISBN 0-618-03377-7   LC 99-35595
Also available in paperback from Puffin Bks.
Rather than marry a cruel king or a seemingly dimwitted prince, Alexandria an enchanted goose girl, endures imprisonment, capture by several ogresses, and other dangers, before learning exactly who she is

"Kindl's humor, the strong characterizations, and vibrant action give the story wings." Booklist

Lost in the labyrinth; a novel. Houghton Mifflin 2002 194p $16   **Fic**
1. Classical mythology—Fiction
ISBN 0-618-16684-X   LC 2002-406
Fourteen-year-old Princess Xenodice tries to prevent the death of her half-brother, the Minotaur, at the hands of the Athenian prince, Theseus, who is aided by Icarus, Daedalus, and her sister Ariadne

"Attentive to both archaeological detail and emotional probity, Kindl fleshes out the Minotaur myth's bare bones and brings it to life." Horn Book

Owl in love. Houghton Mifflin 1993 204p $16; pa $6.99 (6 and up)   **Fic**
1. Supernatural—Fiction 2. Owls—Fiction 3. Teachers—Fiction
ISBN 0-395-66162-5; 0-618-43910-2 (pa)
     LC 92-26952
Also available in paperback from Penguin Bks.
A fourteen-year-old girl, who can transform into an owl, has a crush on her science teacher which leads her into interesting new relationships with both humans and owls

"Kindl's prose is remarkably even in its wit, one of many virtues in this tautly plotted and touching novel." Publ Wkly

The woman in the wall. Houghton Mifflin 1997 185p $16   **Fic**
1. Shyness—Fiction
ISBN 0-395-83014-1   LC 96-24567
Also available in paperback from Penguin Bks.
Anna is "an extremely shy child who retreats behind the walls of her family's large, dilapidated house and

Kindl, Patrice, 1951-—*Continued*
lives alone in her secret rooms until she is 14 years old.
Then . . . Anna finally comes out and faces the world.
. . . This contemporary story is just on the edge of the
surreal. . . . What makes you suspend disbelief is the
authority of Anna's quirky, vulnerable narrative voice,
which pulls you into a touching, dreamy story told with
tender comedy." Booklist

Kirwan, Anna
Victoria, May blossom of Britannia. Scholastic
2001 219p il (Royal diaries) $10.95 **Fic**
1. Victoria, Queen of Great Britain, 1819-1901—Fiction 2. Great Britain—History—19th century—Fiction
ISBN 0-439-21598-6 LC 2001-20031
In 1829, nine-year-old Victoria begins a journal chronicling her life as an English princess. Includes information on the reign, marriage, and family life of Queen
Victoria and English civilization during that period
"A charming portrayal of three years in the childhood
of Queen Victoria." SLJ

Klass, David, 1960-
California Blue. Scholastic 1994 200p pa $5.99
hardcover o.p. **Fic**
1. Butterflies—Fiction 2. Environmental protection—
Fiction
ISBN 0-590 46689-5 LC 93-13705
When seventeen-year-old John Rodgers discovers a
new sub-species of butterfly which may necessitate closing the mill where his dying father works, they find
themselves on opposite sides of the environmental conflict
"The absorbing first-person narration rings true,
projecting the credible voice of a teenager just beginning
to break free from his emotional ties at home, family and
friends. The fears, excitement, anger and energy of this
awkward psychological time are movingly captured
here." Publ Wkly

Danger zone. Scholastic 1996 232p hardcover
o.p. paperback available $4.99 **Fic**
1. Basketball—Fiction 2. Race relations—Fiction
3. African Americans—Fiction
ISBN 0-590-48591-1 (pa) LC 94-20234
When he joins a predominantly black "Teen Dream
Team" that will be representing the United States in an
international basketball tournament in Rome, Jimmy
Doyle makes some unexpected discoveries about prejudice, racism, and politics
"The pace never lags, and Klass does a convincing job
of capturing the feel of the game and depicting Doyle's
attempts to be accepted by his teammates, as well as
showing what happens when some terrorists add fear to
the list of the team's opponents." Booklist

Home of the Braves. Farrar, Straus & Giroux
2002 312p $18 (7 and up) **Fic**
1. Soccer—Fiction 2. School stories
ISBN 0-374-39963-8 LC 2002-19391
"Frances Foster books"

Eighteen-year-old Joe, captain of the soccer team, is
dismayed when a hotshot player shows up from Brazil
and threatens to take over both the team and the girl
whom Joe hopes to date
"A gritty, realistic story of a robust insider with his
feet planted solidly on the ground. . . . More than a
sports story, {this} is a first-rate coming-of-age novel."
Voice Youth Advocates

You don't know me; a novel. Foster Bks. 2001
262p $17 (7 and up) **Fic**
1. School stories 2. Child abuse—Fiction
ISBN 0-374-38706-0 LC 00-22709
Also available in paperback from HarperCollins
Fourteen-year-old John creates alternative realities in
his mind as he tries to deal with his mother's abusive
boyfriend, his crush on a beautiful, but shallow classmate
and other problems at school
"Klass is effective with John's deliberately distanced
voice, his constant dancing with and away from reality,
. . . and his brittle and even dorky defenses, and the rising tension is suspenseful." Bull Cent Child Books

Klass, Sheila Solomon
The un-civil war. Holiday House 1997 162p
$15.95 **Fic**
1. School stories 2. Friendship—Fiction
ISBN 0-8234-1329-2 LC 95-15548
Also available in paperback from Yearling Bks.
Even with her father as principal, Asa Andersen is
certain that sixth grade will be perfect, until a new boy
in school starts making fun of her name and the baby her
mother is expecting is born prematurely
"This novel not only is enjoyable but also explores issues to which many readers will relate." Booklist

Klause, Annette Curtis
Alien secrets. Delacorte Press 1993 227p pa
$5.50 hardcover o.p. (5 and up) **Fic**
1. Science fiction 2. Mystery fiction
ISBN 0-440-41061-4 LC 92-31326
On her journey to the distant planet where her parents
are working, twelve-year-old Puck befriends a troubled
alien and becomes involved in a dangerous mystery involving a precious artifact
"This fast-paced adventure novel features a smart heroine, an appealing alien, plenty of intrigue, and a noble
mission that readers won't be able to resist." SLJ

The silver kiss. Delacorte Press 1990 198p
hardcover o.p. paperback available $4.99
Fic
1. Vampires—Fiction 2. Death—Fiction
ISBN 0-440-21346-0 (pa) LC 89-48880
"One evening, when 17-year-old Zoë is sitting in the
park contemplating her mother's imminent death due to
cancer, her father's lack of support, and her best friend's
move, she meets Simon. Simon is startlingly handsome
and strangely compelling. As their friendship grows over
time, Simon reveals to Zoë his true identity: he is a vampire, trying to kill his younger vampire brother." SLJ
"There's inherent romantic appeal in the vampire legend, and Klause weaves all the gory details into a poignant love story that becomes both sensuous and suspenseful." Booklist

Klise, Kate

Deliver us from Normal; by Kate Klise. 1st ed. Scholastic Press 2005 226p $16.95   **Fic**

1. Family life—Fiction 2. Illinois—Fiction

ISBN 0-439-52322-2   LC 2004-42906

With a mother who buys Christmas cards in August and a younger brother who describes the Trinity as a toasted marshmallow on a graham cracker, life for eleven-year-old Charles Harrisong is anything but normal in Normal, Illinois.

"Through Charles's narration, Klise offers a stunningly realistic look at the concatenations that the boy's obsessive thinking weaves. . . . A superb psychological novel." SLJ

Letters from camp; illustrated by M. Sarah Klise. Avon Bks. 1999 178p il $15.99; pa $5.99   **Fic**

1. Camps—Fiction 2. Siblings—Fiction 3. Letters—Fiction

ISBN 0-380-97539-4; 0-380-79348-2 (pa)

LC 98-52315

Sent to Camp Happy Harmony to learn how to get along with each other, pairs of brothers and sisters chronicle in letters home how they come to suspect the intentions of the singing family running the camp

This is a "delightfully wacky story. . . . The humor is very gentle and tongue-in-cheek. . . . An entirely satisfying camp adventure." Booklist

Koertge, Ronald

The Brimstone journals; {by} Ron Koertge. Candlewick Press 2001 113p $15.99; pa $6.99 (7 and up)   **Fic**

1. Violence—Fiction 2. School stories

ISBN 0-7636-1302-9; 0-7636-1742-3 (pa)

LC 00-37886

"'Brimstone' is the unflattering nickname bestowed on Branston High School by its students; in a collection of free-verse monologues, fifteen of those students offer their individual views of their lives, lives that are on the verge of being changed forever as a bitter and disaffected student joins a plan to amass weapons for massacre of those named on his ever-growing list." Bull Cent Child Books

"Through the very spare and economical text we come to know these 15 children and their lives, and the subplots are surprisingly intricate for such a slim book. . . . Whatever one may think of the characters, the events in this book are all too believable." N Y Times Book Rev

Margaux with an X; Ron Koertge. 1st ed. Candlewick Press 2004 165p $15.99 (7 and up)   **Fic**

1. Domestic violence—Fiction

ISBN 0-7636-2401-2   LC 2003-65279

Margaux, known as a "tough chick" at her Los Angeles high school, makes a connection with Danny, who, like her, struggles with the emotional impact of family violence and abuse.

This book "excels in character development. It is an intriguing story that constantly provokes readers' curiosity. . . . [The author's] language at times is advanced, an accurate reflection of his characters' intellectual capacity." SLJ

Shakespeare bats cleanup; [by] Ron Koertge. Candlewick Press 2003 116p $15.99 (7 and up)   **Fic**

1. Poetry—Fiction

ISBN 0-7636-2116-1   LC 2002-31171

When a fourteen-year-old baseball player catches mononucleosis, he discovers that keeping a journal and experimenting with poetry not only helps fill the time, it also helps him deal with life, love, and loss

"Koertge does an excellent job of creating the authentic voice of a teenage boy exclusively through poems. The poems are funny, touching, and always energetic." Booklist

Stoner & Spaz; {by} Ron Koertge. Candlewick Press 2002 169p $15.99; pa $6.99 (7 and up)   **Fic**

1. Cerebral palsy—Fiction 2. School stories

ISBN 0-7636-1608-7; 0-7636-2150-1 (pa)

LC 2001-43050

A troubled youth with cerebral palsy struggles toward self-acceptance with the help of a drug-addicted young woman

"Funny, touching, and surprising, it is a hopeful yet realistic view of things as they are and as they could be." Booklist

Koja, Kathe

Buddha Boy. Farrar, Straus & Giroux 2003 117p $16 (7 and up)   **Fic**

1. Artists—Fiction 2. Buddhism—Fiction 3. School stories

ISBN 0-374-30998-1   LC 2002-25067

"Frances Foster books"

"When Jinsen arrives at Edward Rucher High School coatless in winter, sporting a bald head, begging for money in the school cafeteria, and talking about karma, he is immediately dubbed 'Buddha Boy' by the resident bullies. Justin, the narrator . . . is forced to work on a school project with Jinsen and discovers the newcomer's incredible artistic talent. . . . Mesmerized by Jinsen's art and philosophy, Justin befriends him and learns about Jinsen's hostile past." Voice Youth Advocates

"A compelling introduction to Buddhism and a credible portrait of how true friendship brings out the best in people." Publ Wkly

Straydog. Farrar, Straus & Giroux 2002 105p $16 (7 and up)   **Fic**

1. Dogs—Fiction 2. Animal shelters—Fiction

ISBN 0-374-37278-0   LC 2001-16030

"Frances Foster books"

Rachel, a teenager with a healthy dose of both aptitude and attitude, begins to feel at home volunteering at an animal shelter until the arrival of a feral dog with whom she senses a special kinship

"The strong characters, rich detail, and well-articulated emotions . . . make a powerful story that will resonate with many teens." Booklist

Koller, Jackie French

Someday. Orchard Bks. 2002 215p $16.95
Fic

1. Family life—Fiction 2. Friendship—Fiction
3. Massachusetts—Fiction

ISBN 0-439-29317-0   LC 2001-21788

In 1938, fourteen-year-old Celie must cope with leaving her Enfield, Massachusetts, home and her life-long friend, Chubby, as the day approaches when the Swift River Valley will be flooded to create a reservoir for Boston

"With complex, finely drawn characters and fluid language that rings true for the period and place, the story is satisfying emotionally as well as intellectually." Publ Wkly

Konigsburg, E. L.

The outcasts of 19 Schuyler Place. Atheneum Bks. for Young Readers 2004 296p $16.95
Fic

1. Social action—Fiction

ISBN 0-689-86636-4   LC 2003-8067

A prequel to Silent to the bone

Upon leaving an oppressive summer camp, twelve-year-old Margaret Rose Kane spearheads a campaign to preserve three unique towers her grand uncles have been building in their back yard for over forty years

"The plot is well paced and has excellent foreshadowing. Konigsburg's characters are particularly well motivated. . . . Funny and thought-provoking by turns, this is Konigsburg at her masterful best." SLJ

A proud taste for scarlet and miniver; written and illustrated by E. L. Konigsburg. Atheneum Pubs. 1973 201p il $18.95 (5 and up)   **Fic**

1. Eleanor, of Aquitaine, Queen, consort of Henry II, King of England, 1122?-1204—Fiction

ISBN 0-689-30111-1

Also available in paperback from Aladdin Bks.

This is an historical novel about the 12th century queen, Eleanor of Aquitaine, wife of kings of France and England and mother of King Richard the Lion Hearted and King John. Impatiently awaiting the arrival of her second husband, King Henry II, in heaven, she recalls her life with the aid of some contemporaries

The author "has succeeded in making history amusing as well as interesting. . . . The characterization is superb. . . . The black-and-white drawings are skillfully as well as appropriately modeled upon medieval manuscript illuminations and add their share of joy to the book." Horn Book

Silent to the bone. Atheneum Bks. for Young Readers 2000 261p $16; pa $5.99 (7 and up)
Fic

1. Siblings—Fiction 2. Babysitters—Fiction
3. Mystery fiction

ISBN 0-689-83601-5; 0-689-83602-3 (pa)

LC 00-20043

"A Jean Karl book"

When he is wrongly accused of gravely injuring his baby half-sister, thirteen-year-old Branwell loses his power of speech and only his friend Connor is able to reach him and uncover the truth about what really happened

"A compelling mystery that is also a moving story of family, friendship, and seduction." Booklist

The view from Saturday. Atheneum Bks. for Young Readers 1996 163p $16.95; pa $5.99 (4 and up)
Fic

1. School stories 2. Friendship—Fiction 3. Physically handicapped—Fiction

ISBN 0-689-80993-X; 0-689-81721-5 (pa)

LC 95-52624

Awarded the Newbery Medal, 1997

"A Jean Karl book"

Four students, with their own individual stories, develop a special bond and attract the attention of their teacher, a paraplegic, who choses them to represent their sixth-grade class in the Academic Bowl competition

"Glowing with humor and dusted with magic. . . . Wrought with deep compassion and a keen sense of balance." Publ Wkly

Korman, Gordon, 1963-

Jake, reinvented. Hyperion 2003 213p $15.99 (7 and up)
Fic

1. School stories

ISBN 0-7868-1957-X   LC 2003-47804

Rick becomes friends with the popular new boy, Jake Garrett, football player and host of superlative parties, and in the process discovers the true nature of his schoolmates and uncovers the mystery of Jake's past.

"Korman's reworking of The Great Gatsby places the action in a modern framework, which makes it more recognizable for today's readers and may lead them to the classic. Teens will find deeper issues to consider about popularity, being true to one's self, and taking responsibility for one's actions as they relate to the setting and characters." SLJ

No more dead dogs. Hyperion Bks. for Children 2000 180p $15.99; pa $5.99   **Fic**

1. Theater—Fiction 2. School stories

ISBN 0-7868-0531-5; 0-7868-1601-5 (pa)

LC 00-24313

Eighth-grade football hero Wallace Wallace is sentenced to detention attending rehearsals of the school play where, in spite of himself, he becomes wrapped up in the production and begins to suggest changes that improve not only the play but his life as well

"Humor abounds here, but underlying is the true angst of the middle school student." Voice Youth Advocates

The sixth grade nickname game. Hyperion Bks. for Children 1998 154p pa $5.99 hardcover o.p. (4 and up)
Fic

1. Nicknames—Fiction 2. School stories

ISBN 0-7868-5190-2   LC 98-12343

Eleven-year-old best friends Jeff and Wiley, who like to give nicknames to their classmates, try to find the right one for the new girl Cassandra, while adjusting to the football coach who has become their new teacher

"This is a funny, fast-paced grade-school romp." Bull Cent Child Books

Korman, Gordon, 1963— *Continued*
Son of the mob. Hyperion Bks. for Children
2002 262p $15.99; pa $5.99 (7 and up)

Fic

1. Mafia—Fiction
ISBN 0-7868-0769-5; 0-7868-1593-0 (pa)

LC 2002-68672

Also available Thorndike Press large print edition
Seventeen-year-old Vince's life is constantly complicated by the fact that he is the son of a powerful Mafia
boss, a relationship that threatens to destroy his romance
with the daughter of an FBI agent
"The fast-paced, tightly focused story addresses the
problems of being an honest kid in a family of outlaws—and loving them anyway. Korman doesn't ignore
the seamier side of mob life, but even when the subject
matter gets violent . . . he keeps things light by relating
his tale in the first-person voice of a humorously sarcastic yet law-abiding wise guy." Horn Book
Another title about Vince is:
Son of the mob: Hollywood hustle (2004)

Kornblatt, Marc, 1954-
Understanding Buddy. Margaret K. McElderry
Bks. 2001 113p $16.95   Fic
1. Death—Fiction 2. Friendship—Fiction 3. Jews—
Fiction
ISBN 0-689-83215-X   LC 99-46913
Also available Thorndike Press large print edition
When Buddy stops speaking because of the sudden
death of his mother, fifth grader Sam tries to befriend
him and risks destroying his relationship with his best
friend Alex
"This is a well-written, easy-to-read, thoughtful novel
about what it means to lose someone you love." Book
Rep

Kositsky, Lynne, 1947-
The thought of high windows. Kids Can Press
2004 175p $16.95 (7 and up)   Fic
1. Jews—Fiction 2. Holocaust, 1933-1945—Fiction
ISBN 1-55337-621-8
"Esther describes her life as one of a group of Jewish
children taken from Germany to France by the Red Cross
during World War II. The novel begins when she is 15
and living in a French castle; her childhood in Berlin is
described through flashbacks. . . . Based on true events,
this is an immediate, painfully honest story." SLJ

Koss, Amy Goldman, 1954-
The girls. Dial Bks. for Young Readers 2000
121p $16.99; pa $5.99 (5 and up)   Fic
1. Friendship—Fiction
ISBN 0-8037-2494-2; 0-14-230033-0 (pa)

LC 99-19318

Also available Thorndike Press large print edition
"One Saturday morning a girl finds out that her group
of friends, for reasons unknown, has decided to exclude
her. As the short novel moves over the course of the
weekend, five girls narrate in turns, each moving the story forward as well as providing sometimes unwitting
commentary on her friends' versions of events." Horn

Book Guide
"This provocative page-turner will be passed from one
girl to the next." SLJ

Stranger in Dadland. Dial Bks. 2001 119p
$16.99 (5 and up)   Fic
1. Father-son relationship—Fiction 2. Divorce—Fic-
tion
ISBN 0-8037-2563-9   LC 99-462100
Twelve-year-old John develops a new understanding
of his divorced father during an eventful summer visit to
California
"What readers will appreciate is John's honest vacilla-
tion between anger and longing for his dad's attention.
The first-person dialogue crisply captures John's angst."
Booklist

Strike two. Dial Bks. for Young Readers 2001
134p $16.99; pa $5.99 (4 and up)   Fic
1. Strikes—Fiction 2. Cousins—Fiction
ISBN 0-8037-2607-4; 0-14-250024-0 (pa)

LC 00-38365

Haley's hope of spending the summer playing softball
and hanging out with her cousin Gwen is ruined when
her father and her uncle land on opposite sides of the local newspaper strike
"Gwen is a wonderfully spunky kid who has real
problems, creative solutions, and the guts to admit that
she has a lot to learn about others' needs." Booklist

Krisher, Trudy
Spite fences. Delacorte Press 1994 283p
hardcover o.p. paperback available $4.99

Fic

1. Race relations—Fiction 2. Mother-daughter relationship—Fiction 3. Georgia—Fiction
ISBN 0-440-22016-5 (pa)   LC 94-8665
"This is the story of a thirteen-year-old girl as much
an outcast from her family as she is from her southern
town. Maggie Pugh is physically abused by her mother,
beaten and nearly raped by a violent neighbor, and re-
viled for her championship of African-American friends
who, during the summer of 1960, are challenging rural
Georgia racism with sit-ins and other forms of protest."
Bull Cent Child Books
"Characters emerge as complex individuals, not pawns
of a political agenda. Hearts will go out to Maggie as
she weathers various forms of physical and emotional
abuse; her final triumph is a tribute to all who have suffered for justice." Publ Wkly

Uncommon Faith. Holiday House 2003 263p
$17.95   Fic
1. Women's rights—Fiction 2. Christian life—Fiction
3. Massachusetts—Fiction
ISBN 0-8234-1791-3   LC 2002-191919
In 1837-38, residents of Millbrook, Massachusetts,
speak in their different voices of major issues of their
day, including women's rights, slavery, religious differences, and one fiery girl named Faith
"The increasingly distinctive voices make this
multilayered story richer and more compelling as it progresses." Booklist

Kropp, Paul
The countess and me. Fitzhenry & Whiteside 2002 144p $14.95; pa $8.95 **Fic**
1. Friendship—Fiction
ISBN 1-55041-680-4; 1-55041-692-8 (pa)
"Jordan befriends an elderly, eccentric neighbor, Mrs. von Loewen, a countess in her younger European days, by helping her around the house. . . . Jordan's stories of the old woman attract the attention of a clique of boys on their way to juvenile delinquenthood. Jordan is offered a chance to become part of their group—at the price of betraying Mrs. von Loewen's trust." Booklist
"Told in first person, the well-paced plot will keep kids involved, and the book is not too difficult for reluctant readers." SLJ

Kudlinski, Kathleen V., 1950-
The spirit catchers; an encounter with Georgia O'Keeffe; by Kathleen Kudlinski. Watson-Guptill Publications 2004 165p il (Art encounters) $15.95 (7 and up) **Fic**
1. O'Keeffe, Georgia, 1887-1986—Fiction 2. Artists—Fiction 3. Great Depression, 1929-1939—Fiction 4. New Mexico—Fiction
ISBN 0-8230-0408-2 LC 2004-3653
"Parker begins his relationship with Georgia O'Keeffe by stealing her property, notably a camera. She is prepared to let him rot in jail when she develops the photos he has taken with the stolen camera and recognizes the boy's raw ability." Publisher's note
"There are enough surprises to keep the pages turning. . . . While teens may not find this title on their own, it would certainly breathe life into a number of curricular-content areas." SLJ
Includes bibliographical references

Kurtz, Jane
Jakarta missing. Greenwillow Bks. 2001 268p lib bdg $16.89 **Fic**
1. Sisters—Fiction 2. North Dakota—Fiction
ISBN 0-06-029402-7 LC 00-56195
When her sister, star-athlete Jakarta, finally joins them, Dakar feels much safer and happier in Cottonwood, North Dakota, where she and their parents are living for a year, but she still longs for their home in Africa
This "offers glimpses outside the usual boxes, gently expanding the reader's understanding of how 'terrifying and wonderful' life can be." Bull Cent Child Books

Saba; under the hyena's foot; illustration by Jean-Paul Tibbles. Pleasant Co. 2003 207p il (Girls of many lands) $15.95; pa $7.95 **Fic**
1. Ethiopia—Fiction 2. Kidnapping—Fiction 3. Kings and rulers—Fiction
ISBN 1-58485-829-X; 1-58485-747-1 (pa)
LC 2002-155613
"American Girl"
After being kidnapped and brought to the emperor's palace in Gondar, Ethiopia, twelve-year-old Saba discovers that she and her brother are part of the emperor's desperate attempt to consolidate political power in the mid-1840's
"Kurtz creates a powerful sense of place with cultural and sensory details, and Saba's strong first-person voice and brave adventures will hook many readers." Booklist

The storyteller's beads. Harcourt Brace & Co. 1998 154p $15 (5 and up) **Fic**
1. Friendship—Fiction 2. Prejudices—Fiction 3. Blind—Fiction 4. Ethiopia—Fiction
ISBN 0-15-201074-2 LC 97-42312
"Gulliver books"
During the political strife and famine of the 1980's, two Ethiopian girls, one Christian and the other Jewish and blind, struggle to overcome many difficulties, including their prejudices about each other, as they make the dangerous journey out of Ethiopia
"The novel presents an involving portrait of Ethiopian culture through the eyes of two well-defined characters." Horn Book Guide

Kwasney, Michelle D., 1960-
Baby Blue; Michelle D. Kwasney. 1st ed. Henry Holt 2004 202p $16.95 **Fic**
1. Wife abuse—Fiction 2. Stepfathers—Fiction 3. Sisters—Fiction 4. Massachusetts—Fiction
ISBN 0-8050-7050-8 LC 2003-56579
In western Massachusetts in 1976, still grieving and guilt-ridden over her father's drowning, twelve-year-old Blue is dealt another blow when her older sister, Star, runs away to escape their stepfather's violence against their mother.
"A sensitive and realistic coming-of-age story about personal loss, love, abuse, and complex family relationships." SLJ

La Fevers, R. L.
The falconmaster. Dutton Children's Bks. 2003 167p $16.99 **Fic**
1. Magic—Fiction 2. Falcons—Fiction
ISBN 0-525-46993-1 LC 2003-48321
Ten-year-old Wat, a crippled boy living in Norman England, rescues two baby falcons and is lead to discover the grandfather he never knew and the powerful magic that resides in the deep forest and in himself
"The author successfully blends rich descriptions of the medieval world and flights of fantasy into an exciting adventure." Booklist

LaFaye, A., 1970-
Edith Shay. Viking 1998 183p (7 and up) **Fic**
1. United States—History—1865-1898—Fiction
ISBN 0-670-87598-8; 0-689-84228-7
LC 98-16832
Leaving her home in Wisconsin in 1865, sixteen-year-old Katherine sets out for Chicago to prove to her family that she can make a life for herself
"LaFaye offers a multidimensional portrait of a young woman in transition . . . revealed in poetic and poignant language." Publ Wkly

LaFaye, A., 1970—— *Continued*
Worth. Simon & Schuster Books for Young
Readers 2004 144p $15.95 (5 and up)   **Fic**
1. Frontier and pioneer life—Fiction 2. Orphans—Fiction 3. Nebraska—Fiction
ISBN 0-689-85730-6   LC 2003-8101
After breaking his leg, eleven-year-old Nate feels useless because he cannot work on the family farm in nineteenth-century Nebraska, so when his father brings home an orphan boy to help with the chores, Nate feels even worse.
"This short tale has a quietly epic sweep." Horn Book Guide

Lamm, C. Drew
Bittersweet; {by} Drew Lamm. Clarion Bks.
2003 214p $15   **Fic**
1. Grandmothers—Fiction 2. Artists—Fiction
ISBN 0-618-16443-X   LC 2003-12503
When her beloved grandmother suffers a stroke, high school junior and talented artist Taylor finds her inspiration and creative energy disappearing until she learns to reconnect with others and herself in unexpected ways
"Lamm has written a dramatic, poignant, realistic first novel with a character who will find a place in readers' hearts." SLJ

Langrish, Katherine
Troll Fell. HarperCollins 2004 264p $15.99; lib bdg $16.89 (5 and up)   **Fic**
1. Orphans—Fiction 2. Fantasy fiction
ISBN 0-06-058304-5; 0-06-058305-3 (lib bdg)
                   LC 2003-17480
Forced to live with his evil identical-twin uncles after his father's death, twelve-year-old Peer tries to find a way to stop their plan to sell the neighbor's children to the trolls.
"Langrish's tense, quick-paced story will keep readers glued to the page." Booklist

Larbalestier, Justine
Magic or madness; by Justine Larbalestier.
Razorbill 2005 288p $16.99 (7 and up)
                     Fic
1. Magic—Fiction 2. Space and time—Fiction 3. Grandmothers—Fiction 4. New York (N.Y.)—Fiction 5. Australia—Fiction
ISBN 1-59514-022-0   LC 2004-18263
From the Sydney, Australia home of a grandmother she believes is a witch, fifteen-year-old Reason Cansino is magically transported to New York City, where she discovers that friends and foes can be hard to distinguish
"Readers looking for layered, understated fantasy will follow the looping paths of Larbalestier's fine writing . . . with gratitude and awe." Booklist

Lasky, Kathryn
Beyond the burning time. Blue Sky Press (NY) 1994 272p pa $5.99 hardcover o.p. (7 and up)
                     Fic
1. Witchcraft—Fiction 2. Salem (Mass.)—Fiction 3. Mother-daughter relationship—Fiction
ISBN 0-590-47332-8 (pa)   LC 94-5231

When, in the winter of 1691, accusations of witchcraft surface in her small New England village, twelve-year-old Mary Chase fights to save her mother from execution
"Well researched and documented with extensive notes. . . . A readable, engrossing, and sometimes exciting tale of an important era in American history." SLJ

Blood secret; by Kathryn Lasky. 1st ed.
HarperCollins 2004 249p $15.99; lib bdg $16.89 (7 and up)   **Fic**
1. Aunts—Fiction 2. Jews—Persecutions—Fiction 3. Spain—Fiction
ISBN 0-06-000066-X; 0-06-000065-1 (lib bdg)
                   LC 2003-22299
Fourteen-year-old Jerry Luna, mute since her mother's disappearance, is sent to her great-great aunt Constanza's house, where she discovers a trunk that draws her into the world of her ancestors during the Spanish Inquisition.
"Lasky's quiet, layered novel introduces history. . . that's rarely covered in books for youth while asking sophisticated questions about faith, the legacy of persecution, the power of silence, and the deep mysteries of what's passed between generations." Booklist

Christmas after all; the Great Depression diary of Minnie Swift. Scholastic 2001 185p (Dear America) $10.95   **Fic**
1. Great Depression, 1929-1939—Fiction 2. Family life—Fiction 3. Orphans—Fiction
ISBN 0-439-21943-4   LC 00-67031
In her fictionalized journal, eleven-year-old Minnie Swift recounts how her family dealt with the difficult times during the Depression and how the arrival of an orphan from Texas changed their lives in Indianapolis just before Christmas 1932
"Overall this is an enjoyable story of a well-off family during the 1930s. A historical note and archival photos are appended." Horn Book Guide

Dreams in the golden country; the diary of Zipporah Feldman, a Jewish immigrant girl. Scholastic 1998 188p il (Dear America) $10.95; lib bdg $12.95 (4 and up)   **Fic**
1. Jews—Fiction 2. Immigrants—Fiction 3. New York (N.Y.)—Fiction
ISBN 0-590-02973-8; 0-439-55502-7 (lib bdg)
                   LC 97-26213
Twelve-year-old Zippy, a Jewish immigrant from Russia, keeps a diary account of the first eighteen months of her family's life on the Lower East Side of New York City in 1903-1904
"The hopes and dreams of a young girl are beautifully portrayed through Lasky's eloquent and engaging narrative." SLJ

Elizabeth I; red rose of the House of Tudor. Scholastic 1999 237p il (Royal diaries) $10.95 (4 and up)   **Fic**
1. Elizabeth I, Queen of England, 1533-1603—Fiction 2. Great Britain—History—1485-1603, Tudors—Fiction
ISBN 0-590-68484-1   LC 99-11178
In a series of diary entries, Princess Elizabeth, the eleven-year-old daughter of King Henry VIII, celebrates holidays and birthdays, relives her mother's execution,

Lasky, Kathryn—*Continued*
revels in her studies, and agonizes over her father's health
"Well written and captivating." Voice Youth Advocates

Jahanara, Princess of Princesses. Scholastic 2002 186p (Royal diaries) $10.95 **Fic**
1. Jahanara Begum—Fiction 2. Shahjahan, Emperor of India, ca. 1592-1666—Fiction 3. Mogul Empire—Fiction
ISBN 0-439-22350-4 LC 2001-57627
Beginning in 1627, Princess Jahanara, first daughter of Shah Jahan of India's Mogul Dynasty, writes in her diary about political intrigues, weddings, battles, and other experiences of her life. Includes historical notes on Jahanara's later life and on the Mogul Empire
"The language seems true to the thoughts and sensitivities of a young teen, and Lasky's meticulous research is evident throughout the journal." Booklist

A journey to the New World; the diary of Remember Patience Whipple. Scholastic 1996 173p (Dear America) $10.95 **Fic**
1. Mayflower (Ship)—Fiction 2. Pilgrims (New England colonists)—Fiction 3. Massachusetts—History—1600-1775, Colonial period—Fiction
ISBN 0-590-50214-X LC 95-25715
Twelve-year-old Mem presents a diary account of the trip she and her family made on the Mayflower in 1620 and their first year in the New World
"The format, with spaces between entries, will appeal to reluctant readers, while the lively writing will hold the attention of good readers. A historical note on the year 1620, maps, a diagram of the Mayflower, and reproductions of historical prints add to the social-studies value of the book." SLJ

Kazunomiya; prisoner of heaven; by Kathryn Lasky. 1st ed. Scholastic 2004 156p (Royal diaries) $10.95 **Fic**
1. Kazunomiya, Princess of Japan, 1846-1877—Fiction 2. Japan—Fiction
ISBN 0-439-16485-0 LC 2003-25474
Princess Kazunomiya, half-sister of the Emperor of Japan, relates in her diary and in poems the confusing events occurring in the Imperial Palace in 1858, including political and romantic intrigue.

Mary, Queen of Scots, queen without a country. Scholastic 2002 206p (Royal diaries) $10.95 **Fic**
1. Mary, Queen of Scots, 1542-1587—Fiction 2. France—History—1328-1589, House of Valois—Fiction
ISBN 0-439-19404-0 LC 2001-31085
Mary, the young Scottish queen, is sent a diary from her mother in which she records her experiences living at the court of France's King Henry II as she awaits her marriage to Henry's son, Francis
"Lasky creates a voice that's both accessible and believable, deftly incorporating historical detail and the intricacies of court life and behavior while showing the teenage queen as a compelling, independent character." Booklist

Memoirs of a bookbat. Harcourt Brace & Co. 1994 216p pa $6 hardcover o.p. (6 and up) **Fic**
1. Censorship—Fiction 2. Books and reading—Fiction
ISBN 0-15-201259-1 LC 93-36402
Fourteen-year-old Harper, an avid reader of fantasy who must hide her books from her fundamentalist parents, comes to realize that their public promotion of censorship threatens her freedom to make her own choices
"In this very smart (and somewhat acerbic) book . . . Lasky . . . combines fictional characters with real-life authors and religious groups (such as Operation Rescue) to create a credible and entertaining story of an emerging independent thinker." Publ Wkly

The night journey; with drawings by Trina Schart Hyman. Warne 1981 149p il o.p. Penguin Bks. paperback available $4.99 (4 and up) **Fic**
1. Jews—Fiction
ISBN 0-14-032048-2 (pa) LC 81-2225
Also available Spanish language edition
This novel "describes the escape of a Jewish family from the persecutions and pogroms of Tsarist Russia. . . . It is told as a story-within-a-story, as thirteen-year-old Rachel learns, bit by bit, what her great-grandmother went through as a child." Bull Cent Child Books
"The novel shifts back and forth from the dangerous journey out of Russia to Rachel's own casual, secure life at home and school. These transitions are handled with a smoothness that doesn't break the intrinsic tension of the story, and the contrast between the two lives demonstrates with poignant clarity the real meaning of freedom. The portrayal of warm, supportive families in both stories becomes a link between past and present." SLJ

Star split. Hyperion Bks. for Children 1999 203p hardcover o.p. paperback available $5.99 (7 and up) **Fic**
1. Genetic engineering—Fiction 2. Cloning—fiction 3. Science fiction
ISBN 0-7868-1568-X (pa) LC 98-43839
In 3038, thirteen-year-old Darci uncovers an underground movement to save the human race from genetic enhancement technology
"On the whole this is gripping fare. . . . Lasky leaves readers with plenty of food for thought." Publ Wkly

A time for courage; the suffragette diary of Kathleen Bowen. Scholastic 2002 c2001 217p il (Dear America) $10.95; lib bdg $12.95 **Fic**
1. Women—Suffrage—Fiction
ISBN 0-590-51141-6; 0-439-55542-6 (lib bdg) LC 2001-49080
A diary account of thirteen-year-old Kathleen Bowen's life in Washington, D.C. in 1917, as she juggles concerns about the national battle for women's suffrage, the war in Europe, and her own school work and family. Includes a historical note
The author "gives a good overview of the harsh treatment these women endured during their picketing and imprisonment." SLJ

Lasky, Kathryn—*Continued*

True north; a novel of the underground railroad. Blue Sky Press (NY) 1996 267p pa $4.99 hardcover o.p. (6 and up)   **Fic**
1. Abolitionists—Fiction 2. Underground railroad—Fiction 3. Slavery—Fiction
ISBN 0-590-20524-2   LC 95-2922
"Fourteen-year-old Lucy is the youngest daughter of a proper, upper-middle-class family living in Boston in 1858. Afrika, a young slave, doesn't know how old she is, but she knows it's time to make a run for freedom via the Underground Railroad. The girls' lives collide when Lucy discovers Afrika hiding in her grandfather's house. . . . Rich imagery and detail add to the suspenseful plot, and the characters, revealed in alternating perspectives, are vivid and believable." Booklist

Lawrence, Caroline

The thieves of Ostia; a Roman mystery. Roaring Brook Press 2002 152p lib bdg $22.90; pa $5.99
                                          Fic
1. Dogs—Fiction 2. Rome—History—Fiction 3. Mystery fiction
ISBN 0-7613-2602-2 (lib bdg); 0-7613-1582-9 (pa)
                              LC 2001-34912
Also available audiobook version
First published 2001 in the United Kingdom

In Rome in the year 79 A.D., a group of children from very different backgrounds work together to discover who beheaded a pet dog—and why
"With adroit and skillful writing, the author hooks the reader into this fast-paced, sharply pieced together mystery, and doesn't let up until she reaches a convincing and satisfying solution. . . . Moreover, the book is filled with appealing and believable characters, interesting historical information, and strong narrative descriptions." ALAN
Other titles in this series are:
The dolphins of Laurentem (2003)
The enemies of Jupiter (2005)
The gladiators of Capua (2005)
The pirates of Pompeii (2003)
The twelve tasks of Flavia Gemina (2004)

Lawrence, Iain, 1955-

B for Buster. Delacorte Press 2004 321p $15.95; lib bdg $17.95 (7 and up)   **Fic**
1. World War, 1939-1945—Fiction 2. Air pilots—Fiction
ISBN 0-385-73086-1; 0-385-90108-9 (lib bdg)
                              LC 2003-17345
In the spring of 1943, sixteen-year-old Kak, desperate to escape his abusive parents, lies about his age to enlist in the Canadian Air Force and soon finds himself based in England as part of a crew flying bombing raids over Germany
"Lawrence writes a gripping, affecting story about the thrill of flying, the terrifying realities of war, and the agony of reconciling personal fears and ideals with duty and bravery." Booklist

The lightkeeper's daughter. Delacorte Press 2002 246p $16.95; lib bdg $18.99; pa $7.95 (7 and up)   **Fic**
1. Teenage mothers—Fiction 2. Islands—Fiction
ISBN 0-385-72925-1; 0-385-90062-7 (lib bdg); 0-385-73127-2 (pa)   LC 2002-578
When, after a four-year absence, seventeen-year-old Squid returns to her childhood home on a remote lighthouse island off British Columbia with her young daughter in tow, she and her parents try to come to terms with each other and the painful events of the past, especially the death of her older brother
This "is not an easy or comfortable read but for sophisticated teens, this lyrical novel is an experience not to be forgotten." SLJ

Lord of the nutcracker men. Delacorte Press 2001 212p map $15.95; lib bdg $17.99; pa $5.99 (5 and up)   **Fic**
1. World War, 1914-1918—Fiction
ISBN 0-385-72924-3; 0-385-90024-4 (lib bdg); 0-440-41812-7 (pa)   LC 2001-17254
Johnny, a ten year old English boy, comes to believe that the battles he enacts with his toy soldiers control the war his father is fighting on the front in World War I
"There's realism in the grief of the village people and also in Dad's poignant letters. . . . This will be a fine introduction to World War I, both for personal interest and for curriculum use." Booklist

The wreckers. Delacorte Press 1998 196p $15.95; pa $5.99 (5 and up)   **Fic**
1. Shipwrecks—Fiction 2. Adventure fiction 3. Great Britain—History—1714-1837—Fiction
ISBN 0-385-32535-5; 0-440-41545-4 (pa)
                              LC 97-31625
Also available Thorndike Press large print edition
"In 1799 fourteen-year-old John Spencer survives a shipwreck on the coast of Cornwall. To his horror, he soon learns that the villagers are not rescuers, but pirates who lure ships ashore in order to plunder their cargoes. . . . Lawrence creates an edge-of-the-chair survival/mystery story. Fast-moving, mesmerizing." Horn Book Guide
Followed by The smugglers (1999) and Ghost boy (2000)

Lawrence, Louise, 1943-

Dream-weaver. Clarion Bks. 1996 231p $15 (7 and up)   **Fic**
1. Science fiction
ISBN 0-395-71812-0   LC 95-25856
"When her frightening dreams about a blue-eyed, alien boy come to the attention of the Dream-Weavers Guild, Eth is accepted for training even though she is unusually young. As she learns the arts of healing and weaving dreams that maintain harmony and stability in her society, a spaceship from Earth is carrying 3,000 colonists to her planet, among them 17-year-old Troy, who fears the colonists' intentions for their new world. . . . The action is intense with lots of twists and turns; Lawrence's characters are striking; and her conclusion is satisfying, though not what readers may expect. All in all, a first-rate piece of science fiction." Booklist

Lawrence, Michael

A crack in the line; Withern Rise, volume I; by Michael Lawrence. 1st ed. Greenwillow Books 2004 c2003 323p (Withern Rise) $15.99; lib bdg $16.89 (7 and up) **Fic**
1. Space and time—Fiction 2. Great Britain—Fiction
ISBN 0-06-072477-3; 0-06-072478-1 (lib bdg)
LC 2003-56860
Sixteen-year-old Alaric discovers how to travel to an alternate reality, where his mother is alive and his place in the family is held by a girl named Naia
"The first in a trilogy, this complex story of choices, fate, and acceptance is demanding. . . . [It] is sure to spark passionate discussion." Booklist

Lawson, Julie, 1947-

Destination gold! Orca Bk. Pubs. 2001 c2000 210p $16.95; pa $7.50 **Fic**
1. Klondike River Valley (Yukon)—Gold discoveries—Fiction
ISBN 1-55143-155-6; 1-55143-157-2 (pa)
"In 1897, sixteen-year-old Ned leaves his home in Victoria, British Columbia, in pursuit of Klondike gold. The novel charts his struggles in the north while following Catherine, a teenage girl running away from her past, and Ned's twelve-year old sister, Sarah, as they, too, make the dangerous trek to the mining town." Horn Book Guide
"The details of gold mining and traveling in the Klondike are well researched and vividly described. . . . This is an exciting, fast-paced adventure." SLJ

Le Guin, Ursula K., 1929-

Gifts. Harcourt 2004 274p $17 (7 and up)
Fic

1. Fantasy fiction
ISBN 0-15-205123-6   LC 2003-21449
When a young man in the Uplands blinds himself rather than use his gift of "unmaking"—a violent talent shared by members of his family—he upsets the precarious balance of power among rival, feuding families, each of which has a strange and deadly talent of its own
"Although intriguing as a coming-of-age allegory, Orrec's story is also rich in . . . earthy magic and intelligent plot twists." Booklist

Leavitt, Martine

Heck, superhero. Front Street 2004 144p $16.95
Fic
1. Mental illness—Fiction 2. Abandoned children—Fiction 3. Cartoons and comics—Fiction
ISBN 1-88691-094-4   LC 2002-192863
Abandoned by his mentally ill mother, thirteen-year-old Heck tries to survive on his own as his mind bounces between the superhero character he imagines himself to be and the harsh reality of his life.
"Strong supporting characters . . . add depth to this engrossing, evocative novel." Booklist

Lee, Marie G.

Necessary roughness. HarperCollins Pubs. 1996 228p (7 and up) **Fic**
1. Korean Americans—Fiction 2. Prejudices—Fiction 3. Football—Fiction 4. Father-son relationship—Fiction
ISBN 0-06-025124-7; 0-06-447169-1
LC 96-34185
Sixteen-year-old Korean American Chan moves from Los Angeles to a small town in Minnesota, where he must cope not only with racism on the football team but also with the tensions in his relationship with his strict father
"Lee's tight characterizations lift this novel above the ordinary, and the football action will appeal to sports' fans." SLJ

Lee, Tanith

Piratica; being a daring tale of a singular girl's adventure upon the high seas; presented most handsomely by the notorious Tanith Lee. Dutton Children's Books 2004 288p $17.99 **Fic**
1. Pirates—Fiction 2. Sex role—Fiction 3. Adventure fiction
ISBN 0-525-47324-6
First published 2003 in the United Kingdom
A bump on the head restores Art's memories of her mother and the exciting life they led, so the sixteen-year-old leaves Angels Academy for Young Maidens, seeks out the pirates who were her family before her mother's death, and leads them back to adventure on the high seas.
"Piratica is a refreshing, tongue-in-cheek, tangled tale that will entice readers who crave adventure and fantasy." SLJ

L'Engle, Madeleine, 1918-

A ring of endless light. Farrar, Straus & Giroux 1980 324p $20 (5 and up) **Fic**
1. Death—Fiction 2. Dolphins—Fiction
ISBN 0-374-36299-8   LC 79-27679
Also available in paperback from Random House
During the summer her grandfather is dying of leukemia and death seems all around, 15-year-old Vicky finds comfort with the pod of dolphins with which she has been doing research
"With customary grace and firm control of an intricate plot, L'Engle has created another irresistible novel about familiar characters, the Austin family." Publ Wkly

A wrinkle in time. Farrar, Straus & Giroux 1962 211p $17 (5 and up) **Fic**
1. Fantasy fiction
ISBN 0-374-38613-7
Also available in paperback from Dell
Awarded the Newbery Medal, 1963
"A brother and sister, together with a friend, go in search of their scientist father who was lost while engaged in secret work for the government on the tesseract problem. A tesseract is a wrinkle in time. The father is a prisoner on a forbidding planet, and after awesome and terrifying experiences, he is rescued, and the little group returns safely to Earth and home." Child Books Too

L'Engle, Madeleine, 1918-—*Continued*
Good to Miss
"It makes unusual demands on the imagination and
consequently gives great rewards." Horn Book
Followed by A wind in the door (1973)

Leonard, Elmore
A coyote's in the house. HarperEntertainment
2004 149p il $15.95 (5 and up)   **Fic**
1. Dogs—Fiction 2. Coyotes—Fiction 3. Hollywood
(Calif.)—Fiction
ISBN 0-06-054404-X   LC 2003-71050
"Hip coyote Antwan. . . . is foraging for garbage
when he makes the acquaintance of German shepherd
Buddy, a retired film star. Buddy is bored and has decided he'd like the freedom of the coyote's life in the wild,
while Antwan. . . . is interested in getting to know Miss
Betty, a prizewinning poodle who lives with Buddy's
family. . . . The story is good fun, but the real pleasure
here . . . lies in listening to the characters banter with
one another. . . . A poignant ending gives the tale just
the right edge." Booklist

Lester, Alison, 1952-
Quicksand pony. Houghton Mifflin 1998 136p
$15   **Fic**
1. Horses—Fiction 2. Australia—Fiction
ISBN 0-395-93749-3   LC 98-6930
"Walter Lorraine books"
First published 1997 in Australia
After her pony Bella, trapped in quicksand, is rescued
by a mysterious unseen person, ten-year-old Biddy fol-
lows the trail into the Australian bush and discovers the
solution to a disappearance that happened years ago
"A multilayered story of survival, love, mystery, and
family relationships." SLJ

The snow pony. Houghton Mifflin 2003 194p il
$15   **Fic**
1. Horses—Fiction 2. Australia—Fiction
ISBN 0-618-25404-8   LC 2002-13388
"Walter Lorraine books"
Prolonged drought has strained Dusty's ranching family to the breaking point, but she finds consolation with
her wild and beautiful horse
"This fast-paced 'horse and girl' adventure story has
interesting, well-developed characters, and the tension
among the family members is well drawn." SLJ

Lester, Julius
Day of tears; a novel in dialogue. Hyperion
2005 177p $15.99 (7 and up)   **Fic**
1. Slavery—Fiction 2. African Americans—Fiction
ISBN 0-7868-0490-4
"Jump at the sun"
Emma has taken care of the Butler children since Sarah and Frances's mother, Fanny, left. Emma wants to
raise the girls to have good hearts, as a rift over slavery
has ripped the Butler household apart. Now, to pay off
debts, Pierce Butler wants to cash in his slave "assets",
possibly including Emma.
"The horror of the auction and its aftermath is unforgettable. . . . The racism is virulent (there's widespread
use of the n-word). The personal voices make this a stirring text for group discussion." Booklist

Othello; a novel. Scholastic 1995 151p $12.95
                                               Fic
ISBN 0-590-41967-6   LC 94-12833
"An interpretation of Shakespeare's play in the form
of a novel casts Othello, Iago, and Iago's wife as African
immigrants in Elizabethan England. The first half of the
book details the courtship and marriage of Othello and
Desdemona; the second half closely follows the plot of
the play and includes, in boldface, quotations and para-
phrases from Shakespeare's play. An ambitious yet accessible reworking." Horn Book Guide

When Dad killed Mom. Harcourt 2001 183p
$17; pa $6.95 (7 and up)   **Fic**
1. Homicide—Fiction 2. Siblings—Fiction
ISBN 0-15-216305-0; 0-15-204698-4 (pa)
                                  LC 00-12033
"After Jeremy, twelve, and Jenna, fourteen, learn that
their father has shot and killed their mother, disturbing
bits and pieces of the truth emerge. Although the story's
roll call of sensational events sometimes takes on a
melodramatic quality, the telling is undeniably gripping,
and readers will find believable the siblings' efforts to
sort through the truth about their parents and begin to
build a new life." Horn Book Guide

Levin, Betty
Shadow-catcher. Greenwillow Bks. 2000 152p
$15.95 (5 and up)   **Fic**
1. Grandfathers—Fiction 2. Photography—Fiction
3. Mystery fiction
ISBN 0-688-17862-6   LC 99-45087
Although he often fancied himself a detective, Jona-
than must become a real sleuth when he attempts to
solve a mystery while accompanying his grandfather, a
Civil War veteran and traveling photographer in Maine
"The well-crafted, engaging mystery . . . neatly
frames a story of character growth and development."
Booklist

Levine, Ellen, 1939-
Catch a tiger by the toe; by Ellen Levine.
Viking 2005 200p $15.99   **Fic**
1. Communism—Fiction 2. Bronx (New York,
N.Y.)—Fiction 3. United States—Politics and government—1945-1953—Fiction
ISBN 0-670-88461-8   LC 2004-17348
In the Bronx, New York, during the McCarthy era,
twelve-year-old Jamie keeps a terrible secret about her
family, but when the truth is exposed, her parents lose
their jobs and she is fired from the school newspaper.
"Tension mounts to the very end. . . . The warmth,
sadness, and anger humanize the issues, which are sure
to spark discussion about the meaning of patriotism -
then and now." Booklist

The journal of Jedediah Barstow; an emigrant
on the Oregon Trail. Scholastic 2002 172p (My
name is America) $10.95   **Fic**
1. Overland journeys to the Pacific—Fiction
2. Orphans—Fiction 3. Frontier and pioneer life—Fiction
ISBN 0-439-06310-8   LC 2001-49559

Levine, Ellen, 1939-—*Continued*

In his 1845 diary, thirteen-year-old orphan Jedediah describes his wagon train journey to Oregon, in which he confronts rivers and sandy plains, bears and rattlesnakes, and the challenges of living with his fellow travelers. Includes historical notes

"Readers will care about the characters and root for them from first page to last." SLJ

Levine, Gail Carson, 1947-

Dave at night. HarperCollins Pubs. 1999 281p lib bdg $16.99; pa $5.99 (5 and up)   **Fic**

1. Orphans—Fiction 2. Jews—Fiction 3. African Americans—Fiction 4. New York (N.Y.)—Fiction

ISBN 0-06-028154-5 (lib bdg); 0-06-440747-0 (pa)

LC 98-50069

Also available Audiobook version

When orphaned Dave is sent to the Hebrew Home for Boys where he is treated cruelly, he sneaks out at night and is welcomed into the music- and culture-filled world of the Harlem Renaissance

"The magic comes from Levine's language and characterization. This novel will provide inspiration for all children while offering a unique view of a culturally diverse New York City." SLJ

Ella enchanted. HarperCollins Pubs. 1997 232p $16.99; lib bdg $17.89; pa $6.50 (5 and up)   **Fic**

1. Fantasy fiction

ISBN 0-06-027510-3; 0-06-027511-1 (lib bdg); 0-06-440705-5 (pa)

LC 96-30734

Also available Thorndike Press large print edition

A Newbery Medal honor book, 1998

In this novel based on the story of Cinderella, Ella struggles against the childhood curse that forces her to obey any order given to her

"As finely designed as a tapestry, Ella's story both neatly incorporates elements of the original tale and mightily expands them." Booklist

The princess test; illustrated by Mark Elliott. HarperCollins Pubs. 1999 91p il (Princess tales) $9.99 (4 and up)   **Fic**

1. Fairy tales

ISBN 0-06-028062-X

LC 98-27960

In this humorous retelling of Hans Christian Andersen's "The Princess and the Pea," Lorelei must pass many difficult tests in order to prove that she is a true princess and win the hand of Prince Nicholas

"Breezily told, with a wealth of comic detail, slyly contemporary dialogue, and genuine affection for the genre that inspired {it}." Bull Cent Child Books

Other available titles in the Princess tales series are:

Cinderellis and the glass hill (2000)
The fairy's mistake (1999)
The fairy's return (2002)
For Biddle's sake (2002)
Princess Sonora and the long sleep (1999)

The two princesses of Bamarre. HarperCollins Pubs. 2001 241p $15.99; lib bdg $16.89; pa $5.99 (5 and up)   **Fic**

1. Fantasy fiction 2. Sisters—Fiction 3. Princesses—Fiction

ISBN 0-06-029315-2; 0-06-029316-0 (lib bdg); 0-06-440966-X (pa)

LC 00-47953

With her adventurous sister, Meryl, suffering from the Gray Death, meek and timid Princess Addie sets out to find a cure

"A lively tale with vivid characters and an exciting plot." Book Rep

The wish. HarperCollins Pubs. 2000 197p $15.99; lib bdg $16.89; pa $5.99   **Fic**

1. School stories

ISBN 0-06-027900-1; 0-06-027901-X (lib bdg); 0-06-447361-9 (pa)

LC 98-19087

When granted her wish to be the most popular girl in school, Wilma, an eighth grader, forgets that she will graduate in three weeks and her popularity will vanish

"There are some laugh-out-loud moments here and plenty of scenes that are believable and fun. Kids will get a kick out of this one." Booklist

Levitin, Sonia, 1934-

The cure. Harcourt Brace & Co. 1999 181p $16   **Fic**

1. Antisemitism—Fiction 2. Science fiction 3. Jews—Fiction 4. Middle Ages—Fiction

ISBN 0-15-201827-1

LC 98-33907

Also available in paperback from HarperCollins Pubs.

Gemm, a young boy living in 2407, collides with the past when he finds himself in Strasbourg in 1348 confronting the antisemitism that sweeps through Europe during the Black Plague

"Levitin weaves a chilling story linking two worlds." ALAN

Dream freedom. Silver Whistle Bks. 2000 178p $17   **Fic**

1. Slavery—Fiction 2. School stories 3. Sudan—Fiction

ISBN 0-15-202404-2

LC 00-35869

Marcus and his classmates learn about the terrible problem of slavery in present-day Sudan and raise money to help buy the freedom of some of the slaves. Alternate chapters tell the stories of the slaves

"Levitin's intended audience is young, but she successfully portrays the horrors of slavery—rapes, massacres, torture—using language that is age appropriate." Voice Youth Advocates

Includes bibliographical references

Journey to America; illustrated by Charles Robinson. Atheneum Pubs. 1993 c1970 150p il pa $4.99 hardcover o.p. (4 and up)   **Fic**

1. World War, 1939-1945—Fiction 2. Jewish refugees—Fiction 3. Family life—Fiction

ISBN 0-689-71130-1 (pa)

LC 93-163980

A reissue of the title first published 1970

"In a strong immigration story, Lisa Platt, the middle daughter, tells how her family is forced to leave Nazi Germany and make a new life in the United States. First

Levitin, Sonia, 1934-—*Continued*
their father leaves, then the others escape to Switzerland, where they endure harsh conditions. After months of separation, the family is reunited in New York." Rochman. Against borders
Followed by Silver days (1989) and Annie's promise (1993)

The return. Atheneum Pubs. 1987 213p map o.p. Fawcett Bks. paperback available $5.99 (6 and up)   **Fic**
1. Jews—Fiction   2. Antisemitism—Fiction 3. Ethiopia—Fiction
ISBN 0-449-70280-4 (pa)   LC 86-25891
"In a docunovel of a Jewish Ethiopian family's flight to Israel, Levitin focuses on an orphan, Desta, whose older brother, Joas, persuades her to leave the village where hunger and political recriminations constantly threaten their lives." Bull Cent Child Books
"A vivid and compelling book. . . . Levitin's tour de force is sensitively written; her command of the language is impressive and she uses Ethiopian terms effectively, interspersing them in ways readers will understand." Booklist

Room in the heart. Dutton Children's Bks. 2003 290p $16.99   **Fic**
1. World War, 1939-1945—Fiction 2. Holocaust, 1933-1945—Fiction 3. Denmark—Fiction
ISBN 0-525-46871-4   LC 2003-41012
After German forces occupy Denmark during World War II, fifteen-year-old Julie Weinstein and fifteen-year-old Niels Nelson and their friends and families try to cope with their daily lives, finding various ways to resist the Nazis and, ultimately, to survive
"Levitin makes clear what she calls the 'disgrace' of human nature, including a horrifying account of Nazi cruelty to residents of a home for the aged. What will grab readers is the picture of young people as survivors and heroic rescuers, the secrets and adventure, the fear and exhilaration." Booklist

Levy, Elizabeth
Seventh grade tango. Hyperion Bks. for Children 2000 153p $15.99 (5 and up)   **Fic**
1. Dancers—Fiction 2. Friendship—Fiction 3. School stories
ISBN 0-7868-0498-X   LC 99-53124
When Rebecca, a seventh-grader, is paired up with her friend Scott for a dance class at school, she learns a lot about who her real friends are
"Descriptive prose, snappy dialogue, and diverse characters enhance the story, which notably portrays ballroom dance as a hip, fun activity." Booklist

Levy, Marilyn, 1937-
Run for your life. Houghton Mifflin 1996 217p pa $5.99 hardcover o.p. (7 and up)   **Fic**
1. Track athletics—Fiction 2. African Americans—Fiction 3. California—Fiction
ISBN 0-698-11608-9   LC 95-24379
Also available in paperback from Putnam Pub. Group

While living in a housing project in Oakland, California, thirteen-year-old Kisha joins a track team which helps her discover that she can be a winner
"This is a highly readable and engrossing story." SLJ

Lewis, C. S. (Clive Staples), 1898-1963
The lion, the witch, and the wardrobe; illustrated by Pauline Baynes. HarperCollins Pubs. 1994 189p il $16.99; lib bdg $17.89; pa $7.99 (4 and up)   **Fic**
1. Spanish language editions 2. Fantasy fiction
ISBN 0-06-023481-4; 0-06-023482-2 (lib bdg); 0-06-440499-4 (pa)   LC 93-8889
Also available Thorndike Press large print edition; Spanish language edition also available
A reissue of the title first published 1950 by Macmillan
Four English schoolchildren find their way through the back of a wardrobe into the magic land of Narnia and assist Aslan, the golden lion, to triumph over the White Witch, who has cursed the land with eternal winter
This begins "the 'Narnia' stories, outstanding modern fairy tales with an underlying theme of good overcoming evil." Child Books Too Good to Miss
Other available titles about Narnia are:
The horse and his boy (1954)
The last battle (1956)
The magician's nephew (1956)
Prince Caspian (1951)
The silver chair (1953)
The voyage of the Dawn Treader (1952)

Lewis, Catherine
Postcards to father Abraham; a novel. Atheneum Bks. for Young Readers 2000 288p $17.95 (7 and up)   **Fic**
1. Lincoln, Abraham, 1809-1865—Fiction 2. Physically handicapped—Fiction
ISBN 0-689-82852-7   LC 99-27005
When sixteen-year-old Meghan loses her leg to cancer and her brother to Vietnam, she expresses intense anger in postcards which she writes to her idol, Abraham Lincoln
"The book works wonderfully well given the sheer strength of Meghan's personality, wicked wit, and the empathy she evokes." Booklist

Lion, Melissa, 1975-
Upstream; Melissa Lion. Wendy Lamb Books 2005 149p $15.95; lib bdg $17.99 (7 and up)   **Fic**
1. Bereavement—Fiction 2. Alaska—Fiction
ISBN 0-385-74643-1; 0-385-90877-6 (lib bdg)   LC 2004-15145
After her boyfriend is killed in a hunting accident, Alaska high school senior Marty, with help from her mother and two younger sisters, tries to get over her grief and begin a new life.
"Lion writes with sensitivity and depth. . . . Teens will want to discuss the morally complex conclusion, which raises questions about accidents, crime, and punishment." Booklist

Lipsyte, Robert

The contender. Harper & Row 1967 182p pa $5.99 hardcover o.p. (7 and up) **Fic**

1. Boxing—Fiction 2. Harlem (New York, N.Y.)—Fiction 3. African Americans—Fiction

ISBN 0-06-447039-3

"After a street fight in which he is the chief target, Alfred wanders into a gym in his neighborhood. He decides not only to improve his physical condition but also to become a boxer. Because of this interest Alfred's life is completely changed. He assumes a more positive outlook on his immediate future, even within the confines of a black ghetto." Shapiro. Fic for Youth. 3d edition

Followed by The brave (1991) and The chief (1993)

One fat summer. Harper & Row 1977 152p hardcover o.p. paperback available $5.95 (7 and up) **Fic**

1. Weight loss—Fiction 2. Obesity—Fiction

ISBN 0-06-447073-3 (pa) LC 76-49746

"Bobby Marks is 14 and fat. How fat, he doesn't know because he jumps off the scale when it hits 200 pounds. In one action-packed summer Bobby learns that altered physical appearance can bolster self-esteem. He's not sure he likes his friend Joanie's new nose and new ego, but he's certainly pleased with his own svelte new image. The slimming is a result of his summer job; tending the grounds of the town miser." West Coast Rev Books

"This is far superior to most of the summer-of-change stories; any change that takes place is logical and the protagonist learns by action and reaction to be both self-reliant and compassionate." Bull Cent Child Books

Followed by Summer rules (1981) and The summerboy (1982)

Lisle, Janet Taylor, 1947-

The art of keeping cool. Atheneum Bks. for Young Readers 2000 207p $17; pa $4.99 (5 and up) **Fic**

1. World War, 1939-1945—Fiction 2. Rhode Island—Fiction

ISBN 0-689-83787-9; 0-689-83788-7 (pa) LC 00-32778

"A Richard Jackson book"

In 1942, Robert and his cousin Elliot uncover long-hidden family secrets while staying in their grandparents' Rhode Island town, where they also become involved with a German artist who is suspected of being a spy

"Lisle develops an unforgettable cast of characters placed against a fully realized setting. Engrossing, challenging, and well paced." Horn Book

The crying rocks. Atheneum Bks. for Young Readers 2003 199p $16.95; pa $6.99 **Fic**

1. Orphans—Fiction 2. Native Americans—Fiction 3. Adoption—Fiction

ISBN 0-689-85319-X; 0-689-85320-3 (pa) LC 2002-151484

"A Richard Jackson book"

Thirteen-year-old Joelle has always wondered about her life before being adopted by the woman she calls Aunt Louise and her husband Vernon, and she makes some surprising discoveries while researching a 17th century Indian tribe

"This lovely portrait of a strong girl facing her past and present with dignity and courage will receive a wide and enthusiastic readership." SLJ

How I became a writer and Oggie learned to drive. Philomel Bks. 2002 155p $16.99; pa $5.99 (4 and up) **Fic**

1. Brothers—Fiction 2. Authorship—Fiction 3. Gangs—Fiction

ISBN 0-399-23394-6; 0-14-250167-0 (pa) LC 2001-36205

"After their parents break up, aspiring writer Archie, eleven, and his six-year-old brother Oggie move to a dangerous neighborhood with their mother. When Oggie's wallet is stolen by a gang, Archie promises to get it back but must join the gang to do so." Horn Book Guide

"It's a tribute to Lisle's powers as a writer that this frightening scenario never overpowers the real essence of the book, which is about how fiction and life are different and equally useful to one another. Such great truths are stated simply and shown in the action at the same time. . . . [A] fast-paced, adventure-filled title." SLJ

Littke, Lael

Haunted sister. Holt & Co. 1998 217p $16.95 (7 and up) **Fic**

1. Near-death experiences—Fiction 2. Twins—Fiction 3. Sisters—Fiction 4. Supernatural—Fiction

ISBN 0-8050-5729-3 LC 98-12144

A sixteen-year-old girl suffers a near-death experience in which her twin sister, who died in an accident twelve years before, returns to forcibly share her body

"A twist at the end both surprises and satisfies. A positive family story with strong psychological overtones." Booklist

Lake of secrets. Holt & Co. 2002 202p $16.95 (7 and up) **Fic**

1. Reincarnation—Fiction 2. Mystery fiction

ISBN 0-8050-6730-2 LC 2001-39933

Having arrived in her mother's home town to try to find her long-missing brother, who disappeared three years before she was born, fifteen-year-old Carlene finds herself haunted by memories from a past life

"The realistic characters and plot make the idea compelling, and the story will intrigue teens." Booklist

London, Jack, 1876-1916

The call of the wild (5 and up) **Fic**

1. Dogs—Fiction 2. Alaska—Fiction

Hardcover and paperback editions available from various publishers

First published 1903 by Macmillan

"Buck, half-St. Bernard, half-Scottish sheepdog, is stolen from his comfortable home in California and pressed into service as a sledge dog in the Klondike. At first he is abused by both man and dog, but he learns to fight ruthlessly. He becomes lead dog on a sledge team, after bettering Spitz, the vicious old leader, in a brutal fight to the death. In John Thornton, he finally finds a master whom he can respect and love. When Thornton

London, Jack, 1876-1916—*Continued*

is killed by Indians, Buck breaks away to the wilds and becomes the leader of a wolf pack, returning each year to the site of Thornton's death." Reader's Ency. 4th edition

White Fang (5 and up)   **Fic**
1. Dogs—Fiction 2. Alaska—Fiction
Hardcover and paperback editions available from various publishers
First published 1906
White Fang "is about a dog, a cross-breed, sold to Beauty Smith. This owner tortures the dog to increase his ferocity and value as a fighter. A new owner Weedom Scott, brings the dog to California, and, by kind treatment, domesticates him. White Fang later sacrifices his life to save Scott." Haydn. Thesaurus of Book Dig

Lord, Bette Bao

In the Year of the Boar and Jackie Robinson; illustrations by Marc Simont. Harper & Row 1984 169p il lib bdg $15.89; pa $4.95 (4-6)
Fic
1. Chinese Americans—Fiction 2. School stories
ISBN 0-06-024004-0 (lib bdg); 0-06-440175-8 (pa)
LC 83-48440
"In a story based in part on the author's experience as an immigrant, Shirley Temple Wong . . . arrives in Brooklyn and spends her first year in public school." Bull Cent Child Books
"Warm-hearted, fresh, and dappled with humor, the episodic book, which successfully encompasses both Chinese dragons and the Brooklyn Dodgers, stands out in the bevy of contemporary problem novels. And the unusual flavor of the text infiltrates the striking illustrations picturing the pert, pigtailed heroine making her way in 'Mei Guo'—her new 'Beautiful Country.'" Horn Book

Love, D. Anne

The puppeteer's apprentice. Margaret K. McElderry Bks. 2003 185p $16.95   **Fic**
1. Puppets and puppet plays—Fiction
ISBN 0-689-84424-7   LC 2001-44868
A medieval orphan girl called Mouse gains the courage she needs to follow her dreams of becoming a puppeteer's apprentice
"Combining a likeable heroine, a colorful setting, and an exciting plot, this historical adventure will capture young readers." Booklist
Includes bibliographical references

A year without rain. Holiday House 2000 118p $15.95 (5 and up)   **Fic**
1. Family life—Fiction 2. Frontier and pioneer life—Fiction 3. Remarriage—Fiction 4. South Dakota—Fiction
ISBN 0-8234-1488-4   LC 99-35825
Her mother's death and a year-long drought has made life difficult for twelve-year-old Rachel and her family on their farm in the Dakotas, but when she learns that her father plans to get married again, it is almost more than Rachel can bear
This "is simply yet artfully told with characters both realistic and endearing." SLJ

Lowry, Brigid, 1953-

Follow the blue; Brigid Lowry. 1st American ed. Holiday House 2004 205p $16.95 (7 and up)
Fic
1. Australia—Fiction
ISBN 0-8234-1827-8   LC 2003-62550
Fifteen-year-old Bec, living with her family in Perth, Australia, decides to stop being sensible and follow her wilder impulses during the summer that her parents are away on a long trip to help her father recover from a breakdown.
This is an "exhilarating novel. . . . A lot goes on in this very funny romp, some of it quite profound, and Lowry manages to remain mercifully nonpreachy throughout." Booklist

Guitar highway Rose. Holiday House 2003 c1997 196p $16.95 (7 and up)   **Fic**
1. Runaway teenagers—Fiction 2. Australia—Fiction
ISBN 0-8234-1790-5   LC 2002-191916
First published 1997 in Australia
Two fifteen-year-olds, Rosie and Asher, upset over the various unhappy circumstances of their lives in the Australian city of Perth, decide to run away.
"This is a romantic, entertaining, and thoughtful novel." SLJ

Lowry, Lois

Anastasia Krupnik. Houghton Mifflin 1979 113p $16 (4-6)   **Fic**
1. Family life—Fiction
ISBN 0-395-28629-8
Also available in paperback from Dell
This book describes the tenth year in the life of fourth-grader Anastasia. As she "experiences rejection of a long labored-over poem, fights acceptance of the coming arrival of a baby sibling, deliberates about becoming Catholic (in order to change her name), has a crush on Washburn Cummings who constantly dribbles an imaginary basketball, and learns to understand her senile grandmother's inward eye, she grows and matures." Booklist
"Anastasia's father and mother—an English professor and an artist—are among the most humorous, sensible, and understanding parents to be found in . . . children's fiction, and Anastasia herself is an amusing and engaging heroine." Horn Book
Other available titles about Anastasia Krupnik and her family are:
All about Sam (1988)
Anastasia, absolutely (1995)
Anastasia again! (1981)
Anastasia, ask your analyst (1984)
Anastasia at this address (1991)
Anastasia at your service (1982)
Anastasia has the answers (1986)
Anastasia on her own (1985)
Anastasia's chosen career (1987)
Attaboy Sam! (1992)
See you around Sam! (1996)
Zooman Sam (1999)

Lowry, Lois—*Continued*

Autumn Street. Houghton Mifflin 1980 188p
$16 (4 and up)   **Fic**
1. World War, 1939-1945—Fiction 2. Friendship—
Fiction
ISBN 0-395-27812-0   LC 80-376
Also available in paperback from Dell

"Elizabeth, the teller of the story, feels danger around
her when her father goes to fight in World War II. She,
her older sister, and her pregnant mother go to live with
her grandparents on Autumn Street. Tatie, the black
cook-housekeeper, and her street-wise grandson Charley
love Elizabeth and reassure her during this difficult
time." Child Book Rev Serv

"Characters, dialogue, believable plot combine in this
well written story to capture the mind and heart of all
who read this memorable and touching book." Voice
Youth Advocates

Gathering blue. Houghton Mifflin 2000 215p
$16 (5 and up)   **Fic**
1. Science fiction
ISBN 0-618-05581-9   LC 00-24359
Also available in paperback from Laurel Leaf

"Walter Lorraine books"

Lame and suddenly orphaned, Kira is mysteriously removed from her squalid village to live in the palatial
Council Edifice, where she is expected to use her gifts
as a weaver to do the bidding of the all-powerful Guardians

"Lowry has once again created a fully realized world
full of drama, suspense, and even humor." SLJ

The giver. Houghton Mifflin 1993 180p $16 (6
and up)   **Fic**
1. Science fiction
ISBN 0-395-64566-2   LC 92-15034
Also available Thorndike Press large print edition and
in paperback from Dell; audiobook version also available

Awarded the Newbery Medal, 1994

Given his lifetime assignment at the Ceremony of
Twelve, Jonas becomes the receiver of memories shared
by only one other in his community and discovers the
terrible truth about the society in which he lives

"A riveting, chilling story that inspires a new appreciation for diversity, love, and even pain. Truly memorable." SLJ

Number the stars. Houghton Mifflin 1989 137p
$16 (4 and up)   **Fic**
1. World War, 1939-1945—Fiction 2. Jews—Fiction
3. Friendship—Fiction 4. Denmark—Fiction
ISBN 0-395-51060-0   LC 88-37134
Also available in paperback from Dell; audiobook version also available

Awarded the Newbery Medal, 1990

In 1943, during the German occupation of Denmark,
ten-year-old Annemarie learns how to be brave and courageous when she helps shelter her Jewish friend from
the Nazis.

"The appended details the historical incidents upon
which Lowry bases her plot. . . . The whole work is
seamless, compelling, and memorable." Horn Book

The one hundredth thing about Caroline.
Houghton Mifflin 1983 150p $16 (5 and up)
                                                  Fic
1. Single parent family—Fiction
ISBN 0-395-34829-3   LC 83-12629

"Caroline, fascinated by dinosaurs, spends much of
her free time prowling New York's Museum of Natural
History; her best friend, Stacy, practices being an investigative reporter. The combination proves disastrous when
Caroline's mother becomes interested in Frederick Fiske,
the mysterious man in the fifth-floor apartment who
looks, Caroline is convinced, like the evil 'Tyrannosaurus
rex' and who seemingly wants to eliminate Caroline and
her brother, J.P." Booklist

"Lowry's style is bright, fast-paced and funny, with
skillfully-drawn, believable characters." SLJ

Followed by Switcharound (1985)

Rabble Starkey. Houghton Mifflin 1987 192p
$16 (5 and up)   **Fic**
1. Friendship—Fiction
ISBN 0-395-43607-9   LC 86-27542
Also available in paperback from Dell

"Parable Starkey and her mother, Sweet Hosanna,
move into the Bigelows' house to take charge of the
children after Mrs. Bigelow's hospitalization for mental
illness. . . . {This is} a smooth first-person narrative that
quietly takes on class as well as individual differences.
In the end, Lowry has managed to portray a large, diverse cast by carefully and consistently focusing the
point of view as one of a maturing observer." Bull Cent
Child Books

The silent boy. Houghton Mifflin 2003 178p
$15   **Fic**
1. Mentally handicapped—Fiction
ISBN 0-618-28231-9   LC 2002-9072

"Walter Lorraine books"

Katy, the precocious eight-year-old daughter of the
town doctor, befriends a retarded boy

"The author balances humor and generosity with the
obstacles and injustice of Katy's world to depict a complete picture of the turn of the 20th century." Publ Wkly

Stay! Keeper's story. Houghton Mifflin 1997
127p il $15 (5 and up)   **Fic**
1. Dogs—Fiction
ISBN 0-395-87048-8   LC 97-1569
Also available in paperback from Dell

"The canine narrator is a mongrel with class, a poetically inclined, refined animal of good upbringing if not
bloodlines. He leaves the relative safety of his first home
(an alley outside a French restaurant) for the perils of the
wide world in search of a human friend." Bull Cent
Child Books

"The author proves she is as well versed in animal behavior as in human sensibilities. Her warm sense of humor and vivid imagination . . . accentuate Keeper's un-
orthodox perceptions of the world." Publ Wkly

Taking care of Terrific. Houghton Mifflin 1983
168p $16 (7 and up)   **Fic**
1. Babysitters—Fiction 2. Boston (Mass.)—Fiction
ISBN 0-395-34070-5   LC 82-23331
Also available in paperback from Yearling Bks.

Lowry, Lois—*Continued*

Taking her overprotected young charge to the public park to broaden his horizons, fourteen-year-old baby sitter Enid enjoys unexpected friendships with a black saxophonist and a bag lady until she is charged with kidnapping.

"The Boston setting is vividly evoked, and the diverse cast of characters adds variety and flavor to the narrative." Horn Book

Your move, J.P.! Houghton Mifflin 1990 122p $16 (5 and up)   **Fic**

1. School stories

ISBN 0-395-53639-1   LC 89-24707

Also available in paperback from Dell

Caroline's older brother, twelve-year-old J.P. Tate, who appeared in The one hundredth thing about Caroline and Switcharound, has a "crush on Angela Galsworthy, newly arrived at his private school from London, England. . . . Anxious to sustain Angela's interest, J.P. tells her that he is suffering from triple framosis, a rare but fatal disease. Angela believes him and J.P. is stuck with his lie." Bull Cent Child Books

"The author makes the most of the humor in J.P.'s antics but maintains a rueful sympathy throughout for his plight and for his eventual admission of truth." Horn Book

Lubar, David, 1954-

Dunk. Clarion Bks. 2002 249p $15; pa $6.99 (7 and up)   **Fic**

1. Amusement parks—Fiction

ISBN 0-618-19455-X; 0-618-43909-9 (pa)

LC 2001-58428

While hoping to work as the clown in an amusement park dunk tank on the New Jersey shore the summer before his junior year in high school, Chad faces his best friend's serious illness, hassles with police, and the girl that got away

"With painful truth, Lubar has created complex, difficult to understand characters that seem straight from real life." Booklist

Wizards of the game. Philomel Bks. 2003 166p $16.99   **Fic**

1. Games—Fiction 2. School stories 3. Magic—Fiction

ISBN 0-399-23706-2   LC 2002-3640

Eighth grader Mercer, whose passion is the fantasy role-playing game Wizards of the Warrior World, hopes to use a fund raiser to bring a gaming convention to his middle school, but instead he attracts four genuine wizards who are trapped on Earth and want his help in returning to their own world

"Short, often funny, and easy to read, the story combines wizardry and the real world of eighth grade in a way that is entirely believable and thought-provoking." SLJ

Lunn, Janet Louise Swoboda

The hollow tree; {by} Janet Lunn. Viking 2000 c1997 208p hardcover o.p. paperback available $5.99   **Fic**

1. United States—History—1775-1783, Revolution—Fiction 2. Vermont—Fiction

ISBN 0-14-230142-6 (pa)   LC 99-76483

First published 1997 in Canada

"During the Revolutionary War, formerly meek Phoebe finds her mettle while crossing wilderness Vermont to deliver a spy's report, joining a group of loyalist refugees—including handsome Jem Morrissay—on their way to Canada." Horn Book Guide

"Using well-crafted characters, believable relationships, and continuous action, Lunn creates a tense, atmospheric story." Booklist

Lupica, Mike

Travel team. Philomel Books 2004 274p $16.99

Fic

1. Basketball—Fiction 2. Father-son relationship—Fiction 3. School stories

ISBN 0-399-24150-7   LC 2003-25072

After he is cut from his travel basketball team - the very same team that his father once led to national prominence - twelve-year-old Danny Walker forms his own team of cast-offs that might have a shot at victory.

"Lupica's mix of rich characterizations and authentic basketball details blend to create an engaging, enjoyable story." Horn Book Guide

Lurie, April

Dancing in the streets of Brooklyn. Delacorte Press 2002 194p $15.95; lib bdg $17.99; pa $5.99

Fic

1. Stepfathers—Fiction 2. World War, 1939-1945—Fiction 3. Brooklyn (New York, N.Y.)—Fiction

ISBN 0-385-72942-1; 0-385-90066-X (lib bdg); 0-440-41825-9 (pa)   LC 2002-170

In 1944, thirteen-year-old Judy grapples with the discovery that "Pa" isn't her biological father, experiences her first romance, and faces hardships dealt to friends in Brooklyn's Norwegian community

"Judy's crises, romantic and domestic, are thoroughly believable, and Lurie ably avoids melodrama by setting them firmly among the realistic ebb and flow of neighborhood life." Bull Cent Child Books

Lynch, Chris

Gold dust. HarperCollins Pubs. 2000 196p lib bdg $16.89; pa $7.99   **Fic**

1. Baseball—Fiction 2. Race relations—Fiction 3. Friendship—Fiction 4. Boston (Mass.)—Fiction

ISBN 0-06-028175-8 (lib bdg); 0-06-447201-9 (pa)

LC 00-24348

In 1975, twelve-year-old Richard befriends Napolean, a Caribbean newcomer to his Catholic school, hoping that Napolean will learn to love baseball and the Red Sox, and will win acceptance in the racially polarized Boston school

"Lynch captures the thrill of the game and an athlete's intense physical and mental concentration with freshness and joy, and issues of race and class are introduced with sensitivity and realism." Booklist

Shadow boxer. HarperCollins Pubs. 1993 215p pa $5.95 hardcover o.p. (7 and up)   **Fic**

1. Boxing—Fiction 2. Brothers—Fiction 3. Father-son relationship—Fiction

ISBN 0-06-447112-8 (pa)   LC 92-47490

Lynch, Chris—*Continued*

"Fourteen-year-old George has felt responsible for his younger brother Monty ever since the death of his father, a heavyweight boxer. George passes on the boxing lessons Dad taught him and is equally intent on teaching Monty about life outside the ring. The fight sequences, fraternal dynamics, and memorable cast of eccentric characters make for some riveting episodes in the rough, tough-talking book." Horn Book Guide

Slot machine. HarperCollins Pubs. 1995 241p pa $5.99 hardcover o.p. (7 and up)   **Fic**
1. Camps—Fiction 2. Sports—Fiction 3. Friendship—Fiction
ISBN 0-06-447140-3 (pa)   LC 94-48235
When overweight thirteen-year-old Elvin Bishop is sent to camp at St. Paul's Seminary Retreat Center, he and his two best friends are forced to try out various sports in order to find out where they belong

"The religious setting is used to heighten the irony. There is some beer drinking. Pornography is discussed and in one scene described in an inoffensive way. Likewise, there is a scene or two of adolescent male exhibitionism, again not graphically described, and finally it is implied that Frank undergoes hazing of a homosexual nature." Book Rep

Followed by Extreme Elvin (1999)

Who the man. HarperCollins Pubs. 2002 186p $15.99; lib bdg $16.89   **Fic**
1. Violence—Fiction 2. Divorce—Fiction
ISBN 0-06-623938-9; 0-06-623939-7 (lib bdg)
                 LC 2002-7969
Thirteen-year-old Earl Pryor is much too big for his age, and much too powerful for the anger that rages within him when classmates tease him, the girl he likes disappoints him, or his parents' problems get too real

"The novel successfully captures the nuances of Earl's character, and is superbly written." SLJ

Lyon, George Ella, 1949-

Gina.Jamie.Father.Bear. Atheneum Bks. for Young Readers 2002 135p $15.95   **Fic**
1. Supernatural—Fiction 2. Fathers—Fiction 3. Single parent family—Fiction 4. Ohio—Fiction
ISBN 0-689-84370-4   LC 2001-22991
"A Richard Jackson book"
The lives of two young people, Gina in Ohio and Jamie in another dimension, intersect as they struggle to hold their single-parent families together and to explain the behavioral changes they see in their fathers

"A thought-provoking contemporary novel with elements of fantasy . . . . Lyon's skillful, poetic use of language gives the situations and characters vitality." SLJ

Sonny's house of spies. Atheneum Books for Young Readers 2004 298p $16.95   **Fic**
1. Race relations—Fiction 2. Homosexuality—Fiction 3. Alabama—Fiction
ISBN 0-689-85168-5   LC 2003-7529
"A Richard Jackson book"
In a small Alabama town in 1947 - 1956, Sonny searches for answers about his father's disappearance, Uncle Marty, who looks after the family, and Mamby, their black housekeeper.

"Lyon conveys a strong sense of Southern life through the cadence of speech, wonderful turns of phrase, and the patterns of daily life. Sonny, smart-mouthed older sister Loretta, and their mother are all well-drawn, realistic characters with whom readers will sympathize." SLJ

Lyon, Steve

The gift moves. Houghton Mifflin 2004 230p $15   **Fic**
1. Science fiction
ISBN 0-618-39128-2   LC 2003-12293
In a futuristic United States devoid of wealth and material things, a teenage baker befriends a talented weaver's apprentice who holds a dark secret.

"Lyon mixes elements of magical realism with a coming-of-age story, incorporating issues that teens will relate to. . . . This is an unusual story that is sure to inspire much thought and contemplation." SLJ

Lyons, Mary E.

Dear Ellen Bee; a Civil War scrapbook of two Union spies; by Mary E. Lyons & Muriel M. Branch. Atheneum Bks. for Young Readers 2000 161p il $17.95   **Fic**
1. Van Lew, Elizabeth, 1818-1900—Fiction
2. Slavery—Fiction 3. Abolitionists—Fiction
4. United States—History—1861-1865, Civil War—Fiction 5. Spies—Fiction
ISBN 0-689-82379-7   LC 99-42050
A scrapbook kept by Liza, a young black girl details her experiences and those of the older white woman, "Miss Bet," who had freed her and her family, sent her north from Richmond to get an education, and then worked to bring an end to slavery. Based on the life of Elizabeth Van Lew

"Terrific research provides a fascinating portrait of these real heroines." Voice Youth Advocates

Letters from a slave girl; the story of Harriet Jacobs. Scribner 1992 146p il pa $4.99 hardcover o.p. (6 and up)   **Fic**
1. Jacobs, Harriet A. (Harriet Ann), 1813-1896 or 7—Fiction 2. Slavery—Fiction 3. African Americans—Fiction 4. Letters—Fiction
ISBN 0-689-80015-0   LC 91-45778
A fictionalized version of the life of Harriet Jacobs, told in the form of letters that she might have written during her slavery in North Carolina and as she prepared for escape to the North in 1842

This "is historical fiction at its best. . . . Mary Lyons has remained faithful to Jacobs's actual autobiography throughout her readable, compelling novel. . . . Her observations of the horrors of slavery are concise and lucid. The letters are written in dialect, based on Jacobs's own writing and on other slave narrations of the period." Horn Book

Mack, Tracy, 1968-

Birdland. Scholastic Press 2003 198p $16.95 (7 and up)   **Fic**
1. Video recording—Fiction 2. Brothers—Fiction 3. New York (N.Y.)—Fiction
ISBN 0-439-53590-5   LC 2002-151863

Mack, Tracy, 1968——_Continued_

Fourteen-year-old, tongue-tied Jed spends Christmas break working on a school project filming a documentary about his East Village, New York City, neighborhood, where he is continually reminded of his older brother, Zeke, a promising poet who died the year before

"Colorful, well-drawn characters add to the story's painful sense of realism." SLJ

Drawing lessons. Scholastic Press 2000 168p hardcover o.p. paperback available $4.99

Fic

1. Father-daughter relationship—Fiction 2. Artists—Fiction 3. Divorce—Fiction
ISBN 0-439-11203-6 (pa)   LC 99-27254

Twelve-year-old Rory begins to lose the passion for making art that she shares with her father after she finds him kissing his female model and fears for the safety of her parents' marriage

This "is a simple book of surprising beauty and depth." Booklist

Mackel, Kathy

Can of worms. Avon Bks. 1999 146p pa $3.99 hardcover o.p.   Fic

1. Extraterrestrial beings—Fiction 2. Science fiction
ISBN 0-380-80050-0 (pa)   LC 98-53346

Bullied and unhappy at school, thirteen-year-old Mike, who has always thought that he might be an alien, sends a distress call into space asking to be rescued from the ignorance and cruelty of his life on Earth

"This humorous, fast-paced science-fiction adventure is set in the real world of adolescent angst, bullies, and first love." SLJ

Other titles in this series are:
Eggs in one basket (2000)
From the horse's mouth (2002)

Mackler, Carolyn

The earth, my butt, and other big, round things. Candlewick Press 2003 246p $15.99 (7 and up)

Fic

1. Family life—Fiction 2. Obesity—Fiction 3. School stories 4. New York (N.Y.)—Fiction
ISBN 0-7636-1958-2   LC 2002-73921

Feeling like she does not fit in with the other members of her family, who are all thin, brilliant, and good-looking, fifteen-year-old Virginia tries to deal with her self-image, her first physical relationship, and her disillusionment with some of the people closest to her

"The e-mails [Virginia] exchanges . . . and the lists she makes (e.g., 'The Fat Girl Code of Conduct') add both realism and insight to her character. The heroine's transformation into someone who finds her own style and speaks her own mind is believable—and worthy of applause." Publ Wkly

Love and other four-letter words. Delacorte Press 2000 247p hardcover o.p. paperback available $5.99 (7 and up)   Fic

1. Divorce—Fiction 2. Mother-daughter relationship—Fiction
ISBN 0-440-22831-X (pa)   LC 00-25189

When she and her mother move to an apartment in New York City after her parents decide on a trial separation, sixteen-year-old Sammie learns to deal with her mother's fragile mental state, her best friend's self-centeredness, several new friendships, and her own budding sexuality

"Mackler gets the contemporary scene with humor and realism." Booklist

MacLachlan, Patricia, 1938-

Journey. Delacorte Press 1991 83p pa $5.50 hardcover o.p. (4 and up)   Fic

1. Family life—Fiction
ISBN 0-440-40809-1 (pa)   LC 90-21052

When their mother goes off, leaving her two children with their grandparents, they feel as if their past has been erased until Grandfather finds a way to restore it to them

"This is a spellbinding tale, lean only in its length. The author's clipped dialogue and meticulously pared-down descriptions convey a deceptive simplicity—there are deep, intricate rumblings beneath the surface calm of MacLachlan's words." Publ Wkly

MacPhail, Catherine, 1946-

Dark waters. Bloomsbury Pub. 2003 175p $15.95   Fic

1. Brothers—Fiction 2. Ghost stories
ISBN 1-58234-846-4   LC 2002-28296

Col McCann becomes a local hero when he saves a boy from drowning but when his older brother is suspected of a serious crime, Col must decide if he should be loyal to his family or tell the truth about what he saw while under the water

"This is a fast-paced, exciting tale with lively characters and realistic family friction." Booklist

Maguire, Gregory

The good liar. Clarion Bks. 1999 129p $15 (4 and up)   Fic

1. World War, 1939-1945—Fiction 2. France—Fiction
ISBN 0-395-90697-0   LC 98-19981

Also available in paperback from HarperTrophy
First published 1995 in Ireland

Now an old man living in the United States, Marcel recalls his childhood in German-occupied France, especially the summer that he and his older brother Rene befriended a young German soldier

"At once poignant, thoughtful, and laced with humor, the book offers readers an unusual perspective on history." Horn Book Guide

Mahy, Margaret

Alchemy. Margaret K. McElderry Bks. 2003 207p $16.95 (7 and up)   Fic

1. Alchemy—Fiction
ISBN 0-689-85053-0   LC 2002-5973

Seventeen-year-old Roland discovers that an unpopular girl in his school is studying alchemy and finds that their destiny is linked with that of a power-hungry magician

"Mahy, whose thrillers are both complex and literary, once again provides a multilayered story that can be appreciated on several levels." Booklist

Mankell, Henning, 1948-
Secrets in the fire; translated by Anne Connie
Stuksrud. Annick Press 2003 166p $17.95; pa
$7.95 (5 and up)   **Fic**
  1. Mozambique—Fiction 2. War stories
  ISBN 1-55037-801-5; 1-55037-800-7 (pa)
  Orginally published in Sweden
Sofia, who lost her legs from landmines in Mozam-
bique, attempts to make a new life for herself.
  "A hard-hitting, eye-opening novel that brings readers
face-to-face with the horrors of war. . . . Mankell's lan-
guage and style are spare, but elicit a deeply emotional
response." SLJ

Marsden, John, 1950-
Checkers. Houghton Mifflin 1998 122p $15 (7
and up)   **Fic**
  1. Psychiatric hospitals—Fiction 2. Dogs—Fiction
  3. Australia—Fiction
  ISBN 0-395-85754-6   LC 97-49405
  Also available in paperback from Laurel Leaf
An unnamed Australian "teenage girl describes her interactions with her fellow patients in a mental hospital
and recalls events that led to her institutionalization. Her
memories center on her pet dog and on a financial scandal that involved her businessman father." Horn Book
Guide
  "Marsden's beautiful prose packs and emotional wallop. . . . This affecting account of a family under siege
by the media is both an engaging read and a strong psychological exploration." Booklist

Tomorrow, when the war began. Houghton
Mifflin 1995 286p $16 (7 and up)   **Fic**
  1. War stories 2. Australia—Fiction
  ISBN 0-395-70673-4   LC 94-29299
  Also available in paperback from Dell
  First published 1993 in Australia
"Australian teenager Ellie and six of her friends return
from a winter break camping trip to find their homes
burned or deserted, their families imprisoned, and their
country occupied by a foreign military force in league
with a band of disaffected Australians. As their shock
wears off, the seven decide they must stick together if
they are to survive." SLJ
  "The novel is a riveting adventure through which
Marsden explores the capacity for evil and the necessity
of working together to oppose it." Horn Book
  Other available titles in this series are:
Burning for revenge (2000)
Darkness, be my friend (1999)
The dead of night (1997)
A killing frost (1998)
The night is for hunting (2001)
The other side of dawn (2002)

Martin, Ann M., 1955-
A corner of the universe. Scholastic Press 2002
189p $15.95; pa $5.99 (5 and up)   **Fic**
  1. Uncles—Fiction 2. Friendship—Fiction
  ISBN 0-439-38880-5; 0-439-38881-3 (pa)
                                   LC 2001-57611

The summer that Hattie turns twelve, she meets the
childlike uncle she never knew and becomes friends with
a girl who works at the carnival that comes to Hattie's
small town
  "Martin delivers wonderfully real characters and an
engrossing plot through the viewpoint of a girl who tries
so earnestly to connect with those around her." SLJ

Here today. Scholastic 2004 308p $16.95 (5 and
up)   **Fic**
  1. Mothers—Fiction 2. Family life—Fiction
  ISBN 0-439-57944-9   LC 2004-41620
In 1963, Ellie's mother was crowned a grocery store
beauty queen, her classmates treated her cruelly, and
President Kennedy was killed. It was also when Ellie realized that in trying to keep her life together she had to
let pieces of it go
  "Martin paints a well-articulated picture of the times,
but it is her memorable child and adult characters that
shine here." SLJ

Martin, Nora
Flight of the Fisherbird. Bloomsbury Children's
Bks. 2003 150p il $16.95 (5 and up)   **Fic**
  1. Uncles—Fiction 2. Chinese Americans—Fiction
  3. Washington (State)—Fiction
  ISBN 1-582-34814-6   LC 2002-35628
In 1889 in the islands off the coast of Washington
State, thirteen-year-old Clementine pulls a nearly
drowned Chinese man out of the sea and begins to sus-
pect that her beloved uncle may have been involved in
his attempted murder as well as other treacherous deeds.
  "A fast-paced, high-stakes historical mystery." SLJ

Masefield, John
Jim Davis; a high-sea adventure. Scholastic
2002 c1911 224p $15.95 (5 and up)   **Fic**
  1. Pirates—Fiction 2. Adventure fiction
  ISBN 0-439-40436-3   LC 2002-21175
  "The Chicken House"
  First published 1911 in the United Kingdom
Jim Davis is a twelve-year-old boy whose life takes a
terrifying turn when he stumbles upon a ring of bloodthirsty pirates
  "Masefield was England's poet laureate, and his prose
has a poet's grace and attention to detail. The language,
however, doesn't get in the way of the rip-roaring plot,
which taps into the rich vein of classic sea stories."
Booklist

Mass, Wendy, 1967-
A mango-shaped space; a novel. Little, Brown
2003 220p $16.95   **Fic**
  1. Synesthesia—Fiction 2. School stories
  ISBN 0-316-52388-7   LC 2002-72989
Afraid that she is crazy, thirteen-year-old Mia, who
sees a special color with every letter, number, and sound,
keeps this a secret until she becomes overwhelmed by
school, changing relationships, and the loss of something
important to her
  "Mass skillfully conveys Mia's emotions, and readers
will be intrigued with this fictional depiction of an actual, and fascinating, condition." Horn Book Guide

Matas, Carol, 1949-

After the war. Simon & Schuster Bks. for Young Readers 1996 116p map pa $4.99 hardcover o.p. (7 and up)   **Fic**
1. Holocaust, 1933-1945—Fiction 2. Jews—Fiction
ISBN 0-689-80722-8   LC 95-43613
After being released from Buchenwald at the end of World War II, fifteen-year-old Ruth risks her life to lead a group of children across Europe to Palestine
"Rich in texture and simple in its honesty, this story resonates with feeling." Voice Youth Advocates
Followed by The garden

Greater than angels. Simon & Schuster Bks. for Young Readers 1998 133p pa $4.99 hardcover o.p. (7 and up)   **Fic**
1. World War, 1939-1945—Fiction 2. Jews—Fiction 3. Holocaust, 1933-1945—Fiction 4. France—Fiction
ISBN 0-689-83084-X   LC 97-27565
Anna, a teenaged German refugee, relates how she and other Jewish children were cared for by the citizens of Le Chambon-sur-Lignon, France, during the German occupation
"This well-researched historical novel will make a good addition to middle-school collections." SLJ

In my enemy's house. Simon & Schuster Bks. for Young Readers 1999 167p pa $4.99 hardcover o.p. (7 and up)   **Fic**
1. World War, 1939-1945—Fiction 2. Jews—Fiction 3. Holocaust, 1933-1945—Fiction 4. Germany—Fiction
ISBN 0-689-82400-9   LC 98-16330
When German soldiers arrive in Zloczow during World War II, a young Jewish girl must decide whether or not to conceal her identity and work for a Nazi in Germany in order to survive
"Although this is fiction, it has the immediacy and impact of a true story. Marisa's ordeal is compelling, moving—and deeply disturbing." SLJ

Sparks fly upward. Clarion Bks. 2002 180p $15 (4 and up)   **Fic**
1. Jews—Fiction 2. Canada—Fiction
ISBN 0-618-15964-9   LC 2001-47188
In 1910, when a family of Russian Jews moves from Saskatchewan to Winnipeg, Canada, twelve-year-old Rebecca must live with Christians temporarily and struggles with anti-Semitism, confusion about God, and changing relationships with family and friends
"There's no sentimentality in the characterization . . . and the history is well researched. Most compelling, though, is Rebecca's personal struggle with faith, friendship, and loyalty." Booklist

The war within; a novel of the Civil War. Simon & Schuster Bks. for Young Readers 2001 151p $16; pa $4.99 (5 and up)   **Fic**
1. United States—History—1861-1865, Civil War—Fiction 2. Jews—Fiction 3. Prejudices—Fiction
ISBN 0-689-82935-3; 0-689-84358-5 (pa)
    LC 00-45068
Also available Thorndike Press large print edition
"Readers will find themselves swept along by the riptide of action and the appealing cast of strong, vivid characters." Booklist

Mathis, Sharon Bell, 1937-

Teacup full of roses. Viking 1972 125p hardcover o.p. paperback available $4.99 (7 and up)   **Fic**
1. African Americans—Fiction 2. Family life—Fiction 3. Drug abuse—Fiction
ISBN 0-14-32328-7 (pa)
"Because of the mother's especially protective concern for her eldest son, Paul, the world of the Brooks family revolves around him—to the detriment of the rest of the family. After a hospital stay for detoxification from heroin, Paul returns home. With him comes tragedy that destroys David, the youngest son, who had an 'outasight' basketball arm, and changes the life of the middle son, Joe, who had a gift for telling stories. This is an exploration of love and loyalty in a black inner-city family." Shapiro. Fic for Youth. 3d edition

Matthews, Kezi, 1928-

Flying lessons. Cricket Bks. 2002 162p $16.95
    Fic
1. Aunts—Fiction 2. Uncles—Fiction 3. Death—Fiction
ISBN 0-8126-2671-0   LC 2002-6047
In 1937, when LaMarr's glamorous mother is lost in a plane crash and she goes to live with her aunt and uncle, it takes the thirteen-year-old some time to reconcile herself to the idea that her mother has not gone to Hollywood to become a movie star
"Beautifully written and emotionally resonant." Horn Book

Mazer, Harry, 1925-

A boy at war; a novel of Pearl Harbor. Simon & Schuster Bks. for Young Readers 2001 104p il $15; pa $4.99 (7 and up)   **Fic**
1. Pearl Harbor (Oahu, Hawaii), Attack on, 1941—Fiction
ISBN 0-689-84161-2; 0-689-84160-4 (pa)
    LC 00-49687
While fishing with his friends off Honolulu on December 7, 1941, teenaged Adam is caught in the midst of the Japanese attack and through the chaos of the subsequent days tries to find his father, a naval officer who was serving on the U.S.S. Arizona when the bombs fell
"Mazer's graphic, sensory descriptions give the narrative immediacy, putting readers alongside Adam, watching with him as 'pieces of the ship and pieces of men rained down around him.' . . . This is a thought-provoking, sobering account of the human costs of war." Horn Book
Other titles in this series are:
Boy no more (2004)
Heroes don't run (2005)

The last mission. Delacorte Press 1979 182p o.p. Dell paperback available $5.99 (7 and up)
    Fic
1. World War, 1939-1945—Fiction 2. Prisoners of war—Fiction 3. Jews—Fiction
ISBN 0-440-94797-9 (pa)   LC 79-50674
In 1944 a 15-year-old Jewish boy tells his family he will travel in the West but instead, enlists in the United

Mazer, Harry, 1925- —*Continued*
States Air Corps and is subsequently taken prisoner by
the Germans
"Told in a rapid journalistic style, occasionally peppered with barrack-room vulgarities, the story is a vivid
and moving account of a boy's experience during World
War II as well as a skillful, convincing portrayal of his
misgivings as a Jew on enemy soil and of his ability to
size up—in mature human fashion—the misery around
him." Horn Book

Snow bound. Delacorte Press 1973 146p o.p.
Dell paperback available $5.99 (7 and up)
Fic
1. Wilderness survival—Fiction 2. Runaway children—Fiction
ISBN 0-440-96134-3 (pa)   LC 72-7958
Also available in hardcover from P. Smith
"Tony Laporte is angry when his parents will not allow him to keep a stray dog, so he takes off in his mother's old car. Driving without a license in the middle of
a snowstorm that soon becomes a blizzard, Tony picks
up a hitchhiker, Cindy Reichert. Trying to impress the
slightly older girl with his driving skill, Tony wrecks the
car, leaving the two stranded in a desolate area far from
a main highway, with little likelihood of rescue for
days." Shapiro. Fic for Youth. 3d edition

The wild kid. Simon & Schuster Bks. for Young
Readers 1998 103p pa $4.99 hardcover o.p. (4 and
up)
Fic
1. Mentally handicapped—Fiction 2. Wild children—
Fiction 3. Runaway children—Fiction
ISBN 0-689-82289-8   LC 97-42578
Twelve-year-old Sammy, who is mildly retarded, runs
away from home and becomes a prisoner of Kevin, a
wild kid living in the woods
"A gripping survival story with flesh-and-blood char-
acters." SLJ

Mazer, Norma Fox, 1931-
After the rain. Morrow 1987 291p $17.99
Fic
1. Grandfathers—Fiction 2. Death—Fiction
ISBN 0-688-06867-7   LC 86-33270
Also available in paperback from Avon Bks.
A Newbery Medal honor book, 1988
"Adolescent Rachel has always been a little afraid of
Grandpa Izzy, her mother's father; sharp-tongued and ir-
ritable, the old man seems to have no kindness or soft-
ness in his nature. After the family learns that he has terminal cancer (which Izzy isn't told), Rachel begins to
visit him and walk with him daily, and by the time he
is near the end and hospitalized, she has come to love
him." Bull Cent Child Books
"A powerful book, dealing with death and dying and
the strength of family affection." Horn Book

Girlhearts. HarperCollins Pubs. 2001 210p
$15.99; lib bdg $16.89; pa $6.99   **Fic**
1. Orphans—Fiction 2. Death—Fiction
ISBN 0-688-13350-9; 0-688-06866-9 (lib bdg);
0-380-72290-9 (pa)   LC 00-63202
Also available Thorndike Press large print edition

Thirteen-year-old Sarabeth Silver's life is turned upside-down when her mother dies suddenly, leaving her
orphaned, confused, and at the mercy of everyone who
seems to know what is best for her
"Mazer's intimate portrait of grief is convincing and
well drawn." Horn Book Guide

Good night, Maman. Harcourt Brace & Co.
1999 185p $16 (5 and up)   **Fic**
1. Holocaust, 1933-1945—Fiction 2. World War,
1939-1945—Fiction 3. Jewish refugees—Fiction
ISBN 0-15-201468-3   LC 98-49220
Also available in paperback from HarperCollins
After spending years fleeing from the Nazis in war-
torn Europe, twelve-year-old Karin Levi and her older
brother Marc find a new home in a refugee camp in Oswego, New York
"Mazer convincingly constructs a fictional yet moving
memoir of one girl's forever-altered life, and in Karin
she gives readers a memorable heroine." Bull Cent Child
Books

Out of control. Morrow Junior Bks. 1993 217p
$16 (7 and up)   **Fic**
1. Sexual harassment—Fiction 2. Friendship—Fiction
ISBN 0-688-10208-5   LC 92-32516
Also available in paperback from HarperCollins Pubs.
"An incident of sexual harassment occurring in a high
school corridor dramatically alters the lives of two of the
students involved. Of the three youths accused of assaulting sharp-tongued Valerie Michon, only Rollo, a junior,
experiences twinges of guilt which evolve into a desperate need to be forgiven by his family as well as his victim. Meanwhile, bitter, fearful Valerie struggles to regain
her independence and trust in men." Publ Wkly
"This is a work of real strength, a book in which every character, every facet of plot, suggests credibility and
provokes introspection." Voice Youth Advocates

Silver. Morrow Junior Bks. 1988 261p $16 (7
and up)   **Fic**
1. Friendship—Fiction
ISBN 0-688-06865-0   LC 88-18652
Also available in paperback from Avon Bks.
"When Sarabeth Silver's mother moves the two of
them to the far end of Roadview Trailer Park, she puts
Sarabeth in the Drumlins school district and scores again
in her relentless drive to ensure that her daughter will
have better. . . . The relative insignificance of wealth
becomes glaringly clear when her enigmatic friend, Patty,
reveals that she is the victim of sexual abuse." Voice
Youth Advocates
"Mazer's story unfolds smoothly. She has an ear for
dialogue that gives her scenes an easy credibility, and the
story's central drama of a girl's physical abuse is handled without oversensationalizing the plot." Booklist

Taking Terri Mueller. Morrow 1983 c1981 212p
pa $5.99 hardcover o.p.   **Fic**
1. Parental kidnapping—Fiction 2. Divorce—Fiction
3. Parent-child relationship—Fiction
ISBN 0-380-79004-1 (pa)   LC 82-18849
First published 1981 in paperback by Avon Bks.
"Thirteen-year-old Terri and her father, Phil, have an
almost idyllic relationship. Together they travel across
the country, moving wherever Phil's carpentry work

Mazer, Norma Fox, 1931-—*Continued*
takes him. Terri has no reason to doubt what her father
has told her about her mother's death in an auto accident
nine years before. No reason, that is, until she overhears
a conversation indicating something is being kept from
her. . . . For a book that begins so benignly, amazing
emotional depths are reached." Booklist

McAllister, Margaret, 1956-
Ghost at the window. Dutton Children's Bks.
2002 160p $15.99 (5 and up)   **Fic**
1. Space and time—Fiction 2. Ghost stories
3. Scotland—Fiction
ISBN 0-525-46852-8   LC 2001-40395
Life at Ninian House, Ewan's Scottish home that slips
back and forth in time, becomes even more unpredictable
when a ghostly girl from 1937 shares a frightening secret
with him.
"McAllister's prose moves quickly, and her characters,
setting, and events are easy to visualize. . . . Part mystery, part ghost story, part morality tale, the novel has a
good deal to offer." Booklist

Hold my hand and run. Dutton 2000 $15.99
                                          Fic
1. Space and time—Fiction 2. Ghost stories
ISBN 0-525-46391-7
Originally published: Oxford, England : Oxford University Press, 1999
Life at Ninian House, Ewan's Scottish home that slips
back and forth in time, becomes even more unpredictable
when a ghostly girl from 1937 shares a frightening secret
with him
"McAllister's prose moves quickly, and her characters,
setting, and events are easy to visualize. . . . Part mystery, part ghost story, part morality tale, the novel has a
good deal to offer." Booklist

McCaffrey, Anne
Black horses for the king. Harcourt Brace & Co.
1996 217p map $17 (7 and up)   **Fic**
1. Arthur, King—Fiction 2. Horses—Fiction
ISBN 0-15-227322-0   LC 95-36366
Also available in paperback from Ballantine Pub.
Group
Galwyn, son of a Roman Celt, escapes from his tyran-
nical uncle and joins Lord Artos, later know as King Arthur, using his talent with languages and way with horses
to help secure and care for the Libyan horses that Artos
hopes to use in battle against the Saxons
"The Arthurian flavor is well maintained throughout,
and both characterizations and events are totally convincing." Booklist

Pegasus in flight. Ballantine Bks. 1990 290p
hardcover o.p. paperback available $5.99 (7 and
up)   **Fic**
1. Science fiction
ISBN 0-345-36897-5 (pa)   LC 90-92901
Sequel to To ride Pegasus (1990)
"A Del Rey book"
"As director of the Jerhatten Center for Parapsychic
Talents, telepath Rhyssa Owen struggles to protect her

psychically gifted people—called 'Talents'—from a
world that both fears and wants to exploit their abilities."
Libr J

{The Pern series} (7 and up)   **Fic**
1. Fantasy fiction
"The people of Pern are in danger of the Threads, and
look to the tamed dragons for protection from the thread-
like spores. . . . McCaffrey has created a vivid and be-
lievable world, alive with interesting characters and
events. There is plenty of action, a good plot, and the
writing is excellent." Roman. Sequences
Fantasy titles set on Pern are:
All the Weyrs of Pern (1991)
The chronicles of Pern: first fall (1993)
The dolphins of Pern (1994)
Dragondrums (1979)
Dragonflight (1968)
Dragonholder (1999)
Dragonquest (1971)
Dragonriders of Pern (1978)
Dragonsdawn (1988)
Dragonseye (1997)
Dragonsinger (1977)
Dragonsong (1976)
The masterharper of Pern (1998)
Moreta: Dragonlady of Pern (1983)
Nerilka's story (1986)
The Renegades of Pern (1989)
The skies of Pern (2001)
White dragon (1978)

McCaffrey, Laura Williams
Alia waking. Clarion Bks. 2003 214p $15
                                          Fic
1. Fantasy fiction 2. Friendship—Fiction
ISBN 0-618-19461-4   LC 2002-8721
Alia and her best friend Kay long to join the
Keentens, a sisterhood of warrior women, but after a
punishment caring for captives, Alia begins to question
everything that once was certain in her life
"The rich characters, vivid descriptions, and suspenseful storytelling are well blended in this novel about war,
enemies, and finding oneself." SLJ

McCaughrean, Geraldine, 1951-
The kite rider; a novel. HarperCollins Pubs.
2002 272p maps $15.95; lib bdg $16.89; pa $6.99
(5 and up)   **Fic**
1. Kublai Khan, 1216-1294—Fiction 2. China—Fiction 3. Kites—Fiction
ISBN 0-06-623874-9; 0-06-623875-7 (lib bdg);
0-06-441091-9 (pa)   LC 2001-39522
In thirteenth-century China, after trying to save his
widowed mother from a horrendous second marriage,
twelve-year-old Haoyou has life-changing adventures
when he takes to the sky as a circus kite rider and ends
up meeting the great Mongol ruler Kublai Khan
"The story is a genuine page-turner. . . .
McCaughrean fully immerses her memorable characters
in the culture and lore of the ancient Chinese and Mongols, which make this not only a solid adventure story
but also a window to a fascinating time and place."
Booklist

McCaughrean, Geraldine, 1951-—*Continued*

The stones are hatching. HarperCollins Pubs. 2000 c1999 130p hardcover o.p. paperback available $5.95 (5 and up)   **Fic**
1. Fantasy fiction
ISBN 0-06-447218-3 (pa)   LC 99-39895
First published 1999 in the United Kingdom
Eleven-year-old Phelim and his companions, a Maiden, a Fool, and a strange black Horse, journey to the Stoor Worm's lair to destroy the long-forgotten Worm and its Hatchlings, who have been roused from their slumber by the sounds of war
"With lyrical language, pieces of old songs and poetry, and wondrous imagery, McCaughrean has created a story of amazing depth and breadth." Horn Book Guide

Stop the train! a novel. HarperCollins Pubs. 2003 289p $16.99; lib bdg $17.89 (5 and up)   **Fic**
1. Frontier and pioneer life—Fiction 2. Oklahoma—Fiction
ISBN 0-06-050749-7; 0-06-050750-0 (lib bdg)   LC 2002-27340
Despite the opposition of the owner of the Red Rock Runner railroad in 1893, the new settlers of Florence, Oklahoma, are determined to build a real town
"There is much tongue-in-cheek humor in this rollicking tale, and wonderful figurative language abounds." SLJ

McCord, Patricia

Pictures in the dark. Bloomsbury Children's Books 2004 288p $16.95 (7 and up)   **Fic**
1. Mental illness—Fiction 2. Child abuse—Fiction 3. Sisters—Fiction
ISBN 1-582-34848-0   LC 2003-56252
Life with their mentally ill mother becomes unbearable for twelve-year-old Sarah and fifteen-year-old Carlie as they are deprived of food and forbidden to use the bathroom.
"McCord has painted a bleak yet often hopeful picture of a family coping with mental illness. . . .A poignant, enlightening read." Booklist

McCormick, Patricia

Cut. Front St. 2000 168p $16.95 (7 and up)   **Fic**
1. Self-mutilation—Fiction 2. Psychiatric hospitals—Fiction
ISBN 1-88691-061-8   LC 00-34840
Also available in paperback from Scholastic Bks.
While confined to a mental hospital, thirteen-year-old Callie slowly comes to understand some of the reasons behind her self-mutilation, and gradually starts to get better
"Realistic, sensitive, and heartfelt." Voice Youth Advocates

McDonald, Janet, 1953-

Spellbound. Frances Foster Bks. 2001 138p $16 (7 and up)   **Fic**
1. Teenage mothers—Fiction 2. African Americans—Fiction
ISBN 0-374-37140-7   LC 00-29381

Also available Thorndike Press large print edition and in paperback from Puffin Bks.
Raven, a teenage mother and high school dropout living in a housing project, decides, with the help and sometime interference of her best friend Aisha, to study for a spelling bee which could lead to a college preparatory program and four-year scholarship
"The dialogue is lively and smart; the characters ring true." Booklist

Twists and turns. Frances Foster Bks./Farrar, Straus & Giroux 2003 135p $16 (7 and up)   **Fic**
1. African Americans—Fiction 2. Public housing—Fiction 3. Sisters—Fiction 4. Brooklyn (New York, N.Y.)—Fiction
ISBN 0-374-39955-7   LC 2002-35313
Also available Thorndike Press large print edition
With the help of a couple of successful friends, eighteen- and nineteen-year-old Teesha and Keeba try to capitalize on their talents by opening a hair salon in the rundown Brooklyn housing project where they live
"The poetry and wit are in the daily details. . . . The story is inspiring—not because of a slick resolution or a heavy message, but because McDonald shows how hard things are, even as she tells a story of teens who find the strength in themselves and in those around them to rebuild and carry on." Booklist

McDonald, Joyce

Devil on my heels. Delacorte Press 2004 263p $15.95; lib bdg $17.99 (7 and up)   **Fic**
1. African Americans—Fiction 2. Race relations—Fiction 3. Migrant labor—Fiction 4. Florida—Fiction
ISBN 0-385-73107-8; 0-385-90133-x (lib bdg)
In 1957 fifteen-year-old Dove, the daughter of a prosperous orange grower in Benevolence, Florida, feels increasingly uneasy after learning of acts of racism against the African American orange pickers by those close to her.
"This is certainly a page-turner and it will give readers insight into a difficult and shameful part of American history." SLJ

Shades of Simon Gray. Delacorte Press 2001 245p $15.95; lib bdg $17.99; pa $5.50 (7 and up)   **Fic**
1. Supernatural—Fiction 2. New Jersey—Fiction
ISBN 0-385-32659-9; 0-385-90026-0 (lib bdg); 0-440-22804-2 (pa)   LC 2001-17424
Seventeen-year-old Simon lies in a coma, finding his space and time overlapping with that of a man who was lynched over 200 years ago, while a member of the cheating ring he has been helping wonders if their actions have caused the plagues assaulting their New Jersey town
"McDonald blends elements of ghost story, thriller, and unrequited romance in this spooky tale from a guilty conscience." Horn Book Guide

Swallowing stones. Delacorte Press 1997 245p pa $6.50 hardcover o.p. (7 and up)   **Fic**
1. Guilt—Fiction 2. Death—Fiction
ISBN 0-440-22672-4   LC 97-1402

McDonald, Joyce—*Continued*

Dual perspectives reveal the aftermath of seventeen-year-old Michael MacKenzie's birthday celebration during which he discharges an antique Winchester rifle and unknowingly kills the father of high school classmate Jenna Ward

"This mesmerizing story largely derives its power from the respect McDonald demonstrates for these teens and their emotions, and her unwavering focus on their changing relationships in response to the tragedy." SLJ

McDonald, Megan, 1959-

All the stars in the sky; the Santa Fe trail diary of Florrie Mack Ryder. Scholastic 2003 187p il (Dear America) $10.95 (4 and up)   **Fic**
1. Santa Fe Trail—Fiction 2. Frontier and pioneer life—Fiction 3. Overland journeys to the Pacific—Fiction
ISBN 0-439-16963-1   LC 2002-44579
Twelve-year-old Florrie's diary records the year 1848 during which she, her brother, mother, and stepfather traveled the Santa Fe trail from Independence, Missouri, to Santa Fe

"The writing is excellent, developing a compelling narrative." SLJ

McGhee, Alison, 1960-

Snap; a novel. Candlewick Press 2004 129p $15.99 (5 and up)   **Fic**
1. Friendship—Fiction 2. Grandmothers—Fiction 3. Death—Fiction
ISBN 0-7636-2002-5   LC 2002-34998
Eleven-year-old Edwina confronts old and new challenges when her longtime best friend Sally faces the inevitable death of the grandmother who raised her.

This "features memorable characters and a tolerance for eccentricity, emotional subtlety and complexity, themes of acceptance of death and love, and a spare and poetic text that begs to be reread and savored." SLJ

McGraw, Eloise Jarvis, 1915-2000

The moorchild; [by] Eloise McGraw. Margaret K. McElderry Bks. 1996 241p $17; pa $4.99 (4 and up)   **Fic**
1. Fantasy fiction 2. Fairies—Fiction
ISBN 0-689-80654-X; 0-689-82033-X (pa)
LC 95-34107
Also available Thorndike Press large print edition
Newbery Medal honor book, 1997

"Saaski, a half-human, half-Moorfolk child, is banished from the Mound and placed as a changeling in a human village, where she is regarded with suspicion and treated with scorn." Horn Book Guide

"Incorporating some classic fantasy motifs and icons, McGraw . . . conjures up an appreciably familiar world that, as evidence of her storytelling power, still strikes an original chord." Publ Wkly

McKay, Hilary, 1959-

Saffy's angel. Margaret K. McElderry Bks. 2002 152p $16; pa $4.99 (5 and up)   **Fic**
1. Family life—Fiction 2. Adoption—Fiction
ISBN 0-689-84933-8; 0-689-84934-6 (pa)
LC 2001-44110

First published 2001 in the United Kingdom

After learning that she was adopted, thirteen-year-old Saffron's relationship with her eccentric, artistic family changes, until they help her go back to Italy where she was born to find a special momento of her past

"Like the Casson household itself, the plot is a chaotic whirl that careens off in several directions simultaneously. But McKay always skillfully draws each clearly defined character back into the story with witty, well-edited details; rapid dialogue; and fine pacing." Booklist
Other titles in this series are:
Indigo's star (2004)
Permanent Rose (2005)

McKinley, Robin

Beauty; a retelling of the story of Beauty & the beast. Harper & Row 1978 247p $15.99; pa $5.99 (7 and up)   **Fic**
1. Fairy tales
ISBN 0-06-024149-7; 0-06-440477-3 (pa)
LC 77-25636
"McKinley's version of this folktale is embellished with rich descriptions and settings and detailed characterizations. The author has not modernized the story but varied the traditional version to attract modern readers. The values of love, honor, and beauty are placed in a magical setting that will please the reader of fantasy." Shapiro. Fic for Youth. 3d edition

The blue sword. Greenwillow Bks. 1982 272p $16.99 (7 and up)   **Fic**
1. Fantasy fiction
ISBN 0-688-00938-7   LC 82-2895
Also available in paperback from Ace Bks.

Harry, bored with her sheltered life in the remote orange-growing colony of Daria, discovers magic in herself when she is kidnapped by a native king with mysterious powers

"This is a zesty, romantic, heroic fantasy with an appealing stalwart heroine, a finely realixed mythical kingdom, and a grounding in reality." Booklist

The hero and the crown. Greenwillow Bks. 1985 246p lib bdg $16.99 (6 and up)   **Fic**
1. Fantasy fiction
ISBN 0-688-02593-5   LC 84-4074
Also available in paperback from Penguin Putnam Bks. for Young Readers
Awarded the Newbery Medal, 1985

"A prequel rather than sequel to 'The Blue Sword' {1982}, McKinley's second novel set in the . . . mythical kingdom of Damar centers on Aerin, daughter of a Damarian king and his second wife, a witchwoman from the feared, demon-ridden North. The narrative follows Aerin as she seeks her birthright, becoming first a dragon killer and eventually the savior of the kingdom." Booklist

The author "has in this suspenseful prequel . . . created an utterly engrossing fantasy, replete with a fairly mature romantic subplot as well as adventure." N Y Times Book Rev

McKinley, Robin—*Continued*

Rose daughter. Greenwillow Bks. 1997 306p $16.95   **Fic**
1. Fairy tales
ISBN 0-688-15439-5   LC 96-48783
Also available in paperback from Ace Bks.
"Nearly twenty years after the publication of *Beauty: A Retelling of the Story of Beauty and the Beast* McKinley has . . . produced another full-length novel retelling the same tale." Horn Book Guide
Compared to Beauty, this "is fuller bodied, with richer characterizations and a more mystical, darker edge. . . . There is more background on the Beast in this version . . . and Beauty's choice at the end, a departure from that in *Beauty*, is just so right. Readers will be enchanted, in the best sense of the word." Booklist

McKissack, Patricia C., 1944-

Nzinga, warrior queen of Matamba; by Patricia McKissack. Scholastic 2000 136p (Royal diaries) $10.95 (5 and up)   **Fic**
1. Nzinga, Queen of Matamba, 1582-1663—Fiction 2. Angola—Fiction 3. Princesses—Fiction 4. Slave trade—Fiction
ISBN 0-439-11210-9   LC 00-24216
Presents the diary of thirteen-year-old Nzingha, a sixteenth-century West African princess who loves to hunt and hopes to lead her kingdom one day against the invasion of the Portuguese slave traders
"The diary format will appeal to readers and the author's use of time lines, seasons, and actual place names makes the story believable and interesting." SLJ

A picture of Freedom; the diary of Clotee, a slave girl. Scholastic 1997 192p il maps (Dear America) $10.95 (4 and up)   **Fic**
1. Slavery—Fiction 2. Underground railroad—Fiction 3. Books and reading—Fiction 4. African Americans—Fiction
ISBN 0-590-25988-1   LC 96-25673
In 1859 twelve-year-old Clotee, a house slave who must conceal the fact that she can read and write, records in her diary her experiences and her struggle to decide whether to escape to freedom
"McKissack brings Clotee alive through touching and sobering details of slave life." SLJ

Run away home. Scholastic 1997 160p pa $4.50 hardcover o.p. (5 and up)   **Fic**
1. African Americans—Fiction 2. Apache Indians—Fiction 3. Alabama—Fiction
ISBN 0-590-46752-2   LC 96-43673
"This story of the young Apache who escaped from the train transporting Geronimo and his companions-in-exile from Florida to Alabama is rooted in the author's family history. The narrator is eleven-year-old Sarah Jane Crossman, who first befriends Sky when, sick and friendless, he seeks shelter in her family's barn." Horn Book
"Grabbing readers with wonderful characters, an engaging plot, and vital themes, McKissack weaves a compelling story of cultural clash, tragedy, accommodation, and ultimate triumph." SLJ

McLaren, Clemence, 1938-

Inside the walls of Troy; a novel of the women who lived the Trojan War. Atheneum Bks. for Young Readers 1996 199p $16 (7 and up)   **Fic**
1. Helen of Troy (Legendary character)—Fiction
ISBN 0-689-31820-0   LC 93-8127
Also available in paperback from Bantam Bks.
The events surrounding the famous battle between the Greeks and the Trojans are told from the points of view of two women, the beautiful Helen and the prophetic Cassandra
"These ancient stories are made as fresh and vivid as any modern tale by the electrifying characters and sensual details." Booklist

McMullan, Margaret

How I found the Strong; a Civil War story. Houghton Mifflin 2004 136p $15 (5 and up)   **Fic**
1. United States—History—1861-1865, Civil War—Fiction 2. Mississippi—Fiction 3. Slavery—Fiction
ISBN 0-618-35008-X   LC 2003-12294
Frank Russell, known as Shanks, wishes he could have gone with his father and brother to fight for Mississippi and the Confederacy, but his experiences with the war and his changing relationship with the family slave, Buck, change his thinking.
"The crisply written narrative is full of regional speech and detail, creating a vivid portrait." Voice Youth Advocates

McNamee, Graham

Acceleration. Wendy Lamb Bks. 2003 210p $15.95; lib bdg $17.99   **Fic**
1. Homicide—Fiction 2. Mystery fiction 3. Canada—Fiction
ISBN 0-385-73119-1; 0-385-90144-5 (lib bdg)
     LC 2003-3708
Stuck working in the Lost and Found of the Toronto Transit Authority for the summer, seventeen-year-old Duncan finds the diary of a serial killer and sets out to stop him
"Never overexploits the sensational potential of the subject and builds suspense layer upon layer, while injecting some surprising comedy relief." Booklist

McNaughton, Janet, 1953-

An earthly knight. HarperCollins Publishers 2004 c2003 261p $15.99; lib bdg $16.89 (7 and up)   **Fic**
1. Fantasy fiction 2. Scotland—Fiction
ISBN 0-06-008992-X; 0-06-008993-8 (lib bdg)
     LC 2003-9561
First published 2003 in Canada
In 1162 in Scotland, sixteen-year-old Jenny Avenel falls in love with the mysterious Tam Lin while being courted by the king's brother and must navigate the tides of tradition and the power of ancient magic to define her own destiny.
"The author does an excellent job of interweaving legend and history to create an exciting and engaging tale." SLJ

McNaughton, Janet, 1953-—*Continued*

The secret under my skin; by Janet McNaughton. . Eos 2005 264p $15.99; lib bdg $16.89 (7 and up)   **Fic**
1. Science fiction
ISBN 0-06-008989-X; 0-06-008990-3 (lib bdg)
LC 2004-12373

In the year 2368, humans exist under dire environmental conditions and one young woman, rescued from a workcamp and chosen for a special duty, uses her love of learning to discover the truth about the planet's future and her own dark past

"The setting and culture of the book are . . . vividly rendered, offering a depth that allows readers to believe fully in its premise. The writing is clear and crisp, evoking a magic that enchants. . . . This [is] one of the top science fiction novels in recent years." SLJ

Mead, Alice, 1952-

Girl of Kosovo. Farrar, Straus & Giroux 2001 113p $16 (5 and up)   **Fic**
1. Kosovo (Serbia)—Fiction
ISBN 0-374-32620-7   LC 00-44239
Also available in paperback from Yearling

Although Zana, an eleven-year-old Albanian girl, experiences the turmoil and violence of the 1999 conflict in her native Kosovo, she remembers her father's admonition to not let her heart become filled with hate

"Mead writes lucidly and honestly about a child of war." Horn Book Guide

Swimming to America; Alice Mead. 1st ed. Farrar, Straus and Giroux 2005 153p $16
Fic
1. Immigrants—Fiction 2. Brooklyn (New York, N.Y.)—Fiction
ISBN 0-374-38047-3   LC 2004-53249

Eighth grader Linda Berati struggles to understand who she is within the context of her mother's secrecy about the family background, her discomfort with her old girlfriends, her involvement with the family problems of her Cuban-American friend Ramon, and an opportunity to attend a school for "free spirits" like herself.

Written with "sensitivity and optimism. . . . [This is] an informative, empathetic, contemporary portrait of the immigrant experience." SLJ

Melling, O. R.

The Hunter's Moon. Amulet Books 2005 284p (Chronicles of Faerie) $16.95 (7 and up)
Fic
1. Magic—Fiction 2. Ireland—Fiction
ISBN 0-8109-5857-0   LC 2004-22216
First published 1992 in Ireland

Two teenage cousins, one Irish, the other from the United States, set out to find a magic doorway to the Faraway Country, where humans must bow to the little people.

"This novel is a compelling blend of Irish mythology and geography. Characters that breathe and connect with readers, and a picturesque landscape that shifts between the present and the past, bring readers into the experience." SLJ

Merrill, Jean, 1923-

The pushcart war; with illustrations by Ronni Solbert. HarperCollins Pubs. 1992 c1964 222p il o.p. Dell paperback available $5.99 (5 and up)
Fic
1. Trucks—Fiction 2. New York (N.Y.)—Fiction
ISBN 0-440-47147-8 (pa)
A reissue of the title first published 1964 by W.R. Scott

"Arrogant, mammoth trucks threaten to crowd people, small cars, pushcarts, and peddlers off the streets of New York. When a truck contemptuously runs down a pushcart, the peddlers rebel and wage a guerrilla war against the trucks, using a primitive, but effective, secret weapon. Funny, dramatic, tongue-in-cheek satire on the sheer bigness which is overwhelming urban life but which is here, for once, defeated by the little people who 'are' the city." Moorachian. What is a City?

Meyer, Carolyn

Beware, Princess Elizabeth. Harcourt 2001 214p $17; pa $5.95   **Fic**
1. Elizabeth I, Queen of England, 1533-1603—Fiction 2. Great Britain—History—1485-1603, Tudors—Fiction
ISBN 0-15-202659-2; 0-15-204556-2 (pa)
LC 00-11700
"Gulliver Books"

After the death of her father, King Henry VIII, in 1547, thirteen-year-old Elizabeth must endure the political intrigues and dangers of the reigns of her half-brother Edward and her half-sister Mary before finally becoming Queen of England eleven years later

"The story moves along swiftly with hints of romance, life-and-death plots, and snippets of everyday life." Book Rep

Drummers of Jericho. Harcourt Brace & Co. 1995 308p $11; pa $6 (7 and up)   **Fic**
1. Prejudices—Fiction 2. Jews—Fiction 3. Friendship—Fiction
ISBN 0-15-200441-6; 0-15-200190-5 (pa)
LC 94-36105
"Gulliver books"

A fourteen-year-old Jewish girl goes to live with her father and stepmother in a small town and soon finds herself the center of a civil rights battle when she objects to the high school band marching in the formation of a cross

"This is a well-crafted and powerfully thought-provoking novel about religious persecution." Voice Youth Advocates

Gideon's people. Harcourt Brace & Co. 1996 297p pa $6 hardcover o.p.   **Fic**
1. Amish—Fiction 2. Jews—Fiction 3. Family life—Fiction
ISBN 0-15-200304-5   LC 95-37917
"Gulliver books"

"Twelve-year-old Isaac Litvak, an Orthodox Jew, wakes up after a wagon accident in the home of an Amish family. . . . Trouble begins when Gideon, the sixteen-year-old son in this kind Amish family, announces to his new-found friend, Isaac, that he is secretly

Meyer, Carolyn—*Continued*
planning to run away." ALAN

"Deft characterizations and juxtaposition of fathers and sons amplify similarities and differences between the families and cultures." SLJ

Jubilee journey. Harcourt Brace & Co. 1997 271p pa $6 hardcover o.p. **Fic**
1. African Americans—Fiction 2. Race relations—Fiction 3. Racially mixed people—Fiction
ISBN 0-15-201591-4 LC 96-44563
"Gulliver books"

This story "takes place three generations after the story of Rose Lee Jefferson {in White lilacs}. . . . We meet Rose Lee's great-granddaughter, thirteen-year-old Emily Rose Chartier, who lives in Connecticut with her white father, black mother, and two brothers. . . . Emily Rose's image of herself is jolted . . . when she, her mother, and brothers go to Texas to visit her great-grandmother. . . . Jubilee journey has all the characteristics of a satisfying sequel. . . . It also succeeds as a stand-alone novel, with well-developed characters, especially the engaging protagonist. The author confronts difficult issues without becoming didactic." Voice Youth Advocates

Mary, Bloody Mary. Harcourt Brace & Co. 1999 227p (Young royals) $17; pa $6 **Fic**
1 Mary I, Queen of England, 1516-1558—Fiction 2. Great Britain—History—1485-1603, Tudors—Fiction
ISBN 0-15-201906-5; 0-15-216456-1 (pa)
LC 99-21185
"Gulliver books"

Mary Tudor, who would reign briefly as Queen of England during the mid sixteenth century, tells the story of her troubled childhood as daughter of King Henry VIII

"This interesting and well-researched fictional biography brings a bit of history vividly and compellingly to life." Voice Youth Advocates

Where the broken heart still beats; the story of Cynthia Ann Parker. Harcourt Brace Jovanovich 1992 197p pa $7 hardcover o.p. **Fic**
1. Parker, Cynthia Ann, 1827?-1864—Fiction 2. Comanche Indians—Fiction
ISBN 0-15-295602-6 LC 92-2578
"Gulliver books"

Having been taken as a child and raised by Comanche Indians, thirty-four-year-old Cynthia Ann Parker is forcibly returned to her white relatives, where she longs for her Indian life and her only friend is her twelve-year-old cousin Lucy

"A thoughtful and thought provoking book, this embroiders liberally but convincingly on the few facts known about the subject, a famous captive who was mother of the Comanche leader Quanah Parker." Bull Cent Child Books

White lilacs. Harcourt Brace Jovanovich 1993 242p il $13; pa $6 (5 and up) **Fic**
1. Race relations—Fiction 2. African Americans—Fiction 3. Texas—Fiction
ISBN 0-15-200641-9; 0-15-295876-2 (pa)
LC 92-30503
"Gulliver books"

In 1921 in Dillon, Texas, twelve-year-old Rose Lee sees trouble threatening her black community when the whites decide to take the land there for a park and forcibly relocate the black families to an ugly stretch of territory outside the town

"This bittersweet novel is poignant and tender, both in its spare vernacular dialogue and delicate description." Publ Wkly

Followed by Jubilee journey

Meyer, L. A., 1942-
Bloody Jack; being an account of the curious adventures of Mary "Jacky" Faber, ship's boy. Harcourt 2002 278p $17; pa $6.95 (7 and up) **Fic**
1. Orphans—Fiction 2. Seafaring life—Fiction 3. Pirates—Fiction 4. Sex role—Fiction
ISBN 0-15-216731-5; 0-15-205085-X (pa)
LC 2002-759

Reduced to begging and thievery in the streets of 18th-century London, a thirteen-year-old orphan disguises herself as a boy and connives her way onto a British warship set for high sea adventure in search of pirates

"From shooting a pirate in battle to foiling a shipmate's sexual attack to surviving when stranded alone on a Caribbean island, the action in Jacky's tale will entertain readers with a taste for adventure." Booklist

Other titles in this series are:
Curse of the blue tatoo (2004)
Under the Jolly Roger (2005)

Mikaelsen, Ben, 1952-
Red midnight. HarperCollins Pubs. 2002 212p $15.95; pa $5.99 **Fic**
1. Boats and boating—Fiction 2. Survival after airplane accidents, shipwrecks, etc.—Fiction 3. Refugees—Fiction 4. Guatemala—Fiction
ISBN 0-380-97745-1; 0-380-80561-8 (pa)
LC 2001-39834

After soldiers kill his family, twelve-year-old Santiago and his four-year-old sister flee Guatemala in a kayak and try to reach the United States

"A poignant, gripping story of survival told simply and realistically." Voice Youth Advocates

Stranded. Hyperion Bks. for Children 1995 247p $15.99; pa $4.95 **Fic**
1. Whales—Fiction 2. Physically handicapped—Fiction 3. Florida—Fiction
ISBN 0-7868-0072-0; 0-7868-1109-9 (pa)
LC 94-27069

Twelve-year-old Koby, who has lost a foot in an accident, sees a chance to prove her self-reliance to her parents when she tries to rescue two stranded pilot whales near her home in the Florida Keys

"This is a heartwarming story, believable and at the same time grist for fantasies of heroism and wonderful deeds." Voice Youth Advocates

Mikaelsen, Ben, 1952-—*Continued*

Touching Spirit Bear. HarperCollins Pubs. 2001
241p $15.99; lib bdg $16.89; pa $5.99

Fic

1. Alaska—Fiction 2. Wilderness survival—Fiction
3. Bears—Fiction
ISBN 0-380-97744-3; 0-06-029149-4 (lib bdg);
0-380-80560-X (pa) LC 00-40702
Also available Thorndike Press large print edition

After his anger erupts into violence, Cole, in order to
avoid going to prison, agrees to participate in a sentencing alternative based on the native American Circle Justice, and he is sent to a remote Alaskan Island where an
encounter with a huge Spirit Bear changes his life

"Mikaelsen's portrayal of this angry, manipulative,
damaged teen is dead on. . . . Gross details about Cole
eating raw worms, a mouse, and worse will appeal to
fans of the outdoor adventure/survival genre." SLJ

Miklowitz, Gloria D., 1927-

The enemy has a face. Eerdmans Bks. for
Young Readers 2003 139p $16; pa $8 (7 and up)

Fic

1. Missing persons—Fiction
ISBN 0-8028-5243-2; 0-8028-5261-0 (pa)
LC 2002-9233

Netta and her family have relocated temporarily from
Israel to Los Angeles, and when her seventeen-year-old
brother mysteriously disappears, she becomes convinced
that he has been abducted by Palestinian terrorists

"Almost unbearably suspenseful, the plot will keep
readers turning pages as fast as they can. Nicely interspersed with the events is a thoughtful examination of
some of the reasons behind the age-old strife between
Palestinians and Israelis. Readers come away with a
greater understanding of the conflict, and Netta is given
the opportunity to modify her attitude about her former
enemies." SLJ

Miller, Mary Beth

Aimee; a novel. Dutton Bks. 2002 276p $16.99;
pa $6.99 (7 and up) **Fic**

1. Suicide—Fiction 2. Friendship—Fiction
ISBN 0-525-46894-3; 0-14-240025-4 (pa)
LC 2002-283987

It seems that everyone believes that Zoe helped her
best friend, Aimee, commit suicide. Zoe is paralyzed by
loneliness, guilt, and anger at everyone's suppression of
the truth

"Despite the topic, there's no gratuitous violence, and
the realistic yet not overly graphic suicide scene doesn't
romanticize Aimee's action. The portrayal of therapy is
especially good, and Miller's wholly believable, often ir-
ritating characters will alienate some readers but feel like
a mirror for others." Booklist

Mills, Claudia, 1954-

Alex Ryan, stop that! Farrar, Straus & Giroux
2003 151p $16 (5 and up) **Fic**

1. School stories 2. Fathers—Fiction
ISBN 0-374-34655-0 LC 2002-25009
Sequel to Lizzie at last

Seventh-grader Alex Ryan enjoys attracting attention,
though he never seems to impress his father, but when
his antics cause problems with his would-be girlfriend on
a school outing, he has second thoughts about his actions

"Mills has a great ear for middle-school dialogue, and
her characters ring true." Booklist

Lizzie at last. Farrar, Straus & Giroux 2000
151p $16 (5 and up) **Fic**

1. School stories
ISBN 0-374-34659-3 LC 99-47621
Also available in paperback from Hyperion

"Sequel to *Losers, Inc.* and *You're a Brave Man, Julius Zimmerman* gives the title character of the latter
novel a minor role, while placing the refreshingly candid
Lizzie Archer center stage. Determined to shake off her
reputation as a nerd, Lizzie puts on a new face at the
start of seventh grade." Publ Wkly

"Mills has all the elements of middle school in place
and deftly weaves a story that is both sensitive and humorous." SLJ

Mochizuki, Ken

Beacon Hill boys. Scholastic Press 2002 201p
$16.95; pa $5.99 (7 and up) **Fic**

1. Japanese Americans—Fiction 2. Washington
(State)—Fiction
ISBN 0-439-26749-8; 0-439-24906-6 (pa)
LC 2002-2343

In 1972 in Seattle, a teenager in a Japanese American
family struggles for his own identity, along with a group
of three friends who share his anger and confusion

"The author nicely balances universal experiences of
male adolescence . . . with scenes that bring readers
right into the complicated era, and his important,
thought-provoking story asks tough questions about racial
and cultural identity, prejudice, and family." Booklist

Montes, Marisa

A circle of time. Harcourt 2002 261p $17

Fic

1. Space and time—Fiction
ISBN 0-15-202626-6 LC 2001-2614
"A Time travel mystery"

In 1996, Allison, a fourteen-year-old girl in a coma,
is forced back in time by Becky, a girl who died in
1906, and who needs help in righting a series of terrible
wrongs

"Fans of both mysteries and time-slip stories will like
the novel, which is liberally spiced with romance and
melodrama, and clarifies a bit of intriguing and tragic
California history." Booklist

Moore, Peter

Blind sighted. Viking 2001 262p $16.99; pa
$6.99 (7 and up) **Fic**

1. School stories 2. Blind—Fiction
ISBN 0-670-03543-2; 0-14-240126-9 (pa)
LC 2001-56813

Kirk, a creative misfit who is in trouble at high school
because he is bored with his classes, learns to deal with
his alcoholic mother, new friends, and life with the help
of a blind young woman who hires him to read to her

Moore, Peter—*Continued*

"The author's plotting is complex and subtle. Moore writes snappy dialogue that is dead-on accurate teenage banter." SLJ

Moore, Yvette

Freedom songs. Orchard Bks. 1991 168p pa $5.99 hardcover o.p.   **Fic**

1. African Americans—Fiction 2. Uncles—Fiction

ISBN 0-14-036017-4   LC 88-43073

"Sheryl is a black fourteen-year-old who launches her narrative with an account of her family's trip to North Carolina on Easter of 1963. There she sees Jim Crow laws in action. . . . Back in Brooklyn, she organizes a concert to raise money for the freedom riders, one of whom, her Uncle Pete, is killed by a bomb at the school where he teaches black southerners registering to vote." Bull Cent Child Books

"Humorous details of typical adolescent concerns and escapades lighten the serious nature of a well-crafted story." Horn Book

Moranville, Sharelle Byars

Over the river. Holt & Co. 2002 228p $16.95 (5 and up)   **Fic**

1. Family life—Fiction 2. Illinois—Fiction

ISBN 0-8050-7049-4   LC 2002-24308

Also available in paperback from Dell

In 1947, after the war, Willa Mae's father returns to the Illinois town where she has lived with her maternal grandparents for the last five of her eleven years, and Willa Mae finds herself struggling to understand old family tensions and secrets

"Suspense builds and the troubling secrets are revealed, but there's no tidy resolution. . . . This is the best kind of historical fiction, where details of time and place are not a picturesque backdrop but an integral part of the story." Booklist

Morgan, Clay

The boy who spoke dog. Dutton Children's Bks. 2003 166p $15.99 (5 and up)   **Fic**

1. Survival after airplane accidents, shipwrecks, etc.—Fiction 2. Dogs—Fiction 3. Orphans—Fiction

ISBN 0-525-47159-6   LC 2003-45223

After being marooned on an island near New Zealand, Jack, an orphaned cabin boy from San Francisco, becomes allied with a group of dogs who protect the local sheep from wild dogs

"Morgan delivers an unusual, engrossing novel, using vivid language to project the reader into the sounds and smells of the animal world as he examines the ancient bonds between humans and dogs." Booklist

Morgan, Nicola, 1961-

Chicken friend; Nicola Morgan. 1st U.S. ed. Candlewick Press 2005 148p $15.99 (5 and up)
Fic

1. Diabetes—Fiction 2. Country life—Fiction 3. Friendship—Fiction 4. Great Britain—Fiction

ISBN 0-7636-2735-6   LC 2004-54608

When her parents decide to move their family to the English countryside, homeschool their children, and raise chickens, Becca tries to make friends with her new neighbors by hiding her diabetes and throwing a twelfth birthday party for herself.

"The girl is believable and likable as both character and narrator, which turns an apparently simple story into one that is funny, insightful, and moving." SLJ

Fleshmarket. Delacorte Press 2004 208p $15.95; lib bdg $17.99 (7 and up)   **Fic**

1. Knox, Robert, 1793-1862—Fiction 2. Medicine—Fiction 3. Physicians—Fiction 4. Poverty—Fiction 5. Scotland—Fiction

ISBN 0-385-73154-X; 0-385-90192-5 (lib bdg)
LC 2003-11441

In nineteenth-century Scotland, following the death of his mother during surgery, Robbie decides to take revenge on the surgeon who performed the operation, Dr. Robert Knox, and in the process, makes a gruesome discovery about the lengths the medical profession will go to advance its knowledge of anatomy.

"The protagonist's need for revenge is palpable, and Morgan's story is fast paced and absorbing. Readers who are fascinated by forensics and anatomy will find this a gripping story." SLJ

Morgenstern, Susie Hoch

Secret letters from 0 to 10; translated by Gill Rosner. Viking 1998 137p $16.99; pa $4.99
Fic

1. Friendship—Fiction 2. School stories 3. Paris (France)—Fiction

ISBN 0-670-88007-8; 0-14-130819-2 (pa)
LC 98-5559

Ten-year-old Ernest lives a boring existence in Paris with his grandmother until a lively girl named Victory enters his class at school

"Morgenstern has created extremely well-drawn, distinct, and sometimes quirky characters with eloquent dialogue." SLJ

Moriarty, Jaclyn

The year of secret assignments. Arthur A. Levine Books 2004 340p $16.95 (7 and up)
Fic

1. Friendship—Fiction 2. School stories 3. Australia—Fiction

ISBN 0-439-49881-3   LC 2003-14278

Three female students from Ashbury High write to three male students from rival Brookfield High as part of a pen pal program, leading to romance, humiliation, revenge plots, and war between the schools

"There are a few coarse moments—a reference to a blow job and some caustic outbursts. . . . This is an unusual novel with an exhilarating pace, irrepressible characters, and a screwball humor that will easily attract teens." Booklist

Morpurgo, Michael

Kensuke's kingdom. Scholastic Press 2003 c1999 164p $16.95 (4 and up)   **Fic**

1. Survival after airplane accidents, shipwrecks, etc.—Fiction

ISBN 0-439-38202-5   LC 2002-9078

Morpurgo, Michael—*Continued*

First published 1999 in the United Kingdom

When Michael is swept off his family's yacht, he washes up on a desert island, where he struggles to survive—until he finds he is not alone

This is "highly readable. . . . The end is bittersweet but believable, and the epilogue is a sad commentary on the long-lasting effects of war." Booklist

Private Peaceful. Scholastic Press 2004 c2003 202p $16.95 (7 and up)   **Fic**

1. World War, 1914-1918—Fiction 2. Great Britain—Fiction

ISBN 0-439-63648-5   LC 2003-65347

First published 2003 in the United Kingdom

When Thomas Peaceful's older brother is forced to join the British Army, Thomas decides to sign up as well, although he is only fourteen years old, to prove himself to his country, his family, his childhood love, Molly, and himself

"In this World War I story, the terse and beautiful narrative of a young English soldier is as compelling about the world left behind as about the horrific daily details of trench warfare. . . . Suspense builds right to the end, which is shocking, honest, and unforgettable." Booklist

Morris, Gerald, 1963-

The squire's tale. Houghton Mifflin 1998 212p (Squire's tales) $15; pa $5.50   **Fic**

1. Gawain (Legendary character)—Fiction 2. Knights and knighthood—Fiction 3. Great Britain—History—0-1066—Fiction

ISBN 0-395-86959-5; 0-440-22823-9 (pa)

LC 97-12447

In medieval England, fourteen-year-old Terence finds his tranquil existence suddenly changed when he becomes the squire of the young Gawain of Orkney and accompanies him on a long quest, proving Gawain's worth as a knight and revealing an important secret about his own true identity

"Well-drawn characters, excellent, snappy dialogue, detailed descriptions of medieval life, and a dry wit put a new spin on this engaging tale of the characters and events of King Arthur's time." Booklist

Other available titles in this series are:

The ballad of Sir Dinadan (2003)

Parsifal's page (2001)

The princess, the crone, and the dung-cart knight (2004)

The savage damsel and the dwarf (2000)

The squire, his knight, & his lady (1999)

Moses, Shelia P.

The legend of Buddy Bush. Margaret K. McElderry Books 2004 216p $15.95   **Fic**

1. Race relations—Fiction 2. African Americans—Fiction 3. North Carolina—Fiction

ISBN 0-689-85839-6   LC 2003-8024

In 1947, twelve-year-old Pattie Mae is sustained by her dreams of escaping Rich Square, North Carolina, and moving to Harlem when her Uncle Buddy is arrested for attempted rape of a white woman and her grandfather is diagnosed with a terminal brain tumor.

"Patti Mae's first-person voice, steeped in the inflec-

tions of the South, rings true, and her observations richly evoke a time, place, and a resilient African American community." Booklist

Mosher, Richard, 1949-

Zazoo. Clarion Bks. 2001 248p $16; pa $6.99

Fic

1. Vietnamese—Fiction 2. Grandfathers—Fiction 3. Orphans—Fiction 4. France—Fiction

ISBN 0-618-13534-0; 0-618-43904-8 (pa)

LC 2001-28291

Amid old secrets revealed and rifts healed, a thirteen-year-old Vietnamese orphan raised in rural France by her aging "Grand-Pierre" learns about life, death, and love

This "is a beautiful and lyrical novel, with poetry woven throughout." SLJ

Mosier, Elizabeth

My life as a girl. Random House 1999 193p pa $12 hardcover o.p.   **Fic**

1. Prisoners—Fiction 2. Waiters and waitresses—Fiction 3. Arizona—Fiction

ISBN 0-375-89522-1   LC 98-8688

During her last summer in Phoenix, Arizona, before going to an eastern college, eighteen-year-old Jaime works two waitress jobs and plans her escape from a life forever changed by her father's prison sentence

"Featuring lifelike dialogue, three-dimensional characters and an upbeat outcome, the novel also serves up glossy, attention-getting prose." Publ Wkly

Mowry, Jess, 1960-

Ghost train. Holt & Co. 1996 164p $14.95

Fic

1. Haitian Americans—Fiction 2. Supernatural—Fiction

ISBN 0-8050-4440-X   LC 96-10291

"On Remi DuMont's first night in his new home, a train thunders past his window and he watches a murder being committed. Remi, 13, is a recent immigrant from Haiti to Oakland, CA. . . . He soon realizes that the late-night train is a ghost train and the murder reenacted on it nightly actually happened more than 50 years ago. As the boy and his new friend Niya investigate, they put together the pieces of an unsolved crime and an unexplained disappearance. They then step into the past to try to right a long-standing wrong." SLJ

"Containing more substance than most thrillers for this age group, this horror story is underscored by strong social commentary on poverty, waste and materialism." Publ Wkly

Murphy, Claire Rudolf

Free radical. Clarion Bks. 2002 198p $15 (7 and up)   **Fic**

1. Baseball—Fiction

ISBN 0-618-11134-4   LC 2001-42268

In Fairbanks, Alaska, in the middle of the summer Little League baseball season, fifteen-year-old Luke is stunned when his mother confesses that she is wanted by the FBI for her role in the death of a student during an anti-Vietnam War protest thirty years ago

Murphy, Claire Rudolf—*Continued*
"The fast action of the baseball scenes will lure teens to the sports story, and the thought-provoking issues of guilt and responsibility will hold their interest." Booklist

Murphy, Jim, 1947-
The journal of James Edmond Pease, a Civil War Union soldier. Scholastic 1998 173p il (My name is America) $10.95; lib bdg $12.95

Fic

1. Orphans—Fiction 2. United States—History—1861-1865, Civil War—Fiction
ISBN 0-590-43814-X; 0-439-55537-X (lib bdg)
LC 98-10738
This "is very well written, and Pease's unassuming personality keeps him a vivid, accessible narrator throughout." Booklist

My face to the wind; the diary of Sarah Jane Price, a prairie teacher. Scholastic 2001 182p (Dear America) $10.95
Fic
1. Teachers—Fiction 2. Frontier and pioneer life—Fiction 3. Nebraska—Fiction
ISBN 0-590-43810-7
LC 2001-20315
Following her father's death from a disease that swept through her Nebraska town in 1881, teenaged Sarah Jane must find work to support herself and records in her diary her experiences as a young school teacher
"This diary brings to life the problems and day-to-day activities of an educator while also providing a glimpse into life in Nebraska during the late 1880s." SLJ

West to a land of plenty; the diary of Teresa Angelino Viscardi. Scholastic 1998 204p il maps (Dear America) $10.95
Fic
1. Frontier and pioneer life—Fiction 2. Italian Americans—Fiction
ISBN 0-590-73888-7
LC 97-23064
While traveling in 1883 with her Italian American family (including a meddlesome little sister) and other immigrant pioneers to a utopian community in Idaho, fourteen-year-old Teresa keeps a diary of her experiences along the way
"Engaging colorful characters abound. . . . Excellent archival photos and notes enhance the presentation of this historical novel." SLJ

Murphy, Rita
Harmony. Delacorte Press 2002 129p $15.95; pa $5.99
Fic
1. Mountain life—Fiction
ISBN 0-385-72938-3; 0-440-22923-5 (pa)
LC 2002-1663
Found as a baby by an old farm couple in the Tennessee mountains, Harmony has always been different, but when she begins developing special powers, she wants nothing more than to be ordinary
"Harmony and her family are lovable and believable characters. . . . A wonderful story of a teen who is coming to terms with being different and learning to accept her gift." SLJ

Murray, Jaye
Bottled up; a novel. Dial Books 2003 220p $16.99 (7 and up)
Fic
1. Brothers—Fiction 2. Alcoholism—Fiction 3. Drug abuse—Fiction
ISBN 0-8037-2897-2
LC 2002-13744
A high school boy comes to terms with his drug addiction, life with an alcoholic father, and a younger brother who looks up to him
"With its rich language and exquisite allegories, the book is a perfect choice for any teen who needs a humorous yet touching push in the right direction." Voice Youth Advocates

Murray, Martine, 1965-
The slightly true story of Cedar B. Hartley; (who planned to live an unusual life). Levine Bks. 2003 233p $15.95 (5 and up)
Fic
1. Acrobats and acrobatics—Fiction 2. Friendship—Fiction 3. Australia—Fiction
ISBN 0-439-48622-X
LC 2002-12113
When twelve-year-old Cedar loses her dog, it sets off a chain of events leading her to find a new friend, become an acrobat, and learn some bitter-sweet truths about family, community, and herself
"With unique and fully realized supporting characters and a multiethnic, urban environment, this story vibrates with authenticity. . . . Small, wonderfully quirky line drawings accompany this breezy yet serious novel." SLJ

Myers, Anna
The keeping room. Walker & Co. 1997 135p $16.95; pa $5.99
Fic
1. United States—History—1775-1783, Revolution—Fiction 2. Father-son relationship—Fiction
ISBN 0-8027-8641-3; 0-14-130468-5 (pa)
LC 97-2964
"The story has plenty of action to keep it going and enough reflection to give it meaning." Booklist

Tulsa burning. Walker & Co. 2002 152p $16.95; pa $6.95 (7 and up)
Fic
1. Race relations—Fiction 2. Riots—Fiction 3. Oklahoma—Fiction
ISBN 0-8027-8829-7; 0-8027-7696-5 (pa)
LC 2002-23457
In 1921, fifteen-year-old Noble Chase hates the sheriff of Wekiwa, Oklahoma, and is more than willing to cross him to help his best friend, a black man, who is injured during race riots in nearby Tulsa
"In this emotional page-turner, Myers expertly captures an era of poisonous racism while conveying the strong, true voice of a courageous young man." Booklist

Myers, Walter Dean, 1937-
The Beast. Scholastic Press 2003 170p $16.95 (7 and up)
Fic
1. Drug abuse—Fiction 2. African Americans—Fiction
ISBN 0-439-36841-3
LC 2002-42776
A visit to his Harlem neighborhood and the discovery that the girl he loves is using drugs give sixteen-year-old Anthony Witherspoon a new perspective both on his

Myers, Walter Dean, 1937-—*Continued*
home and on his life at a Connecticut prep school

"The emotions of the characters, their search for meaning in a harsh setting, and their conclusions will resonate with readers." Libr Media Connect

Fallen angels. Scholastic 1988 309p hardcover
o.p. paperback available $4.99 **Fic**
1. Vietnam War, 1961-1975—Fiction 2. African American soldiers—Fiction
ISBN 0-590-40943-3 (pa) LC 87-23236

"Black, seventeen, perceptive and sensitive, Richie (the narrator) has enlisted and been sent to Vietnam; in telling the story of his year of active service, Richie is candid about the horror of killing and the fear of being killed, the fear and bravery and confusion and tragedy of the war." Bull Cent Child Books

"Except for occasional outbursts, the narration is remarkably direct and understated; and the dialogue, with morbid humor sometimes adding comic relief, is steeped in natural vulgarity, without which verisimilitude would be unthinkable. In fact, the foul talk, which serves as the story's linguistic setting, is not nearly as obscene as are the events." Horn Book

Hoops; a novel. Delacorte Press 1981 183p pa
$5.99 hardcover o.p. **Fic**
1. Basketball—Fiction 2. Harlem (New York, N.Y.)— Fiction 3. African Americans—Fiction
ISBN 0-440-93884-8 (pa) LC 81-65497

"Growing up in the streets of Harlem, seventeen-year-old Lonnie Jackson dreams of making a better life. He has a 'game,' and sees basketball as his way out of the ghetto." ALAN

"This story offers the reader some fast, descriptive basketball action, a love story between Lonnie and girlfriend Mary-Ann, peer friendship problems, and gangster intrigues. Most importantly, however, it portrays the growth of a trusting and deeply caring father-son relationship between [the coach] Cal and [fatherless] Lonnie." Voice Youth Advocates

Followed by The outside shot (1988)

The journal of Biddy Owens, the Negro leagues. Scholastic 2001 141p (My name is America) $10.95; pa $12.95 **Fic**
1. African Americans—Fiction 2. Baseball—Fiction
ISBN 0-439-09503-4; 0-439-55499-3 (pa)
LC 00-44667

Teenager Biddy Owens' 1948 journal about working for the Birmingham Black Barons includes the games and the players, racism the team faces from New Orleans to Chicago, and his family's resistance to his becoming a professional baseball player. Includes a historical note about the evolution of the Negro Leagues

"Myers, with his usual clear, strong writing voice, conveys the excitement, anger, frustration, and poignancy of the last years of the Negro Leagues." Horn Book Guide

The journal of Joshua Loper; a black cowboy. Scholastic 1999 158p il (My name is America) $10.95 (5 and up) **Fic**
1. Cowhands—Fiction 2. African Americans—Fiction 3. West (U.S.)—Fiction
ISBN 0-590-02691-7 LC 98-18661

In 1871 Joshua Loper, a sixteen-year-old black cowboy, records in his journal his experiences while making his first cattle drive under an unsympathetic trail boss

"With characteristic research, sensitivity, and insight, Myers offers a lively, youthful portrait of the life and times of this black cowboy." SLJ

The journal of Scott Pendleton Collins; a World War II soldier. Scholastic 1999 140p il (My name is America) $10.95 (5 and up) **Fic**
1. World War, 1939-1945—Fiction
ISBN 0-439-05013-8 LC 99-13615

A seventeen-year-old soldier from central Virginia records his experiences in a journal as his regiment takes part in the D-Day invasion of Normandy and subsequent battles to liberate France

"This brief novel presents an accurate depiction of the horror of battle. The narrative voice is engaging and believable." SLJ

Me, Mop, and the Moondance Kid; illustrated by Rodney Pate. Delacorte Press 1988 154p il hardcover o.p. paperback available $4.99 (4-6)
Fic
1. Baseball—Fiction 2. Adoption—Fiction 3. Friendship—Fiction
ISBN 0-440-40396-0 (pa) LC 88-6503

"Eleven-year-old T. J. and his younger brother Billy, a.k.a. the Moondance Kid, have been living with their adoptive parents for about six months, and are settling in well. They are worried that their friend Mop, a girl who has not yet been adopted, may be transferred to an orphanage some distance away. Mop decides to join T. J.'s little league team in order to get close to the coach and his wife, whom she suspects are interested in adopting her." SLJ

"Myers's keen sense of humor, quick, natural dialogue and irresistible protagonists make this novel a winner." Publ Wkly

Followed by Mop, Moondance, and the Nagasaki Knights (1992)

Monster; illustrations by Christopher Myers. HarperCollins Pubs. 1999 281p il $14.95; lib bdg $14.89 (7 and up) **Fic**
1. Trials—Fiction 2. African Americans—Fiction
ISBN 0-06-028077-8; 0-06-028078-6 (lib bdg)
LC 98-40958

Coretta Scott King honor book text, 2000

While on trial as an accomplice to a murder, sixteen-year-old Steve Harmon records his experiences in prison and in the courtroom in the form of a film script as he tries to come to terms with the course his life has taken

"Balancing courtroom drama and a sordid jailhouse setting with flashbacks to the crime, Myers adeptly allows each character to speak for him or herself, leaving readers to judge for themselves the truthfulness of the defendants, witnesses, lawyers, and, most compellingly, Steve himself." Horn Book Guide

The Mouse rap. Harper & Row 1990 186p pa $5.99 hardcover o.p. (6 and up) **Fic**
1. African Americans—Fiction 2. Buried treasure— Fiction 3. Harlem (New York, N.Y.)—Fiction
ISBN 0-06-440356-4 LC 89-36419

Myers, Walter Dean, 1937-—*Continued*

During an eventful summer in Harlem, fourteen-year-old Mouse and his friends fall in and out of love and search for a hidden treasure from the days of Al Capone

"A crisp rap beat, an intriguing, intergenerational cast of characters, and the zaniness of events make this story of fourteen-year-old Mouse and his friends a very upbeat adventure." Horn Book Guide

Scorpions. Harper & Row 1988 216p $16.99; lib bdg $16.89; pa $5.99 (6 and up)   **Fic**
1. African Americans—Fiction 2. Juvenile delinquency—Fiction 3. Harlem (New York, N.Y.)—Fiction
ISBN 0-06-024364-3; 0-06-024365-1 (lib bdg); 0-06-447066-0 (pa)   LC 85-45815
A Newbery Medal honor book, 1989
Set in Harlem, this "story presents a brutally honest picture of the tragic influence of gang membership and pressures on a young black adolescent. Jamal Hicks, age twelve, reluctantly follows the orders of his older brother, now serving time in prison for robbery, and takes his place as leader of the Scorpions. When Jamal's leadership is challenged, disaster follows and Jamal learns some tragic lessons about friendship and owning a gun." Child Book Rev Serv

Slam! Scholastic Press 1996 266p $15.95; pa $5.99 (7 and up)   **Fic**
1. Basketball—Fiction 2. African Americans—Fiction 3. School stories
ISBN 0-590-48667-5; 0-590-48668-3 (pa)   LC 95-46647
Coretta Scott King Award for text, 1997
Seventeen-year-old "Slam" Harris is counting on his noteworthy basketball talents to get him out of the inner city and give him a chance to succeed in life, but his coach sees things differently
Myers "descriptions of Slam on the court . . . use crisp details, not flowery language, to achieve their muscular poetry, and Myers is equally vivid in relating the torment Slam feels as he stares at a page of indecipherable algebra formulas. . . . [This is an] admirably realistic coming-of-age novel." Booklist

Somewhere in the darkness. Scholastic 1992 168p pa $5.99 hardcover o.p. (7 and up)   **Fic**
1. Father-son relationship—Fiction 2. Prisoners—Fiction
ISBN 0-439-52356-7 (pa)   LC 91-19295
A Newbery Medal honor book, 1993
A teenage boy accompanies his father, who has recently escaped from prison, on a trip that turns out to be a time of, often painful, discovery for them both
"This is one of Myer's most memorable pieces of writing: there is not an unnecessary word or phrase; the scenes are vivid and emotionally powerful; and the characters are heartbreakingly realistic. A page-turner elevated to a higher plane by its theme of the universal quest of a son for his father." Horn Book

Myracle, Lauren, 1969-
Eleven. Dutton Children's Books 2004 201p $16.99 (4 and up)   **Fic**
1. Friendship—Fiction 2. Family life—Fiction
ISBN 0-525-47165-0   LC 2003-49076

The year between turning eleven and turning twelve bring many changes for Winnie and her friends.
"The inclusion of details about the everyday lives of these girls . . . will make this novel enjoyable, even for reluctant readers. However, it's the book's occasional revelation of harder truths that lifts it out of the ordinary." SLJ

Na, An, 1972-
A step from heaven. Front St. 2000 156p $15.95 (7 and up)   **Fic**
1. Korean Americans—Fiction 2. Family life—Fiction
ISBN 1-88691-058-8   LC 00-41083
Also available Thorndike Press large print edition and in paperback from Speak
A young Korean girl and her family find it difficult to learn English and adjust to life in America
"This isn't a quick read, especially at the beginning when the child is trying to decipher American words and customs, but the coming-of-age drama will grab teens and make them think of their own conflicts between home and outside. As in the best writing, the particulars make the story universal." Booklist

Naidoo, Beverley
Journey to Jo'burg; a South African story; illustrations by Eric Velasquez. Lippincott 1986 80p il lib bdg $16.89; pa $4.99 (5 and up)   **Fic**
1. South Africa—Race relations—Fiction
ISBN 0-397-32169-4 (lib bdg); 0-06-440237-1 (pa)   LC 85-45508
"This touching novel graphically depicts the plight of Africans living in the horror of South Africa. Thirteen-year-old Maledi and her 9-year-old brother leave their small village, take the perilous journey to the city, and encounter, firsthand, the painful struggle for justice, freedom, and dignity in the 'City of Gold.' A provocative story with a message readers will long remember." Soc Educ
Followed by Chain of fire (1990)

No turning back; a novel of South Africa. HarperCollins Pubs. 1997 c1995 189p pa $5.99 hardcover o.p. (5 and up)   **Fic**
1. Runaway children—Fiction 2. South Africa—Fiction
ISBN 0-06-440749-7   LC 96-28980
First published 1995 in the United Kingdom
When the abuse at home becomes too much for twelve-year-old Sipho, he runs away to the streets of Johannesburg and learns to survive in the post-apartheid world
"Charged with a rhythm that begins beating on the first page and carries through until the last, Naidoo's novel is a can't-put-it-down account." Horn Book

The other side of truth. HarperCollins Pubs. 2001 c2000 252p $16.99; lib bdg $17.89; pa $5.99 (5 and up)   **Fic**
1. Africans—Fiction 2. London (England)—Fiction 3. Nigeria—Fiction
ISBN 0-06-029628-3; 0-06-029629-1 (lib bdg); 0-06-441002-1 (pa)   LC 00-54112

Naidoo, Beverley—*Continued*

First published 2000 in the United Kingdom

Smuggled out of Nigeria after their mother's murder, Sade and her younger brother are abandoned in London when their uncle fails to meet them at the airport and they are fearful of their new surroundings and of what may have happened to their journalist father back in Nigeria

"Part survival adventure, part docudrama, the narrative stays true to Sade's viewpoint. . . . This powerful novel brings the news images very close." Booklist

Namioka, Lensey

An ocean apart, a world away. Delacorte Press 2002 197p $15.95; lib bdg $17.99; pa $5.50

Fic

1. Chinese—United States—Fiction

ISBN 0-385-73002-0; 0-385-90053-8 (lib bdg);
0-440-22973-1 (pa)   LC 2002-73550

Companion volume to Ties that bind, ties that break (1998)

Despite the odds facing her decision to become a doctor in 1920's Nanking, China, teenaged Yanyan leaves her family to study at Cornell University where, along with hard work, she finds prejudice and loneliness as well as friendship and a new sense of accomplishment

"Without heavy messages, Namioka explores what it means to be independent." Booklist

Ties that bind, ties that break; a novel. Delacorte Press 1999 154p pa $5.50 hardcover o.p. (5 and up)   **Fic**

1. Sex role—Fiction 2. China—Fiction

ISBN 0-440-41599-3   LC 98-27877

"In early twentieth-century China, Ailin's liberal father allows her to avoid the tradition of foot-binding, but a broken engagement makes her family fear for her future. Ailin's intelligence and hard work—and a lot of luck—lead her to a new life in America." Horn Book Guide

"In lyrical, descriptive prose, Namioka compassionately portrays a young girl's coming-of-age in a repressive, challenging time." Booklist

Napoli, Donna Jo, 1948-

Beast. Atheneum Bks. for Young Readers 2000 260p $17; pa $8 (7 and up)   **Fic**

1. Fairy tales 2. Iran—Fiction

ISBN 0-689-83589-2; 0-689-87005-1 (pa)
LC 99-89923

"In this take on 'Beauty and the Beast,' Napoli focuses on Beast before French beauty Belle enters his life. The first-person story begins in Persia, where proud prince Orasmyn, who loves roses, makes an unfortunate decision that sets in motion a curse: he becomes a lion who can only be restored by the love of a woman." Booklist

"The reader is immersed in the imagery and spirituality of ancient Persia. . . . Although Napoli uses Farsi (Persian) and Arabic words in the text (there is a glossary), this only adds to the texture and richness of her remarkable piece of writing." Book Rep

Bound. Atheneum Books for Young Readers 2004 186p $16.95   **Fic**

1. China—Fiction 2. Sex role—Fiction

ISBN 0-689-86175-3   LC 2004-365

In a novel based on Chinese Cinderella tales, fourteen-year-old stepchild Xing-Xing endures a life of neglect and servitude, as her stepmother cruelly mutilates her own child's feet so that she alone might marry well.

The author "fleshes out and enriches the story with well-rounded characters and with accurate information about a specific time and place in Chinese history; the result is a dramatic and masterful retelling." SLJ

The great god Pan. Wendy Lamb Bks. 2003 149p $15.95; lib bdg $17.99 (7 and up)

Fic

1. Pan (Greek deity)—Fiction 2. Classical mythology—Fiction

ISBN 0-385-32777-3; 0-385-90120-8 (lib bdg)
LC 2002-13139

A retelling of the Greek myths about Pan, both goat and god, whose reed flute frolicking leads him to a meeting with Iphigenia, a human raised as the daughter of King Agamemnon and Queen Clytemnestra

"Filling in gaps that appear in other myths about Pan and Iphigenia, Napoli creates a novel filled with breathtaking language about nature, music, and desire. Teen readers will swoon." Booklist

Song of the Magdalene. Scholastic Press 1996 240p pa $6.99 hardcover o.p. (7 and up)

Fic

1. Mary Magdalene, Saint—Fiction 2. Christian saints—Fiction

ISBN 0-689-87396-4 (pa)   LC 96-7066

Tells the story of Miriam, a young girl being raised by her widowed father in ancient Israel, who grows up to be Mary Magdalene

"Napoli has taken a few Biblical facts about Mary Magdalene and created a possible past in a beautifully written story with well-developed characters." Book Rep

Spinners; {by} Donna Jo Napoli & Richard Tchen. Dutton Children's Bks. 1999 197p $15.99; pa $5.99 (7 and up)   **Fic**

1. Fairy tales 2. Father-daughter relationship—Fiction

ISBN 0-525-46065-9; 0-14-131110-X (pa)
LC 98-54640

Also available in paperback from Puffin Bks.

A "tailor promises that he will clothe his bride in gold; to this end, he steals an elderly woman's spinning wheel and ends up obsessed, turning straw into gold but somehow 'rumpling' his leg—thus earning his lover's disdain and the hated sobriquet Rumpelstiltskin. The narrative then fast-forwards and shifts to Saskia, the miller's daughter (really Rumpelstiltskin's child), whose mother has died in childbirth." Publ Wkly

Stones in water. Dutton Children's Bks. 1997 209p pa $5.99 hardcover o.p. (5 and up)

Fic

1. World War, 1939-1945—Fiction

ISBN 0-14-130600-9   LC 97-14253

After being taken by German soldiers from a local movie theater along with other Italian boys including his

Napoli, Donna Jo, 1948-—*Continued*
Jewish friend, Roberto is forced to work in Germany, escapes into the Ukrainian winter, before desperately trying to make his way back home to Venice

This is a "gripping, meticulously researched story (loosely based on the life of an actual survivor)." Publ Wkly

Three days. Dutton Children's Bks. 2001 151p $15.99; pa $5.99   **Fic**
    1. Kidnapping—Fiction 2. Italy—Fiction
    ISBN 0-525-46790-4; 0-14-250025-9 (pa)
                                             LC 2001-28535
When her father suddenly dies while on a business trip leaving her alone on an Italian highway, eleven-year-old Jackie worries what will happen when she is picked up by two men with unknown motives.

"A taut thriller that races to its complex conclusion." Booklist

Zel. Dutton Children's Bks. 1996 227p pa $5.99 hardcover o.p. (7 and up)   **Fic**
    1. Fairy tales 2. Mother-daughter relationship—Fiction
    ISBN 0-14-130116-3 (pa)   LC 96-15135
Based on the fairy tale Rapunzel, the story is told in alternating chapters from the point of view of Zel, her mother, and the prince, and delves into the psychological motivations of the characters

"This version, with its Faustian overtones, will challenge readers to think about this old story on a deeper level. It begs for discussion in literature classes." SLJ

Naylor, Phyllis Reynolds, 1933-
The fear place. Atheneum Pubs. 1994 118p pa $4.99 hardcover o.p. (5 and up)   **Fic**
    1. Brothers—Fiction 2. Pumas—Fiction 3. Camping—Fiction
    ISBN 0-689-80442-3 (pa)   LC 93-38891
When he and his older brother Gordon are left camping alone in the Rocky Mountains, twelve-year-old Doug faces his fear of heights and his feelings about Gordon—with the help of a cougar

This is "a solid action story, tense and involving. . . . A satisfying wilderness adventure." Publ Wkly

Ice. Atheneum Bks. for Young Readers 1996 194p $16; pa $4.99   **Fic**
    1. Family life—Fiction 2. Farm life—Fiction
    ISBN 0-689-80005-3; 0-689-81872-6 (pa)
                                             LC 95-5279
"A Jean Karl book"
When thirteen-year-old Chrissa is sent to her paternal grandmother's farm, she learns more about her absent father and some of the reasons for her distant relationship with her mother

"Naylor is a master of strong adolescent characterizations. Just the right amount of adventure and suspense keeps the plot moving quickly without getting mired in emotional soul-searching." Book Rep

Jade Green; a ghost story. Atheneum Bks. for Young Readers 2000 168p $16.95; pa $4.99 (7 and up)   **Fic**
    1. Ghost stories 2. Orphans—Fiction
    ISBN 0-689-82005-4; 0-689-82002-X (pa)
                                             LC 99-20740

While living with her uncle in a house haunted by the ghost of a young woman, recently orphaned Judith Sparrow wonders if her one small transgression causes mysterious happenings

"This is unapologetic, craftily constructed romantic melodrama, complete with hurricanes, stolen kisses, {and} bloodstained steps." Bull Cent Child Books

Reluctantly Alice. Atheneum Pubs. 1991 182p $16; pa $4.99   **Fic**
    1. School stories 2. Family life—Fiction
    ISBN 0-689-31681-X; 0-689-81688-X (pa)
                                             LC 90-37956
"A Jean Karl book"
Alice experiences the joys and embarrassments of seventh grade while advising her father and older brother on their love lives

"Naylor combines laugh-out-loud scenes with moments of sudden gentleness. . . . The characters are complex, the dialogue is droll, the junior high world authentic." Booklist

Other titles about Alice are:
Achingly Alice (1998)
Alice alone (2001)
Alice in-between (1994)
Alice in lace (1996)
Alice on her way (2005)
Alice on the outside (1999)
Alice the brave (1995)
All but Alice (1992)
The grooming of Alice (2000)
Including Alice (2004)
Outrageously Alice (1997)
Patiently Alice (2003)
Simply Alice (2002)

Sang Spell. Atheneum Bks. for Young Readers 1998 176p $16; pa $4.99 (7 and up)   **Fic**
    1. Orphans—Fiction 2. Appalachian region—Fiction
    ISBN 0-689-82007-0; 0-689-82006-2 (pa)
                                             LC 97-34067
"A Jean Kark book"
When his mother is killed in an automobile accident, high-schooler Josh decides to hitchhike across country, and finds himself trapped in a mysterious village somewhere in the Appalachian Mountains, among a group of people who call themselves Melungeons

"Naylor's memorable story skillfully combines the real world with a haunting, fantasy one." Voice Youth Advocates

Shiloh. Atheneum Pubs. 1991 144p $15; pa $5.50 (4-6)   **Fic**
    1. Newbery Medal titles 2. Dogs—Fiction 3. West Virginia—Fiction
    ISBN 0-689-31614-3; 0-689-83583-3 (pa)
                                             LC 90-603
Also available Shiloh trilogy as a boxed set $35; pa $14.99 (ISBN 0-689-82327-4; 0-689-01525-9) Audiobook version of trilogy also available

Awarded the Newbery Medal, 1992
When he finds a lost beagle in the hills behind his West Virginia home, Marty tries to hide it from his family and the dog's real owner, a mean-spirited man known to shoot deer out of season and to mistreat his dogs

"A credible plot and characters, a well-drawn setting,

Naylor, Phyllis Reynolds, 1933——*Continued*
and nicely paced narration combine in a story that leaves
the reader feeling good." Horn Book
Other available titles about Shiloh are:
Saving Shiloh (1997)
Shiloh season (1996)

Nelson, Blake, 1960-
New rules of high school. Viking 2003 225p
$16.99 (7 and up)   **Fic**
1. School stories
ISBN 0-670-03644-7   LC 2002-153369
Seventeen-year-old Max Caldwell has been the perfect
high school student—on the honor roll, captain of the debate team, and soon-to-be editor of the school newspaper—but during his senior year, he begins questioning
his approach to life and things start to change
"The teenage voice is dead-on, and Max pulls readers
by the hand, right into his world, without missing a
beat." SLJ

Nelson, Theresa, 1948-
Ruby electric; a novel. Atheneum Bks. for
Young Readers 2003 264p $16.95 (5 and up)
     Fic
1. Fathers—Fiction   2. Siblings—Fiction
3. Authorship—Fiction 4. California—Fiction
ISBN 0-689-83852-2   LC 2002-8034
"A Richard Jackson book"
Twelve-year-old Ruby Miller, movie buff and aspiring
screen writer, tries to resolve the mysteries surrounding
her little brother's stuffed woolly mammoth and their father's five year absence
"Ruby's voice is electric, and she is an unforgettable
character with courage, a cause, and imagination." Booklist

Newman, Robert, 1909-1988
The case of the Baker Street Irregular; a
Sherlock Holmes story. Atheneum Pubs. 1978
216p hardcover o.p. paperback available $4.95 (5
and up)   **Fic**
1. Mystery fiction 2. London (England)—Fiction
ISBN 0-689-70766-5 (pa)   LC 77-15463
Also available in hardcover from P. Smith
Brought to London under mysterious circumstances by
his tutor, young Andrew Tillett seeks the help of Sherlock Holmes when his tutor is kidnapped and he himself
is threatened with the same fate
"The author is as urbane and fluent as the legendary
Mr. Holmes; he seems thoroughly comfortable with the
characters, the atmosphere, and the turn-of-the century
London setting; and the story moves along with unflag-
ging energy." Horn Book

Nickerson, Sara
How to disappear completely and never be
found; illustrations by Sally Wern Comport.
HarperCollins Pubs. 2002 281p il $15.99; lib bdg
$16.89; pa $5.99   **Fic**
1. Mystery fiction
ISBN 0-06-029771-9; 0-06-029772-7 (lib bdg);
0-06-441027-7 (pa)   LC 2001-39517

With a swimming medal, the key to a mansion, and
a comic book about a half-man/half-rat as her only clues,
twelve-year-old Margaret seeks the true story of her father's mysterious death four years earlier near an island
in the Pacific Northwest
"The story's graphic-novel sensibility . . . will intrigue fans of that genre, and readers in general will relish this compelling and offbeat adventure." Bull Cent
Child Books

Nix, Garth, 1963-
Mister Monday; Keys to the kingdom, book
one. Scholastic 2003 361p $15.99; pa $5.99
     Fic
1. Fantasy fiction
ISBN 0-439-70370-0; 0-439-55123-4 (pa)
     LC 2004-540574
Arthur Penhaligon is supposed to die at a young age,
but is saved by a key that is shaped like the minute hand
of a clock. The key causes bizarre creatures to come
from another realm, bringing with them a plague. A man
named Mister Monday will stop at nothing to get the key
back. Arthur goes to a mysterious house that only he can
see, so that he can learn the truth about himself and the
key
"The first in a seven part series for middle graders is
every bit as exciting and suspenseful as the author's previous young adult novels." SLJ
Other titles in the Keys to the Kingdom series are:
Drowned Wednesday (2005)
Grim Tuesday (2004)

Sabriel. HarperCollins Pubs. 1996 c1995 292p
$17.99; pa $7.99   **Fic**
1. Fantasy fiction
ISBN 0-06-027322-4; 0-06-447183-7 (pa)
     LC 96-1295
First published 1995 in Australia
Sabriel, daughter of the necromancer Abhorsen, must
journey into the mysterious and magical Old Kingdom to
rescue her father from the Land of the Dead
"The final battle is gripping, and the bloody cost of
combat is forcefully presented. The story is remarkable
for the level of originality of the fantastic elements . . .
and for the subtle presentation, which leaves readers to
explore for themselves the complex structure and significance of the magic elements." Horn Book
Other titles in this series are:
Abhorsen (2003)
Across the wall (2005)
Lirael, daughter of the Clayr (2001)

Shade's children. HarperCollins Pubs. 1997
310p $18.99; pa $6.99 (7 and up)   **Fic**
1. Science fiction
ISBN 0-06-027324-0; 0-06-447196-9 (pa)
     LC 97-3841
In a savage postnuclear world, four young fugitives attempt to overthrow the bloodthirsty rule of the Overlords
with the help of Shade, their mysterious mentor
"Grim, unusual, and fascinating." Horn Book

Nixon, Joan Lowery, 1927-2003

The haunting. Delacorte Press 1998 184p pa $5.50 hardcover o.p. (7 and up)   **Fic**

1. Ghost stories 2. Louisiana—Fiction

ISBN 0-440-22008-4 (pa)   LC 97-32658

When her mother inherits an old plantation house in the Louisiana countryside, fifteen-year-old Lia seeks to rid it of the evil spirit that haunts it

"This title has it all - a hint of romance, some really scary scenes, and a plucky heroine who successfully routs both outer and inner demons." Horn Book Guide

Murdered, my sweet. Delacorte Press 1997 200p pa $4.99 hardcover o.p. (7 and up)   **Fic**

1. Mystery fiction

ISBN 0-440-41988-3   LC 96-43431

Jenny and her mother hunt a killer while fearing for their own safety, after the reading of their millionaire cousin's will leads to the murder of another cousin

"Another solid Nixon mystery without too much violence and lots of suspense." Booklist

Nightmare. Delacorte Press 2003 166p $15.95; lib bdg $17.99   **Fic**

1. Camps—Fiction 2. Homicide—Fiction 3. Mystery fiction

ISBN 0-385-73026-8; 0-385-90151-8 (lib bdg)   LC 2003-43434

Emily is sent to a camp for underachievers where she discovers a murderer on the staff who might provide an explanation for her recurring nightmares

"Elements of suspense and mystery are cleverly integrated with the teen's problems resulting from what she witnessed as a child. Readers will once again fall under Nixon's spell as they enjoy this page-turner." SLJ

Who are you? Delacorte Press 1999 184p $15.95; pa $5.50 (7 and up)   **Fic**

1. Art museums—Fiction 2. Mystery fiction

ISBN 0-385-32566-5; 0-440-22757-7 (pa)   LC 98-43000

When the police discover that a man who has been shot has been keeping a file of her entire life, sixteen-year-old Kristi, an aspiring artist, suspects a connection with the possible theft of a painting from a museum

"Appealing characters, an interesting scenario, and a fascinating peek into the big-money art world will keep the pages turning." Booklist

Nolan, Han, 1956-

A face in every window. Harcourt Brace & Co. 1999 264p $16 (7 and up)   **Fic**

1. Mentally handicapped—Fiction

ISBN 0-15-201915-4   LC 99-14230

Also available in paperback from Puffin Bks.

After the death of his grandmother, who held the family together, teenage JP is left with a mentally challenged father and a mother who seems ineffectual and constantly sick, and he feels everything sliding out of control

"Only a writer as talented as Nolan could make this improbable story line and bizarre cast of characters not only believable but also ultimately uplifting, intriguing, and memorable." Booklist

Norville, Rod

Moonshine express; with a history of moonshine today and yesterday. Four Seasons Pub. 2003 xxix, 195p pa $13.95   **Fic**

1. Moonshining—Fiction 2. Florida—Fiction

ISBN 1-89129-99-2

"Thirteen-year-old Rob McKinley's world is falling apart. His mother has died and his father is drinking heavily. Rob's barely coping with the support of his friend, Katie. They live on the edge of a north Florida swamp sprinkled with half-breed Seminole moon shiners. Rob and Katie are stunned when they stumble across respectable community citizens behind a local moonshine distribution ring." Publisher's note

"This is an edge-of-the-seat thriller." SLJ

Nye, Naomi Shihab, 1952-

Habibi. Simon & Schuster Bks. for Young Readers 1997 259p $16; pa $5.99   **Fic**

1. Jewish-Arab relations—Fiction 2. Jerusalem—Fiction

ISBN 0-689-80149-1; 0-689-82523-4 (pa)   LC 97-10943

When fourteen-year-old Liyanne Abboud, her younger brother, and her parents move from St. Louis to a new home between Jerusalem and the Palestinian village where her father was born, they face many changes and must deal with the tensions between Jews and Palestinians

"Poetically imaged and leavened with humor, the story renders layered and complex history understandable through character and incident." SLJ

Oates, Joyce Carol, 1938-

Big Mouth & Ugly Girl. HarperCollins Pubs. 2002 265p $16.99; lib bdg $17.89; pa $7.99 (7 and up)   **Fic**

1. School stories 2. Friendship—Fiction

ISBN 0-06-623756-4; 0-06-623758-0 (lib bdg); 0-06-447347-3 (pa)   LC 2001-24601

When sixteen-year-old Matt is falsely accused of threatening to blow up his high school and his friends turn against him, an unlikely classmate comes to his aid

"Readers will be propelled through these pages by an intense curiosity to learn how events will play out. Oates has written a fast-moving, timely, compelling story." SLJ

Freaky green eyes. Harper Tempest 2003 341p $16.99; lib bdg $17.89 (7 and up)   **Fic**

1. Domestic violence—Fiction

ISBN 0-06-623759-9; 0-06-623757-2 (lib bdg)   LC 2002-32868

Fifteen-year-old Frankie relates the events of the year leading up to her mother's mysterious disappearance and her own struggle to discover and accept the truth about her parents' relationship

"Oates pulls readers into a fast-paced, first-person thriller. . . . an absorbing page-turner." Booklist

O'Brien, Robert C., 1918-1973

Mrs. Frisby and the rats of NIMH; illustrated by Zena Bernstein. Atheneum Pubs. 1971 223p il lib bdg $18; pa $5.99 (4 and up)   **Fic**

O'Brien, Robert C., 1918-1973—*Continued*
1. Mice—Fiction 2. Rats—Fiction
ISBN 0-689-20651-8 (lib bdg); 0-689-71068-2 (pa)
Awarded the Newbery Medal, 1972
"Mrs. Frisby, a widowed mouse, is directed by an owl to consult with the rats that live under the rosebush about her problem of moving her sick son from the family's endangered home. Upon entering the rats' quarters, Mrs. Frisby discovers to her astonishment that the rats are not ordinary rodents, but highly intelligent creatures that escaped from an NIMH laboratory after being taught to read." Booklist
"The story is fresh and ingenious, the style witty, and the plot both hilarious and convincing." Saturday Rev
Followed by Racso and the rats of NIMH by Jane Leslie Conly

Z for Zachariah. Atheneum Pubs. 1975 c1974 246p hardcover o.p. paperback available $4.50 (7 and up)   **Fic**
1. Science fiction
ISBN 0-02-044650-0 (pa)
Seemingly the only person left alive after a nuclear war, a sixteen-year-old girl is relieved to see a man arrive into her valley until she realizes that he is a tyrant and she must somehow escape.
"The journal form is used by O'Brien very effectively, with no lack of drama and contrast, and the pace and suspense of the story are adroitly maintained until the dramatic and surprising ending." Bull Cent Child Books

O'Connor, Barbara
Fame and glory in Freedom, Georgia. Frances Foster Bks./Farrar, Straus & Giroux 2003 104p $16 (4 and up)   **Fic**
1. School stories 2. Contests—Fiction
ISBN 0-374-32258-9   LC 2002-190212
Unpopular sixth-grader Burdette "Bird" Weaver persuades the new boy at school, whom everyone thinks is mean and dumb, to be her partner for a spelling bee that might win her everything she's ever wanted
"An idiosyncratic group of characters play out this touching and well-paced story about friendship, family, and connection." Horn Book

O'Dell, Kathleen
Agnes Parker . . . girl in progress. Dial Bks. 2003 156p $16.99 (4 and up)   **Fic**
1. Friendship—Fiction 2. School stories
ISBN 0-8037-2648-1   LC 2001-58256
As she starts in the sixth grade, Agnes faces challenges with her old best friend, a longtime bully, a wonderful new classmate and neighbor, and herself
"This is a thoughtful, gently humorous, and resonant cusp-of-coming-of-age novel." Horn Book Guide
Another available title about Agnes Parker is:
Agnes Parker . . . Happy camper? (2005)

O'Dell, Scott, 1898-1989
The black pearl; illustrated by Milton Johnson. Houghton Mifflin 1967 140p il $17 (6 and up)
Fic

1. Pearl fisheries—Fiction 2. Baja California (Mexico: Peninsula)—Fiction
ISBN 0-395-06961-0
Also available in paperback from Dell
A Newbery Medal honor book, 1968
"The people of Baja California feared a demon creature, a giant ray—El Manta Diablo. He was believed to live in a cave at the end of a lagoon. . . . Yet Ramón Salazar, goaded by the taunts of the greatest pearl diver of his father's fleet, dared to enter the cave to dive for a pearl even more wonderful than the one El Sevillano had boasted of. And he found it—the Paragon of Pearls, the Pearl of Heaven. Then came the encounter with the Manta." Horn Book
"The stark simplicity of the story and the deeper significance it holds in the triumph of good over evil add importance to the book, but even without that the book would be enjoyable as a rousing adventure tale with supernatural overtones and beautifully maintained tempo and suspense." Bull Cent Child Books

Island of the Blue Dolphins; illustrated by Ted Lewin. Houghton Mifflin 1990 181p il $22 (5 and up)   **Fic**
1. Native Americans—Fiction 2. Wilderness survival—Fiction 3. San Nicolas Island (Calif.)—Fiction
ISBN 0-395-53680-4   LC 90-35331
Also available in paperback from Dell; Spanish language edition also available
Awarded the Newbery Medal, 1961
A reissue with new illustrations of the title first published 1960
"Unintentionally left behind by members of her California Native American tribe who fled a tragedy-ridden island, young Karana must construct a life for herself. Without bitterness or self-pity, she is able to extract joy and challenge from her eighteen years of solitude." Shapiro. Fic for Youth. 2d edition
Followed by Zia

Sarah Bishop. Houghton Mifflin 1980 184p $16 (6 and up)   **Fic**
1. United States—History—1775-1783, Revolution—Fiction 2. American Loyalists—Fiction 3. New York (State)—Fiction
ISBN 0-395-29185-2   LC 79-28394
Also available in paperback from Scholastic
"Surrounded by war, prejudice, and fear, fifteen-year-old Sarah Bishop quietly determines to live her own kind of life in the wilderness that was Westchester County, New York, during the Revolution. Orphaned Sarah plucks up her courage when she is wrongfully dealt with by both the American and British forces, and she creates a home for herself and her animal friends in the forest near Long Pond." Child Book Rev Serv
"Despite a series of highly dramatic incidents, the story line is basically sharp and clear; O'Dell's messages about the bitterness and folly of war, the dangers of superstition, and the courage of the human spirit are smoothly woven into the story, as are the telling details of period and place." Bull Cent Child Books

Sing down the moon. Houghton Mifflin 1970 137p $18 (5 and up)   **Fic**
1. Navajo Indians—Fiction
ISBN 0-395-10919-1
Also available in paperback from Laurel Leaf

O'Dell, Scott, 1898-1989—*Continued*
A Newbery Medal honor book, 1971
This story is told "through the eyes of a young Nava-
ho girl as she sees the rich harvest in the Canyon de
Chelly in 1864 destroyed by Spanish slavers and the sub-
sequent destruction by white soldiers which forces the
Navahos on a march to Fort Sumner." Publ Wkly
"There is a poetic sonority of style, a sense of identifi-
cation, and a note of indomitable courage and stoicism
that is touching and impressive." Saturday Rev

Streams to the river, river to the sea; a novel of
Sacagawea. Houghton Mifflin 1986 191p $16 (5
and up) **Fic**
1. Sacagawea, b. 1786—Fiction 2. Lewis and Clark
Expedition (1804-1806)—Fiction 3. Native Ameri-
cans—Fiction
ISBN 0-395-40430-4 LC 86-936
Also available in paperback from Fawcett Bks.
This novel "tells the story of the Lewis and Clark ex-
pedition through the eyes of the young Shoshone woman
who served as interpreter and, often, guide." Soc Educ
"An informative and involving choice for American
history students and pioneer-adventure readers." Bull
Cent Child Books

Thunder rolling in the mountains; {by} Scott
O'Dell and Elizabeth Hall. Houghton Mifflin 1992
128p map $17 (5 and up) **Fic**
1. Nez Percé Indians—Fiction
ISBN 0-395-59966-0 LC 91-15961
Also available in paperback from Yearling
"Told from the point of view of Chief Joseph's
daughter, this historical novel concerns the forced removal of the Nez Perce tribe from their homeland in 1877.
Fourteen-year-old Sound of Running Feet describes her
people's pain at leaving their beloved Wallowa Valley,
their disagreements over whether to resist the government troops that plague them, and their suffering as every act of defense or defiance brings on a more devastating reaction." Booklist
"This is a sad, dark-hued story told in Mr. O'Dell's
lean, affecting prose." Child Book Rev Serv

Zia. Houghton Mifflin 1976 179p $18 (5 and
up) **Fic**
1. Native Americans—Fiction 2. Christian missions—
Fiction
ISBN 0-395-24393-9 LC 75-44156
Also available in paperback from Laurel Leaf
In this sequel to Island of the Blue Dolphins, the author invents a niece for Karana "in the character of Zia,
a young Indian who lives at the Santa Barbara Mission
and who dreams of sailing to the island to rescue her
aunt. After one thwarted attempt to get there, and imprisonment for helping some fellow Indians flee the Mission,
Zia finds her dream realized." N Y Times Book Rev
"Zia is an excellent story in its own right, written in
a clear, quiet, and reflective style which is in harmony
with the plot and characterization." SLJ

Olsen, Sylvia, 1955-
The girl with a baby. Sono Nis Press 2004 203p
pa $8.95 (7 and up) **Fic**

1. Teenage mothers—Fiction 2. Native Americans—
Fiction 3. Canada—Fiction
ISBN 1-55039-142-9
This "novel tells of teenage mother Jane, 14, who
wants to stay in school and raise her baby, Destiny, to
be respectful of tradition and smart in the new ways.
Jane's family left the reservation because of resentment
against Dad, who is white; now in a white area, they
face prejudice for being Indian. . . . Jane's home . . . is
drawn without romanticism, and . . . Jane's first-person
narrative never denies how hard life is, and how thrilling." Booklist

White girl. Sono Nis Press 2004 235p pa $8.95
(7 and up) **Fic**
1. Native Americans—Fiction 2. Prejudices—Fiction
ISBN 1-5503-9147-X
"Until she was fourteen, Josie was pretty ordinary.
Then her Mom meets Martin, 'a real ponytail Indian,'
and before long, Josie finds herself living on a reserve
outside town, with a new stepfather, a new stepbrother,
and a new name 'Blondie.'" Publisher's note
"The talk is contemporary and relaxed, and the characters will hold readers as much as the novel's extraordinary sense of place." Booklist

Oppel, Kenneth
Airborn. Eos 2004 355p $16.99; lib bdg $17.89
(7 and up) **Fic**
1. Fantasy fiction 2. Airships—Fiction
ISBN 0-06-053180-0; 0-06-053181-9 (lib bdg)
LC 2003-15642
Matt, a young cabin boy aboard an airship, and Kate,
a wealthy young girl traveling with her chaperone, team
up to search for the existence of mysterious winged creatures reportedly living hundreds of feet above the Earth's
surface.
"This rousing adventure has something for everyone:
appealing and enterprising characters, nasty villains, and
a little romance." SLJ

Silverwing. Simon & Schuster Bks. for Young
Readers 1997 217p pa $4.99 hardcover o.p. (5 and
up) **Fic**
1. Bats—Fiction
ISBN 0-689-82558-7 LC 97-10977
When a newborn bat named Shade but sometimes
called "Runt" becomes separated from his colony during
migration, he grows in ways that prepare him for even
greater journeys
"Oppel's bats are fully developed characters who, if
not quite cuddly, will certainly earn readers' sympathy
and respect. In *Silverwing* the author has created an intriguing microcosm of rival species, factions, and religions." Horn Book
Other titles in this series are:
Firewing (2003)
Sunwing (2000)

Orenstein, Denise Gosliner, 1950-
Unseen companion. Katherine Tegen Bks. 2003
357p $15.99; lib bdg $16.89 (7 and up)
                                           Fic
1. Inuit—Fiction 2. Alaska—Fiction
ISBN 0-06-052056-6; 0-06-052057-4 (lib bdg)
                              LC 2002-152944
"In distinctive voices, the four narrators tell their own
involving stories. . . . A sensitive observer and a compelling storyteller, Orenstein offers a novel that is both
touching and harsh." Booklist

Orlev, Uri, 1931-
Run, boy, run; a novel; translated from the
Hebrew by Hillel Halkin. Houghton Mifflin 2003
186p $15 (7 and up)   Fic
1. Holocaust, 1933-1945—Fiction 2. Jews—Poland—
Fiction
ISBN 0-618-16465-0   LC 2003-1550
"Walter Lorraine books"
Original Hebrew edition, 2001
Based on the true story of a nine-year-old boy who
escapes the Warsaw Ghetto and must survive throughout
the war in the Nazi-occupied Polish countryside
"The story is totally engrossing as it vividly describes
the hardships faced by so many youngsters during the
war. Orlev has . . . successfully used historical fiction to
illustrate the Holocaust experience." SLJ

Ortiz Cofer, Judith, 1952-
Call me Maria; a novel; . . Orchard Books 2004
127p $16.95   Fic
1. Puerto Ricans—Fiction 2. New York (N.Y.)—Fiction
ISBN 0-439-38577-6   LC 2004-2674
Fifteen-year-old Maria leaves her mother and their
Puerto Rican home to live in the barrio of New York
with her father, feeling torn between the two cultures in
which she has been raised.
"Through a mixture of poems, letters, and prose, María gradually reveals herself as a true student of language
and life. . . . Understated but with a brilliant combination of all the right words to convey events, Cofer aptly
relates the complexities of María's two homes, her parents' lives, and the difficulty of her choice between
them." SLJ

Orwell, George, 1903-1950
Animal farm (7 and up)   Fic
1. Animals—Fiction 2. Totalitarianism—Fiction
Hardcover and paperback editions available from various publishers
First published 1945 in the United Kingdom; first
United States edition 1946
"The animals on Farmer Jones's farm revolt in a
move led by the pigs, and drive out the humans. The
pigs become the leaders, in spite of the fact that their
government was meant to be 'classless.' The other animals soon find that they are suffering varying degrees of
slavery. A totalitarian state slowly evolves in which 'all
animals are equal but some animals are more equal than
others.' This is a biting satire aimed at communism."
Shapiro. Fic for Youth. 3d edition

Nineteen eighty-four (7 and up)   Fic

1. Totalitarianism—Fiction
Hardcover and paperback editions available from various publishers
First published 1949 by Harcourt, Brace
"A dictatorship called Big Brother rules the people in
a collectivist society where Winston Smith works in the
Ministry of Truth. The Thought Police persuade the people that ignorance is strength and war is peace. Winston
becomes involved in a forbidden love affair and joins the
underground to resist this mind control." Shapiro. Fic for
Youth. 3d edition

Osa, Nancy
Cuba 15. Delacorte Press 2003 277p $15.95; lib
bdg $17.99 (7 and up)   Fic
1. Cuban Americans—Fiction
ISBN 0-385-73021-7; 0-385-90086-4 (lib bdg)
                              LC 2002-13389
Violet Paz, who is half Cuban American, half Polish
American, reluctantly prepares for her upcoming
"quince," a Spanish nickname for the celebration of an
Hispanic girl's fifteenth birthday
"Violet's hilarious, cool first-person narrative veers
between slapstick and tenderness, denial and truth."
Booklist

Osborne, Mary Pope, 1949-
Adaline Falling Star. Scholastic Press 2000 170p
$16.95; pa $5.99 (5 and up)   Fic
1. Carson, Kit, 1809-1868—Fiction 2. Arapaho Indians—Fiction 3. Racially mixed people—Fiction
ISBN 0-439-05947-X; 0-439-05948-8 (pa)
                              LC 99-30689
Feeling abandoned by her deceased Arapaho mother
and Kit Carson, her explorer father, Adaline Falling Star
runs away from the prejudiced cousins with whom she
is staying and comes close to death in the wilderness,
with only a mongrel dog for company
"Told in the girl's colorful frontier voice, this is an
engaging tale of true grit and self-discovery." Booklist

Standing in the light; the captive diary of
Catherine Carey Logan. Scholastic 1998 184p il
(Dear America) $10.95   Fic
1. United States—History—1600-1775, Colonial period—Fiction 2. Pennsylvania—Fiction 3. Delaware Indians—Fiction 4. Society of Friends—Fiction
ISBN 0-590-13462-0   LC 97-40083
"Osborne successfully sustains readers' attention with
a strong story line while informing them about American
history." SLJ

Paolini, Christopher
Eragon. Knopf 2003 509p (Inheritance) $18.95;
lib bdg $20.99 (7 and up)   Fic
1. Dragons—Fiction 2. Fantasy fiction
ISBN 0-375-82668-8; 0-375-92668-2 (lib bdg)
                              LC 2003-47481
First published 2002 in different form by Paolini International
In Aagaesia, a fifteen-year-old boy of unknown lineage called Eragon finds a mysterious stone that weaves

Paolini, Christopher—_Continued_
his life into an intricate tapestry of destiny, magic, and power, peopled with dragons, elves, and monsters

"This unusual, powerful tale . . . is the first book in the planned Inheritance trilogy. . . . The telling remains constantly fresh and fluid, and [the author] has done a fine job of creating an appealing and convincing relationship between the youth and the dragon." Booklist

Another title in this series is:
Eldest (2005)

Park, Barbara
The graduation of Jake Moon. Atheneum Bks. for Young Readers 2000 115p $15; pa $4.99
      Fic
1. Alzheimer's disease—Fiction 2. Grandfathers—Fiction
ISBN 0-689-83912-X; 0-689-83985-5 (pa)
      LC 99-87475
Fourteen-year-old Jake recalls how he has spent the last four years of his life watching his grandfather descend slowly but surely into the horrors of Alzheimer's disease

"Jake is a well-rounded and believable character surrounded by colorful and equally realistic supporting characters. . . . This novel . . . is written in an accessible style that will appeal to a wide audience." SLJ

Park, Linda Sue, 1960-
Project Mulberry; a novel. Clarion 2005 225p $16 (5 and up)
      Fic
1. Korean Americans—Fiction
ISBN 0-618-47786-1
While working on a project for an afterschool club, Julia, a Korean American girl, and her friend Patrick learn not just about silkworms, but also about tolerance, prejudice, friendship, patience, and more. Between the chapters are short dialogues between the author and main character about the writing of the book.

"The unforgettable family and friendship story, the quiet, almost unspoken racism, and the excitement of the science make this a great cross-curriculum title." Booklist

A single shard. Clarion Bks. 2001 152p $15 (5 and up)
      Fic
1. Pottery—Fiction 2. Korea—Fiction
ISBN 0-395-97827-0
      LC 00-43102
Also available Thorndike Press large print edition and in paperback from Yearling

Awarded the Newbery Medal, 2002

Tree-ear, a thirteen-year-old orphan in medieval Korea, lives under a bridge in a potters' village, and longs to learn how to throw the delicate celadon ceramics himself

"This quiet, but involving, story draws readers into a very different time and place. . . . A well-crafted novel with an unusual setting." Booklist

When my name was Keoko. Clarion Bks. 2002 199p $16 (5 and up)
      Fic
1. Korea—Fiction 2. World War, 1939-1945—Fiction
ISBN 0-618-13335-6
      LC 2001-32487

With national pride and occasional fear, a brother and sister face the increasingly oppressive occupation of Korea by Japan during World War II, which threatens to suppress Korean culture entirely

"Park is a masterful prose stylist, and her characters are developed beautifully. She excels at making traditional Korean culture accessible to Western readers." Voice Youth Advocates

Includes bibliographical references

Paterson, Katherine
Bridge to Terabithia; illustrated by Donna Diamond. Crowell 1977 128p il $15.99; lib bdg $16.89; pa $5.99 (4 and up)
      Fic
1. Friendship—Fiction 2. Death—Fiction 3. Virginia—Fiction
ISBN 0-690-01359-0; 0-690-04635-9 (lib bdg); 0-06-440184-7 (pa)
      LC 77-2221
Awarded the Newbery Medal, 1978
The life of Jess, a ten-year-old boy in rural Virginia expands when he becomes friends with a newcomer who subsequently meets an untimely death trying to reach their hideaway, Terabithia, during a storm

"Jess and his family are magnificently characterized; the book abounds in descriptive vignettes, humorous sidelights on the clash of cultures, and realistic depictions of rural school life." Horn Book

The great Gilly Hopkins. Crowell 1978 148p $15.99; lib bdg $16.89; pa $5.99 (5 and up)
      Fic
1. Foster home care—Fiction
ISBN 0-690-03837-2; 0-690-03838-0 (lib bdg); 0-06-440201-0 (pa)
      LC 77-27075
"Cool, scheming, and deliberately obstreperous, 11-year-old Gilly is ready to be her usual obnoxious self when she arrives at her new foster home. . . . But Gilly's old tricks don't work against the all-encompassing love of the huge, half-illiterate Mrs. Trotter. . . . Determined not to care she writes a letter full of wild exaggerations to her real mother that brings, in return, a surprising visit from an unknown grandmother." Booklist

"A well-structured story, {this} has vitality of writing style, natural dialogue, deep insight in characterization, and a keen sense of the fluid dynamics in human relationships." Bull Cent Child Books

Jacob have I loved. Crowell 1980 216p $15.99; lib bdg $16.89; pa $6.50
      Fic
1. Twins—Fiction 2. Sisters—Fiction 3. Chesapeake Bay (Md. and Va.)—Fiction
ISBN 0-690-04078-4; 0-690-04079-2 (lib bdg); 0-06-440368-8 (pa)
      LC 80-668
"Sara Louise, called Wheeze, felt like the unloved twin in competition with her sister Caroline. On a small Chesapeake Bay island Louise is isolated and denied the opportunity to fulfill her hopes and goals while everyone caters to her twin sister. The return of an old captain after a 50-year absence, and the advent of the war, gives Louise a chance to grow toward maturity and achieve her wish to work alongside her father." Shapiro. Fic for Youth. 3d edition

Paterson, Katherine—*Continued*

Jip; his story. Lodestar Bks. 1996 181p (5 and up) **Fic**

1. Slavery—Fiction 2. African Americans—Fiction 3. Vermont—Fiction 4. Racially mixed people—Fiction

ISBN 0-525-67543-4; 0-14-038674-2 LC 96-2680

While living on a Vermont poor farm during 1855 and 1856, Jip learns that his mother was a runaway slave, and that his father, the plantation owner, plans to reclaim him as property

"This historically accurate story is full of revelations and surprises, one of which is the return appearance of the heroine of *Lyddie*. . . . The taut, extremely readable narrative and its tender depictions of friendship and loyalty provide first-rate entertainment." Publ Wkly

Lyddie. Lodestar Bks. 1991 182p $17.99; pa $6.99 (5 and up) **Fic**

1. United States—History—1815-1861—Fiction 2. Massachusetts—Fiction 3. Factories—Fiction

ISBN 0-525-67338-5; 0-14-034981-2 (pa)

LC 90-42944

Also available Thorndike Press large print edition

Impoverished Vermont farm girl Lyddie Worthen is determined to gain her independence by becoming a factory worker in Lowell, Massachusetts, in the 1840s

"Not only does the book contain a riveting plot, engaging characters, and a splendid setting, but the language—graceful, evocative, and rhythmic—incorporates the rural speech patterns of Lyddie's folk, the simple Quaker expressions of the farm neighbors, and the lilt of fellow mill girl Bridget's Irish brogue. . . . A superb story of grit, determination, and personal growth." Horn Book

The master puppeteer; illustrated by Haru Wells. Crowell 1976 c1975 179p il hardcover o.p. paperback available $4.95 (6 and up) **Fic**

1. Japan—Fiction 2. Puppets and puppet plays—Fiction

ISBN 0-06-440281-9 (pa)

"In 18th-century Osaka, Japan, Jiro, son of a starving puppetmaker, runs away from home to apprentice himself to Yoshida, the ill-tempered master of the Hanaza puppet theater. As Jiro works to learn the art of the puppeteer and travels among the savage, hunger-crazed bands of night rovers in search of his parents, he becomes aware of a mysterious connection between Saboro, a Robin Hood-like figure, and the Hanaza theater itself." SLJ

"The make-believe world of the Japanese puppet theatre merges excitingly with the hungry, desperate realities of 18th century Osaka in this better-than-average junior novel." Bull Cent Child Books

Park's quest. Lodestar Bks. 1988 148p hardcover o.p. paperback available $4.99 (5 and up) **Fic**

1. Farm life—Fiction 2. Vietnamese Americans—Fiction

ISBN 0-14-034262-1 (pa) LC 87-32422

Also available Spanish language edition

Eleven-year-old Park makes some startling discoveries when he travels to his grandfather's farm in Virginia to learn about his father who died in the Vietnam War and meets a Vietnamese-American girl named Thanh

The author "confronts the complexity, the ambiguity, of the war and the emotions of those it involved with an honesty that young readers are sure to recognize and appreciate." N Y Times Book Rev

Preacher's boy. Clarion Bks. 1999 168p $15; pa $4.95 (5 and up) **Fic**

1. Family life—Fiction 2. Christian life—Fiction 3. Vermont—Fiction

ISBN 0-395-83897-5; 0-06-447233-7 (pa)

LC 98-50083

Also available Thorndike Press large print edition

In 1899, ten-year-old Robbie, son of a preacher in a small Vermont town, gets himself into all kinds of trouble when he decides to give up being Christian in order to make the most of his life before the end of the world

"With warmth, humor, and her powerful yet plain style, Paterson draws empathetic and memorable characters." SLJ

The same stuff as stars. Clarion Bks. 2002 242p $15 (5 and up) **Fic**

ISBN 0-618-24744-0 LC 2002-3967

When Angel's self-absorbed mother leaves her and her younger brother with their poor great-grandmother, the eleven-year-old girl worries not only about her mother and brother, her imprisoned father, the frail old woman, but also about a mysterious man who begins sharing with her the wonder of the stars

"Paterson's deft hand at characterization, her insight into the human soul, and her glorious prose make this book one to rejoice over." Voice Youth Advocates

Paton, Alan

Cry, the beloved country (7 and up)

Fic

1. Race relations—Fiction 2. South Africa—Fiction

Hardcover and paperback editions available from various publishers

First published 1948 by Scribner

"Reverend Kumalo, a black South African preacher, is called to Johannesburg to rescue his sister. There he learns that his son Absalom has been accused of murdering a young white attorney whose interests and sympathies had been with the natives. Despite this, the attorney's father comes to the aid of the minister to help the natives in their struggle to survive a drought." Shapiro. Fic for Youth. 3d edition

Paton Walsh, Jill, 1937-

A parcel of patterns. Farrar, Straus & Giroux 1983 136p pa $5.95 hardcover o.p. **Fic**

1. Plague—Fiction 2. Great Britain—Fiction

ISBN 0-374-45743-3 LC 83-48143

Also available in hardcover from P. Smith

Mall Percival tells how the plague came to her Derbyshire village of Eyam in the year 1665, how the villagers determined to isolate themselves to prevent further spread of the disease, and how three-fourths of them died before the end of the following year

"Historical in broad outline, the narrative blends superb characterizations, skillful plotting, and convincing speech for a hauntingly memorable story that offers a richly textured picture of the period." Child Book Rev Serv

Pattou, Edith

East. Harcourt 2003 498p $18 **Fic**
1. Fairy tales 2. Bears—Fiction
ISBN 0-15-204563-5 LC 2003-2338

A young woman journeys to a distant castle on the back of a great white bear who is the victim of a cruel enchantment

"Readers with a taste for fantasy and folklore will embrace Pattou's . . . lushly rendered retelling of 'East of the Sun and West of the Moon'." Publ Wkly

Paulsen, Gary

Alida's song. Delacorte Press 1999 88p pa $5.50 hardcover o.p. (5 and up) **Fic**
1. Grandmothers—Fiction 2. Farm life—Fiction
ISBN 0-440-41474-1 LC 98-37015

In this sequel to The cookcamp, "Grandma Alida once again steps in at a troubled time in her grandson's life. Now the boy is 14; living with violent, drunken parents. . . . {A} letter arrives from his grandmother offering him a summer job as a hired hand on a farm. . . . He accepts the offer and experiences a season of hard work, music, dancing, and hearty meals served up with warmth, love, and understanding. . . . This beautifully written novella is a quiet tribute to a loving relative." SLJ

The cookcamp. Orchard Bks. 1991 115p $15.95 (5 and up) **Fic**
1. Grandmothers—Fiction 2. World War, 1939-1945—Fiction
ISBN 0-531-05927-8 LC 90-7734

Also available in paperback from Dell

"A Richard Jackson book"

During World War II, a little boy is sent to live with his grandma, a cook in a camp for workers building a road through the wilderness

"Paulsen's simply told story strikes extraordinary emotional chords. . . . Those hungry for adventure stories, as well as more introspective readers, will be spellbound by this stirring novel." Publ Wkly

Followed by Alida's song

Dogsong. Bradbury Press 1985 177p (6 and up) **Fic**
1. Inuit—Fiction 2. Arctic regions—Fiction
LC 84-20443

Available in hardcover $16 (ISBN 0-698-83960-X) and paperback $5.99 (ISBN 0-689-82700-8) from Atheneum

A Newbery Medal honor book, 1986

The author's "mystical tone and blunt prose style are well suited to the spare landscape of his story, and his depictions of Russell's icebound existence add both authenticity and color to a slick rendition of the vision-quest plot, which incorporates human tragedy as well as promise." Booklist

Harris and me; a summer remembered. Harcourt Brace & Co. 1993 157p $16 (5 and up) **Fic**
1. Farm life—Fiction 2. Cousins—Fiction
ISBN 0-15-292877-4 LC 93-19788

Sent to live with relatives on their farm because of his unhappy home life, an eleven-year-old city boy meets his distant cousin Harris and is given an introduction to a whole new world

"Readers will experience hearts as large as farmers' appetites, humor as broad as the country landscape and adventures as wild as boyhood imaginations. All this adds up to a hearty helping of old-fashioned, rip-roaring entertainment." Publ Wkly

Hatchet. Bradbury Press 1987 195p **Fic**
1. Survival after airplane accidents, shipwrecks, etc.—Fiction 2. Divorce—Fiction
ISBN 0-02-770130-1 LC 87-6416

Available in hardcover $16.95 (ISBN 0-689-84092-6) and in paperback $5.99 (ISBN 0-689-82699-0) from Atheneum

A Newbery Medal honor book, 1988

After a plane crash, thirteen-year-old Brian spends fifty-four days in the wilderness, learning to survive initially with only the aid of a hatchet given him by his mother, and learning also to survive his parents' divorce

"Paulsen's knowledge of our national wilderness is obvious and beautifully shared." Voice Youth Advocates

Other titles in this series are:
Brian's return (1999)
Brian's winter (1996)
The river (1991)

The haymeadow; illustrated by Ruth Wright Paulsen. Delacorte Press 1992 195p il hardcover o.p. paperback available $4.99 (6 and up) **Fic**
1. Ranch life—Fiction 2. Sheep—Fiction
ISBN 0-440-40923-3 (pa) LC 91-36666

Also available Audiobook version

Fourteen-year-old John comes of age and gains self-reliance during the summer he spends up in the Wyoming mountains tending his father's herd of sheep

"The protagonist is clearly imagined; the style is both consciously simple and dramatic. . . . There's even a touch of humor." Bull Cent Child Books

The island. Orchard Bks. 1988 202p Dell paperback available $5.50 o.p. **Fic**
1. Islands—Fiction
ISBN 0-440-20632-4 LC 87-24761

"A Richard Jackson book"

"Wil Neuton moves with his parents from Madison, Wis., to a small house in the north woods, miles from the nearest village, because of his father's work with the state highway department. He then discovers a lake with a single island in the middle of it; or rather, he feels as though the island had discovered him and drawn him to it for some mysterious and important purpose." N Y Times Book Rev

"With humor and psychological genius, Paulsen develops strong adolescent characters who lend new power to youth's plea to be allowed to apply individual skills in their risk-taking." Voice Youth Advocates

The monument. Delacorte Press 1991 151p pa $5.50 hardcover o.p. (6 and up) **Fic**
1. Artists—Fiction 2. Physically handicapped—Fiction
ISBN 0-440-40782-6 (pa) LC 91-13919

Thirteen-year-old Rocky, self-conscious about the braces on her leg, has her life changed by the remarkable

Paulsen, Gary—*Continued*

artist named Mick who comes to her small Kansas town to design a war memorial

"In sparse, sensitive, moving prose, Paulsen illuminates a small town and its inhabitants beautiful and ugly sides to create a tribute to art." Voice Youth Advocates

Nightjohn. Delacorte Press 1993 92p $15.95; pa $5.99   **Fic**
1. Slavery—Fiction 2. Reading—Fiction 3. African Americans—Fiction
ISBN 0-385-30838-8; 0-440-21936-1 (pa)
                   LC 92-1222
Also available in paperback from Dell
Twelve-year-old Sarny's brutal life as a slave becomes even more dangerous when a newly arrived slave offers to teach her how to read

"Paulsen is at his best here: the writing is stark and bareboned, without stylistic pretensions of any kind. The narrator's voice is strong and true, the violence real but stylized with an almost mythic tone. . . . The simplicity of the text will make the book ideal for older reluctant readers who can handle violence but can't or won't handle fancy writing in long books. Best of all, the metaphor of reading as an act of freedom speaks for itself through striking action unembroidered by didactic messages." Bull Cent Child Books

The rifle. Harcourt Brace & Co. 1995 105p $17 (7 and up)   **Fic**
1. Rifles—Fiction 2. United States—History—1775-1783, Revolution—Fiction
ISBN 0-15-292880-4   LC 95-730
Also available in paperback from Dell
"The centerpiece of the book is a flintlock rifle made in 1768 by a gifted American gunsmith named Cornish McManus. . . . The story follows . . . the life of the gun as it passes from McManus to a trapper/soldier to century-long storage to a 1993 gun nut and finally into the hands of a gas station owner, who mounts it over his fireplace. On Christmas Eve, a stray spark ignites the loaded weapon and the errant bullet kills a neighbor child." Voice Youth Advocates

"Paulsen's message is clear and cutting: a machine made for killing, no matter how lovingly crafted and benignly kept, remains a machine made for killing." Booklist

The Schernoff discoveries. Delacorte Press 1997 103p pa $4.99 hardcover o.p.   **Fic**
1. Friendship—Fiction 2. School stories
ISBN 0-440-41463-6 (pa)   LC 96-45390
Harold and his best friend, both hopeless geeks and societal misfits, try to survive unusual science experiments, the attacks of the football team, and other dangers of junior high school

"The tone is breezy, funny, and sometimes touching (but not too mushy) and bound to keep the most reluctant reader chuckling." Bull Cent Child Books

Soldier's heart; a novel of the Civil War. Delacorte Press 1998 106p $15.95; pa $5.99 (7 and up)   **Fic**
1. United States—History—1861-1865, Civil War—Fiction 2. Post-traumatic stress disorder—Fiction
ISBN 0-385-32498-7; 0-440-22838-7 (pa)
                   LC 98-10038

"Being the story of the enlistment and due service of the boy Charley Goddard in the First Minnesota Volunteers." Title page

"This compelling and realistic depiction of war is based on a true story. . . . Paulsen's writing is crisp and fast-paced, and this soldier's story will haunt readers long after they finish reading the novel." Book Rep

The Transall saga. Delacorte Press 1998 248p pa $6.50 hardcover o.p.   **Fic**
1. Science fiction
ISBN 0-440-21976-0 (pa)   LC 97-40773
While backpacking in the desert, thirteen-year-old Mark falls into a tube of blue light and is transported into a more primitive world, where he must use his knowledge and skills to survive

"A riveting tale of adventure and action." Voice Youth Advocates

The voyage of the Frog. Orchard Bks. 1989 141p pa $5.50 hardcover o.p. (6 and up)
                            Fic
1. Sea stories
ISBN 0-440-40364-2 (pa)   LC 88-15261
"A Richard Jackson book"
When David goes out on his sailboat to scatter his recently deceased uncle's ashes to the wind, he is caught in a fierce storm and must survive many days on his own as he works out his feelings about life and his uncle

"The author, knowledgeable in sailing lore and lyrical and powerful in descriptions of either silken seas or crashing breakers, has made the ocean both a background and a protagonists in David's transition from boy to young man." Horn Book

The winter room. Orchard Bks. 1989 103p $16.95 (5 and up)   **Fic**
1. Farm life—Fiction 2. Minnesota—Fiction
ISBN 0-531-05839-5   LC 89-42541
Also available in paperback from Dell
A Newbery Medal honor book, 1990
"A Richard Jackson book"
A young boy growing up on a northern Minnesota farm describes the scenes around him and recounts his old Norwegian uncle's tales of an almost mythological logging past

"While this seems at first to be a collection of anecdotes organized around the progression of the farm calendar, Paulsen subtly builds a conflict that becomes apparent in the last brief chapters, forceful and well-prepared. . . . Lyrical and only occasionally sentimental, the prose is clean, clear, and deceptively simple." Bull Cent Child Books

Peck, Richard, 1934-

Are you in the house alone? Viking 1976 156p pa $5.99 hardcover o.p.   **Fic**
1. Rape—Fiction
ISBN 0-14-130693-9 (pa)   LC 76-28810
"Gail is frightened by the obscene telephone calls she receives and the notes that are left on her school locker. It is after she has been raped by a classmate while she is babysitting that she begins to understand the real meaning of fear. Although she is a victim, she is doubted

Peck, Richard, 1934-—*Continued*

by her family, friends, and the police. Most unendurable is the fact that she is forced frequently to cross the path of her attacker, the son of a prominent member of the community." Shapiro. Fic for Youth. 2d edition

Fair weather; a novel. Dial Bks. 2001 130p il $16.99; pa $5.99 (5 and up) **Fic**
1. Buffalo Bill, 1846-1917—Fiction 2. Russell, Lillian, 1861-1922—Fiction 3. Family life—Fiction 4. Chicago (Ill.)—Fiction
ISBN 0-8037-2516-7; 0-14-250034-8 (pa)
LC 00-55561
Also available Thorndike Press large print edition
In 1893, thirteen-year-old Rosie and members of her family travel from their Illinois farm to Chicago to visit Aunt Euterpe and attend the World's Columbian Exposition which, along with an encounter with Buffalo Bill and Lillian Russell, turns out to be a life-changing experience for everyone
"Peck's unforgettable characters, cunning dialogue and fast-paced action will keep readers in stitches." Publ Wkly

The great interactive dream machine; another adventure in cyberspace. Dial Bks. for Young Readers 1996 149p $14.99; pa $4.99 **Fic**
1. Computers—Fiction 2. Space and time—Fiction 3. School stories
ISBN 0-8037-1989-2; 0-14-038264-X (pa)
LC 95-53263
Josh Lewis is unwillingly drawn into the computer experiments of Aaron, his friend and fellow classmate at an exclusive New York private school, and the two find themselves uncontrollably transported through space and time
"Humor, fantasy,science fiction, and even a touch of mystery all cleverly combine to make this book a guaranteed fun, fast-paced adventure." SLJ

The last safe place on earth. Delacorte Press 1995 161p pa $5.99 hardcover o.p. (7 and up) **Fic**
1. Censorship—Fiction 2. Family life—Fiction 3. Christian fundamentalism—Fiction
ISBN 0-440-22007-6 (pa)
LC 94-446
Fifteen-year-old Todd sees his perfect suburban world start to unravel when his little sister has her mind poisoned by a member of a fundamentalist sect and he begins to notice signs of censorship in his community
"Peck writes with wit and warmth that will sweep teens into a world they'll recognize. He has a sharp eye for the poetic image that captures the contemporary scene." Booklist

A long way from Chicago; a novel in stories. Dial Bks. for Young Readers 1998 148p $15.99; pa $5.99 (5 and up) **Fic**
1. Grandmothers—Fiction 2. Great Depression, 1929-1939—Fiction
ISBN 0-8037-2290-7; 0-14-240110-2 (pa)
LC 98-10953
A Newbery Medal honor book, 1999
Joe recounts his annual summer trips to rural Illinois with his sister during the Great Depression to visit their larger-than-life grandmother
"The novel reveals a strong sense of place, a depth of characterization, and a rich sense of humor." Horn Book
Followed by A year down yonder

Lost in cyberspace. Dial Bks. for Young Readers 1995 151p $16.99; pa $5.99 (5 and up) **Fic**
1. Space and time—Fiction 2. School stories 3. Siblings—Fiction
ISBN 0-8037-1931-0; 0-14-037856-1 (pa)
LC 94-48330
While dealing with changes at home, sixth-grader Josh and his friend Aaron use the computer at their New York prep school to travel through time, learning some secrets from the school's past and improving Josh's home situation
This "will appeal to today's computer-literate generation while allowing their imaginations to soar. A time-traveling journey that will keep the reader on the edge of his seat—or computer." Child Book Rev Serv

The river between us. Dial Bks. 2003 164p $16.99 (7 and up) **Fic**
1. United States—History—1861-1865, Civil War—Fiction 2. Racially mixed people—Fiction 3. Race relations—Fiction
ISBN 0-8037-2735-6
LC 2002-34815
During the early days of the Civil War, the Pruitt family takes in two mysterious young ladies who have fled New Orleans to come north to Illinois
"The harsh realities of war are brutally related in a complex, always surprising plot that resonates on mutiple levels." Horn Book

Strays like us. Dial Bks. 1998 155p $15.99; pa $4.99 **Fic**
1. Social isolation—Fiction
ISBN 0-8037-2291-5; 0-14-130619-X (pa)
LC 97-18575
When her drug-addict mother can no longer care for her, twelve-year-old Molly comes to stay with her great-aunt and slowly begins to realize that others in the small town also feel as if they don't belong
This novel's "easy-flowing action readily absorbs the reader into the lives of contemporary characters and a realistic, believable plot." Voice Youth Advocates

The teacher's funeral; a comedy in three parts; Richard Peck. Dial Books 2004 190p $16.99 (5 and up) **Fic**
1. Teachers—Fiction 2. Indiana—Fiction 3. Country life—Fiction
ISBN 0-8037-2736-4
LC 2004-4361
In rural Indiana in 1904, fifteen-year-old Russell's dream of quitting school and joining a wheat threshing crew is disrupted when his older sister takes over the teaching at his one-room schoolhouse after mean, old Myrt Arbuckle "hauls off and dies."
"The dry wit and unpretentious tone make the story's events comical, its characters memorable, and its conclusion unexpectedly moving." Booklist

Peck, Richard, 1934-—Continued

A year down yonder. Dial Bks. for Young
Readers 2000 130p $16.99; pa $5.99 (5 and up)
Fic
1. Grandmothers—Fiction 2. Great Depression, 1929-
1939—Fiction
ISBN 0-8037-2518-3; 0-14-230070-5 (pa)
LC 99-43159
Awarded the Newbery Medal, 2001
This sequel to A long way from Chicago "tells the
story of Joey's younger sister, Mary Alice, 15, who
spends the year of 1937 back with Grandma Dowdel in
a small town in Illinois." Booklist
"Peck has created a delightful, insightful tale that re-
sounds with a storyteller's wit, humor, and vivid description." SLJ

Peck, Robert Newton, 1928-

A day no pigs would die. Knopf 1973 c1972
150p $25; pa $5.50 (6 and up)　　　　　**Fic**
1. Shakers—Fiction 2. Farm life—Fiction
3. Vermont—Fiction
ISBN 0-394-48235-2; 0-679-85306-5 (pa)
"Rob lives a rigorous life on a Shaker farm in Vermont in the 1920s. Since farm life is earthy, this book
is filled with Yankee humor and explicit descriptions of
animals mating. A painful incident that involves the
slaughter of Rob's beloved pet pig is instrumental in urg-
ing him toward adulthood. The death of his father completes the process of his accepting responsibility." Shapiro. Fic for Youth. 3d edition

Horse thief; a novel. HarperCollins Pubs. 2002
231p $16.95; lib bdg $16.89; pa $5.99 (7 and up)
Fic
1. Rodeos—Fiction
ISBN 0-06-623791-2; 0-06-623792-0 (lib bdg);
0-06-441075-7 (pa)　　　　　LC 2001-39733
In 1938, with the help of a doctor and her elderly,
horse-thieving father, a seventeen-year-old orphan steals
thirteen horses from Chickalookee, Florida's doomed rodeo and finds a family in the process
This is "a convoluted and surprisingly funny odyssey,
chock-full of engaging characters. Peck's dialect and
comic timing are right on target. Even sophisticated urban teens may find themselves drawn by the rip-roaring
story and gentle humor." Booklist

Pennebaker, Ruth

Both sides now. Holt & Co. 2000 202p $16.95
(7 and up)　　　　　**Fic**
1. Cancer—Fiction 2. Mother-daughter relationship—
Fiction
ISBN 0-8050-6105-3　　　　　LC 99-58442
Fifteen-year-old Liza tries to deal with the normal everyday crises of life in an Austin, Texas, high school, a
process complicated by her mother's fight with breast
cancer
"Moving and realistic, this taut novel trades a happy
ending for one both honest and empowering." Publ Wkly

Perkins, Lynne Rae

All alone in the universe. Greenwillow Bks.
1999 140p il $15.95; pa $5.99 (5 and up)
Fic
1. Friendship—Fiction
ISBN 0-688-16881-7; 0-380-73302-1 (pa)
LC 98-50093
Also available Audiobook version
Debbie is dismayed when her best friend Maureen
starts spending time with ordinary, boring Glenna
"A poignant story written with sensitivity and tender-
ness." SLJ

Perkins, Mitali, 1963-

Monsoon summer. Delacorte Press 2004 257p
$15.95; lib bdg $17.99 (7 and up)　　　　**Fic**
1. India—Fiction 2. East Indians—United States—Fiction
ISBN 0-385-73123-X; 0-385-90147-X (lib bdg)
LC 2003-15168
Secretly in love with her best friend and business partner Steve, fifteen-year-old Jazz must spend the summer
away from him when her family goes to India during
that country's rainy season to help set up a clinic.
This "novel, written in Jazz's smart, funny, self-
deprecating voice, vividly evokes the smells, sights, and
sounds of India in the monsoon season." Booklist

Peters, Julie Anne, 1952-

Define "normal"; a novel. Little, Brown 2000
196p $14.95; pa $5.95 (7 and up)　　　　**Fic**
1. School stories 2. Friendship—Fiction
ISBN 0-316-70631-0; 0-316-73489-6 (pa)
LC 99-42774
Also available Thorndike Press large print edition
When she agrees to meet with Jasmine as a peer
counselor at their middle school, Antonia never dreams
that this girl with the black lipstick and pierced eyebrow
will end up helping her deal with the serious problems
she faces at home and become a good friend
"Readers who are looking for believable characters
and a good story about friendship, being different, and
growing wiser will appreciate Define 'Normal'." Voice
Youth Advocates

Pevsner, Stella

Is everyone moonburned but me? Clarion Bks.
2000 202p $15　　　　　**Fic**
1. Family life—Fiction 2. Sisters—Fiction
3. Remarriage—Fiction
ISBN 0-395-95770-2　　　　　LC 99-36816
Thirteen-year-old Hannah feels plain and drab compared to her older and younger sisters, but when both of
her divorced parents seem on the verge of remarriage
and a series of crises face the family, she is the only one
who manages to keep her sanity
"Pevsner keeps her tone upbeat and her characters (especially the adults) sensible, leaving plenty of room for
the humor she writes so well." Booklist

Pfeffer, Susan Beth, 1948-
The year without Michael. Delacorte Press 2003 164p $9.95; lib bdg $11.99; pa $4.99 **Fic**
1. Missing children—Fiction 2. Family life—Fiction
ISBN 0-385-73120-5; 0-385-90150-X (lib bdg); 0-553-27373-6 (pa) LC 2004-270004
First published 1987 by Bantam Bks.
"Thirteen year old Michael disappears on a Sunday afternoon. His family may never know what happened to him but they will hope and search until he's found. It falls upon Jody, Michael's older sister, to hold the family together as the stress and uncertainty mount." BAYA Book Rev
This offers "taut structuring, sound characterization, and honest dialogue." SLJ

Philbrick, W. R. (W. Rodman)
Freak the Mighty; [by] Rodman Philbrick. Blue Sky Press (NY) 1993 169p $16.95; pa $5.99 **Fic**
1. Learning disabilities—Fiction 2. Physically handicapped—Fiction 3. Friendship—Fiction
ISBN 0-590-47412-X; 0-439-28606-9 (pa) LC 93-19913
"Large, awkward, learning-disabled Maxwell Kane, whose father is in prison for murdering his mother, and crippled, undersized Kevin are both mocked by their peers. . . . The boys establish a friendship—and a partnership. Kevin defends them with his intelligence, while Max is his friend's 'legs,' affording him a chance to participate in the larger world. Inspired by tales of King Arthur, they become knights fighting for good and true causes. But Kevin's illness progresses, and when he dies, Max is left with the memories of an extraordinary relationship and, perhaps, the insight to think positively about himself and his future." SLJ
"The story is both riveting and poignant, with solid characters, brisk pacing, and even a little humor to carry us along." Booklist
Followed by Max the Mighty (1998)

The journal of Douglas Allen Deeds; the Donner Party expedition; by Rodman Philbrick. Scholastic 2001 155p il (My name is America) $10.95 **Fic**
1. Donner party—Fiction 2. Overland journeys to the Pacific—Fiction 3. Orphans—Fiction
ISBN 0-439-21600-1 LC 2001-17022
Douglas Deeds, a fifteen-year-old orphan, keeps a journal of his travels by wagon train as a member of the ill-fated Donner Party, which became stranded in the Sierra Nevada mountains in the winter of 1846-47
"Philbrick shows the action rather than merely telling about it, but he deals discreetly with the issue of cannibalism. . . . This is historical fiction that will spark discussions about both ethics and leadership." Booklist

The last book in the universe; by Rodman Philbrick. Blue Sky Press (NY) 2001 223p $16.95; pa $5.99 **Fic**
1. Science fiction 2. Epilepsy—Fiction
ISBN 0-439-08758-9; 0-439-08759-7 (pa) LC 99-59878
Expanded from a short story in Tomorrowland edited by Michael Cart, published 1999 by Scholastic Press

After an earthquake has destroyed much of the planet, an epileptic teenager nicknamed Spaz begins the heroic fight to bring human intelligence back to the Earth of a distant future
"Enthralling, thought-provoking, and unsettling." Voice Youth Advocates

The young man and the sea; {by} Rodman Philbrick. Blue Sky Press 2004 192p $16.95 (5 and up) **Fic**
1. Fishing—Fiction
ISBN 0-439-36829-4 LC 2003-050233
After his mother's death, twelve-year-old Skiff Beaman decides that it is up to him to earn money to take care of himself and his father, so he undertakes a dangerous trip alone out on the ocean off the coast of Maine to try to catch a hugh bluefin tuna.
"This excellent maritime bildungsroman has all of the makings of a juvenile classic: wide-open adventure, heart-pounding suspense, and just the right amount of tear-jerking pathos, all neatly wrapped up in an ending that . . . is purely triumphant." SLJ

Pierce, Meredith Ann, 1958-
Treasure at the heart of the Tanglewood. Viking 2001 241p $16.99; pa $6.99 **Fic**
1. Fantasy fiction
ISBN 0-670-89247-5; 0-14-250013-5 (pa) LC 00-51366
Hannah, a healer with unusual powers, leaves the wizard she has always served and, along with her animal companions, begins a journey which uncovers the truth about her real nature
"Pierce draws readers in with a mystery that deepens with each chapter; her feyly arcane language, obtrusive at first, eventually merges with her elemental themes to create a seamless and compelling whole." Horn Book Guide

Pierce, Tamora, 1954-
Circle of magic: Sandry's book. Scholastic Press 1997 252p $15.95; pa $5.99 **Fic**
1. Fantasy fiction
ISBN 0-590-55356-9; 0-590-55408-9 (pa) LC 95-39540
Four young misfits find themselves living in a strictly disciplined temple community where they become friends while also learning to do crafts and to use their powers, especially magic
"Pierce has created an excellent new world where magic is a science and utterly believable and populated it with a cast of well-developed characters." Booklist
Other available titles in this series are:
Circle of magic: Briar's book (1999)
Circle of magic: Daja's book (1998)
Circle of magic: Tris's book (1998)

First test. Random House 1999 216p (Protector of the small) $16; lib bdg $17.99; pa $5.99 **Fic**
1. Fantasy fiction
ISBN 0-679-88914-0; 0-679-98914-5 (lib bdg); 0-679-88917-5 (pa) LC 98-30903
Set in the imaginary kingdom of Tortall, setting for the author's Lioness quartet and the Immortals series

Pierce, Tamora, 1954—*Continued*

First title in the Protector of the small series. Ten-year-old Keladry of Mindalen, daughter of nobles, serves as a page but must prove herself to the males around her if she is ever to fulfill her dream of becoming a knight

"Pierce spins a whopping good yarn, her plot balanced on a solid base of action and characterization." Bull Cent Child Books

Other available titles in this series are:

Lady knight (2002)

Page (2001)

Squire (2002)

Trickster's choice. Random House 2003 422p $17.95; pa $8.95 (7 and up) **Fic**

1. Fantasy fiction

ISBN 0-375-81466-3; 0-375-82879-6 (pa)

LC 2003-5202

Alianne must call forth her mother Alanna's courage and her father's wit in order to survive on the Copper Isles in a royal court rife with political intrigue and murderous conspiracy

"This series opener is packed with Pierce's alluring mix of fantasy, adventure, romance, and humor, making the book an essential purchase for school and public libraries." Voice Youth Advocates

Another title in this series is:

Trickster's queen (2004)

Pinkney, Andrea Davis

Silent thunder; a Civil War story. Hyperion Bks. for Children 1999 218p il $15.99; lib bdg $16.49 **Fic**

1. Slavery—Fiction 2. African Americans—Fiction 3. Virginia—Fiction 4. United States—History—1861-1865, Civil War—Fiction

ISBN 0-7868-0439-4; 0-7868-2388-7 (lib bdg)

LC 98-32071

In 1862 eleven-year-old Summer and her thirteen-year-old brother Rosco take turns describing how life on the quiet Virginia plantation where they are slaves is affected by the Civil War

"This is an excellent, well-written historical novel, with two compelling narrators." SLJ

Placide, Jaira

Fresh girl. Wendy Lamb Bks. 2002 216p $15.95; pa $5.50 (7 and up) **Fic**

1. Haitian Americans—Fiction 2. Haiti—Fiction 3. Brooklyn (New York, N.Y.)—Fiction

ISBN 0-385-32753-6; 0-440-23764-5 (pa)

LC 2001-32427

After having been sent, at a very young age, from New York to live with her grandmother in Haiti, fourteen-year-old Mardi returns to join her parents and try to shape a new life in Brooklyn

"The heart of the story is Mardi's relationship with her uncle, who helps her confront, first, her anger toward him and finally the horror of her rape when the soldiers came. The violence isn't sensationalized, and readers will appreciate that by the end, Mardi is beginning to feel at home." Booklist

Plummer, Louise

The unlikely romance of Kate Bjorkman. Delacorte Press 1995 183p pa $5.99 hardcover o.p. (7 and up) **Fic**

1. Christmas—Fiction 2. Family life—Fiction 3. Love stories

ISBN 0-440-22704-6 (pa)

LC 94-49614

"Neither writing a romance novel nor starring in one is characteristic of Kate Bjorkman, she freely admits; yet she feels compelled to try both when her brother comes home from college for Christmas with the love of her life, a childhood friend of his. The intelligent, thoroughly entertaining romantic comedy contains many laugh-out-loud moments and shrewd asides on the writing process." Horn Book Guide

Polikoff, Barbara Garland

Why does the coqui sing? Holiday House 2004 213p $16.95 (5 and up) **Fic**

1. Puerto Ricans—Fiction 2. Puerto Rico—Fiction 3. Moving—Fiction

ISBN 0-8234-1817-0

LC 2003-56776

When thirteen-year-old Luz and her family move from Chicago to her stepfather's native home of Puerto Rico, she and her brother Rome struggle to adjust and to decide where it is they really belong

"Luz, an aspiring poet, beautifully describes the pain of leaving and resettling in a sensitive, sometimes lyrical voice that's always true to her age." Booklist

Powell, Randy

Three clams and an oyster. Farrar, Straus & Giroux 2002 216p $16 (7 and up) **Fic**

1. Friendship—Fiction 2. Football—Fiction

ISBN 0-374-37526-7

LC 2001-54833

During their humorous search to find a fourth player for their flag football team, three high school juniors are forced to examine their long friendship, their individual flaws, and their inability to try new experiences

"Sometimes philosophical, sometimes comical, but always touching, Randy Powell writes an unusually moving story of adolescent male friends." Book Rep

Pratchett, Terry

The amazing Maurice and his educated rodents. HarperCollins Pubs. 2001 241p $16.95; lib bdg $17.89; pa $6.99 (7 and up) **Fic**

1. Fantasy fiction 2. Rats—Fiction 3. Cats—Fiction

ISBN 0-06-001233-1; 0-06-001234-X (lib bdg); 0-06-001235-8 (pa)

LC 2001-42411

A talking cat, intelligent rats, and a strange boy cooperate in a Pied Piper scam until they try to con the wrong town and are confronted by a deadly evil rat king

"In this laugh-out-loud fantasy, his first 'Discworld' novel for younger readers, Pratchett rethinks a classic story and comes up with a winner." SLJ

Only you can save mankind. HarperCollins 2005 c1992 207p $15.99; lib bdg $16.89 (5 and up) **Fic**

1. Computer games—Fiction 2. War stories

ISBN 0-06-054185-7; 0-06-054186-5 (lib bdg)

First published 1992 in the United Kingdom

Pratchett, Terry—*Continued*

Twelve-year-old Johnny endures tensions between his parents, watches television coverage of the Gulf War, and plays a computer game called Only You Can Save Mankind, in which he is increasingly drawn into the reality of the alien ScreeWee.

This is "a wild ride, full of Pratchett's trademark humor; digs at primitive, low-resolution games . . . ; and some not-so-subtle philosophy about war and peace." Booklist

The Wee Free Men. HarperCollins Pubs. 2003 263p $16.99; lib bdg $17.89 **Fic**
1. Fantasy fiction 2. Witches—Fiction
ISBN 0-06-001236-6; 0-06-001237-4 (lib bdg)
LC 2002-15396

A young witch-to-be named Tiffany teams up with the Wee Free Men, a clan of six-inch-high blue men, to rescue her baby brother and ward off a sinister invasion from Fairyland

"Pratchett invites readers into his well-established realm of Discworld where action, magic, and characters are firmly rooted in literary reality. Humor ripples throughout, making tense, dangerous moments stand out in stark contrast." Bull Cent Child Books

Another title about Tiffany is:
A hat full of sky (2004)

Pressler, Mirjam

Malka; translated by Brian Murdoch. Philomel Bks. 2003 280p $18.99 (7 and up) **Fic**
1. Jews—Poland—Fiction
ISBN 0-399-23984-7
LC 2002-74869

Original German edition 2001; this translation first published 2002 in the United Kingdom

In the winter of 1943, a Polish physician and her older daughter make a dangerous and arduous trek to Hungary while seven-year-old Malka, who they were forced to leave behind when she became ill, fends for herself in a ghetto

"Based on one Jewish family's real escape story, Pressler's novel never romanticizes either the victims or the rescuers. . . . The history is accurate, and the survival adventure will hold readers to the very last page." Booklist

Prose, Francine, 1947-

After. HarperCollins Pubs. 2003 330p $15.99; lib bdg $16.89 (7 and up) **Fic**
1. School stories 2. School violence—Fiction 3. Conspiracies—Fiction
ISBN 0-06-008081-7; 0-06-008082-5 (lib bdg)
LC 2002-14386

In the aftermath of a nearby school shooting, a grief and crisis counselor takes over Central High School and enacts increasingly harsh measures to control students, while those who do not comply disappear

"This drama raises all-too-relevant questions about the fine line between safety as a means of protection versus encroachment on individual rights and free will. Sure to spur heated discussions." Publ Wkly

Pullman, Philip, 1946-

The amber spyglass. Knopf 2000 518p $19.95 (7 and up) **Fic**
1. Fantasy fiction
ISBN 0-679-87926-9
LC 00-44776

Also available in paperback from Del Rey

Third volume in His dark materials trilogy "starts where *The Subtle Knife* . . . left off. Lyra has been hidden away by her mother, and Will is determined to find her. Meanwhile, Lord Asriel is preparing to fight the forces of the Church's Consistorial Court, as well as the God-like Authority's Lieutenant, Metatron, who hungers for ultimate power over all worlds. At the heart of this discord is Dust, the mysterious substance that is linked irrevocably to consciousness; it is streaming away at an increasing rate, causing havoc in its wake. It is Lyra and Will's destiny to determine the outcome of this situation." SLJ

Clockwork; or, All wound up; with illustrations by Leonid Gore. Levine Bks. 1998 c1996 112p il pa $4.99 hardcover o.p. (4 and up) **Fic**
1. Supernatural—Fiction
ISBN 0-590-12998-8 (pa)
LC 97-27458

First published 1996 in the United Kingdom

Long ago in Germany, a storyteller's story and an apprentice clockwork-maker's nightmare meet in a menacing, lifelike figure created by the strange Dr. Kalmenius

"Pullman laces his tale with subtle humor while maintaining the suspense until the end. Misty, moody, and atmospheric black-and-white drawings by Leonid Gore make a perfect fit for this gothic gem." Voice Youth Advocates

The golden compass. Knopf 1996 399p $20 (7 and up) **Fic**
1. Fantasy fiction
ISBN 0-679-87924-2
LC 95-33397

Also available in paperback from Del Rey

First published 1995 in the United Kingdom with title: Northern lights

This first title in a fantasy trilogy "introduces the characters and sets up the basic conflict, namely, a race to unlock the mystery of a newly discovered type of charged particles simply called 'dust' that may be a bridge to an alternate universe. The action follows 11-year-old protagonist Lyra Belacqua from her home at Oxford University to the frozen wastes of the North on a quest to save dozens of kidnapped children from the evil 'Gobblers,' who are using them as part of a sinister experiment involving dust." Libr J

Followed by The subtle knife

The ruby in the smoke. Knopf 1987 c1985 230p hardcover o.p. paperback available $6.50 **Fic**
1. Mystery fiction 2. Orphans—Fiction 3. London (England)—Fiction
ISBN 0-394-89589-4 (pa)
LC 86-20983

First published 1985 in the United Kingdom

This story "begins in 1872 on a 'cold, fretful' October afternoon in London. Sally Lockhart is the 16-year-old heroine who asks some innocent questions about her father's death that lead her into a world of stolen rubies and the opium trade." N Y Times Book Rev

Pullman, Philip, 1946—*Continued*

"Pullman uses a cliff-hanger at the end of each chapter to keep readers enthralled in this fast-paced, intricate, and suspenseful novel. Sally's complex characterization as a resourceful, yet occasionally unsure, young woman, makes her both likable and memorable." Voice Youth Advocates

The subtle knife. Knopf 1997 326p $20 (7 and up)   **Fic**

1. Fantasy fiction
ISBN 0-679-87925-0   LC 97-673
Also available in paperback from Del Rey
Sequel to The golden compass
In the second volume of His dark secret trilogy the boundaries between worlds begin to dissolve, Lyra and her daemon help Will Parry in his search for his father and for a powerful, magical knife
"A heart-thumping pace propels a vast cast of characters through an intricate plot, making for exuberant storytelling." Publ Wkly
Followed by The amber spyglass

Quintana, Anton

The baboon king; translated by John Nieuwenhuizen. Walker & Co. 1999 183p $16.95 (7 and up)   **Fic**

1. Baboons—Fiction 2. Kikuyu (African people)—Fiction 3. Masai (African people)—Fiction 4. Africa—Fiction
ISBN 0-8027-8711-8   LC 99-18322
Son of a Kikuyu mother and a Masai herdsman father, Morengáru the hunter lives on the edges of tribal society until an actual banishment forces him to make a life for himself among a troop of baboons
"The visceral descriptions, explorations of the animals' psychology, and realizations about his own humanity make this a memorable, even mystical novel." SLJ

Randall, David, 1972-

Clovermead; in the shadow of the bear; David Randall. 1st ed. Margaret K. McElderry Books 2004 288p $15.95 (7 and up)   **Fic**

1. Fantasy fiction
ISBN 0-689-86639-9   LC 2003-9934
Clovermead, twelve-year-old tomboy, learns that her father has been lying about the past and that the truth may be the key to ending the epic battle raging between the followers of Lord Ursus and those of Lady Moon.
"Excellent characterization and a well-developed story make for an intricate and action-packed adventure." SLJ

Randle, Kristen D., 1952-

Breaking rank. Morrow Junior Bks. 1999 201p $15.95; pa $6.99 (7 and up)   **Fic**

1. Gangs—Fiction 2. School stories
ISBN 0-688-16243-6; 0-380-73281-5 (pa)
LC 98-27867
Seventeen-year-old Casey has some of her preconceived notions challenged when she begins to tutor Baby, a member of a ganglike non-conformist society called the Clan

"The alternating points of view and Randle's taut, poetic prose provide remarkable character depth and complexity. . . . Gritty, smart, and realistic, the novel perceptively explores issues of religion, sex and sexual abstinence, peer pressure, and integrity with grace and compassion." Booklist

Rao, Sirish

Sophocles' Oedipus the King; retold by Sirish Rao & Gita Wolf ; illustrated by Indrapramit Roy. J. Paul Getty Museum 2004 unp $18.95 (7 and up)
Fic

1. Sophocles. Oedipus Rex 2. Classical mythology—Fiction
ISBN 0-89236-764-4   LC 2004-1682
"This retelling begins with Oedipus' . . . answer to the Sphinx's riddle and his entry into Thebes, and ends with the blind Oedipus stumbling away from the city. A narrator . . . introduces the story and provides background, but most of the text is dialogue, adapted from the play. . . . The book . . . is as elegant as the retelling. Silk-screened illustrations, inspired by ancient Greek art, portray dramatic moments in the story." Booklist

Raskin, Ellen, 1928-1984

The Westing game. Dutton Children's Books 2003 182p $16.99; pa $5.99   **Fic**

1. Mystery fiction
ISBN 0-525-47137-5; 0-14-240120-X (pa)
LC 2004-268658
Awarded the Newbery medal, 1979
First published 1978
"This mystery puzzle . . . centers on the challenge set forth in the will of eccentric multimillionaire Samuel Westing. Sixteen heirs of diverse backgrounds and ages are assembled in the old 'Westing house,' paired off, and given clues to a puzzle they must solve—apparently in order to inherit." SLJ
"The rules of the game make eight pairs of the players; each oddly matched couple is given a ten thousand dollar check and a set of clues. The result is a fascinating medley of word games, disguises, multiple aliases and subterfuges—in a demanding but rewarding book." Horn Book

Rawlings, Marjorie Kinnan, 1896-1953

The yearling; with pictures by N. C. Wyeth. Scribner 1985 c1938 400p il $28; pa $5.95
Fic

1. Florida—Fiction 2. Deer—Fiction
ISBN 0-684-18461-3; 0-02-044931-3 (pa)
LC 85-40301
Reissue of the title first published 1938; awarded Pulitzer Prize, 1939
"Young Jody Baxter lives a lonely life in the scrub forest of Florida until his parents unwillingly consent to his adopting an orphan fawn. The two become inseparable until the fawn destroys the meager crops. Then Jody realizes that this situation offers no compromise. In the sacrifice of what he loves best, he leaves his own yearling days behind." Read Ladders for Hum Relat. 5th edition
"With its excellent descriptions of Florida scrub land-

Rawlings, Marjorie Kinnan, 1896-1953—*Continued*
scapes, its skillful use of native vernacular, its tender relation between Jody and his pet fawn, The Yearling is a simply written, picturesque story of boyhood." Time

Rawls, Wilson, 1913-
Summer of the monkeys. Doubleday 1976 239p $15.95; pa $5.99 (7 and up)   **Fic**
1. Monkeys—Fiction 2. Oklahoma—Fiction
ISBN 0-385-11450-8; 0-440-41580-2 (pa)
LC 75-32295
"When Jay Berry Lee discovers a passel of valuable circus monkeys living in the river bottoms near his home, he thinks his fortune is made. Armed with his crippled sister's advice and his grandpa's ingenious traps, he sets out with the family hound dog to catch the critters, collect the reward, and buy himself the pony and the gun he's always wanted. Nobody, least of all Jay Berry, reckons on the comical problems 29 smart monkeys can make for a 14-year-old Oklahoma farm boy. . . . A heartwarming story that escapes a trite conclusion via a fine blend of folksy humor and delightful characterization." Booklist

Where the red fern grows; the story of two dogs and a boy. Bantam Bks. 212p $16.95; pa $5.99
Fic
1. Dogs—Fiction 2. Ozark Mountains—Fiction
ISBN 0-385-32330-1; 0-440-41267-6 (pa)
First published 1961 by Doubleday
"Looking back more than 50 years to his boyhood in the Ozarks, the narrator, recalls how he achieved his heart's desire in the ownership of two redbone hounds, how he taught them all the tricks of hunting, and how they won the championship coon hunt before Old Dan was killed by a mountain lion and Little Ann died of grief. Although some readers may find this novel hackneyed and entirely too sentimental, others will enjoy the fine coonhunting episodes and appreciate the author's feelings for nature." Booklist

Ray, Delia
Ghost girl; a Blue Ridge Mountain story. Clarion Bks. 2003 216p il $15 (5 and up)
Fic
1. Hoover, Herbert, 1874-1964—Fiction 2. Hoover, Lou Henry, 1874-1944—Fiction 3. School stories 4. Teachers—Fiction 5. Virginia—Fiction
ISBN 0-618-33377-0   LC 2003-4115
Eleven-year-old April is delighted when President and Mrs. Hoover build a school near her Madison County, Virginia, home but her family's poverty, grief over the accidental death of her brother, and other problems may mean that April can never learn to read from the wonderful teacher, Miss Vest
"This excellent portrayal of four important years in a girl's life rises to the top. Based on a real school and teacher, this novel seamlessly incorporates historical facts into the narrative." SLJ

Reeder, Carolyn, 1937-
Across the lines. Atheneum Bks. for Young Readers 1997 220p $17 hardcover o.p. (5 and up)
Fic
1. United States—History—1861-1865, Civil War—Fiction 2. African Americans—Fiction 3. Race relations—Fiction
ISBN 0-689-81133-0   LC 96-31068
Available in paperback from HarperCollins
"Twelve-year-old Edward and his family flee to Petersburg just before the Yankees capture their Virginia plantation; Simon, Edward's former slave and companion, performs various jobs for Union troops advancing on the same city. During the span of a year, the boys make parallel journeys toward a deeper understanding of the complex nature of freedom and friendship. Told in the alternating voices of Edward and Simon, this thoughtful Civil War story resonates with authenticity." Horn Book Guide

Rees, Douglas C.
Vampire High. Delacorte Press 2003 226p $15.95; lib bdg $17.99   **Fic**
1. Vampires—Fiction 2. School stories 3. Massachusetts—Fiction
ISBN 0-385-73117-5; 0-385-90143-7 (lib bdg)
LC 2003-41992
When his family moves from California to New Sodom, Massachusetts and Cody enters Vlad Dracul Magnet School, many things seem strange, from the dark-haired, pale-skinned, supernaturally strong students to Charon, the wolf who guides him around campus on the first day
"There's barely a false note in this rollicking tale of horror, humor, and light romance that will appeal to both girls and boys." Booklist

Reeve, Philip, 1966-
Mortal engines; a novel. Eos 2003 c2001 310p (Hungry city chronicles) $16.99; lib bdg $17.89 (7 and up)   **Fic**
1. Science fiction
ISBN 0-06-008207-0; 0-06-008208-9 (lib bdg)
LC 2002-38801
First published 2001 in the United Kingdom
In the distant future, when cities move about and consume smaller towns, a fifteen-year-old apprentice is pushed out of London by the man he most admires and must seek answers in the perilous Out-Country, aided by one girl and the memory of another
"A page-turner, this adventure in a city-eat-city world will have readers eagerly suspending disbelief to follow the twists and turns of the imaginative plot." Booklist

Reiss, Kathryn, 1957-
PaperQuake; a puzzle. Harcourt Brace & Co. 1998 264p $17; pa $6   **Fic**
1. Sisters—Fiction 2. Earthquakes—Fiction 3. San Francisco (Calif.)—Fiction 4. Mystery fiction
ISBN 0-15-201183-8; 0-15-216782-X (pa)
LC 97-33217
Certain that she is being drawn by more than coincidences into the lives of people living nearly 100 years

Reiss, Kathryn, 1957-—*Continued*
ago, Violet, who feels like the odd sister in a set of triplets, searches for clues to help her avert an imminent tragedy

"Themes of adventure and family relationships, heightened by an atmospheric sense of place, are deftly woven into this clever and skillfully written mystery." Horn Book Guide

Rennison, Louise, 1951-
Angus, thongs and full-frontal snogging; confessions of Georgia Nicolson. HarperCollins Pubs. 2000 c1999 247p $15.95; pa $6.95 (7 and up)   **Fic**
1. Great Britain—Fiction
ISBN 0-06-028814-0; 0-06-447227-2 (pa)
LC 99-40591
First published 1999 in the United Kingdom

Presents the humorous journal of a year in the life of Georgia, a fourteen-year-old British girl who tries to reduce the size of her nose, stop her mad cat from terrorizing the neighborhood animals, and win the love of handsome hunk Robbie

"Georgia is a wonderful character whose misadventures are not only hysterically funny but universally recognizable." Booklist
Other titles about Georgia are:
Away laughing on a fast camel (2004)
Dancing in my nuddy-pants (2003)
Knocked out by my nunga-nungas (2002)
On the bright side, I'm now the girlfriend of a sex god (2001)
Then he ate my boy entrancers (2005)

Richter, Conrad, 1890-1968
The light in the forest. Everyman's Library 2005 c1953 176p $14.95; pa $6.50   **Fic**
1. Frontier and pioneer life—Fiction 2. Delaware Indians—Fiction
ISBN 1-4000-4426-X; 1-4000-7788-5 (pa)
First published 1953 by Knopf
"A boy stolen in early childhood and brought up by the Delawares is at fifteen suddenly returned to the family he has forgotten. He resents his loss of independence, hates the brutality of the white man's civilization, and longs only for a return to the Indians whom he remembers as peace-loving and kind. His return to the Delawares does not, however, bring him peace; rather, he must make a bitter choice between helping his indian brothers kill agroup of unsuspecting white men or helping the white men escape. This is both vivid re-creation of outdoor life and a provocative study in conflicting loyalties." Horn Book

Rinaldi, Ann, 1934-
Amelia's war. Scholastic Press 1999 265p $15.95; pa $4.99   **Fic**
1. United States—History—1861-1865, Civil War—Fiction 2. Maryland—Fiction
ISBN 0-590-11744-0; 0-439-32666-4 (pa)
LC 98-23286

"This gripping, fast-paced story, based on a true incident, particularly shines in its depiction of the subtleties of everyday life." Booklist
Includes bibliographical references

The fifth of March; a story of the Boston Massacre. Harcourt Brace & Co. 1993 335p (Great episodes) pa $6.95 hardcover o.p. (7 and up)
   Fic
1. Adams family—Fiction 2. Boston Massacre, 1770—Fiction 3. United States—History—1600-1775, Colonial period—Fiction
ISBN 0-15-205078-7 (pa)   LC 93-17821
"Gulliver books"
"The story moves along briskly, and details of life in 18th-century Boston are woven into the narrative." SLJ

Girl in blue. Scholastic Press 2001 310p $15.95; pa $5.99   **Fic**
1. Greenhow, Rose O'Neal, 1817-1864—Fiction 2. United States—History—1861-1865, Civil War—Fiction 3. Sex role—Fiction 4. Spies—Fiction
ISBN 0-439-07336-7; 0-439-67646-0 (pa)
LC 00-41945
"This first-person novel will engage readers through its sympathetic main character and exciting action." Booklist

Hang a thousand trees with ribbons; the story of Phillis Wheatley. Harcourt Brace & Co. 1996 336p pa $6 hardcover o.p.   **Fic**
1. Wheatley, Phillis, 1753-1784—Fiction 2. African Americans—Fiction 3. Slavery—Fiction 4. United States—History—1600-1775, Colonial period—Fiction
ISBN 0-15-200877-2 (pa)   LC 96-872
"Rinaldi blends history, romance, and drama into an inspiring novel that will leave a lasting impression on readers and broaden their understanding of slavery in colonial America." Book Rep

In my father's house. Scholastic 1993 323p pa $5.99 hardcover o.p. (7 and up)   **Fic**
1. United States—History—1861-1865, Civil War—Fiction 2. Stepfathers—Fiction
ISBN 0-590-44731-9 (pa)   LC 91-46839
"The story is told from the point of view of Osceola, Wilmer McLean's stepdaughter. Bull Run, the first battle of the war, is fought on the McLean's land and their home is damaged. Flashbacks review pre-War events and develop family characters. The narrative ends in 1865 at Appomattox Court House when Grant receives Lee's surrender in the parlor of the family's new home. . . . Even reluctant history students will enjoy learning about the Civil War by reading this work." Book Rep

A stitch in time. Scholastic 1994 305p pa $5.99 hardcover o.p. (7 and up)   **Fic**
1. Family life—Fiction 2. Quilts—Fiction 3. Frontier and pioneer life—Fiction
ISBN 0-590-46056-0 (pa)   LC 93-8964
"The Chelmsfords of Massachusetts are a respected merchant family after the War of Independence. But there are shadows and silences that Hannah can't understand. Her father behaves unfairly toward her and sister Abigail while favoring a third daughter. The night before

Rinaldi, Ann, 1934-—_Continued_
the sisters go their separate ways, they divide up fabrics intended for a family quilt." Publisher's note

"There is plenty of personal interest, adventure, humor, fear, and joy in this ambitious novel." SLJ

Other titles in this series are:
The blue door (1996)
Broken days (1995)

Taking liberty; the story of Oney Judge, George Washington's runaway slave. Simon & Schuster Bks. for Young Readers 2002 267p $16.95
Fic
1. Washington, George, 1732-1799—Fiction 2. Slavery—Fiction 3. African Americans—Fiction
ISBN 0-689-85187-1   LC 2002-3849

After serving Martha Washington loyally for twenty years, Oney Judge realizes that she is just a slave and must decide if she will run away to find true freedom

"This excellent novel depicts the political conflicts of the new nation and a compelling character." Voice Youth Advocates

Includes bibliographical references

Wolf by the ears. Scholastic 1991 252p hardcover o.p. paperback available $5.99
Fic
1. Jefferson, Thomas, 1743-1826—Fiction 2. Slavery—Fiction 3. African Americans—Fiction
ISBN 0-590-43412-8 (pa)   LC 90-40563

"Set at Monticello from 1819-1822, this provocative historical novel deals with the conflicts of teenage Harriet Hemings, daughter of the slave Sally and allegedly of Thomas Jefferson. A member of two worlds, Harriet is confused about the truth of her parentage, her love of her master, her need to leave home and people she loves, and her eventual plan to pass as white." ALAN

Ritter, John H., 1951-
The boy who saved baseball. Philomel Bks. 2003 216p $17.99 (5 and up)   **Fic**
1. Baseball—Fiction
ISBN 0-399-23622-8   LC 2002-15792

The fate of a small California town rests on the outcome of one baseball game, and Tom Gallagher hopes to lead his team to victory with the secrets of the now disgraced player, Dante Del Gato

"This tale is peppered with both optimism and dilemmas; it has plenty of play-by-play action, lots of humor, and a triumphant ending." SLJ

Choosing up sides. Philomel Bks. 1998 166p $17.99; pa $5.99   **Fic**
1. Left- and right-handedness—Fiction 2. Father-son relationship—Fiction 3. Baseball—Fiction
ISBN 0-399-23185-4; 0-689-11840-5 (pa)
LC 97-39779

"In 1921 Ohio, a minister's son is condemned by his father because of his natural inclination for using his left hand. Luke discovers he has a talent for playing baseball, although Pa disdains sports—especially a game that utilizes Luke's 'evil' hand." Horn Book Guide

"This is an entertaining and thought-provoking coming-of-age story." Book Rep

Roberts, Willo Davis, 1928-
Hostage. Atheneum Bks. for Young Readers 2000 140p $16; pa $4.99   **Fic**
1. Kidnapping—Fiction
ISBN 0-689-81669-3; 0-689-83886-7 (pa)
LC 99-20701

"A Jean Karl book"

When eleven-year-old Kaci interrupts burglars in the process of robbing her house, she and her nosy elderly neighbor Mrs. Banducci are kidnapped and held hostage by the desperate and ruthless criminals

"Roberts blends an exciting well-crafted plot with strong characters." SLJ

The kidnappers. Atheneum Bks. for Young Readers 1998 137p $15; pa $4.99 (4 and up)
Fic
1. Kidnapping—Fiction 2. Wealth—Fiction 3. New York (N.Y.)—Fiction
ISBN 0-689-81394-5; 0-689-81393-7 (pa)
LC 96-53677

"A Jean Karl book"

No one believes eleven-year-old Joey, who has a reputation for telling tall tales, when he claims to have witnessed the kidnapping of the class bully outside their expensive New York City private school

"The combination of a witty narrative and a suspenseful plot makes this a good page-turner that will leave even the most reluctant readers glued to their seats." Booklist

Twisted summer. Atheneum Bks. for Young Readers 1996 156p pa $4.99 hardcover o.p.
Fic
1. Mystery fiction
ISBN 0-689-80600-0 (pa)   LC 95-585

"A Jean Karl book"

Fourteen-year-old Cici hopes for a romantic summer at the beach but instead finds herself trying to solve a murder which had occurred there the previous year

"The brisk pace of this suspenseful murder mystery lures readers right to the gripping ending. . . . This is a well-crafted, sophisticated story." SLJ

Robinet, Harriette Gillem
Walking to the bus-rider blues. Atheneum Bks. for Young Readers 2000 146p $16; pa $4.99 (5 and up)   **Fic**
1. African Americans—Fiction 2. Race relations—Fiction
ISBN 0-689-83191-9; 0-689-83886-7 (pa)
LC 99-29054

"A Jean Karl book"

Twelve-year-old Alfa Merryfield, his older sister, and their grandmother struggle for rent money, food, and their dignity as they participate in the Montgomery, Alabama bus boycott in the summer of 1956

"Ingredients of mystery, suspense, and humor enhance and personalize this well-constructed story that offers insight into a troubled era." SLJ

Robinson, Barbara

The best Christmas pageant ever; pictures by Judith Gwyn Brown. Harper & Row 1972 80p il $15.99; lib bdg $16.89; pa $5.99 (4-6)

Fic

1. Christmas—Fiction 2. Pageants—Fiction
ISBN 0-06-025043-7; 0-06-025044-5 (lib bdg); 0-06-447044-X (pa)
Also available Audiobook version

In this story the six Herdmans, "absolutely the worst kids in the history of the world," discover the meaning of Christmas when they bully their way into the leading roles of the local church nativity play

The story "romps through the festive preparations with comic relish, and if the Herdmans are so gauche as to seem exaggerated, they are still enjoyable, as are the not-so-subtle pokes at pageant-planning in general." Bull Cent Child Books

Other titles about the Herdmans are:
The best Halloween ever (2004)
The best school year ever (1994)

Rodgers, Mary, 1931-

Freaky Friday. Harper & Row 1972 145p $15.95; lib bdg $16.89; pa $5.99 (4 and up)

Fic

1. Mother-daughter relationship—Fiction
ISBN 0-06-025048-8; 0-06-025049-6 (lib bdg); 0-06-057010-5 (pa)
Also available Audiobook version

"'When I woke up this morning, I found I'd turned into my mother.' So begins the most bizarre day in the life of 13-year-old Annabel Andrews, who discovers one Friday morning she has taken on her mother's physical characteristics while retaining her own personality. Readers will giggle in anticipation as Annabel plunges madly from one disaster to another trying to cope with various adult situations." Publ Wkly

"A fresh, imaginative, and entertaining story." Bull Cent Child Books

Rodman, Mary Ann

Yankee girl. Farrar, Straus and Giroux 2004 219p $17 (4 and up)

Fic

1. Race relations—Fiction 2. School stories 3. Mississippi—Fiction
ISBN 0-374-38661-7   LC 2003-49048

When her FBI-agent father is transferred to Jackson, Mississippi, in 1964, eleven-year-old Alice wants to be popular but also wants to reach out to the one black girl in her class in a newly-integrated school.

"Rodman shows characters grappling with hard choices, sometimes courageously, sometimes willfully, sometimes inconsistently, but invariably believably." Publ Wkly

Rodowsky, Colby F., 1932-

Clay; {by} Colby Rodowsky. Farrar, Straus & Giroux 2001 165p $16

Fic

1. Parental kidnapping—Fiction 2. Autism—Fiction
ISBN 0-374-31338-5   LC 00-44225

After their parents divorce, eleven-year-old Elsie and her younger brother Tommy, who is mentally "different," must deal with a terrible secret that causes them and their mother to move from place to place and stay in hiding

"Without sentimentality, Rodowsky's moving story makes vivid the stress of mental illness in a family. Caught up by the suspense, readers will stay for the gripping personal story." Booklist

Rowling, J. K.

Harry Potter and the sorcerer's stone; illustrations by Mary Grandpré. Levine Bks. 1998 c1997 309p il $19.95; pa $6.99 (4 and up)

Fic

1. Fantasy fiction 2. Witches—Fiction
ISBN 0-590-35340-3; 0-590-35342-X (pa)
LC 97-39059

Also available Thorndike Press large print edition
First published 1997 in the United Kingdom with title: Harry Potter and the philosopher's stone

This "is a brilliantly imagined and beautifully written fantasy." Booklist

Other titles about Harry Potter are:
Harry Potter and the Chamber of Secrets (1999)
Harry Potter and the goblet of fire (2000)
Harry Potter and the half-blood prince (2005)
Harry Potter and the Order of the Phoenix (2003)
Harry Potter and the prisoner of Azkaban (1999)

Ruby, Laura

Lily's ghosts. HarperCollins Pubs. 2003 258p $16.99; lib bdg $17.89 (5 and up)   **Fic**

1. Ghost stories
ISBN 0-06-051829-4; 0-06-051830-8 (lib bdg)
LC 2002-154315

Strange goings-on at her great-uncle's summer home in Cape May, New Jersey, draw Lily and a new friend into a mystery involving lost treasure, a fake medium, and ghosts of all sizes, shapes, and dispositions

"Ruby doesn't horrify so much as she insinuates, in gracefully nuanced language that provides chilling support for the action." Bull Cent Child Books

Ruckman, Ivy, 1931-

Night of the twisters. Crowell 1984 153p lib bdg $15.89; pa $5.99 (4 and up)   **Fic**

1. Tornadoes—Fiction 2. Nebraska—Fiction
ISBN 0-690-04409-7 (lib bdg); 0-06-440176-6 (pa)
LC 83-46168

"Twelve-year-old Dan describes the events leading up to the hour that his town was struck seven times by tornadoes. Alone at home, {in Grand Island, Nebraska} Dan, his baby brother, and his best friend Arthur ride out the storm huddled in the shower stall in Dan's basement and then begin the search for their parents." Sci Child

"Ruckman does a good job of creating and maintaining suspense, produces dialogue that sounds appropriate for a stress situation, and gives her characters some depth and differentiation." Bull Cent Child Books

Rupp, Rebecca

The waterstone. Candlewick Press 2002 275p $16.99; pa $5.99   **Fic**

1. Fantasy fiction
ISBN 0-7636-0726-6; 0-7636-2294-X (pa)
LC 2001-52939

Twelve-year-old Tad, finding that he holds an ancient wisdom and the power to draw beings together, embarks on a quest to seek a powerful crystal which, when retrieved from the evil Nixie, will restore balance to the world

"This charming fantasy has strong characters and a fresh, innovative voice." Voice Youth Advocates

Ryan, Pam Muñoz

Becoming Naomi León; Pam Muñoz Ryan. 1st ed. Scholastic Press 2004 246p $16.95 (5 and up)   **Fic**

1. Mexican Americans—Fiction 2. Mexico—Fiction 3. Family life—Fiction
ISBN 0-439-26969-5   LC 2004-346

When Naomi's absent mother resurfaces to claim her, Naomi runs away to Mexico with her great-grandmother and younger brother in search of her father

"Ryan has written a moving book about family dynamics. . . . All of the characters are well drawn." SLJ

Esperanza rising. Scholastic Press 2000 262p $15.95; pa $4.99 (5 and up)   **Fic**

1. Mexican Americans—Fiction 2. Agricultural laborers—Fiction 3. California—Fiction
ISBN 0-439-12041-1; 0-439-12042-X (pa)
LC 00-24186

Esperanza and her mother are forced to leave their life of wealth and privilege in Mexico to go work in the labor camps of Southern California, where they must adapt to the harsh circumstances facing Mexican farm workers on the eve of the Great Depression

"Ryan writes movingly in clear, poetic language that children will sink into, and the {book} offers excellent opportunities for discussion and curriculum support." Booklist

Rylant, Cynthia

A fine white dust. Bradbury Press 1986 106p $16; pa $4.99 (5 and up)   **Fic**

1. Religion—Fiction 2. Friendship—Fiction 3. Family life—Fiction
ISBN 0-02-777240-3; 0-689-80462-8 (pa)
LC 86-1003

Also available Thorndike Press large print edition
A Newbery Medal honor book, 1987

The visit of the traveling Preacher Man to his small North Carolina town gives new impetus to thirteen-year-old Peter's struggle to reconcile his own deeply felt religious belief with the beliefs and non-beliefs of his family and friends

"Blending humor and intense emotion with a poetic use of language, Cynthia Rylant has created a taut, finely drawn portrait of a boy's growth from seeking for belief, through seduction and betrayal, to a spiritual acceptance and a readiness 'for something whole.'" Horn Book

The islander; a novel. DK Ink 1998 96p $14.95   **Fic**

1. Grandfathers—Fiction 2. Islands—Fiction 3. Mermaids and mermen—Fiction
ISBN 0-7894-2490-8   LC 97-36059

Also available in paperback from Bantam Bks.

Living with his grandfather on an island off British Columbia, ten-year-old Daniel feels deep loneliness until the night he meets a mermaid whose identity he tries to learn

"The novel reads quickly and easily, and the voice, though subdued, is compelling." Horn Book Guide

Missing May. Orchard Bks. 1992 89p $14.95; pa $5.99 (5 and up)   **Fic**

1. Death—Fiction 2. West Virginia—Fiction
ISBN 0-531-05996-0; 0-439-61383-3 (pa)
LC 91-23303

Awarded the Newbery Medal, 1993
"A Richard Jackson book"

After the death of the beloved aunt who has raised her, twelve-year-old Summer and her uncle Ob leave their West Virginia trailer in search of the strength to go on living

"There is much to ponder here, from the meaning of life and death to the power of love. That it all succeeds is a tribute to a fine writer who brings to the task a natural grace of language, an earthly sense of humor, and a well-grounded sense of the spiritual." SLJ

Sachar, Louis, 1954-

Holes. Farrar, Straus & Giroux 1998 233p $17 (5 and up)   **Fic**

1. Juvenile delinquency—Fiction 2. Friendship—Fiction 3. Buried treasure—Fiction
ISBN 0-374-33265-7   LC 97-45011

Also available Thorndike Press large print edition and in paperback from Yearling; an Audiobook version is also available

Awarded the Newbery Medal, 1999
"Frances Foster books"

As further evidence of his family's bad fortune which they attribute to a curse on a distant relative, Stanley Yelnats is sent to a hellish correctional camp in the Texas desert where he finds his first real friend, a treasure, and a new sense of himself

"This delightfully clever story is well-crafted and thought-provoking, with a bit of a folklore thrown in for good measure." Voice Youth Advocates

Sage, Angie

Magyk; Septimus Heap, book one; illustrations by Mark Zug. .: . . Katherine Tegen Books 2005 576p il $16.99; lib bdg $17.89 (5 and up)   **Fic**

1. Fantasy fiction 2. Magic—Fiction
ISBN 0-06-057731-2; 0-06-057732-0 (lib bdg)
LC 2003-28185

After learning that she is the Princess, Jenna is whisked from her home and carried toward safety by the Extraordinary Wizard, those she always believed were her father and brother, and a young guard known only as Boy 412, pursued by agents of those who killed her

Sage, Angie—*Continued*
mother ten years earlier.

"Youngsters will lose themselves happily in Sage's fluent, charismatic storytelling, which enfolds supportive allies and horrific enemies, abundant quirky details, and poignant moments of self-discovery." Booklist

Saint-Exupéry, Antoine de, 1900-1944
The little prince; written and illustrated by Antoine de Saint-Exupery; translated from the French by Richard Howard. Harcourt 2000 83p il $18; pa $12   **Fic**
ISBN 0-15-202398-4; 0-15-601219-7 (pa)
               LC 99-50439
A new translation of the title first published 1943 by Reynal & Hitchcock

"This many-dimensional fable of an airplane pilot who has crashed in the desert is for readers of all ages. The pilot comes upon the little prince soon after the crash. The prince tells of his adventures on different planets and on Earth as he attempts to learn about the universe in order to live peacefully on his own small planet. A spiritual quality enhances the seemingly simple observations of the little prince." Shapiro. Fic for Youth. 3d edition

Salisbury, Graham, 1944-
Jungle dogs. Delacorte Press 1998 183p pa $4.99 hardcover o.p.   **Fic**
1. Wild dogs—Fiction 2. Brothers—Fiction 3. Hawaii—Fiction
ISBN 0-440-41573-X (pa)   LC 98-5561
While worrying about the wild dogs that supposedly lurk in the jungle along his paper route, Hawaiian sixth grader Boy Regis also seeks to stop his older brother Damon from fighting all his battles for him

"The novel boasts a compelling narrative voice, a sympathetic protagonist, and throws in enough drama to bring the story to a satisfying end." ALAN

Lord of the deep. Delacorte Press 2001 182p $15.95; lib bdg $17.99; pa $7.99 (5 and up)
                        Fic
1. Fishing—Fiction 2. Stepfathers—Fiction 3. Hawaii—Fiction
ISBN 0-385-72918-9; 0-385-90013-9 (lib bdg); 0-440-22911-1 (pa)   LC 00-60280
Working for Bill, his stepfather, on a charter fishing boat in Hawaii teaches thirteen-year-old Mikey about fishing, and about taking risks, making sacrifices, and facing some of life's difficult choices

"With its vivid Hawaiian setting, this fine novel is a natural for book-discussion groups that enjoy pondering moral ambiguity. Its action-packed scenes will also lure in reluctant readers." SLJ

Under the blood-red sun. Delacorte Press 1994 246p pa $5.99 hardcover o.p.   **Fic**
1. Pearl Harbor (Oahu, Hawaii), Attack on, 1941—Fiction 2. World War, 1939-1945—Fiction 3. Japanese Americans—Fiction 4. Hawaii—Fiction
ISBN 0-440-41139-4 (pa)   LC 94-444

Tomikazu Nakaji's biggest concerns are baseball, homework, and a local bully, until life with his Japanese family in Hawaii changes drastically after the bombing of Pearl Harbor in December 1941

"Character development of major figures is good, the setting is warmly realized, and the pace of the story moves gently though inexorably forward." SLJ

Sanchez, Alex
So hard to say; Alex Sanchez. 1st ed. Simon & Schuster Books for Young Readers 2004 230p $14.95   **Fic**
1. Homosexuality—Fiction 2. Mexican Americans—Fiction 3. California—Fiction
ISBN 0-689-86564-3   LC 2003-21128
Thirteen-year-old Xio, a Mexican American girl, and Frederick, who has just moved to California from Wisconsin, quickly become close friends, but when Xio starts thinking of Frederick as her boyfriend, he must confront his feelings of confusion and face the fear that he might be gay.

"Adventurous, multifaceted, funny, and unpredictably insightful, Sanchez's novel . . . gels well-rounded characterizations with the universal excitement of first love." SLJ

Schmidt, Gary D.
Lizzie Bright and the Buckminster boy. Clarion Books 2004 219p $15 (7 and up)   **Fic**
1. Race relations—Fiction 2. Maine—Fiction
ISBN 0-618-43929-3   LC 2003-20967
A Newbery Medal honor book, 2005
In 1911, Turner Buckminster hates his new home of Phippsburg, Maine, but things improve when he meets Lizzie Bright Griffin, a girl from a poor, nearby island community founded by former slaves that the town fathers—and Turner's—want to change into a tourist spot

"Although the story is hauntingly sad, there is much humor, too. Schmidt's writing is infused with feeling and rich in imagery. With fully developed, memorable characters and a fascinating, little-known piece of history, this novel will leave a powerful impression on readers." SLJ

Schwartz, Virginia Frances
Send one angel down. Holiday House 2000 163p $15.95   **Fic**
1. Slavery—Fiction 2. African Americans—Fiction 3. Racially mixed people—Fiction 4. Cousins—Fiction
ISBN 0-8234-1484-1   LC 99-52818
Also available Thorndike Press large print edition
Abram, a young slave tries to hide the horrors of slavery from his younger cousin Eliza, a light-skinned slave who is the daughter of the plantation owner

"Schwartz's well-developed characters are full of humanity and personality, and the story vividly acknowledges the sustaining power of music . . . in the lives of the slaves. This is a profoundly moving tale that is ultimately hopeful but never glosses over the horrific treatment of slaves." Booklist

Scieszka, Jon, 1954-
Seen Art? Viking 2005 unp il $16.99
                        Fic

Scieszka, Jon, 1954-—*Continued*

1. Museum of Modern Art (New York, N.Y.)—Fiction
2. Art appreciation—Fiction
ISBN 0-670-05986-2

While looking for his friend Art, a boy wanders through the Museum of Modern Art and is amazed by what he discovers there.

"The unusually long and narrow shape of the book and the stylized characters echo the modern-art theme while the muted background tones are an effective foil for the well-reproduced if sometimes diminutive artwork. . . . For anyone planning a trip to MoMA with a youngster, this is a provocative read." SLJ

Scott, Kieran, 1974-

The princess & the pauper; [by] Kate Brian. Simon & Schuster Bks. for Young Readers 2003 266p $14.95 (7 and up)   Fic

1. Princesses—Fiction 2. Los Angeles (Calif.)—Fiction
ISBN 0-689-86173-7   LC 2003-7380

When sixteen-year-old Julia, of Los Angeles, and sixteen-year-old Princess Carina, of Vineland, switch places, Julia dances at the ball with the incredible Markus and Carina escapes rigid protocol to spend time with a rock star

"Although the plot is pure fairy tale, the humor is incisive, the characters of the two girls are well drawn, and the touch of sweet, G-rated romance will thrill the intended audience." Booklist

Sedgwick, Marcus

The book of Dead Days; Marcus Sedgwick. Wendy Lamb Books 2004 273p $15.95; lib bdg $17.99   Fic

1. Magicians—Fiction 2. Orphans—Fiction 3. Horror fiction
ISBN 0-385-73055-1; 0-385-90158-5 (lib bdg)
LC 2004-6444

With the help of his servant and an orphan girl, a magician named Valerian searches graveyards, churches, and underground waterways for a book he hopes will save him from a pact he has made with evil.

"Unexpected twists keep the action moving, and the suspense never flags. . . . Readers who enjoy fast-paced melodrama with an overlay of the supernatural will devour this tale and wait eagerly for the next installment." SLJ

The Dark Horse. Wendy Lamb Bks. 2003 217p il $15.95; lib bdg $17.99 (7 and up)   Fic

1. Adventure fiction
ISBN 0-385-73054-3; 0-385-90091-0 (lib bdg)
LC 2002-5655

Having risen to power as chief of his people, the Storn, sixteen-year-old Sigurd leads them as they try to resist the bloodthirsty invaders known as the Dark Horse and makes a shocking discovery about his foster sister Mouse

"Employing a lean narrative voice and writing in short chapters that encourage page turning, Sedgwick draws readers along. . . . Sedgwick's tale is rich, involving, and vivifying." SLJ

Seidler, Tor, 1952-

Brainboy and the Deathmaster. Laura Geringer Bks. 2003 311p $16.99; lib bdg $17.89 (5 and up)
Fic

1. Orphans—Fiction 2. Video games—Fiction
3. Science fiction
ISBN 0-06-029181-8; 0-06-029182-6 (lib bdg)
LC 2002-33918

When Darryl, a twelve-year-old orphan, is adopted by a technology genius, he finds himself the star of his very own life-threatening video game

"A fast-paced, science-fiction adventure. . . . Seidler has created empathetic characters and writes at a level that is accessible even to readers not usually drawn to this genre." SLJ

Shearer, Alex

The Great Blue Yonder. Clarion Bks. 2002 c2001 184p $15 (5 and up)   Fic

1. Future life—Fiction
ISBN 0-618-21257-4   LC 2001-47741
First published 2001 in the United Kingdom

This "novel tells the story of Harry, killed in a bicycle accident. Initially confused by his new existence in the Other Side, the flippant 12-year-old realizes he cannot move toward the peace of the Great Blue Yonder until he has addressed the unfinished business in his life. . . . Amusing, poignant, and deeply moving. A great main character and unusual topical matter combine to make a unique winner of a book that will leave readers laughing through their tears." SLJ

Sheldon, Dyan

Confessions of a teenage drama queen. Candlewick Press 1999 272p $16.99; pa $7.99 (7 and up)   Fic

1. School stories
ISBN 0-7636-0822-X; 0-7636-2827-1 (pa)
LC 98-53914

In her first year at a suburban New Jersey high school, Mary Elizabeth Cep, who now calls herself "Lola," sets her sights on the lead in the annual drama production, and finds herself in conflict with the most popular girl in school

"An exuberant and hilarious celebration of the ups and downs of high school life. . . . The story is off-beat, outrageous, and utterly charming." SLJ

My perfect life. Candlewick Press 2002 201p $16.99; pa $5.99 (7 and up)   Fic

1. School stories 2. Elections—Fiction
ISBN 0-7636-1839-X; 0-7636-2436-5 (pa)
LC 2001-58118

Ella has no interest in running for class president at her suburban high school, but her off-beat friend Lola tricks her into challenging the rich and overbearing Carla Santini in a less-than-friendly race

"The story is entertaining and well written. The characters reflect the personalities and cliques of kids in any high school." SLJ

Sherlock, Patti

Letters from Wolfie. Viking 2004 232p $16.99
(5 and up)   **Fic**

1. Dogs—Fiction 2. Vietnam War, 1961-1975—Fiction

ISBN 0-670-03694-3   LC 2003-24316

Certain that he is doing the right thing by donating his dog, Wolfie, to the Army's scout program in Vietnam, thirteen-year-old Mark begins to have second thoughts when the Army refuses to say when and if Wolfie will ever return.

"In this topnotch novel, Sherlock weaves together numerous threads of emotion, information, and plot so seamlessly that readers will be surprised by how much they've learned by the time they finish this deceptively simple story." SLJ

Shinn, Sharon, 1957-

The Safe-Keeper's secret. Viking 2004 222p
$16.99   **Fic**

1. Fantasy fiction

ISBN 0-670-05910-2   LC 2003-23538

Fiona is Safe-Keeper in the small village of Tambleham, where neighbors and strangers alike come one by one, in secret, to tell her things they dare not share with anyone else.

"Teens will connect with Shinn's vividly drawn fantasy world as well as her provocative questions about truth, justice, and individual destiny." Booklist

A companion volume to:

The truth-teller's tale (2005)

Shreve, Susan Richards

Under the Watson's porch; [by] Susan Shreve.
1st ed. Alfred A. Knopf 2004 199p $15.95; lib
bdg $17.99 (5 and up)   **Fic**

1. Friendship—Fiction

ISBN 0-375-82630-0; 0-375-92630-5 (lib bdg)
      LC 2003-61383

"Ellie's first-person narration is utterly and immediately believable. . . . Shreve imagines a troubled kid with unusual sensitivity and depth, and this novel will be treasured by readers." Booklist

Shusterman, Neal

Downsiders. Simon & Schuster Bks. for Young
Readers 1999 246p $17.95; pa $4.99   **Fic**

1. Subways—Fiction 2. New York (N.Y.)—Fiction

ISBN 0-689-80375-3; 0-689-83969-3 (pa)
      LC 98-38555

When fourteen-year-old Lindsay meets Talon and discovers the Downsiders world which had evolved from the subway built in New York in 1867 by Alfred Ely Beach, she and her new friend experience the clash of their two cultures

"Shusterman has invented an alternate world in the Downside that is both original and humorous." Voice Youth Advocates

Full tilt; a novel. Simon & Schuster Bks. for
Young Readers 2003 201p $16.95 (7 and up)
       Fic

1. Amusement parks—Fiction 2. Brothers—Fiction
3. Horror fiction

ISBN 0-689-80374-5   LC 2002-13867

"An older, alluring, and slightly mysterious girl invites Blake to an amusement park that's only open from midnight to dawn. The rules: he must finish seven rides, all before sunrise, or the park absorbs him. Blake comes to realize that each ride takes him to his deepest fears." Horn Book Guide

"Shusterman has created a surreal, scary fantasy, packed with suspenseful psychological drama." Booklist

The Schwa was here; Neal Shusterman. 1st ed.
Dutton Children's Books 2004 228p $15.99
       Fic

1. Friendship—Fiction 2. Brooklyn (New York,
N.Y.)—Fiction

ISBN 0-525-47182-0   LC 2004-45072

A Brooklyn eighth-grader nicknamed Antsy befriends the Schwa, an "invisible-ish" boy who is tired of blending into his surroundings and going unnoticed by nearly everyone.

"Antsy is one funny narrator. . . . Shusterman has created yet another very readable and refreshingly different story." Voice Youth Advocates

Siegelson, Kim L., 1962-

Trembling earth. Philomel Books 2004 152p
$17.99   **Fic**

1. Slavery—Fiction 2. United States—History—1861-
1865, Civil War—Fiction 3. Georgia—Fiction
4. Race relations—Fiction

ISBN 0-399-24021-7   LC 2003-23591

"Siegelson weaves a tight story about life in the swamp, and how perceptions can change with experience. Her vivid use of language draws a tangible and satisfying picture of the wild tangle of the Okefenokee Swamp and all of its dangers and beauty." SLJ

Sitomer, Alan Lawrence

The Hoopster. Jump at the Sun/Hyperion Books
for Children 2005 218p $16.99 (7 and up)
       Fic

1. Basketball—Fiction 2. Race relations—Fiction
3. African Americans—Fiction 4. Authorship—Fiction

ISBN 0-7868-5483-9

First published 2002 by Milk Mug Pub.

Andre Anderson, called "The Hoopster" for his basketball skills, is brutally attacked by racists in response to an article he writes for a national magazine.

"The dialogue-filled sparring is fresh and accurately portrays the dynamics among urban teens and their families." SLJ

Skurzynski, Gloria, 1930-

Cliff hanger; by Gloria Skurzynski and Alane Ferguson. National Geographic Soc. 1999 147p il (Mysteries in our National Parks) $15.95; pa $5.95   **Fic**

1. Foster home care—Fiction 2. Mystery fiction
ISBN 0-7922-7036-3; 0-7922-7654-X (pa)
LC 98-8716

Twelve-year-old Jack and his younger sister visit Mesa Verde National Park, where they delve into the park's history while gradually uncovering the mysterious past of their family's teenage foster child Lucky

"The authors do a fine job of integrating lots of material into an exciting story." Booklist

Other titles in the Mysteries in our National Parks series are:
Buried alive (2003)
Deadly waters (1999)
Escape from fear (2002)
Ghost horses (2000)
Hunted (2000)
Out of the deep (2002)
Over the edge (2002)
Rage of fire (1998)
Running scared (2002)
Valley of death (2002)
Wolf stalker (1997)

Rockbuster. Atheneum Bks. for Young Readers 2001 253p $16   **Fic**

1. Hill, Joe, 1879-1915—Fiction 2. Industrial Workers of the World—Fiction 3. Coal mines and mining—Fiction
ISBN 0-689-83991-X   LC 00-50415

In 1915, after being asked to sing at the funeral of executed songwriter and member of the international union, Industrial Workers of the World, Joe Hill, eighteen-year-old Utah coal miner Tommy Quinlan begins to accept his past and make decisions about his future

"Skurzynski's historically based novel is a page-turner from beginning to end. . . . Skurzynski's characters are vibrant, their story is memorable, and a little-known episode in American history gets some needed attention." Booklist

Slade, Arthur G., 1967-

Dust. Wendy Lamb Books 2003 183p $15.95; lib bdg $17.99   **Fic**

1. Supernatural—Fiction
ISBN 0-385-73004-7; 0-385-90093-7 (lib bdg)
LC 2002-7666

Eleven-year-old Robert is the only one who can help when a mysterious stranger arrives, performing tricks and promising to bring rain, at the same time children begin to disappear from a dust bowl farm town in Saskatchewan in the 1930s

"Suspense builds to a searing and satisfying climax. . . . This unusual, well-written story will definitely exercise readers' imaginations." SLJ

Sleator, William

The boy who reversed himself. Dutton 1986 167p hardcover o.p. paperback available $5.99 (5 and up)   **Fic**

1. Science fiction 2. Space and time—Fiction
ISBN 0-14-038965-2 (pa)   LC 86-19700
Available in hardcover from P. Smith

When Laura discovers that the unpopular boy living next door to her has the ability to go into the fourth dimension, she makes the dangerous decision to accompany him on his journeys there

"What follows is a terrifying trip into the fourth dimension, populated by some of Sleator's most unusual characters to date. An utterly fantastic and ultimately satisfying novel by a master storyteller." SLJ

The duplicate. Dutton 1988 154p hardcover o.p. paperback available $5.99 (7 and up)   **Fic**

1. Science fiction
ISBN 0-14-130431-6 (pa)   LC 87-30562

Sixteen-year-old David, finding a strange machine that creates replicas of living organisms, duplicates himself and suffers the horrible consequences when the duplicate turns against him

"There are some points in the story when the roles of the clones (referred to as Duplicates A and B) become congested to the detriment of the book's pace, but fantasy fans will doubtless find the concept fresh enough and eerie enough to compensate for this, and Sleator is, as always, economical in casting and structuring his story." Bull Cent Child Books

House of stairs. Dutton 1974 166p hardcover o.p. paperback available $5.99 (7 and up)   **Fic**

1. Science fiction
ISBN 0-14-034580-9 (pa)
Available in hardcover from P. Smith

"Five 15-year-old orphans with widely ranging personality characteristics are involuntarily placed in a house of endless stairs and subjected to psychological experiments on conditioned human responses." Booklist

"The setting is bleak, dramatic and convincing; the interaction and development of the five young people as characters trapped in an abrasive situation are compelling. A very effective and provocative suspense story that can be read for plot alone or doubly enjoyed for the mystery and the message." Bull Cent Child Books

Interstellar pig. Dutton 1984 197p hardcover o.p. paperback available $6.99 (5 and up)   **Fic**

1. Science fiction
ISBN 0-14-037595-3 (pa)   LC 84-4132

"Solitary and bored, Barney is quickly attracted by the exotic appearance and protean personalities of Zena, Manny, and Joe, who have rented the summer house next door. The interest of the sophisticated adults in sixteen-year-old Barney at first flatters, then intrigues, and finally terrifies him as he becomes absorbed in their compulsion to possess 'The Piggy.' When he realizes that the talisman has power, the game expands in significance." Horn Book

The author "draws the reader in with intimations of danger and horror, but the climactic battle is more slapstick than horrific, and the victor's prize could scarcely

Sleator, William—*Continued*
be more ironic. Problematic as straight science fiction
but great fun as a spoof on human-alien contact." Booklist

Another title about Barney is:
Parasite Pig (2002)

Singularity. Dutton 1985 170p pa $5.99
hardcover o.p. (7 and up)   **Fic**
1. Twins—Fiction 2. Science fiction
ISBN 0-14-037598-8 (pa)   LC 84-26075
Available in hardcover from P. Smith
Sixteen-year-old twins Harry and Barry stumble across
a gateway to another universe, where a distortion in time
and space causes a dramatic change in their competitive
relationship
"The book has a title with a fine double entendre and
is an unusual, suspenseful yarn told by a master storyteller." Horn Book

Smith, Cynthia Leitich
Rain is not my Indian name. HarperCollins
Pubs. 2001 135p $15.99; lib bdg $16.89
    Fic
1. Death—Fiction 2. Photography—Fiction 3. Native
Americans—Fiction
ISBN 0-688-17397-7; 0-06-029504-X (lib bdg)
    LC 00-59705
Tired of staying in seclusion since the death of her
best friend, a fourteen-year-old Native American girl
takes on a photographic assignment with her local newspaper to cover events at the Native American summer
youth camp
"The engaging first-person narrative convincingly portrays Rain's grieving process and addresses the varying
degrees of prejudice she encounters." Horn Book Guide

Smith, Greg Leitich
Ninjas, piranhas, and Galileo; by Greg Leitich
Smith. 1st ed. Little, Brown 2003 179p $15.95
    Fic
1. School stories 2. Japanese Americans—Fiction
ISBN 0-316-77854-0   LC 2003-47629
Honoria, Shohei, and Elias, who are "united together
against That Which Is The Peshtigo School," face conflict over their budding romantic interest and a science
project gone awry.
"A fresh, unusual story of friendship and honesty, rid-
dled with wit, intelligence, and more than a few chuck-
les." SLJ

Smith, Patricia Clark, 1943-
Weetamoo, heart of the Pocassets. Scholastic
2003 203p il (Royal diaries) $10.95   **Fic**
1. Native Americans—Fiction 2. Massachusetts—Fiction
ISBN 0-439-12910-9   LC 00-49243
The 1653-1654 diary of a fourteen-year-old Pocasset
Indian girl, destined to become a leader of her tribe, describes how her life changes with the seasons, after a ritual fast she undertakes, and with her tribe's interaction
with the English "Coat-men" of the nearby Plymouth

Colony
This is "a lively yet ultimately tragic tale that vividly
evokes the time period." Booklist

Smith, Roland, 1951-
The captain's dog; my journey with the Lewis
and Clark tribe. Harcourt Brace & Co. 1999 287p
$17; pa $6   **Fic**
1. Lewis and Clark Expedition (1804-1806)—Fiction
2. Dogs—Fiction 3. West (U.S.)—Fiction
ISBN 0-15-201989-8; 0-15-202696-7 (pa)
    LC 99-25608
"Gulliver books"
Captain Meriwether Lewis's dog Seaman describes his
experiences as he accompanies his master on the Lewis
and Clark Expedition to explore the uncharted western
wilderness
This is a "marvelous piece of historical fiction."
Booklist

The Sasquatch. Hyperion Bks. for Children 1998
188p $15.95; pa $5.99   **Fic**
1. Sasquatch—Fiction 2. Mount Saint Helens
(Wash.)—Fiction
ISBN 0-7868-0368-1; 0-7868-1334-2 (pa)
    LC 97-39650
Thirteen-year-old Dylan follows his father into the
woods on the slopes of Mount St. Helens, which is on
the brink of another eruption, in an attempt to protect the
resident Sasquatch from ruthless hunters
"The prose is well written, the characters well defined,
and the story gripping." Voice Youth Advocates

Smith, Sherwood
Crown duel; book I of the Crown & court duet.
Jane Yolen Bks. 1997 211p $17 (7 and up)
    Fic
1. Fantasy fiction
ISBN 0-15-201608-2   LC 96-44193
Also available in paperback from Penguin Putnam
Books for Young Readers
To fulfill their father's dying wish, teenage Countess
Meliara and her brother Branaric organize a revolution
against a greedy king
"Smith tells a fast-moving tale of adventure, intrigue,
and honor. . . . Characters and setting are well realized."
Booklist

Snyder, Midori, 1954-
Hannah's garden. Viking 2002 247p $16.99 (7
and up)   **Fic**
1. Violinists—Fiction 2. Fantasy fiction
ISBN 0-670-03577-7   LC 2002-3724
When Cassie's grandfather falls ill, she and her mother return to his farm, where Cassie discovers a wonderful, terrible secret about her family
"Snyder's deft weaving of realism and fantasy makes
conflicting truths seem perfectly logical. The story works
well as a suspenseful adventure." Booklist

Snyder, Zilpha Keatley

The Unseen. Delacorte Press 2004 199p $15.95; lib bdg $17.99 (5 and up)   **Fic**
1. Supernatural—Fiction
ISBN 0-385-73084-5; 0-385-90106-2 (lib bdg)
LC 2003-46299
Feeling angry and out-of-place in her large family, twelve-year-old Xandra finds a magical key to a world of ghostly, sometimes frightening, phantoms that help her see herself and her siblings more clearly.
"This book is a wonderful ride into fantasy, with a lot of realistic touches to think about and relationships to ponder. . . . This perceptive story is not to be missed." SLJ

Son, John

Finding my hat. Orchard Bks. 2003 185p (First person fiction) $16.95   **Fic**
1. Korean Americans—Fiction 2. Family life—Fiction
ISBN 0-439-43538-2   LC 2002-44998
Jin-Han describes his life growing up with his mother and father, immigrants from Korea, and his little sister as they move to different cities with his parents' business
This is "a beautifully written and deeply personal account of growing up." SLJ

Sonenklar, Carol

My own worst enemy. Holiday House 1999 151p $15.95   **Fic**
1. School stories 2. Family life—Fiction
ISBN 0-8234-1456-6   LC 98-41952
As she begins classes at a new middle school, Eve decides to try to fit in so that her father, who has just lost his job, will have less to worry about, but she finds that being true to herself is really the best thing to do
"While Sonenklar's . . . moral about being true to yourself is well-worn, her satirical execution of it is fresh, frank and entertaining." Publ Wkly

Sones, Sonya

Stop pretending; what happened when my big sister went crazy. HarperCollins Pubs. 1999 149p lib bdg $14.89; pa $6.99   **Fic**
1. Mental illness—Fiction 2. Sisters—Fiction
ISBN 0-06-028386-6 (lib bdg); 0-06-446218-8 (pa)
LC 99-11473
"Based on the journals Sones wrote at the age of 13 when her 19-year-old sister was hospitalized due to manic depression, the simply crafted but deeply felt poems reflect her thoughts, fears, hopes, and dreams during that troubling time." SLJ

What my mother doesn't know. Simon & Schuster Bks. for Young Readers 2001 259p $17; pa $6.99 (7 and up)   **Fic**
1. Dating (Social customs)—Fiction
ISBN 0-689-84114-0; 0-689-85553-2 (pa)
LC 00-52634
"Fourteen-year-old Sophia is searching for Mr. Right. In a story written in poetry form, Sophia describes her relationships with sexy Dylan, suspicious cyberboy, and, finally, with the mysterious masked 'stranger' who dances with her on Halloween and then disappears." Book Rep
This is "a fast, funny, touching book. . . . The very short, sometimes rhythmic lines make each page fly. Sophie's voice is colloquial and intimate." Booklist

Soto, Gary

The afterlife. Harcourt 2003 161p $16 (7 and up)   **Fic**
1. Mexican Americans—Fiction 2. Ghost stories
ISBN 0-15-204774-3   LC 2003-44995
A senior at East Fresno High School lives on as a ghost after his brutal murder in the restroom of a club where he had gone to dance
"In many ways, this is as much a story about a hardscrabble place as it is about a boy who is murdered. Both pulse with life and will stay in memory." Booklist

Buried onions. Harcourt Brace & Co. 1997 149p $17   **Fic**
1. Violence—Fiction 2. Mexican Americans—Fiction
ISBN 0-15-201333-4   LC 96-53112
Also available in paperback from HarperCollins
When nineteen-year-old Eddie drops out of college, he struggles to find a place for himself as a Mexican American living in a violence-infested neighborhood of Fresno, California
"Soto has created a beautiful, touching, and truthful story. . . . The lyrical language and Spanish phrases add to the immediacy of setting and to the sensitivity the author brings to his character's life." Voice Youth Advocates

Taking sides. Harcourt Brace Jovanovich 1991 138p $17; pa $5.95 (5 and up)   **Fic**
1. Hispanic Americans—Fiction 2. Basketball—Fiction
ISBN 0-15-284076-1; 0-15-204694-1 (pa)
LC 91-11082
Fourteen-year-old Lincoln Mendoza, an aspiring basketball player, must come to terms with his divided loyalties when he moves from the Hispanic inner city to a white suburban neighborhood
This is a "light but appealing story. . . . Because of its subject matter and its clear, straightforward prose, it will be especially good for reluctant readers." SLJ
Includes glossary

Speare, Elizabeth George, 1908-1994

The sign of the beaver. Houghton Mifflin 1983 135p $16 (5 and up)   **Fic**
1. Frontier and pioneer life—Fiction 2. Native Americans—Fiction 3. Friendship—Fiction
ISBN 0-395-33890-5   LC 83-118
Also available in paperback from Dell
A Newbery Medal honor book, 1984
Left alone to guard the family's wilderness home in eighteenth-century Maine, Matt is hard-pressed to survive until local Indians teach him their skills
Matt "begins to understand the Indians' ingenuity and respect for nature and the devastating impact of the encroachment of the white man. In a quiet but not unsuspenseful story . . . the author articulates historical facts along with the adventures and the thoughts, emotions, and developing insights of a young adolescent." Horn Book

Speare, Elizabeth George, 1908-1994—*Continued*

The witch of Blackbird Pond. Houghton Mifflin 1958 249p $16 (6 and up) **Fic**
1. Connecticut—History—1600-1775, Colonial period—Fiction 2. Witchcraft—Fiction 3. Puritans—Fiction
ISBN 0-395-07114-3 LC 58-11063
Also available in paperback from Dell
Awarded the Newbery Medal, 1959
"Headstrong and undisciplined, Barbados-bred Kit Tyler is an embarrassment to her Puritan relatives, and her sincere attempts to aid a reputed witch soon bring her to trial as a suspect." Child Books Too Good to Miss
"Three satisfactorily concluded romances run through this absorbing story [set in Connecticut]. The New England of colonial times—of candle-dipping, soap-boiling, and corn-husking bees—is realisticaly drawn as background for a solidly written character study." Horn Book

Spinelli, Jerry, 1941-
Crash. Knopf 1996 162p $16; pa $4.99 (5 and up) **Fic**
1. Football—Fiction 2. Grandfathers—Fiction 3. Friendship—Fiction
ISBN 0-679-87957-9; 0-679-88550-1 (pa)
LC 95-30942
"Crash is a star football player. He torments Penn, a classmate who is everything Crash is not—friendly, small, and a pacifist. When his beloved grandfather comes to live with his family and suffers a debilitating stroke, Crash begins to see value in many of the things he has scorned." Horn Book Guide
"Readers will devour this humorous glimpse at what jocks are made of while learning that life does not require crashing helmet-headed through it." SLJ

Maniac Magee; a novel. Little, Brown 1990 184p $16.99 (5 and up) **Fic**
1. Orphans—Fiction 2. Homeless persons—Fiction 3. Race relations—Fiction
ISBN 0-316-80722-2 LC 89-27144
Also available Thorndike Press large print edition and in paperback from HarperCollins Pubs.
Awarded the Newbery Medal, 1991
"Orphaned at three, Jeffery Lionel Magee, after eight unhappy years with relatives, one day takes off running. A year later, he ends up 200 miles away in Two Mills, a highly segregated community. Part tall tale and part contemporary realistic fiction, this unusual novel magically weaves timely issues of homelessness, racial prejudice, and illiteracy into an energetic story that bursts with creativity, enthusiasm, and hope for the future. In short, it's a celebration of life." Booklist

Stargirl. Knopf 2000 186p $15.95; lib bdg $17.99; pa $8.95 **Fic**
1. School stories 2. Arizona—Fiction
ISBN 0-679-88637-0; 0-679-98637-5 (lib bdg); 0-375-82233-X (pa) LC 99-87944
Also available Thorndike Press large print edition
In this story about the perils of popularity, the courage of nonconformity, and the thrill of first love, an eccentric student named Stargirl changes Mica High School forever

"As always respectful of his audience, Spinelli poses searching questions about loyalty to one's friends and oneself and leaves readers to form their own answers." Publ Wkly

There's a girl in my hammerlock. Simon & Schuster Bks. for Young Readers 1991 199p hardcover o.p. paperback available $4.99 (5 and up) **Fic**
1. Wrestling—Fiction 2. Sex role—Fiction 3. School stories
ISBN 0-671-86695-8 (pa) LC 91-8765
Thirteen-year-old Maisie joins her school's formerly all-male wrestling team and tries to last through the season, despite opposition from other students, her best friend, and her own teammates
The author "tackles a meaty subject—traditional gender roles—with his usual humor and finesse. The result, written in a breezy, first-person style, is a rattling good sports story that is clever, witty and tightly written." Publ Wkly

Wringer. HarperCollins Pubs. 1997 228p $16.99; lib bdg $16.89; pa $6.50 (4 and up) **Fic**
1. Courage—Fiction 2. Violence—Fiction 3. Pigeons—Fiction
ISBN 0-06-024913-7; 0-06-024914-5 (lib bdg); 0-06-440578-8 (pa) LC 96-37897
A Newbery Medal honor book, 1998
"Joanna Cotler books"
"During the annual pigeon shoot, it is a town tradition for 10-year-old boys to break the necks of wounded birds. In this riveting story told with verve and suspense, Palmer rebels." SLJ

Spinner, Stephanie
Quicksilver; Stephanie Spinner. Knopf 2005 229p $15.95; lib bdg $17.99 (7 and up)
Fic
1. Classical mythology—Fiction
ISBN 0-375-82638-6; 0-375-92638-0 (lib bdg)
LC 2004-10311
Hermes, Prince of Thieves and son of Zeus, relates why the seasons change, the history of the Trojan War, his friendship with Pegasus, and many more adventures.

"Spinner seamlessly weaves necessary background information about the cast of celestial characters into a narrative filled with thrilling action and violence that is drawn straight from the original stories. Teens will connect with Hermes' immediate, often very funny voice." Booklist

Quiver. Knopf 2002 177p $15.95; lib bdg $17.99; pa $5.99 (7 and up) **Fic**
1. Atalanta (Greek mythology)—Fiction
ISBN 0-375-81489-2; 0-375-91489-7 (lib bdg); 0-440-23819-6 (pa) LC 2002-5451
When her father commands that she produce an heir, the huntress Atalanta gives her suitors a seemingly impossible task in order to uphold her pledge of chastity, as the gods of ancient Greece look on
"Spinner gives this Greek myth a fresh face and makes Atalanta a strong heroine." SLJ

Springer, Nancy

I am Mordred; a tale from Camelot. Philomel Bks. 1998 184p $16.99; pa $6.99 (7 and up) **Fic**

1. Arthur, King—Fiction 2. Mordred (Legendary character) 3. Great Britain—History—0-1066—Fiction
ISBN 0-399-23143-9; 0-698-11841-3 (pa)
LC 97-39740

"Mordred, the bad seed, the son of King Arthur and his sister, spends his youth learning who he is and then trying to deal with the prophecy made by Merlin that he will kill his father." SLJ

"Springer humanizes Arthurian archvillain Mordred in a thoroughly captivating and poignant tale." Booklist

I am Morgan le Fay; a tale from Camelot. Philomel Bks. 2001 227p $17.99; pa $5.99 (7 and up) **Fic**

1. Arthur, King—Fiction 2. Morgan le Fay (Legendary character)—Fiction 3. Great Britain—History—0-1066—Fiction
ISBN 0-399-23451-9; 0-698-11974-6 (pa)
LC 99-52847

In a war-torn England where her half-brother Arthur will eventually become king, the young Morgan le Fay comes to realize that she has magic powers and links to the faerie world

"Introspective, yet threaded with intrigue and adventure, this compelling study of the legendary villainess explores the ways that love, hate, jealousy, and the desire for power shape one young woman's fate and affect the destiny of others." Horn Book

Rowan Hood, outlaw girl of Sherwood Forest. Philomel Bks. 2001 170p $16.99 (4 and up) **Fic**

1. Robin Hood (Legendary character)—Fiction 2. Middle Ages—Fiction 3. Adventure fiction
ISBN 0-399-23368-7
LC 00-63694

In her quest to connect with Robin Hood, the father she has never met, thirteen-year-old Rosemary disguises herself as a boy, befriends a half-wolf, half-dog, a runaway princess, and an overgrown boy whose singing is hypnotic, and makes peace with her elfin heritage

"This tale is a charmer, filled with exciting action, plenty of humor, engaging characters, and a nice fantasy twist." Booklist

Other available titles about Rowan Hood are:
Lionclaw (2002)
Outlaw princess of Sherwood (2003)
Wild boy (2004)

Stahler, David, Jr.

A gathering of shades; . . HarperTempest 2005 289p $15.99; lib bdg $16.89 (7 and up) **Fic**

1. Ghost stories 2. Farm life—Fiction 3. Vermont—Fiction
ISBN 0-06-052294-1; 0-06-052295-X (lib bdg)
LC 2004-21498

Having moved with his mother to a remote corner of Vermont after his father's death, sixteen-year-old Aidan learns much about his family, including that ghosts inhabit an ancient orchard on the family farm, sustained by his grandmother.

"Stahler's eloquence on grief and yearning, combined with a vision of ghosts refreshingly distinct from depictions in 'cheesy horror movies,' will exert a powerful hold on many teens' imaginations." Booklist

Stanley, Diane, 1943-

The mysterious matter of I.M. Fine. HarperCollins Pubs. 2001 201p $15.99; lib bdg $16.89; pa $5.99 **Fic**

1. Magic—Fiction 2. Books and reading—Fiction 3. Mystery fiction
ISBN 0-688-17546-5; 0-06-029619-4 (lib bdg); 0-380-73327-7 (pa)
LC 00-54040

Noticing that a popular series of horror novels is having a bizarre effect on the behavior of its readers, Franny and Beamer set out to find the mysterious author

"The solidly constructed mystery, well-rounded characters, and playful jab at wildly successful horror writers go down a treat." Horn Book Guide

Staples, Suzanne Fisher

Dangerous skies. Farrar, Straus & Giroux 1996 231p $17 (7 and up) **Fic**

1. African Americans—Fiction 2. Prejudices—Fiction 3. Friendship—Fiction
ISBN 0-374-31694-5
LC 95-45529

"Frances Foster books"

"At twelve, white boy Buck and black girl Tunes Smith are best friends. . . . The adolescents' idyllic world of fishing and observing nature is shattered when their much older friend Jorge Rodrigues is murdered, and Tunes is accused of the crime. . . . Staples's beautifully written and chilling tale of contemporary racism should keep young adult readers turning pages until they reach the heart-breaking end." Voice Youth Advocates

Shabanu; daughter of the wind. Knopf 1989 240p hardcover o.p. paperback available $6.50 **Fic**

1. Sex role—Fiction 2. Pakistan—Fiction
ISBN 0-440-23856-0 (pa)
LC 89-2714

When eleven-year-old Shabanu, the daughter of a nomad in the Cholistan Desert of present-day Pakistan, is pledged in marriage to an older man whose money will bring prestige to the family, she must either accept the decision, as is the custom, or risk the consequences of defying her father's wishes

"Interspersing native words throughout adds realism, but may trip up readers, who must be patient enough to find meaning through context. This use of language is, however, an important element in helping Staples paint an evocative picture of life in the desert that includes references to the hard facts of reality." Booklist

Followed by Haveli

Shiva's fire. Farrar, Straus & Giroux 1999 275p $17 (7 and up) **Fic**

1. Dance—Fiction 2. India—Fiction
ISBN 0-374-36824-4
LC 99-10626

Also available Thorndike Press large print edition and in paperback from HarperCollins Pubs.

"A Frances Foster book"

Staples, Suzanne Fisher—*Continued*
In India, a talented dancer sacrifices friends and family for her art
"This novel draws the reader into the exotic setting and spiritual world of sacred Hindu classical dance. The glossary with pronunciation guide helps readers understand Indian terminology. . . . Readers will relate to Parvati's dislike of being different and to her relief upon finding her place as a master dancer, a place where her unique abilities are honored, not feared." Voice Youth Advocates

Stauffacher, Sue, 1961-
Donuthead. Knopf 2003 144p $15.95; lib bdg $17.99 (4-6)   **Fic**
1. Fear—Fiction 2. Friendship—Fiction
ISBN 0-375-82468-5; 0-375-92468-X (lib bdg)
LC 2003-40073
Franklin Delano Donuthead, a fifth-grader obsessed with hygiene and safety, finds an unlikely friend and protector in Sarah Kervick, the tough new student who lives in a dirty trailer, bonds with his mother, and is as "irregular" as he is
"It's refreshing for a novel with problem situations to be so light and funny. An appealing story with some memorable characters and a lot of heart." SLJ

Stein, Tammar
Light years; a novel; by Tammar Stein. 1st ed. Knopf, Distributed by Random House 2005 263p (7 and up)   **Fic**
1. Israel-Arab conflicts—Fiction 2. Bereavement—Fiction
ISBN 0-375-83023-5; 0-375-93023-X (lib bdg)
LC 2004-7776
Maya Laor leaves her home in Israel to study astronomy at the University of Virginia after the tragic death of her boyfriend in a suicide bombing.
"This well-paced first novel, a moving study of grief and recovery, is also a love story that should appeal particularly to students interested in other ways of seeing the world." SLJ

Steinbeck, John, 1902-1968
The pearl. John Steinbeck centennial ed. Penguin Books 2002 87p pa $11 (7 and up)   **Fic**
1. Mexico—Fiction 2. Poverty—Fiction
ISBN 0-14-200069-8   LC 2001-56113
First published 1947
"Kino, a poor pearl-fisher, lives a happy albeit spartan life with his wife and their child. When he finds a magnificent pearl, the Pearl of the World, he is besieged by dishonest pearl merchants and envious neighbors. Even a greedy doctor ties his professional treatment of their baby when it is bitten by a scorpion to the possible acquisition of the pearl. After a series of disasters, Kino throws the pearl away since it has brought him only unhappiness." Shapiro. Fic for Youth. 3d edition

The red pony. Viking 100p pa $8 hardcover o.p.
Fic
1. Horses—Fiction 2. Ranch life—Fiction
3. California—Fiction
ISBN 0-14-017736-1 (pa)   LC 86-1610

Also available G.K. Hall large print edition and in paperback from Bantam Bks.
First published 1937
"Jody Tiflin, ten years old, begins to grow up in these four vignettes describing his life on a farm in California. He takes responsibility for his red pony and suffers when it dies. An old man arouses Jody's curiosity about what is beyond the mountains, and he anxiously awaits the birth of a colt. His grandfather's tales are a source of interest and wonder for Jody." Shapiro. Fic for Youth. 3d edition

Stevenson, Robert Louis, 1850-1894
Dr. Jekyll and Mr. Hyde (7 and up)
Fic
Hardcover and paperback editions available from various publishers
First published 1886 with title: The strange case of Dr. Jekyll and Mr. Hyde
"The disturbing tale of the dual personality of Dr. Jekyll, a physician. A generous and philanthropic man, he is preoccupied with the problems of good and evil and with the possibility of separating them into two distinct personalities. He develops a drug that transforms him into the demonic Mr. Hyde, in whose person he exhausts all the latent evil in his nature. He also creates an antidote that will restore him to his respectable existence as Dr. Jekyll. Gradually, however, the unmitigated evil of his darker self predominates, until finally he performs an atrocious murder. . . . The novel is of great psychological perception and strongly concerned with ethical problems." Reader's Ency. 4th edition

Kidnapped (7 and up)   **Fic**
1. Adventure fiction 2. Scotland—Fiction
Various editions available
First published 1886
This historical novel "deals with the adventures of David Balfour, the young hero, and Alan Breck, a Jacobite who is considered one of Stevenson's most interesting and best-drawn characters. A sequel, Catriona, was published in 1893." Reader's Ency. 4th edition

Treasure Island (6 and up)   **Fic**
1. Buried treasure—Fiction 2. Pirates—Fiction
Hardcover and paperback editions available from various publishers
First published 1882
Young Jim Hawkins discovers a treasure map in the chest of an old sailor who dies under mysterious circumstances at his mother's inn. He shows it to Dr. Livesey and Squire Trelawney who agree to outfit a ship and sail to Treasure Island. Among the crew is the pirate Long John Silver and his followers who are in pursuit of the treasure
"A masterpiece among romances. . . . Pew, Black Dog, and Long John Silver are a villainous trio, strongly individualized, shedding an atmosphere of malignancy and terror. The scenery of isle and ocean contrasts vividly with the savagery of the action." Baker. Guide to the Best Fic

Stewart, Jennifer J., 1960-
If that breathes fire, we're toast! Holiday House 1999 118p $15.95 **Fic**
1. Dragons—Fiction 2. Arizona—Fiction
ISBN 0-8234-1430-2 LC 98-36883
Also available in paperback from Scholastic
When twelve-year-old Rick and his mother move from San Diego to Tucson he is not too happy about the change, but when they get a fire-breathing, time-traveling dragon to replace their broken furnace, his new life starts to get more interesting
"The sharp, funny phrasing and the likable, believable characters give the book freshness and zip." Booklist

Stolls, Amy
Palms to the ground; a novel; Amy Stolls. 1st ed. Farrar, Straus and Giroux 2005 243p $17 (7 and up) **Fic**
ISBN 0-374-35731-5 LC 2004-53261
The only child of an over-protective mother and a well-meaning father, and in therapy since the age of seven, eighth-grader Calman Pulowitz spends two weeks with his pen pal in Washington State, getting drunk, running away, and learning a lot about himself.
"Delightfully quirky, but thoroughly believable characters make this . . . novel enjoyable and thought provoking." SLJ

Stolz, Joëlle
The shadows of Ghadames; translated from the French by Catherine Temerson. Delacorte Press 2004 p. cmp $15.95; lib bdg $17.99 **Fic**
1. Muslims—Fiction 2. Sex role—Fiction 3. Libya—Fiction
ISBN 0-385-73104-3; 0-385-90131-3 (lib bdg)
LC 2003-21656
At the end of the nineteenth century in Libya, eleven-year-old Malika simultaneously enjoys and feels constricted by the narrow world of women, but an injured stranger enters her home and disrupts the traditional order of things.
"Stolz invigorates her tale with elegant prose and a deft portrayal of a girl verging on adolescence. The vivid backdrop is intoxicating." Booklist

Strasser, Todd, 1950-
Can't get there from here. Simon & Schuster Books for Young Readers 2004 198p $15.95 (7 and up) **Fic**
1. Runaway teenagers—Fiction 2. Homeless persons—Fiction 3. New York (N.Y.)—Fiction
ISBN 0-689-84169-8 LC 2003-170
Tired of being hungry, cold, and dirty from living on the streets of New York City with a tribe of other homeless teenagers who are dying, one by one, a girl named Maybe ponders her future and longs for someone to care about her
"While the events described in this cautionary tale are shocking, the language is not, making these all-too-real problems accessible to a wide readership." SLJ

Stratton, Allan
Chanda's secrets. Annick Press 2004 193p $19.95; pa $8.95 (7 and up) **Fic**
1. AIDS (Disease)—Fiction 2. Africa—Fiction
ISBN 1-55037-835-X; 1-55037-834-1 (pa)
In this story "Chanda, a 16-year-old . . . girl living in the small city of Bonang in Africa, must confront the undercurrents of shame and stigma associated with HIV/AIDS." Publisher's note
"The details of sub-Saharan African life are convincing and smoothly woven into this moving story of poverty and courage, but the real insight for readers will be the appalling treatment of the AIDS victims. Strong language and frank description are appropriate to the subject matter." SLJ

Stroud, Jonathan, 1970-
The Amulet of Samarkand; the Bartimaeus trilogy, book one. Hyperion Bks. for Children 2003 462p $17.95 (7 and up) **Fic**
1. Fantasy fiction
ISBN 0-7868-1859-X LC 2003-49904
Nathaniel, a magician's apprentice, summons up the djinni Bartimaeus and instructs him to steal the Amulet of Samarkand from the powerful magician Simon Lovelace
"There is plenty of action, mystery, and humor to keep readers turning the pages. This title, the first in a trilogy, is a must for fantasy fans." SLJ
Other titles in this series are:
The golem's eye (2004)
Ptolemy's gate (2006)

Sullivan, Paul, 1939-
Maata's journal; a novel. Atheneum Bks. for Young Readers 2001 221p $16.95 (7 and up) **Fic**
1. Inuit—Fiction
ISBN 0-689-83463-2 LC 99-44103
"This dark chronicle provides thought-provoking supplemental reading for world cultures study. Mature teen girls will identify with Maata's struggle within cultural expectations." Voice Youth Advocates

Sutcliff, Rosemary, 1920-1992
Sword song. Farrar, Straus & Giroux 1998 271p $18; pa $6.95 (7 and up) **Fic**
1. Vikings—Fiction 2. Great Britain—History—0-1066—Fiction
ISBN 0-374-37363-9; 0-374-46984-9 (pa)
LC 98-16827
At sixteen, Bjarni is cast out of the Norse settlement in the Angles' Land for an act of oath-breaking and spends five years sailing the west coast of Scotland and witnessing the feuds of the clan chiefs living there
"This is a well-crafted story that will appeal to sophisticated readers." SLJ

Swallow, Pamela Curtis
It only looks easy. Roaring Brook Press 2003 168p $15.95 **Fic**
1. Alzheimer's disease—Fiction 2. School stories
ISBN 0-7613-1790-2 LC 2002-6611

Swallow, Pamela Curtis—*Continued*

On the first day of seventh grade when Kat "borrows" a bicycle to go see her dog who was hit the day before by a woman with Alzheimer's disease, she learns about the serious consequences of impetuous actions and manages to make some new friends in the process

"Genuine kid humor and a goodhearted, all-too-human heroine distinguish this middle-grade novel." Booklist

Swanson, Julie A., 1964-

Going for the record. Eerdmans Books for Young Readers 2004 217p pa $8 (7 and up)   **Fic**

1. Soccer—Fiction 2. Father-daughter relationship—Fiction 3. Cancer—Fiction

ISBN 0-8028-5273-4

Seventeen-year-old Leah's chance to make the national soccer team does not seem so important when she learns that her father has cancer and may only have months to live.

"Each character rings true. Without being sensational or maudlin, Swanson's novel is real: it's deeply sad and often painful to read, but ultimately hopeful and uplifting." Booklist

Swift, Jonathan, 1667-1745

Gulliver's travels (7 and up)   **Fic**

1. Fantasy fiction

Hardcover and paperback editions available from various publishers

First published 1726

"In the account of his four wonder-countries Swift satirizes contemporary manners and morals, art and politics—in fact the whole social scheme—from four different points of view. The huge Brobdingnagians reduce man to his natural insignificance, the little people of Lilliput parody Europe and its petty broils, in Laputa philosophers are ridiculed, and finally all Swift's hatred and contempt find their satisfaction in degrading humanity to a bestial condition." Baker. Guide to the Best Fic

Tamar, Erika

The midnight train home. Knopf 2000 204p o.p. Dell paperback available $4.99   **Fic**

1. Siblings—Fiction 2. Vaudeville—Fiction

ISBN 0-440-41670-1 (pa)   LC 00-20355

When their mother can no longer care for them, eleven-year-old Deirdre and her brothers board the Orphans' Train for placement with families out West, but Deirdre, a talented singer, finds a different type of family when she joins a traveling vaudeville troupe. Includes a note on the Children's Aid Society which operated the orphan trains from 1854 to 1930

"The importance of family is a strong theme in this story. Deirdre's conflicting emotions are well articulated." Book Rep

Tashjian, Janet, 1956-

The gospel according to Larry. Holt & Co. 2001 227p il $16.95; pa $5.99 (7 and up)   **Fic**

1. Web sites—Fiction

ISBN 0-8050-6378-1; 0-440-23792-0 (pa)

LC 2001-24568

Seventeen-year-old Josh, a loner-philosopher who wants to make a difference in the world, tries to maintain his secret identity as the author of a web site that is receiving national attention

"Tashjian fabricates a cleverly constructed scenario and expertly carries it out to the bittersweet end." Horn Book Guide

Another title about Larry is:

Vote for Larry (2004)

Multiple choice. Holt & Co. 1999 186p $16.95
    Fic

1. Obsessive-compulsive disorder—Fiction

ISBN 0-8050-6086-3   LC 98-43349

Monica, a fourteen-year-old perfectionist and word game expert, tries to break free from all of the suffocating rules in her life by creating a game for living called Multiple Choice

"This eye-opening, multifaceted exploration of obsessive-compulsive disorder is effectively packaged in a creative, compelling story." Booklist

Taylor, Mildred D.

The friendship; pictures by Max Ginsburg. Dial Bks. for Young Readers 1987 53p il $15.99; pa $4.99 (4 and up)   **Fic**

1. African Americans—Fiction 2. Race relations—Fiction 3. Mississippi—Fiction

ISBN 0-8037-0417-8; 0-14-038964-4 (pa)

LC 86-29309

Coretta Scott King Award for text, 1988

This "story about race relations in rural Mississippi during the Depression focuses on an incident between an old Black man, Mr. Tom Bee, and a white storekeeper, Mr. John Wallace. Indebted to Tom for saving his life as a young man, John had promised they would always be friends. But now, years later, John insists that Tom call him 'Mister' and shoots the old man for defiantly—and publicly—calling him by his first name. Narrator Cassie Logan and her brothers . . . are verbally abused by Wallace's villainous sons before witnessing the encounter." Bull Cent Child Books

The gold Cadillac; pictures by Michael Hays. Dial Bks. for Young Readers 1987 43p il $16.99; pa $4.99 (4 and up)   **Fic**

1. African Americans—Fiction 2. Prejudices—Fiction 3. Race relations—Fiction

ISBN 0-8037-0342-2; 0-14-038963-6 (pa)

LC 86-11526

"The shiny gold Cadillac that Daddy brings home one summer evening marks a stepping stone in the lives of Wilma and 'lois, two black sisters growing up in Ohio during the fifties. At first neighbors and relatives shower them with attention. But when the family begins the long journey to the South to show off the car to their Mississippi relatives, the girls, for the first time, encounter the undisguised ugliness of racial prejudice." Horn Book

"Full-page sepia paintings effectively portray the characters, setting, and mood of the story events as Hays ably demonstrates his understanding of the social and emotional environments which existed for blacks during this period." SLJ

Taylor, Mildred D.—*Continued*

The land. Phyllis Fogelman Bks. 2001 375p $17.99; pa $6.99 (7 and up)   **Fic**
1. Racially mixed people—Fiction 2. African Americans—Fiction 3. Race relations—Fiction
ISBN 0-8037-1950-7; 0-14-250146-8 (pa)
      LC 00-39329
Coretta Scott King award for text, 2002
Prequel to Roll of Thunder, Hear My Cry
After the Civil War Paul-Edward Logan, the son of a white father and a black mother, finds himself caught between the two worlds of colored folks and white folks as he pursues his dream of owning land of his own
"Taylor masterfully uses harsh historical realities to frame a powerful coming-of-age story that stands on its own merits." Horn Book Guide

Let the circle be unbroken. Dial Bks. for Young Readers 1981 394p $17.99; pa $7.99 (4 and up)   **Fic**
1. African Americans—Fiction 2. Mississippi—Fiction 3. Great Depression, 1929-1939—Fiction
ISBN 0-8037-4748-9; 0-14-034892-1 (pa)
      LC 81-65854
Sequel to Roll of thunder, hear my cry
This novel featuring the Logans covers "a series of tangential events so that it is a family record, a picture of the depression years in rural Mississippi, and an indictment of black-white relations in the Deep South. A young friend is convicted of a murder of which he is innocent, a pretty cousin is insulted by some white boys and her father taunted because he married a white woman, an elderly neighbor tries to vote, the government pays farmers to plow their crops under, etc." Bull Cent Child Books
The author "provides her readers with a literal sense of witnessing important American history. . . . Moreover, {she} never neglects the details of her volatile 9-year-old heroine's interior life. The daydreams, the jealousy, the incredible ardor of that age come alive." N Y Times Book Rev

Mississippi bridge; by Mildred Taylor; pictures by Max Ginsburg. Dial Bks. for Young Readers 1990 62p il hardcover o.p. paperback available $4.99 (4 and up)   **Fic**
1. Race relations—Fiction 2. African Americans—Fiction 3. Prejudices—Fiction 4. Mississippi—Fiction
ISBN 0-14-130817-6 (pa)   LC 89-27898
Available in hardcover from P. Smith
In this story featuring the children of Mississippi's Logan family, "Jeremy Simms, a 10-year-old white neighbor, describes a harrowing incident after the Logans and other blacks are ordered off the weekly bus in a foggy rainstorm." N Y Times Book Rev
"Taylor has shaped this episode into a haunting meditation that will leave readers vividly informed about segregation practices and the unequal rights that prevailed in that era. . . . The incident and its context constitute a telling piece of social history." Booklist

The road to Memphis; by Mildred Taylor. Dial Bks. 1989 290p $16.99; pa $6.99 (4 and up)   **Fic**
1. Race relations—Fiction 2. African Americans—Fiction 3. Mississippi—Fiction
ISBN 0-8037-0340-6; 0-14-036077-8 (pa)
      LC 88-33654
Coretta Scott King award for text, 1989
Sadistically teased by two white boys in 1940's rural Mississippi, Cassie Logan's friend, Moe, severely injures one of the boys with a tire iron and enlists Cassie's help in trying to flee the state
"Taylor's continued smooth, easy language provides readability for all ages, with a focus on universal human pride, worthy values, and individual responsibility. This action-packed drama is highly recommended." Voice Youth Advocates

Roll of thunder, hear my cry. 25th anniversary ed. Phyllis Fogelman Books 2001 276p $17.99   **Fic**
1. African Americans—Fiction 2. Mississippi—Fiction
ISBN 0-8037-2647-3   LC 00-39378
Awarded the Newbery medal, 1977
First published 1976 by Dial Press
"The time is 1933. The place is Spokane, Mississippi where the Logans, the only black family who own their own land, wage a courageous struggle to remain independent, displeasing a white plantation owner bent on taking their land. But this suspenseful tale is also about the story's young narrator, Cassie, and her three brothers who decide to wage their own personal battles to maintain the self-dignity and pride with which they were raised. . . . Ms. Taylor's richly textured novel shows a strong, proud black family . . . resisting rather than succumbing to oppression." Child Book Rev Serv
Followed by Let the circle be unbroken

Song of the trees; pictures by Jerry Pinkney. Dial Bks. for Young Readers 1975 48p il $16.99; pa $5.99 (4 and up)   **Fic**
1. African Americans—Fiction 2. Great Depression, 1929-1939—Fiction 3. Mississippi—Fiction
ISBN 0-8037-5452-3; 0-14-250075-5 (pa)
Eight-year-old Cassie Logan tells how her family "leaving Mississippi during the Depression was cheated into selling for practically nothing valuable and beautiful giant old pines and hickories, beeches and walnuts in the forest surrounding their house." Adventuring with Books

The well; David's story. Dial Bks. for Young Readers 1995 92p $16.99; pa $5.99 (4 and up)   **Fic**
1. African Americans—Fiction 2. Race relations—Fiction 3. Mississippi—Fiction
ISBN 0-8037-1802-0; 0-14-038642-4 (pa)
      LC 94-25360
"David Logan (Cassie's father) tells this story from his childhood. . . . There's a drought, and the Logans possess the only well in the area that has not gone dry. Black and white alike come for water freely given by the family, but the Simms boys can't seem to stand the necessary charity, and their resentment explodes when David's big brother Hammer beats Charlie Simms after Charlie hits David." Bull Cent Child Books

Taylor, Mildred D.—*Continued*

This story "delivers an emotional wallop in a concentrated span of time and action. . . . This story reverberates in the heart long after the final paragraph is read." Horn Book

Taylor, Theodore, 1921-

The cay. Delacorte Press c1969 137p $16.95; pa $5.50 (5 and up)   **Fic**

1. Race relations—Fiction 2. Caribbean region—Fiction 3. Survival after airplane accidents, shipwrecks, etc.—Fiction 4. Blind—Fiction

ISBN 0-385-07906-0; 0-440-22912-X (pa)

Also available Audiobook version

"When the freighter which was to take Phillip and his mother from wartime Curacao to the United States is torpedoed, Phillip finds himself afloat on a small raft with a huge, old, very black West Indian man. Phillip becomes blind from injuries and resents his dependence upon old Timothy. Through exciting adventures on a very small cay (coral island), Phillip learns to overcome his prejudice toward Timothy and to see him as a man and a friend. Following the aftermath of a fierce tropical storm, Timothy dies. Phillip survives to live a more complete life because of his friend and because he has grown with the changes that occurred in his life." Read Ladders for Hum Relat. 5th edition

"Starkly dramatic, believable and compelling." Saturday Rev

Followed by Timothy of the cay

Lord of the Kill. Blue Sky Press (NY) 2002 246p $16.95; pa $5.99   **Fic**

1. Wild cats—Fiction 2. Zoos—Fiction

ISBN 0-439-33725-9; 0-439-55956-1 (pa)

LC 2001-37829

Sequel to Sniper (1989)

With his parents in India, sixteen-year-old Ben Jepson is in charge of Los Coyotes Preserve, a refuge for big cats near Los Angeles, when two powerful groups try to shut it down by intimidation, murder, and kidnapping the largest tiger in captivity

"Taylor masterfully creates an exciting, accessible mystery while weaving together fascinating information about big cats and their care in captivity and issues of environmental and animal activism." Booklist

Sweet Friday Island. Harcourt Brace & Co. 1994 173p pa $6 hardcover o.p. (7 and up)

Fic

1. Survival after airplane accidents, shipwrecks, etc.—Fiction 2. Father-daughter relationship—Fiction 3. Baja California (Mexico: Peninsula)—Fiction 4. Islands—Fiction

ISBN 0-15-200012-7 (pa)   LC 93-32435

First published 1984 by Scholastic

"Teenage Peg and her father go on a camping vacation to a supposedly uninhabited island in the Sea of Cortez. Ignoring the warnings of the mainland locals . . . they arrive on the island only to become quickly victimized by an unseen assailant they label Señor Psycho." SLJ

"Lots of suspense, lots of tension with a father-daughter combination that is unique and believable. The adventure is plausible, fast moving and sure to please adventure fans." Voice Youth Advocates

Timothy of the cay. Harcourt Brace & Co. 1993 161p $16 (5 and up)   **Fic**

1. Race relations—Fiction 2. Caribbean region—Fiction 3. Survival after airplane accidents, shipwrecks, etc.—Fiction 4. Blind—Fiction

ISBN 0-15-288358-4   LC 93-7898

Also available in paperback from HarperCollins

Sequel to The cay

Having survived being blinded and shipwrecked on a tiny Caribbean island with the old black man Timothy, twelve-year-old white Phillip is rescued and hopes to regain his sight with an operation. Alternate chapters follow the life of Timothy from his days as a young cabin boy

"Somewhat more thoughtful than its well-loved antecedent, this boldly drawn novel is no less commanding." Publ Wkly

Temple, Frances, 1945-1995

The Beduins' gazelle. Orchard Bks. 1996 150p $15.95 hardcover o.p.   **Fic**

1. Bedouins—Fiction 2. Deserts—Fiction 3. Middle East—Fiction

ISBN 0-531-09519-3   LC 95-33530

Also available in paperback from HarperCollins

"A Richard Jackson book"

"In 1302, Atiyah and Halima, cousins betrothed at birth, are separated when Atiyah travels from the desert to Fez to study. . . . While in Fez, Atiyah meets and befriends Etienne, a French pilgrim who is studying Arabic, whom readers met in 'The Ramsay Scallop'. . . . When word travels to Atiyah that Halima is lost, he and Etienne return to the desert to find her. But Halima is rescued by another tribe whose sheikh wants her as his newest wife." Voice Youth Advocates

"Told in short, rapid chapters, Temple's briskly paced story is fueled by a cast of complex, emotionally resonant characters." Publ Wkly

The Ramsay scallop; a novel. Orchard Bks. 1994 310p Harper-Collins paperback available $6.99 o.p. (6 and up)   **Fic**

1. Middle Ages—Fiction 2. Pilgrims and pilgrimages—Fiction

ISBN 0-06-440601-6   LC 93-29697

"A Richard Jackson book"

At the turn of the fourteenth century in England, fourteen-year-old Elenor finds her betrothal to an ambitious lord's son launching her on a memorable pilgrimage to far-off Spain

"With a nod to *The Canterbury Tales*, the book highlights the stories that their fellow pilgrims share with Elenor and Thomas; the stories are sad, romantic, and instructive, and all help shape the journey into the special thing it becomes for the duo. . . . The leisurely pace of the pilgrimage allows the author to introduce a large cast of characters and to decorate her story with historical details that enlighten and intrigue." Booklist

Tonight, by sea; a novel. Orchard Bks. 1995 152p Harper-Collins paperback available $5.95 o.p. (6 and up)   **Fic**

1. Haiti—Fiction 2. Refugees—Fiction

ISBN 0-06-440670-9   LC 94-32167

"A Richard Jackson book"

Temple, Frances, 1945-1995—_Continued_

As governmental brutality and poverty become unbearable, Paulie joins with others in her small Haitian village to help her uncle secretly build a boat they will use to try to escape to the United States

"In an elegant prose style {the author} captures the lyrical cadence of Creole speech and paints an affecting portrait of a proud, resourceful people trying to survive in the face of lawlessness and tyranny." SLJ

Thesman, Jean

The ornament tree. Houghton Mifflin 1996 232p $16 (7 and up)   **Fic**

1. Orphans—Fiction 2. Feminism—Fiction

ISBN 0-395-74278-1   LC 95-17102

Also available in paperback from Avon Bks.

"In 1914 in Seattle, 14-year-old orphan Bonnie moves to the boardinghouse of her independent-minded female relatives and becomes involved with the people who live and work there. . . . The focus is on the events of the times, including the end of World War I, the flu epidemic, the labor riots, the start of Prohibition, and, above all, the struggle for women's rights." Booklist

"The underlying issues are substantial, but the presentation is laced with humor and warmth—no small feat." Horn Book

Followed by The tree of bells

Singer; Jean Thesman. Viking 2005 308p $17.99 (7 and up)   **Fic**

1. Fantasy fiction

ISBN 0-670-05937-4   LC 2004-14905

Imprisoned by her wicked and power-hungry mother, Lady Rhiannon, Gwenore escapes to a women's healing community, later changing her name and becoming nursemaid and protector to the children of the magical king of Lir, who is now married to Rhiannon

The violent world of this "compulsively readable and satisfying medieval fantasy . . . seems a brutish place indeed. . . . Yet it's a breathtakingly magical world as well." Publ Wkly

The tree of bells. Houghton Mifflin 1999 232p $15 (7 and up)   **Fic**

1. Feminism—Fiction

ISBN 0-395-90510-9   LC 98-27787

Sequel to The ornament tree

"Keeping secret her cousin Bonnie's plans to travel to China, sixteen-year-old Clare Harris contemplates her own future. . . . Clare becomes more interested in helping the underprivileged in 1920s Seattle and more involved in the small dramas taking place at her family's lively boarding house. For those who enjoyed the first book, this installment will more than satisfy." Horn Book Guide

Thomson, Sarah L.

The dragon's son. Orchard Bks. 2001 181p $17.95 (7 and up)   **Fic**

1. Arthur, King—Fiction 2. Great Britain—History—0-1066—Fiction

ISBN 0-531-30333-0   LC 00-61177

Based on the Mabinogion, a collection of medieval Welsh tales, as well as later legends, tells of family members and servants important in the life of King Arthur, featuring Nimue, Morgan le Fay, Luned, and Mordred

"Thomson's retellings are straightforward and accessible, eschewing florid language in favor of action-packed storytelling, and emphasizing the personal losses and sorrows of well-developed characters who are caught in a time of tremendous change." Bull Cent Child Books

Thurlo, Aimée

The spirit line; {by} Aimeé & David Thurlo. Viking 2004 216p $15.99   **Fic**

1. Navajo Indians—Fiction 2. New Mexico—Fiction

ISBN 0-670-03645-5

When the special rug Crystal Manyfeathers is weaving for her kinaaldá, the traditional Navajo womanhood ceremony, is stolen from her loom, there are any number of suspects.

"Carefully combining humor and seriousness, this well-paced story contains accurate portrayals of Navajo customs, mostly believable teen dialogue, and a realistic depiction of the conflicts modern Native young people face." SLJ

Tingle, Rebecca

The edge on the sword. Putnam 2001 277p $18.99; pa $6.99   **Fic**

1. Great Britain—History—0-1066—Fiction

ISBN 0-399-23580-9; 0-14-250058-5 (pa)

                              LC 00-55353

Sequel: Far traveler

In ninth-century Britain, fifteen-year-old Aethelflaed, daughter of King Alfred of West Saxony, finds she must assume new responsibilities much sooner than expected when she is betrothed to Ethelred of Mercia in order to strengthen a strategic alliance against the Danes

This "story is filled with exciting action, interesting characters, and convincing historical details of the late ninth century that bring to life this distant and violent time in Britain." SLJ

Far traveler; Rebecca Tingle. G. Putnam's Sons 2005 228p $17.99   **Fic**

1. Great Britain—History—0-1066—Fiction

ISBN 0-399-23890-5   LC 2002-31765

Sequel to The Edge on the Sword

After the death of her mother, Aethelflaed of Mercia, seventeen-year-old Aelfwyn flees imprisonment by her uncle King Edward and, in the guise of a youthful bard, plays her part in the resolution of the tangled political enmities of tenth century Britain

"Tingle is a sure-footed plotter, drawing the reader into the suspense of Aelfwyn's plight by offering dashes of excitement and danger alongside a developing romance and complicated political intrigue." Bull Cent Child Books

Tocher, Timothy

Chief Sunrise, John McGraw, and me; Timothy Tocher. 1st ed. Cricket Books 2004 154p $15.95

Fic

1. Baseball—Fiction 2. Runaway teenagers—Fiction 3. Race relations—Fiction

ISBN 0-8126-2711-3   LC 2003-23407

In 1919, fifteen-year-old Hank escapes an abusive father and goes looking for a chance to become a baseball player, accompanied by a man who calls himself Chief Sunrise and claims to be a full-blooded Seminole.

"The story is both entertaining and thought-provoking." Booklist

Tolan, Stephanie S., 1942-

Flight of the raven. HarperCollins Pubs. 2001 294p $15.95; lib bdg $17.89; pa $7.99 (7 and up)

Fic

1. Militia movements—Fiction 2. Terrorism—Fiction 3. Extrasensory perception—Fiction 4. African Americans—Fiction

ISBN 0-688-17419-1; 0-06-029620-8 (lib bdg); 0-380-73299-8 (pa)   LC 00-54043

Sequel to Welcome to the Ark

Elijah, a nine-year-old African American with unusual mental powers and a special ability to reach into the natural world, becomes a hostage of a terrorist militia group and finds himself in a world of violence

"The premise is undeniably compelling . . . and readers may find this an eye-opening examination of some resonant issues." Bull Cent Child Books

Ordinary miracles. Morrow Junior Bks. 1999 221p $15.95; pa $5.95   **Fic**

1. Twins—Fiction 2. Brothers—Fiction 3. Christian life—Fiction

ISBN 0-688-16269-X; 0-380-73322-6 (pa)

LC 99-13658

Another title about the Firkins family is: Save Halloween! (1993)

Tired of being a twin, Mark tries to spend more time away from his twin brother and meets a scientist who challenges some of Mark's long-held Christian beliefs about heaven, God, prayer, and death

"The pace moves gently at first, then inexorably, and the story comes to a poignant, believable conclusion." Booklist

Surviving the Applewhites. HarperCollins Pubs. 2002 216p $15.99; lib bdg $17.89; pa $5.99

Fic

1. Eccentrics and eccentricities—Fiction 2. Theater—Fiction 3. Family life—Fiction

ISBN 0-06-623602-9; 0-06-623603-7 (lib bdg); 0-06-441044-7 (pa)   LC 2002-1474

Jake, a budding juvenile delinquent, is sent for home schooling to the arty and eccentric Applewhite family's Creative Academy, where he discovers talents and interests he never knew he had

This is a "thoroughly enjoyable book with humor, well-drawn characters, and a super cover." Voice Youth Advocates

Welcome to the Ark. Morrow Junior Bks. 1996 250p pa $7.99 hardcover o.p. (7 and up)

Fic

1. Gifted children—Fiction 2. Parapsychology—Fiction

ISBN 0-380-73319-6 (pa)   LC 96-10163

"Four troubled young people live in a group home: Doug, seventeen, Miranda, sixteen, Taryn, nine, and Elijah, eight. Formerly patients in a psychiatric hospital, they are chosen for the home because of their exceptional intelligence and psychic powers. . . . The kids 'connect' with each other through dreams and telepathy, and reach out to others like themselves all over the world via the Internet. . . . Tolan does a superb job depicting emotionally disturbed, gifted youth." Voice Youth Advocates

Tolkien, J. R. R. (John Ronald Reuel), 1892-1973

The hobbit; or, There and back again; illustrated by the author. Houghton Mifflin 1938 310p il hardcover o.p. paperback available $11.95 (4 and up)   **Fic**

1. Fantasy fiction

ISBN 0-395-28265-9 (pa)

Also available from Houghton Mifflin in an edition with illustrations by Michael Hague for $29.95 (ISBN 0-395-36290-3)

First published 1937 in the United Kingdom

"This fantasy features the adventures of hobbit Bilbo Baggins, who joins a band of dwarves led by Gandalf the Wizard. Together they seek to recover the stolen treasure that is hidden in Lonely Mountain and guarded by Smaug the Dragon. This book precedes the *Lord of the Rings* trilogy." Shapiro. Fic for Youth. 3d edition

The lord of the rings. 50th Anniversary ed. Houghton Mifflin 2004 xxv, 1157p il map slip case $100 (7 and up)   **Fic**

1. Fantasy fiction

ISBN 0-618-51765-0   LC 2004-275215

Also available as separate volumes in hardcover and paperback editions

First published 1954 in the United Kingdom

Contents: The fellowship of the ring; The two towers; The return of the king

"This is a tale of imaginary gnomelike creatures who battle against evil. Led by Frodo, the hobbits embark on a journey to prevent a magic ring from falling into the grasp of the powers of darkness. The forces of good succeed in their fight against the Dark Lord of evil, and Frodo and Sam bring the Ring to Mount Doom, where it is destroyed." Shapiro. Fic for Youth. 3d edition

Torres, Laura

Crossing Montana. Holiday House 2002 119p $16.95 (7 and up)   **Fic**

1. Missing persons—Fiction 2. Fathers—Fiction

ISBN 0-8234-1643-7   LC 2001-59355

While looking for her grandfather who is missing, teenaged Callie examines her father's longtime absence and its damaging effects on her family

"Torres' characters are drawn with spare realism. . . . Callie's brave, desperate, present-tense narrative tells the truth and doesn't let you go." Booklist

Townley, Rod

Sky; a novel in three sets and an encore; by Roderick Townley. 1st ed. Atheneum Books for Young Readers 2004 265p $16.95 (7 and up)
Fic
1. Jazz musicians—Fiction 2. New York (N.Y.)—Fiction
ISBN 0-689-85712-8   LC 2003-11354
"A Richard Jackson book"
In New York City in 1959, fifteen-year-old Alec Schuyler, at odds with his widowed father over his love of music, finds a mentor and friend in a blind, black jazz musician.
"Townley presents a compassionate portrait of a young man who is battling for his own place in life and sets the story in the exciting time of the beat poets and the explosive development of jazz music." SLJ

Trottier, Maxine

Sister to the wolf. Kids Can Press 2004 348p $16.95
Fic
1. Pawnee Indians—Fiction 2. Frontier and pioneer life—Fiction
ISBN 1-55337-519-X
"Cecile, who lives in Quebec in the early 1700s, sees a Lesharo, 'an indien slave,' being branded by his master. She buys Lesharo and frees him, and their paths become further intertwined when he accompanies Cecile and her father to Fort Detroit." Booklist
"In addition to providing a rich historical background and vividly recreating the sense of wilderness, Trottier has drawn her characters and their relationships in a fully satisfying manner. There is plenty of action and a sweet romance in the mix as well." SLJ

Trueman, Terry

Inside out. HarperTempest 2003 117p $15.99; lib bdg $16.99 (7 and up)
Fic
1. Schizophrenia—Fiction
ISBN 0-06-623962-1; 0-06-623963-X (lib bdg)
LC 2002-151604
Zach, a sixteen-year-old with schizophrenia, is caught up in the events surrounding an attempted robbery by two other teens who eventually hold him hostage
"Trueman sometimes captures moments of heartbreaking truth, and his swift, suspenseful plot will have particular appeal to reluctant readers." Booklist

Stuck in neutral. HarperCollins Pubs. 2000 114p $14.95; lib bdg $16.89; pa $6.99
Fic
1. Cerebral palsy—Fiction 2. Euthanasia—Fiction 3. Father-son relationship—Fiction
ISBN 0-06-028519-2; 0-06-028518-4 (lib bdg); 0-06-447213-2 (pa)   LC 99-37098
Fourteen-year-old Shawn McDaniel, who suffers from severe cerebral palsy and cannot function, relates his perceptions of his life, his family, and his condition, especially as he believes his father is planning to kill him
"Trueman has created a compelling novel that poses questions about ability and existence while fostering sympathy for people with severe physical limitations." Bull Cent Child Books

Tunnell, Michael O.

Brothers in valor; a story of resistance. Holiday House 2001 260p $16.95
Fic
1. World War, 1939-1945—Fiction 2. Germany—Fiction
ISBN 0-8234-1541-4   LC 00-54053
Three German teenagers who are members of the Mormon Church join forces to create a youth resistance movement during World War II, putting their lives at risk
This book's "combination of readability and serious focus makes it a strong choice for intergenerational discussion." Voice Youth Advocates

Wishing moon. Dutton Children's Books 2004 272p $17.99
Fic
1. Magic—Fiction 2. Orphans—Fiction 3. Middle East—Fiction
ISBN 0-525-47193-6   LC 2003-62486
After a fourteen-year-old orphan named Aminah comes to possess a magic lamp, the wishes granted her by the genie inside it allow her to alter her life by choosing prosperity, purpose, and romance.
"Aminah strives to do good with her magic, and yet the tale skips preachiness and goes for rich characterizations and a strong, suspenseful plot worthy of the Arabian Nights." Booklist

Turnbull, Ann

No shame, no fear. Candlewick Press 2004 c2003 293p $15.99 (7 and up)
Fic
1. Society of Friends—Fiction 2. Great Britain—Fiction
ISBN 0-7636-2505-1   LC 2003-65280
First published 2003 in the United Kingdom
In England in 1662, a time of religious persecution, fifteen-year-old Susanna, a poor country girl and a Quaker, and seventeen-year-old William, a wealthy Anglican, meet and fall in love against all odds.
"This is a well-told historical tale, engaging and informative." Booklist

Turner, Megan Whalen, 1965-

The thief. Greenwillow Bks. 1996 219p $16.99 (6 and up)
Fic
1. Adventure fiction 2. Thieves—Fiction
ISBN 0-688-14627-9   LC 95-41040
Also available in paperback from Puffin Bks.
A Newbery Medal honor book, 1997
"Gen languishes in prison for boasting of his skill as a thief. The magus—the king's powerful advisor—needing a clever thief to find an ancient ring that gives the owner the right to rule a neighboring country, bails Gen out. Their journey toward the treasure is marked by danger and political intrigue, and features a motley cast, tales of old gods, and the revelation of Gen's true identity." Publisher's note
"A tantalizing, suspenseful, exceptionally clever novel. . . . The author's characterization of Gen is simply superb." Horn Book
Followed by The Queen of Attolia (2000)

Twain, Mark, 1835-1910

The adventures of Huckleberry Finn (5 and up)
Fic

Twain, Mark, 1835-1910—*Continued*
1. Mississippi River—Fiction 2. Missouri—Fiction
Hardcover and paperback editions available from various publishers
First published 1885. This is a companion volume to: The adventures of Tom Sawyer
This novel "begins with Huck's escape from his drunken, brutal father to the river, where he meets up with Jim, a runaway slave. The story of their journey downstream, with occasional forays into the society along the banks, is an American classic that captures the smells, rhythms, and sounds, the variety of dialects and the human activity of life on the great river. It is also a penetrating social commentary that reveals corruption, moral decay, and intellectual impoverishment through Huck and Jim's encounters with traveling actors and con men, lynch mobs, thieves, and Southern gentility." Reader's Ency. 4th edition

The adventures of Tom Sawyer (5 and up)
Fic
1. Mississippi River—Fiction 2. Missouri—Fiction
3. Boys 4. Wit and humor 5. Mississippi River
6. Family life 7. Missouri
Hardcover and paperback editions available from various publishers
First published 1876. This is a companion volume to: The adventures of Huckleberry Finn
"Tom, a shrewd and adventurous boy, is at home in the respectable world of his Aunt Polly, as well as in the self-reliant, parentless world of Huck Finn. The two friends, out in the cemetery under a full moon, attempt to cure warts with a dead cat. They accidentally witness a murder, of which Muff Potter is later wrongly accused. Knowing that the true murderer is Injun Joe, the boys are helpless with fear; they decide to run away to Jackson's Island. After a few pleasant days of smoking and swearing, they realize that the townspeople believe them dead. Returning in time to hear their funeral eulogies, they become town heroes. At the trial of Muff Potter, Tom, unable to let an innocent person be condemned, reveals his knowledge. Injun Joe flees. Later Tom and his sweetheart, Becky Thatcher, get lost in the cave in which the murderer is hiding. They escape, and Tom and Huck return to find the treasure Joe has buried." Reader's Ency. 4th edition

The prince and the pauper **Fic**
1. Edward VI, King of England, 1537-1553—Fiction
2. Great Britain—History—1485-1603, Tudors—Fiction
Hardcover and paperback editions available from various publishers
First published 1881
"Edward VI of England and a little pauper change places a few days before Henry VIII's death. The prince wanders in rags, while Tom Canty suffers the horrors of princedom. At the last moment, the mistake is rectified." Reader's Ency. 4th edition

Twomey, Cathleen
Beachmont letters. Boyds Mills Press 2003 223p $16.95 (7 and up) **Fic**
1. Fires—Fiction 2. Burns and scalds—Fiction
ISBN 1-59078-050-7 LC 2002-111301

Scarred by a fire that killed her father, a seventeen-year-old girl begins a correspondence with a young soldier in 1944
This "has plenty of atmosphere and an appealing, courageous heroine who gradually realizes her own strength. This unusual survivor/love story is certain to be a three-hanky read." Booklist

Uchida, Yoshiko, 1921-1992
A jar of dreams. Atheneum Pubs. 1981 131p $16.95; pa $4.99 (5 and up) **Fic**
1. Japanese Americans—Fiction 2. Family life—Fiction 3. Prejudices—Fiction 4. California—Fiction
ISBN 0-689-50210-9; 0-689-71672-9 (pa)
LC 81-3480
"A Margaret K. McElderry book"
"A story of the Depression Era is told by eleven-year-old Rinko, the only girl in a Japanese-American family living in Oakland and suffering under the double burden of financial pressure and the prejudice that had increased with the tension of economic competition. Into the household comes a visitor who is a catalyst for change." Bull Cent Child Books
"Rinko in her guilelessness is genuine and refreshing, and her worries and concerns seem wholly natural, honest, and convincing." Horn Book
Other available titles about Rinko Tsujimura and her family are:
The best bad thing (1983)
The happiest ending (1985)

Journey to Topaz; a story of the Japanese-American evacuation; illustrated by Donald Carrick. Scribner 1971 149p il o.p. Heyday Bks. paperback available $9.95 (5 and up)
Fic
1. Japanese Americans—Evacuation and relocation, 1942-1945—Fiction
ISBN 1-890771-91-0 (pa)
This is the story of eleven-year-old Yuki, her eighteen-year-old brother and her mother, who were uprooted, evacuated and interned in Topaz, the War Relocation Center in Utah during World War II
"This tragic herding of innocent people is described with dignity and a sorrowful sense of injustice that never becomes bitter." Saturday Rev
Followed by Journey home

Updale, Eleanor
Montmorency; thief, liar, gentleman? Orchard Books 2004 c2003 232p $16.95 **Fic**
1. London (England)—Fiction 2. Great Britain—History—19th century—Fiction 3. Thieves—Fiction
ISBN 0-439-58035-8 LC 2003-56345
First published 2003 in the United Kingdom
In Victorian London, after his life is saved by a young physician, a thief utilizes the knowledge he gains in prison and from the scientific lectures he attends as the physician's case study exhibit to create a new, highly successful, double life for himself.
"Updale adroitly works the tradition of devilish schemes and narrow escapes, and the plot moves as nimbly as the master thief himself." Bull Cent Child Books
Another available title about Montmorency is:

Updale, Eleanor—*Continued*

Montmorency on the rocks: doctor, aristocrat, murderer? (2005)

Van Leeuwen, Jean

Cabin on Trouble Creek. Dial Books for Young Readers 2004 119p $16.99 (4 and up)   **Fic**

1. Frontier and pioneer life—Fiction 2. Brothers—Fiction 3. Ohio—Fiction

ISBN 0-8037-2548-5   LC 2003-14151

In 1803 in Ohio, two young brothers are left to finish the log cabin and guard the land while their father goes back to Pennsylvania to fetch their mother and younger siblings.

"Excellent pacing is what makes this novel work so well. . . . The suspense builds consistently. The boys' struggle is portrayed realistically, without sugarcoating nature's harshness." SLJ

Lucy was there—. Phyllis Fogelman Bks. 2002 165p $16.99   **Fic**

1. Death—Fiction 2. Friendship—Fiction 3. Dogs—Fiction

ISBN 0-8037-2738-0   LC 2001-33974

With the help of new friends and a very special dog, Morgan begins to come to terms with the loss of her mother and five-year-old brother, who boarded a plane and never came back

"Morgan's anguish is palpable but never overwrought, and the short chapters, appealing heroine, and well-told story leavened with humor give this solid . . . appeal." Booklist

Vanasse, Deb

Out of the wilderness. Clarion Bks. 1999 165p $15   **Fic**

1. Father-son relationship—Fiction 2. Brothers—Fiction 3. Wilderness survival—Fiction 4. Alaska—Fiction

ISBN 0-395-91421-3   LC 98-22692

Josh tries to endure living in the Alaskan wilderness with his father and half-brother Nathan, but Nathan's uncompromising reverence for nature and its wild creatures causes difficulties that reinforce Josh's determination to return to city life

"This story succeeds on several levels. The characters are believable and the reader appreciates the interwoven struggles Josh faces. . . . The beauty and danger of the Alaskan wilderness is lined in lyrical prose that rises above most tales of adventure." ALAN

Vande Velde, Vivian, 1951-

Alison, who went away. Houghton Mifflin 2001 211p $15   **Fic**

1. Missing persons—Fiction 2. Sisters—Fiction

ISBN 0-618-04585-6   LC 00-32032

Three years after the disappearance of her older sister, fourteen-year-old Sibyl and her family struggle to continue their lives, separately and together

"Female middle-level readers will find this novel engrossing, whether or not they are mystery fans. Alison's story is true to life." Voice Youth Advocates

Heir apparent. Harcourt 2002 315p $17; pa $6.95   **Fic**

1. Virtual reality—Fiction 2. Science fiction

ISBN 0-15-204560-0; 0-15-205125-2 (pa)

LC 2002-2441

While playing a total immersion virtual reality game of kings and intrigue, fourteen-year-old Giannine learns that demonstrators have damaged the equipment to which she is connected, and she must win the game quickly or be damaged herself

"This adventure includes a cast of intriguing characters and personalities. The feisty heroine has a funny, sarcastic sense of humor and succeeds because of her ingenuity and determination." SLJ

Never trust a dead man. Harcourt Brace & Co. 1999 194p $17; pa $5.99   **Fic**

1. Mystery fiction

ISBN 0-15-201899-9; 0-440-22828-X (pa)

LC 98-39885

Wrongly convicted of murder and punished by being sealed in the tomb with the dead man, seventeen-year-old Selwyn enlists the help of a witch and the resurrected victim to find the true killer

"Filled with engaging characters, witty dialogue, and lots of action, this is an entertaining blend of fantasy, whodunit, and comedy." SLJ

There's a dead person following my sister around. Harcourt Brace & Co. 1999 143p $16 (4 and up)   **Fic**

1. Ghost stories 2. Slavery—Fiction 3. Underground railroad—Fiction

ISBN 0-15-202100-0   LC 99-11462

Also available in paperback from Puffin Bks.

Ted becomes concerned and intrigued when his five-year-old sister Vicki begins receiving visits from the ghosts of two runaway slaves

"There is sufficient humor, action, and scariness to keep readers engaged." SLJ

Vaught, Susan

Stormwitch; Susan Vaught. 1st U.S. ed. Bloomsbury Children's Books 2005 208p $16.95 (7 and up)   **Fic**

1. Voodooism—Fiction 2. Haitian Americans—Fiction 3. Hurricanes—Fiction 4. Mississippi—Fiction

ISBN 1-58234-952-5   LC 2004-54681

In Pass Christian, Mississippi in 1969, sixteen-year-old Ruba, trained by her Haitian grandmother in both voodoo and Amazonian warrior tactics, uses her skills to fight against racism and the African witch Zashar, now coming ashore in the form of Hurricane Camille.

"This story offers a smooth blend of historical fact, suspense, and magic." SLJ

Vaupel, Robin

My contract with Henry. Holiday House 2003 244p $16.95   **Fic**

1. Thoreau, Henry David, 1817-1862—Fiction 2. Friendship—Fiction 3. School stories

ISBN 0-8234-1701-8   LC 2002-27471

Vaupel, Robin—*Continued*

A mission that begins as an eighth-grade project on Henry David Thoreau's experimental living at Walden Pond becomes a life-changing experience for a group of outsider students who become budding philosophers, environmental activists, and loyal friends

"Vaupel creates a painfully accurate portrayal of middle-school social dynamics." Booklist

Veciana-Suarez, Ana

The flight to freedom. Orchard Bks. 2002 215p (First person fiction) $16.95; pa $6.99   **Fic**

1. Cuban Americans—Fiction 2. Immigrants—Fiction

ISBN 0-439-38199-1; 0-439-38200-9 (pa)

              LC 2001-58783

Writing in the diary which her father gave her, thirteen-year-old Yara describes life with her family in Havana, Cuba, in 1967 as well as her experiences in Miami, Florida, after immigrating there to be reunited with some relatives while leaving others behind

"The story and characters ring true in their portrayal of loss, longing, and the hope of starting a new life." SLJ

Velmans, Hester

Isabel of the whales; Hester Velmans. Delacorte Press 2005 181p $15.95; lib bdg $17.99 (5 and up)   **Fic**

1. Whales—Fiction 2. Massachusetts—Fiction

ISBN 0-385-73202-3; 0-385-90233-6 (lib bdg)

              LC 2004-546

On a whale watch trip with her class off the coast of Cape Cod, Isabel, who has always had an affinity for whales, falls overboard and discovers as she finds herself swimming underwater with whales all around her that she is one of the Chosen who can change shape from human to whale and back again.

Verne, Jules, 1828-1905

Around the world in eighty days   **Fic**

1. Voyages around the world—Fiction 2. Adventure fiction

Hardcover and paperback editions available from various publishers

Original French edition, 1873

"The hero, Phileas Fogg, undertakes his hasty world tour as the result of a bet made at his London club. He and his French valet Passepartout, meet with some fantastic adventures, but these are overcome by the loyal servant and the endlessy inventive Fogg. The feat they perform is incredible for its day; Fogg wins his bet, having circled the world in only eighty days." Reader's Ency. 4th edition

Twenty thousand leagues under the sea (5 and up)   **Fic**

1. Submarines—Fiction 2. Sea stories 3. Science fiction

              LC 91-27739

Hardcover and paperback editions available from various publishers

Original French edition, 1870

"*The voyage of the Nautilus* permitted Verne to describe the wonders of an undersea world almost totally unknown to the general public of the period. Indebted to literary tradition for his Atlantis, he made his major innovation in having the submarine completely powered by electricity, although the interest in electrical forces goes back to Poe and Shelley. So far as the enigmatic ending is concerned, his readers had to wait for the three-part *The Mysterious Island* (1874-1875) to learn that Nemo had been the Indian warrior-prince Dakkar, who had been involved in the Sepoy Mutiny of 1857." Anatomy of Wonder 4

Voigt, Cynthia

Bad girls in love. Atheneum Bks. for Young Readers 2002 233p $15.95; pa $4.99   **Fic**

1. School stories 2. Friendship—Fiction

ISBN 0-689-82471-8; 0-689-86620-8 (pa)

              LC 2001-45898

Follows Bad girls (1996) and Bad, badder, baddest (1997)

"An Anne Schwartz book"

Now in the eighth grade, best friends Mikey and Margalo try to figure out boys, crushes, and falling in love

It's the girls' "talk—insulting, furious, funny, needy, and smart—on the telephone, and in the school's cafeteria, bathrooms, and hallways that gets the junior-high jungle exactly right." Booklist

Other titles in this series are:

Bad, badder, baddest (1997)

Bad girls (1996)

It's not easy being bad (2000)

Dicey's song. Atheneum Pubs. 1982 196p $17.95 (6 and up)   **Fic**

1. Grandmothers—Fiction 2. Siblings—Fiction

ISBN 0-689-30944-9   LC 82-3882

Also available in paperback from Fawcett Bks. and Audiobook version

Awarded the Newbery Medal, 1983

Sequel to Homecoming

Dicey "had brought her siblings to the grandmother they'd never seen when their mother (now in a mental institution) had been unable to cope. This is the story of the children's adjustment to Gram (and hers to them) and to a new school and a new life—but with some of the old problems." Bull Cent Child Books

"The vividness of Dicey is striking; Voigt has plumbed and probed her character inside out to fashion a memorable protagonist." Booklist

Homecoming. Atheneum Pubs. 1981 312p $18.95 (6 and up)   **Fic**

1. Siblings—Fiction 2. Abandoned children—Fiction

ISBN 0-689-30833-7   LC 80-36723

Also available in paperback from Fawcett Bks.

"When their momma abandons them in a shopping center, Dicey Tillerman and her three younger brothers and sisters set out on foot for where momma was ostensibly taking them—to Great-Aunt Cilla's in Bridgeport, Connecticut." Booklist

"The characterizations of the children are original and intriguing, and there are a number of interesting minor characters encountered in their travels." SLJ

Voigt, Cynthia—*Continued*
Followed by Dicey's song

Izzy, willy-nilly. Rev ed. Atheneum Pubs. 2005
327p $17.95; pa $5.99 (7 and up)   **Fic**
1. Physically handicapped—Fiction
ISBN 1-416-903402; 1-416-90339-9 (pa)
LC 2005-299062
"An amputee after a drunk-driving accident, Izzy
struggles to accept what has happened and in doing so
becomes not only a deeper, stronger person but also begins to see her family and friends in a new, revealing
light." Booklist
"Voigt shows unusual insight into the workings of a
15-year-old girl's mind. . . . Just as Voigt's perceptive
empathy brings Izzy to life, other characterizations are
memorable, whether of Izzy's shallow former friends or
of her egocentric 10-year-old sister." Publ Wkly

Jackaroo. Atheneum Pubs. 1985 291p $19.95 (7
and up)   **Fic**
1. Adventure fiction
ISBN 0-689-31123-0   LC 85-7954
Also available in paperback from Simon & Schuster
"An Argo book"
"In a far-off feudal kingdom, where the people are
hungry and oppressesd by the lords, 16-year-old Gwyn,
the innkeeper's daughter, takes on the identity of a
masked legendary hero, Jackaroo, whose brave deeds for
the poor have always inspired hope in harsh times."
Booklist
"The style is fluid and consistent with the personalities
of her characters; the setting is evoked through skillfully
crafted description; the situations speak directly to the
human condition. What is most notable, however, is the
skill with which the social and political structures are described without interrupting the flow of the plot." Horn
Book

On fortune's wheel. Atheneum Pubs. 1990 276p
hardcover o.p. paperback available $4.99 (7 and
up)   **Fic**
1. Adventure fiction
ISBN 0-689-82957-4 (pa)   LC 89-39010
Also available in paperback from Fawcett Bks.
Faced with the prospect of an unhappy life in the
Kingdom, fourteen-year-old Birle accompanies a young
runaway nobleman on a journey south and falls into slavery in the citadel of a cruel prince
"*On Fortune's Wheel*, set in the same imaginary world
as *Jackaroo* is a lush narrative woven from elements of
classic fairy tales and legends." Publ Wkly

A solitary blue. Atheneum Pubs. 1983 189p $18
(7 and up)   **Fic**
1. Divorce—Fiction 2. Parent-child relationship—Fiction
ISBN 0-689-31008-0   LC 83-6007
Jeff Greene, a minor character from Dicey's song, "is
abandoned by his mother at age seven and suffers from
the benign neglect of his college professor father. As a
teenager, Jeff again sees and is charmed by his mother
only to become disillusioned by her." Child Book Rev
Serv
"This is the most mature and sophisticated of Voigt's
novels. . . . Beautifully knit . . . compelling and intelligent." Bull Cent Child Books

Wait, Lea, 1946-
Wintering well; Lea Wait. 1st ed. Margaret K.
McElderry Books 2004 186p $16.95 (5 and up)
Fic
1. Siblings—Fiction 2. Handicapped—Fiction
3. Maine—Fiction
ISBN 0-689-85646-6   LC 2003-19322
Fifteen-year-old Will Ames and his sister Cassie go to
stay with their sister in nearby Wiscasset, Maine, after a
disabling accident ruins Will's plans for a career in farming.
"Limned with just the right amount of detail about the
realities of life in the early nineteenth century, this is a
quiet story of seeking." Booklist

Waite, Judy
Shopaholic. Atheneum Bks. for Young Readers
2003 211p $16.95   **Fic**
1. Friendship—Fiction 2. Shopping—Fiction
ISBN 0-689-85138-3   LC 2002-26246
"Fourteen-year-old Taylor feels unloved at home,
where her mother has slipped into a depression after the
death of Taylor's younger sister. When an older friend
offers to take Taylor shopping, Taylor struggles to live
up to Kat's glamorous lifestyle." Horn Book Guide
This is "an engaging, emotionally wrenching read."
SLJ

Wallace, Barbara Brooks, 1922-
Secret in St. Something. Atheneum Bks. for
Young Readers 2001 149p pa $4.99 hardcover o.p.
Fic
1. Orphans—Fiction 2. Homeless persons—Fiction
3. New York (N.Y.)—Fiction
ISBN 0-689-85601-6 (pa)   LC 99-49711
"A Jean Karl book"
Fleeing from a cruel step-father, eleven-year-old Robin
takes his baby brother and finds shelter with street boys
living in a church in a tenement area of New York City
This offers "a plucky main character who is repeatedly
thrust into dangerous situations, cliff-hanging chapters,
vicious enemies, and a period setting so well described
readers will be able to smell the dank hallways and dirty
streets." Booklist

Wallace, Bill, 1947-
Aloha summer. Holiday House 1997 168p
$15.95   **Fic**
1. Moving—Fiction 2. Hawaii—Fiction
ISBN 0-8234-1306-3   LC 96-48778
Also available in paperback from Simon Pulse
In 1925 fourteen-year-old John, an Oklahoma farm
boy, has to accept many changes in his life when his father takes a job on a pineapple plantation in Hawaii and
the family moves there
"Honest, vulnerable John narrates this sweet yet unsentimental look at first love, the poison of prejudice,
and plain folk who know what is right and what is not."
Voice Youth Advocates

Eye of the great bear. Pocket Bks. 1999 162p
$14; pa $4.99   **Fic**

Wallace, Bill, 1947--—*Continued*
1. West (U.S.)—Fiction
ISBN 0-671-02504-X; 0-671-02502-3 (pa)
"A face-to-face encounter with a big grizzly cures a
jumpy 12-year-old of his fear of being afraid in this family adventure set in turn-of-the-century western Texas
and Montana. . . . The tale is vigorously told, with uncomplicated situations, cliff-hangers at many chapter
ends, and incidents both entertaining and suspenseful."
Booklist

Skinny-dipping at Monster Lake. Simon &
Schuster Bks. for Young Readers 2003 212p
$16.95 (4 and up)   **Fic**
ISBN 0-689-85150-2   LC 2002-152820
When twelve-year-old Kent helps his father in a daring underwater rescue, he wins the respect he has always
craved.
"This old-fashioned adventure has wide appeal, and
the youngsters' games and camaraderie will hook even
reluctant readers." SLJ

Wallace, Rich, 1957-
Playing without the ball; a novel in four
quarters. Knopf 2000 213p $15.95; lib bdg $17.99
                                                Fic
1. Basketball—Fiction 2. Pennsylvania—Fiction
ISBN 0-679-88672-9; 0-679-98672-3 (lib bdg)
                                     LC 00-38064
Also avialable in paperback from Laurel Leaf
Feeling abandoned by his parents, who have gone
their separate ways and left him behind in a small Pennsylvania town, seventeen-year-old Jay finds hope for the
future in a church-sponsored basketball team and a female friend
"The game action—so well-written that even church
league takes on the tension of an NBA playoff—will carry the most reluctant reader into a deeper story of the
struggle for identity and self acceptance." Booklist

Wrestling Sturbridge. Knopf 1996 135p pa
$4.99 hardcover o.p. (7 and up)   **Fic**
1. Wrestling—Fiction 2. Friendship—Fiction
ISBN 0-679-88555-2 (pa)   LC 95-20468
"Narrator Ben, a high school senior, doesn't want to
be like his father and so many others in Sturbridge, Pa.,
who after graduating get a job at the cinder block plant.
Seemingly his only alternative is to become a state wrestling champion and thus win an athletic scholarship. But
his way is firmly blocked by his buddy Al, who reigns
supreme in their weight class." Publ Wkly
"The wresting scenes are thrilling. . . . Like Ben,
whose voice is so strong and clear here, Wallace weighs
his words carefully, making every one count in this excellent, understated first novel." Booklist

Wallace-Brodeur, Ruth
Blue eyes better. Dutton Children's Bks. 2002
106p il $15.99; pa $5.99 (4-6)   **Fic**
1. Death—Fiction
ISBN 0-525-46836-6; 0-14-250086-0 (pa)
                                   LC 2001-45205

When her older brother is killed in an accident, ten-
year-old Tessa and her parents find it difficult to overcome their grief and return to living normally
"From the first words, this small, beautiful novel is
rooted in hard fact. . . . The images are simple poetry.
. . . This is gripping family drama." Booklist

Wardlaw, Lee, 1955-
101 ways to bug your teacher; Lee Wardlaw.
Dial Books 2004 246p $16.99   **Fic**
1. School stories
ISBN 0-8037-2658-9   LC 2003-20068
Steve "Sneeze" Wyatt attempts to thwart his parents'
plan to have him skip eighth grade, but he has bigger
problems when his friends disapprove of his new list and
Mrs. "Fierce" Pierce threatens to keep him from the Invention Convention.
"In spite of the title, the characters show respect for
their teachers and parents, and for one another. A delightful read." SLJ

Watkins, Yoko Kawashima
My brother, my sister, and I. Bradbury Press
1994 275p hardcover o.p. paperback available
$5.99 (6 and up)   **Fic**
1. World War, 1939-1945—Fiction 2. Japan—Fiction
3. Korea—Fiction
ISBN 0-689-80656-6 (pa)   LC 93-23535
"The author continues her autobiographical account
begun in *So Far from the Bamboo Grove* with the story
of how the two sisters, Ko and Yoko, now reunited with
their brother Hideyo, try to survive in postwar Japan."
Horn Book
"Watkins's first-person narrative is beautifully direct
and emotionally honest." Publ Wkly

So far from the bamboo grove. Lothrop, Lee &
Shepard Bks. 1986 183p map hardcover o.p.
paperback available $4.95 (6 and up)   **Fic**
1. World War, 1939-1945—Fiction 2. Korea—Fiction
3. Japan—Fiction
ISBN 0-688-13115-8 (pa)   LC 85-15939
A fictionalized autobiography in which eight-year-old
Yoko escapes from Korea to Japan with her mother and
sister at the end of World War II
"An admirably told and absorbing novel." Horn Book
Followed by My brother, my sister and I

Watts, Julia, 1969-
Finding H.F. Alyson Bks. 2001 165p $12.95 (7
and up)   **Fic**
1. Lesbians—Fiction
ISBN 1-55583-622-4   LC 2001-31596
"Abandoned by her teenaged mother and raised in
Kentucky by her religious grandmother, 16-year-old
Heavenly Faith . . . knows she is different. She has a
crush on Wendy, a local college professor's daughter,
and the only person she can tell is her best friend Bo, a
'girlish boy' who is beaten regularly by the local jocks."
SLJ
"This novel, laced with realistic teen voices, should
fill a void for many teens who are coping with the some-
times-confusing realization of who they really are."
ALAN

Weatherly, Lee

Missing Abby. David Fickling Books 2004 208p
$15.95; lib bdg $17.99 **Fic**
1. Missing persons—Fiction 2. Friendship—Fiction
ISBN 0-385-75052-8; 0-385-75053-6 (lib bdg)
LC 2003-26546

As the last one to see thirteen-year-old Abby, Emma
is determined to discover the truth about her mysterious
disappearance, spurred in part by her feelings of guilt
over ending their friendship in order to ensure popularity
at her new school

"The book excels at examining the dissolution of a
friendship when one friend is unconventional and the
other longs for conformity." Horn Book Guide

Weeks, Sarah

So B. it; a novel. Laura Geringer Books 2004
245p $15.99 (5 and up) **Fic**
1. Mentally handicapped—Fiction 2. Mental illness—
Fiction
ISBN 0-06-623622-3 LC 2003-15643

After spending her life with her mentally retarded
mother and agoraphobic neighbor, twelve-year-old Heidi
sets out from Reno, Nevada, to New York to find out
who she is.

"This is lovely writing - real, touching, and pared
cleanly down to the essentials." Booklist

Wein, Elizabeth E., 1964-

The Winter Prince. Atheneum Pubs. 1993 202p
(7 and up) **Fic**
1. Arthur, King—Fiction 2. Mordred (Legendary character)—Fiction
LC 91-39129

Available in paperback from Puffin Bks. $6.99 (0-14-
250014-3)

Medraut, the bitter, illegitimate son of King Artos, is
tempted into joining Morgause, the king's treacherous
sister, in a plot against Lleu, the legitimate Prince of
Britain

"The writing is graceful and steeped in atmosphere,
and the story line includes enough sibling rivalry and ac-
tion to keep the reader going to the end." Publ Wkly
Other titles in this series are:
A coalition of lions (2003)
The sunbird (2004)

Wells, H. G. (Herbert George), 1866-1946

The war of the worlds (7 and up) **Fic**
1. Science fiction
Available from various publishers
First published 1898

"The inhabitants of Mars, a loathsome though highly
organized race, invade England, and by their command
of superior weapons subdue and prey on the people." Baker. Guide to the Best Fic

In this novel the author "introduced the 'Alien' being
into the role which became a cliché—a monstrous invad-
er of Earth, a competitor in a cosmic struggle for existence. Though the Martians were a ruthless and terrible
enemy, HGW was careful to point out that Man had
driven many animal species to extinction, and that human invaders of Tasmania had behaved no less callously
in exterminating their cousins." Sci Fic Ency

Werlin, Nancy, 1961-

Black mirror; a novel. Dial Bks. for Young
Readers 2001 249p $16.99; pa $6.99 (7 and up)
Fic
1. School stories 2. Mystery fiction
ISBN 0-8037-2605-8; 0-14-250028-3 (pa)
LC 00-43082

Convinced her brother's death was murder rather than
suicide, sixteen-year-old Frances begins her own investigation into suspicious student activities at her boarding
school

"This thrilling mystery is also a YA coming-of-age
novel where nothing turns out to be what it seems."
Booklist

Double helix. Dial Books 2004 252p $15.99 (7
and up) **Fic**
1. Genetic engineering—Fiction 2. Bioethics—Fiction
3. Science fiction
ISBN 0-8037-2606-6 LC 2003-12269

Eighteen-year-old Eli discovers a shocking secret
about his life and his family while working for a Nobel
Prizewinning scientist whose specialty is genetic engineering.

"Werlin clearly and dramatically raises fundamental
bioethical issues for teens to ponder. She also creates a
riveting story with sharply etched characters and complex
relationships that will stick with readers long after the
book is closed." SLJ

Locked inside. Delacorte Press 2000 259p
hardcover o.p. paperback available $5.50 (7 and
up) **Fic**
1. Kidnapping—Fiction
ISBN 0-440-22829-8 (pa) LC 99-16577

After she is kidnapped from the exclusive boarding
school she attends, heiress Marnie Skyedottir must
rethink her idealized relationship with her mother, her
own sense of who she is, and her relationships with others

"Werlin offers a compelling thriller that will keep
readers turning pages." Booklist

Westerfeld, Scott

The secret hour. Eos 2004 297p (Midnighters)
$15.99 (7 and up) **Fic**
1. Science fiction
ISBN 0-06-051951-7 LC 2003-6986

Upon moving to Bixby, Oklahoma, fifteen-year-old
Jessica Day learns that she is one of a group of people
who have special abilities that help them fight ancient
creatures living in an hour hidden at midnight; creatures
that seem determined to destroy Jess.

"Part science fiction, part horror story, this novel is
the first in a series. . . . The story is exciting and the
writing compelling." SLJ
Another available title in this series is:
Touching darkness (2005)

So yesterday; a novel. Razorbill 2004 225p
$16.99 (7 and up) **Fic**
1. Missing persons—Fiction 2. Mystery fiction
3. New York (N.Y.)—Fiction
ISBN 1-59514-00-X LC 2004-2302

Westerfeld, Scott—*Continued*

Hunter Braque, a New York City teenager who is paid by corporations to spot what is "cool," combines his analytical skills with girlfriend Jen's creative talents to find a missing person and thwart a conspiracy directed at the heart of consumer culture

"This hip, fascinating thriller aggressively questions consumer culture. . . . Teens will inhale this wholly entertaining, thought-provoking look at a system fueled by their purchasing power. " Booklist

Uglies. Simon Pulse 2005 425p pa $6.99 (7 and up)   **Fic**
1. Science fiction
ISBN 0-689-86538-4

"Fifteen-year-old Tally's eerily harmonious, postapocalyptic society gives extreme makeovers to teens on their sixteenth birthdays. . . . When a top-secret agency threatens to leave Tally ugly forever unless she spies on runaway teens, she agrees to infiltrate the Smoke, a shadowy colony of refugees from the 'tyranny of physical perfection.' " Booklist

"Ethical concerns will provide a good source of discussion. . . . Characterization . . . is strong, and . . . the novel is highly readable with a convincing plot." SLJ

Whelan, Gloria

Angel on the square. HarperCollins Pubs. 2001 293p $15.95; lib bdg $15.89; pa $6.99
                                                          Fic
1. Nicholas II, Emperor of Russia, 1868-1918—Fiction
2. Soviet Union—History—1917-1921, Revolution—Fiction
ISBN 0-06-029030-7; 0-06-029031-5 (lib bdg); 0-06-440879-5 (pa)   LC 2001-16639

In 1913 Russia, twelve-year-old Katya eagerly anticipates leaving her St. Petersburg home, though not her older cousin Misha, to join her mother, a lady in waiting in the household of Tsar Nicholas II, but the ensuing years bring world war, revolution, and undreamed of changes to her life

"The book's uncomplicated language and sensitive treatment of political issues make it an excellent, vibrant introduction to the cause and effects of Tsar Nikolai's fall." Publ Wkly

Burying the sun. HarperCollins Publishers 2004 205p $15.99; lib bdg $16.89   **Fic**
1. Saint Petersburg (Russia)—Siege, 1941-1944—Fiction 2. World War, 1939-1945—Fiction
ISBN 0-06-054112-1; 0-06-054113-X (lib bdg)
                                          LC 2003-12487

In Leningrad in 1941, when Russia and Germany are at war, fourteen-year-old Georgi vows to help his family and his city during the terrible siege.

"Haunting images and elegant prose make this companion to The Impossible Journey . . . and Angel on the Square . . . memorable. . . .The lilting writing style and simple dignity of the characters help construct an honest portrait of everyday life in extraordinary circumstances." SLJ

Chu Ju's house. HarperCollins 2004 227p $15.99; lib bdg $16.89   **Fic**
1. China—Fiction 2. Sex role—Fiction 3. Runaway teenagers—Fiction
ISBN 0-06-050724-1; 0-06-050725-X (lib bdg)
                                          LC 2003-6979

In order to save her baby sister, fourteen-year-old Chu Ju leaves her rural home in modern China and earns food and shelter by working on a sampan, tending silk worms, and planting rice seedlings, while wondering if she will ever see her family again.

"Whelan tells a compelling adventure story, filled with rich cultural detail, about a smart, likable teenage girl who overcomes society's gender restrictions." Booklist

Goodbye, Vietnam. Knopf 1992 135p hardcover o.p. paperback available $3.99 (4 and up)
                                                          Fic
1. Refugees—Fiction 2. Vietnamese—Fiction
ISBN 0-679-82376-X (pa)   LC 91-3660

Thirteen-year-old Mai and her family embark on a dangerous sea voyage from Vietnam to Hong Kong to escape the unpredictable and often brutal Vietnamese government

"While the book has the suspense and appeal of any good escape story, Whelan is neither melodramatic nor sentimental, and the sometimes horrific details of the scary voyage are plain but understated." Bull Cent Child Books

Homeless bird. HarperCollins Pubs. 2000 216p $15.95; lib bdg $16.89; pa $5.99 (6 and up)
                                                          Fic
1. Women—India—Fiction
ISBN 0-06-028454-4; 0-06-028452-8 (lib bdg); 0-06-440819-1 (pa)   LC 99-33241

When thirteen-year-old Koly enters into an ill-fated arranged marriage, she must either suffer a destiny dictated by India's tradition or find the courage to oppose it

"This beautifully told, inspiring story takes readers on a fascinating journey through modern India and the universal intricacies of a young woman's heart." Booklist

The impossible journey. HarperCollins Pubs. 2003 248p $15.99; lib bdg $16.89   **Fic**
1. Voyages and travels—Fiction
ISBN 0-06-623811-0; 0-06-623812-9 (lib bdg)
                                          LC 2002-4694

Companion volume to Angel on the square

In 1934, thirteen-year-old Marya and her younger brother, Georgi, set out alone on a long and arduous journey into Siberia to find their mother after she and their father are exiled for opposing Stalin

"Lyrical prose conveys both a strong sense of place and the tremendous love that compels the protagonist to find her parents." SLJ

White, Andrea

Surviving Antarctica; reality TV 2083; by Andrea White. 1st ed. HarperCollins 2005 327p $15.99; lib bdg $16.89 (7 and up)   **Fic**
1. Antarctica—Fiction 2. Science fiction
ISBN 0-06-055454-1; 0-06-055455-X (lib bdg)
                                          LC 2004-6249

White, Andrea—*Continued*

In the year 2083, five fourteen-year-olds who were deprived by chance of the opportunity to continue their educations reenact Scott's 1910-1913 expedition to the South Pole as contestants on a reality television show, secretly aided by a Department of Entertainment employee

"A real page-turner, this novel will give readers pause as they ponder the ethics of teens risking their lives in adult-contrived situations for the entertainment of the masses." Booklist

White, Ellen Emerson

Kaiulani; the people's princess. Scholastic 2001 238p (Royal diaries) $10.95   **Fic**

1. Kaiulani, Princess of Hawaii, 1875-1899—Fiction 2. Princesses—Fiction 3. Hawaii—Fiction

ISBN 0-439-12909-5   LC 00-57338

This fictional diary follows the life of Victoria Kaiulani Cleghorn from 1889 to 1893 as she studies to be a better princess, even as Hawaii's monarchy, and her throne, are being undermined by American businessmen

"The narrative flows smoothly and the main character is well developed." Horn Book Guide

White, Ruth

Belle Prater's boy. Farrar, Straus & Giroux 1996 196p $17 (5 and up)   **Fic**

1. Cousins—Fiction 2. Virginia—Fiction 3. Appalachian region—Fiction

ISBN 0-374-30668-0   LC 94-43625

Also available in paperback from Random House

A Newbery Medal honor book, 1997

"Gypsy and her cousin Woodrow become close friends after Woodrow's mother disappears. Both sixth-graders feel deserted by their parents—Gypsy discovers that her father committed suicide—and need to define themselves apart from these tragedies. White's prose evokes the coal mining region of Virginia and the emotional quality of her characters' transformations." Horn Book Guide

Another title about Belle Prater is:
The search for Belle Prater (2005)

Memories of Summer. Farrar, Straus & Giroux 2000 135p $16 (7 and up)   **Fic**

1. Mentally ill—Fiction 2. Sisters—Fiction 3. Michigan—Fiction

ISBN 0-374-34945-2   LC 99-54793

Also available Thorndike Press large print edition

In 1955, thirteen-year-old Lyric finds her whole life changing when her family moves from the hills of Virginia to a town in Michigan and her older sister Summer begins descending into mental illness

"A marvelous recreation of time and place and a poignant story that has much to say about compassion." SLJ

White, T. H. (Terence Hanbury), 1906-1964

The once and future king. Putnam 1958 677p $25.95   **Fic**

1. Arthur, King—Fiction 2. Great Britain—History—0-1066—Fiction

ISBN 0-399-10597-2   LC 58-10760

Also available in paperback from Ace Bks.

An omnibus edition of four novels; The sword in the stone (1939), The witch in the wood (1939, now called The Queen of Air and Darkness) and The ill-made knight (1940). A number of alterations have been made in the earlier books. Previously unpublished, The candle in the wind "deals with the plotting of Mordred and his kinsmen of the house of Orkney, and their undying enmity to King Arthur." Times Lit Suppl

"White's contemporary retelling of Malory's *Le Morte d'Arthur* is both romantic and exciting." Shapiro. Fic for Youth. 3d edition

Whitesel, Cheryl Aylward

Rebel; a Tibetan odyssey. HarperCollins Pubs. 2000 190p $16.95   **Fic**

1. Buddhism—Fiction 2. Monks—Fiction 3. Tibet (China)—Fiction

ISBN 0-688-16735-7   LC 99-45556

Although he rebels against life in the Tibetan Buddhist monastery where he had been sent, fourteen-year-old Thunder comes to some amazing realizations about himself

"Although the story provides an insightful background to the cultural and political tension that contemporary Tibet is caught in today, it is told with enough fast-paced verve to make it an enticing adventure story in its own right." Horn Book

Whytock, Cherry

My cup runneth over; the life of Angelica Cookson Potts. Simon & Schuster Bks. for Young Readers 2003 163p il $14.95   **Fic**

1. Weight loss—Fiction 2. School stories

ISBN 0-689-86546-5   LC 2003-45769

Published in the United Kingdom with title: Angel: disasters, diets, and D-cups

Believing she is too big, fourteen-year-old Angel tries dieting and kick-boxing to lose weight, but thanks to her friends and the school fashion show, she discovers that her size is just right

"This is very funny stuff, and Whytock freshens up a potentially trite template with peculiarly British recipes . . . plus amusingly annotated doodles." Booklist

Another available title about Angelica Cookson Potts is:
My scrumpious Scottish dumplings (2005)

Wiesel, Elie, 1928-

Night, Dawn, The accident: three tales. Hill & Wang 1972 318p hardcover o.p. paperback available $12 (7 and up)   **Fic**

1. Jews—Fiction

ISBN 0-374-52140-9 (pa)

In Dawn, Elisha, a young Jewish terrorist fighting for the creation of Israel in the 1940s is faced with an agonizing moral dilemma. He is to be the executioner of a British officer in reprisal for the hanging of a captured terrorist. A survivor of the concentration camps and a victim all of his life, Elisha considers whether he is any different from his oppressors if he can execute a helpless prisoner in cold blood. Night is a memoir. The accident concerns a survivor of Auschwitz who, recovering from a near-fatal accident, questions the meaning of man's existence and purpose, and death

Wilhelm, Doug

The revealers. Farrar, Straus & Giroux 2003
207p $16   **Fic**
1. School stories 2. Internet—Fiction 3. Friendship—
Fiction
ISBN 0-374-36255-6   LC 2002-35321
Tired of being bullied and picked on, three seventh-
grade outcasts join forces and, using scientific methods
and the power of the Internet, begin to create a new atmosphere at Parkland Middle School
"Briskly plotted, the novel shows how bringing the
stories to light transforms stereotypes into real people
and provides a vehicle for others to become involved.
. . . The novel is effective and will fascinate even reluctant readers." SLJ

Wilkinson, Carole, 1950-

Dragon keeper. Hyperion Books for Children
2005 c2003 339p $16.99 (5 and up)   **Fic**
1. Dragons—Fiction 2. China—Fiction
ISBN 0-7868-5581-9
First published 2003 in Australia
An orphan slave girl becomes a Dragon Keeper when
she heroically comes to the aid of an aging dragon and
both go on a dangerous journey across China to protect
a mysterious stone vital to the dragon's legacy.
"The relationship between the child and the beast
stands at the heart of this compelling adventure, which
is infused with humor as well as peril." Booklist

Williams, Carol Lynch, 1959-

If I forget, you remember. Delacorte Press 1998
201p pa $4.99 hardcover o.p.   **Fic**
1. Grandmothers—Fiction 2. Alzheimer's disease—
Fiction
ISBN 0-440-41420-2 (pa)   LC 97-20582
Twelve-year-old Elyse's plan to write an award-
winning novel during the summer is interrupted when her
grandmother, who has Alzheimer's disease, moves in
with the family
"The smooth writing, tenderness, and excellent pacing
keep the reader engrossed." Voice Youth Advocates

Williams, Lori Aurelia

When Kambia Elaine flew in from Neptune.
Simon & Schuster 2000 246p $17; pa $10 (7 and
up)   **Fic**
1. African Americans—Fiction 2. Houston (Tex.)—
Fiction
ISBN 0-689-82468-8; 0-689-84593-6 (pa)
LC 99-65154
Also available Thorndike Press large print edition
"Williams weaves two tales in the first-person narra-
tive of twelve-year-old Shayla: the story of Shayla's old-
er sister and her sexual awakening; and the story of
Kambia, Shayla's soon-to-be best friend, whose fantastic
stories of transformation hide her real-life abuse." Horn
Book Guide
"This is a strong and disturbing novel, told in beauti-
ful language. Teens will find it engrossing." SLJ

Williams, Maiya

The golden hour. Amulet Bks. 2004 259p
$16.95   **Fic**
1. Fantasy fiction 2. Siblings—Fiction
ISBN 0-8109-4823-0   LC 2003-16281
Thirteen-year-old Rowan and his eleven-year-old sister
Nina, still bereft by the death of their mother the year
before, experience an unusual adventure through time
when they come to stay with their two eccentric great-
aunts in a small town on the Maine coast.
"Part realistic fiction, part fantasy, part historical adventure, this entertaining novel features several well-
realized settings and some quirky, original characters.
The story is particularly energized by Rowan's intelligent, wry observations." Booklist

Williams-Garcia, Rita

Like sisters on the homefront. Lodestar Bks.
1995 165p $15.99; pa $5.99 (7 and up)
Fic
1. African Americans—Fiction 2. Family life—Fiction
3. Teenage mothers—Fiction
ISBN 0-525-67465-9; 0-14-038561-4 (pa)
LC 95-3690
"It's bad enough that 14-year-old Gayle has one baby,
but when she becomes pregnant again by another boy,
Mama's had enough. She takes Gayle for an abortion
and then ships her and her baby south to stay with religious relatives. . . . With the help of her dying great-
grandmother, who leaves Gayle the family's African-
American oral tradition, she begins to mature and understand her place in the family and her future." Child Book
Rev Serv
"Beautifully written, the text captures the cadence and
rhythm of New York street talk and the dilemma of being poor, black, and uneducated. This is a gritty, realistic, well-told story." SLJ

No laughter here. HarperCollins 2004 133p
$15.99; lib bdg $16.89 (7 and up)   **Fic**
1. Female circumcision—Fiction 2. Friendship—Fiction 3. African Americans—Fiction 4. New York
(N.Y.)—Fiction
ISBN 0-688-16247-9; 0-688-16248-7 (lib bdg)
LC 2003-9331
In Queens, New York, ten-year-old Akilah is determined to find out why her closest friend, Victoria, is silent and withdrawn after returning from a trip to her
homeland, Nigeria.
This is a "disturbing and poignant coming-of-age novel. . . .This contemporary tale about the ancient rite of
female circumcision will no doubt leave an indelible
mark on preteens." Publ Wkly

Wilson, Jacqueline

The suitcase kid; illustrated by Ying-hwa Hu.
Delacorte Press 1997 140p il pa $4.50 hardcover
o.p.   **Fic**
1. Divorce—Fiction 2. Family life—Fiction
ISBN 0-440-41371-0 (pa)   LC 96-29083
First published 1992 in the United Kingdom
Ten-year-old Andrea tries to deal with her parents' divorce and the presence of stepparents, stepsisters, and
stepbrothers

Wilson, Jacqueline—*Continued*

"Wilson's frank portrayal of the realities of shared custody will ring true for young readers. . . . Andrea's attempts to cope with her challenging life are, at turns, funny, sad, and poignant." Booklist

Wilson, John, 1951-

And in the morning. Kids Can Press 2003 198p $16.95 (7 and up) **Fic**
1. World War, 1914-1918—Fiction
ISBN 1-55337-400-2

"Jim Hay, 16, is caught up in the patriotic fervor sweeping across Scotland as the British troops prepare to enter World War I. . . . His father is killed in action and 10 days later his mother dies from shock and grief. Within weeks, Jim has signed up and is soon in the trenches. . . . A compelling, fascinating, and ultimately disturbing book that is not to be missed." SLJ

Wilson, Nancy Hope, 1947-

Mountain pose. Farrar, Straus & Giroux 2001 233p $17 (5 and up) **Fic**
1. Grandmothers—Fiction 2. Diaries—Fiction 3. Vermont—Fiction
ISBN 0-374-35078-7 LC 00-57269

Also available in paperback from Scholastic

When twelve-year-old Ellie inherits an old Vermont farm from her cruel and heartless grandmother Aurelia, she reads a set of diaries written by an ancestor and discovers secrets from the past

"Beautifully written and suspenseful, this novel explores the many emotions associated with the tragedy of spousal and child abuse." Voice Youth Advocates

Winerip, Michael

Adam Canfield of the Slash. Candlewick Press 2005 326p $15.99 (5 and up) **Fic**
1. Journalism—Fiction 2. School stories
ISBN 0-7636-2340-7

While serving as co-editors of their school newspaper, middle-schoolers Adam and Jennifer uncover fraud and corruption in their school and in the city's government.

"This is a deceptively fun read that somehow manages to present kids with some of the most subtle social and ethical questions currently shaping their futures." SLJ

Wisler, G. Clifton, 1950-

Caleb's choice. Lodestar Bks. 1996 154p pa $4.99 hardcover o.p. **Fic**
1. Underground railroad—Fiction 2. Slavery—Fiction
ISBN 0-14-038256-9 (pa) LC 96-2339

While living in Texas in 1858, fourteen-year-old Caleb faces a dilemma in deciding whether or not to assist fugitive slaves in their run for freedom

"This fast-paced, easy-to-read novel proves that history can be intriguing and exciting, Wisler draws readers into this masterful, and often humorous tale." ALAN

Red Cap. Lodestar Bks. 1991 160p hardcover o.p. paperback available $4.99 (4 and up)
Fic
1. Powell, Ransom J., 1849-1899—Fiction 2. Andersonville Prison—Fiction 3. United States—History—1861-1865, Civil War—Fiction
ISBN 0-14-036936 LC 90-21944

A young Yankee drummer boy displays great courage when he's captured and sent to Andersonville Prison

The author "presents a well-researched view of the war. He effectively interweaves the known facts of Powell's life with first-person accounts of other soldiers and prisoners to create an exciting story." SLJ

Run the blockade. HarperCollins Pubs. 2000 122p $15.95 hardcover o.p.; lib bdg $15.89 hardcover o.p. **Fic**
1. United States—History—1861-1865, Civil War—Fiction 2. Sea stories
ISBN 0-688-16538-9; 0-06-029208-3 (lib bdg) LC 99-87298

During the Civil War, fourteen-year-old Henry finds adventure working as a ship's boy and lookout aboard the "Banshee," a new British ship attempting to get past the Yankee blockade of the Southern coast

The blockade "gets a dramatic presentation children can relate to, and the focus on commerce as opposed to politics is unusual." Booklist

Wittlinger, Ellen, 1948-

Hard love. Simon & Schuster Bks. for Young Readers 1999 224p $16.95; pa $8 (7 and up)
Fic
1. Authorship—Fiction 2. Lesbians—Fiction
ISBN 0-689-82134-4; 0-689-84154-X (pa) LC 98-6668

"John, cynical yet vulnerable, thinks he's immune to emotion until he meets bright, brittle Marisol, the author of his favorite zine. He falls in love, but Marisol, a lesbian, just wants to be friends. A love story of a different sort—funny, poignant, and thoughtful." Booklist

Zigzag. Simon & Schuster Bks. for Young Readers 2003 267p $16.95 (7 and up) **Fic**
1. Automobile travel—Fiction 2. Cousins—Fiction
ISBN 0-689-84996-6 LC 2002-2145

A high-school junior makes a trip with her aunt and two cousins, discovering places she did not know existed and strengths she did not know she had

"Teens will easily hear themselves in Robin's hilarious, sharp observations and feel her excitement as she travels through new country and discovers her own strength." Booklist

Wolf, Allan

New found land; Lewis and Clark's voyage of discovery: a novel. Candlewick Press 2004 500p map $18.99 (7 and up) **Fic**
1. Lewis and Clark Expedition (1804-1806)—Fiction
ISBN 0-7636-2113-7 LC 2003-65254

The letters and thoughts of Thomas Jefferson, members of the Corps of Discovery, their guide Sacagawea, and Captain Lewis's Newfoundland dog, all tell of the

Wolf, Allan—*Continued*

historic exploratory expedition to seek a water route to the Pacific Ocean.

"This is an extraordinary, engrossing book that would appeal most to serious readers, but it should definitely be added to any collection." SLJ

Includes glossary and bibliographical references

Wolff, Virginia Euwer

Make lemonade. Holt & Co. 1993 200p $17.95

Fic

1. Teenage mothers—Fiction 2. Babysitters—Fiction
3. Poverty—Fiction

ISBN 0-8050-2228-7   LC 92-41182

Also available Thorndike Press large print edition and in paperback from Scholastic

"Fourteen-year-old LaVaughn accepts the job of babysitting Jolly's two small children but quickly realizes that the young woman, a seventeen-year-old single mother, needs as much help and nurturing as her two neglected children. The four become something akin to a temporary family, and through their relationship each makes progress toward a better life. Sixty-six brief chapters, with words arranged on the page like poetry, perfectly echo the patterns of teenage speech." Horn Book Guide

Another title about LaVaughn is:
True believer (2001)

The Mozart season. Holt & Co. 1991 249p o.p.

Scholastic paperback available $4.99 (6 and up)

Fic

1. Violinists—Fiction

ISBN 0-439-16309-9 (pa)   LC 90-23635

Allegra spends her twelfth summer practicing a Mozart concerto for a violin competition and finding many significant connections in her world

"With a clear, fresh voice that never falters, Wolff gives readers a delightful heroine, a fully realized setting, and a slowly building tension that reaches a stunning climax." SLJ

Probably still Nick Swansen. Holt & Co. 1988 144p (7 and up)   Fic

1. Learning disabilities—Fiction

ISBN 0-8050-0701-6   LC 88-13175

Available in paperback from Simon & Schuster $7.99 (0-689-85226-6)

Sixteen-year-old learning-disabled Nick struggles to endure a life in which the other kids make fun of him, he has to take special classes, his date for the prom makes an excuse not to go with him, and he is haunted by the memory of his older sister who drowned while he was watching

"It is a poignant, gentle, utterly believable narrative." Booklist

Wood, June Rae, 1946-

The man who loved clowns. Putnam 1992 224p pa $5.99 hardcover o.p.   Fic

1. Down syndrome—Fiction 2. Mentally handicapped—Fiction 3. Uncles—Fiction

ISBN 0-14-240422-5 (pa)   LC 91-33861

Thirteen-year-old Delrita, whose unhappy life has caused her to hide from the world, loves her uncle Punky but sometimes feels ashamed of his behavior because he has Down's syndrome

"Wood's prose is strong and flowing, with a good balance of dialogue and narrative, and with several well-developed and memorable characters." SLJ

Another title about Delrita is:
Turtle on a fence post (1997)

Wooding, Chris, 1977-

The haunting of Alaizabel Cray. Orchard Bks. 2004 292p $16.95 (7 and up)   Fic

1. Horror fiction 2. Supernatural—Fiction 3. London (England)—Fiction

ISBN 0-439-54656-7   LC 2003-69108

First published 2001 in the United Kingdom

In a world similar to Victorian London, Thaniel, a seventeen-year-old hunter of deadly, demonic creatures called the wych-kin, takes in a lost, possessed girl, and becomes embroiled in a plot to unleash evil on the world

"Eerie and exhilarating. . . . [The author] fuses together his best storytelling skills . . . to create a fabulously horrific and ultimately timeless underworld." SLJ

Woodruff, Elvira

Dear Austin; letters from the Underground Railroad; illustrated by Nancy Carpenter. Knopf 1998 137p il $16; lib bdg $17.99; pa $5.50

Fic

1. Underground railroad—Fiction 2. Slavery—Fiction
3. African Americans—Fiction 4. Pennsylvania—Fiction

ISBN 0-679-88594-3; 0-679-98594-8 (lib bdg);
0-375-80356-4 (pa)   LC 98-5314

Sequel to Dear Levi (1994)

In 1853, in letters to his older brother, eleven-year-old Levi describes his adventures in the Pennsylvania countryside with his black friend Jupiter and his experiences with the Underground Railroad

"The smoothly written text is fast paced." Horn Book Guide

Woods, Brenda

The red rose box. Putnam 2002 136p $16.99; pa $5.99 (5 and up)   Fic

1. African Americans—Fiction 2. Louisiana—Fiction

ISBN 0-399-23702-X; 0-14-250151-4 (pa)

LC 2001-18354

In 1953, Leah Hopper dreams of leaving the poverty and segregation of her home in Sulphur, Louisiana, and when Aunt Olivia sends train tickets to Los Angeles as part of her tenth birthday present, Leah gets a first taste of freedom

"In language made musical with southern phrases, this . . . novel shapes the era and characters with both well-chosen particulars and universal emotions." Booklist

Woods, Ron

The hero. Knopf 2002 215p $15.95; lib bdg $17.99; pa $4.99   Fic

1. Rafting (Sports)—Fiction 2. Death—Fiction

ISBN 0-375-80612-1; 0-375-90612-6 (lib bdg);
0-440-22978-2 (pa)   LC 00-54460

Woods, Ron—*Continued*
In the summer of 1957 in Idaho, when 14 year old Jamie and his older cousin Jerry reluctantly include outsider Dennis in their rafting adventure, Dennis drowns and Jamie lies that Dennis made a heroic sacrifice
"The author deftly handles a convincing adventure with emotional depth and tenderness toward his characters." SLJ

Woodson, Jacqueline
Behind you. Putnam 2004 118p $15.99 (7 and up) **Fic**
1. Death—Fiction 2. African Americans—Fiction 3. New York (N.Y.)—Fiction
ISBN 0-399-23988-X
Sequel to If you come softly
After fifteen-year-old Jeremiah is mistakenly shot by police, the people who love him struggle to cope with their loss as they recall his life and death, unaware that 'Miah is watching over them.
"Woodson writes with impressive poetry about race, love, death, and what grief feels like—the things that 'snap the heart' and her characters' open strength and wary optimism will resonate with many teens." Booklist

The house you pass on the way. Delacorte Press 1997 99p $16.99; pa $5.99 (7 and up) **Fic**
1. Cousins—Fiction 2. Racially mixed people—Fiction 3. African Americans—Fiction 4. Lesbians—Fiction
ISBN 0-399-23969-3; 0-14-250191-3 (pa)
LC 97-1620
When fourteen-year-old Staggerlee, the daughter of a racially mixed marriage, spends a summer with her cousin Trout, she begins to question her sexuality to Trout and catches a glimpse of her possible future self
"Woodson writes beautifully about feelings and issues, and this slim novel is packed with them. Racism is discussed clearly, family barriers are built and torn down, and sexuality and young women's coming-of-age are explored. . . . Woodson stops well short of being sexually explicit." Voice Youth Advocates

Hush. Putnam 2002 181p pa $5.99 hardcover o.p. **Fic**
1. Witnesses—Fiction 2. African Americans—Fiction
ISBN 0-14-250049-6 (pa)   LC 2001-19710
Thirteen-year-old Toswiah finds her life changed when her family enters the witness protection program
The author's "poetic, low-key, yet vivid writing style perfectly conveys the story's atmosphere of quiet intensity." Horn Book

I hadn't meant to tell you this. Delacorte Press 1994 115p hardcover o.p. paperback available $4.99 **Fic**
1. African Americans—Fiction 2. Friendship—Fiction 3. Incest—Fiction 4. Child sexual abuse—Fiction
ISBN 0-440-21960-4 (pa)   LC 93-8733
Marie, the only black girl in the eighth grade willing to befriend her white classmate Lena, discovers that Lena's father is doing horrible things to her in private
"Woodson's characters are deftly drawn, whole individuals; her spare prose and crystal images create a haunting, poetic novel." Horn Book Guide

If you come softly. Putnam 1998 181p $15.99; pa $5.99 (7 and up) **Fic**
1. African Americans—Fiction 2. Race relations—Fiction 3. New York (N.Y.)—Fiction
ISBN 0-399-23112-9; 0-698-11862-6 (pa)
LC 97-32212
After meeting at their private school in New York, fifteen-year-old Jeremiah, who is black and whose parents are separated, and Ellie, who is white and whose mother has twice abandoned her, fall in love and then try to cope with people's reactions
"The gentle and melancholy tone of this book makes it ideal for thoughtful readers and fans of romance." Voice Youth Advocates
Followed by Behind you (2004)

Miracle's boys. Putnam 2000 133p $15.99; pa $5.99 **Fic**
1. Brothers—Fiction 2. Orphans—Fiction 3. African Americans—Fiction 4. New York (N.Y.)—Fiction
ISBN 0-399-23113-7; 0-698-11916-9 (pa)
LC 99-40050
Also available Thorndike Press large print edition
Coretta Scott King award for text, 2001
Twelve-year-old Lafayette's close relationship with his older brother Charlie changes after Charlie is released from a detention home and blames Lafayette for the death of their mother
"The fast-paced narrative is physically immediate, and the dialogue is alive with anger and heartbreak." Booklist

Wrede, Patricia C., 1953-
Dealing with dragons. Harcourt Brace Jovanovich 1990 212p $17; pa $5.95 (6 and up) **Fic**
1. Fairy tales 2. Dragons—Fiction
ISBN 0-15-222900-0; 0-15-204566-X (pa)
LC 89-24599
Also available in paperback from Scholastic
"Jane Yolen books"
Bored with traditional palace life, a princess goes off to live with a group of dragons and soon becomes involved with fighting against some disreputable wizards who want to steal away the dragons' kingdom
"A decidedly diverting novel with plenty of action and many slightly skewed fairy-tale conventions that add to the laugh-out-loud reading pleasure and give the story a wide appeal. The good news is that this is book one in the Enchanted Forest Chronicles." Booklist
Other available titles in the Enchanted Forest Chronicles are:
Calling on dragons (1993)
Searching for dragons (1991)
Talking to dragons (1993)

Sorcery and Cecelia, or, The enchanted chocolate pot; being the correspondence of two young ladies of quality regarding various magical scandals in London and the country; {by} Patricia C. Wrede and Caroline Stevermer. Harcourt 2003 316p $17; pa $6.95 (7 and up) **Fic**
1. Cousins—Fiction 2. Supernatural—Fiction 3. Great Britain—Fiction
ISBN 0-15-204615-1; 0-15-205300-X (pa)
LC 2002-38706

Wrede, Patricia C., 1953-—*Continued*

In 1817 in England, two young cousins, Cecilia living in the country and Kate in London, write letters to keep each other informed of their exploits, which take a sinister turn when they find themselves confronted by evil wizards

"This is a fun story that quickly draws in the reader." Voice Youth Advocates

Another available title about Kate and Cecilia is: The grand tour (2004)

Wright, Betty Ren

Out of the dark. Scholastic 1995 149p $13.95 (4 and up) **Fic**

1. Ghost stories 2. Grandmothers—Fiction
ISBN 0-590-43598-1   LC 93-48025

"Jessie and her parents have recently moved to her grandmother's rural home, but her enjoyment of the house is marred by nightmares that are chillingly real. Her parents' frustrations with unemployment have put a strain on the whole family, and she doesn't feel able to share her terror as the threatening ghost of her dreams begins to appear while she is awake. . . . Relationships built on well-defined characters add realism to this supernatural tale. Effective and well crafted." SLJ

Wulffson, Don L., 1943-

Soldier X. Viking 2001 226p $15.99; pa $6.99 (7 and up) **Fic**

1. World War, 1939-1945—Fiction 2. Russia—Fiction
ISBN 0-670-88863-X; 0-14-250073-9 (pa)
            LC 99-49418

"Based on a true story"

In 1943 sixteen-year-old Erik experiences the horrors of war when he is drafted into the German army and sent to fight on the Russian front

"Erik's first-person narrative records battlefield sequences with an unflinching—and occasionally numbing—brutality, in a story notable for its unusual perspective." Horn Book Guide

Wyeth, Sharon Dennis

A piece of heaven. Knopf 2001 200p
            Fic

1. Single parent family—Fiction 2. Mentally ill—Fiction 3. African Americans—Fiction
ISBN 0-679-88535-8; 0-440-418109-0 (pa)
            LC 00-62930

Thirteen-year-old Haley holds her life together with the help of good people after her mother suffers a nervous breakdown and her brother is arrested

"The text combines lively dialogue; appealing, believable characters, and descriptions that . . . ring with authenticity." Booklist

Wynne-Jones, Tim

The boy in the burning house. Farrar, Straus & Giroux 2001 c2000 213p $16; pa $5.95
            Fic

1. Mystery fiction 2. Canada—Fiction
ISBN 0-374-30930-2; 0-374-40887-4 (pa)
            LC 99-89534

"Melanie Kroupa books"

First published 2000 in Canada

Trying to solve the mystery of his father's disappearance from their rural Canadian community, fourteen-year-old Jim gets help from the disturbed Ruth Rose, who suspects her stepfather, a local pastor

"A gripping, fast-moving plot offers the pure adrenaline rush of a thriller." Horn Book Guide

Stephen Fair; a novel. DK Ink 1998 218p (7 and up) **Fic**

1. Family life—Fiction
ISBN 0-7894-2495-9   LC 97-40328

Available in paperback from HarperCollins $5.95 (ISBN 0-06-447206-X)

"A Melanie Kroupa book"

At the age of fifteen Stephen begins having nightmares like the ones that drove his older brother away from home, and eventually the dreams lead to a discovery that is shocking but that ultimately allows his family to come back together

This offers "strong characterization, rich imagery, and well-crafted writing." Horn Book Guide

A thief in the house of memory; by Tim Wynne-Jones. 1st ed. Farrar, Straus and Giroux 2004 210p $17 (7 and up) **Fic**

1. Memory—Fiction 2. Mothers—Fiction 3. Canada—Fiction
ISBN 0-374-37478-3   LC 2004-53263

"Melanie Kroupa books"

The death of an apparent stranger in the Steeple family's old home triggers troubling questions for sixteen-year-old Declan as he tries to make sense of his fragmented dreams, random memories, and unexplained coincidences, hoping to learn the truth about the mother who suddenly left when he was ten.

"This rich and rewarding novel will appeal most to thoughtful readers who appreciate a sad and bittersweet read." SLJ

Yee, Lisa

Millicent Min, girl genius. Arthur A. Levine Books 2003 248p $16.95; pa $4.99 (5 and up)
            Fic

1. Gifted children—Fiction 2. School stories 3. Chinese Americans—Fiction
ISBN 0-439-42519-0; 0-439-42520-4 (pa)
            LC 2003-3747

"At the tender age of eleven, Millicent Min has completed her junior year of high school. Summer school is Millie's idea of fun, so she is excited that her parents are allowing her to take a college poetry course. . . . The tension between Millie's formal, overly intellectual way of expressing herself and her emotional immaturity makes her a very funny narrator. . . . Readers considerably older than Millicent's eleven years will enjoy this strong debut novel." Voice Youth Advocates

Yep, Laurence

Angelfish. Putnam 2001 216p $16.99 (5 and up)
            Fic

1. Chinese Americans—Fiction
ISBN 0-399-23041-6   LC 00-62676

Yep, Laurence—*Continued*

Robin, a young ballet dancer who is half Chinese and half white, works in a fish store for Mr. Tsow, a brusque Chinese who accuses her of being a half-person and who harbors a bitter secret

"An entertaining read with an engaging and resourceful protagonist." SLJ

The case of the Goblin Pearls. HarperCollins Pubs. 1997 179p (Chinatown mystery) pa $4.95 hardcover o.p. **Fic**

1. Mystery fiction 2. Chinese Americans—Fiction 3. San Francisco (Calif.)—Fiction

ISBN 0-06-440552-4 (pa) LC 96-22924

Lily and her aunt, a Chinese American movie actress, join forces to solve the theft of some priceless pearls and stop the operator of a sweatshop in San Francisco's Chinatown

"With enough fun and intrigue to keep the pages turning, this is a worthwhile series title." SLJ

Other available titles in the Chinatown mystery series are:

The case of the firecrackers (1999)
The case of the lion dance (1998)

Child of the owl. Harper & Row 1977 217p pa $6.99 hardcover o.p. (5 and up) **Fic**

1. Chinese Americans—Fiction 2. Grandmothers—Fiction 3. San Francisco (Calif.)—Fiction

ISBN 0-06-440336-X (pa) LC 76-24314

"Casey, a 12-year-old Chinese American girl, is more American than Chinese. When her father, a compulsive gambler, is hospitalized after a severe beating, Casey moves in with her grandmother in San Francisco's Chinatown. Although she is a street-smart child, Casey finds that she is an outsider in this community. Her grandmother teaches her something of her heritage and what it means to be 'a child of the owl.'" Shapiro. Fic for Youth. 3d edition

Dragon's gate. HarperCollins Pubs. 1993 273p $16.99; pa $6.99 (6 and up) **Fic**

1. Chinese—United States—Fiction 2. Railroads Fic tion

ISBN 0-06-022971-3; 0-06-440489-7 (pa)

LC 92-43649

A Newbery Medal honor book, 1994

When he accidentally kills a Manchu, a fifteen-year-old Chinese boy is sent to America to join his father, an uncle, and other Chinese working to build a tunnel for the transcontinental railroad through the Sierra Nevada mountains in 1867

"Yep has succeeded in realizing the primary characters and the irrepressibly dramatic story. . . . The carefully researched details will move students to thought and discussion." Bull Cent Child Books

Dragonwings. Harper & Row 1975 248p lib bdg $16.89; pa $6.99 (5 and up) **Fic**

1. Chinese Americans—Fiction 2. San Francisco (Calif.)—Fiction

ISBN 0-06-026738-0 (lib bdg); 0-06-440085-9 (pa)

"In 1903 Moon Shadow, eight years old, leaves China for the 'Land of the Golden Mountains,' San Francisco, to be with his father, Windrider, a father he has never seen. There, beset by the trials experienced by most foreigners in America, Moonrider shares his father's dream—to fly. This dream enables Windrider to endure the mockery of the other Chinese, the poverty he suffers in this hostile place—the land of the white demons—and his loneliness for his wife and his own country." Shapiro. Fic for Youth. 3d edition

Dream soul. HarperCollins Pubs. 2000 245p $15.95; lib bdg $164.89; pa $6.99 **Fic**

1. Chinese Americans—Fiction 2. Christmas—Fiction 3. West Virginia—Fiction

ISBN 0-06-028389-0; 0-06-028390-4 (lib bdg); 0-06-440788-8 (pa) LC 99-88636

In 1927, as Christmas approaches, fifteen-year-old Joan Lee hopes to get her parents' permission to celebrate the holiday, one of the problems of belonging to the only Chinese American family in her small West Virginia community

In this novel "Yep captures the complex relationships of family members trying to balance between two cultures." Bull Cent Child Books

Hiroshima; a novella. Scholastic 1995 56p pa $4.99 hardcover o.p. (4 and up) **Fic**

1. Hiroshima (Japan)—Bombardment, 1945—Fiction

ISBN 0-590-20833-0 (pa) LC 94-18195

"This moving and detailed narrative chronicles the dropping of the atomic bomb on Hiroshima and its effects on its citizens, especially on twelve-year-old Sachi. Based on true accounts, this book describes the horrors and sadness as well as the courage and hope that result from war." Soc Educ

Thief of hearts. HarperCollins Pubs. 1995 197p pa $6.99 hardcover o.p. (5 and up) **Fic**

1. Chinese Americans—Fiction 2. Friendship—Fiction 3. San Francisco (Calif.)—Fiction

ISBN 0-06-440591-5 (pa) LC 94-18703

"Stacy is not pleased that she's been elected by her parents to show a new girl from China around school, particularly when it turns out that Hong Ch'un is snotty and difficult, even calling Stacy t'ung *chung*, 'mixed seed.' Stacy's mother (whose story was told in Child of the Owl . . . *is of Chine*se descent, and her father Caucasian, and when Hong Ch'un is accused by the other kids of stealing, Stacy feels torn between parental instruction, ethnic loyalty, and peer acceptance." Bull Cent Child Books

"Told with candor and controlled emotion, this first-person narrative presents a difficult topic in a manner accessible to a wide audience." Horn Book

The traitor; Golden Mountain chronicles, 1885. HarperCollins Pubs. 2003 310p $16.99; lib bdg $17.89 (5 and up) **Fic**

1. Prejudices—Fiction 2. Friendship—Fiction 3. Chinese Americans—Fiction

ISBN 0-06-027522-7; 0-06-027523-5 (lib bdg)

LC 2002-22534

Sequel to Dragon's gate

In 1885, a lonely illegitimate American boy and a lonely Chinese American boy develop an unlikely friendship in the midst of prejudices and racial tension in their coal mining town of Rock Springs, Wyoming

"The short chapters read quickly, and readers will be-

Yep, Laurence—*Continued*
come involved through the first-person voices that capture each boy's feelings of being an outsider and a traitor." Booklist

Yolen, Jane
Armageddon summer; {by} Jane Yolen & Bruce Coville. Harcourt Brace & Co. 1998 266p $17; pa $6.95 (7 and up) **Fic**
1. Cults—Fiction
ISBN 0-15-201767-4; 0-15-202268-6 (pa)
LC 98-6920
Fourteen-year-old Marina and sixteen-year-old Jed accompany their parents' religious cult, the Believers, to await the end of the world atop a remote mountain, where they try to decide what they themselves believe
"Yolen and Coville, writing in alternating chapters from Marina's and Jed's points of view, explore their rich, thought-provoking theme with the perfect balance of gripping adventure and understated pathos, leavened by a dollop of humor." Booklist

Briar Rose. Doherty Assocs. 1992 190p (Fairy tale series) hardcover o.p. paperback available $5.99 **Fic**
1. Fantasy fiction
ISBN 0-7653-4230-8 (pa) LC 92-25456
"A TOR book"
"Yolen takes the story of Briar Rose (commonly known as Sleeping Beauty) and links it to the Holocaust. . . . Rebecca Berlin, a young woman who has grown up hearing her grandmother Gemma tell an unusual and frightening version of the Sleeping Beauty legend, realizes when Gemma dies that the fairy tale offers one of the very few clues she has to her grandmother's past. . . . By interpolating Gemma's vivid and imaginative story into the larger narrative, Yolen has created an engrossing novel." Publ Wkly

The devil's arithmetic. Viking Kestrel 1988 170p hardcover o.p. paperback available $4.99 (4 and up) **Fic**
1. Jews—Fiction 2. Holocaust, 1933-1945—Fiction
ISBN 0-14-034535-3 (pa) LC 88-14235
"During a Passover Seder, 12-year-old Hannah finds herself transported from America in 1988 to Poland in 1942, where she assumes the life of young Chaya. Within days the Nazis take Chaya and her neighbors off to a concentration camp, mere components in the death factory. As days pass, Hannah's own memory of her past, and the prisoners' future, fades until she is Chaya completely." Publ Wkly
"Through Hannah, with her memories of the present and the past, Yolen does a fine job of illustrating the importance of remembering. She adds much to children's understanding of the effects of the Holocaust." SLJ

Girl in a cage; {by} Jane Yolen & Robert J. Harris. Philomel Bks. 2002 234p $18.99; pa $6.99 **Fic**
1. Robert I, King of Scotland, 1274-1329—Fiction 2. Scotland—Fiction
ISBN 0-399-23627-9; 0-14-240132-3 (pa)
LC 2001-55978

As English armies invade Scotland in 1306, eleven-year-old Princess Marjorie, daughter of the newly crowned Scottish king, Robert the Bruce, is captured by England's King Edward Longshanks and held in a cage on public display
"Marjorie's first-person narration of her captivity and the events leading up to it is exciting and moving, and her strategies for coping with a hideous imprisonment are models of ingenuity and staying true to oneself." SLJ

Jason and the Gorgon's blood; by Jane Yolen and Robert J. Harris. HarperCollins 2004 246p (Young heroes) $15.99; lib bdg $16.89
Fic
1. Jason (Greek mythology)—Fiction 2. Adventure fiction
ISBN 0-06-029452-3; 0-06-029453-1 (lib bdg)
LC 2003-4096
Jason, who will grow up to become the head of the Argonauts, leads five other boys on a dangerous quest to save the kingdom of Iolcus, learning along the way what it means to be in command.
"There is plenty of action to keep mythology enthusiasts happy, and the band of angry and violent centaurs and attacks by hungry harpies could convert new fans to the genre." SLJ

Passager; the young Merlin trilogy, book one. Harcourt Brace & Co. 1996 76p $16 **Fic**
1. Merlin (Legendary character)—Fiction 2. Fantasy fiction
ISBN 0-15-200391-6 LC 94-27101
Also available one volume paperback compilation of the entire trilogy $6.95 (ISBN 0-15-205211-9)
A foundling rediscovers his identity through the help of the falconer who adopts him
A "stark, poignant, and absorbing tale. . . . This 'skinny' book will entice reluctant readers, but its rich language and poetic phrasing make it compelling and challenging." SLJ
Other titles in the Young Merlin trilogy are:
Hobby (1996)
Merlin (1997)

Prince across the water; [by] Jane Yolen & Robert J. Harris. Philomel Books 2004 290p $18.99 **Fic**
1. Scotland—Fiction 2. War stories
ISBN 0-399-23897-2 LC 2004-44628
In 1746, a year after the Scottish clans have rallied to the call of their exiled prince, Charles Stuart, to take up arms against England's tyranny, fourteen-year-old, epileptic Duncan MacDonald and his cousin, Ewan, run away to join the fight at Culloden and discover the harsh reality of war.
"The convincing depictions of people and relationships earlier in the story deepen the sense of despair during the battle, which is realistically depicted as cruel, violent, and gory. . . . a spirited historical adventure." Booklist

The queen's own fool; a novel of Mary Queen of Scots; {by} Jane Yolen and Robert J. Harris. Philomel Bks. 2000 390p hardcover o.p. paperback available $7.99 **Fic**
1. Mary, Queen of Scots, 1542-1587—Fiction 2. Scotland—Fiction
ISBN 0-698-11918-5 (pa) LC 99-55070

Yolen, Jane—*Continued*

When twelve-year-old Nicola leaves Troupe Brufort and serves as the fool for Mary, Queen of Scots, she experiences the political and religious upheavals in both France and Scotland

"The authors have woven fiction and historical fact into a seamless tapestry." Horn Book Guide

Sword of the rightful king; a novel of King Arthur. Harcourt 2003 349p $17   **Fic**
1. Arthur, King—Fiction 2. Knights and knighthood—Fiction 3. Middle Ages—Fiction 4. Great Britain—History—0-1066—Fiction
ISBN 0-15-202527-8   LC 2002-152622

Merlinnus the magician devises a way for King Arthur to prove himself the rightful king of England—pulling a sword from a stone—but trouble arises when someone else removes the sword first

"Combining old and new, adventure and idealism, this will leave many readers hoping for a sequel that is just as well written and intriguingly crafted." Booklist

Young, Karen Romano, 1959-

The Beetle and me; a love story. Greenwillow Bks. 1999 181p $15.95; pa $5.95 (7 and up)   **Fic**
1. Automobiles—Fiction 2. Family life—Fiction
ISBN 0-688-15922-2; 0-380-73295-5 (pa)
LC 98-16327

Surrounded by her busy extended family and their many cars, fifteen-year-old Daisy pursues her goal of single-handedly restoring the car of her dreams, the old purple Volkswagen Beetle from her childhood

"An oddly endearing, 'tweaked' love story that touches on numerous teen concerns: following your dream; getting along with parents; and, of course, finding that perfect set of wheels." Booklist

Yumoto, Kazumi

The letters; translated by Cathy Hirano. Farrar, Straus & Giroux 2002 165p $16 (7 and up)   **Fic**
1. Death—Fiction 2. Japan—Fiction
ISBN 0-374-34383-7   LC 2001-59768
Original Japanese edition, 1997

In Japan, the death of her former landlady triggers a young woman's memories about her father's death when she was six years old, and the special way the old lady helped her to cope with the loss

This book is "beautifully crafted and affecting." Booklist

Zeises, Lara M.

Contents under pressure. Delacorte Press 2004 244p $15.95; lib bdg $17.99 (7 and up)   **Fic**
1. Family life—Fiction 2. Pregnancy—Fiction
ISBN 0-385-73047-0; 0-385-90162-3 (lib bdg)
LC 2003-5411

Lucy, a fourteen-year-old high school freshman, experiences the happiness and confusion of dating a popular older boy, changing relationships with lifelong friends, and sharing a bedroom with her older brother's pregnant girlfriend.

"Zeises paints a convincing picture of a family facing tough decisions and a fully realistic heroine who's confused and scared. Even secondary characters have depth and add sparkle to an already absorbing plot." SLJ

Zephaniah, Benjamin

Face. Bloomsbury Pub. 2002 c1999 207p $15.95; pa $6.95 (7 and up)   **Fic**
1. Burns and scalds—Fiction 2. Great Britain—Fiction
ISBN 1-58234-774-3; 1-58234-921-5 (pa)
LC 2002-22758
First published 1999 in the United Kingdom

"Something terrible has happened to Martin's face. An automobile crash and fire have left the handsome, popular 15-year-old boy horribly disfigured. . . . His life is about to change drastically." Booklist

"This book will not only be enjoyed by teen readers for its entertaining story, but also for its statement about prejudice." Voice Youth Advocates

Zindel, Paul

The Pigman; a novel. Harper & Row 1968 182p lib bdg $17.89; pa $6.99 (7 and up)   **Fic**
ISBN 0-06-026828-X (lib bdg); 0-06-057353-3 (pa)
Also available in paperback from Bantam Bks.

"John Conlan and Lorraine Jensen, high school sophomores, are both troubled young people who have problems at home. They become friendly with an elderly widower, Mr. Pignati, who welcomes them into his home and shares with them his simple pleasures, including his collection of ceramic pigs, of which he is proud. When the Pigman, as the young people call him, goes to the hospital after a heart attack, they take advantage of his house for a party that becomes destructive. The consequences are tragic and propel the two young friends into more responsible behavior." Shapiro. Fic for Youth. 3d edition

Followed by The Pigman's legacy (1980)

Zinnen, Linda

The dragons of Spratt, Ohio; by Linda Zinnen. 1st ed. HarperCollins Publishers 2004 233p $15.99; lib bdg $16.89 (5 and up)   **Fic**
1. Dragons—Fiction 2. Ohio—Fiction
ISBN 0-06-000021-X; 0-06-000022-8 (lib bdg)
LC 2003-19610

Seventh-grader John Salt, a budding animal behaviorist, and his best friend's sister become unlikely allies in an attempt to protect a pack of dragons from an unscrupulous cosmetics researcher.

"This is an exciting fantasy with a subtle message about self-acceptance and individuality." SLJ

The truth about rats, rules, and seventh grade. HarperCollins Pubs. 2001 153p $14.95   **Fic**
1. School stories 2. Mother-daughter relationship—Fiction 3. Dogs—Fiction 4. Ohio—Fiction
ISBN 0-06-028799-3   LC 00-27126

Zinnen, Linda—*Continued*

Eleven-year-old Larch has depended on her own rules to help her cope with the life she and her mother share in a trailer in a small Ohio town, but her rules do not help her deal with a rat-catching dog, her best friend's crush, and the truth she learns about her father's death

"The seventh-grader's astute, mixed-up perspective rings true, and her words are an uncommon blend of thoughtfulness, wisdom, and fun." Booklist

Zucker, Naomi Flink

Benno's bear; by N.F. Zucker. Dutton Children's Bks. 2001 244p $16.99   **Fic**

1. Theft—Fiction 2. Bears—Fiction

ISBN 0-525-46521-9   LC 2001-28537

After he and his father are arrested as pickpockets, Benno is separated from the bear he had raised and come to love when the bear is sent to a zoo and Benno is taken in by a kindly policeman and his wife

"Benno's tale has a small cast of well-defined characters and a focused, emotionally appealing plot." Bull Cent Child Books

Zusak, Markus, 1975-

Fighting Ruben Wolfe. Levine Bks. 2001 219p $15.95; pa $6.99 (7 and up)   **Fic**

1. Boxing—Fiction 2. Brothers—Fiction 3. Australia—Fiction

ISBN 0-439-24188-X; 0-439-24187-1 (pa)

LC 00-42817

"The Wolfe brothers, Ruben and Cameron, set about to make things right in their down-on-their-luck working class Australian family by becoming boxers with a sleazy promoter of the underground boxing circuit. Ruben is good and has the desire to win, but Cameron is more of a dreamer. The family's plight is poignant and their pain tangible, and the bond between the two brothers . . . is unbreakable. The plot pulls readers in and holds their avid attention. Some of the language is crude and lewd and many of the escapades are sexually suggestive." Book Rep

Another title about the Wolfe brothers is:
Getting the girl (2003)

S C STORY COLLECTIONS

Books in this class include collections of short stories by one author and collections by more than one author. Folklore is in class 398.2

13; thirteen stories that capture the agony and ecstasy of being thirteen; edited by James Howe. Atheneum Books for Young Readers 2003 278p $16.95   **S C**

1. Short stories

ISBN 0-689-82863-2

Contents: What's the worst that could happen? by Bruce Coville; Kate the great by Meg Cabot; If you kiss a boy by Alex Sanchez; Thirteen and a half by Rachel Vail; Jeremy Goldblatt is so not Moses by James Howe; Black holes and basketball sneakers by Lori Aurelia Williams; Picky eater by Stephen Roos; Such foolishness by

Maureen Ryan Griffin; Noodle soup for nincompoops by Ellen Wittlinger; Squid girl by Todd Strasser; Angel & Aly by Ron Koertge; Nobody stole Jason Grayson by Carolyn Mackler; Tina the teen fairy by Ann M. Martin and Laura Godwin.

In this "collection, familiar authors for young adults contribute short fiction about 13-year-old characters who are experiencing bewildering feelings, making discoveries, or undergoing the embarrassments typical of the age." Booklist

"The stories are a mixture of humor, pathos, and poignancy, and most are based on personal experiences. . . . Howe has chosen excellent authors for this volume and they have written oh-so-true stories about that wonderful, terrible first year of being a teenager. " SLJ

Aiken, Joan, 1924-2004

Shadows and moonshine; stories; illustrations by Pamela Johnson. Godine 2001 171p il $18.95 (4 and up)   **S C**

1. Fantasy fiction 2. Short stories

ISBN 1-56792-167-1   LC 2001-23830

This is a collection 13 stories about such things as witches, enchanted pigs, mermaids, and dragons, selected from the author's earlier anthologies

"Whether scary, satiric, or poetic, Aiken's tales have strong settings, memorable characters, insight, and humor." SLJ

Alexander, Lloyd

The foundling and other tales of Prydain. rev & expanded ed. Holt & Co. 1999 98p $19.95 (5 and up)   **S C**

1. Fantasy fiction 2. Short stories

ISBN 0-8050-6130-4   LC 98-42807

Also available in paperback from Penguin

First published 1973; this revised and expanded edition includes two additional stories Coll and his white pig and The truthful harp, first published separately 1965 and 1967 respectively

Eight short stories dealing with events that preceded the birth of Taran, the Assistant Pig-Keeper and key figure in the author's five works on the Kingdom of Prydain which began with The book of three

"The stories are written with vivid grace and humor." Chicago. Children's Book Center {review of 1973 edition}

American eyes; new Asian-American short stories for young adults; edited by Lori M. Carlson; introduction by Cynthia Kadohata. Holt & Co. 1994 144p o.p. Fawcett Bks. paperback available $4.50   **S C**

1. Asian Americans—Fiction 2. Short stories

ISBN 0-449-70448-3 (pa)   LC 94-22391

These ten stories reflect the conflict Asian Americans face in balancing an ancient heritage and an unknown future

"The stories are sensitive, realistic, humorous and eye-opening. The characters represent all facets of human behavior. . . . This well-balanced collection helps us see life through another's eyes no matter what our ancestry." Book Rep

Anaya, Rudolfo A.

My land sings; stories from the Rio Grande; {by} Rudolfo Anaya; illustrated by Amy Córdova. Morrow Junior Bks. 1999 176p $17; pa $5.99

S C

1. New Mexico—Fiction 2. Short stories
ISBN 0-688-15078-0; 0-380-72902-4 (pa)

LC 99-19040

A collection of ten original and traditional stories set in New Mexico, including "Lupe and la Llorona," "The Shepherd Who Knew the Language of Animals," and "Coyote and Raven.'"

"Every story spins its magic effectively. Best of all, beyond their solid entertainment value and read-aloud potential, the engaging tales allegorically extol solid virtues." Booklist

Appelt, Kathi, 1954-

Kissing Tennessee and other stories from the Stardust Dance. Harcourt 2000 118p $15; pa $5.95

S C

1. School stories 2. Short stories
ISBN 0-15-202249-X; 0-15-205127-9 (pa)

LC 99-50505

Graduating eighth graders relate their stories of love and heartbreak that have brought them to Dogwood Junior High's magical Stardust Dance.

"This collection will spark conversation in contemporary literature discussions, will quietly unsettle readers, and will elevate the quality of short-story collections." SLJ

Asimov, Isaac, 1920-1992

I, robot. Gnome Press 1950 253p o.p. Bantam Bks. paperback available $6.99 (7 and up)

S C

1. Science fiction 2. Robots—Fiction 3. Short stories
ISBN 0-553-29438-5 (pa)

"These loosely connected stories cover the career of Dr. Susan Calvin and United States Robots, the industry that she heads, from the time of the public's early distrust of these robots to its later dependency on them. This collection is an important introduction to a theme often found in science fiction: the encroachment of technology on our lives." Shapiro. Fic for Youth. 3d edition

Aspin, Diana

Ordinary miracles. Red Deer Press 2003 168p (Northern Lights young novels) pa $7.95 (7 and up)

S C

1. Canada—Fiction 2. Short stories
ISBN 0-88995-277-9

A collection of 13 short stories concerning life in a small Canadian community, covering such topics as an old man's memories of abandonment by his mother and his abusive life as an orphan, a teen's struggle with his sexuality, and issues such as alcoholism, death, adultery, and poverty.

This is "a riveting collection. . . . The author has created a work that leaves readers awash with feelings of empathy for each young protagonist." SLJ

Avi, 1937-

What do fish have to do with anything? and other stories; illustrated by Tracy Mitchell. Candlewick Press 1997 202p il pa $5.99 hardcover o.p. (4 and up)

S C

1. Short stories
ISBN 0-7636-0412-7 (pa)

LC 97-1354

"Willie believes a homeless man possesses a cure for unhappiness. A minister dares his devilish son to be good. Pet-obsessed Eve receives visitations from two deceased cats. . . . These are among seven . . . stories dealing with communication in troubled relationships." Publisher's note

"While Avi's endings are not tidy, they are effective: each story brings its protagonist beyond childhood self-absorption to the realization that one is an integral part of a bigger picture." Horn Book

The **Book** of dragons; selected and illustrated by Michael Hague. Morrow 1995 146p il $21; pa $9.99

S C

1. Dragons—Fiction 2. Fantasy fiction 3. Short stories
ISBN 0-688-10879-2; 0-06-075968-2 (pa)

LC 94-42958

"Excerpts from classic novels such as J. R. R. Tolkien's *The Hobbit*, C. S. Lewis's *Voyage of the Dawn Treader*, and short stories such as Kenneth Grahame's 'The Reluctant Dragon' are included. In addition, there are folktales from China, Italy, and Germany. Most of the heroes are men, but occasionally children are the only ones who can outsmart the dragon. . . . Hague's beautiful full-page watercolors reflect the different moods of the stories and the temperaments of the dragons depicted." SLJ

The **Boy** of Chancellorville and other Civil War stories; edited by James Marten. Oxford Univ. Press 2002 126p il $20 (7 and up)

S C

1. Short stories 2. United States—History—1861-1865, Civil War—Fiction
ISBN 0-19-514163-6

LC 2001-46117

"A collection of eight stories set during the Civil War, originally published in books and children's magazines from 1865 to 1912. Pieces by several well-known authors, such as Louisa May Alcott and Hamlin Garland, are included." SLJ

"The stories vividly reveal how the war affected the lives of children differently than the adults around them. A well-balanced account is given from virtually every viewpoint." Book Rep

The **Color** of absence; 12 stories about loss and hope; edited by James Howe. Atheneum Bks. for Young Readers 2001 238p $16; pa $6.99

S C

1. Short stories
ISBN 0-689-82862-4; 0-689-8567-9 (pa)

LC 00-44206

A collection of stories dealing with different kinds of loss experienced by young people. Among the authors represented are Angela Johnson, Norma Fox Mazer, Avi, Walter Dean Myers, Jacqueline Woodson, and Chris Lynch

"A solid choice for all collections." SLJ

Conford, Ellen
Crush; stories. HarperCollins Pubs. 1998 138p
(7 and up)   **S C**
1. Dating (Social customs)—Fiction 2. Short stories
3. Valentine's Day—Fiction
ISBN 0-06-025414-9; 0-06-440778-0 (pa)
                            LC 97-34335
A series of romantic episodes in the lives of B.J. and
other students at Cutter's Forge High as they plan for the
Valentine's Day Sweetheart Stomp
"Addressing such issues as peer pressure, self-esteem,
respect, alienation, greed, and heartbreak, the clever stories . . . show how much self-image can differ from outward appearance and reputation." Booklist

Coville, Bruce
Odder than ever; stories by Bruce Coville.
Harcourt Brace & Co. 1999 146p   **S C**
1. Horror fiction 2. Short stories
ISBN 0-15-201747-X; 0-15-202465-4 (pa)
                            LC 98-51102
A collection of nine short stories featuring a ghost, a
goblin, a giant, and other unusual creatures
"From light fantasy to more thought-provoking
themes, this has something for everyone." Booklist

Crutcher, Chris, 1946-
Athletic shorts; six short stories. Greenwillow
Bks. 1991 154p $17.99; pa $6.99 (7 and up)
                                S C
1. Sports—Fiction 2. Short stories
ISBN 0-688-10816-4; 0-06-050783-7 (pa)
                            LC 91-4418
A collection of short stories about high school sports
"The author seamlessly blends humor with more seri-
ous elements. . . These Athletic Shorts will speak to
YAs, touch them deeply, and introduce them to charac-
ters they'll want to know better." SLJ

Dahl, Roald
Skin and other stories. Viking 2000 212p
$15.99; pa $8.99 (7 and up)   **S C**
1. Short stories
ISBN 0-670-89184-3; 0-14-131034-0 (pa)
                            LC 99-58600
A collection of 13 of the author's short stories written
for adults. "Full of irony and unexpected twists, they
smack of the master's touch—every word carefully chosen, characters fully fleshed out in only a few pages, the
sense of place immediate." Booklist

De Lint, Charles, 1951-
Waifs and strays; preface by Terri Windling.
Viking 2002 394p $17.99; pa $7.99 (7 and up)
                                S C
1. Supernatural—Fiction 2. Short stories
ISBN 0-670-03584-X; 0-14-240158-7 (pa)
                          LC 2002-23314
Chiefly a collection of previously published (1986-
2001) stories

"De Lint offers sixteen of his previously published
short stories about coming of age, dividing the collection
into locations familiar from his previous works. . . .
Throughout the stories, characters confront physical,
emotional, and psychological dangers. . . . The book
creates emotionally believable characters and uses their
fantastical settings to deal with powerful archetypal
themes such as abandonment, bereavement, and redemption." Bull Cent Child Books

Delacre, Lulu, 1957-
Salsa stories; stories and linocuts by Lulu
Delacre. Scholastic Press 2000 105p il $15.95; pa
$4.50 (4-6)   **S C**
1. Latin America—Fiction 2. Family life—Fiction
3. Short stories
ISBN 0-590-63118-7; 0-590-63121-7 (pa)
                            LC 99-25534
A collection of stories within the story of a family
celebration where the guests relate their memories of
growing up in various Latin American countries. Also
contains recipes
"Kids will respond to both the warmth and the anxiety
of the family life described in the vivid writing, and in
Delacre's nicely composed linocuts." Booklist

Destination unexpected: short stories; collected by
Donald R. Gallo. Candlewick Press 2003 240p
$16.99 (7 and up)   **S C**
1. Short stories
ISBN 0-7636-1764-4   LC 2002-71599
Contents: Something old, something new, by J. Sweeney; Brutal interlude, by R. Koertge; Bread on the water,
by D. Lubar; My people, by M. P. Haddix; Bad blood,
by W. Weaver; Keep smiling, by A. Flinn; August lights,
by K. W. Holt; Mosquito, by G. Salisbury; The kiss in
the carry-on bag, by R. Peck; Tourist trapped, by E.
Wittlinger
This collection "features teen protagonists experiencing a transforming experience while on some kind of
journey. . . . . Whether humorous or serious, the stories
are consistently well written and engaging." Booklist

Don't cramp my style; stories about that time of
the month; edited by Lisa Rowe Fraustino.
Simon & Schuster for Young Readers 2004
295p $15.95 (7 and up)   **S C**
1. Menstruation—Fiction 2. Short stories
ISBN 0-689-85882-5
A collection of eleven stories concerning menstruation,
by such authors as Pat Brisson, Alice McGill, David
Lubar, and Joan Elizabeth Goodman.
"This highly recommended collection . . . encompasses an impressive variety of times, cultures, attitudes, and
moods. . . . The writing . . . is consistently excellent."
Voice Youth Advocates

Doyle, Sir Arthur Conan, 1859-1930
The complete Sherlock Holmes; with a preface
by Christopher Morley. Doubleday 1960 c1930
1122p $27.95 (7 and up)   **S C**
1. Mystery fiction 2. Short stories
ISBN 0-385-00689-6
Also available in a two-volume paperback edition
from Bantam Bks.

Doyle, Sir Arthur Conan, 1859-1930—*Continued*

First published 1930

Fifty-eight Sherlock Holmes stories which were originally published in nine separate volumes: A study in scarlet (1887); The sign of the four (1890); Adventures of Sherlock Holmes (1892); Memoirs of Sherlock Holmes (1894); The return of Sherlock Holmes (1905); The hound of the Baskervilles (1902); The valley of fear (1915); His last bow (1917); The case book of Sherlock Holmes (1927)

Estevis, Anne

Down Garrapata road; by Anne Estevis. Arte Piñata Books 2003 119p pa $12.95 (7 and up)

S C

1. Mexican Americans—Fiction 2. Texas—Fiction 3. Short stories

ISBN 1-55885-397-9   LC 2003-49837

A collection of short stories set in a small Mexican-American community in southern Texas during the 1940s and 1950s, revealing the traditions, love, and social concerns of the families living there.

"Sly, gentle, and written in lively, simple language, these are stories that will draw readers into the particulars of a culture while capturing universal family dramas." Booklist

Face relations; 11 stories about seeing beyond color. Simon & Schuster Books for Young Readers 2004 224p $17.95 (7 and up)

S C

1. Race relations—Fiction 2. Short stories

ISBN 0-689-85637-7

Contents: Phat acceptance by Jess Mowry; Skins by Joseph Bruchac; Snow by Sherri Winston; The heartbeat of the soul of the world by René Saldaña, Jr.; Hum by Naomi Shihab Nye; Epiphany by Ellen Wittlinger; Black and white by Kyoko Mori; Hearing flower by M.E. Kerr; Gold by Marina Budhos; Mr. Ruben by Rita Williams-Garcia; Negress by Marilyn Singer

"Contributed by familiar writers for young people, including Ellen Wittlinger, M. E. Kerr, Rita Williams-Garcia, Naomi Shihab Nye, and Jess Mowry, the stories ask challenging questions about what role race plays in family life, at school, in friendships, and in love. . . . This is a provocative collection." Booklist

Fire and wings: dragon tales from East and West; edited by Marianne Carus; illustrated by Nilesh Mistry; with an introduction by Jane Yolen. Cricket Bks. 2002 146p il $17.95 (4 and up)

S C

1. Dragons—Fiction 2. Short stories

ISBN 0-8126-2664-8   LC 2002-5792

A collection of stories about all kinds of dragons, by such authors as Jane Yolen, Patricia MacLachlan, Eric A. Kimmel, Vida Chu, and E. Nesbit

"The writing is smooth and the black-and-white illustrations are skillfully done, with especially graceful line work." SLJ

Firebirds: an anthology of original fantasy and science fiction; an anthology of original fantasy and science fiction; edited by Sharyn November. Firebird Press 2003 420p il $19.99 (7 and up)

S C

1. Fantasy fiction 2. Science fiction 3. Short stories

ISBN 0-14-250142-5

A collection of science fiction and fantasy stories by such authors as Nancy Springer, Lloyd Alexander, Patricia A. McKillip, Diana Wynne Jones, Garth Nix, and Nancy Farmer

"Teens will find much to savor and celebrate in this dazzling collection of 16 short stories by some of the best fantasy writers around." SLJ

Flake, Sharon G.

Who am I without him? short stories about girls and the boys in their lives. Jump at the Sun/Hyperion Books for Children 2004 168p $15.99 (7 and up)

S C

1. African Americans—Fiction 2. Short stories

ISBN 0-7868-0693-1

Ten short stories about African American teenage girls and their relationships with boys

"Addressing issues and situations that many girls face in today's often complex society, this book is provocative and thought-provoking." SLJ

A **Glory** of unicorns; compiled by Bruce Coville; illustrated by Alix Berenzy. Scholastic 1998 198p il (5 and up)

S C

1. Unicorns—Fiction 2. Short stories

ISBN 0-590-95943-3; 0-439-06628-X (pa)

LC 97-13689

Eleven stories and one poem, by such authors as Nancy Varian Berberick, Gregory Maguire, and Margaret Bechard, about unicorns in both mythical and contemporary settings

"Exciting and thought-provoking. Even readers who shy away from the science fiction/fantasy genres will enjoy these short tales and their special messages." Voice of Youth Advocates

Gothic!; ten original dark tales; edited by Deborah Noyes. . Candlewick Press 2004 241p $15.99 (7 and up)

S C

1. Horror fiction 2. Short stories

ISBN 0-7636-2243-5   LC 2004-45188

Contents: Lungewater by Joan Aiken; Morgan Roehmar's boys by Vivian Vande Velde; Watch and wake by M.T. Anderson; Forbidden brides of the faceless slaves in the nameless house of the night of dread desire by Neil Gaiman; The dead and the moonstruck by Caitlin R. Kiernan; Have no fear, Crumpot is here! by Barry Yourgrau; Stone tower by Janni Lee Simner; The prank by Gregory Maguire; Writing on the wall by Celia Rees; Endings by Garth Nix

This "collection features short stories by noted young adult authors such as M. T. Anderson, Caitlín R. Kiernan, Garth Nix, Celia Rees, Janni Lee Simner, and Barry Yourgrau. . . . These varied tales take place in the distant past and in the high-tech present. Some are humorous while others have surprising twists or are reminiscent of classic fairy tales full of malevolent characters, but all share a love of the surreal or supernatural. . . . A sophisticated, thought-provoking, and gripping read." SLJ

Half-human; compiled & edited by Bruce Coville; photo illustrations by Marc Tauss. Scholastic Press 2001 212p il $16.95; pa $5.99 (7 and up)
                                                    S C
1. Fantasy fiction 2. Short stories
ISBN 0-590-95944-1; 0-590-95588-8 (pa)
                                    LC 00-50524
A collection of 9 stories and one poem about such creatures as mermaids and centaurs, who are part-human and part-animal or part-plant, by such authors as Jane Yolen, Nancy Springer, Tamora Pierce, and Bruce Coville
Readers "will be intrigued with this unusual collection of well-written fantasies that illustrate the adolescent challenge of discovering both our animal and human natures." Booklist

The **Haunted** house: a collection of original stories; edited by Jane Yolen and Martin H. Greenberg; illustrated by Doron Ben-Ami. HarperCollins Pubs. 1995 88p il lib bdg $15.89
                                                    S C
1. Ghost stories 2. Short stories
ISBN 0-06-024468-2 (lib bdg)   LC 94-25136
"The premise is intriguing: over the years, seven families have moved into the house at 66 Brown's End, and each time, a child has discovered a different ghost. Yolen, Bruce Coville, Barbara Goldin, Mary Whittington, Janet Gill, and Anna and Gary Hines have loaded the house from basement to attic with spirits of all sorts—from abandoned ghost puppies to an insatiable gourmet ghost. The stories are all wonderful—eerie and unsettling enough to be satisfying, but lightened with humor." Booklist

Hearne, Betsy Gould, 1942-
The canine connection: stories about dogs and people; [by] Betsy Hearne. Margaret K. McElderry Bks. 2003 113p $15.95   **S C**
1. Dogs—Fiction 2. Short stories
ISBN 0-689-85258-4   LC 2001-58991
Twelve short stories that reflect the varied ways that dogs and humans relate
"The emotions and dialogue are pitch perfect. . . . A rewarding collection that will stay with readers." Booklist

Join in; multiethnic short stories by outstanding writers for young adults; edited by Donald R. Gallo. Delacorte Press 1993 256p pa $5.99 hardcover o.p.   **S C**
1. Short stories
ISBN 0-440-21957-4 (pa)   LC 92-43169
"The 17 stories cross the boundaries of race and culture and probe the universal themes of belonging, acceptance, family, and friendship." Booklist
"Uneven in quality, this will nevertheless offer grounds for discussion among young adults, who will appreciate the accessibility and brevity of the stories." Bull Cent Child Books

Jones, Diana Wynne
Unexpected magic; collected stories. Greenwillow Books 2004 497p $16.99; lib bdg $17.89   **S C**
1. Fantasy fiction 2. Short stories
ISBN 0-06-055533-5; 0-06-055534-3 (lib bdg)
                                    LC 2003-53118
Contents: The Girl Jones; Nad and Dan Adn Quaffy; The plague of peacocks; The Master; Enna Hittims; The girl who loved the sun; The fluffy pink toadstool; Auntie Bea's day out; Carruthers; What the cat told me; The green stone; The fat wizard; No one; Dragon Reserve, Home Eight; Little Dot; Everard's ride
"This collection of 15 short stories and one novella begins with the autobiographical 'The Girl Jones,' about nine-year-old Diana. Among the selections that follow, readers will find stories about a science-fiction writer who becomes involved in an interstellar revolution, a haunting encounter with werewolves and a sinister fool, and a talking cat cursed with long life. In the concluding novella, four children become embroiled in intrigue over an innocent prince, an evil count, and a brave outlaw. All of the selections have characters that are both appealing and realistically flawed, and the worlds they inhabit are brought to life through detail and humor." SLJ

Kimmel, Eric A.
The jar of fools: eight Hanukkah stories from Chelm; illustrated by Mordicai Gerstein. Holiday House 2000 56p il $18.95 (4 and up)
                                                    S C
1. Hanukkah—Fiction 2. Short stories 3. Jews—Fiction
ISBN 0-8234-1463-9   LC 99-57823
Drawing on traditional Jewish folklore, these Hanukkah stories relate the antics of the people of Chelm, thought—perhaps incorrectly—to be a town of fools
"Kimmel gets the shtetl setting, the humanity, and the farce. . . . Gerstein's detailed ink-on-oil paint artwork, one full-page picture per story, captures the intricate silliness and slapstick." Booklist

Sword of the samurai; adventure stories from Japan. Harcourt Brace & Co. 1999 114p (4 and up)   **S C**
1. Japan—Fiction 2. Adventure fiction 3. Short stories
ISBN 0-15-201985-5   LC 98-16633
Available in paperback from HarperCollins $4.99 (0-06-442131-7)
"Browndeer Press"

Eleven short stories about samurai warriors, their way of life, courage, wit, and foolishness
"These selections offer something for everyone: humor, wisdom and adventure along with a gentle and graceful introduction to the code of ethics that continues to shape Japan today." Publ Wkly

Kipling, Rudyard, 1865-1936
The jungle books (4 and up)   **S C**
1. Animals—Fiction 2. India—Fiction 3. Short stories
Hardcover and paperback editions available from various publishers

Kipling, Rudyard, 1865-1936—*Continued*
A collection of fifteen animal stories first published 1894 and 1895 in two volumes by Macmillan with titles: The jungle book and The second jungle book.

Lester, Julius
Long journey home: stories from black history. Dial Press (NY) 1972 147p pa $5.99 hardcover o.p. **S C**
1. African Americans—Fiction 2. Short stories
ISBN 0-14-038981-4 (pa)
"Six original short stories based on real characters and incidents depict the drama and tragedy of the black experience." Chicago Public Libr
"In a foreword, Julius Lester explains that he has chosen minor figures because the mass of people were the 'movers of history' while the great figures are their symbols. . . . The selections are diversified in their settings and alike in their sharply-etched effectiveness." Bull Cent Child Books

Lynch, Chris
All the old haunts. HarperCollins Pubs. 2001 185p $15.95; lib bdg $15.89 (7 and up)
S C
1. Short stories
ISBN 0-06-028178-2; 0-06-028179 0 (lib bdg)
LC 2001-16638
In this collection of 10 short stories "the 'old haunts' include young love gone wrong, an unexpected pregnancy, exploration of sexuality, father/son relationships, an evil twin, and a visitation from a dead cousin. . . . Teens who enjoy deftly crafted tales with more than a hint of the dark side will appreciate this sophisticated prose." SLJ

Marston, Elsa
Figs and fate; stories about growing up in the Arab world today. Braziller 2005 135p $22.50; pa $15.95 **S C**
1. Arab countries—Fiction 2. Middle East—Fiction 3. Short stories
ISBN 0-8076-1551-X; 0-8076-1554-4 (pa)
Contents: In line; Hand of Fatima; Faces; The plan; Santa Claus in Bagdad
A collection of five stories portraying Arab life in Egypt, Lebanon, Syria, a Palestinian refugee camp in Lebanon, and Iraq today.
"Readers will recognize the universals of coming-of-age, even as they are drawn into the rich diversity and the desperation of daily life." Booklist

McKinley, Robin
The door in the hedge. Greenwillow Bks. 1981 216p **S C**
1. Fairy tales 2. Short stories
ISBN 0-688-00312-5
LC 80-21903
Available in paperback from Penguin $6.99 (ISBN 0-698-11960-6)
The author "presents four romantic tales that elaborate—to a greater or lesser degree—upon the supernatu-ral lore of fairy tale, myth, and legend. Two of the stories are original in plot and in characters. . . . The other two stories are literary recastings of Grimm tales, 'The Princess and the Frog' . . . {and} 'The Twelve Dancing Princesses.'" Horn Book
"These tales are well-written and enjoyable to read. It is too bad they lack illustrations." Child Book Rev Serv

Water: tales of elemental spirits; [by] Robin McKinley, Peter Dickinson. Putnam 2002 266p $18.99; pa $6.99 (7 and up) **S C**
1. Fantasy fiction 2. Mermaids and mermen—Fiction 3. Short stories
ISBN 0-399-23796-8; 0-14-240244-3 (pa)
LC 2001-41642
"These six stories, three by McKinley and three by her husband, Dickinson, feature the elemental spirits that inhabit Earth's waters." Voice Youth Advocates
"The masterfully written stories all feature distinct, richly detailed casts and settings . . . and focus as strongly on action as on character. There's plenty here to excite, enthrall, and move even the pickiest readers." SLJ

Memories of sun; stories of Africa and America; edited by Jane Kurtz. Greenwillow Books 2004 263p $15.99; lib bdg $16.89 **S C**
1. Africa—Fiction 2. Short stories
ISBN 0-06-051050-1; 0-06-051051-X (lib bdg)
LC 2003-49067
A collection of short stories and poems by authors from both continents about life in various African countries and some of the experiences and impressions of Americans in Africa and of Africans in America.
"Providing sharp, contrasting images of splendor and strife, these selections will reverberate in readers' minds." Publ Wkly

Myers, Walter Dean, 1937-
145th Street; short stories. Delacorte Press 2000 151p $15.95; pa $5.50 **S C**
1. Harlem (New York, N.Y.)—Fiction 2. African Americans—Fiction 3. Short stories
ISBN 0-385-32137-6; 0-440-22916-2 (pa)
LC 99-36097
"These ten powerful stories create a vivid mosaic of life in the Harlem neighborhood of 145th Street. Memorable characters range from outgoing Big Joe, who decides to stage his own funeral party in *Big Joe's funeral*, to book-loving *Monkeyman*, who outsmarts the Tigros gang. . . . Beautifully told, Myers's stories offer an enticing collection for teens." Voice Youth Advocates

A time to love; stories from the Old Testament; with artwork by Christopher Myers. Scholastic Press 2003 127p il $19.95 (7 and up)
S C
1. Bible stories 2. Short stories
ISBN 0-439-22000-9
LC 2001-43466
A retelling of six stories from the Old Testament, which explore the complexity of love from the perspective of Ruth, Delilah, Reuben, Isaac, Gamiel, and Zillah
"Myers' thoughtful introduction explains how and why these multilayered stories entice across the ages. . . .

Myers, Walter Dean, 1937-—*Continued*
This is an exquisitely designed book, rich in color. Christopher Myers' illustrations, in mixed media and collage, accompany each story. . . . Suitable across many faiths, these stories show their power once again." Booklist

Naidoo, Beverley
Out of bounds: seven stories of conflict and hope. HarperCollins Pubs. 2003 c2001 175p $16.99; lib bdg $17.89 (5 and up)   **S C**
1. South Africa—Race relations—Fiction 2. Short stories
ISBN 0-06-050799-3; 0-06-050800-0 (lib bdg)
LC 2002-68901
First published 2001 in the United Kingdom
Seven stories, spanning the time period from 1948 to 2000, chronicle the experiences of young people from different races and ethnic groups as they try to cope with the restrictions placed on their lives by South Africa's apartheid laws
"Naidoo's book reveals our humanity and inhumanity with starkness and precision. . . . She honors her country's past, present, and future with these brave tales." Horn Book

Necessary noise: stories about our families as they really are; edited by Michael Cart; illustrations by Charlotte Noruzi. Joanna Cotler Bks. 2003 239p $15.99; lib bdg $16.89 (7 and up)
S C
1. Family life—Fiction 2. Short stories
ISBN 0-06-027499-9; 0-06-027500-6 (lib bdg)
LC 2002-151058
Contents: Hardware, by J. Bauer; Siskiyou Sloan and the eye of the giraffe, by N. Howe; Necessary noise, by E. Donoghue; The throwaway: a suite, by N. Grimes; Visit, by W. D. Myers; A family illness: a mom-son conversation, by J. C. Thomas; A woman's touch, by R. Williams-Garcia; Sailing away, by M. Cart; Dr. Jekyll and Sister Hyde, by S. Sones; Snowbound, by L. Lowry
"Ten original stories provide ten distinct perspectives on the quagmire that is 'family.' The result is a collection with considerable range and depth. . . . The style of the writers varies as much as their subjects: Joyce Carol Thomas offers a 'Mom-Son Conversation' about the frightening onset of schizophrenia; Sonya Sones's prose poems portray a light-and-dark relationship with an abusive sibling in 'Dr. Jekyll and Sister Hyde'. . . . Lois Lowry gives us a terrific finale with a clever and truthful story that reads like a one-act play." Horn Book

New skies: an anthology of today's science fiction; edited by Patrick Nielsen Hayden. Tor 2003 288p $19.95   **S C**
1. Science fiction 2. Short stories
ISBN 0-7653-0016-8   LC 2003-55952
"A Tom Doherty Associates book"
This collection "gathers 17 stories starring aliens and dimensions beyond the 3D world. In 'They're Made Out of Meat' by Terry Bisson, a pair of aliens are stunned to discover an intelligent species made not of machinery or gasses, but of flesh. A boy and his dog exchange bodies with a pair of tentacled aliens in 'Brian and the Aliens' by Will Shetterly. And in the award-winning 'Tangents'

by Greg Bear, a scientist and a kid make contact with the fourth dimension." Publ Wkly
This "is the finest collection of SF short stories published specifically for young adult readers in recent memory. . . . This anthology is a must-purchase for all YA collections." Voice Youth Advocates

Night terrors; stories of shadow and substance; edited by Lois Duncan. Simon & Schuster Bks. for Young Readers 1996 175p pa $5.99 hardcover o.p. (7 and up)   **S C**
1. Horror fiction 2. Short stories
ISBN 0-689-80724-4 (pa)   LC 95-44901
Contents: The monkey's wedding, by J. Aiken; Satan's shadow, by A. Ferguson; The chosen, by M. Harrah; The bogey man, by A. C. Klause; Bearing Paul, by C. Lynch; The beautiful thing, by H. Mazer; The house on Buffalo Street, by N. F. Mazer; The dark beast of death, by J. L. Nixon; Girl at the window, by R. Peck; The grind of an axe, by T. Taylor; Moon kill, by P. Windsor
"The stories deal with madness, witchcraft, homicide and incest. While the book should be popular with students, the subject matter may be too mature for some middle-schoolers." Voice Youth Advocates

Nixon, Joan Lowery, 1927-2003
Ghost town; seven ghostly stories. Delacorte Press 2000 147p $14.95; pa $4.99   **S C**
1. Ghost stories 2. West (U.S.)—Fiction 3. Short stories
ISBN 0-385-32681-5; 0-440-41603-5 (pa)
LC 99-36340
A collection of stories about eerie encounters in various Western ghost towns. Each story is accompanied by an afterword about the actual town on which the story is based
"Readers will get shivers and laughs from this collection. . . . This well-researched and enjoyable book will be useful in cross-curricular units." Book Rep

Oates, Joyce Carol, 1938-
Small avalanches and other stories. HarperCollins Pubs. 2003 390p $16.99; lib bdg $19.89; pa $7.99 (7 and up)   **S C**
1. Short stories
ISBN 0-06-001217-X; 0-06-001218-8 (lib bdg); 0-06-001219-6 (pa)   LC 2002-23311
These "tales are about vulnerable, wild, rebellious, scared young women, several of whom fall victim to older, predatory males who know how to lure them with the thrill of danger and make them betray the best in themselves. . . . Oates makes poetry with ordinary words that take readers right into the restless psyches of young women terrified of their own violence. Far from role models, these characters wrestle with the fearful fantasies they dare not even articulate" Booklist

On the edge: stories at the brink; edited by Lois Duncan. Simon & Schuster Bks. for Young Readers 2000 211p $17; pa $4.99 (7 and up)
S C
1. Short stories
ISBN 0-689-82251-0; 0-689-83256-7 (pa)
LC 99-54262

On the edge: stories at the brink—*Continued*

A collection of twelve stories by such writers as William Sleator, Gail Carson Levine, and Gloria Skurzynsk. In each a young person is physically and\or emotionally on the edge

"Each edgy situation raises provocative questions that will resonate strongly with teens, as will the contemporary details." Booklist

On the fringe; edited by Donald R. Gallo. Dial Bks. for Young Readers 2001 224p $17.99; pa $6.99 **S C**

1. Short stories

ISBN 0-8037-2656-2; 0-14-250026-7 (pa)

LC 00-40521

"Kids who are geeks, unathletic, poor, emotionally fragile, loners, or unattractive by current standards form the heart of this collection of exceptional stories by well-known YA authors such as Joan Bauer, Chris Crutcher, and M. E. Kerr." SLJ

Once upon a cuento; edited by Lyn Miller-Lachman. 1st ed. Curbstone Press 2003 243p pa $15.95 **S C**

1. Hispanic Americans—Fiction 2. Short stories

ISBN 1-88068-499-3   LC 2003-14667

Contents: Heritage, holidays, and contemporary culture: My ciguapa; A Nuyorican Christmas in el Bronx; Adventures in Mexican wrestling; Searching for Peter Z; Family life: Leaving before the snow; A special gift; Initiation; Good trouble for Lucy; The snake; Friends and other relationships: Sara and Panchito; Armpits, hair and other marks of beauty; Learning buddies; Indian summer sun; Dealing with differences: Leti's shoe escandalo; Dancing Miranda; That October; Grease

"Fourteen Latino authors have contributed to this collection of 17 short stories." SLJ

"Writing quality is consistently high throughout. . . . This book . . . succeeds admirably in proving, through literature, that there is no single 'Latino experience.' " Voice Youth Advocates

Ortiz Cofer, Judith, 1952-

An island like you; stories of the barrio. Orchard Bks. 1995 165p Penguin Bks paperback available $5.99 hardcover o.p. (7 and up) **S C**

1. Puerto Ricans—Fiction 2. New Jersey—Fiction 3. Short stories

ISBN 0-14-038868-X   LC 94-32496

"A Melanie Kroupa book"

A collection of twelve stories about young people in Paterson New Jersey caught between their Puerto Rican heritage and their American surroundings

"The combination of interweaving of characters, intensity of emotion, and deft control of language make this a rewarding collection." Bull Cent Child Books

Peck, Richard, 1934-

Past perfect, present tense: new and collected stories. Dial Bks. 2004 177p $16.99 **S C**

1. Short stories

ISBN 0-8037-2998-7   LC 2003-10904

A collection of short stories, including two previously unpublished ones, that deal with the way things could be

"The stories perfectly highlight Peck's range and expertise at characterization. Almost every one is a superb read-aloud. . . . This superior collection is a must for every library." SLJ

Places I never meant to be; original stories by censored writers; edited by Judy Blume. Atheneum Bks. for Young Readers 1999 198p $16.95; pa $10 (7 and up) **S C**

1. Short stories

ISBN 0-689-82034-8; 0-689-84258-9 (pa)

LC 98-30343

"This collection of 11 original short stories and a reprint of the late Norma Klein's college writing is interspersed with personal essays about the authors' views on censorship and its effect upon their work. Among the authors included are Norma Fox Mazer, Jacqueline Woodson, Harry Mazer, and Susan Beth Pfeffer." SLJ

"The contributors are a stellar list of well-known YA authors. . . . The authors' notes about censorship add a thought-provoking dimension to the collection, as does Blume's introduction, and the stories themselves are emotionally intense." Bull Cent Child Books

Poe, Edgar Allan, 1809-1849

Edgar Allan Poe's tales of mystery and madness; illustrated by Gris Grimley. Atheneum Books for Young Readers 2004 135p il $17.95 **S C**

1. Horror fiction 2. Short stories

ISBN 0-689-84837-4   LC 2003-10565

Contents: The black cat; The masque of the Red Death; Hop Frog; The fall of the house of Usher

"With high-production values and gothic sensibilities thoroughly reflected in both text and art, this is an essential purchase for libraries. Adults can use it to lead young people to some great literature; readers will pluck it off the shelves themselves for creepy, entertaining fun." Booklist

The pit and the pendulum and other stories; illustrations by Jame's {sic} Pruniel. Viking 1999 153p (Whole story) $25.99 hardcover o.p.; pa $17.99 hardcover o.p. (7 and up) **S C**

1. Horror fiction 2. Mystery fiction 3. Short stories

ISBN 0-670-88706-4; 0-670-88725-0 (pa)

LC 99-71205

Presents seven stories of horror and mystery from the mid-nineteenth century. Includes illustrated notes throughout the text explaining the historical background of each story

"This lucious, compact compilation should help make Poe accessible." Booklist

Tales of Edgar Allan Poe; illustrated by Barry Moser; afterword by Peter Glassman. Books of Wonder 1991 308p il $24.99 **S C**

1. Horror fiction 2. Short stories

ISBN 0-688-07509-6   LC 91-3277

This illustrated collection includes The gold bug; The tell-tale heart; The fall of the House of Usher and The pit and the pendulum

Poe, Edgar Allan, 1809-1849—_Continued_
"Moser's watercolor paintings for 14 of Poe's best stories are both macabre and understated. The best of them make us further imagine the terrible things beyond the edge." Booklist

Potok, Chaim, 1929-2002
Zebra and other stories. Knopf 1998 146p $18 (7 and up)   **S C**
1. Short stories
ISBN 0-679-85440-1   LC 98-4769
Also available Thorndike Press Large print edition
A collection of stories about six different young people who each experience a life-changing event
"Potok's ability to spin a tale is extraordinary and this collection will be devoured by those who loved his earlier works, and those lucky enough to stumble upon this one." Voice Youth Advocates

Read into the millennium; tales of the future; from the editors of Read magazine. Millbrook Press 1999 160p lib bdg $24.90   **S C**
1. Science fiction 2. Short stories
ISBN 0-7613-0962-4   LC 98-8390
"This collection of futuristic fiction features one of Isaac Asimov's early robot stories, a chilling and mythic look at life after the nuclear age by Stephen Vincent Benét, and a fast-paced tale by Robert Lipsyte. . . . adaptations of _The Time Machine_ and _Frankenstein_ and . . . selections from _The Martian Chronicles_ by Ray Bradbury and Lois Lowry's _The Giver._" Horn Book Guide

Rice, David, 1964-
Crazy loco; stories about growing up Chicano in southern Texas. Dial Bks. for Young Readers 2001 135p $16.99; pa $6.99   **S C**
1. Mexican Americans—Fiction 2. Texas—Fiction 3. Short stories
ISBN 0-8037-2598-1; 0-14-250056-9 (pa)
LC 00-59042
A collection of nine stories about Mexican American kids growing up in the Rio Grande Valley of southern Texas
"Two great strengths of these stories are the pitch-perfect sense for the speech and thought patterns of teens and the vivid depiction of the daily lives of Mexican-Americans in Texas's Rio Grande Valley." SLJ

Saldaña, René
Finding our way: stories; [by] René Saldaña, Jr. Wendy Lamb Bks. 2003 117p $15.95; lib bdg $17.99   **S C**
1. Mexican Americans—Fiction 2. Short stories
ISBN 0-385-73051-9; 0-385-90077-5 (lib bdg)
LC 2002-8249
This is a collection of short stories about Mexican American adolescents "involved in dramas about family, first dates, going to the prom, and getting expelled from school." Booklist
"Saldaña's prose, peppered with Spanish words and phrases (understandable in context), is sharp and colloquial. While much is revealed, just as much is implied, making the stories layered and rich while still rendering them accessible." Bull Cent Child Books

Salisbury, Graham, 1944-
Island boyz: short stories. Wendy Lamb Bks. 2002 260p $16.95; lib bdg $18.99; pa $5.99 (7 and up)   **S C**
1. Hawaii—Fiction 2. Short stories
ISBN 0-385-72970-7; 0-385-90037-6 (lib bdg); 0-440-22955-3 (pa)   LC 2001-32425
"Eleven short stories chronicle pivotal episodes in the lives of teenage boys growing up in the Hawaiian islands. . . . Themes are timeless in their appeal—guys testing their mettle against hurricanes and bullies and the irresponsible dares of their best friends, against fear of sharks and fear of failure and fear of war—and plotting is exceptionally well crafted to maximize suspense and to meticulously develop a teen narrator's frame of mind and state of conscience." Bull Cent Child Books

San Souci, Robert, 1946-
Dare to be scared; thirteen stories to chill and thrill; illustrations by David Ouimet. Cricket Bks. 2003 159p il $15.95 (4 and up)   **S C**
1. Horror fiction 2. Short stories
ISBN 0-8126-2688-5   LC 2002-152827
"From a horrible dream a boy can't wake up from to an alien-driven bus to an eerie house with an alarming inhabitant, these stories cover the gamut of scary themes." SLJ
"With crisp, straightforward delivery and some intriguing endings, these 13 tales are great fun for young readers who like to be spooked." Booklist

Double-dare to be scared: another thirteen chilling tales; {by} Robert D. San Souci ; illustrated by David Ouimet. Cricket Books 2004 170p il $15.95 (4 and up)   **S C**
1. Horror fiction 2. Short stories
ISBN 0-8126-2716-4   LC 2003-26610
Companion volume to Dare to be scared (2003)
This is a "collection of 13 tales . . . . Most of the main characters are menaced by a variety of scary, unexpected threats: a madman in the woods, a giant spider, unforgiving leprechauns, and exceptionally hungry Appalachian children." Booklist
"San Souci uses elements of urban legend and folklore to weave powerful and suspenseful yet age-appropriate stories that youngsters will revisit, finding new meaning with each reading." SLJ

Shattered: stories of children and war; edited by Jennifer Armstrong. Knopf 2002 166p $15.95   **S C**
1. War stories 2. Short stories
ISBN 0-375-81112-5   LC 2001-18609
Also available Thorndike Print large print edition
"This anthology of short stories (and one memoir), mostly by well-known writers for YAs, shows how war's violence affects individual young people in countries across the world." Booklist
"These selections will make teens cry, will make them angry, but most of all they will make them think." SLJ

Shelf life: stories by the book; edited by Gary Paulsen. Simon & Schuster Bks. for Young Readers 2003 173p $16.95 (5 and up)

S C

1. Books and reading—Fiction 2. Short stories
ISBN 0-689-84180-9   LC 2002-66901

Contents: In your hat, by E. Conford; Escape, by M. P. Haddix; Follow the water, by J. L. Holm; Testing, testing 1 . . . 2 . . . 3, by A. La Faye; Tea party ends in bloody massacre, film at 11, by G. Maguire; What's a fellow to do, by K. Karr; Wet hens, by E. Wittlinger; The good deed, by M. D. Bauer; Bacarole for paper and bones, by M. T. Anderson; Clean sweep, by J. Bauer

Ten short stories in which the lives of young people in different circumstances are changed by their encounters with books

"Covering almost every genre of fiction, including mystery, SF, fantasy and realism, these well-crafted stories by familiar authors offer sharply drawn characterizations and intriguing premises." Publ Wkly

Sherwood: original stories from the world of Robin Hood; edited by Jane Yolen; with paintings by Dennis Nolan. Philomel Bks. 2000 134p il $19.99   S C
1. Robin Hood (Legendary character)—Fiction 2. Short stories
ISBN 0-399-23182-X   LC 97-47765

These "tales range from further adventures of Robin and his merry men in the traditional vein, to humor, science fiction, and a dark tale of the violent life led in Sherwood Forest. . . . There is humor and adventure enough for reluctant readers, and several of the stories would be great read-alouds." Voice Youth Advocates

Singer, Isaac Bashevis, 1904-1991
The power of light; eight stories for Hanukkah; with illustrations by Irene Lieblich. Farrar, Straus & Giroux 1980 86p il pa $10.95 hardcover o.p. (4 and up)   S C
1. Hanukkah—Fiction 2. Short stories 3. Jews—Fiction
ISBN 0-374-45984-3 (pa)   LC 80-20263

"The stories, bound together by recurring Hanukkah motifs—the lamp, the dreidel, and the pancakes, tell chiefly of events affecting the lives of Eastern European Jews. Ranging from such somber happenings as the drafting of small Jewish boys to serve in the Russian army during the nineteenth century through the bombing and burning of the Warsaw ghetto, the harrowing events are seen in the context of the celebration of Hanukkah." Horn Book

"The stories vary from realism to incorporation of the miraculous . . . but are united in their strong piety as they are in the polished craftsmanship and warmth with which they are written." Bull Cent Child Books

Sixteen; short stories by outstanding writers for young adults; edited by Donald R. Gallo. Delacorte Press 1984 179p pa $5.99 hardcover o.p. (7 and up)   S C
1. Short stories
ISBN 0-440-97757-6 (pa)   LC 84-3250

"This is a collection of sixteen short stories for young adults especially commissioned from such authors as Joan Aiken, M. E. Kerr, Richard Peck, and Norma and Harry Mazer. Divided into five sections ('Friendships', 'Turmoils', 'Lovers', 'Decisions', and 'Families'), some of the stories are fantasies, some are realistic, others are funny, scary, or poignant, but all are choice examples of their genre." Child Book Rev Serv

Sleator, William
Oddballs; stories. Dutton Children's Bks. 1993 134p pa $5.99 hardcover o.p. (6 and up)

S C

1. Short stories
ISBN 0-14-037438-8 (pa)   LC 92-27666

A collection of stories based on experiences from the author's youth and peopled with an unusual assortment of family and friends

"Fresh, funny, and slightly gross, the quasi-autobiographical glimpses will grab the reader's attention." Horn Book Guide

Somehow tenderness survives; stories of Southern Africa; selected by Hazel Rochman. Harper & Row 1988 147p hardcover o.p. paperback available $5.99   S C
1. Short stories 2. South Africa—Race relations—Fiction
ISBN 0-06-447063-6 (pa)   LC 88-916

A collection of eight short stories and two "autobiographical accounts which vividly evoke what it means to come of age in South Africa under apartheid. The contributors, including Doris Lessing and Nadine Gordimer, as well as lesser-known writers, are of various races and their stories cover a time span of 35 years. . . . This title should be in every YA collection. A glossary and notes on contributors are included." Voice Youth Advocates

Soto, Gary
Baseball in April, and other stories. 10th anniversary ed. Harcourt Brace Jovanovich 2000 c1990 111p $16; pa $6 (5 and up)   S C
1. Mexican Americans—Fiction 2. California—Fiction 3. Short stories
ISBN 0-15-202573-1; 0-15-202567-7 (pa)

Also available Spanish language edition and Audiobook version

A reissue of the title first published 1990

A collection of eleven short stories focusing on the everyday adventures of Hispanic young people growing up in Fresno, California

Each story "gets at the heart of some aspect of growing up. The insecurities, the embarrassments, the triumphs, the inequities of it all are chronicled with wit and charm. Soto's characters ring true and his knowledge of, and affection for, their shared Mexican-American heritage is obvious and infectious." Voice Youth Advocates

Help wanted; stories; by Gary Soto. Harcourt 2005 218p $17   S C
1. Mexican Americans—Fiction 2. California—Fiction 3. Short stories
ISBN 0-15-205201-1   LC 2004-7510

Soto, Gary—*Continued*

"Ten original short stories about Mexican-American teens in central California. The fundamental theme of 'needing help' is the common thread among the stories, which range from the satirical to the peculiar to the humorous to the sad." SLJ

"The stories are sometimes funny, often poignant, and occasionally provocative." Booklist

Local news. Harcourt Brace Jovanovich 1993 148p $13.95; pa $5.95   **S C**
1. Mexican Americans—Fiction 2. California—Fiction 3. Short stories
ISBN 0-15-248117-6; 0-15-204695-X (pa)
LC 92-37905
Also available in paperback from Scholastic

A collection of thirteen short stories about the everyday lives of Mexican American young people in California's Central Valley

"These stories resonate with integrity, verve, and compassion." Horn Book

Soul searching: thirteen stories about faith and belief; edited by Lisa Rowe Fraustino. Simon & Schuster Bks. for Young Readers 2002 267p $17.95   **S C**
1. Religion—Fiction 2. Short stories
ISBN 0-689-83484-5   LC 2002-70571
Contents: The shunning of Sadie B. Zook, by L. O. High; The funeral, by W. Sleator; The olive grove, by E. Marston; A daughter of Abraham, by D. Hess; Words of faith, by D. Lubar; The evil eye, by D. C. Regan; The see-far glasses, by M. Ho; Going to Kashi, by U. Krishnaswami; Dust to dust, by N. Flynn; The moth of God, by J. Armstrong; Star vision, by S. Begay; Elvis lives, by J. Slayton; The tin man, by L. R. Fraustino

"This varied collection seeks to foster thought and discussion on the sometimes-conflicting themes of faith and belief. . . . Overall . . . teens will find new ideas to consider, new worlds to explore, and perhaps see themselves in some of the protagonists." SLJ

Spinelli, Jerry, 1941-
The library card. Scholastic 1997 148p (4 and up)   **S C**
1. Books and reading—Fiction 2. Short stories
ISBN 0-590-46731-X; 0-590-38633-6 (pa)
LC 96-18412

"A library card is the magical object common to each of these four stories in which a budding street thug, a television addict, a homeless orphan, and a lonely girl are all transformed by the power and the possibilities that await them within the walls of the public library. Spinelli's characters . . . are unusual and memorable; his writing both humorous and convincing." Horn Book Guide

Talking leaves; contemporary native American short stories; introduced and edited by Craig Lesley; associate editor, Katheryn Stavrakis. Dell 1991 xxvi, 385p pa $16.95   **S C**
1. Native Americans—Fiction 2. Short stories
ISBN 0-385-31272-5   LC 92-139334
"A Laurel trade paperback"

This anthology includes contributions by such authors as Louise Erdrich, Diane Glancy, Michael Dorris, N. Scott Momaday, Paula Gunn Allen, and Mary Tallmountain

"All these stories have a strong sense of person and place and engagingly inform of the Native American condition." Libr J

Taylor, Theodore, 1921-
Rogue wave and other red-blooded sea stories. Harcourt Brace & Co. 1996 184p $16
S C
1. Sea stories 2. Short stories
ISBN 0-15-201408-X   LC 96-14585
Also available in paperback from Avon Bks.

This "collection comprises five stories previously published in the 1950s and 1960s in such magazines as *Argosy* and three original ones focusing on teenagers' sea adventures. . . . Juicy subjects such as sharks, a cruel captain, and the psychological battle between a captured German U-boat commander and a scholarly British officer are fleshed out in very masculine style, with lots of physical detail and excitement, and most of the stories end with the sort of punchy conclusion that characterizes the best short stories." Booklist

Time capsule: short stories about teenagers throughout the twentieth century; edited by Donald R. Gallo. Delacorte Press 1999 221p hardcover o.p. paperback available $6.50
S C
1. Short stories
ISBN 0-440-22819-0 (pa)   LC 99-13117
Ten stories by such notable authors as Richard Peck, Chris Crutcher, and Chris Lynch, each of which presents the life of a teenager in a different decade of the twentieth century, accompanied by a brief description of the historical and cultural highlights of that decade

This collection is "an outstanding achievement that should win over fiction fans and history buffs alike." Booklist

Tripping over the lunch lady and other school stories; edited by Nancy E. Mercado. Dial Books 2004 177p $16.99 (4 and up)
S C
1. School stories 2. Short stories
ISBN 0-8037-2873-5   LC 2003-15905
Contents: Tripping over the lunch lady by Angela Johnson; How I got my English A by Avi; Experts, incorporated by Sarah Weeks; Apple blossoms by Terry Trueman; Science friction by David Lubar; The grade school zone by James Proimos, illustrated by David Fremont; The desk by Lee Wardlaw; The crush by Rachel Vail; The girls room by Susan Shreve; Tied to Zelda by David Rice

An "anthology of 10 short stories, by authors such as Avi, Angela Johnson, David Lubar, and Rachel Vail." SLJ

"In these first-person narratives, sharply defined details and keenly observed nuances of school life often set the stage for moments of wit, surprise, realization, and tenderness." Booklist

Ultimate sports; short stories by outstanding writers for young adults; edited by Donald R. Gallo. Delacorte Press 1995 333p pa $6.50 hardcover o.p. (7 and up)   S C
1. Sports—Fiction 2. Short stories
ISBN 0-440-22707-0 (pa)   LC 94-49610
This anthologyincludes stories by: Chris Crutcher; Will Weaver; Norma Fox Mazer; Robert Lipsyte; Thomas J. Dygard and Chris Lynch
"There is a terrific mix of the serious and the light-hearted, female and male characters, and traditional and nontraditional games. A winning collection." SLJ

Vampires: a collection of original stories; edited by Jane Yolen and Martin H. Greenberg. HarperCollins Pubs. 1991 228p   S C
1. Vampires—Fiction 2. Short stories
ISBN 0-06-026800-X; 0-06-050222-3 (pa)
        LC 90-27888
A collection of thirteen original stories about vampires by a variety of authors
"In this collection of chilling, funny, and sensitive stories, the undead include piano teachers, mean old aunts, and even the girl next door." Booklist

Vande Velde, Vivian, 1951-
Being dead; stories. Harcourt 2001 203p $17; pa $6.95 (7 and up)   S C
1. Supernatural—Fiction 2. Horror fiction 3. Short stories
ISBN 0-15-216320-4; 0-15-204912-6 (pa)
        LC 00-12996
This is a collection of seven "creepy tales featuring ghosts, cemeteries, suicides, murders, and other death-related themes." SLJ
"Often humorous and sometimes evoking sympathy, this anthology will be enjoyed by lovers of mild horror as well as by those who like clever short stories." Voice Youth Advocates

Tales from the Brothers Grimm and the Sisters Weird. Harcourt Brace & Co. 1995 128p il $17; pa $5.95   S C
1. Fairy tales 2. Short stories
ISBN 0-15-200220-0; 0-15-205572-X (pa)
        LC 94-26341
"Jane Yolen Books"
This collection presents alternative versions of such familiar fairy tales as Rumpelstiltskin, Hansel and Gretel, and The Princess and the Pea
"Vande Velde challenges readers' notions of good, bad, and ugly. . . . Modern references and sensibilities . . . add to the humor (often the gallows variety). Entertaining and provocative, these selections make good read-alouds and can be used to spark discussion or creative writing exercises." SLJ

Visions: nineteen short stories by outstanding writers for young adults; edited by Donald R. Gallo. Delacorte Press 1987 228p hardcover o.p. paperback available $5.99 (7 and up)
        S C
1. Short stories
ISBN 0-440-20208-6 (pa)   LC 87-6787

"Information about the authors follows each of nineteen original short stories, most of them impressive examples of the genre, all of them written by established men and women. Among the familiar names: Joan Aiken, M.E. Kerr, Walter Dean Myers, Richard Peck. The tales are grouped under such headings as 'Adjustments' or 'Kinships,' and include both realistic and fanciful writing, most of the work being of fine quality and the rest only slightly less so." Bull Cent Child Books

Wallace, Rich, 1957-
Losing is not an option: stories. Knopf 2003 127p $15.95; lib bdg $17.99 (7 and up)
        S C
1. Short stories
ISBN 0-375-81351-9; 0-375-91351-3 (lib bdg)
        LC 2002-34036
Nine episodes in the life of a young man, from sneaking into his tenth football game in a row with his best friend in sixth grade to running his last high school race, the Pennsylvania state championships
"Readers will nod with recognition as they follow this jock/poet/regular guy from the cusp of adolescence to the edge of adulthood." Horn Book

What a song can do; 12 riffs on the power of music; edited by Jennifer Armstrong. Knopf 2004 200p $15.95 (7 and up)   S C
1. Music—Fiction 2. Short stories
ISBN 0-375-82499-5   LC 2003-24306
Twelve stories describe the power of music in young people's lives, from forming a community of individuals in a high school band to helping a young man connect to his Indian heritage through ancient songs.
These stories "show the power of both words and music to express the turbulent emotions of growing up." Booklist

Who do you think you are? stories of friends and enemies; selected by Hazel Rochman and Darlene Z. McCampbell. Little, Brown 1993 170p hardcover o.p. paperback available $9.95
        S C
1. Friendship—Fiction 2. Short stories
ISBN 0-316-75320-3 (pa)   LC 93-314
"Joy Street books"
"Louise Erdrich, John Updike, Ray Bradbury, Joyce Carol Oates, Sandra Cisneros, Tim O'Brien, Richard Peck, and Maya Angelou are among the 15 writers represented in this anthology of stories {two prose excerpts and a poem} about friendship and loss of friendship." Booklist
"Meticulously chosen and arranged, these works crystalize moments of vulnerability, sorrow and understanding; together, they serve as an excellent introduction to modern American writing." Publ Wkly

Yee, Paul
Tales from Gold Mountain; stories of the Chinese in the New World; paintings by Simon Ng. Macmillan 1989 64p il (4 and up)
        S C
1. Chinese Americans—Fiction 2. Short stories
ISBN 0-02-793621-X   LC 89-12643

Yee, Paul—*Continued*

Groundwood Bks. reissue available $18.95 (0-88899-098-7)

A collection of eight stories reflecting the gritty optimism of the Chinese who overcame prejudice and adversity to build a unique place for themselves in North America

These "brief, pithy tales strikingly reflect traditional Chinese beliefs and customs in New World circumstances. . . . Romance, family loyalty, and justice are important themes, and an element of surprise is never far away." Booklist

LIST OF RECOMMENDED PERIODICALS

The following list of recommended periodicals for a Middle and Junior High School Library is divided into two parts: Part I, Professional, which lists titles for librarians and teachers, and Part II, Children's and Young Adult, which lists titles for students. It is widely felt that a school library should introduce students to weekly news magazines and other popular general magazines as appropriate, but these types of materials are not listed below. Neither are popular young adult magazines that are strictly for entertainment and have no educational content, which can be collected at the individual library's discretion.

PART I

PROFESSIONAL

Art Education. National Art Education Association $25 per year (members), $50 per year (non-members)
ISSN 0004-3125

http://www.naea-reston.org

Bimonthly.

"Articles on current directions, problems, and exemplary approaches in visual art education at all instructional levels. Articles may focus on the art curriculum, teaching strategies, innovative programs, or a special area of the curriculum such as studio, art criticism, or art history. Each issue of Art Education includes four full-color reproductions of works of art, with commentary and lesson plan suggestions for use at both elementary and secondary levels." NAEA website

Educational Leadership. Association for Supervision and Curriculum Development $49 per year (must be a member of this organization)
ISSN 0004-3125

http://www.ascd.org

Bimonthly September through May.

This magazine discusses "teaching and learning, new ideas and practices relevant to practicing educators, and the latest trends and issues affecting prekindergarten through higher education." ASCD website

Edutopia: The World of Learning. The George Lucas Educational Foundation Free
ISSN 1552-9029

http://www.edutopia.org

Bimonthly.

Published by the George Lucas Foundation and evolved from their website that features multimedia streaming video to support many of the journal articles, Edutopia focuses on the newest research, theories, and practices in K-12 education and relates it to schools around the world that are already implementing them. Best New Publication 2005 Maggie Awards

English Journal. National Council of Teachers of English $25 per year (price for members)
ISSN 0013-8274

http://www.ncte.org

Bimonthly September through July.

"A journal of ideas for English language arts teachers in junior and senior high schools and middle schools. EJ presents information on the teaching of writing and reading, literature, and language. Each issue examines the relationship of theory and research to classroom practice and reviews current materials of interest to English teachers, including books and electronic media." NCTE website

Instructor. Scholastic, Inc. $14 per year
ISSN 1049-5851

http://www.scholastic.com

Monthly August, September, October, March, and April. Bimonthly November/December, January/February, May/June.

This magazine is focused on elementary and middle school teachers with lots of classroom activities as well as feature articles, monthly columns and education news.

JOPERD. American Alliance for Health, Physical Education, Recreation and Dance $145 per year
ISSN 0730-3084

Monthly (except June).

The Journal of Physical Education, Recreation & Dance is the professional magazine for the American Alliance of Health, Physical, Recreation, and Dance. It addresses a variety of HPERD issues including articles on teaching strategies, fitness, legal issues, assessment, dancing, teacher education, adapted physical education, leisure for older adults, the use of technology, and ethics and gender equity in sports and physical education.

Knowledge Quest. American Library Association $40 per year
ISSN 1094-9046

http://www.ala.org/aasl

Bimonthly September through May.

This publication, along with its companion website KQonline, "is devoted to offering substantive information to assist building-level library media specialists, supervisors, library educators, and other decision makers concerned with the development of school library media programs and services. Articles address the integration of theory and practice in school librarianship and new developments in education, learning theory, and relevant disciplines." ALA website

Language Arts. National Council of Teachers of English $25 per year (members)
ISSN 0360-9170

http://www.ncte.org

Bimonthly September-July.

Language Arts—*Continued*

"A professional journal for elementary and middle school teachers and teacher educators. It provides a forum for discussions on all aspects of language arts learning and teaching, primarily as they relate to children in prekindergarten through the eighth grade. Issues discuss both theory and classroom practice, highlight current research, and review children's and young adolescent literature, as well as classroom and professional materials of interest to language arts educators." NCTE website

Learning and Leading with Technology. International Society for Technology in Education $79 per year (members)
ISSN 1082-5754

http://www.iste.org

Monthly (except June, July, August), bimonthly December/January.

Member subscription of the International Society for Technology in Education, introduces classroom applications of newer technology, integration strategies, and leadership strategies for implementing instructional technology into schools.

Middle School Journal. National Middle School Association $40 per year
ISSN 0094-0771

http://www.nmsa.org

5 times per year (September, November, January, March, May).

Peer-reviewed, membership-distributed journal of the National Middle School Association, focusing on topics related to teaching middle school students. Focused on middle school curriculum implementation and teaching strategies.

Phi Delta Kappan. Phi Delta Kappa International, Inc. $58 per year
ISSN 0031-7217

http://www.pdkintl.org/kappan/kappan.htm

Monthly (except July and August).

"The professional print journal for education, addresses policy issues for educators at all levels. Advocating research-based school reform, the Kappan provides a forum for debate on controversial subjects." PDKINTL website

Preventing School Failure. Heldref Publications $113 for institutions, otherwise $28.25 per copy
ISSN 1045-988X

http://www.heldref.org

Quarterly.

"Helps educators and other professionals seeking to promote the success of students who have learning and behavioral problems. It offers examples of programs and practices that help children and youth in schools, clinics, correctional institutions, and other settings." Heldref website

The **Reading** Teacher. International Reading Association $61 per year (members), $15 per issue (non-members)
ISSN 0034-0561

http://www.reading.org

Eight times per year.

Topics range from research-based suggestions about teaching phonics to the latest thinking about technology integration, and from reviews of children's books to ideas that promote learning from nonfiction text.

School Library Media Research. American Library Association Free
ISSN 1523-4320

http://www.ala.org/aasl/SLMR

5 times a year.

This is a web-based only publication

"An official journal of the American Association of School Librarians. It is the successor to School Library Media Quarterly Online. The purpose of School Library Media Research is to promote and publish high quality original research concerning the management, implementation, and evaluation of school library media programs. The journal will also emphasize research on instructional theory, teaching methods, and critical issues relevant to school library media." Publisher's note

Science Books and Films. American Association for the Advancement of Science $45 per year
ISSN 1533-5046

http://SBFonline.com

Bimonthly.

"Published by the American Association for the Advancement of Science (AAAS), SB&F is the only critical review journal devoted exclusively to print and nonprint materials in all of the sciences and for all age groups. Every year, SB&F evaluates nearly 1,000 books, videos and DVDs, and software packages for general audiences, professionals, teachers, and students from kindergarten through college." AAAS website

Science Scope. National Science Teachers Association $67 per year for members
ISSN 0887-2376

http://www.nsta.org

Eight times per year.

National Science Teachers Association's professional journal for middle school science teachers. Practical ideas for teaching science based on middle school theory and practice.

Social Education. National Council for the Social Studies $35 per year (members), otherwise $7.50 per issue
ISSN 0037-7724

http://www.socialstudies.org

Monthly in September, October, March, April. Bimonthly November/December, January/February, May/June.

This journal, which includes the supplement *Middle Level Learning*, which brings together lesson ideas and theoretical content focused on the middle grades (3 times yearly) "contains a balance of theoretical content and practical ideas for classroom use. Our award-winning resources include techniques for using teaching materials in the classroom, information on the latest instructional technology, reviews of educational media, research on significant topics related to social studies, and lesson plans that can be applied to various disciplines." NCSS website

Teacher Magazine. Editorial Projects in Education $17.94 per year
ISSN 1046-6193

http://www.teachermagazine.org

Bimonthly (except for July and single-month October issue).

A sister publication of Education Week, Teacher Magazine is focused upon current news and stories of interest to classroom teachers. Lots of personal experiences and reflection.

Teaching Exceptional Children. Council for Exceptional Children $24 per year
ISSN 0040-0599

http://www.cec.sped.org

Bimonthly September-July.

"TEC, an official publication of the Council for Exceptional Children, is published specifically for teachers and administrators of children with disabilities and children who are gifted. TEC features . . . articles that present methods and materials for classroom use as well as current issues in special education teaching and learning. TEC also brings its readers the latest data on technology, assistive technology, and procedures and techniques with applications to students with exceptionalities." CEC website

Teaching PreK-8: Teacher Resources for Professional Development. Highlights for Children, Inc. $16 per year
ISSN 0891-4508

http://www.Teachingk-8.com

Monthly (except June, July, August, December).

This publication was Highlights Winner of the 2003 Association of Education Publishers Distinguished Achievement Award and includes reviews of classroom products, "Green Pages" listing ideas for classroom activities, and articles and columns written by teachers about their experiences.

Teaching Tolerance Magazine. Teaching Tolerance No charge to educators
ISSN 1066-2847

http://www.teachingtolerance.org

Twice a year.

"Founded in 1991 by the Southern Poverty Law Center, Teaching Tolerance provides educators with free educational materials that promote respect for differences and appreciation of diversity in the classroom and beyond. Published twice a year, our magazine profiles educators, schools and programs promoting diversity and equity in inspirational and replicable ways." Teaching Tolerance website

Technology and Learning. C M P Media Free to qualified personnel
ISSN 1053-6728

http://www.techlearning.com/

Monthly.

"The Resource for Education Technology Leaders" targets teachers as well as technology coordinators and administrators with ideas for and the theory behind the educational use of technology resources in the classroom.

Voices from the Middle. National Council of Teachers of English $20 per year (members)
ISSN 1074-4762

http://www.ncte.org

September, December, March, May.

"Devotes each issue to one topic or concept related to literacy and learning at the middle school level. Each issue includes teachers' descriptions of authentic classroom practices, middle school students' reviews of adolescent literature, a technology column, and reviews of professional resources for teachers." NCTE website

PART II

CHILDREN'S AND YOUNG ADULT

Blackgirl Magazine. Destiny Entertainment $24 per year (4 and up)

http://www.blackgirlmagazine.com/

Bimonthly.

Created by a 14-year-old girl from Atlanta, this magazine "focuses on promoting positive messages and imagery among African-American teens, while offering . . . coverage of history, culture, lifestyle, and entertainment news." Publisher's note

Boys' Life. Boy Scouts of America $21.60 per year (5-9)
ISSN 0006-8608

http://www.boyslife.org

Monthly.

This magazine covers scouting projects and profiles of scouts, as well as sports, science, hobbies, and other topics. It also features comics (including a Bible Heroes graphic strip), craft projects, and fiction. Some commercial content is included.

Brio. Focus on the Family $18 per year (6-10)
ISSN 1048-2873

http://www.briomag.com

Monthly.

This magazine takes a conservative Christian perspective on issues younger teens face. It features an advice column, interviews, profiles of Christian celebrities, and fiction.

Calliope. Carus $29.95 per year (4-6)

http://www.cobblestonepub.com

9 times a year.

Each issue focuses on a single theme in world history, such as Mozart or the Mexican Revolution, and includes theme-related illustrations, maps, time lines, images of art from museums, activities and experiments, puzzles, and bibliographies.

Career World. Weekly Reader Publications $34.50 per year (6-12)
ISSN 0744-1002

http://www.weeklyreader.com/teens/publications.asp

6 times a year.

This magazine features information about careers, education, and the connection between college courses and employment as well as coverage of employment trends, the job market, job-search tips and interviewing techniques.

ChildArt. International Child Art Foundation $30 per year (3-7)
ISSN 1096-9020

http://www.icaf.org

6 times a year.

This magazine focuses on famous art and artists and encourages young readers to express themselves in a variety of art forms. It explores themes, such as refugee art, peace through art, and art and culture, and includes games, wordplay, and profiles.

Cicada. Carus $35.97 per year (4-9)
ISSN 1097-4008

http://www.cricketmag.com

Bimonthly.

This teen literary magazine features fiction and poetry often focused on themes of growing up. Submissions from young people are encouraged.

Cobblestone: discover American history. Carus $19.95 per year (4-8)
ISSN 0199-5197

http://www.cobblestonepub.com

9 times a year.

Each issue of this historical magazine features a theme topic such as cowboys, Russians in America, or libraries, and contains articles, stories, and activities related to the issue's theme.

Creative Kids: the national voice for kids. Prufrock $19.95 per year (3-8)
ISSN 0892-9599

http://www.prufrock.com

4 times a year.

This magazine features "games, stories, and opinions all by and for kids ages 8-14." Publisher's note

Cricket: the magazine for children. Carus $35.97 per year (4-8)
ISSN 0090-6034

http://www.cricketmag.com

Monthly.

This magazine features fiction (including science fiction), biographies, fantasy, poetry, and folktales. It also "offers its readers cartoons, crossword puzzles, crafts, and recipes. In addition, CRICKET features story, poetry, art, and photography contests." Publisher's note

Current Science. Weekly Reader Publications $34.50 per year (6-10)
ISSN 0011-3905

http://www.weeklyreader.com

16 times a year.

This magazine "uses today's news to make science more relevant to students in grades 6-10. . . . Each issue covers every area of the science curriculum—life, earth, and physical science, plus health and technology. . . . [Also available are] Teacher's Guides that link each issue's content to state and NSE standards." Publisher's note

Dig Magazine. Carus $32.97 per year (4-8)
ISSN 1539-7130

http://www.cricketmag.com/

9 times a year.

This magazine features articles on archaeological discoveries, with topics ranging from mummies to dinosaurs. Each issue includes photo-illustrations, projects, puzzles and games.

Faces: people, places, & cultures. Carus $29.95 per year (4-6)
ISSN 0749-1387

http://www.cobblestonepub.com

9 times a year.

Each issue of this 52-page magazine focuses on a different culture and includes maps, photographs, time lines, activities, contests, a crossword puzzle, bibliography, and Webography all related to that theme.

Footsteps: African-American heritage. Carus $23.95 per year (4-6)
ISSN 1521-5865

http://www.footstepsmagazine.com

5 times a year.

Each issue of this magazine explores a African American-related theme, such as Colonial slavery, the Negro Leagues, or the life of an African American historical figure. Issues include theme-related articles, interviews, photographs, artwork, maps, primary source documents, time lines, activities, and projects.

Girls' Life. Monarch Avalon $14.95 per year (6-8)
ISSN 1078-3326

http://www.girlslife.com

Bimonthly.

In addition to articles on boys, school, fashion, celebrities, and family relationships, this magazine also features an advice column, craft projects, reviews, contests, quizzes, and profiles of notable teenage girls.

Guideposts Sweet 16. Guideposts $19.95 per year (6-12)
ISSN 1551-904X

http://www.guidepostssweet16mag.com

Bimonthly.

This spiritual teen magazine features true life stories, advice columns, news, social commentary, and reviews in addition to articles on fashion, beauty, entertainment, celebrities, and boys.

Imagine: opportunities and resources for academically talented youth. Johns Hopkins Center for Talented Youth $30 per year (6-12)
ISSN 1071-605X

http://www.cty.jhu.edu/imagine

5 times a year.

Aimed at career-minded middle and high school students, this magazine features student-penned articles on academic competitions, internships, summer programs, extracurricular activities, and other ways of gaining job experience for the future. It also provides college planning advice, career profiles, and other resources.

Junior Scholastic. Scholastic, Inc. Prices vary according to the number of subscriptions per classroom (5-7)
ISSN 0022-6688

http://www.scholastic.com/juniorscholastic

Biweekly during the school year.

Designed for use in classrooms, this magazine offers news stories from around the world as well as articles on American history and geography. A teacher's edition is also available. Some commercial content is included.

JVibe. Jewish Family & Life! $18 per year (6-12)

http://www.jvibe.com

Bimonthly.

This magazine focuses on Jewish youth culture from around the world, with topics including pop culture, religious issues, social action, and Israel.

Kids Discover. Kids Discover $19.95 per year (4-6)
ISSN 1054-2868

http://www.kidsdiscover.com

10 times a year.

Kids Discover—*Continued*

Each theme-based issue features articles, bibliographies, experiments, and activities. Themes include topics as diverse as space exploration, weather, the pyramids, and the brain.

Muse. Carus $32.97 per year (5 and up)
ISSN 1090-0381

http://www.cricketmag.com

10 times a year.

This magazine aims to encourage kids to be more curious about the world around them and features articles on science, history, and art. "Each issue is filled with engaging photographs and illustrations, cartoons, a contest, activities, Web site recommendations, and reader letters." Publisher's note

New Moon: the magazine for girls and their dreams. New Moon $29.95 per year (5-9)
ISSN 1069-238X

http://www.newmoon.org

Bimonthly.

This periodical is edited by girls eight to 14 years old and features fiction, poems, articles, artwork, and letters from girls around the world.

Odyssey: adventures in science. Carus $29.95 per year (5-9)
ISSN 0163-0946

http://www.cobblestonepub.com

9 times a year.

Each issue features articles on recent scientific discoveries, puzzles, hands-on activities, an animal column, a cartoon featuring astronomer Jack Horkheimer, and a monthly "Star Chart" for young astronomers. The magazine also publishes stories, poems, and artwork by kids.

Owl. Bayard Canada $31.02 per year (4-7)
ISSN 0382-6627

http://www.owlkids.com

10 times a year.

This magazine presents a variety of articles on science, art, and the environment. It also features an advice column, puzzles and activities.

Pack-O-Fun. Clapper $21.97 (4-7)
ISSN 0030-901X

http://www.craftideas.com/packofun

6 times a year.

This magazine offers color photographs of finished themed arts and crafts projects. It includes step-by-step directions and lists of necessary materials for projects.

Scholastic Art. Scholastic, Inc. Price is based on the total number of subscriptions (7-12)
ISSN 1060-832X

http://teacher.scholastic.com/products/classmags/art.htm

6 times a year.

Each issue is centered on an art related theme and explains the historical and cultural contexts in which works or styles of fine art were created. It also includes an "Art Workshop" to teach students how to replicate theme-related techniques.

Skipping Stones: a multicultural magazine. Skipping Stones $35 per year (5-7)
ISSN 0899-529X

http://www.skippingstones.org

6 times a year.

This magazine features the writings and artwork of adults and young people from countries around the world, with an emphasis on international and multicultural education and communication.

Sports Illustrated for Kids. Time $24.95 per year (6-12)
ISSN 1042-394X

http://www.sikids.com

Monthly.

Each issue features stories, trivia, color action photos, and posters for young sports fans.

Stone Soup: the magazine by young writers and artists. Children's Art Foundation $34 per year (4-7)
ISSN 0094-579X

http://www.stonesoup.com

6 times a year.

This magazine publishes works of fiction, poetry, and artwork by young people from around the world. It also pays a nominal fee for admissions that are accepted.

Teen Ink. Young Authors Foundation $25 per year (6-12)

http://www.teenink.com

Monthly.

Each issue of this national magazine written and illustrated by teenagers features fiction, nonfiction, interviews, poetry, photography, and art.

Teen Voices. Women Express $20 per year (6-12)
ISSN 1074-7494

http://www.teenvoices.com

Twice a year.

This magazine written and illustrated by teenage girls addresses such issues as body image, racism, rape, and drug abuse.

Wizard: the comics magazine. Wizard Entertainment $28 per year (5 and up)
ISSN 1065-6499

http://www.wizarduniverse.com/

Monthly.

This comic book and action figure price guide also features interviews, comics industry news, art tips, and other comic book-related topics.

Zoobooks. Wildlife Education Ltd. $20.95 per year (4-6)
ISSN 0737-9005

http://www.zoobooks.com

12 times a year.

Each issue features articles, color photographs, illustrations, and interactive games focused on a specific animal.

LIST OF RECOMMENDED ELECTRONIC RESOURCES

A. Pintura: Art Detective. Educational Web Adventures Free

http://www.eduweb.com/pintura

An online game about art history and art composition, in which players attempt to identify a painting's artist by examining paintings by famous artists from Gauguin to Van Gogh for composition, style and subject. Three other art history games are linked.

Absurd Math. Learningwave Free

http://www.learningwave.com/abmath/

In this online interactive game, players work to overthrow a tyranny which punishes all thought, and mathematical thought in particular. They are presented with a series of pre-algebra problems of increasing difficulty as they approach success. The mathematics requires knowledge of arithmetic up to decimal fractions, and email help is available.

Academy of reading. TE21 Contact producer for pricing (K-12)

http://www.te21.com

By subscription only. Tel. 843-881-7854

Designed to teach reading skills in a developmental continuum, Academy of Reading targets children at all levels, helping them sequentially improve phonemic awareness, reading subskills, word recognition, and oral/silent reading comprehension. Features a "Teacher Time" function that will not allow a child who is having difficulty with a concept to proceed until a teacher intervenes. Includes a management system, a metronome tool for nudging children forward, and student prizes for mastery of concepts (i.e., clues to complete a puzzle, etc.). Educators should note that consistent use of the program in short segments of fifteen to twenty minutes three to five days a week is recommended for optimal results.

Alien Empire. Public Broadcasting Service Free

http://www.pbs.org/wnet/nature/alienempire/metropolis.html

Provides pictures, sounds, animation, and videos on insects. Articles discuss insect reproduction, societies, migration, and survival strategies. Includes animated presentations on monarch butterflies, mayflies, and bees and a list of insect information resources.

Alt HealthWatch. EBSCO Publishing $395/yr.

http://www.epnet.com

By subscription only. Tel. 800-653-2726

Alt HealthWatch is a reference resource Internet tool that focuses on complementary, holistic, and integrated approaches to health care and wellness. It includes nearly 50,000 articles from over 160 international, peer-reviewed and professional journals, magazines, reports, proceedings, and association and consumer newsletters (most from 1990 to the present), pamphlets, booklets, special reports, original research, and book excerpts. The database indexes each article by more than 225 subject categories, 16 article types, and 11 publication types. It provides coverage across the spectrum of subject areas covered by the term, "Alternative Medicine."

Amazon Interactive. Educational Web Adventures Free

http://www.eduweb.com/amazon.html

Explains the geography of the Ecuadorian Amazon and the culture of the Quichua people through online games and activities. In one interactive game, players try to set up and manage a sustainable, community-based ecotourism project along the Río Napo.

America The Beautiful Online. Grolier Educational Contact producer for pricing; minimum of two databases (4 and up)

http://www.go.grolier.com

By subscription only. Tel. 888-326-6546

A national and state reference (including territories) with over 1000 articles covering: history, economy, government, cities and capitals, rivers and lakes, geography and landforms. Articles are enhanced with photos, maps, narrated slide shows, and pre-selected Web links on the Grolier Internet Index. Profiles of famous Americans include every president. Information on national parks, natural wonders, monuments, museums, zoos, and historical places is also included. Key word searches can be limited to article titles or full text with the use of Boolean operators. The site also includes an almanac and a dictionary. Lesson plans and activities are provided for teachers.

American family immigration history center. The statue of liberty—Ellis island foundation, Inc. Free

http://www.ellisisland.org

Explore your family history by accessing the records of all immigrants to pass through Ellis Island and the Port of New York from 1892 to 1924. A simple name search on the home page is the starting point. You can also search ship's manifests, create and maintain a family scrapbook and create printouts.

American Government. ABC-CLIO $499/yr. (6 and up)

http://www.americangovernment.abc-clio.com/

By subscription only. Tel. 800-368-6868

Comprehensive resource on all aspects of American Government that includes topic overviews, essays, court cases, biographies, speeches, and historical documents. Students can explore pre-designed topics such as Congressional Powers, the Presidency, Civil Rights, and Political Parties or search by key word. Advanced searches can be limited by topic and categories (movements, organizations, statistics, quotes, etc.). The Home page provides changing news articles and feature stories linked to related articles in the database. Instructors can customize the site by adding announcements, syllabi, calendar of assignments, tests, etc. Teachers also have access to professional articles and links to additional resources. Includes the *Merriam Webster Dictionary*.

"Well designed, with good content and strategically placed links. Students will enjoy digging deep into this source." Libr J

American History. ABC-CLIO $499/yr. (6 and up)

http://www.americanhistory.abc-clio.com/

By subscription only. Tel. 800-368-6868

Provides coverage and resources on American history from 1350 to the present. The Home page includes feature stories and current events with links to related articles. Information can be searched by key word or phrase as well as through advanced searches by category, including documents, quotes, timelines, and type of multimedia. Instructors can customize the site by adding announcements, syllabi, calendar of assignments, tests, etc. Teachers also have access to professional articles and links to additional resources. Includes the *Merriam Webster Dictionary*.

"An easily navigable, appealing and comprehensive resource that would be extremely useful for the study of United States history." Evalutech

American verse project. University of Michigan Free

http://www.hti.umich.edu/a/amverse/

A collaboration between the University of Michigan Humanities Text Initiative and the University of Michigan Press to assemble an electronic archive of volumes of American poetry prior to 1920. Search types include: simple, proximity, Boolean, and citations. A word index and browse features are also included. There are over 125 volumes available by authors such as Whittier, Teasdale and Poe. Some of the volumes available, including those by a number of African-American and women poets, are the only existing editions of the author's work.

Animal diversity web. University of Michigan Free (6-12)

http://animaldiversity.ummz.umich.edu/site/index.html

An online database of animal natural history, distribution, classification, and conservation biology at the University of Michigan. It has thousands of species accounts about individual animal species and descriptions of levels of organization above the species level. ADW labels itself a searchable encyclopedia of the natural history of animals that facilitates inquiry-driven learning (that is, teaching about science by leading students to use the methods of science), and a virtual museum.

"This is a fantastic site that has a variety of tools including an animal kingdom classification index showing phylum, class, order, and family; and also detailed physical structures." Florida's Instructional Technology Resource Center

Animals A to Z. Oakland Zoo Free

http://www.oaklandzoo.org/atoz/atoz.html

A database of text, pictures, sounds, and video on approximately one hundred zoo animals.

Anne Frank the writer. United States Holocaust Memorial Museum and The Netherlands Institute for War Documentation Free (6-12)

http://www.ushmm.org/museum/exhibit/online/af/htmlsite/

"Presents the essence of Anne's life and writings in multimedia slide shows that include quotations, photographs, and video clips. We gain an appreciation of the precocious wisdom and youthful enthusiasm of Anne through her own words and through an extensive collection of photographs that can be viewed interactively. Excerpts from her 'pen children,' as she called her stories,

and from her diaries are presented in a variety of ways that add a dynamic visual quality to the information. RealPlayer video interviews with relatives and historians provide insight into Anne's personality and experiences, and a moderated discussion section permits visitors to the Web site to share reactions and comments with others." Evalutech

Art explorer. The Art Institute of Chicago Free (6-12)

http://www.artic.edu/artexplorer/

"An interactive website where visitors can search for art, save selections into scrapbooks with notes, and share the scrapbooks with friends and students. Art Explorer focuses on the Art Institute's Impressionist and Postimpressionist collections, and includes original artworks, as well as additional resources, including texts, video clips, artist biographies, activities, and games." Internet Scout

Art Museum Image Gallery. H.W. Wilson Contact producer for pricing

http://www.hwwilson.com

By subscription only. Tel. 800-367-6770

The Art Museum Image Gallery is a digital resource of over 96,000 high-quality art images and related multimedia gathered from the collections of distinguished museums around the world. Each image features a full description, and many include curatorial text, provenance data, detail or multiple views for many images, plus related multimedia where available. The images cover artistic creation from 3000 B.C. to the present, with art from the cultures of Africa, Asia, Europe, and the Americas, including Native American and Meso-American peoples. There is coverage of both fine and decorative art: painting, sculpture, drawings, prints, photographs, textiles, costumes, jewelry, ceramics, furniture, glass, books and manuscripts, archaeological finds, and more. The images can be useful for multicultural studies, area studies, archaeology, history, religion, cultural studies, literature, and related subject areas.

Ask Dr. Math. Drexel University Free (1 and up)

http://mathforum.org/dr.math

This website, run by math majors at Drexel University, answers submitted mathematics questions and offers math advice for elementary, middle, high school, and college students.

Backyard biology. National Zoo Free (4 and up)

http://nationalzoo.si.edu/Animals/BackyardBiology/default.cfm

This site from the National Zoo in Washington, D.C. uses "its own grounds as a lens for learning about the 'backyard biology' that is present right within this major metropolitan area. The right-hand side of the site is well worth starting with, as it contains three thematic areas: 'Celebrate', 'Study', and 'Protect'. In each area, visitors may browse through a set of resources dedicated to science articles, identification guides, and other such materials." Internet Scout

Bartleby.com. Alibris Free

http://www.bartleby.com/

Access to full text of books on the web including reference, verse, fiction and nonfiction. Sections are indexed by author, subject and title and feature a browse function for each section. Reference texts include: Columbia Encyclopedia, American Heritage Dictionary, Roget's II: The new Thesaurus, American Heritage Book of English

Bartleby.com—*Continued*
Usage, Columbia World of Quotations, Simpson's Contemporary Quotations, Bartlett's Familiar Quotations, King James Bible, Oxford Shakespeare, Gray's Anatomy, Strunk's Elements of Style, World Factbook and Columbia Gazetteer. Includes banner advertising.

Become A Historical Detective. Library of Congress Free

http://memory.loc.gov/learn/features/detect/detectiv.html

Teaches research by posing a question about a historical mystery and giving hints on finding the answer. Includes links to the American Memory collection of primary historical source materials.

Ben's guide to U.S. Government. U.S. Government Printing Office Free

http://bensguide.gpo.gov/912/games/interactive.html

Quick facts and information about the U.S. Government designed for students, divided by grade levels. Topics include: Our nation, historical documents, branches of Government, how laws are made, National versus State Government, election process, citizenship, and national high school debate topics. Students can put together, state by state, and interactive puzzle of the nation or access Print games including word searches and crossword puzzles.

Bibliomania. Biblomania.com Ltd. Free

http://www.bibliomania.com

Free access to thousands of e-books, poems, articles, short stories and plays on the Internet. Study guides are written by Oxford and Cambridge University graduates and include summaries, discussions and commentaries on the texts. The reference section includes biographies, classic nonfiction and religious texts. Each section can be quickly accessed by using the search features on the left side of the screen by section type and author. A book store function is also featured.

Big turbo tools. Big6 Learning Tools, LLC. Contact producer for pricing (5-12)

http://www.big6turbotools.com

By subscription only. Tel. 888-342-2446

Students are taken through the 6-step research and writing process: task-definition, information seeking strategies, location and access, use of information, synthesis, and evaluation. The site includes a Locker that allows students to save their projects, TurboCite for notetaking and citations, TurboWrite where they actually write their paper, a dictionary/thesaurus, a built-in e-mail/chat feature, a Bulletin Board of Teacher Tools, Big6 links, and Big6 video clips of students working through the research process.

Biography Reference Bank. H. W. Wilson Contact producer for pricing

http://hwwilson.com

By subscription only. Tel. 800-367-6770

This database features substantial full-text biographies of over 500,000 people, current and historical. Biographies are linked to related indexing, abstracts, full-text articles, and page images from the full range of Wilson databases, covering over 6,000 periodicals, to keep information up to date. There are also over 36,000 pictures of people profiled. Uniform name authority control facilitates searching.

Biography Resource Center. Gale Group Contact producer for pricing (8-12)

http://www.gale.com

By subscription only. Tel. 800-877-4253

More than 330,000 biographies of nearly 220,000 individuals compiled from almost eighty Gale Group products such as Contemporary Authors and Historic World Leaders and full-text biographical articles from more than 250 magazines. Features include Name Search, Advanced Search, Biographical Facts Search, Thumbnail Biographies, and Web site periodical links. Also includes online dictionary and a student Research Guide.

BLS Career Information. U.S. Bureau of Labor Statistics Free

http://www.bls.gov/k12/

Provides ideas for what to do when one grows up, and how to set about doing so, for children interested in the arts, mathematics, science, physical activities, the outdoors, social science, or reading.

Born in Slavery. Library of Congress Free

http://memory.loc.gov/ammem/snhtml/snhome.html

Contains more than 2,300 first-person oral histories of slavery and 500 black-and-white photographs of former slaves collected in the 1930s as part of the Federal Writers' Project. Some narratives contain descriptions of shocking cruelty while others convey an almost nostalgic view of plantation life. Many narratives contain a word commonly used by African Americans in the 1930s South when speaking of themselves that some children may find horrifying.

Build a Prairie. Bell Museum of Natural History Free

http://www.bellmuseum.org/distancelearning/prairie/

In this interactive game, players restore a prairie to its native state. They reintroduce native grasses, wildflowers, birds, animals, and insects, taking care not to introduce exotic, invasive species. Upon successfully completing each stage, they are shown an animation of their prairie's progress.

C.E.R.F. (Curriculum and Education Resource Finder). Media Flex $500/yr.

http://www.cerfinfo.com/search/

By subscription only. Tel. 877-331-1022

A directory of weekly updated Web sites that have been pre-screened and selected for use in the instructional setting. Users can search for sites by key word (with Boolean operators), by topic lists, or by grade level range (including professional). Information about each site includes the title, hyperlinked URL, relevant subject areas, correlations to McREL standards, and cross references to related topics. Sites can also be saved to a bibliography with an option to e-mail results.

"A big plus for C.E.R.F. is the extensive use of links from outside the United States, giving a more global perspective to inquiry." Book Report

Cambridge Dictionaries online. Cambridge University Press Free

http://dictionary.cambridge.org/

A simple to use search functions allows access to Cambridge dictionaries. Enter a word in the box, click search, and users can immediately access dictionary information. Also included are activities and worksheets, information for language researches and top twenty word list.

Cats: Plans for Perfection. National Geographic Society Free

http://www.nationalgeographic.com/features/97/cats

This site is organized around the conceit that all feline species were designed by a team of engineers, who faced engineers' usual difficulties with budgets and schedules. As it tells the story of the design project's progress, the site teaches the relationship between feline structure and function.

Celebrate Hispanic heritage! Scholastic, Inc. Free (2 and up)

http://teacher.scholastic.com/activities/hispanic/

"This innovative site provides students with an opportunity to 'discover the contributions and rich cultures of Hispanics in the United States' through biographies, timelines links, and more. Students can access 'Hispanic History in the Americas' which opens an interactive map linked to information about Hispanic/Latino nations and people, 'Meet Famous Latinos,' a set of profiles of several noted celebrities, and 'Latinos in History,' a database of 25 biographies." SLJ

Celebrate Hispanic Heritage Month with the National Register of Historic Places. National Park Service Free (6 and up)

http://www.cr.nps.gov/nr/feature/hispanic

This site explores various Hispanic-related national parks, buildings and properties, as well as highlights Hispanic American contributions to design and architecture that have made an impact on American culture. It also includes links to publications such as travel itineraries and lesson plans.

Chem4Kids. Andrew Rader Studios Free (6-8)

http://www.chem4kids.com/index.html

"This web site examines the states of matter, such as liquids, solids, gases, plasma, and mixtures. Chem4Kids is written at a middle school level with a fun approach. Information and properties of the cell are covered including its structure, bonding, compounds, and ions. This is a super science resource for students and science teachers." Florida's Instructional Technology Resource Center

Children's Literature Comprehensive Database. CLCD Company, LLC. From $275/yr.

http://www.childrenslit.com/home.htm

By subscription only. Tel. 800-469-2070

The database contains more than 1,200,000 MARC records and 200,000 reviews from baby board books to young adult novels drawn from sources such as *Children's Literature Newsletter*, *Kirkus*, *Science Books and Films*, and *VOYA*. Reviews can be searched by key word with options to limit by category (fiction or nonfiction), genre, age, language, author/illustrator, publisher, publication date, and search term qualifiers such as exact phrase and singular or plural forms. Search results are ranked in relevancy order and each record provides a one-sentence annotation, text of reviews, as well as hyperlinks to related subject terms and other works by the author and reviewers.

"This is a great resource for librarians, media specialists, teachers, and parents." SLJ

The **CIA** world factbook. Central Intelligence Agency Free

http://www.odci.gov/cia/publications/factbook/index.html

Quick reference to information for all countries including: geography (including maps), people, government, economy, military, communication, travel, and transnational issues. All countries can be accessed from the browse list on the left side of the home page. Appendixes include: abbreviations, international organizations and groups, international environmental agreements, cross-reference list of country data codes, cross-reference list of hydrographic data codes, and cross-reference list of geographic names. Also included is a comprehensive collection of reference maps and a definitions and abbreviations section.

Civil rights movement and the legacy of Martin Luther King, Jr. U.S. Department of State Free (6 and up)

http://usinfo.state.gov/products/pubs/civilrts/

A history of the contemporary civil rights movement in the United States, including a chronology of key events, brief biographical information on two centuries of African-American leaders, and excerpts from King's speeches and writings.

Columbia gazetteer of the world. Columbia University Press $595 per site (volume discount pricing available) (6-12)

http://www.columbiagazetteer.org

By subscription only. Tel. 800-944-8648

"The Columbia Gazetteer of the World provides instant access to an encyclopedic compendium of geographical places and features. This comprehensive resource contains over 165,000 entries, including more than 40,000 that are in the U.S. The content of the articles ranges from basic statistical data such as population, elevation, and industrial output to more esoteric facts about transportation lines, shopping malls, and military bases." Evalutech

Connected University. Classroom Connect Contact producer for pricing

http://www.cu.classroom.com

By subscription only. Tel. 800-638-1639

Connected University offers educators 24-hour a day access to instructor-led courses, self-paced courses, technology "how to" tips, and software tutorials. Courses are available on a broad range of topics from teaching reading standards to how to build a Web page. Graduate credits and continuing education units can be obtained from partner universities. Thousands of pre-screened, educator-friendly web sites are provided in the CU Library.

Cosmic Quest. Children's Museum of Indianapolis Free

http://www.childrensmuseum.org/cosmicquest/index.html

Site divided into three separate sections: Living in Space: Design a Space Station (a game); Field Guide to the Universe with detailed information about the planets, spacecraft, and astronomers; and Expedition to the Magnetic North Pole.

Current biography illustrated. H.W. Wilson Contact producer for pricing (6-12)

http://www.hwwilson.com.

By subscription only. Tel. 800-367-6770

"Current Biography Illustrated (CBI) contains the full text of the 25,000 biographies and obituaries that have appeared in Current Biography Yearbook since 1940,

Current biography illustrated—*Continued*

many accompanied by photos (more than 20,000). CBI profiles artists, politicians, businesspeople, journalists, actors, writers, sports figures, scientists, and other prominent individuals in the news. The biography profiles . . . provide information such as full name, preferred name, or pseudonym; birth date; business or home address; field or profession; an account of the subject's life and career; the subject's own views, attitudes, and opinions; and observations of journalists, colleagues, and associates." SLJ

Curriculum Resource Center. Facts on File $650/yr for up to 500 users; $860/yr. for 500-1000 users (4 and up)

http://www.factsonfile.com

By subscription only. Tel. 800-322-8755

Database of copyright-free, reproducible, black-and-white and color maps, historical maps, graphs, charts, timelines, illustrations, and other hand-out materials with visual content and text. Subjects dealt with are environment, geography, health and fitness, general science, United States history and government, and world history. The materials in this database display in Adobe Acrobat (link to free download provided).

DigitalCurriculum.com. AIMS Multimedia Contact producer for pricing

http://www.digitalcurriculum.com/

By subscription only. Tel. 800-367-2467

DigitalCurriculum.com provides access to over a thousand curriculum-based educational videos, or indexed key concept clips of the videos. The program sends these videos to the school via the Internet using video streaming/downloading technology. Schools and districts can also place the videos on their local or wide area network. The general program covers a variety of subjects including Science, Social Science, Language Arts, Reading, Health, Guidance, Mathematics, and Drivers Education.

Dino directory. The Natural History Museum Free (3-10)

http://flood.nhm.ac.uk/cgi-bin/dino/

"This database of dinosaur information and illustrations from the Natural History Museum in London, England, has an interface that provides multiple paths for accessing dinosaur data. The user may browse entries alphabetically, by geologic timeline (Upper Triassic to Upper Cretaceous periods), by geographic location, or by body shape. Each entry contains a black-and-white drawing and an enhanced action drawing (based on speculative estimates of coloring and habitats). . . . The text for each entry indicates such fundamental information as pronunciation, taxonomy, size, diet, and range. . . . Dino Directory serves admirably in its role as a well-organized source of basic information on these fascinating ancient reptiles." Evalutech

Discover the History of Life. University of California Museum of Paleontology Free

http://www.ucmp.berkeley.edu/historyoflife/histoflife.html

Online exhibits explain how the theories of phylogeny, geology, and evolution fit together in paleontology. Also includes pages on special exhibits and a mystery fossil identification game.

Discovering collection 2.0. Gale Group Contact producer for subscription pricing (6-12)

http://www.gale.com

By subscription only. Tel. 800-877-4253

An aggregation of many of the Gale print series (Discovering Series, Exploring Series, Worldmark and Junior Worldmark Encyclopedias, and UXL)) into a single searchable database powered by the Infotrac interface that focuses on literature, history, biography, science, and social studies. Students can access primary sources, biographies, criticism, timelines, and multimedia.

This "will certainly be useful to school, academic, and public library reference librarians assisting these students, and it will have strong appeal for subject buffs as well." Net Connect

Discovering Lewis and Clark. VIAs, Inc. Free (4-12)

http://www.lewis-clark.org/

"Discovering Lewis and Clark provides three paths to explore the most extraordinary journey in American history. Professor Harry Fritz's account of the adventure is divided into 19 segments, accessible from the 'Expedition' menu. Excerpts from the journal may be accessed directly from a menu of the entry dates. Finally, a 'Discovery Paths' menu leads to a fascinating series of special features that offer high interest information about various aspects of the expedition and the historical milieu. Multimedia materials include sound files, photographs, maps, and motion pictures. The value of this site in the American history classroom extends far beyond the scope of the expedition itself, due to its coverage of the societal context of the Jeffersonian era." Evalutech

Discovery School. Discovery Channel Free

http://school.discovery.com/

This site provides "teaching materials for teachers, . . . resources for students, and . . . advice for parents about how to help their kids enjoy learning and excel in school. The site is . . . reviewed for educational relevance by practicing classroom teachers in elementary school, middle school, and high school." Publisher's note

Distinguished women of past and present. Distinguishedwomen.com Free

http://www.distinguishedwomen.com/

Search for biographical information by subject or name of women writers, educators, scientists, heads of state, politicians, civil rights crusaders, artists, and entertainers. This site features bibliography information links to Amazon.com.

Dred Scott v. Sandford. Street Law & the Supreme Court Historical Society Free (5 and up)

http://www.landmarkcases.org/dredscott/home.html.

This "site provides teaching recommendations based on available class time, a summary of the case for three different reading levels, age appropriate discussion questions, and excerpts from both the majority and dissenting opinions of the Supreme Court judges. Additional resources include full-text newspaper editorials from the time and Lincoln's speech on the decision" SLJ

Dynamic Earth. Dynamic Earth Smithsonian Institution Free (6 and up)

http://www.mnh.si.edu/earth/main%5Fframes.html

This geology information resource is offered both in multimedia and text-only versions that explain and demonstrate the various processes that are occurring at and below the surface of the earth. The multimedia version, which requires the free Flash plug-in, includes audiovisual presentations that help explain the dynamic processes that are occurring on Earth.

Earth Science Explorer. Wheeling Jesuit University/NASA Free

http://www.cotf.edu/ete/modules/msese/
explorer.html

This site is organized around the floor plan of a museum, one floor of which is devoted to earth sciences and the other of which is devoted to dinosaurs. The earth sciences section contains tutorials on geologic time, plate tectonics, geological cycles, and biomes. The dinosaur section presents various contending theories of dinosaur extinction and invites one to decide which is most plausible. Teacher section password protected.

Education world: math center. George Washington University Free

http://www.education-world.com/a%5Flesson/
archives/math.shtml

"Education World offers a wealth of instructional resources for teachers. This section of the website is devoted to mathematics resources, primarily articles and lesson ideas. Each lesson idea lists the appropriate grade levels for the activity, the Standards and instructional goals addressed through the activity, supplies needed, key words to learn, and assessment strategies. The articles address various topics in teacher professional development and school administration." Internet Scout

eNature.com. Audubon Society Free

http://www.enature.com

Audubon field guides online and searchable, with descriptions and color photographs of over 4,800 North American plants and animals. If given a zip code, the site will provide descriptions and pictures of birds native to that region.

Encarta. Microsoft Corporation Free

http://encarta.msn.com/

Online access to the Encarta encyclopedia by entering a question or a keyword. Sections include: reference, homework, college prep, grad school, e-learning, parents, genealogy, and products. Quick reference tools include encyclopedia, dictionary and atlas. Content includes text, graphic, audio and video files. Quicktime three is needed for playing video files.

Encyclopedia Americana. Grolier Educational Contact producer for pricing; minimum of two databases

http://www.go.grolier.com

By subscription only. Tel. 888-326-6546

General encyclopedia comprised of 45,000 articles and more than 25 million words contributed by over 6,500 specialists in their respective disciplines covering all academic fields and curriculum topics. The new online addition is organized around four editorial "modules": Americana encyclopedia database, Americana Journal, Profiles, and Editor's Picks and is American with Disabilities Act (ADA)/Section 508 compliant. Many of the articles link to the Online Computer Library Center's (OCLC) WorldCat bibliographic database which contains merged catalogs of libraries from around the world providing up to 25 bibliographic citations per entry which can be filtered by zip or postal code to locate libraries holding the work.

"EA remains a good choice for any highschool, college, or public library collection. Libraries that can afford the online version, updated quarterly, will get the benefit of hundreds of new and revised articles each year that do not appear in the print set, as well as other online features." Booklist

Encyclopedia Britannica. Encyclopedia Britannica, Inc. $69.95/yr.

http://www.britannica.com

By subscription only. Tel. 800-323-1229

This site offers Britannica's well-researched, clearly written articles packaged with a search engine, videos and pictures, a Web site directory, periodical articles, and the Merriam-Webster dictionary and thesaurus. Search results provide topic headings, encyclopedia articles, Web site listings, and an opportunity to search the periodical database. A browse mode gives one access to the topic headings in alphabetical order, although without the cross-references found in print versions. There is also a set of subject classifications bringing together articles on related subjects. Includes banner advertising.

Encyclopedia of educational technology. San Diego State University Department of Educational Technology Free

http://coe.sdsu.edu/eet/admin/index.htm

"Offers a collection of short multimedia articles from various authors discussing topics related to the fields of instructional design, and education and training. . . . The Table of Contents is divided into the following main topics: Cognition and Learning, Analysis, Design, Development, Implementation, and Evaluation. For each subtopic the site provides a short explanation and related video demonstrations, images, or examples to help explain the topic, and links to related topics. Visitors will find overviews of topics such as Vygotsky's Zone of Proximal Development (ZPD), eLearning, Web accessibility, and authentic assessment." Internet Scout

Encyclopedia Smithsonian. Smithsonian Institution Free

http://www.si.edu/resource/faq/start.htm

This site provides an alphabetical list of links to Smithsonian resources, the subjects ranging from advertising to zoology.

Essentials of music. W. W. Norton Free (6-12)

http://www.essentialsofmusic.com

"Essentials of Music is a companion Web site to Sony Classical Music's series of recordings called Essential Classics. The site is divided into three parts: 'Eras,' 'Composers,' and 'Glossary.' 'Eras' includes the Middle Ages, the Renaissance, Baroque, Classical, Romantic, and 20th Century. Click on any of the topics to see a short outline of historical themes, musical context, styles, and names of composers. The main 'Composers' section includes biographical information, including some RealPlayer clips of talents ranging from Hildegarde, Von Bingen, Palestrina, and Handel to Duke Ellington, John Cage, and Richard Rodgers." SLJ

eTAP. eTAP, Inc. $75/yr.

http://www.etap.org

By subscription only. Tel. 949-497-2200

Short for "electronic teaching assistance program," this resource provides a K-12 curriculum in the subjects of mathematics, English, history and science. It provides educators with lesson plans, instructions for assignments, links to web sites on key topics, practice exercises that can be used as worksheet assignments for students, tests modeled after standardized exams, and a problem section that can be printed out and used for student assessment.

Ethnic NewsWatch. Softline Information, Inc. Contact producer for pricing

http://www.slinfo.com

Ethnic NewsWatch—*Continued*

By subscription only. Tel. 1-800-833-8025

Ethnic NewsWatch, a reference resource tool, includes a full-text collection from 240 newspapers, magazines and other publications from the ethnic, minority and native press in America. It includes coverage of issues in Ireland, Israel and the Middle East, Mexico, Bosnia, Armenia, China, Nigeria, and Ukraine among other countries. The resource covers current topics and other social, political and educational subjects, especially African-American and Hispanic topics. The database includes full-text articles in English and Spanish, and roughly 7500 new articles are added each month. It is available in three subscription packages: Complete (coverage from 1990 forward), Select (coverage from 1996 forward), and Current (coverage from 1998 forward).

Ethnologue. SIL International Free

http://www.ethnologue.com/web.asp

Information about 6,800 languages and 41,000 alternative dialects from around the world. Users can search for world language information by using the interactive world map to drill down to particular countries or search by language name, codes or families. Specific information for each language includes population, region, alternate names, classification and comments.

Exploratorium. The museum of science, art and human perception at the Palace of Fine Arts, San Francisco Free (K and up)

http://www.exploratorium.edu

This site features a variety of resources, demonstrations, photos, and streaming video presentations designed to appeal to all ages and interests, with items ranging from the Hubble Spacecraft to a cow's eye dissection. It features five sections: Explore, Educate, Visit, Partner, and Shop.

Exploring Leonardo. Boston Museum of Science Free

http://www.mos.org/sln/Leonardo/ LeoHomePage.html

Interactive site describes some of Leonardo's inventions, and gives a chance to analyze them and design others. Explains his system of perspective, provides a brief biography, and discusses his habit of writing in reverse.

Exploring the Planets. National Air and Space Museum Free

http://www.nasm.si.edu/research/ceps/etp/etp.htm

Explains how the planets of the solar system have been explored from Earth and by spacecraft. Includes information on and photographs of each planet, of asteroids, and of comets. In an activity, one describes satellite photographs and compares one's descriptions to those of an astronomer.

Facts for features and special editions. United States Census Bureau Free (6 and up)

http://www.census.gov/Press-Release/www/releases/ archives/ facts%5Ffor%5Ffeatures%5Fspecial%5Feditions/ index.html

"The U. S. Census Bureau has created an online portal to display the data collected from their Decennial Census (official population census of the United States) and nearly 100 other various surveys that they conduct annually. A bonus for educators is the 'Facts for Features and Special Editions.' Teachers will find collections of information intended to 'commemorate anniversaries or observances.' Each entry contains a short history of the holiday/event followed by single lines of startling facts. In addition, the site provides 'The Photo Zone,' a collection of public domain images to accompany the facts discussed." SLJ

Fake Out. Houghton Mifflin Free

http://www.eduplace.com/fakeout

In this variation of a classic word game, players are given an improbable, but actual, word and a set of plausible definitions among which to select. Players are invited to invent plausible definitions for upcoming words.

Federal Resources for Educational Excellence. U.S. Department of Education Free

http://www.ed.gov/free/index.html

Lists hundreds of educational Web sites supported by U.S. government agencies. Subjects include arts, educational technology, foreign languages, health and safety, language arts, mathematics, physical education, science, social studies, and vocational education.

The Federal Web Locator. The Center for Information law and policy Free

http://www.infoctr.edu/fwl/

A comprehensive guide to federal government information. Also includes extensive list of links to search engines.

FirstGov. Office of Citizen Services and Communications, U.S. General Services Administration Free

http://firstgov.org

The official U.S. Government gateway for citizens, business and government employees. Provides one-click access to federal, state, local, tribal, and international government information.

Gale virtual reference library. Gale Group Contact producer for subscription pricing (6-12)

http://www.galegroup.com

By subscription only. Tel. 800-877-4253

Selected UXL reference titles as well as other Thomson Gale titles can be accessed via the web. It features basic and advanced search functions as well as indexes and tables of contents. This resource "offers more than 85 reference sources including encyclopedias, almanacs, series and more, allowing libraries to provide respected authoritative essays on varied topics from numerous subject areas." Publisher's note

The Gateway to Educational Materials. U. S. Department of Education Free

http://www.thegateway.org

Direct access to collections of educational resources found on various federal, state, university, nonprofit, and commercial Internet sites including lesson plans, activities, and projects. Lists and search functions are organized by title, subject, keyword, and grade level.

Geography Software: USA, World and California. Click and Learn Software $2995/yr.

http://www.clickandlearn.com

By subscription only. Tel. 888-254-2550

Geography Software: USA, World and California—*Continued*

Geography Software: USA, World and California is a Hybrid CD that includes geographical material for students, an instructional video, and lesson plans for the teacher. Included in the program is access to the publisher's Internet site where drills and updates on newly formed or renamed countries are available for downloading.

Get a Clue Vocabulary: Web-Based Edition. FableVision Contact producer for price

http://www.getaclue.com

By subscription only. Tel. 800-860-9228

Get a Clue Vocabulary: Web-Based Edition is a vocabulary development program based on word etymology. Students use the inductive reasoning skills of application, analysis, and synthesis to work through a word's derivation and 5 "Clues," 3 of which mirror PSAT/SAT format. Students develop understanding of word meaning by examining multimedia feedback and explanation at each step. The program provides online progress tracking, review features, and customized printable quizzes.

Ghosts in the Castle. National Geographic Society Free

http://www.nationalgeographic.com/castles/enter.html

As one tours a virtual castle, ghosts reminisce about their lives there.

Gizmos. ExploreLearning $799 teacher and student subscription; $349 teacher only. Contact sales@explorelearning.com for school or district volume discount pricing (6-12)

http://www.explorelearning.com

By subscription only. Tel. 866-882-4141

This "site focuses on concepts grouped by grade levels (6-8 and 9-12) in broad categories, such as biology, earth and space science, algebra, geometry, and number operations. Each Gizmo is an interactive Shockwave demonstration of a concept. Students manipulate variables within a simulation and view the outcomes. Brief assessment is provided with multiple-choice questions based on the concept presented in an activity. Answers are reviewed with detailed explanations for correct and incorrect responses. . . . Gizmos is a dynamic and evolving site that can be used in math and science classes to promote the understanding of key concepts and reinforce learning." Evalutech

Global grocery list project. Landmark Project Free (4-8)

http://landmark-project.com/ggl/

"The Global Grocery List Project was designed by The Landmark Project and is supported by the Global SchoolNet Foundation. Through the Global Grocery List Project students share local grocery prices to build a growing table of data which is then available to use for computation, analysis, and conclusion-building within the context of social studies, science, mathematics and other disciplines. Since 1987, the project has collected grocery prices from classes all over the world." Internet Scout

Great web sites for kids. American Library Association Free

http://www.ala.org/greatsites

Lists children's sites selected for clear statement of authorship and sponsorship, clearly defined purpose, good design, stability, and use of sound information to inform, educate, or entertain. Subjects include arts and entertainment, literature and language, people, geography, and science and technology.

Greenwood daily life online: exploring everyday life past and present. Greenwood Publishing $595 to $995/yr. (7-12)

http://www.greenwood.com

By subscription only. Tel. 203-226-3571

"Based on the Greenwood Encyclopedia of Daily Life, this site provides full-text content from reference works, monographs, and primary source documents. The database includes images (1200 color and b&w), maps, illustrations, and timelines. Daily Life Online provides students with information regarding the daily lives of people from ancient civilizations and cultures of the past (3,000 BC) to those of the modern era. The site is exceptionally navigable and well structured and the main interface enables users to approach the content from period, time, or subject." SLJ

Grolier Multimedia Encyclopedia Online. Grolier Educational Contact producer for pricing; minimum of two databases (5 and up)

http://www.go.grolier.com

By subscription only. Tel. 888-326-6546

General encyclopedia covering all subjects with multimedia and current events. Information can be located by browsing categories such U.S. history, language and literature, life sciences, and technology or by key word searches. Advanced searches can be limited to article titles or full text with the use of Boolean operators. Articles include hyperlinked cross references, related Web links, and bibliographies. There are also links to related magazine articles provided by EBSCO. The Brain Jam feature changes frequently and explores a topic in more depth, enhanced with Web links, activities, and teacher resources.

"A wonderfully easy-to-use title that provides good overviews to large topics, good definitions and brief biographies, and highly useful cross-referencing. . . . Highly recommended for public and school libraries." Libr J

A **Guided** Tour of the Visible Human. MadSci Network Free

http://www.madsci.org/%7Elynn/VH/tour.html

The Visible Human Project has taken over 18,000 sections of a human body, scanned them, and made the images available over the Internet. This site uses some of the scanned images in an anatomy tutorial. Animations are used to explain how to visualize transverse, coronal, and sagittal sections in three dimensions.

Healthfinder. Office of Disease Prevention and Health Promotion/ U.S. Department of Health and Human Services Free

http://www.healthfinder.gov

This government site serves as an all-purpose source of free medical and health information for the general public. It features a Health Library, organized by disease or condition; a section "Just for You," organized by age, race, ethnicity, sex, etc.; a section on information about doctors, dentists, hospitals, health insurance, Medicare, etc.; and a directory of selected health information Web sites from government agencies, clearinghouses, nonprofit organizations, and universities. There is also a Spanish version.

The **Hero's** Journey. Maricopa Center for Learning and Instruction Free

http://www.mcli.dist.maricopa.edu/smc/journey

In The Hero with a Thousand Faces, Joseph Campbell writes that hero myths follow a general formula. This site provides an interactive form based on this formula, with which writers can construct mythic, heroic stories.

History explorer. National Museum of American History Free (4 and up)

http://americanhistory.si.edu/explorer/index.cfm

"Allows those surfing the Web to browse through an interactive timeline of American history. The interface is composed of items from the Museum's various online collections, exhibitions and programs, such as Plymouth Rock and a world map from 1511. Visitors can zoom in and out through the timeline and its objects and also elect to toggle on or off various themes, such as 'Arts and Culture', 'Peopling America', and 'Politics and Reform'. Overall, this is a very well-thought-out tool for learning about American history and one that will engage a wide range of persons." Internet Scout

HistorySolutions.com. History Solutions, Inc. Starting at $49.95/yr.

http://www.historysolutions.com

By subscription only. Tel. 973-701-6770

This history Internet workbook contains 16 units of U.S. History. Each unit contains six lessons. In Historical Simulation students act as advisors to historical figures, weigh options, consider consequences, and try to make the "historically accurate" decision. Students create notes in the interactive Cognitive Organizer. The Primary Source Analysis Guide has students interpret documents. In the Prediction Center students attempt to predict how certain events will affect the United States. The Quiz at the end of each unit checks mastery of the content-based simulations. Students work in the Writer's Workshop where they are guided through the process of writing an expository essay based on the content in the historical simulation, and evaluate their essay. The program provides opportunities for students to learn historical content, critical thinking skills, historical perspective, conceptual thinking, and expository writing.

Homeroom.com. The Princeton Review Contact producer for pricing

http://k12.princetonreview.com/
homeroom%5Findex.asp

By subscription only. Tel. 800-REVIEW-2

Homeroom.com is a web based assessment and diagnostic tool containing over 130,000 math, reading, and language arts questions and over 10,000 instructional resources aligned to all state standards, major classroom textbooks, and specific state and national tests. There are an average of 10 instructional resources per tested skill. The program can be used to assess, analyze, and remediate strengths and weaknesses of student skills. It allows teachers to generate practice assessments that are correlated to state or city standards and the textbook used in the classroom. It directs teachers and students to targeted educational resources, customized to each tested skill, based on individual and group performance.

Homework Center. Multnomah Public Library Free

http://www.multcolib.org/homework/index.html

This browsable selection of internet resources is organized by topics most commonly requested for homework assignments. Sites are selected and annotated by librarians and an online question feature allows immediate access to a librarian of the Mulnomah Public Library.

Hotmath.com. Hotmath.com $29 for 60 days; $49/yr.

http://www.hotmath.com

By subscription only. Tel. 510-524-5525

This website provides tutorial solutions to homework problems in selected state-approved mathematics textbooks. Solutions include hints, Socratic questions, graphs, figures, and steps leading up to and including the final answer.

How stuff works. BYG Publishing, Inc. Free (3-10)

http://www.howstuffworks.com/

This site "tackles typical childhood questions such as 'Why is the sky blue?' as well as more esoteric issues, such as 'What does WD-40 mean?' . . . A 'Question-of-the-Day' feature provides responses to reader questions and includes an archive that may be accessed in chronological order or by category. Additional useful features include a section on how to cite the articles, and lists of related Web sites. The expanded scope of How Stuff Works will make it an invaluable tool for the science class, as well as a potentially useful resource for other disciplines." Evalutech

How Things Work. University of Virginia Free

http://rabi.phys.virginia.edu/HTW/

A professor of physics answers email questions about how things—machines, everyday processes, toys, and games, among others—work. The explanations are as complete as they can be without mathematics, but the language is not needlessly technical. Includes an archive of answered questions.

Hunkin's Experiments. Pelham Projects Ltd. Free

http://www.HunkinsExperiments.com

A cartoonist with an engineering degree provides sketches of how to do hundreds of demonstrations, illusions, and tricks. Examples include how to move a mug of water by balloon, to peel bananas automatically, to photograph the path of a pendulum, to prove $1 = 2$, to prove there is no black in a television picture, to pull a string through your neck, and to push a cube through the middle of a cube the same size.

Infoplease.com. Family Education Network, Inc. Free

http://www.infoplease.com/

A collection of almanacs as well as a searchable dictionary, encyclopedia, and atlas. Contains banner advertising.

InfoTrac Junior Edition. Gale Group Contact producer for pricing (5-8)

http://www.galegroup.com

By subscription only. Tel. 800-877-4253

InfoTrac Junior Edition features full-text articles from periodical titles relevant to the interests and curriculum needs of upper elementary, junior high, and middle school students. Broad search term results offer suggested narrower terms with related subdivisions and types of source documents. An optional child-friendly interface is available that includes a Toolbox with tips for doing research and writing reports. Newspapers and magazines are updated daily. Includes a dictionary feature and maps.

Inside Art. Educational Web Adventures Free

http://www.eduweb.com/insideart/index.html

An online game which explores a painting from the inside out. During an art museum tour, players are sucked into a vortex and find themselves inside Van Gogh's Bank of the Oise at Auvers. Their only hope of escape is, with the help of a fish named Trish, to place the painting in its artistic and historical context.

Interactive Online Exhibits. London Natural History Museum Free

http://www.nhm.ac.uk/interactive/index.html

Among these exhibits are a video feed from a leafcutter ant colony, a database of dinosaur pictures, a multimedia presentation on eclipses, and an online game in which players use various instruments to identify objects from the museum's collection.

The **Internet** Public library. Regents of the University of Michigan Free

http://www.ipl.org/

This virtual library provides easy access to reference resources, books, magazines, and other web sites on the Internet. It is organized the same as a public library around basic content areas using the Dewey decimal system, although the easy to use home page provides quick access to all collections. There is also a section especially for teens.

The **Internet** Scout Report. Internet Scout Project Free

http://scout.cs.wisc.edu/report/sr/current/index.html

Published each Friday online and by email, the report provides information about valuable resources on the Internet. Resources are selected, researched and annotated by a team of professional librarians and subject matter experts.

It's international. Topics Online Magazine Free (4-12)

http://www.topics-mag.com/internatl/center.htm

Published by an online magazine aimed at students and teachers of English as a second language, this site aims to create a forum for ESL students to share their experiences. Sections include "World of Tastes—Food, markets . . . and more!", "Holidays, Festivals, Celebrations" and "Traditional Clothing."

"Vivid details, illustrations, and photos of dress, food, and family traditions enhance instruction and student research." SLJ

JASON Foundation for Education. JASON Foundation for Education Contact producer for pricing

http://www.jasonproject.org

Expeditions and resources paid for individually. Tel. 888-527-6600

Live and previously video-taped expeditions create a multidisciplinary program to enhance teaching and learning in science, mathematics, technology, geography, reading, and writing. It includes print curricula, videos, and interactive Internet programming.

Junior Reference Collection. Gale Group Contact producer for subscription pricing (K-12)

http://www.galegroup.com

By subscription only. Tel. 800-877-4253

This is an online version of the Gale Group's U·X·L electronic resources for students and librarians that combines the information from U·X·L Biographies 2.0, U·X·L Science, U·X·L Junior DISCovering Authors 2.0, U·X·L Junior Worldmark and U·X·L Multicultural, with entries written at an appropriate reading level. The combined database provides an interface that permits searching by person, places, author, book, and multimedia, and it includes three Merriam-Webster dictionaries and a timeline with over 4000 entries.

"This database combines the wonderful UXL reference tools . . . in a user-friendly interface that is appropriate for upper elementary and middle school students." SLJ

Kid Territory. San Diego Zoo Free

http://www.sandiegozoo.org/kids/index.html

Includes biographical profiles of zoo animals, job descriptions of zoo workers, articles on zookeeping, and games.

Kids web: the digital library for K-12 students. Northeast Parallel Architectures Center at Syracuse University Free (K-12)

http://www.npac.syr.edu/textbook/kidsweb/

"Kids Web is a digital library for K-12 students that aims to 'present students with a subset of the Web that is very simple to navigate, and contains information targeted at the K-12 level.' . . . The collection of websites is organized into the following subject areas: Arts, Sciences, Social Studies, and Miscellaneous. The Miscellaneous section currently includes some games and reference resources, such as dictionaries and economic data. The Science section includes websites on topics such as mathematics, computers, technology, and meteorology." Internet Scout

KidsClick!. Ramapo Catskill Library System Free

http://kidsclick.org/

Lists sites selected to inform or entertain children from kindergarten to seventh grade in Dewey Decimal System order. Includes a child's search engine and a child's tutorial on Internet searching.

Landmarks for schools. The Landmark Project Free

http://www.landmark-project.com/index.php

Maintained and created by educator and consultant David Warlick, the site's features include the Blogmeister, a special blog for educators and their students; PiNet, a section that allows an educator to create and house a personal library of links; the New Century Schoolhouse where visitors can adopt a classroom and design it for 21st Century learning; the Education Podcast Network, a compilation of educational podcasting for teacher use; and a Web Tools site that includes a rubric builder and citation machine.

Lands and Peoples Online. Grolier Educational Contact producer for pricing; minimum of two databases (4 and up)

http://www.go.grolier.com

By subscription only. Tel. 888-326-6546

An international geography reference based on the print version. Articles have hyperlinked outlines and cross references and include photos, maps, flags, facts and figures, and Internet links. A Culture Cross feature enables users to compare two countries, continents, or states/provinces from the perspective of land, people, economy, history, or facts and figures. Also included are

Lands and Peoples Online—*Continued*

highlights of current events around the world, an atlas, an almanac, and games and quizzes for students.

"The ease of navigation and the multiple access points make it easy for beginning researchers to find what they need. The ability to create specific searches and locate precise elements of information make Lands and Peoples online attractive for more sophisticated assignments as well." Booklist

Librarians Index to the Internet. Library of California Free

http://lii.org/

A searchable collection of over 10,000 Internet resources selected by librarians at the Library of California for their usefulness to users of public libraries. Browsing and advanced search functions are included.

The **Library** of Congress. Library of Congress Free

http://www.loc.gov/

Provides access to Library of Congress digital collections of text, audio, and graphics. Collections include: American Memory from the Library of Congress (http://memory.loc.gov/); Global Gateway: World Culture and Resources (http://international.loc.gov/intldl/intldlhome.html); America's Library (http://www.americaslibrary.gov/cgi-bin/page.cgi) for kids and family; THOMAS (http://thomas.loc.gov/) legislative information; Exhibitions (http://www.loc.gov/exhibits/) Online galleries. Other services include: search functions, including catalogues and A-Z index, web casting and Ask a Librarian feature.

A **Lifetime** of Color. Sanford Free

http://www.sanford-artedventures.com/index.html

This site features four major sections: Create Art, Hands-on activities, technique demos and more; Study Art, Art history, glossary terms, and artist biographies; Play Art Games, ArtEdventures and online activities about art history and art concepts; and Teach Art, Lesson plans for classroom and art teachers.

LitFinder for Schools. Gale Group Contact producer for subscription pricing (6-12)

http://www.gale.com

By subscription only. Tel. 800-877-4253

An educator's version of Gale's LitFinder, this database contains 126,500 poems, 5,000 short stories, 2,800 essays, 1,800 speeches, 1,000 plays, 850 Spanish-language poems with English translations, and coverage of more than 600 nationalities and ethnicities and approximately 27,000 women writers. It also includes biographies, work summaries, photographs, and a glossary. It focuses on contemporary works, including more than 3,500 full-text poems published for the first time in the current year. Updated quarterly.

This "is a highly recommended resource for student self-directed study and research as well as a reference tool for teachers." Evalutech

MAS Ultra. EBSCO Publishing Contact producer for pricing

http://www.epnet.com

By subscription only. Tel. 800-653-2726

This is a full text, general reference database designed for high school libraries. The database includes: Searchable full text from more than 700 popular high school

magazines, 518 pamphlets, more than 230 reference books (including the CIA World Fact Book), 84,074 biographies, 86,135 primary source documents, an Image Collection of over 100,000 images (including flags and maps), and backfiles for some magazines dating back to 1975.

Math Forum Problems. Drexel University School membership $500/yr.; class membership $75/yr.; teacher membership $20/yr.; student membership $15/yr.

http://mathforum.org/library/problems/

By membership only. Tel. 800-756-7823

An archive of elementary, middle school, geometry, algebra, discrete mathematics, trigonometry, and calculus word problems, each with a variety of solutions.

Medline Plus. National Library of Medicine/ National Institutes of Health Free

http://www.nlm.nih.gov/medlineplus

This site is devoted to medical and health information for the public and for health professionals. It features information on conditions, diseases and wellness topics, and a medical encyclopedia; drug information; several medical dictionaries; access to directories with locations and credentials of doctors, dentists, and hospitals; and access to medical organizations, consumer health libraries, international sites, and medical publications.

Merriam-Webster online. Merriam-Webster Inc. Free

http://www.mw.com/netdict.htm

Site provides quick access to Merriam-Webster's Collegiate Dictionary, Collegiate Thesaurus, and the Merriam-Webster Unabridged Dictionary by entering a word in the appropriate box on the home page. Other features include: Word of the Day, word games, and word for the wise. You can also add a free dictionary button to your browser, add a free dictionary search box on your web site or receive the word of the day by email through the language center.

Mind Over Matter. National Institute on Drug Abuse Free

http://www.nida.nih.gov/mom/momindex.html

Describes the effects of specific drugs or drug types on the anatomy and physiology of the brain and the body and on the way in which these drug-induced changes affect both behavior and emotion. Care is taken to provide necessary background information on brain functioning.

Museum of Ancient Inventions. Smith College Free

http://www.smith.edu/hsc/museum/ancient%5Finventions/hsclist.htm

Pictures and descriptions of replicas of forty-six ancient devices, with explanations of how they work and why they were important. Devices range from the distaff and the hoe, to toys and cosmetics, to a lighthouse and a ship breaker.

The **Mystery** Spot: Access Excellence Mysteries. National Health Museum Free

http://www.accessexcellence.org/AE/mspot

Interactive, online scientific mysteries teach problem-solving and inquiry. In one, players must decide whether an outbreak of sickness on a racing yacht is dangerous enough to require breaking off the race.

NASA Explores. NASA Free

http://www.nasaexplores.com/

This site contains articles discussing recent scientific research at NASA. Each article is available at reading levels appropriate for elementary school students, middle school students, and high school students and comes replete with teacher lesson plans and student worksheets.

National Geographic news. National Geographic Society Free (4 and up)

http://news.nationalgeographic.com/news/

"Provides access to many of the day's most compelling news, including updates on the Space Shuttle launches and new archaeological discoveries. The news stories are thematically organized around such familiar topics as animals and nature, health, and the environment. The feature section titled 'Pulse of the Planet' is a nice find, along with the 'Offbeat' area, which offers a bit of lighter news coverage." Internet Scout

Native American sites. American Indian Library Association Free (6 and up)

http://www.nativeculturelinks.com/indians.html

"This is a one-stop shopping site for information on all things pertaining to American Indians. Click on 'Information on Individual Native Nations' for an alphabetical listing of recognized and unrecognized tribal names. Links to homepages are included, and offer a vast assortment of official tribal sites. Students can find other important sources of information, such as using Indian names and figures as mascots, the history of Indians in military service, a list of Indian businesses, and more." SLJ

Native languages of the Americas: facts for kids. Native Languages of the Americas Free (5 and up)

http://www.native-languages.org/kids.htm

"Over 30 tribal languages are described with alphabets, dictionaries, and pronunciation guides, and many come with sound files. Unfamiliar words, or Indian terms in general are highlighted and are linked to either a glossary, or another site with detailed explanations. Most of the individual language pages come with links to the homepages of the tribes themselves." SLJ

Natural History Notebooks. Canadian Museum of Nature Free

http://www.nature.ca/nature%5Fe.cfm

Provides short descriptions and sketches of 246 animal species. The text is from the museum's book series of the same title and the sketches are by a former chief illustrator.

Nettrekker. Thinkronize $1,195/yr. (K-12)

http://www.nettrekker.com

By subscription only. Tel. 1-877-517-1125

An Internet search engine created specifically for the K-12 education community. Aligned with individual state standards and divided into Elementary and Secondary sites, Nettrekker highlights over 180,000 websites organized by basic subjects such as Math, Science, Technology, and Language Arts that in turn are broken down into smaller subsets that are ranked according to usefulness. Teacher Tools feature lesson plan and exercises, games, pictures, and videos. Also features a Timeline feature showing the cross-curricular connection between important eras, famous people, events, arts and innovations during a specific period.

The **New** Book of Popular Science Online. Grolier Educational Contact producer for pricing; minimum of two databases (5 and up)

http://www.go.grolier.com

By subscription only. Tel. 888-326-6546

A science and technology reference site with articles found in the print version along with science in the news. Articles are organized by broad topics and feature hyperlinked outlines and links to related topics. Key word searches can be limited to the full text of articles or article titles with the use of Boolean operators. Sidebars have options for selected readings, Web links, careers, etc. The resource includes news stories and a Skywatch section featuring a map of the heavens. There are puzzles and games for students and an option to communicate with a science expert via e-mail.

"The quantity and quality of graphics and features such as NewsBytes and SciZone are appealing to students, teachers, parents, and librarians." Libr J

The **New** York Times on the web Learning Network. The New York Times Company Free

http://www.nytimes.com/learning/index.html

Users can search and access front page and news stories from the New York Times for current and past years. Sections for students, teachers and parents provide lesson plans, puzzles, quizzes and information.

North American mammals. The Smithsonian National Museum of Natural History Free (3-12)

http://web4.si.edu/mna/

"The content of two major reference books, The Smithsonian Book of North American Mammals (Don E. Wilson and Sue Ruff) and Mammals of North America (Roland W. Kays and Don E. Wilson), are incorporated into this interactive Web site. . . . Each of the over 400 profiles on the site includes scientific information such as average weight and length, a drawing of the animal, a map with its distribution range, and an explanation of the animal's habits, alternative names, and other characteristics. Some profiles include Quicktime panoramas that can be manipulated by the viewer, and several have sound clips such as a coyote's howl. . . . An interactive map search allows users to select an area of North America and identify the mammals in that range. . . . Students will find North American Mammals to be a delight for browsing as well as a valuable tool for research." Evalutech

NoveList K-8. EBSCO Publishing $750 for public library; $350 high school; $250 middle and elementary/yr. (K-8)

http://www.epnet.com

By subscription only. Tel. 800-653-2726

"An annotated database of 38,000 picture book and fiction titles enhanced by teacher resources. . . . Searches produce lists of titles with Lexile ratings and descriptions, that usually include a book cover graphic, subject headings, plot summary, links to related Web resources, and reviews from standard sources. . . . Teacher resources include more than ten multidisciplinary thematic units, articles on using books with children, several hundred book talks for grades four and higher, and Boolean search options. . . . NoveList K-8 is a versatile and powerful resource for connecting readers with books, whether the need is to guide eager readers, support the curriculum, suggest titles for summer reading, or develop customized reading plans based on Lexile level and personal interest." Evalutech

Nueva enciclopedia Cumbre en linea. Grolier Educational Contact producer for pricing; minimum of two databases (6 and up)

http://www.go.grolier.com

By subscription only. Tel. 888-326-6546

A Spanish-language encyclopedia covering all subjects. Articles can be located by keyword with the option of Boolean operators or by browsing broad categories. Web links, photos, maps, and audio recordings are included.

"Articles in NECEL are well written in clear, easy-to-read Spanish and generally reflect a Latin American perspective." Libr J

NYPL Digital Gallery. New York Public Library Free (6 and up)

http://digitalgallery.nypl.org/nypldigital/index.cfm

This is the New York Public Library's image database, which "contains over 275,000 items for online viewing. . . . Some of the items include Goya's Disasters of War, George Caitlin's North American Indian Portfolio, and of course, some lovely cityscapes of New York City's Fifth Avenue. . . . The site also contains a 'Curator's Choice' section, which features hundreds of American posters printed from 1893 through the early years of the 20th century. Overall, this site will warrant many return visits and is both elegant and easy to use." Internet Scout

Online Exhibits. Field Museum Free

http://www.fmnh.org/exhibits/online_exhib.htm

Collection of exhibits shows such things as photographs of a 19th-century hunt for two lions who had eaten 128 workers building a Ugandan railway bridge, an animated, insect's-eye view of life underground, and paintings of stages in the evolution of life.

PBS: the meaning of food. Public Broadcasting Service Free (6 and up)

http://www.pbs.org/opb/meaningoffood/

"This PBS documentary companion website on the Meaning of Food describes itself as 'an exploration of culture through food. What we consume, how we acquire it, who prepares it, who's at the table, and who eats first is a form of communication that is rich with meaning.' The site shares stories, recipes, beautiful images, and more under the headings: Food & Life, Food & Family, and Food & Culture. The website addresses such subjects as kosher food, the Slow Food Movement, pet food, and heirloom seeds, to name a few." Internet Scout

The **PLANTS** Database. U. S. Department of Agriculture Free

http://plants.usda.gov/

A database of plant information by common name, scientific name and symbol. Also included are special topics such as: alternative crops, cultural significance, distribution update, and fact sheets. Tools include a crop nutrient, erosion prediction, ecological site information system and plant materials.

PLATO Writing Process and Practice. Plato Learning Contact producer for pricing (3-12)

http://www.plato.com

Designed for middle and high school students with skills equivalent to grades 3-12, interactive modules of four different products [PLATO Essential Writing Process and Practice (3-4), PLATO Fundamental Writing Process and Practice (5-6), PLATO Intermediate Writing Process and Practice (7-9), PLATO Advanced Writing Process and Practice (10-12)] assist in the teaching of writing strategies and grammar and mechanics. Speech synthesizer where needed/appropriate and pdf Curriculum Guide. Winner of 2004 ComputED Gazette EDDIE Award, Best Language Arts Web Site and 2004 Media & Methods Magazine Awards Portfolio, English & Language Arts.

Plessy v. Ferguson. Library of Congress, American Memory Historical Collections Free (7 and up)

http://memory.loc.gov/ammem/today/may18.html

"The Library of Congress explores the significance of the 1896 Supreme Court ruling that upheld and legalized the practice of separate but equal facilities. The site offers historic photographs and teaches students about black laws, Jim Crow, and the African American's quest for full citizenship. There are links to additional American Memory resources related to segregation and the African-American struggle." SLJ

ProQuest Historical Newspapers. ProQuest Contact publisher for pricing

http://www.proquestk12.com/

By subscription only. Tel. 1-800-521-0600 x3344

ProQuest Historical Newspapers is a full-text, full-content, and graphics archive of the New York Times from 2000 back to the first issue in 1851. The database is indexed by subject and searchable by keyword. It is intended to support student research activities that require primary sources. It provides models for students of book reviews, letters, speeches, news writing, and editorials. A Student Edition is also available.

Pupil pages. Online Solutions for Educators Contact producer for pricing (1-12)

http://www.pupilpages.com

By subscription only. Tel. 888-203-4704

An online portfolio system that enables students to create and manage electronic collections of their work for a single class, for several subjects, over many years, and among grade levels and/or schools. Each portfolio contains a Resume, a Journal, and a Biography that functions as the student's homepage. A Comment feature, which can be password protected, and a language filter allow visitors to provide low-risk feedback. The Portfolio-to-Go feature enables students to take their work with them when they graduate or transfer to another district.

Raid on Deerfield: the many stories of 1704. Pocumtuck Valley Memorial Association Free (7 and up)

http://www.1704.deerfield.history.museum/

This is a "narrative of the well-known raid on the town which took place on February 29, 1704. Within the site, visitors can learn about the various cultures that converged on this region of the New World, the artifacts produced by these different groups, and of course, a very detailed chronology of the raid on Deerfield. Another way to begin learning about the events of the raid is to peruse the various biographical profiles of the people involved (directly or indirectly) in those events. For those with a penchant for cartography and geography, there is also a fine section that offers some maps of how the raid was conducted and a map of settlement patterns in the Connecticut River Valley." Internet Scout

Readers' Guide Full Text, Mega Edition. H. W. Wilson Contact producer for pricing

http://www.hwwilson.com/

By subscription only. Tel. 800-367-6770

This online version of the Readers' Guide to Periodical Literature features indexing and abstracting of nearly 400 popular magazines and journals (including *The New York Times*) going back to 1983, with full text for around 200 of those back to 1994. The full text is in both HTML files and PDF page images to capture graphics and pictures. The topics covered include art and antiques, business, computers, dance, drama, education, entertainment, fashion, food, health, history, literature, music, news and current events, photography, politics, sports, and travel, among others. Also available as a full-text-only database at a lower price.

RefDesk.com. RefDesk.com Free

http://www.refdesk.com/

A searchable reference source for facts on the Internet. This index provides quick access to information using its search and browse features. Also provides free subscription service to "dailies" such as site, thought and facts.

The **reference** suite @ FACTS.com. Facts on File News Services Contact producer for pricing (6-12)

http://www.facts.com

By subscription only. Tel. 800-363-7976 x4617

Updated weekly and hourly, "this reference site incorporates the complete content from the 'Facts on File World News Digest,' along with selections from four other core reference databases, to provide information on events and issues from 1940-present, with over 100,000 available. Along with the news digest, the 'Reference Suite' leverages content from 'Issues and Controversies on File,' 'Today's Science on File,' 'Editorials on File,' 'Reuters OnLine News Service,' 'The World Almanac and Book of Facts,' and 'The World Almanac Encyclopedia.' Special features include maps, photographs, documents, and information on newsmakers and events since 1980." Evalutech

Resources for K-12 Earth Science. Educators Geological Society of America (GSA) Free

http://www.geosociety.org/educate/resources.htm

"Offers lessons plans and additional resources covering virtually all topics in geology for K-12 students. The materials are divided into 12 topics, such as Environmental Science, Weather and Climate, and Plate Tectonics. Each of the topics has elementary, intermediate, and secondary lesson plans that offer details on the content, time required, materials needed, and directions for the project. The stimulating activities are a great way for students to understand otherwise difficult subjects and excite them about geology." Internet Scout

Riverdeep.net. Riverdeep, Inc. $1800 for one classroom of 30 students for all programs; $600 for one classroom for either the math or science programs; for additional pricing contact producer. (4 and up)

http://www.riverdeep.net

By subscription only. Tel. 888-242-6747

A curriculum resource with a variety of programs, activities, and reference tools. The Destination Math program for grades four and up uses animation and natural language narration to provide self-paced tutorials and activities related to concepts such as numbers, fractions, decimals, and percents. For grades six and up the site offers the Logal Middle School Science Gateways and Explorer simulations and an EarthPulse Center for the middle school earth science curriculum. A Living Library section offers searchable reference materials such as the *World Book International*, Time.com for Kids, *Bartlett's Quotations*, almanacs, dictionaries, etc.

Robotics—Sensing-Thinking-Acting. Tech Museum of Innovation Free

http://www.thetech.org/robotics

This online exhibition explains what robots are, what they do, how they work, and who builds them. Includes video clips of researchers explaining how they design robots, ethicists discussing the moral problems of a successful artificial intelligence program, and artists discussing robots as art. Also includes an activity in which one tries to control an exploratory device over a great distance, so that there is a lag between command and response.

The **ruling** that changed America: Brown v. Board of Education. American School Board Journal Free (6 and up)

http://www.asbj.com/BrownvBoard

"Presents a special online issue of articles that focus on the significance of Brown v. Board of Education, in a historical and current context. The journal successfully asks readers to reflect on the importance of the case to the Civil Rights Movement and whether the promise its ruling gave to end segregation holds true in today's schools and society. The site's 'Teaching Brown' section discusses how educators can introduce a discussion of race and equality in the classroom. An informative narrative civil rights timeline and an extensive book and Web list contribute to the usefulness of the site." Internet Scout

Scholastic READ 180. Scholastic, Inc. Contact producer for pricing (4-12)

http://teacher.scholastic.com/read180/

This research-based program "delivers individualized reading instruction to help students improve fluency, create mental models, and understand more complex written information through word analysis and vocabulary development. This is accomplished through a variety of reading experiences that integrate with History and Geography, People and Cultures, and Science and Math topics. The READ 180 model consists of a 90-minute rotation of activities. The four major components of READ 180 are Instructional Reading, Modeled Reading, Independent Reading, and Teacher-Directed Instruction. The program is available in three stages: Stage A (elementary), Stage B (middle school), and Stage C (high school). . . . Other program components include a management and assessment system that monitors student progress, and a reading diagnostic tool, the Scholastic Reading Inventory, that evaluates reading levels for student placement." Evalutech

Science buzz. Science Museum of Minnesota Free (4 and up)

http://ltc2.smm.org/buzz/

This site provides "information about a variety of science news stories that often do not receive adequate coverage elsewhere in the media. Some of the current stories on the site include West Nile virus, cloning, and even invasive flying carp. Visitors will want to start by perusing the 'What's Abuzz' section on the homepage. Here they

Science buzz—*Continued*
can find about current science news stories and peruse previous stories as well. For persons who know what they are looking for there is a section titled 'I want to learn about', where they can go directly to stories about such topical areas as physical science, math, or the history and nature of science." Internet Scout

Science of cooking. Exploratorium Free (6-12)

http://www.exploratorium.edu/cooking/index.html

"Science, cooking, and history are combined to explain not only how to cook, but also what happens chemically during the cooking process. Choose from 'Eggs,' 'Pickles,' 'Candy,' 'Bread,' 'Seasoning,' and 'Meat' to begin a journey of discovery that cooks and non-cooks alike will appreciate. Kids who enjoy cooking will find recipes for an apple pie that uses no apples, an egg white dessert named after a famous ballerina, and more. Science enthusiasts will be intrigued with taste bud tests using Life Savers, making a salt string sculpture, or dissolving an egg's shell in vinegar." SLJ

Science Online. Facts on File $500 for up to 500 users; $675 for 500-1000 users (6-12)

http://www.factsonfile.com

By subscription only. Tel. 800-322-8755

This curriculum-oriented database provides an overview of the sciences, covering subjects ranging from animal anatomy to atomic physics. It includes more than 600 science experiments, approximately 1,900 biographies of important scientists, more than 2,000 essays on current scientific and technological issues, a timeline of more than 5,600 chronology entries, and over 3,000 printable diagrams.

SciLinks. National Science Teacher's Association Free

http://www.scilinks.org/

This site is the product of a partnership between textbook publishers and the National Science Teachers Association. SciLinks provides access to web sites to expand student's understanding of concepts, science news to add context to learning, activities to expand learning opportunities, and experts to answers questions. A coding system in the margins of the textbooks is used to direct students to the correct teacher selected information on the SciLinks web site. Participating publishers include: Harcourt, Holt, Rinehart, and Winston, Kendall/Hunt Publishing Company and WGBH.

Sharks: myth and mystery. Monterey Bay Aquarium Free (5 and up)

http://www.mbayaq.org/efc/sharks.asp

An online exhibit on the world of sharks that features of a gallery tour, which is organized by geographic region, such as Australia and Central America. In each area, visitors can learn about the individual species of shark in each region and how various human communities interact with these magnificent creatures. Visitors can also take a look through the live "Shark Cam" from the Aquarium's Australia Gallery. While sharks will be the draw here, visitors can also learn about and view penguins, jellyfish, sea otters, and octopi in other sections of the site.

Simple machines. Franklin Institute Online Free (4-8)

http://sln.fi.edu/qa97/spotlight3/spotlight3.html

"Learn about six simple machines and how they work at this Website that is almost as simple as the simple machines themselves. Basic definitions and samples of each simple machine are provided. There are examples of how simple machines are used to change the amount of force needed to move objects. Also given are links to other pages that go into more detail and provide activities and lesson plans." Florida's Instructional Technology Resource Center

SimScience. National Science Foundation Free

http://simscience.org

Provides tutorials on four areas of scientific research that depend on simulations done on supercomputers: membranes, fluid flow, dam cracking, and crackling noise. The tutorials are offered at three reading levels: elementary, secondary, and college-level.

SIRS Discoverer. ProQuest Contact producer for pricing

http://www.proquestk12.com

By subscription only. Tel. 800 521-0600 x3334

Reference database of full-text articles searchable by key words (options for Boolean operators, truncation, phrases, and natural language); subject tree (15 broad categories with sub-topics); and subject headings (primarily Library of Congress). Articles are drawn from newspapers, magazines, and U.S. government documents, as well as contributions by the SIRS staff. Articles are color-coded by reading level: easy (grades 1-4), moderate (grades 5-7), and challenging (grade 8 and beyond). The site includes Current Events articles updated daily, *The World Almanac for Kids*, *Funk and Wagnalls New Encyclopedia*, maps, a dictionary, and a thesaurus.

"SIRS Discoverer on the Web offers well-organized information and simplified search capabilities for student research." Evalutech

Smithsonian Expeditions. Smithsonian Institution Free

http://www.mnh.si.edu/anthro/laexped

Tells the story of the North and Latin American naturalists who collaborated on anthropological, botanical, and zoological expeditions to South America in the 19th and early 20th centuries.

SOS Math. Math Medics, L.L.C. Free

http://www.sosmath.com/index.html

Provides tutorials and practice exams on elementary to college-level mathematics.

Star Journey. National Geographic Free

http://www.nationalgeographic.com/features/97/stars

This site provides a star chart with embedded links to thirty-nine Hubble space telescope photographs of the corresponding heavenly bodies. Also includes articles on the Hubble space telescope and on constellations.

StarChild. NASA Free

http://starchild.gsfc.nasa.gov/docs/StarChild

Contains information on and photographs of the solar system, more distant heavenly bodies, and space exploration. All writing is available at both elementary and secondary reading levels.

State Geography. ABC-CLIO $499/yr. (4 and up)

http://www.stategeography.abc-clio.com/

State Geography—*Continued*

By subscription only. Tel. 800-368-6868

Covers the people, places, events, trends, statistics, news, attractions, politics, culture, environment, government, and history of all 50 states in the U.S. The site also includes biographies and primary source documents. Searchable by key word and advanced search options that allow filtering by categories. Teachers can customize the site by setting up classes and posting information such as announcements, syllabi, discussion questions, handouts, and tests. The Home page has frequently updated news articles and feature stories that are linked to related articles in the database. Includes the *Merriam Webster Dictionary*.

"The site's entries are authoritative and well linked. This online reference would be a boon to busy teachers who want to use the Internet in the instruction of geography. Highly recommended." Book Report

Student Resource Center Junior. Gale Group Contact producer for pricing (4-8)

http://www.galegroup.com

By subscription only. Tel. 800-877-4253

Student Resource Center Junior provides content based on national curriculum standards including literature, science, geography, and multicultural studies, as well as biographical information. The database has original reference material in the form of overview and critical essays; primary source documents from the American Journey series; and articles from periodicals and newspapers updated daily. Search results are returned by document type. The site includes periodical back files from 1986; more than 16,000 timeline event descriptions; more than 15,000 photographs, maps and graphics; and more than 41,000 primary source documents (diaries, letters, recordings, etc.). There are also full-text articles from encyclopedias and almanacs as well as hundreds of audio and video clips. Includes the *Merriam-Webster Collegiate*, *Biographical*, and *Geographical dictionaries*.

testGEAR. Bridges Contact producer for pricing

http://www.testu.com/frameset.asp

By subscription only. Tel. 800-281-1168

This is a test preparation program that provides interactive instruction in English-Language Arts, mathmatics, social studies and science topics tested on the exit-level examination. It supplies lessons on test-taking strategies, and offers practice tests in a variety of formats.

Today's science @ FACTS.com. Facts On File News Service $329/yr. (6-12)

http://www.facts.com

By subscription only. Tel. 800-363-7976 x4300

"Bridges the gap between textbooks and what's happening in science today. From 1992 to the present, Today's Science provides students with a collection of thousands of self-contained, illustrated original articles on breaking news in science, health, and technology. The articles feature large explanatory pictures (2500) and diagrams, and pop-up glossary definitions (4,000) of scientific terms. The pop-up glossary allows students to read the definition without leaving the article. The text includes hyperlinks to relevant news accounts, including archival coverage dating back to 1941 from the Facts On File World News Digest—along with links to overviews from the World Almanac, World Almanac Encyclopedia, and Issues and Controversies@Facts.com." SLJ

Treehouses on the Tree of Life. Tree of Life Project Free

http://tolweb.org/tree/home.pages/treehouses.html

The Tree of Life is a web project developed by biologists around the world that is composed of more than 2,000 web pages and provides information about phylogeny and biodiversity. Treehouses is the section of the Tree of Life aimed at k-16 learners and teachers. The site features "treehouses" or sections including investigations (science reports and experiments with photos, diagrams, and videos), stories, games, and teacher resources.

U. S. government documents ready reference collection. Columbia University Library Free

http://www.columbia.edu/cu/lweb/indiv/dsc/readyref.html

A ready reference collection arranged by subject of the most frequently used depository document titles at Columbia University Libraries. Documents are available in various formats including print, microfiche, web, and CD-ROM.

unitedstreaming.com Mathematics 8-12. AGC United Learning Starting at $995/yr. for K-8 schools and $1,495/yr. for high schools

http://www.unitedstreaming.com

By subscription only. Tel. 800-323-9084

Unitedstreaming.com is an online library of over 10,000 video clips aligned to state standards for grades K-12. The library is searchable by keyword, subject area, grade level, and curriculum strand. Video clips are supported by materials for teachers and students, and can be steamed or downloaded as PDF files, printed, and distributed.

Unraveling the mysteries of King Tutankhamun. National Geographic Society Free (4 and up)

http://magma.nationalgeographic.com/ngm/tut/mysteries/index.html

This site "allows visitors to examine . . . [Tutankhamun's] body through the use of CT scan imagery and see how he might have looked. Clicking on the entrance to this multimedia feature, visitors are greeted by audio narration that complements a 360-degree view of the four walls of King Tut's tomb. Visitors can then look closer at each wall in detail by using a built-in interface to navigate the various decorative and symbolic markings on each side. After this first section, visitors can move to the 'Royal Wrappings' feature, which includes a detailed look at the many layers in which King Tut was entombed. The site is rounded out by a selection of additional links to such resources as articles from National Geographic dealing with Egyptian archaeology." Internet Scout

The USGenWeb Project. The USGenWeb Project Free

http://usgenweb.org/

Provides links to all state and county web sites for genealogical research with resources for postings of unknown county queries, family reunion bulletin boards, state histories, and maps showing the changing county boundaries. Special projects include: transcription of Civil War regiments, the reuniting of families with lost photos and tombstone transcription.

Virtual Renaissance. Twin Groves Junior High School Free

http://www.twingroves.district96.k12.il.us/Renaissance/VirtualRen.html

Virtual Renaissance—*Continued*

This tutorial on Renaissance history is presented as a trip back through time to various sites in Europe and England. Local people explain their lives and Renaissance art, science, exploration, trade, politics, war, religion, and society.

Visual thesaurus. Thinkmap, Inc. Contact producer for pricing (3-12)

http://www.visualthesaurus.com

By subscription only. Tel. 212-381-0552

Provides the meaning of 140,000 words meanings and explores their relationships to other words (ex. Antonym). Pdf Teachers Guide and Student Workbook included.

"The engaging, dynamic, and efficient interface is the great strength of this resource. Its responsive, animated interactivity draws students into a study of words. It also offers an excellent way for ESL students to develop a fuller understanding of English vocabulary." Evalutech

Water science for schools. United States Geological Survey Free (7-12)

http://ga.water.usgs.gov/edu/

"Virtually every aspect of water usage is addressed in both scientific and consumer areas. Topics covered fall under the broad categories of where water is located, its properties, how we study water, water in our bodies, and water quality. In addition to factual articles, there are activities, quizzes, and a glossary. An extensive collection of maps, photos, charts, and graphics are included in the Picture Gallery and the Map Gallery. The Data Library houses a selection of data tables focusing on water usage by state." Evalutech

Web feet. Gale Group Contact producer for subscription pricing (K-12)

http://www.galegroup.com

By subscription only. Tel. 800-877-4253

A collection of preselected, annotated, free websites that have been selected and evaluated by librarian and educators based on the criteria of source, information, timeliness, and appropriate links. Searchable by keyword [subject], grade level, and curriculum area or browsed by LC subject, title of Web site, author or sponsor of the site, or LC or Dewey call number. Sites, both curriculum specific and general interest, added on a bimonthly basis.

"The folks behind WEB FEET have done an outstanding job of selection. Every URL, with rare exception, took me straight to a page containing the exact information I was expecting to find. . . . WEB FEET ONLINE is a functional Internet subject guide, a truly useful resource for finding solid, trustworthy Web sites." Libr J

Webopedia. INT Media Group, Inc. Free

http://www.webopedia.com/

An online dictionary and search engine for computer and Internet technology information. Features include: term of the day, top 15 terms and information, job listings, and quick reference section for information on everything technological. Contains banner advertising.

What works clearinghouse: middle school math curricula. U.S. Department of Education's Institute of Education Sciences Free

http://www.whatworks.ed.gov/
Topic.asp?tid=03&ReturnPage=default.asp

"The What Works Clearinghouse was established 'to provide educators, policy-makers, researchers, and the public with a central and trusted source of scientific evidence of what works in education.' It has posted the results from its review of 'interventions based on a curriculum, which contain learning goals that spell out the mathematics that students should know and be able to do, instructional programs and materials that organize the mathematical content, and assessments.' The reviews are organized into three WWC Topic Reports that cover interventions for middle school mathematics, elementary school mathematics, and high school mathematics. For each intervention with at least one study that 'Meets Evidence Standards' or 'Meets Evidence Standards with Reservations,' the site provides a short review of the study and the findings." Internet Scout

The why files. The University of Wisconsin at Madison, The National Institute for Science Education Free (6-12)

http://whyfiles.org/

"The Why Files delves into the science behind the news headlines and draws a connection between science in the everyday world and science in the classroom. A major science-related story is posted every week in the 'In Depth' section. In addition to the mainstream science disciplines (biology, environmental science, and physical science), these stories also cover the areas of sports, health, social science, and technology. The stories feature excellent navigational aids, and often have online videos and other multimedia enhancements. An archive of articles is maintained, and a site search engine provides flexible access. The 'In Brief' section offers pithy articles dealing with popular science mysteries, while 'In the News' selects stories from the Why Files database and relates them to current events. The site is nicely designed, well-written, and efficiently organized." Evalutech

Wise: Web-based inquiry science environment. Wise, UC Berkeley Free

http://wise.berkeley.edu/

This web-based science learning environment supported by the National Science Foundation helps students learn about and respond to scientific controversies through designing, debating and critiquing solutions. Topics include: genetically modified foods, earthquake prediction, and the deformed frogs mystery.

The Wordsmyth Educational Dictionary-Thesaurus (WEDT). Wordsmyth Collaboratory Free

http://www.wordsmyth.net/

Users can search this online American English dictionary (with an integrated thesaurus of over 50,000 headwords) and hyperlinked synonyms by entering a word on the homepage. Choose from three levels of search: exact, broad, and spelled-like. Entry includes syllabication, part of speech, pronunciation, definitions, browse words alphabetically around entry, and see other entries that contain entry. Also included are discussion area, word of the week, wordlink and thinktank (key discussions on popular topics) features. Includes Glossary Maker, Crossword Puzzle Helper, Quiz Builder, and Anagram Solver.

World Atlas. Facts on File $280/yr. for up to 500 users; $375/yr. for 500-1000 users (6 and up)

http://www.factsonfile.com

By subscription only. Tel. 800-322-8755

An interactive database of maps and information related to geographic regions and countries of the world, as

World Atlas—*Continued*

well as states and Canadian provinces. The site provides full-color political, elevation, and outline maps of each geographic area as well as multiple maps depicting information ranging from political and economic data to energy and natural resources. "Fact Files" have information on countries such as vital statistics, government, history, and chronologies. Links to related Web sites are included.

"Allows for easy access to current information in lieu of hard copy versions that become outdated quickly. This is a worthwhile purchase for classroom and media center use for research." Evalutech

World Book Online. World Book Publishing Contact producer for pricing (4 and up)

http://www.worldbookonline.com

By subscription only. Tel. 800-975-3250

General reference encyclopedia with all articles from the print version of World Book Encyclopedia along with multimedia elements and updated articles and information (750 new articles, 550 new Back in Time articles, 60 special reports, and 4500 revised articles were added in a single year). This online reference also has links to full text articles in over 250 magazines and newspapers as well as links to more than 10,000 editor approved Web sites. Back in Time articles, taken from World Book Yearbooks dating to 1922, provide coverage of people and events from the perspective of the times. A Surf the Millennium feature introduces the major political, cultural, and scientific events of the last 10 centuries. Includes a fully integrated dictionary.

"This flexible, easy-to-use, online resource is an excellent tool for student research. By integrating historical background and current information, it makes history more relevant to events of the day. Highly recommended." Book Report

The World Flag Database. The World Flag Database and Graham Bartram Free

http://www.flags.net/

A comprehensive database of information and graphics of flags around the world. Listed by country, information is given for capital city and main city as well as specific flag information and graphics for national flag, civil ensign, naval ensign, and government ensign. Searchable using the quick buttons on the left side of the home page.

World Geography. ABC-CLIO $499/yr. (6 and up)

http://www.worldgeography.abc-clio.com/

By subscription only. Tel. 800-368-6868

Provides information for a catalog of countries and regions. Each country page provides an overview of the nation, historical and governmental information, facts and figures, important events, biographies, primary source documents, lists of organizations, and maps. Articles are cross-referenced through hyperlinks. In addition to key word searches, there are advanced search options to limit by categories of information. Teachers can customize the site by adding discussion questions, handouts, tests, etc. The site also features daily news articles and feature stories with links to related articles. Includes the *Merriam-Webster Collegiate Dictionary* and *Merriam-Webster's Collegiate Thesaurus*.

"An excellent reference tool . . . that also can be used as a daily organizational resource for students logging on to find their assignments for the day." Evalutech

The Writers Almanac. Minnesota Public Radio Free

http://almanac.mpr.org/

Provides archival access to audio and text files from past programs of The Writers Almanac, a daily program of poetry and history hosted by Garrison Keillor, on National Public Radio stations. Information includes author background and text of reading selections as well as program schedule.

yourDictionary.com. yourDictionary.com Free

http://www.yourdictionary.com

Provides a portal for language and language-related products and services on the web including 1800 dictionaries with more than 250 languages. All dictionaries on the site are searchable via a Google powered search engine and include language, specialty, translation, synonym, acronym, rhyming and more. There is a translation feature and gameroom. Specialty areas include access to endangered languages and research.

The Yuckiest Site on the Internet. Discovery Channel Free

http://yucky.kids.discovery.com

Covers the coarser aspects of biology. Includes scientifically sound discussions of such topics as regurgitation, flatulence, cockroaches, and worms. Includes recordings of vulgar noises and a whack-a-roach game.

AUTHOR, TITLE, SUBJECT, AND ANALYTICAL INDEX

This index to the books in the Classified Catalog includes author, title, subject, and analytical entries; added entries for publishers' series, for joint authors, and for editors of works entered under title; and name and subject cross references; all arranged in one alphabet. The number or symbol in bold face type at the end of each entry refers to the Dewey Decimal Classification or to the Fiction or Story Collection Section where the book will be found. Works classed in 92 will be found under the heading for the person written about. For further information about this index and for examples of entries, see Directions for Use of the Catalog.

6th grade can really kill you. DeClements, B.
    Fic

9.11.01: terrorists attack the U.S. Lalley, P.
    973.931

12 again. Corbett, S.   **Fic**

13   **S C**

19 varieties of gazelle. Nye, N. S.   **811**

The **20th** century
  In World history on file   **909**

20th-century history makers [series]
  Adams, S. Mahatma Gandhi   **92**

20th century inventions [series]
  Hoare, S. Digital revolution   **621.381**
  Morgan, N. Lasers   **621.36**

20th century issues series
  Snedden, R. Medical ethics   **174.2**

20th-century perspectives [series]
  Ross, S. The United Nations   **341.23**
  Taylor, D. The Cold War   **909.82**

21st century debates [series]
  Bowden, R. Water supply   **363.6**
  Dowswell, P. Genetics   **660.6**
  Foley, R. World health   **362.1**
  Fooks, L. The drug trade   **364.1**
  Garlake, T. Global debt   **336.3**
  MccGwire, S. Surveillance   **323.44**
  Petley, J. Media   **302.23**

21st century health and wellness [series]
  Edelson, E. The immune system   **616.07**
  Kittredge, M. The common cold   **616.2**
  Little, M. The endocrine system   **612.4**
  Little, M. Sexually transmitted diseases
    616.95

33 things every girl should know (7 and up)
    810.8

33 things every girl should know about women's history (5 and up)   **305.4**

100 award-winning science fair projects. Vecchione, G.   **507.8**

100 books for girls to grow on. Dodson, S.
    028.1

100 most popular children's authors. McElmeel, S. L.   **810.3**

100 most popular scientists for young adults. Haven, K. F.   **920**

101 amazing optical illusions. Jennings, T.
    152.14

101 essential tips [series]
  Mills, D. Aquarium fish   **639.34**

101 questions about blood and circulation, with answers straight from the heart. Brynie, F. H.
    612.1

101 questions about sex and sexuality—. Brynie, F. H.   **613.9**

101 stories of the great ballets. Balanchine, G.
    792.8

101+ teen programs that work. Honnold, R.
    027.62

101 ways to bug your teacher. Wardlaw, L.
    Fic

111 one-minute monologues. Lamedman, D.
    812.008

111 Shakespeare monologues. See Shakespeare, W. One hundred and eleven Shakespeare monologues   **822.3**

145th Street. Myers, W. D.   **S C**

203 icy, freezing, frosty, cool & wild experiments, Janice Van Cleave's. VanCleave, J. P.
    507.8

300 B.C. Service, P. F.   **930**

800. George, L. S.   **909.07**

882 ½ amazing answers to your questions about the Titanic. Brewster, H.   **910.4**

911: the book of help   **810.8**

1,000 inventions & discoveries. Bridgman, R. F.
    609

1000 playthinks. Moscovich, I.   **793.73**

1,001 facts about dinosaurs. Clark, N.   **567.9**

1200. Service, A.   **909.07**

1500. Schomp, V.   **909.08**

1800. Ashby, R.   **909.8**

The **1918** influenza pandemic. Peters, S. T.
    614.5

1984. See Orwell, G. Nineteen eighty-four   **Fic**

The **1993** World Trade Center bombing. Shields, C. J.   **364.1**

2001: a space odyssey. Clarke, A. C.　　　**Fic**

A

A & E biography [series]
Anderson, D. Saddam Hussein　　　92
Finlayson, R. Colin Powell　　　92
Finlayson, R. Nelson Mandela　　　92
Headlam, G. Yasser Arafat　　　92
Howard, M. Christopher Reeve　　　92
Howard, M. Madeleine Albright　　　92
Kite, L. P. Maya Angelou　　　92
Ruth, A. Jane Austen　　　92
Ruth, A. Louisa May Alcott　　　92
Ruth, A. Mother Teresa　　　92

A **maze** me. Nye, N. S.　　　811

A to Z encyclopedias [series]
Netzley, P. D. The Greenhaven encyclopedia of ancient Egypt　　　932

A **to** Z of Native American women. Sonneborn, L.　　　920.003

A **to** Z of women in science and math. Yount, L.　　　920.003

A.I.D.S. (Disease) See AIDS (Disease)

A. Philip Randolph and the African American labor movement. Miller, C. C.　　　92

A+ projects in earth science, Janice VanCleave's. VanCleave, J. P.　　　550

AACR See Anglo-American cataloguing rules

Aaseng, Nathan, 1953-
Black inventors (7 and up)　　　920
Business builders in real estate　　　920
Construction: building the impossible　　　624
Multiple sclerosis　　　616.8
Navajo code talkers　　　940.54
Poisonous creatures　　　591.6
Wild shots (5 and up)　　　778.9
You are the juror　　　345

Abandoned children
Jocelyn, M. A home for foundlings (7 and up)　　　362.7
Warren, A. Orphan train rider (4 and up)　　　362.7

Fiction
Leavitt, M. Heck, superhero　　　**Fic**
Voigt, C. Homecoming (6 and up)　　　**Fic**

Abarat. Barker, C.　　　**Fic**

ABC-CLIO biographical companion [series]
Wrigley, C. Winston Churchill: a biographical companion　　　92

'Abd al-'Azīz ibn Sa'ūd See Ibn Sa'ūd, King of Saudi Arabia, 1880-1953

Abduction!. Kehret, P.　　　**Fic**

Abelove, Joan
Go and come back (7 and up)　　　**Fic**
Saying it out loud (7 and up)　　　**Fic**

Abernathy, Alexia
See/See also pages in the following book(s):
Thimmesh, C. Girls think of everything (5 and up)　　　920

Abnaki Indians
Bruchac, J. Bowman's store　　　92

Fiction
Bruchac, J. The winter people (5 and up)　　　**Fic**

The **abolition** of American slavery. Tackach, J.　　　326

Abolitionists
Altman, L. J. Slavery and abolition in American history　　　973.7
Brezina, C. Sojourner Truth's "Ain't I a woman?" speech　　　92
Butler, M. G. Sojourner Truth (5 and up)　　　92
Cloud Tapper, S. Voices from slavery's past (7 and up)　　　326
Douglass, F. Escape from slavery　　　92
Edwards, J. Abolitionists and slave resistance (7 and up)　　　326
Fradin, D. B. Bound for the North Star (7 and up)　　　326
Fritz, J. Harriet Beecher Stowe and the Beecher preachers (5 and up)　　　92
January, B. John Brown's raid on Harpers Ferry (4 and up)　　　973.7
Katz, W. L. Black pioneers　　　920
Kenschaft, L. Lydia Maria Child (7 and up)　　　92
Krass, P. Sojourner Truth　　　92
McArthur, D. The Kansas-Nebraska Act and "Bleeding Kansas" in American history　　　978.1
Stein, R. C. John Brown's Raid on Harpers Ferry in American history　　　973.7
Strangis, J. Lewis Hayden and the war against slavery　　　92
Tackach, J. The abolition of American slavery (7 and up)　　　326
Todras, E. H. Angelina Grimké (7 and up)　　　92
Yancey, D. Frederick Douglass　　　92
Zeinert, K. Tragic prelude: bleeding Kansas (7 and up)　　　978.1
See/See also pages in the following book(s):
McKissack, P. C. Black hands, white sails (5 and up)　　　639.2

Fiction
Lasky, K. True north (6 and up)　　　**Fic**
Lyons, M. E. Dear Ellen Bee　　　**Fic**

Abolitionists and slave resistance. Edwards, J.　　　326

Aboriginal art of Australia. Finley, C.　　　759.01

Aboriginal Australians
Arnold, C. Uluru, Australia's Aboriginal heart (5 and up)　　　994
Finley, C. Aboriginal art of Australia　　　759.01

Aborigines, Australian See Aboriginal Australians

Abortion
Abortion: opposing viewpoints (7 and up)　　　363.46
See/See also pages in the following book(s):
Culture wars: opposing viewpoints　　　306
Law and legislation
Gold, S. D. Roe v. Wade　　　344
Payment, S. Roe v. Wade　　　344
Romaine, D. S. Roe v. Wade (7 and up)　　　344

Abortion: opposing viewpoints (7 and up)
363.46

The **abracadabra** kid. Fleischman, S. **92**

Abraham and Isaac. Myers, W. D.
In Myers, W. D. A time to love; stories from
the Old Testament p67-84 **S C**

Abraham-Podietz, Eva
(jt. auth) Fox, A. L. Ten thousand children
940.53

Abrahams, Peter, 1919-
Tell freedom [excerpt]
In Somehow tenderness survives; stories of
Southern Africa p7-18 **S C**

Abrahams, Peter, 1947-
Down the rabbit hole (7 and up) **Fic**

Abrahams, Roger D.
(comp) African folktales. See African folktales
398.2

Abraham's battle. Banks, S. H. **Fic**

Abramovitz, Melissa
Leukemia **616.99**

Abrams, Carol
(jt. auth) Wenger, J. Teen knitting club
746.43

Abrams, Liesa
Chronic fatigue syndrome **616.9**

Abridged Dewey decimal classification and relative index. Dewey, M. **025.4**

Abridged readers' guide to periodical literature
051

Absolutely normal chaos. Creech, S. **Fic**

Abuela invents the zero. Ortiz Cofer, J.
In Ortiz Cofer, J. An island like you; stories
of the barrio p107-11 **S C**

Abuse of children *See* Child abuse

Abuse of wives *See* Wife abuse

Abused women
Battered women **362.82**

Academic achievement
Farmer, L. S. J. Student success and library media programs **027.8**

Academic freedom
Pipkin, G. At the schoolhouse gate **373.1**
Reichman, H. Censorship and selection
025.2

Acceleration. McNamee, G. **Fic**

The **accident.** Wiesel, E.
In Wiesel, E. Night, Dawn, The accident:
three tales p205-318 **Fic**

Accidents
See also types of accidents and subjects
with the subdivision *Accidents*
Fiction
Bauer, M. D. On my honor (4 and up) **Fic**
Prevention
See also Safety education

According to Coyote. Kauffman, J.
In Theatre for young audiences; 20 great
plays for children p170-82 **812.008**

Acculturation
See also Socialization

Achieving a curriculum-based library media center
program. Smith, J. B. **027.8**

Ackerman, Jane, 1948-
Louis Pasteur and the founding of microbiology
(7 and up) **92**

Ackroyd, Peter
The beginning (7 and up) **576.8**
Escape from Earth (7 and up) **629.4**

Acquaintance rape *See* Date rape

Acquired immune deficiency syndrome *See*
AIDS (Disease)

Acrobats and acrobatics
Fiction
Murray, M. The slightly true story of Cedar B.
Hartley (5 and up) **Fic**

Across America on an emigrant train. Murphy, J.
92

Across the lines. Reeder, C. **Fic**

Acting
The Book of monologues for aspiring actors (7
and up) **808.82**
Friedman, L. Break a leg! (4 and up) **792**
Great monologues for young actors **812.008**
Great scenes for young actors from the stage
808.82
Lamedman, D. 111 one-minute monologues
812.008
Millennium monologs **812.008**
O'Brien, L. Lights, camera, action! **791.43**
Shakespeare, W. One hundred and eleven
Shakespeare monologues (7 and up) **822.3**
Surface, M. H. Short scenes and monologues for
middle school actors **812**
Costume
See Costume

Acting out. Gustafson, C. **812**

An **actor** on the Elizabethan stage. Currie, S.
792.09

Actors
See also African American actors
Giblin, J. Good brother, bad brother [biography
of John Wilkes Booth and Edwin Booth] (5
and up) **92**
Howard, M. Christopher Reeve **92**
Fiction
Deaver, J. R. Say goodnight, Gracie (7 and up)
Fic

Actresses *See* Actors

Adair, Gene
George Washington Carver **92**

Adaline Falling Star. Osborne, M. P. **Fic**

Adam and Eve and Pinch-me. Johnston, J. **Fic**

Adam Canfield of the Slash. Winerip, M. **Fic**

Adam marries. Lester, J.
In Lester, J. When the beginning began; stories about God, the creatures, and us
p69-72 **296.1**

Adams, Abigail, 1744-1818
About
Bober, N. Abigail Adams (7 and up) **92**

Adams, Colleen
Women's suffrage **305.4**

Adams, Douglas, 1952-2001
The Hitchhiker's Guide to the Galaxy (7 and up)   **Fic**
See/See also pages in the following book(s):
Reid, S. E. Presenting young adult science fiction   **813.009**

Adams, John
(jt. auth) Dixon, D. The future is wild   **576.8**

Adams, John Quincy, 1767-1848
See/See also pages in the following book(s):
Kennedy, J. F. Profiles in courage   **920**

Adams, Richard, 1920-
Watership Down (6 and up)   **Fic**

Adams, Richard C., 1945-
Energy projects for young scientists (7 and up)   **621**
More ideas for science projects (7 and up)   **507.8**

Adams, Samuel, 1722-1803
About
Fradin, D. B. Samuel Adams (6 and up)   **92**
Irvin, B. Samuel Adams (7 and up)   **92**

Adams, Simon
Castles & forts (5 and up)   **355.7**
Mahatma Gandhi (7 and up)   **92**
Titanic (4 and up)   **910.4**
World War II (4 and up)   **940.53**
World War I (4 and up)   **940.3**

Adams family
Fiction
Rinaldi, A. The fifth of March (7 and up)   **Fic**

Adamson, Joy, 1910-1980
Born free   **599.75**

Adamson, Lynda G.
Literature connections to American history, 7-12   **016.973**
Literature connections to world history, 7-12   **016.9**
(jt. auth) Dickinson, A. T. American historical fiction   **016.813**

ADD *See* Attention deficit disorder

Addiction. Papa, S.   **616.86**

Addiction: opposing viewpoints   **362.29**

Addiction to alcohol *See* Alcoholism

Addictive behavior *See* Compulsive behavior

Addresses *See* Speeches

Addy, Sean
(il) Chin-Lee, C. Amelia to Zora   **920**

ADHD. Trueit, T. S.   **616.85**

Adhesives
See/See also pages in the following book(s):
Knapp, B. J. Materials science   **620.1**

Adirondack Mountains (N.Y.)
Fiction
Bauer, J. Backwater (7 and up)   **Fic**

Adkins, Jan, 1944-
Bridges (4 and up)   **624**

Adler, Bill, 1929-
(ed) Growing up black. See Growing up black   **920**

Adler, C. S. (Carole S.), 1932-
One unhappy horse   **Fic**
Winning   **Fic**

Adler, David A., 1947-
B. Franklin, printer (4 and up)   **92**
George Washington (5 and up)   **92**
The kids' catalog of Jewish holidays   **296.4**
We remember the Holocaust   **940.53**

Adlington, L. J., 1970-
The diary of Pelly D (7 and up)   **Fic**

Administering the school library media center. Morris, B. J.   **027.8**

Administration of criminal justice
Wormser, R. Defending the accused (7 and up)   **345**

Administration of justice
Hile, K. S. The trial of juveniles as adults   **345**
Jacobs, T. A. They broke the law, you be the judge (7 and up)   **345**

Adoff, Arnold, 1935-
The basket counts   **811**
(ed) I am the darker brother. See I am the darker brother   **811.008**
(ed) My black me. See My black me   **811.008**

Adoff, Jaime
The song shoots out of my mouth   **811**

Adolescence
Crump, M. Don't sweat it!   **613**
Daldry, J. The teenage guy's survival guide (7 and up)   **305.23**
Gravelle, K. What's going on down there?   **612.6**
Gray, H. M. Real girl/real world (7 and up)   **305.23**
Gurian, M. From boys to men   **305.23**
Jukes, M. Growing up: it's a girl thing (4 and up)   **612.6**
Jukes, M. The guy book (7 and up)   **305.23**
Jukes, M. It's a girl thing (5 and up)   **305.23**
Shandler, S. Ophelia speaks (7 and up)   **305.23**
Teen dreams   **612.6**

Adolescent mothers *See* Teenage mothers

Adolescent pregnancy *See* Teenage pregnancy

Adolescent psychology
Mental health information for teens (7 and up)   **616.89**
Muharrar, A. More than a label (7 and up)   **305.23**
Ng, G. Everything you need to know about self-mutilation (7 and up)   **616.85**
Wells, D. K. Live aware, not in fear (7 and up)   **155.5**

Adolescent rights. Greenberg, K. E.   **346**

Adolescents *See* Teenagers

Adoption
Adoption: opposing viewpoints (7 and up)   **362.7**
Kaminker, L. Everything you need to know about being adopted (7 and up)   **362.7**

Adoption—*Continued*

Weiss, A. E. Adoptions today (7 and up) **362.7**

See/See also pages in the following book(s):

The Family: opposing viewpoints (7 and up) **306.8**

Warren, A. Orphan train rider (4 and up) **362.7**

Fiction

Alvarez, J. Finding miracles **Fic**
Blacker, T. The angel factory **Fic**
Johnson, A. Heaven (6 and up) **Fic**
Lisle, J. T. The crying rocks **Fic**
McKay, H. Saffy's angel (5 and up) **Fic**
Myers, W. D. Me, Mop, and the Moondance Kid (4-6) **Fic**

Adoption, Interracial *See* Interracial adoption

Adoption: opposing viewpoints (7 and up) **362.7**

Adoptions today. Weiss, A. E. **362.7**

Adventure and adventurers

Alter, J. Extraordinary explorers and adventurers **920**

Explorers & discoverers **920.003**

Fiction

See Adventure fiction

Adventure fiction

See also Science fiction; Sea stories

Alexander, L. The Illyrian adventure (5 and up) **Fic**
Alexander, L. The iron ring (5 and up) **Fic**
Alexander, L. The remarkable journey of Prince Jen (5 and up) **Fic**
Alexander, L. Westmark (5 and up) **Fic**
Allende, I. City of the beasts (7 and up) **Fic**
Campbell, E. The Shark Callers (7 and up) **Fic**
Cross, G. The great American elephant chase **Fic**
Farmer, N. A girl named Disaster (6 and up) **Fic**
Smith, J. A. Bandit's moon (4-6) **Fic**
Fleischman, S. The whipping boy (5 and up) **Fic**
Gavin, J. Coram boy (7 and up) **Fic**
Hobbs, W. Ghost canoe **Fic**
Horowitz, A. The Devil and his boy (5 and up) **Fic**
Karr, K. Skullduggery (5 and up) **Fic**
Kehret, P. The secret journey **Fic**
Kimmel, E. A. Sword of the samurai (4 and up) **S C**
Lawrence, I. The wreckers (5 and up) **Fic**
Lee, T. Piratica **Fic**
Masefield, J. Jim Davis (5 and up) **Fic**
Sedgwick, M. The Dark Horse (7 and up) **Fic**
Springer, N. Rowan Hood, outlaw girl of Sherwood Forest (4 and up) **Fic**
Stevenson, R. L. Kidnapped (7 and up) **Fic**
Turner, M. W. The thief (6 and up) **Fic**
Verne, J. Around the world in eighty days **Fic**
Voigt, C. Jackaroo (7 and up) **Fic**

Voigt, C. On fortune's wheel (7 and up) **Fic**
Yolen, J. Jason and the Gorgon's blood **Fic**

The **adventure** of Black Peter. Doyle, Sir A. C.
In Doyle, Sir A. C. The complete Sherlock Holmes **S C**

The **adventure** of Charles Augustus Milverton. Doyle, Sir A. C.
In Doyle, Sir A. C. The complete Sherlock Holmes **S C**

The **adventure** of Shoscombe Old Place. Doyle, Sir A. C.
In Doyle, Sir A. C. The complete Sherlock Holmes **S C**

The **adventure** of the Abbey Grange. Doyle, Sir A. C.
In Doyle, Sir A. C. The complete Sherlock Holmes **S C**

The **adventure** of the Beryl Coronet. Doyle, Sir A. C.
In Doyle, Sir A. C. The complete Sherlock Holmes **S C**

The **adventure** of the blanched soldier. Doyle, Sir A. C.
In Doyle, Sir A. C. The complete Sherlock Holmes **S C**

The **adventure** of the Blue Carbuncle. Doyle, Sir A. C.
In Doyle, Sir A. C. The complete Sherlock Holmes **S C**

The **adventure** of the Bruce-Partington plans. Doyle, Sir A. C.
In Doyle, Sir A. C. The complete Sherlock Holmes **S C**

The **adventure** of the cardboard box. Doyle, Sir A. C.
In Doyle, Sir A. C. The complete Sherlock Holmes **S C**

The **adventure** of the copper beeches. Doyle, Sir A. C.
In Doyle, Sir A. C. The complete Sherlock Holmes **S C**

The **adventure** of the creeping man. Doyle, Sir A. C.
In Doyle, Sir A. C. The complete Sherlock Holmes **S C**

The **adventure** of the dancing men. Doyle, Sir A. C.
In Doyle, Sir A. C. The complete Sherlock Holmes **S C**

The **adventure** of the devil's foot. Doyle, Sir A. C.
In Doyle, Sir A. C. The complete Sherlock Holmes **S C**

The **adventure** of the dying detective. Doyle, Sir A. C.
In Doyle, Sir A. C. The complete Sherlock Holmes **S C**

The **adventure** of the empty house. Doyle, Sir A. C.
In Doyle, Sir A. C. The complete Sherlock Holmes **S C**

The **adventure** of the engineer's thumb. Doyle, Sir A. C.
In Doyle, Sir A. C. The complete Sherlock Holmes **S C**

The **adventure** of the golden pince-nez. Doyle, Sir A. C.
In Doyle, Sir A. C. The complete Sherlock Holmes **S C**

The **adventure** of the illustrious client. Doyle, Sir A. C.
In Doyle, Sir A. C. The complete Sherlock Holmes **S C**

The **adventure** of the lion's mane. Doyle, Sir A. C.
In Doyle, Sir A. C. The complete Sherlock Holmes **S C**

The **adventure** of the Mazarin stone. Doyle, Sir A. C.
In Doyle, Sir A. C. The complete Sherlock Holmes **S C**

The **adventure** of the missing three-quarter. Doyle, Sir A. C.
In Doyle, Sir A. C. The complete Sherlock Holmes **S C**

The **adventure** of the noble bachelor. Doyle, Sir A. C.
In Doyle, Sir A. C. The complete Sherlock Holmes **S C**

The **adventure** of the Norwood builder. Doyle, Sir A. C.
In Doyle, Sir A. C. The complete Sherlock Holmes **S C**

The **adventure** of the priory school. Doyle, Sir A. C.
In Doyle, Sir A. C. The complete Sherlock Holmes **S C**

The **adventure** of the red circle. Doyle, Sir A. C.
In Doyle, Sir A. C. The complete Sherlock Holmes **S C**

The **adventure** of the retired colourman. Doyle, Sir A. C.
In Doyle, Sir A. C. The complete Sherlock Holmes **S C**

The **adventure** of the second stain. Doyle, Sir A. C.
In Doyle, Sir A. C. The complete Sherlock Holmes **S C**

The **adventure** of the six Napoleons. Doyle, Sir A. C.
In Doyle, Sir A. C. The complete Sherlock Holmes **S C**

The **adventure** of the solitary cyclist. Doyle, Sir A. C.
In Doyle, Sir A. C. The complete Sherlock Holmes **S C**

The **adventure** of the speckled band. Doyle, Sir A. C.
In Doyle, Sir A. C. The complete Sherlock Holmes **S C**

The **adventure** of the Sussex vampire. Doyle, Sir A. C.
In Doyle, Sir A. C. The complete Sherlock Holmes **S C**

The **adventure** of the three gables. Doyle, Sir A. C.
In Doyle, Sir A. C. The complete Sherlock Holmes **S C**

The **adventure** of the three Garridebs. Doyle, Sir A. C.
In Doyle, Sir A. C. The complete Sherlock Holmes **S C**

The **adventure** of the three students. Doyle, Sir A. C.
In Doyle, Sir A. C. The complete Sherlock Holmes **S C**

The **adventure** of the veiled lodger. Doyle, Sir A. C.
In Doyle, Sir A. C. The complete Sherlock Holmes **S C**

The **adventure** of Wisteria Lodge. Doyle, Sir A. C.
In Doyle, Sir A. C. The complete Sherlock Holmes **S C**

The **adventures** of Blue Avenger. Howe, N. **Fic**

The **adventures** of Eustace. Lewis, C. S.
In The Book of dragons p10-15 **S C**

The **adventures** of Huckleberry Finn. Twain, M. **Fic**

Adventures of Sherlock Holmes. Doyle, Sir A. C.
In Doyle, Sir A. C. The complete Sherlock Holmes **S C**

The **adventures** of Simon and Susanna. Lester, J.
In Lester, J. The last tales of Uncle Remus p151-56 **398.2**

The **adventures** of Sojourner. Wunsch, S. T. **629.43**

The **adventures** of Tom Sawyer. Twain, M. **Fic**

Advertising
Day, N. Advertising (7 and up) **659.1**
Dunn, J. M. Advertising (7 and up) **659.1**
Graydon, S. Made you look (5 and up) **659.1**
See/See also pages in the following book(s):
Mass media: opposing viewpoints **302.23**

Aeken, Hieronymus van *See* Bosch, Hieronymus, d. 1516

Aeneas (Legendary character)
See/See also pages in the following book(s):
Hamilton, E. Mythology p21-76 **292**

Aerial photography
Arthus-Bertrand, Y. Earth from above for young readers (4 and up) **779**

Aeronautics
See also Rocketry
Carson, M. K. The Wright Brothers for kids (4 and up) **629.13**
Graham, I. Flight **629.13**

Accidents
See Aircraft accidents

History
Collins, M. Airborne: a photobiography of Wilbur and Orville Wright (4 and up) **92**
Freedman, R. The Wright brothers: how they invented the airplane **92**

Aeronautics—History—*Continued*
Nahum, A. Flying machine (4 and up) **629.133**
Sproule, A. The Wright brothers **92**
Aesthetics
See also Art appreciation
Affirmative action programs
See/See also pages in the following book(s):
Civil rights (7 and up) **323.1**
Afghanistan
Behnke, A. Afghanistan in pictures (5 and up) **958.1**
Corona, L. Afghanistan **958.1**
Greenblatt, M. Afghanistan (5 and up) **958.1**
Kazem, H. Afghanistan (4 and up) **958.1**
Otfinoski, S. Afghanistan **958.1**
Romano, A. A historical atlas of Afghanistan **958.1**
Stewart, G. Life under the Taliban **958.1**
Afghanistan in pictures. Behnke, A. **958.1**
Africa
Biography—Dictionaries
African biography **920.003**
Africa
Africa: opposing viewpoints **960**
Peoples of Africa **960**
Biography
Hansen, J. African princess (5 and up) **920**
Encyclopedias
Africa: an encyclopedia for students (7 and up) **960**
Altman, S. Encyclopedia of African-American heritage **305.8**
Encyclopedia of African nations and civilizations (7 and up) **960**
Fiction
Memories of sun **S C**
Quintana, A. The baboon king (7 and up) **Fic**
Stratton, A. Chanda's secrets (7 and up) **Fic**
Folklore
See Folklore—Africa
History
African history on file **960**
Haskins, J. African beginnings (4 and up) **960**
Politics and government
Downing, D. Africa **960**
Africa, East *See* East Africa
Africa, South *See* South Africa
Africa: an encyclopedia for students (7 and up) **960**
Africa: opposing viewpoints **960**
African-American achievers [series]
Chambers, V. The Harlem Renaissance **700**
DeAngelis, G. The black cowboys **978**
Stovall, T. The Buffalo Soldiers **978**
African American actors
Hill, A. E. Denzel Washington (7 and up) **92**
The **African** American almanac **305.8**
African American art
Bolden, T. Wake up our souls **704**

African American artists
Duggleby, J. Story painter: the life of Jacob Lawrence (4 and up) **92**
Greenberg, J. Romare Bearden (4 and up) **92**
Lyons, M. E. Talking with Tebé: Clementine Hunter, memory artist (4-6) **92**
Lyons, M. E. Catching the fire: Philip Simmons, blacksmith (4 and up) **92**
Rembert, W. Don't hold me back (4 and up) **92**
African American arts
Chambers, V. The Harlem Renaissance **700**
Hardy, P. S. Extraordinary people of the Harlem Renaissance **920**
African American athletes
Green, M. Y. A strong right arm: the story of Mamie "Peanut" Johnson (4 and up) **92**
McCormack, S. Cool Papa Bell **92**
McKissack, P. C. Black diamond (6 and up) **796.357**
Myers, W. D. The greatest: Muhammad Ali (7 and up) **92**
Payment, S. Buck Leonard **92**
Robinson, S. Promises to keep: how Jackie Robinson changed America (4 and up) **92**
Tessitore, J. Muhammed Ali (7 and up) **92**
Twemlow, N. Josh Gibson **92**
Williams, V. Venus & Serena (7 and up) **92**
African American authors
Cuffie, T. A. Maya Angelou (7 and up) **92**
Harper, J. E. Maya Angelou **92**
Hart, J. Native son: the story of Richard Wright (7 and up) **92**
Haskins, J. Toni Morrison (4 and up) **92**
Hill, C. M. Langston Hughes **92**
Kite, L. P. Maya Angelou **92**
Lyons, M. E. Sorrow's kitchen: the life and folklore of Zora Neale Hurston **92**
Myers, W. D. Bad boy (7 and up) **92**
Poetry from the masters: the pioneers (7 and up) **811.008**
Reef, C. Paul Laurence Dunbar **92**
Rhynes, M. E. Gwendolyn Brooks (7 and up) **92**
Richmond, M. A. Phillis Wheatley **92**
Salisbury, C. Phillis Wheatley **92**
Strickland, M. R. African-American poets **920**
African-American biographies [series]
Durden, R. F. Carter G. Woodson **92**
Hill, C. M. John Lewis **92**
Hill, C. M. Langston Hughes **92**
Lisandrelli, E. S. Ida B. Wells-Barnett **92**
Litwin, L. B. Benjamin Banneker **92**
Lommel, C. Mary Church Terrell **92**
Old, W. Duke Ellington: giant of jazz **92**
Old, W. Louis Armstrong **92**
Reef, C. Paul Laurence Dunbar **92**
Rowh, M. Thurgood Marshall **92**
Schraff, A. E. Dr. Charles Drew **92**
Schraff, A. E. Harriet Tubman **92**
Schraff, A. E. Ralph Bunche **92**
Wright, D. K. Paul Robeson **92**
African American biography **920.003**

African American breakthroughs   **305.8**

African American businesspeople
Haskins, J. African American entrepreneurs
    920

African American children
Bolden, T. Tell all the children our story (5 and up)   **305.8**
Parks, R. Dear Mrs. Parks (5 and up)
    305.23

African American cooking
Erdosh, G. The African American kitchen (7 and up)   **641.5**

African-American culture and history   **305.8**

African American dancers
Cruz, B. Alvin Ailey   **92**

African American educators
Meltzer, M. Mary McLeod Bethune   **92**

The **African** American encyclopedia   **305.8**

African American entrepreneurs. Haskins, J.
    920

The **African-American** experience. Spangenburg, R.   **917.3**

African-American experience [series]
Historic speeches of African Americans   **815**

The **African-American** experience on file
    305.8

African-American faith in America. Murphy, L.
    200

The **African** American family album. Hoobler, D.
    305.8

African American folklore See African Americans—Folklore

African-American history from emancipation to today. Byers, A.   **305.8**

African American inventors
Aaseng, N. Black inventors (7 and up)   **920**
Haskins, J. Outward dreams   **609**
Sullivan, O. R. African American inventors (5 and up)   **920**
Sullivan, O. R. African American women scientists and inventors   **920**

The **African** American kitchen. Erdosh, G.
    641.5

African American literature See American literature—African American authors

African American military heroes. Haskins, J.
    920

African American millionaires. Sullivan, O. R.
    920

African American music
Cooper, M. L. Slave spirituals and the Jubilee Singers   **782.42**
Johnson, J. W. Lift every voice and sing
    782.42

African American musicians
Frankl, R. Charlie Parker, musician   **92**
Harrah, M. Blind Boone (5 and up)   **92**
Old, W. Duke Ellington: giant of jazz   **92**
Old, W. Louis Armstrong   **92**
Preston, K. K. Scott Joplin   **92**
Shirley, D. Everyday I sing the blues: the story of B.B. King (7 and up)   **92**
Tate, E. E. African American musicians   **920**

African American pilots
George, L. The Tuskegee Airmen   **940.54**
Hart, P. S. Flying free (4 and up)   **629.13**
Hart, P. S. Up in the air: the story of Bessie Coleman   **92**
Haskins, J. Black eagles (5 and up)   **629.13**
See/See also pages in the following book(s):
Bruning, J. R. Elusive glory   **920**

African American poetry See American poetry—African American authors

African-American poets. Strickland, M. R.
    920

African American reference library [series]
African American biography   **920.003**
African American breakthroughs   **305.8**

African American singers
Freedman, R. The voice that challenged a nation [biography of Marian Anderson] (5 and up)
    92
Kliment, B. Billie Holiday   **92**
Lester, J. The blues singers (5 and up)   **920**
Orgill, R. Mahalia [Jackson] (5 and up)   **92**
Huggins, N. I. Lena Horne   **92**
Steins, R. Leontyne Price, opera superstar
    92
Turk, R. Ray Charles: soul man   **92**

The **African-American** slave trade. Grant, R. G.
    326

African American soldiers
Bruning, J. R. Elusive glory   **920**
Buckley, G. L. American patriots (7 and up)
    355
Clinton, C. The Black soldier (5 and up)
    355
Cox, C. Come all you brave soldiers (6 and up)
    973.3
Cox, C. The forgotten heroes   **978**
Haskins, J. African American military heroes
    920
Stovall, T. The Buffalo Soldiers   **978**
Trudeau, N. A. Like men of war (7 and up)
    973.7
See/See also pages in the following book(s):
Frankel, N. Break those chains at last: African Americans, 1860-1880   **305.8**
Fiction
Myers, W. D. Fallen angels   **Fic**

African American women
Alagna, M. Mae Jemison (4 and up)   **92**
Angelou, M. Maya Angelou   **811**
Bolden, T. And not afraid to dare   **920**
Bolden, T. Maritcha [biography of Maritcha Rémond Lyons] (4 and up)   **92**
Brezina, C. Sojourner Truth's "Ain't I a woman?" speech   **92**
Butler, M. G. Sojourner Truth (5 and up)
    92
Fradin, D. B. Fight on!: Mary Church Terrell's battle for integration   **92**
Freedman, R. The voice that challenged a nation [biography of Marian Anderson] (5 and up)
    92
Hansen, J. Women of hope (4 and up)   **920**
Jemison, M. C. Find where the wind goes (5 and up)   **92**

African American women—*Continued*

Katz, W. L. Black women of the Old West (5 and up) **978**

Kliment, B. Billie Holiday **92**

Klingel, C. F. Coretta Scott King **92**

Krass, P. Sojourner Truth **92**

Lisandrelli, E. S. Ida B. Wells-Barnett (7 and up) **92**

Lommel, C. Mary Church Terrell **92**

Lyons, M. E. Sorrow's kitchen: the life and folklore of Zora Neale Hurston **92**

Meltzer, M. Mary McLeod Bethune **92**

Old, W. Marian Wright Edelman (7 and up) **92**

Orgill, R. Mahalia [Jackson] (5 and up) **92**

Huggins, N. I. Lena Horne **92**

Parks, R. Rosa Parks: my story (5 and up) **92**

Pinkney, A. D. Let it shine (4 and up) **920**

Rhodes, L. R. Coretta Scott King **92**

Schraff, A. E. Harriet Tubman **92**

Steins, R. Leontyne Price, opera superstar **92**

Sullivan, O. R. African American women scientists and inventors **920**

Taylor, M. W. Harriet Tubman **92**

Yannuzzi, D. A. Mae Jemison **92**

Folklore

Hamilton, V. Her stories (4 and up) **398.2**

African American women scientists and inventors. Sullivan, O. R. **920**

African American youth

Rap and hip hop (7 and up) **306**

African Americans

The African American almanac **305.8**

Hoobler, D. The African American family album (5 and up) **305.8**

Katz, W. L. Black Indians **305.8**

McKissack, P. C. Black hands, white sails (5 and up) **639.2**

Biography

Adair, G. George Washington Carver **92**

African American biography **920.003**

Altman, S. Extraordinary African-Americans (5 and up) **920**

Bisson, T. Nat Turner **92**

Blumberg, R. York's adventures with Lewis and Clark (5 and up) **978**

Bolden, T. Portraits of African-American heroes (4 and up) **920**

Distinguished African American scientists of the 20th century (7 and up) **920**

Douglass, F. Escape from slavery **92**

Draper, A. S. The assassination of Malcolm X **92**

Durden, R. F. Carter G. Woodson (7 and up) **92**

Finlayson, R. Colin Powell **92**

Fradin, D. B. My family shall be free!: the life of Peter Still **92**

Growing up black **920**

Hamilton, V. Anthony Burns: the defeat and triumph of a fugitive slave (5 and up) **92**

Hardy, P. S. Extraordinary people of the Harlem Renaissance **920**

Haskins, J. African American entrepreneurs **920**

Haskins, J. Against all opposition (5 and up) **920**

Haskins, J. The life and death of Martin Luther King, Jr. (5 and up) **92**

Hatt, C. Martin Luther King, Jr **92**

Hinman, B. Benjamin Banneker (5 and up) **92**

Hudson, W. Powerful words (5 and up) **808.8**

Kent, D. Thurgood Marshall and the Supreme Court **92**

Lanier, S. Jefferson's children (7 and up) **920**

Lawler, M. Marcus Garvey **92**

Litwin, L. B. Benjamin Banneker **92**

Manheimer, A. S. Martin Luther King Jr (5 and up) **92**

Marston, H. I. Isaac Johnson **92**

Miller, C. C. A. Philip Randolph and the African American labor movement **92**

Rembert, W. Don't hold me back (4 and up) **92**

Rowh, M. Thurgood Marshall **92**

Sanford, W. R. Bill Pickett: African-American rodeo star **92**

Schraff, A. E. Dr. Charles Drew **92**

Schraff, A. E. Ralph Bunche **92**

Slave narratives **326**

Strangis, J. Lewis Hayden and the war against slavery **92**

Sullivan, O. R. African American millionaires **920**

Tillage, L. Leon's story (4 and up) **92**

Troy, D. W.E.B. DuBois **92**

Wright, D. K. Paul Robeson **92**

Yancey, D. Frederick Douglass **92**

Yates, E. Amos Fortune, free man **92**

Biography—Dictionaries

Kranz, R. The biographical dictionary of African Americans **920.003**

Civil rights

Bullard, S. Free at last **323.1**

Civil rights (7 and up) **323.1**

Dubovoy, S. Civil rights leaders (7 and up) **920**

Finlayson, R. We shall overcome **323.1**

Fireside, H. The "Mississippi Burning" civil rights murder conspiracy trial **345**

Fradin, D. B. Fight on!: Mary Church Terrell's battle for integration **92**

Freedman, R. The voice that challenged a nation [biography of Marian Anderson] (5 and up) **92**

George, L. Civil rights marches **323.1**

Haskins, J. The life and death of Martin Luther King, Jr. (5 and up) **92**

Hatt, C. Martin Luther King, Jr **92**

Hill, C. M. John Lewis **92**

King, C. Oh, freedom! (5 and up) **323.1**

King, M. L. The words of Martin Luther King, Jr. **323.1**

Klingel, C. F. Coretta Scott King **92**

Linda Brown, you are not alone (5 and up) **323.1**

African Americans—Civil rights—*Continued*

Lisandrelli, E. S. Ida B. Wells-Barnett (7 and up) **92**

Lommel, C. Mary Church Terrell **92**

Manheimer, A. S. Martin Luther King Jr (5 and up) **92**

McWhorter, D. A dream of freedom (5 and up) **323.1**

Miller, C. C. A. Philip Randolph and the African American labor movement **92**

Miller, C. C. No easy answers [biography of Bayard Rustin] (7 and up) **92**

Parks, R. Rosa Parks: my story (5 and up) **92**

Pinkney, A. D. Let it shine (4 and up) **920**

Rasmussen, R. K. Farewell to Jim Crow (7 and up) **305.8**

Rhodes, L. R. Coretta Scott King **92**

Ribeiro, M. The assassination of Medgar Evers **92**

Ritchie, N. The civil rights movement **323.1**

Sirimarco, E. American voices from the civil rights movement **323.1**

Somerlott, R. The Little Rock school desegregation crisis in American history **373**

Sorensen, L. The Scottsboro Boys Trial **345**

Walsh, F. The Montgomery bus boycott **323.1**

Wexler, S. The civil rights movement (7 and up) **323.1**

Williams, J. Eyes on the prize: America's civil rights years, 1954-1965 (7 and up) **323.1**

Wormser, R. The rise and fall of Jim Crow (7 and up) **305.8**

See/See also pages in the following book(s):

Parks, R. Dear Mrs. Parks (5 and up) **305.23**

Civil rights—Cartoons and caricatures

Civil rights (7 and up) **323.1**

Employment

See also African American businesspeople

Encyclopedias

African-American culture and history **305.8**

The African American encyclopedia **305.8**

Altman, S. Encyclopedia of African-American heritage **305.8**

Fiction

Armstrong, J. Steal away (5 and up) **Fic**

Armstrong, W. H. Sounder (5 and up) **Fic**

Baldwin, J. Go tell it on the mountain (7 and up) **Fic**

Banks, S. H. Abraham's battle **Fic**

Brooks, B. The moves make the man **Fic**

Carbone, E. L. Stealing freedom **Fic**

Childress, A. Rainbow Jordan (7 and up) **Fic**

Collier, J. L. Jump ship to freedom (6 and up) **Fic**

Collier, J. L. War comes to Willy Freeman (6 and up) **Fic**

Collier, J. L. Who is Carrie? **Fic**

Collier, J. L. With every drop of blood (5 and up) **Fic**

Collier, K. Jericho walls (7 and up) **Fic**

Curtis, C. P. Bucking the Sarge (5 and up) **Fic**

Curtis, C. P. Bud, not Buddy (4 and up) **Fic**

Curtis, C. P. The Watsons go to Birmingham—1963 (4 and up) **Fic**

Draper, S. M. Double Dutch **Fic**

Draper, S. M. Forged by fire (7 and up) **Fic**

Draper, S. M. Tears of a tiger (7 and up) **Fic**

English, K. Francie (5 and up) **Fic**

Fenner, C. Yolonda's genius (4-6) **Fic**

Flake, S. G. Money hungry **Fic**

Flake, S. G. The skin I'm in **Fic**

Flake, S. G. Who am I without him? (7 and up) **S C**

Fuqua, J. S. Darby (4 and up) **Fic**

Gaines, E. J. The autobiography of Miss Jane Pittman (7 and up) **Fic**

Grimes, N. Bronx masquerade (7 and up) **Fic**

Grimes, N. Jazmin's notebook **Fic**

Grove, V. The starplace **Fic**

Guy, R. The disappearance **Fic**

Hamilton, V. Cousins (5 and up) **Fic**

Hamilton, V. The house of Dies Drear (5 and up) **Fic**

Hamilton, V. Plain City (5 and up) **Fic**

Hamilton, V. The planet of Junior Brown (6 and up) **Fic**

Hamilton, V. Time pieces (5 and up) **Fic**

Hansen, J. One true friend **Fic**

Hansen, J. Which way freedom? (5 and up) **Fic**

Hewett, L. Dancer (7 and up) **Fic**

Houston, G. Bright Freedom's song **Fic**

Johnson, A. Bird (5 and up) **Fic**

Johnson, A. The first part last (7 and up) **Fic**

Johnson, A. Heaven (6 and up) **Fic**

Johnson, A. Looking for Red **Fic**

Johnson, A. Songs of faith (5 and up) **Fic**

Johnson, A. Toning the sweep **Fic**

Klass, D. Danger zone **Fic**

Lester, J. Day of tears (7 and up) **Fic**

Lester, J. Long journey home: stories from black history **S C**

Levine, G. C. Dave at night (5 and up) **Fic**

Levy, M. Run for your life (7 and up) **Fic**

Lipsyte, R. The contender (7 and up) **Fic**

Lyons, M. E. Letters from a slave girl (6 and up) **Fic**

Mathis, S. B. Teacup full of roses (7 and up) **Fic**

McDonald, J. Spellbound (7 and up) **Fic**

McDonald, J. Twists and turns (7 and up) **Fic**

McDonald, J. Devil on my heels (7 and up) **Fic**

McKissack, P. C. Let my people go (4 and up) **221.9**

McKissack, P. C. A picture of Freedom (4 and up) **Fic**

McKissack, P. C. Run away home (5 and up) **Fic**

Meyer, C. Jubilee journey **Fic**

Meyer, C. White lilacs (5 and up) **Fic**

Moore, Y. Freedom songs **Fic**

African Americans—Fiction—*Continued*

Moses, S. P. The legend of Buddy Bush **Fic**

Myers, W. D. 145th Street **S C**

Myers, W. D. The Beast (7 and up) **Fic**

Myers, W. D. Hoops **Fic**

Myers, W. D. The journal of Biddy Owens, the Negro leagues **Fic**

Myers, W. D. The journal of Joshua Loper (5 and up) **Fic**

Myers, W. D. Monster (7 and up) **Fic**

Myers, W. D. The Mouse rap (6 and up) **Fic**

Myers, W. D. Scorpions (6 and up) **Fic**

Myers, W. D. Slam! (7 and up) **Fic**

Paterson, K. Jip (5 and up) **Fic**

Paulsen, G. Nightjohn **Fic**

Pinkney, A. D. Silent thunder **Fic**

Reeder, C. Across the lines (5 and up) **Fic**

Rinaldi, A. Hang a thousand trees with ribbons **Fic**

Rinaldi, A. Taking liberty **Fic**

Rinaldi, A. Wolf by the ears **Fic**

Robinet, H. G. Walking to the bus-rider blues (5 and up) **Fic**

Schwartz, V. F. Send one angel down **Fic**

Sitomer, A. L. The Hoopster (7 and up) **Fic**

Staples, S. F. Dangerous skies (7 and up) **Fic**

Taylor, M. D. The friendship (4 and up) **Fic**

Taylor, M. D. The gold Cadillac (4 and up) **Fic**

Taylor, M. D. The land (7 and up) **Fic**

Taylor, M. D. Let the circle be unbroken (4 and up) **Fic**

Taylor, M. D. Mississippi bridge (4 and up) **Fic**

Taylor, M. D. The road to Memphis (4 and up) **Fic**

Taylor, M. D. Roll of thunder, hear my cry **Fic**

Taylor, M. D. Song of the trees (4 and up) **Fic**

Taylor, M. D. The well (4 and up) **Fic**

Tolan, S. S. Flight of the raven (7 and up) **Fic**

Williams, L. A. When Kambia Elaine flew in from Neptune (7 and up) **Fic**

Williams-Garcia, R. Like sisters on the homefront (7 and up) **Fic**

Williams-Garcia, R. No laughter here (7 and up) **Fic**

Woodruff, E. Dear Austin **Fic**

Woods, B. The red rose box (5 and up) **Fic**

Woodson, J. Behind you (7 and up) **Fic**

Woodson, J. The house you pass on the way (7 and up) **Fic**

Woodson, J. Hush **Fic**

Woodson, J. I hadn't meant to tell you this **Fic**

Woodson, J. If you come softly (7 and up) **Fic**

Woodson, J. Miracle's boys **Fic**

Wyeth, S. D. A piece of heaven **Fic**

Folklore

Hamilton, V. The people could fly (5 and up) **398.2**

Lester, J. The last tales of Uncle Remus (4 and up) **398.2**

Talk that talk: an anthology of African-American storytelling **398.2**

History

African American breakthroughs **305.8**

The African-American experience on file **305.8**

Bair, B. Though justice sleeps (7 and up) **305.8**

Boyle, D. African Americans **305.8**

Byers, A. African-American history from emancipation to today (7 and up) **305.8**

Collier, C. Reconstruction and the rise of Jim Crow, 1864-1896 **973.8**

The Complete history of American slavery (7 and up) **326**

DeAngelis, G. The black cowboys **978**

Frankel, N. Break those chains at last: African Americans, 1860-1880 **305.8**

Golay, M. Reconstruction and reaction (7 and up) **305.8**

Grant, R. G. The African-American slave trade **326**

Grossman, J. R. A chance to make good (7 and up) **305.8**

Hansen, J. Breaking ground, breaking silence **974.7**

Hansen, J. Bury me not in a land of slaves (7 and up) **973.8**

Haskins, J. Out of the darkness (5 and up) **305.8**

Historic speeches of African Americans **815**

Hudson, W. Powerful words (5 and up) **808.8**

Isserman, M. Journey to freedom (7 and up) **305.8**

Katz, W. L. Black pioneers **920**

Littlefield, D. C. Revolutionary citizens (7 and up) **305.8**

McGowen, T. African-Americans in the Old West **978**

McKissack, P. C. Days of Jubilee (5 and up) **973.7**

Myers, W. D. Now is your time! (6 and up) **305.8**

Patrick, D. The New York Public Library amazing African American history (5 and up) **305.8**

Reef, C. Africans in America: the spread of people and culture **305.8**

Reef, C. This our dark country **966.62**

Schlissel, L. Black frontiers **978**

Spangenburg, R. The African-American experience (7 and up) **917.3**

Student almanac of African American history **305.8**

Thomas, V. M. Lest we forget (7 and up) **326**

Trotter, J. W. From a raw deal to a New Deal? African Americans, 1929-1945 (7 and up) **305.8**

White, D. G. Let my people go: African Americans, 1804-1860 (7 and up) **305.8**

African Americans—History—*Continued*
See/See also pages in the following book(s):
Clinton, C. The Black soldier (5 and up)
355

History—Chronology
Hornsby, A., Jr. Chronology of African American history (7 and up) 305.8
Intellectual life
Hill, L. C. Harlem stomp! (7 and up) 810.9
Music
See African American music
Pictorial works
Myers, W. D. One more river to cross (7 and up) 779
Poetry
Giovanni, N. Ego-tripping and other poems for young people (5 and up) 811
Grimes, N. A dime a dozen (5 and up) 811
Grimes, N. Hopscotch love (4 and up) 811
Hughes, L. The dream keeper and other poems (5 and up) 811
I, too, sing America (6 and up) 811.008
Johnson, A. The other side 811
Johnson, A. Running back to Ludie 811
Lewis, J. P. Freedom like sunlight (5 and up) 811
Myers, W. D. Harlem 811
Myers, W. D. Here in Harlem (7 and up) 811
Nelson, M. Fortune's bones 811
Quiet storm (7 and up) 811.008
Smith, H. A. The way a door closes (4 and up) 811
Weatherford, C. B. Remember the bridge 811
Woodson, J. Locomotion (4 and up) 811
Words with wings (4 and up) 811.008
Quotations
Stretch your wings (7 and up) 808.88
Religion
Murphy, L. African-American faith in America 200
Segregation
Rasmussen, R. K. Farewell to Jim Crow (7 and up) 305.8
Wormser, R. The rise and fall of Jim Crow (7 and up) 305.8
Social conditions
Downing, D. Africa 960
Social life and customs
Bial, R. The strength of these arms (4 and up) 326
Walter, M. P. Kwanzaa: a family affair (4 and up) 394.26
New York (N.Y.)
Bolden, T. Maritcha [biography of Maritcha Rémond Lyons] (4 and up) 92
African Americans in art
Lawrence, J. The great migration 759.13
Words with wings (4 and up) 811.008
African Americans in literature
The Coretta Scott King Awards book, 1970-1999 028.5
Stephens, C. G. Coretta Scott King Award books 028.5

African-Americans in the Old West. McGowen, T. 978
African art
Bingham, J. African art & culture 709.6
Finley, C. The art of African masks (5 and up) 391
African art. Rea, W. R.
In International encyclopedia of art 703
African art & culture. Bingham, J. 709.6
African beginnings. Haskins, J. 960
African biography 920.003
The **African** cats. Saign, G. 599.75
African civilizations [series]
Conrad, D. C. The Songhay Empire 966.2
Green, R. L. The empire of Ghana 966.1
Haynes, J. Egyptian dynasties 932
Russmann, E. R. Nubian kingdoms 939
Wilson, T. H. City states of the Swahili coast 967.6
African folktales 398.2
African history on file 960
African mythology
Lynch, P. A. African mythology A to Z 299.6
African mythology A to Z. Lynch, P. A. 299.6
African poetry
Collections
The Penguin book of modern African poetry 896
Talking drums (5 and up) 896
African princess. Hansen, J. 920
An **African** story. Dahl, R.
In Dahl, R. Skin and other stories S C
African tales, uh-huh, Ashley Bryan's. Bryan, A. 398.2
Africans
Fiction
Naidoo, B. The other side of truth (5 and up) Fic
Africans in America: the spread of people and culture. Reef, C. 305.8
After. Prose, F. Fic
After Celilo. Edmo, E.
In Talking leaves; contemporary native American short stories S C
After Elaine. Dreyer, A. L. Fic
After the death of Anna Gonzales. Fields, T. 811
After the first death. Cormier, R. Fic
After the Holocaust. Greenfeld, H. 940.53
After the last dog died. Bredeson, C. 92
After the rain. Mazer, N. F. Fic
After the shooting stops. Gay, K. 355
After the war. Matas, C. Fic
The **afterlife**. Soto, G. Fic
Against all opposition. Haskins, J. 920
Age *See* Old age
Age and employment
See also Teenagers—Employment

The **age** of chivalry. Bulfinch, T.
In Bulfinch, T. Bulfinch's mythology   **201**

The **age** of discovery. Martell, H. M.   **909.08**

The **age** of fable. Bulfinch, T.
In Bulfinch, T. Bulfinch's mythology   **201**

The **Age** of revolution (1750-1914)
In World history on file   **909**

The **age** of synthesis: 1800-1895. Spangenburg, R.
  509

Agee, Jon
Sit on a potato pan, Otis!   **793.73**
Who ordered the jumbo shrimp? and other oxymorons   **793.73**

Agenbroad, Larry D.
Mammoths   **569**

Aglebemu. Bruchac, J.
In Bruchac, J. and Bruchac, J. When the Chenoo howls; native American tales of terror   **398.2**

Agnes Parker . . . girl in progress. O'Dell, K.
  Fic

Agnesi, Maria Gaetana, 1718-1799
See/See also pages in the following book(s):
Celebrating women in mathematics and science
  920

The **agony** and the eggplant. Hogan, W.
  813.009

Agricultural laborers
Ancona, G. Harvest (4 and up)   **331.5**
Atkin, S. B. Voices from the fields (5 and up)
  331.5

Fiction
Ryan, P. M. Esperanza rising (5 and up)
  Fic

Agriculture
Bial, R. Portrait of a farm family (4 and up)
  630.1
Bowden, R. Food and farming   **363.8**
Halley, N. Farm (4 and up)   **630.1**
Kidd, J. S. Shades of green (7 and up)
  363.7
Marshall, E. L. High-tech harvest (7 and up)
  641.3

Government policy
See/See also pages in the following book(s):
Global resources: opposing viewpoints
  333.71

Aguinaldo. Delacre, L.
In Delacre, L. Salsa stories p62-70   **S C**

Aguirre, Hank, 1932-1994
About
Copley, B. The tall Mexican: the life of Hank Aguirre, all-star pitcher, businessman, humanitarian (7 and up)   **92**

Ahvel. Whittington, M. K.
In Vampires: a collection of original stories p121-33   **S C**

AI (Artificial intelligence) *See* Artificial intelligence

AIDS (Disease)
Check, W. A. AIDS   **616.97**
McPhee, A. T. AIDS (5 and up)   **616.97**
Shein, L. AIDS (7 and up)   **616.97**
Winick, J. Pedro and me (7 and up)   **362.1**

See/See also pages in the following book(s):
Epidemics: opposing viewpoints   **614.4**
Fiction
Kerr, M. E. Night kites (7 and up)   **Fic**
Stratton, A. Chanda's secrets (7 and up)   **Fic**

Aiken, Joan, 1924-2004
Cousin Alice
In Visions: nineteen short stories by outstanding writers for young adults p152-69
  S C
The gift-giving
In Sixteen; short stories by outstanding writers for young adults p134-46   **S C**
Lungewater
In Gothic!; ten original dark tales   **S C**
The monkey's wedding
In Night terrors; stories of shadow and substance   **S C**
Shadows and moonshine (4 and up)   **S C**
Contents: Gift pig; Rocking donkey; Cooks and prophecies; Lilac in the lake; Harp of fishbones; Small pinch of weather; King who stood all night; Cat's cradle; Moonshine in the mustard pot; Wolves and the mermaids; John Sculpin and the witches; Night the stars were gone; Boy with a wolf's foot
The wolves of Willoughby Chase (5 and up)
  Fic

Ailey, Alvin
About
Cruz, B. Alvin Ailey   **92**

Aimee. Miller, M. B.   **Fic**

Ain't gonna study war no more. Meltzer, M.
  303.6

Air
Gardner, R. Science project ideas about air
  533
Meiani, A. Air (4 and up)   **533**
See/See also pages in the following book(s):
Knapp, B. J. Materials science   **620.1**

Air pilots
See also African American pilots; Women air pilots
Giblin, J. Charles A. Lindbergh   **92**
Koopmans, A. Charles Lindbergh   **92**
Maurer, R. The Wright sister [biography of Katharine Wright Haskell] (5 and up)   **92**
Fiction
Lawrence, I. B for Buster (7 and up)   **Fic**

Air pollution
Kidd, J. S. Into thin air (7 and up)   **363.7**

Air raid. McGowen, T.   **940.54**

Airborn. Oppel, K.   **Fic**

Airborne: a photobiography of Wilbur and Orville Wright. Collins, M.   **92**

Aircraft accidents
Cole, M. D. TWA flight 800   **363.1**
Fiction
Cooney, C. B. Flight #116 is down   **Fic**

Aircraft carriers
McGowen, T. Carrier war   **940.54**

Airplanes
Graham, I. Flight   **629.13**
Accidents
See Aircraft accidents

Airships
O'Brien, P. The Hindenburg (4 and up)
    629.133
Fiction
Oppel, K. Airborn (7 and up)   **Fic**

Aiyangar, Srinivasa Ramanujan *See* Ramanujan
 Aiyangar, Srinivasa, 1887-1920

Ajeemah and his son. Berry, J.   **Fic**

Ake, Anne, 1943-
Hungary (7 and up)   943.9

Akers, Michelle, 1966-
See/See also pages in the following book(s):
Kaminsky, M. Uncommon champions **920**

Al Adely, Laith Muhmood
(jt. auth) Hassig, S. M. Iraq   956.7

Al Capone and the roaring twenties. King, D. C.
    92

Al Capone does my shirts. Choldenko, G. **Fic**

Al Qaeda (Organization)
Margulies, P. Al Qaeda: Osama bin Laden's
 army of terrorists   973.931
See/See also pages in the following book(s):
Currie, S. Terrorists and terrorist groups (7 and
 up)   303.6

Al-Windawi, Thura
Thura's diary (7 and up)   956.7

Alabama
Davis, L. Alabama
 In America the beautiful, second series
    973
Shirley, D. Alabama
 In Celebrate the states   973
Fiction
English, K. Francie (5 and up)   **Fic**
Johnson, A. Bird (5 and up)   **Fic**
Lyon, G. E. Sonny's house of spies **Fic**
McKissack, P. C. Run away home (5 and up)
    Fic

Alabiso, Vincent
(ed) Flash!: the Associated Press covers the
 world. See Flash!: the Associated Press covers the world   070.4

Alagna, Magdalena
Mae Jemison (4 and up)   **92**

Alamo (San Antonio, Tex.)
Levy, J. The Alamo   976.4
McNeese, T. The Alamo   976.4
Murphy, J. Inside the Alamo (5 and up)
    976.4

Alaska
Stefoff, R. Alaska
 In Celebrate the states   973
Walsh Shepherd, D. Alaska
 In America the beautiful, second series
    973
Webb, S. Looking for seabirds   598
Fiction
George, J. C. Water sky (5 and up) **Fic**
Hill, K. Minuk (5 and up)   **Fic**
Hobbs, W. Leaving Protection (7 and up)
    Fic
Hobbs, W. Wild Man Island   **Fic**
Lion, M. Upstream (7 and up)   **Fic**

London, J. The call of the wild (5 and up)
    Fic
London, J. White Fang (5 and up) **Fic**
Mikaelsen, B. Touching Spirit Bear **Fic**
Orenstein, D. G. Unseen companion (7 and up)
    Fic
Vanasse, D. Out of the wilderness **Fic**

Albert Einstein [essays about]   **92**

Albert Einstein and the frontiers of physics. Bernstein, J.   **92**

Alberta
Laws, G. D. Alberta
 In Exploring Canada   971

Albinos and albinism
Landau, E. Living with albinism 616.5

Albright, Madeleine Korbel, 1937-
About
Hasday, J. L. Madeleine Albright **92**
Howard, M. Madeleine Albright **92**
See/See also pages in the following book(s):
Jones, V. B. Government & politics **920**

Albyn, Carole Lisa, 1955-
The multicultural cookbook for students
    641.5

Alcatraz Island (Calif.)
Fiction
Bunting, E. Someone is hiding on Alcatraz Island   **Fic**
Choldenko, G. Al Capone does my shirts (5 and
 up)   **Fic**

The **alchemist's** cat. Jarvis, R.   **Fic**

Alchemy
Fiction
Mahy, M. Alchemy (7 and up)   **Fic**

Alcohol 101. Hyde, M. O.   362.292

Alcohol and teenagers *See* Teenagers—Alcohol
use

Alcoholism
Addiction: opposing viewpoints 362.29
Alcoholism (7 and up)   362.292
Banfield, S. Inside recovery   616.86
Chemical dependency: opposing viewpoints (7
 and up)   362.29
Gottfried, T. The facts about alcohol
    362.292
Hyde, M. O. Alcohol 101 (7 and up)
    362.292
Sheen, B. Teen alcoholism (7 and up)
    616.86
Teen alcoholism (7 and up)   362.292
See/See also pages in the following book(s):
Blue, R. Staying out of trouble in a troubled
 family (7 and up)   362.7
Fiction
Brooks, K. Martyn Pig (7 and up) **Fic**
Bruchac, J. The heart of a chief **Fic**
Conly, J. L. Crazy lady! (5 and up) **Fic**
Murray, J. Bottled up (7 and up) **Fic**

Alcoholism (7 and up)   362.292

Alcorn, Stephen, 1958-
(il) Gottfried, T. Children of the slaughter
    940.53
(il) Gottfried, T. Deniers of the Holocaust
    940.53

Alcorn, Stephen, 1958-—*Continued*
(il) Gottfried, T. Heroes of the Holocaust
      940.53
(il) I, too, sing America. See I, too, sing America **811.008**
(il) My America. See My America **811.008**

Alcott, Louisa May, 1832-1888
Nelly's hospital
In The Boy of Chancellorville and other Civil
 War stories p55-73   **S C**
About
Meigs, C. L. Invincible Louisa [May Alcott]
         92
Ruth, A. Louisa May Alcott **92**
See/See also pages in the following book(s):
Ellis, S. From reader to writer **372.6**

Alder, Elizabeth
Crossing the panther's path **Fic**
The king's shadow (7 and up) **Fic**

Alderton, David
Wild cats of the world (7 and up) **599.75**

Alex Ryan, stop that!. Mills, C. **Fic**

Alexander, the Great, 356-323 B.C.
See/See also pages in the following book(s):
Meltzer, M. Ten kings (5 and up) **920**
Stefoff, R. The ancient Mediterranean (5 and
 up)   **938**

Alexander, Lloyd
The Arkadians (5 and up) **Fic**
The book of three (5 and up) **Fic**
Coll and his white pig
 In Alexander, L. The foundling and other
  tales of Prydain p75-83 **S C**
The foundling and other tales of Prydain (5 and
 up)   **S C**
 Contents: The foundling; The stone; The true enchanter; The
rascal crow; The sword; The smith, the weaver, and the harper;
Coll and his white pig; The truthful harp
Gypsy Rizka (5 and up) **Fic**
The high king (5 and up) **Fic**
The Illyrian adventure (5 and up) **Fic**
The iron ring (5 and up) **Fic**
Max Mondrosch
 In Firebirds: an anthology of original fantasy
  and science fiction; an anthology of orig-
  inal fantasy and science fiction **S C**
The rascal crow
 In Alexander, L. The foundling and other
  tales of Prydain p41-50 **S C**
The remarkable journey of Prince Jen (5 and
 up)   **Fic**
The truthful harp
 In Alexander, L. The foundling and other
  tales of Prydain p87-94 **S C**
Westmark (5 and up) **Fic**

Alexander, Sally Hobart
Do you remember the color blue? (4 and up)
        362.4

Alexandria (Egypt)
Nardo, D. Ancient Alexandria (7 and up)
        932

Alexandria (Egypt). Library *See* Alexandrian Library (Egypt)

Alexandrian Library (Egypt)
Trumble, K. The Library of Alexandria (5 and
 up)   **027**

Alger, Neil
(ed) The Palestinians and the disputed territories. See The Palestinians and the disputed
 territories   **956.04**

Algeria
Kagda, F. Algeria (5 and up) **965**

Algonquian Indians
 See also Delaware Indians
Fiction
Dorris, M. Guests **Fic**

Ali, Muhammad, 1942-
About
Freedman, S. Clay v. United States (7 and up)
        343
Myers, W. D. The greatest: Muhammad Ali (7
 and up)   **92**
Tessitore, J. Muhammed Ali (7 and up) **92**

Ali Anugne O Chash (The boy who was). Dunn,
C.
 In The Green Man: tales from the mythic for-
  est p299-309   **808.8**

Alia waking. McCaffrey, L. W. **Fic**

Alice-by-accident. Banks, L. R. **Fic**

Alice, I think. Juby, S. **Fic**

Alida's song. Paulsen, G. **Fic**

Alien abductions: opposing viewpoints. Netzley, P.
D.   **001.9**

The **alien** mind. Dick, P. K.
 In New skies: an anthology of today's science
  fiction   **S C**

Alien secrets. Klause, A. C. **Fic**

Aliens
 See also Immigrants
United States
 See also United States—Immigration and
emigration
Aliens ate my homework. Coville, B. **Fic**

Aliens from outer space *See* Extraterrestrial beings

Aliki
William Shakespeare & the Globe (4 and up)
        792.09

Aliquipiso. Mayer, M.
 In Mayer, M. Women warriors; myths and
  legends of heroic women p71-74 **398**

Alison Dare: Little Miss Adventures. Torres, J.
        741.5

Alison, who went away. Vande Velde, V. **Fic**

All about heroin. Sonder, B. **362.29**

All about hockey. Sullivan, G. **796.962**

All alone in the universe. Perkins, L. R. **Fic**

All-American girl. Cabot, M. **Fic**

The **all-American** slurp. Namioka, L.
 In Visions: nineteen short stories by outstanding writers for young adults p32-41
        S C

All Hallows' Eve *See* Halloween

All shook up: the life and death of Elvis Presley. Denenberg, B. **92**

All that remains. Brooks, B. **Fic**

All that remains [novella] Brooks, B.
In Brooks, B. All that remains p3-61 **Fic**

All the birds of North America. Griggs, J. L. **598**

All the old haunts. Lynch, C. **S C**

All the stars in the sky. McDonald, M. **Fic**

All the way home. Giff, P. R. **Fic**

Allaby, Michael, 1933-
Biomes of the world (5 and up) **577**
Deserts (7 and up) **577.5**
Droughts (7 and up) **551.57**
Floods (7 and up) **551.48**
Makers of science **920.003**
Temperate forests (7 and up) **577.3**
(jt. auth) Bailey, J. Plants and plant life **580**

Allan, Tony, 1946-
The Rhine (4 and up) **943**
Understanding DNA **576.5**

Allegories
Adams, R. Watership Down (6 and up) **Fic**
Golding, W. Lord of the Flies **Fic**

Allen, Ethan, 1738-1789
Fiction
Gauthier, G. The hero of Ticonderoga **Fic**

Allen, Gracie, 1906?-1964
See/See also pages in the following book(s):
Stewart, G. Great women comedians **920**

Allen, Jean, 1964-
Tornadoes **551.55**

Allen, John Logan, 1941-
(ed) Explorers. See Explorers **920.003**

Allen, Michael Geoffrey
Calvin Coolidge (7 and up) **92**

Allen, Paula Gunn
Deer Woman
In Talking leaves; contemporary native American short stories **S C**

Allen, Thomas B., 1929-
George Washington, spymaster **92**
Remember Pearl Harbor (5 and up) **940.54**

Allende, Isabel
City of the beasts (7 and up) **Fic**

Allergy
Latta, S. L. Allergies (7 and up) **616.97**
Out of control **612.8**
Parker, S. Allergies (5 and up) **616.97**

Alles, Gregory D.
(ed) The Encyclopedia of world religions. See The Encyclopedia of world religions **200.3**

The **alley**. Romero, D.
In Join in; multiethnic short stories by outstanding writers for young adults p223-38 **S C**

Alligators
Simon, S. Crocodiles & alligators (4 and up) **597.9**

The **alligators**. Updike, J.
In Who do you think you are?; stories of friends and enemies p64-72 **S C**

Allison, Stephen, 1969-
(ed) Scientists: their lives and works. See Scientists: their lives and works **920.003**

Allusions
Brewer's dictionary of phrase and fable **803**

Almanac of famous people **920.003**

Almanacs
Bigelow, B. C. American Revolution: almanac (5 and up) **973.3**
Encyclopaedia Britannica almanac **031.02**
Hillstrom, K. American Civil War: almanac **973.7**
Information please almanac, atlas & yearbook **031.02**
The New York Times almanac **031.02**
Saari, P. Colonial America: almanac **973.2**
Women's almanac **305.4**
The World almanac and book of facts **031.02**
The World almanac for kids **031.02**

Almond, David, 1951-
Counting stars (7 and up) **Fic**
The fire-eaters **Fic**
Kit's wilderness (5 and up) **Fic**
Skellig (5 and up) **Fic**

Almost home. Baskin, N. R. **Fic**

Aloha summer. Wallace, B. **Fic**

Alone. De Lint, C.
In De Lint, C. Waifs and strays p233-49 **S C**

Alone in the world. Reef, C. **362.7**

Alonso, Karen
The Chicago Seven political protest trial **345**
Korematsu v. United States (7 and up) **323.1**
Loving v. Virginia (7 and up) **346**
Schenck v. United States (7 and up) **342**

Alt ed. Atkins, C. **Fic**

Alter, Judy
Extraordinary explorers and adventurers **920**
Extraordinary women of the American West **920**
The Santa Fe Trail **978**

Alternative. Saldaña, R.
In Saldaña, R. Finding our way: stories p49-59 **S C**

Alternative American religions. Stein, S. J. **209**

Alternative medicine
Billitteri, T. J. Alternative medicine (7 and up) **615.5**
Kowalski, K. M. Alternative medicine (7 and up) **615.5**
Rattenbury, J. Understanding alternative medicine (7 and up) **615.5**

Altman, Linda Jacobs, 1943-
Arkansas
In Celebrate the states **973**
California
In Celebrate the states **973**
The creation of Israel (7 and up) **956.94**
Crimes and criminals of the Holocaust **940.53**

Altman, Linda Jacobs, 1943-—*Continued*
Death: an introduction to medical-ethical dilem-
mas **155.9**
Forever outsiders **909**
The forgotten victims of the Holocaust
940.53
Hitler's rise to power and the Holocaust
943.086
Human rights (7 and up) **323**
Impact of the Holocaust **940.53**
The Jewish victims of the Holocaust **940.53**
Plague and pestilence **614.4**
The politics of slavery (7 and up) **326**
Slavery and abolition in American history
973.7

Altman, Susan
Encyclopedia of African-American heritage
305.8
Extraordinary African-Americans (5 and up)
920

Altmann, Anna E.
(jt. auth) De Vos, G. New tales for old
398.2

Alton, Steve
The Malifex **Fic**

Aluminum
Farndon, J. Aluminum
In The Elements **546**

Alvarez, Julia, 1950-
Before we were free (7 and up) **Fic**
Daughter of invention
In Growing up Latino; memoirs and stories
p3-15 **810.8**
Finding miracles **Fic**
How Tia Lola came to visit/stay (4 and up)
Fic

See/See also pages in the following book(s):
Hill, C. M. Ten Hispanic American authors
920

Alvarez, Luis W., 1911-1988
See/See also pages in the following book(s):
Oleksy, W. G. Hispanic-American scientists (7
and up) **920**

Alvarez Bravo, Lola, 1907-1993
See/See also pages in the following book(s):
Sills, L. In real life: six women photographers
(7 and up) **920**

Alvarez de Cabral, Pedro *See* Cabral, Pedro
Alvares, 1460?-1526?

Always inventing: a photobiography of Alexander
Graham Bell. Matthews, T. L. **92**

Alzheimer's disease
Harmon, D. Life out of focus (7 and up)
616.8
Willett, E. Alzheimer's disease (7 and up)
616.8
See/See also pages in the following book(s):
Hyde, M. O. When the brain dies first (7 and
up) **616.8**
Fiction
Park, B. The graduation of Jake Moon **Fic**
Swallow, P. C. It only looks easy **Fic**
Williams, C. L. If I forget, you remember
Fic

Am I blue? Coville, B.
In Coville, B. Odder than ever **S C**
Amanda and the wounded birds. Rodowsky, C. F.
In Visions: nineteen short stories by outstand-
ing writers for young adults p78-86
S C
Amandine. Griffin, A. **Fic**
Amankamek. Bruchac, J.
In Bruchac, J. and Bruchac, J. When the
Chenoo howls; native American tales of
terror **398.2**
Amari, Suad
Cooking the Lebanese way
In Easy menu ethnic cookbooks **641.5**
Amaryllis. Crist-Evans, C. **Fic**
Amazing amphibians. Miller, S. S. **597.8**
Amazing brain [series]
Brynie, F. H. Perception **612.8**
Brynie, F. H. The physical brain **612.8**
Goldsmith, C. Neurological disorders **616.8**
Papa, S. Addiction **616.86**
The **amazing** Maurice and his educated rodents.
Pratchett, T. **Fic**
The **amazing** thinking machine. Haseley, D.
Fic
The **amazing** two-headed boy. Wallace, R.
In Wallace, R. Losing is not an option: stories
S C
The **Amazon.** Barter, J. **981**
Amazon.com Inc.
Garty, J. Jeff Bezos **92**
Amazon River
Barter, J. The Amazon **981**
Castner, J. L. River life **577.6**
Amazon River valley
Barter, J. The Amazon **981**
Castner, J. L. Layers of life **577.3**
Castner, J. L. Partners and rivals **577.3**
Castner, J. L. Surviving in the rain forest
577.3
Montgomery, S. Encantado (4 and up) **599.5**
Fiction
Ibbotson, E. Journey to the river sea (5 and up)
Fic
The **amber** spyglass. Pullman, P. **Fic**
Ambrose, Stephen E.
The good fight (5 and up) **940.53**
Ambrus, Victor G., 1935-
(il) McCarty, N. The Iliad **883**
Ambush. O'Brien, T.
In Who do you think you are?; stories of
friends and enemies p152-55 **S C**
Amelia Rules!. Gownley, J. **741.5**
Amelia to Zora. Chin-Lee, C. **920**
Amelia's war. Rinaldi, A. **Fic**
Amerasians
Fiction
Garland, S. Song of the buffalo boy **Fic**
Ameri, Anan
(ed) Arab American encyclopedia. See Arab
American encyclopedia **305.8**

America
   See also North America
Antiquities
Lauber, P. Who came first (5 and up)
                        970.01
Wood, M. Ancient America (5 and up)
                        970.01
Exploration
Edwards, J. Henry Hudson and his voyages of exploration in world history (7 and up)
                        92
Faber, H. Samuel de Champlain (5 and up)
                        92
Gaines, A. Hernando de Soto and the Spanish search for gold in world history (7 and up)
                        92
Haskins, J. Against all opposition (5 and up)
                        920
Meltzer, M. Columbus and the world around him   92
Meltzer, M. Francisco Pizarro (5 and up) 92
Otfinoski, S. Juan Ponce de Leon (5 and up)
                        92
Otfinoski, S. Vasco Nuñez de Balboa (5 and up)
                        92
Sonneborn, L. Samuel de Champlain   92
Exploration—Fiction
Dorris, M. Guests   Fic
Dorris, M. Morning Girl (4 and up)   Fic
America as story. Coffey, R. K.   016.813
America at war [series]
  Bosco, P. I. World War I   940.3
  Golay, M. Civil War   973.7
  Greenblatt, M. War of 1812   973.5
  Isserman, M. World War II   940.53
  Marker, S. Plains Indian wars   973.5
  Marquette, S. America under attack 973.931
  Marquette, S. War of 1812   973.5
America in historical fiction. VanMeter, V.
                      016.813
America in the 20th century   973.9
America in the 1950s. Lindop, E. 973.921
America in the 1960s. Kronenwetter, M.
                      973.92
America in the Korean War. Dolan, E. F.
                      951.9
America the beautiful, second series (5 and up)
                      973
America under attack. Marquette, S. 973.931
America under attack. Stewart, G. 973.931
America under attack: primary sources (7 and up)
                      973.931
American art
  Celebrate America in poetry and art (5 and up)
                      811.008
  Danneberg, J. Women artists of the West
                      920
  Heart to heart (5 and up)   811.008
American artists *See* Artists—United States
American Association of School Librarians
  Information power   027.8
  The Information-powered school. See The Information-powered school   027.8
American astronomers. Camp, C. A. 920

American authors, 1600-1900   920.003
American Bird Conservancy
  Griggs, J. L. All the birds of North America
                      598
The American book of days   394.26
An American chronology. Bornstein, J. 973
American civil rights: primary sources 323.1
The American Civil War. Dolan, E. F. 973.7
American Civil War: almanac. Hillstrom, K.
                      973.7
American Civil War: primary sources. Hillstrom, K.   973.7
American colonies *See* United States—History—1600-1775, Colonial period
American Colonization Society
  Reef, C. This our dark country   966.62
American composers *See* Composers—United States
American computer pioneers. Northrup, M.
                      920
American cooking *See* Cooking
American disasters [series]
  Cole, M. D. TWA flight 800   363.1
  Gow, M. Attack on America   973.931
  Houle, M. M. Triangle Shirtwaist Factory fire
                      974.7
  Sherrow, V. The Exxon Valdez   363.7
  Sherrow, V. Hurricane Andrew 551.55
  Sherrow, V. The Oklahoma City bombing
                      364.1
American dragons: twenty-five Asian American voices   810.8
American drama
Collections
  You're on!: seven plays in English and Spanish (4 and up)   812.008
The American ethnic cookbook for students. Zanger, M. H.   641.5
American eyes   S C
American family albums [series]
  Hoobler, D. The African American family album   305.8
  Hoobler, D. The Chinese American family album   305.8
  Hoobler, D. The Cuban American family album   305.8
  Hoobler, D. The German American family album   305.8
  Hoobler, D. The Irish American family album   305.8
  Hoobler, D. The Italian American family album   305.8
  Hoobler, D. The Japanese American family album   305.8
  Hoobler, D. The Mexican American family album   305.8
American fiction
Bibliography
  Dickinson, A. T. American historical fiction
                      016.813
  VanMeter, V. America in historical fiction
                      016.813

American folk art
Panchyk, R. American folk art for kids   **745**

American folk art for kids. Panchyk, R.   **745**

The **American** frontier (7 and up)   **978**

American government at work (7 and up)   **320.4**

American Heritage book of great American speeches for young people (7 and up)   **815**

The **American** Heritage children's science dictionary   **503**

The **American** Heritage encyclopedia of American history   **973.03**

The **American** Heritage science dictionary   **503**

The **American** Heritage student dictionary   **423**

The **American** Heritage student science dictionary   **503**

American historic places [series]
Spangenburg, R. The African-American experience   **917.3**
Spangenburg, R. Literature and the arts   **917.3**
Spangenburg, R. Political and social movements   **917.3**

American historical fiction. Dickinson, A. T.   **016.813**

American history. Ortiz Cofer, J.
In Who do you think you are?; stories of friends and enemies p36-46   **S C**

American history on file   **973**

American history series
Asian Americans: opposing viewpoints   **305.8**
The Industrial revolution: opposing viewpoints   **330.973**
Native Americans: opposing viewpoints   **970.004**

American immigration. Daniels, R.   **325.73**

American Indian Movement
See/See also pages in the following book(s):
Brave Bird, M. Lakota woman   **92**

American Indian myths and legends   **398.2**

The **American** Indian wars. Dolan, E. F.   **970.004**

American Indians *See* Native Americans

American Islam. Wormser, R.   **297**

American jazz musicians. Mour, S. I.   **920**

American Kennel Club
The complete dog book   **636.7**

The **American** kitchen, 1700 to the present. Plante, E. M.   **643**

American landmarks [series]
Nash, G. B. Landmarks of the American Revolution   **973.3**

American Library Association
Anglo-American cataloguing rules. See Anglo-American cataloguing rules   **025.3**

American Library Association. Coretta Scott King Award Task Force
The Coretta Scott King Awards book, 1970-1999. See The Coretta Scott King Awards book, 1970-1999   **028.5**

American literature
See also various forms of American literature, e.g. American poetry
   African American authors
The Coretta Scott King Awards book, 1970-1999   **028.5**
Hudson, W. Powerful words (5 and up)   **808.8**
Stephens, C. G. Coretta Scott King Award books   **028.5**
   Asian American authors—Collections
American dragons: twenty-five Asian American voices   **810.8**
   Bio-bibliography
American authors, 1600-1900   **920.003**
   Black authors
See American literature—African American authors
   Collections
33 things every girl should know (7 and up)   **810.8**
911: the book of help   **810.8**
Girls got game (5 and up)   **810.8**
The Great North American prairie   **810.8**
Guys write for Guys Read   **810.8**
Halloween howls   **810.8**
   Hispanic American authors—Bibliography
York, S. Children's and young adult literature by Latino writers   **028.5**
   Hispanic American authors—Collections
Growing up Latino   **810.8**
Here is my kingdom   **810.8**
   Native American authors
Gleason, K. Native American literature   **897**
   Native American authors Collections
Night is gone, day is still coming (7 and up)   **808.8**

American Loyalists
   Fiction
O'Dell, S. Sarah Bishop (6 and up)   **Fic**

American men & women of science   **920.003**

American mosaic: African American contributions
Asirvatham, S. The history of jazz   **781.65**
Asirvatham, S. The history of the blues   **781.643**

American Museum of Natural History
Murdoch, D. H. North American Indian   **970.004**

American orations *See* American speeches

American patriots. Buckley, G. L.   **355**

An **American** plague. Murphy, J.   **614.5**

American poetry
   African American authors
Strickland, M. R. African-American poets   **920**
   African American authors—Collections
I am the darker brother   **811.008**
I, too, sing America (6 and up)   **811.008**
My black me (5 and up)   **811.008**
Poetry from the masters: the pioneers (7 and up)   **811.008**
Quiet storm (7 and up)   **811.008**
Shimmy shimmy shimmy like my sister Kate   **811.008**

American poetry—African American authors—
Collections—*Continued*
 Soul looks back in wonder (4 and up)
 811.008
 Words with wings (4 and up) 811.008
  Collections
 The Blackbirch treasury of American poetry (5
  and up) 811.008
 Book poems 811.008
 Celebrate America in poetry and art (5 and up)
 811.008
 Committed to memory 821.008
 Heart to heart (5 and up) 811.008
 The Invisible ladder (7 and up) 811.008
 Is this forever, or what? (7 and up) 811.008
 A Jar of tiny stars: poems by NCTE award-
  winning poets 811.008
 The Kingfisher book of funny poems (4 and up)
 821.008
 Lives: poems about famous Americans (4 and
  up) 811.008
 Marvelous math (4 and up) 811.008
 More spice than sugar (4 and up) 811.008
 My America (4 and up) 811.008
 The New Oxford book of American verse (7
  and up) 811.008
 The Oxford book of children's verse in America
 811.008
 The Oxford book of story poems 821.008
 The Oxford treasury of time poems 821.008
 The Pain tree, and other teenage angst-ridden
  poetry (7 and up) 811.008
 Paint me like I am (7 and up) 811.008
 The Place my words are looking for (4 and up)
 811.008
 Poetry from A to Z (5 and up) 808.1
 A Poke in the I (4 and up) 811.008
 The Random House book of poetry for children
 821.008
 Roots & flowers (7 and up) 811.008
 Salting the ocean (4 and up) 811.008
 Seeing the blue between (7 and up) 808.1
 Three centuries of American poetry, 1623-1923
 811.008
 Very best (almost) friends (4 and up)
 811.008
 When the rain sings 811.008
 Whisper and shout (4 and up) 811.008
  Hispanic American authors—Collections
 Cool salsa (5 and up) 811.008
 Red hot salsa (7 and up) 811.008
  Women authors—Collections
 A Poem of her own 811.008
American presidents. Nelson, L. E. 920.003
American presidents in world history 920.003
American profiles [series]
 Aaseng, N. Black inventors 920
 Dubovoy, S. Civil rights leaders 920
 Oleksy, W. G. Hispanic-American scientists
 920
 Yount, L. Asian-American scientists 920
American religious experience [series]
 Williams, J. K. The Amish 289.7
 Williams, J. K. The Christian Scientists
 289.5
 Williams, J. K. The Quakers 289.6

 Williams, J. K. The Shakers 289
The **American** Revolution. Bohannon, L. F.
 973.3
The **American** Revolution. Morton, J. C.
 973.3
The **American** Revolution. Ross, S. 973.3
The **American** Revolution, 1763-1783. Collier, C.
 973.3
American Revolution: almanac. Bigelow, B. C.
 973.3
American Revolution: battles and leaders
 973.3
American Revolution: biographies. Schmittroth, L.
 920
American Revolution: primary sources (5 and up)
 973.3
The **American** revolutionaries: a history in their
 own words, 1750-1800 (6 and up) 973.3
The **American** scene: events 973
The **American** scene: lives 920.003
American Sign Language. Sternberg, M. L. A.
 419
American sign language dictionary, Random
 House. Costello, E. 419
American slavery (7 and up) 326
American social movements [series]
 Animal rights movement 179
American songs
  See also Spirituals (Songs)
American speeches
 American Heritage book of great American
  speeches for young people (7 and up)
 815
 The Founding of America 973.3
 Historic speeches of African Americans 815
 My fellow Americans (7 and up) 352.23
American voices from— [series]
 Beller, S. P. The Civil War 973.7
 Beller, S. P. The Revolutionary War 973.3
 Ruggiero, A. American voices from The Great
  Depression
 Ruggiero, A. World War I 940.3
 Ruggiero, A. World War II 940.53
 Schomp, V. American voices from the Vietnam
  era 973.923
 Sirimarco, E. American voices from the civil
  rights movement 323.1
 Sirimarco, E. American voices from The Cold
  War 909.82
 Stefoff, R. American voices from the new re-
  public, 1783-1830 973.4
 Stefoff, R. Colonial life 973.2
 Stefoff, R. The opening of the West 978
American voices from the civil rights movement.
 Sirimarco, E. 323.1
American voices from The Cold War. Sirimarco,
 E. 909.82
American voices from The Great Depression.
 Ruggiero, A.
American voices from the new republic, 1783-
 1830. Stefoff, R. 973.4

American voices from the Vietnam era. Schomp, V. **973.923**

American war library, American Revolution [series]
Nardo, D. Weapons of war **973.3**
Stewart, G. Life of a soldier in Washington's army **973.3**

American war library, Cold War [series]
Blohm, C. E. An uneasy peace, 1945-1980 **940.55**
Blohm, C. E. Weapons of peace **327.1**
Campbell, G. A. The home front **973.92**
Kallen, S. A. Primary sources **909.82**
Keeley, J. Espionage **327.12**
Uschan, M. V. Political leaders **920**

American war library, Persian Gulf War [series]
Campbell, G. A. Life of an American soldier **956.7**

American war library, Vietnam War [series]
Roberts, R. Leaders and generals **920**
Yancey, D. Life of an American soldier **959.704**

American war series
Carey, C. W. The Mexican War **973.6**
Somerlott, R. The Spanish-American War **973.8**
Stein, R. C. World War II in Europe **940.54**
Stein, R. C. World War II in the Pacific **940.54**
Warrick, K. C. The War of 1812 **973.5**

The **American** West: an illustrated history. Sonneborn, L. **978**

American women of achievement [series]
Richmond, M. A. Phillis Wheatley **92**
Weisberg, B. Susan B. Anthony **92**

American women scientists. Reynolds, M. D. **920**

American women's history. Matthews, G. **305.4**

Americanisms
Bartlett's Roget's thesaurus **423**
Dictionary of American slang **427**
Young, S. The new comprehensive American rhyming dictionary **423**

America's decades **973.9**

America's forests. Staub, F. J. **577.3**

America's freedoms [series]
Spitzer, R. J. The right to bear arms **344**

America's great disasters. Sandler, M. W. **973**

America's prisons: opposing viewpoints (7 and up) **365**

Ames, Lee J., 1921-
[Draw 50 series] (4 and up) **743**
Drawing with Lee Ames **741.2**

Amina, Queen of Zaria
See/See also pages in the following book(s):
Hansen, J. African princess (5 and up) **920**

Amish
Williams, J. K. The Amish (7 and up) **289.7**
Fiction
Meyer, C. Gideon's people **Fic**

Amistad (Schooner)
Hulm, D. United States v. the Amistad **326**
Myers, W. D. Amistad: a long road to freedom (5 and up) **326**

Amnesia
Fiction
Fisk, P. The secret of Sabrina Fludde **Fic**

Amnesty International
Banks, D. Amnesty International **323**

Among the hidden. Haddix, M. P. **Fic**

Among the leaves so green. Lee, T.
In The Green Man: tales from the mythic forest p86-112 **808.8**

Amos Fortune, free man. Yates, E. **92**

Amphibians
Amphibians and reptiles **597.9**
Crump, M. L. Amphibians, reptiles, and their conservation (7 and up) **597.9**
Miller, S. S. Amazing amphibians **597.8**
Reptiles and amphibians **597.9**
Silverstein, A. Snakes & such **639**
Stebbins, R. C. A field guide to Western reptiles and amphibians **597.9**

Amphibians and reptiles **597.9**

Amphibians, reptiles, and their conservation. Crump, M. L. **597.9**

The **Amulet** of Samarkand. Stroud, J. **Fic**

Amusement parks
Fiction
Lubar, D. Dunk (7 and up) **Fic**
Shusterman, N. Full tilt (7 and up) **Fic**

Analgesics
Durham, M. Painkillers and tranquilizers **615**

Ananse the Spider in search of a fool. Bryan, A.
In Bryan, A. Ashley Bryan's African tales, uh-huh p1-8 **398.2**

Anasazi culture See Pueblo Indians

Anastasia See Anastasiía Nikolaevna, Grand Duchess, daughter of Nicholas II, Emperor of Russia, 1901-1918

Anastasia Krupnik. Lowry, L. **Fic**

Anastasiía Nikolaevna, Grand Duchess, daughter of Nicholas II, Emperor of Russia, 1901-1918
See/See also pages in the following book(s):
McGaw, L. To be a princess (4 and up) **920**

Anatomy
See also Musculoskeletal system; Physiology

Anatomy, Human See Human anatomy

Anaya, Rudolfo A.
The apple orchard
In Growing up Latino; memoirs and stories p292-304 **810.8**
Dead end
In Join in; multiethnic short stories by outstanding writers for young adults p101-09 **S C**
My land sings **S C**

Anaya, Rudolfo A.—*Continued*
Contents: Lupe and la Llorona; Dulcinea; The three brothers;
Doña Sebastiana; The shepherd who knew the language of ani-
mals; The fountain of youth; The lost camel; The miller's good
luck; Sipa's choice; Coyote and Raven
See/See also pages in the following book(s):
Hill, C. M. Ten Hispanic American authors
    920

Ancient Alexandria. Nardo, D.   932
Ancient America. Wood, M.   970.01
Ancient architecture
Bentley, D. The seven wonders of the ancient
world   722
Ancient Athens. Nardo, D.   938
Ancient China. Cotterell, A.   931
The ancient Chinese. Schomp, V.   931
Ancient civilization
    See also Classical civilization
Hakim, J. Aristotle leads the way (5 and up)
    509
Knight, J. Ancient civilizations: almanac (7 and
up)   930
McConnell, S. A. Ancient civilizations: biogra-
phies (7 and up)   920
Trumble, K. The Library of Alexandria (5 and
up)   027
Encyclopedias
Ancient civilizations (5 and up)   930
Exploring ancient civilizations   930
Ancient civilizations (5 and up)   930
Ancient Egypt. Harris, G.   932
Ancient Egypt. Hart, G.   932
Ancient Egypt. Nardo, D.   932
Ancient Egyptian jobs. Malam, J.   932
Ancient Egyptians. Baker, R. F.   932
The ancient Egyptians. Perl, L.   932
Ancient Greece!. Hart, A.   938
Ancient Greece. Malam, J.   938
Ancient Greece. Nardo, D.   938
Ancient Greece. Powell, A.   938
Ancient Greece and Rome   938
The ancient Greek Olympics. Woff, R.   796.48
Ancient Greeks. Baker, R. F.   938
The ancient Greeks. Lassieur, A.   938
The ancient Greeks. Nardo, D.   938
The ancient Hebrews. Mann, K.   909
Ancient history
Burrell, R. E. C. Oxford first ancient history
    909
Service, P. F. 300 B.C.   930
The ancient Inca. Calvert, P.   985
The ancient Mediterranean. Stefoff, R.   938
Ancient Mesopotamia. Schomp, V.   935
The ancient Near East. Stefoff, R.   939
The ancient Roman world. Mellor, R.   937
The ancient Romans. Lassieur, A.   937
The ancient Romans. Nardo, D.   937
Ancient Rome. Corbishley, M.   937
Ancient Rome. James, S.   937
Ancient Rome [Daily life series] Nardo, D.
    937

Ancient Rome [History of weapons and warfare
series] Nardo, D.   937
Ancient voices. Hovey, K.   811
Ancient world leaders [series]
Lange, B. Genghis Khan   92
Ancona, George, 1929-
Harvest (4 and up)   331.5
And in the morning. Wilson, J.   Fic
And not afraid to dare. Bolden, T.   920
And round me rings. Spencer, A.   398.2
And sometimes why. Farrell, M.   Fic
And the lights flickered. Goldin, B. D.
    In The Haunted house: a collection of original
    stories   S C
And the soul shall dance. Yamauchi, W.
    In American dragons: twenty-five Asian
    American voices p144-54   810.8
And who cured the princess? Yolen, J.
    In Yolen, J. Mightier than the sword; world
    folktales for strong boys p69-73
    398.2
Andersen, Bethanne
(il) Meltzer, M. Ten kings   920
(il) Meltzer, M. Ten queens   920
Andersen, Hans Christian, 1805-1875
The princess and the pea; adaptation. See
    Levine, G. C. The princess test   Fic
(jt. auth) Levine, G. C. The princess test
    Fic
Anderson, Alan H., 1943-
Geology crafts for kids
    In Diehn, G. and others. Science smart; cool
    projects for exploring the marvels of the
    planet Earth   550
Science smart. See Science smart   550
Anderson, Cynthia
Write grants, get money   025.1
Anderson, Dale, 1953-
Arriving at Ellis Island (5 and up)   325.73
The Cold War years   973.92
Maria Mitchell, astronomer (7 and up)   92
Saddam Hussein   92
Anderson, Elizabeth Garrett, 1836-1917
See/See also pages in the following book(s):
Celebrating women in mathematics and science
    920
Anderson, Janet, 1946-
The last treasure (5 and up)   Fic
Anderson, Kevin J., 1962-
Grumpy old monsters   741.5
Anderson, Laurie Halse
Fever, 1793 (5 and up)   Fic
Speak (7 and up)   Fic
Anderson, M. T., 1968-
Bacarole for paper and bones
    In Shelf life: stories by the book p127-49
    S C
The Game of Sunken Places (5 and up)   Fic
Handel, who knew what he liked (4-6)   92
Watch and wake
    In Gothic!; ten original dark tales   S C
Anderson, Madelyn Klein
North American Indian games   970.004

Anderson, Madelyn Klein—*Continued*
So proudly they served   **940.54**

Anderson, Margaret Jean, 1931-
Aristotle (5 and up)   **92**
Carl Linnaeus   **92**
Isaac Newton (4 and up)   **92**
(jt. auth) Vivian, R. G. Chaco Canyon   **978**

Anderson, Marian, 1897-1993
About
Freedman, R. The voice that challenged a nation [biography of Marian Anderson] (5 and up)   **92**

Anderson, Mary
See/See also pages in the following book(s):
Thimmesh, C. Girls think of everything (5 and up)   **920**

Anderson, Peter, 1956-
(il) Margeson, S. M. Viking   **948**
(il) Redmond, I. Gorilla   **599.8**

Anderson, Vicki
Fiction sequels for readers 10 to 16   **016.8**

Anderson, Wayne, 1966-
Brown v. Board of Education   **344**
Plessy v. Ferguson   **342**

Anderson, William T., 1952-
Laura Ingalls Wilder (4 and up)   **92**

Andersonville Prison
Fiction
Wisler, G. C. Red Cap (4 and up)   **Fic**

Andreessen, Marc
About
Ehrenhaft, D. Marc Andreessen   **92**
See/See also pages in the following book(s):
Northrup, M. American computer pioneers   **920**

Andrew, Ian P., 1962-
(il) Dickinson, P. The kin   **Fic**

Andrew Jackson's America, 1824-1850. Collier, C.   **973.5**

Andrews, John F.
(ed) Shakespeare's world and work. See Shakespeare's world and work   **822.3**

Andrews, Linda Wasmer
Emotional intelligence   **152.4**
Meditation (5 and up)   **158**

Andrews, Roy Chapman, 1884-1960
About
Bausum, A. Dragon bones and dinosaur eggs: a photobiography of Roy Chapman Andrews (5 and up)   **92**
Marrin, A. Secrets from the rocks: dinosaur hunting with Roy Chapman Andrews (4 and up)   **92**

Andronik, Catherine M.
Copernicus   **92**
(comp) Information literacy skills, grades 7-12. See Information literacy skills, grades 7-12   **027.62**

Andryszewski, Tricia, 1956-
Kosovo   **949.7**
School prayer (7 and up)   **344**
Step by step along the Appalachian Trail   **796.51**

Andy and Ruthie. Saldaña, R.
In Saldaña, R. Finding our way: stories p39-48   **S C**

Anecdotes
See also Wit and humor

Angel & Aly. Koertge, R. 13; thirteen stories that capture the agony and ecstasy of being thirteen

Angel-baby. Salisbury, G.
In Salisbury, G. Island boyz: short stories p196-219   **S C**

Angel: disasters, diets, and D-cups. See Whytock, C. My cup runneth over   **Fic**

The **angel** factory. Blacker, T.   **Fic**

The **Angel** of Death. Lester, J.
In Lester, J. When the beginning began; stories about God, the creatures, and us p25-30   **296.1**

The **angel** of dreams. Schwartz, H.
In Schwartz, H. The day the Rabbi disappeared: Jewish holiday tales of magic p49-52   **398.2**

Angel on the square. Whelan, G.   **Fic**

Angela's eyes. Myers, W. D.
In Myers, W. D. 145th Street; short stories   **S C**

Angelfish. Yep, L.   **Fic**

Angell, Judie, 1937-
Turmoil in a blue and beige bedroom
In Sixteen; short stories by outstanding writers for young adults p72-82   **S C**

Angelo, Master, fl. ca. 1370-ca. 1405
(il) Grimes, N. A dime a dozen   **811**

Angelou, Maya
I know why the caged bird sings [excerpt]
In Who do you think you are?; stories of friends and enemies p156-63   **S C**
Maya Angelou   **811**
About
Cuffie, T. A. Maya Angelou (7 and up)   **92**
Harper, J. E. Maya Angelou   **92**
Kite, L. P. Maya Angelou   **92**
See/See also pages in the following book(s):
Hansen, J. Women of hope (4 and up)   **920**

Angels
Fiction
Banks, L. R. Maura's angel   **Fic**
Chaikin, M. Angels sweep the desert floor (4 and up)   **296.1**

Angels of mercy. Kuhn, B.   **940.54**

Angels sweep the desert floor. Chaikin, M.   **296.1**

Anglo-American cataloguing rules
Fritz, D. A. Cataloging with AACR2 and MARC21   **025.3**
Gorman, M. The concise AACR2, 2004 revision   **025.3**

Anglo-American cataloguing rules   **025.3**

Anglo-Saxons
Fiction
Cadnum, M. Raven of the waves (7 and up)   **Fic**

Angola

Fiction

McKissack, P. C. Nzinga, warrior queen of Matamba (5 and up)   **Fic**

The **angry** woman. Lester, J.

In Lester, J. The last tales of Uncle Remus p56-61   **398.2**

Angus, thongs and full-frontal snogging. Rennison, L.   **Fic**

Animal   **590.3**

Animal abuse *See* Animal welfare

Animal anatomy on file   **571.3**

Animal behavior

Gardner, R. Science project ideas about animal behavior   **591.5**

Perry, P. J. Animals under the ground   **591.56**

Settel, J. Exploding ants (4 and up)   **591.5**

Staub, F. J. The signs animals leave   **590**

Animal communication

Sayre, A. P. Secrets of sound p11-23 (4 and up)   **591.59**

Animal defenses

Castner, J. L. Surviving in the rain forest   **577.3**

Perry, P. J. Armor to venom   **591.47**

Animal experimentation

See also Animal welfare

Day, N. Animal experimentation   **179**

See/See also pages in the following book(s):

O'Neill, T. Biomedical ethics (7 and up)   **174.2**

Animal fact-file. Hare, T.   **599**

Animal farm. Orwell, G.   **Fic**

Animal giants. Taylor, B.   **590**

Animal helpers for the disabled. Kent, D.   **636.088**

Animal rights

See also Animal welfare

Day, N. Animal experimentation   **179**

The Rights of animals (7 and up)   **179**

Animal rights movement

Animal rights movement   **179**

Animal rights movement   **179**

Animal sciences   **590.3**

Animal shelters

Fiction

Koja, K. Straydog (7 and up)   **Fic**

Animal stories *See* Animals—Fiction

Animal tracks

Staub, F. J. The signs animals leave   **590**

Animal watch [series]

Stonehouse, B. Bears   **599.78**

Animal welfare

Fiction

Kehret, P. Cages   **Fic**

Animals

See also Invertebrates; Pets and names of orders and classes of the animal kingdom; kinds of animals characterized by their environments; and names of individual species

Kerrod, R. Facts on File wildlife atlas   **578**

Myers, J. On the trail of the Komodo dragon and other explorations of science in action   **590**

Taylor, B. Animal giants (5 and up)   **590**

The Visual dictionary of animals (4 and up)   **591.4**

Wildlife and plants of the world   **578**

Encyclopedias

Animal   **590.3**

Animal sciences   **590.3**

Animals   **596**

Burnie, D. The Kingfisher illustrated animal encyclopedia   **590.3**

The encyclopedia of animals   **590.3**

Visual encyclopedia of animals   **590.3**

Fiction

Hoeye, M. Time stops for no mouse (5 and up)   **Fic**

Jacques, B. Redwall (6 and up)   **Fic**

Kipling, R. The jungle books (4 and up)   **S C**

Lester, J. The last tales of Uncle Remus (4 and up)   **398.2**

Orwell, G. Animal farm (7 and up)   **Fic**

Folklore

See also Dragons; Monsters; Mythical animals

Nigg, J. Wonder beasts (7 and up)   **398**

Photography

See Photography of animals

Training

Kent, D. Animal helpers for the disabled (4 and up)   **636.088**

Africa

Bateman, R. Safari (4 and up)   **599**

Saign, G. The African cats   **599.75**

United States

Patent, D. H. Animals on the trail with Lewis and Clark (4 and up)   **978**

Animals, Domestic *See* Domestic animals

Animals, Fossil *See* Fossils

Animals, Mythical *See* Mythical animals

Animals   **596**

Animals & the environment [series]

McDonald, M. A. Pythons   **597.9**

McDonald, M. A. Rattlesnakes   **597.9**

Animals and the handicapped

Kent, D. Animal helpers for the disabled (4 and up)   **636.088**

Animals in order [series]

Lassieur, A. Crabs, lobsters, and shrimps   **595.3**

Animals of the world. *See* Visual encyclopedia of animals   **590.3**

Animals on the trail with Lewis and Clark. Patent, D. H.   **978**

Animals' rights *See* Animal rights

Animals that hibernate. Perry, P. J.   **591.56**

Animals under the ground. Perry, P. J.   **591.56**

Animalways [series]

Greenberg, D. A. Dolphins   **599.5**

Greenberg, D. A. Lizards   **597.9**

Greenberg, D. A. Whales   **599.5**

Schlaepfer, G. G. Elephants   **599.67**

Animalways—*Continued*
Warhol, T. Eagles **598**
Animated films
Hahn, D. Animation magic **791.43**
Hart, C. Christopher Hart's animation studio
 791.43
Animation (Cinematography)
Hamilton, J. Special effects in film and television (4 and up) **791.43**
Lockman, D. Computer animation **778.5**
Animation magic. Hahn, D. **791.43**
Anna of Byzantium. Barrett, T. **Fic**
Anna Sunday. Keehn, S. M. **Fic**
Annie Christmas. Hamilton, V.
 In Hamilton, V. Her stories; African American folktales, fairy tales, and true tales p84-89 **398.2**
Annie Christmas. San Souci, R.
 In San Souci, R. Cut from the same cloth; American women of myth, legend, and tall tale p35-40 **398.2**
Annie John. Kincaid, J. **Fic**
Anning, Mary, 1799-1847
 About
Goodhue, T. W. Curious bones: Mary Anning and the birth of paleontology **92**
Annotated guides [series]
Philip, N. Myths & legends **398.2**
Anorexia **616.85**
Anorexia and bulimia. Cotter, A. **616.85**
Anorexia and bulimia. Sanders, P. **616.85**
Anorexia nervosa
Anorexia **616.85**
Cotter, A. Anorexia and bulimia **616.85**
Harmon, D. Anorexia nervosa (7 and up)
 616.85
Sanders, P. Anorexia and bulimia **616.85**
Smith, E. Anorexia nervosa (7 and up)
 616.85
Antarctic journal. Dewey, J. **998**
Antarctica
Calvert, P. Sir Ernest Shackleton **92**
Dewey, J. Antarctic journal (4 and up) **998**
Johnson, R. L. Ernest Shackleton **92**
Myers, W. D. Antarctica **998**
Scott, E. Poles apart (5 and up)
Webb, S. My season with penguins (4 and up)
 598
 Exploration
Bredeson, C. After the last dog died **92**
Kimmel, E. C. Ice story (4 and up) **998**
 Fiction
White, A. Surviving Antarctica (7 and up)
 Fic
Anthony, Piers
See/See also pages in the following book(s):
Reid, S. E. Presenting young adult science fiction **813.009**
Anthony, Susan B., 1820-1906
 About
Monroe, J. The Susan B. Anthony women's voting rights trial **324.6**
Weisberg, B. Susan B. Anthony **92**

Anthony, Suzanne
West Indies **972.9**
Anthropologist: scientist of the people. Batten, M.
 301
Anthropologists
Mark, J. T. Margaret Mead (7 and up) **92**
Pollard, M. Margaret Mead **92**
Poynter, M. The Leakeys **92**
 Fiction
Abelove, J. Go and come back (7 and up)
 Fic
Anthropology
Batten, M. Anthropologist: scientist of the people (4 and up) **301**
Anti-apartheid movement
 See also Apartheid
Anti-war poetry *See* War poetry
Antietam (Md.), Battle of, 1862
Hughes, C. The Battle of Antietam **973.7**
Antigua and Barbuda
 Fiction
Kincaid, J. Annie John **Fic**
Antiquities
 See also Archeology
Moloney, N. The young Oxford book of archaeology (7 and up) **930.1**
Antiquity of man *See* Human origins
Antisemitism
 See also Jews—Persecutions
 Fiction
Levitin, S. The cure **Fic**
Levitin, S. The return (6 and up) **Fic**
Antón, Mauricio
(il) Turner, A. National Geographic prehistoric mammals **569**
Antonio, Sam
See/See also pages in the following book(s):
Mendoza, P. M. Extraordinary people in extraordinary times (7 and up) **920**
Antonius, Marcus, ca. 83-30 B.C.
See/See also pages in the following book(s):
Brooks, P. S. Cleopatra (7 and up) **92**
Antram, David, 1958-
(il) Malam, J. Greek town **938**
Ants
Pascoe, E. Ants (4 and up) **595.7**
Ants. San Souci, R.
 In San Souci, R. Dare to be scared; thirteen stories to chill and thrill **S C**
Anxiety
The truth about fear and depression (7 and up)
 616.85
Any small goodness. Johnston, T. **Fic**
Anzaldúa, Gloria, 1942-2004
People should not die in June in South Texas
 In Growing up Latino; memoirs and stories p280-87 **810.8**
Anzovin, Steven, 1954-
(ed) Facts about the states. *See* Facts about the states **973**
(jt. auth) Kane, J. N. Famous first facts
 031.02

Anzovin, Steven, 1954-—*Continued*
(jt. auth) Podell, J. Old worlds to new
    920.003

AP *See* Associated Press

Apache. McIntosh, K. North American Indians today [series]

Apache Indians
McIntosh, K. Apache North American Indians
today [series]
Schwarz, M. Cochise, Apache chief   **92**
Baird, W. D. Geronimo, Apache warrior   **92**
See/See also pages in the following book(s):
Ehrlich, A. Wounded Knee: an Indian history of
the American West (6 and up)   **970.004**
    Fiction
Burks, B. Walks Alone   **Fic**
McKissack, P. C. Run away home (5 and up)
    Fic

Apartheid
Beecroft, S. The release of Nelson Mandela
    968.06
Downing, D. Apartheid in South Africa   **968**
Apartheid in South Africa. Downing, D.   **968**

Apes
   See also Chimpanzees; Gorillas
Saign, G. The great apes   **599.8**

Apfelbaum, Nina
(jt. auth) Rosen, P. Bearing witness
    016.94053

Apollo 11 (Spacecraft)
Green, J. Race to the moon   **629.45**
Hehner, B. First on the moon (4 and up)
    629.45

Apollo Project *See* Project Apollo

Apollo project
Bredeson, C. The moon (4 and up)   **523.3**

An **apology** to the moon furies. Vega, E.
In Growing up Latino; memoirs and stories
p47-72   **810.8**

Appalachia. Rylant, C.   **974**

Appalachian Mountain region *See* Appalachian
region

Appalachian region
Rylant, C. Appalachia   **974**
    Fiction
Cleaver, V. Where the lillies bloom (5 and up)
    Fic
Naylor, P. R. Sang Spell (7 and up)   **Fic**
White, R. Belle Prater's boy (5 and up)   **Fic**

Appalachian Trail
Andryszewski, T. Step by step along the Appalachian Trail   **796.51**

Apparitions. San Souci, R.
In San Souci, R. A terrifying taste of short &
shivery; thirty creepy tales p30-34
    398.2

Appelt, Kathi, 1954-
Kissing Tennessee and other stories from the
Stardust Dance   **S C**
Contents: Dance with me; Rachel's sister; Just a kiss, Annie
P.; Starbears; The right word; Kissing Tennessee; The notes be-
tween the notes; These shoes
Poems from homeroom (7 and up)   **811**

Appetite depressants
Barrett, C. The dangers of diet drugs and other
weight-loss products   **615**
Clayton, L. Diet pill drug dangers   **616.3**
Walker, P. Understanding the risk of diet drugs
    616.85

Appetite disorders *See* Eating disorders

Apple blossoms. Trueman, T.
In Tripping over the lunch lady and other
school stories p43-57   **S C**

The **apple** orchard. Anaya, R. A.
In Growing up Latino; memoirs and stories
p292-304   **810.8**

The **appointment.** Schwartz, A.
In Schwartz, A. Scary stories 3; more tales to
chill your bones p7   **398.2**

Apprentices
    Fiction
Cadnum, M. Ship of fire (7 and up)   **Fic**
DeFelice, C. C. The apprenticeship of Lucas
Whitaker (5 and up)   **Fic**

The **apprenticeship** of Lucas Whitaker. DeFelice,
C. C.   **Fic**

April 2000: the third expedition. Bradbury, R.
In Read into the millennium; tales of the future p73-102   **S C**

April Mendez. Spinelli, J.
In Spinelli, J. The library card   **S C**

April morning. Fast, H.   **Fic**

Aquanauts *See* Underwater exploration

Aquarium fish. Mills, D.   **639.34**

Aquariums
Mills, D. Aquarium fish   **639.34**

Aquatic animals *See* Marine animals

Aquatic life of the world (4 and up)   **578.7**

Aquatic plants *See* Marine plants

Aquino, Corazon
See/See also pages in the following book(s):
Axelrod-Contrada, J. Women who led nations (7
and up)   **920**
Price-Groff, C. Twentieth-century women politi-
cal leaders (7 and up)   **920**

Arab American encyclopedia (7 and up)   **305.8**

Arab American voices. Hall, L.   **305.8**

Arab Americans
Hall, L. Arab American voices   **305.8**
    Encyclopedias
Arab American encyclopedia (7 and up)
    305.8

Arab countries
    Fiction
Marston, E. Figs and fate   **S C**

The **Arab-Israeli** conflict (7 and up)   **956.04**

Arab-Israeli conflicts *See* Israel-Arab conflicts

Arab-Jewish relations *See* Jewish-Arab relations

Arabs
   See also Bedouins; Palestinian Arabs
    Folklore
Yeoman, J. The Seven voyages of Sinbad the
Sailor (5 and up)   **398.2**

Arachnida *See* Spiders

Arafat, Yasir, 1929-2004
About
Headlam, G. Yasser Arafat   **92**
Arapaho Indians
See/See also pages in the following book(s):
Ehrlich, A. Wounded Knee: an Indian history of the American West (6 and up)   **970.004**
Fiction
Osborne, M. P. Adaline Falling Star (5 and up)
Fic
Arawak Indians *See* Taino Indians
Arbuthnot, May Hill, 1884-1969
(jt. auth) Sutherland, Z. Children and books
028.5
Archaeology *See* Archeology
Archaeology. Barnes, T.   **930.1**
Archbold, Rick, 1950-
(jt. auth) Ballard, R. D. The discovery of the Titanic   **910.4**
(jt. auth) Ballard, R. D. Ghost liners   **910.4**
(jt. auth) Bateman, R. Safari   **599**
Archeological specimens *See* Antiquities
Archeologists
Greenberg, L. Digging into the past   **920**
Archeology
    See also Antiquities; Excavations (Archeology); Prehistoric peoples; Rock drawings, paintings, and engravings names of extinct cities; and names of groups of people and of cities (except extinct cities), countries, regions, etc., with the subdivision Antiquities
Barnes, T. Archaeology (5 and up)   **930.1**
Deem, J. M. Bodies from the bog (4 and up)
930.1
Getz, D. Frozen man (5 and up)   **930.1**
Hawass, Z. A. Curse of the pharaohs (5 and up)
932
McIntosh, J. Archeology (4 and up)   **930.1**
Moloney, N. The young Oxford book of archaeology (7 and up)   **930.1**
Patent, D. H. Secrets of the ice man (5 and up)
930.1
Reinhard, J. Discovering the Inca Ice Maiden (5 and up)   **930.1**
Vivian, R. G. Chaco Canyon   **978**
Encyclopedias
Ancient civilizations (5 and up)   **930**
Archer, Jules
Special interests   **324**
They had a dream   **920**
Architects
Rubin, S. G. Frank Lloyd Wright (7 and up)
92
Wright, D. K. Frank Lloyd Wright   **92**
Architectural engineering *See* Building
Architecture
Corbishley, M. The world of architectural wonders   **720**
Kent, P. Great building stories of the past (4 and up)   **624**
Macaulay, D. Building big   **720**
Rubin, S. G. There goes the neighborhood (7 and up)   **720**
Architecture, Gothic *See* Gothic architecture

Architecture, Medieval *See* Medieval architecture
Architecture, Roman *See* Roman architecture
Arctic regions
Beattie, O. Buried in ice (4 and up)   **998**
Scott, E. Poles apart (5 and up)
Exploration
Warrick, K. C. The perilous search for the fabled Northwest Passage in American history
910.4
Fiction
George, J. C. Julie (6 and up)   **Fic**
George, J. C. Julie of the wolves (6 and up)
Fic
Houston, J. A. Frozen fire (6 and up)   **Fic**
Paulsen, G. Dogsong (6 and up)   **Fic**
Arden, Elizabeth, 1878-1966
About
Shuker, N. Elizabeth Arden (7 and up)   **92**
Ardennes, Battle of the, 1944-1945
Fiction
Hughes, D. Soldier boys   **Fic**
Ardley, Neil, 1937-
(jt. auth) Macaulay, D. The new way things work   **600**
Are we alone? Skurzynski, G.   **576.8**
Are you in the house alone? Peck, R.   **Fic**
Are you there God? it's me, Margaret. Blume, J.
Fic
Argentina
Gofen, E. Argentina (5 and up)   **982**
Hintz, M. Argentina (4 and up)   **982**
Argonauts (Greek mythology)
See/See also pages in the following book(s):
Hamilton, E. Mythology p21-76   **292**
Arid regions
    See also Deserts
Aristotle, 384-322 B.C.
About
Anderson, M. J. Aristotle (5 and up)   **92**
Aristotle leads the way. Hakim, J.   **509**
Arithmetic
Julius, E. H. Arithmetricks   **513**
Arithmetricks. Julius, E. H.   **513**
Ariyoshi, Kyoko
Swan, Vol. 1   **741.5**
Arizona
Blashfield, J. F. Arizona
In America the beautiful, second series
973
McDaniel, M. Arizona
In Celebrate the states   **973**
Fiction
Mosier, E. My life as a girl   **Fic**
Spinelli, J. Stargirl   **Fic**
Stewart, J. J. If that breathes fire, we're toast!
Fic
The **Arkadians.** Alexander, L.   **Fic**
Arkansas
Altman, L. J. Arkansas
In Celebrate the states   **973**
McNair, S. Arkansas
In America the beautiful, second series
973

Arkansas—*Continued*

Fiction

Greene, B. Summer of my German soldier (6 and up) **Fic**

Race relations

Fradin, J. B. The power of one [biography of Daisy Bates] (7 and up) **92**

Polakow, A. Daisy Bates (7 and up) **92**

The **Arkansaw** bear. Harris, A.

In Theatre for young audiences; 20 great plays for children p46-71 **812.008**

Armageddon summer. Yolen, J. **Fic**

Armaments *See* Military weapons

Armaments race *See* Arms race

Armenia

Dhilawala, S. Armenia (5 and up) **947.5**

Armenian massacres, 1915-1923

Kherdian, D. The road from home (6 and up) **92**

Fiction

Bagdasarian, A. Forgotten fire (7 and up) **Fic**

Armenians

Turkey

Kherdian, D. The road from home (6 and up) **92**

Armies of the past [series]

Gravett, C. Going to war in Viking times **355**

Armor

Byam, M. Arms & armor (4 and up) **355.8**

Armor to venom. Perry, P. J. **591.47**

Armored cars (Tanks) *See* Military tanks

Arms & armor. Byam, M. **355.8**

Arms and armor *See* Weapons

Arms control

See also Arms race

Blohm, C. E. Weapons of peace **327.1**

Arms race

Blohm, C. E. Weapons of peace **327.1**

See/See also pages in the following book(s):

Collier, C. The United States in the Cold War: 1945-1989 **327.73**

Armstrong, Jennifer, 1961-

The kindling (7 and up) **Fic**

The moth of God

In Soul searching: thirteen stories about faith and belief p203-19 **S C**

Photo by Brady **973.7**

The song of stones river

In What a song can do; 12 riffs on the power of music **S C**

Steal away (5 and up) **Fic**

Witness

In Shattered: stories of children and war p133-38 **S C**

(jt. auth) Jennings, P. The century for young people **909.82**

(jt. auth) Opdyke, I. G. In my hands **940.53**

(ed) Shattered: stories of children and war. See Shattered: stories of children and war **S C**

(ed) What a song can do. See What a song can do **S C**

Armstrong, Lance

About

Stewart, M. Sweet victory: Lance Armstrong's incredible journey (5 and up) **92**

Armstrong, Louis, 1900-1971

About

Old, W. Louis Armstrong **92**

See/See also pages in the following book(s):

Mour, S. I. American jazz musicians **920**

Armstrong, Lynn

(ed) The Vietnam War. See The Vietnam War **959.704**

Armstrong, Neil, 1930-

About

Bredeson, C. Neil Armstrong **92**

Armstrong, Thomas

You're smarter than you think **153.9**

Armstrong, William Howard, 1914-1999

Sounder (5 and up) **Fic**

Army life *See* Soldiers

Army Nurse Corps *See* United States. Army Nurse Corps

Arnold, Arthur

(il) Arnold, C. Uluru, Australia's Aboriginal heart **994**

Arnold, Benedict, 1741-1801

About

Fritz, J. Traitor: the case of Benedict Arnold **92**

King, D. C. Benedict Arnold and the American Revolution **92**

Arnold, Caroline, 1944-

El Niño (4 and up) **551.6**

Easter Island (5 and up) **996**

The geography book (4 and up) **910**

On the brink of extinction (4 and up) **598**

Stories in stone (4 and up) **709.01**

Uluru, Australia's Aboriginal heart (5 and up) **994**

Arnold, Emily *See* McCully, Emily Arnold

Arnold, Roseanne *See* Barr, Roseanne

Aronson, Billy

Meteors (4 and up) **523.5**

Aronson, Marc

Art attack (7 and up) **700**

John Winthrop, Oliver Cromwell, and the Land of Promise (7 and up) **92**

Sir Walter Ralegh and the quest for El Dorado (7 and up) **92**

(ed) 911: the book of help. See 911: the book of help **810.8**

Around the world in— [series]

Ashby, R. 1800 **909.8**

George, L. S. 800 **909.07**

Schomp, V. 1500 **909.08**

Service, A. 1200 **909.07**

Service, P. F. 300 B.C. **930**

Around the world in a hundred years. Fritz, J. **910.4**

Around the world in eighty days. Verne, J. **Fic**

Arrick, Fran
The good girls
In Visions: nineteen short stories by outstanding writers for young adults p107-20
S C

Arrington, Frances
Bluestem (4-6) **Fic**
Prairie whispers (5 and up) **Fic**
Arriving at Ellis Island. Anderson, D. **325.73**
Arruda, Suzanne Middendorf, 1954-
Freedom's martyr [biography of Jose Rizal]
92

Art
Rubin, S. G. Art against the odds (5 and up)
700
15th and 16th centuries
Cole, A. The Renaissance **709.02**
Corrain, L. The art of the Renaissance
709.02

See/See also pages in the following book(s):
Barter, J. A Renaissance painter's studio
759.5
20th century
Heart to heart (5 and up) **811.008**
Mason, A. In the time of Picasso **709.04**
Mason, A. In the time of Warhol **709.04**
Dictionaries
Greenway, S. Art: an A-Z guide **703**
The Oxford dictionary of art **703**
Encyclopedias
International encyclopedia of art **703**
History
Art: a world history **709**
Gardner's art through the ages **709**
Sayre, H. M. Cave paintings to Picasso (5 and up) **709**
Museums
See Art museums
Study and teaching
Luxbacher, I. The jumbo book of art p8-57 (4 and up) **702.8**

Art, African *See* African art
Art, American *See* American art
Art, Medieval *See* Medieval art
Art, Modern *See* Modern art
Art, Renaissance *See* Art—15th and 16th centuries
Art: a world history **709**
Art against the odds. Rubin, S. G. **700**
Art and architecture. Ross, S. **720**
Art and society
Aronson, M. Art attack (7 and up) **700**
Art appreciation
Aronson, M. Art attack (7 and up) **700**
Corrain, L. The art of the Renaissance
709.02
Richardson, J. Looking at pictures (5 and up)
750
Sturgis, A. Optical illusions in art **750.1**
Fiction
Scieszka, J. Seen Art? **Fic**
Art around the world [series]
Finley, C. Aboriginal art of Australia **759.01**
Finley, C. The art of African masks **391**

Mason, A. In the time of Picasso **709.04**
Mason, A. In the time of Warhol **709.04**
Art attack. Aronson, M. **700**
Art encounters [series]
Kudlinski, K. V. The spirit catchers **Fic**
Art museums
See also names of individual art museums
Richardson, J. Looking at pictures (5 and up)
750
Fiction
Nixon, J. L. Who are you? (7 and up) **Fic**
The **art** of African masks. Finley, C. **391**
The **art** of keeping cool. Lisle, J. T. **Fic**
The **art** of making comic books. Pellowski, M.
741.5
Art of the ancient Mediterranean world. Wilson, B.
In International encyclopedia of art **703**
The **art** of the Renaissance. Corrain, L.
709.02
The **art** of Walt Disney. Finch, C. **791.43**
Art revelations [series]
Connolly, S. New Testament miracles **226**
Ward, E. M. Old Testament women **221.9**
Art revolutions [series]
Bolton, L. Impressionism **709.03**
Artell, Mike, 1948-
Cartooning for kids **741.5**
Artemis Fowl. Colfer, E. **Fic**
Arthritis
Gray, S. H. Living with juvenile rheumatoid arthritis **616.7**
Arthur, King
About
Crossley-Holland, K. The world of King Arthur and his court (5 and up) **942.01**
Nardo, D. King Arthur **942.01**
Pyle, H. The story of King Arthur and his knights (7 and up) **398.2**
Pyle, H. The story of the Grail and the passing of Arthur (7 and up) **398.2**
Sutcliff, R. The light beyond the forest (4 and up) **398.2**
Sutcliff, R. The road to Camlann (4 and up)
398.2
Sutcliff, R. The sword and the circle (4 and up)
398.2
Fiction
Crossley-Holland, K. The seeing stone **Fic**
McCaffrey, A. Black horses for the king (7 and up) **Fic**
Springer, N. I am Mordred (7 and up) **Fic**
Springer, N. I am Morgan le Fay (7 and up)
Fic
Thomson, S. L. The dragon's son (7 and up)
Fic
Wein, E. E. The Winter Prince (7 and up)
Fic
White, T. H. The once and future king **Fic**
Yolen, J. Sword of the rightful king **Fic**
Arthur, Alex
Shell (4 and up) **594**

Arthur Sternbach brings the curveball to Mars. Robinson, K. S.
In New skies: an anthology of today's science fiction **S C**

Arthurian romances
See also Grail
Morpurgo, M. Sir Gawain and the Green Knight (5 and up) **398.2**
Pyle, H. The story of King Arthur and his knights (7 and up) **398.2**
Pyle, H. The story of Sir Launcelot and his companions (7 and up) **398.2**
Pyle, H. The story of the champions of the Round Table (7 and up) **398.2**
Pyle, H. The story of the Grail and the passing of Arthur (7 and up) **398.2**
Sutcliff, R. The light beyond the forest (4 and up) **398.2**
Sutcliff, R. The road to Camlann (4 and up) **398.2**
Sutcliff, R. The sword and the circle (4 and up) **398.2**

Arthus-Bertrand, Yann
Earth from above for young readers (4 and up) **779**

Articles of Confederation *See* United States. Articles of Confederation

The **Articles** of Confederation. Feinberg, B. S. **342**

Artificial intelligence
Jefferis, D. Artificial intelligence (4 and up) **629.8**
Margulies, P. Artificial intelligence (5 and up) **006.3**

Artificial limbs
Murphy, W. B. Spare parts (7 and up) **617.9**

Artificial organs
McClellan, M. Organ and tissue transplants (7 and up) **617.9**
Murphy, W. B. Spare parts (7 and up) **617.9**

Artificial satellites
Kupperberg, P. Spy satellites **327.12**
Wolny, P. Weapons satellites **358**

Artificial satellites in telecommunication
Byers, A. Communications satellites **384.5**

Artists
See also African American artists; Architects; Child artists; Illustrators; Photographers; Women artists
Mason, A. In the time of Picasso **709.04**
Mason, A. In the time of Warhol **709.04**
Biography
Ergas, G. A. Artists: from Michelangelo to Maya Lin **920.003**
Dictionaries
Authors & artists for young adults **920.003**
Fiction
Bowler, T. River boy **Fic**
Feiffer, J. The man in the ceiling (4 and up) **Fic**
Giff, P. R. Pictures of Hollis Woods (5 and up) **Fic**

Gilson, J. Stink Alley (4 and up) **Fic**
Grove, V. Destiny (5 and up) **Fic**
Holmes, B. W. Following Fake Man **Fic**
Koja, K. Buddha Boy (7 and up) **Fic**
Kudlinski, K. V. The spirit catchers (7 and up) **Fic**
Lamm, C. D. Bittersweet **Fic**
Mack, T. Drawing lessons **Fic**
Paulsen, G. The monument (6 and up) **Fic**
United States
Berman, A. James McNeill Whistler (7 and up) **92**
Gherman, B. Norman Rockwell (4 and up) **92**
Greenberg, J. Andy Warhol (7 and up) **92**
Greenberg, J. Runaway girl: the artist Louise Bourgeois (7 and up) **92**
Meryman, R. Andrew Wyeth (7 and up) **92**

Artists, Dutch
Bassil, A. Vincent van Gogh (4 and up) **92**
Greenberg, J. Vincent Van Gogh **92**
Schwartz, G. Hieronymus Bosch (7 and up) **92**

Artists, French
Beardsley, J. Pablo Picasso (7 and up) **92**
Greenfeld, H. Paul Gauguin (7 and up) **92**
Hodge, S. Pablo Picasso (4 and up) **92**
Loria, S. Pablo Picasso **92**
MacDonald, P. A. Pablo Picasso (7 and up) **92**
Rayfield, S. Pierre-Auguste Renoir (7 and up) **92**
Scarborough, K. Pablo Picasso (5 and up) **92**
Welton, J. Henri Matisse **92**

Artists, Italian
Barter, J. A Renaissance painter's studio **759.5**
Herbert, J. Leonardo da Vinci for kids (4 and up) **92**
O'Connor, B. Leonardo da Vinci (5 and up) **92**
Stanley, D. Michelangelo **92**

Artists, Mexican
Cruz, B. José Clemente Orozco **92**
Laidlaw, J. A. Frida Kahlo (5 and up) **92**

Artists, Russian
Pozzi, G. Chagall **92**

Artists in their time [series]
Laidlaw, J. A. Frida Kahlo **92**
Scarborough, K. Pablo Picasso **92**
Welton, J. Henri Matisse **92**

Arts
Major, J. S. Caravan to America (4 and up) **920**
Biography
Creative & performing artists for teens **920.003**
History
Ochoa, G. The Wilson chronology of the arts **700**

Arts, African American *See* African American arts

Arts, Japanese *See* Japanese arts

Arts and crafts *See* Handicraft

Arts, leisure, and entertainment. Nardo, D.
937

Arturo's flight. Ortiz Cofer, J.
In Ortiz Cofer, J. An island like you; stories of the barrio p27-40 **S C**

As far as the eye can reach. Kimmel, E. C.
978

Aser and Gamiel. Myers, W. D.
In Myers, W. D. A time to love; stories from the Old Testament p105-23 **S C**

Ash, Russell
The top 10 of everything **031.02**

Ashabranner, Brent K., 1921-
A date with destiny **355**
Remembering Korea (4 and up) **951.9**

Ashabranner, Jennifer
No better hope (4 and up) **975.3**
(il) Ashabranner, B. K. A date with destiny **355**
(il) Ashabranner, B. K. Remembering Korea **951.9**

Ashby, John
Sea gift **Fic**

Ashby, Ruth
1800 **909.8**
Elizabethan England **942.05**
Victorian England **941.081**
(ed) Watkins, S. R. The diary of Sam Watkins, a confederate soldier **973.7**

Asher, Sandra Fenichel, 1942-
See also Asher, Sandy, 1942-
The wise men of Chelm [play]
In Theatre for young audiences; 20 great plays for children p217-43 **812.008**

Asher, Sandy, 1942-
See also Asher, Sandra Fenichel, 1942-
Great moves
In Visions: nineteen short stories by outstanding writers for young adults p130-40 **S C**
A hundred bucks of happy
In Visions: nineteen short stories by outstanding writers for young adults p141-48 **S C**
The wise men of Chelm [play]
In Theatre for young audiences; 20 great plays for children p217-43 **812.008**

Ashes. Pfeffer, S. B.
In Places I never meant to be; original stories by censored writers **S C**

Ashes of roses. Auch, M. J. **Fic**

Ashley Bryan's African tales, uh-huh. Bryan, A. **398.2**

Asia
See also names of individual countries, e.g. China
Peoples of Eastern Asia (5 and up) **950**
History
The Wilson chronology of Asia and the Pacific **950**

The **Asian-American** experience on file **305.8**

Asian American literature *See* American literature—Asian American authors

Asian-American scientists. Yount, L. **920**

Asian American voices. *See* UXL Asian American voices **815**

Asian Americans
The Asian-American experience on file **305.8**
Asian Americans: opposing viewpoints (7 and up) **305.8**
Sakurai, G. Asian-Americans in the old West (4 and up) **978**
UXL Asian American voices **815**
See/See also pages in the following book(s):
Joselit, J. W. Immigration and American religion (7 and up) **200**
Biography
Sinnott, S. Extraordinary Asian Americans and Pacific Islanders (5 and up) **920**
Yount, L. Asian-American scientists (7 and up) **920**
Fiction
American eyes **S C**
Crew, L. Children of the river (7 and up) **Fic**
Religion
Mann, G. S. Buddhists, Hindus, and Sikhs in America (7 and up) **294**

Asian-Americans in the old West. Sakurai, G. **978**

Asian Americans: opposing viewpoints (7 and up) **305.8**

The **Asian** empires. Stefoff, R. **950**

Asian mythology
Roberts, J. Chinese mythology A to Z **299.5**

Asimov, Isaac, 1920-1992
Asimov's guide to the Bible **220.7**
I, robot (7 and up) **S C**
Contents: Robbie; Runaround; Reason; Catch the rabbit; Liar; Little lost robot; Escape; Evidence; The evitable conflict
Reason
In Read into the millennium; tales of the future p57 **S C**

Asimov's guide to the Bible. Asimov, I. **220.7**

Asirvatham, Sandy
The history of jazz **781.65**
The history of the blues **781.643**

Ask the bones. Olson, A. N.
In Olson, A. N. and Schwartz, H. Ask the bones: scary stories from around the world p30-36 **398.2**

Ask the bones: scary stories from around the world. Olson, A. N. **398.2**

ASPCA complete cat care manual. Edney, A. T. B. **636.8**

Aspin, Diana
Ordinary miracles (7 and up) **S C**

The **assassination** of Malcolm X. Draper, A. S. **92**

The **assassination** of Medgar Evers. Ribeiro, M. **92**

Assault from the sky. McGowen, T. **940.54**

The **assault** on the record. Hoffius, S.
In Ultimate sports; short stories by outstanding writers for young adults p161-78 **S C**

Assisted suicide *See* Euthanasia

Associated Press
Flash!: the Associated Press covers the world
070.4

Association for Educational Communications and Technology
American Association of School Librarians. Information power
027.8

Asteroids
Koppes, S. N. Killer rocks from outer space
523.5

Asthma
Greenberg, A. Asthma (7 and up) **616.2**
Lennard-Brown, S. Asthma (5 and up) **616.2**
Murphy, W. B. Asthma (7 and up) **616.2**
Fiction
Bradley, K. B. Weaver's daughter (5 and up)
Fic

Astor, John Jacob, 1864-1912
See/See also pages in the following book(s):
Aaseng, N. Business builders in real estate
920

Astronautics
See also Space flight
Ackroyd, P. Escape from Earth (7 and up)
629.4
Cole, M. D. Hubble Space Telescope (4 and up)
522
Johnstone, M. The history news in space
629.4
Mayell, M. Tragedies of space exploration (5 and up) **363.1**
Spangenburg, R. The history of NASA
629.4
Stott, C. Space exploration (4 and up) **629.4**
Vogt, G. Space mission patches **629.45**

Astronauts
See also Women astronauts
Alagna, M. Mae Jemison (4 and up) **92**
Bredeson, C. Neil Armstrong **92**
Collins, M. Flying to the moon **629.45**
Goodman, S. Ultimate field trip 5 (4 and up)
629.45
Jemison, M. C. Find where the wind goes (5 and up) **92**
Schyffert, B. U. The man who went to the far side of the moon: the story of Apollo 11 astronaut Michael Collins (5 and up) **92**
See/See also pages in the following book(s):
Haskins, J. Black eagles (5 and up) **629.13**

Astronauts of the future. Trondheim, L. **741.5**

Astronomers
See also Women astronomers
Andronik, C. M. Copernicus **92**
Boerst, W. J. Johannes Kepler **92**
Boerst, W. J. Tycho Brahe (7 and up) **92**
Camp, C. A. American astronomers **920**
Datnow, C. L. Edwin Hubble **92**
Fradin, D. B. The planet hunters (5 and up)
523.4
Goble, T. Nicholas Copernicus and the founding of modern astronomy (7 and up) **92**
Gow, M. Tycho Brahe: astronomer **92**
Hinman, B. Benjamin Banneker (5 and up)
92

Litwin, L. B. Benjamin Banneker **92**
Voelkel, J. R. Johannes Kepler and the new astronomy (7 and up) **92**
White, M. Galileo Galilei **92**

Astronomy
Astronomy (7 and up) **520**
Bond, P. DK guide to space (4 and up) **520**
Bramwell, M. Mapping the planets and space
520
Chartrand, M. R. The Audubon Society field guide to the night sky **523**
Cole, M. D. Hubble Space Telescope (4 and up)
522
Dickinson, T. NightWatch (7 and up) **520**
Fradin, D. B. The planet hunters (5 and up)
523.4
Gallant, R. A. The life stories of stars **523.8**
Lippincott, K. Astronomy **520**
Matloff, G. L. More telescope power **522**
Mechler, G. National Audubon Society first field guide: night sky (4 and up) **520**
Pasachoff, J. M. A field guide to the stars and planets **523**
Redfern, M. The Kingfisher young people's book of space **520**
Reed, G. Eyes on the universe (5 and up)
520
Rhatigan, J. Out-of-this-world astronomy (5 and up) **520**
Ridpath, I. Facts on File stars & planets atlas
520
Scagell, R. Children's night sky atlas (5 and up)
520
Silverstein, A. The universe **520**
Simon, S. Destination: space (4 and up) **520**
Space and astronomy on file **520**
Stott, C. New astronomer (7 and up) **520**
VanCleave, J. P. Janice VanCleave's A+ projects in astronomy (7 and up) **520**
See/See also pages in the following book(s):
Earth science on file **550**
Dictionaries
The Facts on File dictionary of astronomy
520.3
Encyclopedias
Exploring earth and space science (7 and up)
550.3

Astronomy (7 and up) **520**

At fountain abbey. Zambreno, M. F.
In Sherwood: original stories from the world of Robin Hood p100-18 **S C**

At her majesty's request [biography of Sarah Forbes Bonetta] Myers, W. D. **92**

At issue [series]
Anorexia **616.85**
Cloning **174.2**
Does capital punishment deter crime? **364.66**
Drugs and sports **362.29**
Welfare reform **361.6**
What is a hate crime? **364.1**

At issue in history [series]
Custer's last stand **973.8**
Japanese American internment camps **940.53**
The McCarthy hearings **973.921**
The Tiananmen Square massacre **951.05**

At Jerusalem's gate. Grimes, N.   **811**

At the beach. Delacre, L.
   In Delacre, L. Salsa stories p18-27   **S C**

At the end of words. Stone, M.   **92**

At the schoolhouse gate. Pipkin, G.   **373.1**

At the sign of the Sugared Plum. Hooper, M.
    Fic

At the stomp. Conford, E.
   In Conford, E. Crush p131-38   **S C**

Atahualpa, d. 1533
   See/See also pages in the following book(s):
   Meltzer, M. Ten kings (5 and up)   **920**

Atalanta (Greek mythology)
              Fiction
   Spinner, S. Quiver (7 and up)   **Fic**

Atangan, Patrick
   The yellow jar   **741.5**

Athens (Greece)
   Nardo, D. Ancient Athens (7 and up)   **938**

Athletes
    See also African American athletes; Women athletes
   Kaminsky, M. Uncommon champions   **920**
              Drug use
   Drugs and sports (7 and up)   **362.29**
   LeVert, S. The facts about steroids   **362.29**

Athletes with disabilities. Kent, D.   **371.9**

Athletic medicine *See* Sports medicine

Athletic shorts. Crutcher, C.   **S C**

Athletics
    See also Sports; Track athletics

Atinsky, Steve
   Tyler on prime time (5 and up)   **Fic**

Atkin, S. Beth
   Voices from the fields (5 and up)   **331.5**

Atkins, Catherine
   Alt ed (7 and up)   **Fic**

Atkinson, Mary, 1938-
   (ed) The Snake book. See The Snake book
    597.9

Atlantis
   Nardo, D. Atlantis   **001.9**

Atlas of American migration. Flanders, S. A.
    304.8

The **Atlas** of endangered species   **333.95**

Atlas of Hispanic-American history. Ochoa, G.
    305.8

The **atlas** of space exploration. Furniss, T.
    520

Atlas of the world   **912**

Atlases
   Atlas of the world   **912**
   DK student atlas   **912**
   Explorer atlas of the world   **912**
   Geography on file   **912**
   Maps on file   **912**
   Oxford new concise world atlas   **912**
   Scholastic atlas of the world (4 and up)   **912**

Atmosphere
    See also Air
   Gallant, R. A. Atmosphere (5 and up)
    551.51

Atocha (Ship) *See* Nuestra Señora de Atocha (Ship)

The **Atom** bomb   **355.8**

Atomic blue pieces. Johnson, A.
   In The Color of absence; 12 stories about loss and hope p41-48   **S C**

Atomic bomb
   The Atom bomb   **355.8**
   Cohen, D. The Manhattan Project (7 and up)
    623.4
   Grant, R. G. Hiroshima and Nagasaki (7 and up)
    940.54
   Lawton, C. Hiroshima (5 and up)   **940.54**
   Making and using the atomic bomb (7 and up)
    355.8

Atomic energy *See* Nuclear energy

Atomic power plants *See* Nuclear power plants

Atomic theory
   Gallant, R. A. The ever changing atom (5 and up)
    539.7

Atoms
   Cooper, C. Matter   **530**
   Gallant, R. A. The ever changing atom (5 and up)
    539.7
   Woodford, C. Atoms and molecules (5 and up)
    540

Atoms and molecules. Woodford, C.   **540**

Attack of the killer video book. Shulman, M.
    778.59

Attack on America. Gow, M.   **973.931**

Attack on Pearl Harbor. Tanaka, S.   **940.54**

Attention deficit disorder
   Beal, E. Everything you need to know about ADD\ADHD (7 and up)   **616.85**
   Sheen, B. Attention deficit disorder   **616.85**
   Trueit, T. S. ADHD (5 and up)   **616.85**
              Fiction
   Gantos, J. Joey Pigza swallowed the key (5 and up)   **Fic**

Attention to detail. Haratani, R.
   In American dragons: twenty-five Asian American voices p120-25   **810.8**

Attila, King of the Huns, d. 453
              About
   Ingram, S. Attila the Hun   **92**
   See/See also pages in the following book(s):
   Meltzer, M. Ten kings (5 and up)   **920**

Attila the Hun. Ingram, S.   **92**

Attoe, Steve
   (il) Thomas, K. Blades, boards & scooters
    796.2

Auch, Mary Jane
   Ashes of roses (7 and up)   **Fic**
   Journey to nowhere   **Fic**
   Wing nut (5 and up)   **Fic**

Audiovisual materials
              Catalogs
   Adamson, L. G. Literature connections to American history, 7-12   **016.973**

Audiovisual materials—Catalogs—*Continued*
Adamson, L. G. Literature connections to world
history, 7-12 **016.9**

The **audition**. James, J. A.
In What a song can do; 12 riffs on the power
of music **S C**

The **Audubon** Society field guide to North
American butterflies. Pyle, R. M. **595.7**

The **Audubon** Society field guide to North
American insects and spiders. Milne, L. J.
595.7

The **Audubon** Society field guide to North
American mushrooms. Lincoff, G. **579.6**

The **Audubon** Society field guide to North
American rocks and minerals. Chesterman, C.
W. **549**

The **Audubon** Society field guide to North
American seashells. Rehder, H. A. **594**

The **Audubon** Society field guide to North
American seashore creatures. Meinkoth, N. A.
592

The **Audubon** Society field guide to the night sky.
Chartrand, M. R. **523**

Augenbraum, Harold
(ed) Growing up Latino. See Growing up Latino
810.8

August, Louise
(il) Musleah, R. Why on this night? **296.4**

August lights. Holt, K. W.
In Destination unexpected: short stories
S C

Augustin, Byron
United Arab Emirates (4 and up) **953**

Augustus, Emperor of Rome, 63 B.C.-14 A.D.
About
Forsyth, F. Augustus: the first emperor **92**

Augustus: the first emperor. Forsyth, F. **92**

Augustyn, Frank
Footnotes (5 and up) **792.8**

Aumakua. Salisbury, G.
In Salisbury, G. Island boyz: short stories
p95-117 **S C**

Aung San Suu Kyi
About
Stewart, W. Aung San Suu Kyi (7 and up)
92

See/See also pages in the following book(s):
Hacker, C. Nobel Prize winners **920**
Hewitt, K. Lives of extraordinary women (4 and
up) **920**
Price-Groff, C. Twentieth-century women politi-
cal leaders (7 and up) **920**

Aunt Horrible's last visit. Hecht, J.
In Vampires: a collection of original stories
p187-201 **S C**

Aunt Millicent. Steele, M.
In Read all about it!; great read-aloud stories,
poems, and newspaper pieces for preteens and teens p12-28 **808.8**

Aunt Moon's young man. Hogan, L.
In Talking leaves; contemporary native
American short stories **S C**

Aunt Parnetta's electric blisters. Glancy, D.
In Talking leaves; contemporary native
American short stories **S C**

Aunts
Fiction
Alvarez, J. How Tia Lola came to visit/stay (4
and up) **Fic**
Bauer, J. Backwater (7 and up) **Fic**
Bauer, J. Hope was here (7 and up) **Fic**
Brokaw, N. S. Leaving Emma **Fic**
Couloumbis, A. Getting near to baby (5 and up)
Fic
Fusco, K. N. Tending to Grace (7 and up)
Fic
Gordon, A. The Gorillas of Gill Park (4 and up)
Fic
Heneghan, J. Flood **Fic**
Horvath, P. The canning season **Fic**
Irwin, H. The original Freddie Ackerman (5 and
up) **Fic**
Lasky, K. Blood secret (7 and up) **Fic**
Matthews, K. Flying lessons **Fic**

Austen, Jane, 1775-1817
About
Ruth, A. Jane Austen **92**
Wagner, H. L. Jane Austen **92**

Austin, Stephen F. (Stephen Fuller), 1793-1836
About
Haley, J. L. Stephen F. Austin and the founding
of Texas **92**
See/See also pages in the following book(s):
Doherty, K. Ranchers, homesteaders, and traders
920

Australia
Arnold, C. Uluru, Australia's Aboriginal heart
(5 and up) **994**
Einfeld, J. Life in the Australian Outback
994
Grabowski, J. F. Australia (7 and up) **994**
Heinrichs, A. Australia (4 and up) **994**
Rajendra, V. Australia (5 and up) **994**
Fiction
Clarke, J. Kalpana's dream **Fic**
Cohn, R. The Steps (4 and up) **Fic**
Corbet, R. Fifteen love (7 and up) **Fic**
French, J. Hitler's daughter **Fic**
French, S. Where in the world (5 and up)
Fic
Goodman, A. Singing the Dogstar blues (7 and
up) **Fic**
Hartnett, S. Thursday's child (7 and up) **Fic**
Larbalestier, J. Magic or madness (7 and up)
Fic
Lester, A. Quicksand pony **Fic**
Lester, A. The snow pony **Fic**
Lowry, B. Follow the blue (7 and up) **Fic**
Lowry, B. Guitar highway Rose (7 and up)
Fic
Marsden, J. Checkers (7 and up) **Fic**
Marsden, J. Tomorrow, when the war began (7
and up) **Fic**
Moriarty, J. The year of secret assignments (7
and up) **Fic**
Murray, M. The slightly true story of Cedar B.
Hartley (5 and up) **Fic**

Australia—Fiction—*Continued*
Zusak, M. Fighting Ruben Wolfe (7 and up)
     Fic
Australian aborigines
Sharp, A. W. Australia   **994**
See/See also pages in the following book(s):
Einfeld, J. Life in the Australian Outback
    994
Australian painting
Finley, C. Aboriginal art of Australia   **759.01**
Austria
Sheehan, S. Austria (5 and up)   **943.6**
    History—Fiction
Denenberg, B. Elisabeth: the princess bride
    Fic
Author talk (4 and up)   **028.5**
Authoritative guide to kids' search engines, subject directories, and portals, Neal-Schuman. Haycock, K.   **025.04**
Authors
    See also Literature—Bio-bibliography; Women authors
Author talk (4 and up)   **028.5**
Gillespie, J. T. The Newbery companion
    028.5
The Newbery & Caldecott medal books, 1986-2000   **028.5**
Newbery and Caldecott Medal books, 1966-1975
    028.5
Newbery and Caldecott Medal books, 1976-1985
    028.5
Newbery Medal books, 1922-1955   **028.5**
Read all about it!   **808.8**
    Dictionaries
Authors & artists for young adults   **920.003**
Favorite children's authors and illustrators
    920.003
Great world writers: twentieth century
    920.003
The ninth book of junior authors and illustrators
    920.003
Something about the author   **920.003**
Something about the author: autobiography series   **920.003**
World authors, 1900-1950   **920.003**
World authors, 1950-1970   **920.003**
World authors, 1970-1975   **920.003**
World authors, 1975-1980   **920.003**
World authors, 1980-1985   **920.003**
World authors, 1985-1990   **920.003**
World authors, 1990-1995   **920.003**
World authors, 1995-2000   **920.003**
    Homes and haunts
    See Literary landmarks
Authors, African American *See* African American authors
Authors, American
Anderson, W. T. Laura Ingalls Wilder (4 and up)   **92**
Bauer, M. D. A writer's story (7 and up)
    92
Bostrom, K. L. Winning authors   **920**
Bruchac, J. Bowman's store   **92**
Byars, B. C. The moon and I (4 and up)
    92

Cammarano, R. Betsy Byars (4 and up)   **92**
Cleary, B. A girl from Yamhill: a memoir (6 and up)   **92**
Cleary, B. My own two feet   **92**
Cook, J. Natural writer: a story about Marjorie Kinnan Rawlings   **92**
Crutcher, C. King of the mild frontier: an ill-advised autobiography   **92**
Dean, T. Theodor Geisel [Dr. Seuss] (4 and up)
    92
Dyer, D. Jack London (7 and up)   **92**
Fine, E. H. Gary Paulsen (5 and up)   **92**
Fleischman, S. The abracadabra kid (5 and up)
    92
Freedman, J. Sid Fleischman (5 and up)   **92**
Fritz, J. Harriet Beecher Stowe and the Beecher preachers (5 and up)   **92**
Gantos, J. Hole in my life (7 and up)   **92**
George, J. C. A tarantula in my purse (4-6)
    92
Giff, P. R. Don't tell the girls (4 and up)
    92
Graham, P. W. Speaking of journals   **920**
Greene, M. Louis Sachar (5 and up)   **92**
Hart, J. Native son: the story of Richard Wright (7 and up)   **92**
Haskins, J. Toni Morrison (4 and up)   **92**
Kenschaft, L. Lydia Maria Child (7 and up)
    92
Kent, Z. Edgar Allan Poe   **92**
Lasky, K. A brilliant streak: the making of Mark Twain (4 and up)   **92**
Lazo, C. E. F. Scott Fitzgerald   **92**
Lowry, L. Looking back (5 and up)   **92**
Ludwig, E. Judy Blume   **92**
Lukes, B. L. Soldier's courage: the story of Stephen Crane (7 and up)   **92**
Mark Twain [essays about]   **92**
Meigs, C. L. Invincible Louisa [May Alcott]
    92
Meltzer, M. Edgar Allan Poe: a biography (7 and up)   **92**
Meltzer, M. Mark Twain himself   **92**
Meltzer, M. Milton Meltzer (7 and up)   **92**
Mirriam-Goldberg, C. Sandra Cisneros   **92**
Myers, W. D. Bad boy (7 and up)   **92**
Nixon, J. L. The making of a writer   **92**
Nuwer, H. To the young writer   **808**
Open your eyes (7 and up)   **910.4**
Paulsen, G. Caught by the sea (5 and up)
    92
Paulsen, G. Guts   **92**
Paulsen, G. How Angel Peterson got his name (5 and up)   **92**
Paulsen, G. My life in dog years (4 and up)
    92
Peet, B. Bill Peet: an autobiography (4 and up)
    92
Reef, C. John Steinbeck (7 and up)   **92**
Ruth, A. Louisa May Alcott   **92**
Seidman, D. Jerry Spinelli (5 and up)   **92**
Shields, C. J. Amy Tan   **92**
Spinelli, J. Knots in my yo-yo string (4 and up)
    92
Stefoff, R. Jack London (7 and up)   **92**
Streissguth, T. Jack London   **92**

Authors, American—*Continued*

Tessitore, J. John Steinbeck, a writer's life (7 and up) **92**

Thomson, S. L. Robert Cormier **92**

Thoreau, H. D. New suns will arise **92**

Trachtenberg, M. P. Anne McCaffrey **92**

Wilson, A. S.E. Hinton **92**

Wilson, S. Stephen King: king of thrillers and horror **92**

Wukovits, J. F. Stephen King (7 and up) **92**

Yannuzzi, D. A. Ernest Hemingway **92**

Yep, L. The lost garden (5 and up) **92**

Dictionaries

American authors, 1600-1900 **920.003**

Great American writers: twentieth century **920.003**

Writers for young adults **920.003**

Authors, English

Boerst, W. J. Generous anger: the story of George Orwell (7 and up) **92**

Carpenter, A. S. Lewis Carroll (7 and up) **92**

Dahl, R. Boy: tales of childhood **92**

Davenport, J. C.S. Lewis **92**

Gormley, B. C.S. Lewis **92**

Kenyon, K. The Brontë family (7 and up) **920**

King-Smith, D. Chewing the cud (5 and up) **92**

Lynch, D. J.R.R. Tolkien **92**

Miller, C. C. Mary Wollstonecraft and the rights of women (7 and up) **92**

Ruth, A. Jane Austen **92**

Stanley, D. Charles Dickens (4 and up) **92**

Wagner, H. L. Jane Austen **92**

Willett, E. J.R.R. Tolkien **92**

Authors, French

Schoell, W. Remarkable journeys: the story of Jules Verne **92**

Authors, Scottish

Murphy, J. Across America on an emigrant train (5 and up) **92**

Pascal, J. B. Arthur Conan Doyle (7 and up) **92**

Authors & artists for young adults **920.003**

Authors series

American authors, 1600-1900 **920.003**

World authors, 1900-1950 **920.003**

World authors, 1950-1970 **920.003**

World authors, 1970-1975 **920.003**

World authors, 1975-1980 **920.003**

World authors, 1980-1985 **920.003**

World authors, 1985-1990 **920.003**

Authors teens love [series]

Willett, E. J.R.R. Tolkien **92**

Authorship

See also Creative writing; Journalism

Bauer, M. D. Our stories (5 and up) **808.3**

Bauer, M. D. What's your story? (5 and up) **808.3**

Fletcher, R. How writers work (4 and up) **808**

Freedman, J. Sid Fleischman (5 and up) **92**

Harrison, D. L. Writing stories (4 and up) **808.3**

Janeczko, P. B. Writing winning reports and essays **808**

Nuwer, H. To the young writer **808**

Peck, R. Invitations to the world **808.06**

Trueit, T. S. Keeping a journal (5 and up) **808**

Young, S. Writing with style (5 and up) **808**

See/See also pages in the following book(s):

Graham, P. W. Speaking of journals **920**

Fiction

Clements, A. The school story (5 and up) **Fic**

Crew, G. Troy Thompson's excellent peotry book (4 and up) **Fic**

Grimes, N. Jazmin's notebook **Fic**

Hahn, M. D. Daphne's book (5 and up) **Fic**

Hinton, S. E. Taming the Star Runner **Fic**

Kimmel, E. C. Lily B. on the brink of cool **Fic**

Lisle, J. T. How I became a writer and Oggie learned to drive (4 and up) **Fic**

Nelson, T. Ruby electric (5 and up) **Fic**

Sitomer, A. L. The Hoopster (7 and up) **Fic**

Wittlinger, E. Hard love (7 and up) **Fic**

Handbooks, manuals, etc.

Henderson, K. The young writer's guide to getting published **808**

Autism

Baldwin, C. Autism (4-6) **616.89**

Fiction

Choldenko, G. Al Capone does my shirts (5 and up) **Fic**

Rodowsky, C. F. Clay **Fic**

The **autobiography** of Miss Jane Pittman. Gaines, E. J. **Fic**

Automata *See* Robots

Automobile accidents *See* Traffic accidents

Automobile drivers

Poetry

Wong, J. S. Behind the wheel (7 and up) **811**

Automobile industry

Bankston, J. Henry Ford and the assembly line **92**

Tilton, R. Henry Ford (7 and up) **92**

Automobile racing

Hodges, D. W. Classic racing cars **629.228**

Owens, T. NASCAR **796.72**

Automobile travel

Fiction

Wittlinger, E. Zigzag (7 and up) **Fic**

Automobiles

Edmonston, L.-P. Car smarts **629.222**

Hodges, D. W. Classic racing cars **629.228**

Willson, Q. Classic American cars (7 and up) **629.222**

Willson, Q. The ultimate classic car book **629.222**

Fiction

Young, K. R. The Beetle and me (7 and up) **Fic**

Autumn Street. Lowry, L. **Fic**

Avery, Ben

The hedge knight **741.5**

Avery, Henry *See* Avery, John, fl. 1695

Avery, John, fl. 1695
See/See also pages in the following book(s):
Wren, L. L. Pirates and privateers of the high
  seas p11-17   **920**

Avery, Susan, 1949-
Extraordinary American Indians   **920**

Avi, 1937-
The barn (4 and up)   **Fic**
Beyond the western sea   **Fic**
The Book Without Words (5 and up)   **Fic**
The Christmas rat   **Fic**
Crispin   **Fic**
Don't you know there's a war on? (4 and up)
    Fic
The fighting ground (5 and up)   **Fic**
How I got my English A
  In Tripping over the lunch lady and other
    school stories p17-28   **S C**
The man who was Poe   **Fic**
Midnight magic (5 and up)   **Fic**
Never mind! (5 and up)   **Fic**
Nothing but the truth (6 and up)   **Fic**
The secret school (4 and up)   **Fic**
The true confessions of Charlotte Doyle (6 and
  up)   **Fic**
What do fish have to do with anything? and
  other stories (4 and up)   **S C**
  Contents: What do fish have to do with anything?; The good-
  ness of Matt Kaizer; Talk to me; Teacher tamer; Pets; What's in-
  side; Fortune cookie
Wolf rider   **Fic**
You're not a winner unless your picture's in the
  paper
  In The Color of absence; 12 stories about loss
    and hope p147-66   **S C**
        About
Bloom, S. P. Presenting Avi (7 and up)
    813.009

Aviation *See* Aeronautics

Aviators *See* Air pilots

Avisson young adult series
Arruda, S. M. Freedom's martyr   **92**
Bruning, J. R. Elusive glory   **920**

Away to the goldfields!. Derby, P.   **Fic**

Axelrod-Contrada, Joan
Women who led nations (7 and up)   **920**

Ayer, Eleanor H.
Colorado
  In Celebrate the states   **973**
A firestorm unleashed   **940.53**
Germany (7 and up)   **943**
In the ghettos (7 and up)   **940.53**
Inferno   **940.53**
(jt. auth) Chicoine, S. From the ashes
    940.53

Ayres, Katherine
Macaroni boy (5 and up)   **Fic**
North by night (6 and up)   **Fic**

Azarian, Mary
See/See also pages in the following book(s):
The Newbery & Caldecott medal books, 1986-
  2000   **028.5**

The **Aztec** news. Steele, P.   **972**

Aztecs
Steele, P. The Aztec news   **972**
Tanaka, S. Lost temple of the Aztecs (4 and up)
    972

B

B. B. Potok, C.
In Potok, C. Zebra and other stories p26-43
    S C

B for Buster. Lawrence, I.   **Fic**

Baa baa, black sheep. Kipling, R.
In McCaffrey, A. {The Pern series}   **S C**

Babbage, Charles, 1791-1871
        About
Collier, B. Charles Babbage and the engines of
  perfection (7 and up)   **92**
See/See also pages in the following book(s):
Henderson, H. Modern mathematicians (7 and
  up)   **920**

Babies *See* Infants

The **baboon** king. Quintana, A.   **Fic**

Baboons
        Fiction
Quintana, A. The baboon king (7 and up)
    Fic

Baby Blue. Kwasney, M. D.   **Fic**

The **Baby** boom (7 and up)   **306**

The **baby** in the night deposit box. Turner, M. W.
In Firebirds: an anthology of original fantasy
  and science fiction; an anthology of original fantasy and science fiction   **S C**

The **baby** who loved pumpkins. Lester, J.
In Lester, J. The last tales of Uncle Remus
  p46-48   **398.2**

Babysitters
        Fiction
Konigsburg, E. L. Silent to the bone (7 and up)
    Fic
Lowry, L. Taking care of Terrific (7 and up)
    Fic
Wolff, V. E. Make lemonade   **Fic**

Bacarole for paper and bones. Anderson, M. T.
In Shelf life: stories by the book p127-49
    S C

Bachel, Beverly K., 1957-
What do you really want?   **153.8**

Bachman, Richard *See* King, Stephen, 1947-

Bacho, Peter
Boxing in black and white (7 and up)   **796.8**
A matter of faith
  In American eyes; new Asian-American short
    stories for young adults p131-42   **S C**

Bachrach, Deborah, 1943-
The Crimean War (7 and up)   **947**

Backpacking
Hart, J. Walking softly in the wilderness
    796.51

Backwater. Bauer, J.   **Fic**

Backyard birds. Latimer, J. P.   **598**

Bacon, Josephine, 1942-
Cooking the Israeli way
In Easy menu ethnic cookbooks   **641.5**
Bacon, Quentin
(il) Lagasse, E. Emeril's there's a chef in my family!   **641.5**
Bacteriologists
Birch, B. Alexander Fleming   **92**
Hantula, R. Alexander Fleming   **92**
Bad blood. Weaver, W.
In Destination unexpected: short stories
   S C
Bad boy. Myers, W. D.   **92**
Bad day for baseball. Salisbury, G.
In Shattered: stories of children and war p23-39   **S C**
Bad girls. Oates, J. C.
In Oates, J. C. Small avalanches and other stories   **S C**
Bad girls in love. Voigt, C.   **Fic**
Bad guys [series]
Blackwood, G. L. Gangsters   **364.1**
Blackwood, G. L. Highwaymen   **364.1**
Blackwood, G. L. Outlaws   **364.1**
Blackwood, G. L. Pirates   **364.1**
Blackwood, G. L. Swindlers   **364.1**
Bad Heart Buffalo, Amos, ca. 1869-1913
The life and death of Crazy Horse (5 and up)
   92
Bad influence. Ortiz Cofer, J.
In Leaving home: stories p63-90   **808.8**
In Ortiz Cofer, J. An island like you; stories of the barrio p1-26   **S C**
Bad man from Brodie. Nixon, J. L.
In Nixon, J. L. Ghost town; seven ghostly stories p102-24   **S C**
The **baddest** dog in Harlem. Myers, W. D.
In Myers, W. D. 145th Street; short stories
   S C
Baez, Joan
See/See also pages in the following book(s):
Orgill, R. Shout, sister, shout! (6 and up)
   920
Bagdasarian, Adam
First French kiss and other traumas (7 and up)
   Fic
Forgotten fire (7 and up)   **Fic**
Baguley, Kitt
(jt. auth) Winter, J. K. Venezuela   **987**
Bahai Faith
Hartz, P. Baha'i Faith (7 and up)   **297**
Bahamas
Barlas, R. Bahamas (5 and up)   **972.96**
Bahrain
Cooper, R. Bahrain   **953.6**
Bahrami, Mansour
See/See also pages in the following book(s):
Kaminsky, M. Uncommon champions   **920**
Bailey, Anne Hennis, 1742-1825
About
Furbee, M. R. Anne Bailey   **92**
Bailey, Jill
Birds of prey   **598**

Plants and plant life   **580**
Baines, Anthony
The Oxford companion to musical instruments (7 and up)   **784.19**
Bair, Barbara
Though justice sleeps (7 and up)   **305.8**
Baird, W. David
Geronimo, Apache warrior   **92**
Baja California (Mexico: Peninsula)
Fiction
O'Dell, S. The black pearl (6 and up)   **Fic**
Taylor, T. Sweet Friday Island (7 and up)
   Fic
Baker, Charles
(jt. auth) Rembert, W. Don't hold me back
   92
Baker, Charles F., III
(jt. auth) Baker, R. F. Ancient Egyptians
   932
(jt. auth) Baker, R. F. Ancient Greeks   **938**
Baker, Daniel B.
(ed) Explorers & discoverers. See Explorers & discoverers   **920.003**
Baker, Ella, 1903-1986
See/See also pages in the following book(s):
Hansen, J. Women of hope (4 and up)   **920**
Pinkney, A. D. Let it shine (4 and up)   **920**
Baker, Julie
Up Molasses Mountain   **Fic**
Baker, Lawrence W.
(jt. auth) Bruno, L. C. Math and mathematicians
   920
Baker, Rosalie F.
Ancient Egyptians (7 and up)   **932**
Ancient Greeks (7 and up)   **938**
In a word (5 and up)   **422**
(jt. auth) Rembert, W. Don't hold me back
   92
Bakke, Allan Paul
About
Banfield, S. The Bakke case (7 and up)   **344**
The **Bakke** case. Banfield, S.   **344**
Bakotahl. San Souci, R.
In San Souci, R. Dare to be scared; thirteen stories to chill and thrill   **S C**
Balance. English, J.
In Girls got game; sports stories and poems
   810.8
Balanchine, George, 1904-1983
101 stories of the great ballets   **792.8**
Balboa, Vasco Núñez de, 1475-1519
About
Otfinoski, S. Vasco Nuñez de Balboa (5 and up)
   92
See/See also pages in the following book(s):
Fritz, J. Around the world in a hundred years (4 and up)   **910.4**
Bald eagle
Barghusen, J. D. The bald eagle (7 and up)
   598
Patent, D. H. The bald eagle returns (4 and up)
   598
The **bald** eagle returns. Patent, D. H.   **598**

The **Bald** Mountain monster. San Souci, R.
   In San Souci, R. Dare to be scared; thirteen
     stories to chill and thrill   **S C**

Baldwin, Carol
   Autism (4-6)   **616.89**
   Sickle cell disease (4-6)   **616.1**

Baldwin, Guy
   Oklahoma
     In Celebrate the states   **973**
   Wyoming
     In Celebrate the states   **973**

Baldwin, James, 1924-1987
   Go tell it on the mountain (7 and up)   **Fic**

Balkin, Karen
   (ed) Anorexia. See Anorexia   **616.85**
   (ed) Tobacco and smoking: opposing view-
     points. See Tobacco and smoking: opposing
     viewpoints   **362.29**

Ball, Lucille, 1911-1989
   See/See also pages in the following book(s):
   Stewart, G. Great women comedians   **920**

Ballad of a prodigy. Mandell, J.
   In What a song can do; 12 riffs on the power
     of music   **S C**

The **ballad** of Lucy Whipple. Cushman, K.
     Fic

Ballard, Robert D., 1942-
   The discovery of the Titanic (7 and up)
     910.4
   Ghost liners (4 and up)   **910.4**

Ballet
   Augustyn, F. Footnotes (5 and up)   **792.8**
   Goh, C. H. Beyond the dance   **92**
       Fiction
   Deans, S. B. Every day and all the time (5 and
     up)   **Fic**
   Freymann-Weyr, G. The kings are already here
     (7 and up)   **Fic**
   Hewett, L. Dancer (7 and up)   **Fic**
       Stories, plots, etc.
   Balanchine, G. 101 stories of the great ballets
     792.8

Ballet dancers
   Glassman, B. Mikhail Baryshnikov   **92**

Balmer, Randall Herbert
   Religion in twentieth century America (7 and
     up)   **200.9**

La **Bamba**. Soto, G.
   In Soto, G. Baseball in April, and other sto-
     ries p81-89   **S C**

Bambara, Toni Cade
   Raymond's run
     In Who do you think you are?; stories of
     friends and enemies p47-57   **S C**

Bandit's moon. Smith, J. A.   **Fic**

Banfield, Susan
   The Bakke case (7 and up)   **344**
   Inside recovery   **616.86**

Bangladesh
   Whyte, M. Bangladesh (5 and up)   **954.92**

A **bank** fraud. Kipling, R.
   In McCaffrey, A. {The Pern series}   **S C**

Banks, Deena
   Amnesty International   **323**

Banks, Kate, 1960-
   Walk softly, Rachel (7 and up)   **Fic**

Banks, Lynne Reid, 1929-
   Alice-by-accident   **Fic**
   Maura's angel   **Fic**

Banks, Sara H., 1942-
   Abraham's battle   **Fic**

Bankston, John
   Henry Ford and the assembly line   **92**
   Stephen Hawking   **92**

Banneker, Benjamin, 1731-1806
       About
   Hinman, B. Benjamin Banneker (5 and up)
     92
   Litwin, L. B. Benjamin Banneker   **92**

Banning, Herman, d. 1933
   See/See also pages in the following book(s):
   Hart, P. S. Flying free (4 and up)   **629.13**

Banning, James Herman *See* Banning, Herman,
   d. 1933

Bansavage, Lisa
   (ed) Shakespeare, W. One hundred and eleven
     Shakespeare monologues   **822.3**

Barakat, Ibtisam
   Piano obsession
     In What a song can do; 12 riffs on the power
     of music   **S C**
   The second day
     In Shattered: stories of children and war p5-
     13   **S C**

Barbados
   Elias, M. L. Barbados (5 and up)   **972.98**

Barbara McClintock, geneticist. Cullen, J. H.
     92

Barber, Daniel Wynn
   Tiger in the snow
     In Beware!; R.L. Stine picks his favorite
     scary stories p127-37   **808.8**

Barber, Nicola
   Music: an A-Z guide (4 and up)   **780.3**
   (jt. auth) Ganeri, A. The young person's guide
     to the opera   **792.5**

The **barber's** wife. Tchana, K. H.
   In Tchana, K. H. The serpent slayer: and oth-
     er stories of strong women p7-12
     398.2

Barbie. Soto, G.
   In Soto, G. Baseball in April, and other sto-
     ries p33-42   **S C**

Barbour, Karen
   (il) Herrera, J. F. Laughing out loud, I fly
     811
   (il) Marvelous math. See Marvelous math
     811.008

Barbour, Scott
   The environment (7 and up)   **363.7**
   (ed) Free speech. See Free speech   **342**

Bard, Mitchell Geoffrey, 1959-
   (ed) The Complete history of the Holocaust. See
     The Complete history of the Holocaust
     940.53

Bard of Avon: the story of William Shakespeare. Stanley, D.   **822.3**

Bardhan-Quallen, Sudipta
Chemotherapy (7 and up)   **616.99**
The Mexican-American War (5 and up)   **973.6**

Barefoot dancer: the story of Isadora Duncan. O'Connor, B.   **92**

The **barefoot** serpent. Morse, S.   **741.5**

Barghusen, Joan D., 1935-
The bald eagle (7 and up)   **598**
Cults (7 and up)   **209**

Barghusen, Laura, 1964-
The bear (7 and up)   **599.78**

Barker, Clive
Abarat (7 and up)   **Fic**

Barker, Keith, d. 1998
Outstanding books for children and young people   **028.5**

Barkin, Carol, 1944-
(jt. auth) James, E. How to write terrific book reports   **808**
(jt. auth) James, E. Social smarts   **395**

Barkley, James
(il) Armstrong, W. H. Sounder   **Fic**

Barlas, Robert
Bahamas (5 and up)   **972.96**
Latvia (5 and up)   **947.9**
Uganda (5 and up)   **967.6**

The **barn**. Avi   **Fic**

Barnard, Alan
(il) Tanaka, S. Graveyards of the dinosaurs   **567.9**

Barnard, Bryn
Dangerous planet   **363.34**

Barnes, Marian E.
(ed) Talk that talk: an anthology of African-American storytelling. See Talk that talk: an anthology of African-American storytelling   **398.2**

Barnes, Trevor
Archaeology (5 and up)   **930.1**
The Kingfisher book of religions   **201**

Barnett, Ida B. Wells- See Wells-Barnett, Ida B., 1862-1931

Barney, William L.
The Civil War and Reconstruction (7 and up)   **973.7**

Barnhart, Robert K.
(ed) The Barnhart dictionary of etymology. See The Barnhart dictionary of etymology   **422.03**

The **Barnhart** dictionary of etymology   **422.03**

The **baron** of Petronia. Vizenor, G. R.
In Talking leaves; contemporary native American short stories   **S C**

Barr, Catherine
(ed) From biography to history. See From biography to history   **016.8**

Barr, Gary, 1951-
Pearl Harbor   **940.54**
World War II home front   **940.53**

Barr, Roseanne
See/See also pages in the following book(s):
Stewart, G. Great women comedians   **920**

Barrett, Cece
The dangers of diet drugs and other weight-loss products   **615**

Barrett, Joanne R., 1960-
Teaching and learning about computers   **004**

Barrett, Paul M.
National Geographic dinosaurs   **567.9**

Barrett, Tracy, 1955-
Anna of Byzantium   **Fic**
Cold in summer (5 and up)   **Fic**
Kentucky
In Celebrate the states   **973**
Tennessee
In Celebrate the states   **973**
Virginia
In Celebrate the states   **973**

Barron, Ann E.
Technologies for education   **371.3**

Barron, Pamela Petrick, 1946-
(jt. auth) Doll, C. A. Managing and analyzing your collection   **025.2**

Barron, Rachel
John Coltrane (7 and up)   **92**
Richard Nixon (7 and up)   **92**

Barron, T. A.
The lost years of Merlin (6 and up)   **Fic**
The Merlin effect   **Fic**

Barron's how to prepare for high school entrance examinations, SSAT, ISEE. See Shostak, J. How to prepare for the SSAT/ ISEE: Secondary School Admissions Test/Independent School Entrance Exam   **373.1**

Barron's science study dictionary. Prescott, C.   **503**

Barry, Dave
Peter and the starcatchers (5 and up)   **Fic**

Barter, James, 1946-
The Amazon   **981**
The Ganges (7 and up)   **954**
Hallucinogens (7 and up)   **362.29**
The Nile   **962**
Renaissance Florence   **945**
A Renaissance painter's studio   **759.5**
Shakespeare's London (7 and up)   **942.06**
A worker on the transcontinental railroad   **331.7**

Barth, Kelly
(ed) The Tiananmen Square massacre. See The Tiananmen Square massacre   **951.05**

Bartimaeus trilogy [series]
Stroud, J. The Amulet of Samarkand   **Fic**

Bartlett, John, 1820-1905
Familiar quotations   **808.88**

Bartlett's Roget's thesaurus   **423**

Bartoletti, Susan Campbell
Hitler Youth (7 and up)   **943.086**

Bartoletti, Susan Campbell, 1958-
Black potatoes (7 and up)   **941.5**
A coal miner's bride (4 and up)   **Fic**
Growing up in coal country (5 and up)   **331.3**

Bartoletti, Susan Campbell, 1958-—_Continued_
The journal of Finn Reardon (4 and up)   **Fic**
Kids on strike! (5 and up)   **331.8**
No man's land (5 and up)   **Fic**

Barton, Clara, 1821-1912
About
Whitelaw, N. Clara Barton   **92**
See/See also pages in the following book(s):
DeAngelis, G. Science & medicine   **920**

Barton, Otis
About
Matsen, B. The incredible record-setting deep-sea dive of the bathysphere (4 and up)   **551.46**

Baryshnikov, Mikhail, 1948-
About
Glassman, B. Mikhail Baryshnikov   **92**

Baseball
See also Softball
Buckley, J., Jr. The visual dictionary of baseball   **796.357**
Geng, D. Play-by-play baseball (5 and up)   **796.357**
Krasner, S. Play ball like the pros (4 and up)   **796.357**
McKissack, P. C. Black diamond (6 and up)   **796.357**
Owens, T. Collecting baseball memorabilia   **790.1**
Smyth, I. The young baseball player (4 and up)   **796.357**
Biography
Copley, B. The tall Mexican: the life of Hank Aguirre, all-star pitcher, businessman, humanitarian (7 and up)   **92**
Gallagher, J. Pedro Martinez   **92**
Green, M. Y. A strong right arm: the story of Mamie "Peanut" Johnson (4 and up)   **92**
McCormack, S. Cool Papa Bell   **92**
Payment, S. Buck Leonard   **92**
Robinson, S. Promises to keep: how Jackie Robinson changed America (4 and up)   **92**
Twemlow, N. Josh Gibson   **92**
Fiction
Brooks, B. Throwing smoke   **Fic**
Chabon, M. Summerland (5 and up)   **Fic**
Deuker, C. Painting the black (7 and up)   **Fic**
Gutman, D. Shoeless Joe & me (4 and up)   **Fic**
Johnston, T. Never so green (7 and up)   **Fic**
Lynch, C. Gold dust   **Fic**
Murphy, C. R. Free radical (7 and up)   **Fic**
Myers, W. D. The journal of Biddy Owens, the Negro leagues   **Fic**
Myers, W. D. Me, Mop, and the Moondance Kid (4-6)   **Fic**
Ritter, J. H. The boy who saved baseball (5 and up)   **Fic**
Ritter, J. H. Choosing up sides   **Fic**
Tocher, T. Chief Sunrise, John McGraw, and me   **Fic**
History
Stewart, M. World Series   **796.357**

Statistics
Neft, D. S. The sports encyclopedia: baseball   **796.357**

Baseball camp. Klass, D.
_In_ Places I never meant to be; original stories by censored writers   **S C**

Baseball cards
Owens, T. Collecting baseball cards   **769**

Baseball Hall of Famers of the Negro leagues [series]
McCormack, S. Cool Papa Bell   **92**
Payment, S. Buck Leonard   **92**
Twemlow, N. Josh Gibson   **92**

Baseball in April. Soto, G.
_In_ Soto, G. Baseball in April, and other stories p13-22   **S C**

Baseball in April, and other stories. Soto, G.   **S C**

Basher five-two. O'Grady, S. F.   **949.7**

Bashfulness _See_ Shyness

Basic Japanese-English dictionary   **495.6**

Basic life skills _See_ Life skills

Basic rights _See_ Civil rights; Human rights

The **basket** counts. Adoff, A.   **811**

Basketball
Burgan, M. Great moments in basketball   **796.323**
Lannin, J. A history of basketball for girls and women   **796.323**
Stewart, M. Basketball (7 and up)   **796.323**
Stewart, M. Jackie Stiles (4 and up)   **92**
Fiction
Deuker, C. Night hoops (7 and up)   **Fic**
Deuker, C. On the Devil's court (7 and up)   **Fic**
Gutman, D. The million dollar shot   **Fic**
Klass, D. Danger zone   **Fic**
Lupica, M. Travel team   **Fic**
Myers, W. D. Hoops   **Fic**
Myers, W. D. Slam! (7 and up)   **Fic**
Sitomer, A. L. The Hoopster (7 and up)   **Fic**
Soto, G. Taking sides (5 and up)   **Fic**
Wallace, R. Playing without the ball   **Fic**
Poetry
Adoff, A. The basket counts   **811**
Burleigh, R. Hoops   **811**
Smith, C. R. Hoop queens   **811**

Basketball's new wave [series]
Stewart, M. Jackie Stiles   **92**

Baskin, Nora Raleigh, 1961-
Almost home   **Fic**
What every girl (except me) knows (4 and up)   **Fic**

Basman, Michael
Chess for kids (4 and up)   **794.1**

Bassil, Andrea
Vincent van Gogh (4 and up)   **92**

Bassis, Volodymyr
Ukraine (5 and up)   **947.7**

Bat-Ami, Miriam, 1950-
Two suns in the sky (7 and up)   **Fic**

Bateman, Robert, 1930-
Safari (4 and up)   **599**

Bateman, Teresa
The dragon at the well
In Fire and wings: dragon tales from East and
West p1-14   **S C**
Red, white, blue, and Uncle who? (4 and up)
    929.9
Waiting for a white knight
In Fire and wings: dragon tales from East and
West p137-40   **S C**

Bates, Daisy
About
Fradin, J. B. The power of one [biography of
Daisy Bates] (7 and up)   **92**
Polakow, A. Daisy Bates (7 and up)   **92**

Bath, K. P.
The secret of Castle Cant (5 and up)   **Fic**

Batman (Comic strip)
Dini, P. The Batman adventures   **741.5**
The **Batman** adventures. Dini, P.   **741.5**

Batmanglij, Najmieh
See/See also pages in the following book(s):
Major, J. S. Caravan to America p[1]-13 (4 and
up)   **920**

Bats
Fiction
Oppel, K. Silverwing (5 and up)   **Fic**

Batten, Mary
Anthropologist: scientist of the people (4 and
up)   **301**

Battered children *See* Child abuse

Battered women   **362.82**

Battering of wives *See* Wife abuse

Batting after Sophie. Macy, S.
In Girls got game; sports stories and poems
    810.8

The **battle** against polio. Peters, S. T.   **614.5**

Battle dress. Efaw, A.   **Fic**

The **Battle** of Antietam. Hughes, C.   **973.7**

The **battle** of birds. Philip, N.
In Philip, N. Celtic fairy tales p15-26
    398.2

The **Battle** of Bull Run. Kops, D.   **973.7**

The **battle** of Chihaya Castle. Kimmel, E. A.
In Kimmel, E. A. Sword of the samurai; adventure stories from Japan p53-62
    Fic

The **Battle** of Gettysburg. King, D. C.   **973.7**

The **Battle** of Jericho. Draper, S. M.   **Fic**

Battle of the Bulge *See* Ardennes, Battle of the,
1944-1945

The **Battle** of the Little Bighorn. Uschan, M. V.
    973.8

The **Battle** of the Little Bighorn in American history. Ferrell, N. W.   **973.8**

The **Battle** of Vicksburg. King, D. C.   **973.7**

Battles and leaders [series]
World War II battles and leaders   **940.54**

Bauer, Joan
Backwater (7 and up)   **Fic**
Clean sweep
In Shelf life: stories by the book p151-64
    S C

Hardware
In Necessary noise: stories about our families
as they really are p1-20   **S C**
Hope was here (7 and up)   **Fic**
A letter from the fringe
In On the fringe p181-91   **S C**
Rules of the road (7 and up)   **Fic**
Squashed   **Fic**
Stand tall   **Fic**

Bauer, Marion Dane, 1938-
An early winter   **Fic**
The good deed
In Shelf life: stories by the book p109-26
    S C
Land of the buffalo bones   **Fic**
On my honor (4 and up)   **Fic**
Our stories (5 and up)   **808.3**
What's your story? (5 and up)   **808.3**
A writer's story (7 and up)   **92**

Baumfree, Isabella *See* Truth, Sojourner, d. 1883

Bausum, Ann
Dragon bones and dinosaur eggs: a
photobiography of Roy Chapman Andrews (5
and up)   **92**
Our country's presidents (5 and up)   **920**
With courage and cloth   **305.4**

Bawden, Nina, 1925-
Granny the Pag (4 and up)   **Fic**
Off the road   **Fic**

Baxter, Kathleen A.
Gotcha!   **028.1**

Baynes, Pauline, 1922-
(il) Lewis, C. S. The lion, the witch, and the
wardrobe   **Fic**

Bazin, Maurice
Math and science across cultures   **510**

Bazler, Judith A.
More science projects for all students   **507.8**
(ed) Science experiments on file. See Science
experiments on file   **507.8**

Be healthy! it's a girl thing. Cheung, L. W.-Y.
    613

Beaches
Fiction
Howe, J. The watcher (7 and up)   **Fic**
Poetry
Fletcher, R. Have you been to the beach lately?
    811

Beachmont letters. Twomey, C.   **Fic**

Beacon Hill boys. Mochizuki, K.   **Fic**

The **beaded** moccasins. Durrant, L.   **Fic**

Beal, Eileen
Everything you need to know about
ADD\ADHD (7 and up)   **616.85**
Ritalin (7 and up)   **616.85**

Beale, Fleur
I am not Esther (7 and up)   **Fic**

Beanie. Woodson, J.
In Girls got game; sports stories and poems
    810.8

Bear, Greg, 1951-
Tangents
In New skies: an anthology of today's science
fiction   **S C**

The **bear** man. Brown, D. A.
   In Brown, D. A. Dee Brown's folktales of the
    Native American; retold for our times
    p18-22   **398.2**

Beard, Hilary
   (jt. auth) Williams, V. Venus & Serena   **92**

Bearden, Romare, 1914-1988
        About
   Greenberg, J. Romare Bearden (4 and up)
                               92

Beardsley, John
   Pablo Picasso (7 and up)   **92**

Bearing, Paul. Lynch, C.
   In Night terrors; stories of shadow and sub-
    stance   **S C**

Bearing witness. Rosen, P.   **016.94053**

Bears
   See also Polar bear
   Barghusen, L. The bear (7 and up)   **599.78**
   Hehner, B. Ice Age cave bear (5 and up)
                              569
   Montgomery, S. Search for the golden moon
    bear (5 and up)   **599.78**
   Stonehouse, B. Bears   **599.78**
   Ward, P. Wild bears of the world   **599.78**
             Fiction
   Mikaelsen, B. Touching Spirit Bear   **Fic**
   Pattou, E. East   **Fic**
   Zucker, N. F. Benno's bear   **Fic**

Bearstone. Hobbs, W.   **Fic**

The **Beast.** Myers, W. D.   **Fic**

Beast. Napoli, D. J.   **Fic**

Beast and Beauty. Vande Velde, V.
   In Vande Velde, V. Tales from the Brothers
    Grimm and the Sisters Weird p109-28
                          S C

The **beast** is in the labyrinth. Myers, W. D.
   In Places I never meant to be; original stories
    by censored writers   **S C**

Beattie, Owen
   Buried in ice (4 and up)   **998**

Beatty, Patricia, 1922-1991
   Jayhawker (5 and up)   **Fic**

Beatty, Richard
   Manganese
    In The Elements   **546**
   Phosphorus
    In The Elements   **546**
   Sulfur
    In The Elements   **546**

Beatty, Scott
   Superman   **741.5**

Beauties and beasts. Hearne, B. G.   **398.2**

The **beautiful** girl of the moon tower. Hamilton,
V.
   In Hamilton, V. The people could fly;
    American black folktales p53-59
                        398.2

The **beautiful** thing. Mazer, H.
   In Night terrors; stories of shadow and sub-
    stance   **S C**

Beauty. McKinley, R.   **Fic**

Beauty. Smith, S.
   In Firebirds: an anthology of original fantasy
    and science fiction; an anthology of orig-
    inal fantasy and science fiction   **S C**

Beauty and the Beast
   In Hearne, B. G. Beauties and beasts p3-13
                          398.2

Beauty lessons. Ortiz Cofer, J.
   In Ortiz Cofer, J. An island like you; stories
    of the barrio p41-54   **S C**

Because of Winn-Dixie. DiCamillo, K.   **Fic**

Beck, Ian
   (il) Geras, A. The Random House book of opera
    stories   **792.5**

Beck, Peggy
   GlobaLinks: resources for world studies, grades
    K-8   **016.9**

Beckelman, Laurie
   The human body   **612**

Beckham, Eugene C.
   (il) Page, L. M. A field guide to freshwater fish-
    es: North America north of Mexico   **597**

Beckwourth, James Pierson, 1798-1866
   See/See also pages in the following book(s):
   Haskins, J. Against all opposition (5 and up)
                           920

Becoming. Springer, N.
   In Half-human p1-17   **S C**

Becoming Joe DiMaggio. Testa, M.   **811**

Becoming Naomi León. Ryan, P. M.   **Fic**

Bedard, Michael, 1949-
   The painted wall and other strange tales (7 and
    up)   **398.2**

Beddows, Eric, 1951-
   (il) Fleischman, P. I am phoenix: poems for two
    voices   **811**
   (il) Fleischman, P. Joyful noise: poems for two
    voices   **811**

Bedouins
             Fiction
   Temple, F. The Beduins' gazelle   **Fic**

Bedtime snacks. Yep, L.
   In Yep, L. The rainbow people p4-10
                          398.2

The **Beduins'** gazelle. Temple, F.   **Fic**

Beebe, William, 1877-1962
          About
   Matsen, B. The incredible record-setting deep-
    sea dive of the bathysphere (4 and up)
                         551.46

Beebyeebyee and the Water God. Tchana, K. H.
   In Tchana, K. H. The serpent slayer: and oth-
    er stories of strong women p37-41
                         398.2

Beech, Olive Ann, 1903-1993
   See/See also pages in the following book(s):
   Jeffrey, L. S. Great American businesswomen
                         920

Beecher family
          About
   Fritz, J. Harriet Beecher Stowe and the Beecher
    preachers (5 and up)   **92**

Beecroft, Simon
The release of Nelson Mandela   968.06
Beekman's big deal. De Guzman, M.   Fic
Been to yesterdays: poems of a life. Hopkins, L.
B.   811
Beer, Amy-Jane
(jt. auth) Morris, P. Mammals   599
Beers, Kylene
(ed) Into focus. See Into focus   028.1
The **Beetle** and me. Young, K. R.   Fic
Beetles
Pascoe, E. Beetles   595.7
Before the storm. Lassieur, A.   970.004
Before we were free. Alvarez, J.   Fic
Before wings. Goobie, B.   Fic
Begay, Shonto, 1954-
Star vision
In Soul searching: thirteen stories about faith
and belief p220-27   S C
The **beginning.** Ackroyd, P.   576.8
Beginning life. Flanagan, G. L.   612.6
The **beginning** of something. Bridgers, S. E.
In Visions: nineteen short stories by outstand-
ing writers for young adults p213-28
S C
The **beginning** of the world. Curry, J. L.
In Curry, J. L. Hold up the sky: and other
Native American tales from Texas and
the Southern Plains p1-6   398.2
Beginning with the ears. Olson, A. N.
In Olson, A. N. and Schwartz, H. Ask the
bones: scary stories from around the
world p42-45   398.2
Behavior, Compulsive *See* Compulsive behavior
Behavior, Sexual *See* Sexual behavior
The **behavior** survival guide for kids. McIntyre, T.
158
Behind barbed wire. Perl, L.   940.53
Behind the Blue and Gray. Ray, D.   973.7
Behind the mask: the life of Queen Elizabeth I.
Thomas, J. R.   92
Behind the mountains. Danticat, E.   Fic
Behind the wheel. Wong, J. S.   811
Behind you. Woodson, J.   Fic
Behnke, Alison
Afghanistan in pictures (5 and up)   958.1
China in pictures   951
Italy in pictures (5 and up)   945
Japan in pictures (5 and up)   952
Beier, Ulli
(ed) The Penguin book of modern African poet-
ry. See The Penguin book of modern African
poetry   896
Beil, Karen Magnuson, 1950-
Fire in their eyes (4 and up)   628.9
Being dead. Vande Velde, V.   S C
Being human   612
Being with Henry. Brooks, M.   Fic
Belanus, Betty J.
(jt. auth) Major, J. S. Caravan to America
920

Belarus
Levy, P. M. Belarus (5 and up)   947.8
Belfast (Northern Ireland)
Fiction
Banks, L. R. Maura's angel   Fic
Belgium
Pateman, R. Belgium (5 and up)   949.3
Belize
Jermyn, L. Belize (5 and up)   972.82
Shields, C. J. Belize (4 and up)   972.82
Bell, Alexander Graham, 1847-1922
About
Matthews, T. L. Always inventing: a
photobiography of Alexander Graham Bell (4
and up)   92
Bell, Cool Papa, 1903-1991
About
McCormack, S. Cool Papa Bell   92
Bell, David C.
(il) Pascoe, E. Scholastic kid's almanac
031.02
Bell, Gertrude Margaret Lowthian, 1868-1926
See/See also pages in the following book(s):
Greenberg, L. Digging into the past   920
Hewitt, K. Lives of extraordinary women (4 and
up)   920
Bell, Hilari, 1958-
Flame   Fic
The Goblin Wood   Fic
A matter of profit (7 and up)   Fic
Bell, Janet Cheatham
(ed) Stretch your wings. See Stretch your wings
808.88
Bell, M. Shayne, 1957-
The pagodas of Ciboure
In The Green Man: tales from the mythic for-
est p322-47   808.8
Bell, Ruth
Changing bodies, changing lives (7 and up)
613.9
Bell, Suzanne
Encyclopedia of forensic science   363.2
Bellairs, John
The curse of the blue figurine (5 and up)
Fic
Bellamy, Samuel, d. 1717
See/See also pages in the following book(s):
Wren, L. L. Pirates and privateers of the high
seas p11-17   920
Belle Prater's boy. White, R.   Fic
Bellenir, Karen
(ed) Diet information for teens. See Diet infor-
mation for teens   613.2
(ed) Mental health information for teens. See
Mental health information for teens
616.89
Beller, Susan Provost, 1949-
Billy Yank & Johnny Reb (5 and up)   973.7
The Civil War   973.7
Confederate ladies of Richmond   973.7
The Revolutionary War   973.3

Bells
Fiction
Spencer, A. And round me rings (7 and up)
398.2

Belpré, Pura
Tropical memories
In You're on!: seven plays in English and
Spanish p34-41   812.008
Belzoni, Giovanni Battista, 1778-1823
See/See also pages in the following book(s):
Greenberg, L. Digging into the past   920
Ben. Lester, J.
In Lester, J. Long journey home: stories from
black history p59-88   S C
Ben Franklin's almanac. Fleming, C.   92
Bender, David L., 1936-
Cloning. See Cloning [At issue]   174.2
The Rise of Christianity. See The Rise of Chris-
tianity   270
Bender, Howard
(il) Pellowski, M. The art of making comic
books   741.5
Bender, Lionel
Invention (4 and up)   609
Benedict Arnold and the American Revolution.
King, D. C.   92
Benét, Stephen Vincent, 1898-1943
By the waters of Babylon
In Read into the millennium; tales of the fu-
ture p147-60   S C
Benet's reader's encyclopedia   803
Benjamin Franklin [essays about] (7 and up)
92
Bennett, Cherie
A heart divided (7 and up)
Life in the fat lane (7 and up)   Fic
Zink   Fic
Bennett, Clayton
Montana
In Celebrate the states   973
Bennett, Jay, 1912-
Coverup (7 and up)   Fic
Sing me a death song (7 and up)   Fic
Bennett, Michelle, 1946-
Missouri
In Celebrate the states   973
Bennett, William John, 1943-
(ed) Our country's founders. See Our country's
founders   973
Benno's bear. Zucker, N. F.   Fic
Benowitz, Steven I.
Cancer (7 and up)   616.99
Benson, Allen C.
Connecting kids & the Web   004.6
Neal-Schuman complete Internet companion for
librarians   004.6
Benson, Kathleen, 1947-
(jt. auth) Haskins, J. African beginnings   960
(jt. auth) Haskins, J. Bound for America
326
(jt. auth) Haskins, J. Out of the darkness
305.8

Benson, Peter L.
What teens need to succeed (7 and up)
305.23
Benson, Sally
Relationships
In Being human   612
Benson, Sonia
Korean War: almanac and primary sources (7
and up)   951.9
Korean War: biographies (7 and up)   920
Bentley, Diana
The seven wonders of the ancient world
722
Benton, Thomas Hart, 1782-1858
See/See also pages in the following book(s):
Kennedy, J. F. Profiles in courage   920
Beowulf. Osborne, M. P.
In Osborne, M. P. Favorite medieval tales p8-
16   398.2
Berberick, Nancy Varian
A song for Croaker Nordge
In A Glory of unicorns p127-43   S C
Bereavement
Dennison, A. Our dad died (4 and up)
155.9
Gootman, M. E. When a friend dies (7 and up)
155.9
Myers, E. When will I stop hurting? (7 and up)
155.9
Schleifer, J. Everything you need to know when
someone you know has been killed (7 and up)
155.9
See/See also pages in the following book(s):
Death and dying: opposing viewpoints p55-96 (7
and up)   155.9
Fiction
Deans, S. B. Every day and all the time (5 and
up)   Fic
Johnson, M. The key to the golden Firebird (7
and up)   Fic
Lion, M. Upstream (7 and up)   Fic
Stein, T. Light years (7 and up)   Fic
Berenice. Poe, E. A.
In Poe, E. A. Tales of Edgar Allan Poe p293-
304   S C
Berenzy, Alix, 1957-
(il) A Glory of unicorns. See A Glory of uni-
corns   S C
Berg, Elizabeth, 1953-
Senegal (5 and up)   966.3
Berger, Gilda
Celebrate! (4 and up)   296.4
(jt. auth) Berger, M. Mummies of the pharaohs
932
Berger, James, 1954-
(ed) Keller, H. The story of my life   92
Berger, Melvin, 1927-
Mummies of the pharaohs   932
Bergin, Mark
(il) Green, J. Race to the moon   629.45
(il) Malam, J. Super structures   624
(il) Morley, J. Viking town   948

Berlin, Irving, 1888-1989
About
Furstinger, N. Say it with music: the story of Irving Berlin   **92**

Berman, Avis
James McNeill Whistler (7 and up)   **92**

Bernard, Catherine
Understanding To kill a mockingbird (7 and up)   **813.009**

Bernard, Nancy Stone
(jt. auth) Malone, C. Stonehenge   **936.2**
(jt. auth) Smith, S. T. Valley of the Kings   **932**

Berndt, Jeff
(jt. auth) Irwin, J. Vögelein   **741.5**

Bernstein, Jeremy, 1929-
Albert Einstein and the frontiers of physics (7 and up)   **92**

Bernstein, Leonard, 1918-1990
About
Blashfield, J. F. Leonard Bernstein (7 and up)   **92**

Bernstein, Zena
(il) O'Brien, R. C. Mrs. Frisby and the rats of NIMH   **Fic**

Berry, James
Ajeemah and his son   **Fic**

Besheer, Margaret
(jt. auth) Janin, H. Saudi Arabia   **953.8**

Beshore, George W.
Science in ancient China (4 and up)   **509**
Science in early Islamic culture (4 and up)   **509**

Bess. Schwartz, A.
In Schwartz, A. Scary stories 3; more tales to chill your bones p27-29   **398.2**

Bess Call. San Souci, R.
In San Souci, R. Cut from the same cloth; American women of myth, legend, and tall tale p13-18   **398.2**

Best books
Best books for young adult readers   **011.6**
Carter, B. Best books for young adults   **028.1**
Jones, P. A core collection for young adults   **011.6**
Jweid, R. Building character through literature   **028.5**
New York Public Library. Books for the teen age   **011.6**
Notable social studies trade books for young people   **016.3**
Outstanding science trade books for students K-12   **016.5**
Your reading   **011.6**

Best books for young adult readers   **011.6**
Best books for young adults. Carter, B.   **028.1**
The **best** Christmas pageant ever. Robinson, B.   **Fic**

Best friends. San Souci, R.
In San Souci, R. Double-dare to be scared: another thirteen chilling tales   **S C**

The **best** of Latino heritage 1996-2002. Schon, I.   **011.6**
The **best** of Shakespeare. Nesbit, E.   **822.3**
The **best** of the Latino heritage. Schon, I.   **011.6**

Bethancourt, T. Ernesto
Blues for Bob. E. Brown
In Join in; multiethnic short stories by outstanding writers for young adults p201-18   **S C**
Fury
In Ultimate sports; short stories by outstanding writers for young adults p21-49   **S C**

Bethune, Mary Jane McLeod, 1875-1955
About
Meltzer, M. Mary McLeod Bethune   **92**
See/See also pages in the following book(s):
Pinkney, A. D. Let it shine (4 and up)   **920**

Better wait till Martin comes. Hamilton, V.
In Hamilton, V. The people could fly; American black folktales p133-37   **398.2**

Betteridge, Harold T.
Cassell's German-English, English-German dictionary. See Cassell's German-English, English-German dictionary   **433**

Beware! (4 and up)   **808.8**

Beware of the dog. Dahl, R.
In Dahl, R. Skin and other stories   **S C**

Beware, Princess Elizabeth. Meyer, C.   **Fic**

The **bewitching** of Sea Pink. Climo, S.
In Climo, S. Magic & mischief; tales from Cornwall p75-84   **398.2**

Beyer, Rick
The greatest stories never told (7 and up)   **904**

Beyond the burning time. Lasky, K.   **Fic**
Beyond the dance. Goh, C. H.   **92**
Beyond the fringe. Maguire, G.
In A Glory of unicorns p45-57   **S C**
Beyond the pale. Kipling, R.
In McCaffrey, A. {The Pern series}   **S C**
Beyond the western sea. Avi   **Fic**

Bezos, Jeffrey
About
Garty, J. Jeff Bezos   **92**

Bhopal. Bryan, N.   **363.1**
Bhopal. Riddle, J.   **363.1**
Bhopal Union Carbide Plant Disaster, Bhopal, India, 1984
Bryan, N. Bhopal (5 and up)   **363.1**
Riddle, J. Bhopal (7 and up)   **363.1**

Bhutan
Cooper, R. Bhutan   **954.9**

Bhutto, Benazir
See/See also pages in the following book(s):
Axelrod-Contrada, J. Women who led nations (7 and up)   **920**
Price-Groff, C. Twentieth-century women political leaders (7 and up)   **920**

Bi-racial people *See* Racially mixed people

Bial, Raymond
The canals | **386**
Lifeways [series] | **970.004**

The Long Walk | **970.004**
Portrait of a farm family (4 and up) | **630.1**
The strength of these arms (4 and up) | **326**
Tenement (4 and up) | **974.7**
The Underground Railroad (4 and up) | **326**
With needle and thread (4 and up) | **746.46**

Bibb, Henry, 1815-1854
See/See also pages in the following book(s):
Cloud Tapper, S. Voices from slavery's past (7 and up) | **326**

Bible
The Holy Bible [King James Bible. American Bible Soc.] | **220.5**

Bible
Good news Bible | **220.5**
The Holy Bible: new revised standard version | **220.5**
The new American Bible | **220.5**
The new Jerusalem Bible | **220.5**
The Holy Bible [King James Bible. Oxford Univ. Press] | **220.5**

Bible. N.T. Selections
The Christmas story | **232.9**

Bible. O.T.
History of Biblical events
Mann, K. The ancient Hebrews | **909**

Bible. O.T. Pentateuch
See also Torah

Bible. O.T. Ecclesiastes
To every thing there is a season | **223**

Biblc. Old Testament *See* Bible. O.T.

Bible (as subject)
Brown, A. The Bible and Christianity (5 and up) | **220**
Feiler, B. S. Walking the Bible | **222**
Antiquities
Tubb, J. N. Bible lands | **220.9**
Commentaries
Asimov, I. Asimov's guide to the Bible | **220.7**
Dictionaries
The Oxford companion to the Bible | **220.3**
The **Bible** and Christianity. Brown, A. | **220**

Bible lands. Tubb, J. N. | **220.9**

Bible stories
Chaikin, M. Angels sweep the desert floor (4 and up) | **296.1**
Gellman, M. Does God have a big toe? (4-6) | **221.9**
Goldin, B. D. Journeys with Elijah (4 and up) | **222**
Lester, J. When the beginning began (4 and up) | **296.1**
Lottridge, C. B. Stories from the life of Jesus (4 and up) | **232.9**
McKissack, P. C. Let my people go (4 and up) | **221.9**
Myers, W. D. A time to love (7 and up) | **S C**

Bibliographic instruction
Developing an information literacy program, K-12 | **025.5**
Foundations for effective school library media programs | **027.8**
Jweid, R. The library-classroom partnership | **027.8**
Rankin, V. The thoughtful researcher | **027.62**
Smith, J. B. Achieving a curriculum-based library media center program | **027.8**
Smith, S. S. Web-based instruction | **005.7**
Yucht, A. H. Flip it! | **025.5**

Bibliographical citations
Shields, N. E. Where credit is due (7 and up) | **808**

Bibliography
See also Books
Books in print | **015.73**
Subject guide to Books in print | **015.73**
Best books
See Best books

Bicenti. Walters, A. L.
In Talking leaves; contemporary native American short stories | **S C**

Bicycle racing
Maurer, T. BMX freestyle | **796.6**
Stewart, M. Sweet victory: Lance Armstrong's incredible journey (5 and up) | **92**

Bicycle science projects. Gardner, R. | **531**

Bicycles
See also Cycling
Gardner, R. Bicycle science projects | **531**

Bicycles and bicycling *See* Cycling

Bicycling for fitness. Gedatus, G. | **613.7**

Bidner, Jenni
The kids' guide to digital photography (5 and up) | **775**

Bierhorst, John, 1936-
The mythology of Mexico and Central America (7 and up) | **299.7**
The mythology of North America (7 and up) | **299.7**
The mythology of South America (7 and up) | **299.8**

Bies, Don
(il) Reynolds, D. W. Star wars: the visual dictionary | **791.43**

Biesty, Stephen
Rome: in spectacular cross section (4 and up) | **937**

The **Big** Burn. Ingold, J. | **Fic**

Big cat conservation. Thomas, P. | **333.95**

The **big** dig. Vanderwerker, P. | **624.1**

The **big** dinin'. Van Laan, N.
In Van Laan, N. With a whoop and a holler; a bushel of lore from way down south p27-31 | **398**

Big fat paycheck. Lawrence, C. | **808.2**

Big foot *See* Sasquatch

Big Joe's funeral. Myers, W. D.
In Myers, W. D. 145th Street; short stories | **S C**

Big Mouth & Ugly Girl. Oates, J. C.   **Fic**

Big talk. Fleischman, P.   **811**

Big Tree People. Bruchac, J.
In Bruchac, J. and Bruchac, J. When the Chenoo howls; native American tales of terror   **398.2**

The **Big** Wander. Hobbs, W.   **Fic**

Bigelow, Barbara Carlisle
American Revolution: almanac (5 and up)   **973.3**
(comp) World War II: primary sources. See World War II: primary sources   **940.53**

Bigfoot *See* Sasquatch

Bigger. Calvert, P.   **Fic**

Bigotry *See* Toleration

The **bijli**. San Souci, R.
In San Souci, R. A terrifying taste of short & shivery; thirty creepy tales p35-38   **398.2**

Bilbo Baggins and Smaug. Tolkien, J. R. R.
In The Book of dragons p39-46   **S C**

Bilingual books
English-Chinese
Liu Siyu. A thousand peaks   **895.1**
English-Spanish
Cool salsa (5 and up)   **811.008**
Herrera, J. F. Laughing out loud, I fly   **811**
Mora, P. The desert is my mother. El desierto es mi madre   **811**
Red hot salsa (7 and up)   **811.008**
The Tree is older than you are (7 and up)   **860.8**
You're on!: seven plays in English and Spanish (4 and up)   **812.008**

Bilingual education
See/See also pages in the following book(s):
Culture wars: opposing viewpoints   **306**

Bill, Buffalo *See* Buffalo Bill, 1846-1917

Bill of rights (U.S.) *See* United States. Constitution. 1st-10th amendments

The **Bill** of Rights. Patrick, J. J.   **342**

Bill Pickett: African-American rodeo star. Sanford, W. R.   **92**

Billinghurst, Jane, 1958-
Growing up royal   **920**

Billings, Charlene W., 1941-
Supercomputers   **004**

Billingsley, Franny
The Folk Keeper (5 and up)   **Fic**

Billitteri, Thomas J.
Alternative medicine (7 and up)   **615.5**

Billy Yank & Johnny Reb. Beller, S. P.   **973.7**

Bin Laden, Osama *See* Osama bin Laden

Binge-purge behavior *See* Bulimia

Bingham, Hiram, 1875-1956
See/See also pages in the following book(s):
Greenberg, L. Digging into the past   **920**

Bingham, Jane
African art & culture   **709.6**
Indian art & culture   **709.5**

The **bingo** van. Erdrich, L.
In Talking leaves; contemporary native American short stories   **S C**

Biodiversity. Patent, D. H.   **333.95**

Bioethics
Biomedical ethics: opposing viewpoints (7 and up)   **174.2**
Dowswell, P. Genetics (7 and up)   **660.6**
O'Neill, T. Biomedical ethics (7 and up)   **174.2**
Tagliaferro, L. Genetic engineering (7 and up)   **576.5**
Fiction
Werlin, N. Double helix (7 and up)   **Fic**

The **biographical** dictionary of African Americans. Kranz, R.   **920.003**

The **biographical** dictionary of black Americans. See Kranz, R. The biographical dictionary of African Americans   **920.003**

Biographical dictionary of Hispanic Americans. Meyer, N. E.   **920.003**

Biography
Bibliography
Biography index   **920**
From biography to history   **016.8**
Dictionaries
UXL encyclopedia of world biography   **920.003**
Indexes
Biography index   **920**
Periodicals
Biography today   **920.003**
Current biography yearbook   **920.003**

Biography [series]
Streissguth, T. Jack London   **92**

Biography almanac. See Almanac of famous people   **920.003**

Biography index   **920**

Biography today   **920.003**

Biological diversity
Conserving the environment (7 and up)   **333.72**
Gallant, R. A. The wonders of biodiversity (5 and up)   **333.95**
Patent, D. H. Biodiversity (5 and up)   **333.95**

Biological invasions
Guiberson, B. Z. Exotic species   **577**

Biological warfare
Gay, K. Silent death (7 and up)   **358**
Judson, K. Chemical and biological warfare (7 and up)   **358**
Levine, H. M. Chemical & biological weapons in our times (7 and up)   **358**
See/See also pages in the following book(s):
Weapons of mass destruction: opposing viewpoints   **358**

Biologists
Yount, L. Antoni van Leeuwenhoek   **92**

Biology
See also Marine biology
Biology   **570**
Biology matters!
Bottone, F. G., Jr. The science of life   **570**

Biology—*Continued*
The Facts on File biology handbook (7 and up)
570

Encyclopedias
Encyclopedia of life sciences   570.3
Biology, Molecular *See* Molecular biology
Biology   570
Biology matters!
Biomedical ethics. O'Neill, T.   174.2
Biomedical ethics: opposing viewpoints (7 and up)
174.2
Biomes atlases [series]
Burnie, D. Shrublands   577.3
Hoare, B. Temperate grasslands   577.4
Jackson, T. Tropical forests   577.3
Biometry
Tocci, S. High-tech IDs (7 and up)   599.9
Bionics
Rosaler, M. Bionics (5 and up)   617.9
Biotechnology
Marshall, E. L. High-tech harvest (7 and up)
641.3
A Student's guide to biotechnology (7 and up)
660.6
Yount, L. Biotechnology and genetic engineering
303.4
See/See also pages in the following book(s):
Hyde, M. O. Medicine's brave new world (7 and up)   610
Biotechnology and genetic engineering. Yount, L.
303.4
Bipolar disorder, depression, and other mood disorders. Demetriades, H. A.   616.85
Birch, Beverley
Alexander Fleming   92
Guglielmo Marconi   92
Marie Curie   92
The **birchbark** house. Erdrich, L.   Fic
Birchfield, D. L., 1948-
(ed) The Encyclopedia of North American Indians. See The Encyclopedia of North American Indians [Marshall Cavendish]
970.004
Bird, Gloria
Turtle Lake
In Talking leaves; contemporary native American short stories   S C
Bird. Johnson, A.   Fic
Bird alert. Thomas, P.   333.95
The **bird** lovers. Jaffe, N.
In Jaffe, N. and Zeitlin, S. J. The cow of no color: riddle stories and justice tales from around the world p59-69   398.2
Bird song *See* Birdsongs
Bird Woman *See* Sacagawea, b. 1786
Birdland. Mack, T.   Fic
Birds
See also Cage birds; Woodpeckers
Birds   598
Bishop, N. Digging for bird-dinosaurs (4 and up)   567.9
Burnie, D. Bird (4 and up)   598

Grzimek's student animal life resource, Birds
598
Harrison, C. Birds of the world (7 and up)
598
Latimer, J. P. Backyard birds (4 and up)
598
Latimer, J. P. Bizarre birds (4 and up)   598
Latimer, J. P. Shorebirds (4 and up)   598
Latimer, J. P. Songbirds (4 and up)   598
National Audubon Society first field guide: birds (4 and up)   598
Sloan, C. Feathered dinosaurs (5 and up)
567.9
Thomas, P. Bird alert   333.95
Webb, S. Looking for seabirds   598
Zeaman, J. Birds   636.5
Fiction
Auch, M. J. Wing nut (5 and up)   Fic
Norman, H. Between heaven and earth (4 and up)   398.2
Migration
Lerner, C. On the wing (4 and up)   598
Poetry
Fleischman, P. I am phoenix: poems for two voices (4 and up)   811
Protection
Patent, D. H. The bald eagle returns (4 and up)
598
Salmansohn, P. Saving birds (5 and up)
333.95
North America
Bull, J. L. The National Audubon Society field guide to North American birds, Eastern region
598
Griggs, J. L. All the birds of North America
598
Kaufman, K. Lives of North American birds (7 and up)   598
Peterson, R. T. A field guide to the birds of eastern and central North America   598
Robbins, C. S. Birds of North America (4 and up)   598
Udvardy, M. D. F. National Audubon Society field guide to North American birds, Western region   598
West (U.S.)
Peterson, R. T. A field guide to western birds
598
Birds   598
Birds of North America. Robbins, C. S.   598
Birds of prey
See also names of birds of prey
Bailey, J. Birds of prey   598
Collard, S. B., III. Birds of prey   598
Latimer, J. P. Birds of prey (4 and up)   598
Laubach, C. M. Raptor! a kid's guide to birds of prey (4 and up)   598
Birds of the world. Harrison, C.   598
Birdseye, Debbie Holsclaw
Under our skin (4 and up)   305.8
What I believe (4 and up)   200
Birdseye, Tom, 1951-
(jt. auth) Birdseye, D. H. Under our skin
305.8

Birdseye, Tom, 1951——*Continued*
(jt. auth) Birdseye, D. H. What I believe
200

Birdsongs
Latimer, J. P. Songbirds (4 and up) **598**
See/See also pages in the following book(s):
Sayre, A. P. Secrets of sound p11-23 (4 and up)
591.59

Birth, Multiple *See* Multiple birth
Birth defects
Fiction
De Guzman, M. Melonhead **Fic**
The **birth** of science: ancient times to 1699.
Spangenburg, R. **509**
Birthday piñata. Delacre, L.
In Delacre, L. Salsa stories p44-54 **S C**
The **birthday** room. Henkes, K. **Fic**
Biscuits of glory. Coville, B.
In Coville, B. Odder than ever **S C**
In The Haunted house: a collection of original
stories **S C**
Bisexuality
Huegel, K. GLBTQ (Gay, Lesbian, Bisexual,
Transgender, Questioning) **306.76**
Bishop, Nic
Digging for bird-dinosaurs (4 and up) **567.9**
(il) Montgomery, S. The tarantula scientist
595.4
Bishop, Nic, 1955-
(il) Montgomery, S. The snake scientist
597.9
Bisignano, Alphonse
Cooking the Italian way
In Easy menu ethnic cookbooks **641.5**
Bismarck (Battleship)
McGowen, T. Sink the Bismarck (5 and up)
940.54
Bisson, Terry
Nat Turner **92**
They're made out of meat
In New skies: an anthology of today's science
fiction **S C**
Bittersweet. Lamm, C. D. **Fic**
Bitton-Jackson, Livia
I have lived a thousand years (7 and up)
940.53
My bridges of hope (7 and up) **92**
Bizarre birds. Latimer, J. P. **598**
Bjorklund, Ruth
Kansas
In Celebrate the states **973**
Nebraska
In Celebrate the states **973**
Black, Angela
(jt. auth) Sheehan, S. Jamaica **972.92**
Black Americans *See* African Americans
Black Americans of achievement [series]
Adair, G. George Washington Carver **92**
Bisson, T. Nat Turner **92**
De Angelis, T. Louis Farrakhan **92**
Dolan, S. Bob Marley **92**
Frankl, R. Charlie Parker, musician **92**
Hill, A. E. Denzel Washington **92**

Kliment, B. Billie Holiday **92**
Krass, P. Sojourner Truth **92**
Lawler, M. Marcus Garvey **92**
Huggins, N. I. Lena Horne **92**
Preston, K. K. Scott Joplin **92**
Rhodes, L. R. Coretta Scott King **92**
Taylor, M. W. Harriet Tubman **92**
Black art (Magic) *See* Witchcraft
Black authors
See also African American authors
The **Black** Bull of Norroway
In Hearne, B. G. Beauties and beasts p92-96
398.2
The **black** bull of Norroway. Philip, N.
In Philip, N. Celtic fairy tales p67-72
398.2
The **Black** Canary. Curry, J. L. **Fic**
The **black** cat. Philip, N.
In Philip, N. Celtic fairy tales p92-104
398.2
The **black** cat. Poe, E. A.
In Poe, E. A. Edgar Allan Poe's tales of mys-
tery and madness **S C**
The **black** cowboys. DeAngelis, G. **978**
Black death *See* Plague
The **Black** Death. Corzine, P. **614.5**
The **Black** Death. Peters, S. T. **614.5**
Black diamond. McKissack, P. C. **796.357**
The **black** dog. Schwartz, A.
In Schwartz, A. Scary stories 3; more tales to
chill your bones p17-19 **398.2**
The **black** dragon princess. Kang, H.
In Fire and wings: dragon tales from East and
West p103-11 **S C**
Black eagles. Haskins, J. **629.13**
The **black** ferris. Bradbury, R.
In Beware!; R.L. Stine picks his favorite
scary stories p3-17 **808.8**
The **black** fox. Bull, E.
In Firebirds: an anthology of original fantasy
and science fiction; an anthology of orig-
inal fantasy and science fiction **S C**
The **black** fox. San Souci, R.
In San Souci, R. A terrifying taste of short &
shivery; thirty creepy tales p137-40
398.2
Black frontiers. Schlissel, L. **978**
Black hands, white sails. McKissack, P. C.
639.2
Black holes and basketball sneakers. Williams, L.
A.
In 13; thirteen stories that capture the agony
and ecstasy of being thirteen **S C**
Black horses for the king. McCaffrey, A. **Fic**
Black Indians. Katz, W. L. **305.8**
Black inventors. Aaseng, N. **920**
Black literature (American) *See* American litera-
ture—African American authors
Black magic (Witchcraft) *See* Magic
Black magic and witches **133.4**
Black mirror. Werlin, N. **Fic**

Black music
See also African American music
Black musicians
See also African American musicians
Black Muslims
De Angelis, T. Louis Farrakhan   92
Draper, A. S. The assassination of Malcolm X
    92
The **black** pearl. O'Dell, S.   Fic
Black pioneers. Katz, W. L.   920
Black poetry (American) See American poetry—
African American authors
Black potatoes. Bartoletti, S. C.   941.5
Black powder. Wu, W. F.
In American dragons: twenty-five Asian
American voices p211-34   810.8
The **black** snake. Olson, A. N.
In Olson, A. N. and Schwartz, H. Ask the
bones: scary stories from around the
world p99-104   398.2
The **Black** soldier. Clinton, C.   355
Black stars [series]
Haskins, J. African American entrepreneurs
    920
Haskins, J. African American military heroes
    920
Sullivan, O. R. African American inventors
    920
Sullivan, O. R. African American millionaires
    920
Sullivan, O. R. African American women scien-
tists and inventors   920
Tate, E. E. African American musicians   920
Black women of the Old West. Katz, W. L.
    978
Blackbeard, 1680?-1718
See/See also pages in the following book(s):
Wren, L. L. Pirates and privateers of the high
seas p11-17   920
The **Blackbirch** kid's visual reference of the Unit-
ed States (4 and up)   973
The **Blackbirch** kid's visual reference of the
world (5 and up)   910
The **Blackbirch** treasury of American poetry (5
and up)   811.008
Blackburn, G. Meredith
(comp) Index to poetry for children and young
people. See Index to poetry for children and
young people   808.81
Blackburn, Lorraine A.
(comp) Index to poetry for children and young
people. See Index to poetry for children and
young people   808.81
Blacker, Terence
The angel factory   Fic
Blacklock, Dyan
The Roman Army (4 and up)   937
Blackmail. Soto, G.
In Soto, G. Local news p1-13   S C
Blackman, Haden
Star Wars: Clone wars adventures, Vol. 1
    741.5

Blacks
See/See also pages in the following book(s):
Reef, C. Africans in America: the spread of
people and culture   305.8
Biography
See also African Americans—Biography
Cameron, A. The kidnapped prince: the life of
Olaudah Equiano (4 and up)   92
Dolan, S. Bob Marley   92
United States
See African Americans
Blacks in art
See also African Americans in art
Feelings, T. The middle passage (7 and up)
    759.13
Blacks in literature
See also African Americans in literature
The **blacksmith** and the Devil. Lester, J.
In Lester, J. The last tales of Uncle Remus
p141-47   398.2
Blacksmithing
See/See also pages in the following book(s):
Lyons, M. E. Catching the fire: Philip Simmons,
blacksmith (4 and up)   92
Blackwater. Bunting, E.   Fic
Blackwater Ben. Durbin, W.   Fic
Blackwell, Elizabeth, 1821-1910
See/See also pages in the following book(s):
Celebrating women in mathematics and science
    920
DeAngelis, G. Science & medicine   920
Blackwood, Gary L.
Extraordinary events and oddball occurrences
    001.9
Gangsters   364.1
Highwaymen   364.1
Life on the Oregon Trail (7 and up)   979.5
Moonshine   Fic
Outlaws   364.1
Pirates   364.1
The Shakespeare stealer (5 and up)   Fic
Swindlers   364.1
The year of the hangman   Fic
Blades, boards & scooters. Thomas, K.   796.2
Blair, Eric See Orwell, George, 1903-1950
Blake, Quentin, 1932-
(il) Yeoman, J. The Seven voyages of Sinbad
the Sailor   398.2
Blakeslee, Ann R.
A different kind of hero   Fic
Blanca Flor. Gerson, M.-J.
In Gerson, M.-J. Fiesta femenina; celebrating
women in Mexican folktale   398.2
Blashfield, Jean F.
Arizona
In America the beautiful, second series
    973
Chlorine
In Blashfield, J. F. Sparks of life; chemical
elements that make life possible   546
Colorado
In America the beautiful, second series
    973

Blashfield, Jean F.—*Continued*
Delaware
In America the beautiful, second series
973
Iron and trace elements
In Blashfield, J. F. Sparks of life; chemical
elements that make life possible   546
Leonard Bernstein (7 and up)   92
Magnesium
In Blashfield, J. F. Sparks of life; chemical
elements that make life possible   546
Phosphorus
In Blashfield, J. F. Sparks of life; chemical
elements that make life possible   546
Sparks of life [series]   546
Virginia
In America the beautiful, second series
973
Washington
In America the beautiful, second series
973
Wisconsin
In America the beautiful, second series
973

Blastoff! [series]
Schwabacher, M. Jupiter   523.4
Stefoff, R. Earth and the moon   550
Stefoff, R. Neptune   523.4
Stone, T. L. Mars   523.4
Stone, T. L. Saturn   523.4

Blauer, Ettagale
Morocco   964
South Africa (4 and up)   968

The **blaze** engulfs. Sherrow, V.   940.53

Bledsoe, Lucy Jane
Rough touch
In Girls got game; sports stories and poems
810.8

The **blessing**. Goldin, B. D.
In Goldin, B. D. Journeys with Elijah; eight
tales of the Prophet p57-63   222

Blind
Alexander, S. H. Do you remember the color
blue? (4 and up)   362.4
Dash, J. The world at her fingertips: the story of
Helen Keller (5 and up)   92
Freedman, R. Out of darkness: the story of Lou-
is Braille (4 and up)   92
Garrett, L. Helen Keller (5 and up)   92
Keller, H. The story of my life   92
Lawlor, L. Helen Keller: rebellious spirit (5 and
up)   92

Fiction
Clements, A. Things not seen (7 and up)
Fic
Kurtz, J. The storyteller's beads (5 and up)
Fic
Moore, P. Blind sighted (7 and up)   Fic
Taylor, T. The cay (5 and up)   Fic
Taylor, T. Timothy of the cay (5 and up)
Fic

Blind sighted. Moore, P.   Fic
Blizzard!: the storm that changed America. Mur-
phy, J.   974.7
A **blizzard** year. Ehrlich, G.   Fic

Blizzards
Fiction
Gray, D. E. Together apart (7 and up)   Fic
Block party—145th Street style. Myers, W. D.
In Myers, W. D. 145th Street; short stories
S C
Blohm, Craig E., 1948-
An uneasy peace, 1945-1980   940.55
Weapons of peace   327.1
Blonde. Min, K.
In American eyes; new Asian-American short
stories for young adults p3-7   S C
Blood
Brynie, F. H. 101 questions about blood and cir-
culation, with answers straight from the heart
(7 and up)   612.1
Circulation
See also Cardiovascular system
Diseases
See also Leukemia
The **blood-ghoul** of Scarsdale. Friesner, E. M.
In Vampires: a collection of original stories
p81-98   S C
Blood gold. Cadnum, M.   Fic
Blood kin. Sherman, D.
In Vampires: a collection of original stories
p35-63   S C
Blood libel. Hussey, L. A.
In Vampires: a collection of original stories
p157-86   S C
Blood red horse. Grant, K. M.   Fic
Blood secret. Lasky, K.   Fic
The **bloody** country. Collier, J. L.   Fic
Bloody Jack. Meyer, L. A.   Fic
Bloom, Susan P.
Presenting Avi (7 and up)   813.009
Bloomability. Creech, S.   Fic
Bloomfield, Michael, 1950-
See/See also pages in the following book(s):
Graham, K. Contemporary environmentalists (7
and up)   920
Bloor, Edward, 1950-
Crusader (7 and up)   Fic
Story time   Fic
Tangerine (7 and up)   Fic
Blowers, Helene
Weaving a library Web   025.04
Blue, Rose
Staying out of trouble in a troubled family (7
and up)   362.7
(jt. auth) Naden, C. J. Dred Scott   342
(jt. auth) Naden, C. J. John Muir   92
Blue eyes better. Wallace-Brodeur, R.   Fic
The **blue** girl. De Lint, C.   Fic
Blue moon soup. Goss, G.   641.8
Blue Spruce, Ida Marx
(il) Bode, J. Kids still having kids   362.7
The **blue** sword. McKinley, R.   Fic
The **bluebird** and the Coyote. Brown, D. A.
In Brown, D. A. Dee Brown's folktales of the
Native American; retold for our times
p146   398.2

Blues for Bob. E. Brown. Bethancourt, T. E.
In Join in; multiethnic short stories by outstanding writers for young adults p201-
18 **S C**

Blues music
See also Jazz music
Asirvatham, S. The history of the blues
781.643
Elmer, H. Blues **781.643**
Lester, J. The blues singers (5 and up) **920**
Shirley, D. Everyday I sing the blues: the story
of B.B. King (7 and up) **92**

The **blues** singers. Lester, J. **920**

Bluestem. Arrington, F. **Fic**

Bluestone, Rose *See* Blue, Rose

Bluford, Guion S., 1942-
About
Haskins, J. Black eagles (5 and up) **629.13**
See/See also pages in the following book(s):
Haskins, J. Against all opposition (5 and up)
920

Bluish. Hamilton, V. **Fic**

Blumberg, Arnold, 1925-
The history of Israel (7 and up) **956.94**

Blumberg, Rhoda, 1917-
Commodore Perry in the land of the Shogun (5
and up) **952**
The incredible journey of Lewis and Clark (5
and up) **978**
Shipwrecked!: the true adventures of a Japanese
boy [biography of Manjiro Nakahama] (5 and
up) **92**
What's the deal? Jefferson, Napoleon and the
Louisiana Purchase (7 and up) **973.4**
York's adventures with Lewis and Clark (5 and
up) **978**

Blume, Judy
Are you there God? it's me, Margaret (5 and
up) **Fic**
Here's to you, Rachel Robinson (5 and up)
Fic
Tiger eyes (7 and up) **Fic**
About
Ludwig, E. Judy Blume **92**
See/See also pages in the following book(s):
Author talk (4 and up) **028.5**
(ed) Places I never meant to be. See Places I
never meant to be **S C**

Blumenthal, Karen
Six days in October (7 and up) **332.6**

Blushing: expressions of love in poems & letters
(7 and up) **821.008**

Bly, Nellie, 1864-1922
About
Davidson, S. Getting the real story: Nellie Bly
and Ida B. Wells **92**

BMX freestyle. Maurer, T. **796.6**

Bo & Mzzz Mad. Fleischman, S. **Fic**

Boadicea, Queen, d. 62
See/See also pages in the following book(s):
Meltzer, M. Ten queens (5 and up) **920**

Boadicea. Mayer, M.
In Mayer, M. Women warriors; myths and
legends of heroic women p51-53 **398**

Board games
King, D. Games (5 and up) **794**

Board of Education v. Pico (1982). Gold, J. C.
344

Boas, Jacob
We are witnesses (7 and up) **940.53**

The **boasting** contest. Yep, L.
In Yep, L. The rainbow people p106-15
398.2

Boat. Kentley, E. **387.2**

Boats, Submarine *See* Submarines

Boats and boating
See also Rafting (Sports); Ships
Kentley, E. Boat (4 and up) **387.2**
Paulsen, G. Caught by the sea (5 and up)
92
Sandler, M. W. On the waters of the USA (5
and up) **387.2**
Fiction
Mikaelsen, B. Red midnight **Fic**

Bobak, Cathy
(il) Poetry from A to Z. See Poetry from A to
Z **808.1**

Bober, Natalie
Abigail Adams (7 and up) **92**

Bobrick, Benson, 1947-
Fight for freedom (5 and up) **973.3**

Bochinski, Julianne Blair, 1966-
The complete handbook of science fair projects
507.8
More award-winning science fair projects (7 and
up) **507.8**

Bochinski-DiBiase, Judy J.
(il) Bochinski, J. B. The complete handbook of
science fair projects **507.8**
(il) Bochinski, J. B. More award-winning science fair projects **507.8**

Bock, William Sauts, 1939-
(il) Bruchac, J. When the Chenoo howls
398.2
(il) Wolfson, E. From Abenaki to Zuni
970.004

Bocón!. Loomer, L.
In Theatre for young audiences; 20 great
plays for children p429-52 **812.008**

Bodart, Joni Richards
Radical reads **028.5**

Boddy, Joe
(il) Sasaki, C. Constellations: the stars and stories **523.8**

Bode, Janet
The colors of freedom **305.8**
For better, for worse **306.89**
Kids still having kids **362.7**
Voices of rape (7 and up) **362.88**

Bodger, Joan
Tales of court and castle (5 and up) **398.2**

Bodies from the bog. Deem, J. M. **930.1**

Body by design. Nagel, R. **612**

Body doubles. Morgan, S. **660.6**

The **Body** eclectic (7 and up) **808.81**

Body focus: injury, illness and health [series]
Parker, S. The reproductive system   **612.6**
Body image. Sneddon, P. S.   **155.9**
Body piercing
Mason, P. Body piercing and tattooing   **391**
Wilkinson, B. Coping with the dangers of tattooing, body piercing, and branding   **617.9**
Body piercing and tattooing. Mason, P.   **391**
Body story [series]
Crash   **617.1**
Out of control   **612.8**
Teen dreams   **612.6**
Bodybuilding (Weight lifting) See Weight lifting
Boerst, William J., 1939-
Generous anger: the story of George Orwell (7 and up)   **92**
Isaac Newton (7 and up)   **92**
Johannes Kepler   **92**
Tycho Brahe (7 and up)   **92**
The **bogey** man. Klause, A. C.
   In Night terrors; stories of shadow and substance   **S C**
The **Boggart**. Cooper, S.   **Fic**
Bohannon, Lisa Frederiksen
The American Revolution (5 and up)   **973.3**
Bohl, Al
Guide to cartooning   **741.5**
Bohr, Niels Henrik David, 1885-1962
       About
Pasachoff, N. E. Niels Bohr   **92**
See/See also pages in the following book(s):
Henderson, H. Nuclear physics (7 and up)
   539.7
Bolden, Tonya
And not afraid to dare   **920**
Maritcha [biography of Maritcha Rémond Lyons] (4 and up)   **92**
Tell all the children our story (5 and up)
   305.8
Wake up our souls   **704**
Portraits of African-American heroes (4 and up)
   920
(ed) 33 things every girl should know. See 33 things every girl should know   **810.8**
(ed) 33 things every girl should know about women's history. See 33 things every girl should know about women's history   **305.4**
(jt. auth) Buckley, G. L. American patriots
   355
Boling, Katharine
January 1905 (5 and up)   **Fic**
Bolotin, Norm, 1951-
Civil War A to Z (4 and up)   **973.7**
Bolshevism See Communism
Bolton, Linda
Impressionism   **709.03**
Bombaugh, Ruth J.
Science fair success (7 and up)   **507.8**
Bombings
Shields, C. J. The 1993 World Trade Center bombing   **364.1**
Bonaparte, Napoleon See Napoleon I, Emperor of the French, 1769-1821

Bonar, Samantha
Comets (4 and up)   **523.6**
Small wildcats   **599.75**
Bond, Peter, 1948-
DK guide to space (4 and up)   **520**
Bone, J.
(jt. auth) Torres, J. Alison Dare: Little Miss Adventures   **741.5**
Bone [excerpt] Ng, F. M.
   In American eyes; new Asian-American short stories for young adults p108-30   **S C**
The **bone** detectives. Jackson, D. M.   **614**
A **bone** from a dry sea. Dickinson, P.   **Fic**
Bone: out from Boneville. Smith, J.   **741.5**
Bones
Simon, S. Bones (4 and up)   **612.7**
Bones. Hearne, B. G.
   In Hearne, B. G. The canine connection: stories about dogs and people p101-09
   S C
Bones. Strasser, T.
   In Ultimate sports; short stories by outstanding writers for young adults p238-50
   S C
Bonetta, Sarah Forbes, b. 1843?
       About
Myers, W. D. At her majesty's request [biography of Sarah Forbes Bonetta] (5 and up)
   92
Bonham-Boveé, Jonita Ruth, d. 1994
See/See also pages in the following book(s):
Mendoza, P. M. Extraordinary people in extraordinary times (7 and up)   **920**
Boni, Simone
(il) Corrain, L. The art of the Renaissance
   709.02
(il) Loria, S. Pablo Picasso   **92**
Bonnet, Robert L.
Science fair projects: chemistry   **540.7**
Bonny, Anne, b. 1700
See/See also pages in the following book(s):
Wren, L. L. Pirates and privateers of the high seas p11-17   **920**
Bonvillian, Nancy
The Hopi Indians of North America series
The Mohawk
   In Indians of North America series
   970.004
The Teton Sioux Indians of North America series
Book illustration See Illustration of books
Book industry
   See also Publishers and publishing
The **book** of Dead Days. Sedgwick, M.   **Fic**
The **Book** of dragons   **S C**
The **Book** of monologues for aspiring actors (7 and up)   **808.82**
Book of Mormon
The Book of Mormon   **289.3**
The **book** of North American owls. Sattler, H. R.
   598
Book of poetry for children, The Random House
   821.008

The **book** of the Lion. Cadnum, M.   **Fic**

The **book** of three. Alexander, L.   **Fic**

Book of twentieth-century English verse, The Oxford   **821.008**

Book poems   **811.008**

Book report biography [series]

Cockcroft, J. D. Latino visions   **704**

Feinberg, B. S. Douglas MacArthur   **92**

Santella, A. Wayne Gretzky   **92**

Book selection

Lyga, A. A. W. Graphic novels in your media center   **025.2**

Book talks

Bromann, J. Booktalking that works   **028.5**

Keane, N. J. Booktalking across the curriculum: the middle years   **028.5**

Langemack, C. The booktalker's bible   **028.5**

The **Book** Without Words. Avi   **Fic**

Books

    See also Printing

Brookfield, K. Book (4 and up)   **070.5**

    Censorship

Scales, P. R. Teaching banned books   **323.44**

    Reviews

Horning, K. T. From cover to cover   **028.1**

James, E. How to write terrific book reports (4 and up)   **808**

Books and newspapers. Graham, I.   **686.2**

Books and reading

Baxter, K. A. Gotcha!   **028.1**

Bouchard, D. The gift of reading   **372.4**

Children's books in children's hands   **028.5**

Closter, K. Fiction, food, and fun   **028.5**

Donelson, K. L. Literature for today's young adults   **028.5**

Jones, P. Connecting young adults and libraries   **027.62**

Keane, N. J. Booktalking across the curriculum: the middle years   **028.5**

Knowles, E. Talk about books!   **372.4**

Lyga, A. A. W. Graphic novels in your media center   **025.2**

Peck, R. Invitations to the world   **808.06**

Ray, V. L. School wide book events   **027.8**

Trelease, J. The read-aloud handbook   **028.5**

Wright, C. M. More hot links   **011.6**

York, S. Children's and young adult literature by Latino writers   **028.5**

    Best books

    See Best books

    Fiction

Hawes, L. Waiting for Christopher (7 and up)   **Fic**

Lasky, K. Memoirs of a bookbat (6 and up)   **Fic**

McKissack, P. C. A picture of Freedom (4 and up)   **Fic**

Shelf life: stories by the book (5 and up)   **S C**

Spinelli, J. The library card (4 and up)   **S C**

Stanley, D. The mysterious matter of I.M. Fine   **Fic**

    Poetry

Book poems   **811.008**

Books for children *See* Children's literature

Books for the teen age. New York Public Library   **011.6**

Books in print   **015.73**

The **booktalker's** bible. Langemack, C.   **028.5**

Booktalking across the curriculum: the middle years. Keane, N. J.   **028.5**

Booktalking that works. Bromann, J.   **028.5**

Boole, George, 1815-1864

See/See also pages in the following book(s):

Henderson, H. Modern mathematicians (7 and up)   **920**

Boon, Kevin A.

The human genome project (7 and up)   **599.93**

Boone, Blind, 1864-1927

    About

Harrah, M. Blind Boone (5 and up)   **92**

Boone, Daniel, 1734-1820

    About

Calvert, P. Daniel Boone   **92**

See/See also pages in the following book(s):

Doherty, K. Ranchers, homesteaders, and traders   **920**

Boone, John William *See* Boone, Blind, 1864-1927

Booth, Edwin, 1833-1893

    About

Giblin, J. Good brother, bad brother [biography of John Wilkes Booth and Edwin Booth] (5 and up)   **92**

Booth, John Wilkes, 1838-1865

    About

Giblin, J. Good brother, bad brother [biography of John Wilkes Booth and Edwin Booth] (5 and up)   **92**

Otfinoski, S. John Wilkes Booth and the Civil War   **92**

Booth, Teena

Falling from fire (7 and up)   **Fic**

Bootleg summer. Weaver, W.

   In Time capsule: short stories about teenagers throughout the twentieth century p39-59   **S C**

Borenstein, Gerri C.

Therapy   **616.89**

Borkowska, Anna, d. 1988

See/See also pages in the following book(s):

Lyman, D. Holocaust rescuers   **920**

Borland, Hal, 1900-1978

When the legends die   **Fic**

Born confused. Desai Hidier, T.   **Fic**

Born free. Adamson, J.   **599.75**

Born naked. Mowat, F.   **92**

Born too short. Elish, D.   **Fic**

The **borning** room. Fleischman, P.   **Fic**

Bornstein, Harry

(ed) The Comprehensive signed English dictionary. See The Comprehensive signed English dictionary   **419**

Bornstein, Jerry

An American chronology   **973**

Bornstein, Ruth Lercher, 1927-
Butterflies and lizards, Beryl and me (4 and up)
Fic

Bortolotti, Dan
Exploring Saturn (5 and up)   **523.4**
Panda rescue (4 and up)   **639.9**
Tiger rescue (4 and up)   **333.95**

Bortz, Alfred B., 1944-
The library of subatomic particles [series]
539.7

Bosch, Hieronymus, d. 1516
    About
Schwartz, G. Hieronymus Bosch (7 and up)
92

Bosco, Antoinette
(jt. auth) Bosco, P. I. World War I   **940.3**

Bosco, Peter I.
World War I (7 and up)   **940.3**

The **Boscombe** Valley mystery. Doyle, Sir A. C.
In Doyle, Sir A. C. The complete Sherlock
Holmes   **S C**

Bosnia and Hercegovina
    See also Sarajevo (Bosnia and Hercegovina)
King, D. C. Bosnia and Herzegovina (5 and up)
949.7
Milivojevic, J. Bosnia and Herzegovina (5 and
up)   **949.7**
War-torn Bosnia (7 and up)   **949.7**
Bosnia and Herzegovina. Milivojevic, J.   **949.7**
The **boss**. Hearne, B. G.
In Hearne, B. G. The canine connection: sto-
ries about dogs and people p93-100
S C

Boston (Mass.)
Vanderwarker, P. The big dig   **624.1**
    Fiction
Harlow, J. H. Joshua's song (4 and up)   **Fic**
Lowry, L. Taking care of Terrific (7 and up)
Fic
Lynch, C. Gold dust   **Fic**
Boston Jane: an adventure. Holm, J. L.   **Fic**

Boston Massacre, 1770
Lukes, B. L. The Boston Massacre (7 and up)
973.3
    Fiction
Rinaldi, A. The fifth of March (7 and up)
Fic

Boston Tea Party, 1773
Hull, M. The Boston Tea Party in American history   **973.3**

Bostrom, Kathleen Long, 1954-
Winning authors   **920**

Botany
    See also Plants
Bailey, J. Plants and plant life   **580**
Perry, P. J. Science fair success with plants (7
and up)   **580.7**
Plant sciences (7 and up)   **580**
Silverstein, A. Plants   **580**
VanCleave, J. P. Janice VanCleave's plants (5
and up)   **580.7**

Botany, Medical *See* Medical botany

Both sides now. Pennebaker, R.   **Fic**

Bottled up. Murray, J.   **Fic**

Bottone, Frank G., Jr.
The science of life   **570**

Bouchard, Dave
The gift of reading   **372.4**

Boudicca *See* Boadicea, Queen, d. 62

Bound. Napoli, D. J.   **Fic**
Bound for America. Haskins, J.   **326**
Bound for America. Meltzer, M.   **325.73**
Bound for the North Star. Fradin, D. B.   **326**

Bourgeois, Louise
    About
Greenberg, J. Runaway girl: the artist Louise
Bourgeois (7 and up)   **92**

Bourke-White, Margaret, 1904-1971
    About
Rubin, S. G. Margaret Bourke-White   **92**
Welch, C. A. Margaret Bourke-White   **92**
Wooten, S. M. Margaret Bourke-White   **92**
See/See also pages in the following book(s):
Colman, P. Where the action was   **070.4**

Bourseiller, Philippe
(il) Burleigh, R. Volcanoes   **551.2**

Boursin, Didier
Origimi paper animals (7 and up)   **736**

Boutilier, Nancy, 1961-
The rhythm of strong
In Girls got game; sports stories and poems
810.8
What the cat contemplates while pretending to
clean herself
In Girls got game; sports stories and poems
810.8

Boveé, Jonita Ruth Bonham- *See* Bonham-
Boveé, Jonita Ruth, d. 1994

Bowden, Rob
Energy (5 and up)   **333.79**
Food and farming   **363.8**
Kenya   **967.62**
The Nile (5 and up)   **962**
Waste   **363.7**
Water supply   **363.6**

Bowen, Gary
Stranded at Plimoth Plantation, 1626 (4 and up)
974.4

Bowie, James, 1799?-1836
    About
Edmondson, J. R. Jim Bowie   **92**

Bowler, Gerald, 1948-
The world encyclopedia of Christmas   **394.26**

Bowler, Tim, 1953-
Firmament (7 and up)   **Fic**
River boy   **Fic**
Storm catchers (7 and up)   **Fic**

Bowling, beatniks, and bell-bottoms   **306**

Bowman-Kruhm, Mary
(jt. auth) Wirths, C. G. Coping with confrontations and encounters with the police   **363.2**

Bowman's store. Bruchac, J.   **92**

The **boxer**. Karr, K.   **Fic**

Boxing
Bacho, P. Boxing in black and white (7 and up) **796.8**
Biography
Myers, W. D. The greatest: Muhammad Ali (7 and up) **92**
Tessitore, J. Muhammed Ali (7 and up) **92**
Fiction
Karr, K. The boxer (7 and up) **Fic**
Lipsyte, R. The contender (7 and up) **Fic**
Lynch, C. Shadow boxer (7 and up) **Fic**
Zusak, M. Fighting Ruben Wolfe (7 and up) **Fic**

Boxing in black and white. Bacho, P. **796.8**
A **boy** and his dog. Brooks, M.
In Who do you think you are?; stories of friends and enemies p58-63 **S C**
A **boy** at war. Mazer, H. **Fic**
The **boy** in the burning house. Wynne-Jones, T. **Fic**
Boy O'Boy. Doyle, B. **Fic**
The **boy** of Chancellorville. Gilmore, J. R.
In The Boy of Chancellorville and other Civil War stories p40-54 **S C**
The **Boy** of Chancellorville and other Civil War stories (7 and up) **S C**
Boy proof. Castellucci, C. **Fic**
Boy: tales of childhood. Dahl, R. **92**
The **boy** who killed the hill. Curry, J. L.
In Curry, J. L. Hold up the sky: and other Native American tales from Texas and the Southern Plains p120-22 **398.2**
The **boy** who reversed himself. Sleator, W. **Fic**
The **boy** who saved baseball. Ritter, J. H. **Fic**
The **boy** who spoke dog. Morgan, C. **Fic**
Boy with a wolf's foot. Aiken, J.
In Aiken, J. Shadows and moonshine; stories **S C**
The **boy** with yellow eyes. Gonzalez, G.
In Visions: nineteen short stories by outstanding writers for young adults p204-12 **S C**

Boyd, Belle, 1844-1900
See/See also pages in the following book(s):
Caravantes, P. Petticoat spies **920**

Boyd, Richard Henry, 1843-1922
See/See also pages in the following book(s):
Haskins, J. African American entrepreneurs **920**

Boyle, David
African Americans **305.8**
Boys
Daldry, J. The teenage guy's survival guide (7 and up) **305.23**
Gravelle, K. What's going on down there? **612.6**
Gurian, M. From boys to men **305.23**
Jukes, M. The guy book (7 and up) **305.23**
Twain, M. The adventures of Tom Sawyer (5 and up) **Fic**
You hear me? (7 and up) **810.8**

Books and reading
Odean, K. Great books for boys **028.1**
Employment
See Child labor
Fiction
Golding, W. Lord of the Flies **Fic**
Boys, Teenage *See* Teenagers
Boys behaving badly. See Daldry, J. The teenage guy's survival guide **305.23**
The **boys'** war. Murphy, J. **973.7**
Brace, Eric
(il) Newquist, H. P. The great brain book **612.8**
(il) Solheim, J. It's disgusting—and we ate it! **641.3**
Bradberry, Sarah
Kids knit! (5 and up) **746.43**
Bradburn, Frances Bryant
Output measures for school library media programs **027.8**
Bradbury, Ray, 1920-
The black ferris
In Beware!; R.L. Stine picks his favorite scary stories p3-17 **808.8**
Good grief
In Who do you think you are?; stories of friends and enemies p3-13 **S C**
The Halloween tree **Fic**
The ravine
In Read all about it!; great read-aloud stories, poems, and newspaper pieces for preteens and teens p252-71 **808.8**
Something wicked this way comes (7 and up) **Fic**
The Martian chronicles; adaptation. See Bradbury, R. April 2000: the third expedition
Bradford, William, 1588-1657
About
Doherty, K. William Bradford **92**
Bradley, James
Flags of our fathers (7 and up) **940.54**
Bradley, Kimberly Brubaker
For freedom **Fic**
Halfway to the sky **Fic**
Weaver's daughter (5 and up) **Fic**
Brady, Mathew B., ca. 1823-1896
About
Armstrong, J. Photo by Brady **973.7**
Pflueger, L. Mathew Brady **92**
Bragg, Janet Harmon, 1907-1993
See/See also pages in the following book(s):
Haskins, J. African American entrepreneurs **920**
Bragg, Linda Wallenberg
Fundamental gymnastics (5 and up) **796.44**
Brahe, Tycho, 1546-1601
About
Boerst, W. J. Tycho Brahe (7 and up) **92**
Gow, M. Tycho Brahe: astronomer **92**
Braille, Louis, 1809-1852
About
Freedman, R. Out of darkness: the story of Louis Braille (4 and up) **92**

Brain

Brynie, F. H. The physical brain   **612.8**

Fleischman, J. Phineas Gage: a gruesome but true story about brain science   **362.1**

Hall, D. The brain and senses

   In Being human   **612**

Landau, E. Head and brain injuries (7 and up)   **617.1**

Newquist, H. P. The great brain book (5 and up)   **612.8**

Out of control   **612.8**

Parker, S. Brain, nerves, and senses   **612.8**

Simon, S. The brain (4 and up)   **612.8**

     Diseases

Goldsmith, C. Neurological disorders   **616.8**

Hyde, M. O. When the brain dies first (7 and up)   **616.8**

The **brain** and senses. Hall, D.

   In Being human   **612**

Brain, nerves, and senses. Parker, S.   **612.8**

Brainboy and the Deathmaster. Seidler, T.   **Fic**

Brainstorm!. Tucker, T.   **609**

Braly, David

The night watchman

   In Read all about it!; great read-aloud stories, poems, and newspaper pieces for pre-teens and teens p244-51   **808.8**

Bramwell, Martyn

Mapping the planets and space   **520**

Brancato, Robin F.

Fourth of July

   In Sixteen; short stories by outstanding writers for young adults p102-12   **S C**

Branch, Muriel Miller

(jt. auth) Lyons, M. E. Dear Ellen Bee   **Fic**

Brandenberger, Barry Max, Jr.

(ed) Mathematics. See Mathematics   **510**

Brandenburg, Jim

(il) Swinburne, S. R. Once a wolf   **333.95**

Brannen, Daniel E., 1968-

Supreme Court drama (7 and up)   **347**

Brant, Beth, 1941-

Swimming upstream

   In Talking leaves; contemporary native American short stories   **S C**

Braude, Ann

Women and American religion (7 and up)   **200.9**

Braun, Eric

Canada in pictures (5 and up)   **971**

Braun, Linda W.

Hooking teens with the Net   **025.04**

Technically involved   **027.62**

Teens.library   **027.62**

Braun, Molly

(il) Waldman, C. Encyclopedia of Native American tribes   **970.004**

Brave Bird, Mary

Lakota woman   **92**

Brave new world. Huxley, A.   **Fic**

Bravo, Lola Alvarez *See* Alvarez Bravo, Lola, 1907-1993

Bravo! brava! a night at the opera. Siberell, A.   **792.5**

Bray, Robin

(jt. auth) Al-Windawi, T. Thura's diary   **956.7**

Brazil

Dicks, B. Brazil   **981**

Richard, C. Brazil (5 and up)   **981**

Streissguth, T. Brazil in pictures (5 and up)   **981**

     Fiction

Ibbotson, E. Journey to the river sea (5 and up)   **Fic**

Brazil in pictures. Streissguth, T.   **981**

Bread on the water. Lubar, D.

   In Destination unexpected: short stories   **S C**

Break a leg!. Friedman, L.   **792**

Break those chains at last: African Americans, 1860-1880. Frankel, N.   **305.8**

The **breaker** boys. Hughes, P.   **Fic**

Breaker's bridge. Yep, L.

   In Yep, L. The rainbow people p124-34   **398.2**

Breaking ground, breaking silence. Hansen, J.   **974.7**

Breaking point. Flinn, A.   **Fic**

Breaking rank. Randle, K. D.   **Fic**

Breaking the chains. Katz, W. L.   **326**

Breaking through. Jiménez, F.   **Fic**

Breakout. Fleischman, P.   **Fic**

Breast cancer

Peacock, J. Breast cancer   **616.99**

     Poetry

Grover, L. A. Loose threads   **811**

Breckinridge, Mary, 1881-1965

     About

Wells, R. Mary on horseback [biography of Mary Breckinridge] (4 and up)   **92**

Bredeson, Carmen

After the last dog died   **92**

The moon (4 and up)   **523.3**

Neil Armstrong   **92**

Pluto   **523.4**

Shannon Lucid   **92**

Texas

   In Celebrate the states   **973**

Tide pools   **577.6**

Breedlove, Sarah *See* Walker, C. J., Madame, 1867-1919

Brenaman, Miriam

Evvy's Civil War   **Fic**

Brenda. Spinelli, J.

   In Spinelli, J. The library card   **S C**

Brennan, Kristine

Sir Edmund Hillary, modern day explorer (4 and up)   **92**

Brenner, Barbara, 1925-

If you were there in 1776 (4 and up)   **973.3**

(ed) Voices: poetry and art from around the world. See Voices: poetry and art from around the world   **808.81**

Brent, Isabelle
(il) Philip, N. In the house of happiness **204**
Brent, Linda *See* Jacobs, Harriet A. (Harriet Ann), 1813-1896 or 7
Brer Bear comes to the community. Lester, J.
In Lester, J. The last tales of Uncle Remus p25-28 **398.2**
Brer Bear exposes Brer Rabbit. Lester, J.
In Lester, J. The last tales of Uncle Remus p37-39 **398.2**
Brer Buzzard and Brer Crow. Lester, J.
In Lester, J. The last tales of Uncle Remus p138-41 **398.2**
Brer Fox and the white grapes. Lester, J.
In Lester, J. The last tales of Uncle Remus p94-98 **398.2**
Brer Rabbit and Aunt Nancy. Lester, J.
In Lester, J. The last tales of Uncle Remus p149-51 **398.2**
Brer Rabbit and Miss Nancy. Lester, J.
In Lester, J. The last tales of Uncle Remus p16-22 **398.2**
Brer Rabbit, King Polecat, and the gingercakes. Lester, J.
In Lester, J. The last tales of Uncle Remus p123-28 **398.2**
Brer Rabbit teaches Brer Bear to comb his hair. Lester, J.
In Lester, J. The last tales of Uncle Remus p39-41 **398.2**
Brer Rabbit throws a party. Lester, J.
In Lester, J. The last tales of Uncle Remus p62-63 **398.2**
Breslin, Theresa
Remembrance (7 and up) **Fic**
Breuilly, Elizabeth
Festivals of the world **394.26**
Religions of the world (7 and up) **201**
Brewer, Ebenezer Cobham, 1810-1897
Brewer's dictionary of phrase and fable. See Brewer's dictionary of phrase and fable **803**
Brewer's dictionary of phrase and fable **803**
Brewster, Hugh
882 ½ amazing answers to your questions about the Titanic **910.4**
(jt. auth) Marschall, K. Inside the Titanic **910.4**
Brewster, Todd
(jt. auth) Jennings, P. The century for young people **909.82**
Brewster, William, 1566 or 7-1644
Fiction
See/See also pages in the following book(s):
Gilson, J. Stink Alley (4 and up) **Fic**
Brewton, John Edmund, 1898-
(comp) Index to poetry for children and young people. See Index to poetry for children and young people **808.81**
Brewton, Sara Westbrook
(comp) Index to poetry for children and young people. See Index to poetry for children and young people **808.81**

Brezina, Corona
Sojourner Truth's "Ain't I a woman?" speech **92**
Brian and the aliens. Shetterly, W.
In New skies: an anthology of today's science fiction **S C**
Briar Rose. Yolen, J. **Fic**
Bricktop, 1894-1984
About
Haskins, J. Out of the darkness (5 and up) **305.8**
See/See also pages in the following book(s):
Haskins, J. African American entrepreneurs **920**
The **bridal** gown. Olson, A. N.
In Olson, A. N. and Schwartz, H. Ask the bones: scary stories from around the world p125-28 **398.2**
Bride price. Crew, L.
In Join in; multiethnic short stories by outstanding writers for young adults p111-26 **S C**
Bridegam, Martha A.
The right to privacy **323.44**
Brides of Eden. Crew, L. **Fic**
The **bridge**. Vande Velde, V.
In Vande Velde, V. Tales from the Brothers Grimm and the Sisters Weird p70-76 **S C**
The **bridge-builders**. Kipling, R.
In McCaffrey, A. {The Pern series} **S C**
Bridge to Terabithia. Paterson, K. **Fic**
Bridgeman, Captain *See* Avery, John, fl. 1695
Bridgers, Jay
Everything you need to know about having an addictive personality (7 and up) **616.86**
Bridgers, Sue Ellen, 1942-
The beginning of something
In Visions: nineteen short stories by outstanding writers for young adults p213-28 **S C**
Bridges
See also Brooklyn Bridge (New York, N.Y.)
Adkins, J. Bridges (4 and up) **624**
See/See also pages in the following book(s):
Macaulay, D. Building big **720**
Bridgman, Roger Francis, 1940-
1,000 inventions & discoveries (5 and up) **609**
Briggs, Eleanor
The man-eating tigers of Sundarbans (4 and up) **599.75**
Bright Freedom's song. Houston, G. **Fic**
Brightling, Geoff
(il) Cotterell, A. Ancient China **931**
(il) Halley, N. Farm **630.1**
(il) Langley, A. Medieval life [y] **940.1**
(il) Murdoch, D. H. Cowboy **978**
(il) Redmond, I. Gorilla **599.8**
Brill, Marlene Targ, 1945-
Illinois
In Celebrate the states **973**

Brill, Marlene Targ, 1945——_Continued_
Indiana
   _In_ Celebrate the states   **973**
Michigan
   _In_ Celebrate the states   **973**
Tourette syndrome (7 and up)   **616.8**
A **brilliant** streak: the making of Mark Twain.
   Lasky, K.   **92**
The **Brimstone** journals. Koertge, R.   **Fic**
Bringing dinosaur bones to life. Farlow, J. O.
     567.9
Bringing mysteries alive for children and young
   adults. Larson, J. C.   **028.5**
Brisson, Pat
Taking care of things
   _In_ Don't cramp my style; stories about that
     time of the month p15-33   **S C**
British Americans
       Fiction
Bauer, M. D. Land of the buffalo bones   **Fic**
British Columbia
Palana, B. J. British Columbia
   _In_ Exploring Canada   **971**
       Fiction
Horvath, P. Everything on a waffle (4 and up)
     Fic
British Library writers' lives [series]
Shellard, D. William Shakespeare   **822.3**
Brittain, Bill
Shape-changer (5 and up)   **Fic**
The wish giver   **Fic**
Broadcast journalism
Garner, J. We interrupt this broadcast   **070.1**
Wakin, E. How TV changed America's mind (7
   and up)   **070.1**
Broberg, Catherine
Kenya in pictures (5 and up)   **967.62**
Saudi Arabia in pictures   **953.8**
Brockman, C. Frank (Christian Frank), 1902-
Trees of North America   **582.16**
Broderick, Dorothy M.
(jt. auth) Makowski, S. Serious about series
     016.8
Brokaw, Nancy Steele
Leaving Emma   **Fic**
The **broken** blade. Durbin, W.   **Fic**
Broken chain. Soto, G.
   _In_ Read all about it!; great read-aloud stories,
    poems, and newspaper pieces for pre-
    teens and teens p29-39   **808.8**
   _In_ Soto, G. Baseball in April, and other sto-
    ries p1-12   **S C**
Bromann, Jennifer
Booktalking that works   **028.5**
Bronchial asthma _See_ Asthma
Brontë family
       About
Kenyon, K. The Brontë family (7 and up)
     920
Bronx (New York, N.Y.)
       Fiction
Grimes, N. Bronx masquerade (7 and up)
     Fic

Levine, E. Catch a tiger by the toe   **Fic**
Bronx masquerade. Grimes, N.   **Fic**
Bronzes
Talbott, H. Leonardo's horse (4 and up)
     730.9
Brooke, Peggy
Jake's orphan   **Fic**
Brookfield, Karen
Book (4 and up)   **070.5**
Brooklyn (New York, N.Y.)
       Fiction
Avi. Don't you know there's a war on? (4 and
   up)   **Fic**
Danticat, E. Behind the mountains   **Fic**
Frank, E. R. Life is funny (7 and up)   **Fic**
Giff, P. R. All the way home (4 and up)
     Fic
Giff, P. R. A house of tailors (5 and up)
     Fic
Lurie, A. Dancing in the streets of Brooklyn
     Fic
McDonald, J. Twists and turns (7 and up)
     Fic
Mead, A. Swimming to America   **Fic**
Placide, J. Fresh girl (7 and up)   **Fic**
Shusterman, N. The Schwa was here   **Fic**
Brooklyn Bridge (New York, N.Y.)
See/See also pages in the following book(s):
Aaseng, N. Construction: building the impossi-
   ble   **624**
Brooks, Bruce, 1950-
All that remains (7 and up)
     Fic
   [novella]
   _In_ Brooks, B. All that remains p3-61   **Fic**
Do you know where your parents are?
   _In_ Time capsule: short stories about teenagers
    throughout the twentieth century p169-79
     S C
Midnight hour encores (7 and up)   **Fic**
The moves make the man   **Fic**
Playing the creeps
   _In_ Brooks, B. All that remains p65-113
     Fic
Teeing up
   _In_ Brooks, B. All that remains p117-68
     Fic
Throwing smoke   **Fic**
Vanishing   **Fic**
See/See also pages in the following book(s):
Author talk (4 and up)   **028.5**
Brooks, Gwendolyn
       About
Rhynes, M. E. Gwendolyn Brooks (7 and up)
     92
Brooks, Kevin, 1959-
Lucas (7 and up)   **Fic**
Martyn Pig (7 and up)   **Fic**
Brooks, Martha, 1944-
Being with Henry   **Fic**
A boy and his dog
   _In_ Who do you think you are?; stories of
    friends and enemies p58-63   **S C**
True confessions of a heartless girl (7 and up)
     Fic

Brooks, Philip, 1963-
Extraordinary Jewish Americans   920
Brooks, Polly Schoyer
Cleopatra (7 and up)   92
Brooks, Terry, 1944-
See/See also pages in the following book(s):
MacRae, C. D. Presenting young adult fantasy
fiction (7 and up)   **813.009**
Brooks Gollobin, Laurie
Selkie [play]
In Theatre for young audiences; 20 great
plays for children p579-604   **812.008**
Brother, can you spare a dream? Koller, J. F.
In Time capsule: short stories about teenagers
throughout the twentieth century p64-83
S C
Brother Imás. Hinojosa, R.
In Growing up Latino; memoirs and stories
p250-58   **810.8**
Brothers
Giblin, J. Good brother, bad brother [biography
of John Wilkes Booth and Edwin Booth] (5
and up)   92

Fiction

Bloor, E. Tangerine (7 and up)   Fic
Brooke, P. Jake's orphan   Fic
Brown, D. Our time on the river   Fic
Clements, B. A chapel of thieves   Fic
Crist-Evans, C. Amaryllis (7 and up)   Fic
Durrant, L. Echohawk   Fic
Dygard, T. J. River danger (7 and up)   Fic
Gregory, K. Orphan runaways   Fic
Hinton, S. E. Rumble fish (7 and up)   Fic
Hinton, S. E. Tex (7 and up)   Fic
Howland, E. The lobster war   Fic
Kerr, M. E. Night kites (7 and up)   Fic
Kerr, M. E. Slap your sides (7 and up)   Fic
Lisle, J. T. How I became a writer and Oggie
learned to drive (4 and up)   Fic
Lynch, C. Shadow boxer (7 and up)   Fic
Mack, T. Birdland (7 and up)   Fic
MacPhail, C. Dark waters   Fic
Murray, J. Bottled up (7 and up)   Fic
Naylor, P. R. The fear place (5 and up)   Fic
Salisbury, G. Jungle dogs   Fic
Shusterman, N. Full tilt (7 and up)   Fic
Tolan, S. S. Ordinary miracles   Fic
Trueman, T. Cruise control
Van Leeuwen, J. Cabin on Trouble Creek (4
and up)   Fic
Vanasse, D. Out of the wilderness   Fic
Woodson, J. Miracle's boys   Fic
Zusak, M. Fighting Ruben Wolfe (7 and up)
Fic

Brothers and sisters *See* Siblings; Twins
Brothers Grimm
See also Grimm, Jacob, 1785-1863
Brothers in valor. Tunnell, M. O.   Fic
Brower, David, 1912-2000
See/See also pages in the following book(s):
Byrnes, P. Environmental pioneers (7 and up)
920
Graham, K. Contemporary environmentalists (7
and up)   920

Brown, Alan
The Bible and Christianity (5 and up)   220
Brown, Dee Alexander
Bury my heart at Wounded Knee   970.004
Dee Brown's folktales of the Native American
398.2
Contents: The Rooster, the Mockingbird and the maiden; The
bear man; How Antelope Carrier saved the Thunderbirds; Why
dogs have long tongues; The great shell of Kintyel; The girl who
climbed to the sky; The Cheyenne prophet; The deeds and prophecies of Old Man; How day and night were divided; How the
buffalo were released on earth; How corn came to the earth;
How Rabbit brought fire to the people; Godasiyo the woman
chief; The return of Ice Man; Ice Man and the messenger of
springtime; How Ioscoda and his friends met the white men from
the east and journeyed across the great waters; Katlian and the
Iron People; How the first white men came to the Cheyennes;
How a Piegan warrior found the first horses; Water Spirit's gift
of horses; How Rabbit fooled Wolf; Coyote and the rolling rock;
Skunk outwits Coyote; Nihancan and the dwarf's arrow; Swift-
Runner and the trickster Tarantula; Buffalo Woman, a story of
magic; The hunter and the Dakwa; The prisoners of Court House
Rock; Red Shield and Running Wolf; The bluebird and the Coy-
ote; The story of the Bat; Crow and Hawk; Why Coyote stopped
imitating his friends; The lame warrior and the skeleton; Heavy
Collar and the ghost woman; The Sioux who wrestled with a
ghost
Bury my heart at Wounded Knee; adaptation.
See Ehrlich, A. Wounded Knee: an Indian
history of the American West   **970.004**
(jt. auth) Ehrlich, A. Wounded Knee: an Indian
history of the American West   **970.004**
Brown, Don, 1949-
Our time on the river   Fic
Brown, Fredric, 1906-1972
Obedience
In Read into the millennium; tales of the fu-
ture p103-17   **S C**
Brown, Gene
Conflict in Europe and the Great Depression
973.9
Duke Ellington: jazz master (7 and up)   92
Brown, Henry, b. 1816
See/See also pages in the following book(s):
Currie, S. Escapes from slavery   326
Brown, James
See/See also pages in the following book(s):
Lester, J. The blues singers (5 and up)   920
Brown, Jean E., 1945-
(jt. auth) Stephens, E. C. Learning about—the
Civil War   **016.973**
(ed) Your reading. *See* Your reading   **011.6**
Brown, Joanne, 1933-
Declarations of independence   **028.5**
Presenting Kathryn Lasky   **813.009**
Brown, John, 1800-1859
About
January, B. John Brown's raid on Harpers Ferry
(4 and up)   **973.7**
Stein, R. C. John Brown's Raid on Harpers Fer-
ry in American history   **973.7**
Brown, Judith Gwyn
(il) Robinson, B. The best Christmas pageant
ever   Fic
Brown, Marcia, 1918-
See/See also pages in the following book(s):
Marcus, L. S. A Caldecott celebration   **741.6**
Brown, Margaret Tobin *See* Brown, Molly,
1867-1932

Brown, Molly, 1867-1932
About
Landau, E. Heroine of the Titanic: the real
unsinkable Molly Brown (5 and up)   **92**
Brown, Oliver, 1919-1961
About
Anderson, W. Brown v. Board of Education
344
Gold, S. D. Brown v. Board of Education
344
Brown, Rod, 1961-
(il) Lester, J. From slave ship to freedom road
326
Brown, Roslind Varghese
Tunisia (5 and up)   **961.1**
Brown, Stephen F.
Protestantism (7 and up)   **280**
Brown, William Wells, 1815-1884
See/See also pages in the following book(s):
Currie, S. Escapes from slavery   **326**
The **brown** bear of the Green Glen. Philip, N.
In Philip, N. Celtic fairy tales p36-43
398.2
Brown v. Board of Education. Anderson, W.
344
Brown v. Board of Education. Gold, S. D.
344
Brownian motion. Wolff, V. E.
In Ultimate sports; short stories by outstand-
ing writers for young adults p207-36
S C
Browning, Eve
(jt. auth) Cole, D. J. Encyclopedia of modern
everyday inventions   **609**
Brownlie, Ali
Why do people fight wars?   **355**
Brownstone, David M.
The young nation: America 1787-1861   **973**
(jt. auth) Franck, I. M. The Wilson chronology
of women's achievements   **305.4**
(ed) The Wilson chronology of Asia and the Pa-
cific. See The Wilson chronology of Asia and
the Pacific   **950**
Bruce, Henry Clay, 1836-1902
See/See also pages in the following book(s):
Katz, W. L. Black pioneers   **920**
Bruce, Robert *See* Robert I, King of Scotland,
1274-1329
Bruchac, James
(jt. auth) Bruchac, J. When the Chenoo howls
398.2
Bruchac, Joseph, 1942-
Bowman's store   **92**
Code talker   **Fic**
Going home
In Talking leaves; contemporary native
American short stories   **S C**
The heart of a chief   **Fic**
Hidden roots   **Fic**
Lasting echoes (7 and up)   **970.004**
Pocahontas (7 and up)   **Fic**
Sacajawea (6 and up)   **Fic**
Skeleton man (4 and up)   **Fic**

Sounds of thunder
In Shattered: stories of children and war
p122-32   **S C**
A warrior song
In What a song can do; 12 riffs on the power
of music   **S C**
When the Chenoo howls (4-6)   **398.2**
Contents: The Stone Giant; The Flying Head; Ugly-face;
Chenoo; Amankamek; Keewahkwee; Yakwawiak; Man Bear; The
Spreaders; Aglebemu; Big Tree People; Toad Woman
The winter people (5 and up)   **Fic**
Bruder, Mikyla
Button girl (5 and up)   **745.5**
Bruh Alligator and Bruh Deer. Hamilton, V.
In Hamilton, V. The people could fly;
American black folktales p26-30
398.2
Bruh Alligator meets Trouble. Hamilton, V.
In Hamilton, V. The people could fly;
American black folktales p35-42
398.2
Bruh Lizard and Bruh Rabbit. Hamilton, V.
In Hamilton, V. The people could fly;
American black folktales p31-34
398.2
Brundtland, Gro Harlem
See/See also pages in the following book(s):
Axelrod-Contrada, J. Women who led nations (7
and up)   **920**
Graham, K. Contemporary environmentalists (7
and up)   **920**
Price-Groff, C. Twentieth-century women politi-
cal leaders (7 and up)   **920**
Brunel, Marc Isambard, 1769-1849
See/See also pages in the following book(s):
Aaseng, N. Construction: building the impossi-
ble   **624**
Bruning, John R.
Elusive glory   **920**
Bruno, Leonard C.
Math and mathematicians   **920**
Bruns, Roger
Jesse James   **92**
Julius Caesar   **92**
Brutal interlude. Koertge, R.
In Destination unexpected: short stories
S C
Bruun, Bertel
(jt. auth) Robbins, C. S. Birds of North America
598
Bryan, Ashley, 1923-
Ashley Bryan's African tales, uh-huh (4-6)
398.2
(il) Salting the ocean. See Salting the ocean
811.008
Bryan, Nichol, 1958-
Los Alamos wildfires (5 and up)   **363.34**
Bhopal (5 and up)   **363.1**
Chernobyl (5 and up)   **363.7**
Danube (5 and up)   **363.7**
Exxon Valdez oil spill (5 and up)   **363.7**
Love Canal (5 and up)   **363.7**
Bryan, Robin
(jt. auth) Blowers, H. Weaving a library Web
025.04

Bryant, Mary, b. 1765
Fiction
Hausman, G. Escape from Botany Bay (7 and up) **Fic**

Bryant, Sharon, 1954-
The earth kitchen **Fic**

Bryner, John
(jt. auth) Lanning, S. Essential reference services for today's school media specialists **025.5**

Brynie, Faith Hickman, 1946-
101 questions about blood and circulation, with answers straight from the heart (7 and up) **612.1**
101 questions about food and digestion that have been eating at you . . . until now **612.3**
101 questions about sex and sexuality— (7 and up) **613.9**
Perception **612.8**
The physical brain **612.8**

Brzycki, Matt, 1957-
Wrestling strength: prepare to win **796.4**
Wrestling strength: the competitive edge **796.4**

Bstan-'dzin-rgya-mtsho *See* Dalai Lama XIV, 1935-

Bubonic plague *See* Plague

Bucking the Sarge. Curtis, C. P. **Fic**

Buckley, Gail Lumet, 1937-
American patriots (7 and up) **355**

Buckley, James, Jr.
Football (4 and up) **796.332**
The visual dictionary of baseball **796.357**

Buckley, Susan
(jt. auth) Leacock, E. Journeys in time **973**
(jt. auth) Leacock, E. Places in time **911**

Bud, not Buddy. Curtis, C. P. **Fic**

Buddha. Demi **294.3**

Buddha Boy. Koja, K. **Fic**

Buddhism
Demi. The Dalai Lama (3-6) **92**
Ganeri, A. The Tipitaka and Buddhism (5 and up) **294.3**
Mann, G. S. Buddhists, Hindus, and Sikhs in America (7 and up) **294**
Wangu, M. B. Buddhism **294.3**
Wilkinson, P. Buddhism (4 and up) **294.3**
Winston, D. Wide awake: a Buddhist guide for teens **294.3**
See/See also pages in the following book(s):
Osborne, M. P. One world, many religions (4 and up) **201**
Fiction
Koja, K. Buddha Boy (7 and up) **Fic**
Whitesel, C. A. Rebel **Fic**

Buddhists, Hindus, and Sikhs in America. Mann, G. S. **294**

Budiansky, Stephen
The world according to horses (4 and up) **636.1**

Buelno, Pero Niño, conde de, ca. 1379-ca. 1453
See/See also pages in the following book(s):
Zohorsky, J. R. Medieval knights and warriors p26-37 **940.1**

Buffalo Bill, 1846-1917
Fiction
Peck, R. Fair weather (5 and up) **Fic**
The **Buffalo** Soldiers. Stovall, T. **978**
Buffalo Woman, a story of magic. Brown, D. A.
In Brown, D. A. Dee Brown's folktales of the Native American; retold for our times p123-28 **398.2**

The **bug** scientists. Jackson, D. M. **595.7**

Building
See also House construction
Macaulay, D. Unbuilding (4 and up) **690**
See/See also pages in the following book(s):
Macaulay, D. Underground (5 and up) **624**

Building. Wilkinson, P. **690**

Building a new nation. Collier, C. **973.4**

Building America [series]
Bial, R. The canals **386**

Building an ESL collection for young adults. McCaffery, L. H. **016.4**

Building big. Macaulay, D. **720**

Building character through literature. Jweid, R. **028.5**

Building history series
Lace, W. W. The Vatican **945**
McNeese, T. The Panama Canal **386**
Nardo, D. The medieval castle **940.1**
Trent, L. The Viking longship **948**

Building materials
Wilkinson, P. Building (4 and up) **690**

Building the book Cathedral. Macaulay, D. **726**

Building your vocabulary. Terban, M. **428**

Buildings
See also Skyscrapers

Built for speed. Thompson, S. E. **599.75**

Built for speed [series]
Murdico, S. J. Concorde **629.133**

Bulfinch, Thomas, 1796-1867
Bulfinch's mythology **201**

Bulfinch's mythology. Bulfinch, T. **201**

Bulgaria
Otfinoski, S. Bulgaria (7 and up) **949.9**

Bulge, Battle of the *See* Ardennes, Battle of the, 1944-1945

Bulimia
Cotter, A. Anorexia and bulimia **616.85**
Harmon, D. Anorexia nervosa (7 and up) **616.85**
Sanders, P. Anorexia and bulimia **616.85**

Bull, Emma, 1954-
The black fox
In Firebirds: an anthology of original fantasy and science fiction; an anthology of original fantasy and science fiction **S C**
Joshua tree
In The Green Man: tales from the mythic forest p262-96 **808.8**

Bull, John L.
The National Audubon Society field guide to North American birds, Eastern region **598**

Bull-of-all-the-Land
In Hearne, B. G. Beauties and beasts p97-98 **398.2**

Bull Run, 1st Battle of, 1861
Kops, D. The Battle of Bull Run **973.7**
Fiction
Fleischman, P. Bull Run (6 and up) **Fic**

The **bull** that thought. Kipling, R.
In McCaffrey, A. {The Pern series} **S C**

Bullard, Sara
Free at last **323.1**

Buller, Laura
Myths and monsters (5 and up) **398**

Bulletin boards
Serritella, J. Look again! **373.1**

Bulls-eye: a photobiography of Annie Oakley. Macy, S. **92**

Bully for you, Teddy Roosevelt!. Fritz, J. **92**

The **bumblebee** flies anyway. Cormier, R. **Fic**

Bunch, Bryan H.
(ed) Diseases. See Diseases **616**

A **Bunch** of laurel blooms for a present
In Hearne, B. G. Beauties and beasts p22-24 **398.2**

Bunche, Ralph J. (Ralph Johnson), 1904-1971
About
Schraff, A. E. Ralph Bunche **92**

Bunting, Eve, 1928-
Blackwater (5 and up) **Fic**
Doll baby **Fic**
The hideout (5 and up) **Fic**
The Presence **Fic**
Someone is hiding on Alcatraz Island **Fic**
SOS Titanic (7 and up) **Fic**
Spying on Miss Müller (5 and up) **Fic**
The summer of Riley **Fic**

Buonarroti, Michel Angelo *See* Michelangelo Buonarroti, 1475-1564

Buoyancy. Farndon, J. **532**

Burbank, Jon
Nepal (5 and up) **954.96**

Burg, David F.
The Great Depression (7 and up) **973.91**

Burgan, Michael
Cold War (7 and up) **909.82**
Colonial and revolutionary times (5 and up) **973.2**
Great moments in basketball **796.323**
John F. Kennedy **92**
Maryland
In America the beautiful, second series **973**

Burger, Carl, 1888-1967
(il) Gipson, F. B. Old Yeller **Fic**

The **burglar.** Kimmel, E. A.
In Kimmel, E. A. Sword of the samurai; adventure stories from Japan p73-83 **Fic**

Burial
Colman, P. Corpses, coffins, and crypts (7 and up) **393**
Sloan, C. Bury the dead (5 and up) **393**

Buried. Nixon, J. L.
In Nixon, J. L. Ghost town; seven ghostly stories p19-32 **S C**

Buried in ice. Beattie, O. **998**

Buried onions. Soto, G. **Fic**

Buried treasure
Matsen, B. The incredible search for the treasure ship Atocha (4 and up) **910.4**
Fiction
Anderson, J. The last treasure (5 and up) **Fic**
Ashby, J. Sea gift **Fic**
Barron, T. A. The Merlin effect **Fic**
Hobbs, W. Ghost canoe **Fic**
Hobbs, W. Leaving Protection (7 and up) **Fic**
Myers, W. D. The Mouse rap (6 and up) **Fic**
Sachar, L. Holes (5 and up) **Fic**
Stevenson, R. L. Treasure Island (6 and up) **Fic**

Burke, Jim
(il) Whitman, W. Walt Whitman **811**

Burks, Brian
Soldier boy **Fic**
Walks Alone **Fic**

Burleigh, Robert, 1936-
Hoops **811**
The sea (5 and up) **551.46**
Volcanoes (4 and up) **551.2**
Who said that? **808.88**
(jt. auth) Arthus-Bertrand, Y. Earth from above for young readers **779**

Burma *See* Myanmar

The **burn** journals. Runyon, B. **92**

Burnfield, Alexander
Multiple sclerosis (5 and up) **616.8**

Burnie, David
Bird (4 and up) **598**
Endangered planet (5 and up) **333.95**
The Kingfisher illustrated animal encyclopedia **590.3**
The Kingfisher illustrated nature encyclopedia (5 and up) **508**
Light (4 and up) **535**
Shrublands (5 and up) **577.3**
Tree (4 and up) **582.16**
(ed) Animal. See Animal **590.3**

The **burning** questions of Bingo Brown. Byars, B. C. **Fic**

Burning up. Cooney, C. B. **Fic**

Burns, Anthony, 1834-1862
About
Hamilton, V. Anthony Burns: the defeat and triumph of a fugitive slave (5 and up) **92**

Burns and scalds
Runyon, B. The burn journals (7 and up) **92**
Fiction
Cummings, P. A face first **Fic**

Burns and scalds—Fiction—*Continued*
Twomey, C. Beachmont letters (7 and up)
Fic
Zephaniah, B. Face (7 and up) **Fic**

Burr, Brooks M.
(jt. auth) Page, L. M. A field guide to freshwater fishes: North America north of Mexico
597

Burrell, R. E. C. (Roy Eric Charles), 1923-
Oxford first ancient history 909

Burroughs, John, 1837-1921
About
Wadsworth, G. John Burroughs (5 and up)
92

Burton, John A.
(ed) The Atlas of endangered species. See The Atlas of endangered species 333.95

Burwell, Letitia M.
See/See also pages in the following book(s):
Cloud Tapper, S. Voices from slavery's past (7 and up) 326

Bury me not in a land of slaves. Hansen, J.
973.8

Bury my heart at Wounded Knee. Brown, D. A.
970.004

Bury the dead. Sloan, C. 393

Burying grounds *See* Cemeteries

Burying the sun. Whelan, G. **Fic**

The **bus** stop. Schwartz, A.
In Schwartz, A. Scary stories 3; more tales to chill your bones p8-9 **398.2**

Busby, Cylin, 1970-
Getting dumped and getting over it! (7 and up)
646.7

Bush, Barbara, 1925-
About
Greenberg, J. E. Barbara Pierce Bush, 1925-
92

Bush, George W.
About
The Election of 2000 and the administration of George W. Bush (7 and up) 324
Kachurek, S. J. George W. Bush (4 and up)
92
McNeese, T. George W. Bush (7 and up)
92
Sergis, D. K. Bush v. Gore 342

Bush v. Gore. Sergis, D. K. 342

Bushman, Claudia L.
Mormons in America (7 and up) 289.3

Bushman, Richard L.
(jt. auth) Bushman, C. L. Mormons in America
289.3

Busiek, Kurt
Shockrockets: we have ignition 741.5
The wizard's tale 741.5

Business builders [series]
Aaseng, N. Business builders in real estate
920
Kent, J. Business builders in fashion 920

Business builders in fashion. Kent, J. 920

Business builders in real estate. Aaseng, N.
920

Business depression, 1929-1939 *See* Great Depression, 1929-1939

Business people, African American *See* African American businesspeople

Businessmen
Copley, B. The tall Mexican: the life of Hank Aguirre, all-star pitcher, businessman, humanitarian (7 and up) 92
Edge, L. B. Andrew Carnegie
Ehrenhaft, D. Larry Ellison 92
Ehrenhaft, D. Marc Andreessen 92
Glassman, B. John Paul Getty (7 and up)
92
Sherman, J. Jerry Yang and David Filo 92

Businesspeople
Aaseng, N. Business builders in real estate
920
Kent, J. Business builders in fashion 920

Businesswomen
See also Women executives
Jeffrey, L. S. Great American businesswomen
920
Shuker, N. Elizabeth Arden (7 and up) 92

Bussing-Burks, Marie, 1958-
Influential economists (7 and up) 920

But for the grace go I. De Lint, C.
In De Lint, C. Waifs and strays p250-71
S C

But what if I don't want to go to college? Unger, H. G. 331.7

Butcher, Grace
The day the horses came
In Girls got game; sports stories and poems
810.8

Butcher, Miriam H.
(jt. auth) Riddick, F. M. Riddick's Rules of procedure 060.4

Butcher, Nancy
(jt. auth) Armstrong, J. The kindling **Fic**

The **butcher**. Taylor, T.
In Taylor, T. Rogue wave and other red-blooded sea stories S C

Butler, Jon
(ed) Braude, A. Women and American religion
200.9
(ed) Noll, M. A. Protestants in America 280

Butler, Mary G.
Sojourner Truth (5 and up) 92

Butler, Octavia E.
See/See also pages in the following book(s):
Reid, S. E. Presenting young adult science fiction 813.009

Butler, Rebecca P.
Copyright for teachers and librarians 346.04

Butterflies
Lasky, K. Monarchs (4 and up) 595.7
Latimer, J. P. Butterflies (4 and up) 595.7
Pascoe, E. Butterflies and moths 595.7
Pringle, L. P. An extraordinary life (5 and up)
595.7
Pyle, R. M. The Audubon Society field guide to North American butterflies 595.7
Whalley, P. E. S. Butterfly & moth (4 and up)
595.7

Butterflies—*Continued*
Fiction
Klass, D. California Blue   **Fic**

Butterflies and lizards, Beryl and me. Bornstein, R. L.   **Fic**

Butterflies and moths. Pascoe, E.   **595.7**

Butterfly, The *See* Whistler, James McNeill, 1834-1903

Butterfly & moth. Whalley, P. E. S.   **595.7**

The **butterfly** man. Yep, L.
In Yep, L. The rainbow people p60-68   **398.2**

Butterworth, Rod R.
The Perigee visual dictionary of signing   **419**

Buttfield, Helen
The secret life of fishes   **597**

Button girl. Bruder, M.   **745.5**

Buttons
Bruder, M. Button girl (5 and up)   **745.5**

Buxbaum, Shelley M.
Jewish faith in America (7 and up)   **296**

Buzzboy: Trouble in paradise. Gallagher, J.   **741.5**

By far the worst pupil at Long Point School. Peck, R.
In Peck, R. Past perfect, present tense: new and collected stories   **S C**

By the waters of Babylon. Benét, S. V.
In Read into the millennium; tales of the future p147-60   **S C**

Byalick, Marcia
Quit it   **Fic**

Byam, Michéle
Arms & armor (4 and up)   **355.8**

Byars, Betsy Cromer, 1928-
The burning questions of Bingo Brown (4 and up)   **Fic**
Cracker Jackson (5 and up)   **Fic**
The dark stairs [and other titles in series] (4 and up)   **Fic**
The keeper of the doves (4 and up)   **Fic**
The moon and I (4 and up)   **92**
The pinballs (5 and up)   **Fic**
The summer of the swans (5 and up)   **Fic**
About
Cammarano, R. Betsy Byars (4 and up)   **92**

Byelorussia *See* Belarus

Byers, Ann
African-American history from emancipation to today (7 and up)   **305.8**
Communications satellites   **384.5**
The Holocaust overview (7 and up)   **940.53**

Byndley. McKillip, P. A.
In Firebirds: an anthology of original fantasy and science fiction; an anthology of original fantasy and science fiction   **S C**

Byrnes, Patricia, 1942-
Environmental pioneers (7 and up)   **920**

Byzantine Empire
Marston, E. The Byzantine Empire   **949.5**

C

Cabin on Trouble Creek. Van Leeuwen, J.   **Fic**

The **cabinet.** Feinberg, B. S.   **352.24**

Cabinet officers
Feinberg, B. S. The cabinet   **352.24**
Hasday, J. L. Madeleine Albright   **92**
Howard, M. Madeleine Albright   **92**

Cabot, John, 1450-1498
See/See also pages in the following book(s):
Fritz, J. Around the world in a hundred years (4 and up)   **910.4**

Cabot, Meg, 1967-
All-American girl (7 and up)   **Fic**
Kate the great
In 13; thirteen stories that capture the agony and ecstasy of being thirteen
The princess diaries   **Fic**

Cabral, Pedro Alvares, 1460?-1526?
See/See also pages in the following book(s):
Fritz, J. Around the world in a hundred years (4 and up)   **910.4**

Cadnum, Michael
Blood gold (7 and up)   **Fic**
The book of the Lion (7 and up)   **Fic**
Daphne
In The Green Man: tales from the mythic forest p44-49   **808.8**
Daughter of the wind (7 and up)   **Fic**
Edge (7 and up)   **Fic**
Forbidden forest (7 and up)   **Fic**
In a dark wood   **Fic**
The leopard sword (7 and up)   **Fic**
Medusa
In Firebirds: an anthology of original fantasy and science fiction; an anthology of original fantasy and science fiction   **S C**
Raven of the waves (7 and up)   **Fic**
Rundown (7 and up)   **Fic**
Ship of fire (7 and up)   **Fic**

Caesar, Julius, 100-44 B.C.
About
Bruns, R. Julius Caesar   **92**
Julius Caesar [essays about]   **92**
See/See also pages in the following book(s):
Brooks, P. S. Cleopatra (7 and up)   **92**

The **cage.** Sender, R. M.   **940.53**

Cage birds
Zeaman, J. Birds   **636.5**

Cages. Kehret, P.   **Fic**

Cain, David, 1951-
(il) Cobb, V. Science experiments you can eat   **507.8**
(il) Martin, L. C. Nature's art box   **745.5**

Calabro, Marian
The perilous journey of the Donner Party (5 and up)   **978**

Calamity Jane, 1852-1903
About
Faber, D. Calamity Jane (5 and up)   **92**
Sanford, W. R. Calamity Jane: frontier original   **92**

A **Caldecott** celebration. Marcus, L. S.   **741.6**

Caldecott Medal

Marcus, L. S. A Caldecott celebration **741.6**

The Newbery & Caldecott medal books, 1986-2000 **028.5**

Newbery and Caldecott Medal books, 1966-1975 **028.5**

Newbery and Caldecott Medal books, 1976-1985 **028.5**

Caldwell, Billy, 1780-1841
Fiction

Alder, E. Crossing the panther's path **Fic**

Caleb's choice. Wisler, G. C. **Fic**

Calendars

Marks, D. F. Let's celebrate today **394.26**

Calhoun, Dia, 1959-

White midnight (7 and up) **Fic**

California

Altman, L. J. California

In Celebrate the states **973**

Heinrichs, A. California

In America the beautiful, second series **973**

Fiction

Cadnum, M. Edge (7 and up) **Fic**

Garland, S. Valley of the Moon **Fic**

Hobbs, V. Charlie's run **Fic**

Hobbs, V. Tender (7 and up) **Fic**

Holman, F. Real **Fic**

Levy, M. Run for your life (7 and up) **Fic**

Nelson, T. Ruby electric (5 and up) **Fic**

Ryan, P. M. Esperanza rising (5 and up) **Fic**

Sanchez, A. So hard to say **Fic**

Soto, G. Baseball in April, and other stories (5 and up) **S C**

Soto, G. Help wanted **S C**

Soto, G. Local news **S C**

Steinbeck, J. The red pony **Fic**

Uchida, Y. A jar of dreams (5 and up) **Fic**

Gold discoveries

Goldsmith, C. Lost in Death Valley **979.4**

O'Donnell, K. The gold rush (4 and up) **979.4**

Gold discoveries—Fiction

Cadnum, M. Blood gold (7 and up) **Fic**

Cushman, K. The ballad of Lucy Whipple (5 and up) **Fic**

Derby, P. Away to the goldfields! **Fic**

Smith, J. A. Bandit's moon (4-6) **Fic**

Gregory, K. Seeds of hope **Fic**

California Blue. Klass, D. **Fic**

California condors *See* Condors

The **California** cousins. Rice, D.

In Rice, D. Crazy loco; stories about growing up Chicano in southern Texas p96-107 **S C**

Calisher, Charles H.

(jt. auth) Hoff, B. H. Mapping epidemics **614**

Calisthenics *See* Gymnastics

Call me Maria. Ortiz Cofer, J. **Fic**

The **call** of the wild. London, J. **Fic**

Call waiting. Conford, E.

In Conford, E. Crush p95-100 **S C**

The **caller**. San Souci, R.

In San Souci, R. Dare to be scared; thirteen stories to chill and thrill **S C**

Calling a dead man. See Cross, G. Phoning a dead man **Fic**

Calvert, Patricia, 1931-

The ancient Inca (5 and up) **985**

Bigger (5 and up) **Fic**

Daniel Boone **92**

Hernando Cortés **92**

Robert E. Peary **92**

Sir Ernest Shackleton **92**

Stand-off at Standing Rock: the story of Sitting Bull and James Mclaughlin (7 and up) **92**

Vasco da Gama (5 and up) **92**

Zebulon Pike (5 and up) **92**

Calvino, Italo

The dragon and the enchanted filly

In The Book of dragons p1-9 **S C**

Cambodia

Green, R. Cambodia (7 and up) **959.6**

The **Cambridge** gazetteer of the United States and Canada **917.3**

Cameras

Price, S. Click! fun with photography (4 and up) **771**

Cameron, Ann, 1943-

Colibri (5 and up) **Fic**

The kidnapped prince: the life of Olaudah Equiano (4 and up) **92**

Camm, Martin

(il) Stonehouse, B. Bears **599.78**

Cammarano, Rita

Betsy Byars (4 and up) **92**

Camp, Carole Ann

American astronomers **920**

The **camp** system. Shuter, J. **940.53**

Campbell, Andrea

Forensic science (7 and up) **363.2**

Campbell, Ann

The New York Public Library incredible Earth **550**

Campbell, Eric

The Shark Callers (7 and up) **Fic**

Campbell, Geoffrey A.

The home front **973.92**

Life of an American soldier **956.7**

A vulnerable America (7 and up) **363.3**

Campbell, Mary, fl. 1764
Fiction

Durrant, L. The beaded moccasins (5 and up) **Fic**

Campbell, Nancy M., 1944-

Panic disorders **616.85**

Campfire tale. San Souci, R.

In San Souci, R. Double-dare to be scared: another thirteen chilling tales **S C**

Camping
Fiction

Naylor, P. R. The fear place (5 and up) **Fic**

Camps

Directories

Peterson's summer opportunities for kids and teenagers **790.1**

Fiction

Cole, B. The goats   Fic
Danziger, P. There's a bat in bunk five   Fic
Goobie, B. Before wings (7 and up)   Fic
Klise, K. Letters from camp   Fic
Lynch, C. Slot machine (7 and up)   Fic
Nixon, J. L. Nightmare   Fic

Can of worms. Mackel, K.   Fic

Canada

Braun, E. Canada in pictures (5 and up)   **971**
Exploring Canada   **971**
Junior Worldmark encyclopedia of the Canadian provinces   **971**
Pang, G.-C. Canada (5 and up)   **971**

Fiction

Aspin, D. Ordinary miracles (7 and up)   S C
Brooks, M. True confessions of a heartless girl (7 and up)   Fic
Cooper, S. The Boggart (4 and up)   Fic
Doyle, B. Boy O'Boy   Fic
Durbin, W. The broken blade   Fic
Gilmore, R. A group of one   Fic
Heneghan, J. Flood   Fic
Jocelyn, M. Mable Riley (5 and up)   Fic
Matas, C. Sparks fly upward (4 and up)   Fic
McNamee, G. Acceleration   Fic
Olsen, S. The girl with a baby (7 and up)   Fic
Wynne-Jones, T. The boy in the burning house   Fic
Wynne-Jones, T. A thief in the house of memory (7 and up)   Fic

Gazetteers

The Cambridge gazetteer of the United States and Canada   **917.3**

History—0-1763 (New France)—**Fiction**

Goodman, J. E. Paradise (7 and up)   Fic

Canada goose *See* Geese

Canada in pictures. Braun, E.   **971**

Canadian dinosaurs. Kelsey, E.   **567.9**

Canady, Alexa, 1950-

See/See also pages in the following book(s):

Hansen, J. Women of hope (4 and up)   **920**

Canals

Bial, R. The canals   **386**

Fiction

Hurst, C. O. Through the lock   Fic

Cancer

See also Leukemia

Benowitz, S. I. Cancer (7 and up)   **616.99**
Lamb, K. Cancer   **616.99**
Stone, M. At the end of words (7 and up)   **92**
Yount, L. Cancer (7 and up)   **616.99**

Chemotherapy

Bardhan-Quallen, S. Chemotherapy (7 and up)   **616.99**

Fiction

Pennebaker, R. Both sides now (7 and up)   Fic

Swanson, J. A. Going for the record (7 and up)   Fic

Candelaria, Nash, 1928-

The day the Cisco Kid shot John Wayne

In Growing up Latino; memoirs and stories p115-30   **810.8**

The **candle** in the wind. White, T. H.

In White, T. H. The once and future king   Fic

Canesso, Claudia

South Africa   **968.06**

Canfield, Jack, 1944-

Chicken soup for the teenage soul {I-III}   **158**

(comp) Chicken soup for the kid's soul. See Chicken soup for the kid's soul   **158**

The **canine** connection. Hearne, B. G.

In Hearne, B. G. The canine connection: stories about dogs and people p83-92   S C

The **canine** connection: stories about dogs and people. Hearne, B. G.   S C

Canning, Jane

(jt. auth) Cockcroft, J. D. Latino visions   **704**

The **canning** season. Horvath, P.   Fic

Cannon, A. E.

Charlotte's Rose (5 and up)   Fic

Canoes and canoeing

Fiction

Brown, D. Our time on the river   Fic
Conly, J. L. Trout summer (5 and up)   Fic
Dygard, T. J. River danger (7 and up)   Fic

Can't get there from here. Strasser, T.   Fic

Canterbury tales. Cohen, B.   **821**

Canto familiar. Soto, G.   **811**

Cantor, Georg, 1845-1918

See/See also pages in the following book(s):

Henderson, H. Modern mathematicians (7 and up)   **920**

Capital punishment

The Death penalty: opposing viewpoints (7 and up)   **364.66**
Does capital punishment deter crime? (7 and up)   **364.66**
Herda, D. J. Furman v. Georgia (7 and up)   **345**

Capitalists and financiers

Kent, Z. Andrew Carnegie   **92**
Segall, G. John D. Rockefeller   **92**

Capone, Al, 1899-1947

About

King, D. C. Al Capone and the roaring twenties   **92**
Yancey, D. Al Capone   **92**

Cappelloni, Nancy

Ethnic cooking the microwave way

In Easy menu ethnic cookbooks   **641.5**

Capricorn. Oates, J. C.

In Oates, J. C. Small avalanches and other stories   S C

Captain Jack *See* Kintpuash, Modoc Chief, 1837?-1873

Captain James Cook. Meltzer, M.   **92**

The **captain's** dog. Smith, R.   **Fic**

Capuzzo, Mike
Close to shore   **597**

Car smarts. Edmonston, L.-P.   **629.222**

Caravan to America. Major, J. S.   **920**

Caravantes, Peggy
Petticoat spies   **920**

Carbone, Elisa Lynn, 1954-
Stealing freedom   **Fic**

Card, Orson Scott
Ender's game (7 and up)   **Fic**
Salvage
    In New skies: an anthology of today's science
        fiction   **S C**
See/See also pages in the following book(s):
    Reid, S. E. Presenting young adult science fic-
        tion   **813.009**

Card games
King, D. Games (5 and up)   **794**

Cardiovascular system
    See also Heart
Brynie, F. H. 101 questions about blood and cir-
    culation, with answers straight from the heart
    (7 and up)   **612.1**
Parker, S. Heart, blood, and lungs   **612.1**
Simon, S. The heart (4 and up)   **612.1**

Cardona, Manuel, 1934-
See/See also pages in the following book(s):
    Oleksy, W. G. Hispanic-American scientists (7
    and up)   **920**

Cards of grief. Yolen, J.
    In New skies: an anthology of today's science
        fiction   **S C**

Cardús, David, 1922-
See/See also pages in the following book(s):
    Oleksy, W. G. Hispanic-American scientists (7
    and up)   **920**

Care of the dying *See* Terminal care

Career discovery encyclopedia   **331.7**

Career guidance *See* Vocational guidance

Careers *See* Occupations

Carey, Charles W.
The Mexican War   **973.6**
(ed) Castro's Cuba. See Castro's Cuba
    972.91

Cargo. Hearne, B. G.
    In Hearne, B. G. The canine connection: sto-
        ries about dogs and people p29-39
    S C

Caribbean region
    See also West Indies
        Antiquities
Macaulay, D. Ship (4 and up)   **387.2**
        Fiction
Taylor, T. The cay (5 and up)   **Fic**
Taylor, T. Timothy of the cay (5 and up)
    Fic

Caricatures *See* Cartoons and caricatures

Carle, Jill
(jt. auth) Carle, M. Teens cook   **641.5**

Carle, Judi
(jt. auth) Carle, M. Teens cook   **641.5**

Carle, Megan
Teens cook   **641.5**

Carlisle, Barbara
The crane wife [play]
    In Theatre for young audiences; 20 great
        plays for children p453-77   **812.008**

Carlson, Lori M.
(ed) American eyes. See American eyes   **S C**
(ed) Cool salsa. See Cool salsa   **811.008**
(ed) Red hot salsa. See Red hot salsa
    811.008
(comp) You're on!: seven plays in English and
    Spanish. See You're on!: seven plays in En-
    glish and Spanish   **812.008**

Carmen Teresa's gift. Delacre, L.
    In Delacre, L. Salsa stories p71-75   **S C**

Carmichael, James H., 1907-1983
(il) Rehder, H. A. The Audubon Society field
    guide to North American seashells   **594**

Carmichael, Polly
Personality and behavior
    In Being human   **612**

Carnagie, Julie
War of 1812 (7 and up)   **973.5**
Renaissance & Reformation: almanac. See Re-
    naissance & Reformation: almanac   **940.2**
Renaissance & Reformation: primary sources.
    See Renaissance & Reformation: primary
    sources   **940.2**
(ed) U.X.L encyclopedia of biomes. See U.X.L
    encyclopedia of biomes   **577.8**

Carnegie, Andrew, 1835-1919
        About
Edge, L. B. Andrew Carnegie
Kent, Z. Andrew Carnegie   **92**

Carnegie medal
Barker, K. Outstanding books for children and
    young people   **028.5**

Carolrhoda earth watch book [series]
Staub, F. J. America's forests   **577.3**
Walker, S. M. Earthquakes   **551.2**
Winner, C. Erosion   **551.3**

Carolrhoda nature watch book [series]
DuTemple, L. A. North American cranes
    598
Quinlan, S. E. Puffins   **598**

Caroselli, Joanne
(il) Hearne, B. G. Beauties and beasts   **398.2**

Carpal tunnel syndrome and other repetitive strain
    injuries. Johansson, P.   **616.8**

Carpenter, Angelica Shirley
Lewis Carroll (7 and up)   **92**

Carpenter, Nancy
(il) Woodruff, E. Dear Austin   **Fic**

A **carpet** for Holy Week. Delacre, L.
    In Delacre, L. Salsa stories p8-17   **S C**

Carpetbag rule *See* Reconstruction (1865-1876)

Carrick, Donald
(il) Uchida, Y. Journey to Topaz   **Fic**

Carrick, Paul, 1946-
Dinosaur parents, dinosaur young (4 and up)
567.9

Carrier war. McGowen, T.   **940.54**

Carrington, Leonora, 1917-
See/See also pages in the following book(s):
Sills, L. Visions (5 and up)   **920**

Carroll, Lewis, 1832-1898
About
Carpenter, A. S. Lewis Carroll (7 and up)
92

See/See also pages in the following book(s):
Ellis, S. From reader to writer   **372.6**

Carroll, Pamela S.
Caroline Cooney: faith and fiction (7 and up)
813.009

Carruthers, Margaret W.
Pioneers of geology   **920**

Carry A. Nation: saloon smasher and prohibition-ist. Harvey, B. C.   **92**

Carrying the running-aways. Hamilton, V.
In Hamilton, V. The people could fly;
American black folktales p141-46
398.2

Cars (Automobiles) *See* Automobiles

Carson, Kit, 1809-1868
Fiction
Osborne, M. P. Adaline Falling Star (5 and up)
Fic

Carson, Mary Kay, 1964-
Epilepsy (7 and up)   **616.8**
The Wright Brothers for kids (4 and up)
629.13

Carson, Rachel, 1907-1964
The edge of the sea (7 and up)   **577.7**
The sea around us (7 and up)   **551.46**
See/See also pages in the following book(s):
Byrnes, P. Environmental pioneers (7 and up)
920
DeAngelis, G. Science & medicine   **920**
Di Domenico, K. Super women in science
920

Carson-DeWitt, Rosalyn
(ed) Drugs, alcohol, and tobacco. See Drugs, al-cohol, and tobacco   **362.29**

Cart, Michael
Sailing away
In Necessary noise: stories about our families
as they really are p145-69   **S C**
(ed) 911: the book of help. See 911: the book
of help   **810.8**
(ed) Necessary noise: stories about our families
as they really are. See Necessary noise: sto-ries about our families as they really are
S C

Cart and cwidder. Jones, D. W.   **Fic**

Carter, Alden R.
Crescent Moon   **Fic**
No Win Phuong
In Join in; multiethnic short stories by out-standing writers for young adults p62-84
S C

Pig brains
In On the edge: stories at the brink p41-55
S C
Satyagraha
In On the fringe p165-77   **S C**
Y2K.CHATRM43
In Time capsule: short stories about teenagers
throughout the twentieth century p205-19
S C

Carter, Betty, 1944-
Best books for young adults   **028.1**

Carter, Howard, 1874-1939
See/See also pages in the following book(s):
Greenberg, L. Digging into the past   **920**

Cartlidge, Cherese
Life of a Nazi soldier (7 and up)   **940.54**

Cartography *See* Maps

Cartooning for kids. Artell, M.   **741.5**

Cartoons, Animated *See* Animated films

Cartoons and caricatures
See also Comic books, strips, etc.
Artell, M. Cartooning for kids   **741.5**
Bohl, A. Guide to cartooning   **741.5**
Hart, C. Christopher Hart's animation studio
791.43
Hart, C. Christopher Hart's cartoon studio
741.5
Hart, C. How to draw comic book bad guys and
gals   **741.5**
Pellowski, M. The art of making comic books
(5 and up)   **741.5**

Cartoons and comics
Mother Goose on the loose   **398.8**
Fiction
Leavitt, M. Heck, superhero   **Fic**

Carus, Marianne
(ed) 911: the book of help. See 911: the book
of help   **810.8**
(ed) Fire and wings: dragon tales from East and
West. See Fire and wings: dragon tales from
East and West   **S C**

Carvalho, Solomon Nunes, 1815-1897
About
Hirschfelder, A. B. Photo odyssey: Solomon
Carvalho's remarkable Western adventure,
1853-54   **92**

Carvell, Marlene
Who will tell my brother? (7 and up)   **Fic**

Carver, George Washington, 1864?-1943
About
Adair, G. George Washington Carver   **92**
Nelson, M. Carver, a life in poems (7 and up)
811

Carver, a life in poems. Nelson, M.   **811**

Carwardine, Mark
Whales, dolphins, and porpoises (7 and up)
599.5

Casanova, Mary
When eagles fall   **Fic**

The **case** book of Sherlock Holmes. Doyle, Sir A.
C.
In Doyle, Sir A. C. The complete Sherlock
Holmes   **S C**

Case closed. Meltzer, M. **363.2**

A **case** of identity. Doyle, Sir A. C.
In Doyle, Sir A. C. The complete Sherlock Holmes **S C**

The **case** of the Baker Street Irregular. Newman, R. **Fic**

The **case** of the Goblin Pearls. Yep, L. **Fic**

The **case** of the monkeys that fell from the trees. Quinlan, S. E. **577.3**

Caseley, Judith, 1951-
Losing Louisa (7 and up) **Fic**

Caselli, Giovanni
In search of Troy (4 and up) **939**

Cash-Walsh, Tina, 1960-
(il) D'Amico, J. The healthy body cookbook **641.5**

The **cask** of Amontillado. Poe, E. A.
In Poe, E. A. Tales of Edgar Allan Poe p51-59 **S C**
In Poe, E. A. The pit and the pendulum and other stories **S C**

Cassady, Marsh, 1936-
(ed) The Book of monologues for aspiring actors. See The Book of monologues for aspiring actors **808.82**

Cassatt, Mary, 1844-1926
See/See also pages in the following book(s):
Sills, L. Visions (5 and up) **920**

Cassell's French dictionary **443**

Cassell's German-English, English-German dictionary **433**

Cassell's Italian dictionary **453**

Cassell's Latin dictionary **473**

Cassell's Spanish dictionary. See Cassell's Spanish-English, English-Spanish dictionary **463**

Cassell's Spanish-English, English-Spanish dictionary **463**

Cassidy, Cathy
Dizzy (5 and up)

Cassirer, Nadine Gordimer *See* Gordimer, Nadine, 1923-

Castaways of the Flying Dutchman. Jacques, B. **Fic**

Castedo, Elena
Luck
In You're on!: seven plays in English and Spanish p84-99 **812.008**

Castellucci, Cecil, 1969-
Boy proof (7 and up) **Fic**

Castle in the air. Jones, D. W. **Fic**

Castles
Adams, S. Castles & forts (5 and up) **355.7**
Macaulay, D. Castle (4 and up) **728.8**
Martin, A. Knights & castles (5 and up) **940.1**
Nardo, D. The medieval castle (7 and up) **940.1**
Nardo, D. The Middle Ages (7 and up) **940.1**

Castles & forts. Adams, S. **355.7**

Castner, James L.
Layers of life **577.3**
Partners and rivals **577.3**
River life **577.6**
Surviving in the rain forest **577.3**

Castro, Chava
(jt. auth) Gravelle, K. What's going on down there? **612.6**

Castro, Fidel, 1926-
About
Castro's Cuba (7 and up) **972.91**
Platt, R. Fidel Castro **92**
Press, P. Fidel Castro **92**
Woog, A. Fidel Castro **92**
See/See also pages in the following book(s):
Uschan, M. V. Political leaders **920**

Castro, Nick
(jt. auth) Gravelle, K. What's going on down there? **612.6**

Castro's Cuba (7 and up) **972.91**

Cat and Mouse. Lester, J.
In Lester, J. When the beginning began; stories about God, the creatures, and us p31-32 **296.1**

The **cat** ate my gymsuit. Danziger, P. **Fic**

Catalanotto, Peter
(il) Berger, G. Celebrate! **296.4**

Cataloging
Anglo-American cataloguing rules **025.3**
Fritz, D. A. Cataloging with AACR2 and MARC21 **025.3**
Gorman, M. The concise AACR2, 2004 revision **025.3**
Intner, S. S. Standard cataloging for school and public libraries **025.3**

Cataloging with AACR2 and MARC21. Fritz, D. A. **025.3**

Cataloging with AACR2R and USMARC. See Fritz, D. A. Cataloging with AACR2 and MARC21 **025.3**

Catalogs *See* Postage stamps—Catalogs

Catalogs, Subject *See* Subject catalogs

Catch a tiger by the toe. Levine, E. **Fic**

Catch that rabbit. Asimov, I.
In Asimov, I. I, robot **S C**

Catch the moon. Ortiz Cofer, J.
In Ortiz Cofer, J. An island like you; stories of the barrio p55-65 **S C**

Catching fire. Gorrell, G. K. **628.9**

Catching the fire: Philip Simmons, blacksmith. Lyons, M. E. **92**

Cate, Fred H.
The Internet and the First Amendment **342**

Catering
Fiction
Dessen, S. The truth about forever (7 and up) **Fic**

Caterpillars
Latimer, J. P. Caterpillars (4 and up) **595.7**

Cathedrals
Macaulay, D. Building the book Cathedral (4 and up) **726**

Cathedrals—*Continued*

Macaulay, D. Cathedral: the story of its construction (4 and up) **726**

Catherine II, the Great, Empress of Russia, 1729-1796

See/See also pages in the following book(s):

Hewitt, K. Lives of extraordinary women (4 and up) **920**

Meltzer, M. Ten queens (5 and up) **920**

Catherine, called Birdy. Cushman, K. **Fic**

Catholic Church

See also Inquisition

Catholics

United States

See/See also pages in the following book(s):

Joselit, J. W. Immigration and American religion (7 and up) **200**

Catlett, Elizabeth

(il) Johnson, J. W. Lift every voice and sing **782.42**

Cato, Vivienne

The Torah and Judaism (5 and up) **222**

Catran, Ken, 1944-

Voyage with Jason **Fic**

Catrow, David

(il) Burleigh, R. Who said that? **808.88**

Cats

Edney, A. T. B. ASPCA complete cat care manual **636.8**

Fiction

Fox, P. One-eyed cat (5 and up) **Fic**

Hunter, E. Into the wild **Fic**

Kehret, P. Don't tell anyone (5 and up) **Fic**

Kehret, P. Searching for Candlestick Park **Fic**

Kobayashi, M. What's Michael? Vol. 10: Sleepless nights **741.5**

Pratchett, T. The amazing Maurice and his educated rodents (7 and up) **Fic**

Cats, Wild *See* Wild cats

Cat's cradle. Aiken, J.

In Aiken, J. Shadows and moonshine; stories **S C**

Catskinella. Hamilton, V.

In Hamilton, V. Her stories; African American folktales, fairy tales, and true tales p23-27 **398.2**

Cattle

Stanley, J. Cowboys & longhorns **636.2**

Caught by the sea. Paulsen, G. **92**

The **causes** of the Cold War. Ross, S. **327.73**

Cavalry (U.S.) *See* United States. Army. Cavalry

The **cavalry** during the Civil War. Uschan, M. V. **973.7**

Cave drawings and paintings

See also Rock drawings, paintings, and engravings

Cave paintings to Picasso. Sayre, H. M. **709**

The **cay**. Taylor, T. **Fic**

CCC *See* Civilian Conservation Corps (U.S.)

CD-ROMs

Catalogs

Culturally diverse videos, audios, and CD-ROMS for children and young adults **011.6**

Reviews

Adamson, L. G. Literature connections to American history, 7-12 **016.973**

Ceban, Bonnie J.

Tornadoes (4 and up) **551.55**

Celebrate!. Berger, G. **296.4**

Celebrate America in poetry and art (5 and up) **811.008**

Celebrate the states (5 and up) **973**

Celebrating women in mathematics and science **920**

Celia behind me. Huggan, I.

In Who do you think you are?; stories of friends and enemies p73-82 **S C**

Celine. Cole, B. **Fic**

Cells

Viegas, J. Stem cell research **616**

Celtic fairy tales. Philip, N. **398.2**

Celtic mythology

Matson, G. Celtic mythology A to Z **299**

Celtic mythology A to Z. Matson, G. **299**

Celts

Folklore

Philip, N. Celtic fairy tales (4 and up) **398.2**

Cemeteries

Hansen, J. Breaking ground, breaking silence **974.7**

Censorship

Fuller, S. B. Hazelwood v. Kuhlmeier (7 and up) **344**

Gold, J. C. Board of Education v. Pico (1982) (7 and up) **344**

Pipkin, G. At the schoolhouse gate **373.1**

Reichman, H. Censorship and selection **025.2**

Steffens, B. Censorship (7 and up) **342**

See/See also pages in the following book(s):

Places I never meant to be (7 and up) **S C**

Pornography: opposing viewpoints (7 and up) **363.4**

Fiction

Garden, N. The year they burned the books (7 and up) **Fic**

Hentoff, N. The day they came to arrest the book (7 and up) **Fic**

Lasky, K. Memoirs of a bookbat (6 and up) **Fic**

Peck, R. The last safe place on earth (7 and up) **Fic**

Censorship and selection. Reichman, H. **025.2**

Centaur field. Yolen, J.

In Half-human p117-37 **S C**

Center stage. Wilson, P. J. **027.8**

Central Artery/Third Harbor Tunnel Project (Mass.)

Vanderwarker, P. The big dig **624.1**

Central Europe
Kort, M. The handbook of the new Eastern Europe (7 and up) **943**
Central heating. Singer, M. **811**
Central High School (Little Rock, Ark.)
Fradin, J. B. The power of one [biography of Daisy Bates] (7 and up) **92**
Polakow, A. Daisy Bates (7 and up) **92**
Somerlott, R. The Little Rock school desegregation crisis in American history **373**
Central Utah Relocation Center
Tunnell, M. O. The children of Topaz (5 and up) **940.53**
The **century**. See Jennings, P. The century for young people **909.82**
The **century** for young people. Jennings, P. **909.82**
A **century** of immigration, 1820-1924. Collier, C. **325.73**
The **Century** that was (7 and up) **973.9**
Ceramics
Kassinger, R. Ceramics: from magic pots to man-made bones **666**
See/See also pages in the following book(s):
Knapp, B. J. Materials science **620.1**
Ceramics: from magic pots to man-made bones. Kassinger, R. **666**
Cerebral palsy
Gold, J. C. Cerebral palsy (4 and up) **616.8**
Gray, S. H. Living with cerebral palsy (4 and up) **362.1**
Fiction
Koertge, R. Stoner & Spaz (7 and up) **Fic**
Trueman, T. Cruise control
Trueman, T. Stuck in neutral **Fic**
Cerisier, Emmanuel
(il) Burleigh, R. The sea **551.46**
Cerullo, Mary M., 1949-
Coral reef (4 and up) **577.7**
Dolphins **599.5**
The truth about great white sharks (4 and up) **597**
Cesar Chavez (7 and up) **92**
Cha, Dia, 1962-
(jt. auth) Livo, N. J. Folk stories of the Hmong **398.2**
Chabon, Michael
Summerland (5 and up) **Fic**
Chaco Canyon. Vivian, R. G. **978**
Chaco Culture National Historical Park (N.M.)
Vivian, R. G. Chaco Canyon **978**
Chagall, Marc, 1887-1985
About
Pozzi, G. Chagall **92**
Chahrour, Janet
Zap! blink! taste! think! (5 and up) **507.8**
Chaikin, Miriam
Angels sweep the desert floor (4 and up) **296.1**
Chair: a story for voices. Wolff, V. E.
In The Color of absence; 12 stories about loss and hope p91-102 **S C**

Chaka, Zulu Chief, 1787?-1828
About
Stanley, D. Shaka, king of the Zulus (4 and up) **92**
Chalk, Gary
(il) Jacques, B. Redwall **Fic**
The **challenge**. Soto, G.
In Soto, G. Local news p80-90 **S C**
Challenger (Space shuttle)
Jeffrey, L. S. Christa McAuliffe **92**
Challoner, Jack
Energy (5 and up) **621**
Chambers, Tina
(il) Platt, R. Shipwreck **910.4**
Chambers, Veronica
Double dutch (4 and up) **796.2**
The Harlem Renaissance **700**
Chamorro, Violeta Barrios de
See/See also pages in the following book(s):
Axelrod-Contrada, J. Women who led nations (7 and up) **920**
Price-Groff, C. Twentieth-century women political leaders (7 and up) **920**
Champagne, Duane
(ed) The Native North American almanac. See The Native North American almanac **970.004**
The **champion** of the world. Dahl, R.
In Dahl, R. Skin and other stories **S C**
Champlain, Samuel de, 1567-1635
About
Faber, H. Samuel de Champlain (5 and up) **92**
Sonneborn, L. Samuel de Champlain **92**
Chan, Elaine
(jt. auth) Ferroa, P. G. China **951**
Chan, Gillian
A foreign field (7 and up) **Fic**
A **chance** to make good. Grossman, J. R. **305.8**
Chancellorsville (Va.), Battle of, 1863
Fiction
Crane, S. The red badge of courage (7 and up) **Fic**
Chanda's secrets. Stratton, A. **Fic**
Chandrasekhar, Subrahmanyan, 1910-1995
See/See also pages in the following book(s):
Yount, L. Asian-American scientists (7 and up) **920**
Chanel, Coco, 1883-1971
See/See also pages in the following book(s):
Kent, J. Business builders in fashion **920**
Chanel, Gabrielle See Chanel, Coco, 1883-1971
Chang, Lan Samantha
Housepainting
In American eyes; new Asian-American short stories for young adults p13-27 **S C**
Chang, Perry
Florida
In Celebrate the states **973**
The **changeling**. Yep, L.
In Yep, L. The rainbow people p170-77 **398.2**

The **changeling** of Brea Vean. Climo, S.
In Climo, S. Magic & mischief; tales from
Cornwall p61-69   **398.2**

Changing bodies, changing lives. Bell, R.   **613.9**

The **changing** face of American society: 1945-
2000. Collier, C.   **973.92**

The **changing** White House. Feinberg, B. S.   **975.3**

Chanticleer and the fox. Osborne, M. P.
In Osborne, M. P. Favorite medieval tales
p67-72   **398.2**

Chanukah *See* Hanukkah

A **chapel** of thieves. Clements, B.   **Fic**

Chapelle, Dickey, d. 1965
See/See also pages in the following book(s):
Colman, P. Where the action was   **070.4**

Chapman, Robert L.
(ed) Dictionary of American slang. See Dictionary of American slang   **427**
(ed) Roget's international thesaurus. See Roget's
international thesaurus   **423**

Characters and characteristics in literature
See also Native Americans in literature
The Dictionary of characters in children's litera-
ture   **028.5**
Jweid, R. Building character through literature   **028.5**

Charlemagne, Emperor, 742-814
See/See also pages in the following book(s):
Bulfinch, T. Bulfinch's mythology   **201**
Meltzer, M. Ten kings (5 and up)   **920**

Charles I, King of Great Britain, 1600-1649
Fiction
Jeapes, B. The new world order (7 and up)   **Fic**

Charles, Ray
About
Turk, R. Ray Charles: soul man   **92**
See/See also pages in the following book(s):
Lester, J. The blues singers (5 and up)   **920**

Charles Babbage and the engines of perfection.
Collier, B.   **92**

Charles Darwin and the evolution revolution.
Stefoff, R.   **92**

Charles the Great *See* Charlemagne, Emperor,
742-814

Charlie's away. Snyder, M.
In The Green Man: tales from the mythic forest p137-65   **808.8**

Charlie's raven. George, J. C.   **Fic**

Charlie's run. Hobbs, V.   **Fic**

Charlotte's Rose. Cannon, A. E.   **Fic**

Charlotte's web [play] Robinette, J.
In Theatre for young audiences; 20 great
plays for children p7-45   **812.008**

Charmed life. Jones, D. W.   **Fic**

Chartrand, Mark R.
The Audubon Society field guide to the night
sky   **523**

Chasing Redbird. Creech, S.   **Fic**

Chasing the wind. Jones, D. W.
In Firebirds: an anthology of original fantasy
and science fiction; an anthology of original fantasy and science fiction   **S C**

Chasing tornadoes. Lindop, L.   **551.55**

**Châtelet, Gabrielle Emilie Le Tonnelier de
Breteuil, marquise du** *See* Du Châtelet,
Gabrielle Emilie Le Tonnelier de Breteuil,
marquise, 1706-1749

Chaucer, Geoffrey, d. 1400
Adaptations
Cohen, B. Canterbury tales (4 and up)   **821**

Chavez, Cesar, 1927-1993
About
Cesar Chavez (7 and up)   **92**
Collins, D. R. Farmworker's friend: the story of
Cesar Chavez   **92**
See/See also pages in the following book(s):
Streissguth, T. Legendary labor leaders (7 and
up)   **920**

Chávez, Denise, 1948-
The closet
In Growing up Latino; memoirs and stories
p85-98   **810.8**

Cheaney, J. B.
The playmaker   **Fic**
The true Prince   **Fic**

Cheating (Education)
Johnson, D. Learning right from wrong in the
digital age   **004.6**

Check, William A.
AIDS   **616.97**

Checkers. Marsden, J.   **Fic**

Cheetahs
Thompson, S. E. Built for speed (5 and up)   **599.75**

Chemical & biological weapons in our times.
Levine, H. M.   **358**

Chemical and biological warfare. Judson, K.   **358**

Chemical dependency: opposing viewpoints (7 and
up)   **362.29**

Chemical elements
Blashfield, J. F. Sparks of life [series]   **546**
Elements [Grolier] (5 and up)   **546**
The Elements [Benchmark Bks.] (5 and up)   **546**
Newton, D. E. Chemical elements   **546**

Chemical engineering
See also Biotechnology

Chemical industry
Accidents
Bryan, N. Bhopal (5 and up)   **363.1**
Riddle, J. Bhopal (7 and up)   **363.1**

Chemical pollution *See* Pollution

Chemical spills
Bryan, N. Danube (5 and up)   **363.7**

Chemical warfare
Gay, K. Silent death (7 and up)   **358**
Judson, K. Chemical and biological warfare (7
and up)   **358**
Levine, H. M. Chemical & biological weapons
in our times (7 and up)   **358**

Chemical warfare—*Continued*
See/See also pages in the following book(s):
Weapons of mass destruction: opposing viewpoints **358**

Chemicals. Farndon, J. **540.7**

Chemistry
Bonnet, R. L. Science fair projects: chemistry **540.7**
The Facts on File chemistry handbook (7 and up) **540**
Farndon, J. Chemicals **540.7**
Gardner, R. Chemistry science fair projects using acids, bases, metals, salts, and inorganic stuff (7 and up) **540**
Gardner, R. Chemistry science fair projects using french fries, gumdrops, soap, and other organic stuff (7 and up) **547**
Gardner, R. Science project ideas about kitchen chemistry **540.7**
Meiani, A. Chemistry (4 and up) **540**
Oxlade, C. Chemistry **540.7**

Chemistry! best science projects [series]
Gardner, R. Chemistry science fair projects using acids, bases, metals, salts, and inorganic stuff **540**
Gardner, R. Chemistry science fair projects using french fries, gumdrops, soap, and other organic stuff **547**
Goodstein, M. Plastics and polymers science fair projects **507.8**

Chemistry science fair projects using acids, bases, metals, salts, and inorganic stuff. Gardner, R. **540**

Chemistry science fair projects using french fries, gumdrops, soap, and other organic stuff. Gardner, R. **547**

Chemists
Birch, B. Marie Curie **92**
Hager, T. Linus Pauling and the chemistry of life (7 and up) **92**
Lassieur, A. Marie Curie **92**
MacLeod, E. Marie Curie (5 and up) **92**
Pasachoff, N. E. Marie Curie and the science of radioactivity **92**
Poynter, M. Marie Curie: discoverer of radium (4 and up) **92**

Chemotherapy. Bardhan-Quallen, S. **616.99**

Chen, Da, 1962-
China's son (7 and up) **92**

Ch'en, Hsing-Shen *See* Chern, Shiing-Shen, 1911-2004

Chen, Mary F.
Knuckles
In American eyes; new Asian-American short stories for young adults p62-79 **S C**

Cheng, Andrea, 1957-
The lace dowry (4 and up) **Fic**

Cheng, I Sao *See* Cheng, Yi Sao, d. 1844

Cheng, Yi Sao, d. 1844
See/See also pages in the following book(s):
Wren, L. L. Pirates and privateers of the high seas p11-17 **920**

Chenoo. Bruchac, J.
In Bruchac, J. and Bruchac, J. When the Chenoo howls; native American tales of terror **398.2**

Chern, Shiing-Shen, 1911-2004
See/See also pages in the following book(s):
Henderson, H. Modern mathematicians (7 and up) **920**

Chernobyl. Bryan, N. **363.7**

Chernobyl Nuclear Accident, Chernobyl, Ukraine, 1986
Bryan, N. Chernobyl (5 and up) **363.7**

Cherokee. Stewart, P. North American Indians today [series]

Cherokee Indians
Elish, D. The Trail of Tears **970.004**
Furbee, M. R. Wild Rose: Nancy Ward and the Cherokee Nation **92**
Klausner, J. Sequoyah's gift (4 and up) **92**
Perdue, T. The Cherokees Indians of North America series
Stewart, P. Cherokee North American Indians today [series]

Cherokee Nation v. Georgia. Sherrow, V. **346**

The Cherokees. Perdue, T. Indians of North America series

Chesapeake Bay (Md. and Va.)
Fiction
Paterson, K. Jacob have I loved **Fic**

Chesnutt, Charles Waddell, 1858-1932
The doll
In The Boy of Chancellorville and other Civil War stories p112-26 **S C**

Chess
Basman, M. Chess for kids (4 and up) **794.1**
King, D. Chess **794.1**
Fiction
Freymann-Weyr, G. The kings are already here (7 and up) **Fic**

Chess for kids. Basman, M. **794.1**

Chesterman, Charles W.
The Audubon Society field guide to North American rocks and minerals **549**

Cheung, Lillian Wai-Yin
Be healthy! it's a girl thing (5 and up) **613**

Chewing the cud. King-Smith, D. **92**

Cheyenne. McIntosh, K. North American Indians today [series]

Cheyenne Indians
McIntosh, K. Cheyenne North American Indians today [series]
Viola, H. J. It is a good day to die (5 and up) **973.8**
See/See also pages in the following book(s):
Ehrlich, A. Wounded Knee: an Indian history of the American West (6 and up) **970.004**

The Cheyenne prophet. Brown, D. A.
In Brown, D. A. Dee Brown's folktales of the Native American; retold for our times p46-59 **398.2**

Cheyenne revenge [excerpt] Trafzer, C. E.
In Talking leaves; contemporary native American short stories **S C**

Chiang, Yeng-Fong, 1947-
(jt. auth) Krasno, R. Cloud weavers   **398.2**

Chicago (Ill.)

Fiction

Cisneros, S. The house on Mango Street (7 and up)   **Fic**
Deaver, J. R. Say goodnight, Gracie (7 and up)   **Fic**
Peck, R. Fair weather (5 and up)   **Fic**

The **Chicago** "Black Sox" baseball scandal. Pellowski, M.   **796.357**
The **Chicago** Seven political protest trial. Alonso, K.   **345**

Chicago White Sox (Baseball team)
Pellowski, M. The Chicago "Black Sox" base-ball scandal   **796.357**

Chicanos See Mexican Americans

Chicken boy. Dowell, F. O.   **Fic**

Chicken friend. Morgan, N.   **Fic**

Chicken soup for the kid's soul   **158**

Chicken soup for the teenage soul {I-III}. Canfield, J.   **158**

Chickenpox
Silverstein, A. Chickenpox and shingles (7 and up)   **616.9**

Chickenpox and shingles. Silverstein, A.   **616.9**

Chickens

Fiction

Dowell, F. O. Chicken boy (4 and up)   **Fic**

Chicoine, Stephen
From the ashes   **940.53**

Chief Joseph See Joseph, Nez Percé Chief, 1840-1904

Chief Joseph and the Nez Percés. Scott, R. A.   **92**

Chief Sunrise, John McGraw, and me. Tocher, T.   **Fic**

Chilcoat, George W.
(jt. auth) Tunnell, M. O. The children of Topaz   **940.53**

Child, Lydia Maria Francis, 1802-1880
The two Christmas evenings
    In The Boy of Chancellorville and other Civil War stories p74-94   **S C**

About

Kenschaft, L. Lydia Maria Child (7 and up)   **92**

The **child**. Lester, J.
    In Join in; multiethnic short stories by out-standing writers for young adults p142-49   **S C**

Child abuse
    See also Child sexual abuse
Child abuse [Current controversies] (7 and up)   **362.7**
Child abuse: opposing viewpoints (7 and up)   **362.7**
Kim, H. H. Child abuse (7 and up)   **362.7**
Pledge, D. S. When something feels wrong (7 and up)   **362.7**

Fiction

Byars, B. C. Cracker Jackson (5 and up)   **Fic**

Coman, C. What Jamie saw (5 and up)   **Fic**
Crutcher, C. Staying fat for Sarah Byrnes   **Fic**
Draper, S. M. Forged by fire (7 and up)   **Fic**
Golding, T. M. The secret within   **Fic**
Hawes, L. Waiting for Christopher (7 and up)   **Fic**
Howe, J. The watcher (7 and up)   **Fic**
Klass, D. You don't know me (7 and up)   **Fic**
McCord, P. Pictures in the dark (7 and up)   **Fic**

Child abuse [Current controversies] (7 and up)   **362.7**

Child abuse: opposing viewpoints (7 and up)   **362.7**

Child and parent See Parent-child relationship

Child and youth security sourcebook   **362.7**

Child artists
—I never saw another butterfly—   **741.9**

Child custody
    See also Parental kidnapping
See/See also pages in the following book(s):
Marriage and divorce (7 and up)   **306.8**

Child labor
Bartoletti, S. C. Growing up in coal country (5 and up)   **331.3**
Bartoletti, S. C. Kids on strike! (5 and up)   **331.8**
Freedman, R. Kids at work (5 and up)   **331.3**
Kuklin, S. Iqbal Masih and the crusaders against child slavery (7 and up)   **331.3**
Parker, D. L. Stolen dreams   **331.3**
Springer, J. Listen to us (7 and up)   **331.3**

Fiction

Boling, K. January 1905 (5 and up)   **Fic**
D'Adamo, F. Iqbal (5 and up)   **Fic**

Child molesting See Child sexual abuse

The **child** of calamity. Yep, L.
    In Yep, L. The rainbow people p46-52   **398.2**

Child of Faerie. Kimberly, G.
    In A Glory of unicorns p165-82   **S C**

Child of the owl. Yep, L.   **Fic**

Child psychiatry
    See also Autism

Child rearing
    See also Socialization

Child sexual abuse
See/See also pages in the following book(s):
Child abuse: opposing viewpoints (7 and up)   **362.7**
Jukes, M. It's a girl thing (5 and up)   **305.23**

Fiction

Doyle, B. Boy O'Boy   **Fic**
Frank, E. R. Friction (7 and up)   **Fic**
Woodson, J. I hadn't meant to tell you this   **Fic**

Child snatching by parents See Parental kidnapping

Childbirth
> *See also* Multiple birth
> Flanagan, G. L. Beginning life   **612.6**

Children
> *See also* Abandoned children; African American children; Boys; Girls; Infants; Runaway children
> Hoose, P. M. We were there, too! (5 and up)   **973**

> #### Abuse
> *See* Child abuse

> #### Adoption
> *See* Adoption

> #### Books and reading
> Children's books from other countries   **028.5**
> Larson, J. C. Bringing mysteries alive for children and young adults   **028.5**

> #### Employment
> *See* Child labor

> #### Law and legislation
> Gold, S. D. In re Gault (1967) (7 and up)   **345**
> Greenberg, K. E. Adolescent rights (7 and up)   **346**
> Landau, E. Your legal rights (7 and up)   **346**

> #### Socialization
> *See* Socialization

> #### United States
> Greenberg, J. E. Young people's letters to the president   **973**
> Miller, B. M. Growing up in revolution and the new nation, 1775 to 1800 (5 and up)   **973.3**

Children, Retarded *See* Mentally handicapped children

Children and books. Sutherland, Z.   **028.5**

Children and war
> Sherrow, V. Encyclopedia of youth and war   **305.23**

Children of divorced parents
> Schultz, M. A. Teens with single parents (7 and up)   **306.8**

Children of immigrants
> Kosof, A. Living in two worlds (7 and up)   **325.73**

Children of single parents *See* Single parent family

Children of the Dust Bowl. Stanley, J.   **371.9**

Children of the river. Crew, L.   **Fic**

Children of the slaughter. Gottfried, T.   **940.53**

The **children** of Topaz. Tunnell, M. O.   **940.53**

Children's and young adult literature by Latino writers. York, S.   **028.5**

Children's Book Council (New York, N.Y.)
> Notable social studies trade books for young people. See Notable social studies trade books for young people   **016.3**
> Outstanding science trade books for students K-12. See Outstanding science trade books for students K-12   **016.5**

Children's books about religion. Dole, P. P.   **016.2**

Children's books from other countries   **028.5**

Children's books in children's hands   **028.5**

Children's catalog   **011.6**

Children's clothing
> Sills, L. From rags to riches (5 and up)   **391**

Children's encyclopedia of American history. King, D. C.   **973.03**

Children's history of the 20th century   **909.82**

Children's libraries
> *See also* Elementary school libraries; Young adults' libraries
> Minkel, W. Delivering Web reference services to young people   **025.04**
> Reid, R. Something funny happened at the library   **027.62**

Children's literature
> *See also* Caldecott Medal; Coretta Scott King Award; Fairy tales; Newbery Medal
> Keane, N. J. Booktalking across the curriculum: the middle years   **028.5**

> #### Bibliography
> Anderson, V. Fiction sequels for readers 10 to 16   **016.8**
> Barker, K. Outstanding books for children and young people   **028.5**
> Children's books from other countries   **028.5**
> Children's catalog   **011.6**
> Day, F. A. Lesbian and gay voices   **016.8**
> Hall, S. Using picture storybooks to teach literary devices v3   **016.8**
> Helbig, A. Many peoples, one land   **016.8**
> Jweid, R. Building character through literature   **028.5**
> Matthew, K. I. Neal-Schuman guide to celebrations & holidays around the world   **394.26**
> Schon, I. The best of Latino heritage 1996-2002   **011.6**
> Schon, I. The best of the Latino heritage   **011.6**
> Schon, I. Recommended books in Spanish for children and young adults, 2000 through 2004   **011.6**
> Steiner, S. F. Promoting a global community through multicultural children's literature   **016.8**
> Subject guide to Children's books in print   **015.73**
> Trelease, J. The read-aloud handbook   **028.5**
> Ward, M. Voices from the margins   **016.8**
> The World through children's books   **011.6**
> Wright, C. M. More hot links   **011.6**
> York, S. Children's and young adult literature by Latino writers   **028.5**
> Your reading   **011.6**

> #### Bio-bibliography
> McElmeel, S. L. 100 most popular children's authors   **810.3**
> The ninth book of junior authors and illustrators   **920.003**
> Something about the author   **920.003**
> Something about the author: autobiography series   **920.003**

> #### Dictionaries
> The Dictionary of characters in children's literature   **028.5**

Children's literature—*Continued*
History and criticism
Children's books in children's hands   **028.5**
The Coretta Scott King Awards book, 1970-1999   **028.5**
Gillespie, J. T. The Newbery companion
    028.5
Horning, K. T. From cover to cover   **028.1**
The Newbery & Caldecott medal books, 1986-2000   **028.5**
Newbery and Caldecott Medal books, 1966-1975
    028.5
Newbery and Caldecott Medal books, 1976-1985
    028.5
Newbery Medal books, 1922-1955   **028.5**
Stephens, C. G. Coretta Scott King Award books   **028.5**
Sutherland, Z. Children and books   **028.5**
The World through children's books   **011.6**
Study and teaching
Ellis, S. From reader to writer   **372.6**
Scales, P. R. Teaching banned books   **323.44**

Children's night sky atlas. Scagell, R.   **520**

Children's poetry
    See also Nonsense verses

Children's quick & easy cookbook. Wilkes, A.
    641.5

The **children's** war. Esaias, T.
    In Sherwood: original stories from the world of Robin Hood p70-83   **S C**

Children's writings
Atkin, S. B. Voices from the fields (5 and up)
    331.5
—I never saw another butterfly—   **741.9**
Salting the ocean (4 and up)   **811.008**
When the rain sings   **811.008**

Childress, Alice, 1920-1994
Rainbow Jordan (7 and up)   **Fic**

Childress, Diana
The War of 1812 (5 and up)   **973.5**

Chile
Dwyer, C. Chile   **983**
Winter, J. K. Chile (5 and up)   **983**

Chilean poets *See* Poets, Chilean

Chilvers, Ian
(ed) The Oxford dictionary of art. See The Oxford dictionary of art   **703**

Chimpanzees
Goodall, J. The chimpanzees I love (4 and up)
    599.8
Goodall, J. With love (4 and up)   **599.8**
Kozleski, L. Jane Goodall (7 and up)   **92**
Fiction
Dickinson, P. Eva (7 and up)   **Fic**
The **chimpanzees** I love. Goodall, J.   **599.8**

Chin, Beverly Ann
(ed) The Dictionary of characters in children's literature. See The Dictionary of characters in children's literature   **028.5**

Chin-Lee, Cynthia, 1958-
Amelia to Zora (4 and up)   **920**

Ch'in Shih-huang, Emperor of China, 259-210 B.C.
Tomb
O'Connor, J. The emperor's silent army (4 and up)   **931**

China
Behnke, A. China in pictures   **951**
Chen, D. China's son (7 and up)   **92**
Ferroa, P. G. China (5 and up)   **951**
Fritz, J. China homecoming (6 and up)
    951.05
Fritz, J. Homesick: my own story (5 and up)
    92
Antiquities
O'Connor, J. The emperor's silent army (4 and up)   **931**
Civilization
Cotterell, A. Ancient China (4 and up)   **931**
Schomp, V. The ancient Chinese (5 and up)
    931
Stefoff, R. The Asian empires (5 and up)
    950

Communism
    See Communism—China
Description and travel
Otfinoski, S. Marco Polo   **92**
Worth, R. The great empire of China and Marco Polo in world history   **92**
Fiction
Alexander, L. The remarkable journey of Prince Jen (5 and up)   **Fic**
McCaughrean, G. The kite rider (5 and up)
    Fic
Namioka, L. Ties that bind, ties that break (5 and up)   **Fic**
Napoli, D. J. Bound   **Fic**
Whelan, G. Chu Ju's house   **Fic**
Wilkinson, C. Dragon keeper (5 and up)   **Fic**
Folklore
    See Folklore—China
History
Immell, M. The Han dynasty   **931**
Major, J. S. The Silk Route   **950**
Stefoff, R. The Asian empires (5 and up)
    950

History—1949-1976
Slavicek, L. C. Mao Zedong   **92**
History—1949-1976—Personal narratives
Jiang, J.-l. Red scarf girl (6 and up)   **951.05**
Zhang, A. Red land, yellow river (5 and up)
    951.05

Poetry
Grimes, N. Tai chi morning (5 and up)   **811**
Social life and customs
Mah, A. Y. Chinese Cinderella   **92**

China Browne. Vizenor, G. R.
    In Talking leaves; contemporary native American short stories   **S C**

China homecoming. Fritz, J.   **951.05**

China in pictures. Behnke, A.   **951**

China's son. Chen, D.   **92**

Chinatown mystery [series]
Yep, L. The case of the Goblin Pearls   **Fic**

Chinese
United States
Perl, L. To the Golden Mountain   **305.8**
United States—Fiction
Namioka, L. An ocean apart, a world away
   Fic
Yep, L. Dragon's gate (6 and up)   **Fic**
The **Chinese** American family album. Hoobler, D.
   305.8

Chinese Americans
   See also Chinese—United States
Chippendale, L. A. Yo-Yo Ma   **92**
Hoobler, D. The Chinese American family al-
   bum   **305.8**
Yep, L. The lost garden (5 and up)   **92**
See/See also pages in the following book(s):
Asian Americans: opposing viewpoints (7 and
   up)   **305.8**
Biography
Shields, C. J. Amy Tan   **92**
Fiction
Currier, K. S. Kai's journey to Gold Mountain
   (4 and up)   **Fic**
Fletcher, S. Walk across the sea   **Fic**
Lord, B. B. In the Year of the Boar and Jackie
   Robinson (4-6)   **Fic**
Martin, N. Flight of the Fisherbird (5 and up)
   Fic
Yee, L. Millicent Min, girl genius (5 and up)
   Fic
Yee, P. Tales from Gold Mountain (4 and up)
   S C
Yep, L. Angelfish (5 and up)   **Fic**
Yep, L. The case of the Goblin Pearls   **Fic**
Yep, L. Child of the owl (5 and up)   **Fic**
Yep, L. Dragonwings (5 and up)   **Fic**
Yep, L. Dream soul   **Fic**
Yep, L. Thief of hearts (5 and up)   **Fic**
Yep, L. The traitor (5 and up)   **Fic**
Poetry
Glenn, M. Split image: a story in poems (7 and
   up)   **811**
Chinese Cinderella. Mah, A. Y.   **92**
Chinese civilization *See* China—Civilization
Chinese mythology A to Z. Roberts, J.   **299.5**
Chinese poetry
Liu Siyu. A thousand peaks   **895.1**
Chinook Indians
Fiction
Holm, J. L. Boston Jane: an adventure   **Fic**
A **chip** of glass ruby. Gordimer, N.
   In Somehow tenderness survives; stories of
   Southern Africa p105-18   **S C**
Chippendale, Lisa A.
Triumph of the imagination: the story of writer
   J.K. Rowling (5 and up)   **92**
Yo-Yo Ma   **92**
Chippewa Indians *See* Ojibwa Indians
Chisholm, Shirley, 1924-2005
See/See also pages in the following book(s):
Pinkney, A. D. Let it shine (4 and up)   **920**
Chivalry
   See also Medieval civilization
Bulfinch, T. Bulfinch's mythology   **201**

Chlorine
Blashfield, J. F. Chlorine
   In Blashfield, J. F. Sparks of life; chemical
   elements that make life possible   **546**
Chlorine. Lynch, C.
   In Lynch, C. All the old haunts p22-37
   S C
The **chocolate** war. Cormier, R.   **Fic**
The **Choctaw**. McKee, J. O. Indians of North
   America series
Choctaw Indians
McKee, J. O. The Choctaw Indians of North
   America series
Folklore
Tingle, T. Walking the Choctaw road (7 and up)
   398.2
Choi, Sook Nyul
Year of impossible goodbyes (5 and up)   **Fic**
Choldenko, Gennifer, 1957-
Al Capone does my shirts (5 and up)   **Fic**
Notes from a liar and her dog (5 and up)
   Fic
Cholera
Peters, S. T. Cholera   **614.5**
Chollet, Louise E., fl. 1865
Dog Carlos
   In The Boy of Chancellorville and other Civil
   War stories p9-22   **S C**
Choosing up sides. Ritter, J. H.   **Fic**
Choreographers
Cruz, B. Alvin Ailey   **92**
Freedman, R. Martha Graham, a dancer's life (7
   and up)   **92**
Chorlton, Windsor
The invention of the silicon chip   **621.381**
The **chosen**. Harrah, M.
   In Night terrors; stories of shadow and sub-
   stance   **S C**
Chotjewitz, David
Daniel half human (7 and up)   **Fic**
Chouteau, Auguste, d. 1829
See/See also pages in the following book(s):
Doherty, K. Ranchers, homesteaders, and traders
   920
Chouteau, René Auguste *See* Chouteau, Auguste,
   d. 1829
Chrisp, Peter
Mesopotamia (5 and up)   **935**
Town and country life (5 and up)   **940.1**
Warfare   **355**
Christ *See* Jesus Christ
Christensen, Bonnie, 1951-
(comp) In my grandmother's house. See In my
   grandmother's house   **306.8**
Christian, Rebecca
Cooking the Spanish way
   In Easy menu ethnic cookbooks   **641.5**
Christian, Spencer
Shake, rattle, and roll   **551.2**
Christian art
Connolly, S. New Testament miracles   **226**

Christian fiction
Bibliography
Walker, B. J. Developing Christian fiction collections for children and adults   **025.2**

Christian fundamentalism
Fiction
Peck, R. The last safe place on earth (7 and up)   **Fic**

Christian life
Fiction
Crew, L. Brides of Eden (7 and up)   **Fic**
Krisher, T. Uncommon Faith   **Fic**
Paterson, K. Preacher's boy (5 and up)   **Fic**
Tolan, S. S. Ordinary miracles   **Fic**

Christian missionaries
Dolan, S. Junípero Serra   **92**

Christian missions
Fiction
O'Dell, S. Zia (5 and up)   **Fic**

Christian saints
Mulvihill, M. The treasury of saints and martyrs (5 and up)   **920**
Stanley, D. Joan of Arc (4 and up)   **92**
Fiction
Napoli, D. J. Song of the Magdalene (7 and up)   **Fic**

Christian Science
Williams, J. K. The Christian Scientists (7 and up)   **289.5**
The **Christian** Scientists. Williams, J. K.   **289.5**

Christiana, David
(il) Bath, K. P. The secret of Castle Cant   **Fic**

Christianity
Brown, A. The Bible and Christianity (5 and up)   **220**
Lace, W. W. Christianity   **230**
See/See also pages in the following book(s):
Osborne, M. P. One world, many religions (4 and up)   **201**
Dictionaries
The Oxford dictionary of the Christian Church   **230.003**
History
See Church history

Christiansen, C. B.
Red seven
In The Color of absence; 12 stories about loss and hope p105-20   **S C**

Christianson, Gale E.
Isaac Newton and the scientific revolution (7 and up)   **92**

Christianson, Stephen G.
Facts about the Congress   **328.73**
(ed) The American book of days. See The American book of days   **394.26**

Christie, Agatha, 1890-1976
The mirror crack'd (7 and up)   **Fic**

Christina, Queen of Sweden, 1626-1689
See/See also pages in the following book(s):
Meltzer, M. Ten queens (5 and up)   **920**

Christmas
McKissack, P. C. Christmas in the big house, Christmas in the quarters (4 and up)   **394.26**
Encyclopedias
Bowler, G. The world encyclopedia of Christmas   **394.26**
Fiction
Avi. The Christmas rat   **Fic**
Cooney, C. B. What child is this?   **Fic**
Fine, A. The true story of Christmas (4 and up)   **Fic**
Plummer, L. The unlikely romance of Kate Bjorkman (7 and up)   **Fic**
Robinson, B. The best Christmas pageant ever (4-6)   **Fic**
Yep, L. Dream soul   **Fic**
Christmas after all. Lasky, K.   **Fic**
Christmas fantasy. Hijuelos, O.
In You're on!: seven plays in English and Spanish p108-31   **812.008**
Christmas in the big house, Christmas in the quarters. McKissack, P. C.   **394.26**
The **Christmas** rat. Avi   **Fic**
Christmas stories *See* Christmas—Fiction
The **Christmas** story.   **232.9**
A **Christmas** story. Myers, W. D.
In Myers, W. D. 145th Street; short stories   **S C**

Christopher, John, 1922-
The White Mountains   **Fic**
Christopher Hart's animation studio. Hart, C.   **791.43**
Christopher Hart's cartoon studio. Hart, C.   **741.5**
Christopher Hart's portable animation studio. See Hart, C. Christopher Hart's animation studio   **791.43**
Christopher Hart's portable cartoon studio. See Hart, C. Christopher Hart's cartoon studio   **741.5**

Chromosome mapping *See* Gene mapping
Chronic fatigue syndrome
Abrams, L. Chronic fatigue syndrome   **616.9**
Chronicle of America's wars [series]
Bohannon, L. F. The American Revolution   **973.3**
Childress, D. The War of 1812   **973.5**
Feldman, R. T. The Korean War   **951.9**
Feldman, R. T. The Mexican-American War   **973.6**
Feldman, R. T. World War I   **940.3**
Goldstein, M. J. World War II, Europe   **940.53**
Levy, D. The Vietnam War   **959.704**
Sherman, J. The Cold War   **909.82**
Williams, B. World War II, Pacific   **940.54**
Chronicles of Prydain [series]
Alexander, L. The book of three   **Fic**
Alexander, L. The high king   **Fic**
Chronology, Historical *See* Historical chronology
Chronology of African American history. Hornsby, A., Jr.   **305.8**
Chu, Ching-Wu *See* Chu, Paul, 1941-

Chu, Paul, 1941-
See/See also pages in the following book(s):
Yount, L. Asian-American scientists (7 and up)
920

Chu, Vida
The fourth question
In Fire and wings: dragon tales from East and
West p55-64 **S C**

Chu Ju's house. Whelan, G. **Fic**

Chung, Okwha
Cooking the Korean way
In Easy menu ethnic cookbooks **641.5**

Church, Audrey P., 1957-
Leverage your library program to help raise test
scores **027.8**

Church
See also Christianity
The **church**. Hinds, K. **274**

Church and education
See/See also pages in the following book(s):
Religion in America: opposing viewpoints (7
and up) **200.9**

Church and state
Andryszewski, T. School prayer (7 and up)
344
Dudley, M. E. Engel v. Vitale (1962) (7 and up)
344
See/See also pages in the following book(s):
Civil liberties: opposing viewpoints (7 and up)
323
Religion in America: opposing viewpoints (7
and up) **200.9**

Church history
The Rise of Christianity (7 and up) **270**
600-1500, Middle Ages
See also Inquisition

Church of Jesus Christ of Latter-day Saints
Bushman, C. L. Mormons in America (7 and
up) **289.3**

The **church** that was at Antioch. Kipling, R.
In McCaffrey, A. {The Pern series} **S C**

Churchill, Sir Winston, 1874-1965
About
Macdonald, F. Winston Churchill **92**
Severance, J. B. Winston Churchill (5 and up)
92
Wrigley, C. Winston Churchill: a biographical
companion (7 and up) **92**
See/See also pages in the following book(s):
Ross, S. Leaders of World War II **920**

Chuy's beginnings. Saldaña, R.
In Saldaña, R. Finding our way: stories p11-
19 **S C**

Ci Xi *See* Tz'u-hsi, Empress dowager of China,
1835-1908

Ciccone, Madonna *See* Madonna, 1958-

Cinderella
Poetry
Whipple, L. If the shoe fits (5 and up) **811**

Cinematography
Graham, I. Film and photography **770**
Hamilton, J. Special effects in film and televi-
sion (4 and up) **791.43**

Ciphers
Janeczko, P. B. Top secret (4 and up) **652**

Cipollone, Rose, d. 1984
About
Sergis, D. K. Cipollone v. Liggett Group (7 and
up) **346.03**
Cipollone v. Liggett Group. Sergis, D. K.
346.03

Circle of magic: Sandry's book. Pierce, T. **Fic**
A circle of time. Montes, M. **Fic**
A circle unbroken. Hotze, S. **Fic**
The circuit. Jiménez, F.
In Leaving home: stories p53-62 **808.8**

Circulatory system *See* Cardiovascular system

Circumnavigation *See* Voyages around the world

Circus
Fiction
Janeczko, P. B. Worlds afire **Fic**
Circus dreams. San Souci, R.
In San Souci, R. Double-dare to be scared:
another thirteen chilling tales **S C**

Cisneros, Sandra
The house on Mango Street (7 and up) **Fic**
The monkey garden
In Growing up Latino; memoirs and stories
p288-91 **810.8**
My Lucy friend who smells like corn
In Who do you think you are?; stories of
friends and enemies p119-21 **S C**
About
Mirriam-Goldberg, C. Sandra Cisneros **92**
See/See also pages in the following book(s):
Hill, C. M. Ten Hispanic American authors
920

Cities and towns
Millard, A. A street through time **936**
United States
Collier, C. The rise of the cities, 1820-1920
307.7

The **city** [Life in the Renaissance series] Hinds, K.
940.2

The **city** [Life in the Roman Empire series] Hinds,
K. **937**

City: a story of Roman planning and construction.
Macaulay, D. **711**

City and town life
Hinds, K. The city [Life in the Renaissance se-
ries] **940.2**
Hinds, K. The city [Life in the Roman Empire
series] **937**
Sandler, M. W. Straphanging in the USA (5 and
up) **388.4**
Fiction
Almond, D. Counting stars (7 and up) **Fic**
Brooks, M. True confessions of a heartless girl
(7 and up) **Fic**
Fleischman, P. Seedfolks (4 and up) **Fic**
Poetry
Glenn, M. Foreign exchange (7 and up) **811**
Stone bench in an empty park (4 and up)
811.008

"The **City** of Dreadful Night". Kipling, R.
In McCaffrey, A. {The Pern series} **S C**

The **city** of Ember. DuPrau, J.   **Fic**

City of one (7 and up)   **810.8**

City of the beasts. Allende, I.   **Fic**

City planning

Rome

Macaulay, D. City: a story of Roman planning and construction (4 and up)   **711**

City states of the Swahili coast. Wilson, T. H.   **967.6**

Civil defense

Campbell, G. A. A vulnerable America (7 and up)   **363.3**

Civil engineering

See also Structural engineering

Aaseng, N. Construction: building the impossible   **624**

Fantastic feats and failures (4 and up)   **624.1**

Levy, M. Engineering the city   **624**

Macaulay, D. City: a story of Roman planning and construction (4 and up)   **711**

Macaulay, D. Underground (5 and up)   **624**

Civil liberties: opposing viewpoints (7 and up)   **323**

Civil rights

See also African Americans—Civil rights; Discrimination; Women's rights

American civil rights: primary sources   **323.1**

Civil liberties: opposing viewpoints (7 and up)   **323**

Engelbert, P. American civil rights: almanac   **323.1**

Engelbert, P. American civil rights: biographies   **920**

Freedman, R. In defense of liberty   **342**

Krull, K. A kid's guide to America's Bill of Rights (4 and up)   **342**

Patrick, J. J. The Bill of Rights (7 and up)   **342**

Pendergast, T. Constitutional amendments: from freedom of speech to flag burning (7 and up)   **342**

See/See also pages in the following book(s):

The information revolution   **303.4**

Civil rights (International law) *See* Human rights

Civil rights (7 and up)   **323.1**

Civil rights leaders. Dubovoy, S.   **920**

Civil rights marches. George, L.   **323.1**

The **civil** rights movement. Ritchie, N.   **323.1**

The **civil** rights movement. Wexler, S.   **323.1**

Civil War

United States

See United States—History—1861-1865, Civil War

The **Civil** War. Beller, S. P.   **973.7**

Civil War. Golay, M.   **973.7**

The **Civil** War. Haugen, D.   **973.7**

The **Civil** War. Nardo, D.   **973.7**

Civil War. Netzley, P. D.   **973.7**

The **Civil** War [Grolier 10v set] (5 and up)   **973.7**

Civil War [series]

Hughes, C. The Battle of Antietam   **973.7**

King, D. C. The Battle of Gettysburg   **973.7**

King, D. C. The Battle of Vicksburg   **973.7**

Kops, D. The Battle of Bull Run   **973.7**

The **Civil** War, 1860-1865. Collier, C.   **973.7**

Civil War A to Z. Bolotin, N.   **973.7**

The **Civil** War and Reconstruction. Barney, W. L.   **973.7**

The **Civil** War and Reconstruction. Kirchberger, J. H.   **973.7**

The **Civil** War at sea. Sullivan, G.   **973.7**

Civil War: battles and leaders   **973.7**

Civilian Conservation Corps (U.S.)

Fiction

Ingold, J. Hitch (7 and up)   **Fic**

Civilization

See also names of continents, countries, states, etc., with the subdivision *Civilization,* e.g. United States—Civilization

Dictionaries

Hirsch, E. D. The new dictionary of cultural literacy   **031**

Encyclopedias

Lands and peoples   **910.3**

History

Ochoa, G. The Wilson chronology of ideas   **909**

Roberts, J. M. The illustrated history of the world (7 and up)   **909**

Civilization, Ancient *See* Ancient civilization

Civilization, Classical *See* Classical civilization

Civilization, Medieval *See* Medieval civilization

Civilization and science *See* Science and civilization

Civilization and technology *See* Technology and civilization

Cixi *See* Tz'u-hsi, Empress dowager of China, 1835-1908

Clan Apis. Hosler, J.   **741.5**

Clapp, Patricia, 1912-

The tamarack tree (7 and up)   **Fic**

Clark, Charles

Islam   **297**

(jt. auth) Cartlidge, C. Life of a Nazi soldier   **940.54**

Clark, Clara Gillow, 1951-

Hill Hawk Hattie (5 and up)   **Fic**

Clark, Donna Lynn

(jt. auth) Haven, K. F. 100 most popular scientists for young adults   **920**

Clark, Eugenie

About

Ross, M. E. Fish watching with Eugenie Clark (4 and up)   **92**

Clark, John O. E. (John Owen Edward), 1937-

Under the microscope: science tools   **530.8**

(ed) Physics matters! See Physics matters!   **530**

Clark, Neil

1,001 facts about dinosaurs   **567.9**

Clark, Peter H., 1829-1925

See/See also pages in the following book(s):

Katz, W. L. Black pioneers   **920**

Clark, Septima Poinsette, 1898-1987
See/See also pages in the following book(s):
Hansen, J. Women of hope (4 and up)   **920**

Clark, Warren
(il) Graydon, S. Made you look   **659.1**

Clark, William, 1770-1838
Off the map   **978**
About
Blumberg, R. The incredible journey of Lewis
  and Clark (5 and up)   **978**
Faber, H. Lewis and Clark   **978**
Kimmel, E. C. As far as the eye can reach (4
  and up)   **978**
Fiction
Bruchac, J. Sacajawea (6 and up)   **Fic**

Clarke, Alicia
Coping with self-mutilation (7 and up)
  616.85

Clarke, Arthur C., 1917-
2001: a space odyssey (7 and up)   **Fic**

Clarke, Jimmy
(il) Lurie, J. Fundamental snowboarding
  796.93

Clarke, Judith, 1943-
Kalpana's dream   **Fic**
Starry nights   **Fic**
Wolf on the fold (7 and up)   **Fic**

Clash of cultures, prehistory-1638. Collier, C.
  970.004

Class cootie. San Souci, R.
In San Souci, R. Double-dare to be scared:
  another thirteen chilling tales   **S C**

Classic American cars. Willson, Q.   **629.222**
Classic racing cars. Hodges, D. W.   **629.228**

Classical antiquities
See also Rome—Antiquities

Classical civilization
See also Rome—Civilization
Encyclopedias
Ancient Greece and Rome   **938**

Classical music *See* Music

Classical mythology
Greek and Roman mythology (7 and up)
  292
Hamilton, E. Mythology p21-76   **292**
McCaughrean, G. Odysseus (5 and up)   **292**
McCaughrean, G. Perseus (5 and up)   **292**
Pickels, D. E. Egyptian kings and queens and
  classical deities   **930**
Fiction
Coville, B. Juliet Dove, Queen of Love (4-6)
  Fic
Kindl, P. Lost in the labyrinth   **Fic**
Napoli, D. J. The great god Pan (7 and up)
  Fic
Rao, S. Sophocles' Oedipus the King (7 and up)
  Fic
Spinner, S. Quicksilver (7 and up)   **Fic**
Poetry
Hovey, K. Ancient voices   **811**

Classified catalogs
Children's catalog   **011.6**
Senior high school library catalog   **011.6**

Clay, Cassius *See* Ali, Muhammad, 1942-
Clay. Rodowsky, C. F.   **Fic**
Clay v. United States. Freedman, S.   **343**

Clayton, Elaine, 1961-
(jt. auth) Wayland, A. H. Girl coming in for a
  landing   **811**

Clayton, L. (Lawrence)
Diet pill drug dangers   **616.3**

Clean sweep. Bauer, J.
In Shelf life: stories by the book p151-64
  S C

Cleanliness
See/See also pages in the following book(s):
Crump, M. Don't sweat it!   **613**

Cleary, Beverly
Dear Mr. Henshaw (4 and up)   **Fic**
A girl from Yamhill: a memoir (6 and up)
  92
My own two feet   **92**
Strider (4 and up)   **Fic**

Cleaver, Bill
(jt. auth) Cleaver, V. Where the lillies bloom
  Fic

Cleaver, Vera
Where the lillies bloom (5 and up)   **Fic**

Clemens, Samuel Langhorne *See* Twain, Mark,
  1835-1910

Clément, Frédéric
(il) Freedman, R. Confucius   **92**

Clement-Davies, David
Fire bringer (7 and up)   **Fic**

Clements, Andrew, 1949-
The school story (5 and up)   **Fic**
Things not seen (7 and up)   **Fic**

Clements, Bruce
A chapel of thieves   **Fic**

Cleopatra, Queen of Egypt, d. 30 B.C.
About
Brooks, P. S. Cleopatra (7 and up)   **92**
Cleopatra [biographical essays] (7 and up)
  92
Morgan, J. Cleopatra   **92**
Stanley, D. Cleopatra (4 and up)   **92**
See/See also pages in the following book(s):
Hewitt, K. Lives of extraordinary women (4 and
  up)   **920**
Meltzer, M. Ten queens (5 and up)   **920**

Cleopatra [biographical essays] (7 and up)   **92**

Clergy
Fiction
Craven, M. I heard the owl call my name (7 and
  up)   **Fic**

Clever Marcela. Tchana, K. H.
In Tchana, K. H. The serpent slayer: and other stories of strong women p19-23
  398.2

Clewer, Carolyn
Kids can knit (4 and up)   **746.43**

Click-clack. San Souci, R.
In San Souci, R. Double-dare to be scared:
  another thirteen chilling tales   **S C**

Click! fun with photography. Price, S.   **771**

Cliff dwellers and cliff dwellings
Vivian, R. G. Chaco Canyon   **978**

Cliff hanger. Skurzynski, G.   **Fic**

Climate
    See also Meteorology; United States—Climate; Weather
Arnold, C. El Niño (4 and up)   **551.6**

Climbing plants
Petrides, G. A. A field guide to trees and shrubs   **582.16**

Climbing your family tree. Wolfman, I.   **929**

Climo, Shirley, 1928-
Magic & mischief (4 and up)   **398.2**
Includes the following stories: The giant of Castle Treen; The very old woman and the Piskey; The widow and the Spriggans of Trencrom Hill; Tom Treverrow and the Knackers; Pleasing Betty Stoggs; The changeling of Brea Vean; The bewitching of Sea Pink; The mermaid of Zennor; The cornish teeny-tiny; Duffy and the Bucca

Clinton, Bill, 1946-
Impeachment
Cohen, D. The impeachment of William Jefferson Clinton (7 and up)   **973.929**

Clinton, Catherine, 1952-
The Black soldier (5 and up)   **355**
(comp) I, too, sing America. See I, too, sing America   **811.008**
(ed) A Poem of her own. See A Poem of her own   **811.008**

Clinton, Cathryn
A stone in my hand   **Fic**

Clinton, Susan
(jt. auth) Carruthers, M. W. Pioneers of geology   **920**

Clinton, William Jefferson See Clinton, Bill, 1946-

Cliques, phonies & other baloney. Romain, T.   **158**

The **cloak**. Jaffe, N.
In Jaffe, N. and Zeitlin, S. J. The cow of no color: riddle stories and justice tales from around the world p23-26   **398.2**

Clocks and watches
Collier, J. L. Clocks   **681.1**
Duffy, T. The clock (4 and up)   **681.1**

Clockwork. Pullman, P.   **Fic**

Cloning
Cloning [At issue] (7 and up)   **174.2**
Cohen, D. Cloning (7 and up)   **571.8**
Goodnough, D. The debate over human cloning   **174.2**
Morgan, S. Body doubles   **660.6**
Nardo, D. Cloning [Great medical discoveries series] (7 and up)   **660.6**
Nardo, D. Cloning [Science on the edge series] (5 and up)   **660.6**
See/See also pages in the following book(s):
Biomedical ethics: opposing viewpoints (7 and up)   **174.2**
Kidd, J. S. Life lines (7 and up)   **576.5**
O'Neill, T. Biomedical ethics (7 and up)   **174.2**
fiction
Lasky, K. Star split (7 and up)   **Fic**
Cloning [At issue] (7 and up)   **174.2**

Close to shore. Capuzzo, M.   **597**

The **closet**. Chávez, D.
In Growing up Latino; memoirs and stories p85-98   **810.8**

Closter, Kathryn, 1950-
Fiction, food, and fun   **028.5**

Clothing and dress
    See also Children's clothing; Costume; Fashion
Pendergast, S. Fashion, costume, and culture   **391**
Rowland-Warne, L. Costume (4 and up)   **391**

Clothing industry
Houle, M. M. Triangle Shirtwaist Factory fire   **974.7**
Lieurance, S. The Triangle Shirtwaist fire and sweatshop reform in American history (7 and up)   **974.7**

Cloud Tapper, Suzanne
Voices from slavery's past (7 and up)   **326**

Cloud weavers. Krasno, R.   **398.2**

Clouds
Gardner, R. Science project ideas about rain   **551.57**

Clovermead. Randall, D.   **Fic**

Clowes, Martin
(jt. auth) Woodford, C. Atoms and molecules   **540**

Clubs
Fiction
Draper, S. M. The Battle of Jericho (7 and up)   **Fic**

A **coal** miner's bride. Bartoletti, S. C.   **Fic**

Coal mines and mining
Bartoletti, S. C. Growing up in coal country (5 and up)   **331.3**
Fiction
Almond, D. Kit's wilderness (5 and up)   **Fic**
Baker, J. Up Molasses Mountain   **Fic**
Bartoletti, S. C. A coal miner's bride (4 and up)   **Fic**
Hughes, P. The breaker boys   **Fic**
Skurzynski, G. Rockbuster   **Fic**

The **Coalwood** way. Hickam, H. H.   **92**

The **coast** mappers. Morrison, T.   **623.89**

Coatsworth, Elizabeth Jane, 1893-1986
The story of Wang Li
In The Book of dragons p78-88   **S C**

Cobain, Bev, 1940-
When nothing matters anymore (7 and up)   **155.9**

Cobb, Allan B.
(ed) Animal sciences. See Animal sciences   **590.3**

Cobb, Vicki, 1938-
Science experiments you can eat (5 and up)   **507.8**
You gotta try this! (4 and up)   **507.8**

Coborn, John
Snakes   **639**

Cochise, Apache Chief, d. 1874
About
Schwarz, M. Cochise, Apache chief   **92**

Cochise, Apache Chief, d. 1874—About—*Continued*
See/See also pages in the following book(s):
Brown, D. A. Bury my heart at Wounded Knee
970.004
Ehrlich, A. Wounded Knee: an Indian history of the American West (6 and up) **970.004**

Cochran, Thomas, 1955-
Roughnecks (7 and up) **Fic**

Cochrane, Elizabeth *See* Bly, Nellie, 1864-1922

Cockcroft, James D.
Latino visions (7 and up) **704**

CoConis, Ted
(il) Byars, B. C. The summer of the swans
Fic

The **code** book. Singh, S. **652**

Code deciphering *See* Cryptography

Code talker. Bruchac, J. **Fic**

Cody, William Frederick *See* Buffalo Bill, 1846-1917

Coe, Lewis, 1911-
The telegraph **621.383**

Coelacanth
Walker, S. M. Fossil fish found alive (5 and up)
597

Coetzee, Frans, 1955-
World War I: a history in documents (7 and up)
940.3

Coetzee, Marilyn Shevin, 1955-
(jt. auth) Coetzee, F. World War I: a history in documents **940.3**

Cofer, Judith Ortiz *See* Ortiz Cofer, Judith, 1952-

Coffey, Rosemary K.
America as story **016.813**

Coffin, Charles Carleton, 1823-1896
Winning his way
In The Boy of Chancellorville and other Civil War stories p23-39 **S C**

Coffin, Tristram Potter, 1922-
(ed) The Folklore of the American holidays. See The Folklore of the American holidays
394.26

Cohen, Barbara, 1932-1992
Canterbury tales (4 and up) **821**
Contents: The nun's priest's tale; The pardoner's tale; The wife of Bath's tale; The franklin's tale

Cohen, Daniel, 1936-
Cloning (7 and up) **571.8**
The impeachment of William Jefferson Clinton (7 and up) **973.929**
The Manhattan Project (7 and up) **623.4**
Prophets of doom (7 and up) **133.3**
Yellow journalism (7 and up) **302.23**

Cohen, Elizabeth Storr, 1946-
Daily life in Renaissance Italy (7 and up)
945

Cohen, Hennig
(ed) The Folklore of the American holidays. See The Folklore of the American holidays
394.26

Cohen, Richard M., 1938-
(jt. auth) Neft, D. S. The sports encyclopedia: baseball **796.357**

Cohen, Thomas V. (Thomas Vance), 1942-
(jt. auth) Cohen, E. S. Daily life in Renaissance Italy **945**

Cohn, Rachel
The Steps (4 and up) **Fic**

Coincoin, Maria Theresa, 1742-1816
See/See also pages in the following book(s):
Haskins, J. African American entrepreneurs
920

Colbert, David
The magical worlds of Harry Potter (5 and up)
823.009

Colby, Vineta
(ed) World authors, 1975-1980. See World authors, 1975-1980 **920.003**
(ed) World authors, 1980-1985. See World authors, 1980-1985 **920.003**
(ed) World authors, 1985-1990. See World authors, 1985-1990 **920.003**

Cold (Disease)
Kittredge, M. The common cold (7 and up)
616.2
Monroe, J. Influenza and other viruses **616.9**

Cold in summer. Barrett, T. **Fic**

A **cold** stake. Karr, P. A.
In Vampires: a collection of original stories p134-56 **S C**

Cold war
Anderson, D. The Cold War years **973.92**
Blohm, C. E. An uneasy peace, 1945-1980
940.55
Burgan, M. Cold War (7 and up) **909.82**
Campbell, G. A. The home front **973.92**
The Cold War [Great speeches in history series]
909.82
Collier, C. The United States in the Cold War: 1945-1989 **327.73**
Kallen, S. A. Primary sources [American war library, The Cold War] **909.82**
Keeley, J. Espionage **327.12**
Ross, S. The causes of the Cold War
327.73
Sherman, J. The Cold War **909.82**
Sirimarco, E. American voices from The Cold War **909.82**
Speakman, J. The Cold War (7 and up)
327.73
Taylor, D. The Cold War **909.82**
Uschan, M. V. Political leaders **920**
Winkler, A. M. The Cold War **909.82**
See/See also pages in the following book(s):
Lindop, E. America in the 1950s (7 and up)
973.921

The **Cold** War [Great speeches in history series]
909.82

Cold War [series]
Ross, S. The causes of the Cold War
327.73

The **Cold** War years. Anderson, D. **973.92**

Cole, Alison
The Renaissance **709.02**

Cole, Brock, 1938-
Celine **Fic**

Cole, Brock, 1938-—*Continued*
The facts speak for themselves (7 and up)
Fic
The goats Fic
Cole, David J.
Encyclopedia of modern everyday inventions (7
and up) 609
Cole, Michael D.
The Columbia space shuttle disaster (4 and up)
629.44
Comets and asteroids (4 and up) 523.6
Galileo spacecraft 629.43
Hubble Space Telescope (4 and up) 522
Living on Mars 629.4
Moon base (4 and up) 629.4
TWA flight 800 363.1
Coleman, Bessie, 1896?-1926
About
Hart, P. S. Up in the air: the story of Bessie
Coleman 92
Haskins, J. Black eagles (5 and up) 629.13
See/See also pages in the following book(s):
Hart, P. S. Flying free (4 and up) 629.13
Coleman, Lori
Fundamental soccer (5 and up) 796.334
Coleridge, Samuel Taylor, 1772-1834
Samuel Taylor Coleridge 821
Coles, Joan M.
(jt. auth) Post, E. L. Emily Post's teen etiquette
395
Colfer, Eoin, 1965-
Artemis Fowl Fic
Colibri. Cameron, A. Fic
Coll and his white pig. Alexander, L.
In Alexander, L. The foundling and other
tales of Prydain p75-83 S C
The **Collapse** of the Soviet Union (7 and up)
947.085
Collard, Sneed B., III
Birds of prey 598
Lizard Island 577.7
The prairie builders (4 and up) 635.9
The **collected** poems of Langston Hughes. Hughes,
L. 811
Collecting baseball cards. Owens, T. 769
Collecting baseball memorabilia. Owens, T.
790.1
Collective biographies [series]
Camp, C. A. American astronomers 920
Hill, C. M. Ten Hispanic American authors
920
Jeffrey, L. S. Great American businesswomen
920
Lyman, D. Holocaust rescuers 920
Mour, S. I. American jazz musicians 920
Northrup, M. American computer pioneers
920
Strickland, M. R. African-American poets
920
Wren, L. L. Pirates and privateers of the high
seas 920
Collectors and collecting
Owens, T. Collecting baseball memorabilia
790.1

Collier, Bruce
Charles Babbage and the engines of perfection
(7 and up) 92
Collier, Bryan
(il) Rappaport, D. John's secret dreams [biogra-
phy of John Lennon] 92
Collier, Christopher, 1930-
The American Revolution, 1763-1783 973.3
Andrew Jackson's America, 1824-1850
973.5
Building a new nation 973.4
A century of immigration, 1820-1924 325.73
The changing face of American society: 1945-
2000 973.92
The Civil War, 1860-1865 973.7
Clash of cultures, prehistory-1638 970.004
Creating the Constitution, 1787 342
The French and Indian War, 1660-1763
973.2
Hispanic America, Texas, and the Mexican War,
1835-1850 973.6
Indians, cowboys, and farmers and the battle for
the Great Plains, 1865-1910 978
The Jeffersonian Republicans, 1800-1823
973.4
The middle road: American politics, 1945-2000
973.92
The paradox of Jamestown, 1585-1700
975.5
Pilgrims and Puritans, 1620-1676 974.4
Progressivism, the Great Depression, and the
New Deal, 1901 to 1941 973.91
Reconstruction and the rise of Jim Crow, 1864-
1896 973.8
The rise of industry, 1860-1900 973.8
The rise of the cities, 1820-1920 307.7
Slavery and the coming of the Civil War, 1831-
1861 973.6
The United States enters the world stage: from
the Alaska Purchase through World War I,
1867-1919 973.8
The United States in the Cold War: 1945-1989
327.73
The United States in World War II: 1941-1945
940.53
(jt. auth) Collier, J. L. The bloody country
Fic
(jt. auth) Collier, J. L. Jump ship to freedom
Fic
(jt. auth) Collier, J. L. My brother Sam is dead
Fic
(jt. auth) Collier, J. L. War comes to Willy
Freeman Fic
(jt. auth) Collier, J. L. Who is Carrie? Fic
(jt. auth) Collier, J. L. With every drop of blood
Fic
Collier, James Lincoln, 1928-
The bloody country Fic
Clocks 681.1
Gunpowder and weaponry 623.4
Jazz (7 and up) 781.65
Jump ship to freedom (6 and up) Fic
Me and Billy (5 and up) Fic
My brother Sam is dead (6 and up) Fic
Vaccines 615

Collier, James Lincoln, 1928-—*Continued*
War comes to Willy Freeman (6 and up)
                       Fic
Who is Carrie?   **Fic**
With every drop of blood (5 and up)   **Fic**
(jt. auth) Collier, C. The American Revolution, 1763-1783   **973.3**
(jt. auth) Collier, C. Andrew Jackson's America, 1824-1850   **973.5**
(jt. auth) Collier, C. Building a new nation
                       973.4
(jt. auth) Collier, C. A century of immigration, 1820-1924   **325.73**
(jt. auth) Collier, C. The changing face of American society: 1945-2000   **973.92**
(jt. auth) Collier, C. The Civil War, 1860-1865
                       973.7
(jt. auth) Collier, C. Clash of cultures, prehistory-1638   **970.004**
(jt. auth) Collier, C. Creating the Constitution, 1787   **342**
(jt. auth) Collier, C. The French and Indian War, 1660-1763   **973.2**
(jt. auth) Collier, C. Hispanic America, Texas, and the Mexican War, 1835-1850   **973.6**
(jt. auth) Collier, C. Indians, cowboys, and farmers and the battle for the Great Plains, 1865-1910   **978**
(jt. auth) Collier, C. The Jeffersonian Republicans, 1800-1823   **973.4**
(jt. auth) Collier, C. The middle road: American politics, 1945-2000   **973.92**
(jt. auth) Collier, C. The paradox of Jamestown, 1585-1700   **975.5**
(jt. auth) Collier, C. Pilgrims and Puritans, 1620-1676   **974.4**
(jt. auth) Collier, C. Progressivism, the Great Depression, and the New Deal, 1901 to 1941
                       973.91
(jt. auth) Collier, C. Reconstruction and the rise of Jim Crow, 1864-1896   **973.8**
(jt. auth) Collier, C. The rise of industry, 1860-1900   **973.8**
(jt. auth) Collier, C. The rise of the cities, 1820-1920   **307.7**
(jt. auth) Collier, C. Slavery and the coming of the Civil War, 1831-1861   **973.6**
(jt. auth) Collier, C. The United States enters the world stage: from the Alaska Purchase through World War I, 1867-1919   **973.8**
(jt. auth) Collier, C. The United States in the Cold War: 1945-1989   **327.73**
(jt. auth) Collier, C. The United States in World War II: 1941-1945   **940.53**

Collier, Kristi
Jericho walls (7 and up)   **Fic**

Collins, David R.
Dr. Shinichi Suzuki   **92**
Farmworker's friend: the story of Cesar Chavez
                       92

Collins, Mary, 1961-
Airborne: a photobiography of Wilbur and Orville Wright (4 and up)   **92**

Collins, Michael, 1930-
Flying to the moon   **629.45**

About
Schyffert, B. U. The man who went to the far side of the moon: the story of Apollo 11 astronaut Michael Collins (5 and up)   **92**

Collins, Suzanne
Gregor the Overlander (4 and up)   **Fic**

Collins, Tracy Brown
(ed) Living through the Great Depression. See Living through the Great Depression
                       973.91

Collyer, Bess
Keeping safe
  In Being human   **612**

Colman, Penny
Corpses, coffins, and crypts (7 and up)   **393**
Girls! (5 and up)   **305.23**
Rosie the riveter (5 and up)   **331.4**
Where the action was   **070.4**

Colmenares, Margarita H., 1957-
See/See also pages in the following book(s):
Oleksy, W. G. Hispanic-American scientists (7 and up)   **920**

Colombia
DuBois, J. Colombia (5 and up)   **986.1**
Haynes, T. Colombia   **986.1**

Colombo, Cristoforo *See* Columbus, Christopher

Colón, Raúl
(il) Johnston, T. Any small goodness   **Fic**
(il) Yolen, J. Mightier than the sword   **398.2**

Colonial America (4 and up)   **973.2**
Colonial America: a history in documents. Gray, E. G.   **973.2**
Colonial America: almanac. Saari, P.   **973.2**
Colonial America: biographies. Saari, P.   **920**
Colonial America: primary sources. Saari, P.
                       973.2
Colonial and revolutionary times. Burgan, M.
                       973.2

Colonial leaders [series]
Hinman, B. Benjamin Banneker   **92**
Colonial life. Stefoff, R.   **973.2**
Colonial places. Howarth, S.   **973.2**

Color
Kassinger, R. Dyes: from sea snails to synthetics   **667**
See/See also pages in the following book(s):
Luxbacher, I. The jumbo book of art p8-57 (4 and up)   **702.8**

Color me a rhyme. Yolen, J.   **811**
The **Color** of absence   **S C**
The **color** of my words. Joseph, L.   **Fic**

Colorado
Ayer, E. H. Colorado
  In Celebrate the states   **973**
Blashfield, J. F. Colorado
  In America the beautiful, second series
                       973

Fiction
Avi. The secret school (4 and up)   **Fic**

Colorado River (Colo.-Mexico)
Rawlins, C. The Colorado River   **979.1**

The **colors** of freedom. Bode, J.   **305.8**

Colton, Mary-Russell Ferrell, 1889-1971
See/See also pages in the following book(s):
Danneberg, J. Women artists of the West
920

Coltrane, John, 1926-1967
About
Barron, R. John Coltrane (7 and up) **92**
See/See also pages in the following book(s):
Mour, S. I. American jazz musicians **920**

Colum, Padraic, 1881-1972
Perseus and Andromeda
In The Book of dragons p16-19 **S C**

Columbia (Space shuttle)
Cole, M. D. The Columbia space shuttle disaster
(4 and up) **629.44**

Columbia. See Cole, M. D. The Columbia space
shuttle disaster **629.44**

The **Columbia** space shuttle disaster. Cole, M. D.
629.44

Columbus, Christopher
About
Meltzer, M. Columbus and the world around
him **92**
See/See also pages in the following book(s):
Fritz, J. Around the world in a hundred years (4
and up) **910.4**

Columbus and the world around him. Meltzer, M.
92

Coman, Carolyn
What Jamie saw (5 and up) **Fic**

Comanche. Libal, J. North American Indians today [series]

Comanche Indians
Libal, J. Comanche North American Indians to-
day [series]
See/See also pages in the following book(s):
Freedman, R. Indian chiefs (6 and up) **920**
Fiction
Meyer, C. Where the broken heart still beats
Fic

Come all you brave soldiers. Cox, C. **973.3**

Comedians
Stewart, G. Great women comedians **920**

Comets
Bonar, S. Comets (4 and up) **523.6**
Cole, M. D. Comets and asteroids (4 and up)
523.6
Koppes, S. N. Killer rocks from outer space
523.5

Comets and asteroids. Cole, M. D. **523.6**

Comfort. Dean, C. **Fic**

Comic books, strips, etc.
See also Cartoons and caricatures; Graphic
novels
Beatty, S. Superman **741.5**
DeFalco, T. The Hulk: the incredible guide
741.5
Dini, P. The Batman adventures **741.5**
Hart, C. How to draw comic book bad guys and
gals **741.5**
Hart, C. Mecha mania (5 and up) **741.5**
Pellowski, M. The art of making comic books
(5 and up) **741.5**
Sanderson, P. Ultimate X-men **741.5**

Coming of age. Forté-Escamilla, K.
In Join in; multiethnic short stories by outstanding writers for young adults p230-
37 **S C**

Coming to America [series]
Boyle, D. African Americans **305.8**
Deignan, T. Irish Americans **305.8**
Moreno, B. Italian Americans **305.8**
Stein, R. Jewish Americans **305.8**

Commander in Chief Abraham Lincoln and the
Civil War. Marrin, A. **973.7**

Committed to memory **821.008**

Commodore Perry in the land of the Shogun.
Blumberg, R. **952**

The **common** cold. Kittredge, M. **616.2**

Commonwealth of Independent States
See also Russia (Federation); Soviet Union

Communicable diseases
See also Epidemiology; Sexually transmit-
ted diseases; Smallpox
Altman, L. J. Plague and pestilence **614.4**
Farrell, J. Invisible enemies (7 and up)
614.4
See/See also pages in the following book(s):
Epidemics: opposing viewpoints **614.4**

Communication
Medlam, B. Communication
In Being human **612**

Communications close-up [series]
Graham, I. Books and newspapers **686.2**
Graham, I. Film and photography **770**
Graham, I. Global networks **384**
Graham, I. Radio and television **621.384**

Communications satellites. Byers, A. **384.5**

Communism
Fiction
Levine, E. Catch a tiger by the toe **Fic**
China
See/See also pages in the following book(s):
Jiang, J.-l. Red scarf girl (6 and up) **951.05**

Community development
See also City planning

Comnena, Anna, 1083-1148
Fiction
Barrett, T. Anna of Byzantium **Fic**

Comparative anatomy
Animal anatomy on file **571.3**

Comparative religion See Religions

Comparative religions on file **201**

Competitions See Contests

Competitive track and field for girls. Manley, C.
B. **796.42**

Competitive volleyball for girls. Manley, C. B.
796.325

Complete American presidents sourcebook. Matuz,
R. **920**

The **complete** book of the Winter Olympics.
Wallechinsky, D. **796.98**

Complete cat care manual. See Edney, A. T. B.
ASPCA complete cat care manual **636.8**

The **complete** dog book. American Kennel Club
636.7

The **Complete** dog book for kids (4 and up)
    636.7

The **complete** handbook of science fair projects. Bochinski, J. B.   **507.8**

Complete history of [series]
    The Complete history of American slavery
        326
    The Complete history of the Holocaust
        940.53

The **Complete** history of American slavery (7 and up)   **326**

The **Complete** history of the Holocaust (7 and up)
    940.53

The **complete** Sherlock Holmes. Doyle, Sir A. C.
    S C

The **complete** twenty thousand leagues under the sea. See Verne, J. Twenty thousand leagues under the sea   **Fic**

The **complete** weather resource. Engelbert, P.
    551.5

Comport, Sally Wern
    (il) Nickerson, S. How to disappear completely and never be found   **Fic**

Composers
    See also Women composers
    Anderson, M. T. Handel, who knew what he liked (4-6)   **92**
    Horowitz, J. Dvořák in America (7 and up)
        92

        United States
    Furstinger, N. Say it with music: the story of Irving Berlin   **92**
    Preston, K. K. Scott Joplin   **92**

Composite guide [series]
    Gallagher, J. The composite guide to wrestling
        796.8
    Macht, N. L. The composite guide to track & field   **796.42**

The **composite** guide to track & field. Macht, N. L.   **796.42**

The **composite** guide to wrestling. Gallagher, J.
    796.8

Composition (Rhetoric) *See* Rhetoric

Compost
    Lavies, B. Compost critters (4 and up)
        591.7

Compost critters. Lavies, B.   **591.7**

The **Comprehensive** signed English dictionary
    419

Compton's encyclopedia & fact-index   **031**

Compton's yearbook. See Compton's encyclopedia & fact-index   **031**

Compulsion (Psychology) *See* Compulsive behavior

Compulsive behavior
    See also Obsessive-compulsive disorder
    Bridgers, J. Everything you need to know about having an addictive personality (7 and up)
        616.86

Compulsory labor *See* Slavery

Computer animation
    Souter, G. Creating animation for your Web page (4 and up)   **006.6**

Computer animation. Lockman, D.   **778.5**

Computer-assisted instruction
    Mendrinos, R. B. Using educational technology with at-risk students   **027.8**
    Smith, S. S. Web-based instruction   **005.7**
    Stephens, M. T. The library Internet trainer's toolkit   **025.04**

Computer crimes
    Wolinsky, A. Safe surfing on the Internet (4 and up)   **004.6**

Computer games
        Fiction
    Pratchett, T. Only you can save mankind (5 and up)   **Fic**

Computer network resources *See* Internet resources

Computer networks
    See also Internet
    Cate, F. H. The Internet and the First Amendment   **342**
    Gordon, R. S. Teaching the Internet in libraries
        025.04
    Graham, I. Global networks   **384**
    Stephens, M. T. The library Internet trainer's toolkit   **025.04**

Computer programming
    See also Computer software

Computer science
    McAlpine, M. Working with computers   **004**

Computer software
    The Software encyclopedia   **005**

Computer software industry
    Ehrenhaft, D. Larry Ellison   **92**
    Sherman, J. Jerry Yang and David Filo   **92**

Computers
    Barrett, J. R. Teaching and learning about computers   **004**
    Northrup, M. American computer pioneers
        920

        Fiction
    Gutman, D. Virtually perfect   **Fic**
    Peck, R. The great interactive dream machine
        Fic

        History
    Collier, B. Charles Babbage and the engines of perfection (7 and up)   **92**

Computers and children
    Haycock, K. Neal-Schuman authoritative guide to kids' search engines, subject directories, and portals   **025.04**
    Johnson, D. Learning right from wrong in the digital age   **004.6**

Con artists *See* Swindlers and swindling

Concentration camps
    See also Holocaust, 1933-1945; Japanese Americans—Evacuation and relocation, 1942-1945

The **conch** bearer. Divakaruni, C. B.   **Fic**

The **concise** AACR2, 2004 revision. Gorman, M.
    025.3

The **concise** Oxford dictionary of music. Kennedy, M.   **780.3**

Concord (Mass.), Battle of, 1775
Whitelaw, N. The shot heard round the world
973.3

Concorde. Murdico, S. J. **629.133**
Condors
Arnold, C. On the brink of extinction (4 and up)
598
Fiction
Hobbs, W. The maze (7 and up) **Fic**
Conduct of life
Benson, P. L. What teens need to succeed (7 and up) **305.23**
Espeland, P. Life lists for teens **646.7**
James, E. Social smarts **395**
McIntyre, T. The behavior survival guide for kids (5 and up) **158**
Muharrar, A. More than a label (7 and up) **305.23**
Rimm, S. B. See Jane win for girls (5 and up) **305.23**
Teen sunshine reflections **808.8**
Weston, C. For teens only **305.23**
Confederate ladies of Richmond. Beller, S. P. **973.7**

Confederate States of America. Army
Biography
Pflueger, L. Stonewall Jackson **92**
Confederate States of America. Army. Cavalry
See/See also pages in the following book(s):
Uschan, M. V. The cavalry during the Civil War **973.7**

Confessions of a not it girl. Kantor, M. **Fic**
Confessions of a teenage drama queen. Sheldon, D. **Fic**
Conflict and change. Reynoldson, F. **909.7**
Conflict in Europe and the Great Depression. Brown, G. **973.9**
Conflict: India vs. Pakistan. Downing, D. **954**
Conflict management
Drew, N. The kids' guide to working out conflicts **303.6**
Conflict of cultures *See* Culture conflict
Conford, Ellen
Crush (7 and up) **S C**
Contents: Room 202; The gifts of the mangy; Have a heart; Metamorphosis; Two coins in the fountain; Russian overture; Call waiting; Cross out where not applicable; Lucky break; At the stomp
In your hat
In Shelf life: stories by the book p11-21 **S C**

Confucianism
Slavicek, L. C. Confucianism **181**
See/See also pages in the following book(s):
Osborne, M. P. One world, many religions (4 and up) **201**
Confucius
About
Freedman, R. Confucius (4 and up) **92**
Congenital diseases *See* Medical genetics
Congo (Brazzaville) *See* Congo (Republic)
Congo (Republic)
Heale, J. Democratic Republic of the Congo (5 and up) **967.51**

Willis, T. Democratic Republic of the Congo (5 and up) **967.51**
Congress (U.S.) *See* United States. Congress
The **Congress.** Horn, G. **328**
The **conjure** brother. McKissack, P. C.
In Beware!; R.L. Stine picks his favorite scary stories p19-33 **808.8**
Conklin, Barbara Gardner
(jt. auth) Gardner, R. Chemistry science fair projects using french fries, gumdrops, soap, and other organic stuff **547**
(jt. auth) Gardner, R. Health science projects about psychology **150**
(jt. auth) Gardner, R. Health science projects about sports performance **612**
Conlan, Kathy
Under the ice (4 and up) **578.7**
Conly, Jane Leslie
Crazy lady! (5 and up) **Fic**
Racso and the rats of NIMH (4 and up) **Fic**
Trout summer (5 and up) **Fic**
What happened on Planet Kid **Fic**
While no one was watching (5 and up) **Fic**
Connecticut
Fiction
Hurst, C. O. Through the lock **Fic**
Janeczko, P. B. Worlds afire **Fic**
Connecticut
McNair, S. Connecticut
In America the beautiful, second series **973**
Sherrow, V. Connecticut
In Celebrate the states **973**
History—1600-1775, Colonial period
Fradin, D. B. The Connecticut colony **974.6**
History—1600-1775, Colonial period—Fiction
Speare, E. G. The witch of Blackbird Pond (6 and up) **Fic**
The **Connecticut** colony. Fradin, D. B. **974.6**
Connecting kids & the Web. Benson, A. C. **004.6**
Connecting young adults and libraries. Jones, P. **027.62**
Connelly, Neil O.
St. Michael's scales (7 and up) **Fic**
Connolly, Peter, 1935-
Pompeii **937**
Connolly, Sean
New Testament miracles **226**
Conrad, David C.
The Songhay Empire **966.2**
Conrad, Pam, 1947-1996
My Daniel (5 and up) **Fic**
Prairie songs (5 and up) **Fic**
Stonewords (5 and up) **Fic**
Conrow, Robert
(jt. auth) Parker, D. L. Stolen dreams **331.3**
Conscientious objectors
Freedman, S. Clay v. United States (7 and up) **343**
Fiction
Kerr, M. E. Slap your sides (7 and up) **Fic**

Conservation of natural resources
>   *See also* Nature conservation; Wildlife conservation
>   Gallant, R. A. Resources   **333.7**
>   Global resources: opposing viewpoints   **333.71**
>   Malaspina, A. Saving the American wilderness   **333.72**

Conservationists
>   Doherty, K. Marjory Stoneman Douglas (7 and up)   **92**

Conserving the environment (7 and up)   **333.72**

Conspiracies
>   **Fiction**
>   Prose, F. After (7 and up)   **Fic**

Constable, Kate
>   The singer of all songs (7 and up)   **Fic**

Constellation (Frigate)
>   Myers, W. D. USS Constellation   **359.8**

Constellation guidebook. Rükl, A.   **523.8**

Constellations
>   Rükl, A. Constellation guidebook (7 and up)   **523.8**
>   Sasaki, C. Constellations: the stars and stories   **523.8**

Constellations: the stars and stories. Sasaki, C.   523.8

Constitution [series]
>   Fireside, H. The Fifth Amendment   **347**
>   Hanson, F. O. The Second Amendment   **344**
>   Schleichert, E. The Thirteenth Amendment   **342**
>   Wetterer, C. M. The Fourth Amendment   **345**

The **Constitution** and its amendments   **342**

The **Constitutional** Convention (7 and up)   **342**

Constitutional history
>   **United States**
>   Collier, C. Creating the Constitution, 1787   **342**
>   The Constitution and its amendments   **342**
>   The Constitutional Convention (7 and up)   **342**
>   Feinberg, B. S. The Articles of Confederation (7 and up)   **342**
>   Moehn, H. The U.S. Constitution   **342**
>   Spitzer, R. J. The right to bear arms   **344**

Constitutional law
>   **United States**
>   Brannen, D. E. Supreme Court drama (7 and up)   **347**
>   The Constitution and its amendments   **342**
>   Pendergast, T. Constitutional amendments: from freedom of speech to flag burning (7 and up)   **342**
>   Vile, J. R. The United States Constitution (7 and up)   **342**
>   **United States—Dictionaries**
>   Feinberg, B. S. The dictionary of the U.S. Constitution   **342**

Constitutional rights *See* Civil rights

Construction *See* Building

Construction, House *See* House construction

Construction: building the impossible. Aaseng, N.   624

Consumer education
>   Menhard, F. R. Teen consumer smarts   **332.024**

Contagious diseases *See* Communicable diseases

Contemporary environmentalists. Graham, K.   **920**

Contemporary issues [series]
>   Netzley, P. D. Issues in the environment   **333.7**

Contemporary issues companion [series]
>   Depression   **616.85**
>   Eating disorders   **616.85**
>   Inner-city poverty   **362.5**
>   Teen alcoholism   **362.292**

The **contender**. Lipsyte, R.   **Fic**

Contents under pressure. Zeises, L. M.   **Fic**

Contests
>   **Fiction**
>   Gutman, D. The million dollar shot   **Fic**
>   O'Connor, B. Fame and glory in Freedom, Georgia (4 and up)   **Fic**

Continental drift
>   Sattler, H. R. Our patchwork planet (5 and up)   **551.1**

Convicts *See* Prisoners

Conway, John Horton
>   *See/See also pages in the following book(s):*
>   Henderson, H. Modern mathematicians (7 and up)   **920**

Coogan, Michael David
>   (ed) The Oxford companion to the Bible. See The Oxford companion to the Bible   **220.3**

Cook, Deanna F., 1965-
>   The kids' multicultural cookbook   **641.5**

Cook, James, 1728-1779
>   **About**
>   Lawlor, L. Magnificent voyage (7 and up)   **910.4**
>   Meltzer, M. Captain James Cook   **92**
>   **Fiction**
>   Hesse, K. Stowaway (5 and up)   **Fic**

Cook, Judy, 1943-
>   Natural writer: a story about Marjorie Kinnan Rawlings   **92**

Cook, Scott
>   (il) Van Laan, N. With a whoop and a holler   **398**

Cook-Lynn, Elizabeth
>   A visit from Reverend Tileston
>   *In* Talking leaves; contemporary native American short stories   **S C**

The **cookcamp**. Paulsen, G.   **Fic**

Cooke, Timothy
>   (ed) History of the modern world. See History of the modern world   **909.08**

Cooking
>   *See also* Vegetarian cooking
>   Albyn, C. L. The multicultural cookbook for students   **641.5**
>   Carle, M. Teens cook   **641.5**

Cooking—*Continued*

Cobb, V. Science experiments you can eat (5 and up) **507.8**

Cook, D. F. The kids' multicultural cookbook **641.5**

Crespo, C. The secret life of food (4 and up) **641.5**

D'Amico, J. The healthy body cookbook (4 and up) **641.5**

D'Amico, J. The United States cookbook **641.5**

Easy menu ethnic cookbooks [series] (5 and up) **641.5**

Lagasse, E. Emeril's there's a chef in my family! (5 and up) **641.5**

Locricchio, M. The international cookbook for kids (5 and up)

Locricchio, M. Super chef {series} **641.5**

Pentland, P. Kitchen science (4 and up) **641**

Plante, E. M. The American kitchen, 1700 to the present (7 and up) **643**

Webb, L. S. Holidays of the world cookbook for students (5 and up) **641.5**

Wilkes, A. Children's quick & easy cookbook **641.5**

Zanger, M. H. The American ethnic cookbook for students **641.5**

Cooks and prophecies. Aiken, J.
In Aiken, J. Shadows and moonshine; stories **S C**

Cool chix [series]
Warrick, L. Hair trix for cool chix **646.7**

A **cool** moonlight. Johnson, A. **Fic**

Cool salsa (5 and up) **811.008**

Cool women, hot jobs . . . and how you can go for it, too!. Schwager, T. **650.14**

Coolidge, Calvin, 1872-1933
About
Allen, M. G. Calvin Coolidge (7 and up) **92**

Coon, Nora
Teen dream jobs (7 and up) **650.14**

Cooney, Caroline B., 1947-
Burning up (7 and up) **Fic**
The face on the milk carton (7 and up) **Fic**
Flight #116 is down **Fic**
Goddess of yesterday (7 and up) **Fic**
The ransom of Mercy Carter **Fic**
What child is this? **Fic**
About
Carroll, P. S. Caroline Cooney: faith and fiction (7 and up) **813.009**

Cooney, Miriam P.
(ed) Celebrating women in mathematics and science. See Celebrating women in mathematics and science **920**

Cooper, Chris
Matter **530**

Cooper, Dan
Enrico Fermi and the revolutions in modern physics (7 and up) **92**

Cooper, Floyd
(jt. auth) Haskins, J. African beginnings **960**
(il) Haskins, J. Bound for America **326**

Cooper, Gail, 1950-
New virtual field trips **025.5**

Cooper, Garry
(jt. auth) Cooper, G. New virtual field trips **025.5**

Cooper, Ilene, 1948-
Jack: the early years of John F. Kennedy **92**

Cooper, Michael L., 1950-
Dust to eat (4 and up) **973.917**
Fighting for honor (6 and up) **940.53**
Indian school **970.004**
Remembering Manzanar **940.53**
Slave spirituals and the Jubilee Singers **782.42**

Cooper, Robert, 1945-
Bahrain **953.6**
Bhutan **954.9**
Croatia (5 and up) **949.7**
(jt. auth) Mirpuri, G. Indonesia **959.8**

Cooper, Susan, 1935-
The Boggart (4 and up) **Fic**
Over sea, under stone (5 and up) **Fic**
See/See also pages in the following book(s):
Ellis, S. From reader to writer **372.6**

Cooper-Mullin, Alison
Once upon a heroine **028.1**

Cop on the beat. Schulman, A. **363.2**

Copernicus, Nicolaus, 1473-1543
About
Andronik, C. M. Copernicus **92**
Goble, T. Nicholas Copernicus and the founding of modern astronomy (7 and up) **92**

Coping with braces and other orthodontic work. Lee, J. **617.6**

Coping with confrontations and encounters with the police. Wirths, C. G. **363.2**

Coping with diabetes. Kelly, P. **616.4**

Coping with hereditary diseases. Jacobs, M. B. **616**

Coping with migraines and other headaches. Votava, A. **616.8**

Coping with scoliosis. Eisenpreis, B. **616.7**

Coping with self-mutilation. Clarke, A. **616.85**

Coping with the dangers of tattooing, body piercing, and branding. Wilkinson, B. **617.9**

Coping with your emotions. Tym, K. **152.4**

Copley, Bob
The tall Mexican: the life of Hank Aguirre, all-star pitcher, businessman, humanitarian (7 and up) **92**

Coppens, Linda Miles, 1944-
What American women did, 1789-1920 (7 and up) **305.4**

Copyright
See also Fair use (Copyright)
Butler, R. P. Copyright for teachers and librarians **346.04**
Crews, K. D. Copyright essentials for librarians and educators **346.04**

Copyright essentials for librarians and educators. Crews, K. D. **346.04**

Copyright for teachers and librarians. Butler, R. P. **346.04**

Coral reef. Cerullo, M. M. **577.7**

Coral reefs and islands
Buttfield, H. The secret life of fishes **597**
Cerullo, M. M. Coral reef (4 and up) **577.7**
Collard, S. B., III. Lizard Island **577.7**

Coraline. Gaiman, N. **Fic**

Coram boy. Gavin, J. **Fic**

Corbeil, Jean-Claude
The Facts on File visual dictionary **423**

Corbet, Robert
Fifteen love (7 and up) **Fic**

Corbett, Sue
12 again **Fic**

Corbishley, Mike
Ancient Rome (5 and up) **937**
The Middle Ages (5 and up) **940.1**
The world of architectural wonders **720**
(jt. auth) Hunter, E. C. D. First civilizations **939**

Cordi, Kevin
(jt. auth) Sima, J. Raising voices **027.62**

Córdova, Amy, 1953-
(il) Anaya, R. A. My land sings **S C**

A **core** collection for young adults. Jones, P. **011.6**

Coretta Scott King Award
The Coretta Scott King Awards book, 1970-1999 **028.5**
Stephens, C. G. Coretta Scott King Award books **028.5**

Coretta Scott King Award books. Stephens, C. G. **028.5**

The **Coretta** Scott King Awards book, 1970-1999 **028.5**

Corey, Melinda
American history on file. See American history on file **973**
(jt. auth) Ochoa, G. The Wilson chronology of ideas **909**
(jt. auth) Ochoa, G. The Wilson chronology of science and technology **502**
(jt. auth) Ochoa, G. The Wilson chronology of the arts **700**

Corfield, Robin Bell
(il) Levy, C. A crack in the clouds and other poems **811**

Corio, Paul
(il) Matsen, B. Go wild in New York City **974.7**

Cormier, Robert
After the first death **Fic**
The bumblebee flies anyway (7 and up) **Fic**
The chocolate war (7 and up) **Fic**
Frenchtown summer (7 and up) **Fic**
Heroes (7 and up) **Fic**
In the heat
In Sixteen; short stories by outstanding writers for young adults p154-64 **S C**
In the middle of the night (7 and up) **Fic**
The rag and bone shop (7 and up) **Fic**
Tunes for bears to dance to (7 and up) **Fic**

We all fall down **Fic**
About
Thomson, S. L. Robert Cormier **92**

Cornell, George L.
Ojibwa
In North American Indians today [series]

A **corner** of the universe. Martin, A. M. **Fic**

Cornerstones of freedom [series]
Alter, J. The Santa Fe Trail **978**
Davis, L. Medicine in the American West **610.9**
Feinberg, B. S. The changing White House **975.3**
George, L. Civil rights marches **323.1**
George, L. The Tuskegee Airmen **940.54**
January, B. The assassination of Abraham Lincoln **973.7**
January, B. The Dred Scott decision **342**
January, B. John Brown's raid on Harpers Ferry **973.7**
January, B. The Lincoln-Douglas debates **973.7**
January, B. Reconstruction **973.8**
Kent, D. Thurgood Marshall and the Supreme Court **92**
McGowen, T. African-Americans in the Old West **978**
Sakurai, G. Asian-Americans in the old West **978**
Sakurai, G. The Thirteen Colonies **973.2**
Winkelman, B. G. The Panama Canal **972.87**

The **Cornish** teeny-tiny. Climo, S.
In Climo, S. Magic & mischief; tales from Cornwall p101-05 **398.2**

Corona, Laurel, 1949-
Afghanistan **958.1**
Israel (7 and up) **956.94**

Coronado, Francisco Vázquez de *See* Vázquez de Coronado, Francisco, 1510-1549

Coronado, Rosa
Cooking the Mexican way
In Easy menu ethnic cookbooks **641.5**

Corpses, coffins, and crypts. Colman, P. **393**

Corrain, Lucia
The art of the Renaissance **709.02**

Correspondence schools and courses
Directory of distance learning opportunities, K-12 **371.3**

Corrick, James A.
The Industrial Revolution (7 and up) **909.81**
The Louisiana Purchase (7 and up) **973.4**

Corrigan, Mairead, 1944-
See/See also pages in the following book(s):
Hacker, C. Nobel Prize winners **920**

Cortés, Hernán, 1485-1547
About
Calvert, P. Hernando Cortés **92**

Corzine, Phyllis
The Black Death (7 and up) **614.5**

Cosgrave, John O'Hara, 1908-1968
(il) Frost, R. The road not taken **811**

Cosmetics
Shuker, N. Elizabeth Arden (7 and up) **92**

Cosmology
Simon, S. The universe (4 and up)   **523**
Zeitlin, S. J. The four corners of the sky (5 and up)   **201**

Costa Rica
Foley, E. Costa Rica (5 and up)   **972.86**
Morrison, M. Costa Rica (4 and up)   **972.86**

Costello, Elaine
Random House American sign language dictionary   **419**

Costume
  See also Clothing and dress; Fashion
Fashions of a decade [series]   **391**
Hoobler, D. Vanity rules   **391**
Jackson, S. Costumes for the stage: a complete handbook for every kind of play   **792**
Miller, B. M. Dressed for the occasion   **391**
Rowland-Warne, L. Costume (4 and up)   **391**
         History
Pendergast, S. Fashion, costume, and culture   **391**

Costume, tradition and culture [series]
Hughes, M. Popular superstitions   **398**
Kozar, R. Inventors and their discoveries   **920**

Costumes for the stage: a complete handbook for every kind of play. Jackson, S.   **792**

Côte d'Ivoire. Sheehan, P.   **966.68**

Cothran, Helen
(ed) Endangered species: opposing viewpoints. See Endangered species: opposing viewpoints   **578.68**
(ed) Global resources: opposing viewpoints. See Global resources: opposing viewpoints   **333.71**
(ed) Police brutality: opposing viewpoints. See Police brutality: opposing viewpoints   **363.2**
(ed) Pornography: opposing viewpoints. See Pornography: opposing viewpoints   **363.4**
(ed) War-torn Bosnia. See War-torn Bosnia   **949.7**

Cotillion. Sherman, D.
  In Firebirds: an anthology of original fantasy and science fiction; an anthology of original fantasy and science fiction   **S C**

Cotner, June, 1950-
(comp) Teen sunshine reflections. See Teen sunshine reflections   **808.8**

The **cottage** of candles. Schwartz, H.
  In Schwartz, H. The day the Rabbi disappeared: Jewish holiday tales of magic p22-25   **398.2**

Cotter, Alison, 1963-
Anorexia and bulimia   **616.85**
Cycling   **796.6**

Cotterell, Arthur
Ancient China (4 and up)   **931**

The **cotton** gin. Meltzer, M.   **633.5**

Cottrell Boyce, Frank
Millions (5 and up)   **Fic**

Cougars *See* Pumas

Couloumbis, Audrey
Getting near to baby (5 and up)   **Fic**

Say yes   **Fic**

Coulter, Laurie
(jt. auth) Brewster, H. 882 ½ amazing answers to your questions about the Titanic   **910.4**
(jt. auth) Brewster, H. To be a princess   **920**

Count on us. Nathan, A.   **355**

Countdown to space [series]
Bredeson, C. Neil Armstrong   **92**
Cole, M. D. The Columbia space shuttle disaster   **629.44**
Cole, M. D. Galileo spacecraft   **629.43**
Cole, M. D. Hubble Space Telescope   **522**
Cole, M. D. Living on Mars   **629.4**
Cole, M. D. Moon base   **629.4**
Jeffrey, L. S. Christa McAuliffe   **92**
Yannuzzi, D. A. Mae Jemison   **92**

The **countess** and me. Kropp, P.   **Fic**

Counting stars. Almond, D.   **Fic**

Countries of the world [series]
Bowden, R. Kenya   **967.62**
Dicks, B. Brazil   **981**
Kazem, H. Afghanistan   **958.1**
Lister, M. England   **942**
NgCheong-Lum, R. France   **944**

Countries of the world and their leaders yearbook   **910.3**

Country life
Hinds, K. The countryside [Life in the Renaissance series]   **940.2**
Hinds, K. The countryside [Life in the Roman Empire series]   **937**
         Fiction
Bauer, J. Squashed   **Fic**
Creech, S. Ruby Holler (4 and up)   **Fic**
Hite, S. Those darn Dithers   **Fic**
Morgan, N. Chicken friend (5 and up)   **Fic**
Peck, R. The teacher's funeral (5 and up)   **Fic**

Country lovers. Gordimer, N.
  In Somehow tenderness survives; stories of Southern Africa p49-59   **S C**

Country music
Kallen, S. A. The history of country music   **781.642**

The **countryside** [Life in the Renaissance series] Hinds, K.   **940.2**

The **countryside** [Life in the Roman Empire series] Hinds, K.   **937**

Courage
Kennedy, J. F. Profiles in courage   **920**
         Fiction
Bloor, E. Crusader (7 and up)   **Fic**
Spinelli, J. Wringer (4 and up)   **Fic**

The **courier**. Delacre, L.
  In Delacre, L. Golden tales; myths, legends, and folktales from Latin America p65-68   **398.2**

The **court**. Hinds, K.   **940.2**

Courtney Crumrin and the night things. Naifeh, T.   **741.5**

Courtroom drama (7 and up)   **347**

Courts and courtiers
> *See also* Princesses; Queens

Hinds, K. The court   **940.2**

Cousin Alice. Aiken, J.
> *In* Visions: nineteen short stories by outstanding writers for young adults p152-69
>   **S C**

Cousins
Fiction
Draper, S. M. The Battle of Jericho (7 and up)   **Fic**

Hamilton, V. Cousins (5 and up)   **Fic**

Koss, A. G. Strike two (4 and up)   **Fic**

Paulsen, G. Harris and me (5 and up)   **Fic**

Schwartz, V. F. Send one angel down   **Fic**

White, R. Belle Prater's boy (5 and up)   **Fic**

Wittlinger, E. Zigzag (7 and up)   **Fic**

Woodson, J. The house you pass on the way (7 and up)   **Fic**

Wrede, P. C. Sorcery and Cecelia, or, The enchanted chocolate pot (7 and up)   **Fic**

Cousteau, Jacques Yves, 1910-1997
See/See also pages in the following book(s):
Graham, K. Contemporary environmentalists (7 and up)   **920**

Cover, Arthur Byron
Macbeth   **741.5**

Coverlets *See* Quilts

Coverup. Bennett, J.   **Fic**

Coville, Bruce
Aliens ate my homework   **Fic**
Biscuits of glory
> *In* The Haunted house: a collection of original stories   **S C**

The guardian of memory
> *In* A Glory of unicorns p1-28   **S C**

The hardest, kindest gift
> *In* Half-human p183-207   **S C**

Juliet Dove, Queen of Love (4-6)   **Fic**
The monsters of Morley Manor   **Fic**
Odder than ever   **S C**
> Includes the following stories: The golden sail; The stinky princess; The giants tooth; The metamorphosis of Justin Jones; Biscuits of glory; There's nothing under the bed; I, Earthling; Am I blue?; The Japanese mirror

The skull of truth (4 and up)   **Fic**
What's the worst that could happen?
> *In* 13; thirteen stories that capture the agony and ecstasy of being thirteen   **S C**

William Shakespeare's A midsummer night's dream   **822.3**
William Shakespeare's Romeo and Juliet   **822.3**
(comp) A Glory of unicorns. See A Glory of unicorns   **S C**
(comp) Half-human. See Half-human   **S C**
(jt. auth) Yolen, J. Armageddon summer   **Fic**

Coville, Katherine
Story hour
> *In* A Glory of unicorns p97-112   **S C**

The **cow** of no color. Jaffe, N.
> *In* Jaffe, N. and Zeitlin, S. J. The cow of no color: riddle stories and justice tales from around the world p10-13   **398.2**

The **cow** of no color: riddle stories and justice tales from around the world. Jaffe, N.
>   **398.2**

The **coward**. Kimmel, E. A.
> *In* Kimmel, E. A. Sword of the samurai; adventure stories from Japan p23-30
>   **Fic**

Cowboy. Murdoch, D. H.   **978**

Cowboys & longhorns. Stanley, J.   **636.2**

Cowhands
DeAngelis, G. The black cowboys   **978**
Faber, D. Calamity Jane (5 and up)   **92**
Freedman, R. In the days of the vaqueros (4 and up)   **636.2**
Murdoch, D. H. Cowboy (4 and up)   **978**
Sandler, M. W. Vaqueros   **973**
Sanford, W. R. Bill Pickett: African-American rodeo star   **92**
Sanford, W. R. Calamity Jane: frontier original   **92**
Stanley, J. Cowboys & longhorns   **636.2**
See/See also pages in the following book(s):
Collier, C. Indians, cowboys, and farmers and the battle for the Great Plains, 1865-1910
>   **978**

Fiction
Myers, W. D. The journal of Joshua Loper (5 and up)   **Fic**

Cowles, Virginia, 1915-1983
See/See also pages in the following book(s):
Colman, P. Where the action was   **070.4**

Cox, Clinton
Come all you brave soldiers (6 and up)
>   **973.3**
The forgotten heroes   **978**

Coye, Jennifer Marmaduke
(jt. auth) Cooper-Mullin, A. Once upon a heroine   **028.1**

Coyote and Mouse. Curry, J. L.
> *In* Curry, J. L. Hold up the sky: and other Native American tales from Texas and the Southern Plains p56-59   **398.2**

Coyote and Raven. Anaya, R. A.
> *In* Anaya, R. A. My land sings; stories from the Rio Grande p161-74   **S C**

Coyote and the rolling rock. Brown, D. A.
> *In* Brown, D. A. Dee Brown's folktales of the Native American; retold for our times p109-11   **398.2**

Coyote and the seven brothers. Curry, J. L.
> *In* Curry, J. L. Hold up the sky: and other Native American tales from Texas and the Southern Plains p40-46   **398.2**

Coyote and the smallest snake. Curry, J. L.
> *In* Curry, J. L. Hold up the sky: and other Native American tales from Texas and the Southern Plains p60-62   **398.2**

Coyote flies with the geese. Curry, J. L.
> *In* Curry, J. L. Hold up the sky: and other Native American tales from Texas and the Southern Plains p63-68   **398.2**

Coyote frees the buffalo. Curry, J. L.
In Curry, J. L. Hold up the sky: and other Native American tales from Texas and the Southern Plains p69-72   **398.2**

Coyote makes the sun. Curry, J. L.
In Curry, J. L. Hold up the sky: and other Native American tales from Texas and the Southern Plains p7-14   **398.2**

Coyotes

Fiction

Leonard, E. A coyote's in the house (5 and up)   **Fic**

Cozic, Charles P., 1957-
(ed) Illegal drugs. See Illegal drugs   **364.1**
(ed) Welfare reform. See Welfare reform   **361.6**

CQ's American government A to Z series
The Presidency A to Z   **352.23**

Crabs
See/See also pages in the following book(s):
Lassieur, A. Crabs, lobsters, and shrimps (4-6)   **595.3**

Crabs, lobsters, and shrimps. Lassieur, A.   **595.3**

A **crack** in the clouds and other poems. Levy, C.   **811**

A **crack** in the line. Lawrence, M.   **Fic**

Cracker Jackson. Byars, B. C.   **Fic**

Craft, Ellen, 1826-1891
See/See also pages in the following book(s):
Currie, S. Escapes from slavery   **326**

Craft, William, 19th cent.
See/See also pages in the following book(s):
Currie, S. Escapes from slavery   **326**

Crafts (Arts) *See* Handicraft

Craig, David, 1945-
(il) Tanaka, S. Attack on Pearl Harbor   **940.54**
(il) Tanaka, S. Earthquake!   **979.4**

Crane, Stephen, 1871-1900
The red badge of courage (7 and up)   **Fic**
About
Lukes, B. L. Soldier's courage: the story of Stephen Crane (7 and up)   **92**
Adaptations
Vansant, W. The red badge of courage   **741.5**

The **crane** wife [play] Carlisle, B.
In Theatre for young audiences; 20 great plays for children p453-77   **812.008**

Cranes (Birds)
DuTemple, L. A. North American cranes (4 and up)   **598**

Crash   **617.1**

Crash. Spinelli, J.   **Fic**

Craven, Margaret
I heard the owl call my name (7 and up)   **Fic**

Craver, Kathleen W.
Creating cyber libraries   **027.8**

Crawford, Andy
(il) Adams, S. World War II   **940.53**
(il) Adams, S. World War I   **940.3**

(il) Hornby, H. Soccer   **796.334**
(il) Lane, B. Crime & detection   **364**

Crazy Horse, Sioux Chief, ca. 1842-1877
About
Bad Heart Buffalo, A. The life and death of Crazy Horse (5 and up)   **92**
See/See also pages in the following book(s):
Kallen, S. A. Native American chiefs and warriors (7 and up)   **920**

Crazy lady!. Conly, J. L.   **Fic**

Crazy loco. Rice, D.   **S C**

Crazy loco [story] Rice, D.
In Rice, D. Crazy loco; stories about growing up Chicano in southern Texas p57-66   **S C**

Cream puff. Due, L. A.
In Girls got game; sports stories and poems   **810.8**

Creating animation for your Web page. Souter, G.   **006.6**

Creating cyber libraries. Craver, K. W.   **027.8**

Creating the Constitution, 1787. Collier, C.   **342**

Creating the full-service homework center in your library. Mediavilla, C.   **027.4**

Creation
Hamilton, V. In the beginning; creation stories from around the world (5 and up)   **201**
Lester, J. When the beginning began (4 and up)   **296.1**
Zeitlin, S. J. The four corners of the sky (5 and up)   **201**

The **creation** of Israel. Altman, L. J.   **956.94**

Creationism
See also Evolution

Creative & performing artists for teens   **920.003**

Creative Media Applications Inc.
American presidents in world history. See American presidents in world history   **920.003**

Creative minds biography [series]
Cook, J. Natural writer: a story about Marjorie Kinnan Rawlings   **92**

Creative writing
Bauer, M. D. Our stories (5 and up)   **808.3**
Bauer, M. D. What's your story? (5 and up)   **808.3**
Fletcher, R. How writers work (4 and up)   **808**
Harrison, D. L. Writing stories (4 and up)   **808.3**
Young, S. Writing with style (5 and up)   **808**

Creech, Sharon
Absolutely normal chaos (5 and up)   **Fic**
Bloomability (5 and up)   **Fic**
Chasing Redbird (5 and up)   **Fic**
Love that dog (4 and up)   **Fic**
Ruby Holler (4 and up)   **Fic**
Walk two moons (6 and up)   **Fic**

Creech, Sharon—*Continued*
See/See also pages in the following book(s):
The Newbery & Caldecott medal books, 1986-
2000 **028.5**

Creek. Libal, A. North American Indians today
[series]

Creek Indians
Libal, A. Creek North American Indians today
[series]

The **cremation** of Sam McGee. Service, R. W.
811

Crescent Moon. Carter, A. R. **Fic**

Crespo, Clare
The secret life of food (4 and up) **641.5**

Crew, Gary, 1947-
Troy Thompson's excellent peotry book (4 and
up) **Fic**

Crew, Hilary S.
Is it really Mommie Dearest? **813.009**

Crew, Linda
Bride price
In Join in; multiethnic short stories by out-
standing writers for young adults p111-
26 **S C**
Brides of Eden (7 and up) **Fic**
Children of the river (7 and up) **Fic**
Fire on the wind **Fic**

Crews, Jeanne Lee
See/See also pages in the following book(s):
Thimmesh, C. Girls think of everything (5 and
up) **920**

Crews, Kenneth D.
Copyright essentials for librarians and educators
346.04

Crews, Nina
(il) Katz, B. Wc thc people **811**

Crews: gang members talk to Maria Hinojosa.
Hinojosa, M. **302.3**

Cribb, Joe
Money (4 and up) **332.4**

Crichton, Michael, 1942-
Jurassic Park (7 and up) **Fic**

Crick, Francis, 1916-2004
About
Edelson, E. James Watson and Francis Crick
and the building blocks of life (7 and up)
92

Crickets
Pascoe, E. Crickets and grasshoppers (4 and up)
595.7

Crickets and grasshoppers. Pascoe, E. **595.7**

Crime
See also Homicide; Trials
Lane, B. Crime & detection (4 and up) **364**
Fiction
Cadnum, M. Edge (7 and up) **Fic**
Ferris, J. Love among the walnuts (7 and up)
Fic

Crime & detection. Lane, B. **364**

Crime and detection [series]
Innes, B. Forensic science **363.2**
Innes, B. International terrorism **303.6**

Kerrigan, M. The history of punishment
364.6
Lock, J. Famous prisons **365**
Rabiger, J. Daily prison life **365**

Crime, justice, and punishment [series]
Campbell, A. Forensic science **363.2**
DeAngelis, G. White-collar crime **364.1**
Faherty, S. Victims and victims' rights
362.88
Worth, R. The insanity defense **345**

Crime scene. Platt, R. **363.2**

Crimean War, 1853-1856
Bachrach, D. The Crimean War (7 and up)
947

Crimes and criminals of the Holocaust. Altman, L.
J. **940.53**

Criminal investigation
See also Forensic sciences
Campbell, A. Forensic science (7 and up)
363.2
Friedlander, M. P. When objects talk **363.2**
Innes, B. Forensic science (7 and up) **363.2**
Jackson, D. M. The bone detectives (5 and up)
614
Lane, B. Crime & detection (4 and up) **364**
Owen, D. Police lab (7 and up) **363.2**
Pcntland, P. Forensic science (4 and up)
363.2
Platt, R. Crime scene **363.2**
See/See also pages in the following book(s):
Chahrour, J. Zap! blink! taste! think! (5 and up)
507.8
MccGwire, S. Surveillance (7 and up)
323.44

Criminal procedure
Fireside, H. The Fifth Amendment (7 and up)
347
Wormser, R. Defending the accused (7 and up)
345

Criminalistics *See* Forensic sciences

Criminals
See also Thieves
Blackwood, G. L. Gangsters **364.1**
King, D. C. Al Capone and the roaring twenties
92
Yancey, D. Al Capone **92**
Dictionaries
Hoehner, J. Outlaws, mobsters & crooks
920.003
Fiction
Kehret, P. Don't tell anyone (5 and up) **Fic**

Crisfield, Deborah
Winning volleyball for girls **796.325**

Crisp, Marty, 1947-
Private Captain **Fic**

Crispin. Avi **Fic**

Crist, James J.
What to do when you're scared & worried (5
and up) **152.4**

Crist-Evans, Craig
Amaryllis (7 and up) **Fic**

Criswell, Sara Dixon, 1945-
Homelessness (7 and up) **362.5**

Croatia
Cooper, R. Croatia (5 and up)   **949.7**
Croatian Americans
Fiction
Franklin, K. L. Grape thief (5 and up)   **Fic**
Crochet. Davis, J.   **746.43**
Crocheting
Davis, J. Crochet (5 and up)   **746.43**
Crocitto, Frank
(ed) Thoreau, H. D. New suns will arise   **92**
Crocker, Carter
The tale of the swamp rat (4 and up)   **Fic**
Crocodiles
Simon, S. Crocodiles & alligators (4 and up)
    597.9
Sloan, C. Supercroc and the origin of crocodiles (5 and up)   **567.9**
Crocodiles & alligators. Simon, S.   **597.9**
Crompton, Samuel
The Third Crusade (7 and up)   **956**
Cromwell, Oliver, 1599-1658
About
Aronson, M. John Winthrop, Oliver Cromwell, and the Land of Promise (7 and up)   **92**
Fiction
Jeapes, B. The new world order (7 and up)
    Fic
Crook, George, 1829-1890
See/See also pages in the following book(s):
Ehrlich, A. Wounded Knee: an Indian history of the American West (6 and up)   **970.004**
The **crooked** man. Doyle, Sir A. C.
In Doyle, Sir A. C. The complete Sherlock Holmes   **S C**
Crooker waits. San Souci, R.
In San Souci, R. A terrifying taste of short & shivery; thirty creepy tales p1-5
    398.2
Crosher, Judith
Technology in the time of ancient Egypt
    609
Technology in the time of ancient Greece
    609
Technology in the time of the Maya   **609**
Cross, Gillian, 1945-
The dark ground   **Fic**
The great American elephant chase   **Fic**
Phoning a dead man (7 and up)   **Fic**
Tightrope (7 and up)   **Fic**
Cross cultural conflict *See* Culture conflict
Cross out where not applicable. Conford, E.
In Conford, E. Crush p101-06   **S C**
Crossing Montana. Torres, L.   **Fic**
Crossing the panther's path. Alder, E.   **Fic**
Crossley-Holland, Kevin
The seeing stone   **Fic**
The world of King Arthur and his court (5 and up)   **942.01**
Crow. McIntosh, K. North American Indians today [series]
Crow & Weasel. Leonard, J.
In Theatre for young audiences; 20 great plays for children p244-83   **812.008**

Crow and Hawk. Brown, D. A.
In Brown, D. A. Dee Brown's folktales of the Native American; retold for our times p148-50   **398.2**
Crow Dog, Mary *See* Brave Bird, Mary
Crow Indians
McIntosh, K. Crow North American Indians today [series]
Crow learns a lesson. Lester, J.
In Lester, J. When the beginning began; stories about God, the creatures, and us p39-42   **296.1**
Crowe, Chris
Getting away with murder: the true story of the Emmett Till case (7 and up)   **364.1**
Mississippi trial, 1955 (7 and up)   **Fic**
Presenting Mildred D. Taylor (7 and up)
    813.009
Crowe, Francis Trenholm, 1882-1946
See/See also pages in the following book(s):
Aaseng, N. Construction: building the impossible   **624**
Crowe, Frank *See* Crowe, Francis Trenholm, 1882-1946
Crown duel. Smith, S.   **Fic**
Crow's sun. Niatum, D.
In Talking leaves; contemporary native American short stories   **S C**
Cruelty to animals *See* Animal welfare
Cruise control. Trueman, T.
Crum, Robert
(il) Birdseye, D. H. Under our skin   **305.8**
(il) Birdseye, D. H. What I believe   **200**
Crum, Shutta
Spitting image   **Fic**
Crump, Marguerite, 1955-
Don't sweat it!   **613**
Crump, Martha L.
Amphibians, reptiles, and their conservation (7 and up)   **597.9**
Crusader. Bloor, E.   **Fic**
Crusades
Crompton, S. The Third Crusade (7 and up)
    956
Hatt, C. The Crusades (7 and up)   **909.07**
Stanley, D. Saladin: noble prince of Islam (4 and up)   **92**
Fiction
Cadnum, M. The book of the Lion (7 and up)
    Fic
Cadnum, M. The leopard sword (7 and up)
    Fic
Grant, K. M. Blood red horse   **Fic**
Jinks, C. Pagan's crusade (7 and up)   **Fic**
Crush. Conford, E.   **S C**
The **crush**. Vail, R.
In Tripping over the lunch lady and other school stories p120-30   **S C**
Crustaceans
Lassieur, A. Crabs, lobsters, and shrimps (4-6)
    595.3
Crutcher, Chris, 1946-
Athletic shorts (7 and up)   **S C**

Crutcher, Chris, 1946-—*Continued*
Fourth and too long
  In Time capsule: short stories about teenagers
    throughout the twentieth century p143-64
      S C
Guns for geeks
  In On the fringe p195-219   **S C**
Ironman   **Fic**
King of the mild frontier: an ill-advised autobi-
  ography   **92**
Running loose (7 and up)   **Fic**
Staying fat for Sarah Byrnes   **Fic**
Stotan! (7 and up)   **Fic**
Superboy
  In Ultimate sports; short stories by outstand-
    ing writers for young adults p51-67
      S C
Whale talk (7 and up)   **Fic**

Cruz, Bárbara
Alvin Ailey   **92**
José Clemente Orozco   **92**
School dress codes   **371.8**

Cruzan, Joe, d. 1996
    About
Donnelly, K. J. Cruzan v. Missouri   **344**
Fridell, R. Cruzan v. Missouri and the right to
  die debate (7 and up)   **344**

Cruzan, Lester *See* Cruzan, Joe, d. 1996

Cruzan, Nancy
    About
Donnelly, K. J. Cruzan v. Missouri   **344**
Fridell, R. Cruzan v. Missouri and the right to
  die debate (7 and up)   **344**

Cruzan v. Missouri. Donnelly, K. J.   **344**

Cruzan v. Missouri and the right to die debate.
  Fridell, R.   **344**

Cry, the beloved country. Paton, A.   **Fic**

Cryptography
Aaseng, N. Navajo code talkers   **940.54**
Durrett, D. Unsung heroes of World War II (7
  and up)   **940.54**
Janeczko, P. B. Top secret (4 and up)   **652**
Singh, S. The code book (7 and up)   **652**

Crystal & gem. Symes, R. F.   **548**

Crystallography *See* Crystals

Crystals
Symes, R. F. Crystal & gem (5 and up)
    548

Cuba
Castro's Cuba (7 and up)   **972.91**
    Politics and government
Platt, R. Fidel Castro   **92**
Press, P. Fidel Castro   **92**
Woog, A. Fidel Castro   **92**
Cuba 15. Osa, N.   **Fic**

The **Cuban** American family album. Hoobler, D.
    305.8

Cuban Americans
Gay, K. Leaving Cuba (7 and up)   **362.87**
Hoobler, D. The Cuban American family album
    305.8
    Fiction
Osa, N. Cuba 15 (7 and up)   **Fic**

Veciana-Suarez, A. The flight to freedom
    Fic

Cuban refugees
Gay, K. Leaving Cuba (7 and up)   **362.87**

Cuffe, Paul, 1759-1817
See/See also pages in the following book(s):
Haskins, J. African American entrepreneurs
    920

Cuffie, Terrasita A., 1964-
Maya Angelou (7 and up)   **92**

Cullen, J. Heather
Barbara McClintock, geneticist (7 and up)
    92

Cullen-DuPont, Kathryn
Encyclopedia of women's history in America
    305.4
(jt. auth) Frost-Knappman, E. Women's rights
  on trial   **346**
(jt. auth) Frost-Knappman, E. Women's suffrage
  in America   **324.6**

Cullinan, Bernice E.
(ed) A Jar of tiny stars: poems by NCTE award-
  winning poets. See A Jar of tiny stars: poems
  by NCTE award-winning poets   **811.008**

Cults
Barghusen, J. D. Cults (7 and up)   **209**
Stein, S. J. Alternative American religions (7
  and up)   **209**
Zeinert, K. Cults (7 and up)   **209**
    Fiction
Beale, F. I am not Esther (7 and up)   **Fic**
Crew, L. Brides of Eden (7 and up)   **Fic**
Haddix, M. P. Leaving Fishers (7 and up)
    Fic
Yolen, J. Armageddon summer (7 and up)
    Fic

Cultural anthropology *See* Ethnology

Cultural atlas for young people [series]
Corbishley, M. Ancient Rome   **937**
Harris, G. Ancient Egypt   **932**
Hunter, E. C. D. First civilizations   **939**
Powell, A. Ancient Greece   **938**
Wood, M. Ancient America   **970.01**

Cultural diversity. Gay, K.   **305.8**

Cultural pluralism *See* Multiculturalism

Culturally diverse videos, audios, and CD-ROMS
  for children and young adults   **011.6**

Culture, Popular *See* Popular culture

Culture conflict
Collier, C. Clash of cultures, prehistory-1638
    970.004

Culture shock *See* Culture conflict

Culture wars: opposing viewpoints   **306**

Cultures of the past [series]
Ashby, R. Elizabethan England   **942.05**
Ashby, R. Victorian England   **941.081**
Hinds, K. The Incas   **985**
Hinds, K. Medieval England   **942.03**
Hinds, K. Venice and its merchant empire
    945
Mann, K. The ancient Hebrews   **909**
Marston, E. The Byzantine Empire   **949.5**
Marston, E. The Phoenicians   **939**

Cultures of the past—*Continued*
Millar, H. Spain in the age of exploration
946
Ruggiero, A. The Ottoman Empire 956.1
Schomp, V. The Italian Renaissance 945
Schomp, V. Japan in the days of the samurai
952

Cultures of the world [series]
Barlas, R. Bahamas 972.96
Barlas, R. Latvia 947.9
Barlas, R. Uganda 967.6
Bassis, V. Ukraine 947.7
Berg, E. Senegal 966.3
Brown, R. V. Tunisia 961.1
Burbank, J. Nepal 954.96
Cooper, R. Bahrain 953.6
Cooper, R. Bhutan 954.9
Cooper, R. Croatia 949.7
Dhilawala, S. Armenia 947.5
DuBois, J. Colombia 986.1
DuBois, J. Greece 949.5
DuBois, J. Israel 956.94
DuBois, J. Korea 951.9
Elias, M. L. Barbados 972.98
Ferroa, P. G. China 951
Foley, E. Costa Rica 972.86
Fuller, B. Germany 943
Gan, D. Sweden 948.5
Gascoigne, I. Papua New Guinea 995.3
Gofen, E. Argentina 982
Gofen, E. France 944
Goodman, J. Thailand 959.3
Gottfried, T. Slovenia 949.7
Hassig, S. M. Iraq 956.7
Hassig, S. M. Somalia 967.73
Heale, J. Democratic Republic of the Congo
967.51
Heale, J. Madagascar 969.1
Heale, J. Tanzania 967.8
Hestler, A. Wales 942.9
Hestler, A. Yemen 953.3
Holmes, T. Zambia 968.94
Janin, H. Saudi Arabia 953.8
Jermyn, L. Belize 972.82
Jermyn, L. Guyana 988.1
Jermyn, L. Paraguay 989.2
Jermyn, L. Uruguay 989.5
Kagda, F. Algeria 965
Kagda, F. Hong Kong 951.25
Kagda, S. Lithuania 947.9
King, D. C. Bosnia and Herzegovina 949.7
Layton, L. Singapore 959.57
Levy, P. M. Belarus 947.8
Levy, P. M. Ghana 966.7
Levy, P. M. Ireland 941.5
Levy, P. M. Liberia 966.62
Levy, P. M. Nigeria 966.9
Levy, P. M. Scotland 941.1
Levy, P. M. Sudan 962.4
Malcolm, P. Libya 961.2
Mansfield, S. Laos 959.4
McGaffey, L. Honduras 972.83
Mirpuri, G. Indonesia 959.8
Munan, H. Malaysia 959.5
NgCheong-Lum, R. Eritrea 963.5
NgCheong-Lum, R. Fiji 996

NgCheong-Lum, R. Tahiti 996
O'Shea, M. Kuwait 953.67
Pang, G.-C. Canada 971
Pang, G.-C. Grenada 972.98
Pang, G.-C. Mongolia 951.7
Pateman, R. Belgium 949.3
Pateman, R. Egypt 962
Pateman, R. Kenya 967.62
Rajendra, V. Australia 994
Rajendra, V. Iran 955
Reilly, M.-J. Mexico 972
Richard, C. Brazil 981
Rosmarin, I. South Africa 968
Seah, A. Vietnam 959.704
Sheehan, P. Côte d'Ivoire 966.68
Sheehan, P. Luxembourg 949.35
Sheehan, P. Moldova 947.6
Sheehan, S. Austria 943.6
Sheehan, S. Guatemala 972.81
Sheehan, S. Jamaica 972.92
Sheehan, S. Lebanon 956.92
Sheehan, S. Malta 945
Sheehan, S. Pakistan 954.91
Sheehan, S. Trinidad & Tobago 972.983
Sheehan, S. Zimbabwe 968.91
Shelley, R. Japan 952
Sioras, E. Czech Republic 943.7
Smelt, R. New Zealand 993
Spilling, M. Cyprus 956.93
Spilling, M. Estonia 947.9
Spilling, M. Georgia 947.5
Srinivasan, R. India 954
Tope, L. R. R. Philippines 959.9
Wanasundera, N. P. Sri Lanka 954.93
Whyte, M. Bangladesh 954.92
Winter, J. K. Chile 983
Winter, J. K. Italy 945
Winter, J. K. Venezuela 987
Yin, S. M. Myanmar 959.1

Cumming, David, 1953-
The Nile (4 and up) 962

Cummings, Pat, 1950-
(ed) Talking with artists {I-III}. See Talking
with artists {I-III} 741.6

Cummings, Priscilla, 1951-
A face first Fic
Red kayak (7 and up) Fic
Saving Grace (5 and up) Fic

Cunningham, Imogen, 1883-1976
See/See also pages in the following book(s):
Sills, L. In real life: six women photographers
(7 and up) 920

Cunningham, Jesse G.
(ed) The McCarthy hearings. See The McCarthy
hearings 973.921

Cupid and Psyche
In Hearne, B. G. Beauties and beasts p41-55
398.2

The **cure**. Levitin, S. Fic
The **cure** for Curtis. Lynch, C.
In Lynch, C. All the old haunts p38-57
S C

Curie, Marie, 1867-1934
About
Birch, B. Marie Curie 92

Curie, Marie, 1867-1934—About—*Continued*
Lassieur, A. Marie Curie   **92**
MacLeod, E. Marie Curie (5 and up)   **92**
Pasachoff, N. E. Marie Curie and the science of radioactivity   **92**
Poynter, M. Marie Curie: discoverer of radium (4 and up)   **92**
See/See also pages in the following book(s):
Celebrating women in mathematics and science   **920**
DeAngelis, G. Science & medicine   **920**
Hacker, C. Nobel Prize winners   **920**
Henderson, H. Nuclear physics (7 and up)   **539.7**

Curie, Pierre, 1859-1906
See/See also pages in the following book(s):
Henderson, H. Nuclear physics (7 and up)   **539.7**

Curiosities and wonders
    See also Monsters; World records
Ash, R. The top 10 of everything   **031.02**
Bentley, D. The seven wonders of the ancient world   **722**
Blackwood, G. L. Extraordinary events and oddball occurrences   **001.9**
Floyd, E. R. Great American mysteries (7 and up)   **001.9**
Guinness book of records   **032.02**
Llewellyn, C. Great discoveries & amazing adventures (4 and up)   **509**
Packard, M. Ripley's believe it or not!   **031.02**

Curious bones: Mary Anning and the birth of paleontology. Goodhue, T. W.   **92**

Curran, Christine Perdan
Sexually transmitted diseases (7 and up)   **616.95**

Current biography yearbook   **920.003**

Current controversies [series]
Alcoholism   **362.292**
Child abuse   **362.7**
Conserving the environment   **333.72**
Family violence   **362.82**
Free speech   **342**
Guns and violence   **363.33**
Illegal drugs   **364.1**
Marriage and divorce   **306.8**
The Rights of animals   **179**
Smoking   **362.29**
Smoking   **363.4**
Youth violence   **364.36**

Curriculum connections through the library   **027.62**

Curriculum materials centers *See* Instructional materials centers

Curriculum partner. Kearney, C. A.   **027.8**

Currie, Stephen, 1960-
An actor on the Elizabethan stage   **792.09**
Escapes from slavery   **326**
The Mississippi   **977**
Slavery (7 and up)   **326**
Terrorists and terrorist groups (7 and up)   **303.6**

Currier, Katrina Saltonstall, 1969-
Kai's journey to Gold Mountain (4 and up)   **Fic**

Curry, Jane Louise, 1932-
The Black Canary (5 and up)   **Fic**
Hold up the sky: and other Native American tales from Texas and the Southern Plains (4 and up)   **398.2**
Contents: The beginning of the world; Coyote makes the sun; Why Bear waddles when he walks; The quarrel between Wind and Thunder; Thunderbird Woman, Skiwis, and Little Big-Belly Boy; The monsters and the flood; Coyote and the seven brothers; Slaying the monsters; Hold up the sky; Coyote and Mouse; Coyote and the smallest snake; Coyote flies with the geese; Coyote frees the buffalo; The great meatball; The fight between the animals and insects; How Rabbit stole Mountain Lion's teeth; Fox and Possum; Sendeh sings to the prairies dogs; The deserted children; Mountain lion and the four sisters; How Poor Boy won his wife; The ghost woman; The boy who killed the hill; White Fox; The tonkawa and the bear; Young Boy Chief and his sister

The **curse** of the blue figurine. Bellairs, J.   **Fic**
Curse of the pharaohs. Hawass, Z. A.   **932**
Curse of the undead. Rothman, C.
    In Vampires: a collection of original stories p19-34   **S C**

Curtis, Christopher Paul
Bucking the Sarge (5 and up)   **Fic**
Bud, not Buddy (4 and up)   **Fic**
The Watsons go to Birmingham—1963 (4 and up)   **Fic**
See/See also pages in the following book(s):
The Newbery & Caldecott medal books, 1986-2000   **028.5**

Cushman, Karen, 1941-
The ballad of Lucy Whipple (5 and up)   **Fic**
Catherine, called Birdy (6 and up)   **Fic**
Matilda Bone (5 and up)   **Fic**
The midwife's apprentice (6 and up)   **Fic**
Rodzina (5 and up)   **Fic**
See/See also pages in the following book(s):
Author talk (4 and up)   **028.5**
The Newbery & Caldecott medal books, 1986-2000   **028.5**

Cushman, Pauline, 1833-1893
See/See also pages in the following book(s):
Caravantes, P. Petticoat spies   **920**

Custer, Elizabeth Bacon, 1842-1933
The diary of Elizabeth Bacon Custer (5 and up)   **973.8**

Custer, George Armstrong, 1839-1876
About
Custer, E. B. The diary of Elizabeth Bacon Custer (5 and up)   **973.8**
Custer's last stand (7 and up)   **973.8**
Uschan, M. V. The Battle of the Little Bighorn (5 and up)   **973.8**
Viola, H. J. It is a good day to die (5 and up)   **973.8**
Fiction
Burks, B. Soldier boy   **Fic**

Custer's last stand (7 and up)   **973.8**

Custody kidnapping *See* Parental kidnapping

Customs, Social *See* Manners and customs

Cut. McCormick, P.   **Fic**
Cut from the same cloth. San Souci, R.   **398.2**

"**Cutta** cord-la". Lester, J.
> *In* Lester, J. The last tales of Uncle Remus
> p115-19   **398.2**

Cutthroat. Mazer, N. F.
> *In* Ultimate sports; short stories by outstanding writers for young adults p148-59
>   **S C**

Cycling
> *See also* Bicycles
> Cotter, A. Cycling   **796.6**
> Gardner, R. Bicycle science projects   **531**
> Gedatus, G. Bicycling for fitness   **613.7**
> King, A. Play-by-play mountain biking
>   **796.6**

Cyclones
> *See also* Hurricanes
> Longshore, D. Encyclopedia of hurricanes, typhoons and cyclones (7 and up)   **551.55**

Cyprus
> Spilling, M. Cyprus (5 and up)   **956.93**

Cystic fibrosis
> Monroe, J. Cystic fibrosis   **616.3**

The **Czarevna** of Muscovy. Goodman, J. E.
> *In* Don't cramp my style; stories about that time of the month p101-30   **S C**

Czech Republic
> Sioras, E. Czech Republic (5 and up)   **943.7**

Czechoslovakia
> *See also* Czech Republic

D

D.N.A. *See* DNA

Da Gama, Vasco *See* Gama, Vasco da, 1469-1524

Da Vinci, Leonardo *See* Leonardo, da Vinci, 1452-1519

D'Adamo, Francesco
> Iqbal (5 and up)   **Fic**

Daddy Boogey. San Souci, R.
> *In* San Souci, R. Double-dare to be scared: another thirteen chilling tales   **S C**

Dad's cool. Sleator, W.
> *In* Sleator, W. Oddballs; stories p113-27
>   **S C**

Dahl, Roald
> Boy: tales of childhood   **92**
> Skin and other stories (7 and up)   **S C**
> Contents: Skin; Lamb to the slaughter; The sound machine; An African story; Galloping Foxley; The wish; The surgeon; Dip in the pool; The champion of the world; Beware of the dog; My lady love, my dove
> The witches
> *In* Beware!; R.L. Stine picks his favorite scary stories p101-19   **808.8**

Daily life [series]
> Nardo, D. Ancient Rome   **937**

Daily life in a Plains Indian village, 1868. Terry, M. B. H.   **970.004**

Daily life in colonial New England. Johnson, C. D.   **974**

Daily life in Renaissance Italy. Cohen, E. S.   **945**

Daily life in the Pilgrim colony, 1636. Erickson, P.   **974.4**

Daily life on a Southern plantation, 1853. Erickson, P.   **975**

Daily life through history [series]
> Cohen, E. S. Daily life in Renaissance Italy
>   **945**
> Johnson, C. D. Daily life in colonial New England   **974**

Daily prison life. Rabiger, J.   **365**

Dakota Indians
> *See also* Oglala Indians
> Bonvillian, N. The Teton Sioux Indians of North America series
> Brave Bird, M. Lakota woman   **92**
> Lonehill, K. Sioux North American Indians today [series]
> *See/See also pages in the following book(s):*
> Ehrlich, A. Wounded Knee: an Indian history of the American West (6 and up)   **970.004**
> Freedman, R. Indian chiefs (6 and up)   **920**
> > **Fiction**
> Hotze, S. A circle unbroken   **Fic**
> > **Wars**
> Viola, H. J. It is a good day to die (5 and up)
>   **973.8**

Dalai Lama XIV, 1935-
> > **About**
> Demi. The Dalai Lama (3-6)   **92**

Daldry, Jeremy, 1969-
> The teenage guy's survival guide (7 and up)
>   **305.23**

Dalkey, Kara, 1953-
> The lady of the ice garden
> *In* Firebirds: an anthology of original fantasy and science fiction; an anthology of original fantasy and science fiction   **S C**

Dallas, Kim
> Fundamental karate   **796.8**

Dallas Independent School District (Tex.)
> Trespacz, K. L. Ferrell v. Dallas I.S.D. (7 and up)   **344**

Dallmeier, Francisco, 1953-
> *See/See also pages in the following book(s):*
> Oleksy, W. G. Hispanic-American scientists (7 and up)   **920**

Daly, Melissa
> (jt. auth) Piquemal, M. When life stinks
>   **305.23**

D'Amico, Joan, 1957-
> The healthy body cookbook (4 and up)
>   **641.5**
> The United States cookbook   **641.5**

Damon, Duane
> Mein Kampf (7 and up)   **943.086**

Dams
> *See/See also pages in the following book(s):*
> Macaulay, D. Building big   **720**

Dana's eyes. Juratovac, N.
> *In* American dragons: twenty-five Asian American voices p75-95   **810.8**

Dance
> *See also* Ballet; Modern dance

Dance—*Continued*

Fiction

Haas, J. Will you, won't you? **Fic**

Staples, S. F. Shiva's fire (7 and up) **Fic**

The **dance** of Elegba. Jaffe, N.

In Jaffe, N. and Zeitlin, S. J. The cow of no color: riddle stories and justice tales from around the world p76-83 **398.2**

Dance of the continents. Gallant, R. A. **551.1**

Dance with me. Appelt, K.

In Appelt, K. Kissing Tennessee and other stories from the Stardust Dance p1-10 **S C**

Dancer. Hewett, L. **Fic**

Dancer. Sears, V.

In Leaving home: stories p19-25 **808.8**

In Talking leaves; contemporary native American short stories **S C**

Dancers

See also African American dancers; Ballet dancers

Freedman, R. Martha Graham, a dancer's life (7 and up) **92**

O'Connor, B. Barefoot dancer: the story of Isadora Duncan **92**

Fiction

Levy, E. Seventh grade tango (5 and up) **Fic**

Dancing in Cadillac light. Holt, K. W. **Fic**

Dancing in the streets of Brooklyn. Lurie, A. **Fic**

Dancing teepees: poems of American Indian youth (4 and up) **897**

Dancing with Marjorie's ghost. Vande Velde, V.

In Vande Velde, V. Being dead; stories **S C**

D'Angelo, Pascal, 1894-1932

About

Murphy, J. Pick & shovel poet: the journeys of Pascal D'Angelo **92**

Danger zone. Klass, D. **Fic**

Dangerous animals

Lewin, T. Tooth and claw (4 and up) **590**

Wilkes, A. Dangerous creatures (5 and up) **591.6**

Dangerous creatures. Wilkes, A. **591.6**

Dangerous hill. San Souci, R.

In San Souci, R. A terrifying taste of short & shivery; thirty creepy tales p73-76 **398.2**

Dangerous planet. Barnard, B. **363.34**

Dangerous planet. Engelbert, P. **363.34**

Dangerous skies. Staples, S. F. **Fic**

Dangerous weather [series]

Allaby, M. Droughts **551.57**

Allaby, M. Floods **551.48**

The **dangers** of diet drugs and other weight-loss products. Barrett, C. **615**

Daniels, Roger

American immigration (7 and up) **325.73**

Dann, Geoff

(il) Gravett, C. Knight **940.1**

(il) Platt, R. Spy **327.12**

(il) Wilkinson, P. Building **690**

Danneberg, Julie, 1958-

Women artists of the West **920**

Danticat, Edwidge

Behind the mountains **Fic**

Danube. Bryan, N. **363.7**

Danziger, Paula, 1944-2004

The cat ate my gymsuit **Fic**

The Divorce Express **Fic**

P.S. Longer letter later (5 and up) **Fic**

The pistachio prescription **Fic**

Snail mail no more (5 and up) **Fic**

There's a bat in bunk five **Fic**

United Tates of America (4 and up) **Fic**

About

Krull, K. Presenting Paula Danziger **813.009**

Daphne. Cadnum, M.

In The Green Man: tales from the mythic forest p44-49 **808.8**

Daphne's book. Hahn, M. D. **Fic**

Darby. Fuqua, J. S. **Fic**

The **dare**. Naidoo, B.

In Naidoo, B. Out of bounds: seven stories of conflict and hope p1-17 **S C**

Dare to be scared. San Souci, R. **S C**

D'Argo, Laura

(il) Carson, M. K. The Wright Brothers for kids **629.13**

Dark Ages *See* Middle Ages

The **dark** beast of death. Nixon, J. L.

In Night terrors; stories of shadow and substance **S C**

The **dark** dark house. San Souci, R.

In San Souci, R. Dare to be scared; thirteen stories to chill and thrill **S C**

The **dark** ground. Cross, G. **Fic**

The **Dark** Horse. Sedgwick, M. **Fic**

The **dark** portal. Jarvis, R. **Fic**

Dark waters. MacPhail, C. **Fic**

Darkness over Denmark. Levine, E. **940.53**

Darling, Jay Norwood, 1876-1962

See/See also pages in the following book(s):

Byrnes, P. Environmental pioneers (7 and up) **920**

Darling, Kathy, 1943-

(jt. auth) Cobb, V. You gotta try this! **507.8**

Darwin, Charles, 1809-1882

About

Patent, D. H. Charles Darwin (7 and up) **92**

Stefoff, R. Charles Darwin and the evolution revolution (7 and up) **92**

Darwinism *See* Evolution

Dasch, E. Julius (Ernest Julius), 1932-

(ed) Explorers. See Explorers **920.003**

Dasch, Ernest Julius *See* Dasch, E. Julius (Ernest Julius), 1932-

Dasch, Pat

(ed) Space sciences. See Space sciences **500.5**

Dash, Joan
The longitude prize [biography of John Harrison] (5 and up) **92**
We shall not be moved (7 and up) **331.4**
The world at her fingertips: the story of Helen Keller (5 and up) **92**

Data processing
See also Artificial intelligence
Barrett, J. R. Teaching and learning about computers **004**

Date rape
Rue, N. N. Everything you need to know about abusive relationships **362.7**

A **date** with destiny. Ashabranner, B. K. **355**

Dating (Social customs)
Busby, C. Getting dumped and getting over it! (7 and up) **646.7**
Rue, N. N. Everything you need to know about abusive relationships **362.7**
Drama
Soto, G. Novio boy (7 and up) **812**
Fiction
Conford, E. Crush (7 and up) **S C**
Dessen, S. This lullaby (7 and up) **Fic**
Eberhardt, T. Rat boys **Fic**
Fredericks, M. Head games (7 and up) **Fic**
Sones, S. What my mother doesn't know (7 and up) **Fic**

Datlow, Ellen
(ed) The Green Man: tales from the mythic forest. See The Green Man: tales from the mythic forest **808.8**

Datnow, Claire L.
Edwin Hubble **92**

A **daughter** of Abraham. Hess, D.
In Soul searching: thirteen stories about faith and belief p67-89 **S C**

Daughter of invention. Alvarez, J.
In Growing up Latino; memoirs and stories p3-15 **810.8**

A **daughter** of the sea. Wartski, M. C.
In Join in; multiethnic short stories by outstanding writers for young adults p86-96 **S C**

Daughter of the wind. Cadnum, M. **Fic**

Daughters and fathers *See* Father-daughter relationship

Daughters and mothers *See* Mother-daughter relationship

Daughters of the desert **220.9**

Dave at night. Levine, G. C. **Fic**

Davenier, Christine, 1961-
(il) Very best (almost) friends. See Very best (almost) friends **811.008**

Davenport, John, 1960-
C.S. Lewis **92**

David, King of Israel
See/See also pages in the following book(s):
Meltzer, M. Ten kings (5 and up) **920**

Davidson, George
About
Morrison, T. The coast mappers (5 and up) **623.89**

Davidson, Sue, 1925-
Getting the real story: Nellie Bly and Ida B. Wells **92**

Davies, Jacqueline
Where the ground meets the sky **Fic**

Davies, Rhys, 1903-1978
Fear
In Read all about it!; great read-aloud stories, poems, and newspaper pieces for preteens and teens p223-29 **808.8**

Davis, Benjamin O., Jr.
About
Haskins, J. Black eagles (5 and up) **629.13**

Davis, Brangien
What's real, what's ideal (7 and up) **616.85**

Davis, Caroline
The young equestrian **798.2**

Davis, Jane
Crochet (5 and up) **746.43**

Davis, Jill
(ed) Open your eyes. See Open your eyes **910.4**

Davis, Lee Allyn
Environmental disasters (7 and up) **363.7**

Davis, Lucile
Alabama
In America the beautiful, second series **973**
Medicine in the American West **610.9**
Puerto Rico
In America the beautiful, second series **973**

Davis, Miles
See/See also pages in the following book(s):
Mour, S. I. American jazz musicians **920**

Davis, Terry
In the Valley of Elephants
In On the edge: stories at the brink p195-209 **S C**

Dawn. Wallace, R.
In Wallace, R. Losing is not an option: stories **S C**

Dawn. Wiesel, E.
In Wiesel, E. Night, Dawn, The accident: three tales **Fic**

Dawn. Wynne-Jones, T.
In Leaving home: stories p91-114 **808.8**

Day, Frances Ann
Lesbian and gay voices **016.8**

Day, Nancy, 1953-
Advertising (7 and up) **659.1**
Animal experimentation **179**
Killer superbugs (7 and up) **616**

Day, Trevor, 1955-
DK guide to savage Earth **550**
Genetics (5 and up) **576.5**
Oceans (7 and up) **551.46**

A **day** in the country. Jacobson, D.
In Somehow tenderness survives; stories of Southern Africa p37-47 **S C**

A **day** no pigs would die. Peck, R. N. **Fic**

Day of tears. Lester, J. **Fic**

The **day** puffins netted Hid-Well. Norman, H.
In Norman, H. The girl who dreamed only geese, and other tales of the Far North **398.2**

Day that changed America [series]
Tanaka, S. Earthquake! **979.4**

The **day** the Cisco Kid shot John Wayne. Candelaria, N.
In Growing up Latino; memoirs and stories p115-30 **810.8**

The **day** the horses came. Butcher, G.
In Girls got game; sports stories and poems **810.8**

The **day** the Rabbi disappeared. Schwartz, H.
In Schwartz, H. The day the Rabbi disappeared: Jewish holiday tales of magic p73-74 **398.2**

The **day** the Rabbi disappeared: Jewish holiday tales of magic. Schwartz, H. **398.2**

The **day** the sky fell. Meltzer, M. **303.6**

The **day** they came to arrest the book. Hentoff, N. **Fic**

Days of Jubilee. McKissack, P. C. **973.7**

Days that changed the world [series]
Beecroft, S. The release of Nelson Mandela **968.06**

Dayspring mishandled. Kipling, R.
In McCaffrey, A. {The Pern series} **S C**

De Angelis, Therese
Louis Farrakhan **92**

De Balboa, Vasco Núñez *See* Balboa, Vasco Núñez de, 1475-1519

De Chamorro, Violeta Barrios *See* Chamorro, Violeta Barrios de

De Champlain, Samuel *See* Champlain, Samuel de, 1567-1635

De Guzman, Michael
Beekman's big deal (5 and up) **Fic**
Melonhead **Fic**

De la Cruz, Melissa, 1971-
Fresh off the boat (7 and up) **Fic**

De Lint, Charles, 1951-
The blue girl (7 and up) **Fic**
Somewhere in my mind there is a painting box
In The Green Man: tales from the mythic forest p51-83 **808.8**
also in De Lint, C. Waifs and strays p355-91 **S C**

There's no such thing
also in Vampires: a collection of original stories p8-18 **S C**
Waifs and strays (7 and up) **S C**
Contents: Merlin dreams in the Moondream Wood; There's no such thing; Sisters; Fairy dust; A wish named Arnold; Wooden bones; The graceless child; A tattoo on her heart; Stick; May this be your last sorrow; One chance; Alone; But for the grace go I; Ghosts of wind and shadow; Waifs and strays; Somewhere in my mind there is a painting box

De Marcken, Gail
(il) Packer, T. A Midsummer night's dream **822.3**
(il) Packer, T. Tales from Shakespeare **822.3**

De' Medici, Lorenzo *See* Medici, Lorenzo de', 1449-1492

De Mejo, Oscar
(il) Gellman, M. Does God have a big toe? **221.9**

De Sable, Jean Baptiste Pointe *See* Pointe de Sable, Jean Baptiste, 1745?-1818

De Santa Anna, Antonio López *See* Santa Anna, Antonio López de, 1794?-1876

De Soto, Hernando *See* Soto, Hernando de, ca. 1500-1542

De Souza, Philip
(jt. auth) Langley, A. The Roman news **937**

De Tonti, Henri *See* Tonti, Henri de, 1650-1704

De Vos, Gail
New tales for old **398.2**

The **dead** and the moonstruck. Kiernan, C. R.
In Gothic!; ten original dark tales **S C**

Dead end. Anaya, R. A.
In Join in; multiethnic short stories by outstanding writers for young adults p101-09 **S C**

The **dead** hand. Schwartz, A.
In Schwartz, A. Scary stories 3; more tales to chill your bones p35-38 **398.2**

Deadly disasters [series]
Ceban, B. J. Tornadoes **551.55**
Reed, J. Earthquakes **551.2**

Deaf
Dash, J. The world at her fingertips: the story of Helen Keller (5 and up) **92**
Garrett, L. Helen Keller (5 and up) **92**
Keller, H. The story of my life **92**
Landau, E. Deafness **617.8**
Lawlor, L. Helen Keller: rebellious spirit (5 and up) **92**

Fiction
Ferris, J. Of sound mind (7 and up) **Fic**
Jordan, S. The raging quiet (7 and up) **Fic**

Means of communication
See also Sign language

Deafness. Landau, E. **617.8**

Dealing with dragons. Wrede, P. C. **Fic**

Dealing with the stuff that makes life tough. Rutledge, J. Z. **305.23**

Dean, Carolee
Comfort (7 and up) **Fic**

Dean, Ruth, 1947-
Teen prostitution **362.7**
Women of the Middle Ages (7 and up) **940.1**
(jt. auth) Thomson, M. Women of the Renaissance **940.2**

Dean, Tanya
Theodor Geisel [Dr. Seuss] (4 and up) **92**

DeAngelis, Gina
The black cowboys **978**
Science & medicine **920**
White-collar crime (7 and up) **364.1**

Deans, Sis Boulos, 1955-
Every day and all the time (5 and up) **Fic**

Dear America [series]
Bartoletti, S. C. A coal miner's bride **Fic**
Bauer, M. D. Land of the buffalo bones **Fic**
Denenberg, B. Early Sunday morning **Fic**

Dear America—*Continued*

Garland, S. Valley of the Moon	Fic
Gregory, K. Seeds of hope	Fic
Hesse, K. A light in the storm	Fic
Janke, K. Survival in the storm	Fic
Lasky, K. Christmas after all	Fic
Lasky, K. Dreams in the golden country	Fic
Lasky, K. A journey to the New World	Fic
Lasky, K. A time for courage	Fic
McDonald, M. All the stars in the sky	Fic
McKissack, P. C. A picture of Freedom	Fic
Murphy, J. My face to the wind	Fic
Osborne, M. P. Standing in the light	Fic

Dear Austin. Woodruff, E.   Fic

Dear Ellen Bee. Lyons, M. E.   Fic

Dear Mr. Henshaw. Cleary, B.   Fic

Dear Mrs. Parks. Parks, R.   305.23

Death

> *See also* Terminal care

Altman, L. J. Death: an introduction to medical-ethical dilemmas   **155.9**

Death and dying: opposing viewpoints p55-96 (7 and up)   **155.9**

Gootman, M. E. When a friend dies (7 and up)   **155.9**

Schleifer, J. Everything you need to know when someone you know has been killed (7 and up)   **155.9**

Stewart, G. Death   **306.9**

Stone, M. At the end of words (7 and up)   **92**

See/See also pages in the following book(s):

Colman, P. Corpses, coffins, and crypts (7 and up)   **393**

Fiction

Abelove, J. Saying it out loud (7 and up)   Fic

Banks, K. Walk softly, Rachel (7 and up)   Fic

Baskin, N. R. What every girl (except me) knows (4 and up)   Fic

Blume, J. Tiger eyes (7 and up)	Fic
Bowler, T. Firmament (7 and up)	Fic
Bowler, T. River boy	Fic
Brooks, B. All that remains (7 and up)	Fic
Brooks, B. Vanishing	Fic
Brooks, K. Martyn Pig (7 and up)	Fic
Bunting, E. Blackwater (5 and up)	Fic
Clarke, J. Starry nights	Fic
Conly, J. L. Crazy lady! (5 and up)	Fic

Cormier, R. The bumblebee flies anyway (7 and up)   Fic

Couloumbis, A. Getting near to baby (5 and up)   Fic

Craven, M. I heard the owl call my name (7 and up)   Fic

Creech, S. Walk two moons (6 and up)   Fic

Cummings, P. Red kayak (7 and up)   Fic

Danziger, P. United Tates of America (4 and up)   Fic

Deaver, J. R. Say goodnight, Gracie (7 and up)   Fic

Dessen, S. The truth about forever (7 and up)   Fic

DiCamillo, K. The tiger rising   Fic

Draper, S. M. The Battle of Jericho (7 and up)   Fic

Draper, S. M. Tears of a tiger (7 and up)   Fic

Dreyer, A. L. After Elaine	Fic
Fletcher, R. Flying solo (5 and up)	Fic

Freymann-Weyr, G. When I was older (7 and up)   Fic

Gilbert, B. S. Stone water (7 and up)	Fic
Goobie, B. Before wings (7 and up)	Fic

Griffin, A. Where I want to be (7 and up)   Fic

Haas, J. Unbroken (5 and up)	Fic
Haddix, M. P. Takeoffs and landings	Fic
Hamilton, V. Cousins (5 and up)	Fic
Henkes, K. Sun & Spoon (4 and up)	Fic
Hesse, K. Phoenix rising	Fic

Holt, K. W. Keeper of the night (7 and up)   Fic

Johnson, A. Toning the sweep	Fic
Klause, A. C. The silver kiss	Fic
Kornblatt, M. Understanding Buddy	Fic

L'Engle, M. A ring of endless light (5 and up)   Fic

Matthews, K. Flying lessons	Fic
Mazer, N. F. After the rain	Fic
Mazer, N. F. Girlhearts	Fic

McDonald, J. Swallowing stones (7 and up)   Fic

McGhee, A. Snap (5 and up)   Fic

Paterson, K. Bridge to Terabithia (4 and up)   Fic

Rylant, C. Missing May (5 and up)   Fic

Smith, C. L. Rain is not my Indian name   Fic

Van Leeuwen, J. Lucy was there—   Fic

Wallace-Brodeur, R. Blue eyes better (4-6)   Fic

Woods, R. The hero	Fic
Woodson, J. Behind you (7 and up)	Fic
Yumoto, K. The letters (7 and up)	Fic

Death, Apparent *See* Near-death experiences

Death and disease. Woolf, A.   **610**

Death and dying: opposing viewpoints (7 and up)   **155.9**

Death at Devil's Bridge. DeFelice, C. C.   Fic

Death be not proud. Gunther, J.   **92**

Death penalty *See* Capital punishment

The **Death** penalty: opposing viewpoints (7 and up)   **364.66**

Deaver, Julie Reece

Say goodnight, Gracie (7 and up)   Fic

The **debate** over human cloning. Goodnough, D.   **174.2**

Debating Supreme Court decisions [series]

Fridell, R. Cruzan v. Missouri and the right to die debate   **344**

Debs, Eugene V. (Eugene Victor), 1855-1926

See/See also pages in the following book(s):

Streissguth, T. Legendary labor leaders (7 and up)   **920**

The **deceitful** heron. Lee, J. M.

In Lee, J. M. I once was a monkey; stories Buddha told   **294.3**

Declaration of Independence *See* United States. Declaration of Independence

Declarations of independence. Brown, J.   **028.5**

DeClements, Barthe, 1920-
6th grade can really kill you (5 and up)   **Fic**

Decoding life. Fridell, R.   **576.5**

Decoy. Huddleston, C.   **741.5**

DeDonato, Collete
(ed) City of one. See City of one   **810.8**

Dee, Ruby
See/See also pages in the following book(s):
Hansen, J. Women of hope (4 and up)   **920**

Dee Brown's folktales of the Native American. Brown, D. A.   **398.2**

The deeds and prophecies of Old Man. Brown, D. A.
In Brown, D. A. Dee Brown's folktales of the Native American; retold for our times p59-62   **398.2**

Deem, James M.
Bodies from the bog (4 and up)   **930.1**

Deep in the Amazon [series]
Castner, J. L. Layers of life   **577.3**
Castner, J. L. Partners and rivals   **577.3**
Castner, J. L. River life   **577.6**
Castner, J. L. Surviving in the rain forest   **577.3**

Deep space observation satellites. Sherman, J.   **629.43**

Deer
Patent, D. H. Deer and elk (4 and up)   **599.65**
Fiction
Rawlings, M. K. The yearling   **Fic**

Deer and elk. Patent, D. H.   **599.65**

Deer Woman. Allen, P. G.
In Talking leaves; contemporary native American short stories   **S C**

DeFalco, Tom
The Hulk: the incredible guide   **741.5**
Spider-girl, Vol. 1: Legacy   **741.5**

DeFelice, Cynthia C.
The apprenticeship of Lucas Whitaker (5 and up)   **Fic**
Death at Devil's Bridge (5 and up)   **Fic**
The ghost and Mrs. Hobbs (4-6)   **Fic**
The ghost of Fossil Glen (4-6)   **Fic**
Nowhere to call home   **Fic**

The defender. Lipsyte, R.
In Ultimate sports; short stories by outstanding writers for young adults p180-92   **S C**

DeFilippis, Nunzio
Once in a blue moon   **741.5**

Define "normal". Peters, J. A.   **Fic**

Defoe, Daniel, 1661?-1731
Robinson Crusoe (7 and up)   **Fic**

DeGeneres, Ellen
See/See also pages in the following book(s):
Stewart, G. Great women comedians   **920**

Deignan, Tom
Irish Americans (7 and up)   **305.8**

Deities *See* Gods and goddesses

Del Vecchio, Gene, 1955-
The Pearl of Anton (7 and up)   **Fic**

Delacre, Lulu, 1957-
Golden tales (5 and up)   **398.2**
Contents: How the sea was born; Guanina; The eleven thousand Virgins; The laughing skull; Sención, the Indian girl; When the sun and the moon were children; How the rainbow was born; The miracle of Our Lady of Guadalupe; El Dorado; Manco Capac and the rod of gold; Kákuy; The courier
Salsa stories (4-6)   **S C**
Contents: New Years Day; A carpet for Holy Week; At the beach; The night of San Juan; Teatime; Birthday piñata; The Lord of Miracles; Aguinaldo; Carmen Teresa's gift

Delano, Marfe Ferguson
Genius [biography of Albert Einstein] (5 and up)   **92**
Inventing the future: a photobiography of Thomas Alva Edison   **92**

Delany, Annie Elizabeth *See* Delany, Bessie

Delany, Bessie
See/See also pages in the following book(s):
Hansen, J. Women of hope (4 and up)   **920**

Delany, Sadie
See/See also pages in the following book(s):
Hansen, J. Women of hope (4 and up)   **920**

Delany, Sarah Louise *See* Delany, Sadie

Delaware
Blashfield, J. F. Delaware
In America the beautiful, second series   **973**
Schuman, M. Delaware
In Celebrate the states   **973**
Fiction
Hesse, K. A light in the storm (5 and up)   **Fic**

Delaware Indians
Fiction
Durrant, L. The beaded moccasins (5 and up)   **Fic**
Osborne, M. P. Standing in the light   **Fic**
Richter, C. The light in the forest   **Fic**

Delinquency, Juvenile *See* Juvenile delinquency

Deliver us from Normal. Klise, K.   **Fic**

The deliverers of their country. Nesbit, E.
In The Book of dragons p50-66   **S C**

Delivering Web reference services to young people. Minkel, W.   **025.04**

Demetriades, Helen A.
Bipolar disorder, depression, and other mood disorders (7 and up)   **616.85**

Demi, 1942-
Buddha (4-6)   **294.3**
The Dalai Lama (3-6)   **92**
Muhammad (4 and up)   **297**

Democratic Republic of the Congo. Heale, J.   **967.51**

Democratic Republic of the Congo. Willis, T.   **967.51**

Demonstrations
Kronenwetter, M. Protest! (7 and up)   **303.4**

Denenberg, Barry
All shook up: the life and death of Elvis Presley (5 and up)   **92**
Early Sunday morning   **Fic**
Elisabeth: the princess bride   **Fic**

Denenberg, Barry—*Continued*
The journal of Ben Uchida, citizen #13559, Mirror Lake internment camp   **Fic**
When will this cruel war be over?   **Fic**

Deniers of the Holocaust. Gottfried, T.   **940.53**

Denkmire, Heather
The truth about fear and depression. See The truth about fear and depression   **616.85**

Denmark
        Fiction
Levitin, S. Room in the heart   **Fic**
Lowry, L. Number the stars (4 and up)   **Fic**
        History
Levine, E. Darkness over Denmark   **940.53**

Dennison, Allie
(jt. auth) Dennison, A. Our dad died   **155.9**

Dennison, Amy
Our dad died (4 and up)   **155.9**

Dennison, David
(jt. auth) Dennison, A. Our dad died   **155.9**

Dent, Charlie, 1919-1994
        About
Talbott, H. Leonardo's horse (4 and up)
   730.9

Dentistry
See also Orthodontics

Denton, Carey
(jt. auth) Glenn, J. The treasury of family games
   793

Depression (Psychology)
Cobain, B. When nothing matters anymore (7 and up)   **155.9**
Demetriades, H. A. Bipolar disorder, depression, and other mood disorders (7 and up)
   616.85
Depression (7 and up)   **616.85**
Moragne, W. Depression (7 and up)   **616.85**
Piquemal, M. When life stinks   **305.23**
Silverstein, A. Depression (7 and up)   **616.85**
The truth about fear and depression (7 and up)
   616.85
Wolff, L. Teen depression   **616.85**
        Fiction
Fritz, A. Y. Waiting to disappear (7 and up)
   Fic

Depression (7 and up)   **616.85**

The **Depression** and New Deal. McElvaine, R. S.
   973.91

Depressions
        1929
See Great Depression, 1929-1939

Derby, Pat
Away to the goldfields!   **Fic**

Des Chenes, Betz
American civil rights: primary sources. See American civil rights: primary sources
   323.1

Des Moines Independent Community School District
Farish, L. Tinker v. Des Moines (7 and up)
   342

Desai Hidier, Tanuja
Born confused (7 and up)   **Fic**

A **descent** into the maelstrom. Poe, E. A.
In Poe, E. A. Tales of Edgar Allan Poe p27-50   **S C**

Desegregation in education *See* School integration

Desert. Sayre, A. P.   **577.5**

Desert ecology
Mudd-Ruth, M. The deserts of the Southwest
   577.5
Sayre, A. P. Desert (5 and up)   **577.5**

The **desert** is my mother. El desierto es mi madre. Mora, P.   **811**

Desert Storm Operation *See* Persian Gulf War, 1991

Desert storm--the first Persian Gulf War in American history. McArthur, D.   **956.7**

The **deserted** children. Curry, J. L.
In Curry, J. L. Hold up the sky: and other Native American tales from Texas and the Southern Plains p95-102   **398.2**

Deserts
Allaby, M. Deserts (7 and up)   **577.5**
        Fiction
Temple, F. The Beduins' gazelle   **Fic**
        Poetry
Mora, P. The desert is my mother. El desierto es mi madre   **811**

The **deserts** of the Southwest. Mudd-Ruth, M.
   577.5

Designing a school library media center for the future. Erikson, R.   **027.8**

The **desk**. Wardlaw, L.
In Tripping over the lunch lady and other school stories p97-117   **S C**

Despite all obstacles: La Salle and the conquest of the Mississippi. Goodman, J. E.   **92**

Dessen, Sarah, 1970-
Dreamland (7 and up)   **Fic**
Someone like you (7 and up)   **Fic**
This lullaby (7 and up)   **Fic**
The truth about forever (7 and up)   **Fic**

Desserts around the world
In Easy menu ethnic cookbooks   **641.5**

Destination gold!. Lawson, J.   **Fic**

Destination: Jupiter. Simon, S.   **523.4**

Destination: space. Simon, S.   **520**

Destination unexpected: short stories (7 and up)
   S C

Destiny. Grove, V.   **Fic**

Deuker, Carl, 1950-
High heat (7 and up)   **Fic**
If you can't be lucky . . .
In Ultimate sports; short stories by outstanding writers for young adults p72-91
   S C
Night hoops (7 and up)   **Fic**
On the Devil's court (7 and up)   **Fic**
Painting the black (7 and up)   **Fic**

Developing an information literacy program, K-12
   025.5

Developing Christian fiction collections for children and adults. Walker, B. J.   **025.2**

Developing countries
Economic conditions
Garlake, T. Global debt (7 and up)   **336.3**

Devereux, Robert, 1566-1601 *See* Essex, Robert Devereux, 2nd Earl of, 1566-1601

Devers, Gail, 1966-
See/See also pages in the following book(s):
Kaminsky, M. Uncommon champions   **920**

Devi, Gayatri *See* Gayatri Devi, Maharani of Jaipur, 1919-

Devi. Mayer, M.
In Mayer, M. Women warriors; myths and legends of heroic women p13-15   **398**

The **Devil** and his boy. Horowitz, A.   **Fic**

The **devil** and his grandmother. Grimm, J.
In The Book of dragons p67-71   **S C**

Devil boy. Kimmel, E. A.
In Kimmel, E. A. Sword of the samurai; adventure stories from Japan p85-94   **Fic**

Devil on my heels. McDonald, J.   **Fic**

The **devil** with the three golden hairs. Yolen, J.
In Yolen, J. Mightier than the sword; world folktales for strong boys p18-27   **398.2**

DeVillers, David
Marbury v. Madison (7 and up)   **347**

The **devil's** arithmetic. Yolen, J.   **Fic**

Dewdroppers, waldos, and slackers. Ostler, R.   **428**

Dewey, Jennifer
Antarctic journal (4 and up)   **998**
Finding your way   **796.5**

Dewey, Melvil, 1851-1931
Abridged Dewey decimal classification and relative index   **025.4**

Dewey Decimal Classification
Dewey, M. Abridged Dewey decimal classification and relative index   **025.4**

Dezago, Todd
Spider-man: Spidey strikes back Vol. 1 digest   **741.5**
Tellos, Vol. 1   **741.5**

Dhilawala, Sakina, 1964-
Armenia (5 and up)   **947.5**

Di Domenico, Kelly, 1977-
Super women in science   **920**

Diabetes
Hyde, M. O. Diabetes   **616.4**
Kelly, P. Coping with diabetes (7 and up)   **616.4**
Sheen, B. Diabetes   **616.4**
Stewart, G. Diabetes (7 and up)   **616.4**
Fiction
Hautman, P. Sweetblood (7 and up)   **Fic**
Morgan, N. Chicken friend (5 and up)   **Fic**

Diagram Group
African history on file. See African history on file   **960**
Comparative religions on file. See Comparative religions on file   **201**
Earth science on file. See Earth science on file   **550**

Encyclopedia of African nations and civilizations. See Encyclopedia of African nations and civilizations   **960**
The Facts on File biology handbook. See The Facts on File biology handbook   **570**
The Facts on File chemistry handbook. See The Facts on File chemistry handbook   **540**
The Facts on File earth science handbook. See The Facts on File earth science handbook   **550**
The Facts on File physics handbook. See The Facts on File physics handbook   **530**
Human anatomy on file. See Human anatomy on file   **611**
Human physiology on file. See Human physiology on file   **612**
Rules of the game. See Rules of the game   **796.03**
Space and astronomy on file. See Space and astronomy on file   **520**
Weapons. See Weapons   **623.4**
Weather and climate on file. See Weather and climate on file   **551.5**
Women in history on file. See Women in history on file   **305.4**
World history on file. See World history on file   **909**

Diallo, Amadou, d. 1999
About
Fireside, B. J. The trial of the police officers in the shooting death of Amadou Diallo (7 and up)

Diamond, Donna, 1950-
(il) Paterson, K. Bridge to Terabithia   **Fic**

Diamond, Shifra N.
Everything you need to know about going to the gynecologist (7 and up)   **618.1**

Diamond Island: Alcatraz. Wilson, D. B.
In Talking leaves; contemporary native American short stories   **S C**

Diaries
Trueit, T. S. Keeping a journal (5 and up)   **808**

See/See also pages in the following book(s):
Graham, P. W. Speaking of journals   **920**
Fiction
Jacobsson, A. In Ned's head   **Fic**
Wilson, N. H. Mountain pose (5 and up)   **Fic**

The **diary** of a young girl. Frank, A.   **92**

The **diary** of a young girl: the definitive edition. Frank, A.   **92**

The **diary** of Elizabeth Bacon Custer. Custer, E. B.   **973.8**

The **diary** of Pelly D. Adlington, L. J.   **Fic**

The **diary** of Sam Watkins, a confederate soldier. Watkins, S. R.   **973.7**

The **diary** of Susie King Taylor, Civil War nurse. Taylor, S. K.   **973.7**

Dias, Bartholomeu, 1450?-1500
See/See also pages in the following book(s):
Fritz, J. Around the world in a hundred years (4 and up)   **910.4**

Diaz, Bartholomeu *See* Dias, Bartholomeu, 1450?-1500

Diaz, David
See/See also pages in the following book(s):
The Newbery & Caldecott medal books, 1986-2000 **028.5**
(il) Soto, G. Neighborhood odes **811**

Diaz, Henry F., 1948-
See/See also pages in the following book(s):
Oleksy, W. G. Hispanic-American scientists (7 and up) **920**

Diaz, Karen R.
IssueWeb: a guide and sourcebook for research-ing controversial issues on the Web **025.04**

DiCamillo, Kate, 1964-
Because of Winn-Dixie (4 and up) **Fic**
The tiger rising **Fic**

Dicey's song. Voigt, C. **Fic**

Dick, Philip K.
The alien mind
In New skies: an anthology of today's science fiction **S C**

Dickens, Charles, 1812-1870
About
Stanley, D. Charles Dickens (4 and up) **92**

Dickinson, A. T.
American historical fiction **016.813**

Dickinson, Emily, 1830-1886
Emily Dickinson
In The Blackbirch treasury of American poet-ry p101-45 **811.008**
About
Dommermuth-Costa, C. Emily Dickinson **92**

Dickinson, Peter, 1927-
A bone from a dry sea **Fic**
Eva (7 and up) **Fic**
The kin **Fic**
Ko's story
In Dickinson, P. The kin p307-459 **Fic**
Kraken
In McKinley, R. and Dickinson, P. Water: tales of elemental spirits p170-207 **S C**
Mana's story
In Dickinson, P. The kin p465-628 **Fic**
Mermaid song
In McKinley, R. and Dickinson, P. Water: tales of elemental spirits p1-29 **S C**
Noli's story
In Dickinson, P. The kin p151-301 **Fic**
Sea serpent
In McKinley, R. and Dickinson, P. Water: tales of elemental spirits p78-118 **S C**
Suth's story
In Dickinson, P. The kin p1-45 **Fic**
Tears of the salamander **Fic**
(jt. auth) McKinley, R. Water: tales of elemental spirits **S C**

Dickinson, Terence
NightWatch (7 and up) **520**

Dicks, Brian
Brazil **981**

Dictators
Giblin, J. The life and death of Adolf Hitler (7 and up) **92**
Ingram, S. Joseph Stalin **92**
Nardo, D. Adolf Hitler **92**

Dictionaries *See* Encyclopedias and dictionaries

Dictionaries, Biographical *See* Biography—Dic-tionaries

Dictionaries, Picture *See* Picture dictionaries

Dictionary for school library media specialists. McCain, M. M. **020**

Dictionary of American slang **427**

The **Dictionary** of characters in children's litera-ture **028.5**

The **dictionary** of cultural literacy. See Hirsch, E. D. The new dictionary of cultural literacy **031**

The **Dictionary** of folklore (4 and up) **398**
Dictionary of phrase and fable, Brewer's **803**
Dictionary of symbols. Liungman, C. G. **302.2**

The **Dictionary** of the environment and its biomes **577**

The **dictionary** of the U.S. Constitution. Feinberg, B. S. **342**

Didrikson, Babe *See* Zaharias, Babe Didrikson, 1911-1956

Diehn, Gwen, 1943-
Making books that fly, fold, wrap, hide, pop up, twist, and turn (4 and up) **736**
Science crafts for kids
In Diehn, G. and others. Science smart; cool projects for exploring the marvels of the planet Earth **550**
Science smart. See Science smart **550**

Diêm, Ngô Dinh *See* Ngô, Dinh Diêm, 1901-1963

Diet
See also Eating customs
Diet information for teens (7 and up) **613.2**
Diet pill drug dangers. Clayton, L. **616.3**
Diet pills *See* Appetite depressants
Diets, Reducing *See* Weight loss

A **different** kind of hero. Blakeslee, A. R. **Fic**
Different kinds of darkness. Langford, D.
In New skies: an anthology of today's science fiction **S C**

Digestion
Brynie, F. H. 101 questions about food and di-gestion that have been eating at you . . . until now **612.3**
Parker, S. Digestion and reproduction **612.3**
Simon, S. Guts (4 and up) **612.3**
Walker, P. The digestive system (7 and up) **612.3**

Digestion and reproduction. Parker, S. **612.3**
The **digestive** system. Walker, P. **612.3**
Digging for bird-dinosaurs. Bishop, N. **567.9**

Digging for the past [series]
Malone, C. Stonehenge **936.2**
Smith, S. T. Valley of the Kings **932**
Vivian, R. G. Chaco Canyon **978**
Digging into the past. Greenberg, L. **920**

Digital photography
Bidner, J. The kids' guide to digital photography (5 and up) **775**

Digital revolution. Hoare, S. **621.381**

Dignifying science: stories about women scientists. Ottaviani, J. **741.5**

Dillon, Diane
(il) Bible. O.T. Ecclesiastes. To every thing there is a season **223**
(il) Engdahl, S. L. Enchantress from the stars **Fic**
(il) Hamilton, V. Her stories **398.2**
(il) Hamilton, V. Many thousand gone **326**
(il) Norman, H. The girl who dreamed only geese, and other tales of the Far North **398.2**
(il) Packer, T. King Lear **822.3**

Dillon, Leo, 1933-
(il) Bible. O.T. Ecclesiastes. To every thing there is a season **223**
(il) Hamilton, V. Her stories **398.2**
(il) Hamilton, V. Many thousand gone **326**
(il) Norman, H. The girl who dreamed only geese, and other tales of the Far North **398.2**
(il) Packer, T. King Lear **822.3**

A **dime** a dozen. Grimes, N. **811**

Diner, Hasia R.
Jews in America (7 and up) **305.8**

Dini, Paul
The Batman adventures **741.5**

Dinkins is dead. San Souci, R.
In San Souci, R. A terrifying taste of short & shivery; thirty creepy tales p82-85 **398.2**

Dinosaur mummies. Halls, K. M. **567.9**

A **dinosaur** named Sue: the story of the colossal fossil: the world's most complete T. rex. Relf, P. **567.9**

Dinosaur parents, dinosaur young. Carrick, P. **567.9**

Dinosaurs
Barrett, P. M. National Geographic dinosaurs **567.9**
Bausum, A. Dragon bones and dinosaur eggs: a photobiography of Roy Chapman Andrews (5 and up) **92**
Bishop, N. Digging for bird-dinosaurs (4 and up) **567.9**
Clark, N. 1,001 facts about dinosaurs **567.9**
Farlow, J. O. Bringing dinosaur bones to life (5 and up) **567.9**
Halls, K. M. Dinosaur mummies (5 and up) **567.9**
Kelsey, E. Canadian dinosaurs **567.9**
Lambert, D. DK guide to dinosaurs **567.9**
Lessem, D. Scholastic dinosaurs A to Z (4 and up) **567.9**
Marrin, A. Secrets from the rocks: dinosaur hunting with Roy Chapman Andrews (4 and up) **92**
Patent, D. H. In search of the maiasaurs **567.9**

Relf, P. A dinosaur named Sue: the story of the colossal fossil: the world's most complete T. rex (5 and up) **567.9**
Sloan, C. Feathered dinosaurs (5 and up) **567.9**
Tanaka, S. Graveyards of the dinosaurs (4-6) **567.9**
Yates, A. Guide to wild dinosaurs **567.9**
Carrick, P. Dinosaur parents, dinosaur young (4 and up) **567.9**
Encyclopedias
Dinosaurs of the world **567.9**
Fiction
Crichton, M. Jurassic Park (7 and up) **Fic**
Foster, A. D. The Hand of Dinotopia **Fic**
Gurney, J. Dinotopia [and other titles in series] **Fic**
TenNapel, D. R. Tommysaurus Rex **741.5**

Dinosaurs of the world **567.9**

Dinotopia [and other titles in series] Gurney, J. **Fic**

Dior, Christian, 1905-1957
See/See also pages in the following book(s):
Kent, J. Business builders in fashion **920**

Dip in the pool. Dahl, R.
In Dahl, R. Skin and other stories **S C**

Diphtheria
Fiction
Haddix, M. P. Running out of time **Fic**

Direction (Motion pictures) *See* Motion pictures—Production and direction

Directory of distance learning opportunities, K-12 **371.3**

Disabled *See* Handicapped

The **disappearance**. Guy, R. **Fic**

The **disappearance** of Lady Frances Carfax. Doyle, Sir A. C.
In Doyle, Sir A. C. The complete Sherlock Holmes **S C**

Disasters
See also Accidents; Natural disasters
Davis, L. A. Environmental disasters (7 and up) **363.7**
Garner, J. We interrupt this broadcast **070.1**
Sandler, M. W. America's great disasters **973**
Fiction
Harlow, J. H. Joshua's song (4 and up) **Fic**

Disasters in space exploration. Vogt, G. **363.1**

Discover Mars. Skurzynski, G. **523.4**

Discoveries (in geography) *See* Exploration

Discovering Central America [series]
Shields, C. J. Belize **972.82**
Shields, C. J. Honduras **972.83**

Discovering mythology [series]
Glick, S. War and peace **201**
Mass, W. Gods and goddesses **201**

Discovering the Inca Ice Maiden. Reinhard, J. **930.1**

Discovering world cultures [series]
The Middle East **956**

Discovery! [series]
Agenbroad, L. D. Mammoths **569**

Discovery!—*Continued*
Fridell, R. Decoding life   **576.5**
Discovery Channel insects & spiders   **595.7**
The **discovery** of the Titanic. Ballard, R. D.
   910.4

Discrimination
Discrimination: opposing viewpoints (7 and up)
   305.8
Senker, C. Why are people prejudiced?
   303.3
     Law and legislation
McKissack, P. C. To establish justice   **342**
Discrimination in education
   See also Segregation in education
     Law and legislation
Banfield, S. The Bakke case (7 and up)   **344**
Discrimination in public accommodations
Anderson, W. Plessy v. Ferguson   **342**
Discrimination: opposing viewpoints (7 and up)
   305.8
Diseases
   See also Chickenpox; Sick names of specific diseases and groups of diseases; and subjects with the subdivision *Diseases*
Day, N. Killer superbugs (7 and up)   **616**
Friedlander, M. P. Outbreak: disease detectives at work   **614.4**
Hoff, B. H. Mapping epidemics (7 and up)
   614
Jacobs, M. B. Coping with hereditary diseases (7 and up)   **616**
Monroe, J. Influenza and other viruses   **616.9**
Sick! diseases and disorders, injuries and infections   **616**
Whiteside, M. Health and illness
   In Being human   **612**
     Encyclopedias
Diseases   **616**
Diseases   **616**
Diseases and disorders [series]
Abramovitz, M. Leukemia   **616.99**
Abrams, L. Chronic fatigue syndrome   **616.9**
Sheen, B. Diabetes   **616.4**
Diseases and disorders series
Cotter, A. Anorexia and bulimia   **616.85**
Girod, C. M. Down syndrome   **616.85**
Goodfellow, G. Epilepsy   **616.8**
Sheen, B. Attention deficit disorder   **616.85**
Stewart, G. Phobias   **616.85**
Diseases and people [series]
Benowitz, S. I. Cancer   **616.99**
Carson, M. K. Epilepsy   **616.8**
Curran, C. P. Sexually transmitted diseases
   616.95
Demetriades, H. A. Bipolar disorder, depression, and other mood disorders   **616.85**
Johansson, P. Carpal tunnel syndrome and other repetitive strain injuries   **616.8**
Landau, E. Head and brain injuries   **617.1**
Latta, S. L. Allergies   **616.97**
Latta, S. L. Food poisoning and foodborne diseases   **615.9**
Silverstein, A. Chickenpox and shingles
   616.9

Silverstein, A. Depression   **616.85**
Silverstein, A. Measles and rubella   **616.9**
Silverstein, A. Parkinson's disease   **616.8**
Silverstein, A. Polio   **616.8**
Silverstein, A. Sickle cell anemia   **616.1**
Veggeberg, S. Lyme disease   **616.9**
Willett, E. Alzheimer's disease   **616.8**
Willett, E. Meningitis   **616.8**
Dishonesty *See* Honesty
Disney, Walt, 1901-1966
     About
Finch, C. The art of Walt Disney (7 and up)
   791.43
See/See also pages in the following book(s):
Aaseng, N. Business builders in real estate
   920
Disney (Walt) Company *See* Walt Disney Company
Disney (Walt) Productions *See* Walt Disney Productions
A **disorderly** table. Goldin, B. D.
   In Goldin, B. D. Journeys with Elijah; eight tales of the Prophet p21-28   **222**
Displaced persons *See* Refugees
Displaced persons. Gottfried, T.   **940.53**
Dissent
Kronenwetter, M. Protest! (7 and up)   **303.4**
Distance education
     Directories
Directory of distance learning opportunities, K-12   **371.3**
Distinguished African American scientists of the 20th century (7 and up)   **920**
The **disturber** of traffic. Kipling, R.
   In McCaffrey, A. {The Pern series}   **S C**
Divakaruni, Chitra Banerjee, 1956-
The conch bearer (5 and up)   **Fic**
The **dive**. Saldaña, R.
   In Saldaña, R. Finding our way: stories p83-93   **S C**
DiVito, Anna
(il) Krull, K. A kid's guide to America's Bill of Rights   **342**
Divorce
   See also Remarriage
Bode, J. For better, for worse   **306.89**
Marriage and divorce (7 and up)   **306.8**
Sanders, P. Divorce and separation   **306.89**
Stewart, G. Divorce   **306.89**
See/See also pages in the following book(s):
The Family: opposing viewpoints (7 and up)
   306.8
     Fiction
Bauer, J. Stand tall   **Fic**
Bunting, E. The summer of Riley   **Fic**
Caseley, J. Losing Louisa (7 and up)   **Fic**
Cleary, B. Dear Mr. Henshaw (4 and up)
   Fic
Cleary, B. Strider (4 and up)   **Fic**
Cole, B. Celine   **Fic**
Danziger, P. The Divorce Express   **Fic**
Doherty, B. Holly Starcross (7 and up)   **Fic**
Friesen, G. Losing forever (7 and up)   **Fic**

Divorce—Fiction—*Continued*

Graham, R. My not-so-terrible time at Hippie Hotel **Fic**

Hobbs, V. Charlie's run **Fic**

Johnson, A. Songs of faith (5 and up) **Fic**

Koss, A. G. Stranger in Dadland (5 and up) **Fic**

Lynch, C. Who the man **Fic**

Mack, T. Drawing lessons **Fic**

Mackler, C. Love and other four-letter words (7 and up) **Fic**

Mazer, N. F. Taking Terri Mueller **Fic**

Paulsen, G. Hatchet **Fic**

Voigt, C. A solitary blue (7 and up) **Fic**

Wilson, J. The suitcase kid **Fic**

Divorce and separation. Sanders, P. **306.89**

The **Divorce** Express. Danziger, P. **Fic**

Dixon, Chuck, 1954-

Hobbit: an illustrated edition of the fantasy classic **741.5**

Dixon, Dougal, 1947-

The future is wild **576.8**

(jt. auth) Clark, N. 1,001 facts about dinosaurs **567.9**

Dizzy. Cassidy, C.

DK backpack books [series]

Clark, N. 1,001 facts about dinosaurs **567.9**

DK biography [series]

Garrett, L. Helen Keller **92**

Sawyer, K. K. Anne Frank **92**

DK dictionary/thesaurus **423**

DK eyewitness books [series]

Adams, S. Titanic **910.4**

Adams, S. World War II **940.53**

Adams, S. World War I **940.3**

Bender, L. Invention **609**

Brookfield, K. Book **070.5**

Burnie, D. Bird **598**

Burnie, D. Tree **582.16**

Byam, M. Arms & armor **355.8**

Cribb, J. Money **332.4**

Gravett, C. Knight **940.1**

Hornby, H. Soccer **796.334**

Langley, A. Medieval life **940.1**

Langley, M. Religion **200**

Lippincott, K. Astronomy **520**

Macquitty, M. Shark **597**

Margeson, S. M. Viking **948**

Matthews, R. Explorer **910.4**

Murdoch, D. H. Cowboy **978**

Murdoch, D. H. North American Indian **970.004**

Nahum, A. Flying machine **629.133**

Parker, S. Human body **612**

Parker, S. Seashore **577.7**

Philip, N. Mythology **201**

Platt, R. Shipwreck **910.4**

Stott, C. Space exploration **629.4**

Symes, R. F. Crystal & gem **548**

Symes, R. F. Eyewitness rocks & minerals **549**

Taylor, P. D. Fossil **560**

Tubb, J. N. Bible lands **220.9**

DK eyewitness guides [series]

Wilkinson, P. Buddhism **294.3**

The **DK** geography of the world **910**

DK guide to dinosaurs. Lambert, D. **567.9**

DK guide to savage Earth. Day, T. **550**

DK guide to space. Bond, P. **520**

DK guide to the human body. Walker, R. **612**

DK nature encyclopedia **508**

The **DK** science encyclopedia (5 and up) **503**

DK secret worlds [series]

Buller, L. Myths and monsters **398**

DK student atlas **912**

DK ultimate visual dictionary of science. See Ultimate visual dictionary of science **503**

DNA

Allan, T. Understanding DNA **576.5**

Boon, K. A. The human genome project (7 and up) **599.93**

Senker, C. Rosalind Franklin (5 and up) **92**

DNA fingerprinting

Fridell, R. DNA fingerprinting (7 and up) **614**

Tocci, S. High-tech IDs (7 and up) **599.9**

Do it right!. Jones, P. **027.62**

Do people grow on family trees? See Wolfman, I. Climbing your family tree **929**

Do you know where your parents are? Brooks, B.
In Time capsule: short stories about teenagers throughout the twentieth century p169-79 **S C**

Do you remember the color blue? Alexander, S. H. **362.4**

Do you want my opinion? Kerr, M. E.
In Sixteen; short stories by outstanding writers for young adults p93-100 **S C**

Dober, Michelle, 1969-

(jt. auth) Haycock, K. Neal-Schuman authoritative guide to kids' search engines, subject directories, and portals **025.04**

Doc Rabbit, Bruh Fox, and Tar Baby. Hamilton, V.
In Hamilton, V. The people could fly; American black folktales p13-19 **398.2**

Doctors *See* Physicians

Documentary photography
See/See also pages in the following book(s):
Schulke, F. Witness to our times **92**

Documenting history [series]

Hatt, C. The Crusades **909.07**

Hatt, C. Scientists and their discoveries **509**

Hatt, C. World War I, 1914-18 **940.3**

Hatt, C. World War II, 1939-45 **940.53**

Ross, S. The American Revolution **973.3**

Ross, S. The industrial revolution **330.9**

Dodgson, Charles Lutwidge *See* Carroll, Lewis, 1832-1898

Dodson, Shireen

100 books for girls to grow on **028.1**

Does capital punishment deter crime? (7 and up) **364.66**

Does God have a big toe? Gellman, M. **221.9**

Dog Carlos. Chollet, L. E.
In The Boy of Chancellorville and other Civil War stories p9-22   **S C**

Dog racing
  See also Iditarod Trail Sled Dog Race, Alaska; Sled dog racing

Dogs
  See also Working dogs
American Kennel Club. The complete dog book   **636.7**
The Complete dog book for kids (4 and up)   **636.7**
Paulsen, G. My life in dog years (4 and up)   **92**
Sidman, J. The world according to dog   **810.8**

Fiction
Armstrong, W. H. Sounder (5 and up)   **Fic**
Bunting, E. The summer of Riley   **Fic**
Calvert, P. Bigger (5 and up)   **Fic**
Cleary, B. Strider (4 and up)   **Fic**
Crisp, M. Private Captain   **Fic**
DiCamillo, K. Because of Winn-Dixie (4 and up)   **Fic**
Gipson, F. B. Old Yeller (6 and up)   **Fic**
Haas, J. Shaper   **Fic**
Hearne, B. G. The canine connection: stories about dogs and people   **S C**
Henkes, K. Protecting Marie (5 and up)   **Fic**
Hickman, J. Ravine   **Fic**
Koja, K. Straydog (7 and up)   **Fic**
Lawrence, C. The thieves of Ostia   **Fic**
Leonard, E. A coyote's in the house (5 and up)   **Fic**
London, J. The call of the wild (5 and up)   **Fic**
London, J. White Fang (5 and up)   **Fic**
Lowry, L. Stay! (5 and up)   **Fic**
Marsden, J. Checkers (7 and up)   **Fic**
Morgan, C. The boy who spoke dog (5 and up)   **Fic**
Naylor, P. R. Shiloh (4-6)   **Fic**
Rawls, W. Where the red fern grows   **Fic**
Sherlock, P. Letters from Wolfie (5 and up)   **Fic**
Smith, R. The captain's dog   **Fic**
Van Leeuwen, J. Lucy was there—   **Fic**
Zinnen, L. The truth about rats, rules, and seventh grade   **Fic**

Dogs, Wild *See* Wild dogs

Dogsong. Paulsen, G.   **Fic**

Dōhaku's head. Kimmel, E. A.
In Kimmel, E. A. Sword of the samurai; adventure stories from Japan p5-10   **Fic**

Doherty, Berlie
Holly Starcross (7 and up)   **Fic**

Doherty, Charles
Far Eastern art
In International encyclopedia of art   **703**

Doherty, Kieran
Marjory Stoneman Douglas (7 and up)   **92**
Ranchers, homesteaders, and traders   **920**
To conquer is to live: the life of Captain John Smith of Jamestown   **92**
William Bradford   **92**

The **doi** store monkey. Salisbury, G.
In Salisbury, G. Island boyz: short stories p165-95   **S C**

Dolan, Edward F., 1924-
America in the Korean War (7 and up)   **951.9**
The American Civil War   **973.7**
The American Indian wars   **970.004**
The Irish potato famine   **941.5**
The Spanish-American War   **973.8**

Dolan, Sean
Bob Marley   **92**
Junípero Serra   **92**

Dole, Patricia Pearl, 1927-
Children's books about religion   **016.2**

Doll, Carol Ann
Managing and analyzing your collection   **025.2**

The **doll.** Chesnutt, C. W.
In The Boy of Chancellorville and other Civil War stories p112-26   **S C**

Doll baby. Bunting, E.   **Fic**

Dolphins
Carwardine, M. Whales, dolphins, and porpoises (7 and up)   **599.5**
Cerullo, M. M. Dolphins   **599.5**
Greenberg, D. A. Dolphins   **599.5**
Montgomery, S. Encantado (4 and up)   **599.5**
Fiction
L'Engle, M. A ring of endless light (5 and up)   **Fic**

Domestic animals
  See also Pets
See/See also pages in the following book(s):
Zeaman, J. Birds   **636.5**

Domestic architecture
  See also House construction

Domestic violence
  See also Child abuse; Wife abuse
Battered women   **362.82**
Domestic violence: opposing viewpoints   **362.82**
Family violence (7 and up)   **362.82**
Pledge, D. S. When something feels wrong (7 and up)   **362.7**
Fiction
Conly, J. L. What happened on Planet Kid   **Fic**
Hahn, M. D. Following my own footsteps (5 and up)   **Fic**
Koertge, R. Margaux with an X (7 and up)   **Fic**
Oates, J. C. Freaky green eyes (7 and up)   **Fic**

Domestic violence: opposing viewpoints   **362.82**

Domingo, Placido
About
Stefoff, R. Plácido Domingo   **92**

Dominican Americans
Fiction
Alvarez, J. How Tia Lola came to visit/stay (4 and up)   **Fic**

Dominican Republic
    Fiction
    Alvarez, J. Before we were free (7 and up)
           Fic
    Joseph, L. The color of my words (5 and up)
           Fic

Dommermuth-Costa, Carol
    Emily Dickinson   **92**

Don José of La Mancha. Ortiz Cofer, J.
    In Ortiz Cofer, J. An island like you; stories
        of the barrio p92-106   **S C**

Doña Sebastiana. Anaya, R. A.
    In Anaya, R. A. My land sings; stories from
        the Rio Grande p71-83   **S C**

Donelson, Kenneth L.
    Literature for today's young adults   **028.5**

Doney, Meryl
    Festivals   **745.5**
    Masks   **745.59**
    Puppets   **745.592**

Donham, Jean
    Enhancing teaching and learning   **027.8**

Donnellan, William Lorne, 1925-
    The miracle of immunity   **616.07**

Donnelly, Karen J.
    Cruzan v. Missouri   **344**

Donnelly, Matt, 1972-
    Theodore Roosevelt: larger than life (7 and up)
           92

Donner party
    Calabro, M. The perilous journey of the Donner
        Party (5 and up)   **978**
    Lavender, D. S. Snowbound (4 and up)   **978**
    Fiction
    Philbrick, W. R. The journal of Douglas Allen
        Deeds   **Fic**

Donoghue, Emma, 1969-
    Necessary noise
    In Necessary noise: stories about our families
        as they really are p51-67   **S C**

Donoughue, Carol, 1935-
    The mystery of the hieroglyphs (4 and up)
           493

Don't be disrespecting me. Flake, S. G.
    In Flake, S. G. Who am I without him?; short
        stories about girls and the boys in their
        lives p70-89   **S C**

Don't cramp my style (7 and up)   **S C**
Don't hold me back. Rembert, W.   **92**
Don't look behind you. Duncan, L.   **Fic**
Don't sweat it!. Crump, M.   **613**
Don't tell anyone. Kehret, P.   **Fic**
Don't tell the girls. Giff, P. R.   **92**
Don't you know there's a war on? Avi   **Fic**
Donuthead. Stauffacher, S.   **Fic**

Doolittle, Michael J.
    (il) Goodman, S. Ultimate field trip 4: a week
        in the 1800s   **973.5**
    (il) Goodman, S. Ultimate field trip 5
           629.45

The door in the hedge. McKinley, R.   **S C**

Dorfman, Elsa, 1937-
    See/See also pages in the following book(s):
    Sills, L. In real life: six women photographers
        (7 and up)   **920**

Dorjee, Yeshi *See* Yeshi Dorjee

Dorling Kindersley children's illustrated encyclopedia

The Dorling Kindersley science encyclopedia. See
    The DK science encyclopedia   **503**

Dorling Kindersley ultimate visual dictionary of science. See Ultimate visual dictionary of science   **503**

Dorling Kindersley visual dictionaries [series]
    Stanchak, J. E. The visual dictionary of the Civil War   **973.7**

Dornfeld, Margaret
    Maine
    In Celebrate the states   **973**

Dorris, Michael
    Guests   **Fic**
    Morning Girl (4 and up)   **Fic**
    Queen of diamonds
    In Talking leaves; contemporary native
        American short stories   **S C**
    Sees Behind Trees (4 and up)   **Fic**

The double dare. San Souci, R.
    In San Souci, R. Dare to be scared; thirteen
        stories to chill and thrill   **S C**

Double-dare to be scared: another thirteen chilling tales. San Souci, R.   **S C**
Double dutch. Chambers, V.   **796.2**
Double Dutch. Draper, S. M.   **Fic**
Double helix. Werlin, N.   **Fic**

The Dough prince
    In Hearne, B. G. Beauties and beasts p151-53
           398.2

Dougherty, Karla
    The rules to be cool (7 and up)   **395**

Douglas, Ann, 1942-
    The family tree detective   **929**

Douglas, H. Ford, 1831-1865
    See/See also pages in the following book(s):
    Katz, W. L. Black pioneers   **920**

Douglas, Marjory Stoneman
    About
    Doherty, K. Marjory Stoneman Douglas (7 and up)   **92**

Douglas, Paul
    Tennis (7 and up)   **796.342**

Douglas, Stephen Arnold, 1813-1861
    About
    January, B. The Lincoln-Douglas debates
           973.7

Douglass, Frederick, 1817?-1895
    Escape from slavery   **92**
    About
    Yancey, D. Frederick Douglass   **92**
    See/See also pages in the following book(s):
    Cloud Tapper, S. Voices from slavery's past (7
        and up)   **326**
    Dubovoy, S. Civil rights leaders (7 and up)
           920

Douglass, Jackie Leatherbury
Peterson first guide to shells of North America
594

Douglass, John
(il) Douglass, J. L. Peterson first guide to shells of North America **594**
(il) Robins, C. R. A field guide to Atlantic coast fishes of North America **597**

Dove song. Franklin, K. L. **Fic**

Doves See Pigeons

Dovey Coe. Dowell, F. O. **Fic**

Dowdle, Mary
(il) Friedman, L. Break a leg! **792**

Dowell, Frances O'Roark
Chicken boy (4 and up) **Fic**
Dovey Coe (5 and up) **Fic**
The secret language of girls (5 and up) **Fic**
Where I'd like to be (4 and up) **Fic**

Down Garrapata road. Estevis, A. **S C**

Down syndrome
Girod, C. M. Down syndrome **616.85**
Tocci, S. Down syndrome (7 and up)
616.85

Fiction
Wood, J. R. The man who loved clowns
Fic

Down the rabbit hole. Abrahams, P. **Fic**

Downer, Ann, 1960-
Hatching magic (4 and up) **Fic**

Downing, David, 1946-
Africa **960**
Apartheid in South Africa **968**
Conflict: India vs. Pakistan **954**

Downriver. Hobbs, W. **Fic**

Downsiders. Shusterman, N. **Fic**

Dowswell, Paul
Genetics (7 and up) **660.6**

Doyle, Sir Arthur Conan, 1859-1930
Adventures of Sherlock Holmes
In Doyle, Sir A. C. The complete Sherlock Holmes **S C**
The case book of Sherlock Holmes
In Doyle, Sir A. C. The complete Sherlock Holmes **S C**
The complete Sherlock Holmes (7 and up)
S C
His last bow
In Doyle, Sir A. C. The complete Sherlock Holmes **S C**
The hound of the Baskervilles
In Doyle, Sir A. C. The complete Sherlock Holmes **S C**
Memoirs of Sherlock Holmes
In Doyle, Sir A. C. The complete Sherlock Holmes **S C**
The return of Sherlock Holmes
In Doyle, Sir A. C. The complete Sherlock Holmes **S C**
The sign of four
In Doyle, Sir A. C. The complete Sherlock Holmes **S C**
A study in scarlet
In Doyle, Sir A. C. The complete Sherlock Holmes **S C**

The valley of fear
In Doyle, Sir A. C. The complete Sherlock Holmes **S C**
About
Pascal, J. B. Arthur Conan Doyle (7 and up)
92

Doyle, Brian
Boy O'Boy **Fic**

Doyle, Conan See Doyle, Sir Arthur Conan, 1859-1930

Doyle, Debra
Uncle Joshua and the Grogglemen
In New skies: an anthology of today's science fiction **S C**

Doyle, Eugenie F.
Stray voltage **Fic**

Doyle, Malachy
Who is Jesse Flood? **Fic**

Dr. Art's guide to planet earth. Sussman, A.
577

Dr. Jekyll and Mr. Hyde. Stevenson, R. L.
Fic

Dr. Jekyll and Sister Hyde. Sones, S.
In Necessary noise: stories about our families as they really are p173-216 **S C**

Dr. Jenner and the speckled monster. Marrin, A.
614.5

Dr. Seuss See Seuss, Dr.

Dr. Shinichi Suzuki. Collins, D. R. **92**

Draanen, Wendelin van
Flipped (6 and up) **Fic**
Sammy Keyes and the hotel thief (4 and up)
Fic

Draft resisters
See also Conscientious objectors

Dragisic, Patricia
How to write a letter (7 and up) **808**

The **dragon** and the enchanted filly. Calvino, I.
In The Book of dragons p1-9 **S C**

The **dragon** at the well. Bateman, T.
In Fire and wings: dragon tales from East and West p1-14 **S C**

Dragon bones and dinosaur eggs: a photobiography of Roy Chapman Andrews. Bausum, A. **92**

A **dragon** in the sky. Marstall, B. **595.7**

Dragon keeper. Wilkinson, C. **Fic**

Dragon rider. Funke, C. C. **Fic**

The **dragon** tamers. Nesbit, E.
In The Book of dragons p128-46 **S C**

Dragonflies
Marstall, B. A dragon in the sky (4 and up)
595.7

Dragons
Drake, E. Dr. Ernest Drake's Dragonology
398
See/See also pages in the following book(s):
Nigg, J. Wonder beasts (7 and up) **398**
Fiction
The Book of dragons **S C**
Downer, A. Hatching magic (4 and up) **Fic**

Dragons—Fiction—*Continued*
Fire and wings: dragon tales from East and West (4 and up)   **S C**
Fletcher, S. Dragon's milk (7 and up)   **Fic**
Jordan, S. The hunting of the last dragon   **Fic**
Paolini, C. Eragon (7 and up)   **Fic**
Stewart, J. J. If that breathes fire, we're toast!   **Fic**
Wilkinson, C. Dragon keeper (5 and up)   **Fic**
Wrede, P. C. Dealing with dragons (6 and up)   **Fic**
Zinnen, L. The dragons of Spratt, Ohio (5 and up)   **Fic**
Dragon's coo. MacLachlan, P.
In Fire and wings: dragon tales from East and West p25-31   **S C**
Dragon's gate. Yep, L.   **Fic**
Dragon's milk. Fletcher, S.   **Fic**
The **dragons** of Spratt, Ohio. Zinnen, L.   **Fic**
The **dragon's** son. Thomson, S. L.   **Fic**
Dragonwings. Yep, L.   **Fic**
Drake, Ernest
Dr. Ernest Drake's Dragonology   **398**
Drake, Sir Francis, 1540?-1596
About
Rice, E. Sir Francis Drake, navigator and pirate   **92**
See/See also pages in the following book(s):
Wren, L. L. Pirates and privateers of the high seas p11-17   **920**
Fiction
Cadnum, M. Ship of fire (7 and up)   **Fic**
Drama
See also English drama
Collections
Great scenes for young actors from the stage   **808.82**
Theatre for young audiences   **812.008**
Indexes
Karp, R. S. Plays for children and young adults   **808.82**
Drama in education
Gustafson, C. Acting out   **812**
Drama of American history [series]
Collier, C. The American Revolution, 1763-1783   **973.3**
Collier, C. Andrew Jackson's America, 1824-1850   **973.5**
Collier, C. Building a new nation   **973.4**
Collier, C. A century of immigration, 1820-1924   **325.73**
Collier, C. The changing face of American society: 1945-2000   **973.92**
Collier, C. The Civil War, 1860-1865   **973.7**
Collier, C. Clash of cultures, prehistory-1638   **970.004**
Collier, C. Creating the Constitution, 1787   **342**
Collier, C. The French and Indian War, 1660-1763   **973.2**
Collier, C. Hispanic America, Texas, and the Mexican War, 1835-1850   **973.6**

Collier, C. Indians, cowboys, and farmers and the battle for the Great Plains, 1865-1910   **978**
Collier, C. The Jeffersonian Republicans, 1800-1823   **973.4**
Collier, C. The middle road: American politics, 1945-2000   **973.92**
Collier, C. The paradox of Jamestown, 1585-1700   **975.5**
Collier, C. Pilgrims and Puritans, 1620-1676   **974.4**
Collier, C. Progressivism, the Great Depression, and the New Deal, 1901 to 1941   **973.91**
Collier, C. Reconstruction and the rise of Jim Crow, 1864-1896   **973.8**
Collier, C. The rise of industry, 1860-1900   **973.8**
Collier, C. The rise of the cities, 1820-1920   **307.7**
Collier, C. Slavery and the coming of the Civil War, 1831-1861   **973.6**
Collier, C. The United States enters the world stage: from the Alaska Purchase through World War I, 1867-1919   **973.8**
Collier, C. The United States in the Cold War: 1945-1989   **327.73**
Collier, C. The United States in World War II: 1941-1945   **940.53**
Dramatists
Nardo, D. Great Elizabethan playwrights   **920**
Stanley, D. Bard of Avon: the story of William Shakespeare (4 and up)   **822.3**
Dramer, Kim
The Mekong River   **959.7**
Draper, Allison Stark
The assassination of Malcolm X   **92**
Draper, Sharon M., 1950-
The Battle of Jericho (7 and up)   **Fic**
Double Dutch   **Fic**
Forged by fire (7 and up)   **Fic**
Tears of a tiger (7 and up)   **Fic**
Draw 3-D. DuBosque, D.   **742**
[**Draw** 50 series]. Ames, L. J.   **743**
Draw insects. DuBosque, D.   **743**
Drawing
Ames, L. J. [Draw 50 series] (4 and up)   **743**
Ames, L. J. Drawing with Lee Ames   **741.2**
Artell, M. Cartooning for kids   **741.5**
Bohl, A. Guide to cartooning   **741.5**
DuBosque, D. Draw 3-D   **742**
DuBosque, D. Draw insects   **743**
Hart, C. How to draw comic book bad guys and gals   **741.5**
Hart, C. Mecha mania (5 and up)   **741.5**
Mayne, D. Drawing horses that look real!   **743**
See/See also pages in the following book(s):
Luxbacher, I. The jumbo book of art p8-57 (4 and up)   **702.8**
Technique
Hart, C. Christopher Hart's animation studio   **791.43**

Drawing horses that look real!. Mayne, D.
743

Drawing lessons. Mack, T.   Fic

Drawing the wind. Schwartz, H.
In Schwartz, H. The day the Rabbi disappeared: Jewish holiday tales of magic p15-29   398.2

Drawing with Lee Ames. Ames, L. J.   741.2

Dray wara yow dee. Kipling, R.
In McCaffrey, A. {The Pern series}   S C

The **dream**. Schwartz, A.
In Schwartz, A. Scary stories 3; more tales to chill your bones p53-54   398.2

Dream flier. Yep, L.
In Yep, L. The rainbow people p154-60
398.2

Dream freedom. Levitin, S.   Fic

A **dream** in the road. Storni, A.
In You're on!: seven plays in English and Spanish p100-07   812.008

Dream job. Sharmat, M. W.
In Visions: nineteen short stories by outstanding writers for young adults p23-29
S C

The **dream** keeper and other poems. Hughes, L.
811

A **dream** of freedom. McWhorter, D.   323.1

The **dream** of the Rabbi's daughter. Schwartz, H.
In Schwartz, H. The day the Rabbi disappeared: Jewish holiday tales of magic p60-63   398.2

Dream soul. Yep, L.   Fic

Dream-weaver. Lawrence, L.   Fic

Dreaming in black and white. Jung, R.   Fic

Dreamland. Dessen, S.   Fic

Dreams in the golden country. Lasky, K.   Fic

The **Dred** Scott decision. January, B.   342

Dress *See* Clothing and dress

Dress codes
Cruz, B. School dress codes   371.8

Dressed for the occasion. Miller, B. M.   391

Dresselhaus, Mildred S., 1930-
See/See also pages in the following book(s):
Lindop, L. Scientists and doctors (7 and up)
920

Drew, Bernard A. (Bernard Alger), 1950-
The 100 most popular young adult authors
810.9

Drew, Charles
          About
Schraff, A. E. Dr. Charles Drew   92

Drew, Naomi
The kids' guide to working out conflicts
303.6

Dreyer, Ann L.
After Elaine   Fic

Drez, Ronald J.
Remember D-day (5 and up)   940.54

Drinking of alcoholic beverages
Gottfried, T. The facts about alcohol
362.292

Drinking problem *See* Alcoholism

The **dripping** cutlass. Olson, A. N.
In Olson, A. N. and Schwartz, H. Ask the bones: scary stories from around the world p92-98   398.2

Driscoll, Jean, 1966-
See/See also pages in the following book(s):
Kaminsky, M. Uncommon champions   920

The **drive**. Hearne, B. G.
In Hearne, B. G. The canine connection: stories about dogs and people p40-50
S C

Driven from the land. Meltzer, M.   978

Drivers, Automobile *See* Automobile drivers

Drohan, Michele Ingber
Weight-loss programs (7 and up)   616.85
(jt. auth) Levchuck, C. M. Healthy living
613

Drop by drop. Vande Velde, V.
In Vande Velde, V. Being dead; stories
S C

Drop dead. Vande Velde, V.
In Vande Velde, V. Being dead; stories
S C

Drop Star. San Souci, R.
In San Souci, R. Cut from the same cloth; American women of myth, legend, and tall tale p21-26   398.2

Droughts
Allaby, M. Droughts (7 and up)   551.57
Cooper, M. L. Dust to eat (4 and up)
973.917

Drug abuse
Addiction: opposing viewpoints   362.29
Banfield, S. Inside recovery   616.86
Barter, J. Hallucinogens (7 and up)   362.29
Bridgers, J. Everything you need to know about having an addictive personality (7 and up)
616.86
Chemical dependency: opposing viewpoints (7 and up)   362.29
Clayton, L. Diet pill drug dangers   616.3
Drug abuse: opposing viewpoints (7 and up)
362.29
Goodwin, W. Marijuana (7 and up)   362.29
Hyde, M. O. Mind drugs (7 and up)   616.86
Illegal drugs p106-57 (7 and up)   364.1
Papa, S. Addiction   616.86
Roza, G. The encyclopedia of drugs and alcohol
615
Shepherd, K. R. Drugs and low self-esteem (7 and up)   616.86
Sonder, B. All about heroin (7 and up)
362.29
Stewart, G. Drugs   362.29
The war on drugs   363.4
See/See also pages in the following book(s):
Blue, R. Staying out of trouble in a troubled family (7 and up)   362.7
Jukes, M. It's a girl thing (5 and up)
305.23

          Encyclopedias
Drugs, alcohol, and tobacco (7 and up)
362.29

Drug abuse—*Continued*
Fiction
Hinton, S. E. That was then, this is now (7 and up)   **Fic**

Mathis, S. B. Teacup full of roses (7 and up)   **Fic**

Murray, J. Bottled up (7 and up)   **Fic**

Myers, W. D. The Beast (7 and up)   **Fic**
Testing
See Drug testing

Drug abuse: opposing viewpoints (7 and up)
    362.29

Drug abuse prevention library [series]
Banfield, S. Inside recovery   **616.86**
Beal, E. Ritalin   **616.85**
Gordon, M. A. Drug interactions   **615**
Shepherd, K. R. Drugs and low self-esteem
    616.86

Drug dangers [series]
Clayton, L. Diet pill drug dangers   **616.3**

Drug education library [series]
Barter, J. Hallucinogens   **362.29**
Goodwin, W. Marijuana   **362.29**

Drug interactions. Gordon, M. A.   **615**

Drug plants *See* Medical botany

Drug testing
Newton, D. E. Drug testing (7 and up)
    363.4
Government policy
See/See also pages in the following book(s):
Illegal drugs p106-57 (7 and up)   **364.1**

Drug therapy
See also Pharmacology

The **drug** trade. Fooks, L.   **364.1**

Drug traffic
Fooks, L. The drug trade   **364.1**
See/See also pages in the following book(s):
The war on drugs   **363.4**
Fiction
DeFelice, C. C. Death at Devil's Bridge (5 and up)   **Fic**

Drugs
See also Pharmacology
Day, N. Killer superbugs (7 and up)   **616**
Facklam, M. Modern medicines (7 and up)
    615
Gordon, M. A. Drug interactions   **615**
Hyde, M. O. Mind drugs (7 and up)   **616.86**
Roza, G. The encyclopedia of drugs and alcohol
    615
Adulteration and analysis
See Pharmacology
Law and legislation
Ruschmann, P. Legalizing marijuana (7 and up)
    345
See/See also pages in the following book(s):
Illegal drugs p106-57 (7 and up)   **364.1**
The war on drugs   **363.4**

Drugs. Stewart, G.   **362.29**

Drugs [series]
Gottfried, T. The facts about alcohol
    362.292

Gottfried, T. The facts about marijuana
    362.29
LeVert, S. The facts about ecstasy   **362.29**
LeVert, S. The facts about steroids   **362.29**
Menhard, F. R. The facts about inhalants
    362.29

Drugs, alcohol, and tobacco (7 and up)
    362.29

Drugs and crime
Fooks, L. The drug trade   **364.1**

Drugs and low self-esteem. Shepherd, K. R.
    616.86

Drugs and sports (7 and up)   **362.29**

Druids and Druidism
Fiction
Farmer, N. The Sea of Trolls (5 and up)
    Fic

Drummers of Jericho. Meyer, C.   **Fic**

Drummond, Karen Eich
(jt. auth) D'Amico, J. The healthy body cookbook   **641.5**
(jt. auth) D'Amico, J. The United States cookbook   **641.5**

The **drums** of the fore and aft. Kipling, R.
In McCaffrey, A. {The Pern series}   **S C**

Du Bois, W. E. B. (William Edward Burghardt), 1868-1963
About
Troy, D. W.E.B. DuBois   **92**

Du Bois, William Edward Burghardt *See* Du
Bois, W. E. B. (William Edward Burghardt),
1868-1963

Du Châtelet, Gabrielle Emilie Le Tonnelier de Breteuil, marquise, 1706-1749
See/See also pages in the following book(s):
Celebrating women in mathematics and science
    920

Du Châtelet-Lomont, Gabrielle Emilie Le Tonnelier de Breteuil *See* Du Châtelet,
Gabrielle Emilie Le Tonnelier de Breteuil,
marquise, 1706-1749

Du Guesclin, Bertrand, comte de Longueville, ca. 1320-1380
See/See also pages in the following book(s):
Zohorsky, J. R. Medieval knights and warriors
p26-37   **940.1**

Duane, Diane, 1952-
Midnight snack
In Sixteen; short stories by outstanding writ-
ers for young adults p22-30   **S C**

DuBois, Jill, 1952-
Colombia (5 and up)   **986.1**
Greece (5 and up)   **949.5**
Israel (5 and up)   **956.94**
Korea (5 and up)   **951.9**

DuBosque, Doug
Draw 3-D   **742**
Draw insects   **743**

Dubovoy, Sina
Civil rights leaders (7 and up)   **920**

Duden, Jane
Vegetarianism for teens   **613.2**

Duder, Tessa, 1940-
Sea changes
In Ultimate sports; short stories by outstanding writers for young adults p252-72
S C

Dudley, Mark E.
Engel v. Vitale (1962) (7 and up)   **344**

Dudley, William, 1964-
(ed) American slavery. See American slavery
326
(ed) Asian Americans: opposing viewpoints. See Asian Americans: opposing viewpoints
305.8
(ed) Drugs and sports. See Drugs and sports
362.29
(ed) Endangered oceans: opposing viewpoints. See Endangered oceans: opposing viewpoints
577.7
(ed) Illegal immigration: opposing viewpoints. See Illegal immigration: opposing viewpoints
325.73
(ed) The Industrial revolution: opposing viewpoints. See The Industrial revolution: opposing viewpoints   **330.973**
(ed) Japanese American internment camps. See Japanese American internment camps
940.53
(ed) Mass media: opposing viewpoints. See Mass media: opposing viewpoints   **302.23**
(ed) Native Americans: opposing viewpoints. See Native Americans: opposing viewpoints
970.004
(ed) Pregnancy. See Pregnancy   **362.7**
(ed) Religion in America: opposing viewpoints. See Religion in America: opposing viewpoints
200.9
(ed) Russia today: opposing viewpoints. See Russia today: opposing viewpoints
947.086

Due, Linnea A., 1948-
Cream puff
In Girls got game; sports stories and poems
810.8

Duffy, Carol Ann
(ed) I wouldn't thank you for a valentine. See I wouldn't thank you for a valentine
808.81

Duffy, Trent
The clock (4 and up)   **681.1**

Duffy and Lady. Tchana, K. H.
In Tchana, K. H. The serpent slayer: and other stories of strong women p71-76
398.2

Duffy and the Bucca. Climo, S.
In Climo, S. Magic & mischief; tales from Cornwall p111-22   **398.2**

Duffy and the devil. Philip, N.
In Philip, N. Celtic fairy tales p78-85
398.2

Dugdale, John, 1960-
(il) Thoreau, H. D. New suns will arise   **92**

Duggleby, John
Story painter: the life of Jacob Lawrence (4 and up)
92

Duke Ellington: giant of jazz. Old, W.   **92**

Dulcinea. Anaya, R. A.
In Anaya, R. A. My land sings; stories from the Rio Grande p39-53   S C

Dull Knife, Cheyenne Chief, ca. 1828-1879 or 1883
See/See also pages in the following book(s):
Ehrlich, A. Wounded Knee: an Indian history of the American West (6 and up)   **970.004**

Dumas, Alexandre, 1802-1870
The three musketeers (7 and up)   **Fic**

Dumas, Nancy Lagow
(jt. auth) McGowan, E. N. Stock market smart
332.6

Dunbar, Paul Laurence, 1872-1906
About
Reef, C. Paul Laurence Dunbar   **92**

Duncan, Isadora, 1878-1927
About
O'Connor, B. Barefoot dancer: the story of Isadora Duncan   **92**

Duncan, Lois, 1934-
Don't look behind you   **Fic**
I know what you did last summer   **Fic**
Killing Mr. Griffin (7 and up)   **Fic**
Locked in time (7 and up)   **Fic**
Stranger with my face (7 and up)   **Fic**
(ed) Night terrors. See Night terrors   S C
(ed) On the edge: stories at the brink. See On the edge: stories at the brink   S C

Dungeon Vol. 1: Duck Heart. Sfar, J.   **741.5**

Dunk. Lubar, D.   **Fic**

Dunkle, Clare B.
The hollow kingdom   **Fic**

Dunn, Carolyn, 1965-
Ali Anugne O Chash (The boy who was)
In The Green Man: tales from the mythic forest p299-309   **808.8**

Dunn, John M., 1949-
Advertising (7 and up)   **659.1**
The Enlightenment (7 and up)   **940.2**

Dunn-Georgiou, Elisha
Everything you need to know about organic foods (7 and up)   **641.3**

Dunning, Stephen
(comp) Reflections on a gift of watermelon pickle—and other modern verse. See Reflections on a gift of watermelon pickle—and other modern verse   **811.008**

Dunton-Downer, Leslie
Essential Shakespeare handbook   **822.3**

The **duplicate.** Sleator, W.   **Fic**

DuPrau, Jeanne, 1944-
The city of Ember (5 and up)   **Fic**
The people of Sparks (5 and up)   **Fic**

Durbin, William, 1951-
Blackwater Ben (5 and up)   **Fic**
The broken blade   **Fic**
The journal of C.J. Jackson: a Dust Bowl migrant (4 and up)   **Fic**
The journal of Otto Peltonen, a Finnish immigrant   **Fic**
The journal of Sean Sullivan (5 and up)   **Fic**
Wintering   **Fic**

Durden, Robert Franklin
Carter G. Woodson (7 and up) 92
Durham, Michael, 1952-
Painkillers and tranquilizers 615
Durrant, Lynda, 1956-
The beaded moccasins (5 and up) Fic
Echohawk Fic
Turtle clan journey Fic
Durrett, Deanne, 1940-
Unsung heroes of World War II (7 and up)
940.54
Dust. Slade, A. G. Fic
The **dust** bowl and the Depression in American
history. McArthur, D. 978
Dust storms
McArthur, D. The dust bowl and the Depression
in American history (7 and up) 978
Fiction
Hesse, K. Out of the dust (5 and up) Fic
Dust to dust. Flynn, N.
In Soul searching: thirteen stories about faith
and belief p177-202 S C
Dust to eat. Cooper, M. L. 973.917
Dutch artists *See* Artists, Dutch
DuTemple, Lesley A., 1952-
The Great Wall of China (5 and up) 931
The New York subways (5 and up) 388.4
North American cranes (4 and up) 598
The Panama Canal 972.87
The Pantheon (5 and up) 726
Seals and sea lions (7 and up) 599.79
The Taj Mahal 726
Dvořák, Antonín, 1841-1904
About
Horowitz, J. Dvořák in America (7 and up)
92
Dwyer, Christopher
Chile 983
Dwyer, James R.
Earth works 016.3637
Dyer, Daniel, 1944-
Jack London (7 and up) 92
Dyer, Jane
(il) Goss, G. Blue moon soup 641.8
Dyes and dyeing
Kassinger, R. Dyes: from sea snails to synthet-
ics 667
See/See also pages in the following book(s):
Knapp, B. J. Materials science 620.1
Dyes: from sea snails to synthetics. Kassinger, R.
667
Dygard, Thomas J., 1931-1996
Just once
In Ultimate sports; short stories by outstand-
ing writers for young adults p196-205
S C
River danger (7 and up) Fic
Second stringer (7 and up) Fic
"**Dymchurch** flit". Kipling, R.
In McCaffrey, A. {The Pern series} S C
Dynamic modern women [series]
Lindop, L. Scientists and doctors 920

Dyslexia
Landau, E. Dyslexia (5 and up) **616.85**
Wiltshire, P. Dyslexia (5 and up) **616.85**
Dyson, Marianne J.
Home on the moon (4 and up) **629.45**
Dzhugashvili, Iosif Vissarionovich *See* Stalin, Jo-
seph, 1879-1953

E

E.S.P. *See* Extrasensory perception
Eagle Cloud and Fawn. Murphy, B.
In Join in; multiethnic short stories by out-
standing writers for young adults p23-33
S C
Eagles
See also Bald eagle
Patent, D. H. Eagles of America (4 and up)
598
Warhol, T. Eagles 598
Fiction
Casanova, M. When eagles fall Fic
Eagles of America. Patent, D. H. 598
Ear
Silverstein, A. Hearing Silverstein, A. and oth-
ers. Senses and sensors [series] 612.8
Simon, S. Eyes and ears (4 and up) 612.8
The **Ear,** the Eye, and the Arm. Farmer, N.
Fic
Earling, Debra
The old marriage
In Talking leaves; contemporary native
American short stories S C
Earls, Irene
Young musicians in world history 920
Early civilizations (Prehistory to 300 C.E.)
In World history on file 909
Early humans. Gallant, R. A. 599.93
The **Early** Middle Ages (7 and up) 909.07
Early Sunday morning. Denenberg, B. Fic
An **early** winter. Bauer, M. D. Fic
Earth
Day, T. DK guide to savage Earth 550
Earth 550
Miller, R. Earth and the moon (5 and up)
525
Simon, S. Earth: our planet in space (4 and up)
525
Stefoff, R. Earth and the moon 550
Tabak, J. A look at earth 550
Internal structure
Gallant, R. A. Structure (5 and up) 551.1
Poetry
Singer, M. Footprints on the roof (4 and up)
811
Earth 550
Earth and the moon. Miller, R. 525
Earth and the moon. Stefoff, R. 550
Earth from above for young readers. Arthus-
Bertrand, Y. 779
The **earth** kitchen. Bryant, S. Fic

The **earth,** my butt, and other big, round things.
Mackler, C. **Fic**

Earth science on file **550**

Earth sciences
See also Geology
Campbell, A. The New York Public Library incredible Earth **550**
Earth science on file **550**
Earth sciences for students (7 and up) **550**
The Facts on File earth science handbook (7 and up) **550**
Knapp, B. J. Earth science **550**
Pentland, P. Earth science (4 and up) **550**
Redfern, M. The Kingfisher young people's book of planet earth **550**
Science smart **550**
VanCleave, J. P. Janice VanCleave's A+ projects in earth science (7 and up) **550**
Encyclopedias
The Environment encyclopedia (7 and up) **363.7**
Exploring earth and space science (7 and up) **550.3**

Earth sciences for students (7 and up) **550**

Earth watch [series]
Morgan, S. Waste disposal **628.4**

Earth works. Dwyer, J. R. **016.3637**

Earthenware *See* Pottery

An **earthly** knight. McNaughton, J. **Fic**

Earthquakes
Christian, S. Shake, rattle, and roll **551.2**
Grace, C. O. Forces of nature (4 and up) **551.2**
Reed, J. Earthquakes (4 and up) **551.2**
Silverstein, A. Plate tectonics (5 and up) **551.1**
Tanaka, S. Earthquake! (4 and up) **979.4**
Trueit, T. S. Earthquakes **551.2**
Walker, S. M. Earthquakes (3-6) **551.2**
See/See also pages in the following book(s):
Day, T. DK guide to savage Earth **550**
Fiction
Reiss, K. PaperQuake **Fic**

Earth's wild winds. Friend, S. **551.51**

Earthworks [series]
Gallant, R. A. Atmosphere **551.51**
Gallant, R. A. History **551.7**
Gallant, R. A. Plates **551.1**
Gallant, R. A. Resources **333.7**
Gallant, R. A. Structure **551.1**
Gallant, R. A. Water **553.7**

Earthworms. Pascoe, E. **592**

Eason, Alethea
The unicorns of Kabustan
In A Glory of unicorns p115-24 **S C**

East *See* Asia

East (Near East) *See* Middle East

East. Pattou, E. **Fic**

East Africa
History
Wilson, T. H. City states of the Swahili coast **967.6**

East Indians
Fiction
Clarke, J. Kalpana's dream **Fic**
Gilmore, R. A group of one **Fic**
United States—Fiction
Desai Hidier, T. Born confused (7 and up) **Fic**
Perkins, M. Monsoon summer (7 and up) **Fic**

East of the sun and west of the moon
In Hearne, B. G. Beauties and beasts p66-75 **398.2**

Easter
Poetry
Grimes, N. At Jerusalem's gate (5 and up) **811**

Easter Island
Arnold, C. Easter Island (5 and up) **996**
Pelta, K. Rediscovering Easter Island **996**

Eastern Africa *See* East Africa

Eastern Europe
Kort, M. The handbook of the new Eastern Europe (7 and up) **943**

The **Eastern** forest. Fielding, E. **577.3**

Eastman, Mary Huse, 1870-1963
Index to fairy tales. See Index to fairy tales **398.2**

Easton, Kelly, 1960-
The life history of a star (7 and up) **Fic**

Easy menu ethnic cookbooks [series] (5 and up) **641.5**

Eating customs
Solheim, J. It's disgusting—and we ate it! (4 and up) **641.3**

Eating disorders
See also Anorexia nervosa; Bulimia
Barrett, C. The dangers of diet drugs and other weight-loss products **615**
Davis, B. What's real, what's ideal (7 and up) **616.85**
Drohan, M. I. Weight-loss programs (7 and up) **616.85**
Eating disorders (7 and up) **616.85**
Eating disorders: opposing viewpoints (7 and up) **616.85**
Frankenberger, E. Food and love (7 and up) **616.85**
Frissell, S. Eating disorders and weight control (7 and up) **616.85**
The truth about eating disorders (7 and up) **616.85**
Vollstadt, E. W. Teen eating disorders (7 and up) **616.85**
Walker, P. Understanding the risk of diet drugs **616.85**
See/See also pages in the following book(s):
Gray, H. M. Real girl/real world (7 and up) **305.23**
Hinds, M. J. Focus on body image **306.4**
Schwager, T. The right moves (7 and up) **613.7**

Eating disorders (7 and up) **616.85**
Eating disorders and weight control. Frissell, S. **616.85**

Eating disorders: opposing viewpoints (7 and up)
616.85

Eating with trolls. Yolen, J.
In Yolen, J. Mightier than the sword; world
folktales for strong boys p28-35
398.2

Eavesdropping
MccGwire, S. Surveillance (7 and up)
323.44

Eberhardt, Thom
Rat boys **Fic**

Eblen, Ruth A.
(ed) The Environment encyclopedia. See The
Environment encyclopedia **363.7**

Eblen, William R.
(ed) The Environment encyclopedia. See The
Environment encyclopedia **363.7**

Eboch, Chris
Turkey (7 and up) **956.1**

Ebola virus
Willett, E. Ebola virus **616.9**

Eccentrics and eccentricities
Fiction
Tolan, S. S. Surviving the Applewhites **Fic**

Echohawk. Durrant, L. **Fic**

Eckert, John Presper, 1919-1995
See/See also pages in the following book(s):
Northrup, M. American computer pioneers
920

Ecology
See also Environmental protection types of
ecology
Allaby, M. Biomes of the world (5 and up)
577
Gardner, R. Science projects about the environ-
ment and ecology (7 and up) **363.7**
Guiberson, B. Z. Exotic species **577**
Kerrod, R. Facts on File wildlife atlas **578**
Snedden, R. The environment **577**
Sussman, A. Dr. Art's guide to planet earth
577
U.X.L encyclopedia of biomes (7 and up)
577.8
VanCleave, J. P. Janice Vancleave's ecology for
every kid (4 and up) **577**
See/See also pages in the following book(s):
Patent, D. H. Biodiversity (5 and up)
333.95
Dictionaries
The Dictionary of the environment and its
biomes **577**
Encyclopedias
The Environment encyclopedia (7 and up)
363.7

Ecology crafts for kids. Needham, B. **745.5**

Economists
Bussing-Burks, M. Influential economists (7 and
up) **920**

Ecosystem [series]
Allaby, M. Deserts **577.5**
Allaby, M. Temperate forests **577.3**
Day, T. Oceans **551.46**

Ecosystems of North America [series]
Fielding, E. The Eastern forest **577.3**

Katz, S. The Great Lakes **577.6**
Mudd-Ruth, M. The deserts of the Southwest
577.5
Ormsby, A. The prairie **577.4**

Ecstasy (Drug)
LeVert, S. The facts about ecstasy **362.29**

Eddy, Mary Baker, 1821-1910
About
Williams, J. K. The Christian Scientists (7 and
up) **289.5**

Edelman, Marian Wright, 1939-
About
Old, W. Marian Wright Edelman (7 and up)
92
See/See also pages in the following book(s):
Hansen, J. Women of hope (4 and up) **920**

Edelson, Edward
The immune system **616.07**

Edelson, Edward, 1932-
Gregor Mendel, and the roots of genetics (7 and
up) **92**
James Watson and Francis Crick and the building blocks of life (7 and up) **92**

Edelson, Paula
Straight talk about teenage pregnancy (7 and up)
362.7
(jt. auth) Presma, F. Straight talk about today's
families **306.8**

Edgar, Kathleen J.
Everything you need to know about media violence **303.6**

Edgar Allan Poe: a biography. Meltzer, M. **92**

Edgar Allan Poe's tales of mystery and madness.
Poe, E. A. **S C**

Edge, Laura Bufano, 1953-
Andrew Carnegie

Edge, Rosalie
See/See also pages in the following book(s):
Byrnes, P. Environmental pioneers (7 and up)
920

Edge. Cadnum, M. **Fic**

The **edge** of the sea. Carson, R. **577.7**

The **edge** on the sword. Tingle, R. **Fic**

Edison, Thomas A. (Thomas Alva), 1847-1931
About
Delano, M. F. Inventing the future: a
photobiography of Thomas Alva Edison
92
Mason, P. Thomas A. Edison **92**
Sproule, A. Thomas A. Edison **92**
Tagliaferro, L. Thomas Edison (7 and up)
92

Edith Shay. LaFaye, A. **Fic**

Edmo, Ed
After Celilo
In Talking leaves; contemporary native
American short stories **S C**

Edmonds, Marie
About
Grace, C. O. Forces of nature (4 and up)
551.2

Edmonds, S. Emma E. (Sarah Emma Evelyn), 1841-1898
See/See also pages in the following book(s):
Caravantes, P. Petticoat spies   **920**

Edmonds, Sarah Emma Evelyn *See* Edmonds, S. Emma E. (Sarah Emma Evelyn), 1841-1898

Edmondson, Belle, 1840-1873
See/See also pages in the following book(s):
Caravantes, P. Petticoat spies   **920**

Edmondson, J. R., 1950-
Jim Bowie   **92**

Edmonston, Louis-Philippe
Car smarts   **629.222**

Edney, A. T. B.
ASPCA complete cat care manual   **636.8**

Education
    See also Internet in education; Schools
See/See also pages in the following book(s):
The information revolution   **303.4**
    Government policy
Hester, J. P. Public school safety   **371.7**
    History
Woolf, A. Education (5 and up)   **940.1**
    Social aspects
Stanley, J. Children of the Dust Bowl (5 and up)   **371.9**
    Developing countries
Fridell, R. Education for all   **370**
    United States—Directories
The Handbook of private schools   **370.25**
    United States—History
Loeper, J. J. Going to school in 1776 (4 and up)   **370.9**

Education, Bilingual *See* Bilingual education

Education, Segregation in *See* Segregation in education

Education for all. Fridell, R.   **370**

Educational counseling
    See also Vocational guidance

Educational media centers *See* Instructional materials centers

Educational tests and measurements
Terkel, M. What's an "A" anyway? (7 and up)   **371.2**

Educators
    See also African American educators

Edward VI, King of England, 1537-1553
    Fiction
Twain, M. The prince and the pauper   **Fic**

Edwards, Barbara
(jt. auth) Haycock, K. Neal-Schuman authoritative guide to kids' search engines, subject directories, and portals   **025.04**

Edwards, Judith
Abolitionists and slave resistance (7 and up)   **326**
Henry Hudson and his voyages of exploration in world history (7 and up)   **92**
Jamestown, John Smith, and Pocahontas in American history (7 and up)   **975.5**
The Plymouth Colony and the Pilgrim adventure in American history (7 and up)   **974.4**

Edwards, Kirsten, 1965-
Teen library events   **027.62**
(jt. auth) Jones, P. A core collection for young adults   **011.6**

The **eel's** disguise. Yep, L.
In Yep, L. The rainbow people p38-44   **398.2**

Efaw, Amy
Battle dress (7 and up)   **Fic**

Egendorf, Laura K., 1973-
(ed) Africa: opposing viewpoints. See Africa: opposing viewpoints   **960**
(ed) Conserving the environment. See Conserving the environment   **333.72**
(ed) The environment: opposing viewpoints. See The environment: opposing viewpoints   **363.7**
(ed) Guns and violence. See Guns and violence [Current controversies]   **363.33**
(ed) Human rights: opposing viewpoints. See Human rights: opposing viewpoints   **323**
(ed) The information revolution. See The information revolution   **303.4**
(ed) The McCarthy hearings. See The McCarthy hearings   **973.921**
(ed) Mental illness: opposing viewpoints. See Mental illness: opposing viewpoints   **362.2**
(ed) Poverty: opposing viewpoints. See Poverty: opposing viewpoints   **362.5**
(ed) Teen alcoholism. See Teen alcoholism   **362.292**
(ed) Teens at risk: opposing viewpoints. See Teens at risk: opposing viewpoints   **362.7**
(ed) Terrorism: opposing viewpoints. See Terrorism: opposing viewpoints   **363.32**
(ed) Violence: opposing viewpoints. See Violence: opposing viewpoints   **303.6**

Egielski, Richard
See/See also pages in the following book(s):
The Newbery & Caldecott medal books, 1986-2000   **028.5**

Eglė, Queen of Serpents
In Hearne, B. G. Beauties and beasts p124-28   **398.2**

Ego-tripping and other poems for young people. Giovanni, N.   **811**

Egypt
Kallen, S. A. Egypt (7 and up)   **962**
Pateman, R. Egypt (5 and up)   **962**
Wilkens, F. Egypt   **962**
Zuehlke, J. Egypt in pictures (5 and up)   **962**
    Antiquities
Berger, M. Mummies of the pharaohs   **932**
Giblin, J. Secrets of the Sphinx (4 and up)   **932**
Green, R. Tutankhamun   **932**
Harris, G. Ancient Egypt (5 and up)   **932**
Hart, G. Ancient Egypt (4 and up)   **932**
Hawass, Z. A. Curse of the pharaohs (5 and up)   **932**
Millard, A. Pyramids   **909**
Perl, L. Mummies, tombs, and treasure (4 and up)   **393**

Egypt—Antiquities—*Continued*
Smith, S. T. Valley of the Kings (4 and up)
932

Antiquities—Encyclopedias
Netzley, P. D. The Greenhaven encyclopedia of ancient Egypt **932**

Biography
Baker, R. F. Ancient Egyptians (7 and up)
932

Civilization
Baker, R. F. Ancient Egyptians (7 and up)
932
Crosher, J. Technology in the time of ancient Egypt **609**
Giblin, J. Secrets of the Sphinx (4 and up)
932
Harris, G. Ancient Egypt (5 and up) **932**
Hart, G. Ancient Egypt (4 and up) **932**
Haynes, J. Egyptian dynasties **932**
Macaulay, D. Pyramid (4 and up) **726**
Nardo, D. Ancient Alexandria (7 and up)
932
Nardo, D. Ancient Egypt (7 and up) **932**
Pemberton, D. Egyptian mummies (4 and up)
393
Perl, L. The ancient Egyptians (5 and up)
932
Pickels, D. E. Egyptian kings and queens and classical deities **930**
Steedman, S. The Egyptian news **932**
Tanaka, S. Secrets of the mummies (4 and up)
393
Trumble, K. The Library of Alexandria (5 and up) **027**

History
Brooks, P. S. Cleopatra (7 and up) **92**
Cleopatra [biographical essays] (7 and up)
92
Morgan, J. Cleopatra **92**
Stanley, D. Cleopatra (4 and up) **92**

Egypt in pictures. Zuehlke, J. **962**

Egyptian dynasties. Haynes, J. **932**

Egyptian kings and queens and classical deities. Pickels, D. E. **930**

Egyptian language
Donoughue, C. The mystery of the hieroglyphs (4 and up) **493**
Giblin, J. The riddle of the Rosetta Stone (5 and up) **493**

Egyptian mummies. Pemberton, D. **393**

Egyptian mythology
Remler, P. Egyptian mythology A to Z (7 and up) **299**

The **Egyptian** news. Steedman, S. **932**

Ehrenhaft, Daniel
Larry Ellison **92**
Marc Andreessen **92**

Ehrlich, Amy, 1942-
Wounded Knee: an Indian history of the American West (6 and up) **970.004**

Ehrlich, Gretel
A blizzard year **Fic**

Eiffel, Alexandre Gustave, 1832-1923
See/See also pages in the following book(s):
Aaseng, N. Construction: building the impossible **624**

Eight hundred. See George, L. S. 800 **909.07**

Eight hundred eighty-two and a half amazing answers to your questions about the Titanic. See Brewster, H. 882 ½ amazing answers to your questions about the Titanic **910.4**

Eight seconds. Ferris, J. **Fic**

Eighteen hundred. See Ashby, R. 1800 **909.8**

Eighteenth century *See* World history—18th century

Einfeld, Jann
Life in the Australian Outback **994**

Einstein, Albert, 1879-1955
About
Albert Einstein [essays about] **92**
Bernstein, J. Albert Einstein and the frontiers of physics (7 and up) **92**
Delano, M. F. Genius [biography of Albert Einstein] (5 and up) **92**
Macdonald, F. Albert Einstein **92**
MacLeod, E. Albert Einstein (4 and up) **92**
Sullivan, A. M. Albert Einstein (4 and up)
92

Eisenhower, Dwight D. (Dwight David), 1890-1969
About
Young, J. C. Dwight D. Eisenhower **92**
See/See also pages in the following book(s):
Ross, S. Leaders of World War II **920**

Eisenpreis, Bettijane
Coping with scoliosis (7 and up) **616.7**

Eisenreich, Jim
See/See also pages in the following book(s):
Kaminsky, M. Uncommon champions **920**

El **Dorado**. Delacre, L.
In Delacre, L. Golden tales; myths, legends, and folktales from Latin America p47-51
398.2

El-Hamamsy, Salwa
(jt. auth) Pateman, R. Egypt **962**

El-hi textbooks and serials in print **016.3713**

El Niño Current
Arnold, C. El Niño (4 and up) **551.6**

El-Shabazz, El-Hajj Malik *See* Malcolm X, 1925-1965

Elder brother. Pierce, T.
In Half-human p65-93 **S C**

Elderly
See also Old age

Eleanor, of Aquitaine, Queen, consort of Henry II, King of England, 1122?-1204
See/See also pages in the following book(s):
Hewitt, K. Lives of extraordinary women (4 and up) **920**
Meltzer, M. Ten queens (5 and up) **920**
Fiction
Gregory, K. Eleanor: crown jewel of Aquitaine
Fic
Konigsburg, E. L. A proud taste for scarlet and miniver (5 and up) **Fic**

Eleanor: crown jewel of Aquitaine. Gregory, K.
Fic

Eleanor's colonel. Watson, A. R.
In The Boy of Chancellorville and other Civil
War stories p95-102 **S C**

The **election** of 1860 and the administration of
Abraham Lincoln (7 and up) **973.7**

The **Election** of 2000 and the administration of
George W. Bush (7 and up) **324**

Election reform. Marzilli, A. **324.6**

Elections
Marzilli, A. Election reform (7 and up)
324.6

Fiction
Howe, J. The misfits **Fic**
Sheldon, D. My perfect life (7 and up) **Fic**

Electric lines
See/See also pages in the following book(s):
Macaulay, D. Underground (5 and up) **624**

Electric power plants
See also Nuclear power plants

The **electric** summer. Peck, R.
In Peck, R. Past perfect, present tense: new
and collected stories **S C**
In Time capsule: short stories about teenagers
throughout the twentieth century p3-16
S C

Electricity
Meiani, A. Electricity (4 and up) **537**
Parker, S. Electricity (4 and up) **537**
Pinna, S. d. Electricity **621.3**
Pollard, M. The light bulb and how it changed
the world **621.3**
Woodford, C. Electricity (5 and up) **537**

Electronic surveillance
MccGwire, S. Surveillance (7 and up)
323.44

Electronics
Hoare, S. Digital revolution **621.381**

Elementary school libraries
See also Children's libraries
Exploring science in the library **027.8**

The **Elements** [Benchmark Bks.] (5 and up)
546

Elements [Grolier] (5 and up) **546**

Elephant and Frog go courting. Bryan, A.
In Bryan, A. Ashley Bryan's African tales,
uh-huh p13-19 **398.2**

Elephants
Levine, S. P. The elephant (7 and up)
599.67
King, D. Elephant **599.67**
Schlaepfer, G. G. Elephants **599.67**
See/See also pages in the following book(s):
Sayre, A. P. Secrets of sound p11-23 (4 and up)
591.59

Fiction
Cross, G. The great American elephant chase
Fic

The **elevator**. Sleator, W.
In Beware!; R.L. Stine picks his favorite
scary stories p87-99 **808.8**

also in Read all about it!; great read-aloud
stories, poems, and newspaper pieces for
preteens and teens p236-43 **808.8**

Eleven. Myracle, L. **Fic**

The **eleven** thousand Virgins. Delacre, L.
In Delacre, L. Golden tales; myths, legends,
and folktales from Latin America p15-18
398.2

Elias *See* Elijah (Biblical figure)

Elias, Marie Louise
Barbados (5 and up) **972.98**

Elijah (Biblical figure)
About
Goldin, B. D. Journeys with Elijah (4 and up)
222

Elijah and the three brothers. Goldin, B. D.
In Goldin, B. D. Journeys with Elijah; eight
tales of the Prophet p39-47 **222**

**Elisabeth, Empress, consort of Franz Joseph I,
Emperor of Austria, 1837-1898**
Fiction
Denenberg, B. Elisabeth: the princess bride
Fic

Elish, Dan, 1960-
Born too short (7 and up) **Fic**
The Trail of Tears **970.004**
Vermont
In Celebrate the states **973**
Washington, D.C.
In Celebrate the states **973**

Elizabeth I, Queen of England, 1533-1603
About
Greenblatt, M. Elizabeth I and Tudor England
942.05
Lace, W. W. Elizabeth I and her court
942.05
Primary sources [Lucent library of historical
eras. Elizabethan England] **942.05**
Stanley, D. Good Queen Bess: the story of Eliz-
abeth I of England (4 and up) **92**
Thomas, J. R. Behind the mask: the life of
Queen Elizabeth I (7 and up) **92**
See/See also pages in the following book(s):
McGaw, L. To be a princess (4 and up)
920
Hewitt, K. Lives of extraordinary women (4 and
up) **920**
Meltzer, M. Ten queens (5 and up) **920**
Fiction
Lasky, K. Elizabeth I (4 and up) **Fic**
Meyer, C. Beware, Princess Elizabeth **Fic**

Elizabeth II, Queen of Great Britain, 1926-
See/See also pages in the following book(s):
McGaw, L. To be a princess (4 and up)
920

Elizabeth, Princess of Toro
See/See also pages in the following book(s):
Hansen, J. African princess (5 and up) **920**

Elizabeth I and her court. Lace, W. W.
942.05

Elizabeth I and Tudor England. Greenblatt, M.
942.05

Elizabethan England. Ashby, R. **942.05**

Elk
Patent, D. H. Deer and elk (4 and up)
599.65

Ella enchanted. Levine, G. C.   Fic

Ellavich, Marie C.
(ed) Scientists: their lives and works. See Scientists: their lives and works   920.003

Ellington, Duke, 1899-1974
About
Brown, G. Duke Ellington: jazz master (7 and up)   92
Old, W. Duke Ellington: giant of jazz   92
See/See also pages in the following book(s):
Mour, S. I. American jazz musicians   920

Elliot-Wright, Susan
Epilepsy (7 and up)   616.8

Elliott, Laura
Under a war-torn sky (7 and up)   Fic

Elliott, Mark
(il) Levine, G. C. The princess test   Fic

Ellis, Deborah, 1960-
Three wishes (5 and up)   956.94

Ellis, Sarah, 1952-
From reader to writer   372.6
A third kind of funny
In What a song can do; 12 riffs on the power of music   S C

Ellis Island Immigration Station
Anderson, D. Arriving at Ellis Island (5 and up)   325.73
I was dreaming to come to America (4 and up)   325.73
Sandler, M. W. Island of hope (5 and up)   325.73

Ellison, Lawrence J., 1944-
About
Ehrenhaft, D. Larry Ellison   92

Ellmann, Richard, 1918-1987
(ed) The New Oxford book of American verse. See The New Oxford book of American verse   811.008

Ellwood, Robert S., 1933-
(ed) The Encyclopedia of world religions. See The Encyclopedia of world religions   200.3

Elmer, Howard
Blues   781.643

Elusive glory. Bruning, J. R.   920

Elvis lives. Slayton, J.
In Soul searching: thirteen stories about faith and belief p228-47   S C

The **Emancipation** Proclamation. Tackach, J.
973.7

Emberley, Michael, 1960-
(il) Harris, R. H. It's perfectly normal   613.9

Emblems See Signs and symbols

Emblems, National See National emblems

Embryology
See also Reproduction
Flanagan, G. L. Beginning life   612.6

Emeril's there's a chef in my family!. Lagasse, E.
641.5

Emigrants See Immigrants

Emily & the intergalactic lemonade stand. Smith, I.   741.5

Emily Post's etiquette. Post, P.   395

Emily Post's teen etiquette. Post, E. L.   395

Emily Post's The guide to good manners for kids. Post, P.   395

Eminem
See/See also pages in the following book(s):
Rap and hip hop (7 and up)   306

Emotional intelligence. Andrews, L. W.   152.4

Emotional stress See Stress (Psychology)

Emotions
Andrews, L. W. Emotional intelligence
152.4
Canfield, J. Chicken soup for the teenage soul {I-III}   158
Chicken soup for the kid's soul   158
Tym, K. Coping with your emotions   152.4

Emperors
Rome
Bruns, R. Julius Caesar   92
Forsyth, F. Augustus: the first emperor   92
Julius Caesar [essays about]   92

The **emperor's** silent army. O'Connor, J.   931

The **empire** of Ghana. Green, R. L.   966.1

Empire State Building (New York, N.Y.)
Macaulay, D. Unbuilding (4 and up)   690

Employees
Training
See also Apprentices

Employment guidance See Vocational guidance

Employment of children See Child labor

Employment of teenagers See Teenagers—Employment

Employment of women See Women—Employment

Emshwiller, Carol
Overlooking
In The Green Man: tales from the mythic forest p223-36   808.8

Encantado. Montgomery, S.   599.5

The **enchanted** menorah. Schwartz, H.
In Schwartz, H. The day the Rabbi disappeared: Jewish holiday tales of magic p38-40   398.2

Enchanted night. Howe, J.
In The Color of absence; 12 stories about loss and hope p207-28   S C

The **Enchanted** prince
In Hearne, B. G. Beauties and beasts p109-14   398.2

The **Enchanted** Tsarevitch
In Hearne, B. G. Beauties and beasts p14-17   398.2

Enchantment of the world, Second series
Augustin, B. United Arab Emirates   953
Blauer, E. Morocco   964
Blauer, E. South Africa   968
Foster, L. M. Kuwait   953.67
Greenblatt, M. Afghanistan   958.1
Heinrichs, A. Australia   994
Heinrichs, A. Japan   952

Enchantment of the world, Second series—*Continued*

Hintz, M. Argentina	982
Hintz, M. Poland	943.8
Kummer, P. K. Tibet	951
Kummer, P. K. Ukraine	947.7
McNair, S. Thailand	959.3
Milivojevic, J. Bosnia and Herzegovina	949.7
Milivojevic, J. Serbia	949.7
Morrison, M. Costa Rica	972.86
Morrison, M. Guyana	988.1
Orr, T. Slovenia	949.7
Orr, T. Turkey	956.1
Stein, R. C. Mexico	972
Willis, T. Democratic Republic of the Congo	967.51

Enchantress from the stars. Engdahl, S. L. **Fic**

Encyclopaedia Britannica almanac **031.02**

The **Encyclopedia** Americana **031**

Encyclopedia of African nations and civilizations (7 and up) **960**

Encyclopedia of American government **320.03**

The **encyclopedia** of animals **590.3**

The **Encyclopedia** of careers and vocational guidance **331.7**

The **encyclopedia** of drugs and alcohol. Roza, G. **615**

Encyclopedia of first ladies [series]
Flanagan, A. K. Edith Bolling Galt Wilson, 1872-1961 **92**
Greenberg, J. E. Barbara Pierce Bush, 1925- **92**

Encyclopedia of forensic science. Bell, S. **363.2**

Encyclopedia of health (4 and up) **610.3**

Encyclopedia of health [series]
Check, W. A. AIDS **616.97**

Encyclopedia of hurricanes, typhoons and cyclones. Longshore, D. **551.55**

Encyclopedia of life sciences **570.3**

Encyclopedia of modern everyday inventions. Cole, D. J. **609**

Encyclopedia of Native American tribes. Waldman, C. **970.004**

The **Encyclopedia** of North American Indians [Marshall Cavendish] **970.004**

Encyclopedia of psychological disorders [series]
Harmon, D. Anorexia nervosa **616.85**

Encyclopedia of technology and applied sciences **603**

Encyclopedia of the aquatic world **578.7**

Encyclopedia of the human body. Walker, R. **612**

Encyclopedia of the Jewish religion. See The Oxford dictionary of the Jewish religion **296.03**

The **encyclopedia** of the Summer Olympics. Fischer, D. **796.48**

Encyclopedia of women [series]
Sonneborn, L. A to Z of Native American women **920.003**
Yount, L. A to Z of women in science and math **920.003**

Encyclopedia of women and sport in America **796.03**

Encyclopedia of women's history in America. Cullen-DuPont, K. **305.4**

Encyclopedia of world biography **920.003**

The **Encyclopedia** of world religions (7 and up) **200.3**

The **encyclopedia** of world sports. Wukovits, J. F. **796.03**

Encyclopedia of youth and war. Sherrow, V. **305.23**

Encyclopedias and dictionaries
See also Picture dictionaries names of languages with the subdivision *Dictionaries* and subjects with the subdivision *Dictionaries* or *Encyclopedias*

Compton's encyclopedia & fact-index **031**

Corbeil, J.-C. The Facts on File visual dictionary **423**

Dorling Kindersley children's illustrated encyclopedia

The Encyclopedia Americana **031**

Kane, J. N. Famous first facts **031.02**

The New Grolier children's encyclopedia **031**

Oxford American children's encyclopedia **031**

Pascoe, E. Scholastic kid's almanac (4 and up) **031.02**

Scholastic children's encyclopedia (4 and up) **031**

The World Book encyclopedia **031**

End of the world
Cohen, D. Prophets of doom (7 and up) **133.3**

Endangered animals **333.95**

Endangered animals & habitats [series]

Barghusen, J. D. The bald eagle	598
Barghusen, L. The bear	599.78
DuTemple, L. A. Seals and sea lions	599.79
Levine, S. P. The elephant	599.67
Levine, S. P. The tiger	599.75
Malaspina, A. The koala	599.2
Presnall, J. J. The giant panda	599.78
Price-Groff, C. The manatee	599.5
Woog, A. The whale	599.5

Endangered in America [series]
Silverstein, A. The grizzly bear **599.78**

Endangered oceans: opposing viewpoints (7 and up) **577.7**

Endangered planet. Burnie, D. **333.95**

Endangered species
See also Wildlife conservation
Arnold, C. On the brink of extinction (4 and up) **598**

The Atlas of endangered species **333.95**

Barghusen, J. D. The bald eagle (7 and up) **598**

Barghusen, L. The bear (7 and up) **599.78**

Endangered species—*Continued*
DuTemple, L. A. Seals and sea lions (7 and up) **599.79**
Endangered animals **333.95**
Endangered species: opposing viewpoints (7 and up) **578.68**
Hoose, P. M. The race to save the Lord God Bird (7 and up) **598**
Levine, S. P. The elephant (7 and up) **599.67**
Levine, S. P. The tiger (7 and up) **599.75**
Malaspina, A. The koala (7 and up) **599.2**
Presnall, J. J. The giant panda (7 and up) **599.78**
Price-Groff, C. The manatee (7 and up) **599.5**
Salmansohn, P. Saving birds (5 and up) **333.95**
Silverstein, A. The grizzly bear **599.78**
Vergoth, K. Endangered species **578.68**
Woog, A. The whale (7 and up) **599.5**
See/See also pages in the following book(s):
Netzley, P. D. Issues in the environment (7 and up) **333.7**

Endangered species: opposing viewpoints (7 and up) **578.68**

Ender's game. Card, O. S. **Fic**

Endings. Nix, G.
In Gothic!; ten original dark tales **S C**

The **endless** steppe: growing up in Siberia. Hautzig, E. R. **92**

Endocrine glands
Little, M. The endocrine system (7 and up) **612.4**

The **endocrine** system. Little, M. **612.4**

Endrezze, Anita
The humming of stars and bees and waves
In Talking leaves; contemporary native American short stories **S C**

Endurance, Physical *See* Physical fitness

Endurance (Ship)
Calvert, P. Sir Ernest Shackleton **92**
Johnson, R. L. Ernest Shackleton **92**
Kimmel, E. C. Ice story (4 and up) **998**

The **enemy** has a face. Miklowitz, G. D. **Fic**

Energy *See* Force and energy

Energy. Bowden, R. **333.79**

Energy. Challoner, J. **621**

Energy. Farndon, J. **531**

Energy. Juettner, B. **333.79**

Energy development
Bowden, R. Energy (5 and up) **333.79**

Energy forever? [series]
Graham, I. Solar power **621.47**
Graham, I. Water power **620.1**
Graham, I. Wind power **621.4**

Energy projects for young scientists. Adams, R. C. **621**

Energy resources
Challoner, J. Energy (5 and up) **621**
Silverstein, A. Energy **621**

See/See also pages in the following book(s):
Global resources: opposing viewpoints **333.71**

Engdahl, Sylvia Louise
The far side of evil **Fic**

Engdahl, Sylvia Louise, 1933-
Enchantress from the stars **Fic**

Engel, Stephen
About
Dudley, M. E. Engel v. Vitale (1962) (7 and up) **344**

Engel v. Vitale (1962). Dudley, M. E. **344**

Engelbert, Phillis
American civil rights: almanac **323.1**
American civil rights: biographies **920**
The complete weather resource **551.5**
Dangerous planet **363.34**
Technology in action **603**
(ed) American civil rights: primary sources. *See* American civil rights: primary sources **323.1**
(ed) Science, technology, and society: the impact of science in the 20th century. *See* Science, technology, and society: the impact of science in the 20th century **509**
(ed) U.X.L science fact finder. *See* U.X.L science fact finder **500**

Engfer, Lee, 1963-
India in pictures (5 and up) **954**
(jt. auth) Parker, D. L. Stolen dreams **331.3**

Engineering
See also Highway engineering
Macaulay, D. Building big **720**

Engineering, Genetic *See* Genetic engineering
Engineering, Structural *See* Structural engineering
Engineering materials *See* Materials
Engineering the city. Levy, M. **624**

Engineers
Oleksy, W. G. Hispanic-American scientists (7 and up) **920**

England
Lace, W. W. England (7 and up) **942**
Lister, M. England **942**
History
See Great Britain—History
Social life and customs
Ashby, R. Elizabethan England **942.05**
Primary sources [Lucent library of historical eras. Elizabethan England] **942.05**

English, June, 1955-
Balance
In Girls got game; sports stories and poems **810.8**
Scholastic encyclopedia of the United States at war **973.03**

English, Karen
Francie (5 and up) **Fic**

English as a second language
Bibliography
McCaffery, L. H. Building an ESL collection for young adults **016.4**

English as a second language—Bibliography—
Continued
Rosow, L. V. Light 'n lively reads for ESL, adult, and teen readers   **011.6**

English drama
History and criticism
Nardo, D. Great Elizabethan playwrights
                                              920
Woog, A. A history of the Elizabethan theater
                                          792.09

English language
Americanisms
See Americanisms
Dictionaries
The American Heritage student dictionary
                                              423
DK dictionary/thesaurus   **423**
Hirsch, E. D. The new dictionary of cultural literacy   **031**
Random House Webster's unabridged dictionary
                                              423
Webster's third new international dictionary of the English language, unabridged   **423**
Etymology
Baker, R. F. In a word (5 and up)   **422**
The Barnhart dictionary of etymology
                                          422.03
Morris, W. Morris dictionary of word and phrase origins   **422.03**
History
See also English language—Etymology
Idioms
Terban, M. Scholastic dictionary of idioms (4 and up)   **423**
Rhyme
Young, S. The new comprehensive American rhyming dictionary   **423**
Slang
Dictionary of American slang   **427**
Ostler, R. Dewdroppers, waldos, and slackers
                                              428
Synonyms and antonyms
Bartlett's Roget's thesaurus   **423**
DK dictionary/thesaurus   **423**
The Facts on File student's thesaurus   **423**
Hellweg, P. The American Heritage children's thesaurus   **423**
Merriam-Webster's dictionary of synonyms
                                              423
Merriam-Webster's school thesaurus   **423**
Roget's 21st century thesaurus in dictionary form   **423**
Roget's II   **423**
Roget's international thesaurus   **423**
Simon & Schuster thesaurus for children
                                              423
Terms and phrases
Morris, W. Morris dictionary of word and phrase origins   **422.03**

English poetry
Collections
Committed to memory   **821.008**
The Kingfisher book of funny poems (4 and up)
                                          821.008
The Oxford book of story poems   **821.008**

The Oxford book of twentieth-century English verse   **821.008**
The Oxford treasury of time poems   **821.008**
The Random House book of poetry for children
                                          821.008

Enhancing teaching and learning. Donham, J.
                                          027.8

Enigmas *See* Curiosities and wonders

Enlightenment
Dunn, J. M. The Enlightenment (7 and up)
                                          940.2

Enrico Fermi and the revolutions in modern physics. Cooper, D.   **92**

Entrepreneurs
Garty, J. Jeff Bezos   **92**

Entrepreneurship
Kiefer, J. Jobs for kids (4 and up)   **650.1**

Environment
See also Environmental degradation
The **environment**. Barbour, S.   **363.7**
The **environment**. Snedden, R.   **577**
The **Environment** encyclopedia (7 and up)
                                          363.7
The **environment:** opposing viewpoints   **363.7**

Environmental degradation
Burnie, D. Endangered planet (5 and up)
                                          333.95

Environmental disasters. Davis, L. A.   **363.7**

Environmental disasters [series]
Bryan, N. Los Alamos wildfires   **363.34**
Bryan, N. Bhopal   **363.1**
Bryan, N. Chernobyl   **363.7**
Bryan, N. Exxon Valdez oil spill   **363.7**
Bryan, N. Love Canal   **363.7**

Environmental movement
Kidd, J. S. Shades of green (7 and up)
                                          363.7

Environmental pioneers. Byrnes, P.   **920**

Environmental policy
Endangered oceans: opposing viewpoints (7 and up)   **577.7**
United States
The environment: opposing viewpoints   **363.7**
Netzley, P. D. Issues in the environment (7 and up)   **333.7**

Environmental pollution *See* Pollution

Environmental protection
The Atlas of endangered species   **333.95**
Barbour, S. The environment (7 and up)
                                          363.7
Conserving the environment (7 and up)
                                          333.72
Gardner, R. Science projects about the environment and ecology (7 and up)   **363.7**
Graham, K. Contemporary environmentalists (7 and up)   **920**
Needham, B. Ecology crafts for kids   **745.5**
Netzley, P. D. Issues in the environment (7 and up)   **333.7**
Bibliography
Dwyer, J. R. Earth works   **016.3637**

Environmental protection—*Continued*
Encyclopedias
Macmillan encyclopedia of the environment
333.7
Fiction
Klass, D. California Blue **Fic**
Environmental sciences
Sussman, A. Dr. Art's guide to planet earth
577
Encyclopedias
The Environment encyclopedia (7 and up)
363.7
Environmentalists
Byrnes, P. Environmental pioneers (7 and up)
920
Graham, K. Contemporary environmentalists (7 and up) **920**
Eolithic period *See* Stone Age
The **epic** of Gilgamesh. McCaughrean, G.
398.2
Epidemic! [series]
Peters, S. T. The 1918 influenza pandemic
614.5
Peters, S. T. The battle against polio **614.5**
Peters, S. T. The Black Death **614.5**
Peters, S. T. Cholera **614.5**
Peters, S. T. Smallpox in the new world
614.5
Epidemics
Epidemics: opposing viewpoints **614.4**
The Black Death [Turning points in world history series] (7 and up) **614.5**
Epidemics: opposing viewpoints **614.4**
Epidemiology
Friedlander, M. P. Outbreak: disease detectives at work **614.4**
Hoff, B. H. Mapping epidemics (7 and up)
614
Epigrams
See also Quotations
Epilepsy
Carson, M. K. Epilepsy (7 and up) **616.8**
Elliot-Wright, S. Epilepsy (7 and up) **616.8**
Gay, K. Epilepsy **616.8**
Goodfellow, G. Epilepsy **616.8**
Routh, K. Epilepsy
Fiction
Philbrick, W. R. The last book in the universe
Fic
Epoch biographies [series]
Archer, J. They had a dream **920**
Equestrianism *See* Horsemanship
Equiano, Olaudah, b. 1745
About
Cameron, A. The kidnapped prince: the life of Olaudah Equiano (4 and up) **92**
See/See also pages in the following book(s):
Cloud Tapper, S. Voices from slavery's past (7 and up) **326**
Eragon. Paolini, C. **Fic**
Erdoes, Richard
(ed) American Indian myths and legends. See American Indian myths and legends **398.2**
(jt. auth) Brave Bird, M. Lakota woman **92**

Erdosh, George, 1935-
The African American kitchen (7 and up)
641.5
Erdrich, Louise
The bingo van
In Talking leaves; contemporary native American short stories **S C**
The birchbark house (5 and up) **Fic**
The game of silence (5 and up) **Fic**
The red convertible
In Who do you think you are?; stories of friends and enemies p134-45 **S C**
Ergas, G. Aimée
Artists: from Michelangelo to Maya Lin
920.003
Erickson, Jon, 1948-
Making of the earth (7 and up) **551.4**
Marine geology (7 and up) **551.46**
Erickson, Paul, 1976-
Daily life in the Pilgrim colony, 1636 **974.4**
Daily life on a Southern plantation, 1853 (4 and up) **975**
Erie Canal (N.Y.)
Levy, J. The Erie Canal **974.7**
Erikson, Rolf
Designing a school library media center for the future **027.8**
Eritrea
NgCheong-Lum, R. Eritrea **963.5**
Erlbach, Arlene
The kids' invention book (4 and up) **608**
The kids' volunteering book (4-6) **302**
The middle school survival guide **373.1**
Worth the risk **302**
Erosion
Winner, C. Erosion **551.3**
Esaias, Timons
The children's war
In Sherwood: original stories from the world of Robin Hood p70-83 **S C**
Escamilla, Kleya Forté- *See* Forté-Escamilla, Kleya
Escape. Asimov, I.
In Asimov, I. I, robot **S C**
Escape. Haddix, M. P.
In Shelf life: stories by the book p23-32
S C
Escape from Botany Bay. Hausman, G. **Fic**
Escape from Earth. Ackroyd, P. **629.4**
The **escape** from home. See Avi. Beyond the western sea **Fic**
Escape from memory. Haddix, M. P. **Fic**
Escape from Saigon. Warren, A. **92**
Escape from slavery. Douglass, F. **92**
Escape from slavery. Rappaport, D. **326**
Escapes from slavery. Currie, S. **326**
Esckilsen, Erik E.
The last mall rat (7 and up) **Fic**
Esherick, Joan
The FDA and psychiatric drugs
Eskimos *See* Inuit

Eskridge, Ann E.
Slave uprisings and runaways 326
ESP *See* Extrasensory perception
ESP 133.8
Espejo, Roman, 1977-
(ed) Adoption: opposing viewpoints. See Adoption: opposing viewpoints 362.7
(ed) America's prisons: opposing viewpoints. See America's prisons: opposing viewpoints 365
(ed) What is a hate crime? See What is a hate crime? 364.1
Espeland, Pamela, 1951-
Life lists for teens 646.7
(jt. auth) Benson, P. L. What teens need to succeed 305.23
Esperanza rising. Ryan, P. M. Fic
Espionage
See also Spies
Keeley, J. Espionage 327.12
Kupperberg, P. Spy satellites 327.12
Platt, R. Spy 327.12
Wiese, J. Spy science 363.2
Essential fishing for teens. Fitzgerald, R. 799.1
Essential reference services for today's school media specialists. Lanning, S. 025.5
Essex, Robert Devereux, 2nd Earl of, 1566-1601
Fiction
Curry, J. L. The Black Canary (5 and up) Fic
Essex (Whale-ship)
Philbrick, N. Revenge of the whale (7 and up) 910.4
Esteban *See* Estevan, d. 1539
Estefan, Gloria
About
Gonzales, D. Gloria Estefan 92
Estes, Sally
(jt. auth) Carter, B. Best books for young adults 028.1
Estevan, d. 1539
See/See also pages in the following book(s):
Haskins, J. Against all opposition (5 and up) 920
Estevanico *See* Estevan, d. 1539
Estevis, Anne
Down Garrapata road (7 and up) S C
Esther, Queen of Persia
See/See also pages in the following book(s):
Meltzer, M. Ten queens (5 and up) 920
Estonia
Spilling, M. Estonia (5 and up) 947.9
Ethics, Medical *See* Medical ethics
Ethics, Social *See* Social ethics
Ethics in school librarianship 174
Ethiopia
Fiction
Kurtz, J. Saba Fic
Kurtz, J. The storyteller's beads (5 and up) Fic
Levitin, S. The return (6 and up) Fic

Ethnic cooking the microwave way. Cappelloni, N.
In Easy menu ethnic cookbooks 641.5
Ethnic groups
See also Minorities; Racially mixed people
Ethnic relations
See also Culture conflict; Multiculturalism; Race relations
Birdseye, D. H. Under our skin (4 and up) 305.8
Ethnology
Mason, A. People around the world 305.8
Encyclopedias
Junior Worldmark encyclopedia of world cultures (5 and up) 306
Africa
Peoples of Africa 960
America
Peoples of the Americas 970
Kenya
See also Masai (African people)
Etiquette
Dougherty, K. The rules to be cool (7 and up) 395
James, E. Social smarts 395
Packer, A. J. How rude! (7 and up) 395
Post, E. L. Emily Post's teen etiquette (7 and up) 395
Post, P. Emily Post's etiquette (7 and up) 395
Post, P. Emily Post's The guide to good manners for kids (5 and up) 395
Euphrates River
Whitcraft, M. The Tigris and Euphrates Rivers 935
Eureka!. Platt, R. 609
Europe
Church history
Hinds, K. The church 274
Civilization
Hinds, K. The city [Life in the Renaissance series] 940.2
Hinds, K. The countryside [Life in the Renaissance series] 940.2
Hinds, K. The court 940.2
Encyclopedias
Peoples of Europe (5 and up) 940
Folklore
See Folklore—Europe
History—476-1492
The Early Middle Ages (7 and up) 909.07
Maps
Europe on file 912
Europe on file 912
European art since 1850. Malloy, N.
In International encyclopedia of art 703
European art to 1850. Lucchesi, T.
In International encyclopedia of art 703
European War, 1914-1918 *See* World War, 1914-1918
Euthanasia
Euthanasia: opposing viewpoints (7 and up) 179.7

Euthanasia—*Continued*
Rebman, R. C. Euthanasia and the "right to die" **179.7**

See/See also pages in the following book(s):
Altman, L. J. Death: an introduction to medical-ethical dilemmas **155.9**
Suicide: opposing viewpoints (7 and up) **362.28**
Terminal illness: opposing viewpoints (7 and up) **362.1**

Fiction
Gilbert, B. S. Stone water (7 and up) **Fic**
Trueman, T. Stuck in neutral **Fic**

Euthanasia and the "right to die". Rebman, R. C. **179.7**

Euthanasia: opposing viewpoints (7 and up) **179.7**

Eva. Dickinson, P. **Fic**

Evacuation and relocation of Japanese Americans, 1942-1945 *See* Japanese Americans—Evacuation and relocation, 1942-1945

Evaluating the school library media center. Everhart, N. **027.8**

Evans, Lawrence Watt- *See* Watt-Evans, Lawrence, 1954-

Evans, Shane
(il) Smith, H. A. The way a door closes **811**

Evans, Walker, 1903-1975
(il) Rylant, C. Something permanent **811**

The **ever** changing atom. Gallant, R. A. **539.7**

Everard's ride. Jones, D. W. Jones, D. W. Unexpected magic; collected stories p303-497

Everglades (Fla.)
Doherty, K. Marjory Stoneman Douglas (7 and up) **92**

Fiction
George, J. C. The talking earth **Fic**

Everhart, Nancy
Evaluating the school library media center **027.8**

Evers, Medgar Wiley, 1925-1963
About
Ribeiro, M. The assassination of Medgar Evers **92**

Every, Henry *See* Avery, John, fl. 1695

Every, John *See* Avery, John, fl. 1695

Every day and all the time. Deans, S. B. **Fic**

Every girl tells a story. Jones, C. **305.23**

Everyday I sing the blues: the story of B.B. King. Shirley, D. **92**

Everyday living skills *See* Life skills

Everything on a waffle. Horvath, P. **Fic**

Everything you need to know about abusive relationships. Rue, N. N. **362.7**

Everything you need to know about ADD\ADHD. Beal, E. **616.85**

Everything you need to know about being adopted. Kaminker, L. **362.7**

Everything you need to know about creating your own support system. Kreiner, A. **158**

Everything you need to know about dealing with sexual assault. Kaminker, L. **364.1**

Everything you need to know about going to the gynecologist. Diamond, S. N. **618.1**

Everything you need to know about having an addictive personality. Bridgers, J. **616.86**

Everything you need to know about media violence. Edgar, K. J. **303.6**

Everything you need to know about mononucleosis. Smart, P. **616.9**

Everything you need to know about organic foods. Dunn-Georgiou, E. **641.3**

Everything you need to know about protecting yourself and others from abduction. Wiloch, T. **613.6**

Everything you need to know about self-mutilation. Ng, G. **616.85**

Everything you need to know when someone you know has been killed. Schleifer, J. **155.9**

Evidence. Asimov, I.
In Asimov, I. I, robot **S C**

Evil *See* Good and evil

The **evil** eye. Olson, A. N.
In Olson, A. N. and Schwartz, H. Ask the bones: scary stories from around the world p134-40 **398.2**

The **evitable** conflict. Asimov, I.
In Asimov, I. I, robot **S C**

Evolution
Ackroyd, P. The beginning (7 and up) **576.8**
Dixon, D. The future is wild **576.8**
Gallant, R. A. Early humans (5 and up) **599.93**
Gamblin, L. Evolution (4 and up) **576.8**
Gardner, R. Human evolution (7 and up) **599.93**
Patent, D. H. Charles Darwin (7 and up) **92**
Sloan, C. The human story (7 and up) **599.93**
Stefoff, R. Charles Darwin and the evolution revolution (7 and up) **92**

See/See also pages in the following book(s):
Gallant, R. A. History **551.7**
Patent, D. H. Biodiversity (5 and up) **333.95**

Study and teaching
Olson, S. P. The trial of John T. Scopes (5 and up)

Evvy's Civil War. Brenaman, M. **Fic**

Examination day. Slesar, H.
In Beware!; R.L. Stine picks his favorite scary stories p169-77 **808.8**

Examinations
Gilbert, S. D. How to do your best on tests (7 and up) **371.2**

Examining issues through political cartoons [series]
Civil rights **323.1**

Examining pop culture [series]
Rap and hip hop **306**

Excavations (Archeology)
Hansen, J. Breaking ground, breaking silence
974.7
Smith, K. Exploring for shipwrecks **930.1**
Waldman, N. Masada (4 and up) **933**
Italy
Connolly, P. Pompeii **937**

Exceptional children
See also Wild children

The **exchange** student. Gilmore, K. **Fic**

Executions *See* Capital punishment

Exercise
See also Physical fitness; Weight lifting
Gedatus, G. Exercise for weight management
613.7
Vedral, J. L. Toning for teens (7 and up)
613.7
See/See also pages in the following book(s):
Schwager, T. The right moves (7 and up)
613.7

Exercise for weight management. Gedatus, G.
613.7

Exercises, Reducing *See* Weight loss

Exiles *See* Refugees

Exotic species. Guiberson, B. Z. **577**

The **Expanding** world (300-1750)
In World history on file **909**

Expedition [series]
Green, J. Race to the moon **629.45**

Experiences, Near-death *See* Near-death experiences

Experiencing the American Civil War. Hillstrom, K. **973.7**

Experiment central (7 and up) **507.8**

Experimental science series
Adams, R. C. More ideas for science projects
507.8
Tocci, S. How to do a science fair project
507.8

Experimentation on animals *See* Animal experimentation

Experimenting with science [series]
Meiani, A. Air **533**
Meiani, A. Chemistry **540**
Meiani, A. Electricity **537**
Meiani, A. Light **535**
Meiani, A. Magnetism **538**
Meiani, A. Water **532**

Experts, Incorporated. Weeks, S.
In Tripping over the lunch lady and other school stories p30-40 **S C**

Exploding ants. Settel, J. **591.5**

Exploration
Grolier student library of explorers and exploration **910.4**
Kimmel, E. C. The look-it-up book of explorers (5 and up) **920**
Matthews, R. Explorer (4 and up) **910.4**
Stefoff, R. Exploration (5 and up) **910**

Explorer atlas of the world **912**

Explorers
Alter, J. Extraordinary explorers and adventurers
920
Aronson, M. Sir Walter Ralegh and the quest for El Dorado (7 and up) **92**
Calvert, P. Hernando Cortés **92**
Calvert, P. Robert E. Peary **92**
Calvert, P. Sir Ernest Shackleton **92**
Calvert, P. Vasco da Gama (5 and up) **92**
Calvert, P. Zebulon Pike (5 and up) **92**
Dolan, S. Junípero Serra **92**
Edwards, J. Henry Hudson and his voyages of exploration in world history (7 and up)
92
Faber, H. John Charles Frémont **92**
Faber, H. La Salle **92**
Faber, H. Samuel de Champlain (5 and up)
92
Fritz, J. Around the world in a hundred years (4 and up) **910.4**
Gaines, A. Hernando de Soto and the Spanish search for gold in world history (7 and up)
92
Goodman, J. E. Despite all obstacles: La Salle and the conquest of the Mississippi (4 and up) **92**
Goodman, J. E. A long and uncertain journey: the 27,000 mile voyage of Vasco da Gama (4 and up) **92**
Grolier student library of explorers and exploration **910.4**
Haskins, J. Against all opposition (5 and up)
920
Johnson, R. L. Ernest Shackleton **92**
Johnstone, M. Explorers **910.4**
Kimmel, E. C. The look-it-up book of explorers (5 and up) **920**
Levinson, N. S. Magellan and the first voyage around the world (5 and up) **92**
Matthews, R. Explorer (4 and up) **910.4**
Meltzer, M. Captain James Cook **92**
Meltzer, M. Columbus and the world around him **92**
Meltzer, M. Ferdinand Magellan **92**
Meltzer, M. Francisco Pizarro (5 and up) **92**
Otfinoski, S. Francisco Coronado **92**
Otfinoski, S. Juan Ponce de Leon (5 and up)
92
Otfinoski, S. Marco Polo **92**
Otfinoski, S. Vasco Nuñez de Balboa (5 and up)
92
Rice, E. Sir Francis Drake, navigator and pirate
92
Santella, A. Henry Hudson **92**
Sonneborn, L. Samuel de Champlain **92**
Warrick, K. C. The perilous search for the fabled Northwest Passage in American history
910.4
Worth, R. The great empire of China and Marco Polo in world history **92**
Dictionaries
Explorers (5 and up) **920.003**
Explorers & discoverers **920.003**
Podell, J. Old worlds to new **920.003**
Explorers (5 and up) **920.003**
Explorers & discoverers **920.003**

Explorers of new worlds [series]
  Brennan, K. Sir Edmund Hillary, modern day explorer **92**
Exploring ancient civilizations **930**
Exploring Canada **971**
Exploring cultural history [series]
  Living in Nazi Germany **943.086**
  Living through the Great Depression **973.91**
Exploring earth and space science (7 and up) **550.3**
Exploring Earth's biomes [series]
  Sayre, A. P. Desert **577.5**
  Sayre, A. P. Grassland **577.4**
  Sayre, A. P. Lake and pond **577.6**
  Sayre, A. P. Ocean **577.7**
  Sayre, A. P. River and stream **577.6**
  Sayre, A. P. Taiga **577.3**
  Sayre, A. P. Temperate deciduous forest **577.3**
  Sayre, A. P. Tropical rain forest **577.3**
Exploring ecosystems [series]
  Martin, P. A. F. Prairies, fields, and meadows **577.4**
  Martin, P. A. F. Rivers and streams **577.6**
  Martin, P. A. F. Woods and forests **577.3**
Exploring for shipwrecks. Smith, K. **930.1**
Exploring our solar system. Ride, S. K. **523.2**
Exploring planet earth [series]
  Friend, S. Earth's wild winds **551.51**
Exploring Saturn. Bortolotti, D. **523.4**
Exploring science in the library **027.8**
Exploring technology (5 and up) **603**
Exploring tough issues [series]
  Brownlie, A. Why do people fight wars? **355**
  Johnson, J. Why do people join gangs? **364.1**
  Senker, C. Why are people prejudiced? **303.3**
The **extinguished** lights. Singer, I. B.
  In Singer, I. B. The power of light; eight stories for Hanukkah p13-20 **S C**
Extraordinary African-Americans. Altman, S. **920**
Extraordinary American Indians. Avery, S. **920**
Extraordinary Asian Americans and Pacific Islanders. Sinnott, S. **920**
Extraordinary Asian-Pacific Americans. See Sinnott, S. Extraordinary Asian Americans and Pacific Islanders **920**
Extraordinary Black Americans. See Altman, S. Extraordinary African-Americans **920**
Extraordinary events and oddball occurrences. Blackwood, G. L. **001.9**
Extraordinary explorers and adventurers. Alter, J. **920**
Extraordinary Jewish Americans. Brooks, P. **920**
An **extraordinary** life. Pringle, L. P. **595.7**
Extraordinary people [series]
  Alter, J. Extraordinary explorers and adventurers **920**

Alter, J. Extraordinary women of the American West **920**
Altman, S. Extraordinary African-Americans **920**
Brooks, P. Extraordinary Jewish Americans **920**
Gulotta, C. Extraordinary women in politics **920**
Hardy, P. S. Extraordinary people of the Harlem Renaissance **920**
Hasday, J. L. Extraordinary women athletes **920**
Kent, D. Extraordinary people with disabilities **920**
Martin, M. Extraordinary people in jazz **920**
Price-Groff, C. Extraordinary women journalists **920**
Sinnott, S. Extraordinary Asian Americans and Pacific Islanders **920**
Stille, D. R. Extraordinary women of medicine **920**
Extraordinary people in extraordinary times. Mendoza, P. M. **920**
Extraordinary people in jazz. Martin, M. **920**
Extraordinary people of the Harlem Renaissance. Hardy, P. S. **920**
Extraordinary people with disabilities. Kent, D. **920**
Extraordinary women athletes. Hasday, J. L. **920**
Extraordinary women in politics. Gulotta, C. **920**
Extraordinary women journalists. Price-Groff, C. **920**
Extraordinary women of medicine. Stille, D. R. **920**
Extraordinary women of the American West. Alter, J. **920**
Extrasensory perception
  ESP **133.8**
  See/See also pages in the following book(s):
  Paranormal phenomena: opposing viewpoints (7 and up) **133**
        Fiction
  Grunwell, J. M. Mind games **Fic**
  Tolan, S. S. Flight of the raven (7 and up) **Fic**
Extrasolar planets. Miller, R. **523**
Extraterrestrial beings
  Netzley, P. D. Alien abductions: opposing viewpoints (7 and up) **001.9**
        Fiction
  Blacker, T. The angel factory **Fic**
  Brittain, B. Shape-changer (5 and up) **Fic**
  Coville, B. Aliens ate my homework **Fic**
  Coville, B. The monsters of Morley Manor **Fic**
  Gilmore, K. The exchange student (7 and up) **Fic**
  Jeapes, B. The xenocide mission **Fic**
  Mackel, K. Can of worms **Fic**
Extreme skateboarding. Ryan, P. **796.22**
Extreme sports [series]
  Masoff, J. Snowboard! **796.93**

Extreme sports—*Continued*
Pollack, P. Ski 796.93
Ryan, P. Extreme skateboarding 796.22
Exxon Valdez (Ship)
Bryan, N. Exxon Valdez oil spill (5 and up)
363.7
Sherrow, V. The Exxon Valdez 363.7
Exxon Valdez oil spill. Bryan, N. 363.7
Eye
Silverstein, A. Seeing Silverstein, A. and others.
Senses and sensors [series] 612.8
Simon, S. Eyes and ears (4 and up) 612.8
The **eye** of Allah. Kipling, R.
In McCaffrey, A. {The Pern series} S C
Eye of the great bear. Wallace, B. Fic
Eyes and ears. Simon, S. 612.8
Eyes like Willy's. Havill, J. Fic
Eyes on the prize: America's civil rights years,
1954-1965. Williams, J. 323.1
Eyes on the universe. Reed, G. 520
Eyewitness art [series]
Cole, A. The Renaissance 709.02
Eyewitness books [series]
Arthur, A. Shell 594
Buckley, J., Jr. Football 796.332
Cotterell, A. Ancient China 931
Halley, N. Farm 630.1
Hart, G. Ancient Egypt 932
James, S. Ancient Rome 937
Kentley, E. Boat 387.2
Lane, B. Crime & detection 364
McCarthy, C. Reptile 597.9
McIntosh, J. Archeology 930.1
Platt, R. Spy 327.12
King, D. Elephant 599.67
Redmond, I. Gorilla 599.8
Rowland-Warne, L. Costume 391
Whalley, P. E. S. Butterfly & moth 595.7
Wilkinson, P. Building 690
Eyewitness classics [series]
Philip, N. The story of Robin Hood 398.2
Eyewitness handbooks [series]
Carwardine, M. Whales, dolphins, and porpoises
599.5
Harrison, C. Birds of the world 598
Eyewitness history series
Burg, D. F. The Great Depression 973.91
Frost-Knappman, E. Women's suffrage in America 324.6
Kirchberger, J. H. The Civil War and Reconstruction 973.7
Kirchberger, J. H. The First World War
940.3
Wepman, D. Immigration 325.73
Westward expansion 978
Wexler, S. The civil rights movement 323.1
Eyewitness rocks & minerals. Symes, R. F.
549
Eyewitness science [series]
Burnie, D. Light 535
Challoner, J. Energy 621
Cooper, C. Matter 530
Gamblin, L. Evolution 576.8
Parker, S. Electricity 537

Parker, S. Medicine 610
Eyewitness visual dictionaries [series]
The Visual dictionary of animals 591.4
The Visual dictionary of the horse 636.1

F

F E G: ridiculous stupid poems for intelligent children. Hirsch, R. 821
Faber, Doris, 1924-
Calamity Jane (5 and up) 92
Faber, Harold
John Charles Frémont 92
Lewis and Clark 978
La Salle 92
Samuel de Champlain (5 and up) 92
Face. Zephaniah, B. Fic
A **face** first. Cummings, P. Fic
A **face** in every window. Nolan, H. Fic
The **face** on the milk carton. Cooney, C. B.
Fic
Face relations (7 and up) S C
Facing the lion. Lekuton, J. 967.62
Facklam, Howard
(jt. auth) Facklam, M. Modern medicines
615
Facklam, Margery, 1927-
Modern medicines (7 and up) 615
Fact or fiction [series]
Black magic and witches 133.4
ESP 133.8
Factories
Houle, M. M. Triangle Shirtwaist Factory fire
974.7
Lieurance, S. The Triangle Shirtwaist fire and sweatshop reform in American history (7 and up) 974.7
Fiction
Paterson, K. Lyddie (5 and up) Fic
Facts, Miscellaneous *See* Curiosities and wonders
The **facts** about alcohol. Gottfried, T. 362.292
The **facts** about ecstasy. LeVert, S. 362.29
The **facts** about inhalants. Menhard, F. R.
362.29
The **facts** about marijuana. Gottfried, T.
362.29
The **facts** about steroids. LeVert, S. 362.29
Facts about the Congress. Christianson, S. G.
328.73
Facts about the presidents. Kane, J. N. 920
Facts about the states 973
The **Facts** on File atlas of stars and planets. See Ridpath, I. Facts on File stars & planets atlas
520
The **Facts** on File biology handbook (7 and up)
570
The **Facts** on File chemistry handbook (7 and up)
540
The **Facts** on File dictionary of astronomy
520.3

The **Facts** on File earth science handbook (7 and up) **550**

Facts on File library of American history [series]
Meyer, N. E. Biographical dictionary of Hispanic Americans **920.003**
Ochoa, G. Atlas of Hispanic-American history **305.8**

Facts on File library of language and literature [series]
The Facts on File student's thesaurus **423**

Facts on File library of world history [series]
Encyclopedia of African nations and civilizations **960**

The **Facts** on File physics handbook (7 and up) **530**

Facts on File reference library [series]
Sports rules on file **796**

Facts on File science library [series]
Bazler, J. A. More science projects for all students **507.8**
The Facts on File dictionary of astronomy **520.3**

Facts on File stars & planets atlas. Ridpath, I. **520**

The **Facts** on File student's thesaurus **423**

The **Facts** on File visual dictionary. Corbeil, J.-C. **423**

Facts on File wildlife atlas. Kerrod, R. **578**

The **facts** speak for themselves. Cole, B. **Fic**

Fagan, Cary
(jt. auth) Goh, C. H. Beyond the dance **92**

Fagan, Eleanora See Holiday, Billie, 1915-1959

Faget, Maxime A., 1921-2004
See/See also pages in the following book(s):
Richie, J. Space flight **920**

Fagles, Robert
(tr) Homer. The Iliad **883**
(tr) Homer. The Odyssey **883**

Fahd, King of Saudi Arabia, 1923-2005
See/See also pages in the following book(s):
Reed, J. The Saudi royal family **920**

Faherty, Sara
Victims and victims' rights (7 and up) **362.88**

Failure is impossible!. Kendall, M. E. **305.4**

Fair, Brown, and Trembling. Philip, N.
In Philip, N. Celtic fairy tales p27-35 **398.2**

Fair use (Copyright)
Butler, R. P. Copyright for teachers and librarians **346.04**

Fair weather. Peck, R. **Fic**

Fairclough, Chris
(il) Oxlade, C. Chemistry **540.7**
(il) Oxlade, C. Weather **551.5**
(il) Pinna, S. d. Electricity **621.3**
(il) Snedden, R. The environment **577**

Fairies
Comic books, strips, etc.
Irwin, J. Vögelein **741.5**
Fiction
Colfer, E. Artemis Fowl **Fic**

De Lint, C. The blue girl (7 and up) **Fic**
McGraw, E. J. The moorchild (4 and up) **Fic**

Fairy dust. De Lint, C.
In De Lint, C. Waifs and strays p73-82 **S C**

The **Fairy** serpent
In Hearne, B. G. Beauties and beasts p29-31 **398.2**

Fairy tale series
Yolen, J. Briar Rose **Fic**

Fairy tales
See also Fantasy fiction
Barry, D. Peter and the starcatchers (5 and up) **Fic**
Ferris, J. Once upon a Marigold **Fic**
Gruber, M. The witch's boy (7 and up) **Fic**
Hale, S. The Goose girl **Fic**
Hearne, B. G. Beauties and beasts **398.2**
Kindl, P. Goose chase **Fic**
Levine, G. C. The princess test (4 and up) **Fic**
McKinley, R. Beauty (7 and up) **Fic**
McKinley, R. The door in the hedge **S C**
McKinley, R. Rose daughter **Fic**
Napoli, D. J. Beast (7 and up) **Fic**
Napoli, D. J. Spinners (7 and up) **Fic**
Napoli, D. J. Zel (7 and up) **Fic**
Pattou, E. East **Fic**
Philip, N. Celtic fairy tales (4 and up) **398.2**
Vande Velde, V. Tales from the Brothers Grimm and the Sisters Weird **S C**
Wrede, P. C. Dealing with dragons (6 and up) **Fic**
Yeoman, J. The Seven voyages of Sinbad the Sailor (5 and up) **398.2**

Faisal, King of Saudi Arabia, 1906-1975
See/See also pages in the following book(s):
Reed, J. The Saudi royal family **920**

Faisal ibn Abdul-Aziz al Saud See Faisal, King of Saudi Arabia, 1906-1975

Un **faite**. Saldaña, R.
In Saldaña, R. Finding our way: stories p67-74 **S C**

Faith
Gaskins, P. I believe in— **200**

Faith in America [series]
Buxbaum, S. M. Jewish faith in America **296**
Murphy, L. African-American faith in America **200**

Faizabad harvest, 1980. Staples, S. F.
In Shattered: stories of children and war p108-21 **S C**

The **falcon**. Palmer, G.
In Theatre for young audiences; 20 great plays for children p338-63 **812.008**

The **falconmaster**. La Fevers, R. L. **Fic**

Falcons
Fiction
La Fevers, R. L. The falconmaster **Fic**

Fall of a kingdom. See Bell, H. Flame **Fic**

The **fall** of the house of Usher. Poe, E. A.
  In Poe, E. A. Edgar Allan Poe's tales of mystery and madness **S C**
  In Poe, E. A. Tales of Edgar Allan Poe p127-52 **S C**
The **fall** of the Roman Empire. Nardo, D. **937**
The **fall** of Ys. Pierce, M. A.
  In Firebirds: an anthology of original fantasy and science fiction; an anthology of original fantasy and science fiction **S C**
Fallen angels. Myers, W. D. **Fic**
Falling from fire. Booth, T. **Fic**
Falling off the Empire State Building. Mazer, H.
  In Ultimate sports; short stories by outstanding writers for young adults p302-13 **S C**
Falling up. Silverstein, S. **811**
The **false** knight on the road. Yolen, J.
  In Yolen, J. Mightier than the sword; world folktales for strong boys p74-77 **398.2**

Falsehood *See* Truthfulness and falsehood
Fame and glory in Freedom, Georgia. O'Connor, B. **Fic**
Familiar quotations. Bartlett, J. **808.88**
Family
  Blue, R. Staying out of trouble in a troubled family (7 and up) **362.7**
  The Family: opposing viewpoints (7 and up) **306.8**
  Presma, F. Straight talk about today's families (7 and up) **306.8**
The **family** Haggadah. Schecter, E. **296.4**
Family histories *See* Genealogy
A **family** illness: a mom-son conversation. Thomas, J. C.
  In Necessary noise: stories about our families as they really are p97-128 **S C**
Family life
  Twain, M. The adventures of Tom Sawyer (5 and up) **Fic**
Fiction
  Almond, D. Counting stars (7 and up) **Fic**
  Alvarez, J. Before we were free (7 and up) **Fic**
  Anderson, J. The last treasure (5 and up) **Fic**
  Armstrong, W. H. Sounder (5 and up) **Fic**
  Arrington, F. Prairie whispers (5 and up) **Fic**
  Banks, K. Walk softly, Rachel (7 and up) **Fic**
  Baskin, N. R. Almost home **Fic**
  Bruchac, J. Hidden roots **Fic**
  Byars, B. C. The keeper of the doves (4 and up) **Fic**
  Caseley, J. Losing Louisa (7 and up) **Fic**
  Choldenko, G. Notes from a liar and her dog (5 and up) **Fic**
  Clarke, J. Wolf on the fold (7 and up) **Fic**
  Clinton, C. A stone in my hand **Fic**
  Cohn, R. The Steps (4 and up) **Fic**
  Creech, S. Absolutely normal chaos (5 and up) **Fic**

Creech, S. Chasing Redbird (5 and up) **Fic**
Creech, S. Walk two moons (6 and up) **Fic**
Crum, S. Spitting image **Fic**
Cummings, P. Saving Grace (5 and up) **Fic**
Curtis, C. P. The Watsons go to Birmingham—1963 (4 and up) **Fic**
Cushman, K. The ballad of Lucy Whipple (5 and up) **Fic**
Danziger, P. The pistachio prescription **Fic**
Delacre, L. Salsa stories (4-6) **S C**
Dowell, F. O. Chicken boy (4 and up) **Fic**
Fine, A. The true story of Christmas (4 and up) **Fic**
Fleischman, S. Bo & Mzzz Mad (5 and up) **Fic**
Fogelin, A. Sister spider knows all (5 and up) **Fic**
Frank, L. K. Oy, Joy! **Fic**
Gantos, J. Jack on the tracks (5 and up) **Fic**
Garland, S. Shadow of the dragon **Fic**
Grove, V. Destiny (5 and up) **Fic**
Hahn, M. D. Daphne's book (5 and up) **Fic**
Hamilton, V. Time pieces (5 and up) **Fic**
Hartnett, S. Thursday's child (7 and up) **Fic**
Henkes, K. The birthday room (5 and up) **Fic**
Henkes, K. Olive's ocean (5 and up) **Fic**
Hite, S. Those darn Dithers **Fic**
Holm, J. L. Our only May Amelia (5 and up) **Fic**
Ingold, J. Mountain solo (7 and up) **Fic**
Janke, K. Survival in the storm **Fic**
Johnson, A. Toning the sweep **Fic**
Joseph, L. The color of my words (5 and up) **Fic**
Juby, S. Alice, I think (7 and up) **Fic**
Kimmel, E. C. Lily B. on the brink of cool **Fic**
Klise, K. Deliver us from Normal **Fic**
Koller, J. F. Someday **Fic**
Lasky, K. Christmas after all **Fic**
Levitin, S. Journey to America (4 and up) **Fic**
Love, D. A. A year without rain (5 and up) **Fic**
Lowry, L. Anastasia Krupnik (4-6) **Fic**
Mackler, C. The earth, my butt, and other big, round things (7 and up) **Fic**
MacLachlan, P. Journey (4 and up) **Fic**
Martin, A. M. Here today (5 and up) **Fic**
Mathis, S. B. Teacup full of roses (7 and up) **Fic**
McKay, H. Saffy's angel (5 and up) **Fic**
Meyer, C. Gideon's people **Fic**
Moranville, S. B. Over the river (5 and up) **Fic**
Myracle, L. Eleven (4 and up) **Fic**
Na, A. A step from heaven (7 and up) **Fic**
Naylor, P. R. Ice **Fic**
Naylor, P. R. Reluctantly Alice **Fic**
Necessary noise: stories about our families as they really are (7 and up) **S C**
Paterson, K. Preacher's boy (5 and up) **Fic**
Peck, R. Fair weather (5 and up) **Fic**
Peck, R. The last safe place on earth (7 and up) **Fic**

Family life—Fiction—*Continued*

Pevsner, S. Is everyone moonburned but me?
    Fic

Pfeffer, S. B. The year without Michael   **Fic**

Plummer, L. The unlikely romance of Kate Bjorkman (7 and up)   **Fic**

Rinaldi, A. A stitch in time (7 and up)   **Fic**

Ryan, P. M. Becoming Naomi León (5 and up)
    Fic

Rylant, C. A fine white dust (5 and up)   **Fic**

Son, J. Finding my hat   **Fic**

Sonenklar, C. My own worst enemy   **Fic**

Tolan, S. S. Surviving the Applewhites   **Fic**

Uchida, Y. A jar of dreams (5 and up)   **Fic**

Williams-Garcia, R. Like sisters on the homefront (7 and up)   **Fic**

Wilson, J. The suitcase kid   **Fic**

Wynne-Jones, T. Stephen Fair (7 and up)
    Fic

Young, K. R. The Beetle and me (7 and up)
    Fic

Zeises, L. M. Contents under pressure (7 and up)   **Fic**

See/See also pages in the following book(s):

Sleator, W. Oddballs (6 and up)   **S C**

Poetry

Smith, H. A. The way a door closes (4 and up)
    811

The **Family:** opposing viewpoints (7 and up)
    306.8

The **family** tree detective. Douglas, A.   **929**

Family violence *See* Domestic violence

Family violence (7 and up)   **362.82**

Famines

Bartoletti, S. C. Black potatoes (7 and up)
    941.5

Dolan, E. F. The Irish potato famine   **941.5**

Feed the children first   **941.5**

Fiction

Giff, P. R. Nory Ryan's song (5 and up)
    Fic

Heneghan, J. The grave   **Fic**

Famous first facts. Kane, J. N.   **031.02**

Famous prisons. Lock, J.   **365**

Famous trials [series]

Lukes, B. L. The Boston Massacre   **973.3**

Romaine, D. S. Roe v. Wade   **344**

Fanaticism

Fiction

Crew, L. Brides of Eden (7 and up)   **Fic**

Fancy dress *See* Costume

The **fantastic** book of snow-boarding. McKenna, L.   **796.93**

Fantastic feats and failures (4 and up)   **624.1**

Fantastic fiction *See* Fantasy fiction

Fantasy fiction

See also Fairy tales; Science fiction

Aiken, J. Shadows and moonshine (4 and up)
    S C

Alexander, L. The Arkadians (5 and up)   **Fic**

Alexander, L. The book of three (5 and up)
    Fic

Alexander, L. The foundling and other tales of Prydain (5 and up)   **S C**

Alexander, L. Gypsy Rizka (5 and up)   **Fic**

Alexander, L. The high king (5 and up)   **Fic**

Almond, D. Skellig (5 and up)   **Fic**

Alton, S. The Malifex   **Fic**

Barker, C. Abarat (7 and up)   **Fic**

Barron, T. A. The lost years of Merlin (6 and up)   **Fic**

Barron, T. A. The Merlin effect   **Fic**

Bath, K. P. The secret of Castle Cant (5 and up)
    Fic

The Book of dragons   **S C**

Bradbury, R. The Halloween tree   **Fic**

Chabon, M. Summerland (5 and up)   **Fic**

Clement-Davies, D. Fire bringer (7 and up)
    Fic

Colfer, E. Artemis Fowl   **Fic**

Collins, S. Gregor the Overlander (4 and up)
    Fic

Constable, K. The singer of all songs (7 and up)
    Fic

Cooper, S. Over sea, under stone (5 and up)
    Fic

Coville, B. The skull of truth (4 and up)
    Fic

Del Vecchio, G. The Pearl of Anton (7 and up)
    Fic

Dunkle, C. B. The hollow kingdom   **Fic**

Farmer, N. The Sea of Trolls (5 and up)
    Fic

Firebirds: an anthology of original fantasy and science fiction (7 and up)   **S C**

Fisher, C. The oracle betrayed   **Fic**

Fisk, P. Midnight blue   **Fic**

Fletcher, S. Dragon's milk (7 and up)   **Fic**

Foster, A. D. The Hand of Dinotopia   **Fic**

Gurney, J. Dinotopia [and other titles in series]
    Fic

Half-human (7 and up)   **S C**

Haptie, C. Otto and the flying twins (4 and up)
    Fic

Hunter, E. Into the wild   **Fic**

Ibbotson, E. Island of the aunts (5 and up)
    Fic

Jacques, B. Castaways of the Flying Dutchman
    Fic

Jacques, B. Redwall (6 and up)   **Fic**

Jarvis, R. The dark portal (5 and up)   **Fic**

Jarvis, R. Thorn ogres of Hagwood   **Fic**

Jones, D. W. Cart and cwidder (7 and up)
    Fic

Jones, D. W. Castle in the air (6 and up)
    Fic

Jones, D. W. Howl's moving castle (6 and up)
    Fic

Jones, D. W. Unexpected magic   **S C**

Jordan, S. The hunting of the last dragon
    Fic

Jordan, S. Secret sacrament (7 and up)   **Fic**

Kaaberbol, L. The Shamer's daughter   **Fic**

Langrish, K. Troll Fell (5 and up)   **Fic**

Le Guin, U. K. Gifts (7 and up)   **Fic**

L'Engle, M. A wrinkle in time (5 and up)
    Fic

Levine, G. C. Ella enchanted (5 and up)
    Fic

Levine, G. C. The two princesses of Bamarre (5 and up)   **Fic**

Fantasy fiction—*Continued*

Lewis, C. S. The lion, the witch, and the wardrobe (4 and up)   **Fic**

McCaffrey, A. {The Pern series} (7 and up)   **Fic**

McCaffrey, L. W. Alia waking   **Fic**

McCaughrean, G. The stones are hatching (5 and up)   **Fic**

McGraw, E. J. The moorchild (4 and up)   **Fic**

McKinley, R. The blue sword (7 and up)   **Fic**

McKinley, R. The hero and the crown (6 and up)   **Fic**

McKinley, R. Water: tales of elemental spirits (7 and up)   **S C**

McNaughton, J. An earthly knight (7 and up)   **Fic**

Nix, G. Mister Monday   **Fic**

Nix, G. Sabriel   **Fic**

Oppel, K. Airborn (7 and up)   **Fic**

Paolini, C. Eragon (7 and up)   **Fic**

Pierce, M. A. Treasure at the heart of the Tanglewood   **Fic**

Pierce, T. Circle of magic: Sandry's book   **Fic**

Pierce, T. First test   **Fic**

Pierce, T. Trickster's choice (7 and up)   **Fic**

Pratchett, T. The amazing Maurice and his educated rodents (7 and up)   **Fic**

Pratchett, T. The Wee Free Men   **Fic**

Pullman, P. The amber spyglass (7 and up)   **Fic**

Pullman, P. The golden compass (7 and up)   **Fic**

Pullman, P. The subtle knife (7 and up)   **Fic**

Randall, D. Clovermead (7 and up)   **Fic**

Rupp, R. The waterstone   **Fic**

Sage, A. Magyk . (5 and up)   **Fic**

Shinn, S. The Safe-Keeper's secret   **Fic**

Smith, S. Crown duel (7 and up)   **Fic**

Snyder, M. Hannah's garden (7 and up)   **Fic**

Stroud, J. The Amulet of Samarkand (7 and up)   **Fic**

Swift, J. Gulliver's travels (7 and up)   **Fic**

Thesman, J. Singer (7 and up)   **Fic**

Tolkien, J. R. R. The hobbit (4 and up)   **Fic**

Tolkien, J. R. R. The lord of the rings (7 and up)   **Fic**

Williams, M. The golden hour   **Fic**

Yolen, J. Briar Rose   **Fic**

Yolen, J. Passager   **Fic**

History and criticism

MacRae, C. D. Presenting young adult fantasy fiction (7 and up)   **813.009**

Fantasy origami. Nguyen, D.   **736**

Far Eastern art. Doherty, C.
In International encyclopedia of art   **703**

Far North. Hobbs, W.   **Fic**

The **far** side of evil. Engdahl, S. L.   **Fic**

Far traveler. Tingle, R.   **Fic**

Faragher, John Mack, 1945-
(ed) The American Heritage encyclopedia of American history. See The American Heritage encyclopedia of American history   **973.03**

Farewell to Jim Crow. Rasmussen, R. K.   **305.8**

Farewell to Manzanar. Houston, J. W.   **940.53**

Farish, Leah
Tinker v. Des Moines (7 and up)   **342**

Farley, Carol J.
Sim Chung and the dragon king
In Fire and wings: dragon tales from East and West p87-94   **S C**

Farlow, James Orville, 1951-
Bringing dinosaur bones to life (5 and up)   **567.9**

Farm animals *See* Domestic animals

A **farm** at Raraba. Havemann, E.
In Somehow tenderness survives; stories of Southern Africa p119-34   **S C**

Farm laborers *See* Agricultural laborers

Farm life
Bial, R. Portrait of a farm family (4 and up)   **630.1**

Fiction

Avi. The barn (4 and up)   **Fic**

Brooke, P. Jake's orphan   **Fic**

Conly, J. L. What happened on Planet Kid   **Fic**

Doyle, E. F. Stray voltage   **Fic**

Hartnett, S. Thursday's child (7 and up)   **Fic**

Hesse, K. Out of the dust (5 and up)   **Fic**

Hite, S. A hole in the world (7 and up)   **Fic**

Naylor, P. R. Ice   **Fic**

Paterson, K. Park's quest (5 and up)   **Fic**

Paulsen, G. Alida's song (5 and up)   **Fic**

Paulsen, G. Harris and me (5 and up)   **Fic**

Paulsen, G. The winter room (5 and up)   **Fic**

Peck, R. N. A day no pigs would die (6 and up)   **Fic**

Stahler, D., Jr. A gathering of shades (7 and up)   **Fic**

Farmer, Lesley S. Johnson, 1949-
Student success and library media programs   **027.8**

Farmer, Nancy, 1941-
The Ear, the Eye, and the Arm (6 and up)   **Fic**

A girl named Disaster (6 and up)   **Fic**

The house of the scorpion (7 and up)   **Fic**

Remember me
In Firebirds: an anthology of original fantasy and science fiction; an anthology of original fantasy and science fiction   **S C**

The Sea of Trolls (5 and up)   **Fic**

Farmers
See/See also pages in the following book(s):
Collier, C. Indians, cowboys, and farmers and the battle for the Great Plains, 1865-1910   **978**

Farming *See* Agriculture

Farms
Halley, N. Farm (4 and up)   **630.1**

Farmworker's friend: the story of Cesar Chavez. Collins, D. R.   **92**

Farndon, John
Aluminum
In The Elements   **546**

Farndon, John—*Continued*
Buoyancy 532
Chemicals 540.7
Energy 531
Gravity 531
Hydrogen
  In The Elements 546
Motion 531
Nitrogen
  In The Elements 546
Oxygen
  In The Elements 546
Rocks and minerals 549
Solids, liquids, and gases 530.4
Time 529
Farnsworth, Bill
(il) Kroll, S. Robert Fulton 92
Farnsworth, Philo T., 1906-1971
About
McPherson, S. S. TV's forgotten hero: the story of Philo Farnsworth 92
Farrakhan, Louis, 1933-
About
De Angelis, T. Louis Farrakhan 92
Farrand, John, 1937-1994
(jt. auth) Bull, J. L. The National Audubon Society field guide to North American birds, Eastern region 598
(il) Udvardy, M. D. F. National Audubon Society field guide to North American birds, Western region 598
Farrell, Donna L.
(il) Marks, D. F. Let's celebrate today
  394.26
Farrell, Jeanette
Invisible allies 579
Invisible enemies (7 and up) 614.4
Farrell, Juliana
High school, the real deal 373.1
Middle school, the real deal 373.1
Farrell, Mame
And sometimes why Fic
Fascism
Germany
  See National socialism
Fashion
  See also Clothing and dress; Costume
Pendergast, S. Fashion, costume, and culture
  391
Fashion, costume, and culture. Pendergast, S.
  391
Fashion design
Kent, J. Business builders in fashion 920
Fashions of a decade [series] 391
Fast, Howard, 1914-2003
April morning (7 and up) Fic
Fast forward [series]
Malam, J. Super structures 624
Faster and faster. Schwartz, A.
  In Schwartz, A. Scary stories 3; more tales to chill your bones p10-11 398.2
Fasts and feasts *See* Religious holidays

Judaism
  See Jewish holidays
Fat kid rules the world. Going, K. L. Fic
The **fata**. San Souci, R.
  In San Souci, R. A terrifying taste of short & shivery; thirty creepy tales p12-14
  398.2
Father-daughter relationship
Fiction
Abelove, J. Saying it out loud (7 and up)
  Fic
Brooks, B. Midnight hour encores (7 and up)
  Fic
Henkes, K. Protecting Marie (5 and up) Fic
Hobbs, V. Tender (7 and up) Fic
Mack, T. Drawing lessons Fic
Napoli, D. J. Spinners (7 and up) Fic
Swanson, J. A. Going for the record (7 and up)
  Fic
Taylor, T. Sweet Friday Island (7 and up)
  Fic
Father-son relationship
Fiction
Avi. The barn (4 and up) Fic
Bartoletti, S. C. No man's land (5 and up)
  Fic
Calvert, P. Bigger (5 and up) Fic
Cormier, R. In the middle of the night (7 and up) Fic
Crist-Evans, C. Amaryllis (7 and up) Fic
Crutcher, C. Ironman Fic
Durbin, W. Blackwater Ben (5 and up) Fic
Fuqua, J. S. The Willoughby Spit wonder
  Fic
Griffin, A. Sons of liberty Fic
Kehret, P. Searching for Candlestick Park
  Fic
Koss, A. G. Stranger in Dadland (5 and up)
  Fic
Lee, M. G. Necessary roughness (7 and up)
  Fic
Lupica, M. Travel team Fic
Lynch, C. Shadow boxer (7 and up) Fic
Myers, A. The keeping room Fic
Myers, W. D. Somewhere in the darkness (7 and up) Fic
Ritter, J. H. Choosing up sides Fic
Trueman, T. Stuck in neutral Fic
Vanasse, D. Out of the wilderness Fic
Fathers
  See also Stepfathers
Dennison, A. Our dad died (4 and up)
  155.9
Fiction
Deuker, C. High heat (7 and up) Fic
Fleischman, P. Seek (7 and up) Fic
Golding, T. M. The secret within Fic
Heneghan, J. Flood Fic
Holmes, B. W. Following Fake Man Fic
Lyon, G. E. Gina.Jamie.Father.Bear Fic
Mills, C. Alex Ryan, stop that! (5 and up)
  Fic
Nelson, T. Ruby electric (5 and up) Fic
Torres, L. Crossing Montana (7 and up) Fic

Fathers—*Continued*
Poetry
Smith, H. A. The way a door closes (4 and up)
811

Fathers, Single parent *See* Single parent family
Fathers and sons *See* Father-son relationship
Favorite children's authors and illustrators
920.003
Favorite medieval tales. Osborne, M. P.   398.2
Fazio, Wende
West Virginia
In America the beautiful, second series
973

FBI *See* United States. Federal Bureau of Investigation

FDA *See* United States. Food and Drug Administration

The **FDA** and psychiatric drugs. Esherick, J.
Fear
Crist, J. J. What to do when you're scared & worried (5 and up)   152.4
Fiction
Stauffacher, S. Donuthead (4-6)   **Fic**
Fear. Davies, R.
In Read all about it!; great read-aloud stories, poems, and newspaper pieces for preteens and teens p223-29   808.8
The **fear** place. Naylor, P. R.   **Fic**
Feast of Lights *See* Hanukkah
Feathered dinosaurs. Sloan, C.   567.9
Federal Bureau of Investigation (U.S.) *See* United States. Federal Bureau of Investigation
Fee, fie, foe, et cetera. Maguire, G.
In The Green Man: tales from the mythic forest p238-59   808.8
Feed the children first   941.5
Feelings, Tom, 1933-2003
The middle passage (7 and up)   759.13
(il) Soul looks back in wonder. See Soul looks back in wonder   811.008
The **Feester** filibuster. Griffis, M. L.   **Fic**
Feiffer, Jules
The man in the ceiling (4 and up)   **Fic**
Feiler, Bruce S.
Walking the Bible   222
Feinberg, Barbara Silberdick, 1938-
The Articles of Confederation (7 and up)
342
The cabinet   352.24
The changing White House   975.3
The dictionary of the U.S. Constitution   342
Douglas MacArthur   92
Feldman, George
Understanding the Holocaust   940.53
World War II: almanac   940.53
Feldman, Jane
(jt. auth) Lanier, S. Jefferson's children   920
Feldman, Roxanne Hsu
(jt. auth) Minkel, W. Delivering Web reference services to young people   025.04
Feldman, Ruth Tenzer
The Korean War (5 and up)   951.9

The Mexican-American War (5 and up)
973.6
World War I   940.3
Felix, Antonia
(jt. auth) Christian, S. Shake, rattle, and roll
551.2
Fellenbaum, Charlie
(il) Jackson, D. M. The bone detectives   614
Female circumcision
Fiction
Williams-Garcia, R. No laughter here (7 and up)
Fic
Female firsts in their fields [series]
DeAngelis, G. Science & medicine   920
Jones, V. B. Government & politics   920
Female role *See* Sex role
Feminine psychology *See* Women—Psychology
Feminism
33 things every girl should know about women's history (5 and up)   305.4
Brezina, C. Sojourner Truth's "Ain't I a woman?" speech   92
Butler, M. G. Sojourner Truth (5 and up)
92
Cullen-DuPont, K. Encyclopedia of women's history in America   305.4
Kendall, M. E. Failure is impossible!   305.4
Krass, P. Sojourner Truth   92
Lazo, C. E. Gloria Steinem (7 and up)   92
Miller, C. C. Mary Wollstonecraft and the rights of women (7 and up)   92
Sigerman, H. Elizabeth Cady Stanton (7 and up)
92
Stearman, K. Feminism (7 and up)   305.4
Todras, E. H. Angelina Grimké (7 and up)
92
Weisberg, B. Susan B. Anthony   92
Wheaton, E. Ms: the story of Gloria Steinem
92

See/See also pages in the following book(s):
Gray, H. M. Real girl/real world (7 and up)
305.23
Fiction
Thesman, J. The ornament tree (7 and up)
Fic
Thesman, J. The tree of bells (7 and up)
Fic
Poetry
I wouldn't thank you for a valentine   808.81
Fenner, Carol
The king of dragons (5 and up)   **Fic**
Randall's wall   **Fic**
Yolonda's genius (4-6)   **Fic**
Feral children *See* Wild children
Ferdinand V, King of Spain, 1452-1516
About
Mann, K. Isabel, Ferdinand and fifteenth-century Spain   946
Ferguson, Alane, 1957-
Satan's shadow
In Night terrors; stories of shadow and substance   **S C**
(jt. auth) Skurzynski, G. Cliff hanger   **Fic**
Ferguson's career biographies [series]
Blashfield, J. F. Leonard Bernstein   92

Fermi, Enrico, 1901-1954
    About
Cooper, D. Enrico Fermi and the revolutions in modern physics (7 and up)   **92**

Ferraro, Geraldine A.
See/See also pages in the following book(s):
Jones, V. B. Government & politics   **920**

Ferrell, L. W.
    About
Trespacz, K. L. Ferrell v. Dallas I.S.D. (7 and up)   **344**

Ferrell, Nancy Warren
The Battle of the Little Bighorn in American history   **973.8**

Ferri, Giuliano
(il) Sullivan, A. M. Albert Einstein   **92**

Ferrie, Richard
The world turned upside down (5 and up)   **973.3**

Ferris, Jean, 1939-
Eight seconds (7 and up)   **Fic**
Love among the walnuts (7 and up)   **Fic**
Of sound mind (7 and up)   **Fic**
Once upon a Marigold   **Fic**

Ferroa, Peggy Grace
China (5 and up)   **951**

Ferry, Joseph, 1954-
Maria Goeppert Mayer, physicist (7 and up)   **92**

Ferry, Steven, 1953-
Ontario
  In Exploring Canada   **971**
Quebec
  In Exploring Canada   **971**
Yukon Territory
  In Exploring Canada   **971**

Fertilization in vitro
Fullick, A. Test tube babies (7 and up)   **618.1**
Orr, T. Test tube babies (5 and up)   **618.1**

Festivals
Breuilly, E. Festivals of the world   **394.26**
Doney, M. Festivals   **745.5**
Festivals and holidays   **394.26**
The Folklore of world holidays   **394.26**
Heath, A. Windows on the world   **394.2**
Holidays, festivals and celebrations of the world dictionary   **394.26**
Junior worldmark encyclopedia of world holidays   **394.26**
Marks, D. F. Let's celebrate today   **394.26**
Rajtar, S. United States holidays and observances   **394.26**
    Bibliography
Matthew, K. I. Neal-Schuman guide to celebrations & holidays around the world   **394.26**
    United States
The American book of days   **394.26**
The Folklore of the American holidays   **394.26**

Festivals and holidays   **394.26**
Festivals of the world. Breuilly, E.   **394.26**
Fever, 1793. Anderson, L. H.   **Fic**

Feynman, Richard Phillips, 1918-1988
See/See also pages in the following book(s):
Henderson, H. Nuclear physics (7 and up)   **539.7**

Fibers
See/See also pages in the following book(s):
Knapp, B. J. Materials science   **620.1**

Fiction
  See also Adventure fiction; Fairy tales; Fantasy fiction; Horror fiction; Love stories; Mystery fiction; School stories; Science fiction; Sea stories; Short stories; War stories
    Bibliography
Anderson, V. Fiction sequels for readers 10 to 16   **016.8**
Makowski, S. Serious about series   **016.8**

Fiction, food, and fun. Closter, K.   **028.5**
Fiction sequels for readers 10 to 16. Anderson, V.   **016.8**

The **fiddler.** San Souci, R.
  In San Souci, R. A terrifying taste of short & shivery; thirty creepy tales p15-19   **398.2**

The **fiddler** in the cave. Philip, N.
  In Philip, N. Celtic fairy tales p119-20   **398.2**

Fiddling with fire. Olson, A. N.
  In Olson, A. N. and Schwartz, H. Ask the bones: scary stories from around the world p46-52   **398.2**

Field, Elinor Whitney, 1889-1980
(ed) Newbery Medal books, 1922-1955. See Newbery Medal books, 1922-1955   **028.5**

Field athletics *See* Track athletics

A **field** guide to Atlantic coast fishes of North America. Robins, C. R.   **597**
A **field** guide to freshwater fishes: North America north of Mexico. Page, L. M.   **597**
A **field** guide to Pacific states wildflowers. Niehaus, T. F.   **582.13**
A **field** guide to rocks and minerals. Pough, F. H.   **549**
A **field** guide to the birds. See Peterson, R. T. A field guide to the birds of eastern and central North America   **598**
A **field** guide to the birds of eastern and central North America. Peterson, R. T.   **598**
A **field** guide to the stars and planets. Pasachoff, J. M.   **523**
A **field** guide to trees and shrubs. Petrides, G. A.   **582.16**
A **field** guide to western birds. Peterson, R. T.   **598**
Field guide to wildflowers, eastern region. See Thieret, J. W. National Audubon Society field guide to North American wildflowers: eastern region   **582.13**

Field Museum of Natural History
Relf, P. A dinosaur named Sue: the story of the colossal fossil: the world's most complete T. rex   **567.9**

Field trips
Cooper, G. New virtual field trips   **025.5**

Fielding, Eileen
The Eastern forest   577.3
Fields, Debbl
See/See also pages in the following book(s):
Jeffrey, L. S. Great American businesswomen
    920
Fields, Terri, 1948-
After the death of Anna Gonzales (7 and up)
    811
Fields of fury. McPherson, J. M.   973.7
Fieser, Stephen
(il) Major, J. S. The Silk Route   950
Fiesta femenina. Gerson, M.-J.   398.2
Fifteen hundred. See Schomp, V. 1500   909.08
Fifteen love. Corbet, R.   Fic
The **Fifth** Amendment. Fireside, H.   347
The **fifth** of March. Rinaldi, A.   Fic
The **fight** between the animals and insects. Curry,
J. L.
    In Curry, J. L. Hold up the sky: and other
    Native American tales from Texas and
    the Southern Plains p77-80   398.2
Fight for freedom. Bobrick, B.   973.3
Fight on!: Mary Church Terrell's battle for inte-
gration. Fradin, D. B.   92
Fighter. Myers, W. D.
    In Myers, W. D. 145th Street; short stories
    S C
Fighting for honor. Cooper, M. L.   940.53
The **fighting** ground. Avi   Fic
Fighting Ruben Wolfe. Zusak, M.   Fic
Figs and fate. Marston, E.   S C
Fiji
    NgCheong-Lum, R. Fiji (5 and up)   996
Filipino Americans
Fiction
De la Cruz, M. Fresh off the boat (7 and up)
    Fic
Filipovic, Zlata
Zlata's diary   92
Film. Jones, S.   791.43
Film and photography. Graham, I.   770
Film direction *See* Motion pictures—Production
and direction
Film production *See* Motion pictures—Production
and direction
Filmmaking *See* Motion pictures—Production and
direction
Films *See* Motion pictures
Filo, David
About
Sherman, J. Jerry Yang and David Filo   92
The **final** problem. Doyle, Sir A. C.
    In Doyle, Sir A. C. The complete Sherlock
    Holmes   S C
Financiers *See* Capitalists and financiers
Finch, Christopher, 1939-
The art of Walt Disney (7 and up)   791.43
Find where the wind goes. Jemison, M. C.   92
Finding H.F. Watts, J.   Fic
Finding miracles. Alvarez, J.   Fic

Finding my hat. Son, J.   Fic
Finding our way. Saldaña, R.
    In Saldaña, R. Finding our way: stories p94-
    [117]   S C
Finding our way: stories. Saldaña, R.   S C
Finding your way. Dewey, J.   796.5
Fine, Anne
Flour babies (6 and up)   Fic
The true story of Christmas (4 and up)   Fic
Up on cloud nine (5 and up)   Fic
Fine, Edith Hope
Barbara McClintock (7 and up)   92
Gary Paulsen (5 and up)   92
Fine?. Haddix, M. P.
    In On the edge: stories at the brink p59-80
    S C
Fine arts *See* Arts
A **fine** white dust. Rylant, C.   Fic
"The **finest** story in the world". Kipling, R.
    In McCaffrey, A. {The Pern series}   S C
Fingerprints
Tocci, S. High-tech IDs (7 and up)   599.9
Finkelstein, Norman H., 1941-
Remember not to forget (4 and up)   940.53
Finlayson, Reggie
Colin Powell   92
Nelson Mandela   92
We shall overcome   323.1
Finley, Carol
Aboriginal art of Australia   759.01
The art of African masks (5 and up)   391
Finn MacCool and the Scottish giant. Philip, N.
    In Philip, N. Celtic fairy tales p73-77
    398.2
Finn Maccoul. Osborne, M. P.
    In Osborne, M. P. Favorite medieval tales
    p1-7   398.2
Finnish Americans
Fiction
Durbin, W. The journal of Otto Peltonen, a
    Finnish immigrant   Fic
Holm, J. L. Our only May Amelia (5 and up)
    Fic
Fiona and Tim. Hearne, B. G.
    In Hearne, B. G. The canine connection: sto-
    ries about dogs and people p63-69
    S C
Fire
Poetry
Singer, M. Central heating (4 and up)   811
Fire!. Masoff, J.   628.9
Fire and wings: dragon tales from East and West
    (4 and up)   S C
Fire bringer. Clement-Davies, D.   Fic
The **fire-eaters**. Almond, D.   Fic
Fire fighters
Beil, K. M. Fire in their eyes (4 and up)
    628.9
Masoff, J. Fire! (4 and up)   628.9
Fire fighting
Gorrell, G. K. Catching fire   628.9
Fire: friend or foe. Patent, D. H.   577.2

Fire in their eyes. Beil, K. M.   **628.9**

Fire on the wind. Crew, L.   **Fic**

The **fire** pond. Rosen, M. J.
   In The Color of absence; 12 stories about loss and hope p73-86   **S C**

Fire-us trilogy [series]
   Armstrong, J. The kindling   **Fic**

Firearms
   Collier, J. L. Gunpowder and weaponry   **623.4**
   Stewart, G. Guns and violence   **303.6**
         Fiction
   Fox, P. One-eyed cat (5 and up)   **Fic**
       Law and legislation
   See Gun control

Firebirds: an anthology of original fantasy and science fiction (7 and up)   **S C**

Fires
         Fiction
   Booth, T. Falling from fire (7 and up)   **Fic**
   Janeczko, P. B. Worlds afire   **Fic**
   Twomey, C. Beachmont letters (7 and up)   **Fic**
         Chicago (Ill.)
   Murphy, J. The great fire (5 and up)   **977.3**

Fireside, Bryna J.
   The trial of the police officers in the shooting death of Amadou Diallo (7 and up)

Fireside, Harvey, 1929-
   The Fifth Amendment (7 and up)   **347**
   The "Mississippi Burning" civil rights murder conspiracy trial   **345**
   New York Times v. Sullivan (7 and up)   **342**

A **firestorm** unleashed. Ayer, E. H.   **940.53**

Firmament. Bowler, T.   **Fic**

First battles [series]
   McNeese, T. Remember the Maine!   **973.8**
   Whitelaw, N. The shot heard round the world   **973.3**

First book [series]
   Anderson, M. K. So proudly they served   **940.54**
   Aronson, B. Meteors   **523.5**
   Bonar, S. Comets   **523.6**
   Bredeson, C. The moon   **523.3**
   Bredeson, C. Tide pools   **577.6**
   Conrad, D. C. The Songhay Empire   **966.2**
   Gowell, E. T. Fountains of life   **577.7**
   Green, R. L. The empire of Ghana   **966.1**
   Green, R. Tutankhamun   **932**
   Haynes, J. Egyptian dynasties   **932**
   Landau, E. Joined at birth   **616**
   Landau, E. Living with albinism   **616.5**
   Landau, E. Multiple births   **618.2**
   McGowen, T. World War II   **940.53**
   Perry, P. J. Armor to venom   **591.47**
   Rauzon, M. J. Hummingbirds   **598**
   Rauzon, M. J. Vultures   **598**
   Russmann, E. R. Nubian kingdoms   **939**
   Saign, G. The African cats   **599.75**
   Saign, G. The great apes   **599.8**
   Walsh Shepherd, D. The Klondike gold rush   **971.9**

Fire Wilson, T. H. City states of the Swahili coast   **967.6**

First civilizations. Hunter, E. C. D.   **939**

The **first** day. Jones, E. P.
   In Leaving home: stories p9-17   **808.8**

First French kiss and other traumas. Bagdasarian, A.   **Fic**

First impressions [series]
   Beardsley, J. Pablo Picasso   **92**
   Berman, A. James McNeill Whistler   **92**
   Greenfeld, H. Paul Gauguin   **92**
   Meryman, R. Andrew Wyeth   **92**
   Rayfield, S. Pierre-Auguste Renoir   **92**
   Rubin, S. G. Frank Lloyd Wright   **92**
   Schwartz, G. Hieronymus Bosch   **92**

First in peace: George Washington, the Constitution, and the presidency. Rosenburg, J. M.   **92**

First job. Soto, G.
   In Soto, G. Local news p26-34   **S C**

First on the moon. Hehner, B.   **629.45**

The **first** part last. Johnson, A.   **Fic**

First peoples [series]
   LoBaido, A. C. The Kurds of Asia   **950**
   Robinson, D. B. The Sami of Northern Europe   **948**
   Theunissen, S. The Maori of New Zealand   **993**

First person America [series]
   Brown, G. Conflict in Europe and the Great Depression   **973.9**

First person fiction [series]
   Danticat, E. Behind the mountains   **Fic**
   Son, J. Finding my hat   **Fic**
   Veciana-Suarez, A. The flight to freedom   **Fic**

First test. Pierce, T.   **Fic**

The **First** World War. Kirchberger, J. H.   **940.3**

Fischer, David
   The encyclopedia of the Summer Olympics (4 and up)   **796.48**

Fish   **597**

Fish culture
   See also Aquariums

The **fish** damsel. Molnár, I.
   In Molnár, I. One-time dog market at Buda and other Hungarian folktales p64-70   **398.2**

A **fish** story. San Souci, R.
   In San Souci, R. A terrifying taste of short & shivery; thirty creepy tales p25-29   **398.2**

Fish watching with Eugenie Clark. Ross, M. E.   **92**

Fisher, Catherine
   The oracle betrayed   **Fic**

Fisher, Jane Smith
   WJHC: on the air!   **741.5**

Fisher, Julieta Dias
   (jt. auth) Hill, A. Tooting your own horn   **021.7**

Fisher, Leonard Everett, 1924-
The Oregon Trail (4 and up)   **979.5**
To bigotry, no sanction (4 and up)   **296**
Fisher, Mel
About
Matsen, B. The incredible search for the treasure
ship Atocha (4 and up)   **910.4**
Fisher, Teresa
France   **641.5**
The **fisherman** and the chamberlain. Yolen, J.
In Yolen, J. Mightier than the sword; world
folktales for strong boys p52-55
     398.2
Fishes
See also Aquariums
Buttfield, H. The secret life of fishes   **597**
Fish   **597**
Mills, D. Aquarium fish   **639.34**
Ross, M. E. Fish watching with Eugenie Clark
(4 and up)   **92**
North America
Page, L. M. A field guide to freshwater fishes:
North America north of Mexico (7 and up)
     597
Robins, C. R. A field guide to Atlantic coast
fishes of North America   **597**
Fishing
Fitzgerald, R. Essential fishing for teens
     799.1
Fiction
Bauer, M. D. An early winter   **Fic**
DeFelice, C. C. Death at Devil's Bridge (5 and
up)   **Fic**
Hobbs, W. Leaving Protection (7 and up)
     Fic
Philbrick, W. R. The young man and the sea (5
and up)   **Fic**
Salisbury, G. Lord of the deep (5 and up)
     Fic
Fisk, Pauline
Midnight blue   **Fic**
The secret of Sabrina Fludde   **Fic**
Fisk Jubilee Singers (Musical group) *See* Jubilee
Singers (Musical group)
Fitzgerald, F. Scott (Francis Scott), 1896-1940
About
Lazo, C. E. F. Scott Fitzgerald   **92**
Fitzgerald, Francis Scott *See* Fitzgerald, F. Scott
(Francis Scott), 1896-1940
Fitzgerald, John J.
(jt. auth) Young, M. B. The Vietnam War: a
history in documents   **959.704**
Fitzgerald, Ron
Essential fishing for teens   **799.1**
Five helpful hints. Peck, R.
In Peck, R. Past perfect, present tense: new
and collected stories   **S C**
The **five** orange pips. Doyle, Sir A. C.
In Doyle, Sir A. C. The complete Sherlock
Holmes   **S C**
Fixed ideas *See* Obsessive-compulsive disorder
Flag lore of all nations. Smith, W.   **929.9**
Flags
Flags of the world (4 and up)   **929.9**

Smith, W. Flag lore of all nations (4 and up)
     929.9
United States
Shearer, B. F. State names, seals, flags, and
symbols   **929.9**
Flags of our fathers. Bradley, J.   **940.54**
Flags of the world (4 and up)   **929.9**
Flake, Sharon G.
Money hungry   **Fic**
The skin I'm in   **Fic**
Who am I without him? (7 and up)   **S C**
Contents: So I ain't no good girl; The ugly one; Wanted: a
thug; I know a stupid boy when I see one; Mookie in love; Don't
be disrespecting me; I like white boys; Jacob's rules; Hunting for
boys; A letter to my daughter
Flame. Bell, H.   **Fic**
Flanagan, Alice K.
Edith Bolling Galt Wilson, 1872-1961   **92**
Flanagan, Geraldine Lux
Beginning life   **612.6**
Flanders, Stephen A.
Atlas of American migration   **304.8**
Flash!: the Associated Press covers the world
     070.4
The **flask.** Jaffe, N.
In Jaffe, N. and Zeitlin, S. J. The cow of no
color: riddle stories and justice tales from
around the world p88-91   **398.2**
Fleischman, Albert Sidney *See* Fleischman, Sid,
1920-
Fleischman, John
Phineas Gage: a gruesome but true story about
brain science   **362.1**
Fleischman, Paul
Big talk (4 and up)   **811**
The borning room (6 and up)   **Fic**
Breakout (7 and up)   **Fic**
Bull Run (6 and up)   **Fic**
A fate totally worse than death (7 and up)
     Fic
I am phoenix: poems for two voices (4 and up)
     811
Joyful noise: poems for two voices (4 and up)
     811
Mind's eye (7 and up)   **Fic**
Saturnalia (6 and up)   **Fic**
Seedfolks (4 and up)   **Fic**
Seek (7 and up)   **Fic**
Whirligig (7 and up)   **Fic**
See/See also pages in the following book(s):
The Newbery & Caldecott medal books, 1986-
2000   **028.5**
Fleischman, Sid, 1920-
The abracadabra kid (5 and up)   **92**
Bo & Mzzz Mad (5 and up)   **Fic**
The whipping boy (5 and up)   **Fic**
About
Freedman, J. Sid Fleischman (5 and up)   **92**
See/See also pages in the following book(s):
The Newbery & Caldecott medal books, 1986-
2000   **028.5**
Fleming, Alexander, 1881-1955
About
Birch, B. Alexander Fleming   **92**
Hantula, R. Alexander Fleming   **92**

Fleming, Candace
Ben Franklin's almanac (5 and up) 92

Fleshmarket. Morgan, N. **Fic**

Fletcher, Alphonse, Jr.
See/See also pages in the following book(s):
Haskins, J. African American entrepreneurs 920

Fletcher, Buddy *See* Fletcher, Alphonse, Jr.

Fletcher, Ralph, 1953-
Flying solo (5 and up) **Fic**
Have you been to the beach lately? 811
How writers work (4 and up) 808
Poetry matters (4 and up) 808.1
Spider Boy **Fic**

Fletcher, Susan, 1951-
Dragon's milk (7 and up) **Fic**
Shadow spinner (6 and up) **Fic**
Walk across the sea **Fic**

Flies
Pascoe, E. Flies 595.7

Flight. Graham, I. 629.13

Flight #116 is down. Cooney, C. B. **Fic**

The **flight** of Red Bird. Rappaport, D. 92

The **flight** of the beasts. Lee, J. M.
In Lee, J. M. I once was a monkey; stories
Buddha told 294.3

Flight of the Fisherbird. Martin, N. **Fic**

Flight of the raven. Tolan, S. S. **Fic**

The **flight** to freedom. Veciana-Suarez, A. **Fic**

Flinn, Alex
Breaking point (7 and up) **Fic**
Keep smiling
In Destination unexpected: short stories **S C**

Flinn, Alexandra *See* Flinn, Alex

Flip it!. Yucht, A. H. 025.5

Flipped. Draanen, W. v. **Fic**

Floca, Brian
(il) Gurian, M. From boys to men 305.23

A **flock** of angels. Schwartz, H.
In Schwartz, H. The day the Rabbi disappeared: Jewish holiday tales of magic p9-
13 398.2

Flodin, Mickey
(jt. auth) Butterworth, R. R. The Perigee visual
dictionary of signing 419

The **flood**. Harjo, J.
In Talking leaves; contemporary native
American short stories **S C**

Flood. Heneghan, J. **Fic**

Floods
Allaby, M. Floods (7 and up) 551.48

Florence (Italy)
History
Barter, J. Renaissance Florence 945
Greenblatt, M. Lorenzo de' Medici and Renais-
sance Italy 945

Florida
Chang, P. Florida
In Celebrate the states 973

Heinrichs, A. Florida
In America the beautiful, second series 973

Fiction
Bloor, E. Tangerine (7 and up) **Fic**
Crist-Evans, C. Amaryllis (7 and up) **Fic**
Crocker, C. The tale of the swamp rat (4 and
up) **Fic**
DiCamillo, K. Because of Winn-Dixie (4 and
up) **Fic**
Hiaasen, C. Hoot (5 and up) **Fic**
McDonald, J. Devil on my heels (7 and up) **Fic**
Mikaelsen, B. Stranded **Fic**
Norville, R. Moonshine express **Fic**
Rawlings, M. K. The yearling **Fic**

Flotsam. Hoffman, N. K.
In Firebirds: an anthology of original fantasy
and science fiction; an anthology of original fantasy and science fiction **S C**

Flour babies. Fine, A. **Fic**

Flourine
Jackson, T. Flourine
In The Elements 546

The **flower** queen's daughter. Lang, A.
In The Book of dragons p26-34 **S C**

Flowers, Helen F.
Public relations for school library media programs 021.7

Flowers
See also Wild flowers
Souza, D. M. Freaky flowers (5 and up) 582.13

Floyd, E. Randall
Great American mysteries (7 and up) 001.9

Flu *See* Influenza

Fluffy the gangbuster. Peck, R.
In Peck, R. Past perfect, present tense: new
and collected stories **S C**

Flying free. Hart, P. S. 629.13

The **Flying** Head. Bruchac, J.
In Bruchac, J. and Bruchac, J. When the
Chenoo howls; native American tales of
terror 398.2

Flying lessons. Matthews, K. **Fic**

Flying machine. Nahum, A. 629.133

The **flying** shoe. Schwartz, H.
In Schwartz, H. The day the Rabbi disappeared: Jewish holiday tales of magic
p33-35 398.2

Flying solo. Fletcher, R. **Fic**

Flying to the moon. Collins, M. 629.45

The **flying** woman. Winter, L.
In Firebirds: an anthology of original fantasy
and science fiction; an anthology of original fantasy and science fiction **S C**

Flynn, Nancy, 1956-
Dust to dust
In Soul searching: thirteen stories about faith
and belief p177-202 **S C**

Foa, Maryclare
(il) Philip, N. Odin's family 293

Focus on body image. Hinds, M. J. 306.4

Fogelin, Adrian, 1951-
Sister spider knows all (5 and up)   **Fic**

Foghorn. Lynch, C.
In Lynch, C. All the old haunts p1-21
    S C

Foley, Erin, 1967-
Costa Rica (5 and up)   **972.86**

Foley, Mike
Fundamental hockey (5 and up)   **796.962**

Foley, Ronan
World health (7 and up)   **362.1**

The **Folk** Keeper. Billingsley, F.   **Fic**

Folk lore *See* Folklore

Folk songs

United States
See also Spirituals (Songs)

Folk stories of the Hmong. Livo, N. J.   **398.2**

Folklore

See also Dragons topics as themes in folklore and names of ethnic or national groups with the subdivision *Folklore*

The Folklore of world holidays   **394.26**
Forest, H. Wisdom tales from around the world   **398.2**
Hearne, B. G. Beauties and beasts   **398.2**
Hughes, M. Popular superstitions   **398**
Jaffe, N. The cow of no color: riddle stories and justice tales from around the world (4 and up)   **398.2**
Norman, H. Between heaven and earth (4 and up)   **398.2**
Olson, A. N. Ask the bones: scary stories from around the world (4 and up)   **398.2**
San Souci, R. A terrifying taste of short & shivery (4 and up)   **398.2**
Sherman, J. Merlin's kin   **398.2**
Spencer, A. And round me rings (7 and up)   **398.2**
Yolen, J. Mightier than the sword (4 and up)   **398.2**

Dictionaries
The Dictionary of folklore (4 and up)   **398**
Myths and legends   **398**

Indexes
Index to fairy tales   **398.2**

Study and teaching
De Vos, G. New tales for old   **398.2**

Africa
African folktales   **398.2**
Bryan, A. Ashley Bryan's African tales, uh-huh (4-6)   **398.2**

China
Krasno, R. Cloud weavers (5 and up)   **398.2**
Yep, L. The rainbow people (4 and up)   **398.2**

England
See Folklore—Great Britain

Europe
Bulfinch, T. Bulfinch's mythology   **201**
Osborne, M. P. Favorite medieval tales (4 and up)   **398.2**

Great Britain
Bodger, J. Tales of court and castle (5 and up)   **398.2**

Climo, S. Magic & mischief (4 and up)   **398.2**
Philip, N. Celtic fairy tales (4 and up)   **398.2**

Hungary
Molnár, I. One-time dog market at Buda and other Hungarian folktales   **398.2**

Iraq
McCaughrean, G. The epic of Gilgamesh (5 and up)   **398.2**

Latin America
Delacre, L. Golden tales (5 and up)   **398.2**

Mexico
Gerson, M.-J. Fiesta femenina (4 and up)   **398.2**

Southern States
Curry, J. L. Hold up the sky: and other Native American tales from Texas and the Southern Plains (4 and up)   **398.2**
Tingle, T. Walking the Choctaw road (7 and up)   **398.2**
Van Laan, N. With a whoop and a holler (4 and up)   **398**

United States
The Folklore of the American holidays   **394.26**
Myths, legends, and folktales of America   **398.2**
San Souci, R. Cut from the same cloth (4 and up)   **398.2**
Schwartz, A. More scary stories to tell in the dark (4 and up)   **398.2**
Schwartz, A. Scary stories 3 (4 and up)   **398.2**
Schwartz, A. Scary stories to tell in the dark (4 and up)   **398.2**

The **Folklore** of the American holidays   **394.26**
The **Folklore** of world holidays   **394.26**

Folktales of the Native American, Dee Brown's. Brown, D. A.   **398.2**

Follow the blue. Lowry, B.   **Fic**

Follow the water. Holm, J. L.
In Shelf life: stories by the book p33-54
    S C

Following Fake Man. Holmes, B. W.   **Fic**

Following my own footsteps. Hahn, M. D.   **Fic**

Foo, Yuk Yee
(jt. auth) Munan, H. Malaysia   **959.5**

Food
Bowden, R. Food and farming   **363.8**
Haduch, B. Food rules!   **613.2**
Marshall, E. L. High-tech harvest (7 and up)   **641.3**
Pentland, P. Kitchen science (4 and up)   **641**
Solheim, J. It's disgusting—and we ate it! (4 and up)   **641.3**
See/See also pages in the following book(s):
Chahrour, J. Zap! blink! taste! think! (5 and up)   **507.8**

History
Whitman, S. What's cooking? (5 and up)   **394.1**

Psychological aspects
Frankenberger, E. Food and love (7 and up)   **616.85**

Food adulteration and inspection
See/See also pages in the following book(s):
Epidemics: opposing viewpoints   **614.4**

Food and Drug Administration (U.S.) *See* United States. Food and Drug Administration

Food and farming. Bowden, R.   **363.8**

Food and festivals [series]
Fisher, T. France   **641.5**

Food and love. Frankenberger, E.   **616.85**

Food chains (Ecology)
Silverstein, A. Food chains   **577**

Food habits *See* Eating customs

Food poisoning
Latta, S. L. Food poisoning and foodborne diseases (7 and up)   **615.9**

Food poisoning and foodborne diseases. Latta, S. L.   **615.9**

Food preparation *See* Cooking

Food rules!. Haduch, B.   **613.2**

Food supply
See also Agriculture
See/See also pages in the following book(s):
Global resources: opposing viewpoints   **333.71**

Fooks, Louie
The drug trade   **364.1**

The **fool**. Lester, J.
In Lester, J. The last tales of Uncle Remus p128-31   **398.2**

Fool John. Van Laan, N.
In Van Laan, N. With a whoop and a holler; a bushel of lore from way down south p14-17   **398**

The **foolish** boy. Bryan, A.
In Bryan, A. Ashley Bryan's African tales, uh-huh p172-98   **398.2**

The **foolish** forest sprite. Lee, J. M.
In Lee, J. M. I once was a monkey; stories Buddha told   **294.3**

Fools crow [excerpt] Welch, J.
In Talking leaves; contemporary native American short stories   **S C**

Football
See also Soccer
Buckley, J., Jr. Football (4 and up)   **796.332**
Biography
Sullivan, G. Power football   **920**
Fiction
Cochran, T. Roughnecks (7 and up)   **Fic**
Dygard, T. J. Second stringer (7 and up)   **Fic**
Lee, M. G. Necessary roughness (7 and up)   **Fic**
Powell, R. Three clams and an oyster (7 and up)   **Fic**
Spinelli, J. Crash (5 and up)   **Fic**

Footnotes. Augustyn, F.   **792.8**

Footprints on the roof. Singer, M.   **811**

Footsteps. Schwartz, A.
In Schwartz, A. Scary stories 3; more tales to chill your bones p20-21   **398.2**

For better, for worse. Bode, J.   **306.89**

For freedom. Bradley, K. B.   **Fic**

For love of him. Vande Velde, V.
In Vande Velde, V. Being dead; stories   **S C**

For teens only. Weston, C.   **305.23**

Forbidden brides of the faceless slaves in the nameless house of the night of dread desire. Gaiman, N.
In Gothic!; ten original dark tales   **S C**

Forbidden forest. Cadnum, M.   **Fic**

Forbidden fruit. Yee, P.
In Yee, P. Tales from Gold Mountain; stories of the Chinese in the New World p45-50   **S C**

Force and energy
Challoner, J. Energy (5 and up)   **621**
Farndon, J. Energy   **531**
Gardner, R. Forces and motion science fair projects   **531**

Forced labor *See* Slavery

Forces and motion science fair projects. Gardner, R.   **531**

Forces of nature. Grace, C. O.   **551.2**

Ford, Eileen, 1922-
See/See also pages in the following book(s):
Jeffrey, L. S. Great American businesswomen   **920**

Ford, George
(il) Giovanni, N. Ego-tripping and other poems for young people   **811**

Ford, Henry, 1863-1947
About
Bankston, J. Henry Ford and the assembly line   **92**
Tilton, R. Henry Ford (7 and up)   **92**

Ford, Jeffrey, 1955-
The green word
In The Green Man: tales from the mythic forest p353-82   **808.8**

Forecasting
Dixon, D. The future is wild   **576.8**

A **foreign** field. Chan, G.   **Fic**

Foreign population *See* Immigrants

Foreigners *See* Immigrants

Foreman, Michael, 1938-
(il) Garfield, L. Shakespeare stories {I}-II   **822.3**
(il) Morpurgo, M. Sir Gawain and the Green Knight   **398.2**

Forensic sciences
Campbell, A. Forensic science (7 and up)   **363.2**
Fridell, R. DNA fingerprinting (7 and up)   **614**
Friedlander, M. P. When objects talk   **363.2**
Innes, B. Forensic science (7 and up)   **363.2**
Jackson, D. M. The bone detectives (5 and up)   **614**
Lane, B. Crime & detection (4 and up)   **364**
Mattern, J. Forensics (5 and up)   **363.2**
Owen, D. Police lab (7 and up)   **363.2**
Pentland, P. Forensic science (4 and up)   **363.2**

Forensic sciences—*Continued*
Platt, R. Crime scene   363.2
                    Encyclopedias
Bell, S. Encyclopedia of forensic science
                                                     363.2
Forensics. Mattern, J.   363.2
Forest, Heather
Wisdom tales from around the world   398.2
Forest animals
Swinburne, S. R. The woods scientist (4 and up)
                                                     591.7
Forest ecology
     See also Rain forest ecology
Allaby, M. Temperate forests (7 and up)
                                                     577.3
Beil, K. M. Fire in their eyes (4 and up)
                                                     628.9
Burnie, D. Shrublands (5 and up)   577.3
Fielding, E. The Eastern forest   577.3
Martin, P. A. F. Woods and forests (7 and up)
                                                     577.3
Patent, D. H. Fire: friend or foe (4 and up)
                                                     577.2
Sayre, A. P. Taiga (5 and up)   577.3
Sayre, A. P. Temperate deciduous forest (5 and
up)   577.3
Simon, S. Wildfires (3-6)   577.2
Staub, F. J. America's forests (4 and up)
                                                     577.3
Forest fires
Beil, K. M. Fire in their eyes (4 and up)
                                                     628.9
Patent, D. H. Fire: friend or foe (4 and up)
                                                     577.2
Simon, S. Wildfires (3-6)   577.2
                    Fiction
Crew, L. Fire on the wind   Fic
Ingold, J. The Big Burn (7 and up)   Fic
Forests and forestry
     See also Trees
Allaby, M. Temperate forests (7 and up)
                                                     577.3
Staub, F. J. America's forests (4 and up)
                                                     577.3
Forever outsiders. Altman, L. J.   909
Forged by fire. Draper, S. M.   Fic
Forging freedom. Talbott, H.   940.53
Forgotten fire. Bagdasarian, A.   Fic
The **forgotten** heroes. Cox, C.   978
The **forgotten** victims of the Holocaust. Altman,
L. J.   940.53
Former Soviet republics
     See also Soviet Union
Forshay-Lunsford, Cin
Saint Agnes sends the golden boy
     In Visions: nineteen short stories by outstand-
     ing writers for young adults p11-22
                                                      S C
Forster, Cathy
                    About
Bishop, N. Digging for bird-dinosaurs (4 and
up)   567.9

Forsyth, Elizabeth Held
(jt. auth) Hyde, M. O. Diabetes   616.4
(jt. auth) Hyde, M. O. Vaccinations   615
Forsyth, Fiona
Augustus: the first emperor   92
Forté-Escamilla, Kleya
Coming of age
     In Join in; multiethnic short stories by out-
     standing writers for young adults p230-
     37   S C
Forten, James, 1766-1842
See/See also pages in the following book(s):
Haskins, J. African American entrepreneurs
                                                     920
Fortification
Adams, S. Castles & forts (5 and up)   355.7
Macaulay, D. Castle (4 and up)   728.8
Fortin, François
(ed) Sports: the complete visual reference. See
     Sports: the complete visual reference   796
Fortune, Amos, 1709 or 10-1801
                    About
Yates, E. Amos Fortune, free man   92
Fortune cookie. Avi
     In Avi. What do fish have to do with any-
     thing? and other stories p175-203
                                                      S C
Fortune teller. Nguyen, M. D.
     In American eyes; new Asian-American short
     stories for young adults p80-107   S C
Fortune's bones. Nelson, M.   811
Forty bucks. Salisbury, G.
     In Salisbury, G. Island boyz: short stories
     p49-67   S C
Fossey, Dian
                    About
Gogerly, L. Dian Fossey   92
Matthews, T. L. Light shining through the mist:
     a photobiography of Dian Fossey (4 and up)
                                                      92
Nicholson, L. Dian Fossey (7 and up)   92
See/See also pages in the following book(s):
Celebrating women in mathematics and science
                                                     920
Fossil fish found alive. Walker, S. M.   597
Fossil hominids
Gallant, R. A. Early humans (5 and up)
                                                  599.93
                    Fiction
Dickinson, P. A bone from a dry sea   Fic
Fossil mammals
Giblin, J. The mystery of the mammoth bones
     (4 and up)   569
Hehner, B. Ice Age cave bear (5 and up)
                                                     569
Turner, A. National Geographic prehistoric
     mammals (5 and up)   569
Fossil reptiles
     See also Dinosaurs
Sloan, C. Supercroc and the origin of crocodiles
     (5 and up)   567.9

Fossils

Bausum, A. Dragon bones and dinosaur eggs: a photobiography of Roy Chapman Andrews (5 and up) **92**

Bishop, N. Digging for bird-dinosaurs (4 and up) **567.9**

Farlow, J. O. Bringing dinosaur bones to life (5 and up) **567.9**

Gallant, J. R. The tales fossils tell (5 and up) **560**

Goodhue, T. W. Curious bones: Mary Anning and the birth of paleontology **92**

Halls, K. M. Dinosaur mummies (5 and up) **567.9**

Marrin, A. Secrets from the rocks: dinosaur hunting with Roy Chapman Andrews (4 and up) **92**

Patent, D. H. In search of the maiasaurs **567.9**

Relf, P. A dinosaur named Sue: the story of the colossal fossil: the world's most complete T. rex (5 and up) **567.9**

Sloan, C. Feathered dinosaurs (5 and up) **567.9**

Tanaka, S. Graveyards of the dinosaurs (4-6) **567.9**

Taylor, P. D. Fossil (4 and up) **560**

Trueit, T. S. Fossils **560**

Carrick, P. Dinosaur parents, dinosaur young (4 and up) **567.9**

Fiction

Dickinson, P. A bone from a dry sea **Fic**

Jennings, R. W. The great whale of Kansas **Fic**

Foster, Alan Dean, 1946-

The Hand of Dinotopia **Fic**

Foster, Leila Merrell

Italy (7 and up) **945**

Kuwait (4 and up) **953.67**

Foster home care

Fiction

Byars, B. C. The pinballs (5 and up) **Fic**

Childress, A. Rainbow Jordan (7 and up) **Fic**

Cooney, C. B. What child is this? **Fic**

Dowell, F. O. Where I'd like to be (4 and up) **Fic**

Giff, P. R. Pictures of Hollis Woods (5 and up) **Fic**

Guy, R. The disappearance **Fic**

Johnston, J. Adam and Eve and Pinch-me (7 and up) **Fic**

Paterson, K. The great Gilly Hopkins (5 and up) **Fic**

Skurzynski, G. Cliff hanger **Fic**

Poetry

Woodson, J. Locomotion (4 and up) **811**

Foundations for effective school library media programs **027.8**

The **Founding** of America **973.3**

The **foundling**. Alexander, L.

In Alexander, L. The foundling and other tales of Prydain p5-14 **S C**

The **foundling** and other tales of Prydain. Alexander, L. **S C**

Foundling Hospital (London, England)

Jocelyn, M. A home for foundlings (7 and up) **362.7**

The **fountain** of youth. Anaya, R. A.

In Anaya, R. A. My land sings; stories from the Rio Grande p103-19 **S C**

Fountains of life. Gowell, E. T. **577.7**

The **four** corners of the sky. Zeitlin, S. J. **201**

The **four-footed** horror. Olson, A. N.

In Olson, A. N. and Schwartz, H. Ask the bones: scary stories from around the world p37-41 **398.2**

Four perfect pebbles. Perl, L. **940.53**

Four who entered paradise. Schwartz, H.

In Schwartz, H. The day the Rabbi disappeared: Jewish holiday tales of magic p28-30 **398.2**

The **Fourth** Amendment. Wetterer, C. M. **345**

Fourth and too long. Crutcher, C.

In Time capsule: short stories about teenagers throughout the twentieth century p143-64 **S C**

Fourth of July. Brancato, R. F.

In Sixteen; short stories by outstanding writers for young adults p102-12 **S C**

The **fourth** question. Chu, V.

In Fire and wings: dragon tales from East and West p55-64 **S C**

Fox, Anne L., 1926-

Ten thousand children (5 and up) **940.53**

Fox, Paula

One-eyed cat (5 and up) **Fic**

The slave dancer (5 and up) **Fic**

Fox and Possum. Curry, J. L.

In Curry, J. L. Hold up the sky: and other Native American tales from Texas and the Southern Plains p84-88 **398.2**

Fox hunt. Namioka, L.

In Join in; multiethnic short stories by outstanding writers for young adults p13-21 **S C**

The **fox,** the bear, and the poor man. Molnár, I.

In Molnár, I. One-time dog market at Buda and other Hungarian folktales p102-05 **398.2**

Foxglove, Lady *See* Blue, Rose

Fradin, Dennis B.

Bound for the North Star (7 and up) **326**

The Connecticut colony **974.6**

Fight on!: Mary Church Terrell's battle for integration **92**

My family shall be free!: the life of Peter Still **92**

The planet hunters (5 and up) **523.4**

Samuel Adams (6 and up) **92**

The signers (4 and up) **920**

(jt. auth) Fradin, J. B. The power of one [biography of Daisy Bates] **92**

Fradin, Judith Bloom

The power of one [biography of Daisy Bates] (7 and up) **92**

(jt. auth) Fradin, D. B. Fight on!: Mary Church Terrell's battle for integration **92**

The **fragrance** of paradise. Goldin, B. D.
In Goldin, B. D. Journeys with Elijah; eight
tales of the Prophet p49-56   **222**

Frampton, David
(il) Fleischman, P. Bull Run   **Fic**
(il) Grimes, N. At Jerusalem's gate   **811**

France
Gofen, E. France   **944**
NgCheong-Lum, R. France (4 and up)   **944**
Fiction
Elliott, L. Under a war-torn sky (7 and up)
       Fic
Jennings, P. The wolving time   **Fic**
Maguire, G. The good liar (4 and up)   **Fic**
Matas, C. Greater than angels (7 and up)
       Fic
Mosher, R. Zazoo   **Fic**
History—0-1328—Fiction
Gregory, K. Eleanor: crown jewel of Aquitaine
       Fic
History—1328-1589, House of Valois
Stanley, D. Joan of Arc (4 and up)   **92**
History—1328-1589, House of Valois—Fiction
Lasky, K. Mary, Queen of Scots, queen without
a country   **Fic**
History—1589-1789, Bourbons—Fiction
Dumas, A. The three musketeers (7 and up)
       Fic
History—1789-1799, Revolution
The French Revolution (7 and up)   **944.04**
Plain, N. Louis XVI, Marie Antoinette, and the
French Revolution   **944**
History—1940-1945, German occupation—Fiction
Bradley, K. B. For freedom   **Fic**
Kings and rulers
Napoleon Bonaparte [essays about]   **92**
Social life and customs
Fisher, T. France   **641.5**

France. Fisher, T.   **641.5**

Francie. English, K.   **Fic**

Francisco Coronado. Otfinoski, S.   **92**

Franck, Irene M.
The Wilson chronology of women's achievements (7 and up)   **305.4**
(jt. auth) Brownstone, D. M. The young nation:
America 1787-1861   **973**
(ed) The Wilson chronology of Asia and the Pacific. See The Wilson chronology of Asia and
the Pacific   **950**

Franco, Betsy
You hear me? See You hear me?   **810.8**
(ed) Night is gone, day is still coming. See
Night is gone, day is still coming   **808.8**
(ed) Things I have to tell you. See Things I
have to tell you   **810.8**

Frank, Anne, 1929-1945
The diary of a young girl (6 and up)   **92**
The diary of a young girl: the definitive edition
(6 and up)   **92**
About
Gold, A. L. Memories of Anne Frank (5 and
up)   **92**
Lee, C. A. A friend called Anne (4 and up)
       940.53
Müller, M. Anne Frank (7 and up)   **92**

Pressler, M. Anne Frank: a hidden life   **92**
Rol, R. v. d. Anne Frank, beyond the diary (5
and up)   **92**
Sawyer, K. K. Anne Frank (5 and up)   **92**
Wukovits, J. F. Anne Frank (7 and up)   **92**
See/See also pages in the following book(s):
Boas, J. We are witnesses (7 and up)
       940.53
Leapman, M. Witnesses to war (5 and up)
       940.53

Frank, E. R.
Friction (7 and up)   **Fic**
Life is funny (7 and up)   **Fic**

Frank, Lucy K.
Oy, Joy!   **Fic**

Frank, Mary, 1933-
See/See also pages in the following book(s):
Sills, L. Visions (5 and up)   **920**

Frank, Mitch
Understanding September 11th (7 and up)
       973.931
Understanding the Holy Land (7 and up)
       956.94

Frankel, Noralee, 1950-
Break those chains at last: African Americans,
1860-1880   **305.8**

Frankenberger, Elizabeth
Food and love (7 and up)   **616.85**

Frankie Diamond is robbing us blind. Salisbury,
G.
In Salisbury, G. Island boyz: short stories
p118-41   **S C**

Frankl, Ron
Charlie Parker, musician   **92**

Franklin, Aretha
See/See also pages in the following book(s):
Lester, J. The blues singers (5 and up)   **920**

Franklin, Benjamin, 1706-1790
About
Adler, D. A. B. Franklin, printer (4 and up)
       92
Benjamin Franklin [essays about] (7 and up)
       92
Fleming, C. Ben Franklin's almanac (5 and up)
       92

Franklin, Sir John, 1786-1847
About
Beattie, O. Buried in ice (4 and up)   **998**

Franklin, Kristine L., 1958-
Dove song   **Fic**
Grape thief (5 and up)   **Fic**

Franklin, Rosalind, 1920-1958
About
Senker, C. Rosalind Franklin (5 and up)   **92**
See/See also pages in the following book(s):
Di Domenico, K. Super women in science
       920

The **franklin's** tale. Cohen, B.
In Cohen, B. Canterbury tales   **821**

Frank's mother. Sleator, W.
In Sleator, W. Oddballs; stories p15-26
       S C

Fraser, Mary Ann
Vicksburg—the battle that won the Civil War (4 and up) **973.7**

Fraud
Schroeder, A. Scams! (5 and up) **364.1**
Fiction
Curtis, C. P. Bucking the Sarge (5 and up) **Fic**

Fraustino, Lisa Rowe, 1961-
Sleeping Beauty
In Don't cramp my style; stories about that time of the month p131-44 **S C**
Things happen
In Shattered: stories of children and war p87-107 **S C**
The tin man
In Soul searching: thirteen stories about faith and belief p248-67 **S C**
(ed) Don't cramp my style. See Don't cramp my style **S C**
(ed) Soul searching: thirteen stories about faith and belief. See Soul searching: thirteen stories about faith and belief **S C**

Freak the Mighty. Philbrick, W. R. **Fic**
Freaky flowers. Souza, D. M. **582.13**
Freaky Friday. Rodgers, M. **Fic**
Freaky green eyes. Oates, J. C. **Fic**

Frederick, Heather Vogel
The voyage of Patience Goodspeed (5 and up) **Fic**

Fredericks, Mariah
Head games (7 and up) **Fic**
The true meaning of cleavage (7 and up) **Fic**

Free at last. Bullard, S. **323.1**
Free radical. Murphy, C. R. **Fic**
Free speech (7 and up) **342**

Freedman, Jeri
Sid Fleischman (5 and up) **92**

Freedman, Russell
Babe Didrikson Zaharias (5 and up) **92**
Confucius (4 and up) **92**
Eleanor Roosevelt (5 and up) **92**
Franklin Delano Roosevelt (5 and up) **92**
Give me liberty! (5 and up) **973.3**
In defense of liberty **342**
In the days of the vaqueros (4 and up) **636.2**
Indian chiefs (6 and up) **920**
Kids at work (5 and up) **331.3**
Lincoln: a photobiography (5 and up) **92**
Martha Graham, a dancer's life (7 and up) **92**
Out of darkness: the story of Louis Braille (4 and up) **92**
The voice that challenged a nation [biography of Marian Anderson] (5 and up) **92**
The Wright brothers: how they invented the airplane **92**
See/See also pages in the following book(s):
Author talk (4 and up) **028.5**
The Newbery & Caldecott medal books, 1986-2000 **028.5**

Freedman, Suzanne, 1932-
Clay v. United States (7 and up) **343**
The **freedom** fighters of Parkview. Sleator, W.
In Sleator, W. Oddballs; stories p27-42 **S C**
Freedom like sunlight. Lewis, J. P. **811**

Freedom of information
See also Censorship

Freedom of religion
See/See also pages in the following book(s):
Religion in America: opposing viewpoints (7 and up) **200.9**

Freedom of speech
Alonso, K. Schenck v. United States (7 and up) **342**
Cate, F. H. The Internet and the First Amendment **342**
Farish, L. Tinker v. Des Moines (7 and up) **342**
Free speech (7 and up) **342**
See/See also pages in the following book(s):
Civil liberties: opposing viewpoints (7 and up) **323**

Freedom of the press
Fireside, H. New York Times v. Sullivan (7 and up) **342**
Fuller, S. B. Hazelwood v. Kuhlmeier (7 and up) **344**
Gold, S. D. The Pentagon papers **342**
Herda, D. J. New York Times v. United States (7 and up) **342**
Freedom roads: searching for the Underground Railroad. Hansen, J. **973.7**
Freedom songs. Moore, Y. **Fic**
Freedom's martyr [biography of Jose Rizal] Arruda, S. M. **92**
The **freeing** of Nelson Mandela. See Beecroft, S. The release of Nelson Mandela **968.06**

Freeman, Evelyn B.
Children's books in children's hands. See Children's books in children's hands **028.5**

Freeman, Lucille Usher
(ed) Stretch your wings. See Stretch your wings **808.88**

Freeman-Villalobos, Tina Marie
The way it was
In Talking leaves; contemporary native American short stories **S C**

Fremon, David K.
The Great Depression in American history **338.5**
The Salem witchcraft trials in American history **133.4**

Fremont, David
(il) Proimos, J. The grade school zone **S C**
Frémont, John Charles, 1813-1890
About
Faber, H. John Charles Frémont **92**
French, Jackie, 1950-
Hitler's daughter **Fic**
French, Michael, 1944-
(jt. auth) Bradley, J. Flags of our fathers **940.54**

French, Michael, 1944-—*Continued*
(jt. auth) O'Grady, S. F. Basher five-two
949.7

French, Simon, 1957-
Where in the world (5 and up)   **Fic**

French and Indian War *See* United States—History—1755-1763, French and Indian War

The **French** and Indian War, 1660-1763. Collier, C.   **973.2**

French art
Sabbeth, C. Monet and the impressionists for kids (5 and up)   **759.05**

French artists *See* Artists, French

French cooking
Fisher, T. France   **641.5**

French language
Dictionaries
Cassell's French dictionary   **443**

The **French** Revolution (7 and up)   **944.04**

Frenchtown summer. Cormier, R.   **Fic**

Frent, David J.
(ed) The election of 1860 and the administration of Abraham Lincoln. See The election of 1860 and the administration of Abraham Lincoln   **973.7**

Fresh girl. Placide, J.   **Fic**

Fresh off the boat. De la Cruz, M.   **Fic**

Freshwater animals
Aquatic life of the world (4 and up)   **578.7**

Freud, Sigmund, 1856-1939
About
Muckenhoupt, M. Sigmund Freud (7 and up)
92
Reef, C. Sigmund Freud: pioneer of the mind (7 and up)   **92**

Freund, Rudolf, 1915-
(il) Robins, C. R. A field guide to Atlantic coast fishes of North America   **597**

Freymann-Weyr, Garret, 1965-
The kings are already here (7 and up)   **Fic**
My heartbeat (7 and up)   **Fic**
When I was older (7 and up)   **Fic**

Friction. Frank, E. R.   **Fic**

Fridell, Ron, 1943-
Cruzan v. Missouri and the right to die debate (7 and up)   **344**
Decoding life   **576.5**
DNA fingerprinting (7 and up)   **614**
Education for all   **370**
Privacy vs. security   **342**
The search for poison-dart frogs (4-6)   **597.8**

Friedlander, Mark P.
Outbreak: disease detectives at work   **614.4**
When objects talk   **363.2**

Friedman, Ina R.
The other victims   **940.53**

Friedman, Lise
Break a leg! (4 and up)   **792**

Friend, Sandra
Earth's wild winds (5 and up)   **551.51**

A **friend** called Anne. Lee, C. A.   **940.53**

Friends, Society of *See* Society of Friends

Friends and enemies. Gaeddert, L. B.   **Fic**

The **friends** of Kwan Ming. Yee, P.
In Yee, P. Tales from Gold Mountain; stories of the Chinese in the New World p25-31
S C

Friendship
Romain, T. Cliques, phonies & other baloney
158
Taylor, J. The girls' guide to friends   **158**
Winick, J. Pedro and me (7 and up)   **362.1**
You be me (7 and up)   **305.23**
Fiction
Adler, C. S. One unhappy horse   **Fic**
Baskin, N. R. Almost home   **Fic**
Baskin, N. R. What every girl (except me) knows (4 and up)   **Fic**
Blume, J. Here's to you, Rachel Robinson (5 and up)   **Fic**
Brokaw, N. S. Leaving Emma   **Fic**
Brooks, B. The moves make the man   **Fic**
Byars, B. C. The pinballs (5 and up)   **Fic**
Cheng, A. The lace dowry (4 and up)   **Fic**
Cole, B. The goats   **Fic**
Collier, J. L. Me and Billy (5 and up)   **Fic**
Collier, K. Jericho walls (7 and up)   **Fic**
Conly, J. L. What happened on Planet Kid
Fic
Cormier, R. The bumblebee flies anyway (7 and up)   **Fic**
Creech, S. Walk two moons (6 and up)   **Fic**
Crutcher, C. Staying fat for Sarah Byrnes
Fic
Cummings, P. Red kayak (7 and up)   **Fic**
Danziger, P. P.S. Longer letter later (5 and up)
Fic
Danziger, P. Snail mail no more (5 and up)
Fic
Danziger, P. United Tates of America (4 and up)   **Fic**
Deaver, J. R. Say goodnight, Gracie (7 and up)
Fic
Desai Hidier, T. Born confused (7 and up)
Fic
Dessen, S. Someone like you (7 and up)
Fic
Deuker, C. Night hoops (7 and up)   **Fic**
DiCamillo, K. The tiger rising   **Fic**
Dowell, F. O. Chicken boy (4 and up)   **Fic**
Dowell, F. O. The secret language of girls (5 and up)   **Fic**
Dowell, F. O. Where I'd like to be (4 and up)
Fic
Draper, S. M. Double Dutch   **Fic**
Elish, D. Born too short (7 and up)   **Fic**
Farrell, M. And sometimes why   **Fic**
Ferris, J. Of sound mind (7 and up)   **Fic**
Fine, A. Up on cloud nine (5 and up)   **Fic**
Flinn, A. Breaking point (7 and up)   **Fic**
Frank, L. K. Oy, Joy!   **Fic**
Fredericks, M. The true meaning of cleavage (7 and up)   **Fic**
Gaeddert, L. B. Friends and enemies   **Fic**
Giff, P. R. All the way home (4 and up)
Fic
Giff, P. R. Lily's crossing (4 and up)   **Fic**

Friendship—Fiction—*Continued*

Going, K. L. Fat kid rules the world (7 and up)   **Fic**

Gordon, A. The Gorillas of Gill Park (4 and up)   **Fic**

Graham, R. My not-so-terrible time at Hippie Hotel   **Fic**

Griffin, A. Amandine (7 and up)   **Fic**

Hahn, M. D. Daphne's book (5 and up)   **Fic**

Hale, M. The truth about sparrows (5 and up)   **Fic**

Hamilton, V. Bluish   **Fic**

Hamilton, V. The planet of Junior Brown (6 and up)   **Fic**

Hansen, J. One true friend   **Fic**

Hautman, P. Invisible (7 and up)   **Fic**

Hawes, L. Waiting for Christopher (7 and up)   **Fic**

Hesse, K. Phoenix rising   **Fic**

Holt, K. W. When Zachary Beaver came to town   **Fic**

Howe, J. The misfits   **Fic**

Keizer, G. God of beer (7 and up)   **Fic**

Kimmel, E. C. Visiting Miss Caples (6 and up)   **Fic**

Klass, S. S. The un-civil war   **Fic**

Koller, J. F. Someday   **Fic**

Konigsburg, E. L. The view from Saturday (4 and up)   **Fic**

Kornblatt, M. Understanding Buddy   **Fic**

Koss, A. G. The girls (5 and up)   **Fic**

Kropp, P. The countess and me   **Fic**

Kurtz, J. The storyteller's beads (5 and up)   **Fic**

Levy, E. Seventh grade tango (5 and up)   **Fic**

Lowry, L. Autumn Street (4 and up)   **Fic**

Lowry, L. Number the stars (4 and up)   **Fic**

Lowry, L. Rabble Starkey (5 and up)   **Fic**

Lynch, C. Gold dust   **Fic**

Lynch, C. Slot machine (7 and up)   **Fic**

Martin, A. M. A corner of the universe (5 and up)   **Fic**

Mazer, N. F. Out of control (7 and up)   **Fic**

Mazer, N. F. Silver (7 and up)   **Fic**

McCaffrey, L. W. Alia waking   **Fic**

McGhee, A. Snap (5 and up)   **Fic**

Meyer, C. Drummers of Jericho (7 and up)   **Fic**

Miller, M. B. Aimee (7 and up)   **Fic**

Morgan, N. Chicken friend (5 and up)   **Fic**

Morgenstern, S. H. Secret letters from 0 to 10   **Fic**

Moriarty, J. The year of secret assignments (7 and up)   **Fic**

Murray, M. The slightly true story of Cedar B. Hartley (5 and up)   **Fic**

Myers, W. D. Me, Mop, and the Moondance Kid (4-6)   **Fic**

Myracle, L. Eleven (4 and up)   **Fic**

Oates, J. C. Big Mouth & Ugly Girl (7 and up)   **Fic**

O'Dell, K. Agnes Parker . . . girl in progress (4 and up)   **Fic**

Paterson, K. Bridge to Terabithia (4 and up)   **Fic**

Paulsen, G. The Schernoff discoveries   **Fic**

Perkins, L. R. All alone in the universe (5 and up)   **Fic**

Peters, J. A. Define "normal" (7 and up)   **Fic**

Philbrick, W. R. Freak the Mighty   **Fic**

Powell, R. Three clams and an oyster (7 and up)   **Fic**

Rylant, C. A fine white dust (5 and up)   **Fic**

Sachar, L. Holes (5 and up)   **Fic**

Shusterman, N. The Schwa was here   **Fic**

Speare, E. G. The sign of the beaver (5 and up)   **Fic**

Spinelli, J. Crash (5 and up)   **Fic**

Staples, S. F. Dangerous skies (7 and up)   **Fic**

Stauffacher, S. Donuthead (4-6)   **Fic**

Van Leeuwen, J. Lucy was there—   **Fic**

Vaupel, R. My contract with Henry   **Fic**

Voigt, C. Bad girls in love   **Fic**

Waite, J. Shopaholic   **Fic**

Wallace, R. Wrestling Sturbridge (7 and up)   **Fic**

Weatherly, L. Missing Abby   **Fic**

Who do you think you are?   **S C**

Wilhelm, D. The revealers   **Fic**

Williams-Garcia, R. No laughter here (7 and up)   **Fic**

Woodson, J. I hadn't meant to tell you this   **Fic**

Yep, L. Thief of hearts (5 and up)   **Fic**

Yep, L. The traitor (5 and up)   **Fic**

See/See also pages in the following book(s):

Sleator, W. Oddballs (6 and up)   **S C**

Poetry

Very best (almost) friends (4 and up)   **811.008**

The **friendship**. Taylor, M. D.   **Fic**

Friesen, Gayle

Losing forever (7 and up)   **Fic**

Friesner, Esther M.

The blood-ghoul of Scarsdale

  In Vampires: a collection of original stories p81-98   **S C**

Frissell, Susan

Eating disorders and weight control (7 and up)   **616.85**

Fritz, April Young

Waiting to disappear (7 and up)   **Fic**

Fritz, Deborah A. (Deborah Angela), 1955-

Cataloging with AACR2 and MARC21   **025.3**

Fritz, Jean

Around the world in a hundred years (4 and up)   **910.4**

Bully for you, Teddy Roosevelt! (5 and up)   **92**

China homecoming (6 and up)   **951.05**

The great little Madison (5 and up)   **92**

Harriet Beecher Stowe and the Beecher preachers (5 and up)   **92**

Homesick: my own story (5 and up)   **92**

Make way for Sam Houston (4 and up)   **92**

Stonewall [biography of Stonewall Jackson] (4 and up)   **92**

Traitor: the case of Benedict Arnold   **92**

Fritz, Jean—*Continued*
Why not, Lafayette? (5 and up)   92
Fritz, Michael
(il) Fritz, J. China homecoming   951.05
Frog. Vande Velde, V.
In Vande Velde, V. Tales from the Brothers
Grimm and the Sisters Weird p27-35
S C
Frog and his two wives. Bryan, A.
In Bryan, A. Ashley Bryan's African tales,
uh-huh p9-12   398.2
Frogs
Fridell, R. The search for poison-dart frogs (4-6)
597.8
Pascoe, E. Tadpoles   597.8
From a raw deal to a New Deal? African Ameri-
cans, 1929-1945. Trotter, J. W.   305.8
From Abenaki to Zuni. Wolfson, E.   970.004
From biography to history   016.8
From boys to men. Gurian, M.   305.23
From cover to cover. Horning, K. T.   028.1
From founding to fall: a history of Rome. Nardo,
D.   937
From rags to riches. Sills, L.   391
From reader to writer. Ellis, S.   372.6
From slave ship to freedom road. Lester, J.
326
From the ashes. Chicoine, S.   940.53
Frontier and pioneer life
Anderson, W. T. Laura Ingalls Wilder (4 and
up)   92
Cook, J. Natural writer: a story about Marjorie
Kinnan Rawlings   92
Furbee, M. R. Anne Bailey   92
Katz, W. L. Black pioneers   920
Pendergast, T. Westward expansion: biographies
(7 and up)   920
Fiction
Arrington, F. Bluestem (4-6)   **Fic**
Arrington, F. Prairie whispers (5 and up)
Fic
Auch, M. J. Journey to nowhere   **Fic**
Avi. The barn (4 and up)   **Fic**
Bauer, M. D. Land of the buffalo bones   **Fic**
Blakeslee, A. R. A different kind of hero
Fic
Bradley, K. B. Weaver's daughter (5 and up)
Fic
Burks, B. Soldier boy   **Fic**
Calvert, P. Bigger (5 and up)   **Fic**
Cannon, A. E. Charlotte's Rose (5 and up)
Fic
Conrad, P. Prairie songs (5 and up)   **Fic**
Cushman, K. The ballad of Lucy Whipple (5
and up)   **Fic**
Durbin, W. Blackwater Ben (5 and up)   **Fic**
Fleischman, P. The borning room (6 and up)
Fic
Gipson, F. B. Old Yeller (6 and up)   **Fic**
Gregory, K. Seeds of hope   **Fic**
Holm, J. L. Boston Jane: an adventure   **Fic**
Holm, J. L. Our only May Amelia (5 and up)
Fic
LaFaye, A. Worth (5 and up)   **Fic**

Levine, E. The journal of Jedediah Barstow
Fic
Love, D. A. A year without rain (5 and up)
Fic
McCaughrean, G. Stop the train! (5 and up)
Fic
McDonald, M. All the stars in the sky (4 and
up)   **Fic**
Murphy, J. My face to the wind   **Fic**
Murphy, J. West to a land of plenty   **Fic**
Richter, C. The light in the forest   **Fic**
Rinaldi, A. A stitch in time (7 and up)   **Fic**
Speare, E. G. The sign of the beaver (5 and up)
Fic
Trottier, M. Sister to the wolf   **Fic**
Van Leeuwen, J. Cabin on Trouble Creek (4
and up)   **Fic**
California
Goldsmith, C. Lost in Death Valley   979.4
O'Donnell, K. The gold rush (4 and up)
979.4
Texas
Haley, J. L. Stephen F. Austin and the founding
of Texas   92
West (U.S.)
The American frontier (7 and up)   978
Blackwood, G. L. Life on the Oregon Trail (7
and up)   979.5
Calabro, M. The perilous journey of the Donner
Party (5 and up)   978
Calvert, P. Daniel Boone   92
Doherty, K. Ranchers, homesteaders, and traders
920
Edmondson, J. R. Jim Bowie   92
Fisher, L. E. The Oregon Trail (4 and up)
979.5
Josephson, J. P. Growing up in pioneer Ameri-
ca, 1800 to 1890   978
Katz, W. L. Black women of the Old West (5
and up)   978
Ketchum, L. Into a new country (7 and up)
920
Lavender, D. S. Snowbound (4 and up)   978
McGowen, T. African-Americans in the Old
West   978
Patent, D. H. Homesteading (4 and up)   978
Pendergast, T. Westward expansion: almanac
978
Schlissel, L. Black frontiers   978
Stefoff, R. The opening of the West   978
Tunis, E. Frontier living (5 and up)   978
Westward expansion [Eyewitness history series]
978
Westward expansion [Interpreting primary docu-
ments] (7 and up)   978
See/See also pages in the following book(s):
Collier, C. Indians, cowboys, and farmers and
the battle for the Great Plains, 1865-1910
978
Frontier living. Tunis, E.   978
Frost, Helen, 1949-
Keesha's house (7 and up)   **Fic**
Frost, Robert, 1874-1963
The road not taken   811

Frost, Robert, 1874-1963—*Continued*
Robert Frost
In The Blackbirch treasury of American poetry p55-99 **811.008**
You come too: favorite poems for young readers **811**

Frost-Knappman, Elizabeth
Women's rights on trial **346**
Women's suffrage in America (7 and up) **324.6**
(ed) Courtroom drama. See Courtroom drama **347**

Frozen fire. Houston, J. A. **Fic**
Frozen in time [series]
Patent, D. H. In search of the maiasaurs **567.9**
Patent, D. H. Secrets of the ice man **930.1**
Frozen man. Getz, D. **930.1**
Fry, Varian, 1907-1967
See/See also pages in the following book(s):
Lyman, D. Holocaust rescuers **920**
Full tilt. Shusterman, N. **Fic**
Fuller, Barbara, 1961-
Germany (5 and up) **943**
Fuller, Sarah Betsy, 1946-2004
Hazelwood v. Kuhlmeier (7 and up) **344**
The **Fuller** brush man. Miklowitz, G. D.
In Visions: nineteen short stories by outstanding writers for young adults p100-06 **S C**
Fullick, Ann
Rebuilding the body (7 and up) **617.9**
Test tube babies (7 and up) **618.1**
Fulton, Robert, 1765-1815
About
Kroll, S. Robert Fulton **92**
Pierce, M. A. Robert Fulton and the development of the steamboat **92**
See/See also pages in the following book(s):
Levinson, I. S. Gibbons v. Ogden (7 and up) **343**
Fundamental gymnastics. Bragg, L. W. **796.44**
Fundamental hockey. Foley, M. **796.962**
Fundamental karate. Dallas, K. **796.8**
Fundamental life skills See Life skills
Fundamental mountain biking. See King, A. Play-by-play mountain biking **796.6**
Fundamental snowboarding. Lurie, J. **796.93**
Fundamental soccer. Coleman, L. **796.334**
Fundamental softball. Nitz, K. W. **796.357**
Fundamental sports [series]
Bragg, L. W. Fundamental gymnastics **796.44**
Coleman, L. Fundamental soccer **796.334**
Dallas, K. Fundamental karate **796.8**
Foley, M. Fundamental hockey **796.962**
Lurie, J. Fundamental snowboarding **796.93**
Nitz, K. W. Fundamental softball **796.357**
Fundamentalism See Christian fundamentalism
The **funeral**. Sleator, W.
In Soul searching: thirteen stories about faith and belief p23-43 **S C**

Funeral rites and ceremonies
Colman, P. Corpses, coffins, and crypts (7 and up) **393**
Perl, L. Mummies, tombs, and treasure (4 and up) **393**
Sloan, C. Bury the dead (5 and up) **393**
Wilcox, C. Mummies, bones & body parts (5 and up) **393**
Fungi
See also Mushrooms
Pascoe, E. Slime, molds, and fungi (4 and up) **579.5**
Souza, D. M. What is a fungus? (5 and up) **579.5**
Funke, Cornelia Caroline
Dragon rider (5 and up) **Fic**
Inkheart **Fic**
The Thief Lord **Fic**
Funnies See Comic books, strips, etc.
Fuqua, Jonathon Scott
Darby (4 and up) **Fic**
The Willoughby Spit wonder **Fic**
Fur trade
Fiction
Durbin, W. The broken blade **Fic**
Durbin, W. Wintering **Fic**
Furbee, Mary R., 1954-
Anne Bailey **92**
Wild Rose: Nancy Ward and the Cherokee Nation **92**
Furlough—1944. Mazer, H.
In Sixteen; short stories by outstanding writers for young adults p83-92 **S C**
Furman, William Henry
About
Herda, D. J. Furman v. Georgia (7 and up) **345**
Furniss, Tim
The atlas of space exploration **520**
Furstinger, Nancy
Say it with music: the story of Irving Berlin **92**
Fury. Bethancourt, T. E.
In Ultimate sports; short stories by outstanding writers for young adults p21-49 **S C**
Fusco, Kimberly Newton
Tending to Grace (7 and up) **Fic**
The **future** is wild. Dixon, D. **576.8**
Future life
See/See also pages in the following book(s):
Death and dying: opposing viewpoints p55-96 (7 and up) **155.9**
Paranormal phenomena: opposing viewpoints (7 and up) **133**
Fiction
Shearer, A. The Great Blue Yonder (5 and up) **Fic**
Future shock See Culture conflict
Future techniques in surgery. Giddens, S. **617**
Future tense. Lipsyte, R.
In Read into the millennium; tales of the future p42-56 **S C**

Future tense—*Continued*

In Sixteen; short stories by outstanding writers for young adults p60-70   **S C**

G

G.I.'s *See* Soldiers—United States

Gaeddert, LouAnn Bigge
Friends and enemies   **Fic**

Gage, Phineas P., d. 1861
About
Fleischman, J. Phineas Gage: a gruesome but true story about brain science   **362.1**

Gaiman, Neil
Coraline (5 and up)   **Fic**

Gaiman, Neil, 1960-
Forbidden brides of the faceless slaves in the nameless house of the night of dread desire *In* Gothic!; ten original dark tales   **S C**

Gaines, Ann
Hernando de Soto and the Spanish search for gold in world history (7 and up)   **92**

Gaines, Ernest J., 1933-
The autobiography of Miss Jane Pittman (7 and up)   **Fic**

Galante, L. R.
(il) Corrain, L. The art of the Renaissance   **709.02**
(il) Loria, S. Pablo Picasso   **92**

Galbraith, Judy
(jt. auth) Benson, P. L. What teens need to succeed   **305.23**

Galdikas, Biruté
See/See also pages in the following book(s):
Di Domenico, K. Super women in science   **920**
Lindop, L. Scientists and doctors (7 and up)   **920**

The **Gale** encyclopedia of Native American tribes   **970.004**

Gale encyclopedia of the unusual and unexplained. Steiger, B.   **130**

Galens, Judy
Middle ages: almanac   **909.07**

Galens, Judy, 1968-
Middle ages: primary sources. See Middle ages: primary sources   **909.07**

Galford, Ellen
The trail West (5 and up)   **978**

Galilei, Galileo, 1564-1642
About
White, M. Galileo Galilei   **92**

Galileo *See* Galilei, Galileo, 1564-1642

Galileo Project
Cole, M. D. Galileo spacecraft   **629.43**

Galileo spacecraft. Cole, M. D.   **629.43**

Gall, Susan B.
Junior worldmark encyclopedia of the nations. See Junior worldmark encyclopedia of the nations   **910.3**

(ed) Junior Worldmark encyclopedia of the Canadian provinces. See Junior Worldmark encyclopedia of the Canadian provinces   **971**
(ed) Junior Worldmark encyclopedia of the Mexican states. See Junior Worldmark encyclopedia of the Mexican states   **972**
(ed) Junior Worldmark encyclopedia of the states. See Junior Worldmark encyclopedia of the states   **973.03**
(ed) Junior Worldmark encyclopedia of world cultures. See Junior Worldmark encyclopedia of world cultures   **306**

Gall, Timothy L.
Junior worldmark encyclopedia of the nations. See Junior worldmark encyclopedia of the nations   **910.3**
(ed) Junior Worldmark encyclopedia of the Canadian provinces. See Junior Worldmark encyclopedia of the Canadian provinces   **971**
(ed) Junior Worldmark encyclopedia of the Mexican states. See Junior Worldmark encyclopedia of the Mexican states   **972**
(ed) Junior Worldmark encyclopedia of the states. See Junior Worldmark encyclopedia of the states   **973.03**
(ed) Junior Worldmark encyclopedia of world cultures. See Junior Worldmark encyclopedia of world cultures   **306**

Gallagher, Amie
(jt. auth) Stott, C. New astronomer   **520**

Gallagher, Jim, 1969-
The composite guide to wrestling   **796.8**
Pedro Martinez   **92**

Gallagher, John
Buzzboy: Trouble in paradise   **741.5**

Gallant, Jonathan R.
The tales fossils tell (5 and up)   **560**

Gallant, Roy A.
Atmosphere (5 and up)   **551.51**
Dance of the continents (5 and up)   **551.1**
Early humans (5 and up)   **599.93**
The ever changing atom (5 and up)   **539.7**
History   **551.7**
The life stories of stars   **523.8**
The origins of life (5 and up)   **576.8**
Plates (5 and up)   **551.1**
Resources   **333.7**
Structure (5 and up)   **551.1**
The treasure of inheritance (5 and up)   **576.5**
Water (5 and up)   **553.7**
The wonders of biodiversity (5 and up)   **333.95**

Galleries, Art *See* Art museums

Gallo, Donald R.
(ed) Destination unexpected: short stories. See Destination unexpected: short stories   **S C**
(ed) Join in. See Join in   **S C**
(ed) On the fringe. See On the fringe   **S C**
(ed) Sixteen. See Sixteen   **S C**
(ed) Time capsule: short stories about teenagers throughout the twentieth century. See Time capsule: short stories about teenagers throughout the twentieth century   **S C**
(ed) Ultimate sports. See Ultimate sports   **S C**

Gallo, Donald R.—*Continued*
(ed) Visions: nineteen short stories by outstanding writers for young adults. See Visions: nineteen short stories by outstanding writers for young adults   **S C**

Galloping Foxley. Dahl, R.
In Dahl, R. Skin and other stories   **S C**

Galvin, Jack
(jt. auth) Pfetzer, M. Within reach: my Everest story   **796.52**

Gama, Vasco da, 1469-1524
About
Calvert, P. Vasco da Gama (5 and up)   **92**
Goodman, J. E. A long and uncertain journey: the 27,000 mile voyage of Vasco da Gama (4 and up)   **92**
See/See also pages in the following book(s):
Fritz, J. Around the world in a hundred years (4 and up)   **910.4**

Gamble, Cyndi
Leopards (7 and up)   **599.75**

Gambler's eyes. Yee, P.
In Yee, P. Tales from Gold Mountain; stories of the Chinese in the New World p39-44   **S C**

Gamblin, Linda
Evolution (4 and up)   **576.8**

The **game** of silence. Erdrich, L.   **Fic**

The **Game** of Sunken Places. Anderson, M. T.   **Fic**

Game protection
See also Birds—Protection

Games
See also Sports; Word games and names of individual games
Glenn, J. The treasury of family games (5 and up)   **793**
Loeffelbein, R. L. The recreation handbook   **793**
Wise, L. The way cool license plate book (4 and up)   **793.7**
Fiction
Anderson, M. T. The Game of Sunken Places (5 and up)   **Fic**
Lubar, D. Wizards of the game   **Fic**

Games. King, D.   **794**

Games. Sleator, W.
In Sleator, W. Oddballs; stories p3-14   **S C**

Gammell, Stephen, 1943-
See/See also pages in the following book(s):
The Newbery & Caldecott medal books, 1986-2000   **028.5**
(il) Dancing teepees: poems of American Indian youth. See Dancing teepees: poems of American Indian youth   **897**
(il) Fritz, J. Stonewall [biography of Stonewall Jackson]   **92**
(il) Schwartz, A. More scary stories to tell in the dark   **398.2**
(il) Schwartz, A. Scary stories 3   **398.2**
(il) Schwartz, A. Scary stories to tell in the dark   **398.2**

Gan, Delice, 1954-
Sweden (5 and up)   **948.5**

Gandhi, Indira, 1917-1984
See/See also pages in the following book(s):
Axelrod-Contrada, J. Women who led nations (7 and up)   **920**
Hewitt, K. Lives of extraordinary women (4 and up)   **920**
Price-Groff, C. Twentieth-century women political leaders (7 and up)   **920**

Gandhi, Mahatma, 1869-1948
About
Adams, S. Mahatma Gandhi (7 and up)   **92**
Hatt, C. Mahatma Ghandhi   **92**
Severance, J. B. Gandhi, great soul (5 and up)   **92**

Gandhi, Mohandas Karamchand *See* Gandhi, Mahatma, 1869-1948

Gandhi, great soul. Severance, J. B.   **92**

Ganeri, Anita, 1961-
The Ramayana and Hinduism (5 and up)   **294.5**
The Tipitaka and Buddhism (5 and up)   **294.3**
The young person's guide to Shakespeare (7 and up)   **822.3**
The young person's guide to the opera (4 and up)   **792.5**
The young person's guide to the orchestra (4 and up)   **784.2**

Ganges River (India and Bangladesh)
Barter, J. The Ganges (7 and up)   **954**

Ganges River valley (India and Bangladesh)
Barter, J. The Ganges (7 and up)   **954**

Gangs
Hinojosa, M. Crews: gang members talk to Maria Hinojosa (7 and up)   **302.3**
Johnson, J. Why do people join gangs?   **364.1**
Fiction
Bunting, E. Someone is hiding on Alcatraz Island   **Fic**
Cross, G. Tightrope (7 and up)   **Fic**
Lisle, J. T. How I became a writer and Oggie learned to drive (4 and up)   **Fic**
Randle, K. D. Breaking rank (7 and up)   **Fic**

Gangsters. Blackwood, G. L.   **364.1**

Gannon, Ed
(jt. auth) Martin, J. Lionheart   **910.4**

Gantos, Jack
Hole in my life (7 and up)   **92**
Jack on the tracks (5 and up)   **Fic**
Joey Pigza swallowed the key (5 and up)   **Fic**
Muzak for Prozac
In On the fringe p75-86   **S C**

Garbage *See* Refuse and refuse disposal

Garcia, Mannie
(il) Lyons, M. E. Catching the fire: Philip Simmons, blacksmith   **92**

Garcia, Rita Williams- *See* Williams-Garcia, Rita

García de Paredes, Angel
(ed) Cassell's Spanish-English, English-Spanish dictionary. See Cassell's Spanish-English, English-Spanish dictionary   **463**

García Lorca, Federico, 1898-1936
The girl who waters basil and the very inquisitive prince
In You're on!: seven plays in English and Spanish p62-83   **812.008**

Garden, Nancy
The year they burned the books (7 and up)   **Fic**

The **gardener**. Kipling, R.
In McCaffrey, A. {The Pern series}   **S C**

Gardening
Winckler, S. Planting the seed   **635**
Fiction
Hoffman, A. Green angel (7 and up)   **Fic**

Gardens
Fiction
Fleischman, P. Seedfolks (4 and up)   **Fic**

Gardiner, Lynton
(il) Murdoch, D. H. North American Indian   **970.004**

Gardner, Robert, 1929-
Bicycle science projects   **531**
Chemistry science fair projects using acids, bases, metals, salts, and inorganic stuff (7 and up)   **540**
Chemistry science fair projects using french fries, gumdrops, soap, and other organic stuff (7 and up)   **547**
Forces and motion science fair projects   **531**
Health science projects about nutrition (7 and up)   **612.3**
Health science projects about psychology (7 and up)   **150**
Health science projects about sports performance (7 and up)   **612**
Human evolution (7 and up)   **599.93**
Light, sound, and waves science fair projects (7 and up)   **507.8**
Science fair projects—planning, presenting, succeeding (7 and up)   **507.8**
Science project ideas about air   **533**
Science project ideas about animal behavior   **591.5**
Science project ideas about kitchen chemistry   **540.7**
Science project ideas about rain   **551.57**
Science project ideas about the moon   **523.3**
Science project ideas about the sun   **523.7**
Science project ideas about trees (5 and up)   **582.16**
Science project ideas in the house   **507.8**
Science projects about physics in the home (5 and up)   **507.8**
Science projects about plants (7 and up)   **580.7**
Science projects about temperature and heat (7 and up)   **536**
Science projects about the environment and ecology (7 and up)   **363.7**
Science projects about weather (7 and up)   **551.5**

(jt. auth) Adams, R. C. Energy projects for young scientists   **621**
(jt. auth) Adams, R. C. More ideas for science projects   **507.8**

Gardner's art through the ages   **709**

Garfield, Leon, 1921-1996
A grave misunderstanding
In Beware!; R.L. Stine picks his favorite scary stories p189-97   **808.8**
Shakespeare stories {I}-II   **822.3**

Garlake, Teresa
Global debt (7 and up)   **336.3**

Garland, Hamlin, 1860-1940
The return of a private
In The Boy of Chancellorville and other Civil War stories p103-11   **S C**

Garland, Judy
See/See also pages in the following book(s):
Orgill, R. Shout, sister, shout! (6 and up)   **920**

Garland, Sherry, 1948-
In the shadow of the Alamo   **Fic**
Shadow of the dragon   **Fic**
The silent storm   **Fic**
Song of the buffalo boy   **Fic**
Valley of the Moon   **Fic**

Garland reference lib. of social science [series]
Karp, R. S. Plays for children and young adults   **808.82**

Garments *See* Clothing and dress

Garner, Alan, 1934-
The owl service   **Fic**

Garner, Joe
We interrupt this broadcast   **070.1**

Garrett, Leslie, 1932-
Helen Keller (5 and up)   **92**

Garrison, William Lloyd, 1805-1879
See/See also pages in the following book(s):
Cloud Tapper, S. Voices from slavery's past (7 and up)   **326**

Garrison, Zina, 1963-
See/See also pages in the following book(s):
Kaminsky, M. Uncommon champions   **920**

Garrison-Jackson, Zina *See* Garrison, Zina, 1963-

Garty, Judy
Jeff Bezos   **92**

Garvey, Marcus, 1887-1940
About
Lawler, M. Marcus Garvey   **92**

Garzarelli, Elaine
See/See also pages in the following book(s):
Jeffrey, L. S. Great American businesswomen   **920**

Gascoigne, Ingrid
Papua New Guinea (5 and up)   **995.3**

Gaskins, Pearl, 1957-
I believe in—   **200**
(ed) What are you? See What are you?   **305.8**

Gaston, A. G.
See/See also pages in the following book(s):
Haskins, J. African American entrepreneurs   **920**

Gates, Bill, 1955-
See/See also pages in the following book(s):
Northrup, M. American computer pioneers
    920

Gates, Phil
Medicine   610.9

Gates, William H., III *See* Gates, Bill, 1955-

Gateway biography [series]
Bredeson, C. Shannon Lucid   92
Haskins, J. Toni Morrison   92
Naden, C. J. John Muir   92

Gath, Tracy
(ed) Exploring science in the library. See Exploring science in the library   027.8

Gathering blue. Lowry, L.   Fic

A **gathering** of shades. Stahler, D., Jr.   Fic

Gauguin, Paul, 1848-1903
About
Greenfeld, H. Paul Gauguin (7 and up)   92

Gault, Gerald
About
Gold, S. D. In re Gault (1967) (7 and up)
    345

Gaustad, Edwin Scott
Roger Williams (7 and up)   92

Gauthier, Gail, 1953-
The hero of Ticonderoga   Fic
Saving the planet & stuff   Fic

Gavin, Jamila, 1941-
Coram boy (7 and up)   Fic

Gawain (Legendary character)
Morpurgo, M. Sir Gawain and the Green Knight (5 and up)   398.2
Fiction
Morris, G. The squire's tale   Fic

Gay, Kathlyn, 1930-
After the shooting stops (7 and up)   355
Cultural diversity (7 and up)   305.8
Epilepsy   616.8
Leaving Cuba (7 and up)   362.87
Persian Gulf War (5 and up)   956.7
Science in ancient Greece (4 and up)   509
Silent death (7 and up)   358
Volunteering (7 and up)   361.3
World War I (5 and up)   940.3

Gay, Martin
(jt. auth) Gay, K. After the shooting stops
    355
(jt. auth) Gay, K. Persian Gulf War   956.7
(jt. auth) Gay, K. World War I   940.3

Gay lifestyle *See* Homosexuality

Gay men
See/See also pages in the following book(s):
Altman, L. J. The forgotten victims of the Holocaust   940.53
Civil rights
Hudson, D. L. Gay rights (7 and up)   342

Gay rights. Hudson, D. L.   342

Gay women *See* Lesbians

Gayatri Devi, Maharani of Jaipur, 1919-
See/See also pages in the following book(s):
McGaw, L. To be a princess (4 and up)
    920

Gedatus, Gus
Bicycling for fitness   613.7
Exercise for weight management   613.7

Geeks bearing gifts. Koertge, R.
In On the fringe p11-26   S C

Geese
Fiction
Kindl, P. Goose chase   Fic

Geiger, John, 1960-
(jt. auth) Beattie, O. Buried in ice   998

Geisel, Theodor Seuss *See* Seuss, Dr.

Gell-Mann, Murray, 1929-
See/See also pages in the following book(s):
Henderson, H. Nuclear physics (7 and up)
    539.7

Gelletly, LeeAnne
Violence in the media (7 and up)   303.6

Gellhorn, Martha
See/See also pages in the following book(s):
Colman, P. Where the action was   070.4

Gellman, Marc
Does God have a big toe? (4-6)   221.9
How do you spell God? (5 and up)   200

Gems
See also Precious stones

Gems. Kallen, S. A.   553.8

Gender identity *See* Sex role

Gene mapping
See/See also pages in the following book(s):
Biomedical ethics: opposing viewpoints (7 and up)   174.2

Gene splicing *See* Genetic engineering

Gene therapy
See/See also pages in the following book(s):
O'Neill, T. Biomedical ethics (7 and up)
    174.2

Genealogy
Douglas, A. The family tree detective   929
Perl, L. The great ancestor hunt (5 and up)
    929
Taylor, M. Through the eyes of your ancestors (4 and up)   929
Wolfman, I. Climbing your family tree   929
Fiction
Bauer, J. Backwater (7 and up)   Fic

Generals
Feinberg, B. S. Douglas MacArthur   92
Finlayson, R. Colin Powell   92
Fritz, J. Stonewall [biography of Stonewall Jackson] (4 and up)   92
Fritz, J. Traitor: the case of Benedict Arnold
    92
King, D. C. Benedict Arnold and the American Revolution   92
Pflueger, L. Stonewall Jackson   92
Robertson, J. I., Jr. Standing like a stone wall: the life of General Thomas J. Jackson (7 and up)   92
Young, J. C. Dwight D. Eisenhower   92

Generous anger: the story of George Orwell. Boerst, W. J.   92

Genes & DNA. Walker, R.   576.5

Genetic engineering

See also Biotechnology; Cloning

Cohen, D. Cloning (7 and up)   **571.8**

Dowswell, P. Genetics (7 and up)   **660.6**

Goodnough, D. The debate over human cloning   **174.2**

Spangenburg, R. Genetic engineering (7 and up)   **660.6**

Tagliaferro, L. Genetic engineering (7 and up)   **576.5**

Yount, L. Biotechnology and genetic engineering   **303.4**

See/See also pages in the following book(s):

Biomedical ethics: opposing viewpoints (7 and up)   **174.2**

Global resources: opposing viewpoints   **333.71**

Hyde, M. O. Medicine's brave new world (7 and up)   **610**

O'Neill, T. Biomedical ethics (7 and up)   **174.2**

Fiction

Crichton, M. Jurassic Park (7 and up)   **Fic**

Lasky, K. Star split (7 and up)   **Fic**

Werlin, N. Double helix (7 and up)   **Fic**

Genetics

See also Gene mapping; Medical genetics

Allan, T. Understanding DNA   **576.5**

Boon, K. A. The human genome project (7 and up)   **599.93**

Cullen, J. H. Barbara McClintock, geneticist (7 and up)   **92**

Day, T. Genetics (5 and up)   **576.5**

Edelson, E. Gregor Mendel, and the roots of genetics (7 and up)   **92**

Edelson, E. James Watson and Francis Crick and the building blocks of life (7 and up)   **92**

Fine, E. H. Barbara McClintock (7 and up)   **92**

Fridell, R. Decoding life   **576.5**

Gallant, R. A. The treasure of inheritance (5 and up)   **576.5**

Hamilton, J. James Watson   **92**

Kidd, J. S. Life lines (7 and up)   **576.5**

Klare, R. Gregor Mendel   **92**

Walker, R. Genes & DNA (5 and up)   **576.5**

Law and legislation

See/See also pages in the following book(s):

Biomedical ethics: opposing viewpoints (7 and up)   **174.2**

Genetics. Dowswell, P.   **660.6**

Geng, Don

Play-by-play baseball (5 and up)   **796.357**

Genghis Khan, 1162-1227

About

Greenblatt, M. Genghis Khan and the Mongol Empire   **950**

Humphrey, J. Genghis Khan   **92**

Lange, B. Genghis Khan (7 and up)   **92**

Genghis Khan and the Mongol Empire. Greenblatt, M.   **950**

Genius [biography of Albert Einstein] Delano, M. F.   **92**

Genocide

Ayer, E. H. A firestorm unleashed   **940.53**

Grant, R. G. Genocide   **303.6**

See/See also pages in the following book(s):

Chicoine, S. From the ashes   **940.53**

Genome mapping *See* Gene mapping

Geographic names

United States

Shearer, B. F. State names, seals, flags, and symbols   **929.9**

Geographical myths

See also Atlantis

Geography

See also Maps; Voyages and travels

Arnold, C. The geography book (4 and up)   **910**

The Blackbirch kid's visual reference of the world (5 and up)   **910**

Countries of the world and their leaders yearbook   **910.3**

The DK geography of the world   **910**

Geography on file   **912**

Dictionaries

Merriam-Webster's geographical dictionary   **910.3**

Encyclopedias

Gifford, C. The Kingfisher geography encyclopedia (4 and up)   **910.3**

Junior worldmark encyclopedia of the nations   **910.3**

Lands and peoples   **910.3**

Worldmark encyclopedia of the nations   **910.3**

The **geography** book. Arnold, C.   **910**

Geography crafts for kids. Rhatigan, J.

In Diehn, G. and others. Science smart; cool projects for exploring the marvels of the planet Earth   **550**

Geography on file   **912**

Geologists

Carruthers, M. W. Pioneers of geology   **920**

Geology

Erickson, J. Making of the earth (7 and up)   **551.4**

Gallant, R. A. Dance of the continents (5 and up)   **551.1**

Gallant, R. A. Structure (5 and up)   **551.1**

Patent, D. H. Shaping the earth (4 and up)   **550**

Sattler, H. R. Our patchwork planet (5 and up)   **551.1**

Geology crafts for kids. Anderson, A. H.

In Diehn, G. and others. Science smart; cool projects for exploring the marvels of the planet Earth   **550**

George III, King of Great Britain, 1738-1820

About

Ingram, S. King George III   **92**

George, Charles, 1949-

Idaho

In America the beautiful, second series   **973**

George, Charles, 1949——Continued
Mississippi
  In America the beautiful, second series
    973
Montana
  In America the beautiful, second series
    973
White-water rafting **797.1**
(jt. auth) George, L. Civil rights marches
    323.1
(jt. auth) George, L. The Tuskegee Airmen
    940.54

George, Jean Craighead, 1919-
Charlie's raven (5 and up) **Fic**
Julie (6 and up) **Fic**
Julie of the wolves (6 and up) **Fic**
The talking earth **Fic**
A tarantula in my purse (4-6) **92**
Water sky (5 and up) **Fic**

George, Kristine O'Connell
Swimming upstream **811**

George, Linda
Civil rights marches **323.1**
Idaho America the beautiful, second series
    973
The Tuskegee Airmen **940.54**
(jt. auth) George, C. White-water rafting
    797.1

George, Linda S., 1949-
800 **909.07**

George-Warren, Holly
(ed) The Rolling Stone encyclopedia of rock &
  roll. See The Rolling Stone encyclopedia of
  rock & roll **781.66**

George Washington, spymaster. Allen, T. B.
    92

Georgia
Otfinoski, S. Georgia
  In Celebrate the states **973**
Robinson Masters, N. Georgia
  In America the beautiful, second series
    973
    Fiction
Krisher, T. Spite fences **Fic**
Siegelson, K. L. Trembling earth **Fic**

Georgia (Republic)
Spilling, M. Georgia (5 and up) **947.5**

Georgia (Soviet Union) See Georgia (Republic)

Geras, Adèle
The Random House book of opera stories (4
  and up) **792.5**
Troy (7 and up) **Fic**

Gerdes, Louise
(ed) Addiction: opposing viewpoints. See Addiction: opposing viewpoints **362.29**
(ed) The Cold War. See The Cold War [Great
  speeches in history series] **909.82**
(ed) Media violence: opposing viewpoints. See
  Media violence: opposing viewpoints
    303.6
(ed) War: opposing viewpoints. See War: opposing viewpoints **355**

Germain, Sophie, 1776-1831
See/See also pages in the following book(s):
  Celebrating women in mathematics and science
    920

Germaine, Elizabeth
Cooking the Australian way
  In Easy menu ethnic cookbooks **641.5**

The **German** American family album. Hoobler, D.
    305.8

German Americans
Hoobler, D. The German American family al-
  bum (5 and up) **305.8**
    Fiction
Giff, P. R. A house of tailors (5 and up)
    Fic
Gündisch, K. How I became an American (4
  and up) **Fic**

German language
    Dictionaries
Cassell's German-English, English-German dictionary **433**

German prisoners of war
    Fiction
Greene, B. Summer of my German soldier (6
  and up) **Fic**

Germans
    Israel—Fiction
Kass, P. Real time (7 and up) **Fic**

Germany
Ayer, E. H. Germany (7 and up) **943**
Fuller, B. Germany (5 and up) **943**
    Fiction
Chotjewitz, D. Daniel half human (7 and up)
    Fic
Ibbotson, E. The star of Kazan (5 and up)
    Fic
Jung, R. Dreaming in black and white (5 and
  up) **Fic**
Matas, C. In my enemy's house (7 and up)
    Fic
Tunnell, M. O. Brothers in valor **Fic**
    History—1918-1933
Giblin, J. The life and death of Adolf Hitler (7
  and up) **92**
Nardo, D. Adolf Hitler **92**
    History—1933-1945
Altman, L. J. Hitler's rise to power and the
  Holocaust **943.086**
Bartoletti, S. C. Hitler Youth (7 and up)
    943.086
Cartlidge, C. Life of a Nazi soldier (7 and up)
    940.54
Damon, D. Mein Kampf (7 and up) **943.086**
Feldman, G. Understanding the Holocaust
    940.53
Giblin, J. The life and death of Adolf Hitler (7
  and up) **92**
Nardo, D. Adolf Hitler **92**
Soumerai, E. N. A voice from the Holocaust
    940.53
    Politics and government—1933-1945
Byers, A. The Holocaust overview (7 and up)
    940.53
Feldman, G. Understanding the Holocaust
    940.53

Germany—Politics and government—1933-1945—*Continued*
Living in Nazi Germany (7 and up)   **943.086**
The Rise of Nazi Germany (7 and up)
943.086

Germany's lightning war. McGowen, T.
940.54

Geronimo, Apache Chief, 1829-1909
About
Baird, W. D. Geronimo, Apache warrior   **92**
See/See also pages in the following book(s):
Brown, D. A. Bury my heart at Wounded Knee
970.004
Ehrlich, A. Wounded Knee: an Indian history of the American West (6 and up)   **970.004**
Kallen, S. A. Native American chiefs and warriors (7 and up)   **920**

Gerontology
See also Old age

Gershator, Phillis, 1942-
Kotoshi the dragon doctor
In Fire and wings: dragon tales from East and West p117-23   **S C**

Gerson, Mary-Joan
Fiesta femenina (4 and up)   **398.2**
Contents: Rosha and the sun; The hungry goddess; The legend of Tangu Yuh; Why the moon is free; Green bird; Blanca Flor; The Virgin of Guadalupe; Malintzin of the Mountain

Gerstein, Mordicai, 1935-
(il) Kimmel, E. A. The jar of fools: eight Hanukkah stories from Chelm   **S C**

Get on board: the story of the Underground Railroad. Haskins, J.   **326**

Get real [series]
Tym, K. Coping with your emotions   **152.4**
Tym, K. School survival   **371.8**

Getting away with murder: the true story of the Emmett Till case. Crowe, C.   **364.1**

Getting dumped and getting over it!. Busby, C.
646.7

Getting graphic!. Gorman, M.   **741.5**

Getting near to baby. Couloumbis, A.   **Fic**

Getting the real story: Nellie Bly and Ida B. Wells. Davidson, S.   **92**

Getty, J. Paul, 1892-1976
About
Glassman, B. John Paul Getty (7 and up)
92

Gettysburg (Pa.), Battle of, 1863
King, D. C. The Battle of Gettysburg   **973.7**
Murphy, J. The long road to Gettysburg (5 and up)   **973.7**
Fiction
Banks, S. H. Abraham's battle   **Fic**
Crisp, M. Private Captain   **Fic**

Getz, David, 1957-
Frozen man (5 and up)   **930.1**

Ghana
Levy, P. M. Ghana (5 and up)   **966.7**

Ghana Empire
Green, R. L. The empire of Ghana   **966.1**
McKissack, P. C. The royal kingdoms of Ghana, Mali, and Songhay (5 and up)   **966.2**

Gherman, Beverly
Norman Rockwell (4 and up)   **92**

Ghermezian family
See/See also pages in the following book(s):
Aaseng, N. Business builders in real estate
920

The **ghost**. Vande Velde, V.
In Vande Velde, V. Being dead; stories
S C

The **ghost** and Mrs. Hobbs. DeFelice, C. C.
Fic

Ghost at the window. McAllister, M.   **Fic**

Ghost canoe. Hobbs, W.   **Fic**

Ghost dance
See/See also pages in the following book(s):
Ehrlich, A. Wounded Knee: an Indian history of the American West (6 and up)   **970.004**

Ghost girl. Ray, D.   **Fic**

The **ghost** in the Tokaido Inn. Hoobler, D.
Fic

Ghost liners. Ballard, R. D.   **910.4**

The **ghost** of Fossil Glen. DeFelice, C. C.   **Fic**

The **ghost** sitter. Griffin, P. R.   **Fic**

Ghost stories
Almond, D. Kit's wilderness (5 and up)   **Fic**
Barrett, T. Cold in summer (5 and up)   **Fic**
Bloor, E. Story time   **Fic**
Bunting, E. The Presence   **Fic**
Clarke, J. Starry nights   **Fic**
Conrad, P. Stonewords (5 and up)   **Fic**
De Lint, C. The blue girl (7 and up)   **Fic**
DeFelice, C. C. The ghost and Mrs. Hobbs (4-6)
Fic
DeFelice, C. C. The ghost of Fossil Glen (4-6)
Fic
Griffin, P. R. The ghost sitter (4 and up)
Fic
The Haunted house: a collection of original stories   **S C**
Hoffman, N. K. A stir of bones (7 and up)
Fic
Kimmel, E. C. In the stone circle (5 and up)
Fic
MacPhail, C. Dark waters   **Fic**
McAllister, M. Ghost at the window (5 and up)
Fic
McAllister, M. Hold my hand and run   **Fic**
Naylor, P. R. Jade Green (7 and up)   **Fic**
Nixon, J. L. Ghost town   **S C**
Nixon, J. L. The haunting (7 and up)   **Fic**
Ruby, L. Lily's ghosts (5 and up)   **Fic**
San Souci, R. A terrifying taste of short & shivery (4 and up)   **398.2**
Schwartz, A. More scary stories to tell in the dark (4 and up)   **398.2**
Schwartz, A. Scary stories 3 (4 and up)
398.2
Schwartz, A. Scary stories to tell in the dark (4 and up)   **398.2**
Soto, G. The afterlife (7 and up)   **Fic**
Stahler, D., Jr. A gathering of shades (7 and up)
Fic
Vande Velde, V. There's a dead person following my sister around (4 and up)   **Fic**

Ghost stories—_Continued_
Wright, B. R. Out of the dark (4 and up)
          Fic

A **ghost** story. Lester, J.
  _In_ Lester, J. The last tales of Uncle Remus
    p33-36   **398.2**
Ghost town. Nixon, J. L.   **S C**
Ghost train. Mowry, J.   **Fic**
The **ghost** woman. Curry, J. L.
  _In_ Curry, J. L. Hold up the sky: and other
    Native American tales from Texas and
    the Southern Plains p114-19 **398.2**
Ghosts
  See/See also pages in the following book(s):
  Paranormal phenomena: opposing viewpoints (7
    and up)   **133**
The **ghost's** bride. Yep, L.
  _In_ Yep, L. The rainbow people p54-59
          398.2
Ghosts of wind and shadow. De Lint, C.
  _In_ De Lint, C. Waifs and strays p272-312
          S C
Giacobbe, Beppe
  (il) Fleischman, P. Big talk   **811**
The **giant** of Castle Treen. Climo, S.
  _In_ Climo, S. Magic & mischief; tales from
    Cornwall p3-10   **398.2**
Giant panda
  Bortolotti, D. Panda rescue (4 and up)
          639.9
  Presnall, J. J. The giant panda (7 and up)
          599.78
  See/See also pages in the following book(s):
  Ward, P. Wild bears of the world **599.78**
Giant stones and earth mounds. McGowen, T.
          930.1
Giants of American industry [series]
  Glassman, B. John Paul Getty   **92**
  Shuker, N. Elizabeth Arden   **92**
Giants of art and culture [series]
  Brown, G. Duke Ellington: jazz master **92**
  Glassman, B. Mikhail Baryshnikov **92**
  MacDonald, P. A. Pablo Picasso **92**
Giants of science [series]
  Birch, B. Alexander Fleming   **92**
  Birch, B. Guglielmo Marconi   **92**
  Birch, B. Marie Curie   **92**
  Pollard, M. Margaret Mead   **92**
  Sproule, A. James Watt   **92**
  Sproule, A. Thomas A. Edison   **92**
  Sproule, A. The Wright brothers   **92**
  White, M. Galileo Galilei   **92**
  White, M. Isaac Newton   **92**
The **giant's** tooth. Coville, B.
  _In_ Coville, B. Odder than ever **S C**
Gibbons, Thomas, 1757-1826
        About
  Levinson, I. S. Gibbons v. Ogden (7 and up)
          343
Gibbons v. Ogden. Levinson, I. S. **343**
Gibbs, Lois Marie
  See/See also pages in the following book(s):
  Reed, J. Love Canal (7 and up) **363.7**

Giblin, James, 1933-
  Charles A. Lindbergh   **92**
  Good brother, bad brother [biography of John
    Wilkes Booth and Edwin Booth] (5 and up)
          92
  The life and death of Adolf Hitler (7 and up)
          92
  The mystery of the mammoth bones (4 and up)
          569
  The riddle of the Rosetta Stone (5 and up)
          493
  Secrets of the Sphinx (4 and up) **932**
  (ed) The Century that was. See The Century that
    was   **973.9**
Gibson, Josh, 1911-1947
        About
  Twemlow, N. Josh Gibson   **92**
Giddens, Owen
  (jt. auth) Giddens, S. Future techniques in sur-
    gery   **617**
Giddens, Sandra
  Future techniques in surgery   **617**
Gideon, Clarence Earl
        About
  Sherrow, V. Gideon v. Wainwright (7 and up)
          345
Gideon v. Wainwright. Sherrow, V. **345**
Gideon's people. Meyer, C.   **Fic**
Giff, Patricia Reilly
  All the way home (4 and up)   **Fic**
  Don't tell the girls (4 and up)   **92**
  A house of tailors (5 and up)   **Fic**
  Lily's crossing (4 and up)   **Fic**
  Nory Ryan's song (5 and up)   **Fic**
  Pictures of Hollis Woods (5 and up) **Fic**
Gifford, Clive
  The Kingfisher geography encyclopedia (4 and
    up)   **910.3**
  Spies (5 and up)   **327.12**
A **gift** for Jerusalem. Schwartz, H.
  _In_ Schwartz, H. The day the Rabbi disap-
    peared: Jewish holiday tales of magic
    p66-70   **398.2**
The **gift-giving.** Aiken, J.
  _In_ Sixteen; short stories by outstanding writ-
    ers for young adults p134-46 **S C**
The **gift** moves. Lyon, S.   **Fic**
A **gift** of laughter. Sherman, A.
  _In_ Leaving home: stories p27-33 **808.8**
The **gift** of reading. Bouchard, D. **372.4**
Gift pig. Aiken, J.
  _In_ Aiken, J. Shadows and moonshine; stories
          S C
Gifted children
        Fiction
  Blume, J. Here's to you, Rachel Robinson (5
    and up)   **Fic**
  Tolan, S. S. Welcome to the Ark (7 and up)
          Fic
  Yee, L. Millicent Min, girl genius (5 and up)
          Fic
Gifts. Le Guin, U. K.   **Fic**
The **gifts** of the mangy. Conford, E.
  _In_ Conford, E. Crush p9-26 **S C**

Gilbert, Adrian
Franklin D. Roosevelt (7 and up)   92

Gilbert, Barbara Snow, 1954-
Stone water (7 and up)   Fic

Gilbert, Grove Karl, 1843-1918
See/See also pages in the following book(s):
Carruthers, M. W. Pioneers of geology   920

Gilbert, Sara D.
How to do your best on tests (7 and up)
371.2

Gilbert and Sullivan set me free. Karr, K.   Fic

The **Gilded** Age: a history in documents (7 and up)   973.8

Giles, Gail
The gypsy's violin
In What a song can do; 12 riffs on the power of music   S C
Shattering Glass (7 and up)   Fic

Gilgamesh
McCaughrean, G. The epic of Gilgamesh (5 and up)   398.2

Gilgamesh the hero. See McCaughrean, G. The epic of Gilgamesh   398.2

Gill, Margery, 1925-
(il) Cooper, S. Over sea, under stone   Fic

Gill-Lonergan, Janet
The gourmet ghost
In The Haunted house: a collection of original stories   S C

Gilles de la Tourette's syndrome See Tourette syndrome

Gillespie, Dizzy, 1917-1993
See/See also pages in the following book(s):
Mour, S. I. American jazz musicians   920

Gillespie, John Birks See Gillespie, Dizzy, 1917-1993

Gillespie, John Thomas
The Newbery companion   028.5

Gillespie, Kellie M., 1960-
Teen volunteer services in libraries   021.2

Gillies, Judi
The jumbo vegetarian cookbook (4 and up)
641.5

Gilmore, James R., 1822-1903
The boy of Chancellorville
In The Boy of Chancellorville and other Civil War stories p40-54   S C

Gilmore, Kate
The exchange student (7 and up)   Fic

Gilmore, Rachna, 1953-
A group of one   Fic

Gilpin, Laura
See/See also pages in the following book(s):
Danneberg, J. Women artists of the West
920

Gilson, Jamie, 1933-
Stink Alley (4 and up)   Fic

Gina.Jamie.Father.Bear. Lyon, G. E.   Fic

Ginger for the heart. Yee, P.
In Yee, P. Tales from Gold Mountain; stories of the Chinese in the New World p33-38   S C

Ginsburg, Max
(il) Taylor, M. D. The friendship   Fic

Giottino, fl. 1369
(il) L'Engle, M. The glorious impossible
232.9

Giovanni, Nikki
Ego-tripping and other poems for young people (5 and up)   811
(ed) Shimmy shimmy shimmy like my sister Kate. See Shimmy shimmy shimmy like my sister Kate   811.008

Gipsies See Gypsies

Gipson, Frederick Benjamin, 1903-1973
Old Yeller (6 and up)   Fic

Girard, Denis
Cassell's French dictionary. See Cassell's French dictionary   443

Giraudon, David
(il) Arthus-Bertrand, Y. Earth from above for young readers   779
(il) Burleigh, R. Volcanoes   551.2

Girl at the window. Peck, R.
In Night terrors; stories of shadow and substance   S C
In Peck, R. Past perfect, present tense: new and collected stories   S C

Girl coming in for a landing. Wayland, A. H.
811

A **girl** from Yamhill: a memoir. Cleary, B.   92

Girl in a cage. Yolen, J.   Fic

Girl in blue. Rinaldi, A.   Fic

A **girl** named Disaster. Farmer, N.   Fic

Girl of Kosovo. Mead, A.   Fic

Girl Scouts of the United States of America
Jones, C. Every girl tells a story   305.23

The **girl** who climbed to the sky. Brown, D. A.
In Brown, D. A. Dee Brown's folktales of the Native American; retold for our times p39-42   398.2

The **girl** who dreamed only geese. Norman, H.
In Norman, H. The girl who dreamed only geese, and other tales of the Far North
398.2

The **girl** who dreamed only geese, and other tales of the Far North. Norman, H.   398.2

The **girl** who stood on a grave. Schwartz, A.
In Beware!; R.L. Stine picks his favorite scary stories p185-87   808.8

The **girl** who watched in the nighttime. Norman, H.
In Norman, H. The girl who dreamed only geese, and other tales of the Far North
398.2

The **girl** who waters basil and the very inquisitive prince. García Lorca, F.
In You're on!: seven plays in English and Spanish p62-83   812.008

The **girl** with a baby. Olsen, S.   Fic

Girlhearts. Mazer, N. F.   Fic

Girls
33 things every girl should know (7 and up)
810.8

Girls—*Continued*
Colman, P. Girls! (5 and up)   **305.23**
Girls know best   **305.23**
Gray, H. M. Real girl/real world (7 and up)   **305.23**
Jones, C. Every girl tells a story   **305.23**
Jukes, M. Growing up: it's a girl thing (4 and up)   **612.6**
Jukes, M. It's a girl thing (5 and up)   **305.23**
Rimm, S. B. See Jane win for girls (5 and up)   **305.23**
Shandler, S. Ophelia speaks (7 and up)   **305.23**
Sills, L. From rags to riches (5 and up)   **391**
Things I have to tell you (7 and up)   **810.8**
Weston, C. Private and personal   **305.23**
You be me (7 and up)   **305.23**
           Books and reading
Cooper-Mullin, A. Once upon a heroine   **028.1**
Dodson, S. 100 books for girls to grow on   **028.1**
O'Dell, K. Library materials and services for teen girls   **027.62**
           Employment
See Child labor
           Health and hygiene
Cheung, L. W.-Y. Be healthy! it's a girl thing (5 and up)   **613**
Irons, D. Teen beauty secrets (7 and up)   **646.7**
Schwager, T. The right moves (7 and up)   **613.7**
           Poetry
Nye, N. S. A maze me (7 and up)   **811**
Girls, Teenage *See* Teenagers
Girls!. Colman, P.   **305.23**
The **girls**. Koss, A. G.   **Fic**
Girls got game (5 and up)   **810.8**
The **girls'** guide to friends. Taylor, J.   **158**
Girls know best   **305.23**
Girls of many lands [series]
Hill, K. Minuk   **Fic**
Kurtz, J. Saba   **Fic**
The **girls'** room. Shreve, S. R.
   In Tripping over the lunch lady and other school stories p133-56   **S C**
Girls think of everything. Thimmesh, C.   **920**
The **Girls'** World book of jewelry: 50 cool designs to make. Newcomb, R.   **745.594**
Girlwonder. Hartman, H.   **305.23**
Girod, Christina M.
Down syndrome   **616.85**
GIs *See* Soldiers—United States
Give me a crab, John. Philip, N.
   In Philip, N. Celtic fairy tales p66   **398.2**
Give me liberty!. Freedman, R.   **973.3**
The **giver**. Lowry, L.   **Fic**
The **giver** [excerpt] Lowry, L.
   In Read into the millennium; tales of the future p139-46   **S C**

Gjertsen, Derek
(jt. auth) Allaby, M. Makers of science   **920.003**
Gladstone, Dale M.
(il) Julius, E. H. Arithmetricks   **513**
Glancy, Diane
Aunt Parnetta's electric blisters
   In Talking leaves; contemporary native American short stories   **S C**
Glass, Andrew, 1949-
(il) Brittain, B. The wish giver   **Fic**
Glass
Kassinger, R. Glass: from Cinderella's slippers to fiber optics   **620.1**
See/See also pages in the following book(s):
Knapp, B. J. Materials science   **620.1**
Glass: from Cinderella's slippers to fiber optics. Kassinger, R.   **620.1**
Glassman, Bruce
John Paul Getty (7 and up)   **92**
Mikhail Baryshnikov   **92**
GLBTQ (Gay, Lesbian, Bisexual, Transgender, Questioning). Huegel, K.   **306.76**
Gleason, Katherine, 1960-
Native American literature   **897**
Glenn, Jim
The treasury of family games (5 and up)   **793**
Glenn, John, 1921-
           About
Vogt, G. John Glenn's return to space   **629.45**
Glenn, Mel, 1943-
Foreign exchange (7 and up)   **811**
Split image: a story in poems (7 and up)   **811**
Glick, Susan
War and peace   **201**
Global debt. Garlake, T.   **336.3**
Global networks. Graham, I.   **384**
Global profiles [series]
Graham, K. Contemporary environmentalists   **920**
Henderson, H. Modern mathematicians   **920**
Price-Groff, C. Twentieth-century women political leaders   **920**
Global resources: opposing viewpoints   **333.71**
Global warming. Oxlade, C.   **363.7**
Global warming. Parks, P. J.   **363.7**
Global warming. Pringle, L. P.   **363.7**
Global warming. Silverstein, A.   **363.7**
Global warming: opposing viewpoints (7 and up)   **363.7**
GlobaLinks: resources for world studies, grades K-8. Beck, P.   **016.9**
Globalization
January, B. Globalize it! (7 and up)   **337**
Globalize it!. January, B.   **337**
Globe Theatre (London, England)
See also Shakespeare's Globe (London, England)

Globe Theatre (London, England)—See also—
Continued
Aliki. William Shakespeare & the Globe (4 and up) **792.09**

The **'Gloria** Scott'. Doyle, Sir A. C.
In Doyle, Sir A. C. The complete Sherlock Holmes **S C**

The **glorious** impossible. L'Engle, M. **232.9**

A **Glory** of unicorns (5 and up) **S C**

Glossaries *See* Encyclopedias and dictionaries

Glossop, Jennifer
(jt. auth) Gillies, J. The jumbo vegetarian cookbook **641.5**

Glover, David M.
The young Oxford book of the human being **612**

Gnat Stokes and the Foggy Bottom Swamp Queen. Keehn, S. M. **Fic**

Go and come back. Abelove, J. **Fic**

Go boy 7, Vol. 1: Ready set go!. Peyer, T. **741.5**

Go for the goal. Hamm, M. **796.334**

Go girl!: The time team. Robbins, T. **741.5**

Go tell it on the mountain. Baldwin, J. **Fic**

Go wild in New York City. Matsen, B. **974.7**

The **goats.** Cole, B. **Fic**

Goble, Todd, 1962-
Nicholas Copernicus and the founding of modern astronomy (7 and up) **92**

The **Goblin** Wood. Bell, H. **Fic**

God battles the Queen of the Waters. Lester, J.
In Lester, J. When the beginning began; stories about God, the creatures, and us p7-10 **296.1**

God confronts Adam, the Woman, and the Snake. Lester, J.
In Goldin, B. D. Journeys with Elijah; eight tales of the Prophet p87-92 **296.1**
In Lester, J. When the beginning began; stories about God, the creatures, and us p87-92 **296.1**

God creates Adam. Lester, J.
In Lester, J. When the beginning began; stories about God, the creatures, and us p59-63 **296.1**

God creates Woman. Lester, J.
In Lester, J. When the beginning began; stories about God, the creatures, and us p64-68 **296.1**

God learns how to create. Lester, J.
In Lester, J. When the beginning began; stories about God, the creatures, and us p1-5 **296.1**

God makes people. Lester, J.
In Lester, J. When the beginning began; stories about God, the creatures, and us p49-57 **296.1**

God of beer. Keizer, G. **Fic**

God returns to Heaven. Lester, J.
In Lester, J. When the beginning began; stories about God, the creatures, and us p93-95 **296.1**

Godasiyo the woman chief. Brown, D. A.
In Brown, D. A. Dee Brown's folktales of the Native American; retold for our times p71-74 **398.2**

Goddard, Robert Hutchings, 1882-1945
See/See also pages in the following book(s):
Richie, J. Space flight **920**

Goddess of yesterday. Cooney, C. B. **Fic**

Goddesses *See* Gods and goddesses

Godfrey, Neale S.
Neale S. Godfrey's ultimate kids' money book (5 and up) **332.024**

Godless. Hautman, P. **Fic**

Godmother. Mathis, S. B.
In Join in; multiethnic short stories by outstanding writers for young adults p173-99 **S C**

Gods and goddesses
See also Religions names of individual gods and goddesses
Mass, W. Gods and goddesses **201**
See/See also pages in the following book(s):
Hamilton, E. Mythology p21-76 **292**

Gods, goddesses, and monsters. Keenan, S. **201**

Goeppert-Mayer, Maria, 1906-1972
About
Ferry, J. Maria Goeppert Mayer, physicist (7 and up) **92**
See/See also pages in the following book(s):
Di Domenico, K. Super women in science **920**

Goethals, George W. (George Washington), 1858-1928
See/See also pages in the following book(s):
Aaseng, N. Construction: building the impossible **624**

Goetz, Bernhard
See/See also pages in the following book(s):
Aaseng, N. You are the juror **345**

Gofen, Ethel, 1937-
Argentina (5 and up) **982**
France **944**

Gogerly, Liz
Dian Fossey **92**

Gogh, Vincent van, 1853-1890
About
Bassil, A. Vincent van Gogh (4 and up) **92**
Greenberg, J. Vincent Van Gogh **92**

Goh, Chan Hon, 1969-
Beyond the dance **92**

Going, K. L.
Fat kid rules the world (7 and up) **Fic**

Going for the record. Swanson, J. A. **Fic**

Going home. Bruchac, J.
In Talking leaves; contemporary native American short stories **S C**

Going sentimental. Vail, R.
In Places I never meant to be; original stories by censored writers **S C**

Going to Kashi. Krishnaswami, U.
In Soul searching: thirteen stories about faith and belief p157-76 **S C**

Going to school in 1776. Loeper, J. J.   **370.9**

Going to war in Viking times. Gravett, C.
   355

Gola, Mark
(jt. auth) Crisfield, D. Winning volleyball for
girls   **796.325**

Golay, Michael, 1951-
Civil War   **973.7**
Reconstruction and reaction (7 and up)
   305.8

Gold, Alison Leslie
Memories of Anne Frank (5 and up)   **92**

Gold, John Coopersmith
Board of Education v. Pico (1982) (7 and up)
   344
Cerebral palsy (4 and up)   **616.8**

Gold, Susan Dudley, 1949-
Brown v. Board of Education   **344**
In re Gault (1967) (7 and up)   **345**
Miranda v. Arizona (1966) (7 and up)   **345**
Multiple sclerosis (4 and up)   **616.8**
The musculoskeletal system and the skin
   612.7
The Pentagon papers   **342**
Roe v. Wade   **344**

Gold
Kassinger, R. Gold: from Greek myth to computer chips   **669**

The **gold** bug. Poe, E. A.
In Poe, E. A. Tales of Edgar Allan Poe p243-
91   **S C**
In Poe, E. A. The pit and the pendulum and
other stories   **S C**

The **gold** Cadillac. Taylor, M. D.   **Fic**

Gold dust. Lynch, C.   **Fic**

Gold: from Greek myth to computer chips.
Kassinger, R.   **669**

Gold mines and mining
See also Klondike River valley (Yukon)—
Gold discoveries
Fiction
Fleischman, S. Bo & Mzzz Mad (5 and up)
   Fic
Gregory, K. Orphan runaways   **Fic**

Gold rush *See* California—Gold discoveries

The **gold** rush. O'Donnell, K.   **979.4**

Goldberg, Jake
Hawaii
In Celebrate the states   **973**

Goldberg, Whoopi
See/See also pages in the following book(s):
Stewart, G. Great women comedians   **920**

Golden, Diana, 1963-2001
See/See also pages in the following book(s):
Kaminsky, M. Uncommon champions   **920**

The **golden** compass. Pullman, P.   **Fic**

Golden Fleece (Greek mythology) *See* Argonauts
(Greek mythology)

Golden glass. Villanueva, A.
In Growing up Latino; memoirs and stories
p259-63   **810.8**

The **golden** hour. Williams, M.   **Fic**

The **golden** sail. Coville, B.
In Coville, B. Odder than ever   **S C**

Golden tales. Delacre, L.   **398.2**

Goldin, Barbara Diamond
And the lights flickered
In The Haunted house: a collection of original
stories   **S C**
Journeys with Elijah (4 and up)   **222**
Contents: A journey with Elijah; Seven good years; A disor-
derly table; The weaver of Yzad; Elijah and the three brothers;
The fragrance of paradise; The blessing; Meeting Elijah

Golding, Theresa Martin
The secret within   **Fic**

Golding, William, 1911-1993
Lord of the Flies   **Fic**

Goldman, David J.
Presidential losers   **920**

Goldman, Martin S.
Richard M. Nixon (7 and up)   **92**

Goldsmith, Connie, 1945-
Lost in Death Valley   **979.4**
Neurological disorders   **616.8**

Goldstein, Bobbye S.
(ed) Mother Goose on the loose. See Mother
Goose on the loose   **398.8**

Goldstein, Margaret J.
World War II, Europe (5 and up)   **940.53**

The **golem**. Rogasky, B.   **398.2**

Gollobin, Laurie Brooks *See* Brooks Gollobin,
Laurie

Golpe de estado. Regan, D. C.
In Shattered: stories of children and war p52-
70   **S C**

Gompers, Samuel, 1850-1924
See/See also pages in the following book(s):
Streissguth, T. Legendary labor leaders (7 and
up)   **920**

Gone a-whaling. Murphy, J.   **639.2**

Gonzales, Doreen
Gloria Estefan   **92**

Gonzalez, Genaro, 1949-
Un hijo del sol
In Growing up Latino; memoirs and stories
p38-46   **810.8**

Gonzalez, Gloria
The boy with yellow eyes
In Visions: nineteen short stories by outstand-
ing writers for young adults p204-12
   S C
Viva New Jersey
In Join in; multiethnic short stories by out-
standing writers for young adults p51-60
   S C

González, Rubén, 1919-2003
See/See also pages in the following book(s):
Kaminsky, M. Uncommon champions   **920**

Goobie, Beth, 1959-
Before wings (7 and up)   **Fic**

Gooch, Anthony
(ed) Cassell's Spanish-English, English-Spanish
dictionary. See Cassell's Spanish-English, English-Spanish dictionary   **463**

Good and evil

Fiction

Cooper, S. Over sea, under stone (5 and up)
Fic

Poetry

Wicked poems (4 and up)   811.008

Good Blanche, bad Rose, and the talking eggs. Hamilton, V.
In Hamilton, V. Her stories; African American folktales, fairy tales, and true tales p28-32   398.2

Good brother, bad brother [biography of John Wilkes Booth and Edwin Booth] Giblin, J.
92

Good-bye is good-bye. Lynch, C.
In Lynch, C. All the old haunts p113-25
S C

The **good** deed. Bauer, M. D.
In Shelf life: stories by the book p109-26
S C

The **good** fight. Ambrose, S. E.   940.53

The **good** girls. Arrick, F.
In Visions: nineteen short stories by outstanding writers for young adults p107-20
S C

Good grief. Bradbury, R.
In Who do you think you are?; stories of friends and enemies p3-13   S C

The **good** liar. Maguire, G.   Fic

Good morning! this is the future. Slesar, H.
In Read into the millennium; tales of the future p120-25   S C

Good news Bible.   220.5

Good night, Maman. Mazer, N. F.   Fic

Good Queen Bess: the story of Elizabeth I of England. Stanley, D.   92

The **good** samaritan. Saldaña, R.
In Saldaña, R. Finding our way: stories p1-10
S C

The **good** sword. Owen, R. B.
In The Book of dragons p110-20   S C

Good women of a well-blessed land. Miller, B. M.
305.4

Goodall, Jane, 1934-
The chimpanzees I love (4 and up)   599.8
With love (4 and up)   599.8

About

Kozleski, L. Jane Goodall (7 and up)   92
See/See also pages in the following book(s):
Celebrating women in mathematics and science
920

Goodbye, Vietnam. Whelan, G.   Fic

Goodfellow, Gregory
Epilepsy   616.8

Goodhue, Thomas W.
Curious bones: Mary Anning and the birth of paleontology   92

Goodman, Alison, 1966-
Singing the Dogstar blues (7 and up)   Fic

Goodman, Benny, 1909-1986
See/See also pages in the following book(s):
Mour, S. I. American jazz musicians   920

Goodman, Jim
Thailand (5 and up)   959.3

Goodman, Joan E., 1950-
The Czarevna of Muscovy
In Don't cramp my style; stories about that time of the month p101-30   S C
Despite all obstacles: La Salle and the conquest of the Mississippi (4 and up)   92
A long and uncertain journey: the 27,000 mile voyage of Vasco da Gama (4 and up)   92
Paradise (7 and up)   Fic

Goodman, Susan, 1952-
Ultimate field trip 3   577.6
Ultimate field trip 4: a week in the 1800s (5 and up)   973.5
Ultimate field trip 5 (4 and up)   629.45

The **goodness** of Matt Kaizer. Avi
In Avi. What do fish have to do with anything? and other stories p35-59   S C

Goodnough, David
The debate over human cloning   174.2
Pablo Neruda   92

Goodsell, Joan
(ed) Sears list of subject headings. See Sears list of subject headings   025.4

Goodstein, Madeline
Plastics and polymers science fair projects (7 and up)   507.8

GoodWeather, Hartley *See* King, Thomas, 1943-

Goodwin, William, 1943-
Marijuana (7 and up)   362.29

Goose chase. Kindl, P.   Fic

The **Goose** girl. Hale, S.   Fic

Gootman, Marilyn E., 1944-
When a friend dies (7 and up)   155.9

GOP (Grand Old Party) *See* Republican Party (U.S.)

Gordeeva, Ekaterina

About

Shea, P. D. Ekaterina Gordeeva   92

Gordimer, Nadine, 1923-
A chip of glass ruby
In Somehow tenderness survives; stories of Southern Africa p105-18   S C
Country lovers
In Somehow tenderness survives; stories of Southern Africa p49-59   S C
See/See also pages in the following book(s):
Hacker, C. Nobel Prize winners   920

Gordon, Amy, 1949-
The Gorillas of Gill Park (4 and up)   Fic

Gordon, Matthew
Islam (7 and up)   297

Gordon, Melanie Apel
Drug interactions   615

Gordon, Rachel Singer
Teaching the Internet in libraries   025.04

Gordy, Berry, Jr.
See/See also pages in the following book(s):
Haskins, J. African American entrepreneurs
920

Gore, Albert, Jr.
      About
  Sergis, D. K. Bush v. Gore   342
Gorge-purge syndrome *See* Bulimia
Gorilla. Redmond, I.   **599.8**
Gorilla doctors. Turner, P. S.   **333.95**
Gorilla walk. Lewin, T.   **599.8**
Gorillas
  Gogerly, L. Dian Fossey   **92**
  Lewin, T. Gorilla walk (4 and up)   **599.8**
  Matthews, T. L. Light shining through the mist: a photobiography of Dian Fossey (4 and up)   **92**
  Nicholson, L. Dian Fossey (7 and up)   **92**
  Turner, P. S. Gorilla doctors (5 and up)   **333.95**
The **Gorillas** of Gill Park. Gordon, A.   **Fic**
Gorman, Michael, 1941-
  The concise AACR2, 2004 revision   **025.3**
Gorman, Michele
  Getting graphic!   **741.5**
  (jt. auth) Jones, P. Connecting young adults and libraries   **027.62**
Gormley, Beatrice, 1942-
  C.S. Lewis   **92**
  Maria Mitchell (7 and up)   **92**
Gorog, Judith, 1938-
  Those three wishes
  In Read all about it!; great read-aloud stories, poems, and newspaper pieces for pre-teens and teens p475-78   **808.8**
Gorrell, Gena K. (Gena Kinton), 1946-
  Catching fire   **628.9**
  Working like a dog (4 and up)   **636.7**
Gorton, Steve
  (il) Platt, R. Spy   **327.12**
  (il) Stott, C. Space exploration   **629.4**
Goslar, Hannah Pick- *See* Pick-Goslar, Hannah
The **gospel** according to Krenzwinkle. Klass, D.
  In Ultimate sports; short stories by outstanding writers for young adults p274-98   **S C**
The **gospel** according to Larry. Tashjian, J.   **Fic**
Gospel music
  See also Spirituals (Songs)
  Orgill, R. Mahalia [Jackson] (5 and up)   **92**
Goss, Gary, 1947-
  Blue moon soup (4-6)   **641.8**
Goss, Linda
  (ed) Talk that talk: an anthology of African-American storytelling. See Talk that talk: an anthology of African-American storytelling   **398.2**
Gotcha!. Baxter, K. A.   **028.1**
Gothic! (7 and up)   **S C**
Gothic architecture
  Macaulay, D. Building the book Cathedral (4 and up)   **726**
  Macaulay, D. Cathedral: the story of its construction (4 and up)   **726**

Gottesfeld, Jeff
  (jt. auth) Bennett, C. A heart divided
Gottfried, Ted, 1928-
  Children of the slaughter (7 and up)   **940.53**
  Deniers of the Holocaust (7 and up)   **940.53**
  Displaced persons (7 and up)   **940.53**
  The facts about alcohol   **362.292**
  The facts about marijuana   **362.29**
  Heroes of the Holocaust (7 and up)   **940.53**
  Nazi Germany (7 and up)   **940.53**
  The road to Communism   **947**
  Slovakia (5 and up)   **943.7**
  Slovenia (5 and up)   **949.7**
  The Stalinist empire   **947.084**
Gough, Barry M.
  (ed) Explorers. See Explorers   **920.003**
Gould, Steven, 1955-
  Peaches for Mad Molly
  In New skies: an anthology of today's science fiction   **S C**
Gourdine, Traci L.
  (ed) Night is gone, day is still coming. See Night is gone, day is still coming   **808.8**
The **gourmet** ghost. Gill-Lonergan, J.
  In The Haunted house: a collection of original stories   **S C**
Gouveia, Pedro Alvares de *See* Cabral, Pedro Alvares, 1460?-1526?
Government *See* Political science
Government & politics. Jones, V. B.   **920**
Government on file. Tomaselli-Moschovitis, V.   **320.4**
Government publications
    United States—Bibliography
  Hoffmann, F. W. Guide to popular U.S. government publications   **015.73**
Gow, Mary
  Attack on America   **973.931**
  Tycho Brahe: astronomer   **92**
Gowell, Elizabeth Tayntor
  Fountains of life   **577.7**
Gownley, Jimmy
  Amelia Rules!   **741.5**
Grabowski, John F.
  Australia (7 and up)   **994**
Grace, Catherine O'Neill
  Forces of nature (4 and up)   **551.2**
The **graceless** child. De Lint, C.
  In De Lint, C. Waifs and strays p111-38   **S C**
The **grade** school zone. Proimos, J.
  In Tripping over the lunch lady and other school stories p85-92   **S C**
Grading and marking (Education)
  Terkel, M. What's an "A" anyway? (7 and up)   **371.2**
The **graduation** of Jake Moon. Park, B.   **Fic**
Grady, Sean M., 1965-
  Virtual reality (7 and up)   **006.8**
  (jt. auth) Billings, C. W. Supercomputers   **004**
  (jt. auth) Facklam, M. Modern medicines   **615**

Graff Hysell, Shannon
(ed) Recommended reference books for small and medium-sized libraries and media centers. See Recommended reference books for small and medium-sized libraries and media centers **011**

Graham, Arleen Pancza- *See* Pancza-Graham, Arleen

Graham, Bette Nesmith, 1924-1980
See/See also pages in the following book(s):
Thimmesh, C. Girls think of everything (5 and up) **920**

Graham, Ian, 1953-
Books and newspapers **686.2**
Film and photography **770**
Flight **629.13**
Global networks **384**
Radio and television **621.384**
Solar power **621.47**
Water power **620.1**
Wind power **621.4**

Graham, Katharine
See/See also pages in the following book(s):
Jeffrey, L. S. Great American businesswomen **920**

Graham, Kevin, 1959-
Contemporary environmentalists (7 and up) **920**

Graham, Martha
About
Freedman, R. Martha Graham, a dancer's life (7 and up) **92**

Graham, Paula W.
Speaking of journals **920**

Graham, Rosemary
My not-so-terrible time at Hippie Hotel **Fic**

Grahame, Deborah A.
World Health Organization **610.6**

Grahame, Kenneth, 1859-1932
The reluctant dragon
In The Book of dragons p20-25 **S C**

Grail
Fiction
Pyle, H. The story of the Grail and the passing of Arthur (7 and up) **398.2**
Sutcliff, R. The light beyond the forest (4 and up) **398.2**

Grand Canyon (Ariz.)
Fiction
Hautman, P. Hole in the sky (7 and up) **Fic**

Grand Central Park. Sherman, D.
In The Green Man: tales from the mythic forest p21-42 **808.8**

The **grand** parade. Lester, J.
In Lester, J. When the beginning began; stories about God, the creatures, and us p43-48 **296.1**

The **granddaughter**. Vande Velde, V.
In Vande Velde, V. Tales from the Brothers Grimm and the Sisters Weird p37-50 **S C**

Grandfathers
Fiction
Bauer, J. Stand tall **Fic**

Bauer, M. D. An early winter **Fic**
Bawden, N. Off the road **Fic**
Bowler, T. River boy **Fic**
Crowe, C. Mississippi trial, 1955 (7 and up) **Fic**
French, S. Where in the world (5 and up) **Fic**
Garland, S. The silent storm **Fic**
George, J. C. Charlie's raven (5 and up) **Fic**
Gilbert, B. S. Stone water (7 and up) **Fic**
Holt, K. W. Dancing in Cadillac light (5 and up) **Fic**
Levin, B. Shadow-catcher (5 and up) **Fic**
Mazer, N. F. After the rain **Fic**
Mosher, R. Zazoo **Fic**
Park, B. The graduation of Jake Moon **Fic**
Rylant, C. The islander **Fic**
Spinelli, J. Crash (5 and up) **Fic**

Grandmothers
In my grandmother's house **306.8**
Fiction
Bawden, N. Granny the Pag (4 and up) **Fic**
Gilmore, R. A group of one **Fic**
Haas, J. Will you, won't you? **Fic**
Hahn, M. D. Following my own footsteps (5 and up) **Fic**
Hamilton, V. Cousins (5 and up) **Fic**
Henkes, K. Olive's ocean (5 and up) **Fic**
Henkes, K. Sun & Spoon (4 and up) **Fic**
Johnson, A. Toning the sweep **Fic**
Lamm, C. D. Bittersweet **Fic**
Larbalestier, J. Magic or madness. (7 and up) **Fic**
McGhee, A. Snap (5 and up) **Fic**
Paulsen, G. Alida's song (5 and up) **Fic**
Paulsen, G. The cookcamp (5 and up) **Fic**
Peck, R. A long way from Chicago (5 and up) **Fic**
Peck, R. A year down yonder (5 and up) **Fic**
Voigt, C. Dicey's song (6 and up) **Fic**
Williams, C. L. If I forget, you remember **Fic**
Wilson, N. H. Mountain pose (5 and up) **Fic**
Wright, B. R. Out of the dark (4 and up) **Fic**
Yep, L. Child of the owl (5 and up) **Fic**

Grandmother's skull. Tchana, K. H.
In Tchana, K. H. The serpent slayer: and other stories of strong women p61-65 **398.2**

Grandparents
Fiction
Creech, S. Walk two moons (6 and up) **Fic**

Grandpré, Mary, 1954-
Much ado about nothing
In Packer, T. Tales from Shakespeare p49-65 **822.3**
(il) Rowling, J. K. Harry Potter and the sorcerer's stone **Fic**

Granfield, Linda
I remember Korea **951.9**

Granny the Pag. Bawden, N. **Fic**

Grant, K. M.
Blood red horse **Fic**

Grant, R. G. (Reg G.)
The African-American slave trade **326**
Genocide **303.6**
The Great Depression **973.917**
Hiroshima and Nagasaki (7 and up) **940.54**

Grant, Ulysses S. (Ulysses Simpson), 1822-1885
See/See also pages in the following book(s):
Marrin, A. Commander in Chief Abraham Lincoln and the Civil War (7 and up) **973.7**

Grants for school libraries. Hall-Ellis, S. D. **025.1**

Grants-in-aid
Anderson, C. Write grants, get money **025.1**
Grantsmanship for small libraries and school library media centers **025.1**
Hall-Ellis, S. D. Grants for school libraries **025.1**

Grantsmanship for small libraries and school library media centers **025.1**

Granville, Evelyn Boyd, 1924-
See/See also pages in the following book(s):
Celebrating women in mathematics and science **920**

Grape thief. Franklin, K. L. **Fic**

Grapes, Bryan J.
(ed) Child abuse. See Child abuse [Current controversies] **362.7**

Graphic fiction *See* Graphic novels

Graphic novels
Anderson, K. J. Grumpy old monsters **741.5**
Ariyoshi, K. Swan, Vol. 1 **741.5**
Atangan, P. The yellow jar **741.5**
Avery, B. The hedge knight **741.5**
Blackman, H. Star Wars: Clone wars adventures, Vol. 1 **741.5**
Cover, A. B. Macbeth **741.5**
DeFalco, T. Spider-girl, Vol. 1: Legacy **741.5**
DeFilippis, N. Once in a blue moon **741.5**
Dezago, T. Spider-man: Spidey strikes back Vol. 1 digest **741.5**
Dezago, T. Tellos, Vol. 1 **741.5**
Dixon, C. Hobbit: an illustrated edition of the fantasy classic **741.5**
Fisher, J. S. WJHC: on the air! **741.5**
Gallagher, J. Buzzboy: Trouble in paradise **741.5**
Gorman, M. Getting graphic! **741.5**
Gownley, J. Amelia Rules! **741.5**
Harris, J. S. Shades of blue, Volume 1 **741.5**
Higuchi, D. Whistle! Volume 1 **741.5**
Hosler, J. Clan Apis **741.5**
Hosler, J. The sandwalk adventures **741.5**
Hotta, Y. Hikaru No Go, Volume 1 **741.5**
Huddleston, C. Decoy **741.5**
Irwin, J. Vögelein **741.5**
Kirkman, R. Tech jacket, Vol. 1: Lost & found **741.5**
Kobayashi, M. What's Michael? Vol. 10: Sleepless nights **741.5**
Kochalka, J. Monkey vs. Robot **741.5**

Konomi, T. The Prince of Tennis, Vol. 1 **741.5**
Lyga, A. A. W. Graphic novels in your media center **025.2**
Morse, S. The barefoot serpent **741.5**
Naifeh, T. Courtney Crumrin and the night things **741.5**
Naruse, K. Prétear, Volume 1 **741.5**
Ottaviani, J. Dignifying science: stories about women scientists **741.5**
Peyer, T. Go boy 7, Vol. 1: Ready set go! **741.5**
Reed, G. Mary Shelley's Frankenstein: the graphic novel **741.5**
Robbins, T. Go girl!: The time team **741.5**
Robinson, J. Leave it to Chance: Shaman's rain **741.5**
Sakai, S. Usagi Yojimbo, Vol. 18 **741.5**
Sava, S. C. The lab: hey . . . test this! **741.5**
Sfar, J. Dungeon Vol. 1: Duck Heart **741.5**
Sizer, P. Little White Mouse collection 1: Dream of the ghost **741.5**
Smith, I. Emily & the intergalactic lemonade stand **741.5**
Smith, J. Bone: out from Boneville **741.5**
TenNapel, D. R. Tommysaurus Rex **741.5**
Torres, J. Alison Dare: Little Miss Adventures **741.5**
Trondheim, L. Astronauts of the future **741.5**
Vansant, W. The red badge of courage **741.5**
Walker, L. Q. Little Gloomy: . . . It was a dark and stormy night **741.5**
Wong, T. Ultraman Tiga, Vol. 1: Return of the warrior **741.5**

Graphic novels in your media center. Lyga, A. A. W. **025.2**

Grasshopper. Molnár, I.
In Molnár, I. One-time dog market at Buda and other Hungarian folktales p42-46 **398.2**

Grasshoppers
Pascoe, E. Crickets and grasshoppers (4 and up) **595.7**

Grassland ecology
Hoare, B. Temperate grasslands (5 and up) **577.4**
Martin, P. A. F. Prairies, fields, and meadows (7 and up) **577.4**
Sayre, A. P. Grassland (5 and up) **577.4**

Grasslands
See also Prairies

Grater, Lindsay
(il) Spencer, A. And round me rings **398.2**

Gratsaniti, Olga
(jt. auth) DuBois, J. Greece **949.5**

The **grave**. Heneghan, J. **Fic**

A **grave** misunderstanding. Garfield, L.
In Beware!; R.L. Stine picks his favorite scary stories p189-97 **808.8**

A **grave** situation. Hearne, B. G.
In Hearne, B. G. The canine connection: stories about dogs and people p51-62
                                                        S C

Gravelle, Jennifer
(jt. auth) Gravelle, K. The period book
                                                        612.6

Gravelle, Karen
The period book (4 and up)   612.6
What's going on down there?   612.6

Graves, Earl G., 1935-
See/See also pages in the following book(s):
Haskins, J. African American entrepreneurs
                                                        920

Gravett, Christopher
Going to war in Viking times   355
Knight (4 and up)   940.1

Graveyards *See* Cemeteries

Graveyards of the dinosaurs. Tanaka, S.
                                                        567.9

Gravitation
Farndon, J. Gravity   531
Parker, B. R. The mystery of gravity (5 and up)
                                                        531

Gravity. Farndon, J.   531

Gray, Dianne E.
Together apart (7 and up)   Fic

Gray, Edward G., 1964-
Colonial America: a history in documents (7 and up)
                                                        973.2

Gray, Heather M.
Real girl/real world (7 and up)   305.23

Gray, Leon, 1974-
Iodine
In The Elements   546
Tin
In The Elements   546

Gray, Mary W., 1939-
See/See also pages in the following book(s):
Celebrating women in mathematics and science
                                                        920

Gray, Susan H.
Living with cerebral palsy (4 and up)   362.1
Living with juvenile rheumatoid arthritis
                                                        616.7

Graydon, Shari
In your face (7 and up)   391
Made you look (5 and up)   659.1

Graymont, Barbara
The Iroquois Indians of North America series

Great American businesswomen. Jeffrey, L. S.
                                                        920

The **great** American elephant chase. Cross, G.
                                                        Fic

Great American memorials [series]
Ashabranner, J. No better hope   975.3
Ashabranner, B. K. Remembering Korea
                                                        951.9

Great American mysteries. Floyd, E. R.   001.9

Great American writers: twentieth century
                                                        920.003

The **great** ancestor hunt. Perl, L.   929

The **great** apes. Saign, G.   599.8

Great-aunts *See* Aunts

Great Barrier Reef (Australia)
Collard, S. B., III. Lizard Island   577.7

Great battles through the ages [series]
Crompton, S. The Third Crusade   956

The **Great** Blue Yonder. Shearer, A.   Fic

Great books for boys. Odean, K.   028.1

The **great** brain book. Newquist, H. P.   612.8

Great Britain
Antiquities
Malone, C. Stonehenge   936.2

Great Britain
See also England
Civilization
Ashby, R. Victorian England   941.081
Fiction
Aiken, J. The wolves of Willoughby Chase (5 and up)
                                                        Fic
Almond, D. Counting stars (7 and up)   Fic
Almond, D. The fire-eaters   Fic
Almond, D. Kit's wilderness (5 and up)   Fic
Banks, L. R. Alice-by-accident   Fic
Brooks, K. Lucas (7 and up)   Fic
Cassidy, C. Dizzy (5 and up)
Cooper, S. Over sea, under stone (5 and up)
                                                        Fic
Cottrell Boyce, F. Millions (5 and up)   Fic
Cushman, K. Catherine, called Birdy (6 and up)
                                                        Fic
Cushman, K. Matilda Bone (5 and up)   Fic
Cushman, K. The midwife's apprentice (6 and up)
                                                        Fic
Gavin, J. Coram boy (7 and up)   Fic
Horowitz, A. Raven's gate (7 and up)   Fic
Horowitz, A. Stormbreaker   Fic
Lawrence, M. A crack in the line (7 and up)
                                                        Fic
Morgan, N. Chicken friend (5 and up)   Fic
Morpurgo, M. Private Peaceful (7 and up)
                                                        Fic
Paton Walsh, J. A parcel of patterns   Fic
Rennison, L. Angus, thongs and full-frontal snogging (7 and up)
                                                        Fic
Turnbull, A. No shame, no fear (7 and up)
                                                        Fic
Wrede, P. C. Sorcery and Cecelia, or, The enchanted chocolate pot (7 and up)
                                                        Fic
Zephaniah, B. Face (7 and up)   Fic
Folklore
See Folklore—Great Britain
History—0-1066
Crossley-Holland, K. The world of King Arthur and his court (5 and up)   942.01
Nardo, D. King Arthur   942.01
History—0-1066—Fiction
Alder, E. The king's shadow (7 and up)   Fic
Avi. The Book Without Words (5 and up)
                                                        Fic
Morris, G. The squire's tale   Fic
Springer, N. I am Mordred (7 and up)   Fic
Springer, N. I am Morgan le Fay (7 and up)
                                                        Fic
Sutcliff, R. Sword song (7 and up)   Fic
Thomson, S. L. The dragon's son (7 and up)
                                                        Fic

Great Britain—History—0-1066—History—0-1066—Fiction—*Continued*

Tingle, R. The edge on the sword   **Fic**
Tingle, R. Far traveler   **Fic**
White, T. H. The once and future king   **Fic**
Yolen, J. Sword of the rightful king   **Fic**
    History—19th century—Fiction
Kirwan, A. Victoria, May blossom of Britannia   **Fic**
Updale, E. Montmorency   **Fic**
    History—1154-1399, Plantagenets
Ruhl, G. In the time of knights (4 and up)   **942.03**
Weatherly, M. William Marshal, medieval England's greatest knight [biography of William Marshal, earl of Pembroke]   **92**
    History—1154-1399, Plantagenets—Fiction
Cadnum, M. Forbidden forest (7 and up)   **Fic**
Cadnum, M. In a dark wood   **Fic**
Crossley-Holland, K. The seeing stone   **Fic**
    History—1485-1603, Tudors
Currie, S. An actor on the Elizabethan stage   **792.09**
Greenblatt, M. Elizabeth I and Tudor England   **942.05**
Lace, W. W. Elizabeth I and her court   **942.05**
Nardo, D. Great Elizabethan playwrights   **920**
Primary sources [Lucent library of historical eras. Elizabethan England]   **942.05**
Stanley, D. Good Queen Bess: the story of Elizabeth I of England (4 and up)   **92**
Stewart, G. Life in Elizabethan London   **942.05**
Thomas, J. R. Behind the mask: the life of Queen Elizabeth I (7 and up)   **92**
Woog, A. A history of the Elizabethan theater   **792.09**
    History—1485-1603, Tudors—Fiction
Blackwood, G. L. The Shakespeare stealer (5 and up)   **Fic**
Cheaney, J. B. The playmaker   **Fic**
Cheaney, J. B. The true Prince   **Fic**
Curry, J. L. The Black Canary (5 and up)   **Fic**
Lasky, K. Elizabeth I (4 and up)   **Fic**
Meyer, C. Beware, Princess Elizabeth   **Fic**
Meyer, C. Mary, Bloody Mary   **Fic**
Twain, M. The prince and the pauper   **Fic**
    History—1603-1714, Stuarts
Aronson, M. John Winthrop, Oliver Cromwell, and the Land of Promise (7 and up)   **92**
Barter, J. Shakespeare's London (7 and up)   **942.06**
    History—1714-1837—Fiction
Lawrence, I. The wreckers (5 and up)   **Fic**
    History—19th century
    See also Industrial revolution
Ashby, R. Victorian England   **941.081**
Price-Groff, C. Queen Victoria and nineteenth-century England   **941.081**
    Kings and rulers
Billinghurst, J. Growing up royal   **920**

Greenblatt, M. Elizabeth I and Tudor England   **942.05**
Price-Groff, C. Queen Victoria and nineteenth-century England   **941.081**
Stanley, D. Good Queen Bess: the story of Elizabeth I of England (4 and up)   **92**
Thomas, J. R. Behind the mask: the life of Queen Elizabeth I (7 and up)   **92**
    Politics and government—20th century
Macdonald, F. Winston Churchill   **92**
Severance, J. B. Winston Churchill (5 and up)   **92**
Wrigley, C. Winston Churchill: a biographical companion (7 and up)   **92**
    Social life and customs
Hinds, K. Medieval England   **942.03**
Price-Groff, C. Queen Victoria and nineteenth-century England   **941.081**

Great building feats [series]
DuTemple, L. A. The Great Wall of China   **931**
DuTemple, L. A. The New York subways   **388.4**
DuTemple, L. A. The Panama Canal   **972.87**
DuTemple, L. A. The Pantheon   **726**
DuTemple, L. A. The Taj Mahal   **726**
Great building stories of the past. Kent, P.   **624**

Great cities of the world [series]
Stacey, G. London   **942.1**

Great decisions [series]
Aaseng, N. You are the juror   **345**

Great Depression, 1929-1939
Blumenthal, K. Six days in October (7 and up)   **332.6**
Burg, D. F. The Great Depression (7 and up)   **973.91**
Collier, C. Progressivism, the Great Depression, and the New Deal, 1901 to 1941   **973.91**
Cooper, M. L. Dust to eat (4 and up)   **973.917**
Fremon, D. K. The Great Depression in American history   **338.5**
Grant, R. G. The Great Depression   **973.917**
The Great Depression (7 and up)   **973.91**
Living through the Great Depression (7 and up)   **973.91**
McArthur, D. The dust bowl and the Depression in American history (7 and up)   **978**
McElvaine, R. S. The Depression and New Deal (7 and up)   **973.91**
Stanley, J. Children of the Dust Bowl (5 and up)   **371.9**
See/See also pages in the following book(s):
Brown, G. Conflict in Europe and the Great Depression   **973.9**
    Fiction
Ayres, K. Macaroni boy (5 and up)   **Fic**
Blackwood, G. L. Moonshine   **Fic**
Bornstein, R. L. Butterflies and lizards, Beryl and me (4 and up)   **Fic**
Cummings, P. Saving Grace (5 and up)   **Fic**
Curtis, C. P. Bud, not Buddy (4 and up)   **Fic**
DeFelice, C. C. Nowhere to call home   **Fic**

Great Depression, 1929-1939—Fiction—*Continued*

Durbin, W. The journal of C.J. Jackson: a Dust Bowl migrant (4 and up) **Fic**

Hale, M. The truth about sparrows (5 and up) **Fic**

Haseley, D. The amazing thinking machine (4 and up) **Fic**

Hesse, K. Out of the dust (5 and up) **Fic**

Ingold, J. Hitch (7 and up) **Fic**

Janke, K. Survival in the storm **Fic**

Kudlinski, K. V. The spirit catchers (7 and up) **Fic**

Lasky, K. Christmas after all **Fic**

Peck, R. A long way from Chicago (5 and up) **Fic**

Peck, R. A year down yonder (5 and up) **Fic**

Taylor, M. D. Let the circle be unbroken (4 and up) **Fic**

Taylor, M. D. Song of the trees (4 and up) **Fic**

The **Great** Depression (7 and up) **973.91**

The **Great** Depression. Burg, D. F. **973.91**

The **Great** Depression in American history. Fremon, D. K. **338.5**

Great disasters, reforms and ramifications [series]

Reed, J. Love Canal **363.7**

Riddle, J. Bhopal **363.1**

Shields, C. J. The 1993 World Trade Center bombing **364.1**

Great discoveries & amazing adventures. Llewellyn, C. **509**

Great Elizabethan playwrights. Nardo, D. **920**

The **great** empire of China and Marco Polo in world history. Worth, R. **92**

Great episodes [series]

Rinaldi, A. The fifth of March **Fic**

Great escapes [series]

Currie, S. Escapes from slavery **326**

Great expectations. Kerr, M. E.

In On the fringe p26-46 **S C**

Great explorations [series]

Calvert, P. Daniel Boone **92**

Calvert, P. Hernando Cortés **92**

Calvert, P. Robert E. Peary **92**

Calvert, P. Sir Ernest Shackleton **92**

Calvert, P. Vasco da Gama **92**

Calvert, P. Zebulon Pike **92**

Faber, H. John Charles Frémont **92**

Faber, H. Lewis and Clark **978**

Faber, H. La Salle **92**

Faber, H. Samuel de Champlain **92**

Meltzer, M. Captain James Cook **92**

Meltzer, M. Ferdinand Magellan **92**

Meltzer, M. Francisco Pizarro **92**

Otfinoski, S. Francisco Coronado **92**

Otfinoski, S. Juan Ponce de Leon **92**

Otfinoski, S. Marco Polo **92**

Otfinoski, S. Vasco Nuñez de Balboa **92**

Rice, E. Sir Francis Drake, navigator and pirate **92**

Great explorers book [series]

Goodman, J. E. Despite all obstacles: La Salle and the conquest of the Mississippi **92**

Goodman, J. E. A long and uncertain journey: the 27,000 mile voyage of Vasco da Gama **92**

The **great** fire. Murphy, J. **977.3**

The **great** Gilly Hopkins. Paterson, K. **Fic**

The **great** god Pan. Napoli, D. J. **Fic**

The **great** goodbye. Wilson, R. C.

In New skies: an anthology of today's science fiction **S C**

Great historic debates and speeches [series]

Brezina, C. Sojourner Truth's "Ain't I a woman?" speech **92**

Great horned owl *See* Owls

The **great** interactive dream machine. Peck, R. **Fic**

Great inventions [series]

Collier, J. L. Clocks **681.1**

Collier, J. L. Gunpowder and weaponry **623.4**

Collier, J. L. Vaccines **615**

Meltzer, M. The cotton gin **633.5**

Meltzer, M. The printing press **686.2**

Great journeys [series]

Bial, R. The Long Walk **970.004**

Dolan, E. F. The Irish potato famine **941.5**

Elish, D. The Trail of Tears **970.004**

Haskins, J. Out of the darkness **305.8**

Meltzer, M. Bound for America **325.73**

Meltzer, M. Driven from the land **978**

Meltzer, M. They came in chains **326**

Perl, L. Behind barbed wire **940.53**

Perl, L. North across the border **305.8**

Perl, L. To the Golden Mountain **305.8**

The **Great** Lakes. Katz, S. **577.6**

Great life stories [series]

Lassieur, A. Marie Curie **92**

Lynch, D. J.R.R. Tolkien **92**

The **great** little Madison. Fritz, J. **92**

The **great** meatball. Curry, J. L.

In Curry, J. L. Hold up the sky: and other Native American tales from Texas and the Southern Plains p73-76 **398.2**

Great medical discoveries [series]

Bardhan-Quallen, S. Chemotherapy **616.99**

Nardo, D. Cloning **660.6**

Nardo, D. Vaccines **615**

The **great** migration. Lawrence, J. **759.13**

Great military leaders of the 20th century [series]

Slavicek, L. C. Mao Zedong **92**

Great minds of science [series]

Anderson, M. J. Aristotle **92**

Anderson, M. J. Isaac Newton **92**

Andronik, C. M. Copernicus **92**

Datnow, C. L. Edwin Hubble **92**

Gow, M. Tycho Brahe: astronomer **92**

Hamilton, J. Lise Meitner **92**

Pasachoff, N. E. Niels Bohr **92**

Poynter, M. The Leakeys **92**

Poynter, M. Marie Curie: discoverer of radium **92**

Great minds of science—*Continued*
Smith, L. W. Louis Pasteur   **92**
Tocci, S. Jonas Salk   **92**
Yount, L. Antoni van Leeuwenhoek   **92**
Great moments in basketball. Burgan, M.
   796.323
Great moments in sports [series]
Burgan, M. Great moments in basketball
   796.323
Teitelbaum, M. Great moments in women's
sports   **796**
Great moments in women's sports. Teitelbaum,
M.   **796**
Great monologues for young actors   **812.008**
Great moves. Asher, S.
In Visions: nineteen short stories by outstand-
ing writers for young adults p130-40
   S C
Great mysteries [series]
Netzley, P. D. Alien abductions: opposing view-
points   **001.9**
The **Great** North American prairie   **810.8**
Great Plains
   History
Collier, C. Indians, cowboys, and farmers and
the battle for the Great Plains, 1865-1910
   978
McArthur, D. The dust bowl and the Depression
in American history (7 and up)   **978**
Great rivers of the world [series]
Allan, T. The Rhine   **943**
Cumming, D. The Nile   **962**
Walsh, K. The Mississippi   **977**
Waterlow, J. The Yangtze   **951.2**
Great scenes for young actors from the stage
   808.82
The **great** shell of Kintyel. Brown, D. A.
In Brown, D. A. Dee Brown's folktales of the
Native American; retold for our times
p28-39   **398.2**
Great speeches in history [series]
The Arab-Israeli conflict   **956.04**
Great speeches in history series
The Cold War   **909.82**
The Founding of America   **973.3**
Human rights   **323**
The Vietnam War   **959.704**
Great trials of the 20th century [series]
Olson, S. P. The trial of John T. Scopes
Sorensen, L. The Scottsboro Boys Trial   **345**
The **great** turkey walk. Karr, K.   **Fic**
Great Wall of China
DuTemple, L. A. The Great Wall of China (5
and up)   **931**
The **great** whale of Kansas. Jennings, R. W.
   Fic
Great women comedians. Stewart, G.   **920**
Great world writers: twentieth century   **920.003**
Greater than angels. Matas, C.   **Fic**
The **greatest**: Muhammad Ali. Myers, W. D.
   92
The **greatest** stories never told. Beyer, R.   **904**

Greece
DuBois, J. Greece (5 and up)   **949.5**
   Biography
Baker, R. F. Ancient Greeks (7 and up)   **938**
   Civilization
Baker, R. F. Ancient Greeks (7 and up)   **938**
Crosher, J. Technology in the time of ancient
Greece   **609**
Hart, A. Ancient Greece! (4 and up)   **938**
Lassieur, A. The ancient Greeks (5 and up)
   938
Malam, J. Greek town   **938**
Nardo, D. Ancient Athens (7 and up)   **938**
Nardo, D. Ancient Greece (7 and up)   **938**
Nardo, D. The ancient Greeks (7 and up)
   938
Powell, A. Ancient Greece (5 and up)   **938**
Powell, A. The Greek news   **938**
Roberts, J. T. The ancient Greek world (7 and
up)
Stefoff, R. The ancient Mediterranean (5 and
up)   **938**
Woff, R. The ancient Greek Olympics (4 and
up)   **796.48**
   History—0-323
Powell, A. Ancient Greece (5 and up)   **938**
Roberts, J. T. The ancient Greek world (7 and
up)
Stefoff, R. The ancient Mediterranean (5 and
up)   **938**
The **greedy** man and the goat. Olson, A. N.
In Olson, A. N. and Schwartz, H. Ask the
bones: scary stories from around the
world p129-33   **398.2**
Greek and Roman mythology (7 and up)   **292**
The **Greek** interpreter. Doyle, Sir A. C.
In Doyle, Sir A. C. The complete Sherlock
Holmes   **S C**
The **Greek** news. Powell, A.   **938**
Greek town. Malam, J.   **938**
Green, Anne Canevari
(il) Scott, N. S. The thinking kid's guide to suc-
cessful soccer   **796.334**
Green, Carl R.
(jt. auth) Sanford, W. R. Bill Pickett: African-
American rodeo star   **92**
(jt. auth) Sanford, W. R. Calamity Jane: frontier
original   **92**
Green, Jared
(ed) Rap and hip hop. See Rap and hip hop
   306
Green, Jen
Medicine (5 and up)   **610**
Race to the moon   **629.45**
Green, Michelle Y.
A strong right arm: the story of Mamie "Pea-
nut" Johnson (4 and up)   **92**
Green, Rayna
High cotton
In Talking leaves; contemporary native
American short stories   **S C**
Green, Rebecca L.
The empire of Ghana   **966.1**

Green, Robert, 1969-
Cambodia (7 and up)   **959.6**
Tutankhamun   **932**

Green angel. Hoffman, A.   **Fic**

Green bird. Gerson, M.-J.
In Gerson, M.-J. Fiesta femenina; celebrating women in Mexican folktale   **398.2**

The Green Man: tales from the mythic forest (7 and up)   **808.8**

The green word. Ford, J.
In The Green Man: tales from the mythic forest p353-82   **808.8**

Greenaway, Frank
(il) The Snake book. See The Snake book   **597.9**

Greenberg, Alissa
Asthma (7 and up)   **616.2**

Greenberg, Daniel A.
Dolphins   **599.5**
Lizards   **597.9**
Whales   **599.5**

Greenberg, Jan, 1942-
Andy Warhol (7 and up)   **92**
Romare Bearden (4 and up)   **92**
Runaway girl: the artist Louise Bourgeois (7 and up)   **92**
Vincent Van Gogh   **92**
(ed) Heart to heart. See Heart to heart   **811.008**

Greenberg, Judith E.
Barbara Pierce Bush, 1925-   **92**
Young people's letters to the president   **973**

Greenberg, Keith Elliot, 1959-
Adolescent rights (7 and up)   **346**

Greenberg, Lorna
Digging into the past   **920**

Greenberg, Martin Harry
(ed) The Haunted house: a collection of original stories. See The Haunted house: a collection of original stories   **S C**
(ed) Vampires: a collection of original stories. See Vampires: a collection of original stories   **S C**

Greenblatt, Miriam
Afghanistan (5 and up)   **958.1**
Elizabeth I and Tudor England   **942.05**
Genghis Khan and the Mongol Empire   **950**
Lorenzo de' Medici and Renaissance Italy   **945**
Süleyman the Magnificent and the Ottoman Empire   **956.1**
War of 1812 (7 and up)   **973.5**

Greene, Bette, 1934-
An ordinary woman
In Sixteen; short stories by outstanding writers for young adults p125-32   **S C**
Summer of my German soldier (6 and up)   **Fic**

Greene, Meg
Louis Sachar (5 and up)   **92**

Greene, Robert, 1558?-1592
See/See also pages in the following book(s):
Nardo, D. Great Elizabethan playwrights   **920**

Greenfeld, Howard
After the Holocaust (6 and up)   **940.53**
Paul Gauguin (7 and up)   **92**

Greenhaven encyclopedia of [series]
Greek and Roman mythology   **292**

The Greenhaven encyclopedia of ancient Egypt. Netzley, P. D.   **932**

Greenhaven encyclopedias [series]
Netzley, P. D. Civil War   **973.7**

Greenhouse effect
Global warming: opposing viewpoints (7 and up)   **363.7**
Oxlade, C. Global warming (5 and up)   **363.7**
Parks, P. J. Global warming (5 and up)   **363.7**
Pringle, L. P. Global warming (4 and up)   **363.7**
Silverstein, A. Global warming   **363.7**

Greenhow, Rose O'Neal, 1817-1864
See/See also pages in the following book(s):
Caravantes, P. Petticoat spies   **920**
Fiction
Rinaldi, A. Girl in blue   **Fic**

Greensmith, Alan
(jt. auth) Harrison, C. Birds of the world   **598**

Greenspan, Alan
See/See also pages in the following book(s):
Bussing-Burks, M. Influential economists (7 and up)   **920**

Greenway, Shirley
Art: an A-Z guide   **703**

Greenwood, Janette Thomas
(comp) The Gilded Age: a history in documents. See The Gilded Age: a history in documents   **973.8**

Greenwood guides to historic events, 1500-1900 [series]
Morton, J. C. The American Revolution   **973.3**

Greenwood histories of the modern nations [series]
Blumberg, A. The history of Israel   **956.94**

Greenwood professional guides for young adult librarians [series]
Edwards, K. Teen library events   **027.62**

Greenwood professional guides in school librarianship [series]
Kearney, C. A. Curriculum partner   **027.8**

Gregor Mendel, and the roots of genetics. Edelson, E.   **92**

Gregor the Overlander. Collins, S.   **Fic**

Gregory, Kristiana
Eleanor: crown jewel of Aquitaine   **Fic**
Orphan runaways   **Fic**
Seeds of hope   **Fic**
The winter of red snow   **Fic**

Grenada
Pang, G.-C. Grenada (5 and up)   **972.98**

Gresham, Sir Thomas, 1519?-1579
See/See also pages in the following book(s):
Bussing-Burks, M. Influential economists (7 and up)   **920**

Gretzky, Wayne
About
Santella, A. Wayne Gretzky   92
Grey. San Souci, R.
  In San Souci, R. Double-dare to be scared:
    another thirteen chilling tales   S C
Grierson's raid. Matthews, T. L.   973.7
Griffin, Adele
  Amandine (7 and up)   Fic
  Hannah, divided (4 and up)   Fic
  The other Shepards (6 and up)   Fic
  Overnight   Fic
  Sons of liberty   Fic
  Where I want to be (7 and up)   Fic
Griffin, Maureen Ryan
  Such foolishness
  In 13; thirteen stories that capture the agony
    and ecstasy of being thirteen   S C
Griffin, Peni R.
  The ghost sitter (4 and up)   Fic
Griffin, Robert, 1951-
  (ed) The Folklore of world holidays. See The
    Folklore of world holidays   394.26
  (ed) Junior worldmark encyclopedia of world
    holidays. See Junior worldmark encyclopedia
    of world holidays   394.26
Griffis, Molly Levite
  The Feester filibuster (4 and up)   Fic
Griffiths, Rodney
  (il) Gamble, C. Leopards   599.75
Griggs, Jack L.
  All the birds of North America   598
Grimes, Nikki
  At Jerusalem's gate (5 and up)   811
  Bronx masquerade (7 and up)   Fic
  A dime a dozen (5 and up)   811
  Hopscotch love (4 and up)   811
  Jazmin's notebook   Fic
  Tai chi morning (5 and up)   811
  The throwaway: a suite
  In Necessary noise: stories about our families
    as they really are p71-78   S C
Grimké, Angelina Emily, 1805-1879
About
Todras, E. H. Angelina Grimké (7 and up)
       92
Grimly, Gris
  (il) Poe, E. A. Edgar Allan Poe's tales of mys-
    tery and madness   S C
Grimm, Jacob, 1785-1863
  The devil and his grandmother
  In The Book of dragons p67-71   S C
The **grind** of an axe. Taylor, T.
  In Night terrors; stories of shadow and sub-
    stance   S C
Grizzly bear
  Silverstein, A. The grizzly bear   599.78
The **Grolier** children's encyclopedia. See The
  New Grolier children's encyclopedia   031
Grolier student library of explorers and explora-
  tion   910.4
Grossman, James R.
  A chance to make good (7 and up)   305.8

Grounded. Hoffman, N. K.
  In The Green Man: tales from the mythic for-
    est p191-220   808.8
A **group** of one. Gilmore, R.   Fic
Groups, Social *See* Social groups
Grove, Vicki, 1948-
  Destiny (5 and up)   Fic
  Reaching Dustin (5 and up)   Fic
  The starplace   Fic
Grover, Lorie Ann
  Loose threads   811
Growing up. Soto, G.
  In Soto, G. Baseball in April, and other sto-
    ries p97-107   S C
Growing up black   920
Growing up in coal country. Bartoletti, S. C.
       331.3
Growing up in pioneer America, 1800 to 1890.
  Josephson, J. P.   978
Growing up in revolution and the new nation,
  1775 to 1800. Miller, B. M.   973.3
Growing up: it's a girl thing. Jukes, M.   612.6
Growing up Latino   810.8
Growing up royal. Billinghurst, J.   920
Gruber, Michael
  The witch's boy (7 and up)   Fic
Grumpy old monsters. Anderson, K. J.   741.5
Grunfeld, A. Tom (Adalbert Tomasz)
  (jt. auth) Young, M. B. The Vietnam War: a
    history in documents   959.704
Grunwell, Jeanne Marie
  Mind games   Fic
Grzimek, Bernhard, 1909-1987
  Grzimek's student animal life resource, Mam-
    mals. See Grzimek's student animal life re-
    source, Mammals   599
  (ed) Grzimek's student animal life resource,
    Birds. See Grzimek's student animal life re-
    source, Birds   598
Grzimek's student animal life resource, Birds
       598
Grzimek's student animal life resource, Mammals
       599
Guam
Fiction
Holt, K. W. Keeper of the night (7 and up)
       Fic
Guanina. Delacre, L.
  In Delacre, L. Golden tales; myths, legends,
    and folktales from Latin America p7-12
       398.2
The **guardian** of memory. Coville, B.
  In A Glory of unicorns p1-28   S C
Guatemala
Sheehan, S. Guatemala (5 and up)   972.81
Fiction
Mikaelsen, B. Red midnight   Fic
Guayaki Indians
  Batten, M. Anthropologist: scientist of the peo-
    ple (4 and up)   301
Guerrilla season. Hughes, P.   Fic

Guerrillas
Fiction
Hughes, P. Guerrilla season (7 and up) **Fic**

Guess, George *See* Sequoyah, 1770?-1843

Guests. Dorris, M. **Fic**

Guiberson, Brenda Z., 1946-
Exotic species **577**

Guidance, Vocational *See* Vocational guidance

Guide dogs
Kent, D. Animal helpers for the disabled (4 and up) **636.088**

Guide to cartooning. Bohl, A. **741.5**

Guide to popular U.S. government publications. Hoffmann, F. W. **015.73**

Guide to reference books for school media centers. See Safford, B. R. Guide to reference materials for school media centers **011.6**

Guide to reference materials for school media centers. Safford, B. R. **011.6**

Guide to savage Earth, DK. Day, T. **550**

Guide to the Bible, Asimov's. Asimov, I. **220.7**

Guide to wild dinosaurs. Yates, A. **567.9**

Guilt
Fiction
Cormier, R. In the middle of the night (7 and up) **Fic**
Fleischman, P. Whirligig (7 and up) **Fic**
McDonald, J. Swallowing stones (7 and up) **Fic**

Guinness book of records **032.02**

Guinness book of world records. See Guinness book of records **032.02**

Guinness world records. See Guinness book of records **032.02**

Guitar highway Rose. Lowry, B. **Fic**

Gulf War, 1991 *See* Persian Gulf War, 1991

Gulliver's travels. Swift, J. **Fic**

Gulotta, Charles
Extraordinary women in politics **920**

"Gulp!". San Souci, R.
In San Souci, R. Double-dare to be scared: another thirteen chilling tales **S C**

The **gun**. Naidoo, B.
In Naidoo, B. Out of bounds: seven stories of conflict and hope p96-119 **S C**

Gun control
Guns and violence [Current controversies] **363.33**
Hanson, F. O. The Second Amendment (7 and up) **344**
O'Neill, T. Gun control (7 and up) **363.33**
Spitzer, R. J. The right to bear arms **344**

Gunderson, Cory Gideon
The need for oil **338.2**

Gündisch, Karin, 1948-
How I became an American (4 and up) **Fic**

Gunpowder
Collier, J. L. Gunpowder and weaponry **623.4**

Gunpowder and weaponry. Collier, J. L. **623.4**

Guns and violence. Stewart, G. **303.6**
[Current controversies] **363.33**

Guns for geeks. Crutcher, C.
In On the fringe p195-219 **S C**

Gunther, John, 1901-1970
Death be not proud (7 and up) **92**

Gunther, John, 1929-1947
About
Gunther, J. Death be not proud (7 and up) **92**

Gurian, Michael
From boys to men **305.23**

Gurney, James, 1958-
Dinotopia [and other titles in series] **Fic**

Gustafson, Chris, 1950-
Acting out **812**

Guthrie, Woody, 1912-1967
About
Neimark, A. E. There ain't nobody that can sing like me: the life of Woody Guthrie (5 and up) **92**
Partridge, E. This land was made for you and me: the life and songs of Woody Guthrie (7 and up) **92**

Gutman, Dan
Gymnastics **796.44**
The million dollar shot **Fic**
Shoeless Joe & me (4 and up) **Fic**
Virtually perfect **Fic**

Guts. Simon, S. **612.3**

Guy, Rosa
The disappearance **Fic**
She
In Sixteen; short stories by outstanding writers for young adults p147-53 **S C**

The **guy** book. Jukes, M. **305.23**

Guyana
Jermyn, L. Guyana (5 and up) **988.1**
Morrison, M. Guyana (4 and up) **988.1**

Guys write for Guys Read **810.8**

Gwendolen. Mayer, M.
In Mayer, M. Women warriors; myths and legends of heroic women p43-49 **398**

Gymnastics
Bragg, L. W. Fundamental gymnastics (5 and up) **796.44**
Gutman, D. Gymnastics **796.44**

Gynecologists
Diamond, S. N. Everything you need to know about going to the gynecologist (7 and up) **618.1**

Gynecology *See* Women—Health and hygiene

Gypsies
Sharp, A. W. The gypsies **909**
See/See also pages in the following book(s):
Altman, L. J. The forgotten victims of the Holocaust **940.53**
Fiction
Alexander, L. Gypsy Rizka (5 and up) **Fic**

Gypsy Rizka. Alexander, L. **Fic**

The **gypsy's** violin. Giles, G.
In What a song can do; 12 riffs on the power of music   **S C**

H

Haas, Jessie
Shaper   **Fic**
Unbroken (5 and up)   **Fic**
Will you, won't you?   **Fic**
Habibi. Nye, N. S.   **Fic**
Habitat (Ecology)
Kerrod, R. Facts on File wildlife atlas   **578**
VanCleave, J. P. Janice Vancleave's ecology for every kid (4 and up)   **577**
Hacker, Carlotta
Nobel Prize winners   **920**
Haddix, Margaret Peterson, 1964-
Among the hidden   **Fic**
Escape
In Shelf life: stories by the book p23-32   **S C**
Escape from memory   **Fic**
Fine?
In On the edge: stories at the brink p59-80   **S C**
Just Ella (7 and up)   **Fic**
Leaving Fishers (7 and up)   **Fic**
My people
In Destination unexpected: short stories   **S C**
Running out of time   **Fic**
Takeoffs and landings   **Fic**
Turnabout (7 and up)   **Fic**
Haduch, Bill
Food rules!   **613.2**
Science fair success secrets (5 and up)   **507.8**
Haesly, Richard, 1969-
(ed) The Constitutional Convention. See The Constitutional Convention   **342**
Hager, Thomas
Linus Pauling and the chemistry of life (7 and up)   **92**
Hague, Michael, 1948-
(comp) The Book of dragons. See The Book of dragons   **S C**
Hahn, Don
Animation magic   **791.43**
Hahn, Mary Downing, 1937-
Daphne's book (5 and up)   **Fic**
Following my own footsteps (5 and up)   **Fic**
Hear the wind blow (5 and up)   **Fic**
Promises to the dead (5 and up)   **Fic**
Stepping on the cracks (5 and up)   **Fic**
Haiku
Stone bench in an empty park (4 and up)   **811.008**
Hair
Warrick, L. Hair trix for cool chix   **646.7**
Hair trix for cool chix. Warrick, L.   **646.7**

The **hairy** hands. San Souci, R.
In San Souci, R. A terrifying taste of short & shivery; thirty creepy tales p52-57   **398.2**
Haiti
           Fiction
Placide, J. Fresh girl (7 and up)   **Fic**
Temple, F. Tonight, by sea (6 and up)   **Fic**
Haitian Americans
           Fiction
Danticat, E. Behind the mountains   **Fic**
Mowry, J. Ghost train   **Fic**
Placide, J. Fresh girl (7 and up)   **Fic**
Vaught, S. Stormwitch (7 and up)   **Fic**
Hakim, Joy
Aristotle leads the way (5 and up)   **509**
A history of US (5 and up)   **973**
Hale, Marian
The truth about sparrows (5 and up)   **Fic**
Hale, Shannon
The Goose girl   **Fic**
Haley, James, 1968-
(ed) Global warming: opposing viewpoints. See Global warming: opposing viewpoints   **363.7**
Haley, James L.
Stephen F. Austin and the founding of Texas   **92**
Half-human (7 and up)   **S C**
Half-past midnight. San Souci, R.
In San Souci, R. Double-dare to be scared: another thirteen chilling tales   **S C**
Halfway to the sky. Bradley, K. B.   **Fic**
Halkin, Hillel, 1939-
(jt. auth) Orlev, U. Run, boy, run   **Fic**
Hall, Derek, 1930-
The brain and senses
In Being human   **612**
The human body
In Being human   **612**
(ed) Being human. See Being human   **612**
Hall, Donald, 1928-
(ed) The Oxford book of children's verse in America. See The Oxford book of children's verse in America   **811.008**
Hall, Eleanor J.
Recycling (5 and up)   **363.7**
Hall, Elizabeth, 1929-
(jt. auth) O'Dell, S. Thunder rolling in the mountains   **Fic**
Hall, Loretta
Arab American voices   **305.8**
Hall, Nelson
(il) Reynolds, D. W. Star wars: the visual dictionary   **791.43**
Hall, Susan, 1940-
Using picture storybooks to teach literary devices v3   **016.8**
Hall-Ellis, Sylvia Dunn, 1949-
Grants for school libraries   **025.1**

Hall-Ellis, Sylvia Dunn, 1949-—*Continued*
Grantsmanship for small libraries and school library media centers. See Grantsmanship for small libraries and school library media centers **025.1**

Halleck, Elaine
(ed) Living in Nazi Germany. See Living in Nazi Germany **943.086**

Hallett, Mark, 1947-
(il) Hehner, B. Ice Age cave bear **569**
(il) Hehner, B. Ice Age sabertooth **569**

Halley, Ned
Farm (4 and up) **630.1**

Halliburton, Warren J.
(comp) Historic speeches of African Americans. See Historic speeches of African Americans **815**

Halloween
Halloween howls **810.8**
Fiction
Bradbury, R. The Halloween tree **Fic**

Halloween howls **810.8**

The **Halloween** spirit. San Souci, R.
In San Souci, R. Dare to be scared; thirteen stories to chill and thrill **S C**

The **Halloween** tree. Bradbury, R. **Fic**

Halls, Kelly Milner, 1957-
Dinosaur mummies (5 and up) **567.9**

Hallucinogens
Barter, J. Hallucinogens (7 and up) **362.29**

Halpin, Mikki
It's your world—if you don't like it, change it (7 and up) **361.2**

Halsey, Megan
(il) Chin-Lee, C. Amelia to Zora **920**

Hamanaka, Sheila
In search of the spirit (5 and up) **920**

Hamas
Rosaler, M. Hamas: Palestinian terrorists **956.94**
See/See also pages in the following book(s):
Currie, S. Terrorists and terrorist groups (7 and up) **303.6**

Hambly, Barbara
See/See also pages in the following book(s):
MacRae, C. D. Presenting young adult fantasy fiction (7 and up) **813.009**

Hamer, Fannie Lou Townsend, 1917-1977
See/See also pages in the following book(s):
Dubovoy, S. Civil rights leaders (7 and up) **920**
Hansen, J. Women of hope (4 and up) **920**
Pinkney, A. D. Let it shine (4 and up) **920**

Hamilton, Alexander, 1757-1804
About
Rosenburg, J. M. Alexander Hamilton **92**

Hamilton, Edith, 1867-1963
Mythology **292**

Hamilton, Jake
Special effects in film and television (4 and up) **791.43**

Hamilton, Janet
Lise Meitner **92**

Hamilton, Janet, 1795-1873
James Watson **92**

Hamilton, Janice
Mexico in pictures (5 and up) **972**

Hamilton, John, 1959-
Weapons of war **623.4**

Hamilton, Lillian B.
(ed) The Comprehensive signed English dictionary. See The Comprehensive signed English dictionary **419**

Hamilton, Virginia, 1936-2002
Anthony Burns: the defeat and triumph of a fugitive slave (5 and up) **92**
Bluish **Fic**
Cousins (5 and up) **Fic**
Her stories (4 and up) **398.2**
Includes the following stories: Little Girl and Buh Rabby; Lena and Big One Tiger; Marie and Redfish; Miz Hattie gets some company; Catskinella; Good Blanche, bad Rose, and the talking eggs; Mary Belle and the mermaid; Mom Bett and the little ones a-glowing; Who you!; Macie and boo hag; Lonna and Cat Woman; Malindy and little devil; Woman and Man started even; Luella and the tame parrot; The mer-woman out of the sea; Annie Christmas
The house of Dies Drear (5 and up) **Fic**
In the beginning; creation stories from around the world (5 and up) **201**
Many thousand gone (5 and up) **326**
The people could fly (5 and up) **398.2**
Plain City (5 and up) **Fic**
The planet of Junior Brown (6 and up) **Fic**
Time pieces (5 and up) **Fic**
See/See also pages in the following book(s):
Ellis, S. From reader to writer **372.6**

Hamlet. Packer, T.
In Packer, T. Tales from Shakespeare p31-47 **822.3**

Hamm, Mia, 1972-
Go for the goal (7 and up) **796.334**

Hammond Explorer atlas of the world. See Explorer atlas of the world **912**

Hammurabi, King of Babylonia
See/See also pages in the following book(s):
Meltzer, M. Ten kings (5 and up) **920**

Hampton, Wilborn
Kennedy assassinated! (5 and up) **973.922**
Meltdown **363.1**
September 11, 2001 **973.931**

The **Han** dynasty. Immell, M. **931**

The **hand** of death. Olson, A. N.
In Olson, A. N. and Schwartz, H. Ask the bones: scary stories from around the world p105-09 **398.2**

The **Hand** of Dinotopia. Foster, A. D. **Fic**

The **Handbook** of private schools **370.25**

Handbook of the best private schools of the United States and Canada. See The Handbook of private schools **370.25**

The **handbook** of the Middle East. Kort, M. **956**

The **handbook** of the new Eastern Europe. Kort, M. **943**

Handedness *See* Left- and right-handedness

Handel, George Frideric, 1685-1759
About
Anderson, M. T. Handel, who knew what he liked (4-6)   **92**
Handel, who knew what he liked. Anderson, M. T.   **92**
Handicapped
    See also Mentally handicapped; Physically handicapped
Kent, D. Extraordinary people with disabilities   **920**
Fiction
Calhoun, D. White midnight (7 and up)   **Fic**
Jung, R. Dreaming in black and white (5 and up)   **Fic**
Wait, L. Wintering well (5 and up)   **Fic**
Fiction—Bibliography
Ward, M. Voices from the margins   **016.8**
Handicapped children
    See also Mentally handicapped children
Handicraft
Adler, D. A. The kids' catalog of Jewish holidays   **296.4**
Bruder, M. Button girl (5 and up)   **745.5**
Diehn, G. Making books that fly, fold, wrap, hide, pop up, twist, and turn (4 and up)   **736**
Doney, M. Festivals   **745.5**
Doney, M. Masks   **745.59**
Doney, M. Puppets   **745.592**
Hart, A. Ancient Greece! (4 and up)   **938**
Hart, A. Knights & castles (4 and up)   **940.1**
Needham, B. Ecology crafts for kids   **745.5**
Newcomb, R. The Girls' World book of jewelry: 50 cool designs to make (5 and up)   **745.594**
Panchyk, R. American folk art for kids   **745**
Science smart   **550**
The **handkerchief**. Olson, A. N.
    In Olson, A. N. and Schwartz, H. Ask the bones: scary stories from around the world p73-77   **398.2**
Handler, Ruth, 1916-2002
See/See also pages in the following book(s):
Jeffrey, L. S. Great American businesswomen   **920**
Hanes, Richard Clay, 1946-
(jt. auth) Brannen, D. E. Supreme Court drama   **347**
Hang a thousand trees with ribbons. Rinaldi, A.   **Fic**
Hannah, Marc, 1956-
See/See also pages in the following book(s):
Northrup, M. American computer pioneers   **920**
Hannah, divided. Griffin, A.   **Fic**
Hannah's garden. Snyder, M.   **Fic**
Hansen, Joyce
African princess (5 and up)   **920**
Breaking ground, breaking silence   **974.7**
Bury me not in a land of slaves (7 and up)   **973.8**
Freedom roads: searching for the Underground Railroad (5 and up)   **973.7**

One true friend   **Fic**
Which way freedom? (5 and up)   **Fic**
Women of hope (4 and up)   **920**
Hansen, Mark Victor
(jt. auth) Canfield, J. Chicken soup for the teenage soul {I-III}   **158**
Hanson, Freya Ottem, 1949-
The Second Amendment (7 and up)   **344**
Hantula, Richard
Alexander Fleming   **92**
Hanukkah
Fiction
Kimmel, E. A. The jar of fools: eight Hanukkah stories from Chelm (4 and up)   **S C**
Singer, I. B. The power of light (4 and up)   **S C**
A **Hanukkah** evening in my parents' house. Singer, I. B.
    In Singer, I. B. The power of light; eight stories for Hanukkah p3-9   **S C**
Hanukkah in the poorhouse. Singer, I. B.
    In Singer, I. B. The power of light; eight stories for Hanukkah p75-87   **S C**
Haptie, Charlotte
Otto and the flying twins (4 and up)   **Fic**
Harada, Violet H.
Inquiry learning through librarian-teacher partnerships   **371.1**
Harassment, Sexual *See* Sexual harassment
Haratani, Richard
Attention to detail
    In American dragons: twenty-five Asian American voices p120-25   **810.8**
Hard love. Wittlinger, E.   **Fic**
Hardaga, Mustafa
See/See also pages in the following book(s):
Lyman, D. Holocaust rescuers   **920**
The **hardest,** kindest gift. Coville, B.
    In Half-human p183-207   **S C**
Harding, R. R., 1938-
(jt. auth) Symes, R. F. Crystal & gem   **548**
Hardware. Bauer, J.
    In Necessary noise: stories about our families as they really are p1-20   **S C**
Hardy, P. Stephen
Extraordinary people of the Harlem Renaissance   **920**
Hardy, Sheila Jackson
(jt. auth) Hardy, P. S. Extraordinary people of the Harlem Renaissance   **920**
Hare, Tony
Animal fact-file   **599**
Hargittai, Magdolna
Cooking the Hungarian way
    In Easy menu ethnic cookbooks   **641.5**
Harik, Ramsay M.
Women in the Middle East   **305.4**
Harjo, Joy, 1951-
The flood
    In Talking leaves; contemporary native American short stories   **S C**

Harjo, Joy, 1951——*Continued*
Northern lights
In Talking leaves; contemporary native
American short stories   **S C**

Harlem (New York, N.Y.)
Fiction
Baldwin, J. Go tell it on the mountain (7 and
up)   **Fic**
Grimes, N. Jazmin's notebook   **Fic**
Lipsyte, R. The contender (7 and up)   **Fic**
Myers, W. D. 145th Street   **S C**
Myers, W. D. Hoops   **Fic**
Myers, W. D. The Mouse rap (6 and up)
     Fic
Myers, W. D. Scorpions (6 and up)   **Fic**
Poetry
Myers, W. D. Harlem   **811**
Myers, W. D. Here in Harlem (7 and up)
     811

Harlem Renaissance
Chambers, V. The Harlem Renaissance   **700**
Hardy, P. S. Extraordinary people of the Harlem
Renaissance   **920**
Hill, L. C. Harlem stomp! (7 and up)   **810.9**
Shimmy shimmy shimmy like my sister Kate
     811.008
Harlem stomp!. Hill, L. C.   **810.9**
Harlow, George E.
(ed) Simon and Schuster's guide to rocks and
minerals. See Simon and Schuster's guide to
rocks and minerals   **549**
Harlow, Joan Hiatt
Joshua's song (4 and up)   **Fic**
Si-Ling and the dragon
In Fire and wings: dragon tales from East and
West p32-42   **S C**
Harmon, Charles T., 1960-
(jt. auth) Symons, A. K. Protecting the right to
read   **025.2**
Harmon, Dan
Anorexia nervosa (7 and up)   **616.85**
Life out of focus (7 and up)   **616.8**
Harmony. Murphy, R.   **Fic**
Harness, Cheryl
(il) Allen, T. B. George Washington, spymaster
     92
Harney, Paula
(jt. auth) Frissell, S. Eating disorders and weight
control   **616.85**
Harold, King of England, 1022?-1066
Fiction
Alder, E. The king's shadow (7 and up)   **Fic**
Harold. Schwartz, A.
In Beware!; R.L. Stine picks his favorite
scary stories p179-84   **808.8**
In Schwartz, A. Scary stories 3; more tales to
chill your bones p30-34   **398.2**
Harp of fishbones. Aiken, J.
In Aiken, J. Shadows and moonshine; stories
     S C
Harper, Judith E., 1953-
Maya Angelou   **92**

Harpers Ferry (W. Va.)
History—John Brown's Raid, 1859
January, B. John Brown's raid on Harpers Ferry
(4 and up)   **973.7**
Stein, R. C. John Brown's Raid on Harpers Fer-
ry in American history   **973.7**
Harrah, Madge
Blind Boone (5 and up)   **92**
The chosen
In Night terrors; stories of shadow and sub-
stance   **S C**
Harriet Beecher Stowe and the Beecher preachers.
Fritz, J.   **92**
Harris, Aurand, 1915-1996
The Arkansaw bear
In Theatre for young audiences; 20 great
plays for children p46-71   **812.008**
Harris, Geraldine
Ancient Egypt (5 and up)   **932**
Harris, Jacqueline L., 1929-
Science in ancient Rome (4 and up)   **509**
Sickle cell disease (7 and up)   **616.1**
Harris, James S.
Shades of blue, Volume 1   **741.5**
Harris, Mary *See* Jones, Mother, 1830-1930
Harris, Nick, 1958-
(il) Philip, N. The story of Robin Hood
     398.2
Harris, Robert J.
Straight and true
In Sherwood: original stories from the world
of Robin Hood p86-97   **S C**
(jt. auth) Yolen, J. Girl in a cage   **Fic**
(jt. auth) Yolen, J. Jason and the Gorgon's
blood   **Fic**
(jt. auth) Yolen, J. Prince across the water
     Fic
(jt. auth) Yolen, J. The queen's own fool
     Fic
Harris, Robie H.
It's perfectly normal (4 and up)   **613.9**
Harris, Tim
The Mackenzie River (5 and up)   **971**
Harris and me. Paulsen, G.   **Fic**
Harrison, Colin, 1926-2003
Birds of the world (7 and up)   **598**
Harrison, David L.
Wild country   **811**
Writing stories (4 and up)   **808.3**
Harrison, John, 1693-1776
About
Dash, J. The longitude prize [biography of John
Harrison] (5 and up)   **92**
See/See also pages in the following book(s):
Duffy, T. The clock (4 and up)   **681.1**
Harrison, Michael, 1939-
(comp) The Oxford book of story poems. See
The Oxford book of story poems   **821.008**
(ed) The Oxford treasury of time poems. See
The Oxford treasury of time poems
     821.008
Harrison, Supenn
Cooking the Thai way
In Easy menu ethnic cookbooks   **641.5**

Harrison, Ted, 1926-
(il) Service, R. W. The cremation of Sam McGee   **811**

Harrison Bergeron. Vonnegut, K.
In Read into the millennium; tales of the future p126-38   **S C**

Harry Potter and the philosopher's stone. See Rowling, J. K. Harry Potter and the sorcerer's stone   **Fic**

Harry Potter and the sorcerer's stone. Rowling, J. K.   **Fic**

Hart, Avery
Ancient Greece! (4 and up)   **938**
Knights & castles (4 and up)   **940.1**

Hart, Christopher
Christopher Hart's animation studio   **791.43**
Christopher Hart's cartoon studio   **741.5**
How to draw comic book bad guys and gals   **741.5**
Mecha mania (5 and up)   **741.5**

Hart, George, 1945-
Ancient Egypt (4 and up)   **932**

Hart, John, 1948-
Walking softly in the wilderness   **796.51**

Hart, Joyce, 1954-
Native son: the story of Richard Wright (7 and up)   **92**

Hart, Philip S.
Flying free (4 and up)   **629.13**
Up in the air: the story of Bessie Coleman   **92**

Hartman, Holly
Girlwonder (5 and up)   **305.23**

Hartman, Thomas
(jt. auth) Gellman, M. How do you spell God?   **200**

Hartnett, Sonya, 1968-
Thursday's child (7 and up)   **Fic**
What the birds see (7 and up)   **Fic**

Hartz, Paula
Baha'i Faith (7 and up)   **297**
Native American religions   **299.7**
Taoism   **299.5**

Harvest. Ancona, G.   **331.5**

Harvey, Bonnie C.
Carry A. Nation: saloon smasher and prohibitionist   **92**
Daniel Webster   **92**
Jane Addams   **92**

Hasday, Judy L., 1957-
Extraordinary women athletes   **920**
Madeleine Albright   **92**

Haseley, Dennis
The amazing thinking machine (4 and up)   **Fic**

Haskell, Katharine Wright, 1874-1929
About
Maurer, R. The Wright sister [biography of Katharine Wright Haskell] (5 and up)   **92**

Haskins, James, 1941-2005
African American entrepreneurs   **920**
African American military heroes   **920**
African beginnings (4 and up)   **960**

Against all opposition (5 and up)   **920**
Black eagles (5 and up)   **629.13**
Bound for America (5 and up)   **326**
Get on board: the story of the Underground Railroad (5 and up)   **326**
The life and death of Martin Luther King, Jr. (5 and up)   **92**
One love, one heart   **781.646**
Out of the darkness (5 and up)   **305.8**
Outward dreams   **609**
Separate, but not equal (5 and up)   **379**
Toni Morrison (4 and up)   **92**
(jt. auth) Parks, R. Rosa Parks: my story   **92**

Hassig, Susan M., 1969-
Iraq (5 and up)   **956.7**
Somalia (5 and up)   **967.73**

Hat of clouds. Salisbury, G.
In Salisbury, G. Island boyz: short stories p220-60   **S C**

Hatasu *See* Hatshepsut, Queen of Egypt

Hatchepset *See* Hatshepsut, Queen of Egypt

Hatchet. Paulsen, G.   **Fic**

Hatching magic. Downer, A.   **Fic**

Hate crimes
Hate groups: opposing viewpoints (7 and up)   **364.1**
Roleff, T. L. Hate groups (7 and up)   **364.1**
What is a hate crime? (7 and up)   **364.1**

Hate groups. Roleff, T. L.   **364.1**

Hate groups: opposing viewpoints (7 and up)   **364.1**

Hating Hansen. Taylor, T.
In Taylor, T. Rogue wave and other red-blooded sea stories   **S C**

Hatshepsut, Queen of Egypt
See/See also pages in the following book(s):
Hansen, J. African princess (5 and up)   **920**

Hatt, Christine
The Crusades (7 and up)   **909.07**
Mahatma Ghandhi   **92**
Martin Luther King, Jr   **92**
Scientists and their discoveries (7 and up)   **509**
World War I, 1914-18 (7 and up)   **940.3**
World War II, 1939-45 (7 and up)   **940.53**

Haugen, David, 1969-
The Civil War (7 and up)   **973.7**
(ed) Domestic violence: opposing viewpoints. See Domestic violence: opposing viewpoints   **362.82**

Hauling gold. Taylor, T.
In Taylor, T. Rogue wave and other red-blooded sea stories   **S C**

Haunted. Oates, J. C.
In Oates, J. C. Small avalanches and other stories   **S C**

The **haunted** forest. Olson, A. N.
In Olson, A. N. and Schwartz, H. Ask the bones: scary stories from around the world p1-9   **398.2**

The **haunted** grove. San Souci, R.
In San Souci, R. A terrifying taste of short & shivery; thirty creepy tales p101-03   **398.2**

The **Haunted** house: a collection of original stories S C

Haunted sister. Littke, L. Fic

The **haunting**. Nixon, J. L. Fic

The **haunting** of Alaizabel Cray. Wooding, C. Fic

Hausman, Gerald
Escape from Botany Bay (7 and up) Fic

Hausman, Loretta
(jt. auth) Hausman, G. Escape from Botany Bay Fic

Hautman, Pete, 1952-
Godless (7 and up) Fic
Hole in the sky (7 and up) Fic
Hot lava
In On the edge: stories at the brink p83-92 S C
Invisible (7 and up) Fic
Sweetblood (7 and up) Fic

Hautzig, Esther Rudomin, 1930-
The endless steppe: growing up in Siberia 92

Have a heart. Conford, E.
In Conford, E. Crush p27-50 S C

Have no fear, Crumpot is here!. Yourgrau, B.
In Gothic!; ten original dark tales S C

Have you been to the beach lately? Fletcher, R. 811

Havemann, Ernst
A farm at Raraba
In Somehow tenderness survives; stories of Southern Africa p119-34 S C

Haven, Kendall F.
100 most popular scientists for young adults (7 and up) 920

Havill, Juanita
Eyes like Willy's Fic

Hawaii
Goldberg, J. Hawaii
In Celebrate the states 973
Hintz, M. Hawaii
In America the beautiful, second series 973

Fiction
Denenberg, B. Early Sunday morning Fic
Salisbury, G. Island boyz: short stories (7 and up) S C
Salisbury, G. Jungle dogs Fic
Salisbury, G. Lord of the deep (5 and up) Fic
Salisbury, G. Under the blood-red sun Fic
Wallace, B. Aloha summer Fic
White, E. E. Kaiulani Fic
History
Linnea, S. Princess Ka'iulani 92

Hawass, Zahi A.
Curse of the pharaohs (5 and up) 932

Hawes, Louise, 1943-
Waiting for Christopher (7 and up) Fic

Hawkes, Kevin
(il) Anderson, M. T. Handel, who knew what he liked 92
(il) Ibbotson, E. Island of the aunts Fic
(il) Ibbotson, E. Journey to the river sea Fic

(il) Ibbotson, E. The star of Kazan Fic

Hawking, S. W. (Stephen W.)
About
Bankston, J. Stephen Hawking 92

Hawking, Stephen W. *See* Hawking, S. W. (Stephen W.)

Hawkwood, Sir John, ca. 1320-1394
See/See also pages in the following book(s):
Zohorsky, J. R. Medieval knights and warriors p26-37 940.1

Hay, Jeff
(ed) The Early Middle Ages. See The Early Middle Ages 909.07
(ed) Immigration. See Immigration 325.73
(ed) The Renaissance. See The Renaissance [World history by era] 940.2

Haycock, Ken
Neal-Schuman authoritative guide to kids' search engines, subject directories, and portals 025.04
(ed) Foundations for effective school library media programs. See Foundations for effective school library media programs 027.8

Haycraft, Howard, 1905-1991
(ed) American authors, 1600-1900. See American authors, 1600-1900 920.003

Hayden, Lewis, 1815-1889
About
Strangis, J. Lewis Hayden and the war against slavery 92

Hayes, Daniel, 1952-
No effect Fic

Hayes, Randy
See/See also pages in the following book(s):
Graham, K. Contemporary environmentalists (7 and up) 920

The **haymeadow**. Paulsen, G. Fic

Haynes, Joyce
Egyptian dynasties 932

Haynes, Tricia
Colombia 986.1

Haywood, Big Bill, 1869-1928
See/See also pages in the following book(s):
Streissguth, T. Legendary labor leaders (7 and up) 920

Haywood, William Dudley *See* Haywood, Big Bill, 1869-1928

Hazelwood v. Kuhlmeier. Fuller, S. B. 344

He Lion, Bruh Bear and Bruh Rabbit. Hamilton, V.
In Hamilton, V. The people could fly; American black folktales p5-12 398.2

Head and brain injuries. Landau, E. 617.1

The **head** bone's connected to the neck bone. McClafferty, C. K. 616.07

Head games. Fredericks, M. Fic

The **head** of the district. Kipling, R.
In McCaffrey, A. {The Pern series} S C

Headache
Votava, A. Coping with migraines and other headaches (7 and up) 616.8

Heading out (7 and up) 331.7

Headlam, George
Yasser Arafat   **92**

Headline court cases [series]
Alonso, K. The Chicago Seven political protest trial   **345**
Fireside, B. J. The trial of the police officers in the shooting death of Amadou Diallo
Fireside, H. The "Mississippi Burning" civil rights murder conspiracy trial   **345**
Monroe, J. The Susan B. Anthony women's voting rights trial   **324.6**
Pellowski, M. The Chicago "Black Sox" baseball scandal   **796.357**
Pellowski, M. The O.J. Simpson murder trial   **345**
Pellowski, M. The terrorist trial of the 1993 bombing of the World Trade Center   **974.7**

Headliners [series]
Andryszewski, T. Kosovo   **949.7**

Heads of state
See also Dictators; Kings and rulers; Presidents
Slavicek, L. C. Mao Zedong   **92**

Heale, Jay
Democratic Republic of the Congo (5 and up)   **967.51**
Madagascar (5 and up)   **969.1**
Tanzania (5 and up)   **967.8**

Healing drugs: the history of pharmacology. See Facklam, M. Modern medicines   **615**

The **healing** truth. Lay, K.
In A Glory of unicorns p145-62   **S C**

Health
See also Physical fitness
Foley, R. World health (7 and up)   **362.1**
Health on file   **613**
Levchuck, C. M. Healthy living   **613**
Whiteside, M. Health and illness
In Being human   **612**

Health and illness. Whiteside, M.
In Being human   **612**

Health issues [series]
Elliot-Wright, S. Epilepsy   **616.8**
Lamb, K. Cancer   **616.99**
Lennard-Brown, S. Asthma   **616.2**
Wiltshire, P. Dyslexia   **616.85**

Health matters [series]
Baldwin, C. Autism   **616.89**
Baldwin, C. Sickle cell disease   **616.1**

Health on file   **613**

Health science projects about nutrition. Gardner, R.   **612.3**

Health science projects about psychology. Gardner, R.   **150**

Health science projects about sports performance. Gardner, R.   **612**

Health watch [series]
Gold, J. C. Cerebral palsy   **616.8**
Gold, S. D. Multiple sclerosis   **616.8**

The **healthy** body cookbook. D'Amico, J.   **641.5**

Healthy eating for weight management. Turck, M.   **613.7**

Healthy living. Levchuck, C. M.   **613**

Hear that train whistle blow!. Meltzer, M.   **385**

Hear the wind blow. Hahn, M. D.   **Fic**

Hearing
Silverstein, A. Hearing Silverstein, A. and others. Senses and sensors [series]   **612.8**
Simon, S. Eyes and ears (4 and up)   **612.8**

Hearing impaired
See also Deaf

Hearne, Betsy Gould, 1942-
Beauties and beasts   **398.2**
The canine connection: stories about dogs and people   **S C**
Contents: Lab; Restaurant; Room 313; Cargo; The drive; A grave situation; Fiona and Tim; The nose; Nameless creek; The canine connection; The boss; Bones

Hearne, Elizabeth G. *See* Hearne, Betsy Gould, 1942-

Hearst, Patricia Campbell
See/See also pages in the following book(s):
Aaseng, N. You are the juror   **345**

Heart
Brynie, F. H. 101 questions about blood and circulation, with answers straight from the heart (7 and up)   **612.1**
Parker, S. Heart, blood, and lungs   **612.1**
Simon, S. The heart (4 and up)   **612.1**

Heart, blood, and lungs. Parker, S.   **612.1**

A **heart** divided. Bennett, C.

The **heart** of a chief. Bruchac, J.   **Fic**

Heart to heart (5 and up)   **811.008**

Heat
Gardner, R. Science projects about temperature and heat (7 and up)   **536**
Poetry
Singer, M. Central heating (4 and up)   **811**

Heath, Alan
Windows on the world   **394.2**

Heaven. Johnson, A.   **Fic**

Heavy Collar and the ghost woman. Brown, D. A.
In Brown, D. A. Dee Brown's folktales of the Native American; retold for our times p160-66   **398.2**

Hecht, Jeff
Aunt Horrible's last visit
In Vampires: a collection of original stories p187-201   **S C**

Heck, superhero. Leavitt, M.   **Fic**

The **hedge** knight. Avery, B.   **741.5**

Hehner, Barbara, 1947-
First on the moon (4 and up)   **629.45**
Ice Age cave bear (5 and up)   **569**
Ice Age mammoth (5 and up)   **569**
Ice Age sabertooth (5 and up)   **569**

Heifetz, Aaron
(jt. auth) Hamm, M. Go for the goal   **796.334**

Height, Dorothy I., 1912-
See/See also pages in the following book(s):
Pinkney, A. D. Let it shine (4 and up)   **920**

Heiligman, Deborah
High hopes [biography of John F. Kennedy] (4 and up)
The New York Public Library kid's guide to research (5 and up) **025.5**
Ritual purity
In Don't cramp my style; stories about that time of the month p209-41 **S C**

Heinemann, Sue, 1948-
The New York Public Library amazing women in American history (5 and up) **305.4**

Heinemann profiles [series]
Press, P. Fidel Castro **92**

Heinrichs, Ann
Australia (4 and up) **994**
California
In America the beautiful, second series **973**
Florida
In America the beautiful, second series **973**
Indiana
In America the beautiful, second series **973**
Japan (4 and up) **952**
New York
In America the beautiful, second series **973**
Ohio
In America the beautiful, second series **973**
Pennsylvania
In America the beautiful, second series **973**
Texas
In America the beautiful, second series **973**
Vermont
In America the beautiful, second series **973**

Heir apparent. Vande Velde, V. **Fic**

Hekeke. San Souci, R.
In San Souci, R. Cut from the same cloth; American women of myth, legend, and tall tale p103-09 **398.2**

Helbig, Alethea
Many peoples, one land **016.8**
Myths and hero tales **398.2**

Helen Keller: rebellious spirit. Lawlor, L. **92**

Helen of Troy (Legendary character)
Fiction
Cooney, C. B. Goddess of yesterday (7 and up) **Fic**
McLaren, C. Inside the walls of Troy (7 and up) **Fic**

Heller, Julek
(il) Mayer, M. Women warriors **398.2**

Hello, Kate!. Schwartz, A.
In Schwartz, A. Scary stories 3; more tales to chill your bones p15-16 **398.2**

Hellweg, Paul
The American Heritage children's thesaurus **423**

Helmer, Diana Star, 1962-
(jt. auth) Owens, T. NASCAR **796.72**

Help wanted. Soto, G. **S C**

Hemings, Sally, 1773-1835
About
Lanier, S. Jefferson's children (7 and up) **920**

Hemings family
About
Lanier, S. Jefferson's children (7 and up) **920**

Hemingway, Ernest, 1899-1961
About
Yannuzzi, D. A. Ernest Hemingway **92**

Hen and Frog. Bryan, A.
In Bryan, A. Ashley Bryan's African tales, uh-huh p43-53 **398.2**

Henderson, Harry, 1951-
Modern mathematicians (7 and up) **920**
Nuclear physics (7 and up) **539.7**

Henderson, Helene, 1963-
(ed) Holidays, festivals and celebrations of the world dictionary. See Holidays, festivals and celebrations of the world dictionary **394.26**

Henderson, Kathy
The young writer's guide to getting published **808**

Heneghan, James
Flood **Fic**
The grave **Fic**

Henkes, Kevin, 1960-
The birthday room (5 and up) **Fic**
Olive's ocean (5 and up) **Fic**
Protecting Marie (5 and up) **Fic**
Sun & Spoon (4 and up) **Fic**

Henry, Infante of Portugal, 1394-1460
See/See also pages in the following book(s):
Fritz, J. Around the world in a hundred years (4 and up) **910.4**

Henry, the Navigator See Henry, Infante of Portugal, 1394-1460

Henry Ford and the assembly line. Bankston, J. **92**

Henry Holt reference book [series]
World mythology **201**

Henry Hudson and his voyages of exploration in world history. Edwards, J. **92**

Henson, Josiah, 1789-1883
See/See also pages in the following book(s):
Currie, S. Escapes from slavery **326**

Henson, Matthew Alexander, 1866-1955
See/See also pages in the following book(s):
Haskins, J. Against all opposition (5 and up) **920**

Hentoff, Nat
The day they came to arrest the book (7 and up) **Fic**

Her Majesty's servants. Kipling, R.
In Kipling, R. The jungle books **S C**

Her other son. Rice, D.
   In Rice, D. Crazy loco; stories about growing
     up Chicano in southern Texas p14-28
                               S C

Her stories. Hamilton, V.   **398.2**

Heracles (Legendary character) *See* Hercules
   (Legendary character)

Herald, Diana Tixier
   Teen genreflecting   **016.8**

Herbal medicine *See* Medical botany

Herbert, Janis, 1956-
   Leonardo da Vinci for kids (4 and up)   **92**

Hercegovina *See* Bosnia and Hercegovina

Hercules (Legendary character)
   See/See also pages in the following book(s):
   Hamilton, E. Mythology p21-76   **292**

Herd, Richard
             About
   Grace, C. O. Forces of nature (4 and up)
                             551.2

Herda, D. J., 1948-
   The Dred Scott case (7 and up)   **342**
   Furman v. Georgia (7 and up)   **345**
   New York Times v. United States (7 and up)
                              342

Here in Harlem. Mycrs, W. D.   **811**

Here is my kingdom   **810.8**

Here today. Martin, A. M.   **Fic**

Heredity
     See also Gene mapping
   Gallant, R. A. The treasure of inheritance (5 and
     up)   **576.5**
   See/See also pages in the following book(s):
   Kidd, J. S. Life lines (7 and up)   **576.5**

Here's to you, Rachel Robinson. Blume, J.
                                 Fic

Hermes, Patricia, 1936-
   Summer secrets (5 and up)   **Fic**

Hernando de Soto and the Spanish search for
   gold in world history. Gaines, A.   **92**

The **hero**. Woods, R.   **Fic**

The **hero** and the crown. McKinley, R.   **Fic**

The **hero** of Ticonderoga. Gauthier, G.   **Fic**

Heroes. Cormier, R.   **Fic**

Heroes [series]
   McCaughrean, G. Odysseus   **292**
   McCaughrean, G. Perseus   **292**

Heroes and villains [series]
   Nardo, D. Adolf Hitler   **92**
   Nardo, D. King Arthur   **942.01**
   Wukovits, J. F. Oskar Schindler   **92**
   Yancey, D. Al Capone   **92**
   Yancey, D. Frederick Douglass   **92**

Heroes of the Holocaust. Gottfried, T.   **940.53**

The **heroic** quest of Douglas McGawain. Lubar,
   D.
   In Don't cramp my style; stories about that
     time of the month p34-44   **S C**

Heroin
   Sonder, B. All about heroin (7 and up)
                              362.29

Heroine of the Titanic: the real unsinkable Molly
   Brown. Landau, E.   **92**

Heroism *See* Courage

Herrera, Juan Felipe, 1948-
   Laughing out loud, I fly   **811**

Herschel, Caroline Lucretia, 1750-1848
   See/See also pages in the following book(s):
   Celebrating women in mathematics and science
                             920

Hershele and Hanukkah. Singer, I. B.
   In Singer, I. B. The power of light; eight sto-
     ries for Hanukkah p63-72   **S C**

Herzegovina *See* Bosnia and Hercegovina

Hess, Dianne
   A daughter of Abraham
   In Soul searching: thirteen stories about faith
     and belief p67-89   **S C**

Hess, Harry Hammond, 1906-1969
   See/See also pages in the following book(s):
   Carruthers, M. W. Pioneers of geology   **920**

Hesse, Karen
   Letters from Rifka (5 and up)   **Fic**
   A light in the storm (5 and up)   **Fic**
   Out of the dust (5 and up)   **Fic**
   Phoenix rising   **Fic**
   Stowaway (5 and up)   **Fic**
   Witness (6 and up)   **Fic**
   See/See also pages in the following book(s):
   The Newbery & Caldecott medal books, 1986-
     2000   **028.5**

Hesser, Terry Spencer
   Kissing doorknobs (7 and up)   **Fic**

Hester, Joseph P.
   Public school safety   **371.7**

Hestler, Anna
   Wales   **942.9**
   Yemen (5 and up)   **953.3**

Heuston, Kimberley Burton
   The Shakeress (7 and up)   **Fic**

Hewett, Lorri
   Dancer (7 and up)   **Fic**

Hewett, Richard
   (il) Arnold, C. Stories in stone   **709.01**

Hewitt, Kathryn
   Lives of extraordinary women (4 and up)
                          920
   (il) Krull, K. Lives of the presidents   **920**

Hiaasen, Carl
   Hoot (5 and up)   **Fic**

Hiawatha and Megissogwon. Longfellow, H. W.
                             811

Hibernation
   Perry, P. J. Animals that hibernate   **591.56**

Hickam, Homer H., 1943-
   The Coalwood way (7 and up)   **92**
   Rocket boys (7 and up)   **92**

Hickman, Janet
   Ravine   **Fic**

Hickock, Martha Jane Canary *See* Calamity
   Jane, 1852-1903

Hicks, Peter, 1952-
   Technology in the time of the Vikings   **609**

The **hidden** children of the Holocaust. Kustanowitz, E.   **940.53**

Hidden roots. Bruchac, J.   **Fic**

Hidden worlds: looking through a scientist's microscope. Kramer, S.   **502.8**

The **hideout**. Bunting, E.   **Fic**

Hiding to survive. Rosenberg, M. B.   **940.53**

Hiera. Mayer, M.
  In Mayer, M. Women warriors; myths and legends of heroic women p27-29   **398**

Hieroglyphics
  See also Picture writing
Donoughue, C. The mystery of the hieroglyphs (4 and up)   **493**
Giblin, J. The riddle of the Rosetta Stone (5 and up)   **493**

Higgins, Marguerite, 1920-1966
See/See also pages in the following book(s):
Colman, P. Where the action was   **070.4**

High, Linda Oatman, 1958-
The shunning of Sadie B. Zook
  In Soul searching: thirteen stories about faith and belief p1-22   **S C**
The uterus fairy
  In Don't cramp my style; stories about that time of the month p265-83   **S C**

High cotton. Green, R.
  In Talking leaves; contemporary native American short stories   **S C**

High heat. Deuker, C.   **Fic**

High hopes [biography of John F. Kennedy] Heiligman, D.

The **high** king. Alexander, L.   **Fic**

High school libraries
  See also Young adults' libraries
    Catalogs
Senior high school library catalog   **011.6**

High school, the real deal. Farrell, J.   **373.1**

High schools
Farrell, J. High school, the real deal   **373.1**
Lieberman, S. A. The real high school handbook (7 and up)   **373.1**
    Entrance requirements
Shostak, J. How to prepare for the SSAT/ ISEE: Secondary School Admissions Test/Independent School Entrance Exam   **373.1**

High tech *See* Technology

High-tech harvest. Marshall, E. L.   **641.3**

High-tech IDs. Tocci, S.   **599.9**

A **higher** truth. Jaffe, N.
  In Jaffe, N. and Zeitlin, S. J. The cow of no color: riddle stories and justice tales from around the world p110-13   **398.2**

Highway engineering
Vanderwarker, P. The big dig   **624.1**

Highwaymen. Blackwood, G. L.   **364.1**

Higuchi, Daisuke
Whistle! Volume 1   **741.5**

Hiiaka. San Souci, R.
  In San Souci, R. Cut from the same cloth; American women of myth, legend, and tall tale p121-28   **398.2**

Un **hijo** del sol. Gonzalez, G.
  In Growing up Latino; memoirs and stories p38-46   **810.8**

Hijuelos, Oscar
Christmas fantasy
  In You're on!: seven plays in English and Spanish p108-31   **812.008**
The Mambo Kings play songs of love [excerpt]
  In Growing up Latino; memoirs and stories p16-21   **810.8**
See/See also pages in the following book(s):
Hill, C. M. Ten Hispanic American authors   **920**

Hikaru No Go, Volume 1. Hotta, Y.   **741.5**

Hiking
Andryszewski, T. Step by step along the Appalachian Trail   **796.51**
    Fiction
Bradley, K. B. Halfway to the sky   **Fic**

Hile, Kevin S.
The trial of juveniles as adults   **345**

Hill, Alan
(il) Cotterell, A. Ancient China   **931**

Hill, Ann
Tooting your own horn   **021.7**

Hill, Anne E., 1974-
Denzel Washington (7 and up)   **92**

Hill, Barbara W., 1941-
Cooking the English way
  In Easy menu ethnic cookbooks   **641.5**

Hill, Christine M.
John Lewis   **92**
Langston Hughes   **92**
Ten Hispanic American authors   **920**

Hill, Douglas, 1935-
See/See also pages in the following book(s):
Reid, S. E. Presenting young adult science fiction   **813.009**

Hill, Joe, 1879-1915
    Fiction
Skurzynski, G. Rockbuster   **Fic**

Hill, Kathleen Shaye
Taking care of business
  In Talking leaves; contemporary native American short stories   **S C**

Hill, Kim
    About
Batten, M. Anthropologist: scientist of the people (4 and up)   **301**

Hill, Kirkpatrick, 1938-
Minuk (5 and up)   **Fic**

Hill, Laban Carrick
Harlem stomp! (7 and up)   **810.9**

Hill Hawk Hattie. Clark, C. G.   **Fic**

Hillary, Sir Edmund
    About
Brennan, K. Sir Edmund Hillary, modern day explorer (4 and up)   **92**

Hillman, Laura, 1923-
I will plant you a lilac tree (7 and up)
    940.53

Hillstrom, Kevin
American Civil War: almanac   **973.7**
American Civil War: biographies   **920**
American Civil War: primary sources   **973.7**
Experiencing the American Civil War   **973.7**
Vietnam War: almanac (7 and up)   **959.704**
Vietnam War: biographies (7 and up)   **920**
Vietnam War: primary sources (7 and up)
    959.704

Hillstrom, Laurie
(jt. auth) Hillstrom, K. American Civil War: almanac   **973.7**
(jt. auth) Hillstrom, K. American Civil War: biographies   **920**
(jt. auth) Hillstrom, K. American Civil War: primary sources   **973.7**
(jt. auth) Hillstrom, K. Experiencing the American Civil War   **973.7**
(jt. auth) Hillstrom, K. Vietnam War: almanac   **959.704**
(jt. auth) Hillstrom, K. Vietnam War: biographies   **920**
(jt. auth) Hillstrom, K. Vietnam War: primary sources   **959.704**

Himler, Ronald
(il) Fritz, J. Why not, Lafayette?   **92**

Hindenburg (Airship)
O'Brien, P. The Hindenburg (4 and up)
    629.133

Hinds, Kathryn, 1962-
The church   **274**
The city [Life in the Renaissance series]
    940.2
[Life in the Roman Empire series]   **937**
The countryside [Life in the Renaissance series]
    940.2
[Life in the Roman Empire series]   **937**
The court   **940.2**
The Incas   **985**
Medieval England   **942.03**
The Patricians   **937**
Religion   **292**
Venice and its merchant empire   **945**

Hinds, Maurene J.
Focus on body image   **306.4**

Hinduism
Ganeri, A. The Ramayana and Hinduism (5 and up)   **294.5**
Mann, G. S. Buddhists, Hindus, and Sikhs in America (7 and up)   **294**
Wangu, M. B. Hinduism (7 and up)   **294.5**
See/See also pages in the following book(s):
Osborne, M. P. One world, many religions (4 and up)   **201**

Hine, Lewis Wickes, 1874-1940
    About
Freedman, R. Kids at work (5 and up)
    331.3

Hines, Anna Grossnickle, 1946-
The paper doll ghost
   In The Haunted house: a collection of original stories   **S C**

Hines, Gary, 1944-
The train room
   In The Haunted house: a collection of original stories   **S C**

Hines, Kim
Home on the mornin' train
   In Theatre for young audiences; 20 great plays for children p308-37   **812.008**

Hinman, Bonnie
Benjamin Banneker (5 and up)   **92**

Hinojosa, Maria
Crews: gang members talk to Maria Hinojosa (7 and up)   **302.3**

Hinojosa, Rolando, 1929-
Brother Imás
   In Growing up Latino; memoirs and stories p250-58   **810.8**

Hinojosa-Smith, R. Rolando *See* Hinojosa, Rolando, 1929-

Hinton, S. E.
The outsiders (7 and up)   **Fic**
Rumble fish (7 and up)   **Fic**
Taming the Star Runner   **Fic**
Tex (7 and up)   **Fic**
That was then, this is now (7 and up)   **Fic**
    About
Wilson, A. S.E. Hinton   **92**

Hintz, Martin, 1945-
Argentina (4 and up)   **982**
Hawaii
   In America the beautiful, second series
    973
Iowa
   In America the beautiful, second series
    973
Louisiana
   In America the beautiful, second series
    973
Michigan
   In America the beautiful, second series
    973
Minnesota
   In America the beautiful, second series
    973
Missouri
   In America the beautiful, second series
    973
North Carolina
   In America the beautiful, second series
    973
North Dakota
   In America the beautiful, second series
    973
   In America the beautiful, second series
    973
Poland (4 and up)   **943.8**

Hipple, Theodore W.
(ed) Writers for young adults. See Writers for young adults   **920.003**

Hirano, Cathy
(tr) Yumoto, K. The letters   **Fic**

Hired hands. Yolen, J.
   In Yolen, J. Mightier than the sword; world folktales for strong boys p78-86
    398.2

Hiroshima (Japan)
Bombardment, 1945
The Atom bomb 355.8
Grant, R. G. Hiroshima and Nagasaki (7 and up)
940.54
Lawton, C. Hiroshima (5 and up) 940.54
Maruki, T. Hiroshima no pika 940.54
Bombardment, 1945—Fiction
Yep, L. Hiroshima (4 and up) Fic
Hiroshima and Nagasaki. Grant, R. G. 940.54
Hiroshima no pika. Maruki, T. 940.54
Hirsch, E. D. (Eric Donald), 1928-
The new dictionary of cultural literacy 031
Hirsch, Robin
F E G: ridiculous stupid poems for intelligent
children (5 and up) 821
Hirschfelder, Arlene B.
Native American (7 and up) 970.004
Photo odyssey: Solomon Carvalho's remarkable
Western adventure, 1853-54 92
Hirschmann, Kris, 1967-
Pollution (5 and up) 363.7
Hirunpidok, Visalaya
Yai
In American dragons: twenty-five Asian
American voices p168-84 810.8
His last bow. Doyle, Sir A. C.
In Doyle, Sir A. C. The complete Sherlock
Holmes S C
Hispanic America, Texas, and the Mexican War,
1835-1850. Collier, C. 973.6
Hispanic American almanac [junior version] (5
and up) 305.8
Hispanic American art
Cockcroft, J. D. Latino visions (7 and up)
704
Here is my kingdom 810.8
Hispanic American authors
Hill, C. M. Ten Hispanic American authors
920
Hispanic-American experience on file 305.8
Hispanic American poetry *See* American poetry—Hispanic American authors
Hispanic-American scientists. Oleksy, W. G.
920
Hispanic Americans
Gonzales, D. Gloria Estefan 92
Hispanic American almanac [junior version] (5
and up) 305.8
Hispanic-American experience on file 305.8
Ochoa, G. The New York Public Library amazing Hispanic American history 305.8
Oleksy, W. G. Hispanic-American scientists (7
and up) 920
Dictionaries
Meyer, N. E. Biographical dictionary of Hispanic Americans 920.003
Drama
You're on!: seven plays in English and Spanish
(4 and up) 812.008
Fiction
Once upon a cuento S C
Soto, G. Taking sides (5 and up) Fic

History
Ochoa, G. Atlas of Hispanic-American history
(7 and up) 305.8
Poetry
Red hot salsa (7 and up) 811.008
Soto, G. Neighborhood odes (4-6) 811
Hispanic biographies [series]
Cruz, B. José Clemente Orozco 92
Gonzales, D. Gloria Estefan 92
Goodnough, D. Pablo Neruda 92
Mirriam-Goldberg, C. Sandra Cisneros 92
Hispanics of achievement [series]
Dolan, S. Junípero Serra 92
Stefoff, R. Plácido Domingo 92
Historians
Durden, R. F. Carter G. Woodson (7 and up)
92
Historic buildings
See also Literary landmarks
Historic sites
Monuments and historic places of America
973
Nash, G. B. Landmarks of the American Revolution 973.3
Spangenburg, R. The African-American experience (7 and up) 917.3
Spangenburg, R. Literature and the arts (7 and
up) 917.3
Spangenburg, R. Political and social movements
(7 and up) 917.3
Historic speeches of African Americans 815
Historical American biographies [series]
Bruns, R. Jesse James 92
Harvey, B. C. Carry A. Nation: saloon smasher
and prohibitionist 92
Harvey, B. C. Daniel Webster 92
Harvey, B. C. Jane Addams 92
Kent, Z. Andrew Carnegie 92
Kent, Z. Edgar Allan Poe 92
McPherson, S. S. Martha Washington 92
Pflueger, L. Mathew Brady 92
Pflueger, L. Stonewall Jackson 92
Salisbury, C. Phillis Wheatley 92
Streissguth, T. J. Edgar Hoover: powerful FBI
Director 92
Warrick, K. C. John Muir: crusader for the wilderness 92
Whitelaw, N. Clara Barton 92
A **historical** atlas of Afghanistan. Romano, A.
958.1
A **historical** atlas of Iran. Ramen, F. 955
**Historical atlases of South Asia, Central Asia,
and the Middle East** [series]
Ramen, F. A historical atlas of Iran 955
Romano, A. A historical atlas of Afghanistan
958.1
Historical chronology
Tomaselli-Moschovitis, V. Junior timelines on
file 902
Historical fiction
Bibliography
Coffey, R. K. America as story 016.813
Dickinson, A. T. American historical fiction
016.813

Historical fiction—Bibliography—*Continued*
VanMeter, V. America in historical fiction
016.813

Historical inventions on file   **609**

Historiography
Jaffe, S. H. Who were the founding fathers? (7 and up)   **973.3**

History
See also Ancient history; Military history; World history
Bibliography
Adamson, L. G. Literature connections to world history, 7-12   **016.9**
Miscellanea
Beyer, R. The greatest stories never told (7 and up)   **904**

History, Ancient *See* Ancient history

History, Modern *See* Modern history

History. Gallant, R. A.   **551.7**

History Channel presents The greatest stories never told. See Beyer, R. The greatest stories never told   **904**

History firsthand [series]
Castro's Cuba   **972.91**
The Constitutional Convention   **342**
Making and using the atomic bomb   **355.8**
War-torn Bosnia   **949.7**

History makers [series]
Kallen, S. A. Native American chiefs and warriors   **920**
Stewart, G. Great women comedians   **920**
Zohorsky, J. R. Medieval knights and warriors   **940.1**

History news [series]
Gates, P. Medicine   **610.9**
Johnstone, M. Explorers   **910.4**

The **history** news in space. Johnstone, M.   **629.4**

A **history** of basketball for girls and women. Lannin, J.   **796.323**

The **history** of classical music. Kallen, S. A.   **781.6**

The **history** of country music. Kallen, S. A.   **781.642**

The **history** of Israel. Blumberg, A.   **956.94**

The **history** of jazz. Asirvatham, S.   **781.65**

The **history** of jazz. Kallen, S. A.   **781.65**

The **history** of NASA. Spangenburg, R.   **629.4**

The **history** of punishment. Kerrigan, M.   **364.6**

The **history** of rock and roll. Kallen, S. A.   **781.66**

The **history** of rockets. Miller, R.   **621.43**

History of science. Whitfield, P.   **509**

History of science [series]
Spangenburg, R. The age of synthesis: 1800-1895   **509**
Spangenburg, R. The birth of science: ancient times to 1699   **509**
Spangenburg, R. Modern science, 1896-1945   **509**

Spangenburg, R. The rise of reason: 1700-1799   **509**
Spangenburg, R. Science frontiers, 1946 to the present   **509**
The **history** of science from 1895 to 1945. See Spangenburg, R. Modern science, 1896-1945   **509**
The **history** of science from 1946 to the 1990s. See Spangenburg, R. Science frontiers, 1946 to the present   **509**
The **history** of science from the ancient Greeks to the scientific revolution. See Spangenburg, R. The birth of science: ancient times to 1699   **509**
The **history** of science in the eighteenth century. See Spangenburg, R. The rise of reason: 1700-1799   **509**
The **history** of science in the nineteenth century. See Spangenburg, R. The age of synthesis: 1800-1895   **509**

History of sports [series]
Cotter, A. Cycling   **796.6**
Sherrow, V. Volleyball   **796.325**

History of terrorism. Taylor, R.   **303.6**

The **history** of the blues. Asirvatham, S.   **781.643**

A **history** of the Elizabethan theater. Woog, A.   **792.09**

History of the modern world   **909.08**

A **history** of US. Hakim, J.   **973**

History of weapons and warfare [series]
Nardo, D. Ancient Egypt   **932**
Nardo, D. Ancient Greece   **938**
Nardo, D. Ancient Rome   **937**
Nardo, D. The Civil War   **973.7**
Nardo, D. The Middle Ages   **940.1**
Nardo, D. The Native Americans   **970.004**

History of World War I   **940.3**

History's great defeats [series]
Nardo, D. The fall of the Roman Empire   **937**

History's villains [series]
Ingram, S. Attila the Hun   **92**
Ingram, S. Joseph Stalin   **92**
Loehfelm, B. Osama bin Laden   **92**

Hitch. Ingold, J.   **Fic**

The **Hitchhiker's** Guide to the Galaxy. Adams, D.   **Fic**

Hite, Sid, 1954-
A hole in the world (7 and up)   **Fic**
Those darn Dithers   **Fic**

Hitler, Adolf, 1889-1945
About
Altman, L. J. Hitler's rise to power and the Holocaust   **943.086**
Damon, D. Mein Kampf (7 and up)   **943.086**
Giblin, J. The life and death of Adolf Hitler (7 and up)   **92**
Gottfried, T. Nazi Germany (7 and up)   **940.53**
Nardo, D. Adolf Hitler   **92**
The Rise of Nazi Germany (7 and up)   **943.086**

Hitler, Adolf, 1889-1945—About—*Continued*
See/See also pages in the following book(s):
Ross, S. Leaders of World War II   **920**
Fiction
French, J. Hitler's daughter   **Fic**
Hitler-Jugend
Gottfried, T. Children of the slaughter (7 and up)   **940.53**
Hitler Youth *See* Hitler-Jugend
Hitler's daughter. French, J.   **Fic**
Hitler's rise to power and the Holocaust. Altman, L. J.   **943.086**
Hitt, Laura
(ed) Human rights. See Human rights   **323**
HIV disease *See* AIDS (Disease)
Hmong (Asian people) *See* Hmong Americans
Hmong Americans
Livo, N. J. Folk stories of the Hmong   **398.2**
Omoto, S. Hmong milestones in America   **305.8**
Hmong milestones in America. Omoto, S.   **305.8**
Ho, Chí Minh, 1890-1969
See/See also pages in the following book(s):
Roberts, R. Leaders and generals   **920**
Uschan, M. V. Political leaders   **920**
Ho, David D., 1952-
See/See also pages in the following book(s):
Yount, L. Asian-American scientists (7 and up)   **920**
Ho, Minfong
The see-far glasses
In Soul searching: thirteen stories about faith and belief p134-56   **S C**
The winter hibiscus
In Join in; multiethnic short stories by outstanding writers for young adults p239-56   **S C**
Hoare, Ben
Temperate grasslands (5 and up)   **577.4**
Hoare, Stephen
Digital revolution   **621.381**
The **hobbit**. Tolkien, J. R. R.   **Fic**
Hobbit: an illustrated edition of the fantasy classic. Dixon, C.   **741.5**
Hobbs, Valerie, 1941-
Charlie's run   **Fic**
Sonny's war (7 and up)   **Fic**
Tender (7 and up)   **Fic**
Hobbs, Will
Bearstone (7 and up)   **Fic**
The Big Wander (7 and up)   **Fic**
Downriver (7 and up)   **Fic**
Far North (7 and up)   **Fic**
Ghost canoe   **Fic**
Jackie's Wild Seattle (5 and up)   **Fic**
Jason's gold (5 and up)   **Fic**
Leaving Protection (7 and up)   **Fic**
The maze (7 and up)   **Fic**
Wild Man Island   **Fic**
The **hobbyist**. Lynch, C.
In Lynch, C. All the old haunts p126-47   **S C**

In Ultimate sports; short stories by outstanding writers for young adults p315-33   **S C**
Hobgood, Debby, 1964-
(jt. auth) Pervola, C. How to get a job if you're a teenager   **650.14**
Hoboes *See* Tramps
Hobson, Archie, 1946-
(ed) The Cambridge gazetteer of the United States and Canada. See The Cambridge gazetteer of the United States and Canada   **917.3**
Hockey
Foley, M. Fundamental hockey (5 and up)   **796.962**
Stewart, M. Hockey (7 and up)   **796.962**
Sullivan, G. All about hockey (5 and up)   **796.962**
Biography
Santella, A. Wayne Gretzky   **92**
Stewart, M. Mario Lemieux   **92**
Hodge, Susie, 1960-
Pablo Picasso (4 and up)   **92**
Hodges, David W.
Classic racing cars   **629.228**
Hodgkin's disease
Peacock, J. Hodgkin's disease   **616.99**
Hoehner, Jane
Outlaws, mobsters & crooks   **920.003**
Hoeye, Michael, 1947-
Time stops for no mouse (5 and up)   **Fic**
Hoff, Brent H.
Mapping epidemics (7 and up)   **614**
Hoffa, James Riddle *See* Hoffa, Jimmy, b. 1913
Hoffa, Jimmy, b. 1913
See/See also pages in the following book(s):
Streissguth, T. Legendary labor leaders (7 and up)   **920**
Hoffius, Stephen
The assault on the record
In Ultimate sports; short stories by outstanding writers for young adults p161-78   **S C**
Hoffman, Alice
Green angel (7 and up)   **Fic**
Hoffman, Mary
Stravaganza: city of masks (7 and up)   **Fic**
Hoffman, Nancy, 1955-
South Carolina
In Celebrate the states   **973**
West Virginia
In Celebrate the states   **973**
Hoffman, Nina Kiriki
Flotsam
In Firebirds: an anthology of original fantasy and science fiction; an anthology of original fantasy and science fiction   **S C**
Grounded
In The Green Man: tales from the mythic forest p191-220   **808.8**
A stir of bones (7 and up)   **Fic**

Hoffmann, Frank W. (Frank William), 1949-
Guide to popular U.S. government publications
015.73
(ed) Grantsmanship for small libraries and school library media centers. See Grantsmanship for small libraries and school library media centers **025.1**

The **hog**. Schwartz, A.
In Schwartz, A. Scary stories 3; more tales to chill your bones p80-81 **398.2**

Hogan, Linda
Aunt Moon's young man
In Talking leaves; contemporary native American short stories **S C**

Hogan, Walter
The agony and the eggplant (7 and up)
813.009

Hoichi the earless. San Souci, R.
In San Souci, R. A terrifying taste of short & shivery; thirty creepy tales p118-22
398.2

Hokanson, Lars
(il) Finkelstein, N. H. Remember not to forget
940.53

Hokanson, Lois
(il) Finkelstein, N. H. Remember not to forget
940.53

Hold them in your heart. Mondowney, J. G.
027.62

Hold up the sky. Curry, J. L.
In Curry, J. L. Hold up the sky: and other Native American tales from Texas and the Southern Plains p53-55 **398.2**

Hold up the sky: and other Native American tales from Texas and the Southern Plains. Curry, J. L. **398.2**

Hole in my life. Gantos, J. **92**

Hole in the sky. Hautman, P. **Fic**

A **hole** in the world. Hite, S. **Fic**

Holes. Sachar, L. **Fic**

Holford, David M.
Herbert Hoover **92**

Holgate, Sharon Ann
(jt. auth) Kerrod, R. The way science works
507.8

Holiday, Billie, 1915-1959
About
Kliment, B. Billie Holiday **92**
See/See also pages in the following book(s):
Lester, J. The blues singers (5 and up) **920**

Holiday cooking around the world
In Easy menu ethnic cookbooks **641.5**

Holidays
See also Christmas; Religious holidays; Valentine's Day
The American book of days **394.26**
Festivals and holidays **394.26**
The Folklore of the American holidays
394.26
The Folklore of world holidays **394.26**
Holidays, festivals and celebrations of the world dictionary **394.26**

Junior worldmark encyclopedia of world holidays **394.26**
Marks, D. F. Let's celebrate today **394.26**
Rajtar, S. United States holidays and observances **394.26**
Webb, L. S. Holidays of the world cookbook for students (5 and up) **641.5**
Bibliography
Matthew, K. I. Neal-Schuman guide to celebrations & holidays around the world **394.26**

Holidays, Jewish *See* Jewish holidays

Holidays, festivals and celebrations of the world dictionary **394.26**

Holidays of the world cookbook for students. Webb, L. S. **641.5**

Holland, Isabelle
The man without a face **Fic**

Holland *See* Netherlands

Hollander, John
(ed) Committed to memory. See Committed to memory **821.008**

Hollerith, Herman, 1860-1929
See/See also pages in the following book(s):
Northrup, M. American computer pioneers
920

The **hollow** kingdom. Dunkle, C. B. **Fic**

The **hollow** tree. Lunn, J. L. S. **Fic**

Holly Starcross. Doherty, B. **Fic**

Hollywood (Calif.)
Fiction
Leonard, E. A coyote's in the house (5 and up)
Fic

Hollywood and the pits. Lee, C.
In American dragons: twenty-five Asian American voices p34-47 **810.8**

Holm, Jennifer L.
Boston Jane: an adventure **Fic**
Follow the water
In Shelf life: stories by the book p33-54
S C
Our only May Amelia (5 and up) **Fic**

Holman, Felice
Real **Fic**
Slake's limbo (6 and up) **Fic**

Holmes, Barbara Ware
Following Fake Man **Fic**

Holmes, Timothy
Zambia (5 and up) **968.94**

Holocaust, 1933-1945
See also Holocaust survivors; World War, 1939-1945—Jews
Altman, L. J. Crimes and criminals of the Holocaust **940.53**
Altman, L. J. The forgotten victims of the Holocaust **940.53**
Altman, L. J. Hitler's rise to power and the Holocaust **943.086**
Altman, L. J. Impact of the Holocaust
940.53
Altman, L. J. The Jewish victims of the Holocaust **940.53**
Ayer, E. H. A firestorm unleashed **940.53**
Ayer, E. H. Inferno **940.53**

Holocaust, 1933-1945—*Continued*

Bartoletti, S. C. Hitler Youth (7 and up)
943.086

Byers, A. The Holocaust overview (7 and up)
940.53

The Complete history of the Holocaust (7 and up)
940.53

Feldman, G. Understanding the Holocaust
940.53

Finkelstein, N. H. Remember not to forget (4 and up)
940.53

Frank, A. The diary of a young girl (6 and up)
92

Frank, A. The diary of a young girl: the definitive edition (6 and up)
92

Gold, A. L. Memories of Anne Frank (5 and up)
92

Gottfried, T. Children of the slaughter (7 and up)
940.53

Gottfried, T. Deniers of the Holocaust (7 and up)
940.53

Gottfried, T. Heroes of the Holocaust (7 and up)
940.53

Gottfried, T. Nazi Germany (7 and up)
940.53

Greenfeld, H. After the Holocaust (6 and up)
940.53

Leapman, M. Witnesses to war (5 and up)
940.53

Lee, C. A. A friend called Anne (4 and up)
940.53

Levine, E. Darkness over Denmark   940.53

Lyman, D. Holocaust rescuers   920

Meltzer, M. Never to forget: the Jews of the Holocaust (6 and up)   940.53

Meltzer, M. Rescue: the story of how Gentiles saved Jews in the Holocaust (6 and up)
940.53

Müller, M. Anne Frank (7 and up)   92

People of the Holocaust   920.003

Pressler, M. Anne Frank: a hidden life   92

Rescue and resistance: portraits of the Holocaust
940.53

Rogasky, B. Smoke and ashes   940.53

Rol, R. v. d. Anne Frank, beyond the diary (5 and up)   92

Sawyer, K. K. Anne Frank (5 and up)   92

Sherrow, V. The blaze engulfs   940.53

Sherrow, V. Smoke to flame   940.53

Spiegelman, A. Maus (7 and up)   940.53

Talbott, H. Forging freedom (4 and up)
940.53

Warren, A. Surviving Hitler (5 and up)
940.53

Wukovits, J. F. Anne Frank (7 and up)   92

Wukovits, J. F. Oskar Schindler   92

Bibliography

Rosen, P. Bearing witness   016.94053

Encyclopedias

The Holocaust   940.53

Fiction

Isaacs, A. Torn thread (7 and up)   Fic

Jung, R. Dreaming in black and white (5 and up)   Fic

Kositsky, L. The thought of high windows (7 and up)   Fic

Levitin, S. Room in the heart   Fic

Matas, C. After the war (7 and up)   Fic

Matas, C. Greater than angels (7 and up)
Fic

Matas, C. In my enemy's house (7 and up)
Fic

Mazer, N. F. Good night, Maman (5 and up)
Fic

Orlev, U. Run, boy, run (7 and up)   Fic

Yolen, J. The devil's arithmetic (4 and up)
Fic

Personal narratives

Adler, D. A. We remember the Holocaust
940.53

Ayer, E. H. In the ghettos (7 and up)
940.53

Bitton-Jackson, L. I have lived a thousand years (7 and up)   940.53

Boas, J. We are witnesses (7 and up)
940.53

Fox, A. L. Ten thousand children (5 and up)
940.53

Friedman, I. R. The other victims   940.53

Hillman, L. I will plant you a lilac tree (7 and up)   940.53

Holocaust memories (5 and up)   940.53

Kustanowitz, E. The hidden children of the Holocaust   940.53

Lobel, A. No pretty pictures (7 and up)   92

Opdyke, I. G. In my hands (7 and up)
940.53

Perl, L. Four perfect pebbles (6 and up)
940.53

Reiss, J. The upstairs room (5 and up)   92

Rosenberg, M. B. Hiding to survive (5 and up)
940.53

Sender, R. M. The cage (7 and up)   940.53

Siegal, A. Upon the head of the goat: a childhood in Hungary, 1939-1944   92

Soumerai, E. N. A voice from the Holocaust
940.53

Voices and visions   940.53

The **Holocaust**   940.53

Holocaust [21st Century Bks. series]

Gottfried, T. Children of the slaughter
940.53

Gottfried, T. Deniers of the Holocaust
940.53

Gottfried, T. Displaced persons   940.53

Gottfried, T. Heroes of the Holocaust
940.53

Gottfried, T. Nazi Germany   940.53

Holocaust [Blackbirch Press series]

Altman, L. J. Forever outsiders   909

Ayer, E. H. A firestorm unleashed   940.53

Ayer, E. H. Inferno   940.53

Chicoine, S. From the ashes   940.53

Sherrow, V. The blaze engulfs   940.53

Sherrow, V. Smoke to flame   940.53

Voices and visions   940.53

Holocaust [Heinemann Lib. series]

Shuter, J. The camp system   940.53

Shuter, J. Resistance to the Nazis   943.086

Holocaust in history [series]

Altman, L. J. Crimes and criminals of the Holocaust   940.53

Holocaust in history—*Continued*

Altman, L. J. The forgotten victims of the Holocaust **940.53**

Altman, L. J. Hitler's rise to power and the Holocaust **943.086**

Altman, L. J. Impact of the Holocaust **940.53**

Altman, L. J. The Jewish victims of the Holocaust **940.53**

Holocaust memories (5 and up) **940.53**

The **Holocaust** overview. Byers, A. **940.53**

Holocaust remembered series

Byers, A. The Holocaust overview **940.53**

Holocaust rescuers. Lyman, D. **920**

Holocaust survivors

Ayer, E. H. Inferno **940.53**

Bitton-Jackson, L. My bridges of hope (7 and up) **92**

Chicoine, S. From the ashes **940.53**

Friedman, I. R. The other victims **940.53**

Gottfried, T. Displaced persons (7 and up) **940.53**

Greenfeld, H. After the Holocaust (6 and up) **940.53**

Lobel, Λ. No pretty pictures (7 and up) **92**

Rescue and resistance: portraits of the Holocaust **940.53**

Voices and visions **940.53**

Wiesel, E. The accident
In Wiesel, E. Night, Dawn, The accident: three tales p205-318 **Fic**

Holt, Kimberly Willis

August lights
In Destination unexpected: short stories **S C**

Dancing in Cadillac light (5 and up) **Fic**

Keeper of the night (7 and up) **Fic**

My Louisiana sky (6 and up) **Fic**

When Zachary Beaver came to town **Fic**

The **Holy** Bible: new revised standard version. **220.5**

Holy days *See* Religious holidays

Holy Grail *See* Grail

Holy Office *See* Inquisition

Holzer, Harold

The president is shot! (5 and up) **973.7**

(ed) Lincoln, A. Abraham Lincoln the writer **92**

Home

Fiction

Frost, H. Keesha's house (7 and up) **Fic**

Home among the giants. Norman, H.
In Norman, H. The girl who dreamed only geese, and other tales of the Far North **398.2**

A **home** for foundlings. Jocelyn, M. **362.7**

The **home** front. Campbell, G. A. **973.92**

The **home** front in World War II. Levy, P. M. **940.53**

Home instruction *See* Home schooling

Home life *See* Family life

Home now. Oba, R.
In American eyes; new Asian-American short stories for young adults p28-36 **S C**

Home of the Braves. Klass, D. **Fic**

Home on the moon. Dyson, M. J. **629.45**

Home on the mornin' train. Hines, K.
In Theatre for young audiences; 20 great plays for children p308-37 **812.008**

Home schooling

Lerch, M. T. Serving homeschooled teens and their parents **027.6**

Home to El Building. Ortiz Cofer, J.
In Ortiz Cofer, J. An island like you; stories of the barrio p131-43 **S C**

Home video systems

See also Video recording

Homecoming. Voigt, C. **Fic**

The **homecoming.** Yep, L.
In Yep, L. The rainbow people p144-51 **398.2**

Homecooking. Woody, E.
In Talking leaves; contemporary native American short stories **S C**

Homeless bird. Whelan, G. **Fic**

The **Homeless:** opposing viewpoints (7 and up) **362.5**

Homeless persons

See also Refugees; Runaway children; Runaway teenagers; Tramps

Criswell, S. D. Homelessness (7 and up) **362.5**

The Homeless: opposing viewpoints (7 and up) **362.5**

Stewart, G. Homeless teens (7 and up) **362.5**

Fiction

Fenner, C. The king of dragons (5 and up) **Fic**

Spinelli, J. Maniac Magee (5 and up) **Fic**

Strasser, T. Can't get there from here (7 and up) **Fic**

Wallace, B. B. Secret in St. Something **Fic**

Homeless teens. Stewart, G. **362.5**

Homelessness. Criswell, S. D. **362.5**

Homer

The Iliad **883**

The Odyssey **883**

Homesick: my own story. Fritz, J. **92**

Homesteading. Patent, D. H. **978**

Homicide

See also Trials (Homicide)

Silverstein, H. Kids who kill (7 and up) **364.1**

Fiction

Cormier, R. The rag and bone shop (7 and up) **Fic**

Lester, J. When Dad killed Mom (7 and up) **Fic**

McNamee, G. Acceleration **Fic**

Nixon, J. L. Nightmare **Fic**

Homosexuality

Homosexuality: opposing viewpoints (7 and up) **306.76**

Homosexuality—*Continued*

Huegel, K. GLBTQ (Gay, Lesbian, Bisexual, Transgender, Questioning) **306.76**

Snow, J. E. How it feels to have a gay or lesbian parent (5 and up) **306.8**

See/See also pages in the following book(s):

Marriage and divorce (7 and up) **306.8**

Fiction

Ferris, J. Eight seconds (7 and up) **Fic**

Freymann-Weyr, G. My heartbeat (7 and up) **Fic**

Garden, N. The year they burned the books (7 and up) **Fic**

Holland, I. The man without a face **Fic**

Kerr, M. E. Night kites (7 and up) **Fic**

Lyon, G. E. Sonny's house of spies **Fic**

Sanchez, A. So hard to say **Fic**

Homosexuality in literature

Bibliography

Day, F. A. Lesbian and gay voices **016.8**

Homosexuality: opposing viewpoints (7 and up) **306.76**

Homosexuals, Female *See* Lesbians

Homosexuals, Male *See* Gay men

Honduras

McGaffey, L. Honduras (5 and up) **972.83**

Shields, C. J. Honduras (4 and up) **972.83**

Honesty

See also Truthfulness and falsehood

Fiction

Fletcher, R. Spider Boy **Fic**

Honey, Elizabeth

Remote man **Fic**

Hong Kong (China)

Kagda, F. Hong Kong (5 and up) **951.25**

Honma, Rebecca

Jijan

In American dragons: twenty-five Asian American voices p203-10 **810.8**

Honnold, RoseMary, 1954-

101+ teen programs that work **027.62**

Hoobler, Dorothy

The African American family album (5 and up) **305.8**

The Chinese American family album **305.8**

The Cuban American family album **305.8**

The German American family album (5 and up) **305.8**

The ghost in the Tokaido Inn **Fic**

The Irish American family album (5 and up) **305.8**

The Italian American family album (5 and up) **305.8**

The Japanese American family album (5 and up) **305.8**

The Mexican American family album (5 and up) **305.8**

Vanity rules **391**

We are Americans (5 and up) **325.73**

Hoobler, Thomas

(jt. auth) Hoobler, D. The African American family album **305.8**

(jt. auth) Hoobler, D. The Chinese American family album **305.8**

(jt. auth) Hoobler, D. The Cuban American family album **305.8**

(jt. auth) Hoobler, D. The German American family album **305.8**

(jt. auth) Hoobler, D. The ghost in the Tokaido Inn **Fic**

(jt. auth) Hoobler, D. The Irish American family album **305.8**

(jt. auth) Hoobler, D. The Italian American family album **305.8**

(jt. auth) Hoobler, D. The Japanese American family album **305.8**

(jt. auth) Hoobler, D. The Mexican American family album **305.8**

(jt. auth) Hoobler, D. Vanity rules **391**

(jt. auth) Hoobler, D. We are Americans **325.73**

Hood, Robin (Legendary character) *See* Robin Hood (Legendary character)

Hooking teens with the Net. Braun, L. W. **025.04**

Hoop queens. Smith, C. R. **811**

Hooper, Mary

At the sign of the Sugared Plum **Fic**

Hoops. Burleigh, R. **811**

Hoops. Myers, W. D. **Fic**

The **Hoopster**. Sitomer, A. L. **Fic**

Hoose, Phillip M., 1947-

The race to save the Lord God Bird (7 and up) **598**

We were there, too! (5 and up) **973**

Hoot. Hiaasen, C. **Fic**

Hoover, H. M., 1935-

See/See also pages in the following book(s):

Reid, S. E. Presenting young adult science fiction **813.009**

Hoover, Herbert, 1874-1964

About

Holford, D. M. Herbert Hoover **92**

Fiction

Ray, D. Ghost girl (5 and up) **Fic**

Hoover, J. Edgar (John Edgar), 1895-1972

About

Streissguth, T. J. Edgar Hoover: powerful FBI Director **92**

Hoover, John Edgar *See* Hoover, J. Edgar (John Edgar), 1895-1972

Hoover, Lou Henry, 1874-1944

Fiction

Ray, D. Ghost girl (5 and up) **Fic**

Hoover Dam (Ariz. and Nev.)

Mann, E. Hoover Dam (4 and up) **627**

See/See also pages in the following book(s):

Aaseng, N. Construction: building the impossible **624**

Hop-frog. Poe, E. A.

In Poe, E. A. Edgar Allan Poe's tales of mystery and madness **S C**

In Poe, E. A. Tales of Edgar Allan Poe p81-93 **S C**

Hope. Miklowitz, G. D.

In Shattered: stories of children and war p148-55 **S C**

Hope chest. Nix, G.
   In Firebirds: an anthology of original fantasy and science fiction; an anthology of original fantasy and science fiction   **S C**

Hope was here. Bauer, J.   **Fic**

The **Hopi**. Bonvillian, N. Indians of North America series

Hopi Indians
   Bonvillian, N. The Hopi Indians of North America series

Hopkins, Dianne McAfee
   (jt. auth) Zweizig, D. Lessons from Library Power   **027.8**

Hopkins, Lee Bennett, 1938-
   Been to yesterdays: poems of a life (4 and up)   **811**
   Pass the poetry, please!   **372.6**
   See/See also pages in the following book(s):
   Author talk (4 and up)   **028.5**
   (comp) Lives: poems about famous Americans. See Lives: poems about famous Americans   **811.008**
   (comp) Marvelous math. See Marvelous math   **811.008**
   (ed) My America. See My America   **811.008**

Hopkinson, Deborah
   Shutting out the sky (5 and up)   **974.7**

Hopper, Grace, 1906-1992
   See/See also pages in the following book(s):
   Celebrating women in mathematics and science   **920**
   Northrup, M. American computer pioneers   **920**
   Thimmesh, C. Girls think of everything (5 and up)   **920**

Hopscotch love. Grimes, N.   **811**

Hormones
   Little, M. The endocrine system (7 and up)   **612.4**

Horn, Geoffrey
   The Congress (5 and up)   **328**
   The presidency (5 and up)   **352.23**
   The Supreme Court (5 and up)   **347**

Hornby, Hugh
   Soccer (4 and up)   **796.334**

Horne, Lena
      About
   Huggins, N. I. Lena Horne   **92**

Horner, Jack *See* Horner, John R.

Horner, John R.
      About
   Patent, D. H. In search of the maiasaurs   **567.9**

Horning, Kathleen T.
   From cover to cover   **028.1**

Hornsby, Alton, Jr.
   Chronology of African American history (7 and up)   **305.8**

Horoscopes
   See/See also pages in the following book(s):
   Chahrour, J. Zap! blink! taste! think! (5 and up)   **507.8**

Horowitz, Anthony, 1955-
   The Devil and his boy (5 and up)   **Fic**

   Public enemy number two   **Fic**
   Raven's gate (7 and up)   **Fic**
   Stormbreaker   **Fic**

Horowitz, Joseph, 1948-
   Dvořák in America (7 and up)   **92**

Horror fiction
   Beware! (4 and up)   **808.8**
   Coville, B. Odder than ever   **S C**
   Gothic! (7 and up)   **S C**
   Jarvis, R. The alchemist's cat (5 and up)   **Fic**
   Night terrors (7 and up)   **S C**
   Poe, E. A. Edgar Allan Poe's tales of mystery and madness   **S C**
   Poe, E. A. The pit and the pendulum and other stories (7 and up)   **S C**
   Poe, E. A. Tales of Edgar Allan Poe   **S C**
   San Souci, R. Dare to be scared (4 and up)   **S C**
   San Souci, R. Double-dare to be scared: another thirteen chilling tales (4 and up)   **S C**
   Schwartz, A. More scary stories to tell in the dark (4 and up)   **398.2**
   Schwartz, A. Scary stories 3 (4 and up)   **398.2**
   Schwartz, A. Scary stories to tell in the dark (4 and up)   **398.2**
   Sedgwick, M. The book of Dead Days   **Fic**
   Shusterman, N. Full tilt (7 and up)   **Fic**
   Vande Velde, V. Being dead (7 and up)   **S C**
   Wooding, C. The haunting of Alaizabel Cray (7 and up)   **Fic**

Horror vacui. Lynch, C.
   In Lynch, C. All the old haunts p102-12   **S C**

Horse, Harry, 1960-
   (il) King-Smith, D. Chewing the cud   **92**

Horse thief. Peck, R. N.   **Fic**

Horseback riding *See* Horsemanship

Horsemanship
   See also Rodeos
   Davis, C. The young equestrian   **798.2**
   Ransford, S. The Kingfisher illustrated horse & pony encyclopedia (4 and up)   **636.1**

Horses
   Budiansky, S. The world according to horses (4 and up)   **636.1**
   Ransford, S. The Kingfisher illustrated horse & pony encyclopedia (4 and up)   **636.1**
   Ryden, H. Wild horses I have known (4 and up)   **599.66**
   The Visual dictionary of the horse (4 and up)   **636.1**
      Fiction
   Adler, C. S. One unhappy horse   **Fic**
   Grant, K. M. Blood red horse   **Fic**
   Haas, J. Unbroken (5 and up)   **Fic**
   Hinton, S. E. Taming the Star Runner   **Fic**
   Hobbs, W. The Big Wander (7 and up)   **Fic**
   Lester, A. Quicksand pony   **Fic**
   Lester, A. The snow pony   **Fic**
   McCaffrey, A. Black horses for the king (7 and up)   **Fic**
   Steinbeck, J. The red pony   **Fic**

Horses in art
Mayne, D. Drawing horses that look real!
743

Horvath, Polly
The canning season **Fic**
Everything on a waffle (4 and up) **Fic**

Horwitz, Margot F.
(jt. auth) Greenberg, L. Digging into the past
920

Hosler, Jay
Clan Apis **741.5**
The sandwalk adventures **741.5**

Hospitals
See also Psychiatric hospitals
Fiction
Brooks, B. Vanishing **Fic**
Hostage. Roberts, W. D. **Fic**
Hot lava. Hautman, P.
In On the edge: stories at the brink p83-92
S C

Hot pro/con issues [series]
Cruz, B. School dress codes **371.8**
Goodnough, D. The debate over human cloning
174.2
Rebman, R. C. Euthanasia and the "right to die"
179.7

Hotta, Yumi
Hikaru No Go, Volume 1 **741.5**

Hotze, Sollace
A circle unbroken **Fic**

Houbolt, John C., 1919-
See/See also pages in the following book(s):
Richie, J. Space flight **920**

Houghton, Gillian
The Transcontinental Railroad (5 and up)
385

Houle, Michelle M.
Triangle Shirtwaist Factory fire **974.7**
(ed) Cesar Chavez. See Cesar Chavez **92**

The **hound** of the Baskervilles. Doyle, Sir A. C.
In Doyle, Sir A. C. The complete Sherlock
Holmes **S C**

An **hour** with Abuelo. Ortiz Cofer, J.
In Ortiz Cofer, J. An island like you; stories
of the barrio p66-71 **S C**

House construction
Wilkinson, P. Building (4 and up) **690**

The **house** of Dies Drear. Hamilton, V. **Fic**

House of stairs. Sleator, W. **Fic**

A **house** of tailors. Giff, P. R. **Fic**

The **house** of the scorpion. Farmer, N. **Fic**

House of Windsor
About
Billinghurst, J. Growing up royal **920**

The **house** on Buffalo Street. Mazer, N. F.
In Night terrors; stories of shadow and substance **S C**

The **house** on Mango Street. Cisneros, S. **Fic**

The **house** surgeon. Kipling, R.
In McCaffrey, A. {The Pern series} **S C**

The **house** you pass on the way. Woodson, J.
Fic

Household moving See Moving

Housepainting. Chang, L. S.
In American eyes; new Asian-American short
stories for young adults p13-27 **S C**

Housewright, Ed
Winning track and field for girls (7 and up)
796.42

Houston, Gloria
Bright Freedom's song **Fic**

Houston, James A., 1921-2005
Frozen fire (6 and up) **Fic**

Houston, James D.
(jt. auth) Houston, J. W. Farewell to Manzanar
940.53

Houston, Jeanne Wakatsuki, 1933-
Farewell to Manzanar (7 and up) **940.53**

Houston, Samuel, 1793-1863
About
Fritz, J. Make way for Sam Houston (4 and up)
92

See/See also pages in the following book(s):
Doherty, K. Ranchers, homesteaders, and traders
920
Kennedy, J. F. Profiles in courage **920**

Houston (Tex.)
Fiction
Williams, L. A. When Kambia Elaine flew in
from Neptune (7 and up) **Fic**

Hovey, Kate
Ancient voices **811**

How a Piegan warrior found the first horses.
Brown, D. A.
In Brown, D. A. Dee Brown's folktales of the
Native American; retold for our times
p98-99 **398.2**

How a student became a king. Molnár, I.
In Molnár, I. One-time dog market at Buda
and other Hungarian folktales p54-59
398.2

How Angel Peterson got his name. Paulsen, G.
92

How animals got their tails. Bryan, A.
In Bryan, A. Ashley Bryan's African tales,
uh-huh p93-110 **398.2**

How Antelope Carrier saved the Thunderbirds.
Brown, D. A.
In Brown, D. A. Dee Brown's folktales of the
Native American; retold for our times
p22-26 **398.2**

How Brer Lion lost his hair. Lester, J.
In Lester, J. The last tales of Uncle Remus
p131-33 **398.2**

How come Ol' Buzzard boards. Van Laan, N.
In Van Laan, N. With a whoop and a holler;
a bushel of lore from way down south
p49-52 **398**

How corn came to the earth. Brown, D. A.
In Brown, D. A. Dee Brown's folktales of the
Native American; retold for our times
p65-70 **398.2**

How day and night were divided. Brown, D. A.
In Brown, D. A. Dee Brown's folktales of the Native American; retold for our times p62-63   **398.2**

How do you spell God? Gellman, M.   **200**

How fear came. Kipling, R.
In Kipling, R. The jungle books   **S C**

How history is invented [series]
Pelta, K. Rediscovering Easter Island   **996**

How I became a writer and Oggie learned to drive. Lisle, J. T.   **Fic**

How I became an American. Gündisch, K.   **Fic**

How I contemplated the world. Oates, J. C.
In Oates, J. C. Small avalanches and other stories   **S C**

How I found the Strong. McMullan, M.   **Fic**

How I got my English A. Avi
In Tripping over the lunch lady and other school stories p17-28   **S C**

How I got to be queen. Sarris, G.
In Talking leaves; contemporary native American short stories   **S C**

How Ioscoda and his friends met the white men from the east and journeyed across the great waters. Brown, D. A.
In Brown, D. A. Dee Brown's folktales of the Native American; retold for our times p84-90   **398.2**

How it feels to have a gay or lesbian parent. Snow, J. E.   **306.8**

How it works: science and technology   **603**

How Nehemiah got free. Hamilton, V.
In Hamilton, V. The people could fly; American black folktales p147-50   **398.2**

How Poor Boy won his wife. Curry, J. L.
In Curry, J. L. Hold up the sky: and other Native American tales from Texas and the Southern Plains p107-13   **398.2**

How Rabbit brought fire to the people. Brown, D. A.
In Brown, D. A. Dee Brown's folktales of the Native American; retold for our times p70-71   **398.2**

How Rabbit fooled Wolf. Brown, D. A.
In Brown, D. A. Dee Brown's folktales of the Native American; retold for our times p106-09   **398.2**

How Rabbit stole Mountain Lion's teeth. Curry, J. L.
In Curry, J. L. Hold up the sky: and other Native American tales from Texas and the Southern Plains p81-83   **398.2**

How rude!. Packer, A. J.   **395**

How the buffalo were released on earth. Brown, D. A.
In Brown, D. A. Dee Brown's folktales of the Native American; retold for our times p63-65   **398.2**

How the first white men came to the Cheyennes. Brown, D. A.
In Brown, D. A. Dee Brown's folktales of the Native American; retold for our times p92-94   **398.2**

How the narwhal got its tusk. Norman, H.
In Norman, H. The girl who dreamed only geese, and other tales of the Far North   **398.2**

How the rainbow was born. Delacre, L.
In Delacre, L. Golden tales; myths, legends, and folktales from Latin America p37-39   **398.2**

How the sea was born. Delacre, L.
In Delacre, L. Golden tales; myths, legends, and folktales from Latin America p3-5   **398.2**

How the witch was caught. Lester, J.
In Lester, J. The last tales of Uncle Remus p66-70   **398.2**

How they play driedel in Chelm. Kimmel, E. A.
In Kimmel, E. A. The jar of fools: eight Hanukkah stories from Chelm p5-8   **S C**

How Tia Lola came to visit/stay. Alvarez, J.   **Fic**

How Tinktum Tidy recruited an army for the king. Lester, J.
In Lester, J. The last tales of Uncle Remus p82-88   **398.2**

How to cook a gooseberry fool. Vaughan, M.
In Easy menu ethnic cookbooks   **641.5**

How to disappear completely and never be found. Nickerson, S.   **Fic**

How to do a science fair project. Tocci, S.   **507.8**

How-to-do-it manuals for libraries [series]
Developing an information literacy program, K-12   **025.5**
Jones, P. Connecting young adults and libraries   **027.62**
Symons, A. K. Protecting the right to read   **025.2**

How to do your best on tests. Gilbert, S. D.   **371.2**

How to draw comic book bad guys and gals. Hart, C.   **741.5**

How to excel in science competitions. Krieger, M. J.   **507.8**

How to get a job if you're a teenager. Pervola, C.   **650.14**

How to play tennis. Williams, V.   **796.342**

How to prepare for the SSAT/ ISEE: Secondary School Admissions Test/Independent School Entrance Exam. Shostak, J.   **373.1**

How to study. Wood, G.   **371.3**

How to take tests. See Gilbert, S. D. How to do your best on tests   **371.2**

How to write a letter. Dragisic, P.   **808**

How to write a short story. Peck, R.
In Peck, R. Past perfect, present tense: new and collected stories   **S C**

How to write poetry. Janeczko, P. B.   **808.1**

How to write terrific book reports. James, E.
808

How to write your best book report. See James, E.
How to write terrific book reports   808

How TV changed America's mind. Wakin, E.
070.1

How writers work. Fletcher, R.   808

Howard, Elizabeth Fitzgerald, 1927-
(jt. auth) Coffey, R. K. America as story
016.813

Howard, Megan
Christopher Reeve   92
Madeleine Albright   92

Howard, Todd, 1964-
(ed) Mark Twain. See Mark Twain [essays
about]   92

Howarth, Sarah
Colonial places (4 and up)   973.2
The Middle Ages   940.1

Howe, James, 1946-
Enchanted night
In The Color of absence; 12 stories about loss
and hope p207-28   S C
Jeremy Goldblatt is so no Moses
In 13; thirteen stories that capture the agony
and ecstasy of being thirteen
The misfits   Fic
The watcher (7 and up)   Fic
See/See also pages in the following book(s):
Author talk (4 and up)   028.5
(ed) 13. See 13   S C
(ed) The Color of absence. See The Color of
absence   S C

Howe, Norma
The adventures of Blue Avenger (7 and up)
Fic
Siskiyou Sloan and the eye of the giraffe
In Necessary noise: stories about our families
as they really are p23-48   S C

Howell, Troy
(il) Osborne, M. P. Favorite medieval tales
398.2

Howes, Kelly King
World War II: biographies   920

Howland, Ethan, 1963-
The lobster war   Fic

Howl's moving castle. Jones, D. W.   Fic

Hubble, Edwin Powell, 1889-1953
About
Datnow, C. L. Edwin Hubble   92

Hubble Space Telescope
Cole, M. D. Hubble Space Telescope (4 and up)
522
Simon, S. Destination: space (4 and up)   520
Spangenburg, R. The Hubble Space Telescope
522

Huddleston, Courtney
Decoy   741.5

Hudson, David L., 1969-
Gay rights (7 and up)   342

Hudson, Henry, d. 1611
About
Edwards, J. Henry Hudson and his voyages of
exploration in world history (7 and up)
92
Santella, A. Henry Hudson   92

Hudson, Wade
Powerful words (5 and up)   808.8
(ed) Poetry from the masters: the pioneers. See
Poetry from the masters: the pioneers
811.008

Hudson River (N.Y. and N.J.)
Whitcraft, M. The Hudson River   974.7

Huegel, Kelly
GLBTQ (Gay, Lesbian, Bisexual, Transgender,
Questioning)   306.76

Huggan, Isabel, 1943-
Celia behind me
In Who do you think you are?; stories of
friends and enemies p73-82   S C

Huggins, Nathan Irvin, 1927-1989
Lena Horne   92

Hughes, Chris
The Battle of Antietam   973.7

Hughes, Dean, 1943-
Soldier boys   Fic

Hughes, Helga
Cooking the Austrian way
In Easy menu ethnic cookbooks   641.5
Cooking the Irish way
In Easy menu ethnic cookbooks   641.5
Cooking the Swiss way
In Easy menu ethnic cookbooks   641.5

Hughes, Langston, 1902-1967
The collected poems of Langston Hughes
811
The dream keeper and other poems (5 and up)
811
Thank you, ma'am
In Read all about it!; great read-aloud stories,
poems, and newspaper pieces for pre-
teens and teens p82-89   808.8
About
Hill, C. M. Langston Hughes   92

Hughes, Mark Peter
I am the wallpaper   Fic

Hughes, Mary
Popular superstitions   398

Hughes, Monica
Invitation to the game (7 and up)   Fic
See/See also pages in the following book(s):
Ellis, S. From reader to writer   372.6

Hughes, Pat, 1933-
The breaker boys   Fic
Guerrilla season (7 and up)   Fic

Hughes-Hassell, Sandra
(ed) Curriculum connections through the library.
See Curriculum connections through the library   027.62
(ed) The Information-powered school. See The
Information-powered school   027.8

Hulk (Comic strip)
DeFalco, T. The Hulk: the incredible guide
741.5

The **Hulk:** the incredible guide. DeFalco, T.
          741.5

Hull, Mary
 The Boston Tea Party in American history
          973.3

Hulm, David
 United States v. the Amistad   **326**

Human anatomy
 Beckelman, L. The human body **612**
 Hall, D. The human body
  In Being human   **612**
 Human anatomy on file   **611**
 Nagel, R. Body by design   **612**
 Parker, S. Human body   **612**
 Walker, R. DK guide to the human body
          612
 Walker, R. Encyclopedia of the human body
          612

Human anatomy on file   **611**

Human beings
 Being human   **612**
 Glover, D. M. The young Oxford book of the
  human being   **612**

The **human** body. Beckelman, L. **612**
The **human** body. Hall, D.
 In Being human   **612**
Human body. Parker, S.   **612**

Human body library [series]
 Gold, S. D. The musculoskeletal system and the
  skin   **612.7**

Human body on file: anatomy. See Human anatomy on file   **611**
Human body on file: physiology. See Human
 physiology on file   **612**

Human body systems [series]
 Silverstein, A. The respiratory system **612.2**

Human ecology
 The environment: opposing viewpoints **363.7**
 Zeaman, J. Overpopulation (7 and up) **363.9**

Human evolution. Gardner, R. **599.93**

Human Genome Project
 Boon, K. A. The human genome project (7 and
 up)   **599.93**
 See/See also pages in the following book(s):
 Kidd, J. S. Life lines (7 and up) **576.5**

Human geography
 Arthus-Bertrand, Y. Earth from above for young
  readers (4 and up)   **779**
 Mason, A. People around the world **305.8**

Human impact. Vogel, C. G.   **333.91**

Human influence on nature
 Burnie, D. Endangered planet (5 and up)
          333.95
 Davis, L. A. Environmental disasters (7 and up)
          363.7
 Vogel, C. G. Human impact (5 and up)
          333.91
 See/See also pages in the following book(s):
 Patent, D. H. Biodiversity (5 and up)
          333.95

Human origins
  See also Evolution; Fossil hominids; Prehistoric peoples

Gallant, R. A. Early humans (5 and up)
          599.93
Gardner, R. Human evolution (7 and up)
          599.93
Poynter, M. The Leakeys   **92**
Sloan, C. The human story (7 and up)
          599.93
See/See also pages in the following book(s):
 Glover, D. M. The young Oxford book of the
  human being   **612**

Human physiology on file   **612**

The **human** race. Steele, P.
 In Being human   **612**

Human relations *See* Interpersonal relations

Human rights
 Altman, L. J. Human rights (7 and up) **323**
 Human rights   **323**
 Human rights: opposing viewpoints (7 and up)
          323
 Kennedy Cuomo, K. Speak truth to power (7
  and up)   **920**
 Stewart, G. Human rights in the Middle East
          323

 See/See also pages in the following book(s):
 Africa: opposing viewpoints   **960**

Human rights   **323**

Human rights in the Middle East. Stewart, G.
          323

Human rights: opposing viewpoints (7 and up)
          323

The **human** story. Sloan, C.   **599.93**

The **humming** of stars and bees and waves.
 Endrezze, A.
  In Talking leaves; contemporary native
   American short stories   **S C**

Hummingbirds
 Rauzon, M. J. Hummingbirds   **598**

Humor *See* Wit and humor

Humorous poetry
 Hirsch, R. F E G: ridiculous stupid poems for
  intelligent children (5 and up) **821**
 The Kingfisher book of funny poems (4 and up)
          821.008
 Silverstein, S. Falling up   **811**
 Silverstein, S. A light in the attic **811**
 Silverstein, S. Where the sidewalk ends **811**

Humphrey, Judy
 Genghis Khan   **92**

A **hundred** bucks of happy. Asher, S.
 In Visions: nineteen short stories by outstanding writers for young adults p141-48
          S C

The **hundredth** skull. San Souci, R.
 In San Souci, R. A terrifying taste of short &
  shivery; thirty creepy tales p43-45
          398.2

Hungary
 Ake, A. Hungary (7 and up)   **943.9**
      Fiction
 Cheng, A. The lace dowry (4 and up) **Fic**

Hungry city chronicles [series]
 Reeve, P. Mortal engines   **Fic**

Hungry ghosts. San Souci, R.
In San Souci, R. Dare to be scared; thirteen
stories to chill and thrill **S C**
The **hungry** goddess. Gerson, M.-J.
In Gerson, M.-J. Fiesta femenina; celebrating
women in Mexican folktale **398.2**
Hunley (Submarine)
Walker, S. M. Secrets of a Civil War submarine
(7 and up) **973.7**
Hunt, Scott
(il) Testa, M. Becoming Joe DiMaggio **811**
Hunter, Erica C. D.
First civilizations (5 and up) **939**
Hunter, Erin
Into the wild **Fic**
The **hunter** and the Dakwa. Brown, D. A.
In Brown, D. A. Dee Brown's folktales of the
Native American; retold for our times
p132-33 **398.2**
Hunter's moon. McKillip, P. A.
In The Green Man: tales from the mythic for-
est p118-34 **808.8**
Hunting for boys. Flake, S. G.
In Flake, S. G. Who am I without him?; short
stories about girls and the boys in their
lives p135-56 **S C**
The **hunting** of the hind. McKinley, R.
In McKinley, R. The door in the hedge p105-
36 **S C**
The **hunting** of the last dragon. Jordan, S. **Fic**
Huntington's chorea
See/See also pages in the following book(s):
Hyde, M. O. When the brain dies first (7 and
up) **616.8**
Hurley, Jennifer A., 1973-
Teen pregnancy (7 and up) **362.7**
(ed) Child abuse: opposing viewpoints. See
Child abuse: opposing viewpoints **362.7**
(ed) Eating disorders: opposing viewpoints. See
Eating disorders: opposing viewpoints
616.85
(ed) The Homeless: opposing viewpoints. See
The Homeless: opposing viewpoints **362.5**
(ed) Teens at risk: opposing viewpoints. See
Teens at risk: opposing viewpoints **362.7**
Huron
In North American Indians today [series]
The **hurricane**. Salisbury, G.
In Salisbury, G. Island boyz: short stories
p68-94 **S C**
Hurricane Andrew. Sherrow, V. **551.55**
Hurricanes
Longshore, D. Encyclopedia of hurricanes, ty-
phoons and cyclones (7 and up) **551.55**
Sherrow, V. Hurricane Andrew **551.55**
Simon, S. Hurricanes (4 and up) **551.55**
Fiction
Garland, S. The silent storm **Fic**
Vaught, S. Stormwitch (7 and up) **Fic**
Hurst, Carol Otis
Through the lock **Fic**

Hurston, Zora Neale, 1891-1960
About
Lyons, M. E. Sorrow's kitchen: the life and
folklore of Zora Neale Hurston **92**
Hurtado, A. Magdalena
About
Batten, M. Anthropologist: scientist of the peo-
ple (4 and up) **301**
Hurwitz, Johanna
See/See also pages in the following book(s):
Author talk (4 and up) **028.5**
Husain, Saddam *See* Hussein, Ṣaddām
Ḥusayn, Ṣaddām *See* Hussein, Ṣaddām
The **husband** who counted the spoonfuls. Bryan,
A.
In Bryan, A. Ashley Bryan's African tales,
uh-huh p70-80 **398.2**
Hush. Woodson, J. **Fic**
Hush: an interview with America. Still, J.
In Theatre for young audiences; 20 great
plays for children p395-428 **812.008**
Hussein, Ṣaddām
About
Anderson, D. Saddam Hussein **92**
Schaffer, D. The Iran-Iraq War (7 and up)
956.7
Hussey, Leigh Ann
Blood libel
In Vampires: a collection of original stories
p157-86 **S C**
Hutchins, Danuta Zamojska- *See* Zamojska-
Hutchins, Danuta
Hutchison, Linda
Lebanon (7 and up) **956.92**
Hutton, James, 1726-1797
See/See also pages in the following book(s):
Carruthers, M. W. Pioneers of geology **920**
Huxley, Aldous, 1894-1963
Brave new world (7 and up) **Fic**
Huynh, Quang Nhuong
The land I lost: adventures of a boy in Vietnam
(5 and up) **92**
Hyde, Margaret Oldroyd, 1917-
Alcohol 101 (7 and up) **362.292**
Diabetes **616.4**
Medicine's brave new world (7 and up) **610**
Mind drugs (7 and up) **616.86**
Vaccinations (7 and up) **615**
When the brain dies first (7 and up) **616.8**
Hydrogen
Farndon, J. Hydrogen
In The Elements **546**
Hygiene
See also Health
Hyman, Bruce M.
Obsessive-compulsive disorder **616.85**
Hyman, Trina Schart, 1939-2004
(il) Cohen, B. Canterbury tales **821**
(il) Lasky, K. The night journey **Fic**
(il) Rogasky, B. The golem **398.2**
(il) Tchana, K. H. The serpent slayer: and other
stories of strong women **398.2**

Hymns
See also Spirituals (Songs)

Hypatia, ca. 370-415
See/See also pages in the following book(s):
Celebrating women in mathematics and science
920
Di Domenico, K. Super women in science
920

Hyperactive children
See also Attention deficit disorder
The **hypnotist**. Sleator, W.
In Sleator, W. Oddballs; stories p43-55
S C

I

I am Mordred. Springer, N. **Fic**
I am Morgan le Fay. Springer, N. **Fic**
I am not Esther. Beale, F. **Fic**
I am phoenix: poems for two voices. Fleischman, P. **811**
I am Regina. Keehn, S. M. **Fic**
I am the darker brother **811.008**
I am the wallpaper. Hughes, M. P. **Fic**
I believe in . Gaskins, P. **200**
I, Earthling. Coville, B.
In Coville, B. Odder than ever **S C**
I feel a little jumpy around you (7 and up) **808.81**
I go along. Peck, R.
In Peck, R. Past perfect, present tense: new and collected stories **S C**
I hadn't meant to tell you this. Woodson, J. **Fic**
I have lived a thousand years. Bitton-Jackson, L. **940.53**
I heard the owl call my name. Craven, M. **Fic**
I, hungry Hannah Cassandra Glen . . . Mazer, N. F.
In Sixteen; short stories by outstanding writers for young adults p2-14 **S C**
I know a stupid boy when I see one. Flake, S. G.
In Flake, S. G. Who am I without him?; short stories about girls and the boys in their lives p29-48 **S C**
I know what you did last summer. Duncan, L. **Fic**
I know why the caged bird sings [excerpt] Angelou, M.
In Who do you think you are?; stories of friends and enemies p156-63 **S C**
I like white boys. Flake, S. G.
In Flake, S. G. Who am I without him?; short stories about girls and the boys in their lives p90-104 **S C**
—I never saw another butterfly— **741.9**
I once was a monkey. Lee, J. M. **294.3**
I remember Korea. Granfield, L. **951.9**
I, robot. Asimov, I. **S C**

I, too, sing America (6 and up) **811.008**
I voted for Mary Ann. Wallace, R.
In Wallace, R. Losing is not an option: stories **S C**
I was dreaming to come to America (4 and up) **325.73**
I was there books [series]
Hehner, B. First on the moon **629.45**
Tanaka, S. Attack on Pearl Harbor **940.54**
Ruhl, G. In the time of knights **942.03**
Tanaka, S. Lost temple of the Aztecs **972**
Tanaka, S. Secrets of the mummies **393**
I will plant you a lilac tree. Hillman, L. **940.53**
I wouldn't thank you for a valentine **808.81**
Ibatoulline, Bagram
(il) Giblin, J. Secrets of the Sphinx **932**
Ibbotson, Eva
Island of the aunts (5 and up) **Fic**
Journey to the river sea (5 and up) **Fic**
The star of Kazan (5 and up) **Fic**
Ibn Sa'ūd, King of Saudi Arabia, 1880-1953
See/See also pages in the following book(s):
Reed, J. The Saudi royal family **920**
Ibo (African people) *See* Igbo (African people)
Ice. Naylor, P. R. **Fic**
Ice Age cave bear. Hehner, B. **569**
Ice Age mammoth. Hehner, B. **569**
Ice Age sabertooth. Hehner, B. **569**
Ice hockey *See* Hockey
Ice Man and the messenger of springtime. Brown, D. A.
In Brown, D. A. Dee Brown's folktales of the Native American; retold for our times p79-80 **398.2**
Ice skating
Biography
Shea, P. D. Ekaterina Gordeeva **92**
Ice story. Kimmel, E. C. **998**
The **ice** wolf. Kraus, J. H.
In Theatre for young audiences; 20 great plays for children p284-307 **812.008**
Idaho
George, C. Idaho
In America the beautiful, second series **973**
George, L. Idaho America the beautiful, second series **973**
Stefoff, R. Idaho
In Celebrate the states **973**
Ideal states *See* Utopias
Ideas of the modern world [series]
Stearman, K. Feminism **305.4**
Tames, R. Nationalism **320.5**
Iditarod dream. Wood, T. **798.8**
Iditarod Trail Sled Dog Race, Alaska
Paulsen, G. Winterdance **798.8**
If I forget, you remember. Williams, C. L. **Fic**
If that breathes fire, we're toast!. Stewart, J. J. **Fic**
If the shoe fits. Whipple, L. **811**

If you can't be lucky . . . Deuker, C.
  In Ultimate sports; short stories by outstanding writers for young adults p72-91 **S C**

If you come softly. Woodson, J. **Fic**

If you kiss a boy. Sanchez, A.
  In 13; thirteen stories that capture the agony and ecstasy of being thirteen

If you were there in 1776. Brenner, B. **973.3**

Igbo (African people)
Nnoromele, S. Life among the Ibo women of Nigeria (7 and up) **966.9**

Igloos
Yue, C. The igloo (4 and up) **728**

Iizuka, Shokansai
See/See also pages in the following book(s):
Hamanaka, S. In search of the spirit (5 and up) **920**

The **Iliad**. Homer **883**

The **Iliad**. McCarty, N. **883**

The **ill-made** knight. White, T. H.
  In White, T. H. The once and future king **Fic**

I'll see you when this war is over. Kerr, M. E.
  In Shattered: stories of children and war p40-51 **S C**

Illegal aliens
Illegal immigration: opposing viewpoints (7 and up) **325.73**
Kuklin, S. Trial: the inside story (7 and up) **345**

Illegal drugs (7 and up) **364.1**

Illegal immigration: opposing viewpoints (7 and up) **325.73**

Illinois
Brill, M. T. Illinois
  In Celebrate the states **973**
Santella, A. Illinois
  In America the beautiful, second series **973**
Fiction
Klise, K. Deliver us from Normal **Fic**
Moranville, S. B. Over the river (5 and up) **Fic**

Illiteracy *See* Literacy

Illness *See* Diseases

The **illustrated** book of myths. Philip, N. **201**

Illustrated dictionary of mythology. Wilkinson, P. **201**

Illustrated histories [series]
Schroeter, D. J. Israel **956.94**

The **illustrated** history of the world. Roberts, J. M. **909**

Illustrated history of the world [series]
Martell, H. M. The age of discovery **909.08**
Reynoldson, F. Conflict and change **909.7**

Illustration of books
Marcus, L. S. A Caldecott celebration **741.6**

Illustrations, Humorous *See* Cartoons and caricatures

Illustrators
Dean, T. Theodor Geisel [Dr. Seuss] (4 and up) **92**
Marcus, L. S. A Caldecott celebration **741.6**
The Newbery & Caldecott medal books, 1986-2000 **028.5**
Newbery and Caldecott Medal books, 1966-1975 **028.5**
Newbery and Caldecott Medal books, 1976-1985 **028.5**
Peet, B. Bill Peet: an autobiography (4 and up) **92**

Dictionaries
Favorite children's authors and illustrators **920.003**
The ninth book of junior authors and illustrators **920.003**
Something about the author **920.003**
Something about the author: autobiography series **920.003**

The **Illyrian** adventure. Alexander, L. **Fic**

I'm a vegetarian. Schwartz, E. **613.2**

I'm not who you think I am. Kehret, P. **Fic**

IMF *See* International Monetary Fund

Imhotep, fl. 2980-2950 B.C.
See/See also pages in the following book(s):
Aaseng, N. Construction: building the impossible **624**

Immell, Myra
The Han dynasty **931**
(ed) Eating disorders. See Eating disorders **616.85**
(ed) World War II. See World War II [Turning points in world history series] **940.53**

Immigrants
Peoples of North America **305.8**
Fiction
Auch, M. J. Ashes of roses (7 and up) **Fic**
Avi. Beyond the western sea **Fic**
Bartoletti, S. C. A coal miner's bride (4 and up) **Fic**
Cannon, A. E. Charlotte's Rose (5 and up) **Fic**
Currier, K. S. Kai's journey to Gold Mountain (4 and up) **Fic**
Danticat, E. Behind the mountains **Fic**
De la Cruz, M. Fresh off the boat (7 and up) **Fic**
Durbin, W. The journal of Otto Peltonen, a Finnish immigrant **Fic**
French, S. Where in the world (5 and up) **Fic**
Giff, P. R. A house of tailors (5 and up) **Fic**
Gündisch, K. How I became an American (4 and up) **Fic**
Hesse, K. Letters from Rifka (5 and up) **Fic**
Hughes, P. The breaker boys **Fic**
Lasky, K. Dreams in the golden country (4 and up) **Fic**
Mead, A. Swimming to America **Fic**
Veciana-Suarez, A. The flight to freedom **Fic**
United States
Bial, R. Tenement (4 and up) **974.7**

Immigrants—United States—*Continued*
Bode, J. The colors of freedom **305.8**
Daniels, R. American immigration (7 and up)
325.73
Hopkinson, D. Shutting out the sky (5 and up)
974.7
Joselit, J. W. Immigration and American religion (7 and up) **200**
Immigration (7 and up) **325.73**
Immigration. Wepman, D. **325.73**
Immigration and American religion. Joselit, J. W.
200

Immigration and emigration
See also Immigrants; Refugees
Immonen, Stuart
(jt. auth) Busiek, K. Shockrockets: we have ignition **741.5**
Immune system
Donnellan, W. L. The miracle of immunity
616.07
Edelson, E. The immune system **616.07**
Walker, P. The immune system (7 and up)
616.07

Immunization *See* Vaccination
The **imp** of the perverse. Poe, E. A.
In Poe, E. A. Tales of Edgar Allan Poe p9-17
S C
Impact biography [series]
Shirley, D. Everyday I sing the blues: the story of B.B. King **92**
Tessitore, J. Muhammed Ali **92**
Impact of the Holocaust. Altman, L. J. **940.53**
The **impeachment** of William Jefferson Clinton.
Cohen, D. **973.929**
Imperial Trans-Antarctic Expedition (1914-1917)
Calvert, P. Sir Ernest Shackleton **92**
Johnson, R. L. Ernest Shackleton **92**
Kimmel, E. C. Ice story (4 and up) **998**
Importance of [series]
Cuffie, T. A. Maya Angelou **92**
Koopmans, A. Charles Lindbergh **92**
Oliver, M. T. Muhammad **297**
Tilton, R. Henry Ford **92**
Uschan, M. V. John F. Kennedy **92**
Woog, A. Fidel Castro **92**
Wukovits, J. F. Anne Frank **92**
The **impossible** journey. Whelan, G. **Fic**
Impressionism (Art)
Bolton, L. Impressionism **709.03**
Sabbeth, C. Monet and the impressionists for kids (5 and up) **759.05**
Impty-Umpty and the blacksmith. Lester, J.
In Lester, J. The last tales of Uncle Remus
p49-56 **398.2**
In a dark wood. Cadnum, M. **Fic**
In a perfect world [series]
Fridell, R. Education for all **370**
In a word. Baker, R. F. **422**
"**In** ambush". Kipling, R.
In McCaffrey, A. {The Pern series} **S C**

In American history [series]
Altman, L. J. Slavery and abolition in American history **973.7**
Edwards, J. Jamestown, John Smith, and Pocahontas in American history **975.5**
Edwards, J. The Plymouth Colony and the Pilgrim adventure in American history **974.4**
Fremon, D. K. The Great Depression in American history **338.5**
Fremon, D. K. The Salem witchcraft trials in American history **133.4**
Kent, Z. The mysterious disappearance of Roanoke Colony in American history
975.6/175
Lieurance, S. The Triangle Shirtwaist fire and sweatshop reform in American history
974.7
McArthur, D. Desert storm--the first Persian Gulf War in American history **956.7**
McArthur, D. The dust bowl and the Depression in American history **978**
McArthur, D. The Kansas-Nebraska Act and "Bleeding Kansas" in American history
978.1
McCormick, A. L. The industrial revolution in American history **338**
McGowen, T. The Spanish-American War and Teddy Roosevelt in American history
973.8
Sawyer, K. K. The underground railroad in American history **326**
Somerlott, R. The Little Rock school desegregation crisis in American history **373**
Stein, R. C. John Brown's Raid on Harpers Ferry in American history **973.7**
Warrick, K. C. The perilous search for the fabled Northwest Passage in American history
910.4
In defense of liberty. Freedman, R. **342**
In letters that would soar a thousand feet high.
Wallace, R.
In Wallace, R. Losing is not an option: stories
S C

In-line skating
Thomas, K. Blades, boards & scooters (5 and up) **796.2**
In my enemy's house. Matas, C. **Fic**
In my father's house. Rinaldi, A. **Fic**
In my grandmother's house **306.8**
In my hands. Opdyke, I. G. **940.53**
In my own words [series]
Custer, E. B. The diary of Elizabeth Bacon Custer **973.8**
Taylor, S. K. The diary of Susie King Taylor, Civil War nurse **973.7**
Watkins, S. R. The diary of Sam Watkins, a confederate soldier **973.7**
Yep, L. The lost garden **92**
In Ned's head. Jacobsson, A. **Fic**
In re Gault (1967). Gold, S. D. **345**
In search of the maiasaurs. Patent, D. H.
567.9
In search of the spirit. Hamanaka, S. **920**
In search of Troy. Caselli, G. **939**

In spite of killer bees. Johnston, J. **Fic**

In the beginning; creation stories from around the world. Hamilton, V. **201**

In the days of the pharoahs. Meltzer, M. **932**

In the days of the Salem witchcraft trials. Roach, M. K. **133.4**

In the days of the vaqueros. Freedman, R. **636.2**

In the ghettos. Ayer, E. H. **940.53**

In the heat. Cormier, R.
In Sixteen; short stories by outstanding writers for young adults p154-64 **S C**

In the house of happiness. Philip, N. **204**

In the house of Suddhoo. Kipling, R.
In McCaffrey, A. {The Pern series} **S C**

In the line of fire. St. George, J. **364.1**

In the middle of the night. Cormier, R. **Fic**

In the shadow of the Alamo. Garland, S. **Fic**

In the stone circle. Kimmel, E. C. **Fic**

In the time of knights. Ruhl, G. **942.03**

In the time of Picasso. Mason, A. **709.04**

In the time of Warhol. Mason, A. **709.04**

In the Valley of Elephants. Davis, T.
In On the edge: stories at the brink p195-209 **S C**

In the Year of the Boar and Jackie Robinson. Lord, B. B. **Fic**

In their own voices [series]
Greenberg, J. E. Young people's letters to the president **973**
Holocaust memories **940.53**
Slave narratives **326**
Tiulana, P. Wise words of Paul Tiulana **92**

In their own words [series]
Sullivan, G. Abraham Lincoln **92**
Sullivan, G. Paul Revere **92**

In world history [series]
Edwards, J. Henry Hudson and his voyages of exploration in world history **92**
Gaines, A. Hernando de Soto and the Spanish search for gold in world history **92**
Worth, R. The great empire of China and Marco Polo in world history **92**
Worth, R. The Spanish Inquisition in world history **272**

In your face. Graydon, S. **391**

In your hat. Conford, E.
In Shelf life: stories by the book p11-21 **S C**

Incas
Calvert, P. The ancient Inca (5 and up) **985**
Hinds, K. The Incas **985**
Reinhard, J. Discovering the Inca Ice Maiden (5 and up) **930.1**

Incest
Fiction
Woodson, J. I hadn't meant to tell you this **Fic**

Incredible deep-sea adventures [series]
Matsen, B. The incredible search for the treasure ship Atocha **910.4**

Incredible Hulk (Comic strip) *See* Hulk (Comic strip)

The **incredible** journey of Lewis and Clark. Blumberg, R. **978**

The **incredible** record-setting deep-sea dive of the bathysphere. Matsen, B. **551.46**

The **incredible** search for the treasure ship Atocha. Matsen, B. **910.4**

Independent schools *See* Private schools

Index to children's poetry **808.81**

Index to fairy tales **398.2**

Index to poetry for children and young people **808.81**

India
Downing, D. Conflict: India vs. Pakistan **954**
Engfer, L. India in pictures (5 and up) **954**
Srinivasan, R. India (5 and up) **954**
Stefoff, R. The Asian empires (5 and up) **950**
Fiction
Alexander, L. The iron ring (5 and up) **Fic**
Divakaruni, C. B. The conch bearer (5 and up) **Fic**
Kipling, R. The jungle books (4 and up) **S C**
Perkins, M. Monsoon summer (7 and up) **Fic**
Staples, S. F. Shiva's fire (7 and up) **Fic**
Politics and government
Adams, S. Mahatma Gandhi (7 and up) **92**
Hatt, C. Mahatma Ghandhi **92**
Severance, J. B. Gandhi, great soul (5 and up) **92**

India in pictures. Engfer, L. **954**

Indian art & culture. Bingham, J. **709.5**

The **Indian** basket. Roberts, M.
In Talking leaves; contemporary native American short stories **S C**

Indian chiefs. Freedman, R. **920**

Indian literature (American) *See* American literature—Native American authors

Indian school. Cooper, M. L. **970.004**

Indiana
Brill, M. T. Indiana
In Celebrate the states **973**
Heinrichs, A. Indiana
In America the beautiful, second series **973**
Fiction
Peck, R. The teacher's funeral (5 and up) **Fic**

Indianapolis (Cruiser)
Nelson, P. Left for dead (7 and up) **940.54**

Indians, cowboys, and farmers and the battle for the Great Plains, 1865-1910. Collier, C. **978**

Indians of North America *See* Native Americans

Indians of North America series [Chelsea House] **970.004**

Indic arts
Bingham, J. Indian art & culture **709.5**

Indigenous peoples *See* Ethnology

Indigenous peoples of the world [series]
Sharp, A. W. Australia   **994**
Sharp, A. W. The gypsies   **909**
Indonesia
Lyle, G. Indonesia   **959.8**
Mirpuri, G. Indonesia   **959.8**
Industrial accidents
Davis, L. A. Environmental disasters (7 and up)
    363.7
Industrial arts
    See also Technology
Industrial materials *See* Materials
Industrial plants *See* Factories
Industrial revolution
Corrick, J. A. The Industrial Revolution (7 and up)   **909.81**
The Industrial revolution: opposing viewpoints (7 and up)   **330.973**
McCormick, A. L. The industrial revolution in American history   **338**
Outman, J. L. Industrial Revolution: almanac   **330.9**
Outman, J. L. Industrial Revolution: biographies   **920**
Outman, J. L. Industrial Revolution: primary sources   **330.9**
Ross, S. The industrial revolution (7 and up)   **330.9**
Woog, A. A sweatshop during the industrial revolution   **331.2**
Industrial Revolution: biographies. Outman, J. L.   **920**
The **industrial** revolution in American history. McCormick, A. L.   **338**
The **Industrial** revolution: opposing viewpoints (7 and up)   **330.973**
Industrial revolution reference library [series]
Outman, J. L. Industrial Revolution: almanac   **330.9**
Outman, J. L. Industrial Revolution: biographies   **920**
Outman, J. L. Industrial Revolution: primary sources   **330.9**
Industrial Workers of the World
Fiction
Skurzynski, G. Rockbuster   **Fic**
Industries
Collier, C. The rise of industry, 1860-1900   **973.8**
Infantile paralysis *See* Poliomyelitis
Infants
Fiction
Bunting, E. Doll baby   **Fic**
Cannon, A. E. Charlotte's Rose (5 and up)   **Fic**
Johnson, A. The first part last (7 and up)   **Fic**
Infection and infectious diseases *See* Communicable diseases
Inferno. Ayer, E. H.   **940.53**
Infertility
Fullick, A. Test tube babies (7 and up)   **618.1**

Influential economists. Bussing-Burks, M.   **920**
Influenza
Monroe, J. Influenza and other viruses   **616.9**
Peters, S. T. The 1918 influenza pandemic   **614.5**
Influenza and other viruses. Monroe, J.   **616.9**
Information literacy series
Rankin, V. The thoughtful researcher   **027.62**
Information literacy skills, grades 7-12   **027.62**
Information networks
    See also Internet
Information please almanac, atlas & yearbook   **031.02**
Information Please girls' almanac. See Hartman, H. Girlwonder   **305.23**
The **Information** please sports almanac   **796**
Information power. American Association of School Librarians   **027.8**
The **Information-powered** school   **027.8**
Information resources
    See also Internet resources
The **information** revolution   **303.4**
Information society
The information revolution   **303.4**
See/See also pages in the following book(s):
Managing the Internet controversy   **025.04**
Information systems
Wolinsky, A. Internet power research using the Big6 approach (5 and up)   **025.04**
Information technology
The information revolution   **303.4**
See/See also pages in the following book(s):
Managing the Internet controversy   **025.04**
Ingold, Jeanette
The Big Burn (7 and up)   **Fic**
Hitch (7 and up)   **Fic**
Mountain solo (7 and up)   **Fic**
Moving on
In Time capsule: short stories about teenagers throughout the twentieth century p21-34   **S C**
Ingpen, Robert R.
(il) Rosen, M. Shakespeare   **822.3**
Ingram, Scott, 1948-
Attila the Hun   **92**
Joseph Stalin   **92**
King George III   **92**
Oregon
In America the beautiful, second series   **973**
The time machine
In Read into the millennium; tales of the future p116-33   **S C**
Inheritance [series]
Paolini, C. Eragon   **Fic**
Injuries *See* Accidents; Wounds and injuries
Inkheart. Funke, C. C.   **Fic**
Inner cities
Inner-city poverty (7 and up)   **362.5**
Inner-city poverty (7 and up)   **362.5**
Innes, Brian, 1928-
Forensic science (7 and up)   **363.2**

Innes, Brian, 1928—*Continued*
International terrorism   **303.6**
Innovators [series]
   Aaseng, N. Construction: building the impossible   **624**
   Richie, J. Space flight   **920**
Innuit *See* Inuit
Inoculation *See* Vaccination
Inquiry learning through librarian-teacher partnerships. Harada, V. H.   **371.1**
Inquisition
   Worth, R. The Spanish Inquisition in world history (7 and up)   **272**
Insane *See* Mentally ill
Hospitals
   See Psychiatric hospitals
Insanity defense
   Worth, R. The insanity defense (7 and up)   **345**
The **insanity** defense. Worth, R.   **345**
Insects
   See also Ants; Butterflies; Moths
   Discovery Channel insects & spiders   **595.7**
   Insects and other invertebrates   **595.7**
   Insects and spiders of the world (5 and up)   **595.7**
   Jackson, D. M. The bug scientists (4 and up)   **595.7**
   Milne, L. J. The Audubon Society field guide to North American insects and spiders   **595.7**
   Wilsdon, C. National Audubon Society first field guide: insects (4 and up)   **595.7**
Poetry
   Fleischman, P. Joyful noise: poems for two voices (4 and up)   **811**
Insects and other invertebrates   **595.7**
Insects and spiders of the world (5 and up)   **595.7**
Insects in art
   DuBosque, D. Draw insects   **743**
Inside a—   **600**
Inside government [series]
   Feinberg, B. S. The cabinet   **352.24**
Inside out. Trueman, T.   **Fic**
Inside recovery. Banfield, S.   **616.86**
Inside the Alamo. Murphy, J.   **976.4**
Inside the Titanic. Marschall, K.   **910.4**
Inside the walls of Troy. McLaren, C.   **Fic**
Inside the world's most infamous terrorist organizations [series]
   Margulies, P. Al Qaeda: Osama bin Laden's army of terrorists   **973.931**
   Rosaler, M. Hamas: Palestinian terrorists   **956.94**
Insignia
   See also National emblems
Instructional materials centers
   See also School libraries
   American Association of School Librarians. Information power   **027.8**
   Bradburn, F. B. Output measures for school library media programs   **027.8**

Church, A. P. Leverage your library program to help raise test scores   **027.8**
Donham, J. Enhancing teaching and learning   **027.8**
Everhart, N. Evaluating the school library media center   **027.8**
Foundations for effective school library media programs   **027.8**
The Information-powered school   **027.8**
Job, A. G. The school library media specialist as manager   **027.8**
Jweid, R. The library-classroom partnership   **027.8**
Kearney, C. A. Curriculum partner   **027.8**
Mendrinos, R. B. Using educational technology with at-risk students   **027.8**
Morris, B. J. Administering the school library media center   **027.8**
Safford, B. R. Guide to reference materials for school media centers   **011.6**
Smith, J. B. Achieving a curriculum-based library media center program   **027.8**
The Whole school library handbook   **027.8**
Wilson, P. J. Center stage   **027.8**
Woolls, E. B. The school library media manager   **027.8**
Yesner, B. L. Operating and evaluating school library media programs   **027.8**
See/See also pages in the following book(s):
Jones, P. Do it right!   **027.62**
Design and construction
Erikson, R. Designing a school library media center for the future   **027.8**
The **instruments** of music. Kallen, S. A.   **784.19**
Integration in education *See* School integration
Intellect
   Armstrong, T. You're smarter than you think   **153.9**
Intellectual freedom
   Intellectual freedom manual   **323.44**
   Symons, A. K. Protecting the right to read   **025.2**
   See/See also pages in the following book(s):
   Managing the Internet controversy   **025.04**
Intellectual freedom manual   **323.44**
Intelligence, Artificial *See* Artificial intelligence
Intelligence service
   Platt, R. Spy   **327.12**
   Wiese, J. Spy science   **363.2**
   See/See also pages in the following book(s):
   MccGwire, S. Surveillance (7 and up)   **323.44**
Internal migration
   Flanders, S. A. Atlas of American migration   **304.8**
International Bank for Reconstruction and Development *See* World Bank
The **international** cookbook for kids. Locricchio, M.
International encyclopedia of art   **703**
International Monetary Fund
   January, B. Globalize it! (7 and up)   **337**

International organizations [series]
Banks, D. Amnesty International   **323**
Grahame, D. A. World Health Organization
    610.6
International politics *See* World politics
International Red Cross *See* Red Cross
International Red Cross. Perkins, R.   **361.7**
International relations
    See also Globalization; World politics
International terrorism. Innes, B.   **303.6**
International wildlife encyclopedia   **590.3**
Internationalization *See* Globalization
Internet
    See also Internet resources
Benson, A. C. Connecting kids & the Web
    004.6
Benson, A. C. Neal-Schuman complete Internet
    companion for librarians   **004.6**
Braun, L. W. Teens.library   **027.62**
Cate, F. H. The Internet and the First Amend-
    ment   **342**
Cooper, G. New virtual field trips   **025.5**
Ehrenhaft, D. Marc Andreessen   **92**
Hill, A. Tooting your own horn   **021.7**
The Internet: opposing viewpoints   **303.4**
Johnson, D. Learning right from wrong in the
    digital age   **004.6**
Managing the Internet controversy   **025.04**
Rosner, M. A. Science fair success using the
    Internet (7 and up)   **507.8**
Wolinsky, A. Safe surfing on the Internet (4 and
    up)   **004.6**
See/See also pages in the following book(s):
Mass media: opposing viewpoints   **302.23**
Pornography: opposing viewpoints (7 and up)
    363.4
            Fiction
Wilhelm, D. The revealers   **Fic**
Internet and children
Raatma, L. Safety on the Internet (4 and up)
    025.04
The **Internet** and the First Amendment. Cate, F.
    H.   **342**
Internet biographies [series]
Garty, J. Jeff Bezos   **92**
Internet in education
Johnson, C. Using internet primary sources to
    teach critical thinking skills in the sciences
    025.04
Internet library [series]
Souter, G. Creating animation for your Web
    page   **006.6**
Souter, G. Researching on the Internet using
    search engines, bulletin boards, and listservs
    004.6
Wolinsky, A. Internet power research using the
    Big6 approach   **025.04**
Wolinsky, A. Safe surfing on the Internet
    004.6
The **Internet**: opposing viewpoints   **303.4**
Internet power research using the Big6 approach.
    Wolinsky, A.   **025.04**

Internet resources
    See also subjects with the subdivision
    Internet resources, for materials about infor-
    mation available on the Internet on a subject,
    e.g. *Job hunting—Internet resources*
Braun, L. W. Hooking teens with the Net
    025.04
Craver, K. W. Creating cyber libraries   **027.8**
Haycock, K. Neal-Schuman authoritative guide
    to kids' search engines, subject directories,
    and portals   **025.04**
Riedling, A. M. Learning to learn   **028.7**
Souter, G. Researching on the Internet using
    search engines, bulletin boards, and listservs
    (4 and up)   **004.6**
Valenza, J. K. Power research tools   **001.4**
Internet searching
Haycock, K. Neal-Schuman authoritative guide
    to kids' search engines, subject directories,
    and portals   **025.04**
Riedling, A. M. Learning to learn   **028.7**
Valenza, J. K. Power research tools   **001.4**
        Study and teaching
Benson, A. C. Connecting kids & the Web
    004.6
Braun, L. W. Hooking teens with the Net
    025.04
Gordon, R. S. Teaching the Internet in libraries
    025.04
Kuntz, J. The KidsClick! Web searching skills
    guide with CD-ROM   **025.04**
Stephens, M. T. The library Internet trainer's
    toolkit   **025.04**
The **internment** of the Japanese. Yancey, D.
    940.53

Interpersonal relations
Canfield, J. Chicken soup for the teenage soul
    {I-III}   **158**
Chicken soup for the kid's soul   **158**
Girls know best   **305.23**
Kreiner, A. Everything you need to know about
    creating your own support system (7 and up)
    158
McIntyre, T. The behavior survival guide for
    kids (5 and up)   **158**
Romain, T. Cliques, phonies & other baloney
    158
Rutledge, J. Z. Dealing with the stuff that makes
    life tough (7 and up)   **305.23**
Zielin, L. Make things happen   **302.2**
Interpreting primary documents [series]
Westward expansion   **978**
Interracial adoption
Warren, A. Escape from Saigon   **92**
Interracial marriage
        Law and legislation
Alonso, K. Loving v. Virginia (7 and up)
    346
Interracial relations *See* Race relations
The **interrupted** wedding. San Souci, R.
    In San Souci, R. A terrifying taste of short &
    shivery; thirty creepy tales p91-94
    398.2

Interstate commerce
Levinson, I. S. Gibbons v. Ogden (7 and up)
343

Interstellar pig. Sleator, W.   **Fic**

Intervention (International law)
See/See also pages in the following book(s):
War: opposing viewpoints   355

Intner, Sheila S., 1935-
Standard cataloging for school and public libraries   **025.3**

Into a new country. Ketchum, L.   **920**

Into focus   **028.1**

Into the game. Williams-Garcia, R.
In Join in; multiethnic short stories by out-
standing writers for young adults p3-11
S C

Into the wild. Hunter, E.   **Fic**

Into thin air. Kidd, J. S.   **363.7**

Intolerance *See* Toleration

The **intruders**. Nixon, J. L.
In Nixon, J. L. Ghost town; seven ghostly
stories p37-53   **S C**

Inuit
Tiulana, P. Wise words of Paul Tiulana   **92**
Yue, C. The igloo (4 and up)   **728**
Fiction
George, J. C. Julie (6 and up)   **Fic**
George, J. C. Julie of the wolves (6 and up)
Fic
George, J. C. Water sky (5 and up)   **Fic**
Hill, K. Minuk (5 and up)   **Fic**
Houston, J. A. Frozen fire (6 and up)   **Fic**
Orenstein, D. G. Unseen companion (7 and up)
Fic
Paulsen, G. Dogsong (6 and up)   **Fic**
Sullivan, P. Maata's journal (7 and up)   **Fic**
Folklore
Norman, H. The girl who dreamed only geese,
and other tales of the Far North (4 and up)
398.2

Invalids *See* Sick

Inventing the future: a photobiography of Thomas
Alva Edison. Delano, M. F.   **92**

The **invention** of the silicon chip. Chorlton, W.
621.381

Inventions
Aaseng, N. Black inventors (7 and up)   **920**
Bender, L. Invention (4 and up)   **609**
Erlbach, A. The kids' invention book (4 and up)
608
Macaulay, D. The new way things work (4 and
up)   **600**
Pollard, M. The light bulb and how it changed
the world   **621.3**
Thimmesh, C. Girls think of everything (5 and
up)   **920**
Tucker, T. Brainstorm! (5 and up)   **609**
Wulffson, D. L. Toys! (4 and up)   **688.7**
History
Bridgman, R. F. 1,000 inventions & discoveries
(5 and up)   **609**
Cole, D. J. Encyclopedia of modern everyday
inventions (7 and up)   **609**
Historical inventions on file   **609**

Platt, R. Eureka! (4 and up)   **609**
Sandler, M. W. Inventors   **609**
Tomecek, S. What a great idea! (4 and up)
609
Wulffson, D. L. The kid who invented the tram-
poline   **609**

Inventors
Birch, B. Guglielmo Marconi   **92**
Delano, M. F. Inventing the future: a
photobiography of Thomas Alva Edison
92
Kozar, R. Inventors and their discoveries
920
Kroll, S. Robert Fulton   **92**
Mason, P. Thomas A. Edison   **92**
Matthews, T. L. Always inventing: a
photobiography of Alexander Graham Bell (4
and up)   **92**
McPherson, S. S. TV's forgotten hero: the story
of Philo Farnsworth   **92**
Northrup, M. American computer pioneers
920
Pierce, M. A. Robert Fulton and the develop-
ment of the steamboat   **92**
Sandler, M. W. Inventors   **609**
Sproule, A. James Watt   **92**
Sproule, A. Thomas A. Edison   **92**
Tagliaferro, L. Thomas Edison (7 and up)
92
Tucker, T. Brainstorm! (5 and up)   **609**

Inventors, African American *See* African
American inventors

Inventors and their discoveries. Kozar, R.   **920**

Invertebrates
Insects and other invertebrates   **595.7**
Meinkoth, N. A. The Audubon Society field
guide to North American seashore creatures
592

Investments
Liebowitz, J. Wall Street wizard   **332.6**
McGowan, E. N. Stock market smart   **332.6**

Invincible Louisa [May Alcott] Meigs, C. L.
92

Invisible. Hautman, P.   **Fic**

Invisible allies. Farrell, J.   **579**

Invisible enemies. Farrell, J.   **614.4**

The **invisible** guest. Olson, A. N.
In Olson, A. N. and Schwartz, H. Ask the
bones: scary stories from around the
world p110-17   **398.2**

The **Invisible** ladder (7 and up)   **811.008**

Invitation to the game. Hughes, M.   **Fic**

Invitations to the world. Peck, R.   **808.06**

Iodine
Gray, L. Iodine
In The Elements   **546**

**Iona and Peter Opie library of children's litera-
ture** [series]
Nesbit, E. The best of Shakespeare   **822.3**

Iowa
Hintz, M. Iowa
In America the beautiful, second series
973

Iowa—*Continued*
Morrice, P. A. Iowa
In Celebrate the states 973
Fiction
Bauer, J. Squashed Fic
Iqbal. D'Adamo, F. Fic
Iqbal Masih and the crusaders against child slavery. Kuklin, S. 331.3
IRA *See* Irish Republican Army
The **IRA** and England. Wagner, H. L. 941.6
Iran
Rajendra, V. Iran (5 and up) 955
Ramen, F. A historical atlas of Iran 955
Fiction
Fletcher, S. Shadow spinner (6 and up) Fic
Napoli, D. J. Beast (7 and up) Fic
Foreign relations—United States
Spencer, W. The United States and Iran (7 and up) 327.73
Politics and government
Spencer, W. The United States and Iran (7 and up) 327.73
Iran-Iraq War, 1980-1988
Schaffer, D. The Iran-Iraq War (7 and up) 956.7
Iraq
Hassig, S. M. Iraq (5 and up) 956.7
Civilization
Chrisp, P. Mesopotamia (5 and up) 935
Schomp, V. Ancient Mesopotamia (5 and up) 935

History—1991, Persian Gulf War
See Persian Gulf War, 1991
Politics and government
Anderson, D. Saddam Hussein 92
Iraq-Kuwait Crisis, 1990-1991 *See* Persian Gulf War, 1991
Iraq War, 2003
Al-Windawi, T. Thura's diary (7 and up) 956.7
Ireland, Norma Olin, 1907-
(comp) Index to fairy tales. See Index to fairy tales 398.2
Ireland
Levy, P. M. Ireland (5 and up) 941.5
Fiction
Bunting, E. Spying on Miss Müller (5 and up) Fic
Giff, P. R. Nory Ryan's song (5 and up) Fic
Heneghan, J. The grave Fic
Melling, O. R. The Hunter's Moon (7 and up) Fic
History
Bartoletti, S. C. Black potatoes (7 and up) 941.5
Dolan, E. F. The Irish potato famine 941.5
Feed the children first 941.5
Wagner, H. L. The IRA and England (7 and up) 941.6
Irish
Fiction
Heneghan, J. Flood Fic

The **Irish** American family album. Hoobler, D. 305.8
Irish Americans
Deignan, T. Irish Americans (7 and up) 305.8
Dolan, E. F. The Irish potato famine 941.5
Hoobler, D. The Irish American family album (5 and up) 305.8
Fiction
Auch, M. J. Ashes of roses (7 and up) Fic
Bartoletti, S. C. The journal of Finn Reardon (4 and up) Fic
The **Irish** potato famine. Dolan, E. F. 941.5
Irish Republican Army
Wagner, H. L. The IRA and England (7 and up) 941.6
See/See also pages in the following book(s):
Currie, S. Terrorists and terrorist groups (7 and up) 303.6
Iron
Blashfield, J. F. Iron and trace elements
In Blashfield, J. F. Sparks of life; chemical elements that make life possible 546
Sparrow, G. Iron
In The Elements 546
Iron and trace elements. Blashfield, J. F.
In Blashfield, J. F. Sparks of life; chemical elements that make life possible 546
The **iron** ring. Alexander, L. Fic
Ironman. Crutcher, C. Fic
Irons, Diane, 1949-
Teen beauty secrets (7 and up) 646.7
The **Iroquois**. Graymont, B. Indians of North America series
Iroquois. McIntosh, K. North American Indians today [series]
Iroquois Indians
Graymont, B. The Iroquois Indians of North America series
McIntosh, K. Iroquois North American Indians today [series]
Folklore
Taylor, C. J. Peace walker 398.2
Irvin, Benjamin
Samuel Adams (7 and up) 92
Irving, Frazer
(il) Reed, G. Mary Shelley's Frankenstein: the graphic novel 741.5
Irwin, Hadley
The original Freddie Ackerman (5 and up) Fic
Irwin, Jane, 1941-
Vögelein 741.5
Is everyone moonburned but me? Pevsner, S. Fic
Is it really Mommie Dearest? Crew, H. S. 813.009
Is something wrong? Schwartz, A.
In Schwartz, A. Scary stories 3; more tales to chill your bones p82 398.2
Is this forever, or what? (7 and up) 811.008
Isaac Newton and the scientific revolution. Christianson, G. E. 92

Isaacs, Anne
Torn thread (7 and up)   **Fic**

Isabel. Potok, C.
In Potok, C. Zebra and other stories p97-120
     S C

Isabel, Ferdinand and fifteenth-century Spain.
Mann, K.   **946**

Isabel of the whales. Velmans, H.   **Fic**

Isabella I, Queen of Spain, 1451-1504
About
Mann, K. Isabel, Ferdinand and fifteenth-century
Spain   **946**
See/See also pages in the following book(s):
Hewitt, K. Lives of extraordinary women (4 and
up)   **920**
Meltzer, M. Ten queens (5 and up)   **920**

Islam
Clark, C. Islam   **297**
Gordon, M. Islam (7 and up)   **297**
The Muslim almanac   **297**
Wormser, R. American Islam (7 and up)
     297

See/See also pages in the following book(s):
Frank, M. Understanding September 11th (7 and
up)   **973.931**
Osborne, M. P. One world, many religions (4
and up)   **201**

Islamic countries
The Muslim almanac   **297**
Civilization
Beshore, G. W. Science in early Islamic culture
(4 and up)   **509**

Islamic fundamentalism
See/See also pages in the following book(s):
Landau, E. Osama bin Laden (7 and up)   **92**

Islamic Resistance Movement *See* Hamas

The **island**. Paulsen, G.   **Fic**

Island boyz. Salisbury, G.
In Salisbury, G. Island boyz: short stories
p1-5   **S C**

Island boyz: short stories. Salisbury, G.   **S C**

An **island** like you. Ortiz Cofer, J.   **S C**

Island of hope. Sandler, M. W.   **325.73**

Island of the aunts. Ibbotson, E.   **Fic**

Island of the Blue Dolphins. O'Dell, S.   **Fic**

Island of the lost children. Osborne, M. P.
In Osborne, M. P. Favorite medieval tales
p25-33   **398.2**

Island Trees Public Schools (Levittown, N.Y.)
Gold, J. C. Board of Education v. Pico (1982)
(7 and up)   **344**

The **islander**. Rylant, C.   **Fic**

Islands
Fiction
Irwin, H. The original Freddie Ackerman (5 and
up)   **Fic**
Lawrence, I. The lightkeeper's daughter (7 and
up)   **Fic**
Paulsen, G. The island   **Fic**
Rylant, C. The islander   **Fic**
Taylor, T. Sweet Friday Island (7 and up)
     Fic

Israel, Fred L.
(ed) The election of 1860 and the administration
of Abraham Lincoln. See The election of
1860 and the administration of Abraham Lincoln   **973.7**
(ed) The Election of 2000 and the administration of George W. Bush. See The Election of
2000 and the administration of George W.
Bush   **324**

Israel
See also Jerusalem
Corona, L. Israel (7 and up)   **956.94**
DuBois, J. Israel (5 and up)   **956.94**
Israel: opposing viewpoints   **956.94**
Zenatti, V. When I was a soldier (7 and up)
     92
Fiction
Kass, P. Real time (7 and up)   **Fic**
History
Altman, L. J. The creation of Israel (7 and up)
     956.94
Blumberg, A. The history of Israel (7 and up)
     956.94
Schroeter, D. J. Israel (7 and up)   **956.94**
See/See also pages in the following book(s):
Chicoine, S. From the ashes   **940.53**

Israel and the werewolf. San Souci, R.
In San Souci, R. A terrifying taste of short &
shivery; thirty creepy tales p114-17
     398.2

Israel-Arab conflicts
The Arab-Israeli conflict (7 and up)   **956.04**
Ellis, D. Three wishes (5 and up)   **956.94**
Frank, M. Understanding the Holy Land (7 and
up)   **956.94**
The Palestinians and the disputed territories (7
and up)   **956.04**
Rosaler, M. Hamas: Palestinian terrorists
     956.94
See/See also pages in the following book(s):
Blumberg, A. The history of Israel (7 and up)
     956.94
Fiction
Stein, T. Light years (7 and up)   **Fic**

Israel: opposing viewpoints   **956.94**

Israeli-Arab relations *See* Jewish-Arab relations

Isserman, Maurice
Journey to freedom (7 and up)   **305.8**
Korean war (7 and up)   **951.9**
World War II (7 and up)   **940.53**

Issues in focus [series]
Altman, L. J. Death: an introduction to medical-
ethical dilemmas   **155.9**
Altman, L. J. Human rights   **323**
Altman, L. J. Plague and pestilence   **614.4**
Andryszewski, T. School prayer   **344**
Boon, K. A. The human genome project
     599.93
Day, N. Advertising   **659.1**
Day, N. Animal experimentation   **179**
Day, N. Killer superbugs   **616**
Fridell, R. Privacy vs. security   **342**
Kowalski, K. M. Alternative medicine   **615.5**
Kowalski, K. M. Poverty in America   **362.5**

Issues in focus—*Continued*
McClellan, M. Organ and tissue transplants
617.9
Sneddon, P. S. Body image **155.9**
Spangenburg, R. TV news **070.1**
Zeinert, K. Cults **209**
Issues in the environment. Netzley, P. D.
333.7
Issues of our time [series]
Greenberg, K. E. Adolescent rights **346**
IssueWeb: a guide and sourcebook for researching controversial issues on the Web. Diaz, K. R.
025.04
It happened to me [series]
Gay, K. Cultural diversity **305.8**
Gay, K. Epilepsy **616.8**
Gay, K. Volunteering **361.3**
Myers, E. When will I stop hurting? **155.9**
Paquette, P. H. Learning disabilities **371.9**
It is a good day to die. Viola, H. J. **973.8**
It only looks easy. Swallow, P. C. **Fic**
The **Italian** American family album. Hoobler, D.
305.8
Italian Americans
Hoobler, D. The Italian American family album (5 and up) **305.8**
Moreno, B. Italian Americans (7 and up)
305.8
Murphy, J. Pick & shovel poet: the journeys of Pascal D'Angelo **92**
Fiction
Murphy, J. West to a land of plenty **Fic**
Poetry
Testa, M. Becoming Joe DiMaggio (4 and up)
811
Italian artists *See* Artists, Italian
Italian painting
Barter, J. A Renaissance painter's studio
759.5
The **Italian** Renaissance. Schomp, V. **945**
Italiano, Bob
(il) Pascoe, E. Scholastic kid's almanac
031.02
Italy
Behnke, A. Italy in pictures (5 and up) **945**
Foster, L. M. Italy (7 and up) **945**
Winter, J. K. Italy (5 and up) **945**
Civilization
Cohen, E. S. Daily life in Renaissance Italy (7 and up) **945**
Schomp, V. The Italian Renaissance **945**
Fiction
Avi. Midnight magic (5 and up) **Fic**
Dickinson, P. Tears of the salamander **Fic**
Napoli, D. J. Three days **Fic**
Italy in pictures. Behnke, A. **945**
It's a girl thing. Jukes, M. **305.23**
It's a woman's world (7 and up) **808.81**
It's all in how you say it. Roberts, M.
In Talking leaves; contemporary native American short stories **S C**
It's disgusting—and we ate it!. Solheim, J.
641.3

It's "Him!". Schwartz, A.
In Schwartz, A. Scary stories 3; more tales to chill your bones p84-85 **398.2**
It's perfectly normal. Harris, R. H. **613.9**
It's quiet now. Mhlophe, G.
In Somehow tenderness survives; stories of Southern Africa p135-37 **S C**
It's your world—if you don't like it, change it. Halpin, M. **361.2**
Ivory Coast
Sheehan, P. Côte d'Ivoire (5 and up) **966.68**
Iwo Jima, Battle of, 1945
Bradley, J. Flags of our fathers (7 and up)
940.54
IWW *See* Industrial Workers of the World
Izzy, willy-nilly. Voigt, C. **Fic**

J

Jack, Roger
The pebble people
In Talking leaves; contemporary native American short stories **S C**
Jack. Vande Velde, V.
In Vande Velde, V. Tales from the Brothers Grimm and the Sisters Weird p53-70
S C
Jack and his companions. Yolen, J.
In Yolen, J. Mightier than the sword; world folktales for strong boys p56-63
398.2
Jack and the Devil. Hamilton, V.
In Hamilton, V. The people could fly; American black folktales p126-32
398.2
Jack on the tracks. Gantos, J. **Fic**
Jack runs off. Van Laan, N.
In Van Laan, N. With a whoop and a holler; a bushel of lore from way down south p83-88 **398**
Jack: the early years of John F. Kennedy. Cooper, I. **92**
Jackal's favorite game. Bryan, A.
In Bryan, A. Ashley Bryan's African tales, uh-huh p152-71 **398.2**
Jackaroo. Voigt, C. **Fic**
Jackie's nine. Robinson, S. **170**
Jackie's Wild Seattle. Hobbs, W. **Fic**
Jackson, Andrew, 1767-1845
About
Collier, C. Andrew Jackson's America, 1824-1850 **973.5**
Marrin, A. Old Hickory [biography of Andrew Jackson] (7 and up) **92**
Jackson, Donna M., 1959-
The bone detectives (5 and up) **614**
The bug scientists (4 and up) **595.7**
Twin tales (4 and up) **618.2**
Jackson, Ellen B., 1943-
Looking for life in the universe (4 and up)
576.8

Jackson, Joe, 1887 or 8-1951
Fiction
Gutman, D. Shoeless Joe & me (4 and up)
                                                            Fic

Jackson, Livia Bitton- *See* Bitton-Jackson, Livia

Jackson, Mahalia, 1911-1972
About
Orgill, R. Mahalia [Jackson] (5 and up)   **92**
See/See also pages in the following book(s):
Lester, J. The blues singers (5 and up)   **920**

Jackson, Sheila, 1956-
Costumes for the stage: a complete handbook
    for every kind of play   **792**

Jackson, Stonewall, 1824-1863
About
Fritz, J. Stonewall [biography of Stonewall Jack-
    son] (4 and up)   **92**
Pflueger, L. Stonewall Jackson   **92**
Robertson, J. I., Jr. Standing like a stone wall:
    the life of General Thomas J. Jackson (7 and
    up)   **92**

Jackson, Thomas Jonathan *See* Jackson, Stone-
    wall, 1824-1863

Jackson, Tom, 1972-
Flourine
    In The Elements   **546**
Tropical forests (5 and up)   **577.3**

Jackson, William Henry, 1843-1942
About
Lawlor, L. Window on the West (7 and up)
                                                            978

**Jacobs, Harriet A. (Harriet Ann), 1813-1896 or
    7**
See/See also pages in the following book(s):
Cloud Tapper, S. Voices from slavery's past (7
    and up)   **326**
Fiction
Lyons, M. E. Letters from a slave girl (6 and
    up)   **Fic**

Jacobs, Marian B.
Coping with hereditary diseases (7 and up)
                                                            616

Jacobs, Thomas A.
They broke the law, you be the judge (7 and
    up)   **345**
What are my rights? (7 and up)   **346**

Jacob's rules. Flake, S. G.
    In Flake, S. G. Who am I without him?; short
        stories about girls and the boys in their
        lives p105-34   **S C**

Jacobson, Dan, 1929-
A day in the country
    In Somehow tenderness survives; stories of
        Southern Africa p37-47   **S C**

Jacobsson, Anders, 1963-
In Ned's head   **Fic**

Jacques, Brian
Castaways of the Flying Dutchman   **Fic**
Redwall (6 and up)   **Fic**

Jade Green. Naylor, P. R.   **Fic**

Jaffe, Nina
The cow of no color: riddle stories and justice
    tales from around the world (4 and up)
                                                            398.2

Contents: The cow of no color; The sound of work; Ximen
Bao and the river spirit; The cloak; The thief and the pig; The
testimony of the fly; Susannah and the elders; The jury; The
magic seed; The bird lovers; An ounce of mud; The dance of
Elegba; The three wives of Nenpetro; The flask; Kim Son Dal
and the water-carriers; The land; Sharing the soup; A higher
truth; The walnut and the pumpkin; The wise king; Josephus in
the cave; The water pot and the necklace; The test

Jaffe, Steven H.
Who were the founding fathers? (7 and up)
                                                            973.3

Jahan, Shah *See* Shahjahan, Emperor of India, ca.
    1592-1666

Jahanara Begum
Fiction
Lasky, K. Jahanara, Princess of Princesses
                                                            Fic

Jahanara, Princess of Princesses. Lasky, K.
                                                            Fic

Jakarta missing. Kurtz, J.   **Fic**

Jake, reinvented. Korman, G.   **Fic**

Jake's orphan. Brooke, P.   **Fic**

Jam!. Lee, J.   **781.65**

Jamaica
Sheehan, S. Jamaica (5 and up)   **972.92**
Fiction
Berry, J. Ajeemah and his son   **Fic**

James, Curtis, 1966-
(il) Linda Brown, you are not alone. See Linda
    Brown, you are not alone   **323.1**

James, Elizabeth
How to write terrific book reports (4 and up)
                                                            808
Social smarts   **395**

James, J. Alison, 1962-
The audition
    In What a song can do; 12 riffs on the power
        of music   **S C**

James, Jesse, 1847-1882
About
Bruns, R. Jesse James   **92**

James, R. S.
Mozambique (7 and up)   **967.9**

James, Simon, 1957-
Ancient Rome (4 and up)   **937**

James Watson and Francis Crick and the building
    blocks of life. Edelson, E.   **92**

Jamestown (Va.)
History
Collier, C. The paradox of Jamestown, 1585-
    1700   **975.5**
Doherty, K. To conquer is to live: the life of
    Captain John Smith of Jamestown   **92**
Edwards, J. Jamestown, John Smith, and Poca-
    hontas in American history (7 and up)
                                                            975.5

Jamestown, John Smith, and Pocahontas in
    American history. Edwards, J.   **975.5**

Jane, Calamity *See* Calamity Jane, 1852-1903

Janeczko, Paul B., 1945-
How to write poetry (5 and up)   **808.1**
Stardust otel (7 and up)   **811**
Top secret (4 and up)   **652**
Worlds afire   **Fic**
Writing winning reports and essays   **808**

Janeczko, Paul B., 1945——*Continued*
(comp) I feel a little jumpy around you. See I feel a little jumpy around you **808.81**
(ed) A kick in the head. See A kick in the head **811.008**
(comp) The Place my words are looking for. See The Place my words are looking for **811.008**
(comp) Poetry from A to Z. See Poetry from A to Z **808.1**
(ed) A Poke in the I. See A Poke in the I **811.008**
(comp) Seeing the blue between. See Seeing the blue between **808.1**
(ed) Stone bench in an empty park. See Stone bench in an empty park **811.008**
(ed) Very best (almost) friends. See Very best (almost) friends **811.008**

The **Janeites**. Kipling, R.
In McCaffrey, A. {The Pern series} **S C**

Janice VanCleave's 203 icy, freezing, frosty, cool & wild experiments. VanCleave, J. P. **507.8**

Janice VanCleave's A+ projects in astronomy. VanCleave, J. P. **520**

Janice VanCleave's A+ projects in earth science. VanCleave, J. P. **550**

Janice Vancleave's ecology for every kid. VanCleave, J. P. **577**

Janice VanCleave's guide to more of the best science fair projects. VanCleave, J. P. **507.8**

Janice VanCleave's guide to the best science fair projects. VanCleave, J. P. **507.8**

Janice VanCleave's plants. VanCleave, J. P. **580.7**

Janice VanCleave's solar system. VanCleave, J. P. **523.2**

Janin, Hunt, 1940-
Saudi Arabia **953.8**

Janke, Katelan
Survival in the storm **Fic**

January, Brendan, 1972-
The assassination of Abraham Lincoln **973.7**
The Dred Scott decision **342**
Globalize it! (7 and up) **337**
John Brown's raid on Harpers Ferry (4 and up) **973.7**
The Lincoln-Douglas debates **973.7**
Reconstruction **973.8**
Science in colonial America (4 and up) **509**

January 1905. Boling, K. **Fic**

Japan
Behnke, A. Japan in pictures (5 and up) **952**
Heinrichs, A. Japan (4 and up) **952**
Shelley, R. Japan **952**
See/See also pages in the following book(s):
Blumberg, R. Commodore Perry in the land of the Shogun (5 and up) **952**
Biography
Hamanaka, S. In search of the spirit (5 and up) **920**
Civilization
Khanduri, K. Japanese art & culture **709.52**

Schomp, V. Japan in the days of the samurai **952**
Fiction
Hoobler, D. The ghost in the Tokaido Inn **Fic**
Kimmel, E. A. Sword of the samurai (4 and up) **S C**
Lasky, K. Kazunomiya **Fic**
Paterson, K. The master puppeteer (6 and up) **Fic**
Watkins, Y. K. My brother, my sister, and I (6 and up) **Fic**
Watkins, Y. K. So far from the bamboo grove (6 and up) **Fic**
Yumoto, K. The letters (7 and up) **Fic**
Foreign relations—United States
Blumberg, R. Commodore Perry in the land of the Shogun (5 and up) **952**
History
Blumberg, R. Shipwrecked!: the true adventures of a Japanese boy [biography of Manjiro Nakahama] (5 and up) **92**
Roberson, J. R. Japan meets the world (7 and up) **952**

Japan in pictures. Behnke, A. **952**

Japan in the days of the samurai. Schomp, V. **952**

Japan meets the world. Roberson, J. R. **952**

The **Japanese** American family album. Hoobler, D. **305.8**

Japanese American internment camps (7 and up) **940.53**

Japanese American internment during World War II. Ng, W. L. **940.53**

Japanese Americans
Hoobler, D. The Japanese American family album (5 and up) **305.8**
See/See also pages in the following book(s):
Asian Americans: opposing viewpoints (7 and up) **305.8**
Evacuation and relocation, 1942-1945
Alonso, K. Korematsu v. United States (7 and up) **323.1**
Cooper, M. L. Fighting for honor (6 and up) **940.53**
Cooper, M. L. Remembering Manzanar **940.53**
Houston, J. W. Farewell to Manzanar (7 and up) **940.53**
Japanese American internment camps (7 and up) **940.53**
Ng, W. L. Japanese American internment during World War II **940.53**
Perl, L. Behind barbed wire **940.53**
Tunnell, M. O. The children of Topaz (5 and up) **940.53**
Yancey, D. The internment of the Japanese **940.53**
Evacuation and relocation, 1942-1945—Fiction
Denenberg, B. The journal of Ben Uchida, citizen #13559, Mirror Lake internment camp **Fic**
Uchida, Y. Journey to Topaz (5 and up) **Fic**

Japanese Americans—*Continued*
Fiction
Mochizuki, K. Beacon Hill boys (7 and up)
Fic
Salisbury, G. Under the blood-red sun   Fic
Smith, G. L. Ninjas, piranhas, and Galileo
Fic
Uchida, Y. A jar of dreams (5 and up)   Fic
Japanese art & culture. Khanduri, K.   **709.52**
Japanese arts
Khanduri, K. Japanese art & culture   **709.52**
See/See also pages in the following book(s):
Hamanaka, S. In search of the spirit (5 and up)
920
Japanese language
Dictionaries
Basic Japanese-English dictionary   **495.6**
The Oxford-Duden pictorial Japanese and English dictionary   **495.6**
The **Japanese** mirror. Coville, B.
In Coville, B. Odder than ever   **S C**
Japanese paper folding *See* Origami
A **jar** of dreams. Uchida, Y.   **Fic**
The **jar** of fools. Kimmel, E. A.
In Kimmel, E. A. The jar of fools: eight Hanukkah stories from Chelm p1-4   **S C**
The **jar** of fools: eight Hanukkah stories from Chelm. Kimmel, E. A.   **S C**
A **Jar** of tiny stars: poems by NCTE award-winning poets   **811.008**
Jarvis, Robin
The alchemist's cat (5 and up)   Fic
The dark portal (5 and up)   Fic
Thorn ogres of Hagwood   Fic
Jason (Greek mythology)
Fiction
Catran, K. Voyage with Jason   Fic
Yolen, J. Jason and the Gorgon's blood   Fic
Jason and the Gorgon's blood. Yolen, J.   **Fic**
Jason Kovak, the quick and the brave. Okimoto, J. D.
In Visions: nineteen short stories by outstanding writers for young adults p42-63
S C
Jason's gold. Hobbs, W.   **Fic**
Jataka stories
Lee, J. M. I once was a monkey (4 and up)
294.3
Jay, Hilda L.
(jt. auth) Yesner, B. L. Operating and evaluating school library media programs   **027.8**
Jayhawker. Beatty, P.   **Fic**
Jazmin's notebook. Grimes, N.   **Fic**
Jazz makers. Shipton, A.   **920**
Jazz music
See also Blues music
Asirvatham, S. The history of jazz   **781.65**
Collier, J. L. Jazz (7 and up)   **781.65**
Kallen, S. A. The history of jazz   **781.65**
Lee, J. Jam! (7 and up)   **781.65**
Martin, M. Extraordinary people in jazz   **920**
Mour, S. I. American jazz musicians   **920**
Shipton, A. Jazz makers (7 and up)   **920**

Jazz musicians
Barron, R. John Coltrane (7 and up)   **92**
Brown, G. Duke Ellington: jazz master (7 and up)   **92**
Frankl, R. Charlie Parker, musician   **92**
Martin, M. Extraordinary people in jazz   **920**
Mour, S. I. American jazz musicians   **920**
Old, W. Duke Ellington: giant of jazz   **92**
Old, W. Louis Armstrong   **92**
Shipton, A. Jazz makers (7 and up)   **920**
Fiction
Townley, R. Sky (7 and up)   **Fic**
Jeanne d'Arc, Saint *See* Joan, of Arc, Saint, 1412-1431
Jeapes, Ben
The new world order (7 and up)   **Fic**
The xenocide mission   **Fic**
Jefferis, David
Artificial intelligence (4 and up)   **629.8**
Jefferson, Thomas, 1743-1826
About
Blumberg, R. What's the deal? Jefferson, Napoleon and the Louisiana Purchase (7 and up)
973.4
Lanier, S. Jefferson's children (7 and up)
920
Severance, J. B. Thomas Jefferson (7 and up)
92
Whitelaw, N. Thomas Jefferson (7 and up)
92
Fiction
Rinaldi, A. Wolf by the ears   **Fic**
Jefferson family
About
Lanier, S. Jefferson's children (7 and up)
920
The **Jeffersonian** Republicans, 1800-1823. Collier, C.   **973.4**
Jefferson's children. Lanier, S.   **920**
Jeffrey, Laura S.
Christa McAuliffe   **92**
Great American businesswomen   **920**
Jehan, Shah *See* Shahjahan, Emperor of India, ca. 1592-1666
Jemison, Mae C.
Find where the wind goes (5 and up)   **92**
About
Alagna, M. Mae Jemison (4 and up)   **92**
Yannuzzi, D. A. Mae Jemison   **92**
See/See also pages in the following book(s):
Di Domenico, K. Super women in science
920
Hansen, J. Women of hope (4 and up)   **920**
Lindop, L. Scientists and doctors (7 and up)
920
Jen, Gish
What means switch
In Who do you think you are?; stories of friends and enemies p96-118   **S C**
Jenkins, A. M. (Amanda McRaney)
Out of order (7 and up)   **Fic**
Jenkins, Steve
The top of the world (2-4)   **796.52**

Jenner, Edward, 1749-1823
About
Marrin, A. Dr. Jenner and the speckled monster (5 and up) **614.5**

Jennings, Coleman A., 1933-
(ed) Theatre for young audiences. See Theatre for young audiences **812.008**

Jennings, Patrick, 1962-
The wolving time **Fic**

Jennings, Peter, 1938-2005
The century for young people **909.82**

Jennings, Richard W., 1945-
The great whale of Kansas **Fic**
My life of crime (5 and up) **Fic**
Orwell's luck (5 and up) **Fic**

Jennings, Terry
101 amazing optical illusions **152.14**

Jennings, Thomas L., 1791-1859
See/See also pages in the following book(s):
Haskins, J. African American entrepreneurs
920

Jensen, Dan
(jt. auth) Huddleston, C. Decoy **741.5**

Jerabek, Ann
(jt. auth) Hall-Ellis, S. D. Grants for school libraries **025.1**

Jeremiah's song. Myers, W. D.
In Visions: nineteen short stories by outstanding writers for young adults p194-203
S C

Jeremy Goldblatt is so no Moses. Howe, J.
In 13; thirteen stories that capture the agony and ecstasy of being thirteen

Jericho walls. Collier, K. **Fic**

Jermyn, Leslie
Belize (5 and up) **972.82**
Guyana (5 and up) **988.1**
Paraguay (5 and up) **989.2**
Uruguay (5 and up) **989.5**
(jt. auth) DuBois, J. Colombia **986.1**
(jt. auth) Gan, D. Sweden **948.5**
(jt. auth) Gofen, E. Argentina **982**
(jt. auth) Reilly, M.-J. Mexico **972**
(jt. auth) Richard, C. Brazil **981**
(jt. auth) Srinivasan, R. India **954**
(jt. auth) Winter, J. K. Italy **945**

Jerry Yang and David Filo. Sherman, J. **92**

Jerusalem
Fiction
Nye, N. S. Habibi **Fic**
Poetry
Yolen, J. O Jerusalem (4 and up) **811**
The **Jerusalem** Bible. See Bible. The new Jerusalem Bible **220.5**

Jesse Ventura tells it like it is. Ventura, J.
320

Jesus Christ
About
L'Engle, M. The glorious impossible **232.9**
Lottridge, C. B. Stories from the life of Jesus (4 and up) **232.9**
Nativity
Bible. N.T. Selections. The Christmas story
232.9

Poetry
Grimes, N. At Jerusalem's gate (5 and up)
811
Jet planes
Murdico, S. J. Concorde (4 and up) **629.133**
Jewelry
Newcomb, R. The Girls' World book of jewelry: 50 cool designs to make (5 and up)
745.594

Jewels *See* Precious stones
Jewish Americans. Stein, R. **305.8**
Jewish-Arab relations
See also Israel-Arab conflicts
Fiction
Nye, N. S. Habibi **Fic**
Jewish faith in America. Buxbaum, S. M. **296**
Jewish holidays
See also Hanukkah; Passover
Adler, D. A. The kids' catalog of Jewish holidays **296.4**
Berger, G. Celebrate! (4 and up) **296.4**
Fiction
Schwartz, H. The day the Rabbi disappeared: Jewish holiday tales of magic (4 and up)
398.2

Jewish holocaust (1933-1945) *See* Holocaust, 1933-1945
Jewish legends
Chaikin, M. Angels sweep the desert floor (4 and up) **296.1**
Goldin, B. D. Journeys with Elijah (4 and up)
222
Lester, J. When the beginning began (4 and up)
296.1
Rogasky, B. The golem (4 and up) **398.2**
Jewish refugees
Fox, A. L. Ten thousand children (5 and up)
940.53
Gottfried, T. Displaced persons (7 and up)
940.53
Greenfeld, H. After the Holocaust (6 and up)
940.53
Wiesel, E. The accident
In Wiesel, E. Night, Dawn, The accident: three tales p205-318 **Fic**
Fiction
Bat-Ami, M. Two suns in the sky (7 and up)
Fic
Levitin, S. Journey to America (4 and up)
Fic
Mazer, N. F. Good night, Maman (5 and up)
Fic
The **Jewish** victims of the Holocaust. Altman, L. J. **940.53**
Jews
Biography
People of the Holocaust **920.003**
Festivals
See Jewish holidays
Fiction
Chotjewitz, D. Daniel half human (7 and up)
Fic
Cormier, R. Tunes for bears to dance to (7 and up) **Fic**

Jews—Fiction—*Continued*

Hesse, K. Letters from Rifka (5 and up)　**Fic**

Isaacs, A. Torn thread (7 and up)　**Fic**

Kimmel, E. A. The jar of fools: eight Hanukkah stories from Chelm (4 and up)　**S C**

Kornblatt, M. Understanding Buddy　**Fic**

Kositsky, L. The thought of high windows (7 and up)　**Fic**

Lasky, K. Dreams in the golden country (4 and up)　**Fic**

Lasky, K. The night journey (4 and up)　**Fic**

Levine, G. C. Dave at night (5 and up)　**Fic**

Levitin, S. The cure　**Fic**

Levitin, S. The return (6 and up)　**Fic**

Lowry, L. Number the stars (4 and up)　**Fic**

Matas, C. After the war (7 and up)　**Fic**

Matas, C. Greater than angels (7 and up)　**Fic**

Matas, C. In my enemy's house (7 and up)　**Fic**

Matas, C. Sparks fly upward (4 and up)　**Fic**

Matas, C. The war within (5 and up)　**Fic**

Mazer, H. The last mission (7 and up)　**Fic**

Meyer, C. Drummers of Jericho (7 and up)　**Fic**

Meyer, C. Gideon's people　**Fic**

Singer, I. B. The power of light (4 and up)　**S C**

Wiesel, E. Night, Dawn, The accident: three tales (7 and up)　**Fic**

Yolen, J. The devil's arithmetic (4 and up)　**Fic**

Folklore

Schwartz, H. The day the Rabbi disappeared: Jewish holiday tales of magic (4 and up)　**398.2**

History

Altman, L. J. Forever outsiders　**909**

Mann, K. The ancient Hebrews　**909**

Waldman, N. Masada (4 and up)　**933**

Legends

See Jewish legends

Persecutions

See also Holocaust, 1933-1945; World War, 1939-1945—Jews—Rescue

Sherrow, V. Smoke to flame　**940.53**

Persecutions—Fiction

Lasky, K. Blood secret (7 and up)　**Fic**

Denmark

Levine, E. Darkness over Denmark　**940.53**

Europe

Altman, L. J. The Jewish victims of the Holocaust　**940.53**

Boas, J. We are witnesses (7 and up)　**940.53**

Chicoine, S. From the ashes　**940.53**

Rosenberg, M. B. Hiding to survive (5 and up)　**940.53**

Germany

Hillman, L. I will plant you a lilac tree (7 and up)　**940.53**

Perl, L. Four perfect pebbles (6 and up)　**940.53**

Wiesel, E. The accident

In Wiesel, E. Night, Dawn, The accident: three tales p205-318　**Fic**

Hungary

Bitton-Jackson, L. I have lived a thousand years (7 and up)　**940.53**

Siegal, A. Upon the head of the goat: a childhood in Hungary, 1939-1944　**92**

Netherlands

Frank, A. The diary of a young girl (6 and up)　**92**

Frank, A. The diary of a young girl: the definitive edition (6 and up)　**92**

Gold, A. L. Memories of Anne Frank (5 and up)　**92**

Lee, C. A. A friend called Anne (4 and up)　**940.53**

Müller, M. Anne Frank (7 and up)　**92**

Reiss, J. The journey back　**92**

Reiss, J. The upstairs room (5 and up)　**92**

Rol, R. v. d. Anne Frank, beyond the diary (5 and up)　**92**

Sawyer, K. K. Anne Frank (5 and up)　**92**

Wukovits, J. F. Anne Frank (7 and up)　**92**

New York (N.Y.)

Wiesel, E. The accident

In Wiesel, E. Night, Dawn, The accident: three tales p205-318　**Fic**

Poland

Lobel, A. No pretty pictures (7 and up)　**92**

Sender, R. M. The cage (7 and up)　**940.53**

Poland—Fiction

Orlev, U. Run, boy, run (7 and up)　**Fic**

Pressler, M. Malka (7 and up)　**Fic**

United States

Buxbaum, S. M. Jewish faith in America (7 and up)　**296**

Diner, H. R. Jews in America (7 and up)　**305.8**

Fisher, L. E. To bigotry, no sanction (4 and up)　**296**

Rubin, S. G. L'chaim! (7 and up)　**305.8**

Stein, R. Jewish Americans (7 and up)　**305.8**

See/See also pages in the following book(s):

Joselit, J. W. Immigration and American religion (7 and up)　**200**

United States—Biography

Brooks, P. Extraordinary Jewish Americans　**920**

Jews in America. Diner, H. R.　**305.8**

Jews in Shushan. Kipling, R.

In McCaffrey, A. {The Pern series}　**S C**

Jiang, Ji-li

Red scarf girl (6 and up)　**951.05**

Jijan. Honma, R.

In American dragons: twenty-five Asian American voices p203-10　**810.8**

Jim Davis. Masefield, J.　**Fic**

Jiménez, Francisco, 1943-

Breaking through (5 and up)　**Fic**

The circuit

In Leaving home: stories p53-62　**808.8**

Jinga *See* Nzinga, Queen of Matamba, 1582-1663

Jinks, Catherine, 1963-

Pagan's crusade (7 and up)　**Fic**

Jip. Paterson, K.　**Fic**

Joan, of Arc, Saint, 1412-1431
About
Stanley, D. Joan of Arc (4 and up)　　92
See/See also pages in the following book(s):
Hewitt, K. Lives of extraordinary women (4 and up)　　920

Job, Amy G.
The school library media specialist as manager
　　027.8

A **job** for Valentín. Ortiz Cofer, J.
In Ortiz Cofer, J. An island like you; stories of the barrio p112-30　　S C

Job hunting
Coon, N. Teen dream jobs (7 and up)
　　650.14
Pervola, C. How to get a job if you're a teenager (7 and up)　　650.14

Job placement guidance *See* Vocational guidance

Jobs, Steven, 1955-
See/See also pages in the following book(s):
Northrup, M. American computer pioneers
　　920

Jobs *See* Occupations

Jobs for kids. Kiefer, J.　　650.1

Jocelyn, Marthe, 1956-
A home for foundlings (7 and up)　　362.7
Mable Riley (5 and up)　　Fic

Joe is not a monster. Stine, R. L.
In Beware!; R.L. Stine picks his favorite scary stories p121-25　　808.8

Joey Pigza swallowed the key. Gantos, J.　　Fic

Johannes Kepler and the new astronomy. Voelkel, J. R.　　92

Johansson, Philip
Carpal tunnel syndrome and other repetitive strain injuries (7 and up)　　616.8

John and the Devil's daughter. Hamilton, V.
In Hamilton, V. The people could fly; American black folktales p107-15
　　398.2

John Brown's Raid, Harpers Ferry, W. Va., 1859 *See* Harpers Ferry (W. Va.)—History—John Brown's Raid, 1859

John Brown's raid on Harpers Ferry. January, B.
　　973.7

John Brown's Raid on Harpers Ferry in American history. Stein, R. C.　　973.7

John Glenn's return to space. Vogt, G.　　629.45

John Sculpin and the witches. Aiken, J.
In Aiken, J. Shadows and moonshine; stories
　　S C

John Steinbeck, a writer's life. Tessitore, J.
　　92

John Wilkes Booth and the Civil War. Otfinoski, S.　　92

John Winthrop, Oliver Cromwell, and the Land of Promise. Aronson, M.　　92

John's secret dreams [biography of John Lennon] Rappaport, D.　　92

Johnson, Angela, 1961-
Atomic blue pieces
In The Color of absence; 12 stories about loss and hope p41-48　　S C

Bird (5 and up)　　Fic
A cool moonlight (5 and up)　　Fic
The first part last (7 and up)　　Fic
Heaven (6 and up)　　Fic
Looking for Red　　Fic
The other side　　811
Running back to Ludie　　811
Songs of faith (5 and up)　　Fic
Through a window
In On the fringe p63-72　　S C
Toning the sweep　　Fic
Tripping over the lunch lady
In Tripping over the lunch lady and other school stories p1-15　　S C

Johnson, Carolyn
Using internet primary sources to teach critical thinking skills in the sciences　　025.04

Johnson, Claudia D.
Daily life in colonial New England (7 and up)
　　974

Johnson, Doug, 1952-
Learning right from wrong in the digital age
　　004.6

Johnson, Isaac, 1844-1905
About
Marston, H. I. Isaac Johnson　　92

Johnson, James Weldon, 1871-1938
Lift every voice and sing　　782.42

Johnson, Jinny
Simon & Schuster children's guide to sea creatures (4 and up)　　591.7

Johnson, John H., 1918-2005
See/See also pages in the following book(s):
Haskins, J. African American entrepreneurs
　　920

Johnson, Julie
Why do people join gangs?　　364.1

Johnson, Lyndon B. (Lyndon Baines), 1908-1973
See/See also pages in the following book(s):
Roberts, R. Leaders and generals　　920

Johnson, Mamie, 1935-
About
Green, M. Y. A strong right arm: the story of Mamie "Peanut" Johnson (4 and up)　　92

Johnson, Maureen
The key to the golden Firebird (7 and up)
　　Fic

Johnson, Milton, 1932-
(il) O'Dell, S. The black pearl　　Fic

Johnson, Neil, 1954-
National Geographic photography guide for kids (4 and up)　　771

Johnson, Pamela
(il) Aiken, J. Shadows and moonshine　　S C

Johnson, Peanut *See* Johnson, Mamie, 1935-

Johnson, Rebecca L., 1956-
Ernest Shackleton　　92

Johnson, Robert, d. 1938
See/See also pages in the following book(s):
Lester, J. The blues singers (5 and up)　　920

Johnson, Stephen, 1964-
(il) Burleigh, R. Hoops　　811

Johnson, Sylvia A.
Mapping the world (4 and up)   912
Johnston, Julie
Adam and Eve and Pinch-me (7 and up)
                                            Fic
In spite of killer bees (7 and up)   Fic
Johnston, Robert D. (Robert Dougall)
The making of America (5 and up)   973
Johnston, Tim, 1962-
Never so green (7 and up)   Fic
Johnston, Tony
Any small goodness (4 and up)   Fic
Johnstone, Leslie, 1959-
(jt. auth) Levine, S. The microscope book
                                            502.8
Johnstone, Michael
Explorers   910.4
The history news in space   629.4
Join in   S C
Joined at birth. Landau, E.   616
Joint Steering Committee for Revision of AACR
Anglo-American cataloguing rules. See Anglo-
American cataloguing rules   025.3
Jones, Mother, 1830-1930
                   About
Bartoletti, S. C. Kids on strike! (5 and up)
                                            331.8
Josephson, J. P. Mother Jones   92
See/See also pages in the following book(s):
Streissguth, T. Legendary labor leaders (7 and
up)   920
Jones, Carolyn
Every girl tells a story   305.23
Jones, Diana Wynne
Cart and cwidder (7 and up)   Fic
Castle in the air (6 and up)   Fic
Charmed life   Fic
Chasing the wind
   In Firebirds: an anthology of original fantasy
   and science fiction; an anthology of orig-
   inal fantasy and science fiction   S C
Everard's ride Jones, D. W. Unexpected magic;
   collected stories p303-497
Howl's moving castle (6 and up)   Fic
Little Dot
   In Firebirds: an anthology of original fantasy
   and science fiction; an anthology of orig-
   inal fantasy and science fiction   S C
Unexpected magic   S C
Jones, Edward P.
The first day
   In Leaving home: stories p9-17   808.8
Jones, Eric
(jt. auth) Walker, L. Q. Little Gloomy: . . . It
   was a dark and stormy night   741.5
Jones, Frederick McKinley, 1893-1961
See/See also pages in the following book(s):
Aaseng, N. Black inventors (7 and up)   920
Jones, Joe, 1896-1987
                   About
Haskins, J. Out of the darkness (5 and up)
                                            305.8

Jones, John Paul, 1747-1792
See/See also pages in the following book(s):
Wren, L. L. Pirates and privateers of the high
   seas p11-17   920
Jones, Mary Harris *See* Jones, Mother, 1830-
1930
Jones, Patrick
Connecting young adults and libraries
                                            027.62
A core collection for young adults   011.6
Do it right!   027.62
What's so scary about R.L. Stine?   813.009
(ed) New directions for library service to young
   adults. See New directions for library service
   to young adults   027.62
Jones, Quincy, 1933-
See/See also pages in the following book(s):
Haskins, J. African American entrepreneurs
                                            920
Jones, Randy, 1950-
(il) Leacock, E. Places in time   911
Jones, Sarah, 1968-
Film (7 and up)   791.43
Jones, Thomas D.
(jt. auth) English, J. Scholastic encyclopedia of
   the United States at war   973.03
Jones, Tim Wynne- *See* Wynne-Jones, Tim
Jones, Veda Boyd, 1948-
Government & politics   920
Jonkel, Charles
                   About
Patent, D. H. A polar bear biologist at work (4
   and up)   599.78
Jonson, Ben, 1573?-1637
See/See also pages in the following book(s):
Nardo, D. Great Elizabethan playwrights
                                            920
Joplin, Scott, 1868-1917
                   About
Preston, K. K. Scott Joplin   92
See/See also pages in the following book(s):
Mour, S. I. American jazz musicians   920
Jordan, Barbara, 1936-1996
See/See also pages in the following book(s):
Jones, V. B. Government & politics   920
Price-Groff, C. Twentieth-century women politi-
   cal leaders (7 and up)   920
Jordan, Sandra
(jt. auth) Greenberg, J. Andy Warhol   92
(jt. auth) Greenberg, J. Runaway girl: the artist
   Louise Bourgeois   92
(jt. auth) Greenberg, J. Vincent Van Gogh
                                            92
Jordan, Sherryl, 1949-
The hunting of the last dragon   Fic
The raging quiet (7 and up)   Fic
Secret sacrament (7 and up)   Fic
Joselit, Jenna Weissman
Immigration and American religion (7 and up)
                                            200
Joseph, Nez Percé Chief, 1840-1904
                   About
Scott, R. A. Chief Joseph and the Nez Percés
                                            92

Joseph, Nez Percé Chief, 1840-1904—About—
Continued
Taylor, M. W. Chief Joseph   **92**
See/See also pages in the following book(s):
Freedman, R. Indian chiefs (6 and up)   **920**

Joseph, Leonard M.
Skyscrapers: inside and out   **720**

Joseph, Lynn
The color of my words (5 and up)   **Fic**

Joseph McCarthy and the Cold War. Sherrow, V.
                                                   92

Josephs, David
Lakes, ponds, and temporary pools   **577.6**

Josephson, Judith Pinkerton
Growing up in pioneer America, 1800 to 1890
                                                   978
Mother Jones   **92**

Josephus in the cave. Jaffe, N.
In Jaffe, N. and Zeitlin, S. J. The cow of no
  color: riddle stories and justice tales from
  around the world p122-27   **398.2**

Joshua tree. Bull, E.
In The Green Man: tales from the mythic forest p262-96   **808.8**

Joshua's song. Harlow, J. H.   **Fic**

Jost, Kenneth
(ed) The Supreme Court A to Z. See The Su
  preme Court A to Z   **347**

The **journal** of Ben Uchida, citizen #13559, Mirror Lake internment camp. Denenberg, B.
                                                   Fic

The **journal** of Biddy Owens, the Negro leagues.
  Myers, W. D.   **Fic**

The **journal** of C.J. Jackson: a Dust Bowl migrant.
  Durbin, W.   **Fic**

The **journal** of Douglas Allen Deeds. Philbrick,
  W. R.   **Fic**

The **journal** of Finn Reardon. Bartoletti, S. C.
                                                   Fic

The **journal** of James Edmond Pease, a Civil War
  Union soldier. Murphy, J.   **Fic**

The **journal** of Jedediah Barstow. Levine, E.
                                                   Fic

The **journal** of Joshua Loper. Myers, W. D.
                                                   Fic

The **journal** of Otto Peltonen, a Finnish immigrant. Durbin, W.   **Fic**

The **journal** of Scott Pendleton Collins. Myers, W.
  D.   **Fic**

The **journal** of Sean Sullivan. Durbin, W.   **Fic**

Journalism
Cohen, D. Yellow journalism (7 and up)
                                                   302.23
Flash!: the Associated Press covers the world
                                                   070.4
Hampton, W. Kennedy assassinated! (5 and up)
                                                   973.922
Fiction
Winerip, M. Adam Canfield of the Slash (5 and
  up)   **Fic**

Journalists
See also Women journalists
Somervill, B. A. Ida Tarbell   **92**
Wiesel, E. The accident
In Wiesel, E. Night, Dawn, The accident:
  three tales p205-318   **Fic**

Journals *See* Periodicals

Journals (Diaries) *See* Diaries

Journey. MacLachlan, P.   **Fic**

The **journey** back. Reiss, J.   **92**

Journey to America. Levitin, S.   **Fic**

Journey to freedom. Isserman, M.   **305.8**

Journey to freedom [series]
Harper, J. E. Maya Angelou   **92**
Klingel, C. F. Coretta Scott King   **92**
Troy, D. W.E.B. DuBois   **92**

Journey to Jo'burg. Naidoo, B.   **Fic**

Journey to nowhere. Auch, M. J.   **Fic**

A **journey** to the New World. Lasky, K.   **Fic**

Journey to the river sea. Ibbotson, E.   **Fic**

Journey to Topaz. Uchida, Y.   **Fic**

A **journey** with Elijah. Goldin, B. D.
In Goldin, B. D. Journeys with Elijah; eight
  tales of the Prophet p1-10   **222**

Journeys *See* Voyages and travels

Journeys in time. Leacock, E.   **973**

Journeys with Elijah. Goldin, B. D.   **222**

The **joy** of signing. Riekehof, L. L.   **419**

Joyful noise: poems for two voices. Fleischman,
  P.   **811**

Joyner, Hermon
(jt. auth) Monaghan, K. You can weave!
                                                   746.41

Joyriding. Naughton, J.
In Ultimate sports; short stories by outstanding writers for young adults p4-19
                                                   S C

Jubilee journey. Meyer, C.   **Fic**

Jubilee Singers (Musical group)
Cooper, M. L. Slave spirituals and the Jubilee
  Singers   **782.42**

Juby, Susan, 1969-
Alice, I think (7 and up)   **Fic**

Judaism
Buxbaum, S. M. Jewish faith in America (7 and
  up)   **296**
Cato, V. The Torah and Judaism (5 and up)
                                                   222
See/See also pages in the following book(s):
Osborne, M. P. One world, many religions (4
  and up)   **201**
Dictionaries
The Oxford dictionary of the Jewish religion
                                                   296.03

Judge for yourself [series]
Hatt, C. Mahatma Ghandhi   **92**
Hatt, C. Martin Luther King, Jr   **92**

Judges
Kent, D. Thurgood Marshall and the Supreme
  Court   **92**
Rowh, M. Thurgood Marshall   **92**

The **judge's** house. Stine, R. L.
In Beware!; R.L. Stine picks his favorite
scary stories p55-75   **808.8**

Judson, Karen, 1941-
Chemical and biological warfare (7 and up)
358

Juettner, Bonnie, 1968-
Energy (5 and up)   **333.79**

Jukes, Mavis
Growing up: it's a girl thing (4 and up)
612.6
The guy book (7 and up)   **305.23**
It's a girl thing (5 and up)   **305.23**
(jt. auth) Cheung, L. W.-Y. Be healthy! it's a
girl thing   **613**

Julian, Hubert Fauntleroy
See/See also pages in the following book(s):
Hart, P. S. Flying free (4 and up)   **629.13**

Julian, Percy L., 1899-1975
See/See also pages in the following book(s):
Aaseng, N. Black inventors (7 and up)   **920**

Julie. George, J. C.   **Fic**

Julie of the wolves. George, J. C.   **Fic**

Juliet Dove, Queen of Love. Coville, B.   **Fic**

Julius, Edward H., 1952-
Arithmetricks   **513**

Julius Caesar [essays about]   **92**

July Saturday. Woodson, J.
In Places I never meant to be; original stories
by censored writers   **S C**

The **jumbo** book of art. Luxbacher, I.   **702.8**

The **jumbo** vegetarian cookbook. Gillies, J.
641.5

Jump in. Ruiz, D.
In You're on!: seven plays in English and
Spanish p42-61   **812.008**

Jump rope *See* Rope skipping

Jump rope rhymes
Chambers, V. Double dutch (4 and up)
796.2

Jump ship to freedom. Collier, J. L.   **Fic**

Jung, Reinhardt
Dreaming in black and white (5 and up)
Fic

Jungalbook [play] Mast, E.
In Theatre for young audiences; 20 great
plays for children p478-517   **812.008**

The **jungle** books. Kipling, R.   **S C**

Jungle dogs. Salisbury, G.   **Fic**

Junior library of American Indians [series]
Gleason, K. Native American literature   **897**

Junior state maps on file (4 and up)   **973**

Junior timelines on file. Tomaselli-Moschovitis,
V.   **902**

Junior Worldmark encyclopedia of the Canadian
provinces   **971**

Junior Worldmark encyclopedia of the Mexican
states   **972**

Junior worldmark encyclopedia of the nations
910.3

Junior Worldmark encyclopedia of the states
973.03

Junior Worldmark encyclopedia of world cultures
(5 and up)   **306**

Junior worldmark encyclopedia of world holidays
394.26

Jupiter (Planet)
Miller, R. Jupiter   **523.4**
Schwabacher, M. Jupiter   **523.4**
Simon, S. Destination: Jupiter (4 and up)
523.4
Exploration
Cole, M. D. Galileo spacecraft   **629.43**

Jurassic Park. Crichton, M.   **Fic**

Juratovac, Nicol
Dana's eyes
In American dragons: twenty-five Asian
American voices p75-95   **810.8**

Jury
Aaseng, N. You are the juror   **345**
The **jury.** Jaffe, N.
In Jaffe, N. and Zeitlin, S. J. The cow of no
color: riddle stories and justice tales from
around the world p47-51   **398.2**

Just a kiss, Annie P. Appelt, K.
In Appelt, K. Kissing Tennessee and other
stories from the Stardust Dance p31-40
S C

Just delicious. Schwartz, A.
In Schwartz, A. Scary stories 3; more tales to
chill your bones p12-14   **398.2**

Just Ella. Haddix, M. P.   **Fic**

Just once. Dygard, T. J.
In Ultimate sports; short stories by outstand-
ing writers for young adults p196-205
S C

Just the facts [series]
Burnfield, A. Multiple sclerosis   **616.8**
Durham, M. Painkillers and tranquilizers
615
Mason, P. Body piercing and tattooing   **391**
Parker, S. Allergies   **616.97**
Routh, K. Epilepsy

Juvenile courts
Gold, S. D. In re Gault (1967) (7 and up)
345
Jacobs, T. A. They broke the law, you be the
judge (7 and up)   **345**

Juvenile delinquency
See also Gangs
Hile, K. S. The trial of juveniles as adults
345
Silverstein, H. Kids who kill (7 and up)
364.1
Youth violence (7 and up)   **364.36**
See/See also pages in the following book(s):
Teens at risk: opposing viewpoints p63-105 (7
and up)   **362.7**
Fiction
Cormier, R. We all fall down   **Fic**
Hinton, S. E. The outsiders (7 and up)   **Fic**
Hinton, S. E. Rumble fish (7 and up)   **Fic**
Hinton, S. E. That was then, this is now (7 and
up)   **Fic**
Myers, W. D. Scorpions (6 and up)   **Fic**
Sachar, L. Holes (5 and up)   **Fic**

Juvenile prostitution
Dean, R. Teen prostitution   362.7
Jweid, Rosann, 1933-
Building character through literature   028.5
The library-classroom partnership   027.8

K

Kaaberbol, Lene
The Shamer's daughter   Fic
Kaa's hunting. Kipling, R.
In Kipling, R. The jungle books   S C
Kachurek, Sandra J.
George W. Bush (4 and up)   92
Kadohata, Cynthia
Kira-Kira (5 and up)   Fic
Singing apples
In American eyes; new Asian-American short stories for young adults p49-61   S C
Kaffir boy [excerpt] Mathabane, M.
In Somehow tenderness survives; stories of Southern Africa p87-103   S C
Kafirs (African people) *See* Zulu (African people)
Kagda, Falaq
Algeria (5 and up)   965
Hong Kong (5 and up)   951.25
Kagda, Sakina, 1939-
Lithuania (5 and up)   947.9
Kahl, Jonathan D.
National Audubon Society first field guide: weather (4 and up)   551.5
Kahlo, Frida, 1907-1954
About
Laidlaw, J. A. Frida Kahlo (5 and up)   92
Kai's journey to Gold Mountain. Currier, K. S.   Fic
Kaiulani, Princess of Hawaii, 1875-1899
About
Linnea, S. Princess Ka'iulani   92
See/See also pages in the following book(s):
McGaw, L. To be a princess (4 and up)   920
Fiction
White, E. E. Kaiulani   Fic
Kákuy. Delacre, L.
In Delacre, L. Golden tales; myths, legends, and folktales from Latin America p59-63   398.2
Kaleidoscope [series]
Lockman, D. Computer animation   778.5
Lockman, D. Robots   629.8
Kallen, Stuart A., 1955-
Egypt (7 and up)   962
Gems (4 and up)   553.8
The history of classical music   781.6
The history of country music   781.642
The history of jazz   781.65
The history of rock and roll   781.66
The instruments of music   784.19
Mummies (4 and up)   393
Native American chiefs and warriors (7 and up)   920

Primary sources [American war library, The Cold War]   909.82
The Rhine   943
The Salem witch trials (7 and up)   133.4
Shamans   201
Shinto   299.5
(ed) The Baby boom. See The Baby boom   306
Kalpana's dream. Clarke, J.   Fic
Kamen, Gloria, 1923-
(ed) Heading out. See Heading out   331.7
Kaminker, Laura
Everything you need to know about being adopted (7 and up)   362.7
Everything you need to know about dealing with sexual assault   364.1
Kaminsky, Marty
Uncommon champions   920
Kan, Katharine
Sizzling summer reading programs for young adults   027.62
Kane, Joseph Nathan, 1899-2002
Facts about the presidents   920
Famous first facts   031.02
(ed) Facts about the states. See Facts about the states   973
Kanellos, Nicolás, 1945-
(ed) Hispanic American almanac. See Hispanic American almanac [junior version]   305.8
Kang, Hildi, 1934-
The black dragon princess
In Fire and wings: dragon tales from East and West p103-11   S C
Kansas
Bjorklund, R. Kansas
In Celebrate the states   973
Robinson Masters, N. Kansas
In America the beautiful, second series   973
Fiction
Gaeddert, L. B. Friends and enemies   Fic
Jennings, R. W. The great whale of Kansas   Fic
History
McArthur, D. The Kansas-Nebraska Act and "Bleeding Kansas" in American history   978.1
Zeinert, K. Tragic prelude: bleeding Kansas (7 and up)   978.1
The **Kansas-Nebraska** Act and "Bleeding Kansas" in American history. McArthur, D.   978.1
Kantor, Melissa
Confessions of a not it girl (7 and up)   Fic
Kanze Tetsunojo *See* Tetsunojo, Kanze
Kaplan, Gisela T.
(jt. auth) Rajendra, V. Iran   955
Karate
Dallas, K. Fundamental karate   796.8
The **Karate** Kid. Soto, G.
In Soto, G. Baseball in April, and other stories p69-80   S C
Karesh, Sara E.
(jt. auth) Buxbaum, S. M. Jewish faith in America   296

Karp, Rashelle Schlessinger
Plays for children and young adults   **808.82**

Karr, Kathleen
The boxer (7 and up)   **Fic**
Gilbert and Sullivan set me free   **Fic**
The great turkey walk (5 and up)   **Fic**
Skullduggery (5 and up)   **Fic**
What's a fellow to do
   In Shelf life: stories by the book p81-90
     S C

Karr, Phyllis Ann, 1944-
A cold stake
   In Vampires: a collection of original stories
     p134-56   **S C**

Karson, Jill
(ed) Civil rights. See Civil rights   **323.1**

Kasnot, Keith
(il) Newquist, H. P. The great brain book
     612.8

Kass, Pnina
Real time (7 and up)   **Fic**

Kassinger, Ruth
Ceramics: from magic pots to man-made bones
     666
Dyes: from sea snails to synthetics   **667**
Glass: from Cinderella's slippers to fiber optics
     620.1
Gold: from Greek myth to computer chips
     669

Katayev, Tamara
See/See also pages in the following book(s):
Major, J. S. Caravan to America p[1]-13 (4 and
up)   **920**

Kate Crackernuts. Tchana, K. H.
   In Tchana, K. H. The serpent slayer: and oth-
     er stories of strong women p43-46
     398.2

Kate Greenaway medal
Barker, K. Outstanding books for children and
young people   **028.5**

Kate the great. Cabot, M.
   In 13; thirteen stories that capture the agony
     and ecstasy of being thirteen

Katlian and the Iron People. Brown, D. A.
   In Brown, D. A. Dee Brown's folktales of the
     Native American; retold for our times
     p90-92   **398.2**

Katz, Bobbi
We the people (5 and up)   **811**

Katz, Sharon
The Great Lakes   **577.6**

Katz, William Loren
Black Indians   **305.8**
Black pioneers   **920**
Black women of the Old West (5 and up)
     978
Breaking the chains (7 and up)   **326**

Kauffman, John, d. 1990
According to Coyote
   In Theatre for young audiences; 20 great
     plays for children p170-82   **812.008**

Kaufman, Cheryl Davidson
Cooking the Caribbean way
   In Easy menu ethnic cookbooks   **641.5**

Kaufman, Kenn
Lives of North American birds (7 and up)
     598

Kazem, Halima
Afghanistan (4 and up)   **958.1**

Kazunomiya, Princess of Japan, 1846-1877
     Fiction
Lasky, K. Kazunomiya   **Fic**

Keane, Nancy J.
Booktalking across the curriculum: the middle
years   **028.5**

Kearney, Carol A.
Curriculum partner   **027.8**

Keckley, Elizabeth, ca. 1818-1907
See/See also pages in the following book(s):
Haskins, J. African American entrepreneurs
     920

Keehn, Sally M., 1947-
Anna Sunday   **Fic**
Gnat Stokes and the Foggy Bottom Swamp
   Queen (5 and up)   **Fic**
I am Regina   **Fic**

Keeley, Jennifer, 1974-
Espionage   **327.12**

Keen, Dan
(jt. auth) Bonnet, R. L. Science fair projects:
   chemistry   **540.7**

Keenan, Sheila
Gods, goddesses, and monsters   **201**
Scholastic book of outstanding Americans (5
   and up)   **920.003**

Keep smiling. Flinn, A.
   In Destination unexpected: short stories
     S C

The **keeper** of the doves. Byars, B. C.   **Fic**

Keeper of the night. Holt, K. W.   **Fic**

Keeping a journal. Trueit, T. S.   **808**

The **keeping** room. Myers, A.   **Fic**

Keeping safe. Collyer, B.
   In Being human   **612**

Keeping unusual pets [series]
McNicholas, J. Rats   **636.9**

Keesha's house. Frost, H.   **Fic**

Keewahkwee. Bruchac, J.
   In Bruchac, J. and Bruchac, J. When the
     Chenoo howls; native American tales of
     terror   **398.2**

Kehret, Peg, 1936-
Abduction! (5 and up)   **Fic**
Cages   **Fic**
Don't tell anyone (5 and up)   **Fic**
I'm not who you think I am   **Fic**
Searching for Candlestick Park   **Fic**
The secret journey   **Fic**

Keintpoos *See* Kintpuash, Modoc Chief, 1837?-
1873

Keith, Eros, 1942-
(il) Fox, P. The slave dancer   **Fic**
(il) Hamilton, V. The house of Dies Drear
     Fic

Keith, Harold, 1903-1998
Rifles for Watie   **Fic**

Keizer, Garret
God of beer (7 and up)   **Fic**
Keller, Helen, 1880-1968
The story of my life   **92**
      About
Dash, J. The world at her fingertips: the story of
     Helen Keller (5 and up)   **92**
Garrett, L. Helen Keller (5 and up)   **92**
Lawlor, L. Helen Keller: rebellious spirit (5 and
     up)   **92**
Keller, Laurie
(il) Wulffson, D. L. Toys!   **688.7**
Kellert, Stephen R.
(ed) Macmillan encyclopedia of the environ-
     ment. See Macmillan encyclopedia of the en-
     vironment   **333.7**
Kelley, True, 1946-
(il) Cobb, V. You gotta try this!   **507.8**
Kelly, Michael
Native American talking signs   **419**
Kelly, Pat
Coping with diabetes (7 and up)   **616.4**
Kelsey, Elin
Canadian dinosaurs   **567.9**
Kemelhor, Joel
(jt. auth) Altman, S. Encyclopedia of African-
     American heritage   **305.8**
Kemer, Eric
(jt. auth) Gardner, R. Science projects about
     temperature and heat   **536**
Kemp Owyne
In Hearne, B. G. Beauties and beasts p143-44
     398.2
Kenda, Margaret
Math wizardry for kids   **793.7**
Kendall, Martha E., 1947-
Failure is impossible!   **305.4**
Kenna, Kathleen
A people apart (4 and up)   **289.7**
Kennebec Indians *See* Abnaki Indians
Kennedy, John F. (John Fitzgerald), 1917-1963
Profiles in courage   **920**
      About
Burgan, M. John F. Kennedy   **92**
Cooper, I. Jack: the early years of John F. Ken-
     nedy   **92**
Heiligman, D. High hopes [biography of John F.
     Kennedy] (4 and up)   **92**
Uschan, M. V. John F. Kennedy (7 and up)
     92

See/See also pages in the following book(s):
Goldman, M. S. Richard M. Nixon (7 and up)
     92
Uschan, M. V. Political leaders   **920**
      Assassination
Hampton, W. Kennedy assassinated! (5 and up)
     973.922
Kennedy, Michael, 1926-
The concise Oxford dictionary of music
     780.3
Kennedy assassinated!. Hampton, W.   **973.922**
Kennedy Cuomo, Kerry
Speak truth to power (7 and up)   **920**

Kennett, David
(il) Blacklock, D. The Roman Army   **937**
Kenny, Maurice, 1929-
Wet moccasins
     In Talking leaves; contemporary native
     American short stories   **S C**
Kenschaft, Lori
Lydia Maria Child (7 and up)   **92**
Kensuke's kingdom. Morpurgo, M.   **Fic**
Kent, Deborah, 1948-
Animal helpers for the disabled (4 and up)
     636.088
Athletes with disabilities (4 and up)   **371.9**
Extraordinary people with disabilities   **920**
Maine
     In America the beautiful, second series
     973
New Mexico
     In America the beautiful, second series
     973
Snake pits, talking cures, & magic bullets
     616.89
Tennessee
     In America the beautiful, second series
     973
Thurgood Marshall and the Supreme Court
     92
Utah
     In America the beautiful, second series
     973
Wyoming
     In America the beautiful, second series
     973
     In America the beautiful, second series
     973
Kent, Jacqueline, 1947-
Business builders in fashion   **920**
Kent, Peter
Great building stories of the past (4 and up)
     624
Kent, Zachary
Andrew Carnegie   **92**
Edgar Allan Poe   **92**
The mysterious disappearance of Roanoke Colo-
     ny in American history (7 and up)
     975.6/175
Kentley, Eric
Boat (4 and up)   **387.2**
Kentucky
Barrett, T. Kentucky
     In Celebrate the states   **973**
Stein, R. C. Kentucky
     In America the beautiful, second series
     973
      Fiction
Byars, B. C. The keeper of the doves (4 and up)
     Fic
Creech, S. Chasing Redbird (5 and up)   **Fic**
Kenya
Bowden, R. Kenya   **967.62**
Broberg, C. Kenya in pictures (5 and up)
     967.62
Lekuton, J. Facing the lion   **967.62**
Pateman, R. Kenya (5 and up)   **967.62**

Kenya—*Continued*
Description and travel
Adamson, J. Born free   **599.75**
Fiction
Kessler, C. Our secret, Siri Aang (7 and up)
                                                          Fic
Kenya in pictures. Broberg, C.   **967.62**
Kenyon, Karen, 1938-
The Brontë family (7 and up)   **920**
Kenyon, Dame Kathleen Mary, 1906-1978
See/See also pages in the following book(s):
Greenberg, L. Digging into the past   **920**
Kepler, Johannes, 1571-1630
About
Boerst, W. J. Johannes Kepler   **92**
Voelkel, J. R. Johannes Kepler and the new as-
tronomy (7 and up)   **92**
Keppler, Johannes *See* Kepler, Johannes, 1571-
1630
Kerley, Barbara
Walt Whitman (4 and up)   **92**
Kerr, M. E., 1927-
Do you want my opinion?
In Sixteen; short stories by outstanding writ-
ers for young adults p93-100   **S C**
Great expectations
In On the fringe p26-46   **S C**
I'll see you when this war is over
In Shattered: stories of children and war p40-
51   **S C**
Night kites (7 and up)   **Fic**
Slap your sides (7 and up)   **Fic**
The sweet perfume of good-bye
In Visions: nineteen short stories by outstand-
ing writers for young adults p186-91
                                         S C
About
Nilsen, A. P. Presenting M.E. Kerr (7 and up)
                                         813.009
Kerrigan, Michael
The history of punishment (7 and up)   **364.6**
Kerrod, Robin, 1938-
Facts on File wildlife atlas   **578**
The moon   **523.3**
The way science works (7 and up)   **507.8**
Kessler, Cristina
Our secret, Siri Aang (7 and up)   **Fic**
Kessler, James H.
Distinguished African American scientists of the
20th century. See Distinguished African
American scientists of the 20th century
                                         920
Ketchum, Liza, 1946-
Into a new country (7 and up)   **920**
Sables mouvants
In On the edge: stories at the brink p141-60
                                         S C
Kett, Joseph F.
(jt. auth) Hirsch, E. D. The new dictionary of
cultural literacy   **031**
The key to the golden Firebird. Johnson, M.
                                         Fic

Keynes, John Maynard, 1883-1946
See/See also pages in the following book(s):
Bussing-Burks, M. Influential economists (7 and
up)   **920**
Keys to the kingdom [series]
Nix, G. Mister Monday   **Fic**
Khalid, King of Saudi Arabia, 1913-1982
See/See also pages in the following book(s):
Reed, J. The Saudi royal family   **920**
Khanduri, Kamini
Japanese art & culture   **709.52**
Kherdian, David, 1931-
The road from home (6 and up)   **92**
Kherdian, Veron, 1907-
About
Kherdian, D. The road from home (6 and up)
                                         92
Khomeini, Ruhollah
About
Schaffer, D. The Iran-Iraq War (7 and up)
                                         956.7
Khorana, Har Gobind, 1922-
See/See also pages in the following book(s):
Yount, L. Asian-American scientists (7 and up)
                                         920
A **kick** in the head   **811.008**
Kid, Thomas *See* Kyd, Thomas, 1558-1594
The **kid** who invented the trampoline. Wulffson,
D. L.   **609**
Kidd, J. S. (Jerry S.)
Into thin air (7 and up)   **363.7**
Life lines (7 and up)   **576.5**
Mother Nature's pharmacy (7 and up)   **615**
Quarks and sparks (7 and up)   **621.48**
Shades of green (7 and up)   **363.7**
Kidd, Renee A.
(jt. auth) Kidd, J. S. Into thin air   **363.7**
(jt. auth) Kidd, J. S. Life lines   **576.5**
(jt. auth) Kidd, J. S. Mother Nature's pharmacy
                                         615
(jt. auth) Kidd, J. S. Quarks and sparks
                                         621.48
(jt. auth) Kidd, J. S. Shades of green   **363.7**
Kidnapped. Stevenson, R. L.   **Fic**
The **kidnapped** prince: the life of Olaudah
Equiano. Cameron, A.   **92**
The **kidnappers**. Roberts, W. D.   **Fic**
Kidnapping
Wiloch, T. Everything you need to know about
protecting yourself and others from abduction
                                         613.6
Fiction
Bowler, T. Storm catchers (7 and up)   **Fic**
Bruchac, J. Skeleton man (4 and up)   **Fic**
Bunting, E. The hideout (5 and up)   **Fic**
Cameron, A. Colibri (5 and up)   **Fic**
Cooney, C. B. The face on the milk carton (7
and up)   **Fic**
Duncan, L. Killing Mr. Griffin (7 and up)
                                         Fic
Griffin, A. Overnight   **Fic**
Haddix, M. P. Escape from memory   **Fic**
Kehret, P. Abduction! (5 and up)   **Fic**
Kurtz, J. Saba   **Fic**

Kidnapping—Fiction—*Continued*
Napoli, D. J. Three days — **Fic**
Roberts, W. D. Hostage — **Fic**
Roberts, W. D. The kidnappers (4 and up) — **Fic**
Werlin, N. Locked inside (7 and up) — **Fic**
Kidnapping, Parental *See* Parental kidnapping
Kids at work. Freedman, R. — **331.3**
Kids can knit. Clewer, C. — **746.43**
The **kids'** catalog of Jewish holidays. Adler, D. A. — **296.4**
Kids' crafts [series]
Davis, J. Crochet — **746.43**
A **kid's** guide to America's Bill of Rights. Krull, K. — **342**
The **kids'** guide to digital photography. Bidner, J. — **775**
The **kids'** guide to working out conflicts. Drew, N. — **303.6**
The **kids'** invention book. Erlbach, A. — **608**
Kids knit!. Bradberry, S. — **746.43**
The **kids'** multicultural cookbook. Cook, D. F. — **641.5**
Kids on strike!. Bartoletti, S. C. — **331.8**
Kids still having kids. Bode, J. — **362.7**
The **kids'** volunteering book. Erlbach, A. — **302**
Kids who kill. Silverstein, H. — **364.1**
The **KidsClick!** Web searching skills guide with CD-ROM. Kuntz, J. — **025.04**
Kiefer, Jeanne
Jobs for kids (4 and up) — **650.1**
Kieler, Jørgen, 1919-
See/See also pages in the following book(s):
Lyman, D. Holocaust rescuers — **920**
Kiernan, Caitlín R.
The dead and the moonstruck
In Gothic!; ten original dark tales — **S C**
Kiesler, Kate, 1971-
(il) Ehrlich, G. A blizzard year — **Fic**
(il) Freedman, R. Out of darkness: the story of Louis Braille — **92**
Kikuyu (African people)
Fiction
Quintana, A. The baboon king (7 and up) — **Fic**
Kilby, Jack, 1923-2005
See/See also pages in the following book(s):
Northrup, M. American computer pioneers — **920**
Killer rocks from outer space. Koppes, S. N. — **523.5**
Killer superbugs. Day, N. — **616**
Killing Mr. Griffin. Duncan, L. — **Fic**
Killing the bear. Minty, J.
In Talking leaves; contemporary native American short stories — **S C**
Kim, Doug
See/See also pages in the following book(s):
Major, J. S. Caravan to America p[1]-13 (4 and up) — **920**
Kim, Henny H., 1968-
Child abuse (7 and up) — **362.7**
(ed) Depression. See Depression — **616.85**
(ed) Youth violence. See Youth violence — **364.36**
Kim Son Dal and the water-carriers. Jaffe, N.
In Jaffe, N. and Zeitlin, S. J. The cow of no color: riddle stories and justice tales from around the world p94-98 — **398.2**
Kimball, Chad T.
(ed) Child and youth security sourcebook. See Child and youth security sourcebook — **362.7**
Kimber, Murray
(il) Hovey, K. Ancient voices — **811**
Kimberly, Gail
Child of Faerie
In A Glory of unicorns p165-82 — **S C**
Kimmel, Elizabeth Cody
As far as the eye can reach (4 and up) — **978**
Ice story (4 and up) — **998**
In the stone circle (5 and up) — **Fic**
Lily B. on the brink of cool — **Fic**
The look-it-up book of explorers (5 and up) — **920**
Visiting Miss Caples (6 and up) — **Fic**
Kimmel, Eric A.
The jar of fools: eight Hanukkah stories from Chelm (4 and up) — **S C**
Contents: The jar of fools; How they play dreidel in Chelm; Sweeter than honey, purer than oil; The Knight of the Golden Slippers; Silent Samson, the Maccabee; The magic spoon; The soul of a menorah; Wisdom for sale
Sword of the samurai (4 and up) — **S C**
Includes the following stories: Dōhaku's head; The samurai and the dragon; The coward; Matajuro's training; The oxcart; The battle of Chihaya Castle; Tomoe Gozen; The burglar; Devil boy; The Rōnin and the tea master; No sword
The three riddles
In Fire and wings: dragon tales from East and West p79-86 — **S C**
Wonders and miracles (4 and up) — **296.4**
Kimmens, Andrew C.
(ed) World authors, 1900-1950. See World authors, 1900-1950 — **920.003**
The **kin**. Dickinson, P. — **Fic**
Kincaid, Jamaica
Annie John — **Fic**
Kindl, Patrice, 1951-
Goose chase — **Fic**
Lost in the labyrinth — **Fic**
Owl in love (6 and up) — **Fic**
The woman in the wall — **Fic**
The **kindling**. Armstrong, J. — **Fic**
Kindness rewarded. Molnár, I.
In Molnár, I. One-time dog market at Buda and other Hungarian folktales p47-53 — **398.2**
King, Ada *See* Lovelace, Ada King, Countess of, 1815-1852
King, Andy
Play-by-play mountain biking — **796.6**
(il) Bragg, L. W. Fundamental gymnastics — **796.44**
(il) Coleman, L. Fundamental soccer — **796.334**
(il) Dallas, K. Fundamental karate — **796.8**
(il) Foley, M. Fundamental hockey — **796.962**

King, Andy—*Continued*
(il) Geng, D. Play-by-play baseball   **796.357**
King, Augusta Ada *See* Lovelace, Ada King,
Countess of, 1815-1852
King, B. B.
About
Shirley, D. Everyday I sing the blues: the story
of B.B. King (7 and up)   **92**
See/See also pages in the following book(s):
Lester, J. The blues singers (5 and up)   **920**
King, Casey
Oh, freedom! (5 and up)   **323.1**
King, Coretta Scott, 1927-
About
Klingel, C. F. Coretta Scott King   **92**
Rhodes, L. R. Coretta Scott King   **92**
(jt. auth) King, M. L. The words of Martin Lu-
ther King, Jr.   **323.1**
King, Daniel, 1963-
Chess   **794.1**
Games (5 and up)   **794**
King, Dave
Elephant   **599.67**
(il) The Snake book. See The Snake book
597.9
(il) Wilkinson, P. Building   **690**
King, David C., 1933-
Al Capone and the roaring twenties   **92**
The Battle of Gettysburg   **973.7**
The Battle of Vicksburg   **973.7**
Benedict Arnold and the American Revolution
92
Bosnia and Herzegovina (5 and up)   **949.7**
Children's encyclopedia of American history
973.03
King, Elizabeth, 1953-
Quinceañera (5 and up)   **392**
King, Martin Luther, 1929-1968
The words of Martin Luther King, Jr.   **323.1**
About
Haskins, J. The life and death of Martin Luther
King, Jr. (5 and up)   **92**
Hatt, C. Martin Luther King, Jr   **92**
Klingel, C. F. Coretta Scott King   **92**
Manheimer, A. S. Martin Luther King Jr (5 and
up)   **92**
Rhodes, L. R. Coretta Scott King   **92**
See/See also pages in the following book(s):
Dubovoy, S. Civil rights leaders (7 and up)
920
King, Mary-Claire, 1946-
See/See also pages in the following book(s):
Lindop, L. Scientists and doctors (7 and up)
920
King, Stephen, 1947-
About
Wilson, S. Stephen King: king of thrillers and
horror   **92**
Wukovits, J. F. Stephen King (7 and up)   **92**
King, Thomas, 1943-
A seat in the garden
In Talking leaves; contemporary native
American short stories   **S C**

The **king** and the workman's daughter. Philip, N.
In Philip, N. Celtic fairy tales p105-12
398.2
King Arthur. Nardo, D.   **942.01**
King Lear. Packer, T.
In Packer, T. Tales from Shakespeare p175-
192   **822.3**
King Matthias and his truthful shepherd. Molnár,
I.
In Molnár, I. One-time dog market at Buda
and other Hungarian folktales p12-16
398.2
King Matthias and the old man. Molnár, I.
In Molnár, I. One-time dog market at Buda
and other Hungarian folktales p1-5
398.2
King Matthias and the Szekler's daughter. Molnár,
I.
In Molnár, I. One-time dog market at Buda
and other Hungarian folktales p6-11
398.2
King Matthias and the weatherman. Molnár, I.
In Molnár, I. One-time dog market at Buda
and other Hungarian folktales p21-22
398.2
The **king** of dragons. Fenner, C.   **Fic**
The **King** of Ireland's son. Philip, N.
In Philip, N. Celtic fairy tales p44-53
398.2
King of the mild frontier: an ill-advised autobiog-
raphy. Crutcher, C.   **92**
King-Smith, Dick, 1922-
Chewing the cud (5 and up)   **92**
King who stood all night. Aiken, J.
In Aiken, J. Shadows and moonshine; stories
S C
Kingdoms of life [series]
Silverstein, A. Plants   **580**
Silverstein, A. Vertebrates   **596**
The **Kingfisher** book of funny poems (4 and up)
821.008
The **Kingfisher** book of religions. Barnes, T.
201
The **Kingfisher** geography encyclopedia. Gifford,
C.   **910.3**
The **Kingfisher** history encyclopedia (5 and up)
909
The **Kingfisher** illustrated animal encyclopedia.
Burnie, D.   **590.3**
The **Kingfisher** illustrated horse & pony encyclo-
pedia. Ransford, S.   **636.1**
The **Kingfisher** illustrated nature encyclopedia.
Burnie, D.   **508**
Kingfisher knowledge [series]
Adams, S. Castles & forts   **355.7**
Barnes, T. Archaeology   **930.1**
Burnie, D. Endangered planet   **333.95**
Gifford, C. Spies   **327.12**
Malam, J. Mummies   **393**
Taylor, B. Animal giants   **590**
Walker, R. Genes & DNA   **576.5**
Wilkes, A. Dangerous creatures   **591.6**
The **Kingfisher** science encyclopedia   **503**

The **Kingfisher** young people's book of planet earth. Redfern, M. **550**

The **Kingfisher** young people's book of space. Redfern, M. **520**

Kingman, Lee, 1919-
  (ed) Newbery and Caldecott Medal books, 1966-1975. See Newbery and Caldecott Medal books, 1966-1975 **028.5**
  (ed) Newbery and Caldecott Medal books, 1976-1985. See Newbery and Caldecott Medal books, 1976-1985 **028.5**

Kings and queens **920.003**

Kings and rulers
  See also Dictators; Emperors; Queens
  Hinds, K. The court **940.2**
  Humphrey, J. Genghis Khan **92**
  Kings and queens **920.003**
  Meltzer, M. Ten kings (5 and up) **920**
  Pickels, D. E. Egyptian kings and queens and classical deities **930**
  Ross, S. Monarchs (5 and up) **940.1**
  Stanley, D. Saladin: noble prince of Islam (4 and up) **92**
         Fiction
  Kurtz, J. Saba **Fic**

The **King's** ankus. Kipling, R.
  In Kipling, R. The jungle books **S C**

The **kings** are already here. Freymann-Weyr, G. **Fic**

The **king's** dragon. Yolen, J.
  In Fire and wings: dragon tales from East and West p112-16 **S C**

Kings Landing Historical Settlement (N.B.)
  Goodman, S. Ultimate field trip 4: a week in the 1800s (5 and up) **973.5**

The **king's** shadow. Alder, E. **Fic**

Kingsley, Ben
  (jt. auth) Ganeri, A. The young person's guide to the orchestra **784.2**

Kingston, Maxine Hong
  A sea worry
  In American dragons: twenty-five Asian American voices p112-17 **810.8**

Kingston, William H. G., 1814-1880
  St. George and the dragon
  In The Book of dragons p89-95 **S C**

Kintpuash, Modoc Chief, 1837?-1873
  See/See also pages in the following book(s):
  Brown, D. A. Bury my heart at Wounded Knee **970.004**

Kiowa Indians
  See/See also pages in the following book(s):
  Freedman, R. Indian chiefs (6 and up) **920**

Kipfer, Barbara Ann
  (ed) Roget's 21st century thesaurus in dictionary form. See Roget's 21st century thesaurus in dictionary form **423**
  (ed) Roget's international thesaurus. See Roget's international thesaurus **423**

Kipling, Rudyard, 1865-1936
  The jungle books (4 and up) **S C**

Contents: Mowgli's brothers; Kaa's hunting; How fear came; "Tiger! Tiger!"; The King's ankus; Letting in the jungle; Red Dog; The spring running; "Rikki-tikki-tavi"; The white seal; The miracle of Purun Bhagat; The undertakers; Quiquern; Toomai of the elephants; Her Majesty's servants

  Rikki-tikki-tavi
    In Read all about it!; great read-aloud stories, poems, and newspaper pieces for preteens and teens p155-74 **808.8**

Kira-Kira. Kadohata, C. **Fic**

Kirberger, Kimberly, 1953-
  (jt. auth) Canfield, J. Chicken soup for the teenage soul {I-III} **158**

Kirchberger, Joe H.
  The Civil War and Reconstruction (7 and up) **973.7**
  The First World War (7 and up) **940.3**

Kirke, Edmund *See* Gilmore, James R., 1822-1903

Kirkman, Robert
  Tech jacket, Vol. 1: Lost & found **741.5**

Kirkpatrick, Helen, 1909-
  See/See also pages in the following book(s):
  Colman, P. Where the action was **070.4**

Kirkpatrick, Patricia
  (comp) Angelou, M. Maya Angelou **811**

Kirwan, Anna
  Under the bending yew
    In Sherwood: original stories from the world of Robin Hood p38-47 **S C**
  Victoria, May blossom of Britannia **Fic**

The **kiss** in the carry-on bag. Peck, R.
  In Destination unexpected: short stories **S C**
  In Peck, R. Past perfect, present tense: new and collected stories **S C**

Kissing doorknobs. Hesser, T. S. **Fic**

Kissing Tennessee. Appelt, K.
  In Appelt, K. Kissing Tennessee and other stories from the Stardust Dance p81-89 **S C**

Kissing Tennessee and other stories from the Stardust Dance. Appelt, K. **S C**

Kissinger, Henry, 1923-
  See/See also pages in the following book(s):
  Roberts, R. Leaders and generals **920**

Kitchen chemistry. See Gardner, R. Science project ideas about kitchen chemistry **540.7**

Kitchen science. Pentland, P. **641**

Kitchens
  Plante, E. M. The American kitchen, 1700 to the present (7 and up) **643**

Kite, L. Patricia, 1940-
  Maya Angelou **92**

The **kite** rider. McCaughrean, G. **Fic**

Kites
         Fiction
  McCaughrean, G. The kite rider (5 and up) **Fic**

Kit's wilderness. Almond, D. **Fic**

Kittleson, Mark J., 1952-
  (ed) The truth about alcohol. See The truth about alcohol **362.292**

Kittleson, Mark J., 1952——_Continued_
(ed) The truth about eating disorders. See The
truth about eating disorders **616.85**
(ed) The truth about fear and depression. See
The truth about fear and depression
616.85

Kittredge, Mary, 1949-
The common cold (7 and up) **616.2**

Kitty and Mack: a love story. Myers, W. D.
_In_ Myers, W. D. 145th Street; short stories
S C

KKK _See_ Ku Klux Klan

Klare, Roger
Gregor Mendel **92**

Klass, David, 1960-
Baseball camp
_In_ Places I never meant to be; original stories
by censored writers **S C**
California Blue **Fic**
Danger zone **Fic**
The gospel according to Krenzwinkle
_In_ Ultimate sports; short stories by outstand-
ing writers for young adults p274-98
S C
Home of the Braves (7 and up) **Fic**
You don't know me (7 and up) **Fic**

Klass, Sheila Solomon
The un-civil war **Fic**

Klause, Annette Curtis
Alien secrets (5 and up) **Fic**
The bogey man
_In_ Night terrors; stories of shadow and sub-
stance **S C**
The silver kiss **Fic**
Summer of love
_In_ The Color of absence; 12 stories about loss
and hope p1-14 **S C**

Klausner, Janet
Sequoyah's gift (4 and up) **92**

Klein, Norma, 1938-1989
Something which is non-existent
_In_ Places I never meant to be; original stories
by censored writers **S C**

Klein, T. E. D., 1947-
Rhode Island
_In_ Celebrate the states **973**

Klein, Ted _See_ Klein, T. E. D., 1947-

Kliment, Bud
Billie Holiday **92**

Klimley, A. Peter
About
Mallory, K. Swimming with hammerhead sharks
(4 and up) **597**

Kline, Michael P.
(il) Cook, D. F. The kids' multicultural cookbook **641.5**
(il) Hart, A. Ancient Greece! **938**

Klingel, Cynthia Fitterer
Coretta Scott King **92**

Klise, Kate
Deliver us from Normal **Fic**
Letters from camp **Fic**

The **Klondike** gold rush. Walsh Shepherd, D.
971.9

Klondike River valley (Yukon)
Gold discoveries
Walsh Shepherd, D. The Klondike gold rush (4
and up) **971.9**
Gold discoveries—Fiction
Hobbs, W. Jason's gold (5 and up) **Fic**
Lawson, J. Destination gold! **Fic**

Knapp, Brian J.
Earth science **550**
Materials science **620.1**

Knappman, Edward W.
(ed) Courtroom drama. See Courtroom drama
347

Knee-high man. Yolen, J.
_In_ Yolen, J. Mightier than the sword; world
folktales for strong boys p36-38
398.2

Knight, Christopher G.
(il) Lasky, K. Monarchs **595.7**
(il) Lasky, K. The most beautiful roof in the
world **577.3**

Knight, Judson
Ancient civilizations: almanac (7 and up)
930
Middle ages: biographies **920**
(jt. auth) McConnell, S. A. Ancient civilizations:
biographies **920**
(comp) Middle ages: primary sources. See Middle ages: primary sources **909.07**

Knight, Margaret, 1838-1914
See/See also pages in the following book(s):
Thimmesh, C. Girls think of everything (5 and
up) **920**

Knight, Virginia Curtin
(ed) African biography. See African biography
920.003

Knight. Gravett, C. **940.1**

The **Knight** of the Golden Slippers. Kimmel, E.
A.
_In_ Kimmel, E. A. The jar of fools: eight Ha-
nukkah stories from Chelm p13-18
S C

Knights & castles. Hart, A. **940.1**
Knights & castles. Martin, A. **940.1**

Knights and knighthood
Chrisp, P. Warfare **355**
Gravett, C. Knight (4 and up) **940.1**
Hart, A. Knights & castles (4 and up) **940.1**
Martin, A. Knights & castles (5 and up)
940.1
Nardo, D. The Middle Ages (7 and up)
940.1
Nicolle, D. Medieval knights **940.1**
Ruhl, G. In the time of knights (4 and up)
942.03
Weatherly, M. William Marshal, medieval Eng-
land's greatest knight [biography of William
Marshal, earl of Pembroke] **92**
Zohorsky, J. R. Medieval knights and warriors
940.1
Fiction
Cadnum, M. The book of the Lion (7 and up)
Fic
Cadnum, M. The leopard sword (7 and up)
Fic

Knights and knighthood—Fiction—*Continued*
Jinks, C. Pagan's crusade (7 and up)   **Fic**
Morris, G. The squire's tale   **Fic**
Yolen, J. Sword of the rightful king   **Fic**

Knights of the Round Table *See* Arthurian romances

Knitting
Bradberry, S. Kids knit! (5 and up)   **746.43**
Clewer, C. Kids can knit (4 and up)   **746.43**
Wenger, J. Teen knitting club (7 and up)   **746.43**

Knots in my yo-yo string. Spinelli, J.   **92**

Know your true enemy. Springer, N.
In Sherwood: original stories from the world of Robin Hood p50-66   **S C**

Knowles, Elizabeth, 1946-
Reading rules!   **028.5**
Talk about books!   **372.4**

Knox, Bernard MacGregor Walker
(jt. auth) Homer. The Odyssey   **883**

Knox, Robert, 1793-1862
Fiction
Morgan, N. Fleshmarket (7 and up)   **Fic**

Knuckles. Chen, M. F.
In American eyes; new Asian-American short stories for young adults p62-79   **S C**

Koalas
Malaspina, A. The koala (7 and up)   **599.2**

Kobayashi, M. (Makoto)
What's Michael? Vol. 10: Sleepless nights   **741.5**

Kobayashi, Makoto *See* Kobayashi, M. (Makoto)

Kochalka, James
Monkey vs. Robot   **741.5**

Kochel, Marcia Agness
(jt. auth) Baxter, K. A. Gotcha!   **028.1**

Koden. Nihei, J.
In American dragons: twenty-five Asian American voices p97-109   **810.8**

Koertge, Ronald
Angel & Aly 13; thirteen stories that capture the agony and ecstasy of being thirteen
The Brimstone journals (7 and up)   **Fic**
Brutal interlude
In Destination unexpected: short stories   **S C**
Geeks bearing gifts
In On the fringe p11-26   **S C**
Margaux with an X (7 and up)   **Fic**
Shakespeare bats cleanup (7 and up)   **Fic**
Stoner & Spaz (7 and up)   **Fic**
Variations on a theme
In What a song can do; 12 riffs on the power of music   **S C**

Koja, Kathe
Buddha Boy (7 and up)   **Fic**
Remnants
In The Green Man: tales from the mythic forest p312-20   **808.8**
Straydog (7 and up)   **Fic**

Koller, Jackie French
Brother, can you spare a dream?
In Time capsule: short stories about teenagers throughout the twentieth century p64-83   **S C**
Someday   **Fic**

Konigsburg, E. L.
The outcasts of 19 Schuyler Place   **Fic**
A proud taste for scarlet and miniver (5 and up)   **Fic**
Silent to the bone (7 and up)   **Fic**
The view from Saturday (4 and up)   **Fic**
See/See also pages in the following book(s):
Author talk (4 and up)   **028.5**
The Newbery & Caldecott medal books, 1986-2000   **028.5**

Konomi, Takeshi
The Prince of Tennis, Vol. 1   **741.5**

Koopmans, Andy
Charles Lindbergh   **92**

Koppes, Steven N.
Killer rocks from outer space   **523.5**

Kops, Deborah
The Battle of Bull Run   **973.7**
(jt. auth) Pascoe, E. Scholastic kid's almanac   **031.02**

Koran
The Koran   **297.1**

Korea
See also Korea (South)
DuBois, J. Korea (5 and up)   **951.9**
Fiction
Choi, S. N. Year of impossible goodbyes (5 and up)   **Fic**
Park, L. S. A single shard (5 and up)   **Fic**
Park, L. S. When my name was Keoko (5 and up)   **Fic**
Watkins, Y. K. My brother, my sister, and I (6 and up)   **Fic**
Watkins, Y. K. So far from the bamboo grove (6 and up)   **Fic**

Korea (North)
North Korea   **951.93**

Korea (Republic) *See* Korea (South)

Korea (South)
Williams, J. K. South Korea (7 and up)   **951.95**

Korean Americans
Fiction
Lee, M. G. Necessary roughness (7 and up)   **Fic**
Na, A. A step from heaven (7 and up)   **Fic**
Park, L. S. Project Mulberry (5 and up)   **Fic**
Son, J. Finding my hat   **Fic**

Korean War, 1950-1953
Ashabranner, B. K. Remembering Korea (4 and up)   **951.9**
Benson, S. Korean War: almanac and primary sources (7 and up)   **951.9**
Dolan, E. F. America in the Korean War (7 and up)   **951.9**
Feldman, R. T. The Korean War (5 and up)   **951.9**
Isserman, M. Korean war (7 and up)   **951.9**

Korean War, 1950-1953—*Continued*
See/See also pages in the following book(s):
Collier, C. The United States in the Cold War: 1945-1989 **327.73**
Lindop, E. America in the 1950s (7 and up) **973.921**

Biography
Benson, S. Korean War: biographies (7 and up) **920**

Personal narratives
Granfield, L. I remember Korea **951.9**
Korean War: almanac and primary sources. Benson, S. **951.9**
Korean War: biographies. Benson, S. **920**
Korean War Veterans Memorial (Washington, D.C.)
Ashabranner, B. K. Remembering Korea (4 and up) **951.9**

Korematsu, Fred, 1919-2005
About
Alonso, K. Korematsu v. United States (7 and up) **323.1**
Korematsu v. United States. Alonso, K. **323.1**

Korman, Gordon, 1963-
Jake, reinvented (7 and up) **Fic**
No more dead dogs **Fic**
The sixth grade nickname game (4 and up) **Fic**
Son of the mob (7 and up) **Fic**

Kornblatt, Marc, 1954-
Understanding Buddy **Fic**

Korolev, Sergei, 1907-1966
See/See also pages in the following book(s):
Richie, J. Space flight **920**

Kort, Michael
The handbook of the Middle East (7 and up) **956**
The handbook of the new Eastern Europe (7 and up) **943**
Russia (7 and up) **947**

Ko's story. Dickinson, P.
In Dickinson, P. The kin p307-459 **Fic**

Kosek, Jane Kelly
(jt. auth) Levchuck, C. M. Healthy living **613**

Koshkin, Alexander
(il) Chaikin, M. Angels sweep the desert floor **296.1**

Kositsky, Lynne, 1947-
The thought of high windows (7 and up) **Fic**

Koslow, Philip
(jt. auth) Kranz, R. The biographical dictionary of African Americans **920.003**

Kosof, Anna
Living in two worlds (7 and up) **325.73**

Kosovo (Serbia)
Andryszewski, T. Kosovo **949.7**
Fiction
Mead, A. Girl of Kosovo (5 and up) **Fic**

Koss, Amy Goldman, 1954-
The girls (5 and up) **Fic**
Stranger in Dadland (5 and up) **Fic**
Strike two (4 and up) **Fic**

Kotoshi the dragon doctor. Gershator, P.
In Fire and wings: dragon tales from East and West p117-23 **S C**

Kovalevskaíà, S. V. (Sof´íà Vasil´evna), 1850-1891
See/See also pages in the following book(s):
Henderson, H. Modern mathematicians (7 and up) **920**

Kovalevskaíà, Sof´íà Vasil´evna *See* Kovalevskaíà, S. V. (Sof´íà Vasil´evna), 1850-1891

Kowalski, Kathiann M., 1955-
Alternative medicine (7 and up) **615.5**
Poverty in America **362.5**

Kozar, Richard
Inventors and their discoveries **920**

Kozleski, Lisa
Jane Goodall (7 and up) **92**

Kraft, Betsy Harvey
Theodore Roosevelt (5 and up) **92**

Kraken. Dickinson, P.
In McKinley, R. and Dickinson, P. Water: tales of elemental spirits p170-207 **S C**

Kramer, Ann, 1946-
Nelson Mandela (7 and up) **92**

Kramer, Gerri Freid
The truth about eating disorders. See The truth about eating disorders **616.85**

Kramer, Stephen
Hidden worlds: looking through a scientist's microscope (4 and up) **502.8**

Kramer, Sydelle
The look-it-up book of first ladies **920**

Kranz, Rachel
The biographical dictionary of African Americans **920.003**

Krashen, Stephen D.
The power of reading **028.5**

Krasner, Steven
Play ball like the pros (4 and up) **796.357**

Krasno, Rena, 1923-
Cloud weavers (5 and up) **398.2**

Krass, Peter
Sojourner Truth **92**

Kraus, Joanna Halpert, 1937-
The ice wolf
In Theatre for young audiences; 20 great plays for children p284-307 **812.008**

Krautwurst, Terry, 1946-
Science smart. See Science smart **550**

Krecek, Joseph
See/See also pages in the following book(s):
Graham, K. Contemporary environmentalists (7 and up) **920**

Kreiner, Anna
Everything you need to know about creating your own support system (7 and up) **158**

Kress, Nancy, 1948-
Out of all them bright stars
In New skies: an anthology of today's science fiction **S C**

Kress, Stephen W.
(jt. auth) Salmansohn, P. Saving birds
333.95

Kricher, John C.
Peterson first guide to seashores (6 and up)
577.7

Krieger, Melanie Jacobs
How to excel in science competitions   507.8

Krisher, Trudy
Spite fences   **Fic**
Uncommon Faith   **Fic**
We loved Lucy
   In Time capsule: short stories about teenagers
      throughout the twentieth century p112-38
                                              S C

Krishnaswami, Uma, 1956-
Going to Kashi
   In Soul searching: thirteen stories about faith
      and belief p157-76   **S C**

Kristina, Queen of Sweden, 1626-1689 *See*
   Christina, Queen of Sweden, 1626-1689

Krizmanic, Judy
A teen's vegetarian cookbook (7 and up)
                                              641.5

Krog, Hazlitt
(jt. auth) Shulman, M. Attack of the killer video
   book   778.59

Kroll, Steven
Robert Fulton   92

Kronenwetter, Michael
America in the 1960s (7 and up)   973.92
Protest! (7 and up)   303.4

Kronzek, Allan Zola
The sorcerer's companion (4 and up)
                                             823.009

Kronzek, Elizabeth, 1969-
(jt. auth) Kronzek, A. Z. The sorcerer's companion   823.009

Kropp, Paul
The countess and me   **Fic**

Krull, Kathleen, 1952-
A kid's guide to America's Bill of Rights (4
   and up)   342
Lives of the presidents   920
Presenting Paula Danziger   813.009

Ku Klux Klan
                 Fiction
Hesse, K. Witness (6 and up)   **Fic**

Kubinyi, Laszlo, 1937-
(il) Custer, E. B. The diary of Elizabeth Bacon
   Custer   973.8
(il) Taylor, S. K. The diary of Susie King Taylor, Civil War nurse   973.7
(il) Watkins, S. R. The diary of Sam Watkins,
   a confederate soldier   973.7

Kublai Khan, 1216-1294
See/See also pages in the following book(s):
Meltzer, M. Ten kings (5 and up)   920
                 Fiction
McCaughrean, G. The kite rider (5 and up)
                                              Fic

Kudlinski, Kathleen V., 1950-
The spirit catchers (7 and up)   **Fic**

Kuhn, Betsy
Angels of mercy (5 and up)   940.54
Kuhn, Dwight
(il) Pascoe, E. Ants   595.7
(il) Pascoe, E. Beetles   595.7
(il) Pascoe, E. Butterflies and moths   595.7
(il) Pascoe, E. Crickets and grasshoppers
                                            595.7
(il) Pascoe, E. Earthworms   592
(il) Pascoe, E. Flies   595.7
(il) Pascoe, E. Seeds and seedlings   582
(il) Pascoe, E. Slime, molds, and fungi
                                            579.5
(il) Pascoe, E. Snails and slugs   594
(il) Pascoe, E. Tadpoles   597.8
Kuklin, Susan
Iqbal Masih and the crusaders against child
   slavery (7 and up)   331.3
Trial: the inside story (7 and up)   345
Kummer, Patricia K.
Tibet (5 and up)   951
Ukraine (4 and up)   947.7
Kunitz, Stanley, 1905-
(ed) American authors, 1600-1900. See
   American authors, 1600-1900   920.003
Kunkel, Dennis
                 About
Kramer, S. Hidden worlds: looking through a
   scientist's microscope (4 and up)   502.8
Kuntz, Jerry, 1956-
The KidsClick! Web searching skills guide with
   CD-ROM   025.04
Kupperberg, Paul
Spy satellites   327.12
Kurds
LoBaido, A. C. The Kurds of Asia   950
The **Kurds** of Asia. LoBaido, A. C.   950
Kurtz, Jane
Jakarta missing   **Fic**
Saba   **Fic**
The storyteller's beads (5 and up)   **Fic**
(ed) Memories of sun. See Memories of sun
                                              S C
Kustanowitz, Esther
The hidden children of the Holocaust   940.53
Kusugak, Michael
See/See also pages in the following book(s):
Ellis, S. From reader to writer   372.6
Kuwait
Foster, L. M. Kuwait (4 and up)   953.67
Marcovitz, H. Kuwait   953.67
O'Shea, M. Kuwait (5 and up)   953.67
         History—1991, Persian Gulf War
   See Persian Gulf War, 1991
Kwanzaa
Walter, M. P. Kwanzaa: a family affair (4 and
   up)   394.26
Kwasney, Michelle D., 1960-
Baby Blue   **Fic**
Kwolek, Stephanie L., 1923-
See/See also pages in the following book(s):
Thimmesh, C. Girls think of everything (5 and
   up)   920

Kyd, Thomas, 1558-1594
See/See also pages in the following book(s):
Nardo, D. Great Elizabethan playwrights
920

Kynaston, Suzanne
(jt. auth) Ward, P. Wild bears of the world
599.78

Kyvelos, Peter
See/See also pages in the following book(s):
Major, J. S. Caravan to America p[1]-13 (4 and up)
920

L

La Fevers, R. L.
The falconmaster **Fic**

La Salle, René Robert Cavelier *See* La Salle, Robert Cavelier, sieur de, 1643-1687

La Salle, Robert Cavelier, sieur de, 1643-1687
About
Faber, H. La Salle **92**
Goodman, J. E. Despite all obstacles: La Salle and the conquest of the Mississippi (4 and up) **92**

Lab. Hearne, B. G.
In Hearne, B. G. The canine connection: stories about dogs and people p1-10
S C

The **lab**: hey . . . test this!. Sava, S. C. **741.5**

Labor
See also Agricultural laborers; Migrant labor; Teenagers—Employment
United States
Woog, A. A sweatshop during the industrial revolution **331.2**

Labor disputes
See also Strikes

Labor movement
Streissguth, T. Legendary labor leaders (7 and up) **920**
Fiction
Hughes, P. The breaker boys **Fic**

Labor supply
See also Teenagers—Employment

Labor unions
Dash, J. We shall not be moved (7 and up)
331.4
Miller, C. C. A. Philip Randolph and the African American labor movement **92**

Laboratory animal experimentation *See* Animal experimentation

Lace, William W.
Christianity **230**
Elizabeth I and her court **942.05**
England (7 and up) **942**
The Vatican **945**

The **lace** dowry. Cheng, A. **Fic**

Lacrosse
Swissler, B. Winning lacrosse for girls (7 and up) **796.34**

The **lady** of the ice garden. Dalkey, K.
In Firebirds: an anthology of original fantasy and science fiction; an anthology of original fantasy and science fiction **S C**

LaFaye, A., 1970-
Edith Shay (7 and up) **Fic**
Testing, testing 1 . . . 2 . . . 3
In Shelf life: stories by the book p55-66
S C
Worth (5 and up) **Fic**

Lafayette, Marie Joseph Paul Yves Roch Gilbert du Motier, marquis de, 1757-1834
About
Fritz, J. Why not, Lafayette? (5 and up) **92**

Laffite, Jean, 1780?-1825?
See/See also pages in the following book(s):
Wren, L. L. Pirates and privateers of the high seas p11-17 **920**

Lafitte, Jean *See* Laffite, Jean, 1780?-1825?

Lagasse, Emeril
Emeril's there's a chef in my family! (5 and up)
641.5

Laidlaw, Jill A.
Frida Kahlo (5 and up) **92**

The **Laidly** worm of Spindleston Heughs
In Hearne, B. G. Beauties and beasts p139-42
398.2

Lake, Kate
(il) Matsen, B. Go wild in New York City
974.7

Lake and pond. Sayre, A. P. **577.6**

Lake ecology
Josephs, D. Lakes, ponds, and temporary pools
577.6
Katz, S. The Great Lakes **577.6**
Sayre, A. P. Lake and pond (5 and up)
577.6

Lake of secrets. Littke, L. **Fic**

Lakes, ponds, and temporary pools. Josephs, D.
577.6

Lakota woman. Brave Bird, M. **92**

Lalley, Pat
9.11.01: terrorists attack the U.S. (4 and up)
973.931

Lamar, Lucius Quintus Cincinnatus, 1825-1893
See/See also pages in the following book(s):
Kennedy, J. F. Profiles in courage **920**

Lamb, Charles, 1775-1834
Tales from Shakespeare **822.3**

Lamb, Kirsten
Cancer **616.99**

Lamb, Mary, 1764-1847
(jt. auth) Lamb, C. Tales from Shakespeare
822.3

Lamb, William Frederick, 1883-1952
See/See also pages in the following book(s):
Aaseng, N. Construction: building the impossible **624**

Lamb to the slaughter. Dahl, R.
In Dahl, R. Skin and other stories **S C**

Lambert, David, 1932-
DK guide to dinosaurs **567.9**

The **lame** warrior and the skeleton. Brown, D. A.
In Brown, D. A. Dee Brown's folktales of the Native American; retold for our times p158-59   **398.2**

Lamedman, Debbie
111 one-minute monologues   **812.008**

Lamm, C. Drew
Bittersweet   **Fic**

Lampton, Christopher
(jt. auth) Vergoth, K. Endangered species   **578.68**

Lancelot (Legendary character)
Pyle, H. The story of Sir Launcelot and his companions (7 and up)   **398.2**

The **land**. Jaffe, N.
In Jaffe, N. and Zeitlin, S. J. The cow of no color: riddle stories and justice tales from around the world p99-100   **398.2**

The **land**. Taylor, M. D.   **Fic**

The **land** I lost: adventures of a boy in Vietnam. Huynh, Q. N.   **92**

Land of the buffalo bones. Bauer, M. D.   **Fic**

Land-otter. San Souci, R.
In San Souci, R. A terrifying taste of short & shivery; thirty creepy tales p20-24   **398.2**

Landau, Elaine
Deafness   **617.8**
Dyslexia (5 and up)   **616.85**
Head and brain injuries (7 and up)   **617.1**
Heroine of the Titanic: the real unsinkable Molly Brown (5 and up)   **92**
Joined at birth   **616**
Living with albinism   **616.5**
Multiple births   **618.2**
Osama bin Laden (7 and up)   **92**
Parkinson's disease (7 and up)   **616.8**
Tourette syndrome (7 and up)   **616.8**
Tuberculosis (7 and up)   **616.2**
Your legal rights (7 and up)   **346**
(comp) Holocaust memories. See Holocaust memories   **940.53**
(comp) Slave narratives. See Slave narratives   **326**

Landis, Geoffrey A.
A walk in the sun
In New skies: an anthology of today's science fiction   **S C**

Landmark events in American history [series]
Anderson, D. Arriving at Ellis Island   **325.73**
Uschan, M. V. The Battle of the Little Bighorn   **973.8**
Uschan, M. V. The bombing of Pearl Harbor   **940.54**
Walsh, F. The Montgomery bus boycott   **323.1**

Landmark Supreme Court cases [series]
Alonso, K. Korematsu v. United States   **323.1**
Alonso, K. Loving v. Virginia   **346**
Alonso, K. Schenck v. United States   **342**
Banfield, S. The Bakke case   **344**
DeVillers, D. Marbury v. Madison   **347**
Farish, L. Tinker v. Des Moines   **342**

Fireside, H. New York Times v. Sullivan   **342**
Freedman, S. Clay v. United States   **343**
Fuller, S. B. Hazelwood v. Kuhlmeier   **344**
Herda, D. J. The Dred Scott case   **342**
Herda, D. J. Furman v. Georgia   **345**
Herda, D. J. New York Times v. United States   **342**
Levinson, I. S. Gibbons v. Ogden   **343**
Persico, D. Mapp v. Ohio   **345**
Sergis, D. K. Bush v. Gore   **342**
Sergis, D. K. Cipollone v. Liggett Group   **346.03**
Sherrow, V. Cherokee Nation v. Georgia   **346**
Sherrow, V. Gideon v. Wainwright   **345**
Trespacz, K. L. Ferrell v. Dallas I.S.D.   **344**

Landmarks, Literary *See* Literary landmarks

Landmarks of the American Revolution. Nash, G. B.   **973.3**

Lands and peoples   **910.3**

Lane, Brian
Crime & detection (4 and up)   **364**

Lang, Andrew, 1844-1912
The flower queen's daughter
In The Book of dragons p26-34   **S C**
Sigurd and Fafnir
In The Book of dragons p72-77   **S C**
Stan Bolovan
In The Book of dragons p96-109   **S C**

Lang, Mark
(il) Bodger, J. Tales of court and castle   **398.2**

Lange, Brenda
Genghis Khan (7 and up)   **92**

Lange, Dorothea, 1895-1965
About
Partridge, E. Restless spirit: the life and work of Dorothea Lange (6 and up)   **92**
See/See also pages in the following book(s):
Danneberg, J. Women artists of the West   **920**
Sills, L. In real life: six women photographers (7 and up)   **920**

Langemack, Chapple
The booktalker's bible   **028.5**

Langford, David
Different kinds of darkness
In New skies: an anthology of today's science fiction   **S C**

Langhorne, Mary Jo
(ed) Developing an information literacy program, K-12. See Developing an information literacy program, K-12   **025.5**

Langley, Andrew
Medieval life [y] (4 and up)   **940.1**
The Roman news   **937**

Langley, Myrtle
Religion   **200**

Langrish, Bob
(il) Ransford, S. The Kingfisher illustrated horse & pony encyclopedia   **636.1**

Langrish, Katherine
Troll Fell (5 and up)   **Fic**

Language and languages
See also Sign language

Language arts
See also Creative writing

Language of the birds. Yolen, J.
In Yolen, J. Mightier than the sword; world folktales for strong boys p39-45 **398.2**

Lanier, Shannon
Jefferson's children (7 and up) **920**

Lannin, Joanne
A history of basketball for girls and women **796.323**

Lanning, Scott
Essential reference services for today's school media specialists **025.5**

Lantz, Francess Lin, 1952-
Standing on the roof naked
In On the fringe p89-113 **S C**

Laos
Mansfield, S. Laos (5 and up) **959.4**
Zickgraf, R. Laos **959.4**

The **Laplander's** drum. Olson, A. N.
In Olson, A. N. and Schwartz, H. Ask the bones: scary stories from around the world p53-59 **398.2**

Larbalestier, Justine
Magic or madness (7 and up) **Fic**

Larcenet, Manu, 1969-
(jt. auth) Trondheim, L. Astronauts of the future **741.5**

LaReau, Jenna
(il) Janeczko, P. B. Top secret **652**

Larkin, Philip
The Oxford book of twentieth-century English verse. See The Oxford book of twentieth-century English verse **821.008**

Laroche, Giles
(il) Sturges, P. Sacred places **203**

Larson, Jeanette C.
Bringing mysteries alive for children and young adults **028.5**

Lasers
Morgan, N. Lasers **621.36**

Lasher, Maureen
(jt. auth) Wenger, J. Teen knitting club **746.43**

Lasky, Kathryn
Beyond the burning time (7 and up) **Fic**
Blood secret (7 and up) **Fic**
A brilliant streak: the making of Mark Twain (4 and up) **92**
Christmas after all **Fic**
Dreams in the golden country (4 and up) **Fic**
Elizabeth I (4 and up) **Fic**
Jahanara, Princess of Princesses **Fic**
A journey to the New World **Fic**
Kazunomiya **Fic**
Mary, Queen of Scots, queen without a country **Fic**
Memoirs of a bookbat (6 and up) **Fic**
Monarchs (4 and up) **595.7**

The most beautiful roof in the world (4 and up) **577.3**
The night journey (4 and up) **Fic**
Star split (7 and up) **Fic**
A time for courage **Fic**
True north (6 and up) **Fic**

About
Brown, J. Presenting Kathryn Lasky **813.009**

Lassieur, Allison
The ancient Greeks (5 and up) **938**
The ancient Romans (5 and up) **937**
Before the storm (7 and up) **970.004**
Crabs, lobsters, and shrimps (4-6) **595.3**
Marie Curie **92**

The **last** book in the universe. Philbrick, W. R. **Fic**

The **last** mall rat. Esckilsen, E. E. **Fic**

Last mass. Rice, D.
In Rice, D. Crazy loco; stories about growing up Chicano in southern Texas p108-35 **S C**

The **last** mission. Mazer, H. **Fic**

The **last** of the dragons. Nesbit, E.
In Fire and wings: dragon tales from East and West p124-36 **S C**

The **last** safe place on earth. Peck, R. **Fic**

The **last** tales of Uncle Remus. Lester, J. **398.2**

The **last** treasure. Anderson, J. **Fic**

Lasting echoes. Bruchac, J. **970.004**

Latchkey children
Mediavilla, C. Creating the full-service homework center in your library **027.4**

Latimer, Jonathan P.
Backyard birds (4 and up) **598**
Birds of prey (4 and up) **598**
Bizarre birds (4 and up) **598**
Butterflies (4 and up) **595.7**
Caterpillars (4 and up) **595.7**
Shorebirds (4 and up) **598**
Songbirds (4 and up) **598**
(ed) Simon & Schuster thesaurus for children. See Simon & Schuster thesaurus for children **423**

Latimer, Lewis Howard, 1848-1928
See/See also pages in the following book(s):
Aaseng, N. Black inventors (7 and up) **920**

Latin America
Encyclopedias
Latin America, history and culture **980**

Latin America
Bibliography
Schon, I. The best of Latino heritage 1996-2002 **011.6**
Schon, I. The best of the Latino heritage **011.6**

Fiction
Delacre, L. Salsa stories (4-6) **S C**
Folklore
See Folklore—Latin America

Latin America, history and culture **980**

Latin American literature
See also Mexican literature

Latin American literature—*Continued*
Bibliography
Schon, I. Recommended books in Spanish for children and young adults, 2000 through 2004
011.6

Latin language
Dictionaries
Cassell's Latin dictionary   **473**
Latin name of Mikojaj Kopernik *See* Copernicus, Nicolaus, 1473-1543
Latino visions. Cockcroft, J. D.   **704**
Latinos (U.S.) *See* Hispanic Americans
Latinos in baseball [series]
Gallagher, J. Pedro Martinez   **92**
Latta, Sara L.
Allergies (7 and up)   **616.97**
Food poisoning and foodborne diseases (7 and up)   **615.9**
Latvia
Barlas, R. Latvia (5 and up)   **947.9**
Laubach, Christyna M.
Raptor! a kid's guide to birds of prey (4 and up)   **598**
Laubach, René
(jt. auth) Laubach, C. M. Raptor! a kid's guide to birds of prey   **598**
Lauber, Patricia, 1924-
Volcano: the eruption and healing of Mount St. Helens (4 and up)   **551.2**
Who came first (5 and up)   **970.01**
Laughing out loud, I fly. Herrera, J. F.   **811**
The **laughing** skull. Delacre, L.
In Delacre, L. Golden tales; myths, legends, and folktales from Latin America p21-23   **398.2**
Laughter. San Souci, R.
In San Souci, R. Double-dare to be scared: another thirteen chilling tales   **S C**
Lauré, Jason, 1940-
(jt. auth) Blauer, E. Morocco   **964**
(jt. auth) Blauer, E. South Africa   **968**
Lauren, Ralph
See/See also pages in the following book(s):
Kent, J. Business builders in fashion   **920**
Lavender, David Sievert, 1910-2003
Mother Earth, Father Sky   **970.004**
Snowbound (4 and up)   **978**
Lavies, Bianca
Compost critters (4 and up)   **591.7**
Law
See also Constitutional law
Law enforcement
Wirths, C. G. Coping with confrontations and encounters with the police (7 and up)   **363.2**
Law for K-12 libraries and librarians. Torrans, L. A.   **344**
Lawler, Mary
Marcus Garvey   **92**
Lawlor, Laurie
Helen Keller: rebellious spirit (5 and up)   **92**
Magnificent voyage (7 and up)   **910.4**

Window on the West (7 and up)   **978**
Lawlor, Veronica
(il) I was dreaming to come to America. See I was dreaming to come to America   **325.73**
Lawrence, Caroline
The thieves of Ostia   **Fic**
Lawrence, Colton, 1968-
Big fat paycheck   **808.2**
Lawrence, Iain, 1955-
B for Buster (7 and up)   **Fic**
The lightkeeper's daughter (7 and up)   **Fic**
Lord of the nutcracker men (5 and up)   **Fic**
The wreckers (5 and up)   **Fic**
Lawrence, Jacob, 1917-2000
The great migration   **759.13**
About
Duggleby, J. Story painter: the life of Jacob Lawrence (4 and up)   **92**
(jt. auth) Duggleby, J. Story painter: the life of Jacob Lawrence   **92**
Lawrence, Louise, 1943-
Dream-weaver (7 and up)   **Fic**
Lawrence, Michael
A crack in the line (7 and up)   **Fic**
Laws, Gordon D.
Alberta
In Exploring Canada   **971**
Manitoba
In Exploring Canada   **971**
Maritime Provinces
In Exploring Canada   **971**
Northwest Territory
In Exploring Canada   **971**
Lawson, Julie, 1947-
Destination gold!   **Fic**
Lawton, Clive
Hiroshima (5 and up)   **940.54**
Lawyers
See also Judges
Wormser, R. Defending the accused (7 and up)   **345**
Lay, Kathryn
The healing truth
In A Glory of unicorns p145-62   **S C**
Layers of life. Castner, J. L.   **577.3**
Layton, Lesley
Singapore (5 and up)   **959.57**
Layton, Neal
(il) Wicked poems. See Wicked poems   **811.008**
Lazan, Marion Blumenthal
(jt. auth) Perl, L. Four perfect pebbles   **940.53**
Lazo, Caroline Evensen
F. Scott Fitzgerald   **92**
Gloria Steinem (7 and up)   **92**
L'chaim!. Rubin, S. G.   **305.8**
Le Guin, Ursula K., 1929-
Gifts (7 and up)   **Fic**
Le Sieg, Theo *See* Seuss, Dr.
Le Vert, Suzanne *See* LeVert, Suzanne
Leacock, Elspeth, 1946-
Journeys in time (4 and up)   **973**

Leacock, Elspeth, 1946-—*Continued*
Places in time (4 and up)   **911**

Leaders and generals. Roberts, R.   **920**

Leaders of ancient Egypt [series]
Morgan, J. Cleopatra   **92**

Leaders of ancient Rome [series]
Forsyth, F. Augustus: the first emperor   **92**

Leaders of World War II. Ross, S.   **920**

Leah's stories. Sleator, W.
In Sleator, W. Oddballs; stories p83-101
   S C

Leakey, Louis Seymour Bazett, 1903-1972
About
Poynter, M. The Leakeys   **92**

Leakey, Mary D., 1913-1996
About
Poynter, M. The Leakeys   **92**
See/See also pages in the following book(s):
Lindop, L. Scientists and doctors (7 and up)
   920

Leapman, Michael, 1938-
Witnesses to war (5 and up)   **940.53**

Learning about—the Civil War. Stephens, E. C.
   016.973

Learning and scholarship
See also Education

Learning disabilities
See also Attention deficit disorder
Paquette, P. H. Learning disabilities   **371.9**
Fiction
DeClements, B. 6th grade can really kill you (5 and up)   **Fic**
Philbrick, W. R. Freak the Mighty   **Fic**
Wolff, V. E. Probably still Nick Swansen (7 and up)   **Fic**

Learning resource centers *See* Instructional materials centers

Learning right from wrong in the digital age.
Johnson, D.   **004.6**

Learning to learn. Riedling, A. M.   **028.7**

Leave it to Chance: Shaman's rain. Robinson, J.
   741.5

Leaving Cuba. Gay, K.   **362.87**

Leaving Emma. Brokaw, N. S.   **Fic**

Leaving Fishers. Haddix, M. P.   **Fic**

Leaving home: stories   **808.8**
Includes the following stories: The first day, by E. P. Jones; Dancer, by V. Sears; A gift of laughter, by A. Sherman; Rules of the game, by A. Tan; The circuit, by F. Jiménez; Bad influence, by J. Ortiz Cofer; Dawn, by T. Wynne-Jones; Trip in a summer dress, by A. Sanford; On the rainy river, by T. O'Brien; The setting sun and the rolling world, by C. Mungoshi; Zelzah: a tale from long ago, by N. F. Mazer; "Recitatif", by T. Morrison

Leaving Protection. Hobbs, W.   **Fic**

Leavitt, Martine
Heck, superhero   **Fic**

Lebanon
Hutchison, L. Lebanon (7 and up)   **956.92**
Sheehan, S. Lebanon (5 and up)   **956.92**

Lechón, Daniel
(il) Mora, P. The desert is my mother. El desierto es mi madre   **811**

LeConte, Joseph, 1823-1901
See/See also pages in the following book(s):
Cloud Tapper, S. Voices from slavery's past (7 and up)   **326**

Ledyard, John, 1751-1789
About
Lawlor, L. Magnificent voyage (7 and up)
   910.4

Lee, Carol Ann
A friend called Anne (4 and up)   **940.53**

Lee, Cherylene
Hollywood and the pits
In American dragons: twenty-five Asian American voices p34-47   **810.8**

Lee, Harper, 1926-
Bernard, C. Understanding To kill a mockingbird (7 and up)   **813.009**
To kill a mockingbird; criticism
In Bernard, C. Understanding To kill a mockingbird   **813.009**

Lee, Jeanne
Jam! (7 and up)   **781.65**

Lee, Jeanne M.
I once was a monkey (4 and up)   **294.3**

Lee, Jordan
Coping with braces and other orthodontic work
   617.6

Lee, Marie G.
Necessary roughness (7 and up)   **Fic**
Summer of my Korean soldier
In American eyes; new Asian-American short stories for young adults p37-48   **S C**

Lee, Spike
See/See also pages in the following book(s):
Haskins, J. African American entrepreneurs
   920

Lee, Tanith
Among the leaves so green
In The Green Man: tales from the mythic forest p86-112   **808.8**
Piratica   **Fic**

Lee, Tanja
(ed) Benjamin Franklin. See Benjamin Franklin [essays about]   **92**

Lee, Tsung Dao, 1926-
See/See also pages in the following book(s):
Yount, L. Asian-American scientists (7 and up)
   920

Leech, Dorothy
(il) Janeczko, P. B. Stardust otel   **811**

Leeming, David Adams, 1937-
(ed) The Dictionary of folklore. See The Dictionary of folklore   **398**
(ed) Myths, legends, and folktales of America. See Myths, legends, and folktales of America
   398.2

Leeuwenhoek, Antoni van, 1632-1723
About
Yount, L. Antoni van Leeuwenhoek   **92**

Left- and right-handedness
Fiction
Ritter, J. H. Choosing up sides   **Fic**

Left for dead. Nelson, P.   **940.54**

Legal aid
Sherrow, V. Gideon v. Wainwright (7 and up)
345

Legalizing marijuana. Ruschmann, P. **345**
The **legend** of Buddy Bush. Moses, S. P. **Fic**
The **legend** of Tangu Yuh. Gerson, M.-J.
In Gerson, M.-J. Fiesta femenina; celebrating
women in Mexican folktale **398.2**
The **legend** of the white stag. Molnár, I.
In Molnár, I. One-time dog market at Buda
and other Hungarian folktales p121-26
398.2

Legendary heroes of the Wild West [series]
Sanford, W. R. Bill Pickett: African-American
rodeo star **92**
Sanford, W. R. Calamity Jane: frontier original
92
Legendary labor leaders. Streissguth, T. **920**
Legends
See also Folklore; Mythology
Philip, N. Myths & legends (7 and up)
398.2

Legends, Jewish *See* Jewish legends
Legends of Charlemagne. Bulfinch, T.
In Bulfinch, T. Bulfinch's mythology **201**
Lehnhausen, Bud
(il) Quinlan, S. E. Puffins **598**
Leidesdorff, William Alexander, 1810-1848
See/See also pages in the following book(s):
Haskins, J. African American entrepreneurs
920

Leighton, Robert
(il) Gravelle, K. What's going on down there?
612.6
Lekuton, Joseph
Facing the lion **967.62**
Lemieux, Mario
About
Stewart, M. Mario Lemieux **92**
LeMond, Greg, 1961-
See/See also pages in the following book(s):
Kaminsky, M. Uncommon champions **920**
Lena and Big One Tiger. Hamilton, V.
In Hamilton, V. Her stories; African
American folktales, fairy tales, and true
tales p7-10 **398.2**
Lenape Indians *See* Delaware Indians
Lend me your ears **808.85**
Lenderman, Lois
(il) Costello, E. Random House American sign
language dictionary **419**
L'Engle, Madeleine, 1918-
The glorious impossible **232.9**
A ring of endless light (5 and up) **Fic**
A wrinkle in time (5 and up) **Fic**
Lennard-Brown, Sarah
Asthma (5 and up) **616.2**
Lennon, Joan, 1953-
Skivvy and cuttle
In Fire and wings: dragon tales from East and
West p43-54 **S C**

Lennon, John, 1940-1980
About
Rappaport, D. John's secret dreams [biography
of John Lennon] (4 and up) **92**
Lent, ReLeah Cossett
(jt. auth) Pipkin, G. At the schoolhouse gate
373.1
Leon, Juan Ponce de *See* Ponce de Leon, Juan,
1460?-1521
Leonard, Buck, 1907-1997
About
Payment, S. Buck Leonard **92**
Leonard, Elmore
A coyote's in the house (5 and up) **Fic**
Leonard, Jim
Crow & Weasel
In Theatre for young audiences; 20 great
plays for children p244-83 **812.008**
Leonardo, da Vinci, 1452-1519
About
Talbott, H. Leonardo's horse (4 and up)
730.9
Herbert, J. Leonardo da Vinci for kids (4 and
up) **92**
O'Connor, B. Leonardo da Vinci (5 and up)
92
Leonardo da Vinci for kids. Herbert, J. **92**
Leonardo's horse. Talbott, H. **730.9**
Leon's story. Tillage, L. **92**
The **leopard** sword. Cadnum, M. **Fic**
Leopards
Gamble, C. Leopards (7 and up) **599.75**
Leopold, Aldo, 1886-1948
See/See also pages in the following book(s):
Byrnes, P. Environmental pioneers (7 and up)
920
Lerch, Maureen T.
Serving homeschooled teens and their parents
027.6
Lerner, Carol, 1927-
On the wing (4 and up) **598**
Lerner biography [series]
Carpenter, A. S. Lewis Carroll **92**
Edge, L. B. Andrew Carnegie
Kenyon, K. The Brontë family **920**
Tagliaferro, L. Thomas Edison **92**
Lerner long biographies [series]
Lazo, C. E. F. Scott Fitzgerald **92**
Lesbian and gay voices. Day, F. A. **016.8**
Lesbians
Civil rights
Hudson, D. L. Gay rights (7 and up) **342**
Fiction
Watts, J. Finding H.F (7 and up) **Fic**
Wittlinger, E. Hard love (7 and up) **Fic**
Woodson, J. The house you pass on the way (7
and up) **Fic**
Lesley, Craig
(ed) Talking leaves. See Talking leaves **S C**
Leslie, Roger
(jt. auth) Wilson, P. J. Center stage **027.8**

Lessem, Don
Scholastic dinosaurs A to Z (4 and up)
567.9

Lessing, Doris May, 1919-
The old chief Mshlanga
In Somehow tenderness survives; stories of
Southern Africa p19-35 **S C**
A **lesson** from the heart. Yabu, J.
In American dragons: twenty-five Asian
American voices p161-65 **810.8**
Lessons from Library Power. Zweizig, D.
027.8

Lest we forget. Thomas, V. M. **326**

Lester, Alison, 1952-
Quicksand pony **Fic**
The snow pony **Fic**

Lester, Julius
The blues singers (5 and up) **920**
The child
In Join in; multiethnic short stories by out-
standing writers for young adults p142-
49 **S C**
Day of tears (7 and up) **Fic**
From slave ship to freedom road (4 and up)
326
The last tales of Uncle Remus (4 and up)
398.2
Contents: Why the cricket has elbows on his legs; Why the
earth is mostly water; The origin of the ocean; Brer Rabbit and
Miss Nancy; The old king and the new king; Brer Bear comes
to the community; The snake; A ghost story; Brer Bear exposes
Brer Rabbit; Brer Rabbit teaches Brer Bear to comb his hair;
Why Brer Possum has no hair on his tail; Why Brer Possum
loves peace; The baby who loved pumpkins; Impty-Umpty and
the blacksmith; The angry woman; Brer Rabbit throws a party;
Why Brer Fox's legs are black; How the witch was caught; The
man who almost married a witch; Why dogs are tame; How
Tinktum Tidy recruited an army for the king; Why guinea fowls
are speckled; Why the Guineas stay awake; Brer Fox and the
white grapes; Why the hawk likes to eat chickens; The little boy
and his dogs; The man and the wild cattle; "Cutta cord-la"; Why
Brer Bull growls and grumbles; Brer Rabbit, King Polecat, and
the gingercakes; The fool; How Brer Lion lost his hair; The man
and the boots; Why the goat has a short tail; Brer Buzzard and
Brer Crow; The blacksmith and the Devil; Why chickens scratch
in the dirt; Brer Rabbit and Aunt Nancy; The adventures of Si-
mon and Susanna
Long journey home: stories from black history
S C
Contents: Satan on my track; Louis; Ben; The man who was
a horse; When freedom came; Long journey home
Othello **Fic**
Spear
In Places I never meant to be; original stories
by censored writers **S C**
When Dad killed Mom (7 and up) **Fic**
When the beginning began (4 and up) **296.1**
Contents: God learns how to create; God battles the Queen of
the Waters; Sun and Moon; Strange creatures; The Angel of
Death; Cat and Mouse; Leviathan and Fox; Crown learns a les-
son; The grand parade; God makes people; God creates Adam;
God creates Woman; Adam marries; The Snake; The Woman,
Adam, and the fruit; God confronts Adam, the Woman, and the
Snake; God returns to Heaven

Let it shine. Pinkney, A. D. **920**
Let my people go. McKissack, P. C. **221.9**
Let my people go: African Americans, 1804-1860.
White, D. G. **305.8**
Let the circle be unbroken. Taylor, M. D. **Fic**

Let's celebrate today. Marks, D. F. **394.26**
Let's visit Indonesia. *See* Lyle, G. Indonesia
959.8
A **letter** from the Clearys. Willis, C.
In New skies: an anthology of today's science
fiction **S C**
A **letter** from the fringe. Bauer, J.
In On the fringe p181-91 **S C**
A **letter** to my daughter. Flake, S. G.
In Flake, S. G. Who am I without him?; short
stories about girls and the boys in their
lives p157-68 **S C**
Letter writing
Dragisic, P. How to write a letter (7 and up)
808
Letters
Fiction
Danziger, P. P.S. Longer letter later (5 and up)
Fic
Danziger, P. Snail mail no more (5 and up)
Fic
Hesse, K. Letters from Rifka (5 and up) **Fic**
Klise, K. Letters from camp **Fic**
Lyons, M. E. Letters from a slave girl (6 and
up) **Fic**
The **letters**. Yumoto, K. **Fic**
Letters from a slave girl. Lyons, M. E. **Fic**
Letters from camp. Klise, K. **Fic**
Letters from Rifka. Hesse, K. **Fic**
Letters from Wolfie. Sherlock, P. **Fic**
Letting in the jungle. Kipling, R.
In Kipling, R. The jungle books **S C**
Leukemia
Abramovitz, M. Leukemia **616.99**
Fiction
Bennett, C. Zink **Fic**
Hamilton, V. Bluish **Fic**
Levchuck, Caroline M.
Healthy living **613**
Leventhal, Alice Walker *See* Walker, Alice,
1944-
Leverage your library program to help raise test
scores. Church, A. P. **027.8**
LeVert, Suzanne
The facts about ecstasy **362.29**
The facts about steroids **362.29**
Louisiana
In Celebrate the states **973**
Massachusetts
In Celebrate the states **973**
Levi-Montalcini, Rita, 1909-
See/See also pages in the following book(s):
Lindop, L. Scientists and doctors (7 and up)
920
Leviathan and Fox. Lester, J.
In Lester, J. When the beginning began; sto-
ries about God, the creatures, and us
p34-38 **296.1**
Levin, Betty
Shadow-catcher (5 and up) **Fic**
Levine, Ellen
Darkness over Denmark **940.53**

Levine, Ellen, 1939-
Catch a tiger by the toe   **Fic**
The journal of Jedediah Barstow   **Fic**

Levine, Gail Carson, 1947-
Dave at night (5 and up)   **Fic**
Ella enchanted (5 and up)   **Fic**
Pluto
    In On the edge: stories at the brink p109-23   **S C**
The princess test (4 and up)   **Fic**
The two princesses of Bamarre (5 and up)   **Fic**
The wish   **Fic**

Levine, Herbert M.
Chemical & biological weapons in our times (7 and up)   **358**

Levine, Laura
Shake, rattle, & roll (4 and up)   **920**

Levine, Shar
The microscope book   **502.8**

Levine, Stuart P., 1968-
The elephant (7 and up)   **599.67**
The tiger (7 and up)   **599.75**

Levinson, David, 1947-
(ed) The Wilson chronology of the world's religions. See The Wilson chronology of the world's religions   **200**

Levinson, Isabel Simone
Gibbons v. Ogden (7 and up)   **343**

Levinson, Nancy Smiler, 1938-
Magellan and the first voyage around the world (5 and up)   **92**

Levitas, Mitchel
(ed) A Nation challenged. See A Nation challenged   **973.931**

Levithan, David, 1972-
What a song can do
    In What a song can do; 12 riffs on the power of music   **S C**

Levitin, Sonia, 1934-
The cure   **Fic**
Dream freedom   **Fic**
Journey to America (4 and up)   **Fic**
The return (6 and up)   **Fic**
Room in the heart   **Fic**

Levitt, William, 1907-1994
See/See also pages in the following book(s):
Aaseng, N. Business builders in real estate   **920**

Levy, Constance, 1931-
A crack in the clouds and other poems (3-5)   **811**

Levy, Debbie
The Vietnam War (5 and up)   **959.704**

Levy, Elizabeth
Seventh grade tango (5 and up)   **Fic**

Levy, Janey
The Alamo   **976.4**
The Erie Canal   **974.7**

Levy, Marilyn, 1937-
Run for your life (7 and up)   **Fic**

Levy, Matthys
Engineering the city   **624**

Levy, Patricia Marjorie, 1951-
Belarus (5 and up)   **947.8**
Ghana (5 and up)   **966.7**
The home front in World War II (7 and up)   **940.53**
Ireland (5 and up)   **941.5**
Liberia (5 and up)   **966.62**
Nigeria (5 and up)   **966.9**
Scotland (5 and up)   **941.1**
Sudan (5 and up)   **962.4**

Lewin, Betsy
(jt. auth) Lewin, T. Gorilla walk   **599.8**

Lewin, Ted, 1935-
Gorilla walk (4 and up)   **599.8**
Tooth and claw (4 and up)   **590**
(il) O'Dell, S. Island of the Blue Dolphins   **Fic**

Lewis, C. S. (Clive Staples), 1898-1963
The adventures of Eustace
    In The Book of dragons p10-15   **S C**
The lion, the witch, and the wardrobe (4 and up)   **Fic**
        About
Davenport, J. C.S. Lewis   **92**
Gormley, B. C.S. Lewis   **92**
See/See also pages in the following book(s):
Ellis, S. From reader to writer   **372.6**

Lewis, Catherine
Postcards to father Abraham (7 and up)   **Fic**

Lewis, Clive Staples See Lewis, C. S. (Clive Staples), 1898-1963

Lewis, Elizabeth, 1967-
Mexican art & culture   **709.72**

Lewis, J. Patrick
Freedom like sunlight (5 and up)   **811**
Monumental verses (5 and up)   **811**

Lewis, John, 1940-
        About
Hill, C. M. John Lewis   **92**

Lewis, John L., 1880-1969
See/See also pages in the following book(s):
Streissguth, T. Legendary labor leaders (7 and up)   **920**

Lewis, Meriwether, 1774-1809
        About
Blumberg, R. The incredible journey of Lewis and Clark (5 and up)   **978**
Faber, H. Lewis and Clark   **978**
Kimmel, E. C. As far as the eye can reach (4 and up)   **978**
(jt. auth) Clark, W. Off the map   **978**

Lewis, Reginald F., 1922-1993
See/See also pages in the following book(s):
Haskins, J. African American entrepreneurs   **920**

Lewis and Clark. Faber, H.   **978**

Lewis and Clark Expedition (1804-1806)
Blumberg, R. The incredible journey of Lewis and Clark (5 and up)   **978**
Blumberg, R. York's adventures with Lewis and Clark (5 and up)   **978**
Clark, W. Off the map   **978**
Faber, H. Lewis and Clark   **978**

Lewis and Clark Expedition (1804-1806)—Con-
tinued
Kimmel, E. C. As far as the eye can reach (4 and up) **978**
Patent, D. H. Animals on the trail with Lewis and Clark (4 and up) **978**
Patent, D. H. The Lewis and Clark trail (4 and up) **978**
Patent, D. H. Plants on the trail with Lewis and Clark (4 and up) **978**
St. George, J. Sacagawea (4-6) **92**
Fiction
Bruchac, J. Sacajawea (6 and up) **Fic**
O'Dell, S. Streams to the river, river to the sea (5 and up) **Fic**
Smith, R. The captain's dog **Fic**
Wolf, A. New found land (7 and up) **Fic**
The **Lewis** and Clark trail. Patent, D. H. **978**
Lewis Hayden and the war against slavery. Strangis, J. **92**
Lexington (Mass.), Battle of, 1775
Whitelaw, N. The shot heard round the world **973.3**
Lexington (Mass.), Battle of, 1775
Fiction
Fast, H. April morning (7 and up) **Fic**
Li **Chi** slays the serpent. Pao, K.
In The Book of dragons p35-38 **S C**
Liability (Law)
Sergis, D. K. Cipollone v. Liggett Group (7 and up) **346.03**
Liar. Asimov, I.
In Asimov, I. I, robot **S C**
Libal, Autumn
Creek North American Indians today [series]
Libal, Joyce
Comanche North American Indians today [series]
Seminole
In North American Indians today [series]
Liberia
Levy, P. M. Liberia (5 and up) **966.62**
History
Reef, C. This our dark country **966.62**
Librarians
Ethics
Ethics in school librarianship **174**
Libraries
See also Instructional materials centers
Gillespie, K. M. Teen volunteer services in libraries **021.2**
Heiligman, D. The New York Public Library kid's guide to research (5 and up) **025.5**
Censorship
Intellectual freedom manual **323.44**
Symons, A. K. Protecting the right to read **025.2**
Collection development
Doll, C. A. Managing and analyzing your collection **025.2**
O'Dell, K. Library materials and services for teen girls **027.62**
Slote, S. J. Weeding library collections **025.2**

Exhibitions
Skaggs, G. On display **027.8**
Law and legislation
Torrans, L. A. Law for K-12 libraries and librarians **344**
Public relations
Flowers, H. F. Public relations for school library media programs **021.7**
Hill, A. Tooting your own horn **021.7**
Valenza, J. K. Power tools recharged **027.8**
Libraries, Children's *See* Children's libraries
Libraries, School *See* School libraries
Libraries, Young adults' *See* Young adults' libraries
Libraries and community
Schuckett, S. Political advocacy for school librarians **027.8**
Libraries and students
Mediavilla, C. Creating the full-service homework center in your library **027.4**
Libraries Unlimited professional guides for young adult librarians [series]
Lerch, M. T. Serving homeschooled teens and their parents **027.6**
O'Dell, K. Library materials and services for teen girls **027.62**
Libraries Unlimited professional guides in school librarianship [series]
Johnson, C. Using internet primary sources to teach critical thinking skills in the sciences **025.04**
Library and information science text series
Woolls, E. B. The school library media manager **027.8**
The **library** card. Spinelli, J. **S C**
Library classification
Intner, S. S. Standard cataloging for school and public libraries **025.3**
The **library-classroom** partnership. Jweid, R. **027.8**
Library information networks
Developing an information literacy program, K-12 **025.5**
Managing the Internet controversy **025.04**
Minkel, W. Delivering Web reference services to young people **025.04**
Smith, S. S. Web-based instruction **005.7**
Library instruction *See* Bibliographic instruction
The **library** Internet trainer's toolkit. Stephens, M. T. **025.04**
Library materials and services for teen girls. O'Dell, K. **027.62**
Library media center programs for middle schools. See Smith, J. B. Achieving a curriculum-based library media center program **027.8**
Library of African American arts and culture [series]
Elmer, H. Blues **781.643**
Erdosh, G. The African American kitchen **641.5**
Lee, J. Jam! **781.65**
Library of African-American history [series]
Golay, M. Reconstruction and reaction **305.8**

Library of African-American history—*Continued*

Isserman, M. Journey to freedom   **305.8**

Rasmussen, R. K. Farewell to Jim Crow   **305.8**

Reef, C. Africans in America: the spread of people and culture   **305.8**

The **Library** of Alexandria. Trumble, K.   **027**

Library of American Indian history [series]

Durrett, D. Unsung heroes of World War II   **940.54**

Lassieur, A. Before the storm   **970.004**

Library of American lives and times [series]

Butler, M. G. Sojourner Truth   **92**

Edmondson, J. R. Jim Bowie   **92**

Pierce, M. A. Robert Fulton and the development of the steamboat   **92**

Library of author biographies [series]

Freedman, J. Sid Fleischman   **92**

Greene, M. Louis Sachar   **92**

Seidman, D. Jerry Spinelli   **92**

Thomson, S. L. Robert Cormier   **92**

Wilson, A. S.E. Hinton   **92**

Library of famous women [series]

Steins, R. Leontyne Price, opera superstar   **92**

Library of future medicine [series]

Giddens, S. Future techniques in surgery   **617**

Viegas, J. The revolution in healing the brain   **612.8**

Viegas, J. Stem cell research   **616**

Library of political assassinations [series]

Draper, A. S. The assassination of Malcolm X   **92**

Ribeiro, M. The assassination of Medgar Evers   **92**

Library of satellites [series]

Byers, A. Communications satellites   **384.5**

Kupperberg, P. Spy satellites   **327.12**

Sherman, J. Deep space observation satellites   **629.43**

Wolny, P. Weapons satellites   **358**

Library Power (Program)

The Information-powered school   **027.8**

Zweizig, D. Lessons from Library Power   **027.8**

Library research skills workbook, grades 7-12. See Information literacy skills, grades 7-12   **027.62**

Library science

Dictionaries

McCain, M. M. Dictionary for school library media specialists   **020**

Library services to children *See* Children's libraries

Library services to young adults *See* Young adults' libraries

Libya

Malcolm, P. Libya (5 and up)   **961.2**

Fiction

Stolz, J. The shadows of Ghadames   **Fic**

Lie, no lie. Lynch, C.

In Places I never meant to be; original stories by censored writers   **S C**

Lieberman, Susan Abel

The real high school handbook (7 and up)   **373.1**

Lieblich, Irene

(il) Singer, I. B. The power of light   **S C**

Liebowitz, Jay

Wall Street wizard   **332.6**

Lieurance, Suzanne

The Triangle Shirtwaist fire and sweatshop reform in American history (7 and up)   **974.7**

Life

See also Death

Origin

Gallant, R. A. The origins of life (5 and up)   **576.8**

Life (Biology)

See also Reproduction

Life after high school. Oates, J. C.

In Oates, J. C. Small avalanches and other stories   **S C**

Life among the Ibo women of Nigeria. Nnoromele, S.   **966.9**

The **life** and death of Adolf Hitler. Giblin, J.   **92**

The **life** and death of Crazy Horse. Bad Heart Buffalo, A.   **92**

The **life** and death of Martin Luther King, Jr. Haskins, J.   **92**

Life balance [series]

Andrews, L. W. Emotional intelligence   **152.4**

Andrews, L. W. Meditation   **158**

Borenstein, G. C. Therapy   **616.89**

Landau, E. Dyslexia   **616.85**

Trueit, T. S. ADHD   **616.85**

Trueit, T. S. Keeping a journal   **808**

Life during the Renaissance. Netzley, P. D.   **940.2**

The **life** history of a star. Easton, K.   **Fic**

Life in Elizabethan London. Stewart, G.   **942.05**

Life in the Australian Outback. Einfeld, J.   **994**

Life in the fat lane. Bennett, C.   **Fic**

Life in the Renaissance [series]

Hinds, K. The church   **274**

Hinds, K. The city   **940.2**

Hinds, K. The countryside   **940.2**

Hinds, K. The court   **940.2**

Life in the Roman Empire [series]

Hinds, K. The city   **937**

Hinds, K. The countryside   **937**

Hinds, K. The Patricians   **937**

Hinds, K. Religion   **292**

Life is funny. Frank, E. R   **Fic**

Life lines. Kidd, J. S.   **576.5**

Life lists for teens. Espeland, P.   **646.7**

Life of a Nazi soldier. Cartlidge, C.   **940.54**

Life of a soldier in Washington's army. Stewart, G. **973.3**

Life of an American soldier. Campbell, G. A. **956.7**

Life of an American soldier. Yancey, D. **959.704**

Life on other planets
Jackson, E. B. Looking for life in the universe (4 and up) **576.8**
Skurzynski, G. Are we alone? (5 and up) **576.8**

Life on the Oregon Trail. Blackwood, G. L. **979.5**

Life: our century in pictures for young people **779**

Life out of focus. Harmon, D. **616.8**

Life sciences
Spangenburg, R. Modern science, 1896-1945 (7 and up) **509**
          Encyclopedias
Encyclopedia of life sciences **570.3**

Life skills
Benson, P. L. What teens need to succeed (7 and up) **305.23**
Erlbach, A. The middle school survival guide **373.1**
Espeland, P. Life lists for teens **646.7**
Morgenstern, J. Organizing from the inside out for teens (7 and up) **646.7**
Weston, C. For teens only **305.23**

The **life** stories of stars. Gallant, R. A. **523.8**

Life under the Taliban. Stewart, G. **958.1**

Lift every voice and sing. Johnson, J. W. **782.42**

Liggett & Myers Tobacco Company
Sergis, D. K. Cipollone v. Liggett Group (7 and up) **346.03**

Light
Burnie, D. Light (4 and up) **535**
Gardner, R. Light, sound, and waves science fair projects (7 and up) **507.8**
Meiani, A. Light (4 and up) **535**

The **light** beyond the forest. Sutcliff, R. **398.2**

The **light** bulb and how it changed the world. Pollard, M. **621.3**

Light-gathering poems (7 and up) **808.81**

A **light** in the attic. Silverstein, S. **811**

The **light** in the forest. Richter, C. **Fic**

A **light** in the storm. Hesse, K. **Fic**

Light 'n lively reads for ESL, adult, and teen readers. Rosow, L. V. **011.6**

Light shining through the mist: a photobiography of Dian Fossey. Matthews, T. L. **92**

Light, sound, and waves science fair projects. Gardner, R. **507.8**

The **lightkeeper's** daughter. Lawrence, I. **Fic**

Lightning
Simon, S. Lightning (4 and up) **551.56**

Lights, Feast of See Hanukkah

Lights, camera, action!. O'Brien, L. **791.43**

Like cats' eyes. Schwartz, A.
In Schwartz, A. Scary stories 3; more tales to chill your bones p23 **398.2**

Like men of war. Trudeau, N. A. **973.7**

Like sisters on the homefront. Williams-Garcia, R. **Fic**

Lilac in the lake. Aiken, J.
In Aiken, J. Shadows and moonshine; stories **S C**

Lilly, Charles
(il) Rappaport, D. Escape from slavery **326**

Lily B. on the brink of cool. Kimmel, E. C. **Fic**

Lily's crossing. Giff, P. R. **Fic**

Lily's ghosts. Ruby, L. **Fic**

Lincoff, Gary
The Audubon Society field guide to North American mushrooms **579.6**

Lincoln, Abraham, 1809-1865
Abraham Lincoln the writer (7 and up) **92**
          About
Ashabranner, J. No better hope (4 and up) **975.3**
The election of 1860 and the administration of Abraham Lincoln (7 and up) **973.7**
Freedman, R. Lincoln: a photobiography (5 and up) **92**
January, B. The Lincoln-Douglas debates **973.7**
Marrin, A. Commander in Chief Abraham Lincoln and the Civil War (7 and up) **973.7**
Sullivan, G. Abraham Lincoln (4 and up) **92**
Sullivan, G. Picturing Lincoln **92**
          Assassination
Giblin, J. Good brother, bad brother [biography of John Wilkes Booth and Edwin Booth] (5 and up) **92**
Holzer, H. The president is shot! (5 and up) **973.7**
January, B. The assassination of Abraham Lincoln **973.7**
Otfinoski, S. John Wilkes Booth and the Civil War **92**
          Fiction
Lewis, C. Postcards to father Abraham (7 and up) **Fic**

Lincoln-Douglas debates, 1858
January, B. The Lincoln-Douglas debates **973.7**

Lincoln Memorial (Washington, D.C.)
Ashabranner, J. No better hope (4 and up) **975.3**

The **Lincoln** train. McHugh, M. F.
In New skies: an anthology of today's science fiction **S C**

Linda Brown, you are not alone (5 and up) **323.1**

Lindbergh, Anne Morrow, 1906-2001
See/See also pages in the following book(s):
Aaseng, N. You are the juror **345**

Lindbergh, Charles, 1902-1974
          About
Giblin, J. Charles A. Lindbergh **92**

Lindbergh, Charles, 1902-1974—About—*Continued*
Koopmans, A. Charles Lindbergh   **92**
See/See also pages in the following book(s):
Aaseng, N. You are the juror   **345**

Lindop, Edmund
America in the 1950s (7 and up)   **973.921**

Lindop, Laurie
Chasing tornadoes   **551.55**
Probing volcanoes (5 and up)   **551.2**
Scientists and doctors (7 and up)   **920**

Lindroth, David
(ed) Hispanic-American experience on file. See Hispanic-American experience on file   **305.8**

Lindsay, Dave
Dave's quick n' easy web pages   **005.7**

Lindsay, William, 1956-
(jt. auth) Clark, N. 1,001 facts about dinosaurs   **567.9**

Ling, Mary
(ed) The Snake book. See The Snake book   **597.9**

Linn, David
(il) Olson, A. N. Ask the bones: scary stories from around the world   **398.2**

Linnaeus, Carl See Linné, Carl von, 1707-1778

Linné, Carl von, 1707-1778
About
Anderson, M. J. Carl Linnaeus   **92**

Linnea, Sharon
Princess Ka'iulani   **92**

Linnea. Malcolm, D. J.
In Half-human p19-45   **S C**

Linus Pauling and the chemistry of life. Hager, T.   **92**

Lion, Melissa, 1975-
Upstream (7 and up)   **Fic**

Lion and the ostrich chicks [story] Bryan, A.
In Bryan, A. Ashley Bryan's African tales, uh-huh p115-34   **398.2**

The **lion**, the witch, and the wardrobe. Lewis, C. S.   **Fic**

Lionheart. Martin, J.   **910.4**

Lions
Adamson, J. Born free   **599.75**

Lippincott, Kristen, 1954-
Astronomy   **520**

Lipsyte, Robert
The contender (7 and up)   **Fic**
The defender
In Ultimate sports; short stories by outstanding writers for young adults p180-92   **S C**
Future tense
In Read into the millennium; tales of the future p42-56   **S C**
In Sixteen; short stories by outstanding writers for young adults p60-70   **S C**
One fat summer (7 and up)   **Fic**

Lisandrelli, Elaine Slivinski, 1951-
Ida B. Wells-Barnett (7 and up)   **92**

Lisker, Emily
(il) Lester, J. When the beginning began   **296.1**

Lisle, Janet Taylor, 1947-
The art of keeping cool (5 and up)   **Fic**
The crying rocks   **Fic**
How I became a writer and Oggie learned to drive (4 and up)   **Fic**

Listen to us. Springer, J.   **331.3**

Listen up!. Trapani, M.   **306.8**

Lister, Maree
England   **942**

Literacy
Krashen, S. D. The power of reading   **028.5**

Literary landmarks
United States
Spangenburg, R. Literature and the arts (7 and up)   **917.3**

Literary prizes
See also Caldecott Medal; Coretta Scott King Award; Newbery Medal

Literary recreations
See also Word games

Literature
See also African Americans in literature; Children's literature; Teenagers' writings; Young adult literature names of national literatures, e.g. *English literature*
Bio-bibliography
Authors & artists for young adults   **920.003**
Great American writers: twentieth century   **920.003**
Great world writers: twentieth century   **920.003**
World authors, 1950-1970   **920.003**
World authors, 1970-1975   **920.003**
World authors, 1975-1980   **920.003**
World authors, 1980-1985   **920.003**
World authors, 1985-1990   **920.003**
World authors, 1990-1995   **920.003**
World authors, 1995-2000   **920.003**
Collections
Beware! (4 and up)   **808.8**
Read all about it!   **808.8**
Teen sunshine reflections   **808.8**
Dictionaries
Benet's reader's encyclopedia   **803**
Brewer's dictionary of phrase and fable   **803**
History and criticism
See also Authors
Masterpieces of world literature   **809**
Study and teaching
Hall, S. Using picture storybooks to teach literary devices v3   **016.8**
Into focus   **028.1**

Literature and the arts. Spangenburg, R.   **917.3**

Literature connections to American history, 7-12. Adamson, L. G.   **016.973**

Literature connections to world history, 7-12. Adamson, L. G.   **016.9**

Literature for today's young adults. Donelson, K. L.   **028.5**

Literature for youth series
Wee, P. H. World War II in literature for youth
016.9

Lithuania
Kagda, S. Lithuania (5 and up) **947.9**

Littke, Lael
Haunted sister (7 and up) **Fic**
Lake of secrets (7 and up) **Fic**

Little, Jean, 1932-
See/See also pages in the following book(s):
Ellis, S. From reader to writer **372.6**

Little, Malcolm *See* Malcolm X, 1925-1965

Little, Marjorie
The endocrine system (7 and up) **612.4**
Sexually transmitted diseases (7 and up)
616.95

Little Bighorn, Battle of the, 1876
Custer's last stand (7 and up) **973.8**
Ferrell, N. W. The Battle of the Little Bighorn
in American history **973.8**
Uschan, M. V. The Battle of the Little Bighorn
(5 and up) **973.8**
Viola, H. J. It is a good day to die (5 and up)
973.8

The **little** bird. Philip, N.
In Philip, N. Celtic fairy tales p137-[38]
398.2

The **little** boy and his dogs. Lester, J.
In Lester, J. The last tales of Uncle Remus
p102-10 **398.2**

Little Crow, Sioux Chief, d. 1863
See/See also pages in the following book(s):
Brown, D. A. Bury my heart at Wounded Knee
970.004

Little Dot. Jones, D. W.
In Firebirds: an anthology of original fantasy
and science fiction; an anthology of original fantasy and science fiction **S C**

Little Eight John. Hamilton, V.
In Hamilton, V. The people could fly;
American black folktales p121-25
398.2

Little Girl and Buh Rabby. Hamilton, V.
In Hamilton, V. Her stories; African
American folktales, fairy tales, and true
tales p3-6 **398.2**

Little Gloomy: . . . It was a dark and stormy
night. Walker, L. Q. **741.5**

Little lost robot. Asimov, I.
In Asimov, I. I, robot **S C**

The **little** prince. Saint-Exupéry, A. d. **Fic**

Little Richard
See/See also pages in the following book(s):
Lester, J. The blues singers (5 and up) **920**

The **Little** Rock school desegregation crisis in
American history. Somerlott, R. **373**

Little White Mouse collection 1: Dream of the
ghost. Sizer, P. **741.5**

Littlefield, Daniel C.
Revolutionary citizens (7 and up) **305.8**

Litwin, Laura Baskes
Benjamin Banneker **92**

Liu, Alan, 1953-
William Wordsworth (7 and up) **821**

Liu Siyu, 1964-
A thousand peaks **895.1**

Liungman, Carl G.
Dictionary of symbols **302.2**

Live aware, not in fear. Wells, D. K. **155.5**

Lives in crisis [series]
Grant, R. G. The African-American slave trade
326

Lives in science [series]
Carruthers, M. W. Pioneers of geology **920**
Greenberg, L. Digging into the past **920**

Lives of extraordinary women. Hewitt, K. **920**

Lives of North American birds. Kaufman, K.
598

Lives of the artists [series]
Bassil, A. Vincent van Gogh **92**
Hodge, S. Pablo Picasso **92**

Lives of the presidents. Krull, K. **920**

Lives: poems about famous Americans (4 and up)
811.008

Living earth [series]
Erickson, J. Making of the earth **551.4**
Erickson, J. Marine geology **551.46**

Living in Nazi Germany (7 and up) **943.086**

Living in two worlds. Kosof, A. **325.73**

Living on Mars. Cole, M. D. **629.4**

Living through the Great Depression (7 and up)
973.91

Living well [series]
Gray, S. H. Living with cerebral palsy
362.1
Gray, S. H. Living with juvenile rheumatoid ar-
thritis **616.7**
Raatma, L. Safety on the Internet **025.04**

Living with albinism. Landau, E. **616.5**

Living with cerebral palsy. Gray, S. H. **362.1**

Living with juvenile rheumatoid arthritis. Gray, S.
H. **616.7**

Livingston, Robert R., 1746-1813
See/See also pages in the following book(s):
Levinson, I. S. Gibbons v. Ogden (7 and up)
343

Livo, Norma J., 1929-
Folk stories of the Hmong **398.2**
Includes the following stories: The beginning of the world;
Legend of the rice seed; How seeds came again into the world
and why dogs eat feces droppings; The origin of the shaman;
Another age of happiness; Creation, flood, naming story; Why
monkey and man do not live together; Why animals cannot talk;
Why people eat three meals a day and why doodle bugs roll balls
of dung; Why farmers have to work so hard; Why birds are never hungry; Why Hmong are forbidden to drink mother's milk;
Why the Hmong live on mountains; Shoa and his fire; The story
of the owl; A bird couple's vow; The monkeys and the grasshoppers; Sister-in-law Yer and the tiger: how a wise woman tricked
the tiger; Zeej Choj Kim, the lazy man; Pumpkin seed and the
snake; The handsome husband; Ngao Nao and Shee Na; The tiger steals Nkauj Ncoom; The orphan and the monkeys; The orphan boy and his wife; The tigers steal Nou Plai's wife,
Ntxawm; Gwa and Uo and their two fish wives

The **Lizard** husband
In Hearne, B. G. Beauties and beasts p35-38
398.2

Lizard Island. Collard, S. B., III **577.7**

Lizards
Greenberg, D. A. Lizards **597.9**

Lizzie at last. Mills, C. **Fic**

Lizzie Bright and the Buckminster boy. Schmidt, G. D. **Fic**

Llewellyn, Claire
Great discoveries & amazing adventures (4 and up) **509**

Lloyd, J. D.
(ed) Family violence. See Family violence **362.82**

LoBaido, Anthony C.
The Kurds of Asia **950**

Lobbying
Archer, J. Special interests **324**
Schuckett, S. Political advocacy for school librarians **027.8**

Lobel, Anita, 1934-
No pretty pictures (7 and up) **92**

Lobel, Arnold
(il) The Random House book of poetry for children. See The Random House book of poetry for children **821.008**

The **lobster** war. Howland, E. **Fic**

Lobsters
See/See also pages in the following book(s):
Lassieur, A. Crabs, lobsters, and shrimps (4-6) **595.3**

Fiction
Howland, E. The lobster war **Fic**

Local government
American government at work (7 and up) **320.4**

Local news. Soto, G. **S C**

Lock, Joan
Famous prisons (7 and up) **365**

Locked in time. Duncan, L. **Fic**

Locked inside. Werlin, N. **Fic**

Lockman, Darcy
Computer animation **778.5**
Robots **629.8**

Lockouts *See* Strikes

Locomotion. Woodson, J. **811**

Locomotives
Zimmermann, K. R. Steam locomotives (4 and up) **385**

Locricchio, Matthew
The international cookbook for kids (5 and up) Super chef {series} **641.5**

Loeffelbein, Robert L.
The recreation handbook **793**

Loehfelm, Bill
Osama bin Laden **92**

Loehle, Richard
(il) Tucker, T. Brainstorm! **609**

Loeper, John J., 1929-
Going to school in 1776 (4 and up) **370.9**

Loertscher, David V., 1940-
(ed) The Whole school library handbook. See The Whole school library handbook **027.8**

Logging *See* Lumber and lumbering

Lommel, Cookie
Mary Church Terrell **92**

London, Jack, 1876-1916
The call of the wild (5 and up) **Fic**
White Fang (5 and up) **Fic**
About
Dyer, D. Jack London (7 and up) **92**
Stefoff, R. Jack London (7 and up) **92**
Streissguth, T. Jack London **92**

London (England)
Stacey, G. London (4 and up) **942.1**
Fiction
Blacker, T. The angel factory **Fic**
Cheaney, J. B. The playmaker **Fic**
Cheaney, J. B. The true Prince **Fic**
Curry, J. L. The Black Canary (5 and up) **Fic**
Hooper, M. At the sign of the Sugared Plum **Fic**
Horowitz, A. The Devil and his boy (5 and up) **Fic**
Jarvis, R. The alchemist's cat (5 and up) **Fic**
Naidoo, B. The other side of truth (5 and up) **Fic**
Newman, R. The case of the Baker Street Irregular (5 and up) **Fic**
Pullman, P. The ruby in the smoke **Fic**
Updale, E. Montmorency **Fic**
Wooding, C. The haunting of Alaizabel Cray (7 and up) **Fic**
History
Barter, J. Shakespeare's London (7 and up) **942.06**
Social life and customs
Stewart, G. Life in Elizabethan London **942.05**

Lonehill, Karen
Sioux North American Indians today [series]

Lonergan, Janet Gill- *See* Gill-Lonergan, Janet

A **long** and uncertain journey: the 27,000 mile voyage of Vasco da Gama. Goodman, J. E. **92**

Long Ben *See* Avery, John, fl. 1695

Long journey home. Lester, J.
In Lester, J. Long journey home: stories from black history p129-47 **S C**

Long journey home: stories from black history. Lester, J. **S C**

The **long** road to Gettysburg. Murphy, J. **973.7**

The **Long** Walk. Bial, R. **970.004**

A **long** way from Chicago. Peck, R. **Fic**

Longevity
See also Old age

Longfellow, Henry Wadsworth, 1807-1882
Henry Wadsworth Longfellow **811**
In The Blackbirch treasury of American poetry p239-83 **811.008**
Hiawatha and Megissogwon **811**

Longitude
Dash, J. The longitude prize [biography of John Harrison] (5 and up) **92**

The **longitude** prize [biography of John Harrison]
Dash, J. **92**

Longshore, David
Encyclopedia of hurricanes, typhoons and cyclones (7 and up) **551.55**

Longueville, Bertrand Du Guesclin, comte de
See Du Guesclin, Bertrand, comte de Longueville, ca. 1320-1380

Lonna and Cat Woman. Hamilton, V.
In Hamilton, V. Her stories; African American folktales, fairy tales, and true tales p56-60 **398.2**

Look again!. Serritella, J. **373.1**

A **look** at earth. Tabak, J. **550**

A **look** at Mercury. Spangenburg, R. **523.4**

A **look** at Neptune. Tabak, J. **523.4**

A **look** at Pluto. Tocci, S. **523.4**

A **look** at Uranus. Tocci, S. **523.4**

The **look-it-up** book of explorers. Kimmel, E. C. **920**

The **look-it-up** book of first ladies. Kramer, S. **920**

Looking at pictures. Richardson, J. **750**

Looking back. Lowry, L. **92**

Looking for life in the universe. Jackson, E. B. **576.8**

Looking for Red. Johnson, A. **Fic**

Looking for seabirds. Webb, S. **598**

Looking into the past: people, places, and customs [series]
Kelly, M. Native American talking signs **419**
Pickels, D. E. Egyptian kings and queens and classical deities **930**

Lookout mountain; or, The legend of the chimney-stack cake. Molnár, I.
In Molnár, I. One-time dog market at Buda and other Hungarian folktales p118-20 **398.2**

Loomer, Lisa
Bocón!
In Theatre for young audiences; 20 great plays for children p429-52 **812.008**

Loose threads. Grover, L. A. **811**

Lopes, Tom
(il) Baker, R. F. In a word **422**

Lorca, Federico García See García Lorca, Federico, 1898-1936

Lord, Bette Bao
In the Year of the Boar and Jackie Robinson (4-6) **Fic**

Lord Kirkle's money. See Avi. Beyond the western sea **Fic**

The **Lord** of Miracles. Delacre, L.
In Delacre, L. Salsa stories p55-61 **S C**

Lord of the deep. Salisbury, G. **Fic**

Lord of the Flies. Golding, W. **Fic**

Lord of the Kill. Taylor, T. **Fic**

Lord of the nutcracker men. Lawrence, I. **Fic**

The **lord** of the rings. Tolkien, J. R. R. **Fic**

The **lord's** daughter and the blacksmith's son. Tchana, K. H.
In Tchana, K. H. The serpent slayer: and other stories of strong women p97-103 **398.2**

Lorenzo de' Medici See Medici, Lorenzo de', 1449-1492

Lorenzo de' Medici and Renaissance Italy. Greenblatt, M. **945**

Loret, John
(ed) Experiment central. See Experiment central **507.8**

Loria, Stephano
Pablo Picasso **92**

Los Alamos wildfires
Bryan, N. Los Alamos wildfires (5 and up) **363.34**

Los Angeles (Calif.)
Fiction
Castellucci, C. Boy proof (7 and up) **Fic**
Currier, K. S. Kai's journey to Gold Mountain (4 and up) **Fic**
Fleischman, P. Breakout (7 and up) **Fic**
Scott, K. The princess & the pauper (7 and up) **Fic**

Losing forever. Friesen, G. **Fic**

Losing is not an option. Wallace, R.
In Wallace, R. Losing is not an option: stories **S C**

Losing is not an option: stories. Wallace, R. **S C**

Losing it. Stockler, J.
In Don't cramp my style; stories about that time of the month p242-64 **S C**

Losing Louisa. Caseley, J. **Fic**

Losleben, Elie
(jt. auth) Malcolm, P. Libya **961.2**

Loss (Psychology)
Busby, C. Getting dumped and getting over it! (7 and up) **646.7**
Dennison, A. Our dad died (4 and up) **155.9**
Myers, E. When will I stop hurting? (7 and up) **155.9**
What have you lost? (7 and up) **808.81**

The **lost** camel. Anaya, R. A.
In Anaya, R. A. My land sings; stories from the Rio Grande p121-32 **S C**

Lost children See Missing children

Lost civilizations [series]
Immell, M. The Han dynasty **931**
Nardo, D. The ancient Greeks **938**
Nardo, D. The ancient Romans **937**

The **lost** garden. Yep, L. **92**

Lost in cyberspace. Peck, R. **Fic**

Lost in Death Valley. Goldsmith, C. **979.4**

Lost in the labyrinth. Kindl, P. **Fic**

Lost temple of the Aztecs. Tanaka, S. **972**

The **lost** years of Merlin. Barron, T. A. **Fic**

Lottridge, Celia Barker
Stories from the life of Jesus (4 and up) **232.9**

Louis XIV, King of France, 1638-1715
See/See also pages in the following book(s):
Meltzer, M. Ten kings (5 and up)   **920**

Louis XVI, King of France, 1754-1793
About
Plain, N. Louis XVI, Marie Antoinette, and the
French Revolution   **944**

Louis. Lester, J.
In Lester, J. Long journey home: stories from
black history p27-58   **S C**

Louis Pasteur and the founding of microbiology.
Ackerman, J.   **92**

Louis XVI, Marie Antoinette, and the French Revolution. Plain, N.   **944**

Louisiana
Hintz, M. Louisiana
In America the beautiful, second series
973
LeVert, S. Louisiana
In Celebrate the states   **973**
Fiction
Duncan, L. Locked in time (7 and up)   **Fic**
Gaines, E. J. The autobiography of Miss Jane
Pittman (7 and up)   **Fic**
Holt, K. W. My Louisiana sky (6 and up)
Fic
Nixon, J. L. The haunting (7 and up)   **Fic**
Woods, B. The red rose box (5 and up)   **Fic**

Louisiana Purchase
Blumberg, R. What's the deal? Jefferson, Napoleon and the Louisiana Purchase (7 and up)
973.4
Corrick, J. A. The Louisiana Purchase (7 and
up)   **973.4**

Love, D. Anne
The puppeteer's apprentice   **Fic**
A year without rain (5 and up)   **Fic**

Love, Susan M.
See/See also pages in the following book(s):
Lindop, L. Scientists and doctors (7 and up)
920

Love
Busby, C. Getting dumped and getting over it!
(7 and up)   **646.7**
Love among the walnuts. Ferris, J.   **Fic**
Love and centipedes. Zindel, P.
In Places I never meant to be; original stories
by censored writers   **S C**
Love and death at the mall. See Peck, R. Invita-
tions to the world   **808.06**
Love and other four-letter words. Mackler, C.
Fic
Love Canal. Bryan, N.   **363.7**
Love Canal. Reed, J.   **363.7**
**Love Canal Chemical Waste Landfill (Niagara
Falls, N.Y.)**
Bryan, N. Love Canal (5 and up)   **363.7**
Reed, J. Love Canal (7 and up)   **363.7**
"Love-o'-women". Kipling, R.
In McCaffrey, A. {The Pern series}   **S C**
Love poetry
Blushing: expressions of love in poems & letters
(7 and up)   **821.008**
Grimes, N. Hopscotch love (4 and up)   **811**

Love stories
Chan, G. A foreign field (7 and up)   **Fic**
Plummer, L. The unlikely romance of Kate
Bjorkman (7 and up)   **Fic**
Love that dog. Creech, S.   **Fic**

Lovelace, Ada King, Countess of, 1815-1852
See/See also pages in the following book(s):
Celebrating women in mathematics and science
920
Henderson, H. Modern mathematicians (7 and
up)   **920**

Loving, Mildred Jeter
About
Alonso, K. Loving v. Virginia (7 and up)
346

Loving, Richard
About
Alonso, K. Loving v. Virginia (7 and up)
346
Loving v. Virginia. Alonso, K.   **346**

Lowe, Joy L.
(jt. auth) Matthew, K. I. Neal-Schuman guide to
celebrations & holidays around the world
394.26

Lower East Side (New York, N.Y.)
Bial, R. Tenement (4 and up)   **974.7**
Hopkinson, D. Shutting out the sky (5 and up)
974.7

Lowman, Margaret
About
Lasky, K. The most beautiful roof in the world
(4 and up)   **577.3**

Lowry, Brigid, 1953-
Follow the blue (7 and up)   **Fic**
Guitar highway Rose (7 and up)   **Fic**

Lowry, Lois
Anastasia Krupnik (4-6)   **Fic**
Autumn Street (4 and up)   **Fic**
Gathering blue (5 and up)   **Fic**
The giver (6 and up)   **Fic**
[excerpt]
In Read into the millennium; tales of the fu-
ture p139-46   **S C**
Looking back (5 and up)   **92**
Number the stars (4 and up)   **Fic**
The one hundredth thing about Caroline (5 and
up)   **Fic**
Rabble Starkey (5 and up)   **Fic**
The silent boy   **Fic**
Snowbound
In Necessary noise: stories about our families
as they really are p219-38   **S C**
Stay! (5 and up)   **Fic**
Taking care of Terrific (7 and up)   **Fic**
Your move, J.P.! (5 and up)   **Fic**
See/See also pages in the following book(s):
Author talk (4 and up)   **028.5**
The Newbery & Caldecott medal books, 1986-
2000   **028.5**

Loyalists, American *See* American Loyalists
Lubar, David, 1954-
Bread on the water
In Destination unexpected: short stories
S C
Dunk (7 and up)   **Fic**

Lubar, David, 1954— *Continued*
The heroic quest of Douglas McGawain
In Don't cramp my style; stories about that
time of the month p34-44   **S C**
Science friction
In Tripping over the lunch lady and other
school stories p60-82   **S C**
War is swell
In Shattered: stories of children and war
p139-47   **S C**
Wizards of the game   **Fic**
Words of faith
In Soul searching: thirteen stories about faith
and belief p90-111   **S C**

Lubin, Leonard B., 1943-
(il) Conly, J. L. Racso and the rats of NIMH
   Fic

Lucas, John
See/See also pages in the following book(s):
Kaminsky, M. Uncommon champions   **920**

Lucas. Brooks, K.   **Fic**

Lucchesi, Tony
European art to 1850
In International encyclopedia of art   **703**

Lucent library of conflict in the Middle East
[series]
Stewart, G. Human rights in the Middle East
   323

**The Lucent library of historical eras, Ancient
Rome** [series]
Nardo, D. Arts, leisure, and entertainment
   937
Nardo, D. The Roman army   **937**
Nardo, D. Words of the ancient Romans
   937

**Lucent library of historical eras, Elizabethan
England** [series]
Lace, W. W. Elizabeth I and her court
   942.05
Nardo, D. Great Elizabethan playwrights
   920
Primary sources   **942.05**
Stewart, G. Life in Elizabethan London
   942.05
Woog, A. A history of the Elizabethan theater
   792.09

Lucent library of homeland security [series]
Campbell, G. A. A vulnerable America
   363.3

Lucent overview series
Barghusen, J. D. Cults   **209**
Criswell, S. D. Homelessness   **362.5**
Dunn, J. M. Advertising   **659.1**
Gelletly, L. Violence in the media   **303.6**
McGowan, K. Sexual harassment   **305.3**
Shein, L. AIDS   **616.97**
Steffens, B. Censorship   **342**
Yount, L. Cancer   **616.99**

Lucent terrorism library [series]
America under attack: primary sources
   973.931
Currie, S. Terrorists and terrorist groups
   303.6

Lucid, Shannon
About
Bredeson, C. Shannon Lucid   **92**

Luck. Castedo, E.
In You're on!: seven plays in English and
Spanish p84-99   **812.008**

Lucky break. Conford, E.
In Conford, E. Crush p107-30   **S C**

Lucy was there—. Van Leeuwen, J.   **Fic**

Ludwig, Elisa
Judy Blume   **92**

Lueders, Edward
(comp) Reflections on a gift of watermelon
pickle—and other modern verse. See Reflections on a gift of watermelon pickle—and
other modern verse   **811.008**

Luella and the tame parrot. Hamilton, V.
In Hamilton, V. Her stories; African
American folktales, fairy tales, and true
tales p75-77   **398.2**

Luhr, James
(ed) Earth. See Earth   **550**

Lukes, Bonnie L.
The Boston Massacre (7 and up)   **973.3**
Soldier's courage: the story of Stephen Crane (7
and up)   **92**

Lum, Darrell H. Y.
Yahk fahn, Auntie
In American dragons: twenty-five Asian
American voices p5-13   **810.8**

Lumber and lumbering
Fiction
Crew, L. Fire on the wind   **Fic**
Durbin, W. Blackwater Ben (5 and up)   **Fic**

Lunar bases
Cole, M. D. Moon base (4 and up)   **629.4**

Lunar expeditions See Space flight to the moon

Lung, Khoo Fuk
(jt. auth) Wong, T. Ultraman Tiga, Vol. 1: Return of the warrior   **741.5**

Lungewater. Aiken, J.
In Gothic!; ten original dark tales   **S C**

Lungs
Diseases
See also Asthma

Lunn, Janet Louise Swoboda
The hollow tree   **Fic**

Lunsford, Cin Forshay- See Forshay-Lunsford,
Cin

Lupe and la Llorona. Anaya, R. A.
In Anaya, R. A. My land sings; stories from
the Rio Grande p19-37   **S C**

Lupica, Mike
Travel team   **Fic**

Lurie, April
Dancing in the streets of Brooklyn   **Fic**

Lurie, Jon
Fundamental snowboarding   **796.93**

Lusitania (Steamship)
Preston, D. Remember the Lusitania (5 and up)
   940.4

Lutey and the mermaid. Philip, N.
In Philip, N. Celtic fairy tales p60-65
398.2

The **lutin**. San Souci, R.
In San Souci, R. A terrifying taste of short & shivery; thirty creepy tales p39-42
398.2

Luxbacher, Irene, 1970-
The jumbo book of art (4 and up)   702.8
Luxembourg
Sheehan, P. Luxembourg (5 and up)   949.35
Lyddie. Paterson, K.   Fic
Lye, Keith
(ed) Encyclopedia of African nations and civilizations. See Encyclopedia of African nations and civilizations   960
Lyell, Sir Charles, 1797-1875
See/See also pages in the following book(s):
Carruthers, M. W. Pioneers of geology   920
Lyga, Allyson A. W.
Graphic novels in your media center   025.2
Lyga, Barry
(jt. auth) Lyga, A. A. W. Graphic novels in your media center   025.2
Lying *See* Truthfulness and falsehood
Lyle, Garry
Indonesia   959.8
Lyly, John, 1554?-1606
See/See also pages in the following book(s):
Nardo, D. Great Elizabethan playwrights
920
Lyman, Darryl, 1944-
Holocaust rescuers   920
Lyme disease
Silverstein, A. Lyme disease   616.9
Veggeberg, S. Lyme disease (7 and up)
616.9
Lynch, Chris
All the old haunts (7 and up)   S C
Contents: Foghorn; Chlorine; The cure for Curtis; Womb to tomb; Off ya go, so; Horror vacui; Good-bye is good-bye; The hobbyist; Two hundred yards; Pissin' and moanin'
Bearing, Paul
In Night terrors; stories of shadow and substance   S C
Gold dust   Fic
The hobbyist
In Ultimate sports; short stories by outstanding writers for young adults p315-33
S C
Lie, no lie
In Places I never meant to be; original stories by censored writers   S C
Rust never sleeps
In Time capsule: short stories about teenagers throughout the twentieth century p184-200   S C
Shadow boxer (7 and up)   Fic
Slot machine (7 and up)   Fic
Who the man   Fic
Lynch, Doris
J.R.R. Tolkien   92

Lynch, P. J., 1962-
Hamlet
In Packer, T. Tales from Shakespeare p31-47
822.3
Lynch, Patricia Ann
African mythology A to Z   299.6
Lynching
Crowe, C. Getting away with murder: the true story of the Emmett Till case (7 and up)
364.1
Lynn, Elizabeth Cook- *See* Cook-Lynn, Elizabeth
Lyon, George Ella, 1949-
Gina.Jamie.Father.Bear   Fic
Sonny's house of spies   Fic
Lyon, Steve
The gift moves   Fic
Lyons, Maritcha Rémond, 1848-1929
About
Bolden, T. Maritcha [biography of Maritcha Rémond Lyons] (4 and up)   92
Lyons, Mary E.
Catching the fire: Philip Simmons, blacksmith (4 and up)   92
Dear Ellen Bee   Fic
Letters from a slave girl (6 and up)   Fic
Sorrow's kitchen: the life and folklore of Zora Neale Hurston   92
Talking with Tebé: Clementine Hunter, memory artist (4-6)   92
(cd) Feed the children first. See Feed the children first   941.5

M

Ma, Yo-Yo, 1955-
About
Chippendale, L. A. Yo-Yo Ma   92
Maarsen, Jacqueline van, 1929-
(jt. auth) Lee, C. A. A friend called Anne
940.53
Maata's journal. Sullivan, P.   Fic
Mabinogion
See/See also pages in the following book(s):
Bulfinch, T. Bulfinch's mythology   201
Mable Riley. Jocelyn, M.   Fic
Macaroni boy. Ayres, K.   Fic
MacArthur, Douglas, 1880-1964
About
Feinberg, B. S. Douglas MacArthur   92
See/See also pages in the following book(s):
Dolan, E. F. America in the Korean War (7 and up)   951.9
Macaulay, David, 1946-
Building big   720
Building the book Cathedral (4 and up)   726
Castle (4 and up)   728.8
Cathedral: the story of its construction (4 and up)   726
City: a story of Roman planning and construction (4 and up)   711
Mill (4 and up)   690
Mosque (4 and up)   726
The new way things work (4 and up)   600

Macaulay, David, 1946-—*Continued*
Pyramid (4 and up)   **726**
Ship (4 and up)   **387.2**
Unbuilding (4 and up)   **690**
Underground (5 and up)   **624**
See/See also pages in the following book(s):
The Newbery & Caldecott medal books, 1986-
2000   **028.5**
Macbeth. Cover, A. B.   **741.5**
Macbeth. Packer, T.
In Packer, T. Tales from Shakespeare p67-83
   822.3

Maccabbees, Feast of the *See* Hanukkah
Macdonald, Fiona
Albert Einstein   **92**
The Stone Age news   **930.1**
Winston Churchill   **92**
Women in 19th-century America   **305.4**
Women in 19th-century Europe   **305.4**
Macdonald, James, 1954-
Nobody has to know
In Vampires: a collection of original stories
p3-7   **S C**
MacDonald, Patricia A.
Pablo Picasso (7 and up)   **92**
MacEachern, Stephen
(il) Douglas, A. The family tree detective
   929
(il) O'Brien, L. Lights, camera, action!
   791.43

Machine quilting *See* Quilting
Machinery
See also Mills
Inside a—   **600**
Macaulay, D. The new way things work (4 and
up)   **600**
Macht, Norman L. (Norman Lee), 1929-
The composite guide to track & field
   796.42
Macie and boo hag. Hamilton, V.
In Hamilton, V. Her stories; African
American folktales, fairy tales, and true
tales p51-55   **398.2**
Mack, Stan
(jt. auth) Bode, J. For better, for worse
   306.89
(il) Bode, J. Kids still having kids   **362.7**
Mack, Tracy, 1968-
Birdland (7 and up)   **Fic**
Drawing lessons   **Fic**
Mackel, Kathy
Can of worms   **Fic**
Mackenzie River (N.W.T.)
Harris, T. The Mackenzie River (5 and up)
   971
Mackler, Carolyn
The earth, my butt, and other big, round things
(7 and up)   **Fic**
Love and other four-letter words (7 and up)
   Fic
Nobody stole Jason Grayson
In 13; thirteen stories that capture the agony
and ecstasy of being thirteen

MacLachlan, James, 1928-
(jt. auth) Collier, B. Charles Babbage and the
engines of perfection   **92**
MacLachlan, Patricia, 1938-
Dragon's coo
In Fire and wings: dragon tales from East and
West p25-31   **S C**
Journey (4 and up)   **Fic**
See/See also pages in the following book(s):
The Newbery & Caldecott medal books, 1986-
2000   **028.5**
MacLeod, Elizabeth
Albert Einstein (4 and up)   **92**
Marie Curie (5 and up)   **92**
(jt. auth) Skreslet, L. To the top of Everest
   796.52
Macmillan encyclopedia of the environment
   333.7
Macmillan Encyclopedia of transportation   **388**
Macmillan encyclopedia of weather. Stein, P.
   551.5
Macmillan illustrated encyclopedia [series]
Animals   **596**
Macmillan profiles [series]
Festivals and holidays   **394.26**
Kings and queens   **920.003**
Monuments and historic places of America
   973
Myths and legends   **398**
Macmillan science library [series]
Animal sciences   **590.3**
MacPhail, Catherine, 1946-
Dark waters   **Fic**
Macquitty, Miranda
Shark (4 and up)   **597**
MacRae, Cathi Dunn
Presenting young adult fantasy fiction (7 and
up)   **813.009**
Macy, Sue, 1954-
Batting after Sophie
In Girls got game; sports stories and poems
   810.8
Bulls-eye: a photobiography of Annie Oakley (4
and up)   **92**
Swifter, higher, stronger (4 and up)   **796.48**
(ed) Girls got game. See Girls got game
   810.8
Madagascar
Bishop, N. Digging for bird-dinosaurs (4 and
up)   **567.9**
Heale, J. Madagascar (5 and up)   **969.1**
Stevens, R. Madagascar   **969.1**
Madavan, Vijay
Cooking the Indian way
In Easy menu ethnic cookbooks   **641.5**
Made you look. Graydon, S.   **659.1**
Madikizela-Mandela, Winnie *See* Mandela,
Winnie
Madison, James, 1751-1836
About
DeVillers, D. Marbury v. Madison (7 and up)
   347
Fritz, J. The great little Madison (5 and up)
   92

Madison, James, 1751-1836—About—*Continued*
Malone, M. James Madison   **92**

Madonna, 1958-
See/See also pages in the following book(s):
Orgill, R. Shout, sister, shout! (6 and up)
    920

A **madonna** of the trenches. Kipling, R.
In McCaffrey, A. {The Pern series}   **S C**

Maestro, Giulio, 1942-
(il) Sattler, H. R. Our patchwork planet
    551.1

Mafia
        Fiction
Korman, G. Son of the mob (7 and up)   **Fic**

Magarian, La Verne J.
See/See also pages in the following book(s):
Major, J. S. Caravan to America p[1]-13 (4 and
up)   **920**

Magazines *See* Periodicals

Magellan, Ferdinand, 1480?-1521
        About
Levinson, N. S. Magellan and the first voyage
around the world (5 and up)   **92**
Meltzer, M. Ferdinand Magellan   **92**
See/See also pages in the following book(s):
Fritz, J. Around the world in a hundred years (4
and up)   **910.4**

Magellan and the first voyage around the world.
Levinson, N. S.   **92**

Magic
Black magic and witches   **133.4**
        Fiction
Avi. The Book Without Words (5 and up)
    Fic
Brittain, B. The wish giver   **Fic**
Chabon, M. Summerland (5 and up)   **Fic**
Constable, K. The singer of all songs (7 and up)
    Fic
Coville, B. Juliet Dove, Queen of Love (4-6)
    Fic
Crossley-Holland, K. The seeing stone   **Fic**
Dickinson, P. Tears of the salamander   **Fic**
Divakaruni, C. B. The conch bearer (5 and up)
    Fic
Downer, A. Hatching magic (4 and up)   **Fic**
Haptie, C. Otto and the flying twins (4 and up)
    Fic
Jennings, R. W. Orwell's luck (5 and up)
    Fic
Jones, D. W. Charmed life   **Fic**
Keehn, S. M. Gnat Stokes and the Foggy Bottom Swamp Queen (5 and up)   **Fic**
La Fevers, R. L. The falconmaster   **Fic**
Larbalestier, J. Magic or madness (7 and up)
    Fic
Lubar, D. Wizards of the game   **Fic**
Melling, O. R. The Hunter's Moon (7 and up)
    Fic
Sage, A. Magyk . (5 and up)   **Fic**
Stanley, D. The mysterious matter of I.M. Fine
    Fic
Tunnell, M. O. Wishing moon   **Fic**

Magic & mischief. Climo, S.   **398.2**

The **magic** brocade. Yolen, J.
In Yolen, J. Mightier than the sword; world
folktales for strong boys p1-10   **398.2**

The **magic** eye. Nixon, J. L.
In Nixon, J. L. Ghost town; seven ghostly
stories p81-98   **S C**

The **magic** lake. Tchana, K. H.
In Tchana, K. H. The serpent slayer: and other stories of strong women p53-59
    398.2

The **magic** seed. Jaffe, N.
In Jaffe, N. and Zeitlin, S. J. The cow of no
color: riddle stories and justice tales from
around the world p55-58   **398.2**

The **magic** spoon. Kimmel, E. A.
In Kimmel, E. A. The jar of fools: eight Hanukkah stories from Chelm p27-34
    S C

The **magic-stealer**. Sherman, J.
In Vampires: a collection of original stories
p99-120   **S C**

The **magic** wine cup. Schwartz, H.
In Schwartz, H. The day the Rabbi disappeared: Jewish holiday tales of magic
p54-58   **398.2**

The **magical** worlds of Harry Potter. Colbert, D.
    823.009

Magicians
        Fiction
Avi. Midnight magic (5 and up)   **Fic**
Sedgwick, M. The book of Dead Days   **Fic**
        Folklore
Sherman, J. Merlin's kin   **398.2**

Magill, Frank Northen, 1907-
(ed) Masterpieces of world literature. See Masterpieces of world literature   **809**

Magnesium
Blashfield, J. F. Magnesium
In Blashfield, J. F. Sparks of life; chemical
elements that make life possible   **546**
Uttley, C. Magnesium
In The Elements   **546**

Magnetism
Meiani, A. Magnetism (4 and up)   **538**

Magnificent voyage. Lawlor, L.   **910.4**

Maguire, Gregory
Beyond the fringe
In A Glory of unicorns p45-57   **S C**
Fee, fie, foe, et cetera
In The Green Man: tales from the mythic forest p238-59   **808.8**
The good liar (4 and up)   **Fic**
The prank
In Gothic!; ten original dark tales   **S C**
Scarecrow
In Half-human p97-115   **S C**
Tea party ends in bloody massacre, film at 11
In Shelf life: stories by the book p67-80
    S C

Magyk . Sage, A.   **Fic**

Mah, Adeline Yen
Chinese Cinderella   **92**

Maher, Terre
(il) Nye, N. S. A maze me   **811**

Mahomet *See* Muḥammad, d. 632

Mahy, Margaret
Alchemy (7 and up)   Fic

Maine
Dornfeld, M. Maine
In Celebrate the states   973
Kent, D. Maine
In America the beautiful, second series
                                                       973

Fiction
Holmes, B. W. Following Fake Man   Fic
Irwin, H. The original Freddie Ackerman (5 and up)   Fic
Schmidt, G. D. Lizzie Bright and the Buckminster boy (7 and up)   Fic
Wait, L. Wintering well (5 and up)   Fic

Maine (Battleship)
McNeese, T. Remember the Maine!   973.8

Major, John S., 1942-
Caravan to America (4 and up)   920
The Silk Route   950

Major, Kevin, 1949-
Three people and two seals
In Sixteen; short stories by outstanding writers for young adults p113-24   S C

Major presidential elections and the administrations that followed [series]
The election of 1860 and the administration of Abraham Lincoln   973.7
The Election of 2000 and the administration of George W. Bush   324

Major world leaders [series]
Reed, J. The Saudi royal family   920

Major world nations [series]
Anthony, S. West Indies   972.9
Canesso, C. South Africa   968.06
Dwyer, C. Chile   983
Haynes, T. Colombia   986.1
James, R. S. Mozambique   967.9
Lyle, G. Indonesia   959.8
McCulla, P. E. Tanzania   967.8
Stevens, R. Madagascar   969.1
Wee, J. The Philippines   959.9
Wilkens, F. Egypt   962
Zickgraf, R. Laos   959.4

Make lemonade. Wolff, V. E.   Fic
Make things happen. Zielin, L.   302.2
Make way for Sam Houston. Fritz, J. 92

Makers of America [series]
Goldman, M. S. Richard M. Nixon   92
Scott, R. A. Chief Joseph and the Nez Percés
                                         92

Makers of science. Allaby, M.   920.003

Making and using the atomic bomb (7 and up)
                                         355.8
Making books that fly, fold, wrap, hide, pop up, twist, and turn. Diehn, G.   736
The **making** of a writer. Nixon, J. L. 92
The **making** of America. Johnston, R. D.   973

Making of America [series]
Anderson, D. The Cold War years   973.92
Making of the earth. Erickson, J.   551.4

Makowski, Silk
Serious about series   016.8

Malam, John, 1957-
Ancient Egyptian jobs (5 and up)   932
Ancient Greece (5 and up)   938
Greek town   938
Mummies (5 and up)   393
Super structures   624

Malaspina, Ann, 1957-
The koala (7 and up)   599.2
Saving the American wilderness   333.72

Malaysia
Munan, H. Malaysia (5 and up)   959.5

Malcolm, D. J.
Linnea
In Half-human p19-45   S C

Malcolm, Peter, 1937-
Libya (5 and up)   961.2

Malcolm X, 1925-1965
About
Draper, A. S. The assassination of Malcolm X
                                         92

Male/female roles: opposing viewpoints   305.3
Male role *See* Sex role

Mali
History
McKissack, P. C. The royal kingdoms of Ghana, Mali, and Songhay (5 and up)   966.2
The **Malifex**. Alton, S.   Fic
Malindy and little devil. Hamilton, V.
In Hamilton, V. Her stories; African American folktales, fairy tales, and true tales p61-65   398.2

Malinowski, Sharon
(ed) The Gale encyclopedia of Native American tribes. See The Gale encyclopedia of Native American tribes   970.004
(ed) U·X·L encyclopedia of Native American tribes. See U·X·L encyclopedia of Native American tribes   970.004

Malintzin of the Mountain. Gerson, M.-J.
In Gerson, M.-J. Fiesta femenina; celebrating women in Mexican folktale   398.2
Malka. Pressler, M.   Fic

Mallory, Kenneth
Swimming with hammerhead sharks (4 and up)
                                         597

Malloy, Nancy
European art since 1850
In International encyclopedia of art   703

Malone, Caroline
Stonehenge   936.2

Malone, Margaret Gay
(ed) Taylor, S. K. The diary of Susie King Taylor, Civil War nurse   973.7

Malone, Mary
James Madison   92

Malone, Peter
(il) Crossley-Holland, K. The world of King Arthur and his court   942.01

Malta
Sheehan, S. Malta (5 and up)   945

The **maltese** cat. Kipling, R.
In McCaffrey, A. {The Pern series} **S C**

Malthus, T. R. (Thomas Robert), 1766-1834
See/See also pages in the following book(s):
Bussing-Burks, M. Influential economists (7 and up) **920**

Malthus, Thomas Robert *See* Malthus, T. R. (Thomas Robert), 1766-1834

Maltz, Leora
(ed) The Founding of America. See The Founding of America **973.3**

Malvin, Harriet
See/See also pages in the following book(s):
Katz, W. L. Black pioneers **920**

Malvin, John, 1795-1880
See/See also pages in the following book(s):
Katz, W. L. Black pioneers **920**

Mama gone. Yolen, J.
In Vampires: a collection of original stories p202-10 **S C**

The **Mambo** Kings play songs of love [excerpt] Hijuelos, O.
In Growing up Latino; memoirs and stories p16-21 **810.8**

Mammals

See also groups of mammals; and names of mammals
Grzimek's student animal life resource, Mammals **599**
Hare, T. Animal fact-file **599**
Morris, P. Mammals **599**
Whitaker, J. O., Jr. National Audubon Society field guide to North American mammals **599**

Mammals, Marine *See* Marine mammals

Mammoths
Agenbroad, L. D. Mammoths **569**
Hehner, B. Ice Age mammoth (5 and up) **569**

Man *See* Human beings

Influence on nature
See Human influence on nature

Origin
See Human origins

Man, Fossil *See* Fossil hominids

Man, Prehistoric *See* Prehistoric peoples

The **man** and the boots. Lester, J.
In Lester, J. The last tales of Uncle Remus p133-36 **398.2**

The **man** and the wild cattle. Lester, J.
In Lester, J. The last tales of Uncle Remus p110-14 **398.2**

Man Bear. Bruchac, J.
In Bruchac, J. and Bruchac, J. When the Chenoo howls; native American tales of terror **398.2**

The **man-child**. Rabin, A.
In Theatre for young audiences; 20 great plays for children p364-94 **812.008**

The **man-eating** tigers of Sundarbans. Briggs, E. **599.75**

The **man** I killed. O'Brien, T.
In Who do you think you are?; stories of friends and enemies p146-51 **S C**

The **man** in the ceiling. Feiffer, J. **Fic**

The **man** who almost married a witch. Lester, J.
In Lester, J. The last tales of Uncle Remus p71-76 **398.2**

The **man** who loved clowns. Wood, J. R. **Fic**

The **man** who married a seagull. Norman, H.
In Norman, H. The girl who dreamed only geese, and other tales of the Far North **398.2**

The **man** who was a horse. Lester, J.
In Lester, J. Long journey home: stories from black history p89-103 **S C**

The **man** who was Poe. Avi **Fic**

The **man** who went to the far side of the moon: the story of Apollo 11 astronaut Michael Collins. Schyffert, B. U. **92**

The **man** who would be king. Kipling, R.
In McCaffrey, A. {The Pern series} **S C**

The **man** with the twisted lip. Doyle, Sir A. C.
In Doyle, Sir A. C. The complete Sherlock Holmes **S C**

The **man** without a face. Holland, I. **Fic**

Managing and analyzing your collection. Doll, C. A. **025.2**

Managing the Internet controversy **025.04**

Mana's story. Dickinson, P.
In Dickinson, P. The kin p465-628 **Fic**

Manatees
Price-Groff, C. The manatee (7 and up) **599.5**

Manco Capac and the rod of gold. Delacre, L.
In Delacre, L. Golden tales; myths, legends, and folktales from Latin America p55-57 **398.2**

Mandela, Nelson
About
Beecroft, S. The release of Nelson Mandela **968.06**
Finlayson, R. Nelson Mandela **92**
Kramer, A. Nelson Mandela (7 and up) **92**

Mandela, Winnie
See/See also pages in the following book(s):
Price-Groff, C. Twentieth-century women political leaders (7 and up) **920**

Mandelbaum, Allen, 1926-
(ed) Three centuries of American poetry, 1623-1923. See Three centuries of American poetry, 1623-1923 **811.008**

Mandelbaum, Jack
About
Warren, A. Surviving Hitler (5 and up) **940.53**

Mandelbrot, Benoit B.
See/See also pages in the following book(s):
Henderson, H. Modern mathematicians (7 and up) **920**

Mandell, Jude
Ballad of a prodigy
In What a song can do; 12 riffs on the power of music **S C**

Mandell, Jude—*Continued*
Princess Dragonblood
In Half-human p139-63   **S C**

Manganese
Beatty, R. Manganese
In The Elements   **546**

A **mango-shaped** space. Mass, W.   **Fic**

Manhattan Project
Cohen, D. The Manhattan Project (7 and up)
     623.4
Making and using the atomic bomb (7 and up)
     355.8

Fiction
Davies, J. Where the ground meets the sky
     Fic

Manheimer, Ann
Riffs
In What a song can do; 12 riffs on the power
of music   **S C**

Manheimer, Ann S.
Martin Luther King Jr (5 and up)   **92**

Maniac Magee. Spinelli, J.   **Fic**

Manic-depressive illness
See also Depression (Psychology)
Demetriades, H. A. Bipolar disorder, depression,
and other mood disorders (7 and up)
     616.85

Manitoba
Laws, G. D. Manitoba
In Exploring Canada   **971**

Mankell, Henning, 1948-
Secrets in the fire (5 and up)   **Fic**

Mankiller, Wilma
See/See also pages in the following book(s):
Kallen, S. A. Native American chiefs and war-
riors (7 and up)   **920**
Hewitt, K. Lives of extraordinary women (4 and
up)   **920**
Price-Groff, C. Twentieth-century women politi-
cal leaders (7 and up)   **920**

Manley, Claudia B.
Competitive track and field for girls   **796.42**
Competitive volleyball for girls   **796.325**

Manmade disasters [series]
Mayell, M. Tragedies of space exploration
     363.1

Mann, Elizabeth, 1948-
Hoover Dam (4 and up)   **627**
The Roman Colosseum   **937**

Mann, Gurinder Singh
Buddhists, Hindus, and Sikhs in America (7 and
up)   **294**

Mann, Jonathan H.
(ed) The Election of 2000 and the administration of George W. Bush. See The Election of
2000 and the administration of George W.
Bush   **324**

Mann, Kenny, 1946-
The ancient Hebrews   **909**
Isabel, Ferdinand and fifteenth-century Spain
     946

Mann, Murray Gell- *See* Gell-Mann, Murray,
1929-

The **manner** of men. Kipling, R.
In McCaffrey, A. {The Pern series}   **S C**

Manners *See* Etiquette

Manners and customs
See also Country life names of ethnic
groups, countries, cities, etc. with the subdivision *Social life and customs*
Cook, D. F. The kids' multicultural cookbook
     641.5

Manny calls. Saldaña, R.
In Saldaña, R. Finding our way: stories p75-
82   **S C**

Mansa Musa *See* Musa, d. 1337

Mansfield, Stephen
Laos (5 and up)   **959.4**

Manslaughter *See* Homicide

Mantell, Paul
(jt. auth) Hart, A. Ancient Greece!   **938**
(jt. auth) Hart, A. Knights & castles   **940.1**

Manuel had a riddle. Hamilton, V.
In Hamilton, V. The people could fly;
American black folktales p65-75
     398.2

Many peoples, one land. Helbig, A.   **016.8**

Many thousand gone. Hamilton, V.   **326**

Manzanar War Relocation Center
Cooper, M. L. Remembering Manzanar
     940.53
Houston, J. W. Farewell to Manzanar (7 and up)
     940.53

Mao, Tse-tung *See* Mao Zedong, 1893-1976

Mao Zedong, 1893-1976
About
Slavicek, L. C. Mao Zedong   **92**
See/See also pages in the following book(s):
Uschan, M. V. Political leaders   **920**

The **Maori** of New Zealand. Theunissen, S.
     993

Maoris
Theunissen, S. The Maori of New Zealand
     993

Mapp, Dollree
About
Persico, D. Mapp v. Ohio (7 and up)   **345**

Mapp v. Ohio. Persico, D.   **345**

Mapping epidemics. Hoff, B. H.   **614**

Mapping the planets and space. Bramwell, M.
     520

Mapping the world. Johnson, S. A.   **912**

Maps
See also Atlases
Johnson, S. A. Mapping the world (4 and up)
     912
Morrison, T. The coast mappers (5 and up)
     623.89
Ross, V. The road to there   **912**

Maps & mapmakers [series]
Bramwell, M. Mapping the planets and space
     520

Maps on file   **912**

The **marble** champ. Soto, G.
 In Soto, G. Baseball in April, and other sto-
  ries p90-96   **S C**
Marbury, William, 1761?-1835
   About
 DeVillers, D. Marbury v. Madison (7 and up)
             347
Marbury v. Madison. DeVillers, D. **347**
Marci, the honest thief. Molnár, I.
 In Molnár, I. One-time dog market at Buda
  and other Hungarian folktales p89-96
            398.2
Marconi, Guglielmo, 1874-1937
   About
 Birch, B. Guglielmo Marconi   **92**
Marcovaldi, Neca
 See/See also pages in the following book(s):
 Graham, K. Contemporary environmentalists (7
  and up)   **920**
Marcovitz, Hal
 Kuwait   **953.67**
Marcus, Leonard S., 1950-
 A Caldecott celebration   **741.6**
 (ed) Author talk. See Author talk **028.5**
Margaret, Princess, Countess of Snowdon, 1930-
 2002
 See/See also pages in the following book(s):
 McGaw, L. To be a princess (4 and up)
            920
Margaux with an X. Koertge, R.   **Fic**
Margeson, Susan M.
 Viking (4 and up)   **948**
Margulies, Phillip
 Al Qaeda: Osama bin Laden's army of terrorists
          973.931
 Artificial intelligence (5 and up) **006.3**
Maria Mitchell, astronomer. Anderson, D. **92**
Maria Theresa, Empress of Austria, 1717-1780
 See/See also pages in the following book(s):
 Meltzer, M. Ten queens (5 and up) **920**
Marian. Trottier, M.
 In Sherwood: original stories from the world
  of Robin Hood p20-34   **S C**
Marie and Redfish. Hamilton, V.
 In Hamilton, V. Her stories; African
  American folktales, fairy tales, and true
  tales p11-14   **398.2**
Marie Antoinette, Queen, consort of Louis XVI,
 King of France, 1755-1793
   About
 Plain, N. Louis XVI, Marie Antoinette, and the
  French Revolution   **944**
 See/See also pages in the following book(s):
 McGaw, L. To be a princess (4 and up)
            920
 Hewitt, K. Lives of extraordinary women (4 and
  up)   **920**
Marijuana
 Goodwin, W. Marijuana (7 and up) **362.29**
 Gottfried, T. The facts about marijuana
           362.29
 Ruschmann, P. Legalizing marijuana (7 and up)
            345

See/See also pages in the following book(s):
 Terminal illness: opposing viewpoints (7 and
  up)   **362.1**
 The war on drugs   **363.4**
Marine animals
 See also Marine mammals
 Johnson, J. Simon & Schuster children's guide
  to sea creatures (4 and up)   **591.7**
 Parker, S. Seashore (4 and up) **577.7**
 Vogel, C. G. Ocean wildlife (5 and up)
           591.7
Marine biology
 Aquatic life of the world (4 and up) **578.7**
 Bredeson, C. Tide pools   **577.6**
 Carson, R. The edge of the sea (7 and up)
           577.7
 Conlan, K. Under the ice (4 and up) **578.7**
 Erickson, J. Marine geology (7 and up)
          551.46
 Goodman, S. Ultimate field trip 3 **577.6**
 Kricher, J. C. Peterson first guide to seashores
  (6 and up)   **577.7**
 Meinkoth, N. A. The Audubon Society field
  guide to North American seashore creatures
           592
 World Book looks at the sea and its marvels
           577.7
   Encyclopedias
 Encyclopedia of the aquatic world **578.7**
Marine Corps (U.S.) *See* United States. Marine
 Corps
Marine ecology
 Cerullo, M. M. Coral reef (4 and up) **577.7**
 Collard, S. B., III. Lizard Island **577.7**
 Endangered oceans: opposing viewpoints (7 and
  up)   **577.7**
 Gowell, E. T. Fountains of life   **577.7**
Marine geology. Erickson, J.   **551.46**
Marine mammal preservation. Thomas, P.
           639.9
Marine mammals
 See also Dolphins; Whales
 Thomas, P. Marine mammal preservation (5 and
  up)   **639.9**
Marine plants
 Parker, S. Seashore (4 and up) **577.7**
Marine pollution
 Conlan, K. Under the ice (4 and up) **578.7**
 Endangered oceans: opposing viewpoints (7 and
  up)   **577.7**
 Vogel, C. G. Human impact (5 and up)
           333.91
Marines (U.S.) *See* United States. Marine Corps
Mariposa. Springer, N.
 In Firebirds: an anthology of original fantasy
  and science fiction; an anthology of orig-
  inal fantasy and science fiction **S C**
Maritcha [biography of Maritcha Rémond Lyons]
 Bolden, T.   **92**
Maritime Provinces
 Laws, G. D. Maritime Provinces
  In Exploring Canada   **971**
Mark, Joan T., 1937-
 Margaret Mead (7 and up)   **92**

The **mark** of the beast. Kipling, R.
  In McCaffrey, A. {The Pern series} **S C**

Mark Twain [essays about] **92**

Mark Twain himself. Meltzer, M. **92**

Marker, Sherry, 1941-
  Plains Indian wars (7 and up) **973.5**

Marks, Alan, 1957-
  (il) Goodall, J. With love **599.8**

Marks, Diana F.
  Let's celebrate today **394.26**

Markuson, Carolyn A.
  (jt. auth) Erikson, R. Designing a school library
  media center for the future **027.8**

Marley, Bob
       About
  Dolan, S. Bob Marley **92**

Marlowe, Christopher, 1564-1593
  See/See also pages in the following book(s):
  Nardo, D. Great Elizabethan playwrights
    920

Maroon. Nolan, H.
  In Don't cramp my style; stories about that
  time of the month p182-208 **S C**

Marquette, Scott
  America under attack (4 and up) **973.931**
  War of 1812 (4 and up) **973.5**

Márquez, Herón
  (jt. auth) Ventura, J. Jesse Ventura tells it like
  it is **320**

Marriage
    See also Divorce; Remarriage
  Marriage and divorce (7 and up) **306.8**

Marriage and divorce (7 and up) **306.8**

The **marriage** of two masters. Tchana, K. H.
  In Tchana, K. H. The serpent slayer: and other stories of strong women p105-09
    398.2

Marrin, Albert, 1936-
  Commander in Chief Abraham Lincoln and the
  Civil War (7 and up) **973.7**
  Dr. Jenner and the speckled monster (5 and up)
    614.5
  Old Hickory [biography of Andrew Jackson] (7
  and up) **92**
  Secrets from the rocks: dinosaur hunting with
  Roy Chapman Andrews (4 and up) **92**

Marriott, Pat, 1920-
  (il) Aiken, J. The wolves of Willoughby Chase
    Fic

Mars (Planet)
  Skurzynski, G. Discover Mars **523.4**
  Stone, T. L. Mars **523.4**
      Exploration
  Cole, M. D. Living on Mars **629.4**
  Wunsch, S. T. The adventures of Sojourner
    629.43

Marsalis, Wynton
  See/See also pages in the following book(s):
  Mour, S. I. American jazz musicians **920**

Marschall, Ken
  Inside the Titanic (4 and up) **910.4**
  (il) Ballard, R. D. Ghost liners **910.4**

  (il) Brewster, H. 882 ½ amazing answers to your
  questions about the Titanic **910.4**

Marsden, John, 1950-
  Checkers (7 and up) **Fic**
  Tomorrow, when the war began (7 and up)
    Fic

Marshal, William *See* Pembroke, William Marshal, Earl of, 1144?-1219

Marshall, Chris, 1962-
  (ed) Dinosaurs of the world. See Dinosaurs of
  the world **567.9**

Marshall, Elizabeth L.
  High-tech harvest (7 and up) **641.3**

Marshall, Samuel D.
      About
  Montgomery, S. The tarantula scientist (4 and
  up) **595.4**

Marshall, Thurgood, 1908-1993
      About
  Kent, D. Thurgood Marshall and the Supreme
  Court **92**
  Rowh, M. Thurgood Marshall **92**
  See/See also pages in the following book(s):
  Dubovoy, S. Civil rights leaders (7 and up)
    920

The **Marshall** Cavendish encyclopedia of health.
  See Encyclopedia of health **610.3**

Marstall, Bob
  A dragon in the sky (4 and up) **595.7**
  (il) Pringle, L. P. An extraordinary life
    595.7

Marston, Elsa
  The Byzantine Empire **949.5**
  Figs and fate **S C**
  Contents: In line; Hand of Fatima; Faces; The plan; Santa
  Claus in Bagdad
  The olive grove
  In Soul searching: thirteen stories about faith
  and belief p44-66 **S C**
  The Phoenicians **939**
  Rima's song
  In Join in; multiethnic short stories by out-
  standing writers for young adults p153-
  71 **S C**
  (jt. auth) Harik, R. M. Women in the Middle
  East **305.4**

Marston, Hope Irvin, 1935-
  Isaac Johnson **92**

Martell, Hazel Mary
  The age of discovery **909.08**

Marten, James, 1956-
  (ed) The Boy of Chancellorville and other Civil
  War stories. See The Boy of Chancellorville
  and other Civil War stories **S C**

Martha Graham, a dancer's life. Freedman, R.
    92

Martha's Vineyard (Mass.)
      Fiction
  DeFelice, C. C. Death at Devil's Bridge (5 and
  up) **Fic**

Martí, José, 1853-1895
  See/See also pages in the following book(s):
  Mendoza, P. M. Extraordinary people in extraor-
  dinary times (7 and up) **920**

Martin, Alex, 1953-
Knights & castles (5 and up)   **940.1**

Martin, Ann M., 1955-
A corner of the universe (5 and up)   **Fic**
Here today (5 and up)   **Fic**
Tina the fairy
In 13; thirteen stories that capture the agony and ecstasy of being thirteen
See/See also pages in the following book(s):
Author talk (4 and up)   **028.5**
(jt. auth) Danziger, P. P.S. Longer letter later   **Fic**
(jt. auth) Danziger, P. Snail mail no more   **Fic**

Martin, George R. R.
The hedge knight; adaptation. See Avery, B.
The hedge knight   **741.5**
(jt. auth) Avery, B. The hedge knight   **741.5**

Martin, Jesse
Lionheart (7 and up)   **910.4**

Martin, Joel
Native American religion (7 and up)   **299.7**

Martin, Joseph Plumb, 1760-1850
About
Murphy, J. A young patriot (5 and up)   **973.3**

Martin, Laura C.
Nature's art box (4 and up)   **745.5**

Martin, Marvin
Extraordinary people in jazz   **920**

Martin, Nora
Flight of the Fisherbird (5 and up)   **Fic**

Martin, Patricia A. Fink, 1955-
Prairies, fields, and meadows (7 and up)   **577.4**
Rivers and streams (7 and up)   **577.6**
Woods and forests (7 and up)   **577.3**

Martin, Patricia Preciado
The ruins
In Growing up Latino; memoirs and stories p73-84   **810.8**

Martin, Rafe, 1946-
The world before this one (4 and up)   **398.2**
Contents: Dangers; Moving; Gaqka, crow; The bow; The rock; Questions; New day; Two boys; Allies; Men's tales; Dream; Stories; The council; The people and the stone; Farewell

Martínez, María Montoya, 1887-1980
About
Morris, J. Tending the fire: the story of Maria Martinez (4 and up)   **92**
See/See also pages in the following book(s):
Danneberg, J. Women artists of the West   **920**

Martinez, Pedro, 1971-
About
Gallagher, J. Pedro Martinez   **92**

Martinez, Sergio
(il) Meltzer, M. Weapons & warfare   **355**

Martyn Pig. Brooks, K.   **Fic**

Maruki, Toshi, 1912-
Hiroshima no pika   **940.54**

Marvelous math (4 and up)   **811.008**

Marxism
See also Communism

Mary I, Queen of England, 1516-1558
See/See also pages in the following book(s):
McGaw, L. To be a princess (4 and up)   **920**
Fiction
Meyer, C. Mary, Bloody Mary   **Fic**

Mary, Queen of Scots, 1542-1587
Fiction
Lasky, K. Mary, Queen of Scots, queen without a country   **Fic**
Yolen, J. The queen's own fool   **Fic**

Mary Belle and the mermaid. Hamilton, V.
In Hamilton, V. Her stories; African American folktales, fairy tales, and true tales p33-37   **398.2**

Mary, Bloody Mary. Meyer, C.   **Fic**

Mary Magdalene, Saint
Fiction
Napoli, D. J. Song of the Magdalene (7 and up)   **Fic**

Mary on horseback [biography of Mary Breckinridge] Wells, R.   **92**

Mary Postgate. Kipling, R.
In McCaffrey, A. {The Pern series}   **S C**

Mary, Queen of Scots, queen without a country. Lasky, K.   **Fic**

Mary Shelley's Frankenstein: the graphic novel. Reed, G.   **741.5**

Mary Tudor *See* Mary I, Queen of England, 1516-1558

Mary Wollstonecraft and the rights of women. Miller, C. C.   **92**

Maryland
Burgan, M. Maryland
In America the beautiful, second series   **973**
Pietrzyk, L. Maryland
In Celebrate the states   **973**
Fiction
Cummings, P. Red kayak (7 and up)   **Fic**
Hahn, M. D. Promises to the dead (5 and up)   **Fic**
Rinaldi, A. Amelia's war   **Fic**

Marzilli, Alan, 1970-
Election reform (7 and up)   **324.6**

Masada Site (Israel)
Waldman, N. Masada (4 and up)   **933**

Masai (African people)
Lekuton, J. Facing the lion   **967.62**
Fiction
Kessler, C. Our secret, Siri Aang (7 and up)   **Fic**
Quintana, A. The baboon king (7 and up)   **Fic**

Masefield, John
Jim Davis (5 and up)   **Fic**

Masih, Iqbal, d. 1995
About
Kuklin, S. Iqbal Masih and the crusaders against child slavery (7 and up)   **331.3**
See/See also pages in the following book(s):
Parker, D. L. Stolen dreams   **331.3**
Fiction
D'Adamo, F. Iqbal (5 and up)   **Fic**

Masks (Facial)
Doney, M. Masks   **745.59**
Finley, C. The art of African masks (5 and up)
    391

Masoff, Joy, 1951-
Fire! (4 and up)   **628.9**
Snowboard!   **796.93**

Mason, Antony
In the time of Picasso   **709.04**
In the time of Warhol   **709.04**
People around the world   **305.8**

Mason, Biddy, 1818-1891
See/See also pages in the following book(s):
Pinkney, A. D. Let it shine (4 and up)   **920**

Mason, Bob
About
Montgomery, S. The snake scientist (4 and up)
    597.9

Mason, Chris, 1944-
(jt. auth) Brownlie, A. Why do people fight
wars?   **355**

Mason, Francis
(jt. auth) Balanchine, G. 101 stories of the great
ballets   **792.8**

Mason, Paul, 1967-
Body piercing and tattooing   **391**
Thomas A. Edison   **92**

The **masque** of the red death. Poe, E. A.
In Poe, E. A. Edgar Allan Poe's tales of mystery and madness   **S C**
In Poe, E. A. Tales of Edgar Allan Poe p117-
25   **S C**

Mass, Wendy, 1967-
Gods and goddesses   **201**
A mango-shaped space   **Fic**

Mass communication *See* Communication

Mass media
Cohen, D. Yellow journalism (7 and up)
    302.23
Edgar, K. J. Everything you need to know about
media violence   **303.6**
Gelletly, L. Violence in the media (7 and up)
    303.6
Mass media: opposing viewpoints   **302.23**
Media violence: opposing viewpoints (7 and up)
    303.6
Petley, J. Media (7 and up)   **302.23**
See/See also pages in the following book(s):
Teens at risk: opposing viewpoints p63-105 (7
and up)   **362.7**

Mass media: opposing viewpoints   **302.23**

Massachusetts
LeVert, S. Massachusetts
In Celebrate the states   **973**
McNair, S. Massachusetts
In America the beautiful, second series
    973
Fiction
Cooney, C. B. The ransom of Mercy Carter
    Fic
Karr, K. Gilbert and Sullivan set me free
    Fic
Koller, J. F. Someday   **Fic**
Krisher, T. Uncommon Faith   **Fic**

Kwasney, M. D. Baby Blue   **Fic**
Paterson, K. Lyddie (5 and up)   **Fic**
Rees, D. C. Vampire High   **Fic**
Smith, P. C. Weetamoo, heart of the Pocassets
    Fic
Velmans, H. Isabel of the whales (5 and up)
    Fic

History—1600-1775, Colonial period
Aronson, M. John Winthrop, Oliver Cromwell,
and the Land of Promise (7 and up)   **92**
Bowen, G. Stranded at Plimoth Plantation, 1626
(4 and up)   **974.4**
Collier, C. Pilgrims and Puritans, 1620-1676
    974.4
Doherty, K. William Bradford   **92**
Edwards, J. The Plymouth Colony and the Pil-
grim adventure in American history (7 and
up)   **974.4**
Erickson, P. Daily life in the Pilgrim colony,
1636   **974.4**
Pilgrim voices   **974.4**
History—1600-1775, Colonial period—Fiction
Lasky, K. A journey to the New World   **Fic**

Mast, Edward
Jungalbook [play]
In Theatre for young audiences; 20 great
plays for children p478-517   **812.008**

The **master** puppeteer. Paterson, K.   **Fic**

Masterpieces of world literature   **809**

Masters, Nancy Robinson *See* Robinson Masters,
Nancy

Masters of art [series]
Corrain, L. The art of the Renaissance
    709.02
Loria, S. Pablo Picasso   **92**
Pozzi, G. Chagall   **92**

Masters of music [series]
Barron, R. John Coltrane   **92**
Furstinger, N. Say it with music: the story of Ir-
ving Berlin   **92**

Mastodon
Giblin, J. The mystery of the mammoth bones
(4 and up)   **569**

Matajuro's training. Kimmel, E. A.
In Kimmel, E. A. Sword of the samurai; adventure stories from Japan p31-39
    Fic

Matas, Carol, 1949-
After the war (7 and up)   **Fic**
Greater than angels (7 and up)   **Fic**
In my enemy's house (7 and up)   **Fic**
Sparks fly upward (4 and up)   **Fic**
The war within (5 and up)   **Fic**

Materia medica
See also Drugs

Material world [series]
Kassinger, R. Ceramics: from magic pots to
man-made bones   **666**
Kassinger, R. Dyes: from sea snails to synthet-
ics   **667**
Kassinger, R. Gold: from Greek myth to com-
puter chips   **669**
Materials
Knapp, B. J. Materials science   **620.1**

Materials science. Knapp, B. J.   **620.1**

Math and mathematicians. Bruno, L. C.   **920**

Math and science across cultures. Bazin, M.   **510**

Math games for middle school. Salvadori, M. G.   **510.7**

Math wizardry for kids. Kenda, M.   **793.7**

Mathabane, Mark
Kaffir boy [excerpt]
In Somehow tenderness survives; stories of Southern Africa p87-103   **S C**

Mathematical recreations
Kenda, M. Math wizardry for kids   **793.7**

Mathematicians
See also Women mathematicians
Bruno, L. C. Math and mathematicians   **920**
Collier, B. Charles Babbage and the engines of perfection (7 and up)   **92**
Henderson, H. Modern mathematicians (7 and up)   **920**
Dictionaries
Notable mathematicians (7 and up)   **920.003**

Mathematics
Bazin, M. Math and science across cultures   **510**
Bruno, L. C. Math and mathematicians   **920**
Mathematics   **510**
Fiction
Griffin, A. Hannah, divided (4 and up)   **Fic**
Poetry
Marvelous math (4 and up)   **811.008**
Study and teaching
Salvadori, M. G. Math games for middle school   **510.7**

Mathematics   **510**

Mathers, Marshall *See* Eminem

Mathis, Sharon Bell, 1937-
Godmother
In Join in; multiethnic short stories by outstanding writers for young adults p173-99   **S C**
Teacup full of roses (7 and up)   **Fic**

Matilda Bone. Cushman, K.   **Fic**

Matisse, Henri
About
Welton, J. Henri Matisse   **92**

Matloff, Gregory L.
More telescope power   **522**

Matoaka *See* Pocahontas, d. 1617

Matoa's mirror. Ortiz Cofer, J.
In Ortiz Cofer, J. An island like you; stories of the barrio p82-91   **S C**

Matsen, Bradford
Go wild in New York City (4 and up)   **974.7**
The incredible record-setting deep-sea dive of the bathysphere (4 and up)   **551.46**
The incredible search for the treasure ship Atocha (4 and up)   **910.4**

Matson, Gienna
Celtic mythology A to Z   **299**

Matsui, Kosei
See/See also pages in the following book(s):
Hamanaka, S. In search of the spirit (5 and up)   **920**

Matter
Cooper, C. Matter   **530**
Farndon, J. Solids, liquids, and gases   **530.4**

A **matter** of faith. Bacho, P.
In American eyes; new Asian-American short stories for young adults p131-42   **S C**

A **matter** of profit. Bell, H.   **Fic**

Mattern, Joanne, 1963-
Forensics (5 and up)   **363.2**

Matthew, Kathryn I.
Neal-Schuman guide to celebrations & holidays around the world   **394.26**

Matthews, Glenna
American women's history   **305.4**

Matthews, Kezi, 1928-
Flying lessons   **Fic**

Matthews, Rupert
Explorer (4 and up)   **910.4**

Matthews, Tom L., 1949-
Always inventing: a photobiography of Alexander Graham Bell (4 and up)   **92**
Grierson's raid (7 and up)   **973.7**
Light shining through the mist: a photobiography of Dian Fossey (4 and up)   **92**

Mattison, Christopher
Snake   **597.9**

Mattresses. Vande Velde, V.
In Vande Velde, V. Tales from the Brothers Grimm and the Sisters Weird p79-87   **S C**

Matulka, Denise I.
Picture this   **011.6**

Matuz, Roger
Complete American presidents sourcebook   **920**

Matzeliger, Jan, 1852-1889
See/See also pages in the following book(s):
Aaseng, N. Black inventors (7 and up)   **920**

Mauchly, John William, 1907-1980
See/See also pages in the following book(s):
Northrup, M. American computer pioneers   **920**

Mauffret, Yvon
(jt. auth) Burleigh, R. The sea   **551.46**

Maura's angel. Banks, L. R.   **Fic**

Maurer, Richard, 1950-
The Wright sister [biography of Katharine Wright Haskell] (5 and up)   **92**

Maurer, Tracy, 1965-
BMX freestyle   **796.6**
Skateboarding   **796.22**

Maus. Spiegelman, A.   **940.53**

Mawson, Sir Douglas, 1882-1958
About
Bredeson, C. After the last dog died   **92**

Max. Potok, C.
In Potok, C. Zebra and other stories p121-46   **S C**

Max Mondrosch. Alexander, L.
In Firebirds: an anthology of original fantasy and science fiction; an anthology of original fantasy and science fiction   **S C**

May I have your autograph? Sharmat, M. W.
In Sixteen; short stories by outstanding writers for young adults p15-21   **S C**

May this be your last sorrow. De Lint, C.
In De Lint, C. Waifs and strays p209-15   **S C**

Mayall, Beth
(jt. auth) Farrell, J. Middle school, the real deal   **373.1**

Mayas
Crosher, J. Technology in the time of the Maya   **609**

Fiction
Cameron, A. Colibri (5 and up)   **Fic**

Maybe you will remember. Schwartz, A.
In Schwartz, A. Scary stories 3; more tales to chill your bones p57-61   **398.2**

Mayell, Mark
Newfoundland
In Exploring Canada   **971**
Saskatchewan
In Exploring Canada   **971**
Tragedies of space exploration (5 and up)   **363.1**

Mayer, Maria Goeppert- *See* Goeppert-Mayer, Maria, 1906-1972

Mayer, Marianna, 1945-
Women warriors (5 and up)   **398.2**
Contents: Devi; Rangada; Semiramis; Hiera; Scathach; Morrigan; Gwendolen; Boadicea; Mella; Yakami; Winyan Ohitika; Aliquipiso

Mayfield, Steven
About
Schulman, A. Cop on the beat   **363.2**

Mayflower (Ship)
Fiction
Lasky, K. A journey to the New World   **Fic**

Mayne, Don, 1961-
Drawing horses that look real!   **743**

Mayo, Edith
(ed) The Smithsonian book of the First Ladies. See The Smithsonian book of the First Ladies   **920**

The **maze.** Hobbs, W.   **Fic**

Mazer, Harry, 1925-
The beautiful thing
In Night terrors; stories of shadow and substance   **S C**
A boy at war (7 and up)   **Fic**
Falling off the Empire State Building
In Ultimate sports; short stories by outstanding writers for young adults p302-13   **S C**
Furlough—1944
In Sixteen; short stories by outstanding writers for young adults p83-92   **S C**
The last mission (7 and up)   **Fic**
The rat children
In Places I never meant to be; original stories by censored writers   **S C**
Snow bound (7 and up)   **Fic**

The wild kid (4 and up)   **Fic**

Mazer, Norma Fox, 1931-
After the rain   **Fic**
Cutthroat
In Ultimate sports; short stories by outstanding writers for young adults p148-59   **S C**
Girlhearts   **Fic**
Good night, Maman (5 and up)   **Fic**
The house on Buffalo Street
In Night terrors; stories of shadow and substance   **S C**
I, hungry Hannah Cassandra Glen . . .
In Sixteen; short stories by outstanding writers for young adults p2-14   **S C**
Meeting the mugger
In Places I never meant to be; original stories by censored writers   **S C**
Out of control (7 and up)   **Fic**
Silver (7 and up)   **Fic**
Taking Terri Mueller   **Fic**
The tin butterfly
In The Color of absence; 12 stories about loss and hope p51-70   **S C**
What happened in the cemetery
In Visions: nineteen short stories by outstanding writers for young adults p64-75   **S C**
Zelzah: a tale from long ago
In Leaving home: stories p179-99   **808.8**
About
Reed, A. J. S. Norma Fox Mazer (7 and up)   **813.009**

McAllister, Margaret, 1956-
Ghost at the window (5 and up)   **Fic**
Hold my hand and run   **Fic**

McAlpine, Margaret
Working with computers   **004**

McArthur, Debra
Desert storm--the first Persian Gulf War in American history   **956.7**
The dust bowl and the Depression in American history (7 and up)   **978**
The Kansas-Nebraska Act and "Bleeding Kansas" in American history   **978.1**

McAuliffe, Christa
About
Jeffrey, L. S. Christa McAuliffe   **92**

McCaffery, Laura Hibbets
Building an ESL collection for young adults   **016.4**

McCaffrey, Anne
Black horses for the king (7 and up)   **Fic**
Pegasus in flight (7 and up)   **Fic**
{The Pern series} (7 and up)   **Fic**
About
Trachtenberg, M. P. Anne McCaffrey   **92**

McCaffrey, Laura Williams
Alia waking   **Fic**

McCain, Mary Maude
Dictionary for school library media specialists   **020**

McCall, Mary Reilly
(ed) Women's almanac. See Women's almanac   **305.4**

McCampbell, Darlene Z., 1942-
(ed) Leaving home: stories. See Leaving home: stories   **808.8**
(comp) Who do you think you are? See Who do you think you are?   **S C**

McCann, Michelle Roehm, 1968-
(comp) Girls know best. See Girls know best   **305.23**

McCarthy, Colin, 1951-
Reptile (4 and up)   **597.9**

McCarthy, Joseph, 1908-1957
About
The McCarthy hearings (7 and up)   **973.921**
Sherrow, V. Joseph McCarthy and the Cold War   **92**
The **McCarthy** hearings (7 and up)   **973.921**

McCarty, Nick
The Iliad   **883**

McCarty, Peter
(il) Getz, D. Frozen man   **930.1**

McCaughrean, Geraldine, 1951-
The epic of Gilgamesh (5 and up)   **398.2**
The kite rider (5 and up)   **Fic**
Odysseus (5 and up)   **292**
Perseus (5 and up)   **292**
The stones are hatching (5 and up)   **Fic**
Stop the train! (5 and up)   **Fic**
Thoughts of a drought dragon
In Fire and wings: dragon tales from East and West p15-24   **S C**

MccGwire, Scarlett
Surveillance (7 and up)   **323.44**

McClafferty, Carla Killough, 1958-
The head bone's connected to the neck bone (7 and up)   **616.07**

McClellan, Marilyn
Organ and tissue transplants (7 and up)   **617.9**

McClintock, Barbara
About
Celebrating women in mathematics and science   **920**
Cullen, J. H. Barbara McClintock, geneticist (7 and up)   **92**
Fine, E. H. Barbara McClintock (7 and up)   **92**

See/See also pages in the following book(s):
Hacker, C. Nobel Prize winners   **920**

McCloskey, Robert, 1914-2003
See/See also pages in the following book(s):
Marcus, L. S. A Caldecott celebration   **741.6**

McConnell, Stacy A.
Ancient civilizations: biographies (7 and up)   **920**
(jt. auth) Schmittroth, L. American Revolution: biographies   **920**

McCord, Patricia
Pictures in the dark (7 and up)   **Fic**

McCormack, Shaun
Cool Papa Bell   **92**

McCormick, Anita Louise
The industrial revolution in American history   **338**

McCormick, Patricia
Cut (7 and up)   **Fic**

McCorvey, Norma
About
Gold, S. D. Roe v. Wade   **344**
Payment, S. Roe v. Wade   **344**
Romaine, D. S. Roe v. Wade (7 and up)   **344**

McCoy, Elijah, 1844-1929
See/See also pages in the following book(s):
Aaseng, N. Black inventors (7 and up)   **920**

McCulla, Patricia E.
Tanzania   **967.8**

McCullers, Carson, 1917-1967
Sucker
In Who do you think you are?; stories of friends and enemies p122-33   **S C**

McCullough, L. E.
(ed) Shakespeare, W. One hundred and eleven Shakespeare monologues   **822.3**

McCully, Emily Arnold
See/See also pages in the following book(s):
The Newbery & Caldecott medal books, 1986-2000   **028.5**

McCurdy, Michael, 1942-
(ed) Douglass, F. Escape from slavery   **92**
(il) Fradin, D. B. The signers   **920**
(il) War and the pity of war. See War and the pity of war   **808.81**

McCutcheon, Marc
(ed) The Facts on File student's thesaurus. See The Facts on File student's thesaurus   **423**

McDade, Melissa C.
(ed) Grzimek's student animal life resource, Birds. See Grzimek's student animal life resource, Birds   **598**
(ed) Grzimek's student animal life resource, Mammals. See Grzimek's student animal life resource, Mammals   **599**

McDaniel, Melissa
Arizona
In Celebrate the states   **973**
New Mexico
In Celebrate the states   **973**
North Dakota Celebrate the states   **973**
South Dakota
In Celebrate the states   **973**

McDonald, Janet, 1953-
Spellbound (7 and up)   **Fic**
Twists and turns (7 and up)   **Fic**

McDonald, Joe
(jt. auth) McDonald, M. A. Pythons   **597.9**
(jt. auth) McDonald, M. A. Rattlesnakes   **597.9**

McDonald, Joyce
Devil on my heels (7 and up)   **Fic**
Shades of Simon Gray (7 and up)   **Fic**
Swallowing stones (7 and up)   **Fic**
Transfusion
In Don't cramp my style; stories about that time of the month p145-81   **S C**

McDonald, Mary Ann, 1956-
Pythons   **597.9**
Rattlesnakes   **597.9**

McDonald, Megan, 1959-
All the stars in the sky (4 and up)   Fic

McElmeel, Sharron L.
100 most popular children's authors   810.3

McElvaine, Robert S.
The Depression and New Deal (7 and up)
973.91

McGaffey, Leta
Honduras (5 and up)   972.83

McGarrahan, Sean
(jt. auth) Gay, K. Epilepsy   616.8

McGaw, Laurie
To be a princess (4 and up)   920
(il) Hansen, J. African princess   920

McGee, Marni
(jt. auth) Mellor, R. The ancient Roman world
937

McGhee, Alison, 1960-
Snap (5 and up)   Fic

McGill, Alice
Moon time child
In Don't cramp my style; stories about that
time of the month p45-67   S C

McGough, Roger, 1937-
(ed) The Kingfisher book of funny poems. See
The Kingfisher book of funny poems
821.008
(ed) Wicked poems. See Wicked poems
811.008

McGowan, Eileen Nixon
Stock market smart   332.6

McGowan, Gary
(jt. auth) Hansen, J. Breaking ground, breaking
silence   974.7
(jt. auth) Hansen, J. Freedom roads: searching
for the Underground Railroad   973.7

McGowan, Keith, 1968-
Sexual harassment (7 and up)   305.3

McGowen, Tom
African-Americans in the Old West   978
Air raid   940.54
Assault from the sky   940.54
Carrier war   940.54
Germany's lightning war (5 and up)   940.54
Giant stones and earth mounds   930.1
Sink the Bismarck (5 and up)   940.54
The Spanish-American War and Teddy
Roosevelt in American history   973.8
World War II (4 and up)   940.53

McGraw, Eloise Jarvis, 1915-2000
The moorchild (4 and up)   Fic
McGraw-Hill encyclopedia of world biography.
See Encyclopedia of world biography
920.003

McHugh, Maureen F.
The Lincoln train
In New skies: an anthology of today's science
fiction   S C

McIntire, Suzanne, 1951-
(ed) American Heritage book of great American
speeches for young people. See American
Heritage book of great American speeches for
young people   815

McIntosh, Jane
Archeology (4 and up)   930.1

McIntosh, Ken
Apache North American Indians today [series]
Cheyenne North American Indians today [series]
Crow North American Indians today [series]
Iroquois North American Indians today [series]
Navajo North American Indians today [series]
Pueblo North American Indians today [series]

McIntyre, Thomas
The behavior survival guide for kids (5 and up)
158

McKain, Mark
(ed) Making and using the atomic bomb. See
Making and using the atomic bomb   355.8

McKay, Hilary, 1959-
Saffy's angel (5 and up)   Fic

McKean, Dave
(il) Gaiman, N. Coraline   Fic

McKee, Jesse O.
The Choctaw Indians of North America series

McKenna, Lesley
The fantastic book of snow-boarding   796.93

McKillip, Patricia A., 1948-
Byndley
In Firebirds: an anthology of original fantasy
and science fiction; an anthology of orig-
inal fantasy and science fiction   S C
Hunter's moon
In The Green Man: tales from the mythic for-
est p118-34   808.8

McKinley, Robin
Beauty (7 and up)   Fic
The blue sword (7 and up)   Fic
The door in the hedge   S C
Contents: The stolen princess; The princess and the frog; The
hunting of the hind; The twelve dancing princesses
The hero and the crown (6 and up)   Fic
The outlaws of Sherwood   398.2
A pool in the desert
In McKinley, R. and Dickinson, P. Water:
tales of elemental spirits p208-66
S C
Rose daughter   Fic
The sea-king's son
In McKinley, R. and Dickinson, P. Water:
tales of elemental spirits p30-77   S C
Water horse
In McKinley, R. and Dickinson, P. Water:
tales of elemental spirits p119-69
S C
Water: tales of elemental spirits (7 and up)
S C

McKissack, Fredrick, 1939-
(jt. auth) McKissack, P. C. Black diamond
796.357
(jt. auth) McKissack, P. C. Black hands, white
sails   639.2
(jt. auth) McKissack, P. C. Christmas in the big
house, Christmas in the quarters   394.26
(jt. auth) McKissack, P. C. Days of Jubilee
973.7
(jt. auth) McKissack, P. C. Let my people go
221.9

McKissack, Fredrick, 1939——_Continued_
(jt. auth) McKissack, P. C. Rebels against slavery **326**
(jt. auth) McKissack, P. C. The royal kingdoms of Ghana, Mali, and Songhay **966.2**

McKissack, Pat _See_ McKissack, Patricia C., 1944-

McKissack, Patricia C., 1944-
Black diamond (6 and up) **796.357**
Black hands, white sails (5 and up) **639.2**
Christmas in the big house, Christmas in the quarters (4 and up) **394.26**
The conjure brother
_In_ Beware!; R.L. Stine picks his favorite scary stories p19-33 **808.8**
Days of Jubilee (5 and up) **973.7**
Let my people go (4 and up) **221.9**
Nzinga, warrior queen of Matamba (5 and up) **Fic**
A picture of Freedom (4 and up) **Fic**
Rebels against slavery (5 and up) **326**
The royal kingdoms of Ghana, Mali, and Songhay (5 and up) **966.2**
Run away home (5 and up) **Fic**
To establish justice **342**

McLaren, Chesley
(il) Packer, T. Twelfth night **822.3**

McLaren, Clemence, 1938-
Inside the walls of Troy (7 and up) **Fic**

McLean, Jacqueline
Women of adventure (7 and up) **920**

McMullan, Margaret
How I found the Strong (5 and up) **Fic**

McNair, Ronald E.
See/See also pages in the following book(s):
Haskins, J. Against all opposition (5 and up) **920**

McNair, Sylvia, 1924-
Arkansas
_In_ America the beautiful, second series **973**
Connecticut
_In_ America the beautiful, second series **973**
Massachusetts
_In_ America the beautiful, second series **973**
Nebraska
_In_ America the beautiful, second series **973**
Rhode Island
_In_ America the beautiful, second series **973**
Thailand (4 and up) **959.3**
U.S. Territories
_In_ America the beautiful, second series **973**

McNally, Robert Aquinas
(ed) Skin health information for teens. See Skin health information for teens **616.5**

McNamee, Graham
Acceleration **Fic**

McNaughton, Janet, 1953-
An earthly knight (7 and up) **Fic**
The secret under my skin (7 and up) **Fic**

McNeely, Tom
(il) Goodman, J. E. Despite all obstacles: La Salle and the conquest of the Mississippi **92**

McNeese, Tim
The Alamo **976.4**
George W. Bush (7 and up) **92**
The Panama Canal (7 and up) **386**
Remember the Maine! **973.8**
The rise and fall of American slavery (7 and up) **326**

McNicholas, June
Rats (4 and up) **636.9**

McPhee, Andrew T.
AIDS (5 and up) **616.97**

McPherson, James M.
Fields of fury (5 and up) **973.7**

McPherson, Stephanie Sammartino
Martha Washington **92**
TV's forgotten hero: the story of Philo Farnsworth **92**

McVay, Charles Butler, III
About
Nelson, P. Left for dead (7 and up) **940.54**

McVeigh, Timothy J.
See/See also pages in the following book(s):
Currie, S. Terrorists and terrorist groups (7 and up) **303.6**
Sherrow, V. The Oklahoma City bombing **364.1**

McWhorter, Diane
A dream of freedom (5 and up) **323.1**

McWorter, Frank, 1777-1854
See/See also pages in the following book(s):
Haskins, J. African American entrepreneurs **920**

Me and Billy. Collier, J. L. **Fic**

Me, Mop, and the Moondance Kid. Myers, W. D. **Fic**

Mead, Alice, 1952-
Girl of Kosovo (5 and up) **Fic**
Swimming to America **Fic**

Mead, Margaret, 1901-1978
About
Mark, J. T. Margaret Mead (7 and up) **92**
Pollard, M. Margaret Mead **92**
See/See also pages in the following book(s):
DeAngelis, G. Science & medicine **920**

Meal planning _See_ Nutrition

Measles
Silverstein, A. Measles and rubella (7 and up) **616.9**

Measles and rubella. Silverstein, A. **616.9**

Measuring instruments
Clark, J. O. E. Under the microscope: science tools **530.8**

Mecha mania. Hart, C. **741.5**

The **mechanical** mind. Soto, G.
_In_ Soto, G. Local news p113-19 **S C**

Mechanics
Pentland, P. Toy and game science (4 and up) **531**

Mechler, Gary
  National Audubon Society first field guide: night sky (4 and up)   **520**

Media *See* Mass media

Media. Petley, J.   **302.23**

Media violence: opposing viewpoints (7 and up)   **303.6**

Media wise [series]
  Jones, S. Film   **791.43**

Media workshop [series]
  Pellowski, M. The art of making comic books   **741.5**

Mediavilla, Cindy
  Creating the full-service homework center in your library   **027.4**

Medical botany
  Kidd, J. S. Mother Nature's pharmacy (7 and up)   **615**

Medical care
  Levchuck, C. M. Healthy living   **613**

Medical ethics
  See also Right to die
  Biomedical ethics: opposing viewpoints (7 and up)   **174.2**
  Hyde, M. O. Medicine's brave new world (7 and up)   **610**
  O'Neill, T. Biomedical ethics (7 and up)   **174.2**
  Snedden, R. Medical ethics   **174.2**

Medical genetics
  Jacobs, M. B. Coping with hereditary diseases (7 and up)   **616**

Medical technology
  Hyde, M. O. Medicine's brave new world (7 and up)   **610**

Medici, Lorenzo de', 1449-1492
       About
  Greenblatt, M. Lorenzo de' Medici and Renaissance Italy   **945**

Medicinal plants *See* Medical botany

Medicine
  See also Alternative medicine; Sports medicine; Women in medicine and names of diseases and groups of diseases
  Green, J. Medicine (5 and up)   **610**
  Parker, S. Medicine   **610**
       Encyclopedias
  Encyclopedia of health (4 and up)   **610.3**
       Fiction
  Morgan, N. Fleshmarket (7 and up)   **Fic**
       History
  Davis, L. Medicine in the American West   **610.9**
  Gates, P. Medicine   **610.9**
  Woolf, A. Death and disease (5 and up)   **610**
       Physiological effect
  See Pharmacology

Medicine in the American West. Davis, L.   **610.9**

Medicine's brave new world. Hyde, M. O.   **610**

Medieval architecture
  Ross, S. Art and architecture (5 and up)   **720**

Medieval art
  Martin, A. Knights & castles (5 and up)   **940.1**
  Ross, S. Art and architecture (5 and up)   **720**

The **medieval** castle. Nardo, D.   **940.1**

Medieval civilization
  Chrisp, P. Town and country life (5 and up)   **940.1**
  Chrisp, P. Warfare   **355**
  Corbishley, M. The Middle Ages (5 and up)   **940.1**
  Dean, R. Women of the Middle Ages (7 and up)   **940.1**
  The Early Middle Ages (7 and up)   **909.07**
  Gravett, C. Knight (4 and up)   **940.1**
  Hart, A. Knights & castles (4 and up)   **940.1**
  Hinds, K. Medieval England   **942.03**
  Howarth, S. The Middle Ages   **940.1**
  Galens, J. Middle ages: almanac   **909.07**
  Knight, J. Middle ages: biographies   **920**
  Langley, A. Medieval life [y] (4 and up)   **940.1**
  Martin, A. Knights & castles (5 and up)   **940.1**
  Medieval world (7 and up)   **909.07**
  Nardo, D. The medieval castle (7 and up)   **940.1**
  Nardo, D. The Middle Ages (7 and up)   **940.1**
  Nicolle, D. Medieval knights   **940.1**
  Ross, S. Monarchs (5 and up)   **940.1**
  Service, A. 1200   **909.07**
  Stefoff, R. The medieval world (5 and up)   **909.07**
  Woolf, A. Death and disease (5 and up)   **610**
  Woolf, A. Education (5 and up)   **940.1**
  Zohorsky, J. R. Medieval knights and warriors   **940.1**

Medieval England. Hinds, K.   **942.03**

Medieval knights. Nicolle, D.   **940.1**

Medieval knights and warriors. Zohorsky, J. R.   **940.1**

Medieval realms [series]
  Chrisp, P. Town and country life   **940.1**
  Chrisp, P. Warfare   **355**
  Ross, S. Art and architecture   **720**
  Ross, S. Monarchs   **940.1**
  Woolf, A. Death and disease   **610**
  Woolf, A. Education   **940.1**

Medieval world (7 and up)   **909.07**

The **medieval** world. Stefoff, R.   **909.07**

Meditation
  Andrews, L. W. Meditation (5 and up)   **158**

Mediterranean region
       History
  Stefoff, R. The ancient Mediterranean (5 and up)   **938**

Medlam, Brigid
Communication
In Being human   **612**

Medusa. Cadnum, M.
In Firebirds: an anthology of original fantasy and science fiction; an anthology of original fantasy and science fiction   **S C**

Meeting Elijah. Goldin, B. D.
In Goldin, B. D. Journeys with Elijah; eight tales of the Prophet p65-74   **222**

Meeting the mugger. Mazer, N. F.
In Places I never meant to be; original stories by censored writers   **S C**

Megalithic monuments
McGowen, T. Giant stones and earth mounds   **930.1**

Megatech [series]
Jefferis, D. Artificial intelligence   **629.8**

Meiani, Antonella
Air (4 and up)   **533**
Chemistry (4 and up)   **540**
Electricity (4 and up)   **537**
Light (4 and up)   **535**
Magnetism (4 and up)   **538**
Water (4 and up)   **532**

Meigs, Cornelia Lynde, 1884-1972
Invincible Louisa [May Alcott]   **92**

Mein Kampf. Damon, D.   **943.086**

Meinkoth, Norman August, 1913-
The Audubon Society field guide to North American seashore creatures   **592**

Meir, Golda, 1898-1978
See/See also pages in the following book(s):
Axelrod-Contrada, J. Women who led nations (7 and up)   **920**
Hewitt, K. Lives of extraordinary women (4 and up)   **920**
Price-Groff, C. Twentieth-century women political leaders (7 and up)   **920**

Meitner, Lise, 1878-1968
About
Hamilton, J. Lise Meitner   **92**
See/See also pages in the following book(s):
Henderson, H. Nuclear physics (7 and up)   **539.7**

Mekong River
Dramer, K. The Mekong River   **959.7**

Mella. Mayer, M.
In Mayer, M. Women warriors; myths and legends of heroic women p55-59   **398**

Melling, O. R.
The Hunter's Moon (7 and up)   **Fic**

Mellor, Ronald
The ancient Roman world (7 and up)   **937**

Melonhead. De Guzman, M.   **Fic**

Meltdown. Hampton, W.   **363.1**

Meltzer, Milton, 1915-
Ain't gonna study war no more   **303.6**
Bound for America (5 and up)   **325.73**
Captain James Cook   **92**
Case closed (5 and up)   **363.2**
Columbus and the world around him   **92**
The cotton gin   **633.5**

The day the sky fell (7 and up)   **303.6**
Driven from the land (4 and up)   **978**
Edgar Allan Poe: a biography (7 and up)   **92**
Ferdinand Magellan   **92**
Francisco Pizarro (5 and up)   **92**
Hear that train whistle blow! (5 and up)   **385**
In the days of the pharoahs (7 and up)   **932**
Mark Twain himself   **92**
Mary McLeod Bethune   **92**
Milton Meltzer (7 and up)   **92**
Never to forget: the Jews of the Holocaust (6 and up)   **940.53**
The printing press   **686.2**
Rescue: the story of how Gentiles saved Jews in the Holocaust (6 and up)   **940.53**
Ten kings (5 and up)   **920**
Ten queens (5 and up)   **920**
There comes a time: the struggle for Civil Rights (5 and up)   **323.1**
They came in chains   **326**
Walt Whitman (7 and up)   **92**
Weapons & warfare (5 and up)   **355**
Witches and witch-hunts (4 and up)   **133.4**
(ed) The American revolutionaries: a history in their own words, 1750-1800. See The American revolutionaries: a history in their own words, 1750-1800   **973.3**

Memoirs of a bookbat. Lasky, K.   **Fic**

Memoirs of Sherlock Holmes. Doyle, Sir A. C.
In Doyle, Sir A. C. The complete Sherlock Holmes   **S C**

Memories of Anne Frank. Gold, A. L.   **92**

Memories of Summer. White, R.   **Fic**

Memories of sun   **S C**

Memory
Fiction
Haddix, M. P. Escape from memory   **Fic**
Wynne-Jones, T. A thief in the house of memory (7 and up)   **Fic**

Menashe and Rachel. Singer, I. B.
In Singer, I. B. The power of light; eight stories for Hanukkah p31-39   **S C**

Menchú, Rigoberta
See/See also pages in the following book(s):
Hewitt, K. Lives of extraordinary women (4 and up)   **920**

Mendel, Gregor, 1822-1884
About
Edelson, E. Gregor Mendel, and the roots of genetics (7 and up)   **92**
Klare, R. Gregor Mendel   **92**

Mendel, Johann Gregor *See* Mendel, Gregor, 1822-1884

Mendoza, Patrick M.
Extraordinary people in extraordinary times (7 and up)   **920**

Mendrinos, Roxanne Baxter
Using educational technology with at-risk students   **027.8**

Menhard, Francha Roffe
The facts about inhalants   **362.29**
Teen consumer smarts   **332.024**

Meningitis
Willett, E. Meningitis (7 and up) **616.8**
Mennonites
See also Amish
Kenna, K. A people apart (4 and up) **289.7**
Fiction
Gaeddert, L. B. Friends and enemies **Fic**
Menstruation
Gravelle, K. The period book (4 and up)
612.6
Jukes, M. Growing up: it's a girl thing (4 and
up) **612.6**
See/See also pages in the following book(s):
Jukes, M. It's a girl thing (5 and up)
305.23
Fiction
Don't cramp my style (7 and up) **S C**
Mental health
Levchuck, C. M. Healthy living **613**
Mental health information for teens (7 and up)
616.89
A student's guide to mental health & wellness
616.89
Mental health information for teens (7 and up)
616.89
Mental illness
Goldsmith, C. Neurological disorders **616.8**
Kent, D. Snake pits, talking cures, & magic bul-
lets **616.89**
Mental illness: opposing viewpoints (7 and up)
362.2
Stewart, G. People with mental illness (7 and
up) **616.89**
A student's guide to mental health & wellness
616.89
Fiction
Franklin, K. L. Dove song **Fic**
Griffin, A. Where I want to be (7 and up)
Fic
Hautman, P. Invisible (7 and up) **Fic**
Hermes, P. Summer secrets (5 and up) **Fic**
Leavitt, M. Heck, superhero **Fic**
McCord, P. Pictures in the dark (7 and up)
Fic
Sones, S. Stop pretending **Fic**
Weeks, S. So B. it (5 and up) **Fic**
Mental illness: opposing viewpoints (7 and up)
362.2
Mentally handicapped
Fiction
Conly, J. L. Crazy lady! (5 and up) **Fic**
Holt, K. W. My Louisiana sky (6 and up)
Fic
Lowry, L. The silent boy **Fic**
Mazer, H. The wild kid (4 and up) **Fic**
Nolan, H. A face in every window (7 and up)
Fic
Weeks, S. So B. it (5 and up) **Fic**
Wood, J. R. The man who loved clowns
Fic
Mentally handicapped children
Fiction
Byars, B. C. The summer of the swans (5 and
up) **Fic**

Mentally ill
Fiction
Bryant, S. The earth kitchen **Fic**
Kehret, P. I'm not who you think I am **Fic**
White, R. Memories of Summer (7 and up)
Fic
Wyeth, S. D. A piece of heaven **Fic**
Institutional care
See also Psychiatric hospitals
The **mer-woman** out of the sea. Hamilton, V.
In Hamilton, V. Her stories; African
American folktales, fairy tales, and true
tales p78-83 **398.2**
Mercado, Nancy E., 1975-
(ed) Tripping over the lunch lady and other
school stories. See Tripping over the lunch
lady and other school stories **S C**
Mercier, Cathryn M.
(jt. auth) Bloom, S. P. Presenting Avi
813.009
Mercury
Watt, S. Mercury
In The Elements **546**
Mercury (Planet)
Miller, R. Mercury and Pluto (5 and up)
523.4
Spangenburg, R. A look at Mercury **523.4**
Spangenburg, R. Mercury **523.4**
Mercury. Watt, S.
In The Elements **546**
Mercury and Pluto. Miller, R. **523.4**
Mercy killing *See* Euthanasia
Meret, Sasha
(il) Feiler, B. S. Walking the Bible **222**
Merlin (Legendary character)
Fiction
Barron, T. A. The lost years of Merlin (6 and
up) **Fic**
Barron, T. A. The Merlin effect **Fic**
Yolen, J. Passager **Fic**
Merlin dreams in the Mondream Wood. De Lint,
C.
In De Lint, C. Waifs and strays p3-20
S C
The **Merlin** effect. Barron, T. A. **Fic**
Merlin's kin. Sherman, J. **398.2**
The **mermaid** of Zennor. Climo, S.
In Climo, S. Magic & mischief; tales from
Cornwall p89-95 **398.2**
Mermaid song. Dickinson, P.
In McKinley, R. and Dickinson, P. Water:
tales of elemental spirits p1-29 **S C**
Mermaids and mermen
Fiction
McKinley, R. Water: tales of elemental spirits
(7 and up) **S C**
Rylant, C. The islander **Fic**
Merman, Ethel, 1908 or 9-1984
See/See also pages in the following book(s):
Orgill, R. Shout, sister, shout! (6 and up)
920
Merriam-Webster's dictionary of synonyms
423

Merriam-Webster's geographical dictionary
910.3

Merriam-Webster's school thesaurus   **423**

Merrill, Jean, 1923-
The pushcart war (5 and up)   **Fic**

Merrill, Martha
(jt. auth) McCain, M. M. Dictionary for school
library media specialists   **020**

The **merry** adventures of Robin Hood of great renown in Notinghamshire. Pyle, H.   **398.2**

Meryman, Richard, 1926-
Andrew Wyeth (7 and up)   **92**

Meserole, Mike
(ed) The Information please sports almanac. See
The Information please sports almanac
796

Mesopotamia *See* Iraq

Mesopotamia. Chrisp, P.   **935**

Metals
See also Aluminum
See/See also pages in the following book(s):
Knapp, B. J. Materials science   **620.1**

Metalwork
See also Metals

Metamorphosis. Conford, E.
In Conford, E. Crush p51-68   **S C**

The **metamorphosis** of Justin Jones. Coville, B.
In Coville, B. Odder than ever   **S C**

Metaoomet, Sachem of the Wampanoags *See*
Philip, Sachem of the Wampanoags, d. 1676

Meteorites
Koppes, S. N. Killer rocks from outer space
523.5
Spangenburg, R. Meteors, mctcoritcs, and meteoroids   **523.5**

Meteorology
See also Droughts; Weather
Engelbert, P. The complete weather resource
551.5
Gallant, R. A. Atmosphere (5 and up)
551.51
Kahl, J. D. National Audubon Society first field
guide: weather (4 and up)   **551.5**
Silverstein, A. Weather and climate   **551.5**
Stein, P. Macmillan encyclopedia of weather
551.5
Weather and climate on file   **551.5**

Meteors
Aronson, B. Meteors (4 and up)   **523.5**
Spangenburg, R. Meteors, meteorites, and mete-
oroids   **523.5**

Meteors. Aronson, B.   **523.5**

Meteors, meteorites, and meteoroids.
Spangenburg, R.   **523.5**

Methylphenidate hydrochloride *See* Ritalin

Metoyer, Maria Theresa Coincoin *See* Coincoin,
Maria Theresa, 1742-1816

Metropolis [series]
Malam, J. Greek town   **938**
Morley, J. Viking town   **948**

Metzger, Bruce Manning
(ed) The Oxford companion to the Bible. See
The Oxford companion to the Bible   **220.3**

Metzger, Lois
Snap, crackle, pop
In Shattered: stories of children and war p71-
86   **S C**

The **Mexican** American family album. Hoobler, D.
305.8

The **Mexican-American** War. Bardhan-Quallen, S.
973.6

The **Mexican-American** War. Feldman, R. T.
973.6

The **Mexican-American** War. Nardo, D.   **973.6**

Mexican Americans
Atkin, S. B. Voices from the fields (5 and up)
331.5
Cesar Chavez (7 and up)   **92**
Collins, D. R. Farmworker's friend: the story of
Cesar Chavez   **92**
Freedman, R. In the days of the vaqueros (4 and
up)   **636.2**
Hoobler, D. The Mexican American family al-
bum (5 and up)   **305.8**
Mirriam-Goldberg, C. Sandra Cisneros   **92**
Perl, L. North across the border   **305.8**
Sandler, M. W. Vaqueros   **973**
   Drama
Soto, G. Novio boy (7 and up)   **812**
   Fiction
Cisneros, S. The house on Mango Street (7 and
up)   **Fic**
Estevis, A. Down Garrapata road (7 and up)
S C
Jiménez, F. Breaking through (5 and up)
Fic
Johnston, T. Any small goodness (4 and up)
Fic
Rice, D. Crazy loco   **S C**
Ryan, P. M. Becoming Naomi León (5 and up)
Fic
Ryan, P. M. Esperanza rising (5 and up)
Fic
Saldaña, R. Finding our way: stories   **S C**
Sanchez, A. So hard to say   **Fic**
Soto, G. The afterlife (7 and up)   **Fic**
Soto, G. Baseball in April, and other stories (5
and up)   **S C**
Soto, G. Buried onions   **Fic**
Soto, G. Help wanted   **S C**
Soto, G. Local news   **S C**
   Poetry
Soto, G. Canto familiar (4-6)   **811**
Soto, G. A natural man (7 and up)   **811**
   Social life and customs
King, E. Quinceañera (5 and up)   **392**

Mexican art
Lewis, E. Mexican art & culture   **709.72**

Mexican art & culture. Lewis, E.   **709.72**

Mexican artists *See* Artists, Mexican

Mexican, Central and South American art. Scott,
J. F.
In International encyclopedia of art   **703**

Mexican literature
Collections
The Tree is older than you are (7 and up)
860.8

Mexican War, 1846-1848
Bardhan-Quallen, S. The Mexican-American
War (5 and up)   973.6
Carey, C. W. The Mexican War   973.6
Collier, C. Hispanic America, Texas, and the
Mexican War, 1835-1850   973.6
Feldman, R. T. The Mexican-American War (5
and up)   973.6
Nardo, D. The Mexican-American War
973.6

Mexicans
United States
See also Mexican Americans
Ancona, G. Harvest (4 and up)   331.5

Mexico
Hamilton, J. Mexico in pictures (5 and up)
972
Junior Worldmark encyclopedia of the Mexican
states   972
Reilly, M.-J. Mexico (5 and up)   972
Stein, R. C. Mexico (4 and up)   972
Fiction
Garland, S. In the shadow of the Alamo **Fic**
Ryan, P. M. Becoming Naomi León (5 and up)
Fic
Steinbeck, J. The pearl (7 and up) **Fic**
Foreign relations—United States
Pascoe, E. Mexico and the United States (7 and
up)   327.73
History
Calvert, P. Hernando Cortés   92
Tanaka, S. Lost temple of the Aztecs (4 and up)
972

Social life and customs
Lewis, E. Mexican art & culture   709.72
Mexico and the United States. Pascoe, E.
327.73
Mexico in pictures. Hamilton, J. 972
Meyer, Carolyn
Beware, Princess Elizabeth   **Fic**
Drummers of Jericho (7 and up)   **Fic**
Gideon's people   **Fic**
Jubilee journey   **Fic**
Mary, Bloody Mary   **Fic**
Where the broken heart still beats **Fic**
White lilacs (5 and up)   **Fic**
Meyer, L. A., 1942-
Bloody Jack (7 and up)   **Fic**
Meyer, Nicholas E.
Biographical dictionary of Hispanic Americans
920.003
Meyerson, Golda *See* Meir, Golda, 1898-1978
Mhlophe, Gcina
It's quiet now
In Somehow tenderness survives; stories of
Southern Africa p135-37   **S C**
The toilet
In Somehow tenderness survives; stories of
Southern Africa p77-86   **S C**

Miami (Fla.)
Fiction
Gantos, J. Jack on the tracks (5 and up) **Fic**
Mice
Fiction
Conly, J. L. Racso and the rats of NIMH (4 and
up)   **Fic**
Hoeye, M. Time stops for no mouse (5 and up)
Fic
Jacques, B. Redwall (6 and up)   **Fic**
Jarvis, R. The dark portal (5 and up) **Fic**
O'Brien, R. C. Mrs. Frisby and the rats of
NIMH (4 and up)   **Fic**
Micheaux, Oscar, 1884-1951
See/See also pages in the following book(s):
Haskins, J. African American entrepreneurs
920
Michelangelo Buonarroti, 1475-1564
About
Stanley, D. Michelangelo   92
Michigan
Brill, M. T. Michigan
In Celebrate the states   973
Hintz, M. Michigan
In America the beautiful, second series
973
Fiction
White, R. Memories of Summer (7 and up)
Fic
Microbiology
See also Biotechnology
Microelectronics
Chorlton, W. The invention of the silicon chip
621.381
Microorganisms
Day, N. Killer superbugs (7 and up) 616
Farrell, J. Invisible allies   579
The **microscope** book. Levine, S. 502.8
Microscopes
Kramer, S. Hidden worlds: looking through a
scientist's microscope (4 and up) 502.8
Levine, S. The microscope book   502.8
Yount, L. Antoni van Leeuwenhoek   92
Middle Ages
See also Medieval civilization
Corbishley, M. The Middle Ages (5 and up)
940.1
Crossley-Holland, K. The world of King Arthur
and his court (5 and up)   942.01
George, L. S. 800   909.07
Hart, A. Knights & castles (4 and up) 940.1
Howarth, S. The Middle Ages   940.1
Galens, J. Middle ages: almanac   909.07
Medieval world (7 and up)   909.07
Middle ages: primary sources   909.07
Peters, S. T. The Black Death   614.5
Schwartz, G. Hieronymus Bosch (7 and up)
92
Stefoff, R. The medieval world (5 and up)
909.07
Zohorsky, J. R. Medieval knights and warriors
940.1
Biography
Knight, J. Middle ages: biographies 920

Middle Ages—*Continued*
Fiction
Avi. The Book Without Words (5 and up)
    Fic
Barrett, T. Anna of Byzantium   **Fic**
Cadnum, M. The book of the Lion (7 and up)
    Fic
Cadnum, M. Forbidden forest (7 and up)
    Fic
Cadnum, M. In a dark wood   **Fic**
Cadnum, M. The leopard sword (7 and up)
    Fic
Crossley-Holland, K. The seeing stone   **Fic**
Cushman, K. Catherine, called Birdy (6 and up)
    Fic
Cushman, K. Matilda Bone (5 and up)   **Fic**
Cushman, K. The midwife's apprentice (6 and
    up)   **Fic**
Grant, K. M. Blood red horse   **Fic**
Jinks, C. Pagan's crusade (7 and up)   **Fic**
Jordan, S. The raging quiet (7 and up)   **Fic**
Levitin, S. The cure   **Fic**
Springer, N. Rowan Hood, outlaw girl of Sher-
    wood Forest (4 and up)   **Fic**
Temple, F. The Ramsay scallop (6 and up)
    Fic
Yolen, J. Sword of the rightful king   **Fic**
The **Middle** Ages. Nardo, D.   **940.1**
Middle ages: almanac. Galens, J.   **909.07**
Middle ages: biographies. Knight, J.   **920**
Middle ages: primary sources   **909.07**
Middle East
Feiler, B. S. Walking the Bible   **222**
Kort, M. The handbook of the Middle East (7
    and up)   **956**
The Middle East   **956**
Stewart, G. Human rights in the Middle East
    323

See/See also pages in the following book(s):
Frank, M. Understanding September 11th (7 and
    up)   **973.931**
Antiquities
Hunter, E. C. D. First civilizations (5 and up)
    939
Civilization
Stefoff, R. The ancient Near East (5 and up)
    939
Fiction
Marston, E. Figs and fate   **S C**
Temple, F. The Beduins' gazelle   **Fic**
Tunnell, M. O. Wishing moon   **Fic**
History
Hunter, E. C. D. First civilizations (5 and up)
    939
Stefoff, R. The ancient Near East (5 and up)
    939
Poetry
Nye, N. S. 19 varieties of gazelle   **811**
The Space between our footsteps (7 and up)
    808.81
Politics and government
Gunderson, C. G. The need for oil   **338.2**
The Middle East: opposing viewpoints (7 and
    up)   **956**
The **Middle** East   **956**

The **Middle** East: opposing viewpoints (7 and up)
    956
Middle East War, 1991 *See* Persian Gulf War,
    1991
The **middle** passage. Feelings, T.   **759.13**
The **middle** road: American politics, 1945-2000.
    Collier, C.   **973.92**
Middle school reference [series]
    American presidents in world history
        920.003
    The Newest Americans   **325.73**
    Student almanac of African American history
        305.8
    Student almanac of Native American history
        970.004
The **middle** school survival guide. Erlbach, A.
    373.1
Middle school, the real deal. Farrell, J.   **373.1**
Middle schools
Erlbach, A. The middle school survival guide
    373.1
Farrell, J. Middle school, the real deal   **373.1**
Middleton, John, 1921-
    (ed) Africa: an encyclopedia for students. See
    Africa: an encyclopedia for students   **960**
Midler, Bette
See/See also pages in the following book(s):
    Orgill, R. Shout, sister, shout! (6 and up)
        920
Midnight blue. Fisk, P.   **Fic**
Midnight hour encores. Brooks, B.   **Fic**
Midnight magic. Avi   **Fic**
Midnight snack. Duane, D.
    In Sixteen; short stories by outstanding writ-
        ers for young adults p22-30   **S C**
The **midnight** train home. Tamar, E.   **Fic**
Midnighters [series]
    Westerfeld, S. The secret hour   **Fic**
A **Midsummer** night's dream. Packer, T.
    In Packer, T. Tales from Shakespeare p15-29
        822.3
A **midsummer** night's dream, William Shake-
    speare's. Coville, B.   **822.3**
Midwifery *See* Midwives
The **midwife's** apprentice. Cushman, K.   **Fic**
Midwives
Fiction
Cushman, K. The midwife's apprentice (6 and
    up)   **Fic**
Mightier than the sword. Yolen, J.   **398.2**
Mighty mikko. Yolen, J.
    In Yolen, J. Mightier than the sword; world
        folktales for strong boys p87-97
        398.2
Migrant labor
Ancona, G. Harvest (4 and up)   **331.5**
Atkin, S. B. Voices from the fields (5 and up)
    331.5
Cesar Chavez (7 and up)   **92**
Collins, D. R. Farmworker's friend: the story of
    Cesar Chavez   **92**
Cooper, M. L. Dust to eat (4 and up)
    973.917

Migrant labor—*Continued*
Stanley, J. Children of the Dust Bowl (5 and up)   **371.9**
Fiction
Durbin, W. The journal of C.J. Jackson: a Dust Bowl migrant (4 and up)   **Fic**
Jiménez, F. Breaking through (5 and up)
                                                      Fic
McDonald, J. Devil on my heels (7 and up)
                                                      Fic
Mikaelsen, Ben, 1952-
Red midnight   **Fic**
Stranded   **Fic**
Touching Spirit Bear   **Fic**
Miklowitz, Gloria D., 1927-
The enemy has a face (7 and up)   **Fic**
The Fuller brush man
In Visions: nineteen short stories by outstanding writers for young adults p100-06
                                                      S C
Hope
In Shattered: stories of children and war p148-55   **S C**
Milbank, Helen Kirkpatrick *See* Kirkpatrick, Helen, 1909-
Milestones in discovery and invention [series]
Henderson, H. Nuclear physics   **539.7**
Military aeronautics
See also World War, 1939-1945—Aerial operations
Military airplanes
McGowen, T. Air raid   **940.54**
Military art and science
Collier, J. L. Gunpowder and weaponry
                                              623.4
Nardo, D. Ancient Egypt (7 and up)   **932**
Nardo, D. Ancient Greece (7 and up)   **938**
Nardo, D. Ancient Rome [History of weapons and warfare series] (7 and up)   **937**
Nardo, D. The Civil War (7 and up)   **973.7**
Nardo, D. The Middle Ages (7 and up)
                                              940.1
Nardo, D. The Native Americans (7 and up)
                                              970.004
Military education
Fiction
Efaw, A. Battle dress (7 and up)   **Fic**
Military history
Brownlie, A. Why do people fight wars?
                                              355
Chrisp, P. Warfare   **355**
Gravett, C. Going to war in Viking times
                                              355
Military might [series]
McGowen, T. Air raid   **940.54**
McGowen, T. Assault from the sky   **940.54**
McGowen, T. Carrier war   **940.54**
McGowen, T. Germany's lightning war
                                              940.54
McGowen, T. Sink the Bismarck   **940.54**
Military personnel
See also Soldiers

Military policy
United States
See/See also pages in the following book(s):
War: opposing viewpoints   **355**
Military tanks
McGowen, T. Germany's lightning war (5 and up)   **940.54**
Military weapons
Hamilton, J. Weapons of war   **623.4**
Nardo, D. Weapons of war   **973.3**
Militia movements
Hate groups: opposing viewpoints (7 and up)
                                              364.1
Fiction
Tolan, S. S. Flight of the raven (7 and up)
                                              Fic
Milivojevic, JoAnn
Bosnia and Herzegovina (5 and up)   **949.7**
Serbia (5 and up)   **949.7**
Mill. Macaulay, D.   **690**
Millar, Heather, 1963-
Spain in the age of exploration   **946**
Millard, Anne
Pyramids   **909**
A street through time   **936**
Millbrook medical library [series]
Murphy, W. B. Asthma   **616.2**
Millennium monologs   **812.008**
Miller, Bertha E. Mahony, 1882-1969
(ed) Newbery Medal books, 1922-1955. See Newbery Medal books, 1922-1955   **028.5**
Miller, Brandon Marie
Dressed for the occasion   **391**
Good women of a well-blessed land   **305.4**
Growing up in revolution and the new nation, 1775 to 1800 (5 and up)   **973.3**
Miller, Calvin Craig, 1954-
A. Philip Randolph and the African American labor movement   **92**
Mary Wollstonecraft and the rights of women (7 and up)   **92**
No easy answers [biography of Bayard Rustin] (7 and up)   **92**
Miller, Debra A.
(ed) North Korea. See North Korea   **951.93**
Miller, James, 1943-
(ed) The Complete history of American slavery. See The Complete history of American slavery   **326**
Miller, Joseph
(ed) Sears list of subject headings. See Sears list of subject headings   **025.4**
Miller, Kathryn Schultz
A thousand cranes
In Theatre for young audiences; 20 great plays for children p518-34   **812.008**
Miller, Lee, 1907-1977
See/See also pages in the following book(s):
Colman, P. Where the action was   **070.4**
Miller, Mary Beth
Aimee (7 and up)   **Fic**
Miller, Mike S.
(il) Avery, B. The hedge knight   **741.5**

Miller, Ralph R.
(il) The Comprehensive signed English dictionary. See The Comprehensive signed English dictionary **419**

Miller, Ron, 1947-
Earth and the moon (5 and up) **525**
Extrasolar planets **523**
The history of rockets **621.43**
Jupiter **523.4**
Mercury and Pluto (5 and up) **523.4**
Saturn (5 and up) **523.4**
The sun **523.7**

Miller, Sara Swan
Amazing amphibians **597.8**
Radical reptiles **597.9**

Miller-Lachmann, Lyn, 1956-
(ed) Once upon a cuento. See Once upon a cuento **S C**

The **Miller's** good luck. Anaya, R. A.
In Anaya, R. A. My land sings; stories from the Rio Grande p135-47 **S C**

Millicent Min, girl genius. Yee, L. **Fic**

The **million** dollar shot. Gutman, D. **Fic**

Millions. Cottrell Boyce, F. **Fic**

Millions for an egg? Molnár, I.
In Molnár, I. One-time dog market at Buda and other Hungarian folktales p60-63 **398.2**

Mills, Claudia, 1954-
Alex Ryan, stop that! (5 and up) **Fic**
Lizzie at last (5 and up) **Fic**

Mills, Dick
Aquarium fish **639.34**

Mills
Macaulay, D. Mill (4 and up) **690**

Mills and millwork *See* Mills

Milne, Lorus Johnson, 1912-
The Audubon Society field guide to North American insects and spiders **595.7**

Milne, Margery Joan Greene, 1914-
(il) Milne, L. J. The Audubon Society field guide to North American insects and spiders **595.7**

Min, Katherine
Blonde
In American eyes; new Asian-American short stories for young adults p3-7 **S C**

Mind drugs. Hyde, M. O. **616.86**

Mind games. Grunwell, J. M. **Fic**

Minderovic, Zoran
(ed) Notable mathematicians. See Notable mathematicians **920.003**

Mind's eye. Fleischman, P. **Fic**

Minerals
Chesterman, C. W. The Audubon Society field guide to North American rocks and minerals **549**
Farndon, J. Rocks and minerals **549**
Pough, F. H. A field guide to rocks and minerals **549**
Simon and Schuster's guide to rocks and minerals **549**

Symes, R. F. Eyewitness rocks & minerals (5 and up) **549**
Trueit, T. S. Rocks, gems, and minerals **552**

Miners
Fiction
Durbin, W. The journal of Otto Peltonen, a Finnish immigrant **Fic**

Mines and mineral resources
See also Coal mines and mining

Minkel, Walter
Delivering Web reference services to young people **025.04**

Minnesota
Hintz, M. Minnesota
In America the beautiful, second series **973**
Paulsen, G. Woodsong (7 and up) **796.5**
Schwabacher, M. Minnesota
In Celebrate the states **973**
Fiction
Durbin, W. The journal of Otto Peltonen, a Finnish immigrant **Fic**
Paulsen, G. The winter room (5 and up) **Fic**

Minor, Wendell
(il) George, J. C. Julie **Fic**

Minorities
See also Discrimination
Bode, J. The colors of freedom **305.8**
Discrimination: opposing viewpoints (7 and up) **305.8**
Peoples of North America **305.8**
Bibliography
Helbig, A. Many peoples, one land **016.8**
Steiner, S. F. Promoting a global community through multicultural children's literature **016.8**
Encyclopedias
The Newest Americans **325.73**

Minty, Judith
Killing the bear
In Talking leaves; contemporary native American short stories **S C**

Mintzer, Richard
The National Institutes of Health **362.1**
The National Transportation Safety Board **363.1**

Minuk. Hill, K. **Fic**

The **miracle** of immunity. Donnellan, W. L. **616.07**

The **miracle** of Our Lady of Guadalupe. Delacre, L.
In Delacre, L. Golden tales; myths, legends, and folktales from Latin America p41-43 **398.2**

The **miracle** of Purun Bhagat. Kipling, R.
In Kipling, R. The jungle books **S C**

Miracles
Christianity
Connolly, S. New Testament miracles **226**

Miracle's boys. Woodson, J. **Fic**

Miranda, Ernesto
About
Gold, S. D. Miranda v. Arizona (1966) (7 and up) **345**

Miranda, Ernesto—About—*Continued*
Sonneborn, L. Miranda v. Arizona   **345**
Miranda v. Arizona. Sonneborn, L.   **345**
Miranda v. Arizona (1966). Gold, S. D.   **345**
Mirpuri, Gouri, 1960-
Indonesia   **959.8**
Mirriam-Goldberg, Caryn
Sandra Cisneros   **92**
The **mirror** crack'd. Christie, A.   **Fic**
The **mirror** crack'd from side to side. See Christie, A. The mirror crack'd   **Fic**
Miscellaneous facts *See* Curiosities and wonders
The **mischief** makers. Swortzell, L.
   In Theatre for young audiences; 20 great plays for children p183-216   **812.008**
The **misfits.** Howe, J.   **Fic**
Miss Butterfly. Mori, T.
   In American dragons: twenty-five Asian American voices p26-33   **810.8**
Miss Emily's roses. Zambreno, M. F.
   In Vampires: a collection of original stories p64-80   **S C**
Missing Abby. Weatherly, L.   **Fic**
Missing children
   See also Runaway children
   Fiction
Hartnett, S. What the birds see (7 and up)   **Fic**
Pfeffer, S. B. The year without Michael   **Fic**
Missing May. Rylant, C.   **Fic**
Missing persons
   See also Runaway teenagers
   Fiction
Johnson, A. Looking for Red   **Fic**
Miklowitz, G. D. The enemy has a face (7 and up)   **Fic**
Torres, L. Crossing Montana (7 and up)   **Fic**
Vande Velde, V. Alison, who went away   **Fic**
Weatherly, L. Missing Abby   **Fic**
Westerfeld, S. So yesterday (7 and up)   **Fic**
Missionaries, Christian *See* Christian missionaries
Missionaries of Charity
Ruth, A. Mother Teresa   **92**
Missions, Christian *See* Christian missions
Mississippi
George, C. Mississippi
   In America the beautiful, second series   **973**
Shirley, D. Mississippi
   In Celebrate the states   **973**
   Fiction
Hermes, P. Summer secrets (5 and up)   **Fic**
McMullan, M. How I found the Strong (5 and up)   **Fic**
Rodman, M. A. Yankee girl (4 and up)   **Fic**
Taylor, M. D. The friendship (4 and up)   **Fic**
Taylor, M. D. Let the circle be unbroken (4 and up)   **Fic**
Taylor, M. D. Mississippi bridge (4 and up)   **Fic**

Taylor, M. D. The road to Memphis (4 and up)   **Fic**
Taylor, M. D. Roll of thunder, hear my cry   **Fic**
Taylor, M. D. Song of the trees (4 and up)   **Fic**
Taylor, M. D. The well (4 and up)   **Fic**
Vaught, S. Stormwitch (7 and up)   **Fic**
   Race relations
Crowe, C. Getting away with murder: the true story of the Emmett Till case (7 and up)   **364.1**
The **Mississippi.** Currie, S.   **977**
Mississippi bridge. Taylor, M. D.   **Fic**
The **"Mississippi** Burning" civil rights murder conspiracy trial. Fireside, H.   **345**
Mississippi River
Currie, S. The Mississippi   **977**
Twain, M. The adventures of Tom Sawyer (5 and up)   **Fic**
Walsh, K. The Mississippi (4 and up)   **977**
   Fiction
Twain, M. The adventures of Huckleberry Finn (5 and up)   **Fic**
Twain, M. The adventures of Tom Sawyer (5 and up)   **Fic**
Mississippi River valley
Currie, S. The Mississippi   **977**
Faber, H. La Salle   **92**
Goodman, J. E. Despite all obstacles: La Salle and the conquest of the Mississippi (4 and up)   **92**
Walsh, K. The Mississippi (4 and up)   **977**
Mississippi trial, 1955. Crowe, C.   **Fic**
Mississippi valley *See* Mississippi River valley
Missouri
Bennett, M. Missouri
   In Celebrate the states   **973**
Hintz, M. Missouri
   In America the beautiful, second series   **973**
Twain, M. The adventures of Tom Sawyer (5 and up)   **Fic**
   Fiction
Twain, M. The adventures of Huckleberry Finn (5 and up)   **Fic**
Twain, M. The adventures of Tom Sawyer (5 and up)   **Fic**
Mister grumpy rides the clouds. Van Laan, N.
   In Van Laan, N. With a whoop and a holler; a bushel of lore from way down south p55-59   **398.2**
   In Van Laan, N. With a whoop and a holler; a bushel of lore from way down south p55-59   **398**
Mister ice cold. Wilson, G.
   In Beware!; R.L. Stine picks his favorite scary stories p199-207   **808.8**
Mister Monday. Nix, G.   **Fic**
Mistry, Nilesh
   (il) Philip, N. The illustrated book of myths   **201**

Mitchell, Maria, 1818-1889
About
Anderson, D. Maria Mitchell, astronomer (7 and up) **92**
Gormley, B. Maria Mitchell (7 and up) **92**
See/See also pages in the following book(s):
Celebrating women in mathematics and science **920**

Mitchell, Tracy
(il) Avi. What do fish have to do with anything? and other stories **S C**

Mixed race people *See* Racially mixed people

Miz Hattie gets some company. Hamilton, V.
In Hamilton, V. Her stories; African American folktales, fairy tales, and true tales p15-19 **398.2**

Mochizuki, Ken
Beacon Hill boys (7 and up) **Fic**

The **model**. Oates, J. C.
In Oates, J. C. Small avalanches and other stories **S C**

Modern art
Aronson, M. Art attack (7 and up) **700**
Cockcroft, J. D. Latino visions (7 and up) **704**

1900-1999 (20th century)
See Art—20th century

Modern dance
Freedman, R. Martha Graham, a dancer's life (7 and up) **92**

Modern history
Martell, H. M. The age of discovery **909.08**
Reynoldson, F. Conflict and change **909.7**

Modern mathematicians. Henderson, H. **920**

Modern medicines. Facklam, M. **615**

Modern nations of the world [series]
Ayer, E. H. Germany **943**
Corona, L. Afghanistan **958.1**
Corona, L. Israel **956.94**
Foster, L. M. Italy **945**
Grabowski, J. F. Australia **994**
Green, R. Cambodia **959.6**
Hutchison, L. Lebanon **956.92**
Kallen, S. A. Egypt **962**
Lace, W. W. England **942**
Williams, J. K. South Korea **951.95**

Modern poetry from Africa. See The Penguin book of modern African poetry **896**

Modern science, 1896-1945. Spangenburg, R. **509**

Moehn, Heather
The U.S. Constitution **342**

Moesta, Rebecca
(jt. auth) Anderson, K. J. Grumpy old monsters **741.5**

Mofsie, Louis B., 1936-
(il) Brown, D. A. Dee Brown's folktales of the Native American **398.2**

Mogul Empire
Fiction
Lasky, K. Jahanara, Princess of Princesses **Fic**

Mohammed *See* Muḥammad, d. 632

Mohammedanism *See* Islam

The **Mohawk**. Bonvillian, N.
In Indians of North America series **970.004**

Mohawk Indians
Bonvillian, N. The Mohawk
In Indians of North America series **970.004**
Fiction
Bruchac, J. Skeleton man (4 and up) **Fic**
Carvell, M. Who will tell my brother? (7 and up) **Fic**
Cooney, C. B. The ransom of Mercy Carter **Fic**

Mohegan Indians
Fiction
Durrant, L. Echohawk **Fic**
Durrant, L. Turtle clan journey **Fic**

Mohican Indians *See* Mohegan Indians

Mohr, Nicholasa, 1935-
Mr. Mendelsohn
In Growing up Latino; memoirs and stories p131-46 **810.8**
See/See also pages in the following book(s):
Author talk (4 and up) **028.5**
Hill, C. M. Ten Hispanic American authors **920**

Mok, Russell
(jt. auth) Shelley, R. Japan **952**

Moldova
Sheehan, P. Moldova (5 and up) **947.6**

Molecular biology
See/See also pages in the following book(s):
Edelson, E. James Watson and Francis Crick and the building blocks of life (7 and up) **92**

Molecules
Cooper, C. Matter **530**
Woodford, C. Atoms and molecules (5 and up) **540**

Molina, Mario, 1943-
See/See also pages in the following book(s):
Oleksy, W. G. Hispanic-American scientists (7 and up) **920**

Molina, Rafael Leónidas Trujillo *See* Trujillo Molina, Rafael Leónidas, 1891-1961

Mollusks
Rehder, H. A. The Audubon Society field guide to North American seashells **594**

Molly Cottontail. San Souci, R.
In San Souci, R. Cut from the same cloth; American women of myth, legend, and tall tale p29-33 **398.2**

Molly Whuppie. Philip, N.
In Philip, N. Celtic fairy tales p86-91 **398.2**

Molnár, Irma
One-time dog market at Buda and other Hungarian folktales **398.2**
Contents: King Matthias and the old man; King Matthias and the Szekler's daughter; King Matthias and his truthful shepherd; One-time dog market at Buda; King Matthias and the weatherman; The quick-witted cobbler at wits' end; The shepherd of rabbits; Peter's taller tale; Grasshopper; Kindness rewarded; How a

Molnár, Irma—*Continued*
student became a king; Millions for an egg?; The fish damsel; Talking grapes, smiling apples, and ringing apricots; To outwit a count; A poor man's bargain; Marci, the honest thief; The strongest creature; The fox, the bear, and the poor man; Twelve at a swat; The three wanderers; Lookout mountain, or, The legend of the chimney-stack cake; The legend of the white stag

Moloney, N. (Norah)
The young Oxford book of archaeology (7 and up)   **930.1**

Mom Bett and the little ones a-glowing. Hamilton, V.
In Hamilton, V. Her stories; African American folktales, fairy tales, and true tales p39-41   **398.2**

MOMA *See* Museum of Modern Art (New York, N.Y.)

MoMA QNS *See* Museum of Modern Art (New York, N.Y.)

Momaday, N. Scott
She is beautiful in her whole being
In Talking leaves; contemporary native American short stories   **S C**

Monaghan, Kathleen
You can weave! (4 and up)   **746.41**

Monarchs *See* Kings and rulers

Monarchs. Lasky, K.   **595.7**

Monarchs. Ross, S.   **940.1**

Monarchy
See also Queens

Monasticism and religious orders for women
See also Nuns

Mondowney, JoAnn G.
Hold them in your heart   **027.62**

Monet and the impressionists for kids. Sabbeth, C.   **759.05**

Money
Cribb, J. Money (4 and up)   **332.4**
Godfrey, N. S. Neale S. Godfrey's ultimate kids' money book (5 and up)   **332.024**
Fiction
Cottrell Boyce, F. Millions (5 and up)   **Fic**

Money hungry. Flake, S. G.   **Fic**

Money-making projects for children
Kiefer, J. Jobs for kids (4 and up)   **650.1**

Mongolia
Pang, G.-C. Mongolia (5 and up)   **951.7**

Mongolians *See* Mongols

Mongols
Greenblatt, M. Genghis Khan and the Mongol Empire   **950**
Lange, B. Genghis Khan (7 and up)   **92**

Mongoose. Spinelli, J.
In Spinelli, J. The library card   **S C**

The **monkey** and the crocodile. Lee, J. M.
In Lee, J. M. I once was a monkey; stories Buddha told   **294.3**

The **monkey** garden. Cisneros, S.
In Growing up Latino; memoirs and stories p288-91   **810.8**

Monkey son-in-law
In Hearne, B. G. Beauties and beasts p32-34   **398.2**

Monkey stew. Van Laan, N.
In Van Laan, N. With a whoop and a holler; a bushel of lore from way down south p11-12   **398**

Monkey vs. Robot. Kochalka, J.   **741.5**

Monkeyman. Myers, W. D.
In Myers, W. D. 145th Street; short stories   **S C**

Monkeys
See also Baboons
Fiction
Rawls, W. Summer of the monkeys (7 and up)   **Fic**

The **monkey's** wedding. Aiken, J.
In Night terrors; stories of shadow and substance   **S C**

Monks
Fiction
Whitesel, C. A. Rebel   **Fic**

Mono (Disease) *See* Mononucleosis

Monologues
The Book of monologues for aspiring actors (7 and up)   **808.82**
Great monologues for young actors   **812.008**
Lamedman, D. 111 one-minute monologues   **812.008**
Millennium monologs   **812.008**
Shakespeare, W. One hundred and eleven Shakespeare monologues (7 and up)   **822.3**
Surface, M. H. Short scenes and monologues for middle school actors   **812**

Mononucleosis
Smart, P. Everything you need to know about mononucleosis (7 and up)   **616.9**

Monroe, Judy
Cystic fibrosis   **616.3**
Influenza and other viruses   **616.9**
The Susan B. Anthony women's voting rights trial   **324.6**

Monson, Dianne L., 1934-
(jt. auth) Sutherland, Z. Children and books   **028.5**

Monsoon summer. Perkins, M.   **Fic**

Monster. Myers, W. D.   **Fic**

Monsters
Buller, L. Myths and monsters (5 and up)   **398**
Fiction
Coville, B. The monsters of Morley Manor   **Fic**

The **monsters** and the flood. Curry, J. L.
In Curry, J. L. Hold up the sky: and other Native American tales from Texas and the Southern Plains p32-39   **398.2**

The **monsters** of Morley Manor. Coville, B.   **Fic**

Montalcini, Rita Levi- *See* Levi-Montalcini, Rita, 1909-

Montana
Fiction
Ingold, J. Hitch (7 and up)   **Fic**

Montana
Bennett, C. Montana
In Celebrate the states **973**
George, C. Montana
In America the beautiful, second series
973
Montardre, Hélène
(jt. auth) Burleigh, R. Volcanoes **551.2**
Montes, Marisa
A circle of time **Fic**
Montgomery, Bernard Law *See* Montgomery of Alamein, Bernard Law Montgomery, Viscount, 1887-1976
Montgomery, L. M. (Lucy Maud), 1874-1942
See/See also pages in the following book(s):
Ellis, S. From reader to writer **372.6**
Montgomery, Lucy Maud *See* Montgomery, L. M. (Lucy Maud), 1874-1942
Montgomery, Sy
Encantado (4 and up) **599.5**
Search for the golden moon bear (5 and up)
599.78
The snake scientist (4 and up) **597.9**
The tarantula scientist (4 and up) **595.4**
Montgomery (Ala.)
Race relations
Walsh, F. The Montgomery bus boycott
323.1
The **Montgomery** bus boycott. Walsh, F.
323.1
Montgomery of Alamein, Bernard Law Montgomery, Viscount, 1887-1976
See/See also pages in the following book(s):
Ross, S. Leaders of World War II **920**
Montmorency. Updale, E. **Fic**
The **monument**. Paulsen, G. **Fic**
Monumental verses. Lewis, J. P. **811**
Monuments
Poetry
Lewis, J. P. Monumental verses (5 and up)
811
Monuments, National *See* National monuments
Monuments and historic places of America
973
Mookie in love. Flake, S. G.
In Flake, S. G. Who am I without him?; short stories about girls and the boys in their lives p49-69 **S C**
Moon, Allan
(il) Thomas, K. Blades, boards & scooters
796.2
Moon
Bredeson, C. The moon (4 and up) **523.3**
Dyson, M. J. Home on the moon (4 and up)
629.45
Gardner, R. Science project ideas about the moon **523.3**
Kerrod, R. The moon **523.3**
Miller, R. Earth and the moon (5 and up)
525
Simon, S. The moon (4 and up) **523.3**
Stefoff, R. Earth and the moon **550**
Exploration
Cole, M. D. Moon base (4 and up) **629.4**

Moon, Voyages to *See* Space flight to the moon
The **moon**. Bredeson, C. **523.3**
Moon. Potok, C.
In Potok, C. Zebra and other stories p44-69
S C
The **moon** and I. Byars, B. C. **92**
Moon base. Cole, M. D. **629.4**
Moon bases *See* Lunar bases
Moon kill. Windsor, P.
In Night terrors; stories of shadow and substance **S C**
Moon time child. McGill, A.
In Don't cramp my style; stories about that time of the month p45-67 **S C**
Moonshine. Blackwood, G. L. **Fic**
Moonshine express. Norville, R. **Fic**
Moonshine in the mustard pot. Aiken, J.
In Aiken, J. Shadows and moonshine; stories
S C
Moonshining
Fiction
Norville, R. Moonshine express **Fic**
The **moorchild**. McGraw, E. J. **Fic**
Moore, Ann
See/See also pages in the following book(s):
Thimmesh, C. Girls think of everything (5 and up) **920**
Moore, Gerald, 1924-
(ed) The Penguin book of modern African poetry. See The Penguin book of modern African poetry **896**
Moore, Peter
Blind sighted (7 and up) **Fic**
Moore, Yvette
Freedom songs **Fic**
Mora, Pat
The desert is my mother. El desierto es mi madre **811**
Moragne, Wendy
Depression (7 and up) **616.85**
New Jersey
In Celebrate the states **973**
Moranville, Sharelle Byars
Over the river (5 and up) **Fic**
Mordred (Legendary character)
Springer, N. I am Mordred (7 and up) **Fic**
Fiction
Wein, E. E. The Winter Prince (7 and up)
Fic
See/See also pages in the following book(s):
Thomson, S. L. The dragon's son (7 and up)
Fic
More award-winning science fair projects. Bochinski, J. B. **507.8**
More hot links. Wright, C. M. **011.6**
More ideas for science projects. Adams, R. C.
507.8
More scary stories to tell in the dark. Schwartz, A. **398.2**
More science projects for all students. Bazler, J. A. **507.8**
More spice than sugar (4 and up) **811.008**

More telescope power. Matloff, G. L.   522

More than a label. Muharrar, A.   305.23

Moreno, Barry
Italian Americans (7 and up)   305.8

Morgan, Clay
The boy who spoke dog (5 and up)   Fic

Morgan, Garrett A., 1877-1963
See/See also pages in the following book(s):
Aaseng, N. Black inventors (7 and up)   920

Morgan, Sir Henry, 1635?-1688
See/See also pages in the following book(s):
Wren, L. L. Pirates and privateers of the high
seas p11-17   920

Morgan, Julian, 1958-
Cleopatra   92

Morgan, Nicola, 1961-
Chicken friend (5 and up)   Fic
Fleshmarket (7 and up)   Fic

Morgan, Nina
Lasers   621.36

Morgan, Sally
Body doubles   660.6
Waste disposal   628.4

Morgan, Thomas Hunt, 1866-1945
See/See also pages in the following book(s):
Kidd, J. S. Life lines (7 and up)   576.5

Morgan le Fay (Legendary character)
Fiction
Springer, N. I am Morgan le Fay (7 and up)
   Fic

Morgan Roehmar's boys. Vande Velde, V.
In Gothic!; ten original dark tales   S C

Morganfield, McKinley *See* Waters, Muddy,
1915-1983

Morgenstern, Julie
Organizing from the inside out for teens (7 and
up)   646.7

Morgenstern, Susie Hoch
Secret letters from 0 to 10   Fic

Morgenstern-Colón, Jessi
(jt. auth) Morgenstern, J. Organizing from the
inside out for teens   646.7

Mori, Toshio, 1910-1980
Miss Butterfly
In American dragons: twenty-five Asian
American voices p26-33   810.8

Moriarty, Jaclyn
The year of secret assignments (7 and up)
   Fic

Moriguchi, Kakō, 1909-
See/See also pages in the following book(s):
Hamanaka, S. In search of the spirit (5 and up)
   920

Morley, Jacqueline
Viking town   948

Mormons
Book of Mormon. The Book of Mormon
   289.3
Fiction
Cannon, A. E. Charlotte's Rose (5 and up)
   Fic

Mormons in America. Bushman, C. L.   289.3

Morning Girl. Dorris, M.   Fic

Morocco
Blauer, E. Morocco   964

Morpurgo, Michael
Kensuke's kingdom (4 and up)   Fic
Private Peaceful (7 and up)   Fic
Sir Gawain and the Green Knight (5 and up)
   398.2

Morrice, Polly Alison
Iowa
In Celebrate the states   973

Morrigan. Mayer, M.
In Mayer, M. Women warriors; myths and
legends of heroic women p39-41   398

Morris, Betty J.
Administering the school library media center
   027.8

Morris, Bruce C.
(jt. auth) Wells, D. K. Live aware, not in fear
   155.5

Morris, Gerald, 1963-
The squire's tale   Fic

Morris, Juddi
Tending the fire: the story of Maria Martinez (4
and up)   92

Morris, Mary, 1913-
(jt. auth) Morris, W. Morris dictionary of word
and phrase origins   422.03

Morris, Pat
Mammals   599

Morris, William, 1913-1994
Morris dictionary of word and phrase origins
   422.03

Morris, Winifred
Secret numbers
In On the edge: stories at the brink p95-106
   S C

Morris dictionary of word and phrase origins.
Morris, W.   422.03

Morrison, Gordon
(il) Kricher, J. C. Peterson first guide to seashores   577.7

Morrison, Lillian, 1917-
(comp) More spice than sugar. See More spice
than sugar   811.008

Morrison, Marion
Costa Rica (4 and up)   972.86
Guyana (4 and up)   988.1

Morrison, Taylor
The coast mappers (5 and up)   623.89

Morrison, Toni, 1931-
"Recitatif"
In Leaving home: stories p201-27   808.8
About
Haskins, J. Toni Morrison (4 and up)   92
See/See also pages in the following book(s):
Hacker, C. Nobel Prize winners   920
Hansen, J. Women of hope (4 and up)   920

Morse, Jenifer Corr
(jt. auth) Pascoe, E. Scholastic kid's almanac
   031.02

Morse, Samuel Finley Breese, 1791-1872
About
Coe, L. The telegraph   621.383

Morse, Scott
The barefoot serpent   **741.5**
Morse, Susan
(jt. auth) Swinburne, S. R. The woods scientist
    591.7
Mortal engines. Reeve, P.   **Fic**
Morton, Joseph C.
The American Revolution (7 and up)   **973.3**
Moscovich, Ivan
1000 playthinks (7 and up)   **793.73**
Moser, Barry
(il) Hamilton, V. In the beginning; creation stories from around the world   **201**
(il) Lasky, K. A brilliant streak: the making of Mark Twain   **92**
(il) MacLachlan, P. Journey   **Fic**
(il) Packer, T. Macbeth   **822.3**
(il) Poe, E. A. Tales of Edgar Allan Poe
    S C
(il) Rylant, C. Appalachia   **974**
Moser, Diane, 1944-
(jt. auth) Spangenburg, R. The African-American experience   **917.3**
(jt. auth) Spangenburg, R. The age of synthesis: 1800-1895   **509**
(jt. auth) Spangenburg, R. The birth of science: ancient times to 1699   **509**
(jt. auth) Spangenburg, R. Genetic engineering
    660.6
(jt. auth) Spangenburg, R. The history of NASA
    629.4
(jt. auth) Spangenburg, R. The Hubble Space Telescope   **522**
(jt. auth) Spangenburg, R. Literature and the arts
    917.3
(jt. auth) Spangenburg, R. A look at Mercury
    523.4
(jt. auth) Spangenburg, R. Mercury   **523.4**
(jt. auth) Spangenburg, R. Meteors, meteorites, and meteoroids   **523.5**
(jt. auth) Spangenburg, R. Modern science, 1896-1945   **509**
(jt. auth) Spangenburg, R. Onboard the space shuttle   **629.44**
(jt. auth) Spangenburg, R. Political and social movements   **917.3**
(jt. auth) Spangenburg, R. Propaganda   **303.3**
(jt. auth) Spangenburg, R. The rise of reason: 1700-1799   **509**
(jt. auth) Spangenburg, R. Science frontiers, 1946 to the present   **509**
(jt. auth) Spangenburg, R. The sun   **523.7**
(jt. auth) Spangenburg, R. TV news   **070.1**
(jt. auth) Spangenburg, R. Venus   **523.4**
Moses (Biblical figure)
About
Chaikin, M. Angels sweep the desert floor (4 and up)   **296.1**
Moses, Shelia P.
The legend of Buddy Bush   **Fic**
Mosher, Richard, 1949-
Zazoo   **Fic**
Mosier, Elizabeth
My life as a girl   **Fic**
Moslemism *See* Islam

Mosque. Macaulay, D.   **726**
Mosques
Design and construction
Macaulay, D. Mosque (4 and up)   **726**
Mosquito. Salisbury, G.
In Destination unexpected: short stories
    S C
Moss, Carol (Carol Marie)
Science in ancient Mesopotamia (4 and up)
    509
Moss, Joyce, 1951-
Profiles in American history   **973**
The **most** beautiful roof in the world. Lasky, K.
    577.3
The **most** important night of Melanie's life. Peck, R.
In Peck, R. Past perfect, present tense: new and collected stories   **S C**
The **most** useful slave. Hamilton, V.
In Hamilton, V. The people could fly; American black folktales p160-65
    398.2
The **moth** of God. Armstrong, J.
In Soul searching: thirteen stories about faith and belief p203-19   **S C**
Mother and daughter. Soto, G.
In Soto, G. Baseball in April, and other stories p60-68   **S C**
The **mother** and death. San Souci, R.
In San Souci, R. A terrifying taste of short & shivery; thirty creepy tales p141-45
    398.2
Mother-daughter relationship
Stone, M. At the end of words (7 and up)
    92
Fiction
Abelove, J. Saying it out loud (7 and up)
    Fic
Brooks, B. Midnight hour encores (7 and up)
    Fic
Cassidy, C. Dizzy (5 and up)
Childress, A. Rainbow Jordan (7 and up)
    Fic
Kehret, P. I'm not who you think I am   **Fic**
Krisher, T. Spite fences   **Fic**
Lasky, K. Beyond the burning time (7 and up)
    Fic
Mackler, C. Love and other four-letter words (7 and up)   **Fic**
Napoli, D. J. Zel (7 and up)   **Fic**
Pennebaker, R. Both sides now (7 and up)
    Fic
Rodgers, M. Freaky Friday (4 and up)   **Fic**
Zinnen, L. The truth about rats, rules, and seventh grade   **Fic**
Poetry
Johnson, A. Running back to Ludie   **811**
Mother-daughter relationships in literature
Crew, H. S. Is it really Mommie Dearest?
    813.009
Mother Earth, Father Sky. Lavender, D. S.
    970.004
Mother Goose on the loose   **398.8**
Mother Jones *See* Jones, Mother, 1830-1930

Mother Nature's pharmacy. Kidd, J. S.   **615**

Mother-son relationship
Fiction
Bennett, J. Sing me a death song (7 and up)
Fic
Corbett, S. 12 again   **Fic**

Mother Teresa *See* Teresa, Mother, 1910-1997

Mother Teresa's Mission of Charity *See* Missionaries of Charity

Mothers
See also Surrogate mothers; Teenage mothers; Unmarried mothers
Fiction
Baskin, N. R. What every girl (except me) knows (4 and up)   **Fic**
Curtis, C. P. Bucking the Sarge (5 and up)
Fic
Fritz, A. Y. Waiting to disappear (7 and up)
Fic
Fusco, K. N. Tending to Grace (7 and up)
Fic
Haddix, M. P. Escape from memory   **Fic**
Haddix, M. P. Takeoffs and landings   **Fic**
Martin, A. M. Here today (5 and up)   **Fic**
Wynne-Jones, T. A thief in the house of memory (7 and up)   **Fic**

Mothers, Single parent *See* Single parent family

Mothers and daughters *See* Mother-daughter relationship

Mothers and sons *See* Mother-son relationship

Moths
Pascoe, E. Butterflies and moths   **595.7**
Whalley, P. E. S. Butterfly & moth (4 and up)
595.7

The **moths**. Viramontes, H. M.
In Growing up Latino; memoirs and stories p32-37   **810.8**

Motion
Farndon, J. Motion   **531**
Gardner, R. Forces and motion science fair projects   **531**

Motion picture actors *See* Actors

Motion picture cartoons *See* Animated films

Motion picture direction *See* Motion pictures—Production and direction

Motion picture photography *See* Cinematography

Motion picture plays
Technique
Lawrence, C. Big fat paycheck   **808.2**

Motion picture producers and directors
Rubin, S. G. Steven Spielberg   **92**

Motion picture production *See* Motion pictures—Production and direction

Motion pictures
Jones, S. Film (7 and up)   **791.43**
Catalogs
Culturally diverse videos, audios, and CD-ROMS for children and young adults
011.6
Fiction
Castellucci, C. Boy proof (7 and up)   **Fic**
Production and direction
O'Brien, L. Lights, camera, action!   **791.43**

Motivation (Psychology)
See also Wishes
Bachel, B. K. What do you really want?
153.8

Moulton, Carroll
(ed) Ancient Greece and Rome. See Ancient Greece and Rome   **938**

Mounds and mound builders
McGowen, T. Giant stones and earth mounds
930.1

Mount Everest (China and Nepal)
Brennan, K. Sir Edmund Hillary, modern day explorer (4 and up)   **92**
Jenkins, S. The top of the world (2-4)
796.52
Pfetzer, M. Within reach: my Everest story (7 and up)   **796.52**
Skreslet, L. To the top of Everest (4 and up)
796.52
Venables, S. To the top (5 and up)   **796.52**

Mount Saint Helens (Wash.)
Lauber, P. Volcano: the eruption and healing of Mount St. Helens (4 and up)   **551.2**
Fiction
Smith, R. The Sasquatch   **Fic**

Mountain bikes
King, A. Play-by-play mountain biking
796.6

Mountain childers. San Souci, R.
In San Souci, R. Double-dare to be scared: another thirteen chilling tales   **S C**

Mountain life
Fiction
Dowell, F. O. Dovey Coe (5 and up)   **Fic**
Murphy, R. Harmony   **Fic**

Mountain lion and the four sisters. Curry, J. L.
In Curry, J. L. Hold up the sky: and other Native American tales from Texas and the Southern Plains p103-06   **398.2**

Mountain lions *See* Pumas

Mountain pose. Wilson, N. H.   **Fic**

Mountain solo. Ingold, J.   **Fic**

Mountaineering
Brennan, K. Sir Edmund Hillary, modern day explorer (4 and up)   **92**
Jenkins, S. The top of the world (2-4)
796.52
Pfetzer, M. Within reach: my Everest story (7 and up)   **796.52**
Skreslet, L. To the top of Everest (4 and up)
796.52
Venables, S. To the top (5 and up)   **796.52**

Mountains
See also Adirondack Mountains (N.Y.); Ozark Mountains
Simon, S. Mountains (3-6)   **551.4**

Mour, Stanley I.
American jazz musicians   **920**

Mouse *See* Mice

The **Mouse** rap. Myers, W. D.   **Fic**

The **mousetrap**. Olson, A. N.
  In Olson, A. N. and Schwartz, H. Ask the bones: scary stories from around the world p78-84   **398.2**
The **moves** make the man. Brooks, B.   **Fic**
Moving
  Fiction
  Auch, M. J. Wing nut (5 and up)   **Fic**
  Bennett, C. A heart divided (7 and up)
  De Guzman, M. Beekman's big deal (5 and up)   **Fic**
  Fletcher, R. Spider Boy   **Fic**
  Hale, M. The truth about sparrows (5 and up)   **Fic**
  Polikoff, B. G. Why does the coqui sing? (5 and up)   **Fic**
  Wallace, B. Aloha summer   **Fic**
Moving on. Ingold, J.
  In Time capsule: short stories about teenagers throughout the twentieth century p21-34   **S C**

Moving pictures *See* Motion pictures
Mowat, Farley
  Born naked (7 and up)   **92**
Mowgli's brothers. Kipling, R.
  In Kipling, R. The jungle books   **S C**
Mowry, Jess, 1960-
  Ghost train   **Fic**
Mozambique
  James, R. S. Mozambique (7 and up)   **967.9**
  Fiction
  Farmer, N. A girl named Disaster (6 and up)   **Fic**
  Mankell, H. Secrets in the fire (5 and up)   **Fic**
The **Mozart** season. Wolff, V. E.   **Fic**
Mr. Mendelsohn. Mohr, N.
  In Growing up Latino; memoirs and stories p131-46   **810.8**
Mrs. Bathurst. Kipling, R.
  In McCaffrey, A. {The Pern series}   **S C**
Mrs. Frisby and the rats of NIMH. O'Brien, R. C.   **Fic**
Mrs. Hauksbee sits out [play]. Kipling, R.
  In McCaffrey, A. {The Pern series}   **S C**
Mrs. Moonlight (Senora de Luna). San Souci, R.
  In San Souci, R. Dare to be scared; thirteen stories to chill and thrill   **S C**
Mrs. Noonan. Salisbury, G.
  In On the fringe p117-41   **S C**
  In Salisbury, G. Island boyz: short stories p20-48   **S C**
Ms. found in a bottle. Poe, E. A.
  In Poe, E. A. Tales of Edgar Allan Poe p153-67   **S C**
Ms: the story of Gloria Steinem. Wheaton, E.   **92**
Much ado about nothing. Packer, T.
  In Packer, T. Tales from Shakespeare p49-65   **822.3**
Muckenhoupt, Margaret
  Sigmund Freud (7 and up)   **92**

Mudd-Ruth, Maria
  The deserts of the Southwest   **577.5**
Muḥammad, d. 632
  About
  Oliver, M. T. Muhammad (7 and up)   **297**
Muhammedanism *See* Islam
Muharrar, Aisha
  More than a label (7 and up)   **305.23**
Muir, John, 1838-1914
  About
  Naden, C. J. John Muir   **92**
  Warrick, K. C. John Muir: crusader for the wilderness   **92**
  See/See also pages in the following book(s):
  Byrnes, P. Environmental pioneers (7 and up)   **920**
Müller, Melissa
  Anne Frank (7 and up)   **92**
The **mulombe**. San Souci, R.
  In San Souci, R. A terrifying taste of short & shivery; thirty creepy tales p95-100   **398.2**
The **multicultural** cookbook for students. Albyn, C. L.   **641.5**
Multiculturalism
  Gay, K. Cultural diversity (7 and up)   **305.8**
  Heath, A. Windows on the world   **394.2**
  See/See also pages in the following book(s):
  Culture wars: opposing viewpoints   **306**
Multiple birth
  Jackson, D. M. Twin tales (4 and up)   **618.2**
  Landau, E. Multiple births   **618.2**
Multiple choice. Tashjian, J.   **Fic**
Multiple sclerosis
  Aaseng, N. Multiple sclerosis   **616.8**
  Burnfield, A. Multiple sclerosis (5 and up)   **616.8**
  Gold, S. D. Multiple sclerosis (4 and up)   **616.8**
Multiracial people *See* Racially mixed people
Mulvihill, Margaret
  The treasury of saints and martyrs (5 and up)   **920**
Mummies
  Berger, M. Mummies of the pharaohs   **932**
  Deem, J. M. Bodies from the bog (4 and up)   **930.1**
  Getz, D. Frozen man (5 and up)   **930.1**
  Kallen, S. A. Mummies (4 and up)   **393**
  Patent, D. H. Secrets of the ice man (5 and up)   **930.1**
  Pemberton, D. Egyptian mummies (4 and up)   **393**
  Perl, L. Mummies, tombs, and treasure (4 and up)   **393**
  Reinhard, J. Discovering the Inca Ice Maiden (5 and up)   **930.1**
  Tanaka, S. Secrets of the mummies (4 and up)   **393**
  Wilcox, C. Mummies, bones & body parts (5 and up)   **393**
Mummies, bones & body parts. Wilcox, C.   **393**
Mummies of the pharaohs. Berger, M.   **932**

Mummies, tombs, and treasure. Perl, L. 393

Munan, Heidi
Malaysia (5 and up) 959.5

Mungoshi, Charles
The setting sun and the rolling world
In Leaving home: stories p157-64 808.8

Municipal engineering
Levy, M. Engineering the city 624

Municipal planning *See* City planning

Munitions *See* Military weapons

Muñoz, William, 1949-
(il) Patent, D. H. Animals on the trail with Lewis and Clark 978
(il) Patent, D. H. The bald eagle returns 598
(il) Patent, D. H. Biodiversity 333.95
(il) Patent, D. H. Deer and elk 599.65
(il) Patent, D. H. Eagles of America 598
(il) Patent, D. H. Fire: friend or foe 577.2
(il) Patent, D. H. Homesteading 978
(il) Patent, D. H. The Lewis and Clark trail 978
(il) Patent, D. H. Plants on the trail with Lewis and Clark 978
(il) Patent, D. H. Prairie dogs 599.3
(il) Patent, D. H. Shaping the earth 550

Munsen, Sylvia
Cooking the Norwegian way
In Easy menu ethnic cookbooks 641.5

Muradi, Abdul Khaliq
See/See also pages in the following book(s):
Major, J. S. Caravan to America p[1]-13 (4 and up) 920

Murder *See* Homicide

Murder trials *See* Trials (Homicide)

Murdered, my sweet. Nixon, J. L. Fic

Murders at the Rue Morgue. Poe, E. A.
In Poe, E. A. The pit and the pendulum and other stories S C

The **murders** in the Rue Morgue. Poe, E. A.
In Poe, E. A. Tales of Edgar Allan Poe p169-216 S C

Murdico, Suzanne J.
Concorde (4 and up) 629.133

Murdoch, David Hamilton, 1937-
Cowboy (4 and up) 978
North American Indian (4 and up) 970.004

Murie, Margaret E., 1902-2003
See/See also pages in the following book(s):
Byrnes, P. Environmental pioneers (7 and up) 920

Murie, Olaus Johan, 1889-1963
See/See also pages in the following book(s):
Byrnes, P. Environmental pioneers (7 and up) 920

Murieta, Joaquín, d. 1853
Fiction
Smith, J. A. Bandit's moon (4-6) Fic

The **murky** secret. Olson, A. N.
In Olson, A. N. and Schwartz, H. Ask the bones: scary stories from around the world p10-16 398.2

Murphy, Barbara, 1933-
Eagle Cloud and Fawn
In Join in; multiethnic short stories by outstanding writers for young adults p23-33 S C

Murphy, Bruce, 1962-
(ed) Benet's reader's encyclopedia. See Benet's reader's encyclopedia 803

Murphy, Claire Rudolf
Free radical (7 and up) Fic
Daughters of the desert. See Daughters of the desert 220.9

Murphy, Donald J.
(ed) World War I. See World War I [Turning points in world history series] 940.3

Murphy, Jim, 1947-
Across America on an emigrant train (5 and up) 92
An American plague (5 and up) 614.5
Blizzard!: the storm that changed America 974.7
The boys' war (5 and up) 973.7
Gone a-whaling (7 and up) 639.2
The great fire (5 and up) 977.3
Inside the Alamo (5 and up) 976.4
The journal of James Edmond Pease, a Civil War Union soldier Fic
The long road to Gettysburg (5 and up) 973.7
My face to the wind Fic
Pick & shovel poet: the journeys of Pascal D'Angelo 92
West to a land of plenty Fic
A young patriot (5 and up) 973.3

Murphy, Larry
African-American faith in America 200

Murphy, Rita
Harmony Fic

Murphy, Wendy B.
Asthma (7 and up) 616.2
Spare parts (7 and up) 617.9

Murray, Aaron R.
(ed) American Revolution: battles and leaders. See American Revolution: battles and leaders 973.3
(ed) Civil War: battles and leaders. See Civil War: battles and leaders 973.7
(ed) World War II battles and leaders. See World War II battles and leaders 940.54

Murray, Jaye
Bottled up (7 and up) Fic

Murray, Martine, 1965-
The slightly true story of Cedar B. Hartley (5 and up) Fic

Murray, Peter, 1952-
See also Hautman, Pete, 1952-

Murrow, Liza Ketchum *See* Ketchum, Liza, 1946-

Murrow, Liza Ketchum, 1946-
Sables Mouvants
In On the edge: stories at the brink p141-60 S C

Musa, d. 1337
See/See also pages in the following book(s):
Meltzer, M. Ten kings (5 and up)   920
Muscles
Simon, S. Muscles (4 and up)   612.7
Musculoskeletal system
    See also Bones
Gold, S. D. The musculoskeletal system and the
    skin   612.7
Parker, S. The skeleton and muscles (5 and up)
              612.7
Parker, S. Skin, muscles, and bones   612.7
The **musculoskeletal** system and the skin. Gold, S.
    D.   612.7
Museum of Modern Art (New York, N.Y.)
    Fiction
Scieszka, J. Seen Art?   Fic
Museums
    See also Art museums
Musgrave, Susan
(ed) You be me. See You be me   305.23
The **Musgrave** ritual. Doyle, Sir A. C.
    In Doyle, Sir A. C. The complete Sherlock
    Holmes   S C
Mushrooms
    See also Fungi
Lincoff, G. The Audubon Society field guide to
    North American mushrooms   579.6
Music
    Analysis, appreciation
    See Music appreciation
    Dictionaries
Barber, N. Music: an A-Z guide (4 and up)
              780.3
Kennedy, M. The concise Oxford dictionary of
    music   780.3
    Encyclopedias
Story of music (7 and up)   780.3
    Fiction
Bowler, T. Firmament (7 and up)   Fic
What a song can do (7 and up)   S C
    History and criticism
Kallen, S. A. The history of classical music
              781.6
    Poetry
Adoff, J. The song shoots out of my mouth
              811
    Study and teaching
Collins, D. R. Dr. Shinichi Suzuki   92
Music, African American *See* African American
    music
Music appreciation
    See also Music—History and criticism
Ganeri, A. The young person's guide to the or-
    chestra (4 and up)   784.2
Music library [series]
Kallen, S. A. The history of classical music
              781.6
Kallen, S. A. The history of country music
              781.642
Kallen, S. A. The history of jazz   781.65
Kallen, S. A. The history of rock and roll
              781.66

Kallen, S. A. The instruments of music
              784.19
Musical instruments
Ganeri, A. The young person's guide to the or-
    chestra (4 and up)   **784.2**
Kallen, S. A. The instruments of music
              784.19
    Dictionaries
Baines, A. The Oxford companion to musical
    instruments (7 and up)   **784.19**
Musicians
    See also Composers; Violoncellists
Earls, I. Young musicians in world history
              920
Levine, L. Shake, rattle, & roll (4 and up)
              920
    Dictionaries
Kennedy, M. The concise Oxford dictionary of
    music   780.3
    Fiction
Brooks, B. Midnight hour encores (7 and up)
              Fic
Corbet, R. Fifteen love (7 and up)   Fic
Dessen, S. This lullaby (7 and up)   Fic
Fenner, C. Yolonda's genius (4-6)   Fic
French, S. Where in the world (5 and up)
              Fic
Going, K. L. Fat kid rules the world (7 and up)
              Fic
    United States
Blashfield, J. F. Leonard Bernstein (7 and up)
              92
Musicians, African American *See* African
    American musicians
Musleah, Rahel
    Why on this night?   296.4
The **Muslim** almanac   297
Muslimism *See* Islam
Muslims
Oliver, M. T. Muhammad (7 and up)   297
    Fiction
Stolz, J. The shadows of Ghadames   Fic
    United States
See/See also pages in the following book(s):
Joselit, J. W. Immigration and American reli-
    gion (7 and up)   200
Muslims, Black *See* Black Muslims
Mussolini, Benito, 1883-1945
See/See also pages in the following book(s):
Ross, S. Leaders of World War II   920
Muzak for Prozac. Gantos, J.
    In On the fringe p75-86   S C
My America (4 and up)   811.008
My big feet out for a walk. Thacker, N.
    In Girls got game; sports stories and poems
              810.8
My black me (5 and up)   811.008
My bridges of hope. Bitton-Jackson, L.   92
My brother, my sister, and I. Watkins, Y. K.
              Fic
My brother Sam is dead. Collier, J. L.   Fic
My contract with Henry. Vaupel, R.   Fic
My cup runneth over. Whytock, C.   Fic

My Daniel. Conrad, P. **Fic**

My face to the wind. Murphy, J. **Fic**

My family shall be free!: the life of Peter Still. Fradin, D. B. **92**

My fellow Americans (7 and up) **352.23**

My future career [series]
McAlpine, M. Working with computers **004**

My heartbeat. Freymann-Weyr, G. **Fic**

My lady love, my dove. Dahl, R.
In Dahl, R. Skin and other stories **S C**

My land sings. Anaya, R. A. **S C**

My life as a girl. Mosier, E. **Fic**

My life in dog years. Paulsen, G. **92**

My life of crime. Jennings, R. W. **Fic**

My Louisiana sky. Holt, K. W. **Fic**

My Lucy friend who smells like corn. Cisneros, S.
In Who do you think you are?; stories of friends and enemies p119-21 **S C**

My name is America [series]
Bartoletti, S. C. The journal of Finn Reardon **Fic**
Denenberg, B. The journal of Ben Uchida, citizen #13559, Mirror Lake internment camp **Fic**
Durbin, W. The journal of C.J. Jackson: a Dust Bowl migrant **Fic**
Durbin, W. The journal of Otto Peltonen, a Finnish immigrant **Fic**
Durbin, W. The journal of Sean Sullivan **Fic**
Levine, E. The journal of Jedediah Barstow **Fic**
Murphy, J. The journal of James Edmond Pease, a Civil War Union soldier **Fic**
Myers, W. D. The journal of Biddy Owens, the Negro leagues **Fic**
Myers, W. D. The journal of Joshua Loper **Fic**
Myers, W. D. The journal of Scott Pendleton Collins **Fic**
Philbrick, W. R. The journal of Douglas Allen Deeds **Fic**

My not-so-terrible time at Hippie Hotel. Graham, R. **Fic**

My own two feet. Cleary, B. **92**

My own worst enemy. Sonenklar, C. **Fic**

My people. Haddix, M. P.
In Destination unexpected: short stories **S C**

My perfect life. Sheldon, D. **Fic**

My season with penguins. Webb, S. **598**

My self myself. Saldaña, R.
In Saldaña, R. Finding our way: stories p60-66 **S C**

My sweet sixteenth. Wilkinson, B. S.
In Join in; multiethnic short stories by outstanding writers for young adults p128-40 **S C**

Myanmar
Yin, S. M. Myanmar (5 and up) **959.1**
Politics and government
Stewart, W. Aung San Suu Kyi (7 and up) **92**

Mycology *See* Fungi

Myers, Anna
The keeping room **Fic**
Tulsa burning (7 and up) **Fic**

Myers, Chris
(ed) The Dictionary of the environment and its biomes. See The Dictionary of the environment and its biomes **577**

Myers, Christopher
(il) Myers, W. D. Harlem **811**

Myers, Edward
When will I stop hurting? (7 and up) **155.9**

Myers, Jack
On the trail of the Komodo dragon and other explorations of science in action **590**

Myers, Steve
(jt. auth) Sanders, P. Anorexia and bulimia **616.85**
(jt. auth) Sanders, P. Divorce and separation **306.89**

Myers, Walter Dean, 1937-
145th Street **S C**
Contents: Big Joe's funeral; The baddest dog in Harlem; Fighter; Angela's eyes; The streak; Monkeyman; Kitty and Mack: a love story; A Christmas story; A story in three parts; Block party—145th Street style
Amistad: a long road to freedom (5 and up) **326**
Antarctica **998**
At her majesty's request [biography of Sarah Forbes Bonetta] (5 and up) **92**
Bad boy (7 and up) **92**
The Beast (7 and up) **Fic**
The beast is in the labyrinth
In Places I never meant to be; original stories by censored writers **S C**
Fallen angels **Fic**
The greatest: Muhammad Ali (7 and up) **92**
Harlem **811**
Here in Harlem (7 and up) **811**
Hoops **Fic**
Jeremiah's song
In Visions: nineteen short stories by outstanding writers for young adults p194-203 **S C**
The journal of Biddy Owens, the Negro leagues **Fic**
The journal of Joshua Loper (5 and up) **Fic**
The journal of Scott Pendleton Collins (5 and up) **Fic**
Me, Mop, and the Moondance Kid (4-6) **Fic**
Monster (7 and up) **Fic**
The Mouse rap (6 and up) **Fic**
Now is your time! (6 and up) **305.8**
One more river to cross (7 and up) **779**
Scorpions (6 and up) **Fic**
Season's end
In The Color of absence; 12 stories about loss and hope p169-82 **S C**
Slam! (7 and up) **Fic**
Somewhere in the darkness (7 and up) **Fic**
A time to love (7 and up) **S C**
Contents: Samson and Delilah; Reuben and Joseph; Ruth and Naomi; Abraham and Isaac; Zillah and Lot; Aser and Gamiel
USS Constellation **359.8**

Myers, Walter Dean, 1937-—*Continued*
Visit
In Necessary noise: stories about our families
as they really are p81-93   **S C**
(jt. auth) Lawrence, J. The great migration
   759.13

Myracle, Lauren, 1969-
Eleven (4 and up)   **Fic**

Mysteries in our National Parks [series]
Skurzynski, G. Cliff hanger   **Fic**

The **mysterious** disappearance of Roanoke Colony
in American history. Kent, Z.   **975.6/175**

The **mysterious** matter of I.M. Fine. Stanley, D.
   Fic

Mystery and detective stories *See* Mystery fiction

Mystery fiction
Abrahams, P. Down the rabbit hole (7 and up)
   Fic
Avi. The man who was Poe   **Fic**
Avi. Wolf rider   **Fic**
Bellairs, J. The curse of the blue figurine (5 and
up)   **Fic**
Bennett, J. Coverup (7 and up)   **Fic**
Bennett, J. Sing me a death song (7 and up)
   Fic
Byars, B. C. The dark stairs [and other titles in
series] (4 and up)   **Fic**
Cheaney, J. B. The playmaker   **Fic**
Cheaney, J. B. The true Prince   **Fic**
Christie, A. The mirror crack'd (7 and up)
   Fic
Cross, G. Tightrope (7 and up)   **Fic**
Doyle, Sir A. C. The complete Sherlock Holmes
(7 and up)   **S C**
Draanen, W. v. Sammy Keyes and the hotel
thief (4 and up)   **Fic**
Duncan, L. Don't look behind you   **Fic**
Duncan, L. I know what you did last summer
   Fic
Duncan, L. Locked in time (7 and up)   **Fic**
Guy, R. The disappearance   **Fic**
Hamilton, V. The house of Dies Drear (5 and
up)   **Fic**
Hoeye, M. Time stops for no mouse (5 and up)
   Fic
Hoobler, D. The ghost in the Tokaido Inn
   Fic
Horowitz, A. Public enemy number two   **Fic**
Ibbotson, E. The star of Kazan (5 and up)
   Fic
Klause, A. C. Alien secrets (5 and up)   **Fic**
Konigsburg, E. L. Silent to the bone (7 and up)
   Fic
Larson, J. C. Bringing mysteries alive for chil-
dren and young adults   **028.5**
Lawrence, C. The thieves of Ostia   **Fic**
Levin, B. Shadow-catcher (5 and up)   **Fic**
Littke, L. Lake of secrets (7 and up)   **Fic**
McNamee, G. Acceleration   **Fic**
Newman, R. The case of the Baker Street Irreg-
ular (5 and up)   **Fic**
Nickerson, S. How to disappear completely and
never be found   **Fic**
Nixon, J. L. Murdered, my sweet (7 and up)
   Fic

Nixon, J. L. Nightmare   **Fic**
Nixon, J. L. Who are you? (7 and up)   **Fic**
Poe, E. A. The pit and the pendulum and other
stories (7 and up)   **S C**
Pullman, P. The ruby in the smoke   **Fic**
Raskin, E. The Westing game   **Fic**
Reiss, K. PaperQuake   **Fic**
Roberts, W. D. Twisted summer   **Fic**
Skurzynski, G. Cliff hanger   **Fic**
Stanley, D. The mysterious matter of I.M. Fine
   Fic
Vande Velde, V. Never trust a dead man
   Fic
Werlin, N. Black mirror (7 and up)   **Fic**
Westerfeld, S. So yesterday (7 and up)   **Fic**
Wynne-Jones, T. The boy in the burning house
   Fic
Yep, L. The case of the Goblin Pearls   **Fic**

Mystery library [series]
Kallen, S. A. Shamans   **201**
Nardo, D. Atlantis   **001.9**

The **mystery** of gravity. Parker, B. R.   **531**

The **mystery** of the hieroglyphs. Donoughue, C.
   493

The **mystery** of the mammoth bones. Giblin, J.
   569

Mythical animals
   See also Dragons; Mermaids and mermen
Buller, L. Myths and monsters (5 and up)
   398

Mythology
   See also Gods and goddesses; Mythical ani-
mals mythology of particular national or eth-
nic groups or of particular geographic areas
Bulfinch, T. Bulfinch's mythology   **201**
Glick, S. War and peace   **201**
Hamilton, V. In the beginning; creation stories
from around the world (5 and up)   **201**
Hearne, B. G. Beauties and beasts   **398.2**
Keenan, S. Gods, goddesses, and monsters
   201
Mass, W. Gods and goddesses   **201**
Philip, N. The illustrated book of myths (5 and
up)   **201**
Philip, N. Mythology   **201**
Philip, N. Myths & legends (7 and up)
   398.2
World mythology   **201**
Zeitlin, S. J. The four corners of the sky (5 and
up)   **201**
Bibliography
Helbig, A. Myths and hero tales   **398.2**
Dictionaries
Myths and legends   **398**
Wilkinson, P. Illustrated dictionary of mytholo-
gy   **201**

Mythology, Classical *See* Classical mythology

Mythology, Norse *See* Norse mythology

Mythology. Hamilton, E.   **292**

Mythology A to Z [series]
Lynch, P. A. African mythology A to Z
   299.6
Matson, G. Celtic mythology A to Z   **299**
Roberts, J. Chinese mythology A to Z   **299.5**

The **mythology** of Mexico and Central America. Bierhorst, J.   **299.7**

The **mythology** of North America. Bierhorst, J.   **299.7**

The **mythology** of South America. Bierhorst, J.   **299.8**

Myths & legends. Philip, N.   **398.2**

Myths and hero tales. Helbig, A.   **398.2**

Myths and legends   **398**

Myths and monsters. Buller, L.   **398**

Myths, legends, and folktales of America   **398.2**

N

Na, An, 1972-
  A step from heaven (7 and up)   **Fic**

Nabwire, Constance R.
  Cooking the East African way
    In Easy menu ethnic cookbooks   **641.5**
  Cooking the West African way
    In Easy menu ethnic cookbooks   **641.5**

Nacho loco. Soto, G.
  In Soto, G. Local news p91-101   **S C**

Nacion, Rachel
  (jt. auth) Harris, J. S. Shades of blue, Volume 1   **741.5**

Naden, Corinne J.
  Dred Scott (7 and up)   **342**
  John Muir   **92**
  (jt. auth) Blue, R. Staying out of trouble in a troubled family   **362.7**
  (jt. auth) Gillespie, J. T. The Newbery companion   **028.5**

Nagasaki (Japan)
      Bombardment, 1945
  The Atom bomb   **355.8**
  Grant, R. G. Hiroshima and Nagasaki (7 and up)   **940.54**

Nagel, Rob
  Body by design   **612**
  (ed) U.X.L encyclopedia of science. See U.X.L encyclopedia of science   **503**

Nahum, Andrew
  Flying machine (4 and up)   **629.133**

Naidoo, Beverley
  Journey to Jo'burg (5 and up)   **Fic**
  No turning back (5 and up)   **Fic**
  The other side of truth (5 and up)   **Fic**
  Out of bounds: seven stories of conflict and hope (5 and up)   **S C**
    Contents: The dare; The noose; One day, Lily, one day; The typewriter; The gun; The playground; Out of bounds

Naifeh, Ted
  Courtney Crumrin and the night things   **741.5**

Nailed. Wallace, R.
  In Wallace, R. Losing is not an option: stories   **S C**

Nailling, Lee, 1917-
      About
  Warren, A. Orphan train rider (4 and up)   **362.7**

Nair, Charissa M.
  (jt. auth) Seah, A. Vietnam   **959.704**

Nakahama, Manjirō, 1827-1898
      About
  Blumberg, R. Shipwrecked!: the true adventures of a Japanese boy [biography of Manjiro Nakahama] (5 and up)   **92**

Nameless creek. Hearne, B. G.
  In Hearne, B. G. The canine connection: stories about dogs and people p77-82   **S C**

Namioka, Lensey
  The all-American slurp
    In Visions: nineteen short stories by outstanding writers for young adults p32-41   **S C**
  Fox hunt
    In Join in; multiethnic short stories by outstanding writers for young adults p13-21   **S C**
  An ocean apart, a world away   **Fic**
  Ties that bind, ties that break (5 and up)   **Fic**
  Who's Hu? [excerpt]
    In American dragons: twenty-five Asian American voices p48-64   **810.8**

Nanji, Azim
  (ed) The Muslim almanac. See The Muslim almanac   **297**

Nanye'hi *See* Ward, Nancy, 1738?-1822

Napoleon I, Emperor of the French, 1769-1821
      About
  Blumberg, R. What's the deal? Jefferson, Napoleon and the Louisiana Purchase (7 and up)   **973.4**
  Napoleon Bonaparte [essays about]   **92**

Napoleon Bonaparte [essays about]   **92**

Napoli, Donna Jo, 1948-
  Beast (7 and up)   **Fic**
  Bound   **Fic**
  The great god Pan (7 and up)   **Fic**
  Song of the Magdalene (7 and up)   **Fic**
  Spinners (7 and up)   **Fic**
  Stones in water (5 and up)   **Fic**
  Three days   **Fic**
  Zel (7 and up)   **Fic**

Narcotics
    See also Marijuana

Nardo, Don, 1947-
  Adolf Hitler   **92**
  Ancient Alexandria (7 and up)   **932**
  Ancient Athens (7 and up)   **938**
  Ancient Egypt (7 and up)   **932**
  Ancient Greece (7 and up)   **938**
  The ancient Greeks (7 and up)   **938**
  The ancient Romans (7 and up)   **937**
  Ancient Rome [Daily life series]   **937**
  [History of weapons and warfare series] (7 and up)   **937**
  Arts, leisure, and entertainment   **937**
  Atlantis   **001.9**
  The Civil War (7 and up)   **973.7**

Nardo, Don, 1947-—*Continued*
Cloning [Great medical discoveries series] (7 and up)
660.6
[Science on the edge series] (5 and up)
660.6
The fall of the Roman Empire (7 and up)
937
From founding to fall: a history of Rome
937
Great Elizabethan playwrights **920**
King Arthur **942.01**
The medieval castle (7 and up) **940.1**
The Mexican-American War **973.6**
The Middle Ages (7 and up) **940.1**
The Native Americans (7 and up) **970.004**
The Roman army **937**
Understanding Frankenstein (7 and up)
823.009
Vaccines (7 and up) **615**
Weapons of war **973.3**
Women of ancient Rome (7 and up) **937**
Words of the ancient Romans **937**
(ed) Cleopatra. See Cleopatra [biographical essays] **92**
(ed) The French Revolution. See The French Revolution **944.04**
(ed) The Great Depression. See The Great Depression **973.91**
(ed) Greek and Roman mythology. See Greek and Roman mythology **292**
(ed) Julius Caesar. See Julius Caesar [essays about] **92**
(ed) The Rise of Christianity. See The Rise of Christianity **270**
(ed) The Rise of Nazi Germany. See The Rise of Nazi Germany **943.086**
(ed) The Black Death. See The Black Death [Turning points in world history series]
614.5

Narrations *See* Monologues

Narrow escape. San Souci, R.
In San Souci, R. A terrifying taste of short & shivery; thirty creepy tales p130-36
398.2

Naruse, Kaori
Prétear, Volume 1 **741.5**

NASA *See* United States. National Aeronautics and Space Administration

NASCAR. Owens, T. **796.72**

Nash, Gary B.
Landmarks of the American Revolution
973.3

Nathan, Amy
Count on us **355**
Yankee doodle gals **940.54**

Nation, Carry Amelia Moore, 1846-1911
About
Harvey, B. C. Carry A. Nation: saloon smasher and prohibitionist **92**

A **Nation** challenged (4 and up) **973.931**

Nation of Islam *See* Black Muslims

A **nation** torn. Ray, D. **973.7**

National Aeronautics and Space Administration (U.S.) *See* United States. National Aeronautics and Space Administration

National Audubon Society
Bull, J. L. The National Audubon Society field guide to North American birds, Eastern region
598
Chartrand, M. R. The Audubon Society field guide to the night sky **523**
Chesterman, C. W. The Audubon Society field guide to North American rocks and minerals
549
Lincoff, G. The Audubon Society field guide to North American mushrooms **579.6**
Milne, L. J. The Audubon Society field guide to North American insects and spiders **595.7**
Pyle, R. M. The Audubon Society field guide to North American butterflies **595.7**
Rehder, H. A. The Audubon Society field guide to North American seashells **594**
Udvardy, M. D. F. National Audubon Society field guide to North American birds, Western region **598**
Whitaker, J. O., Jr. National Audubon Society field guide to North American mammals
599

The **National** Audubon Society field guide to North American birds, Eastern region. Bull, J. L. **598**

National Audubon Society field guide to North American birds, Western region. Udvardy, M. D. F. **598**

National Audubon Society field guide to North American mammals. Whitaker, J. O., Jr.
599

National Audubon Society field guide to North American wildflowers. eastern region. Thieret, J. W. **582.13**

National Audubon Society field guide to North American wildflowers, western region. Spellenberg, R. **582.13**

National Audubon Society first field guide: birds (4 and up) **598**

National Audubon Society first field guide: insects. Wilsdon, C. **595.7**

National Audubon Society first field guide: night sky. Mechler, G. **520**

National Audubon Society first field guide: weather. Kahl, J. D. **551.5**

National Council for the Social Studies
Notable social studies trade books for young people. See Notable social studies trade books for young people **016.3**

National Council of Teachers of English
A Jar of tiny stars: poems by NCTE award-winning poets. See A Jar of tiny stars: poems by NCTE award-winning poets **811.008**

National Council of Teachers of English. Committee on the Junior High and Middle School Booklist
Your reading. See Your reading **011.6**

National emblems
Bateman, T. Red, white, blue, and Uncle who? (4 and up) **929.9**

National Gallery (Great Britain)
 Richardson, J. Looking at pictures (5 and up)
750

National Geographic dinosaurs. Barrett, P. M.
567.9

National Geographic photography guide for kids.
 Johnson, N. **771**

National Geographic prehistoric mammals. Turner,
 A. **569**

National Geographic Society (U.S.)
 Allen, T. B. Remember Pearl Harbor **940.54**
 Barrett, P. M. National Geographic dinosaurs
567.9
 Bausum, A. Dragon bones and dinosaur eggs: a
 photobiography of Roy Chapman Andrews
92
 Blumberg, R. What's the deal? Jefferson, Napo-
 leon and the Louisiana Purchase **973.4**
 Johnson, N. National Geographic photography
 guide for kids **771**
 Longfellow, H. W. Hiawatha and Megissogwon
811
 Macy, S. Bulls-eye: a photobiography of Annie
 Oakley **92**
 Matthews, T. L. Always inventing: a
 photobiography of Alexander Graham Bell
92
 Pollack, P. Ski **796.93**
 Sloan, C. Bury the dead **393**
 Sloan, C. The human story **599.93**
 Sloan, C. Supercroc and the origin of crocodiles
567.9
 Voices: poetry and art from around the world.
 See Voices: poetry and art from around the
 world **808.81**

National Geographic Society atlas of the world.
 See Atlas of the world **912**

National Institutes of Health (U.S.)
 Mintzer, R. The National Institutes of Health
362.1

National monuments
 Bateman, T. Red, white, blue, and Uncle who?
 (4 and up) **929.9**
 Monuments and historic places of America
973

National Museum of American Art (U.S.)
 Celebrate America in poetry and art. See Celebrate America in poetry and art **811.008**

National parks and reserves
 See also National monuments

National Science Teachers Association
 Outstanding science trade books for students K-
 12. See Outstanding science trade books for
 students K-12 **016.5**

National security
 Campbell, G. A. A vulnerable America (7 and
 up) **363.3**
 United States
 See/See also pages in the following book(s):
 Weapons of mass destruction: opposing view-
 points **358**

National socialism
 Altman, L. J. Hitler's rise to power and the
 Holocaust **943.086**

Bartoletti, S. C. Hitler Youth (7 and up)
943.086
 Cartlidge, C. Life of a Nazi soldier (7 and up)
940.54
 Damon, D. Mein Kampf (7 and up) **943.086**
 Giblin, J. The life and death of Adolf Hitler (7
 and up) **92**
 Gottfried, T. Nazi Germany (7 and up)
940.53
 Living in Nazi Germany (7 and up) **943.086**
 Nardo, D. Adolf Hitler **92**
 The Rise of Nazi Germany (7 and up)
943.086
 Fiction
 Chotjewitz, D. Daniel half human (7 and up)
Fic

National Transportation Safety Board (U.S.) *See*
 United States. National Transportation Safety
 Board

The **National** Transportation Safety Board.
 Mintzer, R. **363.1**

Nationalism
 Tames, R. Nationalism (7 and up) **320.5**

Nations in transition [series]
 Kort, M. Russia **947**
 Otfinoski, S. Afghanistan **958.1**
 Otfinoski, S. Ukraine **947.7**

Native American chiefs and warriors. Kallen, S.
 A. **920**

Native American literature. Gleason, K. **897**

Native American religion. Martin, J. **299.7**

Native American religions. Hartz, P. **299.7**

Native American talking signs. Kelly, M. **419**

Native American women
 Sonneborn, L. A to Z of Native American wom-
 en **920.003**

Native Americans
 See also Taino Indians names of Native
 American peoples and linguistic families
 Bial, R. Lifeways [series] **970.004**
 Bruchac, J. Lasting echoes (7 and up)
970.004
 Collier, C. Clash of cultures, prehistory-1638
970.004
 Hirschfelder, A. B. Native American (7 and up)
970.004
 Indians of North America series [Chelsea
 House] **970.004**
 Katz, W. L. Black Indians **305.8**
 Lassieur, A. Before the storm (7 and up)
970.004
 Murdoch, D. H. North American Indian (4 and
 up) **970.004**
 The Native North American almanac
970.004
 North American Indians today [series]
970.004
 Weber, E. N. R. Rattlesnake Mesa (4 and up)
92
 Woods, G. Science of the early Americas (4 and
 up) **509**
 See/See also pages in the following book(s):
 Peoples of the Americas **970**

Native Americans—*Continued*
Antiquities
Arnold, C. Stories in stone (4 and up)
709.01
Wood, M. Ancient America (5 and up)
970.01
Biography
Avery, S. Extraordinary American Indians
920
Freedman, R. Indian chiefs (6 and up) **920**
Kallen, S. A. Native American chiefs and warriors (7 and up) **920**
Dictionaries
Wolfson, E. From Abenaki to Zuni (4 and up)
970.004
Education
Cooper, M. L. Indian school **970.004**
Encyclopedias
The Encyclopedia of North American Indians [Marshall Cavendish] **970.004**
The Gale encyclopedia of Native American tribes **970.004**
Pritzker, B. Native Americans **970.004**
U·X·L encyclopedia of Native American tribes
970.004
Waldman, C. Encyclopedia of Native American tribes **970.004**
Fiction
Abelove, J. Go and come back (7 and up)
Fic
Alder, E. Crossing the panther's path **Fic**
Bruchac, J. The heart of a chief **Fic**
Bruchac, J. Hidden roots **Fic**
Bruchac, J. Sacajawea (6 and up) **Fic**
Craven, M. I heard the owl call my name (7 and up) **Fic**
Dorris, M. Sees Behind Trees (4 and up)
Fic
Holman, F. Real **Fic**
Hotze, S. A circle unbroken **Fic**
Keehn, S. M. I am Regina **Fic**
Lisle, J. T. The crying rocks **Fic**
O'Dell, S. Island of the Blue Dolphins (5 and up) **Fic**
O'Dell, S. Streams to the river, river to the sea (5 and up) **Fic**
O'Dell, S. Zia (5 and up) **Fic**
Olsen, S. The girl with a baby (7 and up)
Fic
Olsen, S. White girl (7 and up) **Fic**
Smith, C. L. Rain is not my Indian name
Fic
Smith, P. C. Weetamoo, heart of the Pocassets
Fic
Speare, E. G. The sign of the beaver (5 and up)
Fic
Talking leaves **S C**
Folklore
American Indian myths and legends **398.2**
Brown, D. A. Dee Brown's folktales of the Native American **398.2**
Bruchac, J. When the Chenoo howls (4-6)
398.2
Curry, J. L. Hold up the sky: and other Native American tales from Texas and the Southern Plains (4 and up) **398.2**
Delacre, L. Golden tales (5 and up) **398.2**

Games
Anderson, M. K. North American Indian games
970.004
Government relations
Sherrow, V. Cherokee Nation v. Georgia (7 and up) **346**
History
Native Americans: opposing viewpoints (7 and up) **970.004**
Student almanac of Native American history
970.004
Origin
Lauber, P. Who came first (5 and up)
970.01
Poetry
Dancing teepees: poems of American Indian youth (4 and up) **897**
Longfellow, H. W. Hiawatha and Megissogwon
811
When the rain sings **811.008**
Religion
American Indian myths and legends **398.2**
Bierhorst, J. The mythology of North America (7 and up) **299.7**
Hartz, P. Native American religions **299.7**
Martin, J. Native American religion (7 and up)
299.7
Rites and ceremonies
Hartz, P. Native American religions **299.7**
Sign language
Kelly, M. Native American talking signs
419
Social life and customs
Kelly, M. Native American talking signs
419
Wars
See also United States—History—1755-1763, French and Indian War
Brown, D. A. Bury my heart at Wounded Knee
970.004
Custer, E. B. The diary of Elizabeth Bacon Custer (5 and up) **973.8**
Dolan, E. F. The American Indian wars
970.004
Ehrlich, A. Wounded Knee: an Indian history of the American West (6 and up) **970.004**
Marker, S. Plains Indian wars (7 and up)
973.5
Nardo, D. The Native Americans (7 and up)
970.004
Central America—Religion
Bierhorst, J. The mythology of Mexico and Central America (7 and up) **299.7**
Great Plains
Collier, C. Indians, cowboys, and farmers and the battle for the Great Plains, 1865-1910
978
Marker, S. Plains Indian wars (7 and up)
973.5
Terry, M. B. H. Daily life in a Plains Indian village, 1868 (4 and up) **970.004**
Mexico
See also Aztecs
Mexico—Religion
Bierhorst, J. The mythology of Mexico and Central America (7 and up) **299.7**

Native Americans—*Continued*
South America
See also Incas
South America—Religion
Bierhorst, J. The mythology of South America (7 and up) **299.8**
West (U.S.)
Brown, D. A. Bury my heart at Wounded Knee **970.004**
Ehrlich, A. Wounded Knee: an Indian history of the American West (6 and up) **970.004**
West Indies
See also Taino Indians
Native Americans. Pritzker, B. **970.004**
Native Americans in literature
Gleason, K. Native American literature **897**
Native Americans: opposing viewpoints (7 and up) **970.004**
The **Native** North American almanac **970.004**
Native son: the story of Richard Wright. Hart, J. **92**

Natural childbirth
See also Midwives
Natural disasters
See also Environmental degradation
Barnard, B. Dangerous planet **363.34**
Day, T. DK guide to savage Earth **550**
Engelbert, P. Dangerous planet **363.34**
Natural disasters [series]
Allen, J. Tornadoes **551.55**
Natural enemies. Yep, L.
In Yep, L. The rainbow people p12-18 **398.2**

Natural foods
Dunn-Georgiou, E. Everything you need to know about organic foods (7 and up) **641.3**
Natural history
Burnie, D. The Kingfisher illustrated nature encyclopedia (5 and up) **508**
Matsen, B. Go wild in New York City (4 and up) **974.7**
Quinlan, S. E. The case of the monkeys that fell from the trees **577.3**
Encyclopedias
DK nature encyclopedia **508**
Maine
Goodman, S. Ultimate field trip 3 **577.6**
Natural History Museum (London, England)
Symes, R. F. Eyewitness rocks & minerals **549**
A **natural** man. Soto, G. **811**
Natural resources
See also Energy resources
Management
Gallant, R. A. Resources **333.7**
Global resources: opposing viewpoints **333.71**
Natural selection
See also Evolution
Natural writer: a story about Marjorie Kinnan Rawlings. Cook, J. **92**

Naturalists
Anderson, M. J. Carl Linnaeus **92**
Bausum, A. Dragon bones and dinosaur eggs: a photobiography of Roy Chapman Andrews (5 and up) **92**
George, J. C. A tarantula in my purse (4-6) **92**
Marrin, A. Secrets from the rocks: dinosaur hunting with Roy Chapman Andrews (4 and up) **92**
Naden, C. J. John Muir **92**
Patent, D. H. Charles Darwin (7 and up) **92**
Stefoff, R. Charles Darwin and the evolution revolution (7 and up) **92**
Thoreau, H. D. New suns will arise **92**
Wadsworth, G. John Burroughs (5 and up) **92**
Warrick, K. C. John Muir: crusader for the wilderness **92**
Fiction
George, J. C. Charlie's raven (5 and up) **Fic**
Naturalist's apprentice [series]
Ross, M. E. Fish watching with Eugenie Clark **92**
Nature
Burnie, D. The Kingfisher illustrated nature encyclopedia (5 and up) **508**
Fiction
Ehrlich, G. A blizzard year **Fic**
Poetry
Levy, C. A crack in the clouds and other poems (3-5) **811**
Nature, Effect of man on *See* Human influence on nature
Nature close-up [series]
Pascoe, E. Ants **595.7**
Pascoe, E. Beetles **595.7**
Pascoe, E. Crickets and grasshoppers **595.7**
Pascoe, E. Earthworms **592**
Pascoe, E. Flies **595.7**
Pascoe, E. Seeds and seedlings **582**
Pascoe, E. Slime, molds, and fungi **579.5**
Pascoe, E. Snails and slugs **594**
Pascoe, E. Tadpoles **597.8**
Nature conservation
See also Wildlife conservation
Collard, S. B., III. The prairie builders (4 and up) **635.9**
Naden, C. J. John Muir **92**
Patent, D. H. Biodiversity (5 and up) **333.95**
Warrick, K. C. John Muir: crusader for the wilderness **92**
Nature craft
Martin, L. C. Nature's art box (4 and up) **745.5**
Nature photography
See also Photography of animals
Nature poetry
Harrison, D. L. Wild country **811**
Singer, M. Footprints on the roof (4 and up) **811**
Yolen, J. Color me a rhyme (4 and up) **811**

Nature study
  Andryszewski, T. Step by step along the Appalachian Trail **796.51**
Nature watch series
  Bailey, J. Birds of prey **598**
Nature's art box. Martin, L. C. **745.5**
Naughton, Jim, 1957-
  Joyriding
    In Ultimate sports; short stories by outstanding writers for young adults p4-19
      S C
Nava. Potok, C.
  In Potok, C. Zebra and other stories p70-96
      S C
Navaho Indians *See* Navajo Indians
Navajo. McIntosh, K. North American Indians today [series]
Navajo code talkers. Aaseng, N. **940.54**
Navajo Indians
  Aaseng, N. Navajo code talkers **940.54**
  Durrett, D. Unsung heroes of World War II (7 and up) **940.54**
  McIntosh, K. Navajo North American Indians today [series]
See/See also pages in the following book(s):
  Ehrlich, A. Wounded Knee: an Indian history of the American West (6 and up) **970.004**
      Fiction
  Bruchac, J. Code talker **Fic**
  Hobbs, W. The Big Wander (7 and up) **Fic**
  O'Dell, S. Sing down the moon (5 and up) **Fic**
  Thurlo, A. The spirit line **Fic**
Naval art and science
  Gravett, C. Going to war in Viking times **355**
Naval history
  See also Military history
The **naval** treaty. Doyle, Sir A. C.
  In Doyle, Sir A. C. The complete Sherlock Holmes **S C**
Naylor, Phyllis Reynolds, 1933-
  The fear place (5 and up) **Fic**
  Ice **Fic**
  Jade Green (7 and up) **Fic**
  Reluctantly Alice **Fic**
  Sang Spell (7 and up) **Fic**
  Shiloh (4-6) **Fic**
      About
  Stover, L. T. Presenting Phyllis Reynolds Naylor **813.009**
See/See also pages in the following book(s):
  The Newbery & Caldecott medal books, 1986-2000 **028.5**
Nazi Germany. Gottfried, T. **940.53**
Nazism *See* National socialism
NCTE bibliography series
  Your reading **011.6**
Neal-Schuman authoritative guide to kids' search engines, subject directories, and portals. Haycock, K. **025.04**
Neal-Schuman complete Internet companion for librarians. Benson, A. C. **004.6**

Neal-Schuman guide to celebrations & holidays around the world. Matthew, K. I. **394.26**
Neal-Schuman net-guide series
  Benson, A. C. Neal-Schuman complete Internet companion for librarians **004.6**
  Kuntz, J. The KidsClick! Web searching skills guide with CD-ROM **025.04**
  Managing the Internet controversy **025.04**
  Stephens, M. T. The library Internet trainer's toolkit **025.04**
Neale S. Godfrey's ultimate kids' money book. Godfrey, N. S. **332.024**
Near-death experiences
      Fiction
  Littke, L. Haunted sister (7 and up) **Fic**
Near East *See* Middle East
Nebraska
  Bjorklund, R. Nebraska
    In Celebrate the states **973**
  McNair, S. Nebraska
    In America the beautiful, second series **973**
      Fiction
  Conrad, P. My Daniel (5 and up) **Fic**
  Conrad, P. Prairie songs (5 and up) **Fic**
  LaFaye, A. Worth (5 and up) **Fic**
  Murphy, J. My face to the wind **Fic**
  Ruckman, I. Night of the twisters (4 and up) **Fic**
Necessary noise. Donoghue, E.
  In Necessary noise: stories about our families as they really are p51-67 **S C**
Necessary noise: stories about our families as they really are (7 and up) **S C**
Necessary roughness. Lee, M. G. **Fic**
The **need** for oil. Gunderson, C. G. **338.2**
Need to know library [series]
  Beal, E. Everything you need to know about ADD\ADHD **616.85**
  Bridgers, J. Everything you need to know about having an addictive personality **616.86**
  Diamond, S. N. Everything you need to know about going to the gynecologist **618.1**
  Dunn-Georgiou, E. Everything you need to know about organic foods **641.3**
  Edgar, K. J. Everything you need to know about media violence **303.6**
  Kaminker, L. Everything you need to know about being adopted **362.7**
  Kreiner, A. Everything you need to know about creating your own support system **158**
  Ng, G. Everything you need to know about self-mutilation **616.85**
  Rue, N. N. Everything you need to know about abusive relationships **362.7**
  Schleifer, J. Everything you need to know when someone you know has been killed **155.9**
  Smart, P. Everything you need to know about mononucleosis **616.9**
  Wiloch, T. Everything you need to know about protecting yourself and others from abduction **613.6**
Needham, Bobbe
  Ecology crafts for kids **745.5**

Neft, David S.
The sports encyclopedia: baseball **796.357**
The **Negro** almanac. See The African American almanac **305.8**
Neighborhood odes. Soto, G. **811**
Neimark, Anne E., 1935-
There ain't nobody that can sing like me: the life of Woody Guthrie (5 and up) **92**
Nelly's hospital. Alcott, L. M.
In The Boy of Chancellorville and other Civil War stories p55-73 **S C**
Nelson, Annika
(il) Soto, G. Canto familiar **811**
Nelson, Blake, 1960-
New rules of high school (7 and up) **Fic**
Nelson, Gaylord
See/See also pages in the following book(s):
Byrnes, P. Environmental pioneers (7 and up) **920**
Nelson, Kadir
(il) Packer, T. Othello **822.3**
Nelson, Lisa W.
(jt. auth) Agenbroad, L. D. Mammoths **569**
Nelson, Lyle Emerson, 1924-
American presidents **920.003**
Nelson, Marilyn, 1946-
Carver, a life in poems (7 and up) **811**
Fortune's bones **811**
Nelson, Michael, 1949-
(ed) The Presidency A to Z. See The Presidency A to Z **352.23**
Nelson, Pete
Left for dead (7 and up) **940.54**
Nelson, Theresa, 1948-
Ruby electric (5 and up) **Fic**
Neolithic period See Stone Age
Nepal
Burbank, J. Nepal (5 and up) **954.96**
Neptune (Planet)
Stefoff, R. Neptune **523.4**
Tabak, J. A look at Neptune **523.4**
Neruda, Pablo, 1904-1973
About
Goodnough, D. Pablo Neruda **92**
Nervous system
Goldsmith, C. Neurological disorders **616.8**
Parker, S. Brain, nerves, and senses **612.8**
Simon, S. The brain (4 and up) **612.8**
Viegas, J. The revolution in healing the brain **612.8**
Diseases
See also Epilepsy; Huntington's chorea; Meningitis; Multiple sclerosis; Tourette syndrome
Nesbit, E. (Edith), 1858-1924
The best of Shakespeare (4 and up) **822.3**
The deliverers of their country
In The Book of dragons p50-66 **S C**
The dragon tamers
In The Book of dragons p128-46 **S C**
The last of the dragons
In Fire and wings: dragon tales from East and West p124-36 **S C**

Nesbit, Edith *See* Nesbit, E. (Edith), 1858-1924
Nesoowa and the Chenoo. Tchana, K. H.
In Tchana, K. H. The serpent slayer: and other stories of strong women p13-18 **398.2**
Nethergrave. Skurzynski, G.
In On the edge: stories at the brink p23-39 **S C**
Netherlands
History—1940-1945, German occupation
Frank, A. The diary of a young girl (6 and up) **92**
Frank, A. The diary of a young girl: the definitive edition (6 and up) **92**
Müller, M. Anne Frank (7 and up) **92**
Reiss, J. The upstairs room (5 and up) **92**
Netscape Communications Corporation
Ehrenhaft, D. Marc Andreessen **92**
Netzley, Patricia D.
Alien abductions: opposing viewpoints (7 and up) **001.9**
Civil War **973.7**
The Greenhaven encyclopedia of ancient Egypt **932**
Issues in the environment (7 and up) **333.7**
Life during the Renaissance (7 and up) **940.2**
Neumann, John Von *See* Von Neumann, John, 1903-1957
Neurological disorders. Goldsmith, C. **616.8**
Neurology *See* Nervous system
Neuroses
See also Obsessive-compulsive disorder
Nevada
Stefoff, R. Nevada
In Celebrate the states **973**
Stein, R. C. Nevada
In America the beautiful, second series **973**
Never mind!. Avi **Fic**
Never quite a Hollywood star. Revard, C.
In Talking leaves; contemporary native American short stories **S C**
Never so green. Johnston, T. **Fic**
Never to forget: the Jews of the Holocaust. Meltzer, M. **940.53**
Never trust a dead man. Vande Velde, V. **Fic**
The **new** American Bible. **220.5**
New and selected poems. Soto, G. **811**
New astronomer. Stott, C. **520**
The **New** Cassell's German dictionary. See Cassell's German-English, English-German dictionary **433**
The **new** comprehensive American rhyming dictionary. Young, S. **423**
New dictionary of American slang. See Dictionary of American slang **427**
The **new** dictionary of cultural literacy. Hirsch, E. D. **031**
New directions for library service to young adults **027.62**

New England
History
Johnson, C. D. Daily life in colonial New England (7 and up) **974**

New found land. Wolf, A. **Fic**

The **new** girl. Stewart, S.
In A Glory of unicorns p185-94 **S C**

The **New** Grolier children's encyclopedia **031**

New Guinea
Fiction
Campbell, E. The Shark Callers (7 and up)
Fic

New Hampshire
Otfinoski, S. New Hampshire
In Celebrate the states **973**
Stein, R. C. New Hampshire
In America the beautiful, second series
973

New Jersey
Moragne, W. New Jersey
In Celebrate the states **973**
Stein, R. C. New Jersey
In America the beautiful, second series
973

Fiction
McDonald, J. Shades of Simon Gray (7 and up)
Fic
Ortiz Cofer, J. An island like you (7 and up)
S C

The **new** Jerusalem Bible. **220.5**

New Mexico
Fiction
Davies, J. Where the ground meets the sky
Fic

New Mexico
Kent, D. New Mexico
In America the beautiful, second series
973
McDaniel, M. New Mexico
In Celebrate the states **973**
Fiction
Anaya, R. A. My land sings **S C**
Kudlinski, K. V. The spirit catchers (7 and up)
Fic
Thurlo, A. The spirit line **Fic**

The **New** Oxford book of American verse (7 and up) **811.008**

New perspectives [series]
Grant, R. G. Hiroshima and Nagasaki
940.54

The **new** Prometheus. Shelley, M. W.
In Read into the millennium; tales of the future p34-40 **S C**

New rules of high school. Nelson, B. **Fic**

New skies: an anthology of today's science fiction
S C
Contents: They're made out of meat / Terry Bisson -- A walk in the sun / Geoffrey A. Landis -- Peaches for Mad Molly / Steven Gould -- Serpents' teeth / Spider Robinson -- Uncle Joshua and the Grooglemen / Debra Doyle and James D. Macdonald -- A letter from the Clearys / Connie Willis -- Brian and the aliens / Will Shetterly -- Different kinds of darkness / David Langford -- Will you be an astronaut? / Greg van Eekhout -- Cards of grief / Jane Yolen -- Tangents / Greg Bear -- The alien

mind / Philip K. Dick -- Out of all them bright stars / Nancy Kress -- The Lincoln train / Maureen F. McHugh -- Arthur Sternbach brings the curveball to Mars / Kim Stanley Robinson -- Salvage / Orson Scott Card -- The great goodbye / Robert Charles Wilson

New suns will arise. Thoreau, H. D. **92**

New tales for old. De Vos, G. **398.2**

New technologies for education. See Barron, A. E.
Technologies for education **371.3**

New Testament miracles. Connolly, S. **226**

New town. Siy, A.
In What a song can do; 12 riffs on the power of music **S C**

New virtual field trips. Cooper, G. **025.5**

The **new** way things work. Macaulay, D. **600**

The **new** world order. Jeapes, B. **Fic**

New Year's Day. Delacre, L.
In Delacre, L. Salsa stories p1-7 **S C**

New Year's Eve. Soto, G.
In Soto, G. Local news p132-44 **S C**

New York (N.Y.)
See also Lower East Side (New York, N.Y.)

Matsen, B. Go wild in New York City (4 and up) **974.7**
Schulman, A. Cop on the beat **363.2**
Antiquities
Hansen, J. Breaking ground, breaking silence
974.7
Fiction
Auch, M. J. Ashes of roses (7 and up) **Fic**
Avi. Never mind! (5 and up) **Fic**
Bartoletti, S. C. The journal of Finn Reardon (4 and up) **Fic**
Byalick, M. Quit it **Fic**
Cabot, M. The princess diaries **Fic**
Couloumbis, A. Say yes **Fic**
De Guzman, M. Beekman's big deal (5 and up)
Fic
Elish, D. Born too short (7 and up) **Fic**
Griffin, A. The other Shepards (6 and up)
Fic
Hamilton, V. Bluish **Fic**
Holman, F. Slake's limbo (6 and up) **Fic**
Karr, K. The boxer (7 and up) **Fic**
Larbalestier, J. Magic or madness (7 and up)
Fic
Lasky, K. Dreams in the golden country (4 and up) **Fic**
Levine, G. C. Dave at night (5 and up) **Fic**
Mack, T. Birdland (7 and up) **Fic**
Mackler, C. The earth, my butt, and other big, round things (7 and up) **Fic**
Merrill, J. The pushcart war (5 and up) **Fic**
Ortiz Cofer, J. Call me Maria **Fic**
Roberts, W. D. The kidnappers (4 and up)
Fic
Shusterman, N. Downsiders **Fic**
Strasser, T. Can't get there from here (7 and up)
Fic
Townley, R. Sky (7 and up) **Fic**
Wallace, B. B. Secret in St. Something **Fic**
Westerfeld, S. So yesterday (7 and up) **Fic**
Williams-Garcia, R. No laughter here (7 and up)
Fic
Woodson, J. Behind you (7 and up) **Fic**

New York (N.Y.)—Fiction—*Continued*
Woodson, J. If you come softly (7 and up)
    Fic
Woodson, J. Miracle's boys   **Fic**
    History
DuTemple, L. A. The New York subways (5
and up)   **388.4**
    Race relations
Bolden, T. Maritcha [biography of Maritcha
Rémond Lyons] (4 and up)   **92**
New York (State)
Heinrichs, A. New York
In America the beautiful, second series
    973
Schomp, V. New York
In Celebrate the states   **973**
    Fiction
Auch, M. J. Journey to nowhere   **Fic**
Bat-Ami, M. Two suns in the sky (7 and up)
    Fic
Bruchac, J. Hidden roots   **Fic**
O'Dell, S. Sarah Bishop (6 and up)   **Fic**
New York Public Library
Books for the teen age   **011.6**
The **New** York Public Library amazing African
American history. Patrick, D.   **305.8**
The **New** York Public Library amazing Hispanic
American history. Ochoa, G.   **305.8**
The **New** York Public Library amazing women in
American history. Heinemann, S.   **305.4**
**New York Public Library answer books for
kids series**
Heinemann, S. The New York Public Library
amazing women in American history
    305.4
Ochoa, G. The New York Public Library amaz-
ing Hispanic American history   **305.8**
Patrick, D. The New York Public Library amaz-
ing African American history   **305.8**
The **New** York Public Library incredible Earth.
Campbell, A.   **550**
The **New** York Public Library kid's guide to re-
search. Heiligman, D.   **025.5**
New York Stock Exchange, Inc.
Blumenthal, K. Six days in October (7 and up)
    332.6
The **New** York subways. DuTemple, L. A.
    388.4
The **New** York Times almanac   **031.02**
New York Times Company
Fireside, H. New York Times v. Sullivan (7 and
up)   **342**
New York Times Company v. United States
Gold, S. D. The Pentagon papers   **342**
Herda, D. J. New York Times v. United States
(7 and up)   **342**
New York Times v. Sullivan. Fireside, H.   **342**
New Zealand
Smelt, R. New Zealand (5 and up)   **993**
The **Newbery** & Caldecott medal books, 1986-
2000   **028.5**
Newbery and Caldecott Medal books, 1966-1975
    028.5

Newbery and Caldecott Medal books, 1976-1985
    028.5
The **Newbery** companion. Gillespie, J. T.
    028.5
Newbery Medal
Bostrom, K. L. Winning authors   **920**
Gillespie, J. T. The Newbery companion
    028.5
The Newbery & Caldecott medal books, 1986-
2000   **028.5**
Newbery and Caldecott Medal books, 1966-1975
    028.5
Newbery and Caldecott Medal books, 1976-1985
    028.5
Newbery Medal books, 1922-1955   **028.5**
Newbery Medal books, 1922-1955   **028.5**
Newbery Medal titles
Fleischman, S. The whipping boy   **Fic**
Kadohata, C. Kira-Kira   **Fic**
Lowry, L. The giver   **Fic**
McKinley, R. The hero and the crown   **Fic**
O'Brien, R. C. Mrs. Frisby and the rats of
NIMH   **Fic**
Paterson, K. Bridge to Terabithia   **Fic**
Peck, R. A year down yonder   **Fic**
Voigt, C. Dicey's song   **Fic**
Naylor, P. R. Shiloh (4-6)   **Fic**
Newbigging, Martha
(il) Shulman, M. Attack of the killer video book
    778.59
Newcomb, Rain
The Girls' World book of jewelry: 50 cool de-
signs to make (5 and up)   **745.594**
(jt. auth) Rhatigan, J. Out-of-this-world astrono-
my   **520**
The **Newest** Americans   **325.73**
Newfoundland
Mayell, M. Newfoundland
In Exploring Canada   **971**
Newman, Robert, 1909-1988
The case of the Baker Street Irregular (5 and
up)   **Fic**
Newman, Roger K.
(ed) The Constitution and its amendments. See
The Constitution and its amendments   **342**
Newquist, H. P. (Harvey P.)
The great brain book (5 and up)   **612.8**
News series
Johnstone, M. The history news in space
    629.4
Langley, A. The Roman news   **937**
Macdonald, F. The Stone Age news   **930.1**
Powell, A. The Greek news   **938**
Steedman, S. The Egyptian news   **932**
Steele, P. The Aztec news   **972**
Wright, R. The Viking news   **948**
Newsboys *See* Newspaper carriers
Newsmakers [series]
Turk, R. Ray Charles: soul man   **92**
Newspaper carriers
    Fiction
Bartoletti, S. C. The journal of Finn Reardon (4
and up)   **Fic**
Harlow, J. H. Joshua's song (4 and up)   **Fic**

Newspapers
See also Journalism; Periodicals
Graham, I. Books and newspapers   **686.2**
Newton, David E.
Chemical elements   **546**
Drug testing (7 and up)   **363.4**
Sick! diseases and disorders, injuries and infections. See Sick! diseases and disorders, injuries and infections   **616**
Newton, Sir Isaac, 1642-1727
About
Anderson, M. J. Isaac Newton (4 and up)
    92
Boerst, W. J. Isaac Newton (7 and up)   **92**
Christianson, G. E. Isaac Newton and the scientific revolution (7 and up)   **92**
White, M. Isaac Newton   **92**
Newton, John, 1725-1807
See/See also pages in the following book(s):
Cloud Tapper, S. Voices from slavery's past (7 and up)   **326**
Next month . . . Hollywood!. Okimoto, J. D.
In Join in; multiethnic short stories by outstanding writers for young adults p35-46
    S C
Next-of-kin. Olson, A. N.
In Olson, A. N. and Schwartz, H. Ask the bones: scary stories from around the world p17-23   **398.2**
Nez Percé Indians
Scott, R. A. Chief Joseph and the Nez Percés
    92
Taylor, M. W. Chief Joseph   **92**
See/See also pages in the following book(s):
Freedman, R. Indian chiefs (6 and up)   **920**
Fiction
O'Dell, S. Thunder rolling in the mountains (5 and up)   **Fic**
Ng, Fae Myenne, 1956-
Bone [excerpt]
In American eyes; new Asian-American short stories for young adults p108-30   **S C**
Ng, Gina
Everything you need to know about self-mutilation (7 and up)   **616.85**
Ng, Simon
(il) Yee, P. Tales from Gold Mountain   **S C**
Ng, Wendy L.
Japanese American internment during World War II   **940.53**
Ng, Yumi
(jt. auth) LoBaido, A. C. The Kurds of Asia
    950
NgCheong-Lum, Roseline, 1962-
Eritrea   **963.5**
Fiji (5 and up)   **996**
France (4 and up)   **944**
Tahiti (5 and up)   **996**
Ngô, Dinh Diêm, 1901-1963
See/See also pages in the following book(s):
Roberts, R. Leaders and generals   **920**
Nguyen, Chi Thien, 1933-
Cooking the Vietnamese way
In Easy menu ethnic cookbooks   **641.5**

Nguyen, Duy
Fantasy origami (7 and up)   **736**
Nguyen, Longhang
Rain music
In American dragons: twenty-five Asian American voices p155-60   **810.8**
Nguyen, Minh Duc
Fortune teller
In American eyes; new Asian-American short stories for young adults p80-107   **S C**
Nguyen Tat Thành *See* Ho, Chí Minh, 1890-1969
Niatum, Duane, 1938-
Crow's sun
In Talking leaves; contemporary native American short stories   **S C**
Nicholas II, Emperor of Russia, 1868-1918
Fiction
Whelan, G. Angel on the square   **Fic**
Nicholas Copernicus and the founding of modern astronomy. Goble, T.   **92**
Nicholls, Calvin
(il) Martin, R. The world before this one
    398.2
Nichols, Margaret Irby
(jt. auth) Safford, B. R. Guide to reference materials for school media centers   **011.6**
Nichols, Terry Lynn
See/See also pages in the following book(s):
Sherrow, V. The Oklahoma City bombing
    364.1
Nicholson, John, 1757-1800
See/See also pages in the following book(s):
Aaseng, N. Business builders in real estate
    920
Nicholson, Lois, 1949-
Dian Fossey (7 and up)   **92**
Nickel
Sparrow, G. Nickel
In The Elements   **546**
Nickel-a-pound plane ride. Soto, G.
In Soto, G. Local news p120-31   **S C**
Nickerson, Sara
How to disappear completely and never be found   **Fic**
Nicklaus, Carol
(il) Otfinoski, S. Speaking up, speaking out
    808.5
Nicknames
Fiction
Korman, G. The sixth grade nickname game (4 and up)   **Fic**
Nicolle, David, 1944-
Medieval knights   **940.1**
Niehaus, Theodore F.
A field guide to Pacific states wildflowers
    582.13
Nielsen Hayden, Patrick
(ed) New skies: an anthology of today's science fiction. See New skies: an anthology of today's science fiction   **S C**
Nieuwenhuizen, John
(jt. auth) Quintana, A. The baboon king   **Fic**

Nigeria
Levy, P. M. Nigeria (5 and up)   **966.9**
Fiction
Naidoo, B. The other side of truth (5 and up)
    Fic
Social life and customs
Nnoromele, S. Life among the Ibo women of
Nigeria (7 and up)   **966.9**

Nigg, Joe
Wonder beasts (7 and up)   **398**

Night. Wiesel, E.
In Wiesel, E. Night, Dawn, The accident:
three tales   **Fic**

Night, Dawn, The accident: three tales. Wiesel, E.
    Fic

Night game. Wallace, R.
In Wallace, R. Losing is not an option: stories
    S C

Night hoops. Deuker, C.   **Fic**

Night is gone, day is still coming (7 and up)
    808.8

The **night** journey. Lasky, K.   **Fic**

Night kites. Kerr, M. E.   **Fic**

The **night** of San Juan. Delacre, L.
In Delacre, L. Salsa stories p28-36   **S C**

A **night** of terror. Olson, A. N.
In Olson, A. N. and Schwartz, H. Ask the
bones: scary stories from around the
world p60-65   **398.2**

Night of the twisters. Ruckman, I.   **Fic**

Night sky. See Mechler, G. National Audubon Society first field guide: night sky   **520**

Night terrors (7 and up)   **S C**

Night the stars were gone. Aiken, J.
In Aiken, J. Shadows and moonshine; stories
    S C

The **night** watchman. Braly, D.
In Read all about it!; great read-aloud stories,
poems, and newspaper pieces for preteens and teens p244-51   **808.8**

Night wolves. Yolen, J.
In The Haunted house: a collection of original
stories   **S C**

Nightingale, Florence, 1820-1910
See/See also pages in the following book(s):
Celebrating women in mathematics and science
    920

Nightjohn. Paulsen, G.   **Fic**

Nightmare. Nixon, J. L.   **Fic**

Nighttown. San Souci, R.
In San Souci, R. Dare to be scared; thirteen
stories to chill and thrill   **S C**

NightWatch. Dickinson, T.   **520**

NIH *See* National Institutes of Health (U.S.)

Nihancan and the dwarf's arrow. Brown, D. A.
In Brown, D. A. Dee Brown's folktales of the
Native American; retold for our times
p114-15   **398.2**

Nihei, Judith
Koden
In American dragons: twenty-five Asian
American voices p97-109   **810.8**

The **Nile**. Barter, J.   **962**
The **Nile**. Bowden, R.   **962**
The **Nile**. Cumming, D.   **962**

Nile River
Barter, J. The Nile   **962**
Bowden, R. The Nile (5 and up)   **962**
Cumming, D. The Nile (4 and up)   **962**

Nile River valley
Barter, J. The Nile   **962**
Bowden, R. The Nile (5 and up)   **962**
Cumming, D. The Nile (4 and up)   **962**

Nilsen, Alleen Pace
Presenting M.E. Kerr (7 and up)   **813.009**
(jt. auth) Donelson, K. L. Literature for today's
young adults   **028.5**

Nine eleven: the book of help. See 911: the book
of help   **810.8**

Nineteen eighty-four. Orwell, G.   **Fic**

Nineteen varieties of gazelle. See Nye, N. S. 19
varieties of gazelle   **811**

Ninjas, piranhas, and Galileo. Smith, G. L.
    Fic

Niño, Pero, conde de Buelno *See* Buelno, Pero
Niño, conde de, ca. 1379-ca. 1453

The **ninth** book of junior authors and illustrators
    920.003

Nitrogen
Farndon, J. Nitrogen
In The Elements   **546**

Nitz, Kristin Wolden
Fundamental softball   **796.357**

Nix, Garth, 1963-
Endings
In Gothic!; ten original dark tales   **S C**
Hope chest
In Firebirds: an anthology of original fantasy
and science fiction; an anthology of orig-
inal fantasy and science fiction   **S C**
Mister Monday   **Fic**
Sabriel   **Fic**
Shade's children (7 and up)   **Fic**

Nixon, Joan Lowery, 1927-2003
The dark beast of death
In Night terrors; stories of shadow and sub-
stance   **S C**
Ghost town   **S C**
Includes the following stories: The shoot-out; Buried; The in-
truders; Payback; The magic eye; Bad man from Bodie; Trade-
off
The haunting (7 and up)   **Fic**
The making of a writer   **92**
Murdered, my sweet (7 and up)   **Fic**
Nightmare   **Fic**
Who are you? (7 and up)   **Fic**

**Nixon, Richard M. (Richard Milhous), 1913-
1994**
About
Barron, R. Richard Nixon (7 and up)   **92**
Goldman, M. S. Richard M. Nixon (7 and up)
    92
See/See also pages in the following book(s):
Roberts, R. Leaders and generals   **920**

Njinga *See* Nzinga, Queen of Matamba, 1582-
1663

Nnoromele, Salome, 1967-
Life among the Ibo women of Nigeria (7 and up) **966.9**
No better hope. Ashabranner, J. **975.3**
No easy answers [biography of Bayard Rustin] Miller, C. C. **92**
No effect. Hayes, D. **Fic**
The **no-guitar** blues. Soto, G.
In Soto, G. Baseball in April, and other stories p43-51 **S C**
No laughter here. Williams-Garcia, R. **Fic**
No man's land. Bartoletti, S. C. **Fic**
No more dead dogs. Korman, G. **Fic**
No pretty pictures. Lobel, A. **92**
No shame, no fear. Turnbull, A. **Fic**
No sword. Kimmel, E. A.
In Kimmel, E. A. Sword of the samurai; adventure stories from Japan p105-09 **Fic**
No, thanks. Schwartz, A.
In Schwartz, A. Scary stories 3; more tales to chill your bones p65 **398.2**
No turning back. Naidoo, B. **Fic**
No Win Phuong. Carter, A. R.
In Join in; multiethnic short stories by outstanding writers for young adults p62-84 **S C**
Noah hunts a wooly mammoth. Norman, H.
In Norman, H. The girl who dreamed only geese, and other tales of the Far North **398.2**
The **Nobel** book of answers (5 and up) **001.4**
Nobel Prize winners. Hacker, C. **920**
Nobel Prize-winning scientists [series]
Hamilton, J. James Watson **92**
Nobel Prizes
Hacker, C. Nobel Prize winners **920**
The Nobel book of answers (5 and up) **001.4**
Nobles, Scott
(il) Bruder, M. Button girl **745.5**
Nobody has to know. Macdonald, J.
In Vampires: a collection of original stories p3-7 **S C**
Nobody stole Jason Grayson. Mackler, C.
In 13; thirteen stories that capture the agony and ecstasy of being thirteen
Noether, Amalie Emmy See Noether, Emmy, 1882-1935
Noether, Emmy, 1882-1935
See/See also pages in the following book(s):
Celebrating women in mathematics and science **920**
Henderson, H. Modern mathematicians (7 and up) **920**
Noguchi, Constance Tom, 1948-
See/See also pages in the following book(s):
Yount, L. Asian-American scientists (7 and up) **920**
Nolan, Dennis, 1945-
(il) Coville, B. William Shakespeare's A midsummer night's dream **822.3**

(il) Coville, B. William Shakespeare's Romeo and Juliet **822.3**
(il) Sherwood: original stories from the world of Robin Hood. See Sherwood: original stories from the world of Robin Hood **S C**
Nolan, Han, 1956-
A face in every window (7 and up) **Fic**
Maroon
In Don't cramp my style; stories about that time of the month p182-208 **S C**
Noli's story. Dickinson, P.
In Dickinson, P. The kin p151-301 **Fic**
Noll, Mark A.
Protestants in America (7 and up) **280**
Nolting, Karen Stray
(jt. auth) Latimer, J. P. Backyard birds **598**
(jt. auth) Latimer, J. P. Birds of prey **598**
(jt. auth) Latimer, J. P. Bizarre birds **598**
(jt. auth) Latimer, J. P. Butterflies **595.7**
(jt. auth) Latimer, J. P. Caterpillars **595.7**
(jt. auth) Latimer, J. P. Shorebirds **598**
(jt. auth) Latimer, J. P. Songbirds **598**
(ed) Simon & Schuster thesaurus for children. See Simon & Schuster thesaurus for children **423**
Nonan-Mercado, Detch P.
(jt. auth) Tope, L. R. R. Philippines **959.9**
Nonsense verses
Silverstein, S. Falling up **811**
Silverstein, S. A light in the attic **811**
Silverstein, S. Where the sidewalk ends **811**
Noodle soup for nincompoops. Wittlinger, E.
In 13; thirteen stories that capture the agony and ecstasy of being thirteen **S C**
Noon, Steve
(il) Millard, A. A street through time **936**
The **noose**. Naidoo, B.
In Naidoo, B. Out of bounds: seven stories of conflict and hope p18-49 **S C**
Norman, Howard
Between heaven and earth (4 and up) **398.2**
The girl who dreamed only geese, and other tales of the Far North (4 and up) **398.2**
Contents: The day puffins netted Hid-Well; Noah hunts a wooly mammoth; Why the rude visitor was flung by walrus; Uteritsoq and the duck-bill dolls; The wolverine's secret; The girl who watched in the nighttime; The man who married a seagull; Home among the giants; How the narwhal got its tusk; The girl who dreamed only geese
Norris, George William, 1861-1944
See/See also pages in the following book(s):
Kennedy, J. F. Profiles in courage **920**
Norse mythology
Hamilton, E. Mythology p21-76 **292**
Philip, N. Odin's family (4-6) **293**
Fiction
Farmer, N. The Sea of Trolls (5 and up) **Fic**
Norsemen See Vikings
North, Sterling, 1906-1974
Rascal (5 and up) **599.7**
North across the border. Perl, L. **305.8**
North America
Population
Peoples of North America **305.8**

North American art since 1900. Turner, C. M. E.
P.
In International encyclopedia of art   **703**
North American art to 1900. Pancza-Graham, A.
In International encyclopedia of art   **703**
North American cranes. DuTemple, L. A.   **598**
North American Indian. Murdoch, D. H.
   970.004
North American Indian games. Anderson, M. K.
   970.004
North American Indians *See* Native Americans
North American Indians of achievement [series]
Schwarz, M. Cochise, Apache chief   **92**
Baird, W. D. Geronimo, Apache warrior   **92**
Taylor, M. W. Chief Joseph   **92**
North American Indians today [series]   **970.004**
North by night. Ayres, K.   **Fic**
North Carolina
Hintz, M. North Carolina
In America the beautiful, second series
   973
Shirley, D. North Carolina
In Celebrate the states   **973**
Fiction
Dowell, F. O. Dovey Coe (5 and up)   **Fic**
Moses, S. P. The legend of Buddy Bush
   Fic
Race relations
Tillage, L. Leon's story (4 and up)   **92**
North Dakota
Hintz, M. North Dakota
In America the beautiful, second series
   973
Hintz, M. North Dakota
In America the beautiful, second series
   973
McDaniel, M. North Dakota Celebrate the states
   973
Fiction
Kurtz, J. Jakarta missing   **Fic**
North Korea   **951.93**
North Pole
See also Arctic regions
Calvert, P. Robert E. Peary   **92**
Northern Ireland
Fiction
Doyle, M. Who is Jesse Flood?   **Fic**
Northern Ireland
Wagner, H. L. The IRA and England (7 and up)
   941.6
Northern lights. Harjo, J.
In Talking leaves; contemporary native
American short stories   **S C**
Northern lights. See Pullman, P. The golden com-
pass   **Fic**
Northern Lights young novels [series]
Aspin, D. Ordinary miracles   **S C**
Northern Rhodesia *See* Zambia
Northmen *See* Vikings
Northrup, Mary
American computer pioneers   **920**
Northwest, Pacific *See* Pacific Northwest

Northwest Passage
Warrick, K. C. The perilous search for the fa-
bled Northwest Passage in American history
   910.4
Northwest Territories
Laws, G. D. Northwest Territory
In Exploring Canada   **971**
Fiction
Hobbs, W. Far North (7 and up)   **Fic**
Northwest Territory. Laws, G. D.
In Exploring Canada   **971**
Norville, Rod
Moonshine express   **Fic**
Nory Ryan's song. Giff, P. R.   **Fic**
Nose
Silverstein, A. Smelling and tasting
In Silverstein, A. and others. Senses and
sensors [series]   **612.8**
The **nose**. Hearne, B. G.
In Hearne, B. G. The canine connection: sto-
ries about dogs and people p70-76
   S C
Notable Americans [series]
Barron, R. Richard Nixon   **92**
Young, J. C. Dwight D. Eisenhower   **92**
Notable mathematicians (7 and up)   **920.003**
Notable social studies trade books for young peo-
ple   **016.3**
Notable women scientists (7 and up)   **920.003**
The **notes** between the notes. Appelt, K.
In Appelt, K. Kissing Tennessee and other
stories from the Stardust Dance p90-100
   S C
Notes from a liar and her dog. Choldenko, G.
   Fic
Nothing at all. Pferdehirt, J.
In Fire and wings: dragon tales from East and
West p65-78   **S C**
Nothing but the truth. Avi   **Fic**
Notorious Americans and their times [series]
King, D. C. Al Capone and the roaring twenties
   92
King, D. C. Benedict Arnold and the American
Revolution   **92**
Otfinoski, S. John Wilkes Booth and the Civil
War   **92**
Sherrow, V. Joseph McCarthy and the Cold War
   92
Nova Scotia
Fiction
Ashby, J. Sea gift   **Fic**
Novello, Antonia
See/See also pages in the following book(s):
DeAngelis, G. Science & medicine   **920**
November, Sharyn
(ed) Firebirds: an anthology of original fantasy
and science fiction. See Firebirds: an antholo-
gy of original fantasy and science fiction
   S C
Novio boy. Soto, G.   **812**
Now is your time!. Myers, W. D.   **305.8**
Nowhere to call home. DeFelice, C. C.   **Fic**

Nowhere to hide. Olson, A. N.
  In Olson, A. N. and Schwartz, H. Ask the
    bones: scary stories from around the
    world p66-72   **398.2**

Noyce, Robert, 1927-1990
  See/See also pages in the following book(s):
  Northrup, M. American computer pioneers
      920

Noyes, Deborah, 1965-
  (ed) Gothic! See Gothic!   **S C**

NTSB *See* United States. National Transportation
  Safety Board

Nubia
  Russmann, E. R. Nubian kingdoms   **939**

Nubian kingdoms. Russmann, E. R.   **939**

Nuclear energy
  Hampton, W. Meltdown   **363.1**
  Kidd, J. S. Quarks and sparks (7 and up)
      621.48
  Scarborough, K. Nuclear waste (5 and up)
      363.7

Nuclear physics
  Gallant, R. A. The ever changing atom (5 and
    up)   **539.7**
  Hamilton, J. Lise Meitner   **92**
  Henderson, H. Nuclear physics (7 and up)
      539.7

Nuclear power plants
  See also Nuclear energy
  Hampton, W. Meltdown   **363.1**
      Environmental aspects
  Bryan, N. Chernobyl (5 and up)   **363.7**
      Fiction
  Hesse, K. Phoenix rising   **Fic**

Nuclear waste. Scarborough, K.   **363.7**

Nuclear weapons
  See also Atomic bomb
  Blohm, C. E. Weapons of peace   **327.1**
  See/See also pages in the following book(s):
  Weapons of mass destruction: opposing view-
    points   **358**

Nuestra Señora de Atocha (Ship)
  Matsen, B. The incredible search for the treasure
    ship Atocha (4 and up)   **910.4**

Number the stars. Lowry, L.   **Fic**

Numrich, Paul David, 1952-
  (jt. auth) Mann, G. S. Buddhists, Hindus, and
    Sikhs in America   **294**

Nunn, Laura Silverstein, 1968-
  (jt. auth) Silverstein, A. Chickenpox and shin-
    gles   **616.9**
  (jt. auth) Silverstein, A. Depression   **616.85**
  (jt. auth) Silverstein, A. Energy   **621**
  (jt. auth) Silverstein, A. Food chains   **577**
  (jt. auth) Silverstein, A. Global warming
      363.7
  (jt. auth) Silverstein, A. The grizzly bear
      599.78
  (jt. auth) Silverstein, A. Lyme disease   **616.9**
  (jt. auth) Silverstein, A. Parkinson's disease
      616.8
  (jt. auth) Silverstein, A. Plate tectonics
      551.1
  (jt. auth) Silverstein, A. Polio   **616.8**

  (jt. auth) Silverstein, A. Senses and sensors [se-
    ries]   **612.8**
  (jt. auth) Silverstein, A. Sickle cell anemia
      616.1
  (jt. auth) Silverstein, A. Snakes & such   **639**
  (jt. auth) Silverstein, A. Symbiosis   **577.8**
  (jt. auth) Silverstein, A. The universe   **520**
  (jt. auth) Silverstein, A. Weather and climate
      551.5

Nuns
  Ruth, A. Mother Teresa   **92**

The **nun's** priest's tale. Cohen, B.
  In Cohen, B. Canterbury tales   **821**

**Nuremberg Trial of Major German War Crimi-
nals, 1945-1946**
  Altman, L. J. Crimes and criminals of the Holo-
    caust   **940.53**

Nurse Corps (Army) *See* United States. Army
  Nurse Corps

Nursery rhymes
  Mother Goose on the loose   **398.8**

Nurses
  Wells, R. Mary on horseback [biography of
    Mary Breckinridge] (4 and up)   **92**
  Whitelaw, N. Clara Barton   **92**

Nutrition
    See also Eating customs
  Brynie, F. H. 101 questions about food and di-
    gestion that have been eating at you . . . until
    now   **612.3**
  Cheung, L. W.-Y. Be healthy! it's a girl thing
    (5 and up)   **613**
  D'Amico, J. The healthy body cookbook (4 and
    up)   **641.5**
  Diet information for teens (7 and up)   **613.2**
  Gardner, R. Health science projects about nutri-
    tion (7 and up)   **612.3**
  Haduch, B. Food rules!   **613.2**
  Turck, M. Healthy eating for weight manage-
    ment   **613.7**
  Walker, P. The digestive system (7 and up)
      612.3
  See/See also pages in the following book(s):
  Schwager, T. The right moves (7 and up)
      613.7

Nutrition and fitness [series]
  Duden, J. Vegetarianism for teens   **613.2**
  Gedatus, G. Bicycling for fitness   **613.7**
  Gedatus, G. Exercise for weight management
      613.7
  Turck, M. Healthy eating for weight manage-
    ment   **613.7**

Nuts! Nuts! Nuts!. Van Laan, N.
  In Van Laan, N. With a whoop and a holler;
    a bushel of lore from way down south
    p61-64   **398**

Nutzhorn, Dorothea *See* Lange, Dorothea, 1895-
  1965

Nuwer, Hank
  To the young writer   **808**

Nye, Michael
  (il) What have you lost? See What have you
    lost?   **808.81**

Nye, Naomi Shihab, 1952-
19 varieties of gazelle   **811**
A maze me (7 and up)   **811**
Habibi   **Fic**
Shoofly pie
   In The Color of absence; 12 stories about loss
     and hope p123-44   **S C**
(comp) I feel a little jumpy around you. See I
   feel a little jumpy around you   **808.81**
(ed) Is this forever, or what? See Is this forever,
   or what?   **811.008**
(comp) Salting the ocean. See Salting the ocean
     811.008
(comp) The Space between our footsteps. See
   The Space between our footsteps   **808.81**
(comp) The Tree is older than you are. See The
   Tree is older than you are   **860.8**
(comp) What have you lost? See What have you
   lost?   **808.81**
NYSE *See* New York Stock Exchange, Inc.
Nzinga, Queen of Matamba, 1582-1663
See/See also pages in the following book(s):
Hansen, J. African princess (5 and up)   **920**
Hewitt, K. Lives of extraordinary women (4 and
   up)   **920**
Fiction
McKissack, P. C. Nzinga, warrior queen of
   Matamba (5 and up)   **Fic**
Nzinga, warrior queen of Matamba. McKissack, P.
   C.   **Fic**

O

The **O.J.** Simpson murder trial. Pellowski, M.
   345
O **Jerusalem**. Yolen, J.   **811**
Oakley, Annie, 1860-1926
About
Macy, S. Bulls-eye: a photobiography of Annie
   Oakley (4 and up)   **92**
Oates, Joyce Carol, 1938-
Big Mouth & Ugly Girl (7 and up)   **Fic**
Freaky green eyes (7 and up)   **Fic**
Small avalanches and other stories (7 and up)
   S C
   Contents: Where are you going, where have you been?; The
   sky blue bell; Small avalanches; Haunted; Bad girls; How I con-
   templated the world; "Shot"; Why don't you come live with me:
   it's time; Life after high school; Capricorn; The visit; The model
Where are you going, where have you been?
   also in Who do you think you are?; stories of
     friends and enemies p14-35   **S C**
Oba, Ryan
Home now
   In American eyes; new Asian-American short
     stories for young adults p28-36   **S C**
Obata, Takeshi
(jt. auth) Hotta, Y. Hikaru No Go, Volume 1
   741.5
Obedience. Brown, F.
   In Read into the millennium; tales of the fu-
     ture p103-17   **S C**

Obesity
Control
   See Weight loss
Fiction
Bennett, C. Life in the fat lane (7 and up)
   Fic
Crutcher, C. Staying fat for Sarah Byrnes
   Fic
Going, K. L. Fat kid rules the world (7 and up)
   Fic
Holt, K. W. When Zachary Beaver came to
   town   **Fic**
Lipsyte, R. One fat summer (7 and up)   **Fic**
Mackler, C. The earth, my butt, and other big,
   round things (7 and up)   **Fic**
Object lesson. Queen, E.
   In Read all about it!; great read-aloud stories,
     poems, and newspaper pieces for pre-
     teens and teens p53-66   **808.8**
   In Read all about it!; great read-aloud stories,
     poems, and newspaper pieces for pre-
     teens and teens p53-66   **808.88**
O'Brien, Dan
See/See also pages in the following book(s):
Kaminsky, M. Uncommon champions   **920**
O'Brien, Joanne
(jt. auth) Breuilly, E. Religions of the world
   201
O'Brien, Joanne, 1959-
(jt. auth) Breuilly, E. Festivals of the world
   394.26
O'Brien, John, 1953-
(il) Bateman, T. Red, white, blue, and Uncle
   who?   **929.9**
O'Brien, Lisa, 1963-
Lights, camera, action!   **791.43**
O'Brien, Patrick
The Hindenburg (4 and up)   **629.133**
O'Brien, Robert C., 1918-1973
Mrs. Frisby and the rats of NIMH (4 and up)
   Fic
Z for Zachariah (7 and up)   **Fic**
O'Brien, Tim, 1946-
Ambush
   In Who do you think you are?; stories of
     friends and enemies p152-55   **S C**
The man I killed
   In Who do you think you are?; stories of
     friends and enemies p146-51   **S C**
On the rainy river
   In Leaving home: stories p133-56   **808.8**
Obscenity (Law)
   See also Pornography
Obsession (Psychology) *See* Obsessive-compulsive
   disorder
Obsessive-compulsive disorder
Hyman, B. M. Obsessive-compulsive disorder
   616.85
Fiction
Hesser, T. S. Kissing doorknobs (7 and up)
   Fic
Tashjian, J. Multiple choice   **Fic**
Obsessive-compulsive neuroses *See* Obsessive-
   compulsive disorder

Obstfeld, Loretta
(ed) Napoleon Bonaparte. See Napoleon Bonaparte [essays about]   92

Obstfeld, Raymond, 1952-
(ed) Napoleon Bonaparte. See Napoleon Bonaparte [essays about]   92

Ocampo, Adriana C., 1955-
See/See also pages in the following book(s):
Oleksy, W. G. Hispanic-American scientists (7 and up)   920

Occultism
See also Prophecies
Steiger, B. Gale encyclopedia of the unusual and unexplained   130

Occupational guidance *See* Vocational guidance

Occupational outlook handbook. United States. Bureau of Labor Statistics   331.7

Occupational training
Unger, H. G. But what if I don't want to go to college? (7 and up)   331.7

Occupations
Career discovery encyclopedia   331.7
The Encyclopedia of careers and vocational guidance   331.7
Heading out (7 and up)   331.7
Schwager, T. Cool women, hot jobs . . . and how you can go for it, too! (7 and up)   650.14
United States. Bureau of Labor Statistics. Occupational outlook handbook   331.7
Young person's occupational outlook handbook   331.7

Ocean
See also Seashore
Burleigh, R. The sea (5 and up)   551.46
Carson, R. The sea around us (7 and up)   551.46
Sayre, A. P. Ocean (5 and up)   577.7
Scholastic atlas of oceans (4 and up)   551.46
An **ocean** apart, a world away. Namioka, L.   Fic

Ocean bottom
Gowell, E. T. Fountains of life   577.7
Matsen, B. The incredible record-setting deep-sea dive of the bathysphere (4 and up)   551.46

Ocean travel
Paulsen, G. Caught by the sea (5 and up)   92

Ocean wildlife. Vogel, C. G.   591.7

Oceania
Lawlor, L. Magnificent voyage (7 and up)   910.4

Oceanography
Day, T. Oceans (7 and up)   551.46

Oceans. Day, T.   551.46

Ochiltree, Dianne, 1953-
The women's house
In Don't cramp my style; stories about that time of the month p68-100   S C

Ochoa, Annette Piña
(ed) Night is gone, day is still coming. See Night is gone, day is still coming   808.8

Ochoa, Ellen, 1958-
See/See also pages in the following book(s):
Oleksy, W. G. Hispanic-American scientists (7 and up)   920

Ochoa, George
Atlas of Hispanic-American history (7 and up)   305.8
The New York Public Library amazing Hispanic American history   305.8
The Wilson chronology of ideas   909
The Wilson chronology of science and technology   502
The Wilson chronology of the arts   700
American history on file. See American history on file   973

O'Connor, Barbara
Barefoot dancer: the story of Isadora Duncan   92
Fame and glory in Freedom, Georgia (4 and up)   Fic
Leonardo da Vinci (5 and up)   92

O'Connor, Jane, 1947-
The emperor's silent army (4 and up)   931

O'Connor, Sandra Day
See/See also pages in the following book(s):
Jones, V. B. Government & politics   920

Octavian *See* Augustus, Emperor of Rome, 63 B.C.-14 A.D.

October chill. Vande Velde, V.
In Vande Velde, V. Being dead; stories   S C

O'Day, Anita, 1919-
See/See also pages in the following book(s):
Orgill, R. Shout, sister, shout! (6 and up)   920

Oddballs. Sleator, W.   S C

Oddballs. Sleator, W.
In Sleator, W. Oddballs; stories p129-34   S C

Odder than ever. Coville, B.   S C

Oddities *See* Curiosities and wonders

Odean, Kathleen
Great books for boys   028.1

O'Dell, Kathleen
Agnes Parker . . . girl in progress (4 and up)   Fic

O'Dell, Katie
Library materials and services for teen girls   027.62

O'Dell, Scott, 1898-1989
The black pearl (6 and up)   Fic
Island of the Blue Dolphins (5 and up)   Fic
Sarah Bishop (6 and up)   Fic
Sing down the moon (5 and up)   Fic
Streams to the river, river to the sea (5 and up)   Fic
Thunder rolling in the mountains (5 and up)   Fic
Zia (5 and up)   Fic

Odhiambo, Thomas
See/See also pages in the following book(s):
Graham, K. Contemporary environmentalists (7 and up)   920

Odin's family. Philip, N.   293

O'Donnell, Kerri, 1972-
The gold rush (4 and up)   **979.4**

Odysseus (Greek mythology)
McCaughrean, G. Odysseus (5 and up)   **292**
See/See also pages in the following book(s):
Hamilton, E. Mythology p21-76   **292**

The **Odyssey**. Homer   **883**

Oedipus the King. See Rao, S. Sophocles' Oedipus the King   **Fic**

Of sound mind. Ferris, J.   **Fic**

Off the map. Clark, W.   **978**

Off the road. Bawden, N.   **Fic**

Off ya go, so. Lynch, C.
In Lynch, C. All the old haunts p79-101
   S C

Offenses against the person
See also Homicide; Kidnapping; Rape

Ogden, Aaron, 1756-1839
About
Levinson, I. S. Gibbons v. Ogden (7 and up)
   343

Oglala Indians
Bad Heart Buffalo, A. The life and death of
Crazy Horse (5 and up)   **92**
See/See also pages in the following book(s):
Freedman, R. Indian chiefs (6 and up)   **920**

Oglesby, Carole A.
(ed) Encyclopedia of women and sport in America. See Encyclopedia of women and sport in
America   **796.03**

O'Grady, Scott F.
Basher five-two (5 and up)   **949.7**

The **ogre's** arm. San Souci, R.
In San Souci, R. A terrifying taste of short &
shivery; thirty creepy tales p46-51
   398.2

Oh, freedom!. King, C.   **323.1**

O'Hanlon, Nancy
(jt. auth) Diaz, K. R. IssueWeb: a guide and
sourcebook for researching controversial issues on the Web   **025.04**

Ohio
Heinrichs, A. Ohio
In America the beautiful, second series
   973
Sherrow, V. Ohio
In Celebrate the states   **973**
Fiction
Fleischman, P. The borning room (6 and up)
   Fic
Hamilton, V. Time pieces (5 and up)   **Fic**
Lyon, G. E. Gina.Jamie.Father.Bear   **Fic**
Van Leeuwen, J. Cabin on Trouble Creek (4
and up)   **Fic**
Zinnen, L. The dragons of Spratt, Ohio (5 and
up)   **Fic**
Zinnen, L. The truth about rats, rules, and sev-
enth grade   **Fic**

Ohmi, Ayano, 1959-
(jt. auth) Hamanaka, S. In search of the spirit
   920

Oil painting *See* Painting

Oil spills
Bryan, N. Exxon Valdez oil spill (5 and up)
   363.7
Sherrow, V. The Exxon Valdez   **363.7**

Ojeda, Auriana, 1977-
(ed) Civil liberties: opposing viewpoints. See
Civil liberties: opposing viewpoints   **323**
(ed) Homosexuality: opposing viewpoints. See
Homosexuality: opposing viewpoints
   306.76
(ed) Male/female roles: opposing viewpoints.
See Male/female roles: opposing viewpoints
   305.3
(ed) Smoking. See Smoking   **363.4**

Ojibwa. Cornell, G. L.
In North American Indians today [series]

Ojibwa Indians
Cornell, G. L. Ojibwa
In North American Indians today [series]
Fiction
Carter, A. R. Crescent Moon   **Fic**
Erdrich, L. The birchbark house (5 and up)
   Fic
Erdrich, L. The game of silence (5 and up)
   Fic

O'Keeffe, Georgia, 1887-1986
See/See also pages in the following book(s):
Danneberg, J. Women artists of the West
   920
Fiction
Kudlinski, K. V. The spirit catchers (7 and up)
   Fic

Okie, Susan
(jt. auth) Ride, S. K. To space & back
   629.45

Okimoto, Jean Davies, 1942-
Jason Kovak, the quick and the brave
In Visions: nineteen short stories by outstand-
ing writers for young adults p42-63
   S C
Next month . . . Hollywood!
In Join in; multiethnic short stories by out-
standing writers for young adults p35-46
   S C

Oklahoma
Baldwin, G. Oklahoma
In Celebrate the states   **973**
Reedy, J. Oklahoma
In America the beautiful, second series
   973
Fiction
Griffis, M. L. The Feester filibuster (4 and up)
   Fic
Grove, V. The starplace   **Fic**
Hesse, K. Out of the dust (5 and up)   **Fic**
McCaughrean, G. Stop the train! (5 and up)
   Fic
Myers, A. Tulsa burning (7 and up)   **Fic**
Rawls, W. Summer of the monkeys (7 and up)
   Fic

Oklahoma City (Okla.) bombing, 1995
Sherrow, V. The Oklahoma City bombing
   364.1

Okutoro, Lydia Omolola
(comp) Quiet storm. See Quiet storm
811.008

Ol' Gally Mander. Van Laan, N.
In Van Laan, N. With a whoop and a holler;
a bushel of lore from way down south
p76-81　　**398**

Ol' Master Biggety. Van Laan, N.
In Van Laan, N. With a whoop and a holler;
a bushel of lore from way down south
p43-46　　**398**

Old, Wendie
Duke Ellington: giant of jazz　　**92**
Louis Armstrong　　**92**
Marian Wright Edelman (7 and up)　　**92**

Old age

Fiction
Auch, M. J. Wing nut (5 and up)　　**Fic**
Bauer, J. Rules of the road (7 and up)　　**Fic**
Fleischman, P. Mind's eye (7 and up)　　**Fic**
Giff, P. R. Pictures of Hollis Woods (5 and up)
　　Fic
Holt, K. W. Dancing in Cadillac light (5 and
up)　　**Fic**
Kimmel, E. C. Visiting Miss Caples (6 and up)
　　Fic

The old chief Mshlanga. Lessing, D. M.
In Somehow tenderness survives; stories of
Southern Africa p19-35　　**S C**

Old Hickory [biography of Andrew Jackson]
Marrin, A.　　**92**

The old jar. Yep, L.
In Yep, L. The rainbow people p96-105
　　398.2

The old king and the new king. Lester, J.
In Lester, J. The last tales of Uncle Remus
p22-25　　**398.2**

**Old Man Coyote, the young man and two otter
sisters**
In Hearne, B. G. Beauties and beasts p154-56
　　398.2

The old marriage. Earling, D.
In Talking leaves; contemporary native
American short stories　　**S C**

Old Nan's ghost. San Souci, R.
In San Souci, R. A terrifying taste of short &
shivery; thirty creepy tales p86-90
　　398.2

Old Sally Cato. San Souci, R.
In San Souci, R. Cut from the same cloth;
American women of myth, legend, and
tall tale p67-73　　**398.2**

Old Testament *See* Bible. O.T.

Old Testament women. Ward, E. M.　　**221.9**

The old woman and the Devil. Tchana, K. H.
In Tchana, K. H. The serpent slayer: and other stories of strong women p47-51
　　398.2

Old worlds to new. Podell, J.　　**920.003**

Old Yeller. Gipson, F. B.　　**Fic**

Oleksy, Walter G., 1930-
Hispanic-American scientists (7 and up)　　**920**

The olive grove. Marston, E.
In Soul searching: thirteen stories about faith
and belief p44-66　　**S C**

Oliver, Marilyn Tower, 1935-
Muhammad (7 and up)　　**297**

Olive's ocean. Henkes, K.　　**Fic**

Olliffe, Pat
(jt. auth) DeFalco, T. Spider-girl, Vol. 1: Legacy
　　741.5

Olsen, Sylvia, 1955-
The girl with a baby (7 and up)　　**Fic**
White girl (7 and up)　　**Fic**

Olson, Arielle North, 1932-
Ask the bones: scary stories from around the
world (4 and up)　　**398.2**
Contents: The haunted forest; The murky secret; Next-of-kin;
The bloody fangs; Ask the bones; The four-footed horror; Beginning with the ears; Fiddling with fire; The Laplander's drum; A
night of terror; Nowhere to hide; The handkerchief; The mousetrap; The speaking head; The dripping cutlass; The black snake;
The hand of death; The invisible guest; A trace of blood; The
bridal gown; The greedy man and the goat; The evil eye

Olson, Steven P.
The trial of John T. Scopes (5 and up)

Olsson, Sören, 1964-
(jt. auth) Jacobsson, A. In Ned's head　　**Fic**

Olympic games
Fischer, D. The encyclopedia of the Summer
Olympics (4 and up)　　**796.48**
Macy, S. Swifter, higher, stronger (4 and up)
　　796.48
Olympism　　**796.48**
Wallechinsky, D. The complete book of the
Winter Olympics　　**796.98**
Woff, R. The ancient Greek Olympics (4 and
up)　　**796.48**

Olympic guides [series]
Olympism　　**796.48**

Olympism　　**796.48**

Omoto, Susan, 1955-
Hmong milestones in America　　**305.8**

On display. Skaggs, G.　　**027.8**

On fortune's wheel. Voigt, C.　　**Fic**

On Greenhow Hill. Kipling, R.
In McCaffrey, A. {The Pern series}　　**S C**

On my honor. Bauer, M. D.　　**Fic**

On the bridge. Strasser, T.
In Visions: nineteen short stories by outstand-
ing writers for young adults p122-29
　　S C

On the brink of extinction. Arnold, C.　　**598**

On the Devil's court. Deuker, C.　　**Fic**

On the edge: stories at the brink (7 and up)
　　S C

On the fringe　　**S C**

On the rainy river. O'Brien, T.
In Leaving home: stories p133-56　　**808.8**

On the road to Texas: Pete Fonseca. Rivera, T.
In Growing up Latino; memoirs and stories
p147-54　　**810.8**

**On the trail of the Komodo dragon and other ex-
plorations of science in action.** Myers, J.
　　590

On the waters of the USA. Sandler, M. W.
387.2

On the wing. Lerner, C.   598

Onboard the space shuttle. Spangenburg, R.
629.44

Once a wolf. Swinburne, S. R.   333.95

The once and future king. White, T. H.   Fic

Once in a blue moon. DeFilippis, N.   741.5

Once upon a cuento   S C

Once upon a heroine. Cooper-Mullin, A.   028.1

Once upon a Marigold. Ferris, J.   Fic

One chance. De Lint, C.
In De Lint, C. Waifs and strays p220-32
S C

One cold day. Van Laan, N.
In Van Laan, N. With a whoop and a holler;
a bushel of lore from way down south
p5-8   398

One day, Lily, one day. Naidoo, B.
In Naidoo, B. Out of bounds: seven stories of
conflict and hope p50-71   S C

One-eyed cat. Fox, P.   Fic

One fat summer. Lipsyte, R.   Fic

One hundred and eleven Shakespeare monologues.
Shakespeare, W.   822.3

One hundred and one amazing optical illusions.
See Jennings, T. 101 amazing optical illusions
152.14

One hundred and one questions about blood and
circulation, with answers straight from the
heart. See Brynie, F. H. 101 questions about
blood and circulation, with answers straight
from the heart   612.1

One hundred and one questions about sex and sexuality. See Brynie, F. H. 101 questions about
sex and sexuality—   613.9

One hundred and one ways to bug your teacher.
See Wardlaw, L. 101 ways to bug your teacher   Fic

One hundred award-winning science fair projects.
See Vecchione, G. 100 award-winning science
fair projects   507.8

One hundred eleven one-minute monologues. See
Lamedman, D. 111 one-minute monologues
812.008

One hundred most popular children's authors. See
McElmeel, S. L. 100 most popular children's
authors   810.3

The one hundred most popular young adult authors. See Drew, B. A. The 100 most popular
young adult authors   810.9

One hundred one questions about food that have
been eating at you . . . until now. See
Brynie, F. H. 101 questions about food and
digestion that have been eating at you . . .
until now   612.3

One hundred one stories of the great ballets. See
Balanchine, G. 101 stories of the great ballets
792.8

The one hundredth thing about Caroline. Lowry,
L.   Fic

One love, one heart. Haskins, J.   781.646

One more river to cross. Myers, W. D.   779

One parent family *See* Single parent family

One thousand and one facts about dinosaurs. See
Clark, N. 1,001 facts about dinosaurs
567.9

One thousand inventions & discoveries. See
Bridgman, R. F. 1,000 inventions & discoveries   609

One thousand playthinks. See Moscovich, I. 1000
playthinks   793.73

One-time dog market at Buda. Molnár, I.
In Molnár, I. One-time dog market at Buda
and other Hungarian folktales p17-20
398.2

One-time dog market at Buda and other Hungarian folktales. Molnár, I.   398.2

One true friend. Hansen, J.   Fic

One unhappy horse. Adler, C. S.   Fic

The one who watches. Ortiz Cofer, J.
In Ortiz Cofer, J. An island like you; stories
of the barrio p72-81   S C

One world, many religions. Osborne, M. P.
201

O'Neal, Rose *See* Greenhow, Rose O'Neal, 1817-
1864

O'Neil, Patrick M., d. 2002
(ed) Great world writers: twentieth century. See
Great world writers: twentieth century
920.003

O'Neill, Ruth
Stealing dreams
In A Glory of unicorns p59-73   S C

O'Neill, Terry
Gun control (7 and up)   363.33

O'Neill, Terry, 1944-
Biomedical ethics (7 and up)   174.2
(ed) ESP. See ESP   133.8

O'Neill, William L.
World War II: a student companion (7 and up)
940.53

Only you can save mankind. Pratchett, T.   Fic

Ontario
Ferry, S. Ontario
In Exploring Canada   971

Opdyke, Irene Gut, 1921-
In my hands (7 and up)   940.53
See/See also pages in the following book(s):
Lyman, D. Holocaust rescuers   920

Open for debate [series]
Judson, K. Chemical and biological warfare
358

Perl, L. Terrorism
Spangenburg, R. Genetic engineering   660.6

Open your eyes (7 and up)   910.4

The opening of the West. Stefoff, R.   978

Opera
Ganeri, A. The young person's guide to the opera (4 and up)   792.5
Siberell, A. Bravo! brava! a night at the opera
(4 and up)   792.5

Stories, plots, etc.
Geras, A. The Random House book of opera
stories (4 and up)   792.5

Operating and evaluating school library media programs. Yesner, B. L. **027.8**

Operation Desert Storm *See* Persian Gulf War, 1991

Ophelia speaks. Shandler, S. **305.23**

Oppel, Kenneth
Airborn (7 and up) **Fic**
Silverwing (5 and up) **Fic**

Opposing viewpoints digests [series]
Barbour, S. The environment **363.7**
Currie, S. Slavery **326**
Haugen, D. The Civil War **973.7**
Hurley, J. A. Teen pregnancy **362.7**
Kim, H. H. Child abuse **362.7**
O'Neill, T. Gun control **363.33**
O'Neill, T. Biomedical ethics **174.2**
Roleff, T. L. Hate groups **364.1**
Speakman, J. The Cold War **327.73**

Opposing viewpoints in world history series
Slavery **326**

Opposing viewpoints series
Abortion: opposing viewpoints **363.46**
Addiction: opposing viewpoints **362.29**
Adoption: opposing viewpoints **362.7**
Africa: opposing viewpoints **960**
America's prisons: opposing viewpoints **365**
Biomedical ethics: opposing viewpoints **174.2**
Chemical dependency: opposing viewpoints **362.29**
Child abuse: opposing viewpoints **362.7**
Civil liberties: opposing viewpoints **323**
Culture wars: opposing viewpoints **306**
Death and dying: opposing viewpoints **155.9**
The Death penalty: opposing viewpoints **364.66**
Discrimination: opposing viewpoints **305.8**
Domestic violence: opposing viewpoints **362.82**
Drug abuse: opposing viewpoints **362.29**
Eating disorders: opposing viewpoints **616.85**
Endangered oceans: opposing viewpoints **577.7**
Endangered species: opposing viewpoints **578.68**
The environment: opposing viewpoints **363.7**
Epidemics: opposing viewpoints **614.4**
Euthanasia: opposing viewpoints **179.7**
The Family: opposing viewpoints **306.8**
Global resources: opposing viewpoints **333.71**
Global warming: opposing viewpoints **363.7**
Hate groups: opposing viewpoints **364.1**
The Homeless: opposing viewpoints **362.5**
Homosexuality: opposing viewpoints **306.76**
Human rights: opposing viewpoints **323**
Illegal immigration: opposing viewpoints **325.73**
The Internet: opposing viewpoints **303.4**
Israel: opposing viewpoints **956.94**
Male/female roles: opposing viewpoints **305.3**
Mass media: opposing viewpoints **302.23**
Media violence: opposing viewpoints **303.6**
Mental illness: opposing viewpoints **362.2**

The Middle East: opposing viewpoints **956**
Paranormal phenomena: opposing viewpoints **133**
Police brutality: opposing viewpoints **363.2**
Pollution: opposing viewpoints **363.7**
Pornography: opposing viewpoints **363.4**
Poverty: opposing viewpoints **362.5**
Race relations: opposing viewpoints **305.8**
Religion in America: opposing viewpoints **200.9**
Russia today: opposing viewpoints **947.086**
Sex: opposing viewpoints **306.7**
Suicide: opposing viewpoints **362.28**
Teenage pregnancy: opposing viewpoints **362.7**
Teens at risk: opposing viewpoints **362.7**
Terminal illness: opposing viewpoints **362.1**
Terrorism: opposing viewpoints **363.32**
Tobacco and smoking: opposing viewpoints **362.29**
Violence: opposing viewpoints **303.6**
The war on drugs **363.4**
War: opposing viewpoints **355**
Weapons of mass destruction: opposing viewpoints **358**

Optical illusions
Jennings, T. 101 amazing optical illusions **152.14**
Sturgis, A. Optical illusions in art **750.1**
Wick, W. Walter Wick's Optical tricks (4 and up) **152.14**

Optical illusions in art. Sturgis, A. **750.1**

The **oracle** betrayed. Fisher, C. **Fic**

Oracle Corp.
Ehrenhaft, D. Larry Ellison **92**

Orations *See* Speeches

Orchestra
Ganeri, A. The young person's guide to the orchestra (4 and up) **784.2**

Ordinary miracles. Aspin, D. **S C**

Ordinary miracles. Tolan, S. S. **Fic**

An **ordinary** woman. Greene, B.
In Sixteen; short stories by outstanding writers for young adults p125-32 **S C**

Ordnance
See also Military weapons

O'Ree, Willie, 1935-
See/See also pages in the following book(s):
Kaminsky, M. Uncommon champions **920**

Oregon
Ingram, S. Oregon
In America the beautiful, second series **973**
Stefoff, R. Oregon
In Celebrate the states **973**
Fiction
Crew, L. Fire on the wind **Fic**

Oregon country *See* Pacific Northwest

Oregon Trail
Blackwood, G. L. Life on the Oregon Trail (7 and up) **979.5**
Fisher, L. E. The Oregon Trail (4 and up) **979.5**

Orenstein, Denise Gosliner, 1950-
Unseen companion (7 and up) Fic

Organ and tissue transplants. McClellan, M.
617.9

Organ transplantation *See* Transplantation of organs, tissues, etc.

Organic gardening
Dunn-Georgiou, E. Everything you need to know about organic foods (7 and up)
641.3

Organized crime
Yancey, D. Al Capone 92
See/See also pages in the following book(s):
King, D. C. Al Capone and the roaring twenties
92

Fiction
Cross, G. Phoning a dead man (7 and up)
Fic

Organizing from the inside out for teens.
Morgenstern, J. 646.7

Orgill, Roxane
Mahalia [Jackson] (5 and up) 92
Shout, sister, shout! (6 and up) 920

Orient *See* Asia

Orienteering
Dewey, J. Finding your way 796.5

Origami
Boursin, D. Origimi paper animals (7 and up)
736
Nguyen, D. Fantasy origami (7 and up) 736

Origimi paper animals. Boursin, D. 736

Origin of man *See* Human origins

Origin of species *See* Evolution

The **origin** of the ocean. Lester, J.
In Lester, J. The last tales of Uncle Remus p13-16 398.2

The **original** Freddie Ackerman. Irwin, H. Fic

The **origins** of life. Gallant, R. A. 576.8

Orlev, Uri, 1931-
Run, boy, run (7 and up) Fic

Ormsby, Alison
The prairie 577.4

The **ornament** tree. Thesman, J. Fic

Orozco, José Clemente, 1883-1949
Juvenile literature
Cruz, B. José Clemente Orozco 92

Orphan runaways. Gregory, K. Fic

Orphan train rider. Warren, A. 362.7

Orphanages
Reef, C. Alone in the world 362.7

Orphans
Reef, C. Alone in the world 362.7
Warren, A. Orphan train rider (4 and up)
362.7
Warren, A. We rode the orphan trains (4 and up) 362.7

Fiction
Alder, E. The king's shadow (7 and up) Fic
Avi. Crispin Fic
Bath, K. P. The secret of Castle Cant (5 and up)
Fic
Blackwood, G. L. The Shakespeare stealer (5 and up) Fic

Brooke, P. Jake's orphan Fic
Cleaver, V. Where the lillies bloom (5 and up)
Fic
Collier, J. L. Me and Billy (5 and up) Fic
Creech, S. Ruby Holler (4 and up) Fic
Curtis, C. P. Bud, not Buddy (4 and up)
Fic
Cushman, K. Rodzina (5 and up) Fic
DeFelice, C. C. The apprenticeship of Lucas Whitaker (5 and up) Fic
DeFelice, C. C. Nowhere to call home Fic
Fleischman, S. Bo & Mzzz Mad (5 and up)
Fic
Garland, S. The silent storm Fic
Gregory, K. Orphan runaways Fic
Haas, J. Unbroken (5 and up) Fic
Heuston, K. B. The Shakeress (7 and up)
Fic
Hobbs, W. Jason's gold (5 and up) Fic
Horowitz, A. Stormbreaker Fic
Hurst, C. O. Through the lock Fic
Ibbotson, E. Journey to the river sea (5 and up)
Fic
Jinks, C. Pagan's crusade (7 and up) Fic
Karr, K. Gilbert and Sullivan set me free
Fic
Karr, K. Skullduggery (5 and up) Fic
LaFaye, A. Worth (5 and up) Fic
Langrish, K. Troll Fell (5 and up) Fic
Lasky, K. Christmas after all Fic
Levine, E. The journal of Jedediah Barstow
Fic
Levine, G. C. Dave at night (5 and up) Fic
Lisle, J. T. The crying rocks Fic
Mazer, N. F. Girlhearts Fic
Meyer, L. A. Bloody Jack (7 and up) Fic
Morgan, C. The boy who spoke dog (5 and up)
Fic
Mosher, R. Zazoo Fic
Murphy, J. The journal of James Edmond Pease, a Civil War Union soldier Fic
Naylor, P. R. Jade Green (7 and up) Fic
Naylor, P. R. Sang Spell (7 and up) Fic
Philbrick, W. R. The journal of Douglas Allen Deeds Fic
Pullman, P. The ruby in the smoke Fic
Sedgwick, M. The book of Dead Days Fic
Seidler, T. Brainboy and the Deathmaster (5 and up) Fic
Spinelli, J. Maniac Magee (5 and up) Fic
Thesman, J. The ornament tree (7 and up)
Fic
Tunnell, M. O. Wishing moon Fic
Wallace, B. B. Secret in St. Something Fic
Woodson, J. Miracle's boys Fic

Orr, Tamra
Slovenia (5 and up) 949.7
Test tube babies (5 and up) 618.1
Turkey (4 and up) 956.1
Violence in our schools (7 and up) 371.7

Orthodontics
Lee, J. Coping with braces and other orthodontic work 617.6

Ortiz, Alfonso, 1939-1997
(ed) American Indian myths and legends. See American Indian myths and legends 398.2

Ortiz Cofer, Judith, 1952-
American history
  In Who do you think you are?; stories of
    friends and enemies p36-46   **S C**
Bad influence
  In Leaving home: stories p63-90   **808.8**
Call me Maria   **Fic**
An island like you (7 and up)   **S C**
See/See also pages in the following book(s):
Hill, C. M. Ten Hispanic American authors
    920

Orwell, George, 1903-1950
Animal farm (7 and up)   **Fic**
Nineteen eighty-four (7 and up)   **Fic**
    About
Boerst, W. J. Generous anger: the story of
  George Orwell (7 and up)   **92**
Orwell's luck. Jennings, R. W.   **Fic**
Oryx multicultural folktale series
Hearne, B. G. Beauties and beasts   **398.2**
Osa, Nancy
Cuba 15 (7 and up)   **Fic**
Osage. Stewart, P. North American Indians today
  [series]
Osage Indians
Stewart, P. Osage North American Indians today
  [series]
Osama bin Laden
    About
Landau, E. Osama bin Laden (7 and up)   **92**
Loehfelm, B. Osama bin Laden   **92**
See/See also pages in the following book(s):
Currie, S. Terrorists and terrorist groups (7 and
  up)   **303.6**
Frank, M. Understanding September 11th (7 and
  up)   **973.931**
Osborn, Elinor, 1939-
Project UltraSwan (4 and up)   **598**
Osborne, Linda Barrett, 1949-
(jt. auth) King, C. Oh, freedom!   **323.1**
Osborne, Mary Pope, 1949-
Adaline Falling Star (5 and up)   **Fic**
Favorite medieval tales (4 and up)   **398.2**
  Contents: Finn Maccoul; Beowulf; The sword in the stone; Is-
land of the lost children; The song of Roland; The werewolf; Sir
Gawain and the Green Knight; Robin Hood and his merry men;
Chanticleer and the fox
One world, many religions (4 and up)   **201**
Standing in the light   **Fic**
O'Shaughnessy, Tam
(jt. auth) Ride, S. K. Exploring our solar system
    523.2
O'Shea, Maria
Kuwait (5 and up)   **953.67**
Ostler, Rosemarie
Dewdroppers, waldos, and slackers   **428**
The **O'Tannenbaum** affair. Taylor, T.
  In Taylor, T. Rogue wave and other red-
    blooded sea stories   **S C**
Otfinoski, Steven, 1949-
Afghanistan   **958.1**
Bulgaria (7 and up)   **949.9**
Francisco Coronado   **92**
Georgia
  In Celebrate the states   **973**

John Wilkes Booth and the Civil War   **92**
Juan Ponce de Leon (5 and up)   **92**
Marco Polo   **92**
New Hampshire
  In Celebrate the states   **973**
Speaking up, speaking out (5 and up)   **808.5**
Ukraine (7 and up)   **947.7**
Vasco Nuñez de Balboa (5 and up)   **92**
Othello. Lester, J.   **Fic**
Othello. Packer, T.
  In Packer, T. Tales from Shakespeare p103-
    119   **822.3**
Other America [series]
Stewart, G. Homeless teens   **362.5**
Stewart, G. People with mental illness
    616.89
Other half of history [series]
Macdonald, F. Women in 19th-century America
    305.4
Macdonald, F. Women in 19th-century Europe
    305.4
The **other** Shepards. Griffin, A.   **Fic**
The **other** side. Johnson, A.   **811**
The **other** side of truth. Naidoo, B.   **Fic**
The **other** victims. Friedman, I. R.   **940.53**
Otoonah. San Souci, R.
  In San Souci, R. Cut from the same cloth;
    American women of myth, legend, and
    tall tale p111-18   **398.2**
Ottaviani, Jim
Dignifying science: stories about women scien-
  tists   **741.5**
Otto and the flying twins. Haptie, C.   **Fic**
The **Ottoman** Empire. Ruggiero, A.   **956.1**
Ouimet, David
(il) San Souci, R. Double-dare to be scared: an-
  other thirteen chilling tales   **S C**
An **ounce** of mud. Jaffe, N.
  In Jaffe, N. and Zeitlin, S. J. The cow of no
    color: riddle stories and justice tales from
    around the world p70-73   **398.2**
Our America [series]
Josephson, J. P. Growing up in pioneer Ameri-
  ca, 1800 to 1890   **978**
Miller, B. M. Growing up in revolution and the
  new nation, 1775 to 1800   **973.3**
Our bodies [series]
Parker, S. The skeleton and muscles   **612.7**
Our country's founders (7 and up)   **973**
Our country's presidents. Bausum, A.   **920**
Our dad died. Dennison, A.   **155.9**
Our endangered planet [series]
Malaspina, A. Saving the American wilderness
    333.72
Our environment [series]
Hall, E. J. Recycling   **363.7**
Hirschmann, K. Pollution   **363.7**
Juettner, B. Energy   **333.79**
Parks, P. J. Global warming   **363.7**
Our Lady of the Greenwood. Yolen, J.
  In Sherwood: original stories from the world
    of Robin Hood p6-16   **S C**

Our only May Amelia. Holm, J. L.   **Fic**

Our patchwork planet. Sattler, H. R.   **551.1**

Our planet in peril [series]
   Oxlade, C. Global warming   **363.7**
   Scarborough, K. Nuclear waste   **363.7**

Our stories. Bauer, M. D.   **808.3**

Our time on the river. Brown, D.   **Fic**

Out of all them bright stars. Kress, N.
   In New skies: an anthology of today's science
     fiction   **S C**

Out of bounds. Naidoo, B.
   In Naidoo, B. Out of bounds: seven stories of
     conflict and hope p145-69   **S C**

Out of bounds: seven stories of conflict and hope.
   Naidoo, B.   **S C**

Out of bounds [story]. Naidoo, B.
   In Naidoo, B. Out of bounds: seven stories of
     conflict and hope p145-69   **S C**

Out of control   **612.8**

Out of control. Mazer, N. F.   **Fic**

Out of darkness: the story of Louis Braille. Freedman, R.   **92**

Out of order. Jenkins, A. M.   **Fic**

Out of sight. Simon, S.   **502.8**

Out of the dark. Wright, B. R.   **Fic**

Out of the darkness. Haskins, J.   **305.8**

Out of the dust. Hesse, K.   **Fic**

Out of the wilderness. Vanasse, D.   **Fic**

Out of this world [series]
   Spangenburg, R. The history of NASA
     629.4
   Spangenburg, R. The Hubble Space Telescope
     522
   Spangenburg, R. A look at Mercury   **523.4**
   Spangenburg, R. Meteors, meteorites, and mete-
     oroids   **523.5**
   Spangenburg, R. Onboard the space shuttle
     629.44
   Tabak, J. A look at earth   **550**
   Tabak, J. A look at Neptune   **523.4**
   Tocci, S. A look at Pluto   **523.4**
   Tocci, S. A look at Uranus   **523.4**

Out-of-this-world astronomy. Rhatigan, J.   **520**

Out there. Taylor, T.
   In Taylor, T. Rogue wave and other red-
     blooded sea stories   **S C**

Outbreak: disease detectives at work. Friedlander,
   M. P.   **614.4**

The **outcasts** of 19 Schuyler Place. Konigsburg, E.
   L.   **Fic**

Outdoor life
   See also Camping
   Paulsen, G. Woodsong (7 and up)   **796.5**

Outdoor life [series]
   Fitzgerald, R. Essential fishing for teens
     799.1

Outdoor survival *See* Wilderness survival

Outer space
   Bramwell, M. Mapping the planets and space
     520

     Exploration
   Ackroyd, P. Escape from Earth (7 and up)
     629.4
   Astronomy (7 and up)   **520**
   Furniss, T. The atlas of space exploration
     520
   Johnstone, M. The history news in space
     629.4
   Redfern, M. The Kingfisher young people's
     book of space   **520**
   Sherman, J. Deep space observation satellites
     629.43
   Spangenburg, R. The history of NASA
     629.4
   Stott, C. Space exploration (4 and up)   **629.4**
   See/See also pages in the following book(s):
   Miller, R. The history of rockets   **621.43**

Outlaws. Blackwood, G. L.   **364.1**

Outlaws, mobsters & crooks. Hoehner, J.
     920.003

The **outlaws** of Sherwood. McKinley, R.
     398.2

Outman, Elisabeth M., 1951-
   (jt. auth) Outman, J. L. Industrial Revolution:
     almanac   **330.9**
   (jt. auth) Outman, J. L. Industrial Revolution:
     biographies   **920**
   (jt. auth) Outman, J. L. Industrial Revolution:
     primary sources   **330.9**

Outman, James L., 1946-
   Industrial Revolution: almanac   **330.9**
   Industrial Revolution: biographies   **920**
   Industrial Revolution: primary sources   **330.9**

Output measures for school library media programs. Bradburn, F. B.   **027.8**

The **outsiders.** Hinton, S. E.   **Fic**

Outstanding books for children and young people.
   Barker, K.   **028.5**

Outstanding science trade books for students
   K-12   **016.5**

Outstanding women athletes. Woolum, J.
     920.003

Outward dreams. Haskins, J.   **609**

Oval portrait. Poe, E. A.
   In Poe, E. A. The pit and the pendulum and
     other stories   **S C**

Over sea, under stone. Cooper, S.   **Fic**

Over the river. Moranville, S. B.   **Fic**

Overcoming adversity [series]
   Chippendale, L. A. Triumph of the imagination:
     the story of writer J.K. Rowling   **92**

Overland journeys to the Pacific
   See also West (U.S.)—Exploration
   Blackwood, G. L. Life on the Oregon Trail (7
     and up)   **979.5**
   Calabro, M. The perilous journey of the Donner
     Party (5 and up)   **978**
   Fisher, L. E. The Oregon Trail (4 and up)
     979.5
   Lavender, D. S. Snowbound (4 and up)   **978**
     Fiction
   Levine, E. The journal of Jedediah Barstow
     Fic

Overland journeys to the Pacific—Fiction—*Continued*
  McDonald, M. All the stars in the sky (4 and up)   **Fic**
  Philbrick, W. R. The journal of Douglas Allen Deeds   **Fic**
Overlooking. Emshwiller, C.
  In The Green Man: tales from the mythic forest p223-36   **808.8**
Overnight. Griffin, A.   **Fic**
Overpopulation. Zeaman, J.   **363.9**
Ovsyanikov, Nikita
  Polar bears (7 and up)   **599.78**
Owen, David, 1939-
  Police lab (7 and up)   **363.2**
Owen, Ruth Bryan, 1885-1954
  The good sword
    In The Book of dragons p110-20   **S C**
Owens, Tom, 1960-
  Collecting baseball cards   **769**
  Collecting baseball memorabilia   **790.1**
  NASCAR   **796.72**
Owl in love. Kindl, P.   **Fic**
The **owl** service. Garner, A.   **Fic**
Owls
  Sattler, H. R. The book of North American owls (4 and up)   **598**
                                  Fiction
  Iliaasen, C. Hoot (5 and up)   **Fic**
  Kindl, P. Owl in love (6 and up)   **Fic**
The **ox** of the wonderful horns [story] Bryan, A.
  In Bryan, A. Ashley Bryan's African tales, uh-huh p27-39   **398.2**
The **oxcart**. Kimmel, E. A.
  In Kimmel, E. A. Sword of the samurai; adventure stories from Japan p41-51
                                                                                           Fic
Oxford American children's encyclopedia   **031**
Oxford book of American verse, The New   **811.008**
The **Oxford** book of children's verse in America   **811.008**
The **Oxford** book of story poems   **821.008**
The **Oxford** book of twentieth-century English verse   **821.008**
The **Oxford** book of war poetry   **808.81**
The **Oxford** companion to musical instruments. Baines, A.   **784.19**
The **Oxford** companion to the Bible   **220.3**
The **Oxford** dictionary of art   **703**
The **Oxford** dictionary of the Christian Church   **230.003**
The **Oxford** dictionary of the Jewish religion   **296.03**
The **Oxford-Duden** pictorial Japanese and English dictionary   **495.6**
Oxford first ancient history. Burrell, R. E. C.   **909**
Oxford new concise world atlas   **912**
Oxford portraits [series]
  Gaustad, E. S. Roger Williams   **92**
  Irvin, B. Samuel Adams   **92**

  Kenschaft, L. Lydia Maria Child   **92**
  Pascal, J. B. Arthur Conan Doyle   **92**
  Segall, G. John D. Rockefeller   **92**
  Sigerman, H. Elizabeth Cady Stanton   **92**
  Stefoff, R. Jack London   **92**
Oxford portraits in science [series]
  Bernstein, J. Albert Einstein and the frontiers of physics   **92**
  Christianson, G. E. Isaac Newton and the scientific revolution   **92**
  Collier, B. Charles Babbage and the engines of perfection   **92**
  Cooper, D. Enrico Fermi and the revolutions in modern physics   **92**
  Edelson, E. Gregor Mendel, and the roots of genetics   **92**
  Edelson, E. James Watson and Francis Crick and the building blocks of life   **92**
  Hager, T. Linus Pauling and the chemistry of life   **92**
  Mark, J. T. Margaret Mead   **92**
  Muckenhoupt, M. Sigmund Freud   **92**
  Pasachoff, N. E. Marie Curie and the science of radioactivity   **92**
  Robbins, L. E. Louis Pasteur   **92**
  Stefoff, R. Charles Darwin and the evolution revolution   **92**
  Voelkel, J. R. Johannes Kepler and the new astronomy   **92**
Oxford profiles [series]
  Baker, R. F. Ancient Egyptians   **932**
  Baker, R. F. Ancient Greeks   **938**
  Shipton, A. Jazz makers   **920**
Oxford student companions to American history [series]
  Barney, W. L. The Civil War and Reconstruction   **973.7**
  Daniels, R. American immigration   **325.73**
  Matthews, G. American women's history   **305.4**
  O'Neill, W. L. World War II: a student companion   **940.53**
The **Oxford** treasury of time poems   **821.008**
Oxlade, Chris
  Chemistry   **540.7**
  Global warming (5 and up)   **363.7**
  Weather   **551.5**
Oxygen
  Farndon, J. Oxygen
    In The Elements   **546**
Oy, Joy!. Frank, L. K.   **Fic**
Ozark Mountains
                                  Fiction
  Rawls, W. Where the red fern grows   **Fic**

                                    P

P.O.W.'s *See* Prisoners of war
P.S. Longer letter later. Danziger, P.   **Fic**
Pacific Coast (North America)
  Morrison, T. The coast mappers (5 and up)   **623.89**

Pacific Northwest
Fiction
Hobbs, W. Ghost canoe   Fic
Pacific region
History
The Wilson chronology of Asia and the Pacific
950
Pacific rim
Pascoe, E. The Pacific rim (7 and up)   950
Pacifism
See also Conscientious objectors
Packard, Mary
Ripley's believe it or not!   031.02
Packer, Alex J., 1951-
How rude! (7 and up)   395
Packer, Tina, 1938-
Tales from Shakespeare   822.3
Contents: A midsummer night's dream illustrated by Gail de
Marcken; Hamlet illustrated by P.J. Lynch; Much ado about
nothing illustrated by Mary GrandPré; King Lear illustrated by
Leo & Diane Dillon; As you like it illustrated by Barbara
McClintock; The Tempest illustrated by Mark Teague; Othello il-
lustrated by Kadir Nelson; Romeo and Juliet illustrated by David
Shannon; Twelfth night illustrated by Chesley McLaren
Paddock, Lisa
(ed) Courtroom drama. See Courtroom drama
347
Pagan's crusade. Jinks, C.   Fic
Page, Jake
(ed) Myths, legends, and folktales of America.
See Myths, legends, and folktales of America
398.2
Page, Lawrence M.
A field guide to freshwater fishes: North Ameri-
ca north of Mexico (7 and up)   597
Pageants
Fiction
Robinson, B. The best Christmas pageant ever
(4-6)   Fic
Pages from history [series]
Coetzee, F. World War I: a history in docu-
ments   940.3
The Gilded Age: a history in documents
973.8
Gray, E. G. Colonial America: a history in doc-
uments   973.2
McElvaine, R. S. The Depression and New Deal
973.91
Patrick, J. J. The Bill of Rights   342
Seidman, R. F. The Civil war: a history in doc-
uments   973.7
Winkler, A. M. The Cold War   909.82
Young, M. B. The Vietnam War: a history in
documents   959.704
The **pagodas** of Ciboure. Bell, M. S.
In The Green Man: tales from the mythic for-
est p322-47   808.8
Pain
See also Headache
The **Pain** tree, and other teenage angst-ridden po-
etry (7 and up)   811.008
Painkillers and tranquilizers. Durham, M.   615
Paint
See/See also pages in the following book(s):
Knapp, B. J. Materials science   620.1

Paint me like I am (7 and up)   811.008
The **painted** wall and other strange tales. Bedard,
M.   398.2
Painters
See also Artists
Painting
Richardson, J. Looking at pictures (5 and up)
750
See/See also pages in the following book(s):
Luxbacher, I. The jumbo book of art p8-57 (4
and up)   702.8
Australian
See Australian painting
Painting the black. Deuker, C.   Fic
Paisley, Tom *See* Bethancourt, T. Ernesto
Pakistan
Downing, D. Conflict: India vs. Pakistan
954
Fiction
D'Adamo, F. Iqbal (5 and up)   Fic
Staples, S. F. Shabanu   Fic
Palana, Brett J.
British Columbia
In Exploring Canada   971
Pale-Faced Lightning. San Souci, R.
In San Souci, R. Cut from the same cloth;
American women of myth, legend, and
tall tale p77-85   398.2
Palen, Debbie
(il) Gravelle, K. The period book   612.6
Paleolithic period *See* Stone Age
Paleontology *See* Fossils
Palestine
Civilization
Sherman, J. Your travel guide to ancient Israel
933
Palestine problem, 1917- *See* Israel-Arab con-
flicts; Jewish-Arab relations
Palestinian Arabs
Ellis, D. Three wishes (5 and up)   956.94
Headlam, G. Yasser Arafat   92
Israel: opposing viewpoints   956.94
Rosaler, M. Hamas: Palestinian terrorists
956.94
Fiction
Clinton, C. A stone in my hand   Fic
The **Palestinians** and the disputed territories (7
and up)   956.04
Palmer, Greg
The falcon
In Theatre for young audiences; 20 great
plays for children p338-63   812.008
Palmer, Martin
(jt. auth) Breuilly, E. Festivals of the world
394.26
(jt. auth) Breuilly, E. Religions of the world
201
Palms to the ground. Stolls, A.   Fic
Pamphlets
Bibliography
Vertical file index   015.73

Pan (Greek deity)
Fiction
Napoli, D. J. The great god Pan (7 and up)
Fic

Panama Canal
DuTemple, L. A. The Panama Canal   972.87
McNeese, T. The Panama Canal (7 and up)
386
Winkelman, B. G. The Panama Canal
972.87
See/See also pages in the following book(s):
Aaseng, N. Construction: building the impossible   624

Panchyk, Richard, 1970-
American folk art for kids   745
(jt. auth) Levy, M. Engineering the city   624

Pancza-Graham, Arleen
North American art to 1900
In International encyclopedia of art   703

Panda *See* Giant panda
Panda rescue. Bortolotti, D.   639.9
Pang, Alex
(il) Jennings, T. 101 amazing optical illusions
152.14

Pang, Guek-Cheng
Canada (5 and up)   971
(jt. auth) Layton, L. Singapore   959.57

Pang, Guek-Cheng, 1950-
Grenada (5 and up)   972.98
Mongolia (5 and up)   951.7

Panic disorders
Campbell, N. M. Panic disorders   616.85

Pantheon (Rome, Italy)
DuTemple, L. A. The Pantheon (5 and up)
726

Pantheon fairy tale & folklore library [series]
African folktales   398.2

Panzer, Nora
(ed) Celebrate America in poetry and art. See
Celebrate America in poetry and art
811.008

Pao, Kan
Li Chi slays the serpent
In The Book of dragons p35-38   S C

Paolini, Christopher
Eragon (7 and up)   Fic

Papa, Susan
Addiction   616.86

Papa John's tall tale. Hamilton, V.
In Hamilton, V. The people could fly;
American black folktales p76-80
398.2

Papa Lalo. Rice, D.
In Rice, D. Crazy loco; stories about growing
up Chicano in southern Texas p39-56
S C

Paper
See/See also pages in the following book(s):
Knapp, B. J. Materials science   620.1

Paper crafts
See also Origami
Diehn, G. Making books that fly, fold, wrap,
hide, pop up, twist, and turn (4 and up)
736
The **paper** doll ghost. Hines, A. G.
In The Haunted house: a collection of original
stories   S C
PaperQuake. Reiss, K.   Fic
Papua New Guinea
Gascoigne, I. Papua New Guinea (5 and up)
995.3
Paquette, Penny Hutchins
Learning disabilities   371.9
Parachute troops
McGowen, T. Assault from the sky   940.54
Paradise. Goodman, J. E.   Fic
The **paradox** of Jamestown, 1585-1700. Collier,
C.   975.5
Paraguay
Jermyn, L. Paraguay (5 and up)   989.2
See/See also pages in the following book(s):
Batten, M. Anthropologist: scientist of the people (4 and up)   301
The **parakeet** named Dreidel. Singer, I. B.
In Singer, I. B. The power of light; eight stories for Hanukkah p23-28   S C
Paramilitary militia movements *See* Militia
movements
Paranormal phenomena: opposing viewpoints (7
and up)   133
Parapsychology
See also Extrasensory perception
Blackwood, G. L. Extraordinary events and oddball occurrences   001.9
Paranormal phenomena: opposing viewpoints (7
and up)   133
Steiger, B. Gale encyclopedia of the unusual
and unexplained   130
Fiction
Tolan, S. S. Welcome to the Ark (7 and up)
Fic
A **parcel** of patterns. Paton Walsh, J.   Fic
The **pardoner's** tale. Cohen, B.
In Cohen, B. Canterbury tales   821
Parent and child *See* Parent-child relationship
Parent-child relationship
Snow, J. E. How it feels to have a gay or lesbian parent (5 and up)   306.8
Fiction
Bawden, N. Granny the Pag (4 and up)   Fic
Bunting, E. The hideout (5 and up)   Fic
Cleary, B. Dear Mr. Henshaw (4 and up)
Fic
Danziger, P. The Divorce Express   Fic
Mazer, N. F. Taking Terri Mueller   Fic
Voigt, C. A solitary blue (7 and up)   Fic
Parental kidnapping
Fiction
Mazer, N. F. Taking Terri Mueller   Fic
Rodowsky, C. F. Clay   Fic
Parenting
Trapani, M. Reality check (7 and up)   306.8

Parents, Single *See* Single parent family

Parents, Unmarried *See* Unmarried mothers

Paris (France)

Fiction

Clements, B. A chapel of thieves   **Fic**

Morgenstern, S. H. Secret letters from 0 to 10   **Fic**

Park, Barbara

The graduation of Jake Moon   **Fic**

Park, Linda Sue, 1960-

Project Mulberry (5 and up)   **Fic**

A single shard (5 and up)   **Fic**

When my name was Keoko (5 and up)   **Fic**

Parker, Barry R.

The mystery of gravity (5 and up)   **531**

Parker, Charlie, 1920-1955

About

Frankl, R. Charlie Parker, musician   **92**

See/See also pages in the following book(s):

Mour, S. I. American jazz musicians   **920**

Parker, Cynthia Ann, 1827?-1864

Fiction

Meyer, C. Where the broken heart still beats   **Fic**

Parker, David L., 1951-

Stolen dreams   **331.3**

Parker, Ely Samuel, 1828-1895

See/See also pages in the following book(s):

Brown, D. A. Bury my heart at Wounded Knee   **970.004**

Ehrlich, A. Wounded Knee: an Indian history of the American West (6 and up)   **970.004**

Parker, Quanah, Comanche Chief, 1854?-1911

See/See also pages in the following book(s):

Freedman, R. Indian chiefs (6 and up)   **920**

Parker, Robert Andrew

(il) Hesse, K. Stowaway   **Fic**

Parker, Steve

Allergies (5 and up)   **616.97**

Brain, nerves, and senses   **612.8**

Digestion and reproduction   **612.3**

Electricity (4 and up)   **537**

Heart, blood, and lungs   **612.1**

Human body   **612**

Medicine   **610**

The reproductive system   **612.6**

Science experiments   **507.8**

Seashore (4 and up)   **577.7**

The skeleton and muscles (5 and up)   **612.7**

Skin, muscles, and bones   **612.7**

Parkins, David

(il) McCaughrean, G. The epic of Gilgamesh   **398.2**

Parkinson's disease

Landau, E. Parkinson's disease (7 and up)   **616.8**

Silverstein, A. Parkinson's disease (7 and up)   **616.8**

See/See also pages in the following book(s):

Hyde, M. O. When the brain dies first (7 and up)   **616.8**

Parks, Henry G., 1916-1989

See/See also pages in the following book(s):

Haskins, J. African American entrepreneurs   **920**

Parks, Peggy J., 1951-

Global warming (5 and up)   **363.7**

Parks, Rosa, 1913-

Dear Mrs. Parks (5 and up)   **305.23**

Rosa Parks: my story (5 and up)   **92**

See/See also pages in the following book(s):

Dubovoy, S. Civil rights leaders (7 and up)   **920**

Pinkney, A. D. Let it shine (4 and up)   **920**

Parks

Fiction

Gordon, A. The Gorillas of Gill Park (4 and up)   **Fic**

Park's quest. Paterson, K.   **Fic**

Parliamentary practice

Riddick, F. M. Riddick's Rules of procedure   **060.4**

Robert, H. M. The Scott, Foresman Robert's Rules of order newly revised   **060.4**

Parnell, Helga

Cooking the German way

In Easy menu ethnic cookbooks   **641.5**

Cooking the South American way

In Easy menu ethnic cookbooks   **641.5**

Parrots

Fiction

Jennings, R. W. My life of crime (5 and up)   **Fic**

Particles (Nuclear physics)

Bortz, A. B. The library of subatomic particles [series]   **539.7**

Partners and rivals. Castner, J. L.   **577.3**

Partridge, Elizabeth

Restless spirit: the life and work of Dorothea Lange (6 and up)   **92**

This land was made for you and me: the life and songs of Woody Guthrie (7 and up)   **92**

Party science. Pentland, P.   **507.8**

Pasachoff, Jay M.

A field guide to the stars and planets   **523**

Pasachoff, Naomi E., 1947-

Marie Curie and the science of radioactivity   **92**

Niels Bohr   **92**

Pascal, Janet B.

Arthur Conan Doyle (7 and up)   **92**

Pascoe, Elaine

Ants (4 and up)   **595.7**

Beetles   **595.7**

Butterflies and moths   **595.7**

Crickets and grasshoppers (4 and up)   **595.7**

Earthworms   **592**

Flies   **595.7**

Mexico and the United States (7 and up)   **327.73**

The Pacific rim (7 and up)   **950**

Scholastic kid's almanac (4 and up)   **031.02**

Seeds and seedlings   **582**

Slime, molds, and fungi (4 and up)   **579.5**

Pascoe, Elaine—*Continued*
Snails and slugs (4 and up)   **594**
Tadpoles   **597.8**
(ed) Crash. See Crash   **617.1**
Pass the poetry, please!. Hopkins, L. B.   **372.6**
Passager. Yolen, J.   **Fic**
Passicot, Monique
(il) Schwartz, H. The day the Rabbi disappeared: Jewish holiday tales of magic
   398.2
Passive resistance
Adams, S. Mahatma Gandhi (7 and up)   **92**
Hatt, C. Mahatma Ghandhi   **92**
Severance, J. B. Gandhi, great soul (5 and up)
   92
Passover
Kimmel, E. A. Wonders and miracles (4 and up)
   296.4
Musleah, R. Why on this night?   **296.4**
Schecter, E. The family Haggadah   **296.4**
Passport to history [series]
Sherman, J. Your travel guide to ancient Israel
   933
Past perfect, present tense: new and collected stories. Peck, R.   **S C**
Pasteur, Louis, 1822-1895
About
Ackerman, J. Louis Pasteur and the founding of microbiology (7 and up)   **92**
Robbins, L. E. Louis Pasteur (7 and up)   **92**
Smith, L. W. Louis Pasteur   **92**
Patchwork quilts *See* Quilts
Pate, Rodney
(il) Myers, W. D. Me, Mop, and the Moondance Kid   **Fic**
Pateman, Robert, 1954-
Belgium (5 and up)   **949.3**
Egypt (5 and up)   **962**
Kenya (5 and up)   **967.62**
Patent, Dorothy Hinshaw
Animals on the trail with Lewis and Clark (4 and up)   **978**
The bald eagle returns (4 and up)   **598**
Biodiversity (5 and up)   **333.95**
Charles Darwin (7 and up)   **92**
Deer and elk (4 and up)   **599.65**
Eagles of America (4 and up)   **598**
Fire: friend or foe (4 and up)   **577.2**
Homesteading (4 and up)   **978**
In search of the maiasaurs   **567.9**
The Lewis and Clark trail (4 and up)   **978**
Plants on the trail with Lewis and Clark (4 and up)   **978**
A polar bear biologist at work (4 and up)
   599.78
Prairie dogs (4 and up)   **599.3**
Secrets of the ice man (5 and up)   **930.1**
Shaping the earth (4 and up)   **550**
Paterson, Katherine
Bridge to Terabithia (4 and up)   **Fic**
The great Gilly Hopkins (5 and up)   **Fic**
Jacob have I loved   **Fic**
Jip (5 and up)   **Fic**
Lyddie (5 and up)   **Fic**

The master puppeteer (6 and up)   **Fic**
Park's quest (5 and up)   **Fic**
Preacher's boy (5 and up)   **Fic**
The red dragonfly
In Places I never meant to be; original stories by censored writers   **S C**
The same stuff as stars (5 and up)   **Fic**
See/See also pages in the following book(s):
Ellis, S. From reader to writer   **372.6**
Paton, Alan
Cry, the beloved country (7 and up)   **Fic**
Paton Walsh, Jill, 1937-
A parcel of patterns   **Fic**
The **Patricians**. Hinds, K.   **937**
Patrick, Diane, 1955-
The New York Public Library amazing African American history (5 and up)   **305.8**
Patrick, John J.
The Bill of Rights (7 and up)   **342**
Patton, George S. (George Smith), 1885-1945
See/See also pages in the following book(s):
Ross, S. Leaders of World War II   **920**
Pattou, Edith
East   **Fic**
Pauling, Linus C., 1901-1994
About
Hager, T. Linus Pauling and the chemistry of life (7 and up)   **92**
Paulsen, Gary
Alida's song (5 and up)   **Fic**
Caught by the sea (5 and up)   **92**
The cookcamp (5 and up)   **Fic**
Dogsong (6 and up)   **Fic**
Guts   **92**
Harris and me (5 and up)   **Fic**
Hatchet   **Fic**
The haymeadow (6 and up)   **Fic**
How Angel Peterson got his name (5 and up)
   92
The island   **Fic**
The monument (6 and up)   **Fic**
My life in dog years (4 and up)   **92**
Nightjohn   **Fic**
The rifle (7 and up)   **Fic**
The Schernoff discoveries   **Fic**
Soldier's heart (7 and up)   **Fic**
The Transall saga   **Fic**
The voyage of the Frog (6 and up)   **Fic**
The winter room (5 and up)   **Fic**
Winterdance   **798.8**
Woodsong (7 and up)   **796.5**
About
Fine, E. H. Gary Paulsen (5 and up)   **92**
See/See also pages in the following book(s):
Author talk (4 and up)   **028.5**
(ed) Shelf life: stories by the book. See Shelf life: stories by the book   **S C**
Pawnee Indians
Fiction
Trottier, M. Sister to the wolf   **Fic**
Payback. Nixon, J. L.
In Nixon, J. L. Ghost town; seven ghostly stories p57-77   **S C**
Payment, Simone
Buck Leonard   **92**

Payment, Simone—*Continued*
Roe v. Wade   344
Payton, Philip A., 1876-1917
See/See also pages in the following book(s):
Haskins, J. African American entrepreneurs
    920

Peace
Glick, S. War and peace   201
Peace walker. Taylor, C. J.   398.2
Peaches for Mad Molly. Gould, S.
In New skies: an anthology of today's science
fiction   S C
Peacock, Judith, 1942-
Breast cancer   616.99
Hodgkin's disease   616.99
Peacock's ghost. San Souci, R.
In San Souci, R. A terrifying taste of short &
shivery; thirty creepy tales p109-13
    398.2

Peale, Charles Willson, 1741-1827
        About
Giblin, J. The mystery of the mammoth bones
(4 and up)   569
Pear, Nancy
(ed) Explorers & discoverers. See Explorers &
discoverers   920.003
Pearce, Philippa, 1920-
Who's afraid?
In Read all about it!; great read-aloud stories,
poems, and newspaper pieces for pre-
teens and teens p230-35   808.8
The **pearl**. Steinbeck, J.   Fic
Pearl fisheries
        Fiction
O'Dell, S. The black pearl (6 and up)   Fic
Pearl Harbor (Oahu, Hawaii), Attack on, 1941
Allen, T. B. Remember Pearl Harbor (5 and up)
    940.54
Barr, G. Pearl Harbor   940.54
Tanaka, S. Attack on Pearl Harbor (4 and up)
    940.54
Uschan, M. V. The bombing of Pearl Harbor
    940.54
        Fiction
Denenberg, B. Early Sunday morning   Fic
Mazer, H. A boy at war (7 and up)   Fic
Salisbury, G. Under the blood-red sun   Fic
The **Pearl** of Anton. Del Vecchio, G.   Fic
Pearson, Kit
See/See also pages in the following book(s):
Ellis, S. From reader to writer   372.6
Pearson, Ridley
(jt. auth) Barry, D. Peter and the starcatchers
    Fic
Peary, Robert Edwin, 1856-1920
        About
Calvert, P. Robert E. Peary   92
The **pebble** people. Jack, R.
In Talking leaves; contemporary native
American short stories   S C
Peck, Richard, 1934-
Are you in the house alone?   Fic

The electric summer
In Time capsule: short stories about teenagers
throughout the twentieth century p3-16
    S C
Fair weather (5 and up)   Fic
Girl at the window
In Night terrors; stories of shadow and sub-
stance   S C
The great interactive dream machine   Fic
How to write a short story
In Peck, R. Past perfect, present tense: new
and collected stories   S C
Invitations to the world   808.06
The kiss in the carry-on bag
In Destination unexpected: short stories
    S C
The last safe place on earth (7 and up)   Fic
A long way from Chicago (5 and up)   Fic
Lost in cyberspace (5 and up)   Fic
Past perfect, present tense: new and collected
stories   S C
Contents: Priscilla and the wimps; The electric summer; Shot-
gun Cheatham's last night above ground; The special powers of
Blossom Culp; By far the worst pupil at Long Point School; Girl
at the window; The most important night of Melanie's life; Wait-
ing for Sebastian; Shadows; Fluffy the gangbuster; I go along;
The kiss in the carry-on bag; The three-century woman; How to
write a short story; Five helpful hints
Priscilla and the wimps
In Sixteen; short stories by outstanding writ-
ers for young adults p42-46   S C
In Who do you think you are?; stories of
friends and enemies p92-95   S C
The river between us (7 and up)   Fic
Shadows
In Visions: nineteen short stories by outstand-
ing writers for young adults p2-10
    S C
Strays like us   Fic
The teacher's funeral (5 and up)   Fic
A year down yonder (5 and up)   Fic
Peck, Robert Newton, 1928-
A day no pigs would die (6 and up)   Fic
Horse thief (7 and up)   Fic
The **peculiar** such thing. Hamilton, V.
In Hamilton, V. The people could fly;
American black folktales p116-20
    398.2
Peden, Margaret Sayers
(jt. auth) Allende, I. City of the beasts   Fic
Pederson, Jay P.
(ed) African American breakthroughs. See
African American breakthroughs   305.8
Pederson, Judy
(il) Fleischman, P. Seedfolks   Fic
Pedrick, Cherry
(jt. auth) Hyman, B. M. Obsessive-compulsive
disorder   616.85
Pedro and me. Winick, J.   362.1
Peele, George, 1558?-1597?
See/See also pages in the following book(s):
Nardo, D. Great Elizabethan playwrights
    920
Peer group influence *See* Peer pressure
Peer pressure
Tym, K. School survival   371.8

Peet, Bill
  Bill Peet: an autobiography (4 and up)   92

Pegasus in flight. McCaffrey, A.   **Fic**

Pellowski, Michael, 1949-
  The art of making comic books (5 and up)
     741.5
  The Chicago "Black Sox" baseball scandal
     796.357
  The O.J. Simpson murder trial   **345**
  The terrorist trial of the 1993 bombing of the
    World Trade Center   **974.7**

Pelta, Kathy
  Rediscovering Easter Island   **996**

Pemberton, Delia
  Egyptian mummies (4 and up)   **393**

Pembroke, William Marshal, Earl of, 1144?-
1219
     About
  Ruhl, G. In the time of knights (4 and up)
     942.03
  Weatherly, M. William Marshal, medieval Eng-
    land's greatest knight [biography of William
    Marshal, earl of Pembroke]   **92**
  See/See also pages in the following book(s):
  Zohorsky, J. R. Medieval knights and warriors
    p26-37   **940.1**

Pendergast, Sara
  Fashion, costume, and culture   **391**
  (cd) Bowling, beatniks, and bell-bottoms. See
    Bowling, beatniks, and bell-bottoms   **306**
  (jt. auth) Pendergast, T. Constitutional amend-
    ments: from freedom of speech to flag burn-
    ing   **342**
  (jt. auth) Pendergast, T. Westward expansion:
    almanac   **978**
  (jt. auth) Pendergast, T. Westward expansion:
    primary sources   **978**
  (jt. auth) Pendergast, T. World War I almanac
     940.3
  (jt. auth) Pendergast, T. World War I primary
    sources   **940.3**
  (jt. auth) Pendergast, T. World War I: biogra-
    phies   **920**

Pendergast, Tom, 1964-
  Constitutional amendments: from freedom of
    speech to flag burning (7 and up)   **342**
  Westward expansion: almanac   **978**
  Westward expansion: biographies (7 and up)
     920
  Westward expansion: primary sources (7 and
    up)   **978**
  World War I almanac (7 and up)   **940.3**
  World War I primary sources (7 and up)
     940.3
  World War I: biographies (7 and up)   **920**
  (ed) Bowling, beatniks, and bell-bottoms. See
    Bowling, beatniks, and bell-bottoms   **306**
  (jt. auth) Pendergast, S. Fashion, costume, and
    culture   **391**

The **Penguin** book of modern African poetry
     896

Penguins
  Webb, S. My season with penguins (4 and up)
     598

Penicillin
  Birch, B. Alexander Fleming   **92**
  Hantula, R. Alexander Fleming   **92**

Penn, William, 1644-1718
  See/See also pages in the following book(s):
  Williams, J. K. The Quakers (7 and up)
     289.6

Pennebaker, Ruth
  Both sides now (7 and up)   **Fic**

Penniman, Richard *See* Little Richard

Pennsylvania
  Heinrichs, A. Pennsylvania
    In America the beautiful, second series
     973
      Fiction
  Collier, J. L. The bloody country   **Fic**
  Hughes, P. The breaker boys   **Fic**
  Osborne, M. P. Standing in the light   **Fic**
  Wallace, R. Playing without the ball   **Fic**
  Woodruff, E. Dear Austin   **Fic**

Penraat, Jaap
      About
  Talbott, H. Forging freedom (4 and up)
     940.53

Penrose, Lee Miller *See* Miller, Lee, 1907-1977

Pentagon (Va.) terrorist attack, 2001 *See* Sep-
    tember 11 terrorist attacks, 2001

Pentagon Papers
  Herda, D. J. New York Times v. United States
    (7 and up)   **342**

Pentland, Peter
  Earth science (4 and up)   **550**
  Forensic science (4 and up)   **363.2**
  Kitchen science (4 and up)   **641**
  Party science (4 and up)   **507.8**
  Space science (4 and up)   **500.5**
  Toy and game science (4 and up)   **531**

People and places [series]
  Howarth, S. Colonial places   **973.2**

A **people** apart. Kenna, K.   **289.7**

People around the world. Mason, A.   **305.8**

People at odds [series]
  Wagner, H. L. The IRA and England   **941.6**

People at the center of [series]
  Bardhan-Quallen, S. The Mexican-American
    War   **973.6**

The **people** could fly. Hamilton, V.   **398.2**

The **people** could fly [story] Hamilton, V.
    In Hamilton, V. The people could fly;
      American black folktales p166-73
     398.2

People in the news [series]
  Wukovits, J. F. Stephen King   **92**

People in the past [series]
  Malam, J. Ancient Egyptian jobs   **932**

The **people** of Sparks. DuPrau, J.   **Fic**

People of the ancient world [series]
  Calvert, P. The ancient Inca   **985**
  Lassieur, A. The ancient Greeks   **938**
  Lassieur, A. The ancient Romans   **937**
  Perl, L. The ancient Egyptians   **932**
  Schomp, V. The ancient Chinese   **931**
  Schomp, V. Ancient Mesopotamia   **935**

People of the Holocaust   **920.003**

People should not die in June in South Texas. Anzaldúa, G.
In Growing up Latino; memoirs and stories p280-87   **810.8**

People to know [series]
Chippendale, L. A. Yo-Yo Ma   **92**
Fine, E. H. Barbara McClintock   **92**
Fine, E. H. Gary Paulsen   **92**
Old, W. Marian Wright Edelman   **92**
Trachtenberg, M. P. Anne McCaffrey   **92**
Wilson, S. Stephen King: king of thrillers and horror   **92**
Wooten, S. M. Margaret Bourke-White   **92**
Wright, D. K. Frank Lloyd Wright   **92**
Yannuzzi, D. A. Ernest Hemingway   **92**

People who made history [series]
Albert Einstein   **92**
Benjamin Franklin   **92**
Cesar Chavez   **92**
Cleopatra   **92**
Julius Caesar   **92**
Mark Twain   **92**
Napoleon Bonaparte   **92**

People with mental illness. Stewart, G.   **616.89**

People's history [series]
Finlayson, R. We shall overcome   **323.1**
Kendall, M. E. Failure is impossible!   **305.4**
Miller, B. M. Good women of a well-blessed land   **305.4**
Whitman, S. What's cooking?   **394.1**

Peoples of Africa   **960**

Peoples of Eastern Asia (5 and up)   **950**

Peoples of Europe (5 and up)   **940**

Peoples of North America   **305.8**

Peoples of the Americas   **970**

People's Republic of China *See* China

Perception
Brynie, F. H. Perception   **612.8**

Perdue, Theda
The Cherokees Indians of North America series

Perez, German
(il) Hinojosa, M. Crews: gang members talk to Maria Hinojosa   **302.3**

The **Perigee** visual dictionary of signing. Butterworth, R. R.   **419**

The **perilous** journey of the Donner Party. Calabro, M.   **978**

The **perilous** search for the fabled Northwest Passage in American history. Warrick, K. C.   **910.4**

The **period** book. Gravelle, K.   **612.6**

Periodicals
Bibliography
El-hi textbooks and serials in print   **016.3713**
Indexes
Abridged readers' guide to periodical literature   **051**
Readers' guide to periodical literature   **051**

Perkins, Agnes
(jt. auth) Helbig, A. Many peoples, one land   **016.8**

(jt. auth) Helbig, A. Myths and hero tales   **398.2**

Perkins, Lynne Rae
All alone in the universe (5 and up)   **Fic**

Perkins, Mitali, 1963-
Monsoon summer (7 and up)   **Fic**

Perkins, Ralf
International Red Cross   **361.7**

Perl, Lila
The ancient Egyptians (5 and up)   **932**
Behind barbed wire   **940.53**
Four perfect pebbles (6 and up)   **940.53**
The great ancestor hunt (5 and up)   **929**
Mummies, tombs, and treasure (4 and up)   **393**
North across the border   **305.8**
Terrorism
To the Golden Mountain   **305.8**

{The **Pern** series}. McCaffrey, A.   **Fic**

Perón, Eva, 1919-1952
See/See also pages in the following book(s):
Hewitt, K. Lives of extraordinary women (4 and up)   **920**
Price-Groff, C. Twentieth-century women political leaders (7 and up)   **920**

Perry, Matthew Calbraith, 1794-1858
About
Blumberg, R. Commodore Perry in the land of the Shogun (5 and up)   **952**

Perry, Phyllis J., 1933-
Animals that hibernate   **591.56**
Animals under the ground   **591.56**
Armor to venom   **591.47**
Science fair success with plants (7 and up)   **580.7**

Perseus (Greek mythology)
McCaughrean, G. Perseus (5 and up)   **292**
See/See also pages in the following book(s):
Hamilton, E. Mythology p21-76   **292**

Perseus and Andromeda. Colum, P.
In The Book of dragons p16-19   **S C**

Persia *See* Iran

Persian Gulf War, 1991
Campbell, G. A. Life of an American soldier   **956.7**
Gay, K. Persian Gulf War (5 and up)   **956.7**
McArthur, D. Desert storm--the first Persian Gulf War in American history   **956.7**

Persico, Deborah
Mapp v. Ohio (7 and up)   **345**

Personal appearance
Graydon, S. In your face (7 and up)   **391**
Hinds, M. J. Focus on body image   **306.4**
Hoobler, D. Vanity rules   **391**
Irons, D. Teen beauty secrets (7 and up)   **646.7**

Personal conduct *See* Conduct of life

Personal finance
Godfrey, N. S. Neale S. Godfrey's ultimate kids' money book (5 and up)   **332.024**
Liebowitz, J. Wall Street wizard   **332.6**

Personal grooming
Irons, D. Teen beauty secrets (7 and up)   **646.7**

Personal life skills *See* Life skills

Personality and behavior. Carmichael, P.
 In Being human   **612**

Perspective
 DuBosque, D. Draw 3-D   **742**

Perspectives on disease and illness [series]
 Monroe, J. Cystic fibrosis   **616.3**
 Monroe, J. Influenza and other viruses **616.9**
 Peacock, J. Breast cancer   **616.99**
 Peacock, J. Hodgkin's disease **616.99**

Perspectives on mental health [series]
 Campbell, N. M. Panic disorders **616.85**

Peru

    Antiquities
 Reinhard, J. Discovering the Inca Ice Maiden (5
  and up)   **930.1**

    Fiction
 Abelove, J. Go and come back (7 and up)
         Fic

Pervola, Cindy, 1956-
 How to get a job if you're a teenager (7 and up)
         650.14

Pesach *See* Passover

Peter II, Emperor of Russia, 1715-1730
 See/See also pages in the following book(s):
 Meltzer, M. Ten kings (5 and up) **920**

Peter and the starcatchers. Barry, D. **Fic**

Peters, Joseph J., 1951-
 (ed) Simon and Schuster's guide to rocks and
 minerals. See Simon and Schuster's guide to
 rocks and minerals   **549**

Peters, Julie Anne, 1952-
 Define "normal" (7 and up)   **Fic**

Peters, Max, 1906-
 (jt. auth) Shostak, J. How to prepare for the
 SSAT/ ISEE: Secondary School Admissions
 Test/Independent School Entrance Exam
         373.1

Peters, Stephanie True, 1965-
 The 1918 influenza pandemic **614.5**
 The battle against polio   **614.5**
 The Black Death   **614.5**
 Cholera   **614.5**
 Smallpox in the new world   **614.5**

Peter's taller tale. Molnár, I.
 In Molnár, I. One-time dog market at Buda
  and other Hungarian folktales p39-41
         398.2

Peterson, Roger Tory, 1908-1996
 A field guide to the birds of eastern and central
  North America   **598**
 A field guide to western birds **598**
 (il) Latimer, J. P. Backyard birds **598**
 (il) Latimer, J. P. Birds of prey **598**
 (il) Latimer, J. P. Bizarre birds **598**
 (il) Latimer, J. P. Shorebirds **598**
 (il) Latimer, J. P. Songbirds **598**

Peterson, Virginia Marie, 1925-
 (jt. auth) Peterson, R. T. A field guide to the
 birds of eastern and central North America
         598

Peterson field guide series
 Pasachoff, J. M. A field guide to the stars and
 planets   **523**

Peterson field guides for young naturalists [se-
 ries]
 Latimer, J. P. Backyard birds **598**
 Latimer, J. P. Birds of prey **598**
 Latimer, J. P. Bizarre birds **598**
 Latimer, J. P. Butterflies **595.7**
 Latimer, J. P. Caterpillars **595.7**
 Latimer, J. P. Shorebirds **598**
 Latimer, J. P. Songbirds **598**

Peterson first guide to seashores. Kricher, J. C.
         577.7

Peterson first guide to shells of North America.
 Douglass, J. L.   **594**

Peterson first guide to the seashore. See Kricher,
 J. C. Peterson first guide to seashores
         577.7

Peterson natural history companions [series]
 Kaufman, K. Lives of North American birds
         598

Peterson's summer opportunities for kids and
 teenagers   **790.1**

Petley, Julian
 Media (7 and up)   **302.23**

Petricic, Dusan
 (il) Dash, J. The longitude prize [biography of
 John Harrison]   **92**

Petrides, George A.
 A field guide to trees and shrubs **582.16**

Petroglyphs *See* Rock drawings, paintings, and
 engravings

Petroleum industry
 Glassman, B. John Paul Getty (7 and up)
         92
 Gunderson, C. G. The need for oil **338.2**

Petroleum trade *See* Petroleum industry

Pets
   See also Domestic animals names of ani-
  mals, e.g. *Cats; Dogs;* etc.
 George, J. C. A tarantula in my purse (4-6)
         92

Pets. Avi
 In Avi. What do fish have to do with anything? and other stories p121-50 **S C**

Petticoat spies. Caravantes, P. **920**

Pevsner, Stella
 Is everyone moonburned but me? **Fic**

Peyer, Tom, 1954-
 Go boy 7, Vol. 1: Ready set go! **741.5**

Pfeffer, Susan Beth, 1948-
 Ashes
  In Places I never meant to be; original stories
   by censored writers   **S C**
 Pigeon humor
  In Sixteen; short stories by outstanding writ-
   ers for young adults p32-41 **S C**
 The year without Michael   **Fic**

Pferdehirt, Julia, 1952-
 Nothing at all
  In Fire and wings: dragon tales from East and
   West p65-78   **S C**

Pfetzer, Mark
 Within reach: my Everest story (7 and up)
         796.52

Pflueger, Lynda
Mathew Brady   92
Stonewall Jackson   92
Pharmacology
See also Drugs
Facklam, M. Modern medicines (7 and up)
                                      615
Kidd, J. S. Mother Nature's pharmacy (7 and
up)   615
Philadelphia (Pa.)
History
Murphy, J. An American plague (5 and up)
                                      614.5
Philanthropists
Edge, L. B. Andrew Carnegie
Kent, Z. Andrew Carnegie   92
Segall, G. John D. Rockefeller   92
Philbrick, Nathaniel
Revenge of the whale (7 and up)   910.4
Philbrick, W. R. (W. Rodman)
Freak the Mighty   Fic
The journal of Douglas Allen Deeds   Fic
The last book in the universe   Fic
The young man and the sea (5 and up)   Fic
Philip, Sachem of the Wampanoags, d. 1676
See/See also pages in the following book(s):
Kallen, S. A. Native American chiefs and war-
riors (7 and up)   920
Philip, Neil
Celtic fairy tales (4 and up)   398.2
Contents: The battle of the birds; Fair, Brown, and Trembling;
The brown bear of the Green Glen; The King of Ireland's son;
The three blows; Rory the fox; Lutey and the mermaid; Give me
a crab, John; The black bull of Norroway; Finn MacCool and the
Scottish giant; Duffy and the devil; Molly Whuppie; The black
cat; The king and the workman's daughter; The soul cages; The
fiddler in the cave; The well at the world's end; The ship that
went to America; The little bird; The tail
The illustrated book of myths (5 and up)
                                      201
In the house of happiness   204
Mythology   201
Myths & legends (7 and up)   398.2
Odin's family (4-6)   293
The story of Robin Hood   398.2
(ed) It's a woman's world. See It's a woman's
world   808.81
(ed) War and the pity of war. See War and the
pity of war   808.81
Philippines
Arruda, S. M. Freedom's martyr [biography of
Jose Rizal]   92
Tope, L. R. R. Philippines (5 and up) 959.9
Wee, J. The Philippines   959.9
Philip's concise world atlas. See Oxford new con-
cise world atlas   912
Philip's wildlife atlas. See Kerrod, R. Facts on
File wildlife atlas   578
Phillips, Samantha, 1967-
(jt. auth) Gray, H. M. Real girl/real world
                                      305.23
Phillips, Terry M.
(jt. auth) Friedlander, M. P. When objects talk
                                      363.2
Philosophers
Anderson, M. J. Aristotle (5 and up)   92

Freedman, R. Confucius (4 and up)   92
Weate, J. A young person's guide to philosophy
(5 and up)   100
Philosophy
Ochoa, G. The Wilson chronology of ideas
                                      909
Weate, J. A young person's guide to philosophy
(5 and up)   100
Phineas Gage: a gruesome but true story about
brain science. Fleischman, J.   362.1
Phobias
Stewart, G. Phobias   616.85
Phoenicians
Marston, E. The Phoenicians   939
Phoenix rising. Hesse, K.   Fic
Phoning a dead man. Cross, G.   Fic
Phosphorus
Beatty, R. Phosphorus
In The Elements   546
Phosphorus. Blashfield, J. F.
In Blashfield, J. F. Sparks of life; chemical
elements that make life possible   546
Photo by Brady. Armstrong, J.   973.7
Photo odyssey: Solomon Carvalho's remarkable
Western adventure, 1853-54. Hirschfelder, A.
B.   92
Photographers
See also Women photographers
Hirschfelder, A. B. Photo odyssey: Solomon
Carvalho's remarkable Western adventure,
1853-54   92
Pflueger, L. Mathew Brady   92
Schulke, F. Witness to our times   92
Photography
See also Cinematography; Digital photogra-
phy
Graham, I. Film and photography   770
Johnson, N. National Geographic photography
guide for kids (4 and up)   771
Price, S. Click! fun with photography (4 and up)
                                      771
Digital techniques
See Digital photography
Equipment and supplies
See also Cameras
Fiction
Levin, B. Shadow-catcher (5 and up)   Fic
Smith, C. L. Rain is not my Indian name
                                      Fic
History
Armstrong, J. Photo by Brady   973.7
Scientific applications
Simon, S. Out of sight (4 and up)   502.8
Photography, Documentary *See* Documentary
photography
Photography of animals
Aaseng, N. Wild shots (5 and up)   778.9
Photojournalism
Flash!: the Associated Press covers the world
                                      070.4
Life: our century in pictures for young people
                                      779

Phrenology
Fiction
Karr, K. Skullduggery (5 and up)   **Fic**

Physical anthropology
See also Human origins
The **physical** brain. Brynie, F. H.   **612.8**

Physical education
Medical aspects
See Sports medicine

Physical fitness
Cheung, L. W.-Y. Be healthy! it's a girl thing (5 and up)   **613**
Gedatus, G. Bicycling for fitness   **613.7**
Gedatus, G. Exercise for weight management   **613.7**
Porter, D. Winning weight training for girls (7 and up)   **613.7**
Schwager, T. The right moves (7 and up)   **613.7**
Vedral, J. L. Toning for teens (7 and up)   **613.7**

Physically handicapped
See also Blind; Deaf
Bankston, J. Stephen Hawking   **92**
Howard, M. Christopher Reeve   **92**
Fiction
Fleischman, P. Mind's eye (7 and up)   **Fic**
Fletcher, S. Shadow spinner (6 and up)   **Fic**
Konigsburg, E. L. The view from Saturday (4 and up)   **Fic**
Lewis, C. Postcards to father Abraham (7 and up)   **Fic**
Mikaelsen, B. Stranded   **Fic**
Paulsen, G. The monument (6 and up)   **Fic**
Philbrick, W. R. Freak the Mighty   **Fic**
Voigt, C. Izzy, willy-nilly (7 and up)   **Fic**

Physicians
See also Surgeons; Women physicians
Fiction
Cushman, K. Matilda Bone (5 and up)   **Fic**
Morgan, N. Fleshmarket (7 and up)   **Fic**

Physicists
Albert Einstein [essays about]   **92**
Bankston, J. Stephen Hawking   **92**
Bernstein, J. Albert Einstein and the frontiers of physics (7 and up)   **92**
Cooper, D. Enrico Fermi and the revolutions in modern physics (7 and up)   **92**
Ferry, J. Maria Goeppert Mayer, physicist (7 and up)   **92**
Hamilton, J. Lise Meitner   **92**
Henderson, H. Nuclear physics (7 and up)   **539.7**
Macdonald, F. Albert Einstein   **92**
MacLeod, E. Albert Einstein (4 and up)   **92**
Sullivan, A. M. Albert Einstein (4 and up)   **92**

Physics
See also Nuclear physics
The Facts on File physics handbook (7 and up)   **530**
Gardner, R. Bicycle science projects   **531**
Gardner, R. Science project ideas in the house   **507.8**

Gardner, R. Science projects about physics in the home (5 and up)   **507.8**
Physics matters!   **530**

Physics! best science projects [series]
Gardner, R. Light, sound, and waves science fair projects   **507.8**
Physics matters!   **530**

Physiognomy
See also Phrenology

Physiology
Gardner, R. Health science projects about sports performance (7 and up)   **612**
Hall, D. The human body
In Being human   **612**
Human physiology on file   **612**
Nagel, R. Body by design   **612**
Parker, S. Human body   **612**
Walker, R. DK guide to the human body   **612**
Walker, R. Encyclopedia of the human body   **612**

See/See also pages in the following book(s):
Glover, D. M. The young Oxford book of the human being   **612**

Pianists
Reich, S. Clara Schumann (5 and up)   **92**

Piano obsession. Barakat, I.
In What a song can do; 12 riffs on the power of music   **S C**

Picasso, Pablo, 1881-1973
About
Beardsley, J. Pablo Picasso (7 and up)   **92**
Hodge, S. Pablo Picasso (4 and up)   **92**
Loria, S. Pablo Picasso   **92**
MacDonald, P. A. Pablo Picasso (7 and up)   **92**
Mason, A. In the time of Picasso   **709.04**
Scarborough, K. Pablo Picasso (5 and up)   **92**

Pick & shovel poet: the journeys of Pascal D'Angelo. Murphy, J.   **92**

Pick-Goslar, Hannah
About
Gold, A. L. Memories of Anne Frank (5 and up)   **92**

Pickels, Dwayne E.
Egyptian kings and queens and classical deities   **930**

Pickering, William H., 1910-2004
See/See also pages in the following book(s):
Richie, J. Space flight   **920**

Picketing *See* Strikes

Pickett, Bill, ca. 1860-1932
About
Sanford, W. R. Bill Pickett: African-American rodeo star   **92**

Picky eater. Roos, S. 13; thirteen stories that capture the agony and ecstasy of being thirteen

Pico, Steven A.
About
Gold, J. C. Board of Education v. Pico (1982) (7 and up)   **344**

Picture books for children
Bibliography
Hall, S. Using picture storybooks to teach literary devices v3 **016.8**
Matulka, D. I. Picture this **011.6**
Picture dictionaries
Corbeil, J.-C. The Facts on File visual dictionary **423**
The Oxford-Duden pictorial Japanese and English dictionary **495.6**
A **picture** of Freedom. McKissack, P. C. **Fic**
Picture that! [series]
Galford, E. The trail West **978**
Martin, A. Knights & castles **940.1**
Picture this. Matulka, D. I. **011.6**
Picture writing
See also Hieroglyphics
Liungman, C. G. Dictionary of symbols **302.2**
Pictures in the dark. McCord, P. **Fic**
Pictures of Hollis Woods. Giff, P. R. **Fic**
Picturing Lincoln. Sullivan, G. **92**
Picturing the past [series]
Chrisp, P. Mesopotamia **935**
Malam, J. Ancient Greece **938**
A **piece** of heaven. Wyeth, S. D. **Fic**
Pierce, Meredith Ann, 1958-
The fall of Ys
In Firebirds: an anthology of original fantasy and science fiction; an anthology of original fantasy and science fiction **S C**
Treasure at the heart of the Tanglewood **Fic**
See/See also pages in the following book(s):
MacRae, C. D. Presenting young adult fantasy fiction (7 and up) **813.009**
Pierce, Morris A.
Robert Fulton and the development of the steamboat **92**
Pierce, Tamora, 1954-
Circle of magic: Sandry's book **Fic**
Elder brother
In Half-human p65-93 **S C**
First test **Fic**
Trickster's choice (7 and up) **Fic**
Pietrzyk, Leslie
Maryland
In Celebrate the states **973**
Pig. Kipling, R.
In McCaffrey, A. {The Pern series} **S C**
Pig brains. Carter, A. R.
In On the edge: stories at the brink p41-55 **S C**
Pigeon humor. Pfeffer, S. B.
In Sixteen; short stories by outstanding writers for young adults p32-41 **S C**
Pigeons
Fiction
Spinelli, J. Wringer (4 and up) **Fic**
The **Pigman**. Zindel, P. **Fic**
Pike, Zebulon Montgomery, 1779-1813
About
Calvert, P. Zebulon Pike (5 and up) **92**

Pilger, Mary Anne
Science experiments index for young people **507.8**
Pilgrim voices **974.4**
Pilgrims (New England colonists)
Bowen, G. Stranded at Plimoth Plantation, 1626 (4 and up) **974.4**
Collier, C. Pilgrims and Puritans, 1620-1676 **974.4**
Doherty, K. William Bradford **92**
Edwards, J. The Plymouth Colony and the Pilgrim adventure in American history (7 and up) **974.4**
Erickson, P. Daily life in the Pilgrim colony, 1636 **974.4**
Pilgrim voices **974.4**
Fiction
Lasky, K. A journey to the New World **Fic**
Pilgrims and pilgrimages
Fiction
Temple, F. The Ramsay scallop (6 and up) **Fic**
Pilgrims and Puritans, 1620-1676. Collier, C. **974.4**
Pilots, Airplane *See* Air pilots
The **pinballs**. Byars, B. C. **Fic**
Pinkney, Andrea Davis
Let it shine (4 and up) **920**
Silent thunder **Fic**
Pinkney, Brian, 1961-
(il) Hughes, L. The dream keeper and other poems **811**
(il) San Souci, R. Cut from the same cloth **398.2**
Pinkney, Jerry, 1939-
(il) Goldin, B. D. Journeys with Elijah **222**
(il) Lester, J. The last tales of Uncle Remus **398.2**
(il) Taylor, M. D. Song of the trees **Fic**
Pinkwater, Daniel Manus, 1941-
About
Hogan, W. The agony and the eggplant (7 and up) **813.009**
Pinkwater, Manus *See* Pinkwater, Daniel Manus, 1941-
Pinna, Simon de
Electricity **621.3**
Pinto Smalto
In Hearne, B. G. Beauties and beasts p145-50 **398.2**
Pioneer life *See* Frontier and pioneer life
Pioneers of geology. Carruthers, M. W. **920**
Pipes, Rose
Rain forests **577.3**
Pipkin, Gloria
At the schoolhouse gate **373.1**
Piquemal, Michel, 1954-
When life stinks **305.23**
Piracy & plunder. Waldman, B. **910.4**
Pirates
Blackwood, G. L. Pirates **364.1**
Wren, L. L. Pirates and privateers of the high seas **920**

Pirates—*Continued*
Fiction
Barry, D. Peter and the starcatchers (5 and up) **Fic**
Lee, T. Piratica **Fic**
Masefield, J. Jim Davis (5 and up) **Fic**
Meyer, L. A. Bloody Jack (7 and up) **Fic**
Rosen, M. Shakespeare **822.3**
Stevenson, R. L. Treasure Island (6 and up) **Fic**
Pirates and privateers of the high seas. Wren, L. L. **920**
Piratica. Lee, T. **Fic**
Pissin' and moanin'. Lynch, C.
In Lynch, C. All the old haunts p155-85 **S C**
The **pistachio** prescription. Danziger, P. **Fic**
The **pit** and the pendulum. Poe, E. A.
In Poe, E. A. Tales of Edgar Allan Poe p95-115 **S C**
In Poe, E. A. The pit and the pendulum and other stories **S C**
The **pit** and the pendulum and other stories. Poe, E. A. **S C**
Pitcairn, Ansel
(il) Bolden, T. Portraits of African-American heroes **920**
The **pitiful** encounter. Sleator, W.
In Sleator, W. Oddballs; stories p71-81 **S C**
Pituh-plays. Sleator, W.
In Sleator, W. Oddballs; stories p103-12 **S C**
Pizarro, Francisco, ca. 1475-1541
About
Meltzer, M. Francisco Pizarro (5 and up) **92**
A **place** for winter. See Tiulana, P. Wise words of Paul Tiulana **92**
The **Place** my words are looking for (4 and up) **811.008**
Places I never meant to be (7 and up) **S C**
Places in time. Leacock, E. **911**
Placide, Jaira
Fresh girl (7 and up) **Fic**
Plague
Corzine, P. The Black Death (7 and up) **614.5**
Peters, S. T. The Black Death **614.5**
The Black Death [Turning points in world history series] (7 and up) **614.5**
Fiction
Hooper, M. At the sign of the Sugared Plum **Fic**
Paton Walsh, J. A parcel of patterns **Fic**
Plague and pestilence. Altman, L. J. **614.4**
Plain, Nancy
Louis XVI, Marie Antoinette, and the French Revolution **944**
(jt. auth) Custer, E. B. The diary of Elizabeth Bacon Custer **973.8**
Plain City. Hamilton, V. **Fic**
Plains Indian wars. Marker, S. **973.5**
The **planet** hunters. Fradin, D. B. **523.4**

The **planet** of Junior Brown. Hamilton, V. **Fic**
Planets
Bramwell, M. Mapping the planets and space **520**
Fradin, D. B. The planet hunters (5 and up) **523.4**
Miller, R. Extrasolar planets **523**
Ride, S. K. Exploring our solar system (4 and up) **523.2**
Ridpath, I. Facts on File stars & planets atlas **520**
Plant sciences (7 and up) **580**
Plantation life
Bial, R. The strength of these arms (4 and up) **326**
Erickson, P. Daily life on a Southern plantation, 1853 (4 and up) **975**
McKissack, P. C. Christmas in the big house, Christmas in the quarters (4 and up) **394.26**
Worth, R. Slave life on the plantation (7 and up) **326**
Plante, Ellen M.
The American kitchen, 1700 to the present (7 and up) **643**
Planting the seed. Winckler, S. **635**
Plants
See also Climbing plants
Bailey, J. Plants and plant life **580**
Gardner, R. Science projects about plants (7 and up) **580.7**
Kerrod, R. Facts on File wildlife atlas **578**
Perry, P. J. Science fair success with plants (7 and up) **580.7**
Plant sciences (7 and up) **580**
Silverstein, A. Plants **580**
VanCleave, J. P. Janice VanCleave's plants (5 and up) **580.7**
Wildlife and plants of the world **578**
United States
Patent, D. H. Plants on the trail with Lewis and Clark (4 and up) **978**
Plants, Industrial *See* Factories
Plants and plant life. Bailey, J. **580**
Plants on the trail with Lewis and Clark. Patent, D. H. **978**
Plastics
Goodstein, M. Plastics and polymers science fair projects (7 and up) **507.8**
See/See also pages in the following book(s):
Knapp, B. J. Materials science **620.1**
Plastics and polymers science fair projects. Goodstein, M. **507.8**
Plate tectonics
Gallant, R. A. Dance of the continents (5 and up) **551.1**
Gallant, R. A. Plates (5 and up) **551.1**
Sattler, H. R. Our patchwork planet (5 and up) **551.1**
Silverstein, A. Plate tectonics (5 and up) **551.1**
Plates. Gallant, R. A. **551.1**

Platinum
Wood, I. Platinum
In The Elements   546
Platinum. Wood, I.
In The Elements   546
Platt, Richard, 1953-
Crime scene   363.2
Eureka! (4 and up)   609
Fidel Castro   92
Shipwreck (4 and up)   910.4
Spy   327.12
Play ball like the pros. Krasner, S.   796.357
Play-by-play baseball. Geng, D.   796.357
Play-by-play mountain biking. King, A.   796.6
The **playground**. Naidoo, B.
In Naidoo, B. Out of bounds: seven stories of
conflict and hope p120-44   S C
Playing God. Sebestyen, O.
In Visions: nineteen short stories by outstand-
ing writers for young adults p87-99
    S C
Playing the creeps. Brooks, B.
In Brooks, B. All that remains p65-113
    Fic
Playing without the ball. Wallace, R.   Fic
Playland. San Souci, R.
In San Souci, R. Dare to be scared; thirteen
stories to chill and thrill   S C
The **playmaker**. Cheaney, J. B.   Fic
Plays *See* Drama—Collections
Plays for children and young adults. Karp, R. S.
    808.82
Playwrights *See* Dramatists
Pleasing Betty Stoggs. Climo, S.
In Climo, S. Magic & mischief; tales from
Cornwall p49-55   398.2
Pledge, Deanna S., 1956-
When something feels wrong (7 and up)
    362.7
Plessy, Homer
About
Anderson, W. Plessy v. Ferguson   342
Plessy v. Ferguson. Anderson, W.   342
Plisson, Philip
(il) Burleigh, R. The sea   551.46
Plotkin, Gregory
Cooking the Russian way
In Easy menu ethnic cookbooks   641.5
Plugged in [series]
Gurian, M. From boys to men   305.23
Plummer, Louise
The unlikely romance of Kate Bjorkman (7 and
up)   Fic
Pluralism (Social sciences) *See* Multiculturalism
Pluto (Planet)
Bredeson, C. Pluto   523.4
Miller, R. Mercury and Pluto (5 and up)
    523.4
Tocci, S. A look at Pluto   523.4
Pluto. Levine, G. C.
In On the edge: stories at the brink p109-23
    S C

The **Plymouth** Colony and the Pilgrim adventure
in American history. Edwards, J.   974.4
Pocahontas, d. 1617
About
Edwards, J. Jamestown, John Smith, and Poca-
hontas in American history (7 and up)
    975.5
Fiction
Bruchac, J. Pocahontas (7 and up)   Fic
Pocho. Villarreal, J. A.
In Growing up Latino; memoirs and stories
p165-92   810.8
Podell, Janet
Old worlds to new   920.003
(ed) Facts about the states. See Facts about the
states   973
(jt. auth) Kane, J. N. Famous first facts
    031.02
Poe, Edgar Allan, 1809-1849
Edgar Allan Poe
In The Blackbirch treasury of American poet-
ry p147-91   811.008
Edgar Allan Poe's tales of mystery and madness
    S C
Contents: The black cat; The masque of the Red Death; Hop
Frog; The fall of the house of Usher
The pit and the pendulum and other stories (7
and up)   S C
Contents: Gold-bug; Oval portrait; Pit and the pendulum; Cask
of Amontillado; Some words with a mummy; Tell-tale heart;
Murders in the Rue Morgue
Tales of Edgar Allan Poe   S C
Contents: The imp of the perverse; The tell-tale heart; A de-
scent into the maelstrom; The cask of Amontillado; The prema-
ture burial; Hop-frog; The pit and the pendulum; The masque of
the Red Death; The fall of the House of Usher; Ms. found in a
bottle; The murders in the Rue Morgue; The purloined letter; The
gold bug; Berenice
About
Kent, Z. Edgar Allan Poe   92
Meltzer, M. Edgar Allan Poe: a biography (7
and up)   92
Fiction
Avi. The man who was Poe   Fic
A **Poem** of her own   811.008
Poems from homeroom. Appelt, K.   811
Poetics
Appelt, K. Poems from homeroom (7 and up)
    811
Fletcher, R. Poetry matters (4 and up)   808.1
Janeczko, P. B. How to write poetry (5 and up)
    808.1
The Place my words are looking for (4 and up)
    811.008
Poetry from A to Z (5 and up)   808.1
Seeing the blue between (7 and up)   808.1
Poetry
See also African poetry; American poetry;
English poetry; Native Americans—Poetry
and types of poetry; subjects with the subdivi-
sion *Poetry*
Collections
Blushing: expressions of love in poems & letters
(7 and up)   821.008
The Body eclectic (7 and up)   808.81
I feel a little jumpy around you (7 and up)
    808.81

Poetry—Collections—*Continued*
I wouldn't thank you for a valentine **808.81**
It's a woman's world (7 and up) **808.81**
A kick in the head **811.008**
Light-gathering poems (7 and up) **808.81**
The Oxford book of war poetry **808.81**
Revenge and forgiveness (7 and up) **808.81**
The Space between our footsteps (7 and up)
  808.81
Step lightly (7 and up) **808.81**
Stone bench in an empty park (4 and up)
  811.008
Truth & lies: an anthology of poems (7 and up)
  808.81
Voices: poetry and art from around the world
  808.81
War and the pity of war (5 and up) **808.81**
What have you lost? (7 and up) **808.81**
Wicked poems (4 and up) **811.008**
          Fiction
Creech, S. Love that dog (4 and up) **Fic**
Crew, G. Troy Thompson's excellent peotry
  book (4 and up) **Fic**
Dean, C. Comfort (7 and up) **Fic**
Koertge, R. Shakespeare bats cleanup (7 and up)
  Fic
          Indexes
Index to children's poetry **808.81**
Index to poetry for children and young people
  808.81
     Study and teaching
Hopkins, L. B. Pass the poetry, please!
  372.6
Poetry for young people [series]
Coleridge, S. T. Samuel Taylor Coleridge
  821
Liu, A. William Wordsworth **821**
Longfellow, H. W. Henry Wadsworth Longfel-
  low **811**
Whitman, W. Walt Whitman **811**
Poetry from A to Z (5 and up) **808.1**
Poetry from the masters: the pioneers (7 and up)
  811.008
Poetry matters. Fletcher, R. **808.1**
Poets
     See also Women poets
Poets, American
Angelou, M. Maya Angelou **811**
Dommermuth-Costa, C. Emily Dickinson **92**
Hill, C. M. Langston Hughes **92**
The Invisible ladder (7 and up) **811.008**
Kerley, B. Walt Whitman (4 and up) **92**
Meltzer, M. Walt Whitman (7 and up) **92**
Reef, C. Paul Laurence Dunbar **92**
Reef, C. Walt Whitman (7 and up) **92**
Rhynes, M. E. Gwendolyn Brooks (7 and up)
  92
Richmond, M. A. Phillis Wheatley **92**
Roots & flowers (7 and up) **811.008**
Salisbury, C. Phillis Wheatley **92**
Strickland, M. R. African-American poets
  920
Poets, Chilean
Goodnough, D. Pablo Neruda **92**

Pohaha. San Souci, R.
  In San Souci, R. Cut from the same cloth;
    American women of myth, legend, and
    tall tale p87-91 **398.2**
Point-counterpoint [series]
Bridegam, M. A. The right to privacy
  323.44
Hile, K. S. The trial of juveniles as adults
  345
Hudson, D. L. Gay rights **342**
Marzilli, A. Election reform **324.6**
Ruschmann, P. Legalizing marijuana **345**
Point of impact [series]
Allan, T. Understanding DNA **576.5**
Chorlton, W. The invention of the silicon chip
  621.381
Pointe de Sable, Jean Baptiste, 1745?-1818
  See/See also pages in the following book(s):
Haskins, J. Against all opposition (5 and up)
  920
Poisonous animals
Aaseng, N. Poisonous creatures **591.6**
Poisonous creatures. Aaseng, N. **591.6**
Poisons and poisoning
     See also Food poisoning
A **Poke** in the I (4 and up) **811.008**
Polakow, Amy, 1958-
Daisy Bates (7 and up) **92**
Poland
Hintz, M. Poland (4 and up) **943.8**
Polar bear
Ovsyanikov, N. Polar bears (7 and up)
  599.78
Patent, D. H. A polar bear biologist at work (4
  and up) **599.78**
A **polar** bear biologist at work. Patent, D. H.
  599.78
Polar expeditions *See* Antarctica—Exploration
Polar regions
     See also Antarctica; Arctic regions
Conlan, K. Under the ice (4 and up) **578.7**
Poles apart. Scott, E.
Police
Schulman, A. Cop on the beat **363.2**
Wirths, C. G. Coping with confrontations and
  encounters with the police (7 and up)
  363.2
          Fiction
Cormier, R. The rag and bone shop (7 and up)
  Fic
Police brutality
Fireside, B. J. The trial of the police officers in
  the shooting death of Amadou Diallo (7 and
  up)
Police brutality: opposing viewpoints (7 and up)
  363.2
Police brutality: opposing viewpoints (7 and up)
  363.2
Police lab. Owen, D. **363.2**
Polikoff, Barbara Garland
Why does the coqui sing? (5 and up) **Fic**
Polio. Silverstein, A. **616.8**

Poliomyelitis
Peters, S. T. The battle against polio   **614.5**
Silverstein, A. Polio (7 and up)   **616.8**
Fiction
Giff, P. R. All the way home (4 and up)
   Fic

Poliomyelitis vaccine
Tocci, S. Jonas Salk   **92**

Polish Americans
Fiction
Bartoletti, S. C. A coal miner's bride (4 and up)
   Fic
Cushman, K. Rodzina (5 and up)   **Fic**
Political advocacy for school librarians. Schuckett,
S.   **027.8**
Political and social movements. Spangenburg, R.
   917.3
Political leaders. Uschan, M. V.   **920**
Political science
Countries of the world and their leaders year-
book   **910.3**
The Statesman's year-book   **310.5**
Politicians
See also Women politicians
Countries of the world and their leaders year-
book   **910.3**
United States
Hill, C. M. John Lewis   **92**
Kennedy, J. F. Profiles in courage   **920**
Politics
See also Political science
Marzilli, A. Election reform (7 and up)
   324.6
See/See also pages in the following book(s):
Mass media: opposing viewpoints   **302.23**
Politics and religion *See* Religion and politics
The **politics** of slavery. Altman, L. J.   **326**
Pollack, Pam
Ski (7 and up)   **796.93**
Pollard, Michael, 1931-
The light bulb and how it changed the world
   621.3
Margaret Mead   **92**
Pollution
See also Environmental protection
Bryan, N. Love Canal (5 and up)   **363.7**
Conserving the environment (7 and up)
   333.72
Davis, L. A. Environmental disasters (7 and up)
   363.7
The environment: opposing viewpoints   **363.7**
Hirschmann, K. Pollution (5 and up)   **363.7**
Pollution: opposing viewpoints (7 and up)
   363.7
Reed, J. Love Canal (7 and up)   **363.7**
Pollution control industry
See also Recycling
Pollution: opposing viewpoints (7 and up)
   363.7
Polo, Marco, 1254-1323?
About
Otfinoski, S. Marco Polo   **92**

Worth, R. The great empire of China and Marco
Polo in world history   **92**
Polymers
Goodstein, M. Plastics and polymers science fair
projects (7 and up)   **507.8**
Pometacom, Sachem of the Wampanoags *See*
Philip, Sachem of the Wampanoags, d. 1676
Pompeii (Extinct city)
Connolly, P. Pompeii   **937**
Ponce de Leon, Juan, 1460?-1521
About
Otfinoski, S. Juan Ponce de Leon (5 and up)
   92
See/See also pages in the following book(s):
Fritz, J. Around the world in a hundred years (4
and up)   **910.4**
Pond ecology
Josephs, D. Lakes, ponds, and temporary pools
   577.6
Sayre, A. P. Lake and pond (5 and up)
   577.6
Pontiac, Ottawa Chief, d. 1769
See/See also pages in the following book(s):
Kallen, S. A. Native American chiefs and war-
riors (7 and up)   **920**
A **pool** in the desert. McKinley, R.
In McKinley, R. and Dickinson, P. Water:
tales of elemental spirits p208-66
   S C
Poor
Bial, R. Tenement (4 and up)   **974.7**
Hopkinson, D. Shutting out the sky (5 and up)
   974.7
Kowalski, K. M. Poverty in America   **362.5**
Fiction
Flake, S. G. Money hungry   **Fic**
Fogelin, A. Sister spider knows all (5 and up)
   Fic
A **poor** man's bargain. Molnár, I.
In Molnár, I. One-time dog market at Buda
and other Hungarian folktales p83-88
   398.2
Pop art
Greenberg, J. Andy Warhol (7 and up)   **92**
Popular authors series
Bostrom, K. L. Winning authors   **920**
McElmeel, S. L. 100 most popular children's
authors   **810.3**
Popular culture
United States
Bowling, beatniks, and bell-bottoms   **306**
Culture wars: opposing viewpoints   **306**
Rap and hip hop (7 and up)   **306**
Popular mechanics for kids [series]
Thomas, K. Blades, boards & scooters   **796.2**
Popular music
See also Blues music; Rock music
Orgill, R. Shout, sister, shout! (6 and up)
   920
Popular science: science year by year   **509**
Popular superstitions. Hughes, M.   **398**
Population
Zeaman, J. Overpopulation (7 and up)   **363.9**

Pordes, Laurence
(il) Brookfield, K. Book   **070.5**
Pornography
Pornography: opposing viewpoints (7 and up)
     363.4
See/See also pages in the following book(s):
Cate, F. H. The Internet and the First Amendment   **342**
Mass media: opposing viewpoints   **302.23**
Pornography: opposing viewpoints (7 and up)
     363.4
Porpoises
Carwardine, M. Whales, dolphins, and porpoises (7 and up)   **599.5**
Porter, David, 1960-
Winning weight training for girls (7 and up)
     613.7
Portrait of a farm family. Bial, R.   **630.1**
Portraits of Black Americans [series]
Miller, C. C. A. Philip Randolph and the African American labor movement   **92**
Possum plays dead. Van Laan, N.
In Van Laan, N. With a whoop and a holler; a bushel of lore from way down south p18-19   **398.2**
In Van Laan, N. With a whoop and a holler; a bushel of lore from way down south p18-19   **398**
Post, Elizabeth L.
Emily Post's teen etiquette (7 and up)   **395**
Post, Peggy, 1945-
Emily Post's etiquette (7 and up)   **395**
Emily Post's The guide to good manners for kids (5 and up)   **395**
Post-traumatic stress disorder
     Fiction
Paulsen, G. Soldier's heart (7 and up)   **Fic**
Postage stamps
Postal Service guide to U.S. stamps   **769.56**
     Catalogs
Scott standard postage stamp catalogue
     769.56
Postal Service guide to U.S. stamps   **769.56**
Postcards to father Abraham. Lewis, C.   **Fic**
Potassium
Blashfield, J. F. Potassium
In Blashfield, J. F. Sparks of life; chemical elements that make life possible   **546**
Potawatomi
In North American Indians today [series]
Potok, Chaim, 1929-2002
Zebra and other stories (7 and up)   **S C**
Contents: Zebra; B.B.; Moon; Nava; Isabel; Max
Potter, Beatrix, 1866-1943
See/See also pages in the following book(s):
Ellis, S. From reader to writer   **372.6**
Pottery
See/See also pages in the following book(s):
Morris, J. Tending the fire: the story of Maria Martinez (4 and up)   **92**
     Fiction
Park, L. S. A single shard (5 and up)   **Fic**
Pough, Frederick H. (Frederick Harvey), 1906-
A field guide to rocks and minerals   **549**

Poultry
     See also Geese; Turkeys
Poverty
     See also Poor
Inner-city poverty (7 and up)   **362.5**
Kowalski, K. M. Poverty in America   **362.5**
Poverty: opposing viewpoints (7 and up)
     362.5
     Fiction
Conly, J. L. While no one was watching (5 and up)   **Fic**
Fenner, C. Randall's wall   **Fic**
Hartnett, S. Thursday's child (7 and up)   **Fic**
Haseley, D. The amazing thinking machine (4 and up)   **Fic**
Morgan, N. Fleshmarket (7 and up)   **Fic**
Steinbeck, J. The pearl (7 and up)   **Fic**
Wolff, V. E. Make lemonade   **Fic**
Poverty in America. Kowalski, K. M.   **362.5**
Poverty: opposing viewpoints (7 and up)
     362.5
Powell, Anton
Ancient Greece (5 and up)   **938**
The Greek news   **938**
Powell, Colin L., 1937-
     About
Finlayson, R. Colin Powell   **92**
Powell, Randy
Three clams and an oyster (7 and up)   **Fic**
Powell, Ransom J., 1849-1899
     Fiction
Wisler, G. C. Red Cap (4 and up)   **Fic**
Powell, William J., 1899-1942
     About
Haskins, J. Black eagles (5 and up)   **629.13**
See/See also pages in the following book(s):
Hart, P. S. Flying free (4 and up)   **629.13**
Power (Mechanics)
     See also Water power; Wind power
Adams, R. C. Energy projects for young scientists (7 and up)   **621**
Farndon, J. Energy   **531**
Power football. Sullivan, G.   **920**
The **power** of light. Singer, I. B.   **S C**
The **power** of light [story] Singer, I. B.
     In Singer, I. B. The power of light; eight stories for Hanukkah p53-60   **S C**
The **power** of one [biography of Daisy Bates] Fradin, J. B.   **92**
The **power** of reading. Krashen, S. D.   **028.5**
Power research tools. Valenza, J. K.   **001.4**
Power resources *See* Energy resources
Power tools. See Valenza, J. K. Power tools recharged   **027.8**
Power tools recharged. Valenza, J. K.   **027.8**
Powerful words. Hudson, W.   **808.8**
Powers, Ron
(jt. auth) Bradley, J. Flags of our fathers
     940.54
Powhatan, ca. 1550-1618
     About
Collier, C. The paradox of Jamestown, 1585-1700   **975.5**

Powhatan Indians
Fiction
Bruchac, J. Pocahontas (7 and up)   **Fic**
POWs *See* Prisoners of war
Poynter, Margaret
The Leakeys   **92**
Marie Curie: discoverer of radium (4 and up)
    92
Pozzi, Gianni
Chagall   **92**
The **prairie**. Ormsby, A.   **577.4**
The **prairie** builders. Collard, S. B., III   **635.9**
Prairie dogs
Patent, D. H. Prairie dogs (4 and up)   **599.3**
Prairie ecology
Martin, P. A. F. Prairies, fields, and meadows (7
and up)   **577.4**
Ormsby, A. The prairie   **577.4**
Patent, D. H. Prairie dogs (4 and up)   **599.3**
Sayre, A. P. Grassland (5 and up)   **577.4**
Prairie songs. Conrad, P.   **Fic**
Prairie whispers. Arrington, F.   **Fic**
Prairies
Collard, S. B., III. The prairie builders (4 and
up)   **635.9**
The Great North American prairie   **810.8**
Prairies, fields, and meadows. Martin, P. A. F.
    577.4
The **prank**. Maguire, G.
In Gothic!; ten original dark tales   **S C**
Pratchett, Terry
The amazing Maurice and his educated rodents
(7 and up)   **Fic**
Only you can save mankind (5 and up)   **Fic**
The Wee Free Men   **Fic**
Prato, Rodica
(il) Leacock, E. Journeys in time   **973**
Prayers
Philip, N. In the house of happiness   **204**
Preacher's boy. Paterson, K.   **Fic**
Precious stones
Kallen, S. A. Gems (4 and up)   **553.8**
Symes, R. F. Crystal & gem (5 and up)
    548
Trueit, T. S. Rocks, gems, and minerals   **552**
Pregnancy
Flanagan, G. L. Beginning life   **612.6**
Fiction
Bunting, E. Doll baby   **Fic**
Caseley, J. Losing Louisa (7 and up)   **Fic**
Dessen, S. Someone like you (7 and up)
    Fic
Zeises, L. M. Contents under pressure (7 and
up)   **Fic**
Pregnancy, Teenage *See* Teenage pregnancy
Pregnancy, Termination of *See* Abortion
Pregnancy (7 and up)   **362.7**
Prehistoric animals
See also Dinosaurs
Gallant, J. R. The tales fossils tell (5 and up)
    560

Prehistoric art
See also Rock drawings, paintings, and en-
gravings
Prehistoric man *See* Fossil hominids
Prehistoric peoples
Deem, J. M. Bodies from the bog (4 and up)
    930.1
Dickinson, P. The kin   **Fic**
Getz, D. Frozen man (5 and up)   **930.1**
Macdonald, F. The Stone Age news   **930.1**
Patent, D. H. Secrets of the ice man (5 and up)
    930.1
Prejudices
See also Antisemitism; Discrimination
Gay, K. Cultural diversity (7 and up)   **305.8**
Senker, C. Why are people prejudiced?
    303.3
Fiction
Blakeslee, A. R. A different kind of hero
    Fic
Brooks, K. Lucas (7 and up)   **Fic**
Bruchac, J. Hidden roots   **Fic**
Conly, J. L. Crazy lady! (5 and up)   **Fic**
Cormier, R. Tunes for bears to dance to (7 and
up)   **Fic**
Curtis, C. P. The Watsons go to Birmingham—
1963 (4 and up)   **Fic**
Ferris, J. Eight seconds (7 and up)   **Fic**
Fletcher, S. Walk across the sea   **Fic**
Grove, V. The starplace   **Fic**
Hesse, K. Witness (6 and up)   **Fic**
Jordan, S. The raging quiet (7 and up)   **Fic**
Kurtz, J. The storyteller's beads (5 and up)
    Fic
Lee, M. G. Necessary roughness (7 and up)
    Fic
Matas, C. The war within (5 and up)   **Fic**
Meyer, C. Drummers of Jericho (7 and up)
    Fic
Olsen, S. White girl (7 and up)   **Fic**
Staples, S. F. Dangerous skies (7 and up)
    Fic
Taylor, M. D. The gold Cadillac (4 and up)
    Fic
Taylor, M. D. Mississippi bridge (4 and up)
    Fic
Uchida, Y. A jar of dreams (5 and up)   **Fic**
Yep, L. The traitor (5 and up)   **Fic**
Prelutsky, Jack
(ed) The Random House book of poetry for
children. See The Random House book of po-
etry for children   **821.008**
The **premature** burial. Poe, E. A.
In Poe, E. A. Tales of Edgar Allan Poe p61-
80   **S C**
Prescott, Chris
Barron's science study dictionary (7 and up)
    503
The **Presence**. Bunting, E.   **Fic**
Presenting Avi. Bloom, S. P.   **813.009**
Presenting Cynthia Voigt. Reid, S. E.   **813.009**
Presenting Kathryn Lasky. Brown, J.   **813.009**
Presenting M.E. Kerr. Nilsen, A. P.   **813.009**

Presenting Mildred D. Taylor. Crowe, C.
813.009

Presenting Paula Danziger. Krull, K.   813.009

Presenting Phyllis Reynolds Naylor. Stover, L. T.
813.009

Presenting young adult fantasy fiction. MacRae,
C. D.   813.009

Presenting young adult science fiction. Reid, S. E.
813.009

Preservation of wildlife *See* Wildlife conservation

The **presidency**. Horn, G.   352.23

The **Presidency** A to Z   352.23

The **president** is shot!. Holzer, H.   973.7

Presidential losers. Goldman, D. J.   920

Presidents
Fiction
Cabot, M. All-American girl (7 and up)   Fic
United States
Adler, D. A. George Washington (5 and up)
92

Allen, M. G. Calvin Coolidge (7 and up)
92

Allen, T. B. George Washington, spymaster
92

American presidents in world history
920.003

Barron, R. Richard Nixon (7 and up)   92

Bausum, A. Our country's presidents (5 and up)
920

Burgan, M. John F. Kennedy   92

Cooper, I. Jack: the early years of John F. Kennedy
92

Donnelly, M. Theodore Roosevelt: larger than life (7 and up)   92

Feinberg, B. S. The changing White House
975.3

Freedman, R. Franklin Delano Roosevelt (5 and up)   92

Freedman, R. Lincoln: a photobiography (5 and up)   92

Fritz, J. Bully for you, Teddy Roosevelt! (5 and up)   92

Fritz, J. The great little Madison (5 and up)
92

Gilbert, A. Franklin D. Roosevelt (7 and up)
92

Goldman, M. S. Richard M. Nixon (7 and up)
92

Greenberg, J. E. Young people's letters to the president   973

Heiligman, D. High hopes [biography of John F. Kennedy] (4 and up)

Holford, D. M. Herbert Hoover   92

Horn, G. The presidency (5 and up)   352.23

Kachurek, S. J. George W. Bush (4 and up)
92

Kane, J. N. Facts about the presidents   920

Kraft, B. H. Theodore Roosevelt (5 and up)
92

Krull, K. Lives of the presidents   920

Lincoln, A. Abraham Lincoln the writer (7 and up)   92

Malone, M. James Madison   92

Marrin, A. Old Hickory [biography of Andrew Jackson] (7 and up)   92

Matuz, R. Complete American presidents sourcebook   920

McNeese, T. George W. Bush (7 and up)
92

My fellow Americans (7 and up)   352.23

Nelson, L. E. American presidents   920.003

Rosenburg, J. M. First in peace: George Washington, the Constitution, and the presidency (7 and up)   92

Rubel, D. Scholastic encyclopedia of the presidents and their times (5 and up)   920

Severance, J. B. Thomas Jefferson (7 and up)
92

Sullivan, G. Abraham Lincoln (4 and up)
92

Sullivan, G. Picturing Lincoln   92

Uschan, M. V. John F. Kennedy (7 and up)
92

Whitelaw, N. Thomas Jefferson (7 and up)
92

World Book of America's presidents   920

Young, J. C. Dwight D. Eisenhower   92
United States—Election
The election of 1860 and the administration of Abraham Lincoln (7 and up)   973.7

Goldman, D. J. Presidential losers   920
United States—Election—2000
The Election of 2000 and the administration of George W. Bush (7 and up)   324

Sergis, D. K. Bush v. Gore   342
United States—Encyclopedias
The Presidency A to Z   352.23
United States—Spouses
See Presidents' spouses—United States

Presidents' spouses
United States
Bober, N. Abigail Adams (7 and up)   92

Flanagan, A. K. Edith Bolling Galt Wilson, 1872-1961   92

Freedman, R. Eleanor Roosevelt (5 and up)
92

Greenberg, J. E. Barbara Pierce Bush, 1925-
92

Kramer, S. The look-it-up book of first ladies
920

McPherson, S. S. Martha Washington   92

The Smithsonian book of the First Ladies (7 and up)   920

Presley, Elvis, 1935-1977
About
Denenberg, B. All shook up: the life and death of Elvis Presley (5 and up)   92

Presma, Frances
Straight talk about today's families (7 and up)
306.8

Presnall, Judith Janda
The giant panda (7 and up)   599.78

Press, Petra
Fidel Castro   92

Press
See also Freedom of the press

Pressler, Mirjam
Anne Frank: a hidden life   92

Malka (7 and up)   Fic

Preston, Diana
Remember the Lusitania (5 and up)   **940.4**
Preston, Katherine K.
Scott Joplin   **92**
Prétear, Volume 1. Naruse, K.   **741.5**
Price, Leontyne
    Juvenile literature
Steins, R. Leontyne Price, opera superstar
    92
Price, Susanna
Click! fun with photography (4 and up)   **771**
Price-Groff, Claire
Extraordinary women journalists   **920**
The manatee (7 and up)   **599.5**
Queen Victoria and nineteenth-century England
    941.081
Twentieth-century women political leaders (7 and up)   **920**
Primary sources [Lucent library of historical eras. Elizabethan England]   **942.05**
Primary sources in American history [series]
Adams, C. Women's suffrage   **305.4**
Houghton, G. The Transcontinental Railroad
    385
Levy, J. The Alamo   **976.4**
Levy, J. The Erie Canal   **974.7**
O'Donnell, K. The gold rush   **979.4**
Primates
Redmond, I. Gorilla (4 and up)   **599.8**
Primavera, Elise, 1954-
(il) Fritz, J. Make way for Sam Houston   **92**
Primm, E. Russell, 1958-
(ed) Favorite children's authors and illustrators. See Favorite children's authors and illustrators
    920.003
Prince across the water. Yolen, J.   **Fic**
The **prince** and the pauper. Twain, M.   **Fic**
The **Prince** of Tennis, Vol. 1. Konomi, T.
    741.5
Prince White Hog
In Hearne, B. G. Beauties and beasts p99-108
    398.2
Princes
Billinghurst, J. Growing up royal   **920**
Princes and princesses *See* Princesses
The **princess** & the pauper. Scott, K.   **Fic**
The **princess** and the frog. McKinley, R.
In McKinley, R. The door in the hedge p79-103   **S C**
The **Princess** and the pig
In Hearne, B. G. Beauties and beasts p18-21
    398.2
The **princess** diaries. Cabot, M.   **Fic**
Princess Dragonblood. Mandell, J.
In Half-human p139-63   **S C**
Princess Ka'iulani. Linnea, S.   **92**
Princess tales [series]
Levine, G. C. The princess test   **Fic**
The **princess** test. Levine, G. C.   **Fic**
Princesses
McGaw, L. To be a princess (4 and up)
    920

Hansen, J. African princess (5 and up)   **920**
Linnea, S. Princess Ka'iulani   **92**
    Fiction
Cabot, M. The princess diaries   **Fic**
Ferris, J. Once upon a Marigold   **Fic**
Haddix, M. P. Just Ella (7 and up)   **Fic**
Hale, S. The Goose girl   **Fic**
Levine, G. C. The two princesses of Bamarre (5 and up)   **Fic**
McKissack, P. C. Nzinga, warrior queen of Matamba (5 and up)   **Fic**
Scott, K. The princess & the pauper (7 and up)
    Fic
White, E. E. Kaiulani   **Fic**
Princeton Language Institute
Roget's 21st century thesaurus in dictionary form. See Roget's 21st century thesaurus in dictionary form   **423**
Principles and practice series
Curriculum connections through the library
    027.62
Pringle, Laurence P.
An extraordinary life (5 and up)   **595.7**
Global warming (4 and up)   **363.7**
Strange animals, new to science (4 and up)
    591.68
Printing
Graham, I. Books and newspapers   **686.2**
The **printing** press. Meltzer, M.   **686.2**
Prinz, Martin, 1931-2000
(ed) Simon and Schuster's guide to rocks and minerals. See Simon and Schuster's guide to rocks and minerals   **549**
Prior, Katherine
UNICEF   **362.7**
Priscilla and the wimps. Peck, R.
In Peck, R. Past perfect, present tense: new and collected stories   **S C**
In Sixteen; short stories by outstanding writers for young adults p42-46   **S C**
In Who do you think you are?; stories of friends and enemies p92-95   **S C**
Prisoners
Rabiger, J. Daily prison life (7 and up)   **365**
    Fiction
Hausman, G. Escape from Botany Bay (7 and up)   **Fic**
Mosier, E. My life as a girl   **Fic**
Myers, W. D. Somewhere in the darkness (7 and up)   **Fic**
The **prisoners** of Court House Rock. Brown, D. A.
In Brown, D. A. Dee Brown's folktales of the Native American; retold for our times p133-34   **398.2**
Prisoners of war
    Fiction
Mazer, H. The last mission (7 and up)   **Fic**
Prisons
Lock, J. Famous prisons (7 and up)   **365**
Rabiger, J. Daily prison life (7 and up)   **365**
    Fiction
Karr, K. Gilbert and Sullivan set me free
    Fic

Prisons—*Continued*
United States
America's prisons: opposing viewpoints (7 and up) **365**

Pritchard, Marion
See/See also pages in the following book(s):
Lyman, D. Holocaust rescuers **920**

Pritchett, Shelley
(il) Pilgrim voices. See Pilgrim voices **974.4**

Pritzker, Barry
Native Americans **970.004**

Privacy vs. security. Fridell, R. **342**

Private and personal. Weston, C. **305.23**

Private Captain. Crisp, M. **Fic**

Private Peaceful. Morpurgo, M. **Fic**

Private schools
Directories
The Handbook of private schools **370.25**

Pro/Con [series]
Tagliaferro, L. Genetic engineering **576.5**

Probably still Nick Swansen. Wolff, V. E.
Fic

Probing volcanoes. Lindop, L. **551.2**

Problem drinking *See* Alcoholism

The **problem** of Thor Bridge. Doyle, Sir A. C.
In Doyle, Sir A. C. The complete Sherlock
Holmes **S C**

Professional growth series
Yucht, A. H. Flip it! **025.5**

Professions
See also Occupations
The **professor** of smells. Yep, L.
In Yep, L. The rainbow people p20-35
398.2

Proffitt, Pamela, 1966-
(ed) Notable women scientists. See Notable
women scientists **920.003**

Profiles [series]
Byrnes, P. Environmental pioneers **920**
McLean, J. Women of adventure **920**
Streissguth, T. Legendary labor leaders **920**

Profiles and pathways series
Haven, K. F. 100 most popular scientists for
young adults **920**

Profiles in American history. Moss, J. **973**

Profiles in courage. Kennedy, J. F. **920**

Programs, Computer *See* Computer software

Programs, Twelve-step *See* Twelve-step programs

Progressivism, the Great Depression, and the New
Deal, 1901 to 1941. Collier, C. **973.91**

Prohibition
Harvey, B. C. Carry A. Nation: saloon smasher
and prohibitionist **92**
See/See also pages in the following book(s):
King, D. C. Al Capone and the roaring twenties
92

Proimos, James
The grade school zone
In Tripping over the lunch lady and other
school stories p85-92 **S C**

Project Apollo
Bredeson, C. The moon (4 and up) **523.3**

Green, J. Race to the moon **629.45**

Project Mulberry. Park, L. S. **Fic**

Project UltraSwan. Osborn, E. **598**

Projects for young scientists [series]
Adams, R. C. Energy projects for young scientists **621**

Proliferation of arms *See* Arms race

Promises to keep: how Jackie Robinson changed
America. Robinson, S. **92**

Promises to the dead. Hahn, M. D. **Fic**

Promoting a global community through
multicultural children's literature. Steiner, S.
F. **016.8**

Propaganda
Spangenburg, R. Propaganda (7 and up)
303.3

Prophecies
Cohen, D. Prophets of doom (7 and up)
133.3

Prophets of doom. Cohen, D. **133.3**

Prose, Francine, 1947-
After (7 and up) **Fic**

Protecting Marie. Henkes, K. **Fic**

Protecting the right to read. Symons, A. K.
025.2

Protection of birds *See* Birds—Protection

Protection of environment *See* Environmental
protection

Protection of wildlife *See* Wildlife conservation

Protector of the small [series]
Pierce, T. First test **Fic**

Protest!. Kronenwetter, M. **303.4**

Protestant churches
Noll, M. A. Protestants in America (7 and up)
280

Protestantism
Brown, S. F. Protestantism (7 and up) **280**

Protestants
United States
See/See also pages in the following book(s):
Joselit, J. W. Immigration and American religion (7 and up) **200**

Protestants in America. Noll, M. A. **280**

Protopopescu, Orel Odinov
(jt. auth) Liu Siyu. A thousand peaks **895.1**

A **proud** taste for scarlet and miniver. Konigsburg,
E. L. **Fic**

Proud to be an American. Rice, D.
In Rice, D. Crazy loco; stories about growing
up Chicano in southern Texas p67-77
S C

Prunier, James
(il) Poe, E. A. The pit and the pendulum and
other stories **S C**

Psychiatric disorders [series]
Esherick, J. The FDA and psychiatric drugs

Psychiatric hospitals
Fiction
Marsden, J. Checkers (7 and up) **Fic**
McCormick, P. Cut (7 and up) **Fic**

Psychiatrists
Muckenhoupt, M. Sigmund Freud (7 and up)
    92
Reef, C. Sigmund Freud: pioneer of the mind (7 and up)
    92

Psychical research *See* Parapsychology

Psychological novels
Wiesel, E. The accident
    In Wiesel, E. Night, Dawn, The accident: three tales p205-318
    Fic

Psychologists
    See also Psychiatrists

Psychology
    See also Adolescent psychology
Carmichael, P. Personality and behavior
    In Being human
    612
Gardner, R. Health science projects about psychology (7 and up)
    150
A student's guide to mental health & wellness
    616.89
See/See also pages in the following book(s):
Chahrour, J. Zap! blink! taste! think! (5 and up)
    507.8
Glover, D. M. The young Oxford book of the human being
    612

Psychotherapy
Borenstein, G. C. Therapy
    616.89
    Fiction
Juby, S. Alice, I think (7 and up)
    Fic

Psychotropic drugs
Durham, M. Painkillers and tranquilizers
    615
Esherick, J. The FDA and psychiatric drugs

PTSD *See* Post-traumatic stress disorder

Pu Songling
    (jt. auth) Bedard, M. The painted wall and other strange tales
    398.2

Puberty
Teen dreams
    612.6

Public debts
Garlake, T. Global debt (7 and up)
    336.3

Public documents *See* Government publications

Public Education Information Network
The Information-powered school. See The Information-powered school
    027.8

Public enemy number two. Horowitz, A.
    Fic

Public health
    See also Epidemiology
Foley, R. World health (7 and up)
    362.1

Public housing
    Fiction
McDonald, J. Twists and turns (7 and up)
    Fic

Public libraries
Edwards, K. Teen library events
    027.62
Jones, P. Do it right!
    027.62
Mediavilla, C. Creating the full-service homework center in your library
    027.4

Public relations for school library media programs. Flowers, H. F.
    021.7

Public school safety. Hester, J. P.
    371.7

Public schools
Pipkin, G. At the schoolhouse gate
    373.1

Public speaking
Otfinoski, S. Speaking up, speaking out (5 and up)
    808.5

Public utilities
See/See also pages in the following book(s):
Macaulay, D. Underground (5 and up)
    624

Public welfare
Inner-city poverty (7 and up)
    362.5
Poverty: opposing viewpoints (7 and up)
    362.5
Welfare reform (7 and up)
    361.6

Publishers and publishing
Graham, I. Books and newspapers
    686.2
    Fiction
Clements, A. The school story (5 and up)
    Fic

Pueblo. McIntosh, K. North American Indians today [series]

Pueblo Indians
Lavender, D. S. Mother Earth, Father Sky
    970.004
McIntosh, K. Pueblo North American Indians today [series]
Morris, J. Tending the fire: the story of Maria Martinez (4 and up)
    92
Vivian, R. G. Chaco Canyon
    978

Puerto Ricans
    Fiction
Ortiz Cofer, J. Call me Maria
    Fic
Ortiz Cofer, J. An island like you (7 and up)
    S C
Polikoff, B. G. Why does the coqui sing? (5 and up)
    Fic

Puerto Rico
Davis, L. Puerto Rico
    In America the beautiful, second series
    973
Schwabacher, M. Puerto Rico
    In Celebrate the states
    973
    Fiction
Polikoff, B. G. Why does the coqui sing? (5 and up)
    Fic

Puffins
Quinlan, S. E. Puffins
    598

Pullman, Philip, 1946-
The amber spyglass (7 and up)
    Fic
Clockwork (4 and up)
    Fic
The golden compass (7 and up)
    Fic
The ruby in the smoke
    Fic
The subtle knife (7 and up)
    Fic

Pumas
    Fiction
Naylor, P. R. The fear place (5 and up)
    Fic

Pumping iron *See* Weight lifting

Punishment
Kerrigan, M. The history of punishment (7 and up)
    364.6

The **puppeteer's** apprentice. Love, D. A.
    Fic

Puppets and puppet plays
Doney, M. Puppets
    745.592
    Fiction
Love, D. A. The puppeteer's apprentice
    Fic
Paterson, K. The master puppeteer (6 and up)
    Fic

Puritans

Aronson, M. John Winthrop, Oliver Cromwell, and the Land of Promise (7 and up) **92**

Collier, C. Pilgrims and Puritans, 1620-1676 **974.4**

Gaustad, E. S. Roger Williams (7 and up) **92**

Fiction

Gilson, J. Stink Alley (4 and up) **Fic**

Speare, E. G. The witch of Blackbird Pond (6 and up) **Fic**

The **purloined** letter. Poe, E. A.

In Poe, E. A. Tales of Edgar Allan Poe p217-42 **S C**

Push-up. Soto, G.

In Soto, G. Local news p47-59 **S C**

The **pushcart** war. Merrill, J. **Fic**

Pyle, Howard, 1853-1911

The merry adventures of Robin Hood of great renown in Notinghamshire (7 and up) **398.2**

The story of King Arthur and his knights (7 and up) **398.2**

The story of Sir Launcelot and his companions (7 and up) **398.2**

The story of the champions of the Round Table (7 and up) **398.2**

The story of the Grail and the passing of Arthur (7 and up) **398.2**

Pyle, Robert Michael

The Audubon Society field guide to North American butterflies **595.7**

Pyramids

Macaulay, D. Pyramid (4 and up) **726**

Millard, A. Pyramids **909**

See/See also pages in the following book(s):

Aaseng, N. Construction: building the impossible **624**

Pythons

McDonald, M. A. Pythons **597.9**

Q

Qaeda (Organization) *See* Al Qaeda (Organization)

Qi Shu Fang *See* Qi Shufang

Qi Shufang

See/See also pages in the following book(s):

Major, J. S. Caravan to America p[1]-13 (4 and up) **920**

Qin Shi Huang, Emperor of China *See* Ch'in Shih-huang, Emperor of China, 259-210 B.C.

Quakers *See* Society of Friends

Qualls, Sean

(il) Hudson, W. Powerful words **808.8**

Quant, Mary, 1934-

See/See also pages in the following book(s):

Kent, J. Business builders in fashion **920**

Quantrill, William Clarke, 1837-1865

Fiction

Hughes, P. Guerrilla season (7 and up) **Fic**

Quarks and sparks. Kidd, J. S. **621.48**

The **quarrel** between Wind and Thunder. Curry, J. L.

In Curry, J. L. Hold up the sky: and other Native American tales from Texas and the Southern Plains p20-21 **398.2**

Québec (Province)

Ferry, S. Quebec

In Exploring Canada **971**

Queen, Ellery

Object lesson

In Read all about it!; great read-aloud stories, poems, and newspaper pieces for pre-teens and teens p53-66 **808.8**

In Read all about it!; great read-aloud stories, poems, and newspaper pieces for pre-teens and teens p53-66 **808.88**

The **Queen** of Air and Darkness. White, T. H.

In White, T. H. The once and future king **Fic**

Queen of diamonds. Dorris, M.

In Talking leaves; contemporary native American short stories **S C**

Queen Victoria and nineteenth-century England. Price-Groff, C. **941.081**

Queens

See also names of queens and countries with the subdivision *Kings and rulers*

Brooks, P. S. Cleopatra (7 and up) **92**

Cleopatra [biographical essays] (7 and up) **92**

Greenblatt, M. Elizabeth I and Tudor England **942.05**

Kings and queens **920.003**

Meltzer, M. Ten queens (5 and up) **920**

Morgan, J. Cleopatra **92**

Price-Groff, C. Queen Victoria and nineteenth-century England **941.081**

Stanley, D. Cleopatra (4 and up) **92**

Stanley, D. Good Queen Bess: the story of Elizabeth I of England (4 and up) **92**

Thomas, J. R. Behind the mask: the life of Queen Elizabeth I (7 and up) **92**

The **queen's** own fool. Yolen, J. **Fic**

Quick, Jennifer

(jt. auth) DeFilippis, N. Once in a blue moon **741.5**

Quick starts for kids! [series]

Mayne, D. Drawing horses that look real! **743**

The **quick-witted** cobbler at wits' end. Molnár, I.

In Molnár, I. One-time dog market at Buda and other Hungarian folktales p23-30 **398.2**

Quicksand pony. Lester, A. **Fic**

Quiet storm (7 and up) **811.008**

The **quilt**. San Souci, R.

In San Souci, R. Double-dare to be scared: another thirteen chilling tales **S C**

Quilt trilogy [series]

Rinaldi, A. A stitch in time **Fic**

Quilting

Bial, R. With needle and thread (4 and up) **746.46**

Quilts
Bial, R. With needle and thread (4 and up)
746.46
Fiction
Rinaldi, A. A stitch in time (7 and up)   **Fic**
Quinceañera (Social custom)
King, E. Quinceañera (5 and up)   **392**
Quinlan, Kathryn A.
(jt. auth) Kent, D. Extraordinary people with disabilities   **920**
Quinlan, Susan E., 1954-
The case of the monkeys that fell from the trees
577.3
Puffins   **598**
Quintana, Anton
The baboon king (7 and up)   **Fic**
Quiquern. Kipling, R.
In Kipling, R. The jungle books   **S C**
Quit it. Byalick, M.   **Fic**
Quiver. Spinner, S.   **Fic**
Quotations
Bartlett, J. Familiar quotations   **808.88**
Burleigh, R. Who said that?   **808.88**
Weston, C. For teens only   **305.23**

R

Raatma, Lucia
Safety on the Internet (4 and up)   **025.04**
Rabbits
Fiction
Adams, R. Watership Down (6 and up)   **Fic**
Jennings, R. W. Orwell's luck (5 and up)
Fic
Rabble Starkey. Lowry, L.   **Fic**
Rabiger, Joanna
Daily prison life (7 and up)   **365**
Rabin, Arnold
The man-child
In Theatre for young audiences; 20 great plays for children p364-94   **812.008**
Raccoons
North, S. Rascal (5 and up)   **599.7**
Race discrimination
Police brutality: opposing viewpoints (7 and up)
363.2
Race relations
See also Culture conflict; Multiculturalism names of countries, cities, etc., with the subdivision *Race relations*
Fiction
Bennett, C. A heart divided (7 and up)
Collier, J. L. With every drop of blood (5 and up)   **Fic**
Collier, K. Jericho walls (7 and up)   **Fic**
Cooney, C. B. Burning up (7 and up)   **Fic**
English, K. Francie (5 and up)   **Fic**
Face relations (7 and up)   **S C**
Fuqua, J. S. Darby (4 and up)   **Fic**
Hermes, P. Summer secrets (5 and up)   **Fic**
Klass, D. Danger zone   **Fic**
Krisher, T. Spite fences   **Fic**

Lynch, C. Gold dust   **Fic**
Lyon, G. E. Sonny's house of spies   **Fic**
McDonald, J. Devil on my heels (7 and up)
Fic
Meyer, C. Jubilee journey   **Fic**
Meyer, C. White lilacs (5 and up)   **Fic**
Moses, S. P. The legend of Buddy Bush
Fic
Myers, A. Tulsa burning (7 and up)   **Fic**
Paton, A. Cry, the beloved country (7 and up)
Fic
Peck, R. The river between us (7 and up)
Fic
Reeder, C. Across the lines (5 and up)   **Fic**
Robinet, H. G. Walking to the bus-rider blues (5 and up)   **Fic**
Rodman, M. A. Yankee girl (4 and up)   **Fic**
Schmidt, G. D. Lizzie Bright and the Buckminster boy (7 and up)   **Fic**
Siegelson, K. L. Trembling earth   **Fic**
Sitomer, A. L. The Hoopster (7 and up)   **Fic**
Spinelli, J. Maniac Magee (5 and up)   **Fic**
Taylor, M. D. The friendship (4 and up)
Fic
Taylor, M. D. The gold Cadillac (4 and up)
Fic
Taylor, M. D. The land (7 and up)   **Fic**
Taylor, M. D. Mississippi bridge (4 and up)
Fic
Taylor, M. D. The road to Memphis (4 and up)
Fic
Taylor, M. D. The well (4 and up)   **Fic**
Taylor, T. The cay (5 and up)   **Fic**
Taylor, T. Timothy of the cay (5 and up)
Fic
Tocher, T. Chief Sunrise, John McGraw, and me   **Fic**
Woodson, J. If you come softly (7 and up)
Fic
Race relations: opposing viewpoints   **305.8**
The **race** to save the Lord God Bird. Hoose, P. M.
598
Race to the moon. Green, J.   **629.45**
Races of people *See* Ethnology
Rachel's sister. Appelt, K.
In Appelt, K. Kissing Tennessee and other stories from the Stardust Dance p11-30
S C
Racial balance in schools *See* School integration
Racially mixed people
Lanier, S. Jefferson's children (7 and up)
920
What are you? (7 and up)   **305.8**
Fiction
Crutcher, C. Whale talk (7 and up)   **Fic**
Curry, J. L. The Black Canary (5 and up)
Fic
Hamilton, V. Plain City (5 and up)   **Fic**
Meyer, C. Jubilee journey   **Fic**
Osborne, M. P. Adaline Falling Star (5 and up)
Fic
Paterson, K. Jip (5 and up)   **Fic**
Peck, R. The river between us (7 and up)
Fic
Schwartz, V. F. Send one angel down   **Fic**

Racially mixed people—Fiction—*Continued*
Taylor, M. D. The land (7 and up)　　**Fic**
Woodson, J. The house you pass on the way (7 and up)　　**Fic**
Racism
Crowe, C. Getting away with murder: the true story of the Emmett Till case (7 and up) **364.1**
Gay, K. Cultural diversity (7 and up)　**305.8**
Fiction
Crowe, C. Mississippi trial, 1955 (7 and up)
　　　　　　　　　　Fic
Rackers, Mark
(ed) The Arab-Israeli conflict. See The Arab-Israeli conflict　　**956.04**
Racso and the rats of NIMH. Conly, J. L.　**Fic**
Racz, Michael
(il) Mann, E. The Roman Colosseum　**937**
Radical reads. Bodart, J. R.　　**028.5**
Radical reptiles. Miller, S. S.　　**597.9**
Radicalism
See also Militia movements
Radio
Graham, I. Radio and television　**621.384**
Fiction
Fleischman, P. Seek (7 and up)　　**Fic**
History
Birch, B. Gugliclmo Marconi　　**92**
El **radio**. Soto, G.
In Soto, G. Local news p35-46　　**S C**
Radio and television. Graham, I.　**621.384**
Radioactive waste disposal
Scarborough, K. Nuclear waste (5 and up)
　　　　　　　　　　363.7
Rafferty, Trisha
(il) I wouldn't thank you for a valentine. See I wouldn't thank you for a valentine　**808.81**
Rafting (Sports)
George, C. White-water rafting　　**797.1**
Fiction
Woods, R. The hero　　**Fic**
The **rag** and bone shop. Cormier, R.　**Fic**
The **raging** quiet. Jordan, S.　　**Fic**
Raicht, Mike
(jt. auth) Dezago, T. Spider-man: Spidey strikes back Vol. 1 digest　　**741.5**
The **Raiders** jacket. Soto, G.
In Soto, G. Local news p69-79　　**S C**
Railroad engineering
Barter, J. A worker on the transcontinental railroad　　**331.7**
Railroads
See/See also pages in the following book(s):
Collier, C. Indians, cowboys, and farmers and the battle for the Great Plains, 1865-1910
　　　　　　　　　　978
Fiction
Durbin, W. The journal of Sean Sullivan (5 and up)　　**Fic**
Yep, L. Dragon's gate (6 and up)　　**Fic**
History
Barter, J. A worker on the transcontinental railroad　　**331.7**

Murphy, J. Across America on an emigrant train (5 and up)　　**92**
United States
Houghton, G. The Transcontinental Railroad (5 and up)　　**385**
Perl, L. To the Golden Mountain　　**305.8**
Rain
See also Droughts
Gardner, R. Science project ideas about rain
　　　　　　　　　　551.57
Rain forest ecology
Castner, J. L. Layers of life　　**577.3**
Castner, J. L. Partners and rivals　**577.3**
Castner, J. L. Surviving in the rain forest
　　　　　　　　　　577.3
Jackson, T. Tropical forests (5 and up)
　　　　　　　　　　577.3
Lasky, K. The most beautiful roof in the world (4 and up)　　**577.3**
Pipes, R. Rain forests　　**577.3**
Quinlan, S. E. The case of the monkeys that fell from the trees　　**577.3**
Sayre, A. P. Tropical rain forest (5 and up)
　　　　　　　　　　577.3
Rain forests
See/See also pages in the following book(s):
Global resources: opposing viewpoints
　　　　　　　　　　333.71
Encyclopedias
Rain forests of the world　　**577.3**
Rain forests. Pipes, R.　　**577.3**
Rain forests of the world　　**577.3**
Rain is not my Indian name. Smith, C. L.　**Fic**
Rain music. Nguyen, L.
In American dragons: twenty-five Asian American voices p155-60　　**810.8**
Rainbow Jordan. Childress, A.　　**Fic**
The **rainbow** people. Yep, L.　　**398.2**
The **rainbow** people [story] Yep, L.
In Yep, L. The rainbow people p178-90
　　　　　　　　　　398.2
Rainey, Ma, 1886-1939
See/See also pages in the following book(s):
Orgill, R. Shout, sister, shout! (6 and up)
　　　　　　　　　　920
Raising voices. Sima, J.　　**027.62**
Rajendra, Rudi
(jt. auth) Rajendra, V. Iran　　**955**
Rajendra, Sundran, 1967-
(jt. auth) Rajendra, V. Australia　　**994**
Rajendra, Vijeya, 1936-
Australia (5 and up)　　**994**
Iran (5 and up)　　**955**
Rajtar, Steve, 1951-
United States holidays and observances
　　　　　　　　　　394.26
Ralegh, Walter *See* Raleigh, Sir Walter, 1552?-1618
Raleigh, Sir Walter, 1552?-1618
About
Aronson, M. Sir Walter Ralegh and the quest for El Dorado (7 and up)　　**92**

Ramanujan Aiyangar, Srinivasa, 1887-1920
See/See also pages in the following book(s):
Henderson, H. Modern mathematicians (7 and up) **920**

The **Ramayana** and Hinduism. Ganeri, A. **294.5**

Ramen, Fred
A historical atlas of Iran **955**

Ramey, Dawn
(ed) Arab American encyclopedia. See Arab American encyclopedia **305.8**

The **Ramsay** scallop. Temple, F. **Fic**

Ranch life
Freedman, R. In the days of the vaqueros (4 and up) **636.2**
Fiction
Ehrlich, G. A blizzard year **Fic**
Paulsen, G. The haymeadow (6 and up) **Fic**
Steinbeck, J. The red pony **Fic**

Ranchers, homesteaders, and traders. Doherty, K. **920**

Randall, David, 1972-
Clovermead (7 and up) **Fic**

Randall's wall. Fenner, C. **Fic**

Randle, Kristen D., 1952-
Breaking rank (7 and up) **Fic**

Randolph, Asa Philip, 1889-1979
About
Miller, C. C. A. Philip Randolph and the African American labor movement **92**
See/See also pages in the following book(s):
Dubovoy, S. Civil rights leaders (7 and up) **920**
Streissguth, T. Legendary labor leaders (7 and up) **920**

Random House American sign language dictionary. Costello, E. **419**

The **Random** House book of opera stories. Geras, A. **792.5**

The **Random** House book of poetry for children **821.008**

Random House Webster's unabridged dictionary **423**

Rangada. Mayer, M.
In Mayer, M. Women warriors; myths and legends of heroic women p17-19 **398**

Rankin, Jeannette, 1880-1973
See/See also pages in the following book(s):
Hewitt, K. Lives of extraordinary women (4 and up) **920**
Mendoza, P. M. Extraordinary people in extraordinary times (7 and up) **920**

Rankin, Virginia
The thoughtful researcher **027.62**

Ransford, Sandy
The Kingfisher illustrated horse & pony encyclopedia (4 and up) **636.1**

The **ransom** of Mercy Carter. Cooney, C. B. **Fic**

Ransome, Arthur, 1884-1967
See/See also pages in the following book(s):
Ellis, S. From reader to writer **372.6**

Ransome, James
(il) McKissack, P. C. Let my people go **221.9**

Rao, Sirish
Sophocles' Oedipus the King (7 and up) **Fic**
Rap and hip hop (7 and up) **306**

Rap music
Rap and hip hop (7 and up) **306**

Rape
See also Date rape
Bode, J. Voices of rape (7 and up) **362.88**
Kaminker, L. Everything you need to know about dealing with sexual assault **364.1**
Fiction
Anderson, L. H. Speak (7 and up) **Fic**
Cadnum, M. Rundown (7 and up) **Fic**
Cole, B. The facts speak for themselves (7 and up) **Fic**
Peck, R. Are you in the house alone? **Fic**

Rappaport, Doreen, 1939-
Escape from slavery (4 and up) **326**
The flight of Red Bird (7 and up) **92**
John's secret dreams [biography of John Lennon] (4 and up) **92**

Raptor! a kid's guide to birds of prey. Laubach, C. M. **598**

Rare animals
See also Endangered species
Pringle, L. P. Strange animals, new to science (4 and up) **591.68**

Rare plants
See also Endangered species

Rascal. North, S. **599.7**

The **rascal** crow. Alexander, L.
In Alexander, L. The foundling and other tales of Prydain p41-50 **S C**

Raschka, Christopher
(il) A kick in the head. See A kick in the head **811.008**
(il) Zeitlin, S. J. The four corners of the sky **201**

Raskin, Ellen, 1928-1984
The Westing game **Fic**

Rasmussen, R. Kent
Farewell to Jim Crow (7 and up) **305.8**
(ed) The African American encyclopedia. See The African American encyclopedia **305.8**
(ed) Encyclopedia of American government. See Encyclopedia of American government **320.03**

Rat boys. Eberhardt, T. **Fic**

The **rat** children. Mazer, H.
In Places I never meant to be; original stories by censored writers **S C**

Rathmann, Peggy
See/See also pages in the following book(s):
The Newbery & Caldecott medal books, 1986-2000 **028.5**

Rationalism
See also Enlightenment

Ratliff, Gerald Lee
(ed) Millennium monologs. See Millennium monologs **812.008**

Rats
McNicholas, J. Rats (4 and up)   **636.9**
      Fiction
Avi. The Christmas rat   **Fic**
Conly, J. L. Racso and the rats of NIMH (4 and up)   **Fic**
Crocker, C. The tale of the swamp rat (4 and up)   **Fic**
Jarvis, R. The dark portal (5 and up)   **Fic**
O'Brien, R. C. Mrs. Frisby and the rats of NIMH (4 and up)   **Fic**
Pratchett, T. The amazing Maurice and his educated rodents (7 and up)   **Fic**

Rattenbury, Jeanne
Understanding alternative medicine (7 and up)   **615.5**

Rattlesnake Mesa. Weber, E. N. R.   **92**

Rattlesnakes
McDonald, M. A. Rattlesnakes   **597.9**

Rauzon, Mark J.
Hummingbirds   **598**
Vultures   **598**

Raven of the waves. Cadnum, M.   **Fic**

Ravens
      Fiction
George, J. C. Charlie's raven (5 and up)   **Fic**

Raven's gate. Horowitz, A.   **Fic**

The **ravine**. Bradbury, R.
   In Read all about it!; great read-aloud stories, poems, and newspaper pieces for pre-teens and teens p252-71   **808.8**

Ravine. Hickman, J.   **Fic**

The **ravine**. Salisbury, G.
   In On the edge: stories at the brink p177-91   **S C**
   In Salisbury, G. Island boyz: short stories p6-19   **S C**

Rawlings, Marjorie Kinnan, 1896-1953
The yearling   **Fic**
      About
Cook, J. Natural writer: a story about Marjorie Kinnan Rawlings   **92**

Rawlins, Carol
The Colorado River   **979.1**

Rawls, Wilson, 1913-
Summer of the monkeys (7 and up)   **Fic**
Where the red fern grows   **Fic**

Ray, Delia
Behind the Blue and Gray (5 and up)   **973.7**
Ghost girl (5 and up)   **Fic**
A nation torn (5 and up)   **973.7**

Ray, G. Carleton
(jt. auth) Robins, C. R. A field guide to Atlantic coast fishes of North America   **597**

Ray, Virginia Lawrence
School wide book events   **027.8**

Rayfield, Susan
Pierre-Auguste Renoir (7 and up)   **92**

Raymond's run. Bambara, T. C.
   In Who do you think you are?; stories of friends and enemies p47-57   **S C**

Rea, William R.
African art
   In International encyclopedia of art   **703**

Reaching Dustin. Grove, V.   **Fic**

Reaching reluctant young adult readers. Sullivan, E. T.   **028.5**

Read, Mary, 1680-1721
See/See also pages in the following book(s):
Wren, L. L. Pirates and privateers of the high seas p11-17   **920**

Read all about it!   **808.8**

The **read-aloud** handbook. Trelease, J.   **028.5**

Read into the millennium   **S C**

Reader's Digest explores [series]
Astronomy   **520**

Reader's Digest pathfinders [series]
Beckelman, L. The human body   **612**

Reader's encyclopedia, Benét's   **803**

Readers' guide to periodical literature   **051**

Readers' theater
Gustafson, C. Acting out   **812**

Reading
Bouchard, D. The gift of reading   **372.4**
Into focus   **028.1**
Krashen, S. D. The power of reading   **028.5**
      Fiction
Paulsen, G. Nightjohn   **Fic**

Reading rules!. Knowles, E.   **028.5**

Reagan, Ronald, 1911-2004
See/See also pages in the following book(s):
Uschan, M. V. Political leaders   **920**

Real. Holman, F.   **Fic**

Real estate business
Aaseng, N. Business builders in real estate   **920**

Real girl/real world. Gray, H. M.   **305.23**

The **real** high school handbook. Lieberman, S. A.   **373.1**

Real time. Kass, P.   **Fic**

Real world (Television program)
Winick, J. Pedro and me (7 and up)   **362.1**

Reality check. Trapani, M.   **306.8**

Really Rosie [play] Sendak, M.
   In Theatre for young audiences; 20 great plays for children p72-98   **812.008**

Reason. Asimov, I.
   In Asimov, I. I, robot   **S C**
   In Read into the millennium; tales of the future p57   **S C**

Rebel. Whitesel, C. A.   **Fic**

The **rebel** princess. Tchana, K. H.
   In Tchana, K. H. The serpent slayer: and other stories of strong women p31-36   **398.2**

Rebels against slavery. McKissack, P. C.   **326**

Rebman, Renee C.
Euthanasia and the "right to die"   **179.7**

Rebora, Piero
(comp) Cassell's Italian dictionary. See Cassell's Italian dictionary   **453**

Rebuilding the body. Fullick, A.   **617.9**

Rebuilding the past [series]
Burrell, R. E. C. Oxford first ancient history
909

Recipes *See* Cooking

"Recitatif". Morrison, T.
In Leaving home: stories p201-27 **808.8**

Recitations *See* Monologues

Recommended reference books for small and medium-sized libraries and media centers
011

Reconstruction (1865-1876)
See also Ku Klux Klan
Barney, W. L. The Civil War and Reconstruction (7 and up) **973.7**
Collier, C. Reconstruction and the rise of Jim Crow, 1864-1896 **973.8**
Golay, M. Reconstruction and reaction (7 and up) **305.8**
Hansen, J. Bury me not in a land of slaves (7 and up) **973.8**
January, B. Reconstruction **973.8**
Kirchberger, J. H. The Civil War and Reconstruction (7 and up) **973.7**
See/See also pages in the following book(s):
Frankel, N. Break those chains at last: African Americans, 1860-1880 **305.8**

Reconstruction and reaction. Golay, M. **305.8**

Reconstruction and the rise of Jim Crow, 1864-1896. Collier, C. **973.8**

Records, World *See* World records

Recreation

Directories
Peterson's summer opportunities for kids and teenagers **790.1**
The **recreation** handbook. Loeffelbein, R. L. **793**

Recycling
Hall, E. J. Recycling (5 and up) **363.7**
Needham, B. Ecology crafts for kids **745.5**

The **red** badge of courage. Crane, S. **Fic**
The **red** badge of courage. Vansant, W. **741.5**
Red Cap. Wisler, G. C. **Fic**

Red Cloud, Sioux Chief, 1822-1909
See/See also pages in the following book(s):
Brown, D. A. Bury my heart at Wounded Knee **970.004**
Ehrlich, A. Wounded Knee: an Indian history of the American West (6 and up) **970.004**
Freedman, R. Indian chiefs (6 and up) **920**

The **red** convertible. Erdrich, L.
In Who do you think you are?; stories of friends and enemies p134-45 **S C**

Red Cross
Perkins, R. International Red Cross **361.7**

Red Dog. Kipling, R.
In Kipling, R. The jungle books **S C**

The **red** dragonfly. Paterson, K.
In Places I never meant to be; original stories by censored writers **S C**

The **Red-headed** League. Doyle, Sir A. C.
In Doyle, Sir A. C. The complete Sherlock Holmes **S C**

Red hot salsa (7 and up) **811.008**

Red kayak. Cummings, P. **Fic**
Red land, yellow river. Zhang, A. **951.05**
Red midnight. Mikaelsen, B. **Fic**
The **red** pony. Steinbeck, J. **Fic**
The **red** rose box. Woods, B. **Fic**
Red scarf girl. Jiang, J.-l. **951.05**
Red seven. Christiansen, C. B.
In The Color of absence; 12 stories about loss and hope p105-20 **S C**

Red Shield and Running Wolf. Brown, D. A.
In Brown, D. A. Dee Brown's folktales of the Native American; retold for our times p135-41 **398.2**

The **red** spot. Schwartz, A.
In Schwartz, A. Scary stories 3; more tales to chill your bones p62 **398.2**

Red, white, blue, and Uncle who? Bateman, T.
929.9

Redfern, Martin
The Kingfisher young people's book of planet earth **550**
The Kingfisher young people's book of space **520**

Rediscovering Easter Island. Pelta, K. **996**

Redmond, Ian
Gorilla (4 and up) **599.8**

Reducing *See* Weight loss

Redwall. Jacques, B. **Fic**

Reed, Arthea J. S.
Norma Fox Mazer (7 and up) **813.009**

Reed, Dale
See/See also pages in the following book(s):
Richie, J. Space flight **920**

Reed, Gary
Mary Shelley's Frankenstein: the graphic novel **741.5**

Reed, George
Eyes on the universe (5 and up) **520**

Reed, Gregory J.
(jt. auth) Parks, R. Dear Mrs. Parks **305.23**

Reed, Jennifer
Earthquakes (4 and up) **551.2**
Love Canal (7 and up) **363.7**
The Saudi royal family **920**

Reeder, Carolyn, 1937-
Across the lines (5 and up) **Fic**

Reedy, Jerry
Oklahoma
In America the beautiful, second series
973

Reef, Catherine
Africans in America: the spread of people and culture **305.8**
Alone in the world **362.7**
John Steinbeck (7 and up) **92**
Paul Laurence Dunbar **92**
Sigmund Freud: pioneer of the mind (7 and up) **92**
This our dark country **966.62**
Walt Whitman (7 and up) **92**

Rees, Celia, 1949-
Writing on the wall
  In Gothic!; ten original dark tales   **S C**
Rees, Douglas C.
Vampire High   **Fic**
Reeve, Christopher, 1952-2004
  About
Howard, M. Christopher Reeve   **92**
Reeve, Philip, 1966-
Mortal engines (7 and up)   **Fic**
Reference books
  Bibliography
Recommended reference books for small and
  medium-sized libraries and media centers
   011
Safford, B. R. Guide to reference materials for
  school media centers   **011.6**
  Reviews
Recommended reference books for small and
  medium-sized libraries and media centers
   011
Reference services (Libraries)
Lanning, S. Essential reference services for to-
  day's school media specialists   **025.5**
Reflections on a gift of watermelon pickle—and
  other modern verse (6 and up)   **811.008**
Reformation
  See also World history—16th century
Hinds, K. The church   **274**
Renaissance & Reformation: almanac   **940.2**
Renaissance & Reformation: primary sources
   940.2
Reformers
Josephson, J. P. Mother Jones   **92**
Refugees
  Fiction
Crew, L. Children of the river (7 and up)
   Fic
Mikaelsen, B. Red midnight   **Fic**
Temple, F. Tonight, by sea (6 and up)   **Fic**
Whelan, G. Goodbye, Vietnam (4 and up)
   Fic
Refugees, Jewish *See* Jewish refugees
Refuse and refuse disposal
  See also Recycling
Bowden, R. Waste   **363.7**
Morgan, S. Waste disposal   **628.4**
See/See also pages in the following book(s):
Netzley, P. D. Issues in the environment (7 and
  up)   **333.7**
Regan, Dian Curtis
Golpe de estado
  In Shattered: stories of children and war p52-
  70   **S C**
Regan, Dian Curtis, 1950-
Tangled notes in watermelon
  In What a song can do; 12 riffs on the power
  of music   **S C**
Reggae music
Dolan, S. Bob Marley   **92**
Rehder, Harald Alfred, 1907-1996
The Audubon Society field guide to North
  American seashells   **594**

Reich, Susanna, 1954-
Clara Schumann (5 and up)   **92**
Reichman, Henry, 1947-
Censorship and selection   **025.2**
Reichmann, Paul
See/See also pages in the following book(s):
Aaseng, N. Business builders in real estate
   920
Reid, Rob
Something funny happened at the library
   027.62
Reid, Suzanne Elizabeth
Presenting Cynthia Voigt   **813.009**
Presenting young adult science fiction
   813.009
The **Reigate** puzzle. Doyle, Sir A. C.
  In Doyle, Sir A. C. The complete Sherlock
  Holmes   **S C**
Reilly, Mary-Jo
Mexico (5 and up)   **972**
Reincarnation
  Fiction
Littke, L. Lake of secrets (7 and up)   **Fic**
Reinhard, Johan
Discovering the Inca Ice Maiden (5 and up)
   930.1
Reiss, Johanna
The journey back   **92**
The upstairs room (5 and up)   **92**
Reiss, Kathryn, 1957-
PaperQuake   **Fic**
Reiter, Chris
(jt. auth) Warhol, T. Eagles   **598**
Relationships. Benson, S.
  In Being human   **612**
The **release** of Nelson Mandela. Beccroft, S.
   968.06
Relf, Patricia
A dinosaur named Sue: the story of the colossal
  fossil: the world's most complete T. rex (5
  and up)   **567.9**
Religion
Langley, M. Religion   **200**
  Bibliography
Dole, P. P. Children's books about religion
   016.2
  Fiction
Blume, J. Are you there God? it's me, Margaret
  (5 and up)   **Fic**
Hautman, P. Godless (7 and up)   **Fic**
Rylant, C. A fine white dust (5 and up)   **Fic**
Soul searching: thirteen stories about faith and
  belief   **S C**
  History—Chronology
The Wilson chronology of the world's religions
   200
  Social aspects
See/See also pages in the following book(s):
Culture wars: opposing viewpoints   **306**
Religion. Hinds, K.   **292**
Religion and politics
See/See also pages in the following book(s):
The Middle East: opposing viewpoints (7 and
  up)   **956**

Religion in America: opposing viewpoints (7 and up) **200.9**

Religion in American life [series]
Balmer, R. H. Religion in twentieth century America **200.9**
Braude, A. Women and American religion **200.9**
Bushman, C. L. Mormons in America **289.3**
Diner, H. R. Jews in America **305.8**
Joselit, J. W. Immigration and American religion **200**
Mann, G. S. Buddhists, Hindus, and Sikhs in America **294**
Martin, J. Native American religion **299.7**
Noll, M. A. Protestants in America **280**
Stein, S. J. Alternative American religions **209**

Religion in the public schools
Andryszewski, T. School prayer (7 and up) **344**
Dudley, M. E. Engel v. Vitale (1962) (7 and up) **344**

Religion in twentieth century America. Balmer, R. H. **200.9**

Religions
See also Gods and goddesses
Barnes, T. The Kingfisher book of religions **201**
Birdseye, D. H. What I believe (4 and up) **200**
Breuilly, E. Religions of the world (7 and up) **201**
Comparative religions on file **201**
The Encyclopedia of world religions (7 and up) **200.3**
Gellman, M. How do you spell God? (5 and up) **200**
Osborne, M. P. One world, many religions (4 and up) **201**
Philip, N. Mythology **201**
Sturges, P. Sacred places (4 and up) **203**

Religions of the world. Breuilly, E. **201**

Religions of the world [series]
Clark, C. Islam **297**
Kallen, S. A. Shinto **299.5**
Lace, W. W. Christianity **230**
Slavicek, L. C. Confucianism **181**

Religious cults *See* Cults

Religious holidays
See also Jewish holidays
Breuilly, E. Festivals of the world **394.26**

Relocation of Japanese Americans, 1942-1945
See Japanese Americans—Evacuation and relocation, 1942-1945

The **reluctant** dragon. Grahame, K.
In The Book of dragons p20-25 **S C**

Reluctantly Alice. Naylor, P. R. **Fic**

The **remarkable** journey of Prince Jen. Alexander, L. **Fic**

Remarkable journeys: the story of Jules Verne. Schoell, W. **92**

Remarriage
Bode, J. For better, for worse **306.89**

Fiction
Cole, B. Celine **Fic**
Love, D. A. A year without rain (5 and up) **Fic**
Pevsner, S. Is everyone moonburned but me? **Fic**

Rembert, Winfred
Don't hold me back (4 and up) **92**
About
Rembert, W. Don't hold me back (4 and up) **92**

Rembrandt Harmenszoon van Rijn, 1606-1669
Fiction
See/See also pages in the following book(s):
Gilson, J. Stink Alley (4 and up) **Fic**

Remember D-day. Drez, R. J. **940.54**

Remember me. Farmer, N.
In Firebirds: an anthology of original fantasy and science fiction; an anthology of original fantasy and science fiction **S C**

Remember not to forget. Finkelstein, N. H. **940.53**

Remember Pearl Harbor. Allen, T. B. **940.54**
Remember the bridge. Weatherford, C. B. **811**
Remember the Lusitania. Preston, D. **940.4**
Remember the Maine!. McNeese, T. **973.8**
Remembering Korea. Ashabranner, B. K. **951.9**

Remembering Manzanar. Cooper, M. L. **940.53**

Remembrance. Breslin, T. **Fic**

Remler, Pat
Egyptian mythology A to Z (7 and up) **299**

Remnants. Koja, K.
In The Green Man: tales from the mythic forest p312-20 **808.8**

Remote man. Honey, E. **Fic**

Renaissance
See also World history—16th century
Barter, J. Renaissance Florence **945**
Barter, J. A Renaissance painter's studio **759.5**
Cohen, E. S. Daily life in Renaissance Italy (7 and up) **945**
Greenblatt, M. Lorenzo de' Medici and Renaissance Italy **945**
Hinds, K. The church **274**
Hinds, K. The city [Life in the Renaissance series] **940.2**
Hinds, K. The countryside [Life in the Renaissance series] **940.2**
Hinds, K. The court **940.2**
Netzley, P. D. Life during the Renaissance (7 and up) **940.2**
Renaissance [Grolier Educ.] (7 and up) **940.2**
The Renaissance [World history by era] **940.2**
Renaissance & Reformation: almanac **940.2**
Renaissance & Reformation: primary sources **940.2**
Schomp, V. The Italian Renaissance **945**
Thomson, M. Women of the Renaissance **940.2**

Renaissance—*Continued*
Wood, T. The Renaissance (4 and up)   **940.2**
Biography
Renaissance & Reformation: biographies   **920**
Fiction
Avi. Midnight magic (5 and up)   **Fic**
The **Renaissance**. Cole, A.
709.02
[Grolier Educ.] (7 and up)   **940.2**
The **Renaissance** [World history by era]   **940.2**
Renaissance & Reformation: almanac   **940.2**
Renaissance & Reformation: biographies   **920**
Renaissance & Reformation: primary sources
940.2
Renaissance art *See* Art—15th and 16th centuries
Renaissance Florence. Barter, J.   **945**
Renaissance Florence. See Barter, J. Renaissance
Florence   **945**
A **Renaissance** painter's studio. Barter, J.
759.5
Renaissance scientists [series]
Boerst, W. J. Johannes Kepler   **92**
Boerst, W. J. Tycho Brahe   **92**
Goble, T. Nicholas Copernicus and the founding
of modern astronomy   **92**
Rendeiro, Charlene
(il) Hopkins, L. B. Been to yesterdays: poems of
a life   **811**
Renewable energy resources
Bowden, R. Energy (5 and up)   **333.79**
Rennison, Louise, 1951-
Angus, thongs and full-frontal snogging (7 and
up)   **Fic**
Renoir, Auguste, 1841-1919
About
Rayfield, S. Pierre-Auguste Renoir (7 and up)
92
Repetitive strain injuries, Carpal tunnel syndrome
and other. Johansson, P.   **616.8**
Report writing
James, E. How to write terrific book reports (4
and up)   **808**
Janeczko, P. B. Writing winning reports and es-
says   **808**
Sullivan, H. Research reports (7 and up)
808
Valenza, J. K. Power research tools   **001.4**
Reporters and reporting
See also Journalism
Reproduction
See also Genetics
Fullick, A. Test tube babies (7 and up)
618.1
Parker, S. The reproductive system   **612.6**
Reproductive system
Parker, S. Digestion and reproduction   **612.3**
The **reproductive** system. Parker, S.   **612.6**
Reptiles
See also Snakes
Amphibians and reptiles   **597.9**
Crump, M. L. Amphibians, reptiles, and their
conservation (7 and up)   **597.9**
McCarthy, C. Reptile (4 and up)   **597.9**

Miller, S. S. Radical reptiles   **597.9**
Reptiles and amphibians   **597.9**
Silverstein, A. Snakes & such   **639**
Stebbins, R. C. A field guide to Western reptiles
and amphibians   **597.9**
Reptiles and amphibians   **597.9**
Republican Party (U.S.)
History
Collier, C. The Jeffersonian Republicans, 1800-
1823   **973.4**
Rescue and resistance: portraits of the Holocaust
940.53
Rescue of Jews, 1939-1945 *See* World War, 1939-
1945—Jews—Rescue
Rescue: the story of how Gentiles saved Jews in
the Holocaust. Meltzer, M.   **940.53**
Research
See also Animal experimentation
Heiligman, D. The New York Public Library
kid's guide to research (5 and up)   **025.5**
Rankin, V. The thoughtful researcher   **027.62**
Riedling, A. M. Learning to learn   **028.7**
Shields, N. E. Where credit is due (7 and up)
808
Souter, G. Researching on the Internet using
search engines, bulletin boards, and listservs
(4 and up)   **004.6**
Sullivan, H. Research reports (7 and up)
808
Valenza, J. K. Power research tools   **001.4**
Wolinsky, A. Internet power research using the
Big6 approach (5 and up)   **025.04**
Research paper writing *See* Report writing
Research reports. Sullivan, H.   **808**
Researching on the Internet using search engines,
bulletin boards, and listservs. Souter, G.
004.6
The **resident** patient. Doyle, Sir A. C.
In Doyle, Sir A. C. The complete Sherlock
Holmes   **S C**
Residential construction *See* House construction
Resistance to government
See also Passive resistance
Resistance to the Nazis. Shuter, J.   **943.086**
Resolution (Ship)
Lawlor, L. Magnificent voyage (7 and up)
910.4
Resources. Gallant, R. A.   **333.7**
Respiration
See also Respiratory system
Respiratory system
Parker, S. Heart, blood, and lungs   **612.1**
Silverstein, A. The respiratory system (5 and
up)   **612.2**
Restaurant. Hearne, B. G.
In Hearne, B. G. The canine connection: sto-
ries about dogs and people p11-18
S C
Restaurants
Fiction
Bauer, J. Hope was here (7 and up)   **Fic**

Restless sea [series]
Vogel, C. G. Human impact   **333.91**

Restless spirit: the life and work of Dorothea Lange. Partridge, E.   **92**

Retarded children *See* Mentally handicapped children

The **return**. Levitin, S.   **Fic**

The **return** of a private. Garland, H.
In The Boy of Chancellorville and other Civil War stories p103-11   **S C**

The **return** of Ice Man. Brown, D. A.
In Brown, D. A. Dee Brown's folktales of the Native American; retold for our times p78-79   **398.2**

The **return** of Sherlock Holmes. Doyle, Sir A. C.
In Doyle, Sir A. C. The complete Sherlock Holmes   **S C**

Reuben and Joseph. Myers, W. D.
In Myers, W. D. A time to love; stories from the Old Testament p27-46   **S C**

Reusable space vehicles *See* Space shuttles

Revard, Carter, 1931-
Never quite a Hollywood star
In Talking leaves; contemporary native American short stories   **S C**

The **revealers**. Wilhelm, D.   **Fic**

Revenge and forgiveness (7 and up)   **808.81**

The **revenge** of the Iron Chink. Yee, P.
In Yee, P. Tales from Gold Mountain; stories of the Chinese in the New World p57-62   **S C**

Revenge of the whale. Philbrick, N.   **910.4**

Revere, Paul, 1735-1818
About
Sullivan, G. Paul Revere   **92**

Revolution, Industrial *See* Industrial revolution

The **revolution** in healing the brain. Viegas, J.   **612.8**

Revolutionary citizens. Littlefield, D. C.   **305.8**

The **Revolutionary** War   **973.3**

The **Revolutionary** War. Beller, S. P.   **973.3**

Reymann, Blandine Pengili
(jt. auth) Gofen, E. France   **944**

Reynolds, David West
Star wars: the visual dictionary   **791.43**

Reynolds, Moira Davison
American women scientists (7 and up)   **920**

Reynoldson, Fiona
Conflict and change   **909.7**

Reznicki, Jack
(il) Masoff, J. Fire!   **628.9**

Rhatigan, Joe
Geography crafts for kids
In Diehn, G. and others. Science smart; cool projects for exploring the marvels of the planet Earth   **550**
Out-of-this-world astronomy (5 and up)   **520**
Sure-to-win science fair projects (5 and up)   **507.8**
Science smart. See Science smart   **550**

Rhetoric
Study and teaching
Ellis, S. From reader to writer   **372.6**

The **Rhine**. Allan, T.   **943**

Rhine River
Allan, T. The Rhine (4 and up)   **943**
Kallen, S. A. The Rhine   **943**

Rhinoceros
Fiction
Kessler, C. Our secret, Siri Aang (7 and up)   **Fic**

Rhode Island
Klein, T. E. D. Rhode Island
In Celebrate the states   **973**
McNair, S. Rhode Island
In America the beautiful, second series   **973**
Fiction
Griffin, A. Where I want to be (7 and up)   **Fic**
Lisle, J. T. The art of keeping cool (5 and up)   **Fic**

Rhodes, Lisa Renee
Coretta Scott King   **92**

Rhodesia, Northern *See* Zambia

Rhodesia, Southern *See* Zimbabwe

Rhue, Morton *See* Strasser, Todd, 1950-

Rhyme
See also English language—Rhyme

Rhynes, Martha E., 1929-
Gwendolyn Brooks (7 and up)   **92**

The **rhythm** of strong. Boutilier, N.
In Girls got game; sports stories and poems   **810.8**

The **Rialto**. Woodson, J.
In The Color of absence; 12 stories about loss and hope p185-204   **S C**

Ribeiro, Myra
The assassination of Medgar Evers   **92**

Rice, David, 1964-
Crazy loco   **S C**
Contents: Sugarcane fire; Her other son; Valentine; Papa Lalo; Crazy loco; Proud to be an American; She flies; The California cousins; Last mass
Tied to Zelda
In Tripping over the lunch lady and other school stories p158-77   **S C**

Rice, Earle
Sir Francis Drake, navigator and pirate   **92**

Rice, John, 1958-
(il) Myers, J. On the trail of the Komodo dragon and other explorations of science in action   **590**

Rich, Mari
(ed) World authors, 1995-2000. See World authors, 1995-2000   **920.003**

Rich, Mary Perrotta
(ed) Book poems. See Book poems   **811.008**

Richard I, King of England, 1157-1199
About
Crompton, S. The Third Crusade (7 and up)   **956**

Richard I, King of England, 1157-1199—
About—*Continued*
See/See also pages in the following book(s):
Zohorsky, J. R. Medieval knights and warriors p26-37 **940.1**

Richard, the Lion Heart *See* Richard I, King of England, 1157-1199

Richard, Christopher, 1959-
Brazil (5 and up) **981**

Richardson, Joy
Looking at pictures (5 and up) **750**

Richardson, Robert D., 1934-
(ed) Three centuries of American poetry, 1623-1923. See Three centuries of American poetry, 1623-1923 **811.008**

Richie, Jason, 1966-
Space flight **920**

Richie. Watt-Evans, L.
In Vampires: a collection of original stories p211-25 **S C**

Richmond, M. A. (Merle A.)
Phillis Wheatley **92**

Richmond (Va.)
History
Beller, S. P. Confederate ladies of Richmond **973.7**

Richter, Conrad, 1890-1968
The light in the forest **Fic**

Riddick, Floyd M.
Riddick's Rules of procedure **060.4**

Riddick's Rules of procedure. Riddick, F. M. **060.4**

Riddle, John
Bhopal (7 and up) **363.1**

The **riddle** of the Rosetta Stone. Giblin, J. **493**

The **riddle** tale of freedom. Hamilton, V.
In Hamilton, V. The people could fly; American black folktales p156-59 **398.2**

Ride, Sally K.
Exploring our solar system (4 and up) **523.2**
To space & back **629.45**

Rider Chan and the night river. Yee, P.
In Yee, P. Tales from Gold Mountain; stories of the Chinese in the New World p51-56 **S C**

Riding, Alan
(jt. auth) Dunton-Downer, L. Essential Shakespeare handbook **822.3**

Riding *See* Horsemanship

Ridpath, Ian
Facts on File stars & planets atlas **520**

Riedling, Ann Marlow, 1952-
Learning to learn **028.7**

Riekehof, Lottie L.
The joy of signing **419**

Riffs. Manheimer, A.
In What a song can do; 12 riffs on the power of music **S C**

The **rifle**. Paulsen, G. **Fic**

Rifles
Fiction
Paulsen, G. The rifle (7 and up) **Fic**

Rifles for Watie. Keith, H. **Fic**

Rigg, Sharon *See* Creech, Sharon

Right- and left-handedness *See* Left- and right-handedness

The **right** moves. Schwager, T. **613.7**

Right of privacy
Bridegam, M. A. The right to privacy **323.44**
Fridell, R. Privacy vs. security **342**
MccGwire, S. Surveillance (7 and up) **323.44**
Persico, D. Mapp v. Ohio (7 and up) **345**
Wetterer, C. M. The Fourth Amendment (7 and up) **345**
See/See also pages in the following book(s):
Civil liberties: opposing viewpoints (7 and up) **323**

The **right** to bear arms. Spitzer, R. J. **344**

Right to die
See also Euthanasia
Rebman, R. C. Euthanasia and the "right to die" **179.7**
See/See also pages in the following book(s):
Death and dying: opposing viewpoints p55-96 (7 and up) **155.9**
Hyde, M. O. When the brain dies first (7 and up) **616.8**
Terminal illness: opposing viewpoints (7 and up) **362.1**
Law and legislation
Donnelly, K. J. Cruzan v. Missouri **344**
Fridell, R. Cruzan v. Missouri and the right to die debate (7 and up) **344**

The **right** to privacy. Bridegam, M. A. **323.44**

The **right** word. Appelt, K.
In Appelt, K. Kissing Tennessee and other stories from the Stardust Dance p66-80 **S C**

Rights, Civil *See* Civil rights

Rights, Human *See* Human rights

Rights of animals *See* Animal rights

The **Rights** of animals (7 and up) **179**

"Rikki-tikki-tavi". Kipling, R.
In Kipling, R. The jungle books **S C**
In Read all about it!; great read-aloud stories, poems, and newspaper pieces for preteens and teens p155-74 **808.8**

Rillieux, Norbert, 1806-1894
See/See also pages in the following book(s):
Aaseng, N. Black inventors (7 and up) **920**

Rima's song. Marston, E.
In Join in; multiethnic short stories by outstanding writers for young adults p153-71 **S C**

Rimm, Sylvia B., 1935-
See Jane win for girls (5 and up) **305.23**

Rinaldi, Ann, 1934-
Amelia's war **Fic**
The fifth of March (7 and up) **Fic**
Girl in blue **Fic**

Rinaldi, Ann, 1934-—*Continued*
Hang a thousand trees with ribbons　Fic
In my father's house (7 and up)　Fic
A stitch in time (7 and up)　Fic
Taking liberty　Fic
Wolf by the ears　Fic

Riots
Alonso, K. The Chicago Seven political protest
trial　345
　　　　　Fiction
Myers, A. Tulsa burning (7 and up)　Fic

Ripley's believe it or not!. Packard, M.
031.02

Ripple, Jeff, 1963-
Sea turtles (7 and up)　597.9

The **rise** and fall of American slavery. McNeese,
T.　326

The **rise** and fall of Jim Crow. Wormser, R.
305.8

The **Rise** of Christianity (7 and up)　270

The **rise** of industry, 1860-1900. Collier, C.
973.8

The **Rise** of Nazi Germany (7 and up)
943.086

The **rise** of reason: 1700-1799. Spangenburg, R.
509

The **rise** of the cities, 1820-1920. Collier, C.
307.7

The **Rise** of the Soviet Union (7 and up)
947.084

Risk-taking (Psychology)
Erlbach, A. Worth the risk　302

A **risky** prescription. Stiefer, S.　613.7

Rissik, Dee
(jt. auth) Rosmarin, I. South Africa　968

Ritalin
Beal, E. Ritalin (7 and up)　616.85

Ritchie, Nigel
The civil rights movement　323.1

Rites and ceremonies
Comparative religions on file　201

Ritter, John H., 1951-
The boy who saved baseball (5 and up)　Fic
Choosing up sides　Fic

Ritual purity. Heiligman, D.
In Don't cramp my style; stories about that
time of the month p209-41　S C

River and stream. Sayre, A. P.　577.6

The **river** between us. Peck, R.　Fic

River boy. Bowler, T.　Fic

River danger. Dygard, T. J.　Fic

River ecology
Castner, J. L. River life　577.6
Martin, P. A. F. Rivers and streams (7 and up)
577.6
Sayre, A. P. River and stream (5 and up)
577.6

River journey [series]
Bowden, R. The Nile　962

River life. Castner, J. L.　577.6

Rivera, Frida Kahlo *See* Kahlo, Frida, 1907-1954

Rivera, Tomás
On the road to Texas: Pete Fonseca
In Growing up Latino; memoirs and stories
p147-54　810.8

Rivers
See also Mississippi River; Nile River

Rivers and streams. Martin, P. A. F.　577.6

Rivers of North America [series]
Harris, T. The Mackenzie River　971

Rivers of the world [series]
Barter, J. The Amazon　981
Barter, J. The Ganges　954
Barter, J. The Nile　962
Currie, S. The Mississippi　977
Kallen, S. A. The Rhine　943

Rivlin, Alice M.
See/See also pages in the following book(s):
Jeffrey, L. S. Great American businesswomen
920

Rizal, José, 1861-1896
　　　　　About
Arruda, S. M. Freedom's martyr [biography of
Jose Rizal]　92

Rizzo, Margaret
(jt. auth) Jweid, R. Building character through
literature　028.5
(jt. auth) Jweid, R. The library-classroom partnership　027.8

Roach, Marilynne K.
In the days of the Salem witchcraft trials (4 and
up)　133.4

Road engineering *See* Highway engineering

The **road** not taken. Frost, R.　811

The **road** to Camlann. Sutcliff, R.　398.2

The **road** to Communism. Gottfried, T.　947

The **road** to Memphis. Taylor, M. D.　Fic

The **road** to there. Ross, V.　912

Roanoke Island (N.C.)
　　　　　History
Kent, Z. The mysterious disappearance of Roanoke Colony in American history (7 and up)
975.6/175

Robbers and outlaws *See* Thieves

Robbie. Asimov, I.
In Asimov, I. I, robot　S C

Robbins, Chandler S., 1918-
Birds of North America (4 and up)　598

Robbins, Louise E.
Louis Pasteur (7 and up)　92

Robbins, Trina, 1938-
Go girl!: The time team　741.5

Roberson, John R., 1930-
Japan meets the world (7 and up)　952

Robert I, King of Scotland, 1274-1329
　　　　　Fiction
Yolen, J. Girl in a cage　Fic

Robert, Henry Martyn, 1837-1923
The Scott, Foresman Robert's Rules of order
newly revised　060.4

Robert, Sarah Corbin
(ed) Robert, H. M. The Scott, Foresman Robert's Rules of order newly revised　060.4

Robert Fulton and the development of the steamboat. Pierce, M. A.   **92**

Robert the Bruce *See* Robert I, King of Scotland, 1274-1329

Roberts, Bartholomew, 1682?-1722
See/See also pages in the following book(s):
Wren, L. L. Pirates and privateers of the high seas p11-17   **920**

Roberts, J. M.
The illustrated history of the world (7 and up)   **909**

Roberts, Jennifer Tolbert
The ancient Greek world (7 and up)

Roberts, Jeremy
Chinese mythology A to Z   **299.5**

Roberts, Mickey
The Indian basket
In Talking leaves; contemporary native American short stories   **S C**
It's all in how you say it
In Talking leaves; contemporary native American short stories   **S C**

Roberts, Russell
Leaders and generals   **920**

Roberts, Willo Davis, 1928-
Hostage   **Fic**
The kidnappers (4 and up)   **Fic**
Twisted summer   **Fic**
Robert's Rules of order. Robert, H. M.   **060.4**

Robertson, James I., Jr.
Standing like a stone wall: the life of General Thomas J. Jackson (7 and up)   **92**

Robeson, Paul, 1898-1976
About
Wright, D. K. Paul Robeson   **92**

Robin Hood (Legendary character)
McKinley, R. The outlaws of Sherwood   **398.2**
Philip, N. The story of Robin Hood   **398.2**
Pyle, H. The merry adventures of Robin Hood of great renown in Notinghamshire (7 and up)   **398.2**
Fiction
Cadnum, M. Forbidden forest (7 and up)   **Fic**
Cadnum, M. In a dark wood   **Fic**
Sherwood: original stories from the world of Robin Hood   **S C**
Springer, N. Rowan Hood, outlaw girl of Sherwood Forest (4 and up)   **Fic**
Robin Hood and his merry men. Osborne, M. P.
In Osborne, M. P. Favorite medieval tales p60-66   **398.2**
Robin Hood v. 1.5.3. Stemple, A.
In Sherwood: original stories from the world of Robin Hood p122-30   **S C**
Robinet, Harriette Gillem
Walking to the bus-rider blues (5 and up)   **Fic**

Robinette, Joseph
Charlotte's web [play]
In Theatre for young audiences; 20 great plays for children p7-45   **812.008**

Robins, C. Richard
A field guide to Atlantic coast fishes of North America   **597**

Robinson, Barbara
The best Christmas pageant ever (4-6)   **Fic**

Robinson, Charles, 1931-
(il) Levitin, S. Journey to America   **Fic**

Robinson, Deborah B.
The Sami of Northern Europe   **948**

Robinson, Heath *See* Robinson, William Heath, 1872-1944

Robinson, Jackie, 1919-1972
About
Robinson, S. Jackie's nine   **170**
Robinson, S. Promises to keep: how Jackie Robinson changed America (4 and up)   **92**

Robinson, James
Leave it to Chance: Shaman's rain   **741.5**

Robinson, Julia B., 1919-1985
See/See also pages in the following book(s):
Celebrating women in mathematics and science   **920**
Henderson, H. Modern mathematicians (7 and up)   **920**

Robinson, Kim Stanley
Arthur Sternbach brings the curveball to Mars
In New skies: an anthology of today's science fiction   **S C**

Robinson, Richard, 1956-
(ed) Biology. See Biology   **570**
(ed) Plant sciences. See Plant sciences   **580**

Robinson, Sharon, 1950-
Jackie's nine   **170**
Promises to keep: how Jackie Robinson changed America (4 and up)   **92**

Robinson, Spider
Serpents' teeth
In New skies: an anthology of today's science fiction   **S C**

Robinson, Tim, 1963-
(jt. auth) Kenda, M. Math wizardry for kids   **793.7**

Robinson, William Heath, 1872-1944
Uncle Lubin and the dragon
In The Book of dragons p47-49   **S C**
Robinson Crusoe. Defoe, D.   **Fic**

Robinson Masters, Nancy
Georgia
In America the beautiful, second series   **973**
Kansas
In America the beautiful, second series   **973**

Robotics *See* Robots

Robots
Jefferis, D. Artificial intelligence (4 and up)   **629.8**
Lockman, D. Robots   **629.8**
Fiction
Asimov, I. I, robot (7 and up)   **S C**

Rochelle, Belinda
(ed) Words with wings. See Words with wings   **811.008**

Rochman, Hazel
(ed) Leaving home: stories. See Leaving home: stories **808.8**
(comp) Somehow tenderness survives. See Somehow tenderness survives **S C**
(comp) Who do you think you are? See Who do you think you are? **S C**

Rock and roll music See Rock music

Rock drawings, paintings, and engravings
Arnold, C. Stories in stone (4 and up) **709.01**

Rock music
Levine, L. Shake, rattle, & roll (4 and up) **920**
Kallen, S. A. The history of rock and roll **781.66**

Encyclopedias
The Rolling Stone encyclopedia of rock & roll (7 and up) **781.66**

Rock musicians
Denenberg, B. All shook up: the life and death of Elvis Presley (5 and up) **92**
Rappaport, D. John's secret dreams [biography of John Lennon] (4 and up) **92**

Rock paintings See Rock drawings, paintings, and engravings

Rockbuster. Skurzynski, G. **Fic**

Rockefeller, John D. (John Davison), 1839-1937
About
Segall, G. John D. Rockefeller **92**

Rocket boys. Hickam, H. H. **92**

Rocketry
Miller, R. The history of rockets **621.43**

Rocking donkey. Aiken, J.
In Aiken, J. Shadows and moonshine; stories **S C**

Rockman, Connie C.
(ed) The ninth book of junior authors and illustrators. See The ninth book of junior authors and illustrators **920.003**

Rocks
Chesterman, C. W. The Audubon Society field guide to North American rocks and minerals **549**
Farndon, J. Rocks and minerals **549**
Pough, F. H. A field guide to rocks and minerals **549**
Simon and Schuster's guide to rocks and minerals **549**
Symes, R. F. Eyewitness rocks & minerals (5 and up) **549**
Trueit, T. S. Rocks, gems, and minerals **552**

Rocks and minerals. Farndon, J. **549**

Rocks, gems, and minerals. Trueit, T. S. **552**

Rockwell, Norman, 1894-1978
About
Gherman, B. Norman Rockwell (4 and up) **92**

Rockwood, Richard
(il) McKenna, L. The fantastic book of snowboarding **796.93**

Roddick, Anita
See/See also pages in the following book(s):
Graham, K. Contemporary environmentalists (7 and up) **920**

Rodeos
Fiction
Ferris, J. Eight seconds (7 and up) **Fic**
Peck, R. N. Horse thief (7 and up) **Fic**

Rodgers, Mary, 1931-
Freaky Friday (4 and up) **Fic**

Rodman, Mary Ann
Yankee girl (4 and up) **Fic**

Rodowsky, Colby F., 1932-
Amanda and the wounded birds
In Visions: nineteen short stories by outstanding writers for young adults p78-86 **S C**
Clay **Fic**

Rodriguez, Richard, 1944-
See/See also pages in the following book(s):
Hill, C. M. Ten Hispanic American authors **920**

Rodzina. Cushman, K. **Fic**

Roe, Jane See McCorvey, Norma

Roe v. Wade. Gold, S. D. **344**
Roe v. Wade. Payment, S. **344**
Roe v. Wade. Romaine, D. S. **344**

Roebling, John Augustus
See/See also pages in the following book(s):
Aaseng, N. Construction: building the impossible **624**

Roebling, Washington Augustus, 1837-1926
See/See also pages in the following book(s):
Aaseng, N. Construction: building the impossible **624**

Rogasky, Barbara, 1933-
The golem (4 and up) **398.2**
Smoke and ashes **940.53**

Roget's 21st century thesaurus in dictionary form **423**
Roget's II **423**
Roget's international thesaurus **423**

Rogue wave. Taylor, T.
In Taylor, T. Rogue wave and other red-blooded sea stories **S C**

Rogue wave and other red-blooded sea stories. Taylor, T. **S C**

Rol, Ruud van der
Anne Frank, beyond the diary (5 and up) **92**

Roleff, Tamara L., 1959-
Hate groups (7 and up) **364.1**
(ed) America under attack: primary sources. See America under attack: primary sources **973.931**
(ed) The Atom bomb. See The Atom bomb **355.8**
(ed) Biomedical ethics: opposing viewpoints. See Biomedical ethics: opposing viewpoints **174.2**
(ed) Black magic and witches. See Black magic and witches **133.4**

Roleff, Tamara L., 1959-—*Continued*
(ed) Drug abuse: opposing viewpoints. See Drug abuse: opposing viewpoints **362.29**
(ed) Hate groups: opposing viewpoints. See Hate groups: opposing viewpoints **364.1**
(ed) Inner-city poverty. See Inner-city poverty **362.5**
(ed) Marriage and divorce. See Marriage and divorce **306.8**
(ed) Mental illness: opposing viewpoints. See Mental illness: opposing viewpoints **362.2**
(ed) Pollution: opposing viewpoints. See Pollution: opposing viewpoints **363.7**
(ed) The Rights of animals. See The Rights of animals **179**
(ed) Suicide: opposing viewpoints. See Suicide: opposing viewpoints **362.28**
(ed) The war on drugs. See The war on drugs **363.4**

Roller skating
See also Skateboarding
The **Rolling** Stone encyclopedia of rock & roll (7 and up) **781.66**

Romain, Trevor
Cliques, phonies & other baloney **158**

Romaine, Deborah S., 1956-
Roe v. Wade (7 and up) **344**

Roman architecture
DuTemple, L. A. The Pantheon (5 and up) **726**
Macaulay, D. City: a story of Roman planning and construction (4 and up) **711**
The **Roman** Army. Blacklock, D. **937**
The **Roman** army. Nardo, D. **937**
The **Roman** Colosseum. Mann, E. **937**

Roman emperors *See* Emperors—Rome

Roman Empire *See* Rome
The **Roman** news. Langley, A. **937**

Romance novels *See* Love stories

Romances
See also Arthurian romances

Romano, Amy, 1978-
A historical atlas of Afghanistan **958.1**

Romanov, Nikolaï *See* Nicholas II, Emperor of Russia, 1868-1918

Romanowski, Patricia
(ed) The Rolling Stone encyclopedia of rock & roll. See The Rolling Stone encyclopedia of rock & roll **781.66**

Rome
History—Fiction
Lawrence, C. The thieves of Ostia **Fic**

Rome
Antiquities
James, S. Ancient Rome (4 and up) **937**
Civilization
Biesty, S. Rome: in spectacular cross section (4 and up) **937**
Corbishley, M. Ancient Rome (5 and up) **937**
Hinds, K. The city [Life in the Roman Empire series] **937**

Hinds, K. The countryside [Life in the Roman Empire series] **937**
Hinds, K. The Patricians **937**
Hinds, K. Religion **292**
James, S. Ancient Rome (4 and up) **937**
Langley, A. The Roman news **937**
Lassieur, A. The ancient Romans (5 and up) **937**
Mellor, R. The ancient Roman world (7 and up) **937**
Nardo, D. The ancient Romans (7 and up) **937**
Nardo, D. Ancient Rome [Daily life series] **937**
Nardo, D. Ancient Rome [History of weapons and warfare series] (7 and up) **937**
Nardo, D. Arts, leisure, and entertainment **937**
Nardo, D. The Roman army **937**
Nardo, D. Women of ancient Rome (7 and up) **937**
Snedden, R. Technology in the time of ancient Rome **609**
Stefoff, R. The ancient Mediterranean (5 and up) **938**
History
Bruns, R. Julius Caesar **92**
Corbishley, M. Ancient Rome (5 and up) **937**
Ingram, S. Attila the Hun **92**
Julius Caesar [essays about] **92**
Mellor, R. The ancient Roman world (7 and up) **937**
Nardo, D. The fall of the Roman Empire (7 and up) **937**
Nardo, D. From founding to fall: a history of Rome **937**
Military history
Blacklock, D. The Roman Army (4 and up) **937**
Nardo, D. The Roman army **937**
Religion
Hinds, K. Religion **292**
Social life and customs
Biesty, S. Rome: in spectacular cross section (4 and up) **937**

Romeo and Juliet. Packer, T.
In Packer, T. Tales from Shakespeare p139-153 **822.3**

Romero, Danny
The alley
In Join in; multiethnic short stories by outstanding writers for young adults p223-38 **S C**

Rommel, Erwin, 1891-1944
See/See also pages in the following book(s):
Ross, S. Leaders of World War II **920**
The **rōnin** and the tea master. Kimmel, E. A.
In Kimmel, E. A. Sword of the samurai; adventure stories from Japan p95-103 **Fic**

Ronto, Craig W.
(il) Page, L. M. A field guide to freshwater fishes: North America north of Mexico **597**

Rood, Ronald N.
(jt. auth) Campbell, A. The New York Public Library incredible Earth **550**

Room, Adrian
(ed) Brewer's dictionary of phrase and fable. See Brewer's dictionary of phrase and fable **803**

Room 202. Conford, E.
In Conford, E. Crush p1-7 **S C**

Room 313. Hearne, B. G.
In Hearne, B. G. The canine connection: stories about dogs and people p19-28 **S C**

Room in the heart. Levitin, S. **Fic**

Roop, Connie, 1951-
(ed) Clark, W. Off the map **978**
(ed) Pilgrim voices. See Pilgrim voices **974.4**

Roop, Peter, 1951-
(ed) Clark, W. Off the map **978**
(ed) Pilgrim voices. See Pilgrim voices **974.4**

Roos, Stephen
Picky eater 13; thirteen stories that capture the agony and ecstasy of being thirteen

Roosevelt, Eleanor, 1884-1962
About
Freedman, R. Eleanor Roosevelt (5 and up) **92**

See/See also pages in the following book(s):
Hewitt, K. Lives of extraordinary women (4 and up) **920**

Roosevelt, Franklin D. (Franklin Delano), 1882-1945
About
Freedman, R. Franklin Delano Roosevelt (5 and up) **92**
Gilbert, A. Franklin D. Roosevelt (7 and up) **92**

See/See also pages in the following book(s):
Fremon, D. K. The Great Depression in American history **338.5**
Ross, S. Leaders of World War II **920**

Roosevelt, Theodore, 1858-1919
About
Donnelly, M. Theodore Roosevelt: larger than life (7 and up) **92**
Fritz, J. Bully for you, Teddy Roosevelt! (5 and up) **92**
Kraft, B. H. Theodore Roosevelt (5 and up) **92**
McGowen, T. The Spanish-American War and Teddy Roosevelt in American history **973.8**

The **Rooster,** the Mockingbird and the maiden. Brown, D. A.
In Brown, D. A. Dee Brown's folktales of the Native American; retold for our times p14-18 **398.2**

Roots & flowers (7 and up) **811.008**

Rope skipping
Chambers, V. Double dutch (4 and up) **796.2**

Fiction
Draper, S. M. Double Dutch **Fic**

Roraff, Susan
(jt. auth) Winter, J. K. Chile **983**

Rory the fox. Philip, N.
In Philip, N. Celtic fairy tales p57-58 **398.2**

Rosaler, Maxine
Bionics (5 and up) **617.9**
Hamas: Palestinian terrorists **956.94**

Rosales, Melodye
(il) Grimes, N. Hopscotch love **811**

Rosalie. San Souci, R.
In San Souci, R. Double-dare to be scared: another thirteen chilling tales **S C**

Rose daughter. McKinley, R. **Fic**

Roseanne *See* Barr, Roseanne

Rosen, Michael, 1946-
Shakespeare **822.3**

Rosen, Michael J., 1954-
The fire pond
In The Color of absence; 12 stories about loss and hope p73-86 **S C**

Rosen, Philip, 1928-
Bearing witness **016.94053**

Rosenberg, Liz
(ed) The Invisible ladder. See The Invisible ladder **811.008**
(ed) Light-gathering poems. See Light-gathering poems **808.81**
(ed) Roots & flowers. See Roots & flowers **811.008**

Rosenberg, Maxine B., 1939-
Hiding to survive (5 and up) **940.53**

Rosenburg, John M.
Alexander Hamilton **92**
First in peace: George Washington, the Constitution, and the presidency (7 and up) **92**

Rosenthal, Joe, 1911-
About
Bradley, J. Flags of our fathers (7 and up) **940.54**

Rosetta stone
Donoughue, C. The mystery of the hieroglyphs (4 and up) **493**
Giblin, J. The riddle of the Rosetta Stone (5 and up) **493**

Rosh, Mair
(jt. auth) DuBois, J. Israel **956.94**

Rosha and the sun. Gerson, M.-J.
In Gerson, M.-J. Fiesta femenina; celebrating women in Mexican folktale **398.2**

Rosie the riveter. Colman, P. **331.4**

Rosmarin, Ike, 1915-
South Africa (5 and up) **968**

Rosner, Marc Alan
Science fair success using the Internet (7 and up) **507.8**

Rosow, La Vergne
Light 'n lively reads for ESL, adult, and teen readers **011.6**

Ross, Edmund Gibson, 1826-1907
See/See also pages in the following book(s):
Kennedy, J. F. Profiles in courage   **920**
Ross, Michael Elsohn
Fish watching with Eugenie Clark (4 and up)
                                          92

Ross, Stewart
The American Revolution (7 and up)   **973.3**
Art and architecture (5 and up)   **720**
The causes of the Cold War   **327.73**
The industrial revolution (7 and up)   **330.9**
Leaders of World War II   **920**
Monarchs (5 and up)   **940.1**
The technology of World War I   **940.3**
The United Nations   **341.23**
Ross, Val
The road to there   **912**
Rosteck, Mary Kay
(ed) People of the Holocaust. See People of the
  Holocaust   **920.003**
(jt. auth) Schmittroth, L. American Revolution:
  biographies   **920**
Roth, Susan L.
(il) Tillage, L. Leon's story   **92**
Rothman, Chuck
Curse of the undead
  In Vampires: a collection of original stories
  p19-34   **S C**
Rotman, Jeffrey L.
(il) Cerullo, M. M. Coral reef   **577.7**
(il) Cerullo, M. M. The truth about great white
  sharks   **597**
Rough touch. Bledsoe, L. J.
  In Girls got game; sports stories and poems
                                      810.8
Roughnecks. Cochran, T.   **Fic**
Routes of science [series]
Day, T. Genetics   **576.5**
Green, J. Medicine   **610**
Woodford, C. Atoms and molecules   **540**
Woodford, C. Electricity   **537**
Routh, Kristina
Epilepsy
Rowan Hood, outlaw girl of Sherwood Forest.
  Springer, N.   **Fic**
Rowh, Mark
Thurgood Marshall   **92**
Rowland-Warne, L.
Costume (4 and up)   **391**
Rowling, J. K.
Harry Potter and the sorcerer's stone (4 and up)
                                       Fic
Roy, Indrapramit
(il) Rao, S. Sophocles' Oedipus the King
                                       Fic
Royal diaries [series]
Denenberg, B. Elisabeth: the princess bride
                                       Fic
Gregory, K. Eleanor: crown jewel of Aquitaine
                                       Fic
Kirwan, A. Victoria, May blossom of Britannia
                                       Fic
Lasky, K. Elizabeth I   **Fic**

Lasky, K. Jahanara, Princess of Princesses
                                       Fic
Lasky, K. Kazunomiya   **Fic**
Lasky, K. Mary, Queen of Scots, queen without
  a country   **Fic**
McKissack, P. C. Nzinga, warrior queen of
  Matamba   **Fic**
Smith, P. C. Weetamoo, heart of the Pocassets
                                       Fic
White, E. E. Kaiulani   **Fic**
The **royal** kingdoms of Ghana, Mali, and Songhay.
  McKissack, P. C.   **966.2**
Royalty *See* Kings and rulers; Princesses; Queens
Roza, Greg
The encyclopedia of drugs and alcohol **615**
Rozario, Paul
(jt. auth) LoBaido, A. C. The Kurds of Asia
                                       950
Rubel, David
Scholastic atlas of the United States **912**
Scholastic encyclopedia of the presidents and
  their times (5 and up)   **920**
Rubella
Silverstein, A. Measles and rubella (7 and up)
                                      616.9
Rubin, Susan Goldman, 1939-
Art against the odds (5 and up)   **700**
Frank Lloyd Wright (7 and up)   **92**
L'chaim! (7 and up)   **305.8**
Margaret Bourke-White   **92**
Steven Spielberg   **92**
There goes the neighborhood (7 and up)
                                       720
Ruby, Laura
Lily's ghosts (5 and up)   **Fic**
Ruby electric. Nelson, T.   **Fic**
Ruby Holler. Creech, S.   **Fic**
The **ruby** in the smoke. Pullman, P. **Fic**
Ruckman, Ivy, 1931-
Night of the twisters (4 and up)   **Fic**
Rudin, Mary Ellen, 1924-
See/See also pages in the following book(s):
Celebrating women in mathematics and science
                                       920
Rue, Nancy N., 1951-
Everything you need to know about abusive re-
  lationships   **362.7**
Ruggiero, Adriane
American voices from The Great Depression
The Ottoman Empire   **956.1**
World War I   **940.3**
World War II   **940.53**
Ruggles, David, 1810-1849
See/See also pages in the following book(s):
Haskins, J. African American entrepreneurs
                                       920
Ruhl, Greg
In the time of knights (4 and up)   **942.03**
(il) Hehner, B. First on the moon   **629.45**
(il) Tanaka, S. Lost temple of the Aztecs
                                       972
(il) Tanaka, S. Secrets of the mummies **393**
Ruins *See* Excavations (Archeology)

The **ruins**. Martin, P. P.
 In Growing up Latino; memoirs and stories
  p73-84   **810.8**

Ruiz, Denise
 Jump in
 In You're on!: seven plays in English and
  Spanish p42-61   **812.008**

Rükl, Antonín
 Constellation guidebook (7 and up) **523.8**
The **rule** book. See Rules of the game **796.03**

Rulers *See* Emperors; Heads of state; Kings and
 rulers; Queens

Rulers and their times [series]
 Greenblatt, M. Elizabeth I and Tudor England
           942.05
 Greenblatt, M. Genghis Khan and the Mongol
  Empire   **950**
 Greenblatt, M. Lorenzo de' Medici and Renais-
  sance Italy   **945**
 Greenblatt, M. Süleyman the Magnificent and
  the Ottoman Empire   **956.1**
 Mann, K. Isabel, Ferdinand and fifteenth-century
  Spain   **946**
 Plain, N. Louis XVI, Marie Antoinette, and the
  French Revolution   **944**
 Price-Groff, C. Queen Victoria and nineteenth-
  century England   **941.081**

Rules of order *See* Parliamentary practice
Rules of procedure, Riddick's. Riddick, F. M.
           060.4
Rules of the game   **796.03**
Rules of the game. Tan, A.
 In Leaving home: stories p35-52 **808.8**
Rules of the road. Bauer, J. **Fic**
The **rules** to be cool. Dougherty, K. **395**
Rumble fish. Hinton, S. E. **Fic**
Run away home. McKissack, P. C. **Fic**
Run, boy, run. Orlev, U. **Fic**
Run for your life. Levy, M. **Fic**
Run the blockade. Wisler, G. C. **Fic**
Runaround. Asimov, I.
 In Asimov, I. I, robot **S C**

Runaway children
     Fiction
 Bunting, E. The hideout (5 and up) **Fic**
 De Guzman, M. Melonhead **Fic**
 Hobbs, V. Charlie's run **Fic**
 Holman, F. Slake's limbo (6 and up) **Fic**
 Kehret, P. Searching for Candlestick Park
           Fic
 Mazer, H. Snow bound (7 and up) **Fic**
 Mazer, H. The wild kid (4 and up) **Fic**
 Naidoo, B. No turning back (5 and up) **Fic**
Runaway girl: the artist Louise Bourgeois. Green-
 berg, J.   **92**

Runaway teenagers
 Veladota, C. Teen runaways (7 and up)
          362.7
     Fiction
 Fleischman, P. Breakout (7 and up) **Fic**
 Griffin, A. Sons of liberty **Fic**
 Hobbs, W. The maze (7 and up) **Fic**
 Johnson, A. Bird (5 and up) **Fic**

 Lowry, B. Guitar highway Rose (7 and up)
           Fic
 Strasser, T. Can't get there from here (7 and up)
           Fic
 Tocher, T. Chief Sunrise, John McGraw, and
  me   **Fic**
 Whelan, G. Chu Ju's house **Fic**
Rundown. Cadnum, M.   **Fic**
Running back to Ludie. Johnson, A. **811**
Running loose. Crutcher, C. **Fic**
Running out of time. Haddix, M. P. **Fic**

Runyon, Brent
 The burn journals (7 and up) **92**

Rupp, Rebecca
 The waterstone   **Fic**

Rural life *See* Country life; Farm life

Ruschmann, Paul
 Legalizing marijuana (7 and up) **345**

Rush, Colleen
 (jt. auth) Farrell, J. High school, the real deal
          373.1

Russell, Lillian, 1861-1922
     Fiction
 Peck, R. Fair weather (5 and up) **Fic**

Russia
  See also Russia (Federation); Soviet Union
     Fiction
 Wulffson, D. L. Soldier X (7 and up) **Fic**

Russia (Federation)
  See also Russia; Soviet Union
 Kort, M. Russia (7 and up) **947**
   Politics and government
 The Collapse of the Soviet Union (7 and up)
         947.085
 Russia today: opposing viewpoints (7 and up)
         947.086
Russia today: opposing viewpoints (7 and up)
         947.086

Russian Empire *See* Russia

Russian overture. Conford, E.
 In Conford, E. Crush p85-93 **S C**

Russian revolution *See* Soviet Union—History—
 1917-1921, Revolution

Russmann, Edna R.
 Nubian kingdoms   **939**

Rust never sleeps. Lynch, C.
 In Time capsule: short stories about teenagers
  throughout the twentieth century p184-
  200   **S C**

Rustin, Bayard, 1910-1987
     About
 Miller, C. C. No easy answers [biography of
  Bayard Rustin] (7 and up) **92**

Ruth, Amy
 Jane Austen   **92**
 Louisa May Alcott   **92**
 Mother Teresa   **92**

Ruth and Naomi. Myers, W. D.
 In Myers, W. D. A time to love; stories from
  the Old Testament p49-65 **S C**

Rutherford, Ernest, 1871-1937
See/See also pages in the following book(s):
Henderson, H. Nuclear physics (7 and up)
539.7

Rutledge, Jill Zimmerman
Dealing with the stuff that makes life tough (7
and up)   **305.23**

Ryan, Bryan
(ed) Hispanic American almanac. See Hispanic
American almanac [junior version]   **305.8**

Ryan, Pam Muñoz
Becoming Naomi León (5 and up)   **Fic**
Esperanza rising (5 and up)   **Fic**

Ryan, Pat
Extreme skateboarding   **796.22**

Rybolt, Leah M.
(jt. auth) Rybolt, T. R. Science fair success with
scents, aromas, and smells   **612.8**

Rybolt, Thomas R.
Science fair success with scents, aromas, and
smells (7 and up)   **612.8**

Ryden, Hope
Wild horses I have known (4 and up)
599.66
Wildflowers around the year (5 and up)
582.13

Rylant, Cynthia
Appalachia   **974**
A fine white dust (5 and up)   **Fic**
The islander   **Fic**
Missing May (5 and up)   **Fic**
Something permanent (7 and up)   **811**
See/See also pages in the following book(s):
The Newbery & Caldecott medal books, 1986-
2000   **028.5**

S

Saar, Betye, 1926-
See/See also pages in the following book(s):
Sills, L. Visions (5 and up)   **920**

Saar, David
The yellow boat
In Theatre for young audiences; 20 great
plays for children p535-78   **812.008**

Saari, Aaron Maurice
(ed) Renaissance & Reformation: almanac. See
Renaissance & Reformation: almanac
940.2
(ed) Renaissance & Reformation: biographies.
See Renaissance & Reformation: biographies
920
(ed) Renaissance & Reformation: primary
sources. See Renaissance & Reformation: primary sources   **940.2**

Saari, Peggy
Colonial America: almanac   **973.2**
Colonial America: biographies   **920**
Colonial America: primary sources   **973.2**
(ed) Explorers & discoverers. See Explorers &
discoverers   **920.003**
(ed) Renaissance & Reformation: almanac. See
Renaissance & Reformation: almanac
940.2

(ed) Renaissance & Reformation: biographies.
See Renaissance & Reformation: biographies
920
(ed) Renaissance & Reformation: primary
sources. See Renaissance & Reformation: primary sources   **940.2**
(ed) Scientists: their lives and works. See Scientists: their lives and works   **920.003**

Saba. Kurtz, J.   **Fic**

Sabbeth, Carol, 1957-
Monet and the impressionists for kids (5 and
up)   **759.05**

Saber-toothed tigers
Hehner, B. Ice Age sabertooth (5 and up)
569

Sable, Jean Baptiste Pointe de *See* Pointe de Sable, Jean Baptiste, 1745?-1818

Sables mouvants. Ketchum, L.
In On the edge: stories at the brink p141-60
S C

Sables Mouvants. Murrow, L. K.
In On the edge: stories at the brink p141-60
S C

Sabriel. Nix, G.   **Fic**
Sabrina Fludde. See Fisk, P. The secret of Sabrina
Fludde   **Fic**

Sacagawea, b. 1786
About
St. George, J. Sacagawea (4-6)   **92**
Fiction
Bruchac, J. Sacajawea (6 and up)   **Fic**
O'Dell, S. Streams to the river, river to the sea
(5 and up)   **Fic**

Sacajawea *See* Sacagawea, b. 1786

Sachar, Louis, 1954-
Holes (5 and up)   **Fic**
About
Greene, M. Louis Sachar (5 and up)   **92**
See/See also pages in the following book(s):
The Newbery & Caldecott medal books, 1986-
2000   **028.5**

Sacred places. Sturges, P.   **203**
Sacred places. Yolen, J.   **811**
Sacred texts [series]
Brown, A. The Bible and Christianity   **220**
Cato, V. The Torah and Judaism   **222**
Ganeri, A. The Ramayana and Hinduism
294.5
Ganeri, A. The Tipitaka and Buddhism
294.3

Ṣaddām Hussein *See* Hussein, Ṣaddām
Sadur, Russell
(il) Williams, V. How to play tennis
796.342

Safari. Bateman, R.   **599**
The **Safe-Keeper's** secret. Shinn, S. **Fic**
Safe surfing on the Internet. Wolinsky, A.
004.6

Safety education
Child and youth security sourcebook   **362.7**
Collyer, B. Keeping safe
In Being human   **612**

Safety education—*Continued*

Raatma, L. Safety on the Internet (4 and up)
025.04

Wiloch, T. Everything you need to know about protecting yourself and others from abduction
613.6

Safety on the Internet. Raatma, L. **025.04**

Safford, Barbara Ripp
Guide to reference materials for school media centers **011.6**

Saffy's angel. McKay, H. **Fic**

Safire, William
(comp) Lend me your ears. See Lend me your ears **808.85**

Sagaunash *See* Caldwell, Billy, 1780-1841

Sage, Angie
Magyk (5 and up) **Fic**

A **sahibs'** war. Kipling, R.
In McCaffrey, A. {The Pern series} **S C**

Saign, Geoffrey, 1955-
The African cats **599.75**
The great apes **599.8**

Sailing away. Cart, M.
In Necessary noise: stories about our families as they really are p145-69 **S C**

Sailors' life *See* Seafaring life

Saint Agnes sends the golden boy. Forshay-Lunsford, C.
In Visions: nineteen short stories by outstanding writers for young adults p11-22 **S C**

Saint-Exupéry, Antoine de, 1900-1944
The little prince **Fic**

Saint Helens, Mount (Wash.) *See* Mount Saint Helens (Wash.)

Saint Petersburg (Russia)
Siege, 1941-1944—Fiction
Whelan, G. Burying the sun **Fic**

Saint Valentine's Day *See* Valentine's Day

Saints
See also Christian saints

Sakai, Stan
Usagi Yojimbo, Vol. 18 **741.5**

Sakurai, Gail, 1952-
Asian-Americans in the old West (4 and up)
978
The Thirteen Colonies **973.2**

Sal Fink. San Souci, R.
In San Souci, R. Cut from the same cloth; American women of myth, legend, and tall tale p51-55 **398.2**

Saladin, Sultan of Egypt and Syria, 1137-1193
About
Crompton, S. The Third Crusade (7 and up)
956
Stanley, D. Saladin: noble prince of Islam (4 and up) **92**
See/See also pages in the following book(s):
Zohorsky, J. R. Medieval knights and warriors p26-37 **940.1**

Saladin: noble prince of Islam. Stanley, D. **92**

Salariya, David
(jt. auth) Malam, J. Super structures **624**

Saldaña, René
Finding our way: stories **S C**
Contents: The good Samaritan; Chuy's beginnings; SylvieSylvieSylvie; Los Twelve Days of Christmas; Andy and Ruthie; Alternative; My self myself; Un faite; Manny calls; The dive; Finding our way

Salem (Mass.)
Fiction
Lasky, K. Beyond the burning time (7 and up)
Fic

History
Fremon, D. K. The Salem witchcraft trials in American history **133.4**
Kallen, S. A. The Salem witch trials (7 and up)
133.4
Roach, M. K. In the days of the Salem witchcraft trials (4 and up) **133.4**

The **Salem** witch trials. Kallen, S. A. **133.4**

The **Salem** witchcraft trials in American history. Fremon, D. K. **133.4**

Salisbury, Cynthia
Phillis Wheatley **92**

Salisbury, Graham, 1944-
Bad day for baseball
In Shattered: stories of children and war p23-39 **S C**
Island boyz: short stories (7 and up) **S C**
Contents: Island boyz; The ravine; Mrs. Noonan; Forty bucks; The hurricane; Aumakua; Frankie Diamond is robbing us blind; Waiting for the war; The doi store monkey; Angel-baby; Hat of clouds
Jungle dogs **Fic**
Lord of the deep (5 and up) **Fic**
Mosquito
In Destination unexpected: short stories
S C
Mrs. Noonan
In On the fringe p117-41 **S C**
The ravine
In On the edge: stories at the brink p177-91
S C
Shark bait
In Ultimate sports; short stories by outstanding writers for young adults p118-44
S C
Under the blood-red sun **Fic**
Waiting for the war
also in Time capsule: short stories about teenagers throughout the twentieth century p88-107 **S C**

Salk, Jonas, 1914-1995
About
Tocci, S. Jonas Salk **92**

Salmansohn, Pete, 1947-
Saving birds (5 and up) **333.95**

Salmonson, Jessica Amanda
The ugly unicorn
In A Glory of unicorns p79-94 **S C**

Salsa stories. Delacre, L. **S C**

Salting the ocean (4 and up) **811.008**

Salvadori, Mario George, 1907-1997
Math games for middle school **510.7**

Salvage. Card, O. S.
In New skies: an anthology of today's science fiction   **S C**

Salzman, Jack
African-American culture and history. See African-American culture and history
     305.8

The **same** stuff as stars. Paterson, K.   **Fic**

Sami (European people)
Robinson, D. B. The Sami of Northern Europe
     948

The **Sami** of Northern Europe. Robinson, D. B.
     948

Sammy Keyes and the hotel thief. Draanen, W. v.
     Fic

Sam's new pet. Schwartz, A.
In Schwartz, A. Scary stories 3; more tales to chill your bones p55-56   **398.2**

Samson and Delilah. Myers, W. D.
In Myers, W. D. A time to love; stories from the Old Testament p1-24   **S C**

Samuels, Barbara G.
(ed) Into focus. See Into focus   **028.1**

The **samurai** and the dragon. Kimmel, E. A.
In Kimmel, E. A. Sword of the samurai; adventure stories from Japan p11-21
     Fic

San Francisco (Calif.)
Fiction
Reiss, K. PaperQuake   **Fic**
Yep, L. The case of the Goblin Pearls   **Fic**
Yep, L. Child of the owl (5 and up)   **Fic**
Yep, L. Dragonwings (5 and up)   **Fic**
Yep, L. Thief of hearts (5 and up)   **Fic**
History
Tanaka, S. Earthquake! (4 and up)   **979.4**

San Nicolas Island (Calif.)
Fiction
O'Dell, S. Island of the Blue Dolphins (5 and up)   **Fic**

San Souci, Robert, 1946-
Cut from the same cloth (4 and up)   **398.2**
Contents: The Star Maiden; Bess Call; Drop Star; Molly Cottontail; Annie Christmas; Susanna and Simon; Sal Fink; Sweet Betsey from Pike; Old Sally Cato; Pale-Face Lightning; Pohaha; Sister Fox and Brother Coyote; Hekeke; Otoonah; Hiiaka

Dare to be scared (4 and up)   **S C**
Contents: Nighttown; The dark dark house; The caller; The double dare; Space is the place; Ants; The Halloween spirit; The Bald Mountain monster; Playland; Smoke; Mrs. Moonlight (Senora de Luna); Hungry ghosts; Bakotahl

Double-dare to be scared: another thirteen chilling tales (4 and up)   **S C**
Contents: Campfire tale; Best friends; The quilt; Circus dreams; Rosalie; Mountain childers; Class cootie; Half-past midnight; Laughter; Click-clack; Daddy Boogey; Grey; "Gulp!"

A terrifying taste of short & shivery (4 and up)
     398.2
Contents: Crooker waits; Yara-ma-yha-who; The fata; The fiddler; Land-otter; A fish story; Apparitions; The bijli; The lutin; The hundredth skull; The ogre's arm; The hairy hands; The snow husband; The zimwi; Witchbirds; Dangerous hill; The witch's head; Dinkins is dead; Old Nan's ghost; The interrupted wedding; The mulombe; The haunted grove; The tiger woman; Peacock's ghost; Israel and the werewolf; Hoichi the earless; A snap of the fingers; Narrow escape; The black fox; The mother and death

Sanchez, Alex
So hard to say   **Fic**

Sanchez, Alex, 1957-
If you kiss a boy
In 13; thirteen stories that capture the agony and ecstasy of being thirteen

Sanchez, Pedro A., 1940-
See/See also pages in the following book(s):
Oleksy, W. G. Hispanic-American scientists (7 and up)   **920**

Sanctuary movement
See also Refugees

Sand Creek, Battle of, 1864
See/See also pages in the following book(s):
Ehrlich, A. Wounded Knee: an Indian history of the American West (6 and up)   **970.004**
Mendoza, P. M. Extraordinary people in extraordinary times (7 and up)   **920**

Sandburg, Carl, 1878-1967
Carl Sandburg
In The Blackbirch treasury of American poetry p9-52   **811.008**

Sanders, Pete
Anorexia and bulimia   **616.85**
Divorce and separation   **306.89**

Sanderson, Peter
Ultimate X-men   **741.5**

Sandler, Martin W.
America's great disasters   **973**
Inventors   **609**
Island of hope (5 and up)   **325.73**
On the waters of the USA (5 and up)   **387.2**
Straphanging in the USA (5 and up)   **388.4**
Vaqueros   **973**

The **sandwalk** adventures. Hosler, J.   **741.5**

Sanford, Annette
Trip in a summer dress
In Leaving home: stories p119-31   **808.8**

Sanford, William R.
Bill Pickett: African-American rodeo star   **92**
Calamity Jane: frontier original   **92**

Sang Spell. Naylor, P. R.   **Fic**

Santa Anna, Antonio López de, 1794?-1876
Fiction
Garland, S. In the shadow of the Alamo   **Fic**

Santa Fe Trail
Alter, J. The Santa Fe Trail   **978**
Fiction
McDonald, M. All the stars in the sky (4 and up)   **Fic**

Santella, Andrew
Henry Hudson   **92**
Illinois
In America the beautiful, second series
     973
Wayne Gretzky   **92**

Santiago, Esmeralda
See/See also pages in the following book(s):
Hill, C. M. Ten Hispanic American authors
     920

Sarah Bishop. O'Dell, S.   **Fic**

Sarajevo (Bosnia and Hercegovina)
Filipovic, Z. Zlata's diary   **92**

Sargent, Pamela
See/See also pages in the following book(s):
Reid, S. E. Presenting young adult science fiction **813.009**

Sarris, Greg
How I got to be queen
In Talking leaves; contemporary native American short stories **S C**

Sasaki, Chris
Constellations: the stars and stories **523.8**

Saskatchewan
Mayell, M. Saskatchewan
In Exploring Canada **971**

Sasquatch
Fiction
Smith, R. The Sasquatch **Fic**

Satan on my track. Lester, J.
In Lester, J. Long journey home: stories from black history p1-25 **S C**

Satan's shadow. Ferguson, A.
In Night terrors; stories of shadow and substance **S C**

Satanta, Kiowa Chief, 1820-1878
See/See also pages in the following book(s):
Freedman, R. Indian chiefs (6 and up) **920**

Sattler, Helen Roney
The book of North American owls (4 and up) **598**
Our patchwork planet (5 and up) **551.1**

Saturn (Planet)
Bortolotti, D. Exploring Saturn (5 and up) **523.4**
Miller, R. Saturn (5 and up) **523.4**
Stone, T. L. Saturn **523.4**

Saturnalia. Fleischman, P. **Fic**

Satyagraha. Carter, A. R.
In On the fringe p165-77 **S C**

Saud, King of Saudi Arabia, 1902-1969
See/See also pages in the following book(s):
Reed, J. The Saudi royal family **920**

Sa'ūd, Ibn *See* Ibn Sa'ūd, King of Saudi Arabia, 1880-1953

Saudi Arabia
Broberg, C. Saudi Arabia in pictures **953.8**
Janin, H. Saudi Arabia **953.8**
Kings and rulers
Reed, J. The Saudi royal family **920**

Saudi Arabia in pictures. Broberg, C. **953.8**

The **Saudi** royal family. Reed, J. **920**

Sauganash *See* Caldwell, Billy, 1780-1841

Saulnier, Karen Luczak
(ed) The Comprehensive signed English dictionary. See The Comprehensive signed English dictionary **419**

Sava, Scott Christian
The lab: hey . . . test this! **741.5**

Savage, Stephen, 1965-
(jt. auth) Martin, P. A. F. Woods and forests **577.3**

Saving birds. Salmansohn, P. **333.95**

Saving Grace. Cummings, P. **Fic**

Saving the American wilderness. Malaspina, A. **333.72**

Saving the planet & stuff. Gauthier, G. **Fic**

Sawa, Maureen
(jt. auth) Edmonston, L.-P. Car smarts **629.222**

Sawyer, Kem Knapp
Anne Frank (5 and up) **92**
The underground railroad in American history **326**

Say, Allen, 1937-
See/See also pages in the following book(s):
The Newbery & Caldecott medal books, 1986-2000 **028.5**

Say goodnight, Gracie. Deaver, J. R. **Fic**

Say it with music: the story of Irving Berlin. Furstinger, N. **92**

Say yes. Couloumbis, A. **Fic**

Saying it out loud. Abelove, J. **Fic**

Sayre, April Pulley
Desert (5 and up) **577.5**
Grassland (5 and up) **577.4**
Lake and pond (5 and up) **577.6**
Ocean (5 and up) **577.7**
River and stream (5 and up) **577.6**
Secrets of sound (4 and up) **591.59**
Taiga (5 and up) **577.3**
Temperate deciduous forest (5 and up) **577.3**
Tropical rain forest (5 and up) **577.3**

Sayre, Henry M.
Cave paintings to Picasso (5 and up) **709**

Scagell, Robin, 1946-
Children's night sky atlas (5 and up) **520**

Scales, Pat R.
Teaching banned books **323.44**

Scams!. Schroeder, A. **364.1**

A **scandal** in Bohemia. Doyle, Sir A. C.
In Doyle, Sir A. C. The complete Sherlock Holmes **S C**

Scandinavians
See also Vikings

Scarborough, Kate
Nuclear waste (5 and up) **363.7**
Pablo Picasso (5 and up) **92**

Scarecrow. Maguire, G.
In Half-human p97-115 **S C**

Scarecrow studies in young adult literature [series]
Brown, J. Declarations of independence **028.5**
Carroll, P. S. Caroline Cooney: faith and fiction **813.009**
Hogan, W. The agony and the eggplant **813.009**
Reed, A. J. S. Norma Fox Mazer **813.009**

Scary stories 3. Schwartz, A. **398.2**

Scary stories to tell in the dark. Schwartz, A. **398.2**

Scathach. Mayer, M.
In Mayer, M. Women warriors; myths and legends of heroic women p31-36 **398**

Schaffer, David
The Iran-Iraq War (7 and up) **956.7**

Schecter, Ellen
The family Haggadah   296.4
Schenck, Charles
About
Alonso, K. Schenck v. United States (7 and up)
    342
Schenck v. United States. Alonso, K.   342
The **Schernoff** discoveries. Paulsen, G.   Fic
Scheuer, Philip
(il) Haduch, B. Science fair success secrets
    507.8
Schindler, Oskar, 1908-1974
About
Wukovits, J. F. Oskar Schindler   92
See/See also pages in the following book(s):
Lyman, D. Holocaust rescuers   920
Schizophrenia
Fiction
Trueman, T. Inside out (7 and up)   Fic
Schlaepfer, Gloria G.
Elephants   599.67
Schleichert, Elizabeth, 1945-
The Thirteenth Amendment (7 and up)   342
Schleifer, Jay
Everything you need to know when someone
you know has been killed (7 and up)
    155.9
Schlein, Lonnie, 1949-
(ed) A Nation challenged. See A Nation chal
lenged   973.931
Schlesinger, Arthur M., 1917-
(ed) The election of 1860 and the administration
of Abraham Lincoln. See The election of
1860 and the administration of Abraham Lin-
coln   973.7
(ed) The Election of 2000 and the administra-
tion of George W. Bush. See The Election of
2000 and the administration of George W.
Bush   324
Schlessinger, June H.
(jt. auth) Karp, R. S. Plays for children and
young adults   808.82
Schliemann, Heinrich, 1822-1890
About
Caselli, G. In search of Troy (4 and up)
    939
Schlissel, Lillian
Black frontiers   978
Schmidt, Gary D.
Lizzie Bright and the Buckminster boy (7 and
up)   Fic
Schmittroth, Linda
American Revolution: biographies (5 and up)
    920
(comp) American Revolution: primary sources.
See American Revolution: primary sources
    973.3
(ed) People of the Holocaust. See People of the
Holocaust   920.003
(ed) U·X·L encyclopedia of Native American
tribes. See U·X·L encyclopedia of Native
American tribes   970.004
(ed) Women's almanac. See Women's almanac
    305.4

Schnare, Mary Kay W.
(jt. auth) Job, A. G. The school library media
specialist as manager   027.8
Schoell, William
Remarkable journeys: the story of Jules Verne
    92
Schoenherr, Ian
(il) Jacques, B. Castaways of the Flying Dutch-
man   Fic
Schoenherr, John, 1935-
See/See also pages in the following book(s):
The Newbery & Caldecott medal books, 1986-
2000   028.5
(il) George, J. C. Julie of the wolves   Fic
(il) North, S. Rascal   599.7
Scholastic atlas of oceans (4 and up)   551.46
Scholastic atlas of the United States. Rubel, D.
    912
Scholastic atlas of the world (4 and up)   912
Scholastic atlas of weather (5 and up)   551.5
Scholastic book of outstanding Americans.
Keenan, S.   920.003
Scholastic children's encyclopedia (4 and up)
    031
Scholastic dictionary of idioms. Terban, M.
    423
Scholastic dictionary of spelling. Terban, M.
    428
Scholastic dinosaurs A to Z. Lessem, D.
    567.9
Scholastic encyclopedia of the presidents and their
times. Rubel, D.   920
Scholastic encyclopedia of the United States at
war. English, J.   973.03
Scholastic guides [series]
Harrison, D. L. Writing stories   808.3
Janeczko, P. B. How to write poetry   808.1
Janeczko, P. B. Writing winning reports and es-
says   808
Terban, M. Building your vocabulary   428
Young, S. Writing with style   808
Scholastic kid's almanac. Pascoe, E.   031.02
Scholastic visual sports encyclopedia (4 and up)
    796.03
Schomp, Virginia, 1953-
1500   909.08
American voices from the Vietnam era
    973.923
The ancient Chinese (5 and up)   931
Ancient Mesopotamia (5 and up)   935
The Italian Renaissance   945
Japan in the days of the samurai   952
New York
In Celebrate the states   973
Schon, Isabel
The best of Latino heritage 1996-2002   011.6
The best of the Latino heritage   011.6
Recommended books in Spanish for children
and young adults, 2000 through 2004
    011.6

Schonebaum, Stephen E., 1961-
(ed) Does capital punishment deter crime? See
Does capital punishment deter crime?
364.66

School dress codes. Cruz, B.   **371.8**

School integration
Fradin, J. B. The power of one [biography of
Daisy Bates] (7 and up)   **92**
Linda Brown, you are not alone (5 and up)
323.1
Polakow, A. Daisy Bates (7 and up)   **92**
Somerlott, R. The Little Rock school desegrega-
tion crisis in American history   **373**

School librarianship series
Job, A. G. The school library media specialist as
manager   **027.8**

School libraries
See also Children's libraries; Elementary
school libraries
American Association of School Librarians. In-
formation power   **027.8**
Bradburn, F. B. Output measures for school li-
brary media programs   **027.8**
Church, A. P. Leverage your library program to
help raise test scores   **027.8**
Craver, K. W. Creating cyber libraries   **027.8**
Curriculum connections through the library
027.62
Developing an information literacy program,
K-12   **025.5**
Donham, J. Enhancing teaching and learning
027.8
Ethics in school librarianship   **174**
Everhart, N. Evaluating the school library media
center   **027.8**
Farmer, L. S. J. Student success and library me-
dia programs   **027.8**
Flowers, H. F. Public relations for school library
media programs   **021.7**
Foundations for effective school library media
programs   **027.8**
Hall-Ellis, S. D. Grants for school libraries
025.1
Harada, V. H. Inquiry learning through librari-
an-teacher partnerships   **371.1**
The Information-powered school   **027.8**
Job, A. G. The school library media specialist as
manager   **027.8**
Jweid, R. The library-classroom partnership
027.8
Kearney, C. A. Curriculum partner   **027.8**
Lanning, S. Essential reference services for to-
day's school media specialists   **025.5**
Mendrinos, R. B. Using educational technology
with at-risk students   **027.8**
Morris, B. J. Administering the school library
media center   **027.8**
Rankin, V. The thoughtful researcher   **027.62**
Ray, V. L. School wide book events   **027.8**
Reichman, H. Censorship and selection
025.2
Scales, P. R. Teaching banned books   **323.44**
Schuckett, S. Political advocacy for school li-
brarians   **027.8**
Skaggs, G. On display   **027.8**

Smith, J. B. Achieving a curriculum-based li-
brary media center program   **027.8**
Torrans, L. A. Law for K-12 libraries and librar-
ians   **344**
Valenza, J. K. Power tools recharged   **027.8**
The Whole school library handbook   **027.8**
Wilson, P. J. Center stage   **027.8**
Woolls, E. B. The school library media manager
027.8
Yesner, B. L. Operating and evaluating school
library media programs   **027.8**
Yucht, A. H. Flip it!   **025.5**
Zweizig, D. Lessons from Library Power
027.8

Activity projects
Honnold, R. 101+ teen programs that work
027.62

Catalogs
Children's catalog   **011.6**
Safford, B. R. Guide to reference materials for
school media centers   **011.6**

Design and construction
Erikson, R. Designing a school library media
center for the future   **027.8**

The **school** library media manager. Woolls, E. B.
027.8

The **school** library media specialist as manager.
Job, A. G.   **027.8**

School media centers *See* Instructional materials
centers

The **school** play. Soto, G.
In Soto, G. Local news p60-68   **S C**
School prayer. Andryszewski, T.   **344**
School science projects *See* Science projects
School stories
Alvarez, J. Finding miracles   **Fic**
Anderson, L. H. Speak (7 and up)   **Fic**
Appelt, K. Kissing Tennessee and other stories
from the Stardust Dance   **S C**
Atkins, C. Alt ed (7 and up)   **Fic**
Avi. Nothing but the truth (6 and up)   **Fic**
Avi. The secret school (4 and up)   **Fic**
Ayres, K. Macaroni boy (5 and up)   **Fic**
Banks, L. R. Alice-by-accident   **Fic**
Bennett, C. A heart divided (7 and up)
Bloor, E. Story time   **Fic**
Bunting, E. Spying on Miss Müller (5 and up)
Fic
Byars, B. C. The burning questions of Bingo
Brown (4 and up)   **Fic**
Carvell, M. Who will tell my brother? (7 and
up)   **Fic**
Clarke, J. Kalpana's dream   **Fic**
Cleary, B. Dear Mr. Henshaw (4 and up)
Fic
Connelly, N. O. St. Michael's scales (7 and up)
Fic
Cormier, R. The chocolate war (7 and up)
Fic
Creech, S. Bloomability (5 and up)   **Fic**
Creech, S. Love that dog (4 and up)   **Fic**
Crutcher, C. Ironman   **Fic**
Crutcher, C. Running loose (7 and up)   **Fic**
Crutcher, C. Whale talk (7 and up)   **Fic**
Danziger, P. The cat ate my gymsuit   **Fic**

School stories—*Continued*

Danziger, P. The pistachio prescription   **Fic**

Danziger, P. United Tates of America (4 and up)   **Fic**

De la Cruz, M. Fresh off the boat (7 and up)   **Fic**

De Lint, C. The blue girl (7 and up)   **Fic**

Deuker, C. High heat (7 and up)   **Fic**

Deuker, C. Painting the black (7 and up)   **Fic**

Dowell, F. O. The secret language of girls (5 and up)   **Fic**

Draper, S. M. The Battle of Jericho (7 and up)   **Fic**

Dreyer, A. L. After Elaine   **Fic**

Duncan, L. Killing Mr. Griffin (7 and up)   **Fic**

Fenner, C. Randall's wall   **Fic**

Fine, A. Flour babies (6 and up)   **Fic**

Flake, S. G. The skin I'm in   **Fic**

Fleischman, P. A fate totally worse than death (7 and up)   **Fic**

Fletcher, R. Flying solo (5 and up)   **Fic**

Flinn, A. Breaking point (7 and up)   **Fic**

Fredericks, M. Head games (7 and up)   **Fic**

Fredericks, M. The true meaning of cleavage (7 and up)   **Fic**

Gantos, J. Jack on the tracks (5 and up)   **Fic**

Gantos, J. Joey Pigza swallowed the key (5 and up)   **Fic**

Garden, N. The year they burned the books (7 and up)   **Fic**

Gauthier, G. The hero of Ticonderoga   **Fic**

Giles, G. Shattering Glass (7 and up)   **Fic**

Griffin, A. Amandine (7 and up)   **Fic**

Griffis, M. L. The Feester filibuster (4 and up)   **Fic**

Grimes, N. Bronx masquerade (7 and up)   **Fic**

Grunwell, J. M. Mind games   **Fic**

Hahn, M. D. Daphne's book (5 and up)   **Fic**

Hamilton, V. Bluish   **Fic**

Hayes, D. No effect   **Fic**

Hentoff, N. The day they came to arrest the book (7 and up)   **Fic**

Howe, J. The misfits   **Fic**

Jenkins, A. M. Out of order (7 and up)   **Fic**

Jennings, R. W. My life of crime (5 and up)   **Fic**

Kantor, M. Confessions of a not it girl (7 and up)   **Fic**

Keizer, G. God of beer (7 and up)   **Fic**

Klass, D. Home of the Braves (7 and up)   **Fic**

Klass, D. You don't know me (7 and up)   **Fic**

Klass, S. S. The un-civil war   **Fic**

Koertge, R. The Brimstone journals (7 and up)   **Fic**

Koertge, R. Stoner & Spaz (7 and up)   **Fic**

Koja, K. Buddha Boy (7 and up)   **Fic**

Konigsburg, E. L. The view from Saturday (4 and up)   **Fic**

Korman, G. Jake, reinvented (7 and up)   **Fic**

Korman, G. No more dead dogs   **Fic**

Korman, G. The sixth grade nickname game (4 and up)   **Fic**

Levine, G. C. The wish   **Fic**

Levitin, S. Dream freedom   **Fic**

Levy, E. Seventh grade tango (5 and up)   **Fic**

Lord, B. B. In the Year of the Boar and Jackie Robinson (4-6)   **Fic**

Lowry, L. Your move, J.P.! (5 and up)   **Fic**

Lubar, D. Wizards of the game   **Fic**

Lupica, M. Travel team   **Fic**

Mackler, C. The earth, my butt, and other big, round things (7 and up)   **Fic**

Mass, W. A mango-shaped space   **Fic**

Mills, C. Alex Ryan, stop that! (5 and up)   **Fic**

Mills, C. Lizzie at last (5 and up)   **Fic**

Moore, P. Blind sighted (7 and up)   **Fic**

Morgenstern, S. H. Secret letters from 0 to 10   **Fic**

Moriarty, J. The year of secret assignments (7 and up)   **Fic**

Myers, W. D. Slam! (7 and up)   **Fic**

Naylor, P. R. Reluctantly Alice   **Fic**

Nelson, B. New rules of high school (7 and up)   **Fic**

Oates, J. C. Big Mouth & Ugly Girl (7 and up)   **Fic**

O'Connor, B. Fame and glory in Freedom, Georgia (4 and up)   **Fic**

O'Dell, K. Agnes Parker . . . girl in progress (4 and up)   **Fic**

Paulsen, G. The Schernoff discoveries   **Fic**

Peck, R. The great interactive dream machine   **Fic**

Peck, R. Lost in cyberspace (5 and up)   **Fic**

Peters, J. A. Define "normal" (7 and up)   **Fic**

Prose, F. After (7 and up)   **Fic**

Randle, K. D. Breaking rank (7 and up)   **Fic**

Ray, D. Ghost girl (5 and up)   **Fic**

Rees, D. C. Vampire High   **Fic**

Rodman, M. A. Yankee girl (4 and up)   **Fic**

Sheldon, D. Confessions of a teenage drama queen (7 and up)   **Fic**

Sheldon, D. My perfect life (7 and up)   **Fic**

Smith, G. L. Ninjas, piranhas, and Galileo   **Fic**

Sonenklar, C. My own worst enemy   **Fic**

Spinelli, J. Stargirl   **Fic**

Spinelli, J. There's a girl in my hammerlock (5 and up)   **Fic**

Swallow, P. C. It only looks easy   **Fic**

Tripping over the lunch lady and other school stories (4 and up)   **S C**

Vaupel, R. My contract with Henry   **Fic**

Voigt, C. Bad girls in love   **Fic**

Wardlaw, L. 101 ways to bug your teacher   **Fic**

Werlin, N. Black mirror (7 and up)   **Fic**

Whytock, C. My cup runneth over   **Fic**

Wilhelm, D. The revealers   **Fic**

Winerip, M. Adam Canfield of the Slash (5 and up)   **Fic**

Yee, L. Millicent Min, girl genius (5 and up)   **Fic**

Zinnen, L. The truth about rats, rules, and seventh grade   **Fic**

The **school** story. Clements, A.   **Fic**
School survival. Tym, K.   **371.8**
School survival guide [series]
   James, E. How to write terrific book reports
     808
School violence
   Child and youth security sourcebook   **362.7**
   Hester, J. P. Public school safety   **371.7**
   Orr, T. Violence in our schools (7 and up)
     371.7
   See/See also pages in the following book(s):
   Stewart, G. Guns and violence   **303.6**
     Fiction
   Prose, F. After (7 and up)   **Fic**
School wide book events. Ray, V. L.   **027.8**
The **schoolie**. Taylor, T.
   In Taylor, T. Rogue wave and other red-
     blooded sea stories   **S C**
Schools
   See also Education
   Tym, K. School survival   **371.8**
     Fiction
   See School stories
     Poetry
   George, K. O. Swimming upstream   **811**
   Wayland, A. H. Girl coming in for a landing (7
     and up)   **811**
     United States—History
   Loeper, J. J. Going to school in 1776 (4 and up)
     370.9
Schraff, Anne E.
   Dr. Charles Drew   **92**
   Harriet Tubman   **92**
   Ralph Bunche   **92**
Schroeder, Andreas, 1946-
   Scams! (5 and up)   **364.1**
Schroeder, Becky
   See/See also pages in the following book(s):
   Thimmesh, C. Girls think of everything (5 and
     up)   **920**
Schroeder, Fred E. H.
   (jt. auth) Cole, D. J. Encyclopedia of modern
     everyday inventions   **609**
Schroeter, Daniel J.
   Israel (7 and up)   **956.94**
Schuckett, Sandy
   Political advocacy for school librarians
     027.8
Schudel, Matt
   (jt. auth) Schulke, F. Witness to our times
     92
Schuerger, Michele, 1961-
   (jt. auth) Schwager, T. Cool women, hot jobs
     . . . and how you can go for it, too!
     650.14
   (jt. auth) Schwager, T. The right moves
     613.7
Schulke, Flip
   Witness to our times   **92**
Schulman, Arlene
   Cop on the beat   **363.2**
Schultz, Margaret A.
   Teens with single parents (7 and up)   **306.8**

Schulz, Carol D., 1948-
   (jt. auth) Soumerai, E. N. A voice from the
     Holocaust   **940.53**
Schuman, Michael, 1953-
   Delaware
     In Celebrate the states   **973**
Schumann, Clara, 1819-1896
     About
   Reich, S. Clara Schumann (5 and up)   **92**
The **Schwa** was here. Shusterman, N.   **Fic**
Schwabacher, Martin
   Jupiter   **523.4**
   Minnesota
     In Celebrate the states   **973**
   Puerto Rico
     In Celebrate the states   **973**
Schwager, Tina, 1964-
   Cool women, hot jobs . . . and how you can go
     for it, too! (7 and up)   **650.14**
   The right moves (7 and up)   **613.7**
Schwartz, Alvin, 1927-1992
   The girl who stood on a grave
     In Beware!; R.L. Stine picks his favorite
     scary stories p185-87   **808.8**
   Harold
     In Beware!; R.L. Stine picks his favorite
     scary stories p179-84   **808.8**
   More scary stories to tell in the dark (4 and up)
     398.2
   Scary stories 3 (4 and up)   **398.2**
   Scary stories to tell in the dark (4 and up)
     398.2
   The wendigo
     In Schwartz, A. Scary stories to tell in the
     dark p49-53   **398.2**
Schwartz, Ellen, 1949-
   I'm a vegetarian   **613.2**
Schwartz, Gary, 1940-
   Hieronymus Bosch (7 and up)   **92**
Schwartz, Howard, 1945-
   The day the Rabbi disappeared: Jewish holiday
     tales of magic (4 and up)   **398.2**
   Contents: A flock of angels; Drawing the wind; The cottage of
   candles; Four who entered paradise; The flying shoe; The en-
   chanted menorah; The souls of trees; The angel of dreams; The
   magic wine cup; The dream of the Rabbi's daughter; A gift for
   Jerusalem; The day the Rabbi disappeared
   (jt. auth) Olson, A. N. Ask the bones: scary sto-
     ries from around the world   **398.2**
Schwartz, Virginia Frances
   Send one angel down   **Fic**
Schwarz, Melissa
   Cochise, Apache chief   **92**
Schyffert, Bea Uusma
   The man who went to the far side of the moon:
     the story of Apollo 11 astronaut Michael Col-
     lins (5 and up)   **92**
Science
   Bazin, M. Math and science across cultures
     510
   Llewellyn, C. Great discoveries & amazing ad-
     ventures (4 and up)   **509**
   Pentland, P. Kitchen science (4 and up)   **641**
   Pentland, P. Party science (4 and up)   **507.8**

Science—*Continued*

Thimmesh, C. The sky's the limit (5 and up) **500**

U.X.L science fact finder **500**

Bibliography

Outstanding science trade books for students K-12 **016.5**

Dictionaries

The American Heritage children's science dictionary **503**

The American Heritage science dictionary **503**

The American Heritage student science dictionary **503**

Prescott, C. Barron's science study dictionary (7 and up) **503**

Ultimate visual dictionary of science **503**

Encyclopedias

The DK science encyclopedia (5 and up) **503**

How it works: science and technology **603**

The Kingfisher science encyclopedia **503**

U.X.L encyclopedia of science **503**

Visual science encyclopedia (5 and up) **503**

The World Book encyclopedia of science **503**

The Young Oxford Library of science **503**

Experiments

See also particular branches of science with the subdivision Experiments

Adams, R. C. Energy projects for young scientists (7 and up) **621**

Adams, R. C. More ideas for science projects (7 and up) **507.8**

Bazler, J. A. More science projects for all students **507.8**

Bochinski, J. B. More award-winning science fair projects (7 and up) **507.8**

Bombaugh, R. J. Science fair success (7 and up) **507.8**

Bonnet, R. L. Science fair projects: chemistry **540.7**

Bottone, F. G., Jr. The science of life **570**

Carson, M. K. The Wright Brothers for kids (4 and up) **629.13**

Chahrour, J. Zap! blink! taste! think! (5 and up) **507.8**

Cobb, V. Science experiments you can eat (5 and up) **507.8**

Cobb, V. You gotta try this! (4 and up) **507.8**

Experiment central (7 and up) **507.8**

Farndon, J. Buoyancy **532**

Farndon, J. Chemicals **540.7**

Farndon, J. Energy **531**

Farndon, J. Gravity **531**

Farndon, J. Motion **531**

Farndon, J. Rocks and minerals **549**

Farndon, J. Solids, liquids, and gases **530.4**

Farndon, J. Time **529**

Gardner, R. Bicycle science projects **531**

Gardner, R. Chemistry science fair projects using acids, bases, metals, salts, and inorganic stuff (7 and up) **540**

Gardner, R. Chemistry science fair projects using french fries, gumdrops, soap, and other organic stuff (7 and up) **547**

Gardner, R. Forces and motion science fair projects **531**

Gardner, R. Health science projects about nutrition (7 and up) **612.3**

Gardner, R. Health science projects about sports performance (7 and up) **612**

Gardner, R. Light, sound, and waves science fair projects (7 and up) **507.8**

Gardner, R. Science fair projects—planning, presenting, succeeding (7 and up) **507.8**

Gardner, R. Science project ideas about air **533**

Gardner, R. Science project ideas about animal behavior **591.5**

Gardner, R. Science project ideas about kitchen chemistry **540.7**

Gardner, R. Science project ideas about rain **551.57**

Gardner, R. Science project ideas about the moon **523.3**

Gardner, R. Science project ideas about the sun **523.7**

Gardner, R. Science project ideas about trees (5 and up) **582.16**

Gardner, R. Science project ideas in the house **507.8**

Gardner, R. Science projects about physics in the home (5 and up) **507.8**

Gardner, R. Science projects about plants (7 and up) **580.7**

Gardner, R. Science projects about temperature and heat (7 and up) **536**

Gardner, R. Science projects about the environment and ecology (7 and up) **363.7**

Gardner, R. Science projects about weather (7 and up) **551.5**

Goodstein, M. Plastics and polymers science fair projects (7 and up) **507.8**

Haduch, B. Science fair success secrets (5 and up) **507.8**

Kerrod, R. The way science works (7 and up) **507.8**

Krieger, M. J. How to excel in science competitions **507.8**

Levine, S. The microscope book **502.8**

Martin, P. A. F. Rivers and streams (7 and up) **577.6**

Martin, P. A. F. Woods and forests (7 and up) **577.3**

Matloff, G. L. More telescope power **522**

Meiani, A. Air (4 and up) **533**

Meiani, A. Chemistry (4 and up) **540**

Meiani, A. Electricity (4 and up) **537**

Meiani, A. Light (4 and up) **535**

Meiani, A. Magnetism (4 and up) **538**

Meiani, A. Water (4 and up) **532**

Oxlade, C. Chemistry **540.7**

Oxlade, C. Weather **551.5**

Parker, S. Science experiments **507.8**

Perry, P. J. Science fair success with plants (7 and up) **580.7**

Pinna, S. d. Electricity **621.3**

Rhatigan, J. Sure-to-win science fair projects (5 and up) **507.8**

Science—Experiments—*Continued*

Rosner, M. A. Science fair success using the Internet (7 and up) **507.8**

Rybolt, T. R. Science fair success with scents, aromas, and smells (7 and up) **612.8**

Science activities (4 and up) **507.8**

Science experiments on file **507.8**

Snedden, R. The environment **577**

Tocci, S. How to do a science fair project **507.8**

VanCleave, J. P. Janice VanCleave's 203 icy, freezing, frosty, cool & wild experiments (4 and up) **507.8**

VanCleave, J. P. Janice VanCleave's A+ projects in astronomy (7 and up) **520**

VanCleave, J. P. Janice VanCleave's A+ projects in earth science (7 and up) **550**

VanCleave, J. P. Janice Vancleave's ecology for every kid (4 and up) **577**

VanCleave, J. P. Janice VanCleave's guide to more of the best science fair projects (5 and up) **507.8**

VanCleave, J. P. Janice VanCleave's guide to the best science fair projects (4 and up) **507.8**

VanCleave, J. P. Janice VanCleave's plants (5 and up) **580.7**

VanCleave, J. P. Janice VanCleave's solar system (4 and up) **523.2**

Vecchione, G. 100 award-winning science fair projects (7 and up) **507.8**

Experiments—Indexes

Pilger, M. A. Science experiments index for young people **507.8**

History

Allaby, M. Makers of science **920.003**

Beshore, G. W. Science in early Islamic culture (4 and up) **509**

Hakim, J. Aristotle leads the way (5 and up) **509**

Hatt, C. Scientists and their discoveries (7 and up) **509**

Ochoa, G. The Wilson chronology of science and technology **502**

Popular science: science year by year **509**

Science, technology, and society: the impact of science in the 20th century **509**

Spangenburg, R. The age of synthesis: 1800-1895 (7 and up) **509**

Spangenburg, R. The birth of science: ancient times to 1699 (7 and up) **509**

Spangenburg, R. Modern science, 1896-1945 (7 and up) **509**

Spangenburg, R. The rise of reason: 1700-1799 (7 and up) **509**

Spangenburg, R. Science frontiers, 1946 to the present (7 and up) **509**

Whitfield, P. History of science **509**

Woods, G. Science of the early Americas (4 and up) **509**

Pictorial works

Simon, S. Out of sight (4 and up) **502.8**

Study and teaching

Exploring science in the library **027.8**

Johnson, C. Using internet primary sources to teach critical thinking skills in the sciences **025.04**

China—History

Beshore, G. W. Science in ancient China (4 and up) **509**

Egypt—History

Woods, G. Science in ancient Egypt (4 and up) **509**

Greece—History

Gay, K. Science in ancient Greece (4 and up) **509**

India—History

Stewart, M. Science in ancient India (4 and up) **509**

Iraq—History

Moss, C. Science in ancient Mesopotamia (4 and up) **509**

Rome—History

Harris, J. L. Science in ancient Rome (4 and up) **509**

United States—History

January, B. Science in colonial America (4 and up) **509**

Science & medicine. DeAngelis, G. **920**

Science & technology in focus [series]

Facklam, M. Modern medicines **615**

Grady, S. M. Virtual reality **006.8**

Science activities (4 and up) **507.8**

Science and civilization

Beshore, G. W. Science in ancient China (4 and up) **509**

Beshore, G. W. Science in early Islamic culture (4 and up) **509**

Gay, K. Science in ancient Greece (4 and up) **509**

Harris, J. L. Science in ancient Rome (4 and up) **509**

January, B. Science in colonial America (4 and up) **509**

Moss, C. Science in ancient Mesopotamia (4 and up) **509**

Science, technology, and society: the impact of science in the 20th century **509**

Stewart, M. Science in ancient India (4 and up) **509**

Woods, G. Science in ancient Egypt (4 and up) **509**

Woods, G. Science of the early Americas (4 and up) **509**

Science and scientists [series]

Pentland, P. Earth science **550**

Pentland, P. Forensic science **363.2**

Pentland, P. Kitchen science **641**

Pentland, P. Party science **507.8**

Pentland, P. Space science **500.5**

Pentland, P. Toy and game science **531**

Science and society [series]

Kidd, J. S. Into thin air **363.7**

Kidd, J. S. Life lines **576.5**

Kidd, J. S. Mother Nature's pharmacy **615**

Kidd, J. S. Quarks and sparks **621.48**

Kidd, J. S. Shades of green **363.7**

Science around the house. See Gardner, R. Science project ideas in the house **507.8**

Science at the edge [series]

Fullick, A. Rebuilding the body **617.9**

Fullick, A. Test tube babies **618.1**

Science concepts [series]
Silverstein, A. Global warming   **363.7**
Silverstein, A. Plate tectonics   **551.1**
Silverstein, A. The universe   **520**
Science crafts for kids. Diehn, G.
    In Diehn, G. and others. Science smart; cool
    projects for exploring the marvels of the
    planet Earth   **550**
Science experiments [series]
Farndon, J. Buoyancy   **532**
Farndon, J. Chemicals   **540.7**
Farndon, J. Energy   **531**
Farndon, J. Motion   **531**
Farndon, J. Rocks and minerals   **549**
Farndon, J. Solids, liquids, and gases   **530.4**
Farndon, J. Time   **529**
Science experiments index for young people.
    Pilger, M. A.   **507.8**
Science experiments on file   **507.8**
Science experiments you can eat. Cobb, V.
    507.8
Science fair projects *See* Science projects
Science fair projects: chemistry. Bonnet, R. L.
    540.7
Science fair projects—planning, presenting, suc-
    ceeding. Gardner, R.   **507.8**
Science fair success. Bombaugh, R. J.   **507.8**
Science fair success [series]
Gardner, R. Bicycle science projects   **531**
Krieger, M. J. How to excel in science competi-
    tions   **507.8**
Perry, P. J. Science fair success with plants
    580.7
Rosner, M. A. Science fair success using the
    Internet   **507.8**
Rybolt, T. R. Science fair success with scents,
    aromas, and smells   **612.8**
Science fair success secrets. Haduch, B.   **507.8**
Science fair success using the Internet. Rosner, M.
    A.   **507.8**
Science fair success with plants. Perry, P. J.
    580.7
Science fair success with scents, aromas, and
    smells. Rybolt, T. R.   **612.8**
Science fairs: ideas and activities   **507.8**
Science fiction
    See also Fantasy fiction
Adams, D. The Hitchhiker's Guide to the Gal-
    axy (7 and up)   **Fic**
Adlington, L. J. The diary of Pelly D (7 and up)
    Fic
Armstrong, J. The kindling (7 and up)   **Fic**
Asimov, I. I, robot (7 and up)   **S C**
Bawden, N. Off the road   **Fic**
Brittain, B. Shape-changer (5 and up)   **Fic**
Card, O. S. Ender's game (7 and up)   **Fic**
Christopher, J. The White Mountains   **Fic**
Clarke, A. C. 2001: a space odyssey (7 and up)
    Fic
Clements, A. Things not seen (7 and up)
    Fic
Coville, B. Aliens ate my homework   **Fic**
Crichton, M. Jurassic Park (7 and up)   **Fic**

Cross, G. The dark ground   **Fic**
Dickinson, P. Eva (7 and up)   **Fic**
DuPrau, J. The city of Ember (5 and up)
    Fic
DuPrau, J. The people of Sparks (5 and up)
    Fic
Engdahl, S. L. The far side of evil   **Fic**
Engdahl, S. L. Enchantress from the stars
    Fic
Farmer, N. The Ear, the Eye, and the Arm (6
    and up)   **Fic**
Firebirds: an anthology of original fantasy and
    science fiction (7 and up)   **S C**
Gilmore, K. The exchange student (7 and up)
    Fic
Goodman, A. Singing the Dogstar blues (7 and
    up)   **Fic**
Gutman, D. Virtually perfect   **Fic**
Haddix, M. P. Among the hidden   **Fic**
Haddix, M. P. Turnabout (7 and up)   **Fic**
Hautman, P. Hole in the sky (7 and up)   **Fic**
Hughes, M. Invitation to the game (7 and up)
    Fic
Jeapes, B. The xenocide mission   **Fic**
Klause, A. C. Alien secrets (5 and up)   **Fic**
Lasky, K. Star split (7 and up)   **Fic**
Lawrence, L. Dream-weaver (7 and up)   **Fic**
Levitin, S. The cure   **Fic**
Lowry, L. Gathering blue (5 and up)   **Fic**
Lowry, L. The giver (6 and up)   **Fic**
Lyon, S. The gift moves   **Fic**
Mackel, K. Can of worms   **Fic**
McCaffrey, A. Pegasus in flight (7 and up)
    Fic
McNaughton, J. The secret under my skin (7
    and up)   **Fic**
New skies: an anthology of today's science fic-
    tion   **S C**
Nix, G. Shade's children (7 and up)   **Fic**
O'Brien, R. C. Z for Zachariah (7 and up)
    Fic
Paulsen, G. The Transall saga   **Fic**
Philbrick, W. R. The last book in the universe
    Fic
Read into the millennium   **S C**
Reeve, P. Mortal engines (7 and up)   **Fic**
Seidler, T. Brainboy and the Deathmaster (5 and
    up)   **Fic**
Sleator, W. The boy who reversed himself (5
    and up)   **Fic**
Sleator, W. The duplicate (7 and up)   **Fic**
Sleator, W. House of stairs (7 and up)   **Fic**
Sleator, W. Interstellar pig (5 and up)   **Fic**
Sleator, W. Singularity (7 and up)   **Fic**
Vande Velde, V. Heir apparent   **Fic**
Verne, J. Twenty thousand leagues under the
    sea (5 and up)   **Fic**
Wells, H. G. The war of the worlds (7 and up)
    Fic
Werlin, N. Double helix (7 and up)   **Fic**
Westerfeld, S. The secret hour (7 and up)
    Fic
Westerfeld, S. Uglies (7 and up)   **Fic**
White, A. Surviving Antarctica (7 and up)
    Fic

Science fiction—*Continued*
History and criticism
Reid, S. E. Presenting young adult science fiction   **813.009**

Science for every kid series
VanCleave, J. P. Janice Vancleave's ecology for every kid   **577**

Science friction. Lubar, D.
In Tripping over the lunch lady and other school stories p60-82   **S C**

Science frontiers, 1946 to the present. Spangenburg, R.   **509**

Science in ancient China. Beshore, G. W.   **509**

Science in ancient Egypt. Woods, G.   **509**

Science in ancient Greece. Gay, K.   **509**

Science in ancient India. Stewart, M.   **509**

Science in ancient Mesopotamia. Moss, C.   **509**

Science in ancient Rome. Harris, J. L.   **509**

Science in colonial America. January, B.   **509**

Science in early Islamic culture. Beshore, G. W.   **509**

The **science** of life. Bottone, F. G., Jr.   **570**

Science of saving animals [series]
Thomas, P. Big cat conservation   **333.95**
Thomas, P. Bird alert   **333.95**

Science of the early Americas. Woods, G.   **509**

Science of the past [series]
Beshore, G. W. Science in ancient China   **509**
Beshore, G. W. Science in early Islamic culture   **509**
Gay, K. Science in ancient Greece   **509**
Harris, J. L. Science in ancient Rome   **509**
January, B. Science in colonial America   **509**
Moss, C. Science in ancient Mesopotamia   **509**
Stewart, M. Science in ancient India   **509**
Woods, G. Science in ancient Egypt   **509**
Woods, G. Science of the early Americas   **509**

Science on the edge [series]
Lindop, L. Chasing tornadoes   **551.55**
Lindop, L. Probing volcanoes   **551.2**
Margulies, P. Artificial intelligence   **006.3**
Mattern, J. Forensics   **363.2**
Nardo, D. Cloning   **660.6**
Orr, T. Test tube babies   **618.1**
Tesar, J. Stem cells   **616**
Wyborny, S. Virtual reality   **006.8**

Science project ideas [series]
Gardner, R. Science project ideas about air   **533**
Gardner, R. Science project ideas about animal behavior   **591.5**
Gardner, R. Science project ideas about rain   **551.57**
Gardner, R. Science project ideas about the moon   **523.3**
Gardner, R. Science project ideas about the sun   **523.7**
Gardner, R. Science project ideas about trees   **582.16**

Gardner, R. Science project ideas in the house   **507.8**

Science project ideas about air. Gardner, R.   **533**

Science project ideas about animal behavior. Gardner, R.   **591.5**

Science project ideas about kitchen chemistry. Gardner, R.   **540.7**

Science project ideas about rain. Gardner, R.   **551.57**

Science project ideas about the moon. Gardner, R.   **523.3**

Science project ideas about the sun. Gardner, R.   **523.7**

Science project ideas about trees. Gardner, R.   **582.16**

Science project ideas in the house. Gardner, R.   **507.8**

Science projects
Adams, R. C. Energy projects for young scientists (7 and up)   **621**
Adams, R. C. More ideas for science projects (7 and up)   **507.8**
Bazler, J. A. More science projects for all students   **507.8**
Bochinski, J. B. The complete handbook of science fair projects   **507.8**
Bochinski, J. B. More award-winning science fair projects (7 and up)   **507.8**
Bombaugh, R. J. Science fair success (7 and up)   **507.8**
Bonnet, R. L. Science fair projects: chemistry   **540.7**
Chahrour, J. Zap! blink! taste! think! (5 and up)   **507.8**
Gardner, R. Bicycle science projects   **531**
Gardner, R. Chemistry science fair projects using acids, bases, metals, salts, and inorganic stuff (7 and up)   **540**
Gardner, R. Chemistry science fair projects using french fries, gumdrops, soap, and other organic stuff (7 and up)   **547**
Gardner, R. Forces and motion science fair projects   **531**
Gardner, R. Health science projects about nutrition (7 and up)   **612.3**
Gardner, R. Health science projects about psychology (7 and up)   **150**
Gardner, R. Health science projects about sports performance (7 and up)   **612**
Gardner, R. Light, sound, and waves science fair projects (7 and up)   **507.8**
Gardner, R. Science fair projects—planning, presenting, succeeding (7 and up)   **507.8**
Gardner, R. Science project ideas about air   **533**
Gardner, R. Science project ideas about animal behavior   **591.5**
Gardner, R. Science project ideas about kitchen chemistry   **540.7**
Gardner, R. Science project ideas about rain   **551.57**
Gardner, R. Science project ideas about the moon   **523.3**

Science projects—*Continued*

Gardner, R. Science project ideas about the sun
523.7

Gardner, R. Science project ideas about trees (5 and up) **582.16**

Gardner, R. Science project ideas in the house
507.8

Gardner, R. Science projects about physics in the home (5 and up) **507.8**

Gardner, R. Science projects about plants (7 and up) **580.7**

Gardner, R. Science projects about the environment and ecology (7 and up) **363.7**

Gardner, R. Science projects about weather (7 and up) **551.5**

Goodstein, M. Plastics and polymers science fair projects (7 and up) **507.8**

Haduch, B. Science fair success secrets (5 and up) **507.8**

Krieger, M. J. How to excel in science competitions **507.8**

Oxlade, C. Chemistry **540.7**

Oxlade, C. Weather **551.5**

Perry, P. J. Science fair success with plants (7 and up) **580.7**

Rhatigan, J. Sure-to-win science fair projects (5 and up) **507.8**

Rosner, M. A. Science fair success using the Internet (7 and up) **507.8**

Rybolt, T. R. Science fair success with scents, aromas, and smells (7 and up) **612.8**

Science fairs: ideas and activities **507.8**

Snedden, R. The environment **577**

Tocci, S. How to do a science fair project
507.8

VanCleave, J. P. Janice VanCleave's A+ projects in astronomy (7 and up) **520**

VanCleave, J. P. Janice VanCleave's A+ projects in earth science (7 and up) **550**

VanCleave, J. P. Janice VanCleave's guide to more of the best science fair projects (5 and up) **507.8**

VanCleave, J. P. Janice VanCleave's guide to the best science fair projects (4 and up)
507.8

VanCleave, J. P. Janice VanCleave's plants (5 and up) **580.7**

VanCleave, J. P. Janice VanCleave's solar system (4 and up) **523.2**

Vecchione, G. 100 award-winning science fair projects (7 and up) **507.8**

Science projects [Enslow series]

Gardner, R. Health science projects about nutrition **612.3**

Gardner, R. Health science projects about psychology **150**

Gardner, R. Health science projects about sports performance **612**

Gardner, R. Science fair projects—planning, presenting, succeeding **507.8**

Gardner, R. Science projects about physics in the home **507.8**

Gardner, R. Science projects about plants
580.7

Gardner, R. Science projects about temperature and heat **536**

Gardner, R. Science projects about the environment and ecology **363.7**

Gardner, R. Science projects about weather
551.5

Science projects [Raintree series]

Oxlade, C. Chemistry **540.7**

Oxlade, C. Weather **551.5**

Pinna, S. d. Electricity **621.3**

Snedden, R. The environment **577**

Science projects about physics in the home. Gardner, R. **507.8**

Science projects about plants. Gardner, R.
580.7

Science projects about temperature and heat. Gardner, R. **536**

Science projects about the environment and ecology. Gardner, R. **363.7**

Science projects about weather. Gardner, R.
551.5

Science smart **550**

Science, technology, and society: the impact of science in the 20th century **509**

Science tools. See Clark, J. O. E. Under the microscope: science tools **530.8**

Science year by year. See Popular science: science year by year **509**

Scientific American sourcebooks [series]

Aaseng, N. Poisonous creatures **591.6**

Scientific apparatus and instruments

Clark, J. O. E. Under the microscope: science tools **530.8**

Scientific expeditions

See also Exploration

Scientific experiments See Science—Experiments

Scientific recreations

Cobb, V. You gotta try this! (4 and up)
507.8

Moscovich, I. 1000 playthinks (7 and up)
793.73

Scientists

See also Environmentalists; Women scientists

Ackerman, J. Louis Pasteur and the founding of microbiology (7 and up) **92**

Adair, G. George Washington Carver **92**

Allaby, M. Makers of science **920.003**

Anderson, M. J. Aristotle (5 and up) **92**

Anderson, M. J. Isaac Newton (4 and up)
92

Boerst, W. J. Isaac Newton (7 and up) **92**

Christianson, G. E. Isaac Newton and the scientific revolution (7 and up) **92**

Delano, M. F. Genius [biography of Albert Einstein] (5 and up) **92**

Distinguished African American scientists of the 20th century (7 and up) **920**

Edelson, E. James Watson and Francis Crick and the building blocks of life (7 and up)
92

Hamilton, J. James Watson **92**

Hatt, C. Scientists and their discoveries (7 and up) **509**

Haven, K. F. 100 most popular scientists for young adults (7 and up) **920**

Scientists—*Continued*
Kozar, R. Inventors and their discoveries
                                                        920
Oleksy, W. G. Hispanic-American scientists (7
    and up)   **920**
Pasachoff, N. E. Niels Bohr   **92**
Richie, J. Space flight   **920**
Robbins, L. E. Louis Pasteur (7 and up)   **92**
Smith, L. W. Louis Pasteur   **92**
Tocci, S. Jonas Salk   **92**
White, M. Isaac Newton   **92**
Yount, L. Asian-American scientists (7 and up)
                                                        920

Dictionaries
American men & women of science   **920.003**
Podell, J. Old worlds to new   **920.003**
Scientists: their lives and works   **920.003**
World Book's biographical encyclopedia of sci-
    entists   **920.003**
Scientists and doctors. Lindop, L.   **920**
Scientists and their discoveries. Hatt, C. **509**
Scientists in the field [series]
    Batten, M. Anthropologist: scientist of the peo-
        ple   **301**
    Collard, S. B., III. The prairie builders
                                                 635.9
    Jackson, D. M. The bug scientists   **595.7**
    Jackson, E. B. Looking for life in the universe
                                                 576.8
    Kramer, S. Hidden worlds: looking through a
        scientist's microscope   **502.8**
    Mallory, K. Swimming with hammerhead sharks
                                                 597
    Montgomery, S. The tarantula scientist   **595.4**
    Osborn, E. Project UltraSwan   **598**
    Sayre, A. P. Secrets of sound   **591.59**
    Swinburne, S. R. The woods scientist   **591.7**
    Turner, P. S. Gorilla doctors   **333.95**
Scientists: their lives and works   **920.003**
Scientists who made history [series]
    Gogerly, L. Dian Fossey   **92**
    Mason, P. Thomas A. Edison   **92**
    Senker, C. Rosalind Franklin   **92**
Scieszka, Jon, 1954-
    Seen Art?   **Fic**
    See/See also pages in the following book(s):
    Author talk (4 and up)   **028.5**
    (ed) Guys write for Guys Read. See Guys write
        for Guys Read   **810.8**
Scoliosis
    Eisenpreis, B. Coping with scoliosis (7 and up)
                                                616.7
Scopes, John Thomas
                About
    Olson, S. P. The trial of John T. Scopes (5 and
        up)
Scorpions. Myers, W. D.   **Fic**
Scotland
    Levy, P. M. Scotland (5 and up)   **941.1**
                Fiction
    Cooper, S. The Boggart (4 and up)   **Fic**
    McAllister, M. Ghost at the window (5 and up)
                                                Fic
    McNaughton, J. An earthly knight (7 and up)
                                                Fic

    Morgan, N. Fleshmarket (7 and up)   **Fic**
    Stevenson, R. L. Kidnapped (7 and up)   **Fic**
    Yolen, J. Girl in a cage   **Fic**
    Yolen, J. Prince across the water   **Fic**
    Yolen, J. The queen's own fool   **Fic**
Scott, Dred, ca. 1795-1858
                About
    Herda, D. J. The Dred Scott case (7 and up)
                                                342
    January, B. The Dred Scott decision   **342**
    Naden, C. J. Dred Scott (7 and up)   **342**
Scott, Elaine
    Poles apart (5 and up)
Scott, Hunter
                About
    Nelson, P. Left for dead (7 and up)   **940.54**
Scott, John F., 1936-
    Mexican, Central and South American art
    In International encyclopedia of art   **703**
Scott, Kieran, 1974-
    The princess & the pauper (7 and up)   **Fic**
Scott, Nina Savin
    The thinking kid's guide to successful soccer (4
        and up)   **796.334**
Scott, Robert Alan
    Chief Joseph and the Nez Percés   **92**
The **Scott,** Foresman Robert's Rules of order new-
    ly revised. Robert, H. M.   **060.4**
Scott standard postage stamp catalogue   **769.56**
Scottish authors *See* Authors, Scottish
The **Scottsboro** Boys Trial. Sorensen, L.   **345**
The **Scrowrers.** Doyle, Sir A. C.
    In Doyle, Sir A. C. The complete Sherlock
        Holmes   **S C**
Sculpture
    See/See also pages in the following book(s):
    Luxbacher, I. The jumbo book of art p8-57 (4
        and up)   **702.8**
The **sea.** Burleigh, R.   **551.46**
Sea animals *See* Marine animals
The **sea** around us. Carson, R.   **551.46**
Sea changes. Duder, T.
    In Ultimate sports; short stories by outstand-
        ing writers for young adults p252-72
                                                S C
Sea gift. Ashby, J.   **Fic**
The **sea-king's** son. McKinley, R.
    In McKinley, R. and Dickinson, P. Water:
        tales of elemental spirits p30-77   **S C**
Sea life *See* Seafaring life
The **Sea** of Trolls. Farmer, N.   **Fic**
Sea serpent. Dickinson, P.
    In McKinley, R. and Dickinson, P. Water:
        tales of elemental spirits p78-118
                                                S C
Sea shells *See* Shells
Sea stories
    Avi. The true confessions of Charlotte Doyle (6
        and up)   **Fic**
    Fox, P. The slave dancer (5 and up)   **Fic**
    Hesse, K. Stowaway (5 and up)   **Fic**

Sea stories—*Continued*

Paulsen, G. The voyage of the Frog (6 and up) **Fic**

Taylor, T. Rogue wave and other red-blooded sea stories **S C**

Verne, J. Twenty thousand leagues under the sea (5 and up) **Fic**

Wisler, G. C. Run the blockade **Fic**

Sea turtles

Ripple, J. Sea turtles (7 and up) **597.9**

A **sea** worry. Kingston, M. H.

In American dragons: twenty-five Asian American voices p112-17 **810.8**

Seafaring life

Fiction

Frederick, H. V. The voyage of Patience Goodspeed (5 and up) **Fic**

Meyer, L. A. Bloody Jack (7 and up) **Fic**

Rosen, M. Shakespeare **822.3**

Seah, Audrey, 1958-

Vietnam (5 and up) **959.704**

Seals (Animals)

DuTemple, L. A. Seals and sea lions (7 and up) **599.79**

Seals (Numismatics)

Shearer, B. F. State names, seals, flags, and symbols **929.9**

Seals and sea lions. DuTemple, L. A. **599.79**

The **séance**. Sleator, W.

In Sleator, W. Oddballs; stories p57-70 **S C**

The **search** for poison-dart frogs. Fridell, R. **597.8**

Search for the golden moon bear. Montgomery, S. **599.78**

Searching for Candlestick Park. Kehret, P. **Fic**

Searching the internet *See* Internet searching

Sears, Vickie, 1941-

Dancer

In Leaving home: stories p19-25 **808.8**

In Talking leaves; contemporary native American short stories **S C**

Sears list of subject headings **025.4**

Seashore

Carson, R. The edge of the sea (7 and up) **577.7**

Kricher, J. C. Peterson first guide to seashores (6 and up) **577.7**

Parker, S. Seashore (4 and up) **577.7**

Seashore ecology

Bredeson, C. Tide pools **577.6**

Goodman, S. Ultimate field trip 3 **577.6**

Seasons

See also Summer

Fiction

Ehrlich, G. A blizzard year **Fic**

Season's end. Myers, W. D.

In The Color of absence; 12 stories about loss and hope p169-82 **S C**

A **seat** in the garden. King, T.

In Talking leaves; contemporary native American short stories **S C**

Sebestyen, Ouida, 1924-

Playing God

In Visions: nineteen short stories by outstanding writers for young adults p87-99 **S C**

Welcome

In Sixteen; short stories by outstanding writers for young adults p47-59 **S C**

The **Second** Amendment. Hanson, F. O. **344**

The **second** day. Barakat, I.

In Shattered: stories of children and war p5-13 **S C**

The **second** jungle book. See Kipling, R. The jungle books **S C**

Second stringer. Dygard, T. J. **Fic**

Secondary schools *See* High schools

The **secret** garden [play] Sterling, P.

In Theatre for young audiences; 20 great plays for children p99-141 **812.008**

The **secret** hour. Westerfeld, S. **Fic**

Secret in St. Something. Wallace, B. B. **Fic**

The **secret** journey. Kehret, P. **Fic**

The **secret** language of girls. Dowell, F. O. **Fic**

Secret letters from 0 to 10. Morgenstern, S. H. **Fic**

The **secret** life of fishes. Buttfield, H. **597**

The **secret** life of food. Crespo, C. **641.5**

Secret numbers. Morris, W.

In On the edge: stories at the brink p95-106 **S C**

The **secret** of Castle Cant. Bath, K. P. **Fic**

The **secret** of Sabrina Fludde. Fisk, P. **Fic**

Secret sacrament. Jordan, S. **Fic**

The **secret** school. Avi **Fic**

Secret service

See also Spies

The **secret** under my skin. McNaughton, J. **Fic**

The **secret** within. Golding, T. M. **Fic**

Secret writing *See* Cryptography

Secrets from the rocks: dinosaur hunting with Roy Chapman Andrews. Marrin, A. **92**

Secrets in the fire. Mankell, H. **Fic**

Secrets of a Civil War submarine. Walker, S. M. **973.7**

Secrets of sound. Sayre, A. P. **591.59**

Secrets of the ice man. Patent, D. H. **930.1**

Secrets of the mummies. Tanaka, S. **393**

Secrets of the Sphinx. Giblin, J. **932**

Secrets of the unexplained [series]

Blackwood, G. L. Extraordinary events and oddball occurrences **001.9**

Sects

Stein, S. J. Alternative American religions (7 and up) **209**

Security reference series

Child and youth security sourcebook **362.7**

Sedgwick, Marcus

The book of Dead Days **Fic**

Sedgwick, Marcus—*Continued*
The Dark Horse (7 and up)   **Fic**
The **see-far** glasses. Ho, M.
  In Soul searching: thirteen stories about faith
     and belief p134-56   **S C**
See Jane win for girls. Rimm, S. B.   **305.23**
See through history [series]
  Howarth, S. The Middle Ages   **940.1**
  Nicolle, D. Medieval knights   **940.1**
  Wood, T. The Renaissance   **940.2**
Seedfolks. Fleischman, P.   **Fic**
Seeds
  Pascoe, E. Seeds and seedlings   **582**
Seeds and seedlings. Pascoe, E.   **582**
Seeds of hope. Gregory, K.   **Fic**
Seeing. Silverstein, A. Silverstein, A. and others.
    Senses and sensors [series]   **612.8**
The **seeing** stone. Crossley-Holland, K.   **Fic**
Seeing the blue between (7 and up)   **808.1**
Seek. Fleischman, P.   **Fic**
Seen Art? Scieszka, J.   **Fic**
Sees Behind Trees. Dorris, M.   **Fic**
Segall, Grant
  John D. Rockefeller   **92**
Segregation
     See also Apartheid; Discrimination
         Fiction
  Collier, K. Jericho walls (7 and up)   **Fic**
       Law and legislation
  Anderson, W. Plessy v. Ferguson   **342**
Segregation in education
  Anderson, W. Brown v. Board of Education
       344
  Gold, S. D. Brown v. Board of Education
       344
Seidler, Tor, 1952-
  Brainboy and the Deathmaster (5 and up)
       Fic
Seidman, David
  Jerry Spinelli (5 and up)   **92**
Seidman, Rachel Filene
  The Civil war: a history in documents   **973.7**
Seismology *See* Earthquakes
Selby, David
  (jt. auth) Willson, Q. The ultimate classic car
     book   **629.222**
Self-acceptance
  Sneddon, P. S. Body image (7 and up)
       155.9
Self-esteem
  Hinds, M. J. Focus on body image   **306.4**
  Shepherd, K. R. Drugs and low self-esteem (7
     and up)   **616.86**
Self-help programs *See* Twelve-step programs
Self-love (Psychology) *See* Self-esteem
Self-mutilation
  Clarke, A. Coping with self-mutilation (7 and
     up)   **616.85**
  Ng, G. Everything you need to know about self-
     mutilation (7 and up)   **616.85**
         Fiction
  McCormick, P. Cut (7 and up)   **Fic**

Self-perception
  Davis, B. What's real, what's ideal (7 and up)
       616.85
  Sneddon, P. S. Body image (7 and up)
       155.9
Self-respect *See* Self-esteem
Selkie [play] Brooks Gollobin, L.
  In Theatre for young audiences; 20 great
     plays for children p579-604   **812.008**
Selznick, Brian
  (il) Clements, A. The school story   **Fic**
  (il) Kerley, B. Walt Whitman   **92**
Semiconductors
  Chorlton, W. The invention of the silicon chip
       621.381
Seminole. Libal, J.
  In North American Indians today [series]
Seminole Indians
  Libal, J. Seminole
     In North American Indians today [series]
         Fiction
  George, J. C. The talking earth   **Fic**
Semiramis. Mayer, M.
  In Mayer, M. Women warriors; myths and
     legends of heroic women p21-24   **398**
Sención, the Indian girl. Delacre, L.
  In Delacre, L. Golden tales; myths, legends,
     and folktales from Latin America p25-27
       398.2
Send one angel down. Schwartz, V. F.   **Fic**
Sendak, Maurice
  Really Rosie [play]
     In Theatre for young audiences; 20 great
       plays for children p72-98   **812.008**
  See/See also pages in the following book(s):
  Marcus, L. S. A Caldecott celebration   **741.6**
Sendeh sings to the prairie dogs. Curry, J. L.
  In Curry, J. L. Hold up the sky: and other
     Native American tales from Texas and
     the Southern Plains p89-94   **398.2**
Sender, Ruth Minsky, 1926-
  The cage (7 and up)   **940.53**
Seneca Indians
         Folklore
  Martin, R. The world before this one (4 and up)
       398.2
Senegal
  Berg, E. Senegal (5 and up)   **966.3**
Senior high school library catalog   **011.6**
Senker, Cath
  Rosalind Franklin (5 and up)   **92**
  Why are people prejudiced?   **303.3**
Senning, Cindy Post
  (jt. auth) Post, P. Emily Post's The guide to
     good manners for kids   **395**
Senses and sensation
  Brynie, F. H. Perception   **612.8**
  Hall, D. The brain and senses
     In Being human   **612**
  Parker, S. Brain, nerves, and senses   **612.8**
  Silverstein, A. Senses and sensors [series]
       612.8

Senses and sensors [series]. Silverstein, A.
612.8

Senungetuk, Vivian
(ed) Tiulana, P. Wise words of Paul Tiulana
92

Separate, but not equal. Haskins, J.   **379**

September 11, 2001. Hampton, W.   **973.931**

September 11, 2001: the day that changed America. Wheeler, J. C.   **973.931**

September 11 terrorist attacks, 2001
911: the book of help   **810.8**
America under attack: primary sources (7 and up)   **973.931**
Frank, M. Understanding September 11th (7 and up)   **973.931**
Gow, M. Attack on America   **973.931**
Hampton, W. September 11, 2001   **973.931**
Lalley, P. 9.11.01: terrorists attack the U.S. (4 and up)   **973.931**
Margulies, P. Al Qaeda: Osama bin Laden's army of terrorists   **973.931**
Marquette, S. America under attack (4 and up)   **973.931**
Stewart, G. America under attack (7 and up)   **973.931**
Stewart, G. Terrorism (4 and up)   **303.6**
Wells, D. K. Live aware, not in fear (7 and up)   **155.5**
Wheeler, J. C. September 11, 2001: the day that changed America   **973.931**
Drama
With their eyes (7 and up)   **812**
Pictorial works
A Nation challenged (4 and up)   **973.931**
Sequoyah, 1770?-1843
About
Klausner, J. Sequoyah's gift (4 and up)   **92**
Sequoyah's gift. Klausner, J.   **92**
Serbia
Milivojevic, J. Serbia (5 and up)   **949.7**
Sergis, Diana K.
Bush v. Gore   **342**
Cipollone v. Liggett Group (7 and up)   **346.03**
Serious about series. Makowski, S.   **016.8**
Sernoff, Linda
(jt. auth) Sullivan, H. Research reports   **808**
The **Serpent** and the grape-grower's daughter
In Hearne, B. G. Beauties and beasts p56-59   **398.2**
The **serpent** slayer. Tchana, K. H.
In Tchana, K. H. The serpent slayer: and other stories of strong women p1-5   **398.2**
The **serpent** slayer: and other stories of strong women. Tchana, K. H.   **398.2**
Serpents' teeth. Robinson, S.
In New skies: an anthology of today's science fiction   **S C**
Serra, Junípero, 1713-1784
About
Dolan, S. Junípero Serra   **92**
Serra, Miguel José See Serra, Junípero, 1713-1784

Serritella, Judy, 1948-
Look again!   **373.1**
Service, Alexandra
1200   **909.07**
Service, Pamela F.
300 B.C.   **930**
See/See also pages in the following book(s):
Reid, S. E. Presenting young adult science fiction   **813.009**
(jt. auth) Service, A. 1200   **909.07**
Service, Robert W., 1874-1958
The cremation of Sam McGee (4 and up)   **811**
Serving from the hip. See Williams, V. Venus & Serena   **92**
Serving homeschooled teens and their parents. Lerch, M. T.   **027.6**
Servitude See Slavery
Setaro, John F.
(jt. auth) Hyde, M. O. Alcohol 101   **362.292**
(jt. auth) Hyde, M. O. Medicine's brave new world   **610**
(jt. auth) Hyde, M. O. When the brain dies first   **616.8**
Settel, Joanne
Exploding ants (4 and up)   **591.5**
The **setting** sun and the rolling world. Mungoshi, C.
In Leaving home: stories p157-64   **808.8**
Setzer, Paul M.
(il) Costello, E. Random House American sign language dictionary   **419**
Seuss, Dr.
About
Dean, T. Theodor Geisel [Dr. Seuss] (4 and up)   **92**
Seven good years. Goldin, B. D.
In Goldin, B. D. Journeys with Elijah; eight tales of the Prophet p11-19   **222**
The **Seven** voyages of Sinbad the Sailor. Yeoman, J.   **398.2**
The **seven** wonders of the ancient world. Bentley, D.   **722**
Seventh grade. Soto, G.
In Soto, G. Baseball in April, and other stories p52-59   **S C**
Seventh grade tango. Levy, E.   **Fic**
Severance, John B.
Gandhi, great soul (5 and up)   **92**
Skyscrapers   **720**
Thomas Jefferson (7 and up)   **92**
Winston Churchill (5 and up)   **92**
Sevier, John, 1745-1815
See/See also pages in the following book(s):
Doherty, K. Ranchers, homesteaders, and traders   **920**
Sevier, Marti
(jt. auth) Lister, M. England   **942**
Sewerage
See/See also pages in the following book(s):
Macaulay, D. Underground (5 and up)   **624**
Sex See Sexual behavior

Sex crimes

See also Child sexual abuse

Sex education

Bell, R. Changing bodies, changing lives (7 and up) **613.9**

Brynie, F. H. 101 questions about sex and sexuality— (7 and up) **613.9**

Daldry, J. The teenage guy's survival guide (7 and up) **305.23**

Diamond, S. N. Everything you need to know about going to the gynecologist (7 and up) **618.1**

Gravelle, K. What's going on down there? **612.6**

Gray, H. M. Real girl/real world (7 and up) **305.23**

Gurian, M. From boys to men **305.23**

Harris, R. H. It's perfectly normal (4 and up) **613.9**

Jukes, M. The guy book (7 and up) **305.23**

Jukes, M. It's a girl thing (5 and up) **305.23**

Parker, S. The reproductive system **612.6**

Sex: opposing viewpoints **306.7**

Sex role

Male/female roles: opposing viewpoints **305.3**

Fiction

Barrett, T. Anna of Byzantium **Fic**

Brenaman, M. Evvy's Civil War **Fic**

Cheng, A. The lace dowry (4 and up) **Fic**

Gray, D. E. Together apart (7 and up) **Fic**

Haddix, M. P. Just Ella (7 and up) **Fic**

Keehn, S. M. Anna Sunday **Fic**

Kessler, C. Our secret, Siri Aang (7 and up) **Fic**

Lee, T. Piratica **Fic**

Meyer, L. A. Bloody Jack (7 and up) **Fic**

Namioka, L. Ties that bind, ties that break (5 and up) **Fic**

Napoli, D. J. Bound **Fic**

Rinaldi, A. Girl in blue **Fic**

Spinelli, J. There's a girl in my hammerlock (5 and up) **Fic**

Staples, S. F. Shabanu **Fic**

Stolz, J. The shadows of Ghadames **Fic**

Whelan, G. Chu Ju's house **Fic**

Sexual behavior

Sex: opposing viewpoints **306.7**

Sexual harassment

McGowan, K. Sexual harassment (7 and up) **305.3**

Fiction

Mazer, N. F. Out of control (7 and up) **Fic**

Sexuality *See* Sexual behavior

Sexually transmitted diseases

Curran, C. P. Sexually transmitted diseases (7 and up) **616.95**

Little, M. Sexually transmitted diseases (7 and up) **616.95**

See/See also pages in the following book(s):

Jukes, M. It's a girl thing (5 and up) **305.23**

Seymour-Smith, Martin

(ed) World authors, 1900-1950. See World authors, 1900-1950 **920.003**

Sfar, Joann

Dungeon Vol. 1: Duck Heart **741.5**

Shabanu. Staples, S. F. **Fic**

Shackleton, Sir Ernest Henry, 1874-1922

About

Calvert, P. Sir Ernest Shackleton **92**

Johnson, R. L. Ernest Shackleton **92**

Kimmel, E. C. Ice story (4 and up) **998**

Shade's children. Nix, G. **Fic**

Shades of blue, Volume 1. Harris, J. S. **741.5**

Shades of green. Kidd, J. S. **363.7**

Shades of Simon Gray. McDonald, J. **Fic**

Shadow boxer. Lynch, C. **Fic**

Shadow brother. Vande Velde, V.

In Vande Velde, V. Being dead; stories **S C**

Shadow-catcher. Levin, B. **Fic**

Shadow of the dragon. Garland, S. **Fic**

Shadow spinner. Fletcher, S. **Fic**

Shadows. Peck, R.

In Peck, R. Past perfect, present tense: new and collected stories **S C**

In Visions: nineteen short stories by outstanding writers for young adults p2-10 **S C**

Shadows and moonshine. Aiken, J. **S C**

The **shadows** of Ghadames. Stolz, J. **Fic**

Shahjahan, Emperor of India, ca. 1592-1666

Fiction

Lasky, K. Jahanara, Princess of Princesses **Fic**

Shaka *See* Chaka, Zulu Chief, 1787?-1828

Shaka, king of the Zulus. Stanley, D. **92**

Shake, rattle, & roll. Levine, L. **920**

Shake, rattle, and roll. Christian, S. **551.2**

The **Shakeress**. Heuston, K. B. **Fic**

Shakers

Williams, J. K. The Shakers (7 and up) **289**

Fiction

Heuston, K. B. The Shakeress (7 and up) **Fic**

Peck, R. N. A day no pigs would die (6 and up) **Fic**

Shakespeare, William, 1564-1616

One hundred and eleven Shakespeare monologues (7 and up) **822.3**

About

Aliki. William Shakespeare & the Globe (4 and up) **792.09**

Dunton-Downer, L. Essential Shakespeare handbook **822.3**

Ganeri, A. The young person's guide to Shakespeare (7 and up) **822.3**

Rosen, M. Shakespeare **822.3**

Shakespeare's world and work (7 and up) **822.3**

Shellard, D. William Shakespeare (7 and up) **822.3**

Shakespeare, William, 1564-1616—About—*Continued*
Stanley, D. Bard of Avon: the story of William Shakespeare (4 and up)   **822.3**
See/See also pages in the following book(s):
Nardo, D. Great Elizabethan playwrights   **920**
Adaptations
Coville, B. William Shakespeare's A midsummer night's dream   **822.3**
Coville, B. William Shakespeare's Romeo and Juliet   **822.3**
Garfield, L. Shakespeare stories {I}-II   **822.3**
Lamb, C. Tales from Shakespeare   **822.3**
Nesbit, E. The best of Shakespeare (4 and up)   **822.3**
Packer, T. Tales from Shakespeare   **822.3**
Williams, M. Tales from Shakespeare   **822.3**
Fiction
Blackwood, G. L. The Shakespeare stealer (5 and up)   **Fic**
Macbeth; adaptation. See Cover, A. B. Macbeth   **741.5**
Othello; adaptation. See Lester, J. Othello   **Fic**
Romeo and Juliet. See Coville, B. William Shakespeare's Romeo and Juliet   **822.3**
(jt. auth) Cover, A. B. Macbeth   **741.5**
(jt. auth) Coville, B. William Shakespeare's Romeo and Juliet   **822.3**
(jt. auth) Lester, J. Othello   **Fic**
Shakespeare bats cleanup. Koertge, R.   **Fic**
The **Shakespeare** stealer. Blackwood, G. L.   **Fic**
Shakespeare's Globe (London, England)
Aliki. William Shakespeare & the Globe (4 and up)   **792.09**
Shakespeare's London. Barter, J.   **942.06**
Shakespeare's world and work (7 and up)   **822.3**
Shamanism
Kallen, S. A. Shamans   **201**
Shamans. Kallen, S. A.   **201**
The **Shamer's** daughter. Kaaberbol, L.   **Fic**
Shan Jahan *See* Shahjahan, Emperor of India, ca. 1592-1666
Shandler, Sara
Ophelia speaks (7 and up)   **305.23**
Shane-Armstrong, Ryn
(ed) The Vietnam War. See The Vietnam War   **959.704**
Shannon, David, 1959-
(il) Packer, T. Romeo and Juliet   **822.3**
(il) Yolen, J. Sacred places   **811**
Shannon, Joyce Brennfleck
(ed) Sports injuries information for teens. See Sports injuries information for teens   **617.1**
Shape-changer. Brittain, B.   **Fic**
Shaper. Haas, J.   **Fic**
Shaping America [series]
Doherty, K. Ranchers, homesteaders, and traders   **920**
Shaping the earth. Patent, D. H.   **550**

Sharing the soup. Jaffe, N.
In Jaffe, N. and Zeitlin, S. J. The cow of no color: riddle stories and justice tales from around the world p104-09   **398.2**
Shark bait. Salisbury, G.
In Ultimate sports; short stories by outstanding writers for young adults p118-44   **S C**
The **Shark** Callers. Campbell, E.   **Fic**
Sharks
Capuzzo, M. Close to shore   **597**
Cerullo, M. M. The truth about great white sharks (4 and up)   **597**
Macquitty, M. Shark (4 and up)   **597**
Mallory, K. Swimming with hammerhead sharks (4 and up)   **597**
Fiction
Campbell, E. The Shark Callers (7 and up)   **Fic**
Sharmat, Marjorie Weinman, 1928-
Dream job
In Visions: nineteen short stories by outstanding writers for young adults p23-29   **S C**
May I have your autograph?
In Sixteen; short stories by outstanding writers for young adults p15-21   **S C**
Sharp, Anne Wallace
Australia   **994**
The gypsies   **909**
Sharrar, Jack F., 1949-
(ed) Great monologues for young actors. See Great monologues for young actors   **812.008**
(ed) Great scenes for young actors from the stage. See Great scenes for young actors from the stage   **808.82**
Shattered. Singer, M.
In Shattered: stories of children and war p14-22   **S C**
Shattered: stories of children and war   **S C**
Shattering Glass. Giles, G.   **Fic**
Shaw, Elizabeth M.
(jt. auth) Brannen, D. E. Supreme Court drama   **347**
Shaw, Patricia Hearst *See* Hearst, Patricia Campbell
She. Guy, R.
In Sixteen; short stories by outstanding writers for young adults p147-53   **S C**
She flies. Rice, D.
In Rice, D. Crazy loco; stories about growing up Chicano in southern Texas p78-95   **S C**
She is beautiful in her whole being. Momaday, N. S.
In Talking leaves; contemporary native American short stories   **S C**
Shea, Pegi Deitz, 1960-
Ekaterina Gordeeva   **92**
Shearer, Alex
The Great Blue Yonder (5 and up)   **Fic**

Shearer, Barbara Smith
(jt. auth) Shearer, B. F. State names, seals, flags, and symbols **929.9**
Shearer, Benjamin F.
State names, seals, flags, and symbols **929.9**
Sheehan, Patricia, 1954-
Côte d'Ivoire (5 and up) **966.68**
Luxembourg (5 and up) **949.35**
Moldova (5 and up) **947.6**
Sheehan, Sean, 1951-
Austria (5 and up) **943.6**
Guatemala (5 and up) **972.81**
Jamaica (5 and up) **972.92**
Lebanon (5 and up) **956.92**
Malta (5 and up) **945**
Pakistan (5 and up) **954.91**
The technology of World War II **940.54**
Trinidad & Tobago (5 and up) **972.983**
Turkey (5 and up) **956.1**
Zimbabwe (5 and up) **968.91**
(jt. auth) Powell, A. Ancient Greece **938**
Sheen, Barbara, 1949-
Attention deficit disorder **616.85**
Diabetes **616.4**
Teen alcoholism (7 and up) **616.86**
Sheep
Fiction
Paulsen, G. The haymeadow (6 and up) **Fic**
Sheets, Anna J.
(ed) U·X·L encyclopedia of Native American tribes. See U·X·L encyclopedia of Native American tribes **970.004**
Shein, Lori, 1957-
AIDS (7 and up) **616.97**
(jt. auth) Haugen, D. The Civil War **973.7**
Sheldon, Dyan
Confessions of a teenage drama queen (7 and up) **Fic**
My perfect life (7 and up) **Fic**
Shelf life: stories by the book (5 and up) **S C**
Shellard, Dominic
William Shakespeare (7 and up) **822.3**
Shelley, Mary Wollstonecraft, 1797-1851
The new Prometheus
In Read into the millennium; tales of the future p34-40 **S C**
About
Nardo, D. Understanding Frankenstein (7 and up) **823.009**
Frankenstein; adaptation. See Reed, G. Mary Shelley's Frankenstein: the graphic novel **741.5**
Frankenstein; adaptation. See Shelley, M. W. The new Prometheus
(jt. auth) Reed, G. Mary Shelley's Frankenstein: the graphic novel **741.5**
Shelley, Rex, 1930-
Japan **952**
Shellfish
See also Mollusks
Shells
Arthur, A. Shell (4 and up) **594**
Douglass, J. L. Peterson first guide to shells of North America **594**

Rehder, H. A. The Audubon Society field guide to North American seashells **594**
Shepherd, Donna Walsh *See* Walsh Shepherd, Donna, 1948-
South Dakota America the beautiful, second series **973**
Shepherd, K. R. (Kenneth Ronald)
Drugs and low self-esteem (7 and up)
616.86
The **shepherd** of rabbits. Molnár, I.
In Molnár, I. One-time dog market at Buda and other Hungarian folktales p31-38
398.2
The **shepherd** who fought for a princess. Skurzynski, G.
In Fire and wings: dragon tales from East and West p95-102 **S C**
The **shepherd** who knew the language of animals. Anaya, R. A.
In Anaya, R. A. My land sings; stories from the Rio Grande p85-101 **S C**
Sheptyts´kyĭ, Andriĭ, 1865-1944
See/See also pages in the following book(s):
Lyman, D. Holocaust rescuers **920**
Sherlock, Patti
Letters from Wolfie (5 and up) **Fic**
Sherman, Allan, 1924-1973
A gift of laughter
In Leaving home: stories p27-33 **808.8**
Sherman, Cindy
See/See also pages in the following book(s):
Sills, L. In real life: six women photographers (7 and up) **920**
Sherman, Delia
Blood kin
In Vampires: a collection of original stories p35-63 **S C**
Cotillion
In Firebirds: an anthology of original fantasy and science fiction; an anthology of original fantasy and science fiction **S C**
Grand Central Park
In The Green Man: tales from the mythic forest p21-42 **808.8**
Sherman, Josepha
The Cold War **909.82**
Deep space observation satellites **629.43**
Jerry Yang and David Filo **92**
The magic-stealer
In Vampires: a collection of original stories p99-120 **S C**
Merlin's kin **398.2**
Your travel guide to ancient Israel **933**
Sherman, Patsy O., 1930-
See/See also pages in the following book(s):
Thimmesh, C. Girls think of everything (5 and up) **920**
Sherman, Whitney
(il) Jaffe, N. The cow of no color: riddle stories and justice tales from around the world
398.2
Sherrod, John
(il) Page, L. M. A field guide to freshwater fishes: North America north of Mexico **597**

Sherrow, Victoria
The blaze engulfs — **940.53**
Cherokee Nation v. Georgia (7 and up) — **346**
Connecticut
In Celebrate the states — **973**
Encyclopedia of youth and war — **305.23**
The Exxon Valdez — **363.7**
Gideon v. Wainwright (7 and up) — **345**
Hurricane Andrew — **551.55**
Joseph McCarthy and the Cold War — **92**
Ohio
In Celebrate the states — **973**
The Oklahoma City bombing — **364.1**
Smoke to flame — **940.53**
Volleyball — **796.325**

Sherwood: original stories from the world of Robin Hood — **S C**

Shetterly, Will
Brian and the aliens
In New skies: an anthology of today's science fiction — **S C**

Shields, Charles J.
Amy Tan — **92**

Shields, Charles J., 1951-
The 1993 World Trade Center bombing — **364.1**
Belize (4 and up) — **972.82**
Honduras (4 and up) — **972.83**

Shields, Nancy E., 1928-
Where credit is due (7 and up) — **808**

Shih Huang-ti, Emperor of China *See* Ch'in Shih-huang, Emperor of China, 259-210 B.C.

Shiloh. Naylor, P. R. — **Fic**

Shimmy shimmy shimmy like my sister Kate — **811.008**

Shimomura, Tsutomu
See/See also pages in the following book(s):
Yount, L. Asian-American scientists (7 and up) — **920**

Shingles (Disease)
Silverstein, A. Chickenpox and shingles (7 and up) — **616.9**

Shinn, Sharon, 1957-
The Safe-Keeper's secret — **Fic**

Shinto
Kallen, S. A. Shinto — **299.5**

Ship. Macaulay, D. — **387.2**

Ship of fire. Cadnum, M. — **Fic**

The **ship** that went to America. Philip, N.
In Philip, N. Celtic fairy tales p125-36 — **398.2**

Shipping
United States
Sandler, M. W. On the waters of the USA (5 and up) — **387.2**

Ships
See also Steamboats
Kentley, E. Boat (4 and up) — **387.2**
Sandler, M. W. On the waters of the USA (5 and up) — **387.2**
Trent, L. The Viking longship (7 and up) — **948**

Shipton, Alyn
Jazz makers (7 and up) — **920**

Shipwrecked!: the true adventures of a Japanese boy [biography of Manjiro Nakahama] Blumberg, R. — **92**

Shipwrecks
Adams, S. Titanic (4 and up) — **910.4**
Ballard, R. D. The discovery of the Titanic (7 and up) — **910.4**
Ballard, R. D. Ghost liners (4 and up) — **910.4**
Brewster, H. 882 ½ amazing answers to your questions about the Titanic — **910.4**
Macaulay, D. Ship (4 and up) — **387.2**
Marschall, K. Inside the Titanic (4 and up) — **910.4**
Matsen, B. The incredible search for the treasure ship Atocha (4 and up) — **910.4**
Philbrick, N. Revenge of the whale (7 and up) — **910.4**
Platt, R. Shipwreck (4 and up) — **910.4**
Smith, K. Exploring for shipwrecks — **930.1**
Walker, S. M. Secrets of a Civil War submarine (7 and up) — **973.7**
Fiction
Bunting, E. SOS Titanic (7 and up) — **Fic**
Lawrence, I. The wreckers (5 and up) — **Fic**

Shirley, David, 1955-
Alabama
In Celebrate the states — **973**
Everyday I sing the blues: the story of B.B. King (7 and up) — **92**
Mississippi
In Celebrate the states — **973**
North Carolina
In Celebrate the states — **973**

Shiva's fire. Staples, S. F. — **Fic**

Shocking, slimy, stinky, shiny science experiments. See Parker, S. Science experiments — **507.8**

Shockrockets: we have ignition. Busiek, K. — **741.5**

Shoeless Joe & me. Gutman, D. — **Fic**

Shoeless Joe Jackson *See* Jackson, Joe, 1887 or 8-1951

Shoemaker, Eugene Merle, 1928-1997
See/See also pages in the following book(s):
Carruthers, M. W. Pioneers of geology — **920**

Shoemaker, Joel
(jt. auth) Jones, P. Do it right! — **027.62**

Shoofly pie. Nye, N. S.
In The Color of absence; 12 stories about loss and hope p123-44 — **S C**

The **shoot-out.** Nixon, J. L.
In Nixon, J. L. Ghost town; seven ghostly stories p3-15 — **S C**

Shopaholic. Waite, J. — **Fic**

Shoplifting
Fiction
Kehret, P. Cages — **Fic**

Shopping
Fiction
Waite, J. Shopaholic — **Fic**

Shopping centers and malls
Fiction
Esckilsen, E. E. The last mall rat (7 and up)
Fic
Shorebirds. Latimer, J. P.   598
Short scenes and monologues for middle school
actors. Surface, M. H.   812
Short stories
13   S C
Aiken, J. Shadows and moonshine (4 and up)
S C
Alexander, L. The foundling and other tales of
Prydain (5 and up)   S C
American eyes   S C
Anaya, R. A. My land sings   S C
Appelt, K. Kissing Tennessee and other stories
from the Stardust Dance   S C
Asimov, I. I, robot (7 and up)   S C
Aspin, D. Ordinary miracles (7 and up)   S C
Avi. What do fish have to do with anything?
and other stories (4 and up)   S C
The Book of dragons   S C
The Boy of Chancellorville and other Civil War
stories (7 and up)   S C
The Color of absence   S C
Conford, E. Crush (7 and up)   S C
Coville, B. Odder than ever   S C
Crutcher, C. Athletic shorts (7 and up)   S C
Dahl, R. Skin and other stories (7 and up)
S C
De Lint, C. Waifs and strays (7 and up)
S C
Delacre, L. Salsa stories (4-6)   S C
Destination unexpected: short stories (7 and up)
S C
Don't cramp my style (7 and up)   S C
Doyle, Sir A. C. The complete Sherlock Holmes
(7 and up)   S C
Estevis, A. Down Garrapata road (7 and up)
S C
Face relations (7 and up)   S C
Fire and wings: dragon tales from East and
West (4 and up)   S C
Firebirds: an anthology of original fantasy and
science fiction (7 and up)   S C
Flake, S. G. Who am I without him? (7 and up)
S C
A Glory of unicorns (5 and up)   S C
Gothic! (7 and up)   S C
Half-human (7 and up)   S C
The Haunted house: a collection of original sto-
ries   S C
Hearne, B. G. The canine connection: stories
about dogs and people   S C
Join in   S C
Jones, D. W. Unexpected magic   S C
Kimmel, E. A. The jar of fools: eight Hanukkah
stories from Chelm (4 and up)   S C
Kimmel, E. A. Sword of the samurai (4 and up)
S C
Kipling, R. The jungle books (4 and up)
S C
Leaving home: stories   808.8
Lester, J. Long journey home: stories from
black history   S C

Lynch, C. All the old haunts (7 and up)
S C
Marston, E. Figs and fate   S C
McKinley, R. The door in the hedge   S C
McKinley, R. Water: tales of elemental spirits
(7 and up)   S C
Memories of sun   S C
Myers, W. D. 145th Street   S C
Myers, W. D. A time to love (7 and up)
S C
Naidoo, B. Out of bounds: seven stories of con-
flict and hope (5 and up)   S C
Necessary noise: stories about our families as
they really are (7 and up)   S C
New skies: an anthology of today's science fic-
tion   S C
Night terrors (7 and up)   S C
Nixon, J. L. Ghost town   S C
Oates, J. C. Small avalanches and other stories
(7 and up)   S C
On the edge: stories at the brink (7 and up)
S C
On the fringe   S C
Once upon a cuento   S C
Ortiz Cofer, J. An island like you (7 and up)
S C
Peck, R. Past perfect, present tense: new and
collected stories   S C
Places I never meant to be (7 and up)   S C
Poe, E. A. Edgar Allan Poe's tales of mystery
and madness   S C
Poe, E. A. The pit and the pendulum and other
stories (7 and up)   S C
Poe, E. A. Tales of Edgar Allan Poe   S C
Potok, C. Zebra and other stories (7 and up)
S C
Read into the millennium   S C
Rice, D. Crazy loco   S C
Saldaña, R. Finding our way: stories   S C
Salisbury, G. Island boyz: short stories (7 and
up)   S C
San Souci, R. Dare to be scared (4 and up)
S C
San Souci, R. Double-dare to be scared: another
thirteen chilling tales (4 and up)   S C
Shattered: stories of children and war   S C
Shelf life: stories by the book (5 and up)
S C
Sherwood: original stories from the world of
Robin Hood   S C
Singer, I. B. The power of light (4 and up)
S C
Sixteen (7 and up)   S C
Sleator, W. Oddballs (6 and up)   S C
Somehow tenderness survives   S C
Soto, G. Baseball in April, and other stories (5
and up)   S C
Soto, G. Help wanted   S C
Soto, G. Local news   S C
Soul searching: thirteen stories about faith and
belief   S C
Spinelli, J. The library card (4 and up)   S C
Talking leaves   S C
Taylor, T. Rogue wave and other red-blooded
sea stories   S C
Time capsule: short stories about teenagers
throughout the twentieth century   S C

Short stories—*Continued*
Tripping over the lunch lady and other school stories (4 and up) **S C**
Ultimate sports (7 and up) **S C**
Vampires: a collection of original stories **S C**
Vande Velde, V. Being dead (7 and up) **S C**
Vande Velde, V. Tales from the Brothers Grimm and the Sisters Weird **S C**
Visions: nineteen short stories by outstanding writers for young adults (7 and up) **S C**
Wallace, R. Losing is not an option: stories (7 and up) **S C**
What a song can do (7 and up) **S C**
Who do you think you are? **S C**
Yee, P. Tales from Gold Mountain (4 and up) **S C**

History and criticism
Short stories for students **809.3**
Indexes
Short story index **808.83**
Short stories for students **809.3**
Short story index **808.83**
Shortcut. Werlin, N.
In On the fringe p49-60 **S C**
Shoshoni Indians
St. George, J. Sacagawea (4-6) **92**
See/See also pages in the following book(s):
Freedman, R. Indian chiefs (6 and up) **920**
Shostak, Jerome
How to prepare for the SSAT/ ISEE: Secondary School Admissions Test/Independent School Entrance Exam **373.1**
"Shot". Oates, J. C.
In Oates, J. C. Small avalanches and other stories **S C**
The **shot** heard round the world. Whitelaw, N. **973.3**
Shotgun Cheatham's last night above ground. Peck, R.
In Peck, R. Past perfect, present tense: new and collected stories **S C**
Shout, sister, shout!. Orgill, R. **920**
Shreve, Susan Richards
The girls' room
In Tripping over the lunch lady and other school stories p133-56 **S C**
Under the Watson's porch (5 and up) **Fic**
Shrimps
See/See also pages in the following book(s):
Lassieur, A. Crabs, lobsters, and shrimps (4-6) **595.3**
Shrines
Sturges, P. Sacred places (4 and up) **203**
Shrublands. Burnie, D. **577.3**
Shrubs
Petrides, G. A. A field guide to trees and shrubs **582.16**
Shuker, Nancy
Elizabeth Arden (7 and up) **92**
Shulman, Mark, 1962-
Attack of the killer video book (5 and up) **778.59**

Shulman, William L.
(comp) Voices and visions. See Voices and visions **940.53**
Shuman, R. Baird (Robert Baird), 1929-
(ed) Great American writers: twentieth century. See Great American writers: twentieth century **920.003**
The **shunning** of Sadie B. Zook. High, L. O.
In Soul searching: thirteen stories about faith and belief p1-22 **S C**
Shurgin, Ann H., 1952-
(ed) The Folklore of world holidays. See The Folklore of world holidays **394.26**
(ed) Junior worldmark encyclopedia of world holidays. See Junior worldmark encyclopedia of world holidays **394.26**
Shusterman, Neal
Downsiders **Fic**
Full tilt (7 and up) **Fic**
The Schwa was here **Fic**
Shuter, Jane, 1955-
The camp system (7 and up) **940.53**
Resistance to the Nazis **943.086**
Shutting out the sky. Hopkinson, D. **974.7**
Shuttles, Space *See* Space shuttles
Shyness
Fiction
Kindl, P. The woman in the wall **Fic**
Si-Ling and the dragon. Harlow, J. H.
In Fire and wings: dragon tales from East and West p32-42 **S C**
Siamese twins
Landau, E. Joined at birth **616**
Siberell, Anne
Bravo! brava! a night at the opera (4 and up) **792.5**
Siberia (Russia)
Hautzig, E. R. The endless steppe: growing up in Siberia **92**
Siblings
See also Twins
Fiction
Avi. Beyond the western sea **Fic**
Blume, J. Here's to you, Rachel Robinson (5 and up) **Fic**
Byars, B. C. The summer of the swans (5 and up) **Fic**
Choldenko, G. Al Capone does my shirts (5 and up) **Fic**
Cleaver, V. Where the lillies bloom (5 and up) **Fic**
Conly, J. L. Trout summer (5 and up) **Fic**
Conrad, P. My Daniel (5 and up) **Fic**
Dorris, M. Morning Girl (4 and up) **Fic**
Draper, S. M. Forged by fire (7 and up) **Fic**
Easton, K. The life history of a star (7 and up) **Fic**
Fenner, C. Yolonda's genius (4-6) **Fic**
Franklin, K. L. Dove song **Fic**
Freymann-Weyr, G. My heartbeat (7 and up) **Fic**
Haddix, M. P. Takeoffs and landings **Fic**

Siblings—Fiction—*Continued*

Hahn, M. D. Hear the wind blow (5 and up)
Fic

Johnson, A. Looking for Red   Fic

Joseph, L. The color of my words (5 and up)
Fic

Klise, K. Letters from camp   Fic

Konigsburg, E. L. Silent to the bone (7 and up)
Fic

Lester, J. When Dad killed Mom (7 and up)
Fic

Nelson, T. Ruby electric (5 and up)   Fic

Peck, R. Lost in cyberspace (5 and up)   Fic

Tamar, E. The midnight train home   Fic

Voigt, C. Dicey's song (6 and up)   Fic

Voigt, C. Homecoming (6 and up)   Fic

Wait, L. Wintering well (5 and up)   Fic

Williams, M. The golden hour   Fic

Sick

Fiction

Fuqua, J. S. The Willoughby Spit wonder
Fic

Sick! diseases and disorders, injuries and infections   **616**

Sickle cell anemia

Baldwin, C. Sickle cell disease (4-6)   **616.1**

Harris, J. L. Sickle cell disease (7 and up)
616.1

Silverstein, A. Sickle cell anemia (7 and up)
616.1

Sickle cell disease. Baldwin, C.   **616.1**

Sickle cell disease. Harris, J. L.   **616.1**

Sickness *See* Diseases

Sidman, Joyce, 1956-

The world according to dog   **810.8**

Siegal, Aranka

Upon the head of the goat: a childhood in Hungary, 1939-1944   **92**

Siegelson, Kim L., 1962-

Trembling earth   Fic

Sieges that changed the world [series]

McNeese, T. The Alamo   **976.4**

Sierra Club

Hart, J. Walking softly in the wilderness
796.51

Sierra Club outdoor adventure guide [series]

Hart, J. Walking softly in the wilderness
796.51

Sigerman, Harriet

Elizabeth Cady Stanton (7 and up)   **92**

Sight *See* Vision

Sign language

Butterworth, R. R. The Perigee visual dictionary of signing   **419**

Costello, E. Random House American sign language dictionary   **419**

Riekehof, L. L. The joy of signing   **419**

Sternberg, M. L. A. American Sign Language
419

Dictionaries

The Comprehensive signed English dictionary
419

The **sign** of four. Doyle, Sir A. C.

In Doyle, Sir A. C. The complete Sherlock Holmes   **S C**

The **sign** of the beaver. Speare, E. G.   Fic

The **signers**. Fradin, D. B.   **920**

Signs and symbols

See also Sign language

Liungman, C. G. Dictionary of symbols
302.2

The **signs** animals leave. Staub, F. J.   **590**

Sigurd and Fafnir. Lang, A.

In The Book of dragons p72-77   **S C**

Sikhism

Mann, G. S. Buddhists, Hindus, and Sikhs in America (7 and up)   **294**

Silberman, Henri

(il) Stone bench in an empty park. See Stone bench in an empty park   **811.008**

The **silent** boy. Lowry, L.   Fic

Silent death. Gay, K.   **358**

Silent Samson, the Maccabee. Kimmel, E. A.

In Kimmel, E. A. The jar of fools: eight Hanukkah stories from Chelm p19-26
S C

The **silent** storm. Garland, S.   Fic

Silent thunder. Pinkney, A. D.   Fic

Silent to the bone. Konigsburg, E. L.   Fic

The **Silk** Route. Major, J. S.   **950**

Sills, Leslie

From rags to riches (5 and up)   **391**

In real life: six women photographers (7 and up)
920

Visions (5 and up)   **920**

Silver. Mazer, N. F.   Fic

Silver Blaze. Doyle, Sir A. C.

In Doyle, Sir A. C. The complete Sherlock Holmes   **S C**

The **silver** kiss. Klause, A. C.   Fic

Silverman, Jerry

Songs and stories from the American Revolution (6 and up)   **782.42**

Songs and stories of the Civil War   **782.42**

Silverstein, Alvin

Chickenpox and shingles (7 and up)   **616.9**

Depression (7 and up)   **616.85**

Energy   **621**

Food chains   **577**

Global warming   **363.7**

The grizzly bear   **599.78**

Hearing Silverstein, A. and others. Senses and sensors [series]   **612.8**

Lyme disease   **616.9**

Measles and rubella (7 and up)   **616.9**

Parkinson's disease (7 and up)   **616.8**

Plants   **580**

Plate tectonics (5 and up)   **551.1**

Polio (7 and up)   **616.8**

The respiratory system (5 and up)   **612.2**

Seeing Silverstein, A. and others. Senses and sensors [series]   **612.8**

Senses and sensors [series]   **612.8**

Sickle cell anemia (7 and up)   **616.1**

Silverstein, Alvin—*Continued*
Smelling and tasting
In Silverstein, A. and others. Senses and
sensors [series] **612.8**
Snakes & such **639**
Symbiosis **577.8**
Touching and feeling Silverstein, A. and others.
Senses and sensors [series] **612.8**
The universe **520**
Vertebrates (5 and up) **596**
Weather and climate **551.5**
Silverstein, Herma
Kids who kill (7 and up) **364.1**
Silverstein, Robert A.
(jt. auth) Silverstein, A. Measles and rubella
616.9
(jt. auth) Silverstein, A. Plants **580**
(jt. auth) Silverstein, A. The respiratory system
612.2
(jt. auth) Silverstein, A. Vertebrates **596**
Silverstein, Shel
Falling up **811**
A light in the attic **811**
Where the sidewalk ends **811**
Silverstein, Virginia B.
(jt. auth) Silverstein, A. Chickenpox and shingles **616.9**
(jt. auth) Silverstein, A. Depression **616.85**
(jt. auth) Silverstein, A. Energy **621**
(jt. auth) Silverstein, A. Food chains **577**
(jt. auth) Silverstein, A. Global warming
363.7
(jt. auth) Silverstein, A. The grizzly bear
599.78
(jt. auth) Silverstein, A. Lyme disease **616.9**
(jt. auth) Silverstein, A. Measles and rubella
616.9
(jt. auth) Silverstein, A. Parkinson's disease
616.8
(jt. auth) Silverstein, A. Plants **580**
(jt. auth) Silverstein, A. Plate tectonics
551.1
(jt. auth) Silverstein, A. Polio **616.8**
(jt. auth) Silverstein, A. The respiratory system
612.2
(jt. auth) Silverstein, A. Senses and sensors [series] **612.8**
(jt. auth) Silverstein, A. Sickle cell anemia
616.1
(jt. auth) Silverstein, A. Snakes & such **639**
(jt. auth) Silverstein, A. Symbiosis **577.8**
(jt. auth) Silverstein, A. The universe **520**
(jt. auth) Silverstein, A. Vertebrates **596**
(jt. auth) Silverstein, A. Weather and climate
551.5
Silverwing. Oppel, K. **Fic**
Sim Chung and the dragon king. Farley, C. J.
In Fire and wings: dragon tales from East and
West p87-94 **S C**
Sima, Judy
Raising voices **027.62**
Simmons, Jake, 1901-1981
See/See also pages in the following book(s):
Haskins, J. African American entrepreneurs
920

Simmons, Philip
About
Lyons, M. E. Catching the fire: Philip Simmons,
blacksmith (4 and up) **92**
Simner, Janni Lee
Stone tower
In Gothic!; ten original dark tales **S C**
Tearing down the unicorns
In A Glory of unicorns p31-42 **S C**
Water's edge
In Half-human p47-63 **S C**
Simon, Seymour, 1931-
Bones (4 and up) **612.7**
The brain (4 and up) **612.8**
Crocodiles & alligators (4 and up) **597.9**
Destination: Jupiter (4 and up) **523.4**
Destination: space (4 and up) **520**
Earth: our planet in space (4 and up) **525**
Eyes and ears (4 and up) **612.8**
Guts (4 and up) **612.3**
The heart (4 and up) **612.1**
Hurricanes (4 and up) **551.55**
Lightning (4 and up) **551.56**
The moon (4 and up) **523.3**
Mountains (3-6) **551.4**
Muscles (4 and up) **612.7**
Out of sight (4 and up) **502.8**
Snakes (4 and up) **597.9**
Spiders (4 and up) **595.4**
Tornadoes (4 and up) **551.55**
The universe (4 and up) **523**
Wildfires (3-6) **577.2**
See/See also pages in the following book(s):
Author talk (4 and up) **028.5**
Simon & Schuster children's guide to sea creatures. Johnson, J. **591.7**
Simon & Schuster thesaurus for children **423**
Simon and Schuster's guide to rocks and minerals
549
Simont, Marc, 1915-
(il) Lord, B. B. In the Year of the Boar and
Jackie Robinson **Fic**
Simpson, Carol
(ed) Ethics in school librarianship. See Ethics in
school librarianship **174**
Simpson, D. P.
Cassell's Latin dictionary. See Cassell's Latin
dictionary **473**
Simpson, O. J., 1947-
About
Pellowski, M. The O.J. Simpson murder trial
345
See/See also pages in the following book(s):
Aaseng, N. You are the juror **345**
Sinbad the Sailor, The Seven voyages of. Yeoman, J. **398.2**
Sing down the moon. O'Dell, S. **Fic**
Sing me a death song. Bennett, J. **Fic**
Singapore
Layton, L. Singapore (5 and up) **959.57**
Singer, Isaac Bashevis, 1904-1991
The power of light (4 and up) **S C**

Singer, Isaac Bashevis, 1904-1991—*Continued*
Contents: A Hanukkah evening in my parents' house; The extinguished lights; The parakeet named Dreidel; Menashe and Rachel; The squire; The power of light; Hershele and Hanukkah; Hanukkah in the poorhouse

Singer, Marilyn, 1948-
Central heating (4 and up)   **811**
Footprints on the roof (4 and up)   **811**
Shattered
  In Shattered: stories of children and war p14-22   **S C**
(ed) Face relations. See Face relations   **S C**

Singer. Thesman, J.   **Fic**

The **singer** of all songs. Constable, K.   **Fic**

Singers
  See also African American singers
Dolan, S. Bob Marley   **92**
Gonzales, D. Gloria Estefan   **92**
Neimark, A. E. There ain't nobody that can sing like me: the life of Woody Guthrie (5 and up)   **92**
Orgill, R. Shout, sister, shout! (6 and up)   **920**
Partridge, E. This land was made for you and me: the life and songs of Woody Guthrie (7 and up)   **92**
Stefoff, R. Plácido Domingo   **92**
        Fiction
Curry, J. L. The Black Canary (5 and up)   **Fic**

Singh, Simon
The code book (7 and up)   **652**

Singing apples. Kadohata, C.
  In American eyes; new Asian-American short stories for young adults p49-61   **S C**

The **Singing,** soaring lark
  In Hearne, B. G. Beauties and beasts p60-65   **398.2**

Singing the Dogstar blues. Goodman, A.   **Fic**

Single parent family
  See also Unmarried mothers
Schultz, M. A. Teens with single parents (7 and up)   **306.8**
        Fiction
Banks, L. R. Alice-by-accident   **Fic**
Lowry, L. The one hundredth thing about Caroline (5 and up)   **Fic**
Lyon, G. E. Gina.Jamie.Father.Bear   **Fic**
Wyeth, S. D. A piece of heaven   **Fic**

A **single** shard. Park, L. S.   **Fic**

Singularity. Sleator, W.   **Fic**

Sink the Bismarck. McGowen, T.   **940.54**

Sinnott, Susan
Extraordinary Asian Americans and Pacific Islanders (5 and up)   **920**

Sioras, Efstathia
Czech Republic (5 and up)   **943.7**

Siouan Indians
  See also Dakota Indians; Oglala Indians; Osage Indians

Sioux. Lonehill, K. North American Indians today [series]

Sioux Indians *See* Dakota Indians

The **Sioux** who wrestled with a ghost. Brown, D. A.
  In Brown, D. A. Dee Brown's folktales of the Native American; retold for our times p166-67   **398.2**

Sipa's choice. Anaya, R. A.
  In Anaya, R. A. My land sings; stories from the Rio Grande p149-58   **S C**

Sipes, Karen L., 1953-
(jt. auth) Closter, K. Fiction, food, and fun   **028.5**

Sir Edmund Hillary, modern day explorer. Brennan, K.   **92**

Sir Gawain and the Green Knight. Morpurgo, M.   **398.2**

Sir Gawain and the Green Knight. Osborne, M. P.
  In Osborne, M. P. Favorite medieval tales p50-59   **398.2**

Sir Gawain and the loathly lady
  In Hearne, B. G. Beauties and beasts p131-38   **398.2**

Sir Walter Ralegh and the quest for El Dorado. Aronson, M.   **92**

Sirimarco, Elizabeth, 1966-
American voices from the civil rights movement   **323.1**
American voices from The Cold War   **909.82**

Sís, Peter, 1949-
Tibet   **951**
(il) Fleischman, S. The whipping boy   **Fic**

Siskiyou Sloan and the eye of the giraffe. Howe, N.
  In Necessary noise: stories about our families as they really are p23-48   **S C**

Sister Fox and Brother Coyote. San Souci, R.
  In San Souci, R. Cut from the same cloth; American women of myth, legend, and tall tale p93-99   **398.2**

Sister Lace. Tchana, K. H.
  In Tchana, K. H. The serpent slayer: and other stories of strong women p25-29   **398.2**

Sister spider knows all. Fogelin, A.   **Fic**

Sister to the wolf. Trottier, M.   **Fic**

Sisters
        Fiction
Arrington, F. Bluestem (4-6)   **Fic**
Boling, K. January 1905 (5 and up)   **Fic**
Byars, B. C. The keeper of the doves (4 and up)   **Fic**
Couloumbis, A. Getting near to baby (5 and up)   **Fic**
Dreyer, A. L. After Elaine   **Fic**
Griffin, A. The other Shepards (6 and up)   **Fic**
Griffin, A. Where I want to be (7 and up)   **Fic**
Hooper, M. At the sign of the Sugared Plum   **Fic**
Johnson, M. The key to the golden Firebird (7 and up)   **Fic**
Johnston, J. In spite of killer bees (7 and up)   **Fic**
Kurtz, J. Jakarta missing   **Fic**

Sisters—Fiction—*Continued*
Kwasney, M. D. Baby Blue **Fic**
Levine, G. C. The two princesses of Bamarre (5 and up) **Fic**
Littke, L. Haunted sister (7 and up) **Fic**
McCord, P. Pictures in the dark (7 and up) **Fic**
McDonald, J. Twists and turns (7 and up) **Fic**
Paterson, K. Jacob have I loved **Fic**
Pevsner, S. Is everyone moonburned but me? **Fic**
Reiss, K. PaperQuake **Fic**
Sones, S. Stop pretending **Fic**
Vande Velde, V. Alison, who went away **Fic**
White, R. Memories of Summer (7 and up) **Fic**

Sisters (in religious orders, congregations, etc.) *See* Nuns

Sisters. De Lint, C.
In De Lint, C. Waifs and strays p32-72 **S C**

Sisters and brothers *See* Siblings

Sit on a potato pan, Otis!. Agee, J. **793.73**

Sitomer, Alan Lawrence
The Hoopster (7 and up) **Fic**

Sitting Bull, Dakota Chief, 1831-1890
See/See also pages in the following book(s):
Ehrlich, A. Wounded Knee: an Indian history of the American West (6 and up) **970.004**
Freedman, R. Indian chiefs (6 and up) **920**

Six days in October. Blumenthal, K. **332.6**

Sixteen (7 and up) **S C**

Sixteenth century *See* World history—16th century

Sixth grade can really kill you. See DeClements, B. 6th grade can really kill you **Fic**

The **sixth** grade nickname game. Korman, G. **Fic**

Siy, Alexandra
New town
In What a song can do; 12 riffs on the power of music **S C**

Sizer, Paul
Little White Mouse collection 1: Dream of the ghost **741.5**

Sizzling summer reading programs for young adults. Kan, K. **027.62**

Skaggs, Gayle
On display **027.8**

Skateboarding
Maurer, T. Skateboarding **796.22**
Ryan, P. Extreme skateboarding **796.22**
Thomas, K. Blades, boards & scooters (5 and up) **796.2**

Skating *See* Ice skating

Skeleton
Simon, S. Bones (4 and up) **612.7**
The **skeleton** and muscles. Parker, S. **612.7**
Skeleton man. Bruchac, J. **Fic**
Skellig. Almond, D. **Fic**
Ski. Pollack, P. **796.93**

Skiing
Pollack, P. Ski (7 and up) **796.93**

Skills, Life *See* Life skills

Skin
Gold, S. D. The musculoskeletal system and the skin **612.7**
Parker, S. Skin, muscles, and bones **612.7**
Diseases—Fiction
Johnson, A. A cool moonlight (5 and up) **Fic**

Skin. Dahl, R.
In Dahl, R. Skin and other stories **S C**

Skin and other stories. Dahl, R. **S C**

Skin health information for teens (7 and up) **616.5**

The **skin** I'm in. Flake, S. G. **Fic**

Skin, muscles, and bones. Parker, S. **612.7**

Skinner, Linda
(jt. auth) Avery, S. Extraordinary American Indians **920**

Skinny-dipping at Monster Lake. Wallace, B. **Fic**

Skivvy and cuttle. Lennon, J.
In Fire and wings: dragon tales from East and West p43-54 **S C**

Sklansky, Amy E.
(ed) Life: our century in pictures for young people. See Life: our century in pictures for young people **779**

Skoura, Xenia
(jt. auth) DuBois, J. Greece **949.5**

Skreslet, Laurie
To the top of Everest (4 and up) **796.52**

The **skull** of truth. Coville, B. **Fic**

Skullduggery. Karr, K. **Fic**

Skunk outwits Coyote. Brown, D. A.
In Brown, D. A. Dee Brown's folktales of the Native American; retold for our times p111-13 **398.2**

Skurzynski, Gloria, 1930-
Are we alone? (5 and up) **576.8**
Cliff hanger **Fic**
Discover Mars **523.4**
Nethergrave
In On the edge: stories at the brink p23-39 **S C**
Rockbuster **Fic**
The shepherd who fought for a princess
In Fire and wings: dragon tales from East and West p95-102 **S C**

Sky. Townley, R. **Fic**

The **sky** blue bell. Oates, J. C.
In Oates, J. C. Small avalanches and other stories **S C**

The **sky's** the limit. Thimmesh, C. **500**

Skyscrapers
Joseph, L. M. Skyscrapers: inside and out **720**
Macaulay, D. Unbuilding (4 and up) **690**
Severance, J. B. Skyscrapers **720**
See/See also pages in the following book(s):
Macaulay, D. Building big **720**

Slade, Arthur G., 1967-
Dust   **Fic**

Slaight, Craig
(ed) Great monologues for young actors. See
Great monologues for young actors
  812.008
(ed) Great scenes for young actors from the
stage. See Great scenes for young actors from
the stage   **808.82**

Slake's limbo. Holman, F.   **Fic**

Slam!. Myers, W. D.   **Fic**

Slap your sides. Kerr, M. E.   **Fic**

Slater, Ann Tashi
There's no reason to get romantic
  In American dragons: twenty-five Asian
   American voices p185-99   **810.8**

The **slave** dancer. Fox, P.   **Fic**

Slave life on the plantation. Worth, R.   **326**

Slave narratives   **326**

Slave spirituals and the Jubilee Singers. Cooper,
M. L.   **782.42**

Slave trade
Grant, R. G. The African-American slave trade
  326
Thomas, V. M. Lest we forget (7 and up)
  326
Worth, R. The slave trade in America (7 and
up)   **326**
See/See also pages in the following book(s):
Reef, C. Africans in America: the spread of
people and culture   **305.8**
     Fiction
Fox, P. The slave dancer (5 and up)   **Fic**
McKissack, P. C. Nzinga, warrior queen of
Matamba (5 and up)   **Fic**

The **slave** trade in America. Worth, R.   **326**

Slave uprisings and runaways. Eskridge, A. E.
  326

Slavery
Cameron, A. The kidnapped prince: the life of
Olaudah Equiano (4 and up)   **92**
See/See also pages in the following book(s):
Reef, C. Africans in America: the spread of
people and culture   **305.8**
     Fiction
Armstrong, J. Steal away (5 and up)   **Fic**
Ayres, K. North by night (6 and up)   **Fic**
Berry, J. Ajeemah and his son   **Fic**
Carbone, E. L. Stealing freedom   **Fic**
Collier, J. L. Jump ship to freedom (6 and up)
  Fic
Collier, J. L. War comes to Willy Freeman (6
and up)   **Fic**
Collier, J. L. Who is Carrie?   **Fic**
Hahn, M. D. Promises to the dead (5 and up)
  Fic
Houston, G. Bright Freedom's song   **Fic**
Lasky, K. True north (6 and up)   **Fic**
Lester, J. Day of tears (7 and up)   **Fic**
Levitin, S. Dream freedom   **Fic**
Lyons, M. E. Dear Ellen Bee   **Fic**
Lyons, M. E. Letters from a slave girl (6 and
up)   **Fic**

McKissack, P. C. Let my people go (4 and up)
  221.9
McKissack, P. C. A picture of Freedom (4 and
up)   **Fic**
McMullan, M. How I found the Strong (5 and
up)   **Fic**
Paterson, K. Jip (5 and up)   **Fic**
Paulsen, G. Nightjohn   **Fic**
Pinkney, A. D. Silent thunder   **Fic**
Rinaldi, A. Hang a thousand trees with ribbons
  Fic
Rinaldi, A. Taking liberty   **Fic**
Rinaldi, A. Wolf by the ears   **Fic**
Schwartz, V. F. Send one angel down   **Fic**
Siegelson, K. L. Trembling earth   **Fic**
Vande Velde, V. There's a dead person follow-
ing my sister around (4 and up)   **Fic**
Wisler, G. C. Caleb's choice   **Fic**
Woodruff, E. Dear Austin   **Fic**
     History
Watkins, R. R. Slavery: bondage throughout his-
tory (7 and up)   **326**
    Pictorial works
Feelings, T. The middle passage (7 and up)
  759.13
     Poetry
Nelson, M. Fortune's bones   **811**
    United States
  See also Abolitionists
Altman, L. J. The politics of slavery (7 and up)
  326
Altman, L. J. Slavery and abolition in American
history   **973.7**
American slavery (7 and up)   **326**
Bial, R. The strength of these arms (4 and up)
  326
Bial, R. The Underground Railroad (4 and up)
  326
Bisson, T. Nat Turner   **92**
Cloud Tapper, S. Voices from slavery's past (7
and up)   **326**
Collier, C. The paradox of Jamestown, 1585-
1700   **975.5**
Collier, C. Slavery and the coming of the Civil
War, 1831-1861   **973.6**
The Complete history of American slavery (7
and up)   **326**
Currie, S. Escapes from slavery   **326**
Currie, S. Slavery (7 and up)   **326**
Edwards, J. Abolitionists and slave resistance (7
and up)   **326**
Erickson, P. Daily life on a Southern plantation,
1853 (4 and up)   **975**
Eskridge, A. E. Slave uprisings and runaways
  326
Fradin, D. B. Bound for the North Star (7 and
up)   **326**
Fradin, D. B. My family shall be free!: the life
of Peter Still   **92**
Frankel, N. Break those chains at last: African
Americans, 1860-1880   **305.8**
Golay, M. Reconstruction and reaction (7 and
up)   **305.8**
Grant, R. G. The African-American slave trade
  326

Slavery—United States—*Continued*

Hamilton, V. Anthony Burns: the defeat and triumph of a fugitive slave (5 and up) **92**

Hamilton, V. Many thousand gone (5 and up) **326**

Hansen, J. Freedom roads: searching for the Underground Railroad (5 and up) **973.7**

Herda, D. J. The Dred Scott case (7 and up) **342**

Hulm, D. United States v. the Amistad **326**

January, B. The Dred Scott decision **342**

Katz, W. L. Breaking the chains (7 and up) **326**

Lester, J. From slave ship to freedom road (4 and up) **326**

Marston, H. I. Isaac Johnson **92**

McArthur, D. The Kansas-Nebraska Act and "Bleeding Kansas" in American history **978.1**

McKissack, P. C. Christmas in the big house, Christmas in the quarters (4 and up) **394.26**

McKissack, P. C. Days of Jubilee (5 and up) **973.7**

McKissack, P. C. Rebels against slavery (5 and up) **326**

McNeese, T. The rise and fall of American slavery (7 and up) **326**

Myers, W. D. Amistad: a long road to freedom (5 and up) **326**

Naden, C. J. Dred Scott (7 and up) **342**

Reef, C. This our dark country **966.62**

Sawyer, K. K. The underground railroad in American history **326**

Schleichert, E. The Thirteenth Amendment (7 and up) **342**

Slave narratives **326**

Slavery **326**

Tackach, J. The abolition of American slavery (7 and up) **326**

Tackach, J. The Emancipation Proclamation (7 and up) **973.7**

Thomas, V. M. Lest we forget (7 and up) **326**

White, D. G. Let my people go: African Americans, 1804-1860 (7 and up) **305.8**

Worth, R. Slave life on the plantation (7 and up) **326**

Worth, R. The slave trade in America (7 and up) **326**

Yates, E. Amos Fortune, free man **92**

Zeinert, K. Tragic prelude: bleeding Kansas (7 and up) **978.1**

See/See also pages in the following book(s):

Marrin, A. Commander in Chief Abraham Lincoln and the Civil War (7 and up) **973.7**

Slavery **326**

Slavery and abolition in American history. Altman, L. J. **973.7**

Slavery and the coming of the Civil War, 1831-1861. Collier, C. **973.6**

Slavery in American history [series]

Altman, L. J. The politics of slavery **326**

Byers, A. African-American history from emancipation to today **305.8**

Cloud Tapper, S. Voices from slavery's past **326**

Edwards, J. Abolitionists and slave resistance **326**

Eskridge, A. E. Slave uprisings and runaways **326**

McNeese, T. The rise and fall of American slavery **326**

Worth, R. Slave life on the plantation **326**

Worth, R. The slave trade in America **326**

Slavicek, Louise Chipley, 1956-

Confucianism **181**

Mao Zedong **92**

Women of the American Revolution (7 and up) **973.3**

Slaying the monsters. Curry, J. L.

In Curry, J. L. Hold up the sky: and other Native American tales from Texas and the Southern Plains p47-52 **398.2**

Slayton, John

Elvis lives

In Soul searching: thirteen stories about faith and belief p228-47 **S C**

Sleator, William

The boy who reversed himself (5 and up) **Fic**

The duplicate (7 and up) **Fic**

The elevator

In Beware!; R.L. Stine picks his favorite scary stories p87-99 **808.8**

also in Read all about it!; great read-aloud stories, poems, and newspaper pieces for preteens and teens p236-43 **808.8**

The funeral

In Soul searching: thirteen stories about faith and belief p23-43 **S C**

House of stairs (7 and up) **Fic**

Interstellar pig (5 and up) **Fic**

Oddballs (6 and up) **S C**

Singularity (7 and up) **Fic**

Unbalanced

In On the edge: stories at the brink p127-39 **S C**

Sled dog racing

See also Iditarod Trail Sled Dog Race, Alaska

Paulsen, G. Winterdance **798.8**

Paulsen, G. Woodsong (7 and up) **796.5**

Wood, T. Iditarod dream (4 and up) **798.8**

Sleeping Beauty. Fraustino, L. R.

In Don't cramp my style; stories about that time of the month p131-44 **S C**

Slesar, Henry, 1927-

Examination day

In Beware!; R.L. Stine picks his favorite scary stories p169-77 **808.8**

Good morning! this is the future

In Read into the millennium; tales of the future p120-25 **S C**

The **slightly** true story of Cedar B. Hartley. Murray, M. **Fic**

Slime, molds, and fungi. Pascoe, E. **579.5**

Slippers. Yep, L.

In Yep, L. The rainbow people p162-68 **398.2**

Sloan, Christopher
Bury the dead (5 and up)   **393**
Feathered dinosaurs (5 and up)   **567.9**
The human story (7 and up)   **599.93**
Supercroc and the origin of crocodiles (5 and up)   **567.9**
Slot machine. Lynch, C.   **Fic**
Slote, Stanley J.
Weeding library collections   **025.2**
Slovakia
Gottfried, T. Slovakia (5 and up)   **943.7**
Slovenia
Gottfried, T. Slovenia (5 and up)   **949.7**
Orr, T. Slovenia (5 and up)   **949.7**
Slovey, Christine
(jt. auth) Pendergast, T. World War I almanac   **940.3**
(ed) World War II: primary sources. See World War II: primary sources   **940.53**
Slow learning children
See also Mentally handicapped children
Slugs (Mollusks)
Pascoe, E. Snails and slugs (4 and up)   **594**
Small avalanches. Oates, J. C.
In Oates, J. C. Small avalanches and other stories   **S C**
Small avalanches and other stories. Oates, J. C.   **S C**
Small pinch of weather. Aiken, J.
In Aiken, J. Shadows and moonshine; stories   **S C**
The **Small-tooth** dog
In Hearne, B. G. Beauties and beasts p25-28   **398.2**
Small wildcats. Bonar, S.   **599.75**
Smallpox
Marrin, A. Dr. Jenner and the speckled monster (5 and up)   **614.5**
Peters, S. T. Smallpox in the new world   **614.5**
Smallpox in the new world. Peters, S. T.   **614.5**
Smart, P. (Paul), 1957-
Everything you need to know about mononucleosis (7 and up)   **616.9**
Smell
Rybolt, T. R. Science fair success with scents, aromas, and smells (7 and up)   **612.8**
Silverstein, A. Smelling and tasting
In Silverstein, A. and others. Senses and sensors [series]   **612.8**
Smelling and tasting. Silverstein, A.
In Silverstein, A. and others. Senses and sensors [series]   **612.8**
Smelt, Roselynn
New Zealand (5 and up)   **993**
Smith, Ada Beatrice Queen Victoria Louisa Virginia *See* Bricktop, 1894-1984
Smith, Barry D., 1957-
(il) Masoff, J. Fire!   **628.9**
Smith, Bessie, 1894-1937
See/See also pages in the following book(s):
Lester, J. The blues singers (5 and up)   **920**

Orgill, R. Shout, sister, shout! (6 and up)   **920**
Smith, Carter, 1962-
(ed) The African-American experience on file. See The African-American experience on file   **305.8**
(ed) The Asian-American experience on file. See The Asian-American experience on file   **305.8**
(ed) Hispanic-American experience on file. See Hispanic-American experience on file   **305.8**
(jt. auth) Hoff, B. H. Mapping epidemics   **614**
Smith, Charles R.
Hoop queens   **811**
Smith, Charles W. G.
(jt. auth) Laubach, C. M. Raptor! a kid's guide to birds of prey   **598**
Smith, Craig, 1955-
(il) Crew, G. Troy Thompson's excellent peotry book   **Fic**
Smith, Cynthia Leitich
Rain is not my Indian name   **Fic**
Smith, Dick King- *See* King-Smith, Dick, 1922-
Smith, Erica
Anorexia nervosa (7 and up)   **616.85**
Smith, Greg Leitich
Ninjas, piranhas, and Galileo   **Fic**
Smith, Heather, 1974-
Science smart. See Science smart   **550**
(jt. auth) Rhatigan, J. Sure-to-win science fair projects   **507.8**
Smith, Henrietta M.
(ed) The Coretta Scott King Awards book, 1970-1999. See The Coretta Scott King Awards book, 1970-1999   **028.5**
Smith, Hope Anita
The way a door closes (4 and up)   **811**
Smith, Hugh L., 1921-1968
(comp) Reflections on a gift of watermelon pickle—and other modern verse. See Reflections on a gift of watermelon pickle—and other modern verse   **811.008**
Smith, Ian
Emily & the intergalactic lemonade stand   **741.5**
Smith, Jane Bandy
Achieving a curriculum-based library media center program   **027.8**
Smith, Jeff
Bone: out from Boneville   **741.5**
Smith, Jessie Carney, 1930-
(ed) African American breakthroughs. See African American breakthroughs   **305.8**
Smith, John, 1580-1631
About
Doherty, K. To conquer is to live: the life of Captain John Smith of Jamestown   **92**
Edwards, J. Jamestown, John Smith, and Pocahontas in American history (7 and up)   **975.5**
Fiction
Bruchac, J. Pocahontas (7 and up)   **Fic**

Smith, Joseph A., 1936-
Bandit's moon (4-6) **Fic**
(il) Gellman, M. How do you spell God?
200

Smith, KC
Exploring for shipwrecks **930.1**

Smith, Lane
(il) Scieszka, J. Seen Art? **Fic**

Smith, Laura Lee, 1968-
(jt. auth) Cook, J. Natural writer: a story about Marjorie Kinnan Rawlings **92**

Smith, Linda Wasmer
Louis Pasteur **92**

Smith, Mark, 1956-
(ed) Managing the Internet controversy. See Managing the Internet controversy **025.04**

Smith, Martha, 1946-
(jt. auth) Knowles, E. Reading rules! **028.5**
(jt. auth) Knowles, E. Talk about books!
372.4

Smith, Patricia Clark, 1943-
Weetamoo, heart of the Pocassets **Fic**

Smith, Paul
(jt. auth) Robinson, J. Leave it to Chance: Shaman's rain **741.5**

Smith, Roland, 1951-
The captain's dog **Fic**
The Sasquatch **Fic**

Smith, Rosamond, 1938-
See also Oates, Joyce Carol, 1938-

Smith, Sherwood
Beauty
In Firebirds: an anthology of original fantasy and science fiction; an anthology of original fantasy and science fiction **S C**
Crown duel (7 and up) **Fic**

Smith, Stuart Tyson
Valley of the Kings (4 and up) **932**

Smith, Susan S.
Web-based instruction **005.7**

Smith, Tyson
(jt. auth) Smith, I. Emily & the intergalactic lemonade stand **741.5**

Smith, Wendy
(il) Ross, M. E. Fish watching with Eugenie Clark **92**

Smith, Whitney
Flag lore of all nations (4 and up) **929.9**

Smith, Adam
See/See also pages in the following book(s):
Bussing-Burks, M. Influential economists (7 and up) **920**

The **smith,** the weaver, and the harper. Alexander, L.
In Alexander, L. The foundling and other tales of Prydain p65-72 **S C**

The **Smithsonian** book of the First Ladies (7 and up) **920**

Smoke. San Souci, R.
In San Souci, R. Dare to be scared; thirteen stories to chill and thrill **S C**

Smoke and ashes. Rogasky, B. **940.53**

Smoke to flame. Sherrow, V. **940.53**

Smoking
See also Marijuana
Smoking (7 and up) **362.29**
Smoking (7 and up) **363.4**
Tobacco and smoking: opposing viewpoints **362.29**
See/See also pages in the following book(s):
Teens at risk: opposing viewpoints p63-105 (7 and up) **362.7**

Smoking (7 and up) **363.4**

Smuggling
Fiction
Honey, E. Remote man **Fic**

Smyth, Ian
The young baseball player (4 and up)
796.357

Snail mail no more. Danziger, P. **Fic**

Snails
Pascoe, E. Snails and slugs (4 and up) **594**

Snails and slugs. Pascoe, E. **594**

The **snake.** Lester, J.
In Lester, J. The last tales of Uncle Remus p28-33 **398.2**
also in Lester, J. When the beginning began; stories about God, the creatures, and us p73-80 **296.1**

The **Snake** book (4-6) **597.9**

Snake pits, talking cures, & magic bullets. Kent, D. **616.89**

The **snake** scientist. Montgomery, S. **597.9**

Snake-spoke. Yep, L.
In Yep, L. The rainbow people p86-95
398.2

Snakes
Coborn, J. Snakes **639**
Mattison, C. Snake **597.9**
Montgomery, S. The snake scientist (4 and up) **597.9**
Simon, S. Snakes (4 and up) **597.9**
The Snake book (4-6) **597.9**
See/See also pages in the following book(s):
Byars, B. C. The moon and I (4 and up)
92

Snakes & such. Silverstein, A. **639**

Snap. McGhee, A. **Fic**

Snap, crackle, pop. Metzger, L.
In Shattered: stories of children and war p71-86 **S C**

A **snap** of the fingers. San Souci, R.
In San Souci, R. A terrifying taste of short & shivery; thirty creepy tales p123-29
398.2

Snatched away. TallMountain, M.
In Talking leaves; contemporary native American short stories **S C**

Snedden, Robert
The environment **577**
Medical ethics **174.2**
Technology in the time of ancient Rome
609

Sneddon, Pamela Shires
Body image (7 and up) **155.9**

Sneve, Virginia Driving Hawk
(comp) Dancing teepees: poems of American Indian youth. See Dancing teepees: poems of American Indian youth   **897**

Snow, Judith E.
How it feels to have a gay or lesbian parent (5 and up)   **306.8**

Snow bound. Mazer, H.   **Fic**

The **snow** husband. San Souci, R.
In San Souci, R. A terrifying taste of short & shivery; thirty creepy tales p58-61   **398.2**

The **snow** pony. Lester, A.   **Fic**

Snowboard!. Masoff, J.   **796.93**

Snowboarding
Lurie, J. Fundamental snowboarding   **796.93**
Masoff, J. Snowboard!   **796.93**
McKenna, L. The fantastic book of snowboarding   **796.93**
Thomas, K. Blades, boards & scooters (5 and up)   **796.2**

Snowbound. Lavender, D. S.   **978**

Snowbound. Lowry, L.
In Necessary noise: stories about our families as they really are p219-38   **S C**

Snyder, Midori, 1954-
Charlie's away
In The Green Man: tales from the mythic forest p137-65   **808.8**
Hannah's garden (7 and up)   **Fic**

Snyder, Zilpha Keatley
The Unseen (5 and up)   **Fic**

So, Meilo
(il) Singer, M. Central heating   **811**
(il) Singer, M. Footprints on the roof   **811**

So B. it. Weeks, S.   **Fic**

So far from the bamboo grove. Watkins, Y. K.   **Fic**

So hard to say. Sanchez, A.   **Fic**

So I ain't no good girl. Flake, S. G.
In Flake, S. G. Who am I without him?; short stories about girls and the boys in their lives p1-9   **S C**

So proudly they served. Anderson, M. K.   **940.54**

So yesterday. Westerfeld, S.   **Fic**

Soaring. Waggoner, T.
In Half-human p165-81   **S C**

Soccer
Coleman, L. Fundamental soccer (5 and up)   **796.334**
Hamm, M. Go for the goal (7 and up)   **796.334**
Hornby, H. Soccer (4 and up)   **796.334**
Scott, N. S. The thinking kid's guide to successful soccer (4 and up)   **796.334**
Stewart, M. Soccer (7 and up)   **796.334**
    Fiction
Bloor, E. Tangerine (7 and up)   **Fic**
Higuchi, D. Whistle! Volume 1   **741.5**
Klass, D. Home of the Braves (7 and up)   **Fic**

Swanson, J. A. Going for the record (7 and up)   **Fic**

Social action
Halpin, M. It's your world—if you don't like it, change it (7 and up)   **361.2**
    Fiction
Konigsburg, E. L. The outcasts of 19 Schuyler Place   **Fic**

Social anthropology *See* Ethnology

Social classes
Hinds, K. The Patricians   **937**
    Fiction
Calhoun, D. White midnight (7 and up)   **Fic**

Social customs *See* Manners and customs

Social ethics
    See also Bioethics
Our country's founders (7 and up)   **973**

Social groups
Romain, T. Cliques, phonies & other baloney   **158**

Social isolation
    Fiction
Peck, R. Strays like us   **Fic**

Social learning *See* Socialization

Social life and customs *See* Manners and customs

Social problems
See/See also pages in the following book(s):
Blue, R. Staying out of trouble in a troubled family (7 and up)   **362.7**

Social sciences
Benson, S. Relationships
In Being human   **612**
    Bibliography
Notable social studies trade books for young people   **016.3**

Social smarts. James, E.   **395**

Socialization
Tym, K. School survival   **371.8**

Society and art *See* Art and society

Society of Friends
Williams, J. K. The Quakers (7 and up)   **289.6**
    Fiction
Kerr, M. E. Slap your sides (7 and up)   **Fic**
Osborne, M. P. Standing in the light   **Fic**
Turnbull, A. No shame, no fear (7 and up)   **Fic**

Softball
Nitz, K. W. Fundamental softball   **796.357**

Software, Computer *See* Computer software

The **Software** encyclopedia   **005**

Soil ecology
Lavies, B. Compost critters (4 and up)   **591.7**

Sojourner Truth *See* Truth, Sojourner, d. 1883

Sojourner Truth's "Ain't I a woman?" speech. Brezina, C.   **92**

Solar energy
Graham, I. Solar power   **621.47**

Solar power. Graham, I.   **621.47**

Solar system
 Ride, S. K. Exploring our solar system (4 and up) **523.2**
 VanCleave, J. P. Janice VanCleave's solar system (4 and up) **523.2**

Solbert, Ronni
 (il) Merrill, J. The pushcart war   **Fic**

Soldier boy. Burks, B.   **Fic**

Soldier boys. Hughes, D.   **Fic**

Soldier X. Wulffson, D. L.   **Fic**

Soldiers
 See also Women soldiers
   Fiction
 Garland, S. In the shadow of the Alamo   **Fic**
 Hughes, D. Soldier boys   **Fic**
   United States
 Beller, S. P. Billy Yank & Johnny Reb (5 and up) **973.7**
 Stewart, G. Life of a soldier in Washington's army **973.3**
 Uschan, M. V. The cavalry during the Civil War **973.7**

Soldier's courage: the story of Stephen Crane. Lukes, B. L.   **92**

Soldier's heart. Paulsen, G.   **Fic**

Solheim, James
 It's disgusting—and we ate it! (4 and up) **641.3**

Solids, liquids, and gases. Farndon, J.   **530.4**

A **solitary** blue. Voigt, C.   **Fic**

Solvent abuse
 Menhard, F. R. The facts about inhalants **362.29**

Solway, Andrew
 (jt. auth) Biesty, S. Rome: in spectacular cross section **937**

Somalia
 Hassig, S. M. Somalia (5 and up)   **967.73**

Some words with a mummy. Poe, E. A.
 In Poe, E. A. The pit and the pendulum and other stories **S C**

Someday. Koller, J. F.   **Fic**

Somehow tenderness survives   **S C**

Someone is hiding on Alcatraz Island. Bunting, E. **Fic**

Someone like you. Dessen, S.   **Fic**

Somerlott, Robert, 1928-
 The Little Rock school desegregation crisis in American history **373**
 The Spanish-American War **973.8**

Somers, Jane *See* Lessing, Doris May, 1919-

Somervill, Barbara A.
 Ida Tarbell   **92**

Somerville, Mary, 1780-1872
 See/See also pages in the following book(s):
 Celebrating women in mathematics and science **920**

Something about the author **920.003**

Something about the author: autobiography series **920.003**

Something funny happened at the library. Reid, R. **027.62**

Something old, something new. Sweeney, J.
 In Destination unexpected: short stories **S C**

Something permanent. Rylant, C.   **811**

Something which is non-existent. Klein, N.
 In Places I never meant to be; original stories by censored writers **S C**

Something wicked this way comes. Bradbury, R. **Fic**

Somewhere a puppy cries. Whittington, M. K.
 In The Haunted house: a collection of original stories **S C**

Somewhere in my mind there is a painting box. De Lint, C.
 In The Green Man: tales from the mythic forest p51-83 **808.8**
 also in De Lint, C. Waifs and strays p355-91 **S C**

Somewhere in the darkness. Myers, W. D. **Fic**

Sommariva, Jon
 (jt. auth) Peyer, T. Go boy 7, Vol. 1: Ready set go! **741.5**

Son, John
 Finding my hat   **Fic**

Son of the mob. Korman, G.   **Fic**

The **son** of the wind. Bryan, A.
 In Bryan, A. Ashley Bryan's African tales, uh-huh p136-71 **398.2**

Sonder, Ben, 1954-
 All about heroin (7 and up) **362.29**

Sonenklar, Carol
 My own worst enemy   **Fic**

Sones, Sonya
 Dr. Jekyll and Sister Hyde
  In Necessary noise: stories about our families as they really are p173-216 **S C**
 Stop pretending   **Fic**
 What my mother doesn't know (7 and up) **Fic**

A **song** for Croaker Nordge. Berberick, N. V.
 In A Glory of unicorns p127-43 **S C**

The **song** of Roland. Osborne, M. P.
 In Osborne, M. P. Favorite medieval tales p34-41 **398.2**

The **song** of stones river. Armstrong, J.
 In What a song can do; 12 riffs on the power of music **S C**

Song of the buffalo boy. Garland, S.   **Fic**

Song of the Magdalene. Napoli, D. J.   **Fic**

Song of the trees. Taylor, M. D.   **Fic**

The **song** shoots out of my mouth. Adoff, J. **811**

Songbirds. Latimer, J. P.   **598**

Songhai Empire
 Conrad, D. C. The Songhay Empire **966.2**
 McKissack, P. C. The royal kingdoms of Ghana, Mali, and Songhay (5 and up) **966.2**

The **Songhay** Empire. Conrad, D. C. **966.2**

Songs

See also Popular music; Spirituals (Songs)
Johnson, J. W. Lift every voice and sing
782.42

Songs and stories from the American Revolution.
Silverman, J. 782.42

Songs and stories of the Civil War. Silverman, J.
782.42

Songs of faith. Johnson, A. Fic

Songs of our ancestors [series]
Atangan, P. The yellow jar 741.5

Songwriters *See* Composers

Sonneborn, Liz
A to Z of Native American women 920.003
The American West: an illustrated history (7
and up) 978
Miranda v. Arizona 345
Samuel de Champlain 92

Sonny's house of spies. Lyon, G. E. Fic

Sonny's war. Hobbs, V. Fic

Sons and daughters. Yee, P.
In Yee, P. Tales from Gold Mountain; stories
of the Chinese in the New World p17-23
S C

Sons and fathers *See* Father-son relationship

Sons and mothers *See* Mother-son relationship

Sons of liberty. Griffin, A. Fic

Sonseray. Spinelli, J.
In Spinelli, J. The library card S C

Sophocles
Rao, S. Sophocles' Oedipus the King (7 and up)
Fic
Oedipus Rex; criticism
In Rao, S. Sophocles' Oedipus the King
Fic

Sophocles' Oedipus the King. Rao, S. Fic

The **sorcerer's** companion. Kronzek, A. Z.
823.009

Sorcery *See* Magic

Sorcery and Cecelia, or, The enchanted chocolate
pot. Wrede, P. C. Fic

Sorensen, Lita
The Scottsboro Boys Trial 345

Sorrow's kitchen: the life and folklore of Zora
Neale Hurston. Lyons, M. E. 92

SOS Titanic. Bunting, E. Fic

Sosa, Maria
(ed) Exploring science in the library. See Exploring science in the library 027.8

Soto, Gary
The afterlife (7 and up) Fic
Baseball in April, and other stories (5 and up)
S C
Contents: Broken chain; Baseball in April; Two dreamers;
Barbie; The no-guitar blues; Seventh grade; Mother and daughter;
The Karate Kid; La Bamba; The marble champ; Growing up
Broken chain
In Read all about it!; great read-aloud stories,
poems, and newspaper pieces for pre-
teens and teens p29-39 808.8
Buried onions Fic
Canto familiar (4-6) 811
Help wanted S C

Contents: Paintball in the wild; Sorry, wrong family; Yeah,
right; How Becky Garza learned golf; the cadet; The sounds of
love; Teenage chimps; The sounds of the house; One last kiss;
Raiders nation
Local news S C
Contents: Blackmail; Trick-or-treating; First job; El radio;
Push-up; The school play; The Raiders jacket; The challenge;
Nacho loco; The squirrels; The mechanical mind; Nickel-a-pound
plane ride; New Year's Eve
A natural man (7 and up) 811
Neighborhood odes (4-6) 811
New and selected poems 811
Novio boy (7 and up) 812
Taking sides (5 and up) Fic
These shoes of mine
In You're on!: seven plays in English and
Spanish p12-32 812.008
See/See also pages in the following book(s):
Hill, C. M. Ten Hispanic American authors
920

Soto, Hernando de, ca. 1500-1542
About
Gaines, A. Hernando de Soto and the Spanish
search for gold in world history (7 and up)
92

The **soul** cages. Philip, N.
In Philip, N. Celtic fairy tales p113-18
398.2

Soul looks back in wonder (4 and up)
811.008

The **soul** of a menorah. Kimmel, E. A.
In Kimmel, E. A. The jar of fools: eight Ha-
nukkah stories from Chelm p35-41
S C

Soul searching: thirteen stories about faith and belief S C

The **souls** of trees. Schwartz, H.
In Schwartz, H. The day the Rabbi disappeared: Jewish holiday tales of magic
p42-45 398.2

Soumerai, Eve Nussbaum
A voice from the Holocaust 940.53

Sound
Gardner, R. Light, sound, and waves science
fair projects (7 and up) 507.8

The **sound** machine. Dahl, R.
In Dahl, R. Skin and other stories S C

The **sound** of work. Jaffe, N.
In Jaffe, N. and Zeitlin, S. J. The cow of no
color: riddle stories and justice tales from
around the world p14-17 398.2

Sounder. Armstrong, W. H. Fic

Sounds of thunder. Bruchac, J.
In Shattered: stories of children and war
p122-32 S C

Sousanis, John
(jt. auth) Pendergast, T. Constitutional amendments: from freedom of speech to flag burning 342

Souter, Allison
(jt. auth) Souter, G. Creating animation for your
Web page 006.6
(jt. auth) Souter, G. Researching on the Internet
using search engines, bulletin boards, and listservs 004.6

Souter, Gerry
Creating animation for your Web page (4 and up) **006.6**
Researching on the Internet using search engines, bulletin boards, and listservs (4 and up) **004.6**

Souter, Janet, 1940-
(jt. auth) Souter, G. Creating animation for your Web page **006.6**
(jt. auth) Souter, G. Researching on the Internet using search engines, bulletin boards, and listservs **004.6**

South Africa
Blauer, E. South Africa (4 and up) **968**
Canesso, C. South Africa **968.06**
Rosmarin, I. South Africa (5 and up) **968**
    Fiction
Naidoo, B. No turning back (5 and up) **Fic**
Paton, A. Cry, the beloved country (7 and up) **Fic**
    Politics and government
Beecroft, S. The release of Nelson Mandela **968.06**
Finlayson, R. Nelson Mandela **92**
Kramer, A. Nelson Mandela (7 and up) **92**
    Race relations
    See also Apartheid
Downing, D. Apartheid in South Africa **968**
Finlayson, R. Nelson Mandela **92**
Kramer, A. Nelson Mandela (7 and up) **92**
    Race relations—Fiction
Naidoo, B. Journey to Jo'burg (5 and up) **Fic**
Naidoo, B. Out of bounds: seven stories of conflict and hope (5 and up) **S C**
Somehow tenderness survives **S C**

South Carolina
Hoffman, N. South Carolina
    In Celebrate the states **973**
Stein, R. C. South Carolina
    In America the beautiful, second series **973**
    Fiction
Fuqua, J. S. Darby (4 and up) **Fic**

South Dakota
McDaniel, M. South Dakota
    In Celebrate the states **973**
Shepherd, D. W. South Dakota America the beautiful, second series **973**
    Fiction
Arrington, F. Prairie whispers (5 and up) **Fic**
Love, D. A. A year without rain (5 and up) **Fic**

South Korea *See* Korea (South)

South Pole
    See also Antarctica

Southern Rhodesia *See* Zimbabwe

Southern States
    Folklore
    See Folklore—Southern States

Southwest, New *See* Southwestern States

Southwestern States
    Antiquities
Lavender, D. S. Mother Earth, Father Sky **970.004**
    History
Collier, C. Hispanic America, Texas, and the Mexican War, 1835-1850 **973.6**

Southwestern States
Freedman, R. In the days of the vaqueros (4 and up) **636.2**

Souza, D. M. (Dorothy M.)
Freaky flowers (5 and up) **582.13**
What is a fungus? (5 and up) **579.5**

Sovereigns *See* Emperors; Kings and rulers; Queens

Soviet Union
    See also Russia; Russia (Federation)
    Foreign relations—United States
Burgan, M. Cold War (7 and up) **909.82**
The Cold War [Great speeches in history series] **909.82**
Collier, C. The United States in the Cold War: 1945-1989 **327.73**
Kallen, S. A. Primary sources [American war library, The Cold War] **909.82**
Ross, S. The causes of the Cold War **327.73**
Sherman, J. The Cold War **909.82**
Speakman, J. The Cold War (7 and up) **327.73**
Winkler, A. M. The Cold War **909.82**
    History
Gottfried, T. The Stalinist empire **947.084**
Ingram, S. Joseph Stalin **92**
The Rise of the Soviet Union (7 and up) **947.084**
    History—1917-1921, Revolution
Gottfried, T. The road to Communism **947**
    History—1917-1921, Revolution—Fiction
Whelan, G. Angel on the square **Fic**
    Politics and government
The Collapse of the Soviet Union (7 and up) **947.085**

Space, Outer *See* Outer space

Space and astronomy on file **520**

Space and time
    Fiction
Conrad, P. Stonewords (5 and up) **Fic**
Haddix, M. P. Running out of time **Fic**
Hickman, J. Ravine **Fic**
Hoffman, M. Stravaganza: city of masks (7 and up) **Fic**
Holman, F. Real **Fic**
Jeapes, B. The new world order (7 and up) **Fic**
Larbalestier, J. Magic or madness (7 and up) **Fic**
Lawrence, M. A crack in the line (7 and up) **Fic**
McAllister, M. Ghost at the window (5 and up) **Fic**
McAllister, M. Hold my hand and run **Fic**
Montes, M. A circle of time **Fic**
Peck, R. The great interactive dream machine **Fic**

Space and time—Fiction—*Continued*
Peck, R. Lost in cyberspace (5 and up) **Fic**
Sleator, W. The boy who reversed himself (5 and up) **Fic**
The **Space** between our footsteps (7 and up) **808.81**
Space Camp (Huntsville, Ala.) *See* U.S. Space Camp (Huntsville, Ala.)
Space exploration. Stott, C. **629.4**
Space flight
Goodman, S. Ultimate field trip 5 (4 and up) **629.45**
Richie, J. Space flight **920**
Ride, S. K. To space & back **629.45**
Schyffert, B. U. The man who went to the far side of the moon: the story of Apollo 11 astronaut Michael Collins (5 and up) **92**
Spangenburg, R. Onboard the space shuttle **629.44**
Vogt, G. John Glenn's return to space **629.45**
Space flight to Mars
Cole, M. D. Living on Mars **629.4**
Wunsch, S. T. The adventures of Sojourner **629.43**
Space flight to the moon
See also Moon—Exploration
Collins, M. Flying to the moon **629.45**
Green, J. Race to the moon **629.45**
Hehner, B. First on the moon (4 and up) **629.45**
Space is the place. San Souci, R.
In San Souci, R. Dare to be scared; thirteen stories to chill and thrill **S C**
Space mission patches. Vogt, G. **629.45**
Space probes
Sherman, J. Deep space observation satellites **629.43**
Space science (5 and up) **500.5**
Space sciences
Furniss, T. The atlas of space exploration **520**
Pentland, P. Space science (4 and up) **500.5**
Space and astronomy on file **520**
Space science (5 and up) **500.5**
Space sciences **500.5**
Encyclopedias
Exploring earth and space science (7 and up) **550.3**
Space sciences **500.5**
Space shuttles
Ride, S. K. To space & back **629.45**
Spangenburg, R. Onboard the space shuttle **629.44**
Space stations
Spangenburg, R. Onboard the space shuttle **629.44**
Space vehicle accidents
Cole, M. D. The Columbia space shuttle disaster (4 and up) **629.44**
Mayell, M. Tragedies of space exploration (5 and up) **363.1**
Vogt, G. Disasters in space exploration **363.1**

Space vehicles
See also Space shuttles
Space warfare
Wolny, P. Weapons satellites **358**
Space weapons
Wolny, P. Weapons satellites **358**
Spain
Fiction
Lasky, K. Blood secret (7 and up) **Fic**
History
Mann, K. Isabel, Ferdinand and fifteenth-century Spain **946**
Millar, H. Spain in the age of exploration **946**
Worth, R. The Spanish Inquisition in world history (7 and up) **272**
History—1898, War of 1898
See Spanish-American War, 1898
Spain in the age of exploration. Millar, H. **946**
Spangenburg, Ray, 1939-
The African-American experience (7 and up) **917.3**
The age of synthesis: 1800-1895 (7 and up) **509**
The birth of science: ancient times to 1699 (7 and up) **509**
Genetic engineering (7 and up) **660.6**
The history of NASA **629.4**
The Hubble Space Telescope **522**
Literature and the arts (7 and up) **917.3**
A look at Mercury **523.4**
Mercury **523.4**
Meteors, meteorites, and meteoroids **523.5**
Modern science, 1896-1945 (7 and up) **509**
Onboard the space shuttle **629.44**
Political and social movements (7 and up) **917.3**
Propaganda (7 and up) **303.3**
The rise of reason: 1700-1799 (7 and up) **509**
Science frontiers, 1946 to the present (7 and up) **509**
The sun **523.7**
TV news (7 and up) **070.1**
Venus **523.4**
Spanish-American War, 1898
Collier, C. The United States enters the world stage: from the Alaska Purchase through World War I, 1867-1919 **973.8**
Dolan, E. F. The Spanish-American War **973.8**
McGowen, T. The Spanish-American War and Teddy Roosevelt in American history **973.8**
McNeese, T. Remember the Maine! **973.8**
Somerlott, R. The Spanish-American War **973.8**
See/See also pages in the following book(s):
Stovall, T. The Buffalo Soldiers **978**
The **Spanish-American** War and Teddy Roosevelt in American history. McGowen, T. **973.8**
Spanish-English bilingual books *See* Bilingual books—English-Spanish

The **Spanish** Inquisition in world history. Worth, R.   **272**

Spanish language
    Dictionaries
    Cassell's Spanish-English, English-Spanish dictionary   **463**

Spanish literature
    Bibliography
    Schon, I. Recommended books in Spanish for children and young adults, 2000 through 2004   **011.6**

Spare parts. Murphy, W. B.   **617.9**

Sparks fly upward. Matas, C.   **Fic**

Sparks of life [series] Blashfield, J. F.   **546**

Sparrow, Giles
    Iron
      In The Elements   **546**
    Nickel
      In The Elements   **546**

Spastic paralysis *See* Cerebral palsy

Spaulding, Charles Clinton, 1874-1952
    See/See also pages in the following book(s):
    Haskins, J. African American entrepreneurs   **920**

Speak. Anderson, L. H.   **Fic**

Speak out, write on! book [series]
    Dragisic, P. How to write a letter   **808**

Speak truth to power. Kennedy Cuomo, K.   **920**

The **speaking** head. Olson, A. N.
    In Olson, A. N. and Schwartz, H. Ask the bones: scary stories from around the world p85-91   **398.2**

Speaking of journals. Graham, P. W.   **920**

Speaking up, speaking out. Otfinoski, S.   **808.5**

Speakman, Jay
    The Cold War (7 and up)   **327.73**

Spear. Lester, J.
    In Places I never meant to be; original stories by censored writers   **S C**

Speare, Elizabeth George, 1908-1994
    The sign of the beaver (5 and up)   **Fic**
    The witch of Blackbird Pond (6 and up)   **Fic**

Spears, Rick
    (il) Halls, K. M. Dinosaur mummies   **567.9**

Special effects in film and television. Hamilton, J.   **791.43**

Special interests. Archer, J.   **324**

The **special** powers of Blossom Culp. Peck, R.
    In Peck, R. Past perfect, present tense: new and collected stories   **S C**

Spectacular science projects series
    VanCleave, J. P. Janice VanCleave's plants   **580.7**

Speech disorders
    Fiction
    Fusco, K. N. Tending to Grace (7 and up)   **Fic**

Speeches
    The Arab-Israeli conflict (7 and up)   **956.04**
    Civil rights (7 and up)   **323.1**

    The Cold War [Great speeches in history series]   **909.82**
    Lend me your ears   **808.85**
    UXL Asian American voices   **815**
    The Vietnam War (7 and up)   **959.704**

Speeches, addresses, etc., American *See* American speeches

Spellbound. McDonald, J.   **Fic**

Spellenberg, Richard
    National Audubon Society field guide to North American wildflowers, western region   **582.13**

Spellers
    Terban, M. Scholastic dictionary of spelling (4 and up)   **428**

Spells *See* Magic

Spencer, Ann, 1955-
    And round me rings (7 and up)   **398.2**

Spencer, William
    The United States and Iran (7 and up)   **327.73**

Sperling, Andrea
    (il) Fletcher, R. Have you been to the beach lately?   **811**

Spider Boy. Fletcher, R.   **Fic**

Spider-girl, Vol. 1: Legacy. DeFalco, T.   **741.5**

Spider-man: Spidey strikes back Vol. 1 digest. Dezago, T.   **741.5**

Spiders
    See also Tarantulas
    Discovery Channel insects & spiders   **595.7**
    Insects and spiders of the world (5 and up)   **595.7**
    Milne, L. J. The Audubon Society field guide to North American insects and spiders   **595.7**
    Simon, S. Spiders (4 and up)   **595.4**
    Fiction
    Fletcher, R. Spider Boy   **Fic**

Spiegelman, Art
    Maus (7 and up)   **940.53**

Spiegelman, Vladek
    About
    Spiegelman, A. Maus (7 and up)   **940.53**

Spielberg, Steven, 1947-
    About
    Rubin, S. G. Steven Spielberg   **92**

Spies
    Allen, T. B. George Washington, spymaster   **92**
    Caravantes, P. Petticoat spies   **920**
    Gifford, C. Spies (5 and up)   **327.12**
    Fiction
    Beatty, P. Jayhawker (5 and up)   **Fic**
    Horowitz, A. Stormbreaker   **Fic**
    Lyons, M. E. Dear Ellen Bee   **Fic**
    Rinaldi, A. Girl in blue   **Fic**

Spilling, Michael
    Cyprus (5 and up)   **956.93**
    Estonia (5 and up)   **947.9**
    Georgia (5 and up)   **947.5**

Spinelli, Jerry, 1941-
    Crash (5 and up)   **Fic**
    Knots in my yo-yo string (4 and up)   **92**

Spinelli, Jerry, 1941——*Continued*
The library card (4 and up)   **S C**
Includes the following stories: Mongoose; Brenda; Sonseray; April Mendez
    Maniac Magee (5 and up)   **Fic**
    Stargirl   **Fic**
    There's a girl in my hammerlock (5 and up)   **Fic**
    Wringer (4 and up)   **Fic**
       About
    Seidman, D. Jerry Spinelli (5 and up)   **92**
See/See also pages in the following book(s):
    The Newbery & Caldecott medal books, 1986-2000   **028.5**
Spinner, Stephanie
    Quicksilver (7 and up)   **Fic**
    Quiver (7 and up)   **Fic**
Spinners. Napoli, D. J.   **Fic**
Spirin, Gennadii
    (il) Bible. N.T. Selections. The Christmas story   **232.9**
The **spirit** catchers. Kudlinski, K. V.   **Fic**
The **spirit** line. Thurlo, A.   **Fic**
Spirits *See* Angels
Spirits of the railway. Yee, P.
    In Yee, P. Tales from Gold Mountain; stories of the Chinese in the New World p9-15   **S C**
Spirituals (Songs)
    Cooper, M. L. Slave spirituals and the Jubilee Singers   **782.42**
Spite fences. Krisher, T.   **Fic**
Spitting image. Crum, S.   **Fic**
Spitzer, Robert J.
    The right to bear arms   **344**
Sports
    See also Games
    Girls got game (5 and up)   **810.8**
    The Information please sports almanac   **796**
    Loeffelbein, R. L. The recreation handbook   **793**
    Sports Illustrated . . . sports almanac   **796**
    Sports rules on file   **796**
    Sports: the complete visual reference   **796**
       Encyclopedias
    Encyclopedia of women and sport in America   **796.03**
    Rules of the game   **796.03**
    Scholastic visual sports encyclopedia (4 and up)   **796.03**
    Wukovits, J. F. The encyclopedia of world sports   **796.03**
       Fiction
    Crutcher, C. Athletic shorts (7 and up)   **S C**
    Lynch, C. Slot machine (7 and up)   **Fic**
    Ultimate sports (7 and up)   **S C**
       Medical aspects
    See Sports medicine
Sports alive! [series]
    George, C. White-water rafting   **797.1**
Sports cards
    See also Baseball cards

The **sports** encyclopedia: baseball. Neft, D. S.   **796.357**
Sports for the handicapped
    Kent, D. Athletes with disabilities (4 and up)   **371.9**
Sports Illustrated . . . sports almanac   **796**
Sports injuries information for teens (7 and up)   **617.1**
Sports issues [series]
    Stiefer, S. A risky prescription   **613.7**
Sports medicine
    Gardner, R. Health science projects about sports performance (7 and up)   **612**
    Sports injuries information for teens (7 and up)   **617.1**
    Stiefer, S. A risky prescription   **613.7**
Sports rules on file   **796**
Sports stories *See* Sports—Fiction
Sports: the complete visual reference   **796**
Sportsgirl [series]
    Manley, C. B. Competitive track and field for girls   **796.42**
    Manley, C. B. Competitive volleyball for girls   **796.325**
Spotted Tail, Brulé Sioux Chief, 1823-1881
    See/See also pages in the following book(s):
    Brown, D. A. Bury my heart at Wounded Knee   **970.004**
The **Spreaders**. Bruchac, J.
    In Bruchac, J. and Bruchac, J. When the Chenoo howls; native American tales of terror   **398.2**
The **spring** running. Kipling, R.
    In Kipling, R. The jungle books   **S C**
Springer, Jane
    Listen to us (7 and up)   **331.3**
Springer, Nancy
    Becoming
       In Half-human p1-17   **S C**
    I am Mordred (7 and up)   **Fic**
    I am Morgan le Fay (7 and up)   **Fic**
    Know your true enemy
       In Sherwood: original stories from the world of Robin Hood p50-66   **S C**
    Mariposa
       In Firebirds: an anthology of original fantasy and science fiction; an anthology of original fantasy and science fiction   **S C**
    Rowan Hood, outlaw girl of Sherwood Forest (4 and up)   **Fic**
Sproule, Anna
    James Watt   **92**
    Thomas A. Edison   **92**
    The Wright brothers   **92**
Sprug, Joseph W., 1922-
    (comp) Index to fairy tales. See Index to fairy tales   **398.2**
Spy. Platt, R.   **327.12**
Spy satellites. Kupperberg, P.   **327.12**
Spy science. Wiese, J.   **363.2**
Spying on Miss Müller. Bunting, E.   **Fic**
Squashed. Bauer, J.   **Fic**

Squid girl. Strasser, T. 13; thirteen stories that capture the agony and ecstasy of being thirteen

The **squire**. Singer, I. B.
  In Singer, I. B. The power of light; eight stories for Hanukkah p43-50   **S C**

The **squire's** tale. Morris, G.   **Fic**

Squire's tales [series]
  Morris, G. The squire's tale   **Fic**

The **squirrels**. Soto, G.
  In Soto, G. Local news p102-12   **S C**

Sri Lanka
  Wanasundera, N. P. Sri Lanka   **954.93**

Srinivasan, Radhika
  India (5 and up)   **954**

St. Antoine, Sara, 1966-
  (ed) The Great North American prairie. See The Great North American prairie   **810.8**

St. Clair, Nancy
  (jt. auth) Brown, J. Declarations of independence   **028.5**

St. George, Judith, 1931-
  In the line of fire (4 and up)   **364.1**
  Sacagawea (4-6)   **92**

St. George and the dragon. Kingston, W. H. G.
  In The Book of dragons p89-95   **S C**

St. Michael's scales. Connelly, N. O.   **Fic**

St. Valentine's Day *See* Valentine's Day

Staal, Flossie Wong- *See* Wong-Staal, Flossie, 1947-

Stacey, Gill
  London (4 and up)   **942.1**

Stahler, David, Jr.
  A gathering of shades (7 and up)   **Fic**

Stalin, Joseph, 1879-1953
       About
  Gottfried, T. The Stalinist empire   **947.084**
  Ingram, S. Joseph Stalin   **92**
  See/See also pages in the following book(s):
  Ross, S. Leaders of World War II   **920**
  Uschan, M. V. Political leaders   **920**

The **Stalinist** empire. Gottfried, T.   **947.084**

Stallworthy, Jon
  (ed) The Oxford book of war poetry. See The Oxford book of war poetry   **808.81**

Stamina, Physical *See* Physical fitness

Stamp Act, 1765
  See/See also pages in the following book(s):
  Collier, C. The American Revolution, 1763-1783   **973.3**

Stamps, Postage *See* Postage stamps

Stan, Susan
  (ed) The World through children's books. See The World through children's books   **011.6**

Stan Bolovan. Lang, A.
  In The Book of dragons p96-109   **S C**

Stanchak, John E.
  The visual dictionary of the Civil War   **973.7**

Stand-off at Standing Rock: the story of Sitting Bull and James Mclaughlin. Calvert, P.   **92**

Stand tall. Bauer, J.   **Fic**

Standard catalog series
  Children's catalog   **011.6**

Standard cataloging for school and public libraries. Intner, S. S.   **025.3**

Standard Oil Co. (Ohio)
  See also Standard Oil Company

Standard Oil Company
  See/See also pages in the following book(s):
  Segall, G. John D. Rockefeller   **92**

Standing Bear, Ponca Chief, 1829?-1908
  See/See also pages in the following book(s):
  Brown, D. A. Bury my heart at Wounded Knee   **970.004**

Standing in the light. Osborne, M. P.   **Fic**

Standing like a stone wall: the life of General Thomas J. Jackson. Robertson, J. I., Jr.   **92**

Standing on the roof naked. Lantz, F. L.
  In On the fringe p89-113   **S C**

Stanley, Diane, 1943-
  Bard of Avon: the story of William Shakespeare (4 and up)   **822.3**
  Charles Dickens (4 and up)   **92**
  Cleopatra (4 and up)   **92**
  Good Queen Bess: the story of Elizabeth I of England (4 and up)   **92**
  Joan of Arc (4 and up)   **92**
  Michelangelo   **92**
  The mysterious matter of I.M. Fine   **Fic**
  Saladin: noble prince of Islam (4 and up)   **92**
  Shaka, king of the Zulus (4 and up)   **92**

Stanley, Jerry, 1941-
  Children of the Dust Bowl (5 and up)   **371.9**
  Cowboys & longhorns   **636.2**

Stanton, Elizabeth Cady, 1815-1902
       About
  Sigerman, H. Elizabeth Cady Stanton (7 and up)   **92**

Staples, Suzanne Fisher
  Dangerous skies (7 and up)   **Fic**
  Faizabad harvest, 1980
    In Shattered: stories of children and war p108-21   **S C**
  Shabanu   **Fic**
  Shiva's fire (7 and up)   **Fic**

The **Star** Maiden. San Souci, R.
  In San Souci, R. Cut from the same cloth; American women of myth, legend, and tall tale p3-10   **398.2**

The **star** of Kazan. Ibbotson, E.   **Fic**

Star split. Lasky, K.   **Fic**

Star trek (Motion picture)
  See/See also pages in the following book(s):
  Reid, S. E. Presenting young adult science fiction   **813.009**

Star vision. Begay, S.
  In Soul searching: thirteen stories about faith and belief p220-27   **S C**

Star Wars: Clone wars adventures, Vol. 1. Blackman, H.   **741.5**

Star Wars films
Reynolds, D. W. Star wars: the visual dictionary
791.43

Star wars: the visual dictionary. Reynolds, D. W.
791.43

Starbears. Appelt, K.
In Appelt, K. Kissing Tennessee and other stories from the Stardust Dance p41-65
S C

Stardust otel. Janeczko, P. B.   **811**

Stargirl. Spinelli, J.   **Fic**

The **starplace**. Grove, V.   **Fic**

Starry nights. Clarke, J.   **Fic**

Stars
Gallant, R. A. The life stories of stars   **523.8**
Ridpath, I. Facts on File stars & planets atlas
520
Sasaki, C. Constellations: the stars and stories
523.8
See/See also pages in the following book(s):
Rükl, A. Constellation guidebook (7 and up)
523.8

State, Heads of *See* Heads of state

State governments
American government at work (7 and up)
320.4
Facts about the states   **973**

State names, seals, flags, and symbols. Shearer, B. F.   **929.9**

The **Statesman's** year-book   **310.5**

Statesmen
See also Heads of state; Politicians
United States
Benjamin Franklin [essays about] (7 and up)
92
Finlayson, R. Colin Powell   **92**
Fradin, D. B. The signers (4 and up)   **920**

Statistical abstract of the United States. United States. Bureau of the Census   **317.3**

Statistics
Encyclopaedia Britannica almanac   **031.02**
Information please almanac, atlas & yearbook
031.02
The New York Times almanac   **031.02**
The Statesman's year-book   **310.5**
United States. Bureau of the Census. Statistical abstract of the United States   **317.3**
The World almanac and book of facts
031.02

Staub, Frank J.
America's forests (4 and up)   **577.3**
The signs animals leave   **590**

Staub, Leslie, 1957-
(il) Lives: poems about famous Americans. See Lives: poems about famous Americans
811.008

Stauffacher, Sue, 1961-
Donuthead (4-6)   **Fic**

Stavans, Ilan
(ed) Growing up Latino. See Growing up Latino
810.8

(ed) Wáchale! poetry and prose on growing up Latino in America. See Wáchale! poetry and prose on growing up Latino in America
810.8

Staver and Vassilissa. Tchana, K. H.
In Tchana, K. H. The serpent slayer: and other stories of strong women p85-89
398.2

Stawicki, Andrew
(il) Kenna, K. A people apart   **289.7**

Stay!. Lowry, L.   **Fic**

Staying fat for Sarah Byrnes. Crutcher, C.   **Fic**

Staying out of trouble in a troubled family. Blue, R.   **362.7**

Steal away. Armstrong, J.   **Fic**

Stealing dreams. O'Neill, R.
In A Glory of unicorns p59-73   **S C**

Stealing for girls. Weaver, W.
In Ultimate sports; short stories by outstanding writers for young adults p93-116
S C

Stealing freedom. Carbone, E. L.   **Fic**

Steam engines
Zimmermann, K. R. Steam locomotives (4 and up)   **385**

Steam locomotives. Zimmermann, K. R.   **385**

Steamboats
Kroll, S. Robert Fulton   **92**
Pierce, M. A. Robert Fulton and the development of the steamboat   **92**

Stearman, Kaye, 1951-
Feminism (7 and up)   **305.4**

Stebbins, Robert C. (Robert Cyril), 1915-
A field guide to Western reptiles and amphibians   **597.9**

Steck, Jim
(il) Lawrence, C. Big fat paycheck   **808.2**

Steedman, Scott
The Egyptian news   **932**

Steele, Mary
Aunt Millicent
In Read all about it!; great read-aloud stories, poems, and newspaper pieces for preteens and teens p12-28   **808.8**

Steele, Philip
The Aztec news   **972**
The human race
In Being human   **612**
(jt. auth) Powell, A. The Greek news   **938**

Steffens, Bradley
Censorship (7 and up)   **342**

Stefoff, Rebecca, 1951-
Alaska
In Celebrate the states   **973**
American voices from the new republic, 1783-1830   **973.4**
The ancient Mediterranean (5 and up)   **938**
The ancient Near East (5 and up)   **939**
The Asian empires (5 and up)   **950**
Charles Darwin and the evolution revolution (7 and up)   **92**
Colonial life   **973.2**
Earth and the moon   **550**

Stefoff, Rebecca, 1951——_Continued_
Exploration (5 and up)   **910**
Idaho
   _In_ Celebrate the states   **973**
Jack London (7 and up)   **92**
The medieval world (5 and up)   **909.07**
Neptune   **523.4**
Nevada
   _In_ Celebrate the states   **973**
The opening of the West   **978**
Oregon
   _In_ Celebrate the states   **973**
Plácido Domingo   **92**
Utah
   _In_ Celebrate the states   **973**
Washington
   _In_ Celebrate the states   **973**
Steig, William, 1907-2003
See/See also pages in the following book(s):
Marcus, L. S. A Caldecott celebration   **741.6**
Steiger, Brad
Gale encyclopedia of the unusual and unexplained   **130**
Steiger, Sherry Hansen
(jt. auth) Steiger, B. Gale encyclopedia of the unusual and unexplained   **130**
Stein, Paul, 1968-
Macmillan encyclopedia of weather   **551.5**
Stein, R. Conrad, 1937-
John Brown's Raid on Harpers Ferry in American history   **973.7**
Kentucky
   _In_ America the beautiful, second series   **973**
Mexico (4 and up)   **972**
Nevada
   _In_ America the beautiful, second series   **973**
New Hampshire
   _In_ America the beautiful, second series   **973**
New Jersey
   _In_ America the beautiful, second series   **973**
South Carolina
   _In_ America the beautiful, second series   **973**
Washington, D.C.
   _In_ America the beautiful, second series   **973**
World War II in Europe   **940.54**
World War II in the Pacific   **940.54**
Stein, Robert
Jewish Americans (7 and up)   **305.8**
Stein, Ross S.
   About
Grace, C. O. Forces of nature (4 and up)   **551.2**
Stein, Stephen J.
Alternative American religions (7 and up)   **209**
Stein, Tammar
Light years (7 and up)   **Fic**
Steinbeck, John, 1902-1968
The pearl (7 and up)   **Fic**

The red pony   **Fic**
   About
Reef, C. John Steinbeck (7 and up)   **92**
Tessitore, J. John Steinbeck, a writer's life (7 and up)   **92**
Steinem, Gloria
   About
Lazo, C. E. Gloria Steinem (7 and up)   **92**
Wheaton, E. Ms: the story of Gloria Steinem   **92**
Steiner, Matt
   About
Warren, A. Escape from Saigon   **92**
Steiner, Stanley F.
Promoting a global community through multicultural children's literature   **016.8**
Steins, Richard
Leontyne Price, opera superstar   **92**
Stem cell research
Tesar, J. Stem cells (5 and up)   **616**
Stem cell research. Viegas, J.   **616**
Stem cells. Tesar, J.   **616**
Stemple, Adam
Robin Hood v. 1.5.3.
   _In_ Sherwood: original stories from the world of Robin Hood p122-30   **S C**
Stemple, Jane H. Yolen _See_ Yolen, Jane
Step by step along the Appalachian Trail. Andryszewski, T.   **796.51**
A **step** from heaven. Na, A.   **Fic**
Step lightly (7 and up)   **808.81**
Stepfamilies
   Fiction
Cohn, R. The Steps (4 and up)   **Fic**
Johnston, T. Never so green (7 and up)   **Fic**
Stepfathers
   Fiction
Johnson, A. Bird (5 and up)   **Fic**
Kwasney, M. D. Baby Blue   **Fic**
Lurie, A. Dancing in the streets of Brooklyn   **Fic**
Rinaldi, A. In my father's house (7 and up)   **Fic**
Salisbury, G. Lord of the deep (5 and up)   **Fic**
Stephen Fair. Wynne-Jones, T.   **Fic**
Stephen King: king of thrillers and horror. Wilson, S.   **92**
Stephens, Claire Gatrell
Coretta Scott King Award books   **028.5**
Stephens, Elaine C., 1943-
Learning about—the Civil War   **016.973**
(ed) Your reading. See Your reading   **011.6**
Stephens, Michael T., 1965-
The library Internet trainer's toolkit   **025.04**
Stephens, Tim
(jt. auth) Price, S. Click! fun with photography   **771**
Stephenson, Karen F.
(jt. auth) Anderson, M. J. Aristotle   **92**
Stepmothers
   Fiction
Baskin, N. R. Almost home   **Fic**

Stepmothers—Fiction—*Continued*
Couloumbis, A. Say yes   **Fic**

Stepparents
   See also Stepfathers

Steppin' Eddie. Wallace, R.
   In On the edge: stories at the brink p163-73
                                      S C

Stepping on the cracks. Hahn, M. D.   **Fic**
The **Steps**. Cohn, R.   **Fic**

Sterling, Pamela
   The secret garden [play]
   In Theatre for young audiences; 20 great
      plays for children p99-141   **812.008**

Sternberg, Martin L. A.
   American Sign Language   **419**

Steroids
   LeVert, S. The facts about steroids   **362.29**

Stetler, Susan L.
   (ed) Almanac of famous people. See Almanac
     of famous people   **920.003**

Stevens, Rita
   Madagascar   **969.1**

Stevenson, Robert Louis, 1850-1894
   Dr. Jekyll and Mr. Hyde (7 and up)   **Fic**
   Kidnapped (7 and up)   **Fic**
   Treasure Island (6 and up)   **Fic**
              About
   Murphy, J. Across America on an emigrant train
     (5 and up)   **92**
   See/See also pages in the following book(s):
   Ellis, S. From reader to writer   **372.6**

Stevermer, Caroline
   (jt. auth) Wrede, P. C. Sorcery and Cecelia, or,
     The enchanted chocolate pot   **Fic**

Stevie in the mirror. Wittlinger, E.
   In On the edge: stories at the brink p1-20
                                      S C

Stewart, Gail, 1949-
   America under attack (7 and up)   **973.931**
   Death   **306.9**
   Diabetes (7 and up)   **616.4**
   Divorce   **306.89**
   Drugs   **362.29**
   Great women comedians   **920**
   Guns and violence   **303.6**
   Homeless teens (7 and up)   **362.5**
   Human rights in the Middle East   **323**
   Life in Elizabethan London   **942.05**
   Life of a soldier in Washington's army
                                  973.3
   Life under the Taliban   **958.1**
   People with mental illness (7 and up)
                                 616.89
   Phobias   **616.85**
   Terrorism (4 and up)   **303.6**

Stewart, Jennifer J., 1960-
   If that breathes fire, we're toast!   **Fic**

Stewart, Mark
   Basketball (7 and up)   **796.323**
   Hockey (7 and up)   **796.962**
   Jackie Stiles (4 and up)   **92**
   Mario Lemieux   **92**
   Soccer (7 and up)   **796.334**

   Sweet victory: Lance Armstrong's incredible
     journey (5 and up)   **92**
   World Series   **796.357**

Stewart, Melissa, 1968-
   Science in ancient India (4 and up)   **509**

Stewart, Philip
   Cherokee North American Indians today [series]
   Osage North American Indians today [series]

Stewart, Sean, 1965-
   The new girl
   In A Glory of unicorns p185-94   **S C**

Stewart, Whitney, 1959-
   Aung San Suu Kyi (7 and up)   **92**

Stick. De Lint, C.
   In De Lint, C. Waifs and strays p154-208
                                      S C

Stidworthy, John
   (jt. auth) Kerrod, R. Facts on File wildlife atlas
                                    578

Stiefer, Sandy
   A risky prescription   **613.7**

Stiekel, Bettina
   (ed) The Nobel book of answers. See The Nobel
     book of answers   **001.4**

Stiles, Jackie, 1978-
              About
   Stewart, M. Jackie Stiles (4 and up)   **92**

Still, James
   Hush: an interview with America
   In Theatre for young audiences; 20 great
      plays for children p395-428   **812.008**

Still, Peter, b. 1801
              About
   Fradin, D. B. My family shall be free!: the life
     of Peter Still   **92**

Stille, Darlene R., 1942-
   Extraordinary women of medicine   **920**

Stine, R. L., 1943-
   Joe is not a monster
   In Beware!; R.L. Stine picks his favorite
      scary stories p121-25   **808.8**
   The judge's house
   In Beware!; R.L. Stine picks his favorite
      scary stories p55-75   **808.8**
   The surprise guest
   In Beware!; R.L. Stine picks his favorite
      scary stories p39-53   **808.8**
   The terrifying adventures of the golem
   In Beware!; R.L. Stine picks his favorite
      scary stories p147-67   **808.8**
              About
   Jones, P. What's so scary about R.L. Stine?
                              813.009
   (comp) Beware! See Beware!   **808.8**

Stink Alley. Gilson, J.   **Fic**

The **stinky** princess. Coville, B.
   In Coville, B. Odder than ever   **S C**

A **stir** of bones. Hoffman, N. K.   **Fic**

A **stitch** in time. Rinaldi, A.   **Fic**

Stock, Catherine
   (il) Bunting, E. Doll baby   **Fic**

The **stock-broker's** clerk. Doyle, Sir A. C.
In Doyle, Sir A. C. The complete Sherlock
Holmes **S C**

Stock market smart. McGowan, E. N. **332.6**

Stockler, Julie
Losing it
In Don't cramp my style; stories about that
time of the month p242-64 **S C**

Stocks
McGowan, E. N. Stock market smart **332.6**

Stolen dreams. Parker, D. L. **331.3**

The **stolen** princess. McKinley, R.
In McKinley, R. The door in the hedge p1-77
S C

Stolley, Richard B.
(ed) Life: our century in pictures for young people. See Life: our century in pictures for
young people **779**

Stolls, Amy
Palms to the ground (7 and up) **Fic**

Stolz, Joëlle
The shadows of Ghadames **Fic**

Stone, Martha Kaufman, 1949-1999
About
Stone, M. At the end of words (7 and up)
92

Stone, Miriam
At the end of words (7 and up) **92**

Stone, Tanya Lee
Mars **523.4**
Saturn **523.4**
(ed) Scientists: their lives and works. See Scientists: their lives and works **920.003**

The **stone**. Alexander, L.
In Alexander, L. The foundling and other
tales of Prydain p17-26 **S C**

Stone Age
Macdonald, F. The Stone Age news **930.1**
McGowen, T. Giant stones and earth mounds
930.1

The **Stone** Age news. Macdonald, F. **930.1**

Stone bench in an empty park (4 and up)
811.008

The **Stone** Giant. Bruchac, J.
In Bruchac, J. and Bruchac, J. When the
Chenoo howls; native American tales of
terror **398.2**

A **stone** in my hand. Clinton, C. **Fic**

Stone tower. Simner, J. L.
In Gothic!; ten original dark tales **S C**

Stone water. Gilbert, B. S. **Fic**

Stonehenge (England)
Malone, C. Stonehenge **936.2**

Stonehouse, Bernard
Bears **599.78**

Stoner & Spaz. Koertge, R. **Fic**

The **stones** are hatching. McCaughrean, G. **Fic**

Stones in water. Napoli, D. J. **Fic**

Stonewall [biography of Stonewall Jackson] Fritz,
J. **92**

Stoneware *See* Pottery

Stonewords. Conrad, P. **Fic**

Stop pretending. Sones, S. **Fic**

Stop the train!. McCaughrean, G. **Fic**

Stoplight. Yoon, S. C.-N.
In American dragons: twenty-five Asian
American voices p14-25 **810.8**

Stories from the life of Jesus. Lottridge, C. B.
232.9

Stories from where we live [series]
The Great North American prairie **810.8**

Stories in stone. Arnold, C. **709.01**

Storm catchers. Bowler, T. **Fic**

Stormbreaker. Horowitz, A. **Fic**

Storms
See also Dust storms; Hurricanes; Tornadoes

Storni, Alfonsina, 1892-1938
A dream in the road
In You're on!: seven plays in English and
Spanish p100-07 **812.008**

Story hour. Coville, K.
In A Glory of unicorns p97-112 **S C**

A **story** in three parts. Myers, W. D.
In Myers, W. D. 145th Street; short stories
S C

The **Story** of Five Heads
In Hearne, B. G. Beauties and beasts p115-19
398.2

The **story** of King Arthur and his knights. Pyle, H.
398.2

Story of music (7 and up) **780.3**

The **story** of my life. Keller, H. **92**

The **story** of Robin Hood. Philip, N. **398.2**

Story of science [series]
Donnellan, W. L. The miracle of immunity
616.07
Gallant, J. R. The tales fossils tell **560**
Gallant, R. A. Dance of the continents
551.1
Gallant, R. A. Early humans **599.93**
Gallant, R. A. The ever changing atom
539.7
Gallant, R. A. The life stories of stars **523.8**
Gallant, R. A. The origins of life **576.8**
Gallant, R. A. The treasure of inheritance
576.5
Gallant, R. A. The wonders of biodiversity
333.95
Hakim, J. Aristotle leads the way **509**
Parker, B. R. The mystery of gravity **531**
Reed, G. Eyes on the universe **520**

The **story** of Sir Launcelot and his companions.
Pyle, H. **398.2**

The **story** of the Bat. Brown, D. A.
In Brown, D. A. Dee Brown's folktales of the
Native American; retold for our times
p147 **398.2**

The **story** of the champions of the Round Table.
Pyle, H. **398.2**

The **story** of the Grail and the passing of Arthur.
Pyle, H. **398.2**

The **story** of Wang Li. Coatsworth, E. J.
In The Book of dragons p78-88 **S C**

Story painter: the life of Jacob Lawrence. Duggleby, J. **92**

Story time. Bloor, E. **Fic**

The **storyteller's** beads. Kurtz, J. **Fic**

Storytelling
Reid, R. Something funny happened at the library **027.62**
Sima, J. Raising voices **027.62**
Fiction
Fletcher, S. Shadow spinner (6 and up) **Fic**
French, J. Hitler's daughter **Fic**

Stotan!. Crutcher, C. **Fic**

Stott, Carole
New astronomer (7 and up) **520**
Space exploration (4 and up) **629.4**

Stout, Harry S.
(ed) Braude, A. Women and American religion **200.9**
(ed) Noll, M. A. Protestants in America **280**

Stovall, TaRessa
The Buffalo Soldiers **978**

Stover, Lois T.
Presenting Phyllis Reynolds Naylor **813.009**

Stowaway. Hesse, K. **Fic**

Stowe, Harriet Beecher, 1811-1896
About
Fritz, J. Harriet Beecher Stowe and the Beecher preachers (5 and up) **92**

Stoyles, Pennie
(jt. auth) Pentland, P. Earth science **550**
(jt. auth) Pentland, P. Forensic science **363.2**
(jt. auth) Pentland, P. Kitchen science **641**
(jt. auth) Pentland, P. Party science **507.8**
(jt. auth) Pentland, P. Space science **500.5**
(jt. auth) Pentland, P. Toy and game science **531**

Straight and true. Harris, R. J.
In Sherwood: original stories from the world of Robin Hood p86-97 **S C**

Straight talk about teenage pregnancy. Edelson, P. **362.7**

Straight talk about today's families. Presma, F. **306.8**

Strain (Psychology) *See* Stress (Psychology)

Stranded. Mikaelsen, B. **Fic**

Stranded at Plimoth Plantation, 1626. Bowen, G. **974.4**

Strange animals, new to science. Pringle, L. P. **591.68**

The **strange** case of Dr. Jekyll and Mr. Hyde. See Stevenson, R. L. Dr. Jekyll and Mr. Hyde **Fic**

Strange creatures. Lester, J.
In Lester, J. When the beginning began; stories about God, the creatures, and us p18-24 **296.1**

The **strange** ride of Morrowbie Jukes. Kipling, R.
In McCaffrey, A. {The Pern series} **S C**

Stranger in Dadland. Koss, A. G. **Fic**

Stranger with my face. Duncan, L. **Fic**

Strangers. Schwartz, A.
In Schwartz, A. Scary stories 3; more tales to chill your bones p79 **398.2**

Strangis, Joel, 1948-
Lewis Hayden and the war against slavery **92**

Straphanging in the USA. Sandler, M. W. **388.4**

Strasser, Todd, 1950-
Bones
In Ultimate sports; short stories by outstanding writers for young adults p238-50 **S C**
Can't get there from here (7 and up) **Fic**
On the bridge
In Visions: nineteen short stories by outstanding writers for young adults p122-29 **S C**
Squid girl 13; thirteen stories that capture the agony and ecstasy of being thirteen

Stratigraphic geology
Gallant, R. A. History **551.7**

Stratton, Allan
Chanda's secrets (7 and up) **Fic**

Straub, Deborah Gillan
(ed) UXL Asian American voices. See UXL Asian American voices **815**

Strauss, Levi, 1829-1902
See/See also pages in the following book(s):
Kent, J. Business builders in fashion **920**

Stravaganza: city of masks. Hoffman, M. **Fic**

Straw into gold. Vande Velde, V.
In Vande Velde, V. Tales from the Brothers Grimm and the Sisters Weird p1-26 **S C**

Stray voltage. Doyle, E. F. **Fic**

Straydog. Koja, K. **Fic**

Strays like us. Peck, R. **Fic**

The **streak**. Myers, W. D.
In Myers, W. D. 145th Street; short stories **S C**

Streams to the river, river to the sea. O'Dell, S. **Fic**

Street gangs *See* Gangs

Street literature *See* Pamphlets

Street people *See* Homeless persons

Street railroads
Sandler, M. W. Straphanging in the USA (5 and up) **388.4**

A **street** through time. Millard, A. **936**

Streissguth, Thomas
Brazil in pictures (5 and up) **981**
J. Edgar Hoover: powerful FBI Director **92**
Jack London **92**
Legendary labor leaders (7 and up) **920**
(ed) Custer's last stand. See Custer's last stand **973.8**
(ed) The Rise of the Soviet Union. See The Rise of the Soviet Union **947.084**

The **strength** of these arms. Bial, R. **326**

Stress (Psychology)
See also Post-traumatic stress disorder
Rutledge, J. Z. Dealing with the stuff that makes life tough (7 and up)   **305.23**
Wells, D. K. Live aware, not in fear (7 and up)   **155.5**
Stretch your wings (7 and up)   **808.88**
Strickland, Michael R., 1965-
African-American poets   **920**
Strider. Cleary, B.   **Fic**
Strike two. Koss, A. G.   **Fic**
Strikes
Bartoletti, S. C. Kids on strike! (5 and up)   **331.8**
Dash, J. We shall not be moved (7 and up)   **331.4**
Fiction
Koss, A. G. Strike two (4 and up)   **Fic**
Stripling, Barbara K.
(ed) Curriculum connections through the library. See Curriculum connections through the library   **027.62**
Stromoski, Rick, 1958-
(il) Haduch, B. Food rules!   **613.2**
A **strong** right arm: the story of Mamie "Peanut" Johnson. Green, M. Y.   **92**
The **strongest** creature. Molnár, I.
In Molnár, I. One-time dog market at Buda and other Hungarian folktales p97-101   **398.2**
Stroud, Jonathan, 1970-
The Amulet of Samarkand (7 and up)   **Fic**
Structural engineering
Corbishley, M. The world of architectural wonders   **720**
Wilkinson, P. Building (4 and up)   **690**
Structure. Gallant, R. A.   **551.1**
Stuart-Clark, Christopher
(comp) The Oxford book of story poems. See The Oxford book of story poems   **821.008**
(ed) The Oxford treasury of time poems. See The Oxford treasury of time poems   **821.008**
Stuck in neutral. Trueman, T.   **Fic**
Stuckenschneider, Dan
(il) Tomecek, S. What a great idea!   **609**
Student almanac of African American history   **305.8**
Student almanac of Native American history   **970.004**
Student success and library media programs. Farmer, L. S. J.   **027.8**
Students
Law and legislation
Fuller, S. B. Hazelwood v. Kuhlmeier (7 and up)   **344**
Trespacz, K. L. Ferrell v. Dallas I.S.D. (7 and up)   **344**
A **Student's** guide to biotechnology (7 and up)   **660.6**
A **student's** guide to mental health & wellness   **616.89**

A **study** in scarlet. Doyle, Sir A. C.
In Doyle, Sir A. C. The complete Sherlock Holmes   **S C**
Study skills
Wood, G. How to study (7 and up)   **371.3**
Sturges, Philemon
Sacred places (4 and up)   **203**
Sturgis, Alexander
Optical illusions in art   **750.1**
Stuyvesant High School (New York, N.Y.)
With their eyes (7 and up)   **812**
Su, E. J.
(jt. auth) Kirkman, R. Tech jacket, Vol. 1: Lost & found   **741.5**
Subject catalogs
Subject guide to Books in print   **015.73**
Subject guide to Children's books in print   **015.73**
Subject guide to Books in print   **015.73**
Subject guide to Children's books in print   **015.73**
Subject headings
Sears list of subject headings   **025.4**
Submarine exploration *See* Underwater exploration
Submarine geology
Erickson, J. Marine geology (7 and up)   **551.46**
Submarines
Walker, S. M. Secrets of a Civil War submarine (7 and up)   **973.7**
Fiction
Verne, J. Twenty thousand leagues under the sea (5 and up)   **Fic**
Substance abuse *See* Drug abuse
The **subtle** knife. Pullman, P.   **Fic**
Subways
DuTemple, L. A. The New York subways (5 and up)   **388.4**
Sandler, M. W. Straphanging in the USA (5 and up)   **388.4**
See/See also pages in the following book(s):
Macaulay, D. Underground (5 and up)   **624**
Fiction
Holman, F. Slake's limbo (6 and up)   **Fic**
Shusterman, N. Downsiders   **Fic**
Success
Bachel, B. K. What do you really want?   **153.8**
Rimm, S. B. See Jane win for girls (5 and up)   **305.23**
Such foolishness. Griffin, M. R.
In 13; thirteen stories that capture the agony and ecstasy of being thirteen   **S C**
Such things happen. Schwartz, A.
In Schwartz, A. Scary stories 3; more tales to chill your bones p39-43   **398.2**
Sucker. McCullers, C.
In Who do you think you are?; stories of friends and enemies p122-33   **S C**
Sudan
Levy, P. M. Sudan (5 and up)   **962.4**

Sudan—*Continued*

Fiction

Levitin, S. Dream freedom — **Fic**

Suellentrop, Tricia

(jt. auth) Jones, P. Connecting young adults and libraries — **027.62**

Suffrage

See also Women—Suffrage

Sugarcane fire. Rice, D.

In Rice, D. Crazy loco; stories about growing up Chicano in southern Texas p1-13 — **S C**

Sugihara, Chiune *See* Sugihara, Sempo, 1900-1986

Sugihara, Sempo, 1900-1986

See/See also pages in the following book(s):

Lyman, D. Holocaust rescuers — **920**

Suicide

Runyon, B. The burn journals (7 and up) — **92**

Suicide: opposing viewpoints (7 and up) — **362.28**

Fiction

Connelly, N. O. St. Michael's scales (7 and up) — **Fic**

Draper, S. M. Tears of a tiger (7 and up) — **Fic**

Fine, A. Up on cloud nine (5 and up) — **Fic**

Holt, K. W. Keeper of the night (7 and up) — **Fic**

Miller, M. B. Aimee (7 and up) — **Fic**

Poetry

Fields, T. After the death of Anna Gonzales (7 and up) — **811**

Glenn, M. Split image: a story in poems (7 and up) — **811**

Suicide: opposing viewpoints (7 and up) — **362.28**

The **suitcase** kid. Wilson, J. — **Fic**

Suleiman I, Sultan of the Turks, 1495-1566 *See* Süleyman I, Sultan of the Turks, 1495-1566

Süleyman I, Sultan of the Turks, 1495-1566

About

Greenblatt, M. Süleyman the Magnificent and the Ottoman Empire — **956.1**

Süleyman the Magnificent and the Ottoman Empire. Greenblatt, M. — **956.1**

Sulfur *See* Sulphur

Sulfur. Blashfield, J. F.

In Blashfield, J. F. Sparks of life; chemical elements that make life possible — **546**

Sullivan, Anne Marie

Albert Einstein (4 and up) — **92**

Sullivan, Charles, 1933-

(ed) Here is my kingdom. See Here is my kingdom — **810.8**

Sullivan, Edward T.

Reaching reluctant young adult readers — **028.5**

Sullivan, George, 1933-

Abraham Lincoln (4 and up) — **92**

All about hockey (5 and up) — **796.962**

The Civil War at sea — **973.7**

Paul Revere — **92**

Picturing Lincoln — **92**

Power football — **920**

Sullivan, Helen

Research reports (7 and up) — **808**

Sullivan, L. B.

About

Fireside, H. New York Times v. Sullivan (7 and up) — **342**

Sullivan, Otha Richard, 1941-

African American inventors (5 and up) — **920**

African American millionaires — **920**

African American women scientists and inventors — **920**

Sullivan, Paul, 1939-

Maata's journal (7 and up) — **Fic**

Sulphur

Beatty, R. Sulfur

In The Elements — **546**

Blashfield, J. F. Sulfur

In Blashfield, J. F. Sparks of life; chemical elements that make life possible — **546**

Sumerians

See/See also pages in the following book(s):

Moss, C. Science in ancient Mesopotamia (4 and up) — **509**

Sumitani, Masamine

See/See also pages in the following book(s):

Hamanaka, S. In search of the spirit (5 and up) — **920**

Summer

Fiction

Conly, J. L. Trout summer (5 and up) — **Fic**

Summer camps *See* Camps

Summer employment

See also Teenagers—Employment

Fiction

Gauthier, G. Saving the planet & stuff — **Fic**

Summer girl. Whiteman, R. H.

In Talking leaves; contemporary native American short stories — **S C**

Summer of love. Klause, A. C.

In The Color of absence; 12 stories about loss and hope p1-14 — **S C**

Summer of my German soldier. Greene, B. — **Fic**

Summer of my Korean soldier. Lee, M. G.

In American eyes; new Asian-American short stories for young adults p37-48 — **S C**

The **summer** of Riley. Bunting, E. — **Fic**

Summer of the monkeys. Rawls, W. — **Fic**

The **summer** of the swans. Byars, B. C. — **Fic**

Summer secrets. Hermes, P. — **Fic**

Summerland. Chabon, M. — **Fic**

Sun

Gardner, R. Science project ideas about the sun — **523.7**

Miller, R. The sun — **523.7**

Spangenburg, R. The sun — **523.7**

Sun & Spoon. Henkes, K. — **Fic**

Sun and Moon. Lester, J.
    In Lester, J. When the beginning began; stories about God, the creatures, and us p11-17 **296.1**

Sun-Girl and Dragon-Prince. Tchana, K. H.
    In Tchana, K. H. The serpent slayer: and other stories of strong women p77-83
        398.2

Super structures. Malam, J.   **624**

Super women in science. Di Domenico, K.
        920

Superboy. Crutcher, C.
    In Ultimate sports; short stories by outstanding writers for young adults p51-67
        S C

Supercomputers
    Billings, C. W. Supercomputers   **004**

Supercroc and the origin of crocodiles. Sloan, C.
        567.9

The **superior** pet. Yep, L.
    In Yep, L. The rainbow people p80-85
        398.2

Superman (Comic strip)
    Beatty, S. Superman   **741.5**

Supernatural
    Steiger, B. Gale encyclopedia of the unusual and unexplained   **130**
        Fiction
    Allende, I. City of the beasts (7 and up)
        Fic
    Avi. The Book Without Words (5 and up)
        Fic
    Brooks, B. Throwing smoke   **Fic**
    Cooper, S. The Boggart (4 and up)   **Fic**
    De Lint, C. Waifs and strays (7 and up)
        S C
    Duncan, L. Stranger with my face (7 and up)
        Fic
    Farmer, N. A girl named Disaster (6 and up)
        Fic
    Gaiman, N. Coraline (5 and up)   **Fic**
    Horowitz, A. Raven's gate (7 and up)   **Fic**
    Kindl, P. Owl in love (6 and up)   **Fic**
    Littke, L. Haunted sister (7 and up)   **Fic**
    Lyon, G. E. Gina.Jamie.Father.Bear   **Fic**
    McDonald, J. Shades of Simon Gray (7 and up)
        Fic
    Mowry, J. Ghost train   **Fic**
    Pullman, P. Clockwork (4 and up)   **Fic**
    Slade, A. G. Dust   **Fic**
    Snyder, Z. K. The Unseen (5 and up)   **Fic**
    Vande Velde, V. Being dead (7 and up)
        S C
    Wooding, C. The haunting of Alaizabel Cray (7 and up)   **Fic**
    Wrede, P. C. Sorcery and Cecelia, or, The enchanted chocolate pot (7 and up)   **Fic**

Superstition
    Hughes, M. Popular superstitions   **398**

Superstructures. See Corbishley, M. The world of architectural wonders   **720**

Suppressants, Appetite *See* Appetite depressants

Supreme Court (U.S.) *See* United States. Supreme Court

The **Supreme** Court. Horn, G.   **347**

The **Supreme** Court A to Z   **347**

Supreme Court cases through primary sources [series]
    Anderson, W. Brown v. Board of Education
        344
    Anderson, W. Plessy v. Ferguson   **342**
    Donnelly, K. J. Cruzan v. Missouri   **344**
    Hulm, D. United States v. the Amistad   **326**
    Payment, S. Roe v. Wade   **344**
    Sonneborn, L. Miranda v. Arizona   **345**

Supreme Court decisions [series]
    Dudley, M. E. Engel v. Vitale (1962)   **344**
    Gold, J. C. Board of Education v. Pico (1982)   **344**
    Gold, S. D. In re Gault (1967)   **345**
    Gold, S. D. Miranda v. Arizona (1966)   **345**

Supreme Court drama. Brannen, D. E.   **347**

Supreme Court milestones [series]
    Gold, S. D. Brown v. Board of Education
        344
    Gold, S. D. Roe v. Wade   **344**
    Naden, C. J. Dred Scott   **342**

Sure-to-win science fair projects. Rhatigan, J.
        507.8

Surface, Mary Hall
    Short scenes and monologues for middle school actors   **812**

The **surgeon.** Dahl, R.
    In Dahl, R. Skin and other stories   **S C**

Surgeons
    Schraff, A. E. Dr. Charles Drew   **92**

Surgery
    Giddens, S. Future techniques in surgery
        617

Suriname
    Fridell, R. The search for poison-dart frogs (4-6)
        597.8

The **surprise** guest. Stine, R. L.
    In Beware!; R.L. Stine picks his favorite scary stories p39-53   **808.8**

Surrogate mothers
    See/See also pages in the following book(s):
    Biomedical ethics: opposing viewpoints (7 and up)   **174.2**

Surveillance. MccGwire, S.   **323.44**

Surveying
    Morrison, T. The coast mappers (5 and up)
        623.89

Survival after airplane accidents, shipwrecks, etc.
        Fiction
    Defoe, D. Robinson Crusoe (7 and up)   **Fic**
    Golding, W. Lord of the Flies   **Fic**
    Kehret, P. The secret journey   **Fic**
    Mikaelsen, B. Red midnight   **Fic**
    Morgan, C. The boy who spoke dog (5 and up)
        Fic
    Morpurgo, M. Kensuke's kingdom (4 and up)
        Fic
    Paulsen, G. Hatchet   **Fic**
    Taylor, T. The cay (5 and up)   **Fic**
    Taylor, T. Sweet Friday Island (7 and up)
        Fic

Survival after airplane accidents, shipwrecks, etc.—Fiction—*Continued*
Taylor, T. Timothy of the cay (5 and up)
    Fic

Survival in the storm. Janke, K.   Fic
Surviving Antarctica. White, A.   Fic
Surviving Hitler. Warren, A.   940.53
Surviving in the rain forest. Castner, J. L.
    577.3
Surviving the Applewhites. Tolan, S. S.   Fic
The **Susan** B. Anthony women's voting rights trial. Monroe, J.   324.6
Susanna and Simon. San Souci, R.
    In San Souci, R. Cut from the same cloth; American women of myth, legend, and tall tale p43-48   398.2
Susannah and the elders. Jaffe, N.
    In Jaffe, N. and Zeitlin, S. J. The cow of no color: riddle stories and justice tales from around the world p40-46   398.2
Sussman, Art
    Dr. Art's guide to planet earth   577
Sustainable world [series]
    Bowden, R. Energy   333.79
    Bowden, R. Food and farming   363.8
    Bowden, R. Waste   363.7
Sutcliff, Rosemary, 1920-1992
    The light beyond the forest (4 and up)
    398.2
    The road to Camlann (4 and up)   398.2
    The sword and the circle (4 and up)   398.2
    Sword song (7 and up)   Fic
Sutherland, Zena, 1915-2002
    Children and books   028.5
Suth's story. Dickinson, P.
    In Dickinson, P. The kin p1-45   Fic
Sutton, Wendy K.
    (jt. auth) Bouchard, D. The gift of reading
    372.4
Suu Kyi *See* Aung San Suu Kyi
Suzuki, Shin'ichi, 1898-1998
    About
    Collins, D. R. Dr. Shinichi Suzuki   92
Swallow, Pamela Curtis
    It only looks easy   Fic
Swallowing stones. McDonald, J.   Fic
Swan, Vol. 1. Ariyoshi, K.   741.5
Swans
    Osborn, E. Project UltraSwan (4 and up)
    598
Swanson, Julie A., 1964-
    Going for the record (7 and up)   Fic
A **sweatshop** during the industrial revolution. Woog, A.   331.2
Sweden
    Gan, D. Sweden (5 and up)   948.5
Sweeney, Joyce, 1955-
    Something old, something new
    In Destination unexpected: short stories
    S C

Sweet, Melissa
    (il) Thimmesh, C. Girls think of everything
    920
    (il) Thimmesh, C. The sky's the limit   500
Sweet Betsey from Pike. San Souci, R.
    In San Souci, R. Cut from the same cloth; American women of myth, legend, and tall tale p57-64   398.2
Sweet Friday Island. Taylor, T.   Fic
The **sweet** perfume of good-bye. Kerr, M. E.
    In Visions: nineteen short stories by outstanding writers for young adults p186-91
    S C
Sweet victory: Lance Armstrong's incredible journey. Stewart, M.   92
Sweetblood. Hautman, P.   Fic
Sweeter than honey, purer than oil. Kimmel, E. A.
    In Kimmel, E. A. The jar of fools: eight Hanukkah stories from Chelm p9-12
    S C
"**Swept** and garnished". Kipling, R.
    In McCaffrey, A. {The Pern series}   S C
Swift, Jonathan, 1667-1745
    Gulliver's travels (7 and up)   Fic
Swift-Runner and the trickster Tarantula. Brown, D. A.
    In Brown, D. A. Dee Brown's folktales of the Native American; retold for our times p115-23   398.2
Swifter, higher, stronger. Macy, S.   796.48
Swimming
    Fiction
    Crutcher, C. Staying fat for Sarah Byrnes
    Fic
    Crutcher, C. Stotan! (7 and up)   Fic
    Crutcher, C. Whale talk (7 and up)   Fic
Swimming to America. Mead, A.   Fic
Swimming upstream. Brant, B.
    In Talking leaves; contemporary native American short stories   S C
Swimming upstream. George, K. O.   811
Swimming with hammerhead sharks. Mallory, K.
    597
Swinburne, Stephen R.
    Once a wolf (4 and up)   333.95
    The woods scientist (4 and up)   591.7
Swindlers. Blackwood, G. L.   364.1
Swindlers and swindling
    Blackwood, G. L. Swindlers   364.1
    Schroeder, A. Scams! (5 and up)   364.1
    Fiction
    Collier, J. L. Me and Billy (5 and up)   Fic
Swisher, Clarice, 1933-
    (ed) Albert Einstein. See Albert Einstein [essays about]   92
    (ed) Primary sources. See Primary sources [Lucent library of historical eras. Elizabethan England]   942.05
Swissler, Becky
    Winning lacrosse for girls (7 and up)
    796.34

Switzerland
Fiction
Creech, S. Bloomability (5 and up)   **Fic**
The **sword**. Alexander, L.
  In Alexander, L. The foundling and other
    tales of Prydain p53-62   **S C**
The **sword** and the circle. Sutcliff, R.   **398.2**
The **sword** in the stone. Osborne, M. P.
  In Osborne, M. P. Favorite medieval tales
    p17-24   **398.2**
The **sword** in the stone. White, T. H.
  In White, T. H. The once and future king
          Fic
Sword of the rightful king. Yolen, J.   **Fic**
Sword of the samurai. Kimmel, E. A.   **S C**
Sword song. Sutcliff, R.   **Fic**
Swortzell, Lowell
  The mischief makers
    In Theatre for young audiences; 20 great
      plays for children p183-216   **812.008**
SylvieSylvieSylvie. Saldaña, R.
  In Saldaña, R. Finding our way: stories p20-
    28   **S C**
Symbiosis
  Silverstein, A. Symbiosis   **577.8**
Symbols *See* Signs and symbols
Symes, R. F.
  Crystal & gem (5 and up)   **548**
  Eyewitness rocks & minerals (5 and up)
          549
Symons, Ann K.
  Protecting the right to read   **025.2**
Synesthesia
  Fiction
  Mass, W. A mango-shaped space   **Fic**
Szeptycki, Andreas *See* Sheptyts´kyĭ, Andriĭ,
  1865-1944

T

T-H-U-P-P-P-P-P-P-P-P!. Schwartz, A.
  In Schwartz, A. Scary stories 3; more tales to
    chill your bones p86-88   **398.2**
Taback, Simms, 1932-
  See/See also pages in the following book(s):
  The Newbery & Caldecott medal books, 1986-
    2000   **028.5**
Tabak, John
  A look at earth   **550**
  A look at Neptune   **523.4**
Tackach, James, 1954-
  The abolition of American slavery (7 and up)
          326
  The Emancipation Proclamation (7 and up)
          973.7
Tadpoles. Pascoe, E.   **597.8**
Taft, Robert A., 1889-1953
  See/See also pages in the following book(s):
  Kennedy, J. F. Profiles in courage   **920**
Tagliaferro, Linda
  Genetic engineering (7 and up)   **576.5**

Thomas Edison (7 and up)   **92**
Tahiti (French Polynesia)
  NgCheong-Lum, R. Tahiti (5 and up)   **996**
Tai chi morning. Grimes, N.   **811**
Taiga. Sayre, A. P.   **577.3**
The **tail**. Philip, N.
  In Philip, N. Celtic fairy tales p[140]
          398.2
Taino Indians
  Fiction
  Dorris, M. Morning Girl (4 and up)   **Fic**
**Taitu, Empress, consort of Menelik II, Negus of
  Ethiopia, d. 1918**
  See/See also pages in the following book(s):
  Hansen, J. African princess (5 and up)   **920**
Taj Mahal (Agra, India)
  DuTemple, L. A. The Taj Mahal   **726**
Takeoffs and landings. Haddix, M. P.   **Fic**
Taking care of business. Hill, K. S.
  In Talking leaves; contemporary native
    American short stories   **S C**
Taking care of Terrific. Lowry, L.   **Fic**
Taking care of things. Brisson, P.
  In Don't cramp my style; stories about that
    time of the month p15 33   **S C**
Taking liberty. Rinaldi, A.   **Fic**
Taking sides. Soto, G.   **Fic**
Taking Terri Mueller. Mazer, N. F.   **Fic**
Talbott, Hudson
  Forging freedom (4 and up)   **940.53**
  Leonardo's horse (4 and up)   **730.9**
The **tale** of the swamp rat. Crocker, C.   **Fic**
The **tales** fossils tell. Gallant, J. R.   **560**
Tales from Gold Mountain. Yee, P.   **S C**
Tales from Shakespeare. Lamb, C.   **822.3**
Tales from Shakespeare. Packer, T.   **822.3**
Tales from Shakespeare. Williams, M.   **822.3**
Tales from the Brothers Grimm and the Sisters
  Weird. Vande Velde, V.   **S C**
Tales of court and castle. Bodger, J.   **398.2**
Tales of Edgar Allan Poe. Poe, E. A.   **S C**
Talk about books!. Knowles, E.   **372.4**
Talk that talk: an anthology of African-American
  storytelling   **398.2**
Talk to me. Avi
  In Avi. What do fish have to do with any-
    thing? and other stories p61-91   **S C**
Talk to the deaf. See Riekehof, L. L. The joy of
  signing   **419**
The **talking** cooter. Hamilton, V.
  In Hamilton, V. The people could fly;
    American black folktales p151-55
          398.2
Talking drums (5 and up)   **896**
The **talking** earth. George, J. C.   **Fic**
Talking grapes, smiling apples, and ringing apri-
  cots. Molnár, I.
  In Molnár, I. One-time dog market at Buda
    and other Hungarian folktales p71-78
          398.2
Talking leaves   **S C**

Talking points [series]
Grant, R. G. Genocide   303.6

Talking with artists {I-III}   741.6

Talking with Tebé: Clementine Hunter, memory artist. Lyons, M. E.   92

The **tall** Mexican: the life of Hank Aguirre, all-star pitcher, businessman, humanitarian. Copley, B.   92

Tall Mountain, Mary See TallMountain, Mary, 1918-1994

Tall tales
San Souci, R. Cut from the same cloth (4 and up)   398.2

TallMountain, Mary, 1918-1994
Snatched away
    In Talking leaves; contemporary native American short stories   S C

Tamai, Tony Leonard
(il) Cover, A. B. Macbeth   741.5

Tamar, Erika
The midnight train home   Fic

The **tamarack** tree. Clapp, P.   Fic

Tames, Richard
Nationalism (7 and up)   320.5

Tamez, Modesto, 1947-
(jt. auth) Bazin, M. Math and science across cultures   510

Taming the Star Runner. Hinton, S. E.   Fic

Tan, Amy
Rules of the game
    In Leaving home: stories p35-52   808.8
         About
Shields, C. J. Amy Tan   92

Tanacredi, John T.
(ed) Experiment central. See Experiment central   507.8

Tanaka, Shelley
Attack on Pearl Harbor (4 and up)   940.54
Earthquake! (4 and up)   979.4
Graveyards of the dinosaurs (4-6)   567.9
Lost temple of the Aztecs (4 and up)   972
Secrets of the mummies (4 and up)   393
(jt. auth) Augustyn, F. Footnotes   792.8
(jt. auth) Beattie, O. Buried in ice   998

Taney, Kimberly Bolan
Teen spaces   022

Tangents. Bear, G.
    In New skies: an anthology of today's science fiction   S C

Tangerine. Bloor, E.   Fic

Tangled notes in watermelon. Regan, D. C.
    In What a song can do; 12 riffs on the power of music   S C

Tanks (Military science) See Military tanks

Tanner, Tim
(il) Clark, W. Off the map   978

Tanzania
Heale, J. Tanzania (5 and up)   967.8
McCulla, P. E. Tanzania   967.8

Taoism
Hartz, P. Taoism   299.5

See/See also pages in the following book(s):
Osborne, M. P. One world, many religions (4 and up)   201

Tappin, the land turtle. Hamilton, V.
    In Hamilton, V. The people could fly; American black folktales p20-25   398.2

A **tarantula** in my purse. George, J. C.   92

The **tarantula** scientist. Montgomery, S.   595.4

Tarantulas
Montgomery, S. The tarantula scientist (4 and up)   595.4

Tarbell, Ida M., 1857-1944
         About
Somervill, B. A. Ida Tarbell   92

Tarter, Jill Cornell, 1944-
         About
Jackson, E. B. Looking for life in the universe (4 and up)   576.8

Tashjian, Janet, 1956-
The gospel according to Larry (7 and up)   Fic
Multiple choice   Fic

Taste
Silverstein, A. Smelling and tasting
    In Silverstein, A. and others. Senses and sensors [series]   612.8

Tata Ajach, Queen of Dahomey
See/See also pages in the following book(s):
Hansen, J. African princess (5 and up)   920

Tate, Eleanora E., 1948-
African American musicians   920

A **tattoo** on her heart. De Lint, C.
    In De Lint, C. Waifs and strays p139-49   S C

Tattooing
Mason, P. Body piercing and tattooing   391
Wilkinson, B. Coping with the dangers of tattooing, body piercing, and branding   617.9

Taussig, Helen Brooke, 1898-1986
See/See also pages in the following book(s):
Lindop, L. Scientists and doctors (7 and up)   920

Taylor, Barbara, 1954-
Animal giants (5 and up)   590

Taylor, C. J. (Carrie J.), 1952-
Peace walker   398.2

Taylor, David
The Cold War   909.82

Taylor, Julie, 1971-
The girls' guide to friends   158

Taylor, M. W. (Marian W.)
Chief Joseph   92
Harriet Tubman   92

Taylor, Maureen, 1955-
Through the eyes of your ancestors (4 and up)   929

Taylor, Mildred D.
The friendship (4 and up)   Fic
The gold Cadillac (4 and up)   Fic
The land (7 and up)   Fic
Let the circle be unbroken (4 and up)   Fic
Mississippi bridge (4 and up)   Fic

Taylor, Mildred D.—*Continued*
The road to Memphis (4 and up)   **Fic**
Roll of thunder, hear my cry   **Fic**
Song of the trees (4 and up)   **Fic**
The well (4 and up)   **Fic**
About
Crowe, C. Presenting Mildred D. Taylor (7 and up)   **813.009**
Taylor, Patricia, 1952-
(jt. auth) Jones, P. A core collection for young adults   **011.6**
Taylor, Paul D., 1953-
Fossil (4 and up)   **560**
Taylor, Robert, 1948-
History of terrorism (7 and up)   **303.6**
Taylor, Susie King, 1848-1912
The diary of Susie King Taylor, Civil War nurse (5 and up)   **973.7**
Taylor, Theodore, 1921-
The cay (5 and up)   **Fic**
The grind of an axe
In Night terrors; stories of shadow and substance   **S C**
Lord of the Kill   **Fic**
Rogue wave and other red-blooded sea stories   **S C**
Contents: Rogue wave; Hauling gold; Wingman, fly me down; Out there; Hating Hansen; The butcher; The schoolie; The O'Tannenbaum Affair
Sweet Friday Island (7 and up)   **Fic**
Timothy of the cay (5 and up)   **Fic**
Tchana, Katrin Hyman, 1963-
The serpent slayer: and other stories of strong women   **398.2**
Contents: The serpent slayer; The barber's wife; Nesoowa and the Chenoo; Clever Marcela; Sister Lace; The rebel princess; Beebyecbyee and the Water God; Kate Crackernuts; The old woman and the Devil; The magic lake; Grandmother's skull; Three whiskers from a lion's chin; Duffy the Lady; Sun-Girl and Dragon-Prince; Staver and Vassilissa; Tokoyo; The lord's daughter and the blacksmith's son; The marriage of two masters
Tchen, Richard
(jt. auth) Napoli, D. J. Spinners   **Fic**
Tea party ends in bloody massacre, film at 11. Maguire, G.
In Shelf life: stories by the book p67-80   **S C**
Teach, Edward *See* Blackbeard, 1680?-1718
Teacher tamer. Avi
In Avi. What do fish have to do with anything? and other stories p93-119   **S C**
Teachers
Fiction
Avi. Don't you know there's a war on? (4 and up)   **Fic**
Danziger, P. The cat ate my gymsuit   **Fic**
Flake, S. G. The skin I'm in   **Fic**
Frank, E. R. Friction (7 and up)   **Fic**
Jocelyn, M. Mable Riley (5 and up)   **Fic**
Kindl, P. Owl in love (6 and up)   **Fic**
Murphy, J. My face to the wind   **Fic**
Peck, R. The teacher's funeral (5 and up)   **Fic**
Ray, D. Ghost girl (5 and up)   **Fic**
The **teacher's** funeral. Peck, R.   **Fic**

Teaching
Aids and devices
Barron, A. E. Technologies for education   **371.3**
Teaching and learning about computers. Barrett, J. R.   **004**
Teaching at home *See* Home schooling
Teaching banned books. Scales, P. R.   **323.44**
Teaching teams
Harada, V. H. Inquiry learning through librarian-teacher partnerships   **371.1**
Teaching the Internet in libraries. Gordon, R. S.   **025.04**
Teacup full of roses. Mathis, S. B.   **Fic**
Tearing down the unicorns. Simner, J. L.
In A Glory of unicorns p31-42   **S C**
Tears of a tiger. Draper, S. M.   **Fic**
Tears of the salamander. Dickinson, P.   **Fic**
Teatime. Delacre, L.
In Delacre, L. Salsa stories p37-43   **S C**
Tech jacket, Vol. 1: Lost & found. Kirkman, R.   **741.5**
Techies [series]
Ehrenhaft, D. Larry Ellison   **92**
Ehrenhaft, D. Marc Andreessen   **92**
Sherman, J. Jerry Yang and David Filo   **92**
Technically involved. Braun, L. W.   **027.62**
Technologies for education. Barron, A. E.   **371.3**
Technology
See also Engineering
Inside a—   **600**
Macaulay, D. The new way things work (4 and up)   **600**
Ross, S. The technology of World War I   **940.3**
Shcehan, S. The technology of World War II   **940.54**
U.X.L science fact finder   **500**
Encyclopedias
Encyclopedia of technology and applied sciences   **603**
Engelbert, P. Technology in action   **603**
Exploring technology (5 and up)   **603**
How it works: science and technology   **603**
History
Crosher, J. Technology in the time of ancient Egypt   **609**
Crosher, J. Technology in the time of ancient Greece   **609**
Crosher, J. Technology in the time of the Maya   **609**
Hicks, P. Technology in the time of the Vikings   **609**
Ochoa, G. The Wilson chronology of science and technology   **502**
Popular science: science year by year   **509**
Science, technology, and society: the impact of science in the 20th century   **509**
Snedden, R. Technology in the time of ancient Rome   **609**

Technology and civilization
Science, technology, and society: the impact of science in the 20th century **509**
Fiction
Huxley, A. Brave new world (7 and up)   **Fic**
Technology—blueprints of the future [series]
Joseph, L. M. Skyscrapers: inside and out **720**
Technology in action. Engelbert, P.   **603**
Technology in the time of ancient Egypt. Crosher, J.   **609**
Technology in the time of ancient Greece. Crosher, J.   **609**
Technology in the time of ancient Rome. Snedden, R.   **609**
Technology in the time of the Maya. Crosher, J.   **609**
Technology in the time of the Vikings. Hicks, P.   **609**
The **technology** of World War I. Ross, S.   **940.3**
The **technology** of World War II. Sheehan, S.   **940.54**
Tecumseh, Shawnee Chief, 1768-1813
Fiction
Alder, E. Crossing the panther's path   **Fic**
Teeing up. Brooks, B.
In Brooks, B. All that remains p117-68   **Fic**
Teen age *See* Adolescence
Teen alcoholism (7 and up)   **362.292**
Teen alcoholism. Sheen, B.   **616.86**
Teen beauty secrets. Irons, D.   **646.7**
Teen Book Project
Bell, R. Changing bodies, changing lives   **613.9**
Teen consumer smarts. Menhard, F. R.   **332.024**
Teen decisions [series]
Pregnancy   **362.7**
Teen depression. Wolff, L.   **616.85**
Teen dream jobs. Coon, N.   **650.14**
Teen dreams   **612.6**
Teen eating disorder prevention book [series]
Walker, P. Understanding the risk of diet drugs   **616.85**
Teen eating disorders. Vollstadt, E. W.   **616.85**
Teen genreflecting. Herald, D. T.   **016.8**
Teen health library of eating disorder prevention [series]
Barrett, C. The dangers of diet drugs and other weight-loss products   **615**
Davis, B. What's real, what's ideal   **616.85**
Drohan, M. I. Weight-loss programs   **616.85**
Frankenberger, E. Food and love   **616.85**
Smith, E. Anorexia nervosa   **616.85**
Teen health series
Diet information for teens   **613.2**
Mental health information for teens   **616.89**
Skin health information for teens   **616.5**
Sports injuries information for teens   **617.1**

Teen issues [series]
Dougherty, K. The rules to be cool   **395**
Frissell, S. Eating disorders and weight control   **616.85**
Hinds, M. J. Focus on body image   **306.4**
Menhard, F. R. Teen consumer smarts   **332.024**
Schultz, M. A. Teens with single parents   **306.8**
Sheen, B. Teen alcoholism   **616.86**
Spangenburg, R. Propaganda   **303.3**
Veladota, C. Teen runaways   **362.7**
Vollstadt, E. W. Teen eating disorders   **616.85**
Wolff, L. Teen depression   **616.85**
Teen knitting club. Wenger, J.   **746.43**
Teen library events. Edwards, K.   **027.62**
Teen pregnancy. Hurley, J. A.   **362.7**
Teen pregnancy prevention library [series]
Trapani, M. Listen up!   **306.8**
Trapani, M. Reality check   **306.8**
Teen prostitution. Dean, R.   **362.7**
Teen runaways. Veladota, C.   **362.7**
Teen spaces. Taney, K. B.   **022**
Teen sunshine reflections   **808.8**
Teen volunteer services in libraries. Gillespie, K. M.   **021.2**
Teen witnesses to the Holocaust [series]
Ayer, E. H. In the ghettos   **940.53**
Kustanowitz, E. The hidden children of the Holocaust   **940.53**
Teenage fathers
Trapani, M. Reality check (7 and up)   **306.8**
Fiction
Johnson, A. The first part last (7 and up)   **Fic**
Teenage gangs *See* Gangs
The **teenage** guy's survival guide. Daldry, J.   **305.23**
Teenage mothers
Bode, J. Kids still having kids   **362.7**
Edelson, P. Straight talk about teenage pregnancy (7 and up)   **362.7**
Teenage pregnancy: opposing viewpoints (7 and up)   **362.7**
Trapani, M. Listen up! (7 and up)   **306.8**
Fiction
Lawrence, I. The lightkeeper's daughter (7 and up)   **Fic**
McDonald, J. Spellbound (7 and up)   **Fic**
Olsen, S. The girl with a baby (7 and up)   **Fic**
Williams-Garcia, R. Like sisters on the homefront (7 and up)   **Fic**
Wolff, V. E. Make lemonade   **Fic**
Teenage pregnancy
Bode, J. Kids still having kids   **362.7**
Edelson, P. Straight talk about teenage pregnancy (7 and up)   **362.7**
Hurley, J. A. Teen pregnancy (7 and up)   **362.7**
Pregnancy (7 and up)   **362.7**
Teenage pregnancy: opposing viewpoints (7 and up)   **362.7**

Teenage pregnancy—*Continued*
Trapani, M. Listen up! (7 and up) **306.8**
See/See also pages in the following book(s):
Teens at risk: opposing viewpoints p63-105 (7
and up) **362.7**
Teenage pregnancy: opposing viewpoints (7 and
up) **362.7**
Teenagers
See also Runaway teenagers
Bode, J. The colors of freedom **305.8**
Busby, C. Getting dumped and getting over it!
(7 and up) **646.7**
Erlbach, A. The middle school survival guide
373.1
Hartman, H. Girlwonder (5 and up) **305.23**
Jones, C. Every girl tells a story **305.23**
Piquemal, M. When life stinks **305.23**
Teens at risk: opposing viewpoints p63-105 (7
and up) **362.7**
What are you? (7 and up) **305.8**
You be me (7 and up) **305.23**
Alcohol use
Sheen, B. Teen alcoholism (7 and up)
616.86
Teen alcoholism (7 and up) **362.292**
Books and reading
Bodart, J. R. Radical reads **028.5**
Bromann, J. Booktalking that works **028.5**
Herald, D. T. Teen genreflecting **016.8**
Honnold, R. 101+ teen programs that work
027.62
Kan, K. Sizzling summer reading programs for
young adults **027.62**
Knowles, E. Reading rules! **028.5**
Larson, J. C. Bringing mysteries alive for chil-
dren and young adults **028.5**
Serritella, J. Look again! **373.1**
Sullivan, E. T. Reaching reluctant young adult
readers **028.5**
Drug use
See/See also pages in the following book(s):
Teens at risk: opposing viewpoints p63-105 (7
and up) **362.7**
Employment
Zielin, L. Make things happen **302.2**
Health and hygiene
Diet information for teens (7 and up) **613.2**
Mental health information for teens (7 and up)
616.89
Vedral, J. L. Toning for teens (7 and up)
613.7

Psychology
See Adolescent psychology
Religious life
Gaskins, P. I believe in— **200**
Teenagers' library services *See* Young adults' li-
braries
Teenagers' writings
City of one (7 and up) **810.8**
The Pain tree, and other teenage angst-ridden
poetry (7 and up) **811.008**
Paint me like I am (7 and up) **811.008**
Sidman, J. The world according to dog
810.8
Things I have to tell you (7 and up) **810.8**

You hear me? (7 and up) **810.8**
Teens at risk: opposing viewpoints (7 and up)
362.7
Teens cook. Carle, M. **641.5**
Teens.library. Braun, L. W. **027.62**
Teens @ the library series
Braun, L. W. Hooking teens with the Net
025.04
Bromann, J. Booktalking that works **028.5**
Honnold, R. 101+ teen programs that work
027.62
Jones, P. A core collection for young adults
011.6
Jones, P. Do it right! **027.62**
Mondowney, J. G. Hold them in your heart
027.62
A **teen's** vegetarian cookbook. Krizmanic, J.
641.5
Teens with single parents. Schultz, M. A.
306.8
Teitelbaum, Michael, 1953-
Great moments in women's sports **796**
Telecommunication
Graham, I. Global networks **384**
Telegraph
Coe, L. The telegraph **621.383**
Telescopes
Matloff, G. L. More telescope power **522**
Television
Graham, I. Radio and television **621.384**
McPherson, S. S. TV's forgotten hero: the story
of Philo Farnsworth **92**
See/See also pages in the following book(s):
Mass media: opposing viewpoints **302.23**
Equipment and supplies
See also Video recording
Fiction
Atinsky, S. Tyler on prime time (5 and up)
Fic
Television actors *See* Actors
Television and children
See/See also pages in the following book(s):
Mass media: opposing viewpoints **302.23**
Television broadcasting of news
Garner, J. We interrupt this broadcast **070.1**
Spangenburg, R. TV news (7 and up) **070.1**
Tell all the children our story. Bolden, T.
305.8
Tell freedom [excerpt] Abrahams, P.
In Somehow tenderness survives; stories of
Southern Africa p7-18 **S C**
The **tell-tale** heart. Poe, E. A.
In Poe, E. A. Tales of Edgar Allan Poe p19-
25 **S C**
also in Poe, E. A. The pit and the pendulum
and other stories **S C**
Temperate deciduous forest. Sayre, A. P.
577.3
Temperate forests. Allaby, M. **577.3**
Temperate grasslands. Hoare, B. **577.4**
Temperature
Gardner, R. Science projects about temperature
and heat (7 and up) **536**

Temple, Charles A.
Children's books in children's hands. See Children's books in children's hands   **028.5**

Temple, Frances, 1945-1995
The Beduins' gazelle   **Fic**
The Ramsay scallop (6 and up)   **Fic**
Tonight, by sea (6 and up)   **Fic**

Temple, Lewis, 1800-1854
See/See also pages in the following book(s):
Aaseng, N. Black inventors (7 and up)   **920**

Temples
DuTemple, L. A. The Pantheon (5 and up)   **726**

Ten Hispanic American authors. Hill, C. M.   **920**

Ten kings. Meltzer, M.   **920**

Ten queens. Meltzer, M.   **920**

The **Ten** serpents
In Hearne, B. G. Beauties and beasts p120-23   **398.2**

Ten thousand children. Fox, A. L.   **940.53**

Tender. Hobbs, V.   **Fic**

Tending the fire: the story of Maria Martinez. Morris, J.   **92**

Tending to Grace. Fusco, K. N.   **Fic**

Tenement. Bial, R.   **974.7**

Tenenbaum, Barbara A., 1946-
(ed) Latin America, history and culture. See Latin America, history and culture   **980**

TenNapel, Douglas R.
Tommysaurus Rex   **741.5**

Tennessee
Barrett, T. Tennessee
In Celebrate the states   **973**
Kent, D. Tennessee
In America the beautiful, second series   **973**
Fiction
Barrett, T. Cold in summer (5 and up)   **Fic**
Bennett, C. A heart divided (7 and up)   **Fic**
Bradley, K. B. Weaver's daughter (5 and up)   **Fic**
Dowell, F. O. Where I'd like to be (4 and up)   **Fic**
Keehn, S. M. Gnat Stokes and the Foggy Bottom Swamp Queen (5 and up)   **Fic**

Tennis
Douglas, P. Tennis (7 and up)   **796.342**
Williams, V. How to play tennis (5 and up)   **796.342**
Williams, V. Venus & Serena (7 and up)   **92**
Fiction
Adler, C. S. Winning   **Fic**
Corbet, R. Fifteen love (7 and up)   **Fic**
Konomi, T. The Prince of Tennis, Vol. 1   **741.5**

Tension (Psychology) *See* Stress (Psychology)

Tepee tales of the American Indian. See Brown, D. A. Dee Brown's folktales of the Native American   **398.2**

Terban, Marvin
Building your vocabulary (4 and up)   **428**

Scholastic dictionary of idioms (4 and up)   **423**
Scholastic dictionary of spelling (4 and up)   **428**

Teresa, Mother, 1910-1997
About
Ruth, A. Mother Teresa   **92**

Terezin (Czechoslovakia: Concentration camp)
—I never saw another butterfly—   **741.9**

Terkel, Marni
What's an "A" anyway? (7 and up)   **371.2**

Terkel, Susan Neiburg, 1948-
(jt. auth) Terkel, M. What's an "A" anyway?   **371.2**

Term paper writing *See* Report writing

Terminal care
Terminal illness: opposing viewpoints (7 and up)   **362.1**
Ethical aspects
See/See also pages in the following book(s):
Death and dying: opposing viewpoints p55-96 (7 and up)   **155.9**
Fiction
Cormier, R. The bumblebee flies anyway (7 and up)   **Fic**

Terminal illness: opposing viewpoints (7 and up)   **362.1**

Terrell, Mary Church, 1863-1954
About
Fradin, D. B. Fight on!: Mary Church Terrell's battle for integration   **92**
Lommel, C. Mary Church Terrell   **92**
See/See also pages in the following book(s):
Dubovoy, S. Civil rights leaders (7 and up)   **920**

The **terrifying** adventures of the golem. Stine, R. L.
In Beware!; R.L. Stine picks his favorite scary stories p147-67   **808.8**

A **terrifying** taste of short & shivery. San Souci, R.   **398.2**

Terrorism
911: the book of help   **810.8**
America under attack: primary sources (7 and up)   **973.931**
Campbell, G. A. A vulnerable America (7 and up)   **363.3**
Currie, S. Terrorists and terrorist groups (7 and up)   **303.6**
Frank, M. Understanding September 11th (7 and up)   **973.931**
Gay, K. Silent death (7 and up)   **358**
Gow, M. Attack on America   **973.931**
Hampton, W. September 11, 2001   **973.931**
Innes, B. International terrorism   **303.6**
Lalley, P. 9.11.01: terrorists attack the U.S. (4 and up)   **973.931**
Landau, E. Osama bin Laden (7 and up)   **92**
Loehfelm, B. Osama bin Laden   **92**
Margulies, P. Al Qaeda: Osama bin Laden's army of terrorists   **973.931**
Marquette, S. America under attack (4 and up)   **973.931**
A Nation challenged (4 and up)   **973.931**

Terrorism—*Continued*

Pellowski, M. The terrorist trial of the 1993 bombing of the World Trade Center **974.7**

Perl, L. Terrorism

Rosaler, M. Hamas: Palestinian terrorists **956.94**

Sherrow, V. The Oklahoma City bombing **364.1**

Shields, C. J. The 1993 World Trade Center bombing **364.1**

Stewart, G. America under attack (7 and up) **973.931**

Stewart, G. Terrorism (4 and up) **303.6**

Taylor, R. History of terrorism (7 and up) **303.6**

Terrorism: opposing viewpoints **363.32**

Wagner, H. L. The IRA and England (7 and up) **941.6**

Wells, D. K. Live aware, not in fear (7 and up) **155.5**

Wheeler, J. C. September 11, 2001: the day that changed America **973.931**

See/See also pages in the following book(s):

Civil liberties: opposing viewpoints (7 and up) **323**

Weapons of mass destruction: opposing viewpoints **358**

Fiction

Cormier, R. After the first death **Fic**

Horowitz, A. Stormbreaker **Fic**

Kass, P. Real time (7 and up) **Fic**

Tolan, S. S. Flight of the raven (7 and up) **Fic**

Terrorism library [series]

Stewart, G. America under attack **973.931**

Taylor, R. History of terrorism **303.6**

Terrorism: opposing viewpoints **363.32**

Terrorist attacks, September 11, 2001 *See* September 11 terrorist attacks, 2001

The **terrorist** trial of the 1993 bombing of the World Trade Center. Pellowski, M. **974.7**

The **terrorists.** See Meltzer, M. The day the sky fell **303.6**

Terrorists and terrorist groups. Currie, S. **303.6**

Terry, Michael Bad Hand

Daily life in a Plains Indian village, 1868 (4 and up) **970.004**

Tesar, Jenny

Stem cells (5 and up) **616**

Tessitore, John

John Steinbeck, a writer's life (7 and up) **92**

Muhammed Ali (7 and up) **92**

The **test.** Jaffe, N.

In Jaffe, N. and Zeitlin, S. J. The cow of no color: riddle stories and justice tales from around the world p134-36 **398.2**

Test tube babies. Fullick, A. **618.1**

Test tube babies. Orr, T. **618.1**

Testa, Maria

Becoming Joe DiMaggio (4 and up) **811**

The **testimony** of the fly. Jaffe, N.

In Jaffe, N. and Zeitlin, S. J. The cow of no color: riddle stories and justice tales from around the world p32-39 **398.2**

Testing for drug abuse *See* Drug testing

Testing, testing 1 . . . 2 . . . 3. LaFaye, A.

In Shelf life: stories by the book p55-66 **S C**

The **Teton** Sioux. Bonvillian, N. Indians of North America series

Tetsunojo, Kanze

See/See also pages in the following book(s):

Hamanaka, S. In search of the spirit (5 and up) **920**

Tex. Hinton, S. E. **Fic**

Texas

Bredeson, C. Texas

In Celebrate the states **973**

Heinrichs, A. Texas

In America the beautiful, second series **973**

Fiction

Estevis, A. Down Garrapata road (7 and up) **S C**

Gipson, F. B. Old Yeller (6 and up) **Fic**

Holt, K. W. Dancing in Cadillac light (5 and up) **Fic**

Holt, K. W. When Zachary Beaver came to town **Fic**

Meyer, C. White lilacs (5 and up) **Fic**

Rice, D. Crazy loco **S C**

History

Levy, J. The Alamo **976.4**

McNeese, T. The Alamo **976.4**

Murphy, J. Inside the Alamo (5 and up) **976.4**

Poetry

Is this forever, or what? (7 and up) **811.008**

Texas in art

Is this forever, or what? (7 and up) **811.008**

Textbooks

Bibliography

El-hi textbooks and serials in print **016.3713**

Textile industry

History

Macaulay, D. Mill (4 and up) **690**

Thacker, Nola

My big feet out for a walk

In Girls got game; sports stories and poems **810.8**

Thailand

Goodman, J. Thailand (5 and up) **959.3**

McNair, S. Thailand (4 and up) **959.3**

Thank you, ma'am. Hughes, L.

In Read all about it!; great read-aloud stories, poems, and newspaper pieces for pre-teens and teens p82-89 **808.8**

Thanksgiving. Wallace, R.

In Wallace, R. Losing is not an option: stories **S C**

That was then, this is now. Hinton, S. E. **Fic**

Thatch, Edward *See* Blackbeard, 1680?-1718

Thatcher, Margaret
See/See also pages in the following book(s):
Axelrod-Contrada, J. Women who led nations (7 and up) **920**
Price-Groff, C. Twentieth-century women political leaders (7 and up) **920**

Thayer, Eli, 1819-1899
See/See also pages in the following book(s):
Doherty, K. Ranchers, homesteaders, and traders **920**

The **100** most popular young adult authors. Drew, B. A. **810.9**

The **Black** Death [Turning points in world history series] (7 and up) **614.5**

T[King James Bible. American Bible Soc.] **220.5**

T[King James Bible. Oxford Univ. Press] **220.5**

Theater
See also Acting
Fiction
Blackwood, G. L. The Shakespeare stealer (5 and up) **Fic**
Cheaney, J. B. The playmaker **Fic**
Cheaney, J. B. The true Prince **Fic**
Horowitz, A. The Devil and his boy (5 and up) **Fic**
Karr, K. Gilbert and Sullivan set me free **Fic**
Korman, G. No more dead dogs **Fic**
Tolan, S. S. Surviving the Applewhites **Fic**
History
Currie, S. An actor on the Elizabethan stage **792.09**
Nardo, D. Great Elizabethan playwrights **920**
Woog, A. A history of the Elizabethan theater **792.09**

Production and direction
See also Motion pictures—Production and direction
Friedman, L. Break a leg! (4 and up) **792**

Theatre for young audiences **812.008**
Contents: Charlotte's web, by J. Robinette; The Arkansaw bear, by A. Harris; Really Rosie, by M. Sendak; The secret garden, by P. Sterling; Wiley and the Hairy Man, by S. Zeder; According to Coyote, by J. Kauffman; The mischief makers, by L. Swortzell; The wise men of Chelm, by S. F. Asher; Crow & Weasel, by J. Leonard; The ice wolf, by J. H. Kraus; Home on the mornin' train, by K. Hines; The falcon, by G. Palmer; The man-child, by A. Rabin; Hush: an interview with America, by J. Still; Bocón! by L. Loomer; The crane wife, by B. Carlisle; Jungalbook, by E. Mast; A thousand cranes, by K. S. Miller; The yellow boat, by D. Saar; Selkie, by L. B. Gollobin

Theatrical costume *See* Costume
Theft
See also Shoplifting
Fiction
Zucker, N. F. Benno's bear **Fic**

Theodore Roosevelt: larger than life. Donnelly, M. **92**

Therapeutics
See also Gene therapy
Therapy, Gene *See* Gene therapy
Therapy. Borenstein, G. C. **616.89**

There ain't nobody that can sing like me: the life of Woody Guthrie. Neimark, A. E. **92**

There comes a time: the struggle for Civil Rights. Meltzer, M. **323.1**

There goes the neighborhood. Rubin, S. G. **720**

There's a bat in bunk five. Danziger, P. **Fic**

There's a dead person following my sister around. Vande Velde, V. **Fic**

There's a girl in my hammerlock. Spinelli, J. **Fic**

There's no reason to get romantic. Slater, A. T.
In American dragons: twenty-five Asian American voices p185-99 **810.8**

There's no such thing. De Lint, C.
In De Lint, C. Waifs and strays p23-31 **S C**
also in Vampires: a collection of original stories p8-18 **S C**

There's nothing under the bed. Coville, B.
In Coville, B. Odder than ever **S C**

These shoes. Appelt, K.
In Appelt, K. Kissing Tennessee and other stories from the Stardust Dance p101-13 **S C**

These shoes of mine. Soto, G.
In You're on!: seven plays in English and Spanish p12-32 **812.008**

Theseus (Greek mythology)
See/See also pages in the following book(s):
Hamilton, E. Mythology p21-76 **292**

Thesman, Jean
The ornament tree (7 and up) **Fic**
Singer (7 and up) **Fic**
The tree of bells (7 and up) **Fic**

Theunissen, Steve
The Maori of New Zealand **993**

They broke the law, you be the judge. Jacobs, T. A. **345**

They came in chains. Meltzer, M. **326**

They changed the world [series]
Podell, J. Old worlds to new **920.003**

They had a dream. Archer, J. **920**

They're made out of meat. Bisson, T.
In New skies: an anthology of today's science fiction **S C**

Thick-head. Yolen, J.
In Yolen, J. Mightier than the sword; world folktales for strong boys p46-51 **398.2**

The **thief.** Turner, M. W. **Fic**

The **thief** and the pig. Jaffe, N.
In Jaffe, N. and Zeitlin, S. J. The cow of no color: riddle stories and justice tales from around the world p28-31 **398.2**

A **thief** in the house of memory. Wynne-Jones, T. **Fic**

The **Thief** Lord. Funke, C. C. **Fic**

Thief of hearts. Yep, L. **Fic**

Thieret, John W.
National Audubon Society field guide to North American wildflowers: eastern region
582.13

Thieves
Blackwood, G. L. Highwaymen   **364.1**
Blackwood, G. L. Outlaws   **364.1**
Bruns, R. Jesse James   **92**
Fiction
Smith, J. A. Bandit's moon (4-6)   **Fic**
Fleischman, S. The whipping boy (5 and up)   **Fic**
Turner, M. W. The thief (6 and up)   **Fic**
Updale, E. Montmorency   **Fic**
The **thieves** of Ostia. Lawrence, C.   **Fic**

Thimmesh, Catherine
Girls think of everything (5 and up)   **920**
The sky's the limit (5 and up)   **500**

Things happen. Fraustino, L. R.
In Shattered: stories of children and war p87-107   **S C**

Things I have to tell you (7 and up)   **810.8**

Things not seen. Clements, A.   **Fic**

The **thinking** kid's guide to successful soccer. Scott, N. S.   **796.334**

The **Third** Crusade. Crompton, S.   **956**

A **third** kind of funny. Ellis, S.
In What a song can do; 12 riffs on the power of music   **S C**

Thirteen. See 13   **S C**

Thirteen and a half. Vail, R.
In 13; thirteen stories that capture the agony and ecstasy of being thirteen   **S C**

The **Thirteen** Colonies. Sakurai, G.   **973.2**

The **Thirteenth** Amendment. Schleichert, E.   **342**

Thirty three things every girl should know. See 33 things every girl should know   **810.8**

Thirty three things every girl should know about women's history. See 33 things every girl should know about women's history   **305.4**

This boy's life [excerpt] Wolff, T.
In Who do you think you are?; stories of friends and enemies p83-91   **S C**

This land was made for you and me: the life and songs of Woody Guthrie. Partridge, E.   **92**

This lullaby. Dessen, S.   **Fic**

This our dark country. Reef, C.   **966.62**

Thomas, Jane Resh, 1936-
Behind the mask: the life of Queen Elizabeth I (7 and up)   **92**

Thomas, Joyce Carol
A family illness: a mom-son conversation
In Necessary noise: stories about our families as they really are p97-128   **S C**
(ed) Linda Brown, you are not alone. See Linda Brown, you are not alone   **323.1**

Thomas, Keltie
Blades, boards & scooters (5 and up)   **796.2**

Thomas, Peggy
Big cat conservation   **333.95**
Bird alert   **333.95**

Marine mammal preservation (5 and up)   **639.9**

Thomas, Piri, 1928-
See/See also pages in the following book(s):
Hill, C. M. Ten Hispanic American authors   **920**

Thomas, Valerie
See/See also pages in the following book(s):
Thimmesh, C. Girls think of everything (5 and up)   **920**

Thomas, Velma Maia
Lest we forget (7 and up)   **326**

Thomas, Vickie, 1950-
(jt. auth) Closter, K. Fiction, food, and fun   **028.5**

Thomas A. Edison. Mason, P.   **92**

Thompson, Cliff
(ed) World authors, 1990-1995. See World authors, 1990-1995   **920.003**
(ed) World authors, 1995-2000. See World authors, 1995-2000   **920.003**

Thompson, Frank *See* Edmonds, S. Emma E. (Sarah Emma Evelyn), 1841-1898

Thompson, John, 1940-
(il) Lewis, J. P. Freedom like sunlight   **811**
(il) McKissack, P. C. Christmas in the big house, Christmas in the quarters   **394.26**
(il) Yolen, J. O Jerusalem   **811**

Thompson, Sharon Elaine, 1952-
Built for speed (5 and up)   **599.75**

Thompson, Stephen P., 1953-
(ed) Teenage pregnancy: opposing viewpoints. See Teenage pregnancy: opposing viewpoints   **362.7**

Thompson, Sue Ellen, 1948-
(ed) Holidays, festivals and celebrations of the world dictionary. See Holidays, festivals and celebrations of the world dictionary   **394.26**

Thoms, Annie
(ed) With their eyes. See With their eyes   **812**

Thomson, Melissa
Women of the Renaissance   **940.2**
(jt. auth) Dean, R. Teen prostitution   **362.7**
(jt. auth) Dean, R. Women of the Middle Ages   **940.1**

Thomson, Sarah L.
The dragon's son (7 and up)   **Fic**
Robert Cormier   **92**

Thoreau, Henry David, 1817-1862
New suns will arise   **92**
Fiction
Vaupel, R. My contract with Henry   **Fic**

Thorn ogres of Hagwood. Jarvis, R.   **Fic**

Those courageous women of the Civil War. Zeinert, K.   **973.7**

Those darn Dithers. Hite, S.   **Fic**

Those extraordinary women of World War I. Zeinert, K.   **940.3**

Those remarkable women of the revolution. Zeinert, K.   **973.3**

Those three wishes. Gorog, J.
In Read all about it!; great read-aloud stories, poems, and newspaper pieces for preteens and teens p475-78   **808.8**

Though justice sleeps. Bair, B.   **305.8**

Thought and thinking
See also Perception

The **thought** of high windows. Kositsky, L.
Fic

The **thoughtful** researcher. Rankin, V.   **027.62**

Thoughts of a drought dragon. McCaughrean, G.
In Fire and wings: dragon tales from East and West p15-24   **S C**

A **thousand** cranes. Miller, K. S.
In Theatre for young audiences; 20 great plays for children p518-34   **812.008**

A **thousand** peaks. Liu Siyu   **895.1**

Threatened species *See* Endangered species

The **three** blows. Philip, N.
In Philip, N. Celtic fairy tales p54-56
398.2

The **three** brothers. Anaya, R. A.
In Anaya, R. A. My land sings; stories from the Rio Grande p55-69   **S C**

Three centuries of American poetry, 1623-1923
811.008

The **three-century** woman. Peck, R.
In Peck, R. Past perfect, present tense: new and collected stories   **S C**

Three clams and an oyster. Powell, R.   **Fic**

The **Three** daughters of King O'Hara
In Hearne, B. G. Beauties and beasts p84-91
398.2

Three days. Napoli, D. J.   **Fic**

Three Foots. Van Laan, N.
In Van Laan, N. With a whoop and a holler; a bushel of lore from way down south p91-94   **398**

Three friends in a forest. Lee, J. M.
In Lee, J. M. I once was a monkey; stories Buddha told   **294.3**

Three hundred B.C. See Service, P. F. 300 B.C.
930

Three Mile Island Nuclear Power Plant (Pa.)
Hampton, W. Meltdown   **363.1**

The **three** musketeers. Dumas, A.   **Fic**

Three people and two seals. Major, K.
In Sixteen; short stories by outstanding writers for young adults p113-24   **S C**

The **three** riddles. Kimmel, E. A.
In Fire and wings: dragon tales from East and West p79-86   **S C**

The **three** wanderers. Molnár, I.
In Molnár, I. One-time dog market at Buda and other Hungarian folktales p113-17
398.2

Three whiskers from a lion's chin. Tchana, K. H.
In Tchana, K. H. The serpent slayer: and other stories of strong women p67-70
398.2

Three wishes. Ellis, D.   **956.94**

The **three** wives of Nenpetro. Jaffe, N.
In Jaffe, N. and Zeitlin, S. J. The cow of no color: riddle stories and justice tales from around the world p84-87   **398.2**

Through a window. Johnson, A.
In On the fringe p63-72   **S C**

Through the eyes of your ancestors. Taylor, M.
929

Through the lock. Hurst, C. O.   **Fic**

The **throwaway:** a suite. Grimes, N.
In Necessary noise: stories about our families as they really are p71-78   **S C**

Throwing smoke. Brooks, B.   **Fic**

Thunder rolling in the mountains. O'Dell, S.
Fic

Thunderbird Woman, Skiwis, and Little Big-Belly Boy. Curry, J. L.
In Curry, J. L. Hold up the sky: and other Native American tales from Texas and the Southern Plains p22-31   **398.2**

Thura's diary. Al-Windawi, T.   **956.7**

Thurgood Marshall and the Supreme Court. Kent, D.   **92**

Thurlo, Aimée
The spirit line   **Fic**

Thurlo, David
(jt. auth) Thurlo, A. The spirit line   **Fic**

Thursday's child. Hartnett, S.   **Fic**

Tiananmen Square Incident, Beijing (China), 1989
The Tiananmen Square massacre (7 and up)
951.05

The **Tiananmen** Square massacre (7 and up)
951.05

Tibet (China)
Demi. The Dalai Lama (3-6)   **92**
Kummer, P. K. Tibet (5 and up)   **951**
Sís, P. Tibet   **951**
Fiction
Whitesel, C. A. Rebel   **Fic**

Ticks
See also Lyme disease

Tide pools. Bredeson, C.   **577.6**

Tied to Zelda. Rice, D.
In Tripping over the lunch lady and other school stories p158-77   **S C**

Ties that bind, ties that break. Namioka, L.
Fic

Tiger eyes. Blume, J.   **Fic**

Tiger in the snow. Barber, D. W.
In Beware!; R.L. Stine picks his favorite scary stories p127-37   **808.8**

Tiger rescue. Bortolotti, D.   **333.95**

The **tiger** rising. DiCamillo, K.   **Fic**

"**Tiger!** Tiger!". Kipling, R.
In Kipling, R. The jungle books   **S C**

The **tiger** woman. San Souci, R.
In San Souci, R. A terrifying taste of short & shivery; thirty creepy tales p104-08
398.2

Tigers
Bortolotti, D. Tiger rescue (4 and up)
333.95
Levine, S. P. The tiger (7 and up) **599.75**
Briggs, E. The man-eating tigers of Sundarbans
(4 and up) **599.75**
Fiction
DiCamillo, K. The tiger rising **Fic**
Tightrope. Cross, G. **Fic**
The **Tigris** and Euphrates Rivers. Whitcraft, M.
935

Tigris River
Whitcraft, M. The Tigris and Euphrates Rivers
935

Till, Emmett
About
Crowe, C. Getting away with murder: the true
story of the Emmett Till case (7 and up)
364.1
Fiction
Crowe, C. Mississippi trial, 1955 (7 and up)
Fic

Tillage, Leon, 1936-
Leon's story (4 and up) **92**
Tilley, Debbie
(il) Jukes, M. Growing up: it's a girl thing
612.6
(il) Jukes, M. It's a girl thing **305.23**
Tilton, Rafael, 1929-
Henry Ford (7 and up) **92**
Time
Collier, J. L. Clocks **681.1**
Duffy, T. The clock (4 and up) **681.1**
Farndon, J. Time **529**
Poetry
The Oxford treasury of time poems **821.008**
Time and space See Space and time
Time capsule: short stories about teenagers
throughout the twentieth century **S C**
A **time** for courage. Lasky, K. **Fic**
The **time** machine. Ingram, S.
In Read into the millennium; tales of the fu-
ture p116-33 **S C**
Time management
Morgenstern, J. Organizing from the inside out
for teens (7 and up) **646.7**
Time pieces. Hamilton, V. **Fic**
Time quest book [series]
Beattie, O. Buried in ice **998**
Time stops for no mouse. Hoeye, M. **Fic**
A **time** to love. Myers, W. D. **S C**
The **timeline** book of the arts. See Ochoa, G. The
Wilson chronology of the arts **700**
Timm, Bruce W.
(jt. auth) Dini, P. The Batman adventures
741.5
Timmons, Anne
(jt. auth) Robbins, T. Go girl!: The time team
741.5
Timothy of the cay. Taylor, T. **Fic**
Tin
Gray, L. Tin
In The Elements **546**

The **tin** butterfly. Mazer, N. F.
In The Color of absence; 12 stories about loss
and hope p51-70 **S C**
The **tin** man. Fraustino, L. R.
In Soul searching: thirteen stories about faith
and belief p248-67 **S C**
Tina the fairy. Martin, A. M.
In 13; thirteen stories that capture the agony
and ecstasy of being thirteen
Ting, S. C. C. (Samuel Chao-chung), 1936-
See/See also pages in the following book(s):
Yount, L. Asian-American scientists (7 and up)
920
Ting, Samuel Chao-chung See Ting, S. C. C.
(Samuel Chao-chung), 1936-
Tingle, Rebecca
The edge on the sword **Fic**
Far traveler **Fic**
Tingle, Tim
Walking the Choctaw road (7 and up) **398.2**
Tinker, John Frederick
About
Farish, L. Tinker v. Des Moines (7 and up)
342
Tinker v. Des Moines. Farish, L. **342**
The **Tipitaka** and Buddhism. Ganeri, A. **294.3**
Tirion, Wil
(jt. auth) Chartrand, M. R. The Audubon Socie-
ty field guide to the night sky **523**
Titanic (Steamship)
Adams, S. Titanic (4 and up) **910.4**
Ballard, R. D. The discovery of the Titanic (7
and up) **910.4**
Brewster, H. 882 ½ amazing answers to your
questions about the Titanic **910.4**
Marschall, K. Inside the Titanic (4 and up)
910.4
See/See also pages in the following book(s):
Landau, E. Heroine of the Titanic: the real
unsinkable Molly Brown (5 and up) **92**
Fiction
Bunting, E. SOS Titanic (7 and up) **Fic**
Tiulana, Paul, 1921-1994
Wise words of Paul Tiulana **92**
TMI Nuclear Power Plant (Pa.) See Three Mile
Island Nuclear Power Plant (Pa.)
To be a princess. McGaw, L. **920**
To bigotry, no sanction. Fisher, L. E. **296**
To conquer is to live: the life of Captain John
Smith of Jamestown. Doherty, K. **92**
To establish justice. McKissack, P. C. **342**
To every thing there is a season. **223**
To know the land [series]
Omoto, S. Hmong milestones in America
305.8
To outwit a count. Molnár, I.
In Molnár, I. One-time dog market at Buda
and other Hungarian folktales p79-82
398.2
To space & back. Ride, S. K. **629.45**
To the Golden Mountain. Perl, L. **305.8**
To the top. Venables, S. **796.52**

To the top of Everest. Skreslet, L.   **796.52**

To the young writer. Nuwer, H.   **808**

Toad Woman. Bruchac, J.
    In Bruchac, J. and Bruchac, J. When the Chenoo howls; native American tales of terror   **398.2**

Tobacco and smoking: opposing viewpoints   **362.29**

Tobacco habit
    Addiction: opposing viewpoints   **362.29**
    Smoking (7 and up)   **362.29**
    Tobacco and smoking: opposing viewpoints   **362.29**

Tobacco industry
    Sergis, D. K. Cipollone v. Liggett Group (7 and up)   **346.03**
    Tobacco and smoking: opposing viewpoints   **362.29**

Tobago *See* Trinidad and Tobago

Tocci, Salvatore
    Down syndrome (7 and up)   **616.85**
    High-tech IDs (7 and up)   **599.9**
    How to do a science fair project   **507.8**
    Jonas Salk   **92**
    A look at Pluto   **523.4**
    A look at Uranus   **523.4**

Tocher, Timothy
    Chief Sunrise, John McGraw, and me   **Fic**

Todd, Mark
    (ed) The Pain tree, and other teenage angst-ridden poetry. See The Pain tree, and other teenage angst-ridden poetry   **811.008**

Todras, Ellen H., 1947-
    Angelina Grimké (7 and up)   **92**

Together apart. Gray, D. E.   **Fic**

The **toilet**. Mhlophe, G.
    In Somehow tenderness survives; stories of Southern Africa p77-86   **S C**

Tōjō, Hideki, 1884-1948
See/See also pages in the following book(s):
    Ross, S. Leaders of World War II   **920**

Tokoyo. Tchana, K. H.
    In Tchana, K. H. The serpent slayer: and other stories of strong women p91-95   **398.2**

Tolan, Stephanie S., 1942-
    Flight of the raven (7 and up)   **Fic**
    Ordinary miracles   **Fic**
    Surviving the Applewhites   **Fic**
    Welcome to the Ark (7 and up)   **Fic**

Toleration
    Gay, K. Cultural diversity (7 and up)   **305.8**
    Fiction
    Calhoun, D. White midnight (7 and up)   **Fic**

Tolkien, J. R. R. (John Ronald Reuel), 1892-1973
    Bilbo Baggins and Smaug
    In The Book of dragons p39-46   **S C**
    The hobbit (4 and up)   **Fic**
    The lord of the rings (7 and up)   **Fic**
    About
    Lynch, D. J.R.R. Tolkien   **92**
    Willett, E. J.R.R. Tolkien   **92**

See/See also pages in the following book(s):
    Ellis, S. From reader to writer   **372.6**
    The hobbit; adaptation. See Dixon, C. Hobbit: an illustrated edition of the fantasy classic   **741.5**
    (jt. auth) Dixon, C. Hobbit: an illustrated edition of the fantasy classic   **741.5**

Tolkien, John Ronald Reuel *See* Tolkien, J. R. R. (John Ronald Reuel), 1892-1973

Toltecs
    See also Aztecs

Tom, Linda C.
    (il) Costello, E. Random House American sign language dictionary   **419**

Tom Treverrow and the Knackers. Climo, S.
    In Climo, S. Magic & mischief; tales from Cornwall p35-44   **398.2**

Tomaselli-Moschovitis, Valerie
    Government on file   **320.4**
    Junior timelines on file   **902**

Tombs
    See also Cemeteries

Tomecek, Steve
    What a great idea! (4 and up)   **609**

Tomes, Margot, 1917-1991
    (il) Fritz, J. Homesick: my own story   **92**

Tomlinson, Carl M.
    (ed) Children's books from other countries. See Children's books from other countries   **028.5**

Tommysaurus Rex. TenNapel, D. R.   **741.5**

Tomoe Gozen. Kimmel, E. A.
    In Kimmel, E. A. Sword of the samurai; adventure stories from Japan p63-72   **Fic**

Tomorrow, when the war began. Marsden, J.   **Fic**

Tonegawa, Susumu, 1939-
See/See also pages in the following book(s):
    Yount, L. Asian-American scientists (7 and up)   **920**

Tonight, by sea. Temple, F.   **Fic**

Toning for teens. Vedral, J. L.   **613.7**

Toning the sweep. Johnson, A.   **Fic**

The **tonkawa** and the bear. Curry, J. L.
    In Curry, J. L. Hold up the sky: and other Native American tales from Texas and the Southern Plains p128-32   **398.2**

Tonti, Henri de, 1650-1704
See/See also pages in the following book(s):
    Doherty, K. Ranchers, homesteaders, and traders   **920**

Toomai of the elephants. Kipling, R.
    In Kipling, R. The jungle books   **S C**

Tooth and claw. Lewin, T.   **590**

Tooting your own horn. Hill, A.   **021.7**

The **top** 10 of everything. Ash, R.   **031.02**

The **top** of the world. Jenkins, S.   **796.52**

Top secret. Janeczko, P. B.   **652**

Tope, Lily Rose R.
    Philippines (5 and up)   **959.9**

Topeka (Kan.). Board of Education
Anderson, W. Brown v. Board of Education
344
Gold, S. D. Brown v. Board of Education
344
Torah
Cato, V. The Torah and Judaism (5 and up)
222
The **Torah** and Judaism. Cato, V.   **222**
Tories, American *See* American Loyalists
Torn thread. Isaacs, A.   **Fic**
Tornadoes
Allen, J. Tornadoes   **551.55**
Ceban, B. J. Tornadoes (4 and up)   **551.55**
Grace, C. O. Forces of nature (4 and up)
551.2
Lindop, L. Chasing tornadoes   **551.55**
Simon, S. Tornadoes (4 and up)   **551.55**
Fiction
Ruckman, I. Night of the twisters (4 and up)
Fic
Torr, James D., 1974-
(ed) Alcoholism. See Alcoholism   **362.292**
(ed) The American frontier. See The American
frontier   **978**
(ed) Euthanasia: opposing viewpoints. See Euthanasia: opposing viewpoints   **179.7**
(ed) The Internet: opposing viewpoints. See The
Internet: opposing viewpoints   **303.4**
(ed) Race relations: opposing viewpoints. See
Race relations: opposing viewpoints   **305.8**
(ed) Slavery. See Slavery   **326**
(ed) Weapons of mass destruction: opposing
viewpoints. See Weapons of mass destruction:
opposing viewpoints   **358**
(ed) Westward expansion. See Westward expan-
sion [Interpreting primary documents]   **978**
Torrans, Lee Ann, 1952-
Law for K-12 libraries and librarians   **344**
Torres, J., 1969-
Alison Dare: Little Miss Adventures   **741.5**
Torres, Laura
Crossing Montana (7 and up)   **Fic**
Tortoise, Hare, and the sweet potatoes. Bryan, A.
In Bryan, A. Ashley Bryan's African tales,
uh-huh p20-26   **398.2**
Tossan, Olivier
(il) Piquemal, M. When life stinks   **305.23**
Totalitarianism
See also Dictators
Fiction
Orwell, G. Animal farm (7 and up)   **Fic**
Orwell, G. Nineteen eighty-four (7 and up)
Fic
Touch
Silverstein, A. Touching and feeling Silverstein,
A. and others. Senses and sensors [se-
ries]   **612.8**
Touching and feeling. Silverstein, A. Silverstein,
A. and others. Senses and sensors [se-
ries]   **612.8**
Touching Spirit Bear. Mikaelsen, B.   **Fic**

Tourette syndrome
Brill, M. T. Tourette syndrome (7 and up)
616.8
Landau, E. Tourette syndrome (7 and up)
616.8
Fiction
Byalick, M. Quit it   **Fic**
Tourist trapped. Wittlinger, E.
In Destination unexpected: short stories
S C
Touro Synagogue (Newport, R.I.)
Fisher, L. E. To bigotry, no sanction (4 and up)
296
Toussaint, Pierre, 1766-1853?
See/See also pages in the following book(s):
Haskins, J. African American entrepreneurs
920
Town and country life. Chrisp, P.   **940.1**
Town planning *See* City planning
Townley, Rod
Sky (7 and up)   **Fic**
What are you good at?
In The Color of absence; 12 stories about loss
and hope p17-38   **S C**
Towns *See* Cities and towns
Toy and game science. Pentland, P.   **531**
Toys
Pentland, P. Toy and game science (4 and up)
531
Wulffson, D. L. Toys! (4 and up)   **688.7**
A **trace** of blood. Olson, A. N.
In Olson, A. N. and Schwartz, H. Ask the
bones: scary stories from around the
world p118-24   **398.2**
Trachtenberg, Martha P.
Anne McCaffrey   **92**
Track athletics
Housewright, E. Winning track and field for
girls (7 and up)   **796.42**
Macht, N. L. The composite guide to track &
field   **796.42**
Manley, C. B. Competitive track and field for
girls   **796.42**
Fiction
Levy, M. Run for your life (7 and up)   **Fic**
Trade-off. Nixon, J. L.
In Nixon, J. L. Ghost town; seven ghostly
stories p129-40   **S C**
Trade routes
Major, J. S. The Silk Route   **950**
Trades *See* Occupations
Traditions *See* Manners and customs
Traffic accidents
Crash   **617.1**
Mintzer, R. The National Transportation Safety
Board   **363.1**
Wiesel, E. The accident
In Wiesel, E. Night, Dawn, The accident:
three tales p205-318   **Fic**
Trafzer, Clifford E.
Cheyenne revenge [excerpt]
In Talking leaves; contemporary native
American short stories   **S C**

Tragedies of space exploration. Mayell, M.
363.1

The **tragedy** of Birlstone. Doyle, Sir A. C.
In Doyle, Sir A. C. The complete Sherlock Holmes **S C**

Tragic prelude: bleeding Kansas. Zeinert, K.
978.1

The **Trail** of Tears. Elish, D.   970.004

The **trail** West. Galford, E.   978

Trailblazer biography [series]
Harrah, M. Blind Boone   92
Johnson, R. L. Ernest Shackleton   92
Manheimer, A. S. Martin Luther King Jr   92
O'Connor, B. Leonardo da Vinci   92

Trailblazers [series]
Collins, D. R. Farmworker's friend: the story of Cesar Chavez   92
Hart, P. S. Up in the air: the story of Bessie Coleman   92
McPherson, S. S. TV's forgotten hero: the story of Philo Farnsworth   92
O'Connor, B. Barefoot dancer: the story of Isadora Duncan   92

Trailblazers of the modern world [series]
Burgan, M. John F. Kennedy   92
Hantula, R. Alexander Fleming   92
Macdonald, F. Winston Churchill   92

The **train** room. Hines, G.
In The Haunted house: a collection of original stories **S C**

Trains, Railroad *See* Railroads

The **traitor**. Yep, L.   **Fic**

Traitor: the case of Benedict Arnold. Fritz, J.
92

Tramps
Fiction
DeFelice, C. C. Nowhere to call home   **Fic**

The **Transall** saga. Paulsen, G.   **Fic**

The **Transcontinental** Railroad. Houghton, G.
385

Transfusion. McDonald, J.
In Don't cramp my style; stories about that time of the month p145-81 **S C**

Transplantation of organs, tissues, etc.
Fullick, A. Rebuilding the body (7 and up)
617.9
McClellan, M. Organ and tissue transplants (7 and up)   617.9
Murphy, W. B. Spare parts (7 and up)
617.9
See/See also pages in the following book(s):
Biomedical ethics: opposing viewpoints (7 and up)   174.2
O'Neill, T. Biomedical ethics (7 and up)
174.2

Transportation
Encyclopedias
Macmillan Encyclopedia of transportation
388

Transportation in America [series]
Sandler, M. W. On the waters of the USA
387.2

Sandler, M. W. Straphanging in the USA
388.4

Transsexualism
Huegel, K. GLBTQ (Gay, Lesbian, Bisexual, Transgender, Questioning)   306.76

Trapani, Margi
Listen up! (7 and up)   306.8
Reality check (7 and up)   306.8

Travel guide to [series]
Barter, J. Renaissance Florence   945
Barter, J. Shakespeare's London   942.06
Nardo, D. Ancient Alexandria   932
Nardo, D. Ancient Athens   938

Travel team. Lupica, M.   **Fic**

Travels *See* Voyages and travels

Travers, P. L. (Pamela L.), 1899-1996
See/See also pages in the following book(s):
Ellis, S. From reader to writer   372.6

Travers, Pamela L. *See* Travers, P. L. (Pamela L.), 1899-1996

Travis, Dempsey, 1920-
See/See also pages in the following book(s):
Haskins, J. African American entrepreneurs
920

Treasure at the heart of the Tanglewood. Pierce, M. A.   **Fic**

Treasure Island. Stevenson, R. L.   **Fic**

The **treasure** of inheritance. Gallant, R. A.
576.5

The **treasury** of family games. Glenn, J.   793

The **treasury** of saints and martyrs. Mulvihill, M.
920

Treaties
See/See also pages in the following book(s):
Weapons of mass destruction: opposing viewpoints   358

The **Tree** is older than you are (7 and up)
860.8

The **tree** of bells. Thesman, J.   **Fic**

Trees
Burnie, D. Tree (4 and up)   582.16
Gardner, R. Science project ideas about trees (5 and up)   582.16
North America
Brockman, C. F. Trees of North America
582.16
Petrides, G. A. A field guide to trees and shrubs
582.16

Trees of North America. Brockman, C. F.
582.16

Trefil, James S., 1938-
(jt. auth) Hirsch, E. D. The new dictionary of cultural literacy   031

Trelease, Jim
The read-aloud handbook   028.5
(ed) Read all about it! See Read all about it!
808.8

Trembling earth. Siegelson, K. L.   **Fic**

Trent, Lynda
The Viking longship (7 and up)   948

Trespacz, Karen L.
Ferrell v. Dallas I.S.D. (7 and up)   344

The **trial** of John T. Scopes. Olson, S. P.

The **trial** of juveniles as adults. Hile, K. S.
345

The **trial** of the police officers in the shooting death of Amadou Diallo. Fireside, B. J.

Trial: the inside story. Kuklin, S. 345

Trials
Aaseng, N. You are the juror 345
Alonso, K. The Chicago Seven political protest trial 345
Courtroom drama (7 and up) 347
Fireside, B. J. The trial of the police officers in the shooting death of Amadou Diallo (7 and up)
Frost-Knappman, E. Women's rights on trial
346
Pellowski, M. The Chicago "Black Sox" baseball scandal 796.357
Pellowski, M. The terrorist trial of the 1993 bombing of the World Trade Center 974.7
Sergis, D. K. Cipollone v. Liggett Group (7 and up) 346.03
Sorensen, L. The Scottsboro Boys Trial 345
Fiction
Myers, W. D. Monster (7 and up) Fic

Trials (Homicide)
Crowe, C. Getting away with murder: the true story of the Emmett Till case (7 and up)
364.1
Fireside, H. The "Mississippi Burning" civil rights murder conspiracy trial 345
Pellowski, M. The O.J. Simpson murder trial
345

Trials (Kidnapping)
Kuklin, S. Trial: the inside story (7 and up)
345

Trials (Murder) See Trials (Homicide)

Triangle histories, Revolutionary War [series]
Ingram, S. King George III 92

Triangle Shirtwaist Company, Inc.
Houle, M. M. Triangle Shirtwaist Factory fire
974.7
Lieurance, S. The Triangle Shirtwaist fire and sweatshop reform in American history (7 and up) 974.7
Fiction
Auch, M. J. Ashes of roses (7 and up) Fic
Triangle Shirtwaist Factory fire. Houle, M. M.
974.7
The **Triangle** Shirtwaist fire and sweatshop reform in American history. Lieurance, S. 974.7

Triathlon
Fiction
Crutcher, C. Ironman Fic

Trick-or-treating. Soto, G.
In Soto, G. Local news p14-25 S C
Trickster's choice. Pierce, T. Fic

Trinidad and Tobago
Sheehan, S. Trinidad & Tobago (5 and up)
972.983

Trip in a summer dress. Sanford, A.
In Leaving home: stories p119-31 808.8

Tripping over the lunch lady. Johnson, A.
In Tripping over the lunch lady and other school stories p1-15 S C
Tripping over the lunch lady and other school stories (4 and up) S C
Triumph of the imagination: the story of writer J.K. Rowling. Chippendale, L. A. 92
Trivia See Curiosities and wonders
Trojan War
Homer. The Iliad 883
McCarty, N. The Iliad 883
See/See also pages in the following book(s):
Hamilton, E. Mythology p21-76 292
Fiction
Geras, A. Troy (7 and up) Fic
Troll Fell. Langrish, K. Fic
Trondheim, Lewis
Astronauts of the future 741.5
(jt. auth) Sfar, J. Dungeon Vol. 1: Duck Heart
741.5
Tropical forests. Jackson, T. 577.3
Tropical memories. Belpré, P.
In You're on!: seven plays in English and Spanish p34-41 812.008
Tropical rain forest. Sayre, A. P. 577.3
Tropical rain forests See Rain forests
Trotter, Joe William, 1945-
From a raw deal to a New Deal? African Americans, 1929-1945 (7 and up) 305.8
Trotter, William Monroe, 1872-1934
See/See also pages in the following book(s):
Dubovoy, S. Civil rights leaders (7 and up)
920
Trottier, Maxine
Marian
In Sherwood: original stories from the world of Robin Hood p20-34 S C
Sister to the wolf Fic
The **trouble.** Schwartz, A.
In Schwartz, A. Scary stories 3; more tales to chill your bones p69-76 398.2
Trouble snake. Yep, L.
In Yep, L. The rainbow people p118-23
398.2
Troubled world [series]
Downing, D. Africa 960
Downing, D. Conflict: India vs. Pakistan
954
Trout summer. Conly, J. L. Fic
Troy, Don
W.E.B. DuBois 92
Troy (Extinct city)
Caselli, G. In search of Troy (4 and up)
939
Troy. Geras, A. Fic
Troy Thompson's excellent peotry book. Crew, G.
Fic
Trucks
Fiction
Merrill, J. The pushcart war (5 and up) Fic
Trudeau, Noah Andre, 1949-
Like men of war (7 and up) 973.7

True confessions of a heartless girl. Brooks, M.
Fic

The **true** confessions of Charlotte Doyle. Avi
Fic

The **true** enchanter. Alexander, L.
In Alexander, L. The foundling and other tales of Prydain p29-38 **S C**

The **true** meaning of cleavage. Fredericks, M.
Fic

True north. Lasky, K. **Fic**

The **true** Prince. Cheaney, J. B. **Fic**

True stories from the edge [series]
Schroeder, A. Scams! **364.1**

The **true** story of Christmas. Fine, A. **Fic**

Trueit, Trudi Strain
ADHD (5 and up) **616.85**
Earthquakes **551.2**
Fossils **560**
Keeping a journal (5 and up) **808**
Rocks, gems, and minerals **552**
Volcanoes **551.2**

Trueman, Terry
Apple blossoms
In Tripping over the lunch lady and other school stories p43-57 **S C**
Cruise control
Inside out (7 and up) **Fic**
Stuck in neutral **Fic**

Trujillo Molina, Rafael Leónidas, 1891-1961
Fiction
Alvarez, J. Before we were free (7 and up) **Fic**

Truman, Harry S., 1884-1972
See/See also pages in the following book(s):
Dolan, E. F. America in the Korean War (7 and up) **951.9**
Uschan, M. V. Political leaders **920**

Trumble, Kelly
The Library of Alexandria (5 and up) **027**

Truth, Sojourner, d. 1883
About
Brezina, C. Sojourner Truth's "Ain't I a woman?" speech **92**
Butler, M. G. Sojourner Truth (5 and up) **92**
Krass, P. Sojourner Truth **92**
See/See also pages in the following book(s):
Pinkney, A. D. Let it shine (4 and up) **920**

Truth & lies: an anthology of poems (7 and up) **808.81**

The **truth** about alcohol (7 and up) **362.292**

The **truth** about eating disorders (7 and up) **616.85**

The **truth** about fear and depression (7 and up) **616.85**

The **truth** about forever. Dessen, S. **Fic**

The **truth** about great white sharks. Cerullo, M. M. **597**

The **truth** about rats, rules, and seventh grade. Zinnen, L. **Fic**

The **truth** about sparrows. Hale, M. **Fic**

The **truthful** harp. Alexander, L.
In Alexander, L. The foundling and other tales of Prydain p87-94 **S C**

The **truthful** shepherd. Yolen, J.
In Yolen, J. Mightier than the sword; world folktales for strong boys p64-68 **398.2**

Truthfulness and falsehood
See also Honesty
Fiction
Cadnum, M. Rundown (7 and up) **Fic**
Choldenko, G. Notes from a liar and her dog (5 and up) **Fic**
Coville, B. The skull of truth (4 and up) **Fic**

Tubb, Jonathan N.
Bible lands **220.9**

Tuberculosis
Landau, E. Tuberculosis (7 and up) **616.2**
Yancey, D. Tuberculosis (7 and up) **616.2**

Tubman, Harriet, 1815?-1913
About
Schraff, A. E. Harriet Tubman **92**
Taylor, M. W. Harriet Tubman **92**
See/See also pages in the following book(s):
Currie, S. Escapes from slavery **326**
Hewitt, K. Lives of extraordinary women (4 and up) **920**
Pinkney, A. D. Let it shine (4 and up) **920**

Tucker, Sophie, 1884-1966
See/See also pages in the following book(s):
Orgill, R. Shout, sister, shout! (6 and up) **920**

Tucker, Tom, 1944-
Brainstorm! (5 and up) **609**

Tulsa burning. Myers, A. **Fic**

Tunes for bears to dance to. Cormier, R. **Fic**

Tungsten
Turrell, K. Tungsten
In The Elements **546**

Tunis, Edwin, 1897-1973
Frontier living (5 and up) **978**

Tunisia
Brown, R. V. Tunisia (5 and up) **961.1**

Tunnell, Michael O.
Brothers in valor **Fic**
The children of Topaz (5 and up) **940.53**
Wishing moon **Fic**

Tunnels
See/See also pages in the following book(s):
Macaulay, D. Building big **720**

Tunney, Kelly Smith
(ed) Flash!: the Associated Press covers the world. See Flash!: the Associated Press covers the world **070.4**

Turck, Mary, 1950-
Healthy eating for weight management **613.7**

Turing, Alan Mathison, 1912-1954
See/See also pages in the following book(s):
Henderson, H. Modern mathematicians (7 and up) **920**

Turk, Ruth, 1917-
Ray Charles: soul man **92**

Turkey
 Eboch, C. Turkey (7 and up)   **956.1**
 Orr, T. Turkey (4 and up)   **956.1**
 Sheehan, S. Turkey (5 and up)   **956.1**
 Stefoff, R. The Asian empires (5 and up)
     950

    Fiction
 Bagdasarian, A. Forgotten fire (7 and up)
     Fic

    History
 Greenblatt, M. Süleyman the Magnificent and
  the Ottoman Empire   **956.1**
 Ruggiero, A. The Ottoman Empire   **956.1**

Turkey vultures See Vultures

Turkeys
    Fiction
 Karr, K. The great turkey walk (5 and up)
     Fic

Turmoil in a blue and beige bedroom. Angell, J.
 In Sixteen; short stories by outstanding writers for young adults p72-82   **S C**

Turnabout. Haddix, M. P.   **Fic**

Turnbull, Ann
 No shame, no fear (7 and up)   **Fic**

Turner, Alan
 National Geographic prehistoric mammals (5
  and up)   **569**

Turner, C. M. E. P.
 North American art since 1900
 In International encyclopedia of art   **703**

Turner, Megan Whalen, 1965-
 The baby in the night deposit box
 In Firebirds: an anthology of original fantasy
  and science fiction; an anthology of orig-
  inal fantasy and science fiction   **S C**
 The thief (6 and up)   **Fic**

Turner, Nat, 1800?-1831
    About
 Bisson, T. Nat Turner   **92**

Turner, Pamela S.
 Gorilla doctors (5 and up)   **333.95**

Turning point inventions series
 Duffy, T. The clock   **681.1**

Turning points in world history [series]
 The American frontier   **978**
 American slavery   **326**
 The Atom bomb   **355.8**
 The Baby boom   **306**
 The Collapse of the Soviet Union   **947.085**
 The Early Middle Ages   **909.07**
 The French Revolution   **944.04**
 The Great Depression   **973.91**
 Immigration   **325.73**
 The Rise of Christianity   **270**
 The Rise of Nazi Germany   **943.086**
 The Rise of the Soviet Union   **947.084**
 The Black Death   **614.5**
 World War I   **940.3**
 World War II   **940.53**

Turrell, Kerry
 Tungsten
 In The Elements   **546**

Turtle clan journey. Durrant, L.   **Fic**

Turtle Lake. Bird, G.
 In Talking leaves; contemporary native
  American short stories   **S C**

Tuskegee airmen See African American pilots

Tuskegee Institute
 Washington, B. T. Up from slavery   **92**

Tutankhamen, King of Egypt
    About
 Green, R. Tutankhamun   **932**

Tuttle, Cheryl Gerson
 (jt. auth) Paquette, P. H. Learning disabilities
     371.9

TV news. Spangenburg, R.   **070.1**

TV's forgotten hero: the story of Philo Farnsworth. McPherson, S. S.   **92**

TWA flight 800. Cole, M. D.   **363.1**

Twain, Mark, 1835-1910
 The adventures of Huckleberry Finn (5 and up)
     Fic
 The adventures of Tom Sawyer (5 and up)
     Fic
 The prince and the pauper   **Fic**
    About
 Lasky, K. A brilliant streak: the making of
  Mark Twain (4 and up)   **92**
 Mark Twain [essays about]   **92**
 Meltzer, M. Mark Twain himself   **92**

Twayne's United States authors series
 Crowe, C. Presenting Mildred D. Taylor
     813.009

Twayne's young adult authors series
 Bloom, S. P. Presenting Avi   **813.009**
 Brown, J. Presenting Kathryn Lasky   **813.009**
 Krull, K. Presenting Paula Danziger   **813.009**
 MacRae, C. D. Presenting young adult fantasy
  fiction   **813.009**
 Nilsen, A. P. Presenting M.E. Kerr   **813.009**
 Reid, S. E. Presenting Cynthia Voigt
     813.009
 Reid, S. E. Presenting young adult science fic-
  tion   **813.009**
 Stover, L. T. Presenting Phyllis Reynolds
  Naylor   **813.009**

Twelfth night. Packer, T.
 In Packer, T. Tales from Shakespeare p155-
  173   **822.3**

Twelve again. See Corbett, S. 12 again   **Fic**

Twelve at a swat. Molnár, I.
 In Molnár, I. One-time dog market at Buda
  and other Hungarian folktales p106-12
     398.2

The **twelve** dancing princesses. McKinley, R.
 In McKinley, R. The door in the hedge p137-
  216   **S C**

Los **twelve** days of Christmas. Saldaña, R.
 In Saldaña, R. Finding our way: stories p29-
  38   **S C**

Twelve-step programs
 Banfield, S. Inside recovery   **616.86**

Twemlow, Nick
 Josh Gibson   **92**

Twentieth century authors. See World authors,
 1900-1950   **920.003**

Twentieth-century history makers [series]
Gilbert, A. Franklin D. Roosevelt   92
Kramer, A. Nelson Mandela   92
Platt, R. Fidel Castro   92

Twentieth-century women political leaders. Price-Groff, C.   920

Twenty-first century medical library [series]
Billitteri, T. J. Alternative medicine   615.5
Brill, M. T. Tourette syndrome   616.8
Harris, J. L. Sickle cell disease   616.1
Hyman, B. M. Obsessive-compulsive disorder   616.85
Moragne, W. Depression   616.85
Yancey, D. Tuberculosis   616.2

Twenty thousand leagues under the sea. Verne, J.   **Fic**

Twin tales. Jackson, D. M.   618.2

Twins
Jackson, D. M. Twin tales (4 and up)   618.2
  Fiction
Avi. Never mind! (5 and up)   **Fic**
Boling, K. January 1905 (5 and up)   **Fic**
Creech, S. Ruby Holler (4 and up)   **Fic**
Duncan, L. Stranger with my face (7 and up)   **Fic**
Littke, L. Haunted sister (7 and up)   **Fic**
Paterson, K. Jacob have I loved   **Fic**
Sleator, W. Singularity (7 and up)   **Fic**
Tolan, S. S. Ordinary miracles   **Fic**

Twins. Vande Velde, V.
In Vande Velde, V. Tales from the Brothers Grimm and the Sisters Weird p88-106   **S C**

Twisted summer. Roberts, W. D.   **Fic**

Twists and turns. McDonald, J.   **Fic**

The **two** Christmas evenings. Child, L. M. F.
In The Boy of Chancellorville and other Civil War stories p74-94   **S C**

Two coins in the fountain. Conford, E.
In Conford, E. Crush p69-84   **S C**

Two dreamers. Soto, G.
In Soto, G. Baseball in April, and other stories p23-32   **S C**

Two hundred and three icy, freezing, frosty, cool & wild experiments, Janice Van Cleave's. See VanCleave, J. P. Janice VanCleave's 203 icy, freezing, frosty, cool & wild experiments   507.8

Two hundred yards. Lynch, C.
In Lynch, C. All the old haunts p148-54   **S C**

The **two** Johns. Hamilton, V.
In Hamilton, V. The people could fly; American black folktales p81-89   398.2

The **two** princesses of Bamarre. Levine, G. C.   **Fic**

Two suns in the sky. Bat-Ami, M.   **Fic**

Two thousand and one: a space odyssey. See Clarke, A. C. 2001: a space odyssey   **Fic**

Twomey, Cathleen
Beachmont letters (7 and up)   **Fic**

Tyge *See* Brahe, Tycho, 1546-1601

Tyle, Laura B.
(ed) UXL encyclopedia of world biography. See UXL encyclopedia of world biography   920.003

Tyler on prime time. Atinsky, S.   **Fic**

Tym, Kate
Coping with your emotions   152.4
School survival   371.8

The **typewriter**. Naidoo, B.
In Naidoo, B. Out of bounds: seven stories of conflict and hope p72-95   **S C**

Typhoons
  See also Hurricanes
Longshore, D. Encyclopedia of hurricanes, typhoons and cyclones (7 and up)   551.55

Typography *See* Printing

Tz'u-hsi, Empress dowager of China, 1835-1908
See/See also pages in the following book(s):
Hewitt, K. Lives of extraordinary women (4 and up)   920

U

The **U.S.** Constitution. Moehn, H.   342

U.S.S.R. *See* Soviet Union

U.S. Space Camp (Huntsville, Ala.)
Goodman, S. Ultimate field trip 5 (4 and up)   629.45

U.S. Territories. McNair, S.
In America the beautiful, second series   973

U.X.L encyclopedia of biomes (7 and up)   577.8

U.X.L encyclopedia of science   503

U.X.L science fact finder   500

Uchida, Yoshiko, 1921-1992
A jar of dreams (5 and up)   **Fic**
Journey to Topaz (5 and up)   **Fic**

Udvardy, Miklos D. F., 1919-1998
National Audubon Society field guide to North American birds, Western region   598

Uganda
Barlas, R. Uganda (5 and up)   967.6

Uglies. Westerfeld, S.   **Fic**

Ugly-face. Bruchac, J.
In Bruchac, J. and Bruchac, J. When the Chenoo howls; native American tales of terror   398.2

The **ugly** one. Flake, S. G.
In Flake, S. G. Who am I without him?; short stories about girls and the boys in their lives p10-18   **S C**

The **ugly** unicorn. Salmonson, J. A.
In A Glory of unicorns p79-94   **S C**

Uhle, Mary E.
(jt. auth) Shields, N. E. Where credit is due   808

Ukraine
Bassis, V. Ukraine (5 and up)   947.7
Kummer, P. K. Ukraine (4 and up)   947.7
Otfinoski, S. Ukraine (7 and up)   947.7

Ulam, Stanislaw M.
See/See also pages in the following book(s):
Henderson, H. Modern mathematicians (7 and up) **920**
The **ultimate** audition book for teens. See Lamedman, D. 111 one-minute monologues **812.008**
The **ultimate** classic car book. Willson, Q. **629.222**
Ultimate field trip 4: a week in the 1800s. Goodman, S. **973.5**
Ultimate field trip 5. Goodman, S. **629.45**
Ultimate kids' money book, Neale S. Godfrey's. Godfrey, N. S. **332.024**
Ultimate sports (7 and up) **S C**
Ultimate visual dictionary of science **503**
Ultimate X-men. Sanderson, P. **741.5**
Ultraman Tiga, Vol. 1: Return of the warrior. Wong, T. **741.5**
Uluru, Australia's Aboriginal heart. Arnold, C. **994**
Uluru-Kata Tjuta National Park (Australia)
Arnold, C. Uluru, Australia's Aboriginal heart (5 and up) **994**
UN *See* United Nations
The **un-civil** war. Klass, S. S. **Fic**
Unbalanced. Sleator, W.
In On the edge: stories at the brink p127-39 **S C**
Unbroken. Haas, J. **Fic**
Unbuilding. Macaulay, D. **690**
Uncle Joshua and the Grogglemen. Doyle, D.
In New skies: an anthology of today's science fiction **S C**
Uncle Lubin and the dragon. Robinson, W. H.
In The Book of dragons p47-49 **S C**
Uncles
Fiction
Carter, A. R. Crescent Moon **Fic**
Ferris, J. Love among the walnuts (7 and up) **Fic**
Frank, L. K. Oy, Joy! **Fic**
Henkes, K. The birthday room (5 and up) **Fic**
Hobbs, W. The Big Wander (7 and up) **Fic**
Hobbs, W. Jackie's Wild Seattle (5 and up) **Fic**
Horvath, P. Everything on a waffle (4 and up) **Fic**
Martin, A. M. A corner of the universe (5 and up) **Fic**
Martin, N. Flight of the Fisherbird (5 and up) **Fic**
Matthews, K. Flying lessons **Fic**
Moore, Y. Freedom songs **Fic**
Wood, J. R. The man who loved clowns **Fic**
Uncommon champions. Kaminsky, M. **920**
Uncommon Faith. Krisher, T. **Fic**
Under a war-torn sky. Elliott, L. **Fic**
Under our skin. Birdseye, D. H. **305.8**

Under the bending yew. Kirwan, A.
In Sherwood: original stories from the world of Robin Hood p38-47 **S C**
Under the blood-red sun. Salisbury, G. **Fic**
Under the ice. Conlan, K. **578.7**
Under the microscope: science tools. Clark, J. O. E. **530.8**
Under the Watson's porch. Shreve, S. R. **Fic**
Underground. Macaulay, D. **624**
Underground railroad
Bial, R. The Underground Railroad (4 and up) **326**
Eskridge, A. E. Slave uprisings and runaways **326**
Fradin, D. B. Bound for the North Star (7 and up) **326**
Hamilton, V. Many thousand gone (5 and up) **326**
Hansen, J. Freedom roads: searching for the Underground Railroad (5 and up) **973.7**
Katz, W. L. Black pioneers **920**
Sawyer, K. K. The underground railroad in American history **326**
Schraff, A. E. Harriet Tubman **92**
Taylor, M. W. Harriet Tubman **92**
Fiction
Armstrong, J. Steal away (5 and up) **Fic**
Ayres, K. North by night (6 and up) **Fic**
Beatty, P. Jayhawker (5 and up) **Fic**
Carbone, E. L. Stealing freedom **Fic**
Houston, G. Bright Freedom's song **Fic**
Lasky, K. True north (6 and up) **Fic**
McKissack, P. C. A picture of Freedom (4 and up) **Fic**
Vande Velde, V. There's a dead person following my sister around (4 and up) **Fic**
Wisler, G. C. Caleb's choice **Fic**
Woodruff, E. Dear Austin **Fic**
The **underground** railroad in American history. Sawyer, K. K. **326**
Understanding alternative medicine. Rattenbury, J. **615.5**
Understanding Buddy. Kornblatt, M. **Fic**
Understanding DNA. Allan, T. **576.5**
Understanding Frankenstein. Nardo, D. **823.009**
Understanding great literature [series]
Bernard, C. Understanding To kill a mockingbird **813.009**
Nardo, D. Understanding Frankenstein **823.009**
Understanding illness [series]
Landau, E. Deafness **617.8**
Understanding issues [series]
Stewart, G. Death **306.9**
Stewart, G. Divorce **306.89**
Stewart, G. Drugs **362.29**
Stewart, G. Guns and violence **303.6**
Stewart, G. Terrorism **303.6**
Understanding September 11th. Frank, M. **973.931**
Understanding the Holocaust. Feldman, G. **940.53**

Understanding the Holy Land. Frank, M.
956.94

Understanding the human body [series]
Parker, S. Brain, nerves, and senses 612.8
Parker, S. Digestion and reproduction 612.3
Parker, S. Heart, blood, and lungs 612.1
Parker, S. Skin, muscles, and bones 612.7
Walker, P. The digestive system 612.3
Walker, P. The immune system 616.07

Understanding the risk of diet drugs. Walker, P.
616.85

Understanding To kill a mockingbird. Bernard, C.
813.009

The **undertakers**. Kipling, R.
In Kipling, R. The jungle books S C

Underwater exploration
Ballard, R. D. The discovery of the Titanic (7
and up) 910.4
Macaulay, D. Ship (4 and up) 387.2
Matsen, B. The incredible record-setting deep-
sea dive of the bathysphere (4 and up)
551.46
Smith, K. Exploring for shipwrecks 930.1
Walker, S. M. Secrets of a Civil War submarine
(7 and up) 973.7

An **uneasy** peace, 1945-1980. Blohm, C. E.
940.55

Unexpected magic. Jones, D. W. S C

Unger, Harlow G., 1931-
But what if I don't want to go to college? (7
and up) 331.7

UNIA *See* Universal Negro Improvement Association

UNICEF
Prior, K. UNICEF 362.7

Unicorns
See/See also pages in the following book(s):
Nigg, J. Wonder beasts (7 and up) 398
Fiction
A Glory of unicorns (5 and up) S C
The **unicorns** of Kabustan. Eason, A.
In A Glory of unicorns p115-24 S C

Unidentified flying objects
Netzley, P. D. Alien abductions: opposing view-
points (7 and up) 001.9
See/See also pages in the following book(s):
Paranormal phenomena: opposing viewpoints (7
and up) 133

Union of South Africa *See* South Africa

Union of Soviet Socialist Republics *See* Soviet
Union

Union Pacific Railroad Company
Houghton, G. The Transcontinental Railroad (5
and up) 385

United Arab Emirates
Augustin, B. United Arab Emirates (4 and up)
953

United Nations
Ross, S. The United Nations 341.23
See/See also pages in the following book(s):
Worldmark encyclopedia of the nations
910.3

United Nations International Children's Fund
See UNICEF

United States
America the beautiful, second series (5 and up)
973
The Blackbirch kid's visual reference of the
United States (4 and up) 973
Celebrate the states (5 and up) 973
Armed forces
Haskins, J. African American military heroes
920
Biography
The American scene: lives 920.003
Engelbert, P. American civil rights: biographies
920
Hillstrom, K. Vietnam War: biographies (7 and
up) 920
Keenan, S. Scholastic book of outstanding
Americans (5 and up) 920.003
Mendoza, P. M. Extraordinary people in extraor-
dinary times (7 and up) 920
Moss, J. Profiles in American history 973
Saari, P. Colonial America: biographies 920
Schmittroth, L. American Revolution: biogra-
phies (5 and up) 920
Biography—Poetry
Lives: poems about famous Americans (4 and
up) 811.008
Civilization
America in the 20th century 973.9
America's decades 973.9
Bowling, beatniks, and bell-bottoms 306
Lindop, E. America in the 1950s (7 and up)
973.921
See/See also pages in the following book(s):
Culture wars: opposing viewpoints 306
Civilization—Chronology
Bornstein, J. An American chronology 973
Climate—Statistics
Weather almanac 551.6
Colonies
See United States—Territories and posses-
sions
Constitutional history
See Constitutional history—United States
Constitutional law
See Constitutional law—United States
Defenses
See/See also pages in the following book(s):
Weapons of mass destruction: opposing view-
points 358
Description and travel
Murphy, J. Across America on an emigrant train
(5 and up) 92
Economic conditions
The Industrial revolution: opposing viewpoints
(7 and up) 330.973
Inner-city poverty (7 and up) 362.5
Poverty: opposing viewpoints (7 and up)
362.5
Economic conditions—1865-1918
Collier, C. The rise of industry, 1860-1900
973.8
Woog, A. A sweatshop during the industrial
revolution 331.2

United States—*Continued*
Economic conditions—1919-1933
Blumenthal, K. Six days in October (7 and up)
332.6
Burg, D. F. The Great Depression (7 and up)
973.91
See/See also pages in the following book(s):
Trotter, J. W. From a raw deal to a New Deal?
African Americans, 1929-1945 (7 and up)
305.8
Economic conditions—1933-1945
Burg, D. F. The Great Depression (7 and up)
973.91
Collier, C. Progressivism, the Great Depression,
and the New Deal, 1901 to 1941   **973.91**
Fremon, D. K. The Great Depression in
American history   **338.5**
The Great Depression (7 and up)   **973.91**
McElvaine, R. S. The Depression and New Deal
(7 and up)   **973.91**
See/See also pages in the following book(s):
Trotter, J. W. From a raw deal to a New Deal?
African Americans, 1929-1945 (7 and up)
305.8

Emigration
See United States—Immigration and emi-
gration
Encyclopedias
Junior Worldmark encyclopedia of the states
973.03
Worldmark encyclopedia of the states
973.03
Ethnic relations
Buxbaum, S. M. Jewish faith in America (7 and
up)   **296**
Exploration
See also West (U.S.)—Exploration
Foreign population
See Immigrants—United States
Foreign relations
American presidents in world history
920.003
Collier, C. The United States enters the world
stage: from the Alaska Purchase through
World War I, 1867-1919   **973.8**
See/See also pages in the following book(s):
War: opposing viewpoints   **355**
Foreign relations—Iran
Spencer, W. The United States and Iran (7 and
up)   **327.73**
Foreign relations—Japan
Blumberg, R. Commodore Perry in the land of
the Shogun (5 and up)   **952**
Foreign relations—Mexico
Pascoe, E. Mexico and the United States (7 and
up)   **327.73**
Foreign relations—Middle East
Marquette, S. America under attack (4 and up)
973.931
Foreign relations—Soviet Union
Burgan, M. Cold War (7 and up)   **909.82**
The Cold War [Great speeches in history series]
909.82
Collier, C. The United States in the Cold War:
1945-1989   **327.73**

Kallen, S. A. Primary sources [American war li-
brary, The Cold War]   **909.82**
Ross, S. The causes of the Cold War
327.73
Sherman, J. The Cold War   **909.82**
Speakman, J. The Cold War (7 and up)
327.73
Winkler, A. M. The Cold War   **909.82**
Gazetteers
The Cambridge gazetteer of the United States
and Canada   **917.3**
Government
See United States—Politics and government
Government publications
See Government publications—United
States
Historical geography
Leacock, E. Journeys in time (4 and up)
973
Leacock, E. Places in time (4 and up)   **911**
History
See also West (U.S.)—History
American history on file   **973**
The American scene: events   **973**
Hakim, J. A history of US (5 and up)   **973**
Hoose, P. M. We were there, too! (5 and up)
973
Johnston, R. D. The making of America (5 and
up)   **973**
Leacock, E. Journeys in time (4 and up)
973
Moss, J. Profiles in American history   **973**
Sandler, M. W. America's great disasters
973
History—1600-1775, Colonial period
Burgan, M. Colonial and revolutionary times (5
and up)   **973.2**
Collier, C. Clash of cultures, prehistory-1638
970.004
Collier, C. The French and Indian War, 1660-
1763   **973.2**
Collier, C. The paradox of Jamestown, 1585-
1700   **975.5**
Colonial America (4 and up)   **973.2**
Doherty, K. To conquer is to live: the life of
Captain John Smith of Jamestown   **92**
Edwards, J. Jamestown, John Smith, and Poca-
hontas in American history (7 and up)
975.5
Gaustad, E. S. Roger Williams (7 and up)
92
Gray, E. G. Colonial America: a history in doc-
uments (7 and up)   **973.2**
Saari, P. Colonial America: almanac   **973.2**
Saari, P. Colonial America: biographies   **920**
Saari, P. Colonial America: primary sources
973.2
Stefoff, R. Colonial life   **973.2**
History—1600-1775, Colonial period—Fiction
Osborne, M. P. Standing in the light   **Fic**
Rinaldi, A. The fifth of March (7 and up)
Fic
Rinaldi, A. Hang a thousand trees with ribbons
Fic

United States—Continued
History—1755-1763, French and Indian War
The American revolutionaries: a history in their own words, 1750-1800 (6 and up) **973.3**
Collier, C. The French and Indian War, 1660-1763 **973.2**

History—1775-1783, Revolution
Allen, T. B. George Washington, spymaster **92**
American Revolution: battles and leaders **973.3**
American Revolution: primary sources (5 and up) **973.3**
The American revolutionaries: a history in their own words, 1750-1800 (6 and up) **973.3**
Beller, S. P. The Revolutionary War **973.3**
Bigelow, B. C. American Revolution: almanac (5 and up) **973.3**
Bobrick, B. Fight for freedom (5 and up) **973.3**
Bohannon, L. F. The American Revolution (5 and up) **973.3**
Burgan, M. Colonial and revolutionary times (5 and up) **973.2**
Collier, C. The American Revolution, 1763-1783 **973.3**
Cox, C. Come all you brave soldiers (6 and up) **973.3**
Fradin, D. B. Samuel Adams (6 and up) **92**
Fritz, J. Traitor: the case of Benedict Arnold **92**
Fritz, J. Why not, Lafayette? (5 and up) **92**
Hull, M. The Boston Tea Party in American history **973.3**
Ingram, S. King George III **92**
Irvin, B. Samuel Adams (7 and up) **92**
Jaffe, S. H. Who were the founding fathers? (7 and up) **973.3**
King, D. C. Benedict Arnold and the American Revolution **92**
Littlefield, D. C. Revolutionary citizens (7 and up) **305.8**
Miller, B. M. Growing up in revolution and the new nation, 1775 to 1800 (5 and up) **973.3**
Morton, J. C. The American Revolution (7 and up) **973.3**
Murphy, J. A young patriot (5 and up) **973.3**
Nardo, D. Weapons of war **973.3**
Nash, G. B. Landmarks of the American Revolution **973.3**
The Revolutionary War **973.3**
Ross, S. The American Revolution (7 and up) **973.3**
Schmittroth, L. American Revolution: biographies (5 and up) **920**
Slavicek, L. C. Women of the American Revolution (7 and up) **973.3**
Stewart, G. Life of a soldier in Washington's army **973.3**
Sullivan, G. Paul Revere **92**
Whitelaw, N. The shot heard round the world **973.3**
Zeinert, K. Those remarkable women of the revolution (7 and up) **973.3**

History—1775-1783, Revolution—Fiction
Avi. The fighting ground (5 and up) **Fic**
Blackwood, G. L. The year of the hangman **Fic**
Collier, J. L. My brother Sam is dead (6 and up) **Fic**
Collier, J. L. War comes to Willy Freeman (6 and up) **Fic**
Fast, H. April morning (7 and up) **Fic**
Gregory, K. The winter of red snow **Fic**
Lunn, J. L. S. The hollow tree **Fic**
Myers, A. The keeping room **Fic**
O'Dell, S. Sarah Bishop (6 and up) **Fic**
Paulsen, G. The rifle (7 and up) **Fic**

History—1775-1783, Revolution—Songs
Silverman, J. Songs and stories from the American Revolution (6 and up) **782.42**

History—1783-1809
See also Louisiana Purchase
Blumberg, R. What's the deal? Jefferson, Napoleon and the Louisiana Purchase (7 and up) **973.4**
Collier, C. Building a new nation **973.4**

History—1783-1809—Fiction
Collier, J. L. Jump ship to freedom (6 and up) **Fic**
Collier, J. L. Who is Carrie? **Fic**

History—1783-1865
Brownstone, D. M. The young nation: America 1787-1861 **973**
Littlefield, D. C. Revolutionary citizens (7 and up) **305.8**
Stefoff, R. American voices from the new republic, 1783-1830 **973.4**

History—1812-1815, War of 1812
See War of 1812

History—1815-1861
Collier, C. Andrew Jackson's America, 1824-1850 **973.5**
Collier, C. Slavery and the coming of the Civil War, 1831-1861 **973.6**

History—1815-1861—Fiction
Paterson, K. Lyddie (5 and up) **Fic**

History—1845-1848, War with Mexico
See Mexican War, 1846-1848

History—1861-1865, Civil War
Armstrong, J. Photo by Brady **973.7**
Barney, W. L. The Civil War and Reconstruction (7 and up) **973.7**
Beller, S. P. Billy Yank & Johnny Reb (5 and up) **973.7**
Beller, S. P. The Civil War **973.7**
Beller, S. P. Confederate ladies of Richmond **973.7**
Bolotin, N. Civil War A to Z (4 and up) **973.7**
The Civil War [Grolier 10v set] (5 and up) **973.7**
Civil War: battles and leaders **973.7**
Collier, C. The Civil War, 1860-1865 **973.7**
Collier, C. Slavery and the coming of the Civil War, 1831-1861 **973.6**
Dolan, E. F. The American Civil War **973.7**
Freedman, R. Lincoln: a photobiography (5 and up) **92**

United States—History—1861-1865, Civil War—*Continued*

Fritz, J. Stonewall [biography of Stonewall Jackson] (4 and up) **92**

Giblin, J. Good brother, bad brother [biography of John Wilkes Booth and Edwin Booth] (5 and up) **92**

Golay, M. Civil War **973.7**

Haugen, D. The Civil War (7 and up) **973.7**

Hillstrom, K. American Civil War: almanac **973.7**

Hillstrom, K. Experiencing the American Civil War **973.7**

Lincoln, A. Abraham Lincoln the writer (7 and up) **92**

Marrin, A. Commander in Chief Abraham Lincoln and the Civil War (7 and up) **973.7**

McKissack, P. C. Days of Jubilee (5 and up) **973.7**

McPherson, J. M. Fields of fury (5 and up) **973.7**

Murphy, J. The boys' war (5 and up) **973.7**

Nardo, D. The Civil War (7 and up) **973.7**

Otfinoski, S. John Wilkes Booth and the Civil War **92**

Pflueger, L. Mathew Brady **92**

Pflueger, L. Stonewall Jackson **92**

Ray, D. Behind the Blue and Gray (5 and up) **973.7**

Ray, D. A nation torn (5 and up) **973.7**

Robertson, J. I., Jr. Standing like a stone wall: the life of General Thomas J. Jackson (7 and up) **92**

Stanchak, J. E. The visual dictionary of the Civil War **973.7**

Sullivan, G. Abraham Lincoln (4 and up) **92**

Sullivan, G. Picturing Lincoln **92**

Taylor, S. K. The diary of Susie King Taylor, Civil War nurse (5 and up) **973.7**

Trudeau, N. A. Like men of war (7 and up) **973.7**

Uschan, M. V. The cavalry during the Civil War **973.7**

Watkins, S. R. The diary of Sam Watkins, a confederate soldier (5 and up) **973.7**

Wisler, G. C. When Johnny went marching (5 and up) **973.7**

Zeinert, K. Those courageous women of the Civil War (7 and up) **973.7**

See/See also pages in the following book(s):

Currie, S. Slavery (7 and up) **326**

Frankel, N. Break those chains at last: African Americans, 1860-1880 **305.8**

History—1861-1865, Civil War—Bibliography

Stephens, E. C. Learning about—the Civil War **016.973**

History—1861-1865, Civil War—Biography

Hillstrom, K. American Civil War: biographies **920**

History—1861-1865, Civil War—Campaigns

Matthews, T. L. Grierson's raid (7 and up) **973.7**

History—1861-1865, Civil War—Encyclopedias

Netzley, P. D. Civil War **973.7**

History—1861-1865, Civil War—Fiction

Banks, S. H. Abraham's battle **Fic**

Bartoletti, S. C. No man's land (5 and up) **Fic**

Beatty, P. Jayhawker (5 and up) **Fic**

The Boy of Chancellorville and other Civil War stories (7 and up) **S C**

Brenaman, M. Evvy's Civil War **Fic**

Clapp, P. The tamarack tree (7 and up) **Fic**

Collier, J. L. With every drop of blood (5 and up) **Fic**

Crisp, M. Private Captain **Fic**

Denenberg, B. When will this cruel war be over? **Fic**

Fleischman, P. Bull Run (6 and up) **Fic**

Hahn, M. D. Hear the wind blow (5 and up) **Fic**

Hahn, M. D. Promises to the dead (5 and up) **Fic**

Hansen, J. Which way freedom? (5 and up) **Fic**

Hesse, K. A light in the storm (5 and up) **Fic**

Hughes, P. Guerrilla season (7 and up) **Fic**

Keehn, S. M. Anna Sunday **Fic**

Keith, H. Rifles for Watie **Fic**

Lyons, M. E. Dear Ellen Bee **Fic**

Matas, C. The war within (5 and up) **Fic**

McMullan, M. How I found the Strong (5 and up) **Fic**

Murphy, J. The journal of James Edmond Pease, a Civil War Union soldier **Fic**

Paulsen, G. Soldier's heart (7 and up) **Fic**

Peck, R. The river between us (7 and up) **Fic**

Pinkney, A. D. Silent thunder **Fic**

Reeder, C. Across the lines (5 and up) **Fic**

Rinaldi, A. Amelia's war **Fic**

Rinaldi, A. Girl in blue **Fic**

Rinaldi, A. In my father's house (7 and up) **Fic**

Siegelson, K. L. Trembling earth **Fic**

Wisler, G. C. Red Cap (4 and up) **Fic**

Wisler, G. C. Run the blockade **Fic**

History—1861-1865, Civil War—Naval operations

Sullivan, G. The Civil War at sea **973.7**

Walker, S. M. Secrets of a Civil War submarine (7 and up) **973.7**

History—1861-1865, Civil War—Reconstruction

See Reconstruction (1865-1876)

History—1861-1865, Civil War—Songs

Silverman, J. Songs and stories of the Civil War **782.42**

History—1861-1865, Civil War—Sources

Hillstrom, K. American Civil War: primary sources **973.7**

Kirchberger, J. H. The Civil War and Reconstruction (7 and up) **973.7**

Seidman, R. F. The Civil war: a history in documents **973.7**

History—1861-1865, Civil War—Women

Caravantes, P. Petticoat spies **920**

History—1865-1898

Bair, B. Though justice sleeps (7 and up) **305.8**

United States—History—1865-1898—*Continued*
Collier, C. The United States enters the world stage: from the Alaska Purchase through World War I, 1867-1919   **973.8**
The Gilded Age: a history in documents (7 and up)   **973.8**
     History—1865-1898—**Fiction**
LaFaye, A. Edith Shay (7 and up)   **Fic**
     History—1898, War of 1898
See Spanish-American War, 1898
     History—1898-1919
Collier, C. The United States enters the world stage: from the Alaska Purchase through World War I, 1867-1919   **973.8**
     History—20th century
America in the 20th century   **973.9**
America's decades   **973.9**
Brown, G. Conflict in Europe and the Great Depression   **973.9**
The Century that was (7 and up)   **973.9**
Collier, C. Progressivism, the Great Depression, and the New Deal, 1901 to 1941   **973.91**
     History—1914-1918, World War
See World War, 1914-1918—United States
     History—1919-1933
See/See also pages in the following book(s):
King, D. C. Al Capone and the roaring twenties   **92**
     History—1933-1945
Isserman, M. World War II (7 and up)   **940.53**
     History—1939-1945, World War
See World War, 1939-1945—United States
     History—1945-
Anderson, D. The Cold War years   **973.92**
Campbell, G. A. The home front   **973.92**
Collier, C. The changing face of American society: 1945-2000   **973.92**
     History—1945-1953
Lindop, E. America in the 1950s (7 and up)   **973.921**
     History—1953-1961
Lindop, E. America in the 1950s (7 and up)   **973.921**
     History—1961-1974
Kronenwetter, M. America in the 1960s (7 and up)   **973.92**
Schomp, V. American voices from the Vietnam era   **973.923**
     History—1991, Persian Gulf War
See Persian Gulf War, 1991
     History—Bibliography
Adamson, L. G. Literature connections to American history, 7-12   **016.973**
     History—Dictionaries
Kane, J. N. Famous first facts   **031.02**
     History—Encyclopedias
The American Heritage encyclopedia of American history   **973.03**
King, D. C. Children's encyclopedia of American history   **973.03**
     History—Fiction—Bibliography
Dickinson, A. T. American historical fiction   **016.813**

VanMeter, V. America in historical fiction   **016.813**
     History—Poetry
Katz, B. We the people (5 and up)   **811**
     History—Sources
Our country's founders (7 and up)   **973**
     History, Military
See United States—Military history
Immigration and emigration
See also Immigrants—United States
Anderson, D. Arriving at Ellis Island (5 and up)   **325.73**
Bode, J. The colors of freedom   **305.8**
Collier, C. A century of immigration, 1820-1924   **325.73**
Daniels, R. American immigration (7 and up)   **325.73**
Dolan, E. F. The Irish potato famine   **941.5**
Hoobler, D. We are Americans (5 and up)   **325.73**
I was dreaming to come to America (4 and up)   **325.73**
Illegal immigration: opposing viewpoints (7 and up)   **325.73**
Immigration (7 and up)   **325.73**
Kosof, A. Living in two worlds (7 and up)   **325.73**
Moreno, B. Italian Americans (7 and up)   **305.8**
Perl, L. To the Golden Mountain   **305.8**
Sandler, M. W. Island of hope (5 and up)   **325.73**
Wepman, D. Immigration (7 and up)   **325.73**
Immigration and emigration—Encyclopedias
The Newest Americans   **325.73**
     Local history
Facts about the states   **973**
Monuments and historic places of America   **973**
     Maps
Junior state maps on file (4 and up)   **973**
Rubel, D. Scholastic atlas of the United States   **912**
     Military history
Buckley, G. L. American patriots (7 and up)   **355**
Gay, K. After the shooting stops (7 and up)   **355**
Haskins, J. African American military heroes   **920**
     Military history—Encyclopedias
English, J. Scholastic encyclopedia of the United States at war   **973.03**
     Poetry
Celebrate America in poetry and art (5 and up)   **811.008**
My America (4 and up)   **811.008**
     Politics and government
Altman, L. J. The politics of slavery (7 and up)   **326**
American government at work (7 and up)   **320.4**
American presidents in world history   **920.003**
Christianson, S. G. Facts about the Congress   **328.73**

United States—Politics and government—*Continued*

The Founding of America   **973.3**
Horn, G. The presidency (5 and up)   **352.23**
My fellow Americans (7 and up)   **352.23**
Nelson, L. E. American presidents   **920.003**
Spangenburg, R. Political and social movements (7 and up)   **917.3**
Tomaselli-Moschovitis, V. Government on file   **320.4**

Politics and government—1775-1783, Revolution

Feinberg, B. S. The Articles of Confederation (7 and up)   **342**
Fradin, D. B. The signers (4 and up)   **920**
Freedman, R. Give me liberty! (5 and up)   **973.3**
Moehn, H. The U.S. Constitution   **342**

Politics and government—1783-1809

Collier, C. Building a new nation   **973.4**
Collier, C. Creating the Constitution, 1787   **342**
Rosenburg, J. M. Alexander Hamilton   **92**

Politics and government—1783-1865

Collier, C. The Jeffersonian Republicans, 1800-1823   **973.4**

Politics and government—1815-1861

Collier, C. Andrew Jackson's America, 1824-1850   **973.5**
Ray, D. A nation torn (5 and up)   **973.7**
See/See also pages in the following book(s):
Harvey, B. C. Daniel Webster   **92**

Politics and government—1861-1865

The election of 1860 and the administration of Abraham Lincoln (7 and up)   **973.7**

Politics and government—1865-1898

January, B. Reconstruction   **973.8**

Politics and government—20th century

Greenberg, J. E. Young people's letters to the president   **973**

Politics and government—1933-1945

Freedman, R. Franklin Delano Roosevelt (5 and up)   **92**
Gilbert, A. Franklin D. Roosevelt (7 and up)   **92**

Politics and government—1945-

Collier, C. The middle road: American politics, 1945-2000   **973.92**

Politics and government—1945-1953

The McCarthy hearings (7 and up)   **973.921**
Sherrow, V. Joseph McCarthy and the Cold War   **92**

Politics and government—1945-1953—Fiction

Levine, E. Catch a tiger by the toe   **Fic**

Politics and government—1953-1961

The McCarthy hearings (7 and up)   **973.921**
Sherrow, V. Joseph McCarthy and the Cold War   **92**

Politics and government—1989-

Cohen, D. The impeachment of William Jefferson Clinton (7 and up)   **973.929**
The Election of 2000 and the administration of George W. Bush (7 and up)   **324**
Ventura, J. Jesse Ventura tells it like it is   **320**

Politics and government—Encyclopedias

Encyclopedia of American government   **320.03**

Politics and government—Handbooks, manuals, etc.

United States government manual   **352.2**

Politics and government—Sources

Matuz, R. Complete American presidents sourcebook   **920**

Popular culture

See Popular culture—United States

Presidents

See Presidents—United States

Race relations

Altman, L. J. The politics of slavery (7 and up)   **326**
Anderson, W. Plessy v. Ferguson   **342**
Birdseye, D. H. Under our skin (4 and up)   **305.8**
Bolden, T. Tell all the children our story (5 and up)   **305.8**
Buckley, G. L. American patriots (7 and up)   **355**
Bullard, S. Free at last   **323.1**
Civil rights (7 and up)   **323.1**
Collier, C. Reconstruction and the rise of Jim Crow, 1864-1896   **973.8**
Engelbert, P. American civil rights: biographies   **920**
Finlayson, R. We shall overcome   **323.1**
George, L. Civil rights marches   **323.1**
Hansen, J. Bury me not in a land of slaves (7 and up)   **973.8**
Haskins, J. Out of the darkness (5 and up)   **305.8**
Isserman, M. Journey to freedom (7 and up)   **305.8**
King, C. Oh, freedom! (5 and up)   **323.1**
King, M. L. The words of Martin Luther King, Jr.   **323.1**
Lanier, S. Jefferson's children (7 and up)   **920**
Linda Brown, you are not alone (5 and up)   **323.1**
McWhorter, D. A dream of freedom (5 and up)   **323.1**
Pinkney, A. D. Let it shine (4 and up)   **920**
Race relations: opposing viewpoints   **305.8**
Rasmussen, R. K. Farewell to Jim Crow (7 and up)   **305.8**
Ritchie, N. The civil rights movement   **323.1**
Sirimarco, E. American voices from the civil rights movement   **323.1**
Trotter, J. W. From a raw deal to a New Deal? African Americans, 1929-1945 (7 and up)   **305.8**
Wexler, S. The civil rights movement (7 and up)   **323.1**
What are you? (7 and up)   **305.8**
Williams, J. Eyes on the prize: America's civil rights years, 1954-1965 (7 and up)   **323.1**
Wormser, R. The rise and fall of Jim Crow (7 and up)   **305.8**
See/See also pages in the following book(s):
Discrimination: opposing viewpoints (7 and up)   **305.8**

Religion

Balmer, R. H. Religion in twentieth century America (7 and up)   **200.9**

United States—Religion—*Continued*

Braude, A. Women and American religion (7 and up)   **200.9**

Joselit, J. W. Immigration and American religion (7 and up)   **200**

Religion in America: opposing viewpoints (7 and up)   **200.9**

Stein, S. J. Alternative American religions (7 and up)   **209**

Social conditions

Anderson, D. The Cold War years   **973.92**

The Baby boom (7 and up)   **306**

Campbell, G. A. The home front   **973.92**

Collier, C. The changing face of American society: 1945-2000   **973.92**

Living through the Great Depression (7 and up)   **973.91**

Woog, A. A sweatshop during the industrial revolution   **331.2**

Social life and customs

The Baby boom (7 and up)   **306**

Brenner, B. If you were there in 1776 (4 and up)   **973.3**

Collier, C. The changing face of American society: 1945-2000   **973.92**

Goodman, S. Ultimate field trip 4: a week in the 1800s (5 and up)   **973.5**

Hoobler, D. Vanity rules   **391**

Miller, B. M. Growing up in revolution and the new nation, 1775 to 1800 (5 and up)
973.3

Myths, legends, and folktales of America
398.2

Plante, E. M. The American kitchen, 1700 to the present (7 and up)   **643**

Whitman, S. What's cooking? (5 and up)
394.1

Social life and customs—1600-1775, Colonial period

Howarth, S. Colonial places (4 and up)
973.2

Johnson, C. D. Daily life in colonial New England (7 and up)   **974**

Loeper, J. J. Going to school in 1776 (4 and up)
370.9

Miller, B. M. Good women of a well-blessed land   **305.4**

Social policy

Welfare reform (7 and up)   **361.6**

Soldiers

See Soldiers—United States

Statistics

Encyclopaedia Britannica almanac   **031.02**

Information please almanac, atlas & yearbook
031.02

The New York Times almanac   **031.02**

United States. Bureau of the Census. Statistical abstract of the United States   **317.3**

The World almanac and book of facts
031.02

Territorial expansion

The American frontier (7 and up)   **978**

Pendergast, T. Westward expansion: primary sources (7 and up)   **978**

Westward expansion [Eyewitness history series]
978

Territories and possessions

McNair, S. U.S. Territories

In America the beautiful, second series
973

Travel

See United States—Description and travel

United States. Army. Cavalry

See/See also pages in the following book(s):

Uschan, M. V. The cavalry during the Civil War
973.7

United States. Army Nurse Corps

Kuhn, B. Angels of mercy (5 and up)
940.54

United States. Articles of Confederation

Feinberg, B. S. The Articles of Confederation (7 and up)   **342**

United States. Bureau of Labor Statistics

Occupational outlook handbook   **331.7**

United States. Bureau of the Census

Statistical abstract of the United States
317.3

United States. Civilian Conservation Corps *See* Civilian Conservation Corps (U.S.)

United States. Congress

Christianson, S. G. Facts about the Congress
328.73

Horn, G. The Congress (5 and up)   **328**

United States. Constitution

The Constitution and its amendments   **342**

Vile, J. R. The United States Constitution (7 and up)   **342**

United States. Constitution. 1st-10th amendments

Freedman, R. In defense of liberty   **342**

Krull, K. A kid's guide to America's Bill of Rights (4 and up)   **342**

Patrick, J. J. The Bill of Rights (7 and up)
342

Pendergast, T. Constitutional amendments: from freedom of speech to flag burning (7 and up)
342

United States. Constitutional Convention (1787)

Collier, C. Creating the Constitution, 1787
342

United States. Declaration of Independence

Brenner, B. If you were there in 1776 (4 and up)   **973.3**

Fradin, D. B. The signers (4 and up)   **920**

Freedman, R. Give me liberty! (5 and up)
973.3

See/See also pages in the following book(s):

Collier, C. The American Revolution, 1763-1783
973.3

United States. Dept. of Justice. Federal Bureau of Investigation *See* United States. Federal Bureau of Investigation

United States. Dept. of Transportation. National Transportation Safety Board *See* United States. National Transportation Safety Board

United States. Federal Bureau of Investigation

Streissguth, T. J. Edgar Hoover: powerful FBI Director   **92**

United States. Food and Drug Administration

Esherick, J. The FDA and psychiatric drugs

United States. Marine Corps
Bradley, J. Flags of our fathers (7 and up)
940.54

United States. National Aeronautics and Space Administration
Spangenburg, R. The history of NASA
629.4
Vogt, G. Space mission patches **629.45**

United States. National Institutes of Health *See* National Institutes of Health (U.S.)

United States. National Transportation Safety Board
Mintzer, R. The National Transportation Safety Board **363.1**

United States. President (1861-1865: Lincoln)
Tackach, J. The Emancipation Proclamation (7 and up) **973.7**

United States. Supreme Court
Brannen, D. E. Supreme Court drama (7 and up) **347**
DeVillers, D. Marbury v. Madison (7 and up) **347**
Kent, D. Thurgood Marshall and the Supreme Court **92**
Rowh, M. Thurgood Marshall **92**
The Supreme Court A to Z **347**

The **United** States and Iran. Spencer, W.
327.73

The **United** States cookbook. D'Amico, J.
641.5

The **United** States enters the world stage: from the Alaska Purchase through World War I, 1867-1919. Collier, C. **973.8**

United States government manual **352.2**

United States holidays and observances. Rajtar, S.
394.26

United States Holocaust Memorial Museum
—I never saw another butterfly—. See —I never saw another butterfly— **741.9**

The **United** States in the Cold War: 1945-1989. Collier, C. **327.73**

The **United** States in World War II: 1941-1945. Collier, C. **940.53**

United States Military Academy
Fiction
Efaw, A. Battle dress (7 and up) **Fic**

United States Naval Expedition to Japan (1852-1854)
Blumberg, R. Commodore Perry in the land of the Shogun (5 and up) **952**

United States Olympic Committee
Olympism. See Olympism **796.48**

United States presidents [series]
Holford, D. M. Herbert Hoover **92**
Kachurek, S. J. George W. Bush **92**

United States stamps and stories. See Postal Service guide to U.S. stamps **769.56**

United States v. the Amistad. Hulm, D. **326**

United Tates of America. Danziger, P. **Fic**

Universal Negro Improvement Association
Lawler, M. Marcus Garvey **92**

Universe
Silverstein, A. The universe **520**

The **universe**. Simon, S. **523**

The **unlikely** romance of Kate Bjorkman. Plummer, L. **Fic**

Unlocking the secrets of science [series]
Bankston, J. Henry Ford and the assembly line **92**

Unmarried couples
See/See also pages in the following book(s):
Marriage and divorce (7 and up) **306.8**

Unmarried fathers
See also Single parent family

Unmarried mothers
See also Single parent family
Fiction
Bunting, E. Doll baby **Fic**
Dessen, S. Someone like you (7 and up)
Fic

The **Unseen**. Snyder, Z. K. **Fic**

Unseen companion. Orenstein, D. G. **Fic**

Unsung heroes of World War II. Durrett, D.
940.54

Up from slavery. Washington, B. T. **92**

Up in the air: the story of Bessie Coleman. Hart, P. S. **92**

Up Molasses Mountain. Baker, J. **Fic**

Up on cloud nine. Fine, A. **Fic**

Updale, Eleanor
Montmorency **Fic**

Updike, John
The alligators
In Who do you think you are?; stories of friends and enemies p64-72 **S C**

Upon the head of the goat: a childhood in Hungary, 1939-1944. Siegal, A. **92**

The **upstairs** room. Reiss, J. **92**

Upstream. Lion, M. **Fic**

Uranus (Planet)
Tocci, S. A look at Uranus **523.4**

Urban areas *See* Cities and towns

Urban life *See* City and town life

Urban planning *See* City planning

Uruguay
Jermyn, L. Uruguay (5 and up) **989.5**

Uschan, Michael V., 1948-
The Battle of the Little Bighorn (5 and up)
973.8
The bombing of Pearl Harbor **940.54**
The cavalry during the Civil War **973.7**
John F. Kennedy (7 and up) **92**
Political leaders **920**

Using educational technology with at-risk students. Mendrinos, R. B. **027.8**

Using internet primary sources to teach critical thinking skills in the sciences. Johnson, C.
025.04

Using picture storybooks to teach literary devices v3. Hall, S. **016.8**

USMA *See* United States Military Academy

USS Constellation. Myers, W. D. **359.8**

Ussama bin Laden *See* Osama bin Laden

Utah
Kent, D. Utah
In America the beautiful, second series
973
Stefoff, R. Utah
In Celebrate the states 973

Ute Indians
Fiction
Borland, H. When the legends die **Fic**
Hobbs, W. Bearstone (7 and up) **Fic**

Uteritsoq and the duck-bill dolls. Norman, H.
In Norman, H. The girl who dreamed only geese, and other tales of the Far North
398.2

The **uterus** fairy. High, L. O.
In Don't cramp my style; stories about that time of the month p265-83 **S C**

Utomo, Gabhor
(il) Currier, K. S. Kai's journey to Gold Mountain **Fic**

Utopias
Fiction
Huxley, A. Brave new world (7 and up) **Fic**

Uttley, Colin
Magnesium
In The Elements 546

UXL Asian American voices 815

U·X·L encyclopedia of Native American tribes
970.004

UXL encyclopedia of world biography 920.003

V

V.C.R.'s *See* Video recording
V.D. *See* Sexually transmitted diseases
Vaccination
Collier, J. L. Vaccines 615
Hyde, M. O. Vaccinations (7 and up) 615
Nardo, D. Vaccines (7 and up) 615
See/See also pages in the following book(s):
Epidemics: opposing viewpoints 614.4

Vaccines. Collier, J. L. 615
Vaccines. Nardo, D. 615

Vagabonds *See* Tramps
Vagrants *See* Tramps

Vail, Rachel
The crush
In Tripping over the lunch lady and other school stories p120-30 **S C**
Going sentimental
In Places I never meant to be; original stories by censored writers **S C**
Thirteen and a half
In 13; thirteen stories that capture the agony and ecstasy of being thirteen **S C**
(jt. auth) Avi. Never mind! **Fic**

Valdez (Ship) *See* Exxon Valdez (Ship)
Valentine. Rice, D.
In Rice, D. Crazy loco; stories about growing up Chicano in southern Texas p29-38
S C

Valentine's Day
Fiction
Conford, E. Crush (7 and up) **S C**

Valenza, Joyce Kasman
Power research tools 001.4
Power tools recharged 027.8

The **valley** of fear. Doyle, Sir A. C.
In Doyle, Sir A. C. The complete Sherlock Holmes **S C**

Valley of the Kings. Smith, S. T. 932
Valley of the Moon. Garland, S. **Fic**

Values
Robinson, S. Jackie's nine 170

Vampire High. Rees, D. C. **Fic**

Vampires
Fiction
Klause, A. C. The silver kiss **Fic**
Rees, D. C. Vampire High **Fic**
Vampires: a collection of original stories
S C

Vampires: a collection of original stories **S C**

Van Allsburg, Chris
See/See also pages in the following book(s):
Marcus, L. S. A Caldecott celebration 741.6
The Newbery & Caldecott medal books, 1986-2000 028.5

Van Eekhout, Greg
Will you be an astronaut?
In New skies: an anthology of today's science fiction **S C**

Van Gogh, Vincent *See* Gogh, Vincent van, 1853-1890

Van Laan, Nancy
With a whoop and a holler (4 and up) 398
Includes the following stories: One cold day; Monkey stew; Fool John; Possum plays dead; The big dinin'; The watermillion patch; Ol' Mister Biggety; How come Ol' Buzzard boards; Mister Grumpy rides the clouds; Nuts! Nuts! Nuts!; We hunted and we hollered; Ol' Gally Mander; Jack runs off; Three Foots

Van Leeuwen, Jean
Cabin on Trouble Creek (4 and up) **Fic**
Lucy was there— **Fic**

Van Lew, Elizabeth, 1818-1900
See/See also pages in the following book(s):
Caravantes, P. Petticoat spies 920
Fiction
Lyons, M. E. Dear Ellen Bee **Fic**

Van Maarsen, Jacqueline *See* Maarsen, Jacqueline van, 1929-

Vanasse, Deb
Out of the wilderness **Fic**

VanCleave, Janice Pratt
Janice VanCleave's 203 icy, freezing, frosty, cool & wild experiments (4 and up)
507.8
Janice VanCleave's A+ projects in astronomy (7 and up) 520
Janice VanCleave's A+ projects in earth science (7 and up) 550
Janice Vancleave's ecology for every kid (4 and up) 577
Janice VanCleave's guide to more of the best science fair projects (5 and up) 507.8
Janice VanCleave's guide to the best science fair projects (4 and up) 507.8

VanCleave, Janice Pratt—*Continued*
Janice VanCleave's plants (5 and up)   **580.7**
Janice VanCleave's solar system (4 and up)   **523.2**

Vande Velde, Vivian, 1951-
Alison, who went away   **Fic**
Being dead (7 and up)   **S C**
Includes the following stories: Dancing with Marjorie's ghost; Shadow brother; For love of him; October chill; Drop by drop; The ghost; Drop dead
Heir apparent   **Fic**
Morgan Roehmar's boys
   In Gothic!; ten original dark tales   **S C**
Never trust a dead man   **Fic**
Tales from the Brothers Grimm and the Sisters Weird   **S C**
Includes the following stories: Straw into gold; Frog; The granddaughter; Jack; The bridge; Mattresses; Twins; Beast and Beauty
There's a dead person following my sister around (4 and up)   **Fic**

Vanderwarker, Peter
The big dig   **624.1**

Vanishing. Brooks, B.   **Fic**

Vanishing species *See* Endangered species

Vanity rules. Hoobler, D.   **391**

VanMeter, Vandelia
America in historical fiction   **016.813**

Vansant, Wayne
The red badge of courage   **741.5**

Vaqueros. Sandler, M. W.   **973**

Variations on a theme. Koertge, R.
   In What a song can do; 12 riffs on the power of music   **S C**

Vatican City
Lace, W. W. The Vatican   **945**

Vaudeville
Fiction
Tamar, E. The midnight train home   **Fic**

Vaughan, Marcia, 1951-
How to cook a gooseberry fool
   In Easy menu ethnic cookbooks   **641.5**

Vaught, Susan
Stormwitch (7 and up)   **Fic**

Vaupel, Robin
My contract with Henry   **Fic**

Vaz, Katherine
A world painted by birds
   In The Green Man: tales from the mythic forest p168-88   **808.8**

Vázquez de Coronado, Francisco, 1510-1549
About
Otfinoski, S. Francisco Coronado   **92**

VCRs *See* Video recording

VD *See* Sexually transmitted diseases

Vecchione, Glen
100 award-winning science fair projects (7 and up)   **507.8**

Vecchione, Patrice
(ed) The Body eclectic. See The Body eclectic   **808.81**
(ed) Revenge and forgiveness. See Revenge and forgiveness   **808.81**
(ed) Truth & lies: an anthology of poems. See Truth & lies: an anthology of poems   **808.81**
(ed) Whisper and shout. See Whisper and shout   **811.008**

Veciana-Suarez, Ana
The flight to freedom   **Fic**

Vedral, Joyce L.
Toning for teens (7 and up)   **613.7**

Vega, Ed
An apology to the moon furies
   In Growing up Latino; memoirs and stories p47-72   **810.8**

Vegetarian cooking
Gillies, J. The jumbo vegetarian cookbook (4 and up)   **641.5**
Krizmanic, J. A teen's vegetarian cookbook (7 and up)   **641.5**

Vegetarian cooking around the world
   In Easy menu ethnic cookbooks   **641.5**

Vegetarianism
Duden, J. Vegetarianism for teens   **613.2**
Schwartz, E. I'm a vegetarian   **613.2**

Vegetarianism for teens. Duden, J.   **613.2**

Veggeberg, Scott
Lyme disease (7 and up)   **616.9**

Veladota, Christina
Teen runaways (7 and up)   **362.7**

Velasquez, Eric
(il) Naidoo, B. Journey to Jo'burg   **Fic**

Velmans, Hester
Isabel of the whales (5 and up)   **Fic**

Venables, Stephen, 1954-
To the top (5 and up)   **796.52**

Venereal diseases *See* Sexually transmitted diseases

Venezuela
Winter, J. K. Venezuela   **987**

Venice (Italy)
History
Hinds, K. Venice and its merchant empire   **945**

Venice and its merchant empire. Hinds, K.   **945**

Vennema, Peter
(jt. auth) Stanley, D. Bard of Avon: the story of William Shakespeare   **822.3**
(jt. auth) Stanley, D. Charles Dickens   **92**
(jt. auth) Stanley, D. Cleopatra   **92**
(jt. auth) Stanley, D. Good Queen Bess: the story of Elizabeth I of England   **92**
(jt. auth) Stanley, D. Shaka, king of the Zulus   **92**

Venti, Anthony Bacon
(il) Climo, S. Magic & mischief   **398.2**
(il) Fritz, J. Around the world in a hundred years   **910.4**

Ventura, Jesse
Jesse Ventura tells it like it is   **320**

Venus (Planet)
Spangenburg, R. Venus   **523.4**

Venus & Serena. Williams, V.   **92**

Verdick, Elizabeth
(ed) Schwager, T. The right moves   613.7
Vergoth, Karin
Endangered species   578.68
Verhoeven, Rian
(jt. auth) Rol, R. v. d. Anne Frank, beyond the diary   92
Vermont
Elish, D. Vermont
In Celebrate the states   973
Heinrichs, A. Vermont
In America the beautiful, second series   973

Fiction
Alvarez, J. How Tia Lola came to visit/stay (4 and up)   Fic
Anderson, M. T. The Game of Sunken Places (5 and up)   Fic
Doyle, E. F. Stray voltage   Fic
Gauthier, G. The hero of Ticonderoga   Fic
Hesse, K. Witness (6 and up)   Fic
Lunn, J. L. S. The hollow tree   Fic
Paterson, K. Jip (5 and up)   Fic
Paterson, K. Preacher's boy (5 and up)   Fic
Peck, R. N. A day no pigs would die (6 and up)   Fic
Stahler, D., Jr. A gathering of shades (7 and up)   Fic
Wilson, N. H. Mountain pose (5 and up)   Fic

Verne, Jules, 1828-1905
Around the world in eighty days   Fic
Twenty thousand leagues under the sea (5 and up)   Fic

About
Schoell, W. Remarkable journeys: the story of Jules Verne   92

Verougstraete, Randy
(il) Godfrey, N. S. Neale S. Godfrey's ultimate kids' money book   332.024
Vertebrates
Animals   596
Silverstein, A. Vertebrates (5 and up)   596
Vertical file index   015.73
Very best (almost) friends (4 and up)   811.008
The **very** old woman and the Piskey. Climo, S.
In Climo, S. Magic & mischief; tales from Cornwall p15-20   398.2
Vespucci, Amerigo, 1451-1512
See/See also pages in the following book(s):
Fritz, J. Around the world in a hundred years (4 and up)   910.4
Vess, Charles
(il) The Green Man: tales from the mythic forest. See The Green Man: tales from the mythic forest   808.8
Veterans

Fiction
Cormier, R. Heroes (7 and up)   Fic
Vicksburg (Miss.)
Siege, 1863
Fraser, M. A. Vicksburg—the battle that won the Civil War (4 and up)   973.7
King, D. C. The Battle of Vicksburg   973.7

Siege, 1863—Fiction
Clapp, P. The tamarack tree (7 and up)   Fic
Vicksburg—the battle that won the Civil War. Fraser, M. A.   973.7
Victims and victims' rights. Faherty, S.   362.88
Victims of crimes
Faherty, S. Victims and victims' rights (7 and up)   362.88
Victoria, Queen of Great Britain, 1819-1901
About
Price-Groff, C. Queen Victoria and nineteenth-century England   941.081
See/See also pages in the following book(s):
McGaw, L. To be a princess (4 and up)   920
Hewitt, K. Lives of extraordinary women (4 and up)   920
Myers, W. D. At her majesty's request [biography of Sarah Forbes Bonetta] (5 and up)   92

Fiction
Kirwan, A. Victoria, May blossom of Britannia   Fic
Victoria Chapman & Associates
Health on file. See Health on file   613
Victoria, May blossom of Britannia. Kirwan, A.   Fic
Victorian England. Ashby, R.   941.081
Victorio, Apache Chief, d. 1880
See/See also pages in the following book(s):
Stovall, T. The Buffalo Soldiers   978
Video cassette recorders and recording *See* Video recording
Video games
Fiction
Seidler, T. Brainboy and the Deathmaster (5 and up)   Fic
Video recording
Shulman, M. Attack of the killer video book (5 and up)   778.59
Fiction
Mack, T. Birdland (7 and up)   Fic
Videorecorders *See* Video recording
Videotape recorders and recording *See* Video recording
Videotapes
Catalogs
Culturally diverse videos, audios, and CD-ROMS for children and young adults   011.6
Viegas, Jennifer
The revolution in healing the brain   612.8
Stem cell research   616
Vienna (Austria)
Fiction
Ibbotson, E. The star of Kazan (5 and up)   Fic
Vietnam
Seah, A. Vietnam (5 and up)   959.704
Fiction
Garland, S. Song of the buffalo boy   Fic
Social life and customs
Huynh, Q. N. The land I lost: adventures of a boy in Vietnam (5 and up)   92

Vietnam War, 1961-1975
Hillstrom, K. Vietnam War: almanac (7 and up) **959.704**
Hillstrom, K. Vietnam War: primary sources (7 and up) **959.704**
Levy, D. The Vietnam War (5 and up) **959.704**
Schomp, V. American voices from the Vietnam era **973.923**
The Vietnam War (7 and up) **959.704**
Warren, A. Escape from Saigon **92**
Yancey, D. Life of an American soldier **959.704**
Young, M. B. The Vietnam War: a history in documents (7 and up) **959.704**
See/See also pages in the following book(s):
Collier, C. The United States in the Cold War: 1945-1989 **327.73**
Goldman, M. S. Richard M. Nixon (7 and up) **92**

Biography
Hillstrom, K. Vietnam War: biographies (7 and up) **920**
Roberts, R. Leaders and generals **920**
Fiction
Easton, K. The life history of a star (7 and up) **Fic**
Franklin, K. L. Dove song **Fic**
Hobbs, V. Sonny's war (7 and up) **Fic**
Myers, W. D. Fallen angels **Fic**
Sherlock, P. Letters from Wolfie (5 and up) **Fic**

Protest movements
Farish, L. Tinker v. Des Moines (7 and up) **342**
The **Vietnam** War (7 and up) **959.704**
Vietnam War: almanac. Hillstrom, K. **959.704**
Vietnam War: biographies. Hillstrom, K. **920**
Vietnam War: primary sources. Hillstrom, K. **959.704**

Vietnamese
Fiction
Mosher, R. Zazoo **Fic**
Whelan, G. Goodbye, Vietnam (4 and up) **Fic**
Vietnamese Americans
Warren, A. Escape from Saigon **92**
Fiction
Garland, S. Shadow of the dragon **Fic**
Paterson, K. Park's quest (5 and up) **Fic**
Vietnamese Conflict, 1961-1975
Fiction
Crist-Evans, C. Amaryllis (7 and up) **Fic**
The **view** from Saturday. Konigsburg, E. L. **Fic**
The **Viking** longship. Trent, L. **948**
The **Viking** news. Wright, R. **948**
Viking town. Morley, J. **948**
Vikings
Gravett, C. Going to war in Viking times **355**
Hicks, P. Technology in the time of the Vikings **609**
Margeson, S. M. Viking (4 and up) **948**

Morley, J. Viking town **948**
Trent, L. The Viking longship (7 and up) **948**
Wright, R. The Viking news **948**
Fiction
Cadnum, M. Daughter of the wind (7 and up) **Fic**
Cadnum, M. Raven of the waves (7 and up) **Fic**
Farmer, N. The Sea of Trolls (5 and up) **Fic**
Sutcliff, R. Sword song (7 and up) **Fic**
Vile, John R.
The United States Constitution (7 and up) **342**
Villalobos, Tina Marie Freeman- *See* Freeman-Villalobos, Tina Marie
Villanueva, Alma, 1944-
Golden glass
In Growing up Latino; memoirs and stories p259-63 **810.8**
Villarreal, José Antonio
Pocho
In Growing up Latino; memoirs and stories p165-92 **810.8**
Villios, Lynne W.
Cooking the Greek way
In Easy menu ethnic cookbooks **641.5**
Vinci, Leonardo da *See* Leonardo, da Vinci, 1452-1519
Viola, Herman J., 1938-
It is a good day to die (5 and up) **973.8**
(jt. auth) Lekuton, J. Facing the lion **967.62**
Violence
See also Domestic violence; School violence
Edgar, K. J. Everything you need to know about media violence **303.6**
Gelletly, L. Violence in the media (7 and up) **303.6**
Guns and violence [Current controversies] **363.33**
Media violence: opposing viewpoints (7 and up) **303.6**
Stewart, G. Guns and violence **303.6**
Violence: opposing viewpoints (7 and up) **303.6**
Youth violence (7 and up) **364.36**
See/See also pages in the following book(s):
Mass media: opposing viewpoints **302.23**
Teens at risk: opposing viewpoints p63-105 (7 and up) **362.7**
Fiction
Cadnum, M. Edge (7 and up) **Fic**
Dessen, S. Dreamland (7 and up) **Fic**
Giles, G. Shattering Glass (7 and up) **Fic**
Koertge, R. The Brimstone journals (7 and up) **Fic**
Lynch, C. Who the man **Fic**
Soto, G. Buried onions **Fic**
Spinelli, J. Wringer (4 and up) **Fic**
Violence in our schools. Orr, T. **371.7**
Violence in the media. Gelletly, L. **303.6**
Violence: opposing viewpoints (7 and up) **303.6**

Violinists
Fiction
Ingold, J. Mountain solo (7 and up)   **Fic**
Snyder, M. Hannah's garden (7 and up)   **Fic**
Wolff, V. E. The Mozart season (6 and up)
  Fic

Violinists, violoncellists, etc. *See* Violoncellists

Violoncellists
Chippendale, L. A. Yo-Yo Ma   **92**

Viramontes, Helena Maria, 1954-
The moths
  In Growing up Latino; memoirs and stories
    p32-37   **810.8**

The **Virgin** of Guadalupe. Gerson, M.-J.
  In Gerson, M.-J. Fiesta femenina; celebrating
    women in Mexican folktale   **398.2**

Virginia
Barrett, T. Virginia
  In Celebrate the states   **973**
Blashfield, J. F. Virginia
  In America the beautiful, second series
    973
Fiction
Brenaman, M. Evvy's Civil War   **Fic**
Fuqua, J. S. The Willoughby Spit wonder
  Fic
Hite, S. Those darn Dithers   **Fic**
Paterson, K. Bridge to Terabithia (4 and up)
  Fic
Pinkney, A. D. Silent thunder   **Fic**
Ray, D. Ghost girl (5 and up)   **Fic**
White, R. Belle Prater's boy (5 and up)   **Fic**

Virtual reality
Grady, S. M. Virtual reality (7 and up)
  006.8
Wyborny, S. Virtual reality   **006.8**
Fiction
Bloor, E. Crusader (7 and up)   **Fic**
Vande Velde, V. Heir apparent   **Fic**

Virtually perfect. Gutman, D.   **Fic**

Virtue goes to town. Yep, L.
  In Yep, L. The rainbow people p136-42
    398.2

Viruses
  See also Chickenpox
Monroe, J. Influenza and other viruses   **616.9**

Vision
Silverstein, A. Seeing Silverstein, A. and others.
  Senses and sensors [series]   **612.8**
Simon, S. Eyes and ears (4 and up)   **612.8**

Vision disorders
Fiction
Dorris, M. Sees Behind Trees (4 and up)
  Fic

Visions. Sills, L.   **920**

Visions: nineteen short stories by outstanding writers for young adults (7 and up)   **S C**

Visit. Myers, W. D.
  In Necessary noise: stories about our families
    as they really are p81-93   **S C**

The **visit**. Oates, J. C.
  In Oates, J. C. Small avalanches and other
    stories   **S C**

A **visit** from Reverend Tileston. Cook-Lynn, E.
  In Talking leaves; contemporary native
    American short stories   **S C**

Visiting Miss Caples. Kimmel, E. C.   **Fic**

The **Visual** dictionary of animals (4 and up)
  591.4

The **visual** dictionary of baseball. Buckley, J., Jr.
  796.357

The **visual** dictionary of the Civil War. Stanchak,
  J. E.   **973.7**

The **Visual** dictionary of the horse (4 and up)
  636.1

Visual encyclopedia of animals   **590.3**

Visual geography series
Behnke, A. Afghanistan in pictures   **958.1**
Behnke, A. China in pictures   **951**
Behnke, A. Italy in pictures   **945**
Behnke, A. Japan in pictures   **952**
Braun, E. Canada in pictures   **971**
Broberg, C. Kenya in pictures   **967.62**
Broberg, C. Saudi Arabia in pictures   **953.8**
Engfer, L. India in pictures   **954**
Hamilton, J. Mexico in pictures   **972**
Streissguth, T. Brazil in pictures   **981**
Zuehlke, J. Egypt in pictures   **962**

Visual science encyclopedia (5 and up)   **503**

Vitale, William J.
About
Dudley, M. E. Engel v. Vitale (1962) (7 and up)
  344

Viva New Jersey. Gonzalez, G.
  In Join in; multiethnic short stories by outstanding writers for young adults p51-60
    S C

Vivian, R. Gwinn
Chaco Canyon   **978**

Vizenor, Gerald Robert, 1934-
The baron of Petronia
  In Talking leaves; contemporary native
    American short stories   **S C**
China Browne
  In Talking leaves; contemporary native
    American short stories   **S C**

Vo, Dinh Mai, 1933-
(il) Huynh, Q. N. The land I lost: adventures of
  a boy in Vietnam   **92**

Vo, Quy
See/See also pages in the following book(s):
Graham, K. Contemporary environmentalists (7
  and up)   **920**

Voake, Charlotte
(il) Richardson, J. Looking at pictures   **750**

Vocabulary
Terban, M. Building your vocabulary (4 and up)
  428

Vocational education
Unger, H. G. But what if I don't want to go to
  college? (7 and up)   **331.7**

Vocational guidance
Career discovery encyclopedia   **331.7**
Coon, N. Teen dream jobs (7 and up)
  650.14

Vocational guidance—*Continued*

The Encyclopedia of careers and vocational guidance **331.7**

Heading out (7 and up) **331.7**

Jones, S. Film (7 and up) **791.43**

McAlpine, M. Working with computers **004**

Pervola, C. How to get a job if you're a teenager (7 and up) **650.14**

Schwager, T. Cool women, hot jobs . . . and how you can go for it, too! (7 and up) **650.14**

Unger, H. G. But what if I don't want to go to college? (7 and up) **331.7**

United States. Bureau of Labor Statistics. Occupational outlook handbook **331.7**

Young person's occupational outlook handbook **331.7**

Vocations *See* Occupations

Voelkel, James R.

Johannes Kepler and the new astronomy (7 and up) **92**

Vogel, Carole Garbuny

Human impact (5 and up) **333.91**

Ocean wildlife (5 and up) **591.7**

Vögelein. Irwin, J. **741.5**

Vogt, Gregory

Disasters in space exploration **363.1**

John Glenn's return to space **629.45**

Space mission patches **629.45**

A **voice** from the Holocaust. Soumerai, E. N. **940.53**

The **voice** that challenged a nation [biography of Marian Anderson] Freedman, R. **92**

Voices and visions **940.53**

Voices from slavery's past. Cloud Tapper, S. **326**

Voices from the fields. Atkin, S. B. **331.5**

Voices from the margins. Ward, M. **016.8**

Voices from the past [series]

Gay, K. Persian Gulf War **956.7**

Gay, K. World War I **940.3**

Voices in poetry [series]

Angelou, M. Maya Angelou **811**

Voices of rape. Bode, J. **362.88**

Voices of twentieth century conflict [series]

Soumerai, E. N. A voice from the Holocaust **940.53**

Voices: poetry and art from around the world **808.81**

Voigt, Cynthia

Bad girls in love **Fic**

Dicey's song (6 and up) **Fic**

Homecoming (6 and up) **Fic**

Izzy, willy-nilly (7 and up) **Fic**

Jackaroo (7 and up) **Fic**

On fortune's wheel (7 and up) **Fic**

A solitary blue (7 and up) **Fic**

About

Reid, S. E. Presenting Cynthia Voigt **813.009**

Volavková, Hana

(ed) —I never saw another butterfly—. See —I never saw another butterfly— **741.9**

Volcanoes

Burleigh, R. Volcanoes (4 and up) **551.2**

Christian, S. Shake, rattle, and roll **551.2**

Grace, C. O. Forces of nature (4 and up) **551.2**

Lauber, P. Volcano: the eruption and healing of Mount St. Helens (4 and up) **551.2**

Lindop, L. Probing volcanoes (5 and up) **551.2**

Silverstein, A. Plate tectonics (5 and up) **551.1**

Trueit, T. S. Volcanoes **551.2**

See/See also pages in the following book(s):

Day, T. DK guide to savage Earth **550**

Fiction

Campbell, E. The Shark Callers (7 and up) **Fic**

Dickinson, P. Tears of the salamander **Fic**

Volleyball

Crisfield, D. Winning volleyball for girls **796.325**

Manley, C. B. Competitive volleyball for girls **796.325**

Sherrow, V. Volleyball **796.325**

Vollstadt, Elizabeth Weiss, 1942-

Teen eating disorders (7 and up) **616.85**

Volpe, Lane E., 1976-

(ed) Battered women. See Battered women **362.82**

Volunteer work

Erlbach, A. The kids' volunteering book (4-6) **302**

Gay, K. Volunteering (7 and up) **361.3**

Gillespie, K. M. Teen volunteer services in libraries **021.2**

Volunteering. Gay, K. **361.3**

Von Braun, Wernher, 1912-1977

See/See also pages in the following book(s):

Richie, J. Space flight **920**

Von Grawbadger, Wade

(jt. auth) Busiek, K. Shockrockets: we have ignition **741.5**

Von Linné, Carl *See* Linné, Carl von, 1707-1778

Von Neumann, John, 1903-1957

See/See also pages in the following book(s):

Northrup, M. American computer pioneers **920**

Vonnegut, Kurt, 1922-

Harrison Bergeron

In Read into the millennium; tales of the future p126-38 **S C**

Voodooism

Fiction

Vaught, S. Stormwitch (7 and up) **Fic**

Vossmeyer, Gabriele

(jt. auth) Fuller, B. Germany **943**

Votava, Andrea

Coping with migraines and other headaches (7 and up) **616.8**

Voting *See* Elections

Voudouism *See* Voodooism

VOYA guides [series]

Gillespie, K. M. Teen volunteer services in libraries **021.2**

The **voyage** of Patience Goodspeed. Frederick, H. V.   **Fic**

The **voyage** of the Frog. Paulsen, G.   **Fic**

Voyage with Jason. Catran, K.   **Fic**

Voyages and travels
Open your eyes (7 and up)   **910.4**
Otfinoski, S. Marco Polo   **92**
Worth, R. The great empire of China and Marco Polo in world history   **92**
Fiction
Clements, B. A chapel of thieves   **Fic**
Derby, P. Away to the goldfields!   **Fic**
Hobbs, W. Jason's gold (5 and up)   **Fic**
Whelan, G. The impossible journey   **Fic**

Voyages around the world
Levinson, N. S. Magellan and the first voyage around the world (5 and up)   **92**
Martin, J. Lionheart (7 and up)   **910.4**
Meltzer, M. Captain James Cook   **92**
Meltzer, M. Ferdinand Magellan   **92**
Fiction
Hesse, K. Stowaway (5 and up)   **Fic**
Verne, J. Around the world in eighty days   **Fic**

Voyages through time [series]
Ackroyd, P. The beginning   **576.8**
Ackroyd, P. Escape from Earth   **629.4**

A **vulnerable** America. Campbell, G. A.   **363.3**

Vultures
Rauzon, M. J. Vultures   **598**

W

Wáchale! poetry and prose on growing up Latino in America (5 and up)   **810.8**

Waddle, Linda L.
(jt. auth) Carter, B. Best books for young adults   **028.1**
(ed) New directions for library service to young adults. See New directions for library service to young adults   **027.62**

Wade, Henry, 1914-2001
About
Gold, S. D. Roe v. Wade   **344**
Payment, S. Roe v. Wade   **344**
Romaine, D. S. Roe v. Wade (7 and up)   **344**

Wadsworth, Ginger
John Burroughs (5 and up)   **92**

Waggoner, Tim
Soaring
In Half-human p165-81   **S C**

Wagner, Heather Lehr
The IRA and England (7 and up)   **941.6**
Jane Austen   **92**

Waifs and strays. De Lint, C.   **S C**

Waifs and strays [story] De Lint, C.
In De Lint, C. Waifs and strays p313-54   **S C**

Wainwright, Louie L.
About
Sherrow, V. Gideon v. Wainwright (7 and up)   **345**

Wait, Lea, 1946-
Wintering well (5 and up)   **Fic**

Waite, Judy
Shopaholic   **Fic**

Waiters and waitresses
Fiction
Mosier, E. My life as a girl   **Fic**

Waiting for a white knight. Bateman, T.
In Fire and wings: dragon tales from East and West p137-40   **S C**

Waiting for Christopher. Hawes, L.   **Fic**

Waiting for Sebastian. Peck, R.
In Peck, R. Past perfect, present tense: new and collected stories   **S C**

Waiting for the war. Salisbury, G.
In Salisbury, G. Island boyz: short stories p142-64   **S C**
also in Time capsule: short stories about teenagers throughout the twentieth century p88-107   **S C**

Waiting to disappear. Fritz, A. Y.   **Fic**

Waitresses *See* Waiters and waitresses

Wake up our souls. Bolden, T.   **704**

Wakefield, Ruth
See/See also pages in the following book(s):
Thimmesh, C. Girls think of everything (5 and up)   **920**

Wakeman, John, 1928-
(ed) World authors, 1950-1970. See World authors, 1950-1970   **920.003**
(ed) World authors, 1970-1975. See World authors, 1970-1975   **920.003**

Wakin, Edward
How TV changed America's mind (7 and up)   **070.1**

Waldee, Lynne Marie
Cooking the French way
In Easy menu ethnic cookbooks   **641.5**

Waldman, Bruce
Piracy & plunder (7 and up)   **910.4**

Waldman, Carl
Encyclopedia of Native American tribes   **970.004**

Waldman, Michael, 1960-
(comp) My fellow Americans. See My fellow Americans   **352.23**

Waldman, Neil, 1947-
Masada (4 and up)   **933**
(il) Schecter, E. The family Haggadah   **296.4**

Wales
Hestler, A. Wales   **942.9**
Fiction
Garner, A. The owl service   **Fic**
Kimmel, E. C. In the stone circle (5 and up)   **Fic**

Walk across the sea. Fletcher, S.   **Fic**

A **walk** in the sun. Landis, G. A.
In New skies: an anthology of today's science fiction   **S C**

Walk softly, Rachel. Banks, K.   **Fic**

Walk two moons. Creech, S.   **Fic**

Walker, Alice, 1944-
See/See also pages in the following book(s):
Hansen, J. Women of hope (4 and up)　**920**

Walker, Barbara J.
Developing Christian fiction collections for children and adults　**025.2**

Walker, C. J., Madame, 1867-1919
See/See also pages in the following book(s):
Aaseng, N. Black inventors (7 and up)　**920**
Haskins, J. African American entrepreneurs
　920
Jeffrey, L. S. Great American businesswomen
　920

Walker, Landry Q.
Little Gloomy: . . . It was a dark and stormy night　**741.5**

Walker, Madame C. J. *See* Walker, C. J., Madame, 1867-1919

Walker, Maggie Lena, 1867-1934
See/See also pages in the following book(s):
Haskins, J. African American entrepreneurs
　920
Jeffrey, L. S. Great American businesswomen
　920

Walker, Pamela
The digestive system (7 and up)　**612.3**
The immune system (7 and up)　**616.07**
Understanding the risk of diet drugs　**616.85**

Walker, Richard, 1951-
DK guide to the human body　**612**
Encyclopedia of the human body　**612**
Genes & DNA (5 and up)　**576.5**

Walker, Sally M.
Earthquakes (3-6)　**551.2**
Fossil fish found alive (5 and up)　**597**
Secrets of a Civil War submarine (7 and up)
　973.7

Walker, Sarah Breedlove *See* Walker, C. J., Madame, 1867-1919

Walking softly in the wilderness. Hart, J.
　796.51
Walking the Bible. Feiler, B. S.　**222**
Walking the Choctaw road. Tingle, T.　**398.2**
Walking to the bus-rider blues. Robinet, H. G.
　Fic
Walks Alone. Burks, B.　**Fic**
Wall Street wizard. Liebowitz, J.　**332.6**

Wallace, Barbara Brooks, 1922-
Secret in St. Something　**Fic**

Wallace, Bill, 1947-
Aloha summer　**Fic**
Eye of the great bear　**Fic**
Skinny-dipping at Monster Lake (4 and up)
　Fic

Wallace, Chad
(il) Longfellow, H. W. Henry Wadsworth Longfellow　**811**

Wallace, Michael Phillip
(jt. auth) Arnold, C. On the brink of extinction
　598

Wallace, Rich, 1957-
Losing is not an option: stories (7 and up)
　S C

Contents: Night game; Nailed; The amazing two-headed boy; I voted for Mary Ann; In letters that would soar a thousand feet high; What it all goes back to; Dawn; Thankgiving; Losing is not an option
Playing without the ball　**Fic**
Steppin' Eddie
　In On the edge: stories at the brink p163-73
　S C
Wrestling Sturbridge (7 and up)　**Fic**

Wallace, Ruby Ann *See* Dee, Ruby

Wallace-Brodeur, Ruth
Blue eyes better (4-6)　**Fic**

Wallechinsky, David, 1948-
The complete book of the Winter Olympics
　796.98

Wallenberg, Raoul
See/See also pages in the following book(s):
Lyman, D. Holocaust rescuers　**920**

The **walnut** and the pumpkin. Jaffe, N.
　In Jaffe, N. and Zeitlin, S. J. The cow of no color: riddle stories and justice tales from around the world p114-16　**398.2**

Walsh, Frank
The Montgomery bus boycott　**323.1**

Walsh, Kieran
The Mississippi (4 and up)　**977**

Walsh Shepherd, Donna, 1948-
Alaska
　In America the beautiful, second series
　973
The Klondike gold rush (4 and up)　**971.9**

Walt Disney Company
Finch, C. The art of Walt Disney (7 and up)
　791.43
Hahn, D. Animation magic　**791.43**

Walt Disney Productions
　See also Walt Disney Company
Peet, B. Bill Peet: an autobiography (4 and up)
　92

Walter, Mildred Pitts, 1922-
Kwanzaa: a family affair (4 and up)　**394.26**

Walter Wick's Optical tricks. Wick, W.
　152.14

Walters, Anna Lee, 1946-
Bicenti
　In Talking leaves; contemporary native American short stories　**S C**

Wanasundera, Nanda P.
Sri Lanka　**954.93**

Wand, Kelly
(ed) Animal rights movement. See Animal rights movement　**179**

Wang, An, 1920-1990
See/See also pages in the following book(s):
Northrup, M. American computer pioneers
　920

Wang, Vera
See/See also pages in the following book(s):
Kent, J. Business builders in fashion　**920**

Wangu, Madhu Bazaz
Buddhism　**294.3**
Hinduism (7 and up)　**294.5**

Wanted: a thug. Flake, S. G.
In Flake, S. G. Who am I without him?; short stories about girls and the boys in their lives p19-28   **S C**

War
Brownlie, A. Why do people fight wars?   **355**
Glick, S. War and peace   **201**
War: opposing viewpoints   **355**
Fiction
See War stories

War and civilization
Gay, K. After the shooting stops (7 and up)   **355**
War and peace. Glick, S.   **201**
War and the pity of war (5 and up)   **808.81**
War comes to Willy Freeman. Collier, J. L.   **Fic**

War crime trials
See also Nuremberg Trial of Major German War Criminals, 1945-1946

War crimes
See/See also pages in the following book(s):
Chicoine, S. From the ashes   **940.53**
War is swell. Lubar, D.
In Shattered: stories of children and war p139-47   **S C**

War of 1812
Childress, D. The War of 1812 (5 and up)   **973.5**
Collier, C. The Jeffersonian Republicans, 1800-1823   **973.4**
Greenblatt, M. War of 1812 (7 and up)   **973.5**
Carnagie, J. War of 1812 (7 and up)   **973.5**
Marquette, S. War of 1812 (4 and up)   **973.5**
Warrick, K. C. The War of 1812   **973.5**
Fiction
Alder, E. Crossing the panther's path   **Fic**
The **war** of the worlds. Wells, H. G.   **Fic**
The **war** on drugs   **363.4**

War on terrorism [series]
Hamilton, J. Weapons of war   **623.4**
Wheeler, J. C. September 11, 2001: the day that changed America   **973.931**
War: opposing viewpoints   **355**

War poetry
The Oxford book of war poetry   **808.81**
War and the pity of war (5 and up)   **808.81**

War stories
Mankell, H. Secrets in the fire (5 and up)   **Fic**
Marsden, J. Tomorrow, when the war began (7 and up)   **Fic**
Pratchett, T. Only you can save mankind (5 and up)   **Fic**
Shattered: stories of children and war   **S C**
Yolen, J. Prince across the water   **Fic**
War-torn Bosnia (7 and up)   **949.7**
The **war** within. Matas, C.   **Fic**

Ward, Catherine
(il) McKenna, L. The fantastic book of snowboarding   **796.93**
Ward, Elaine M.
Old Testament women (5 and up)   **221.9**
Ward, Marilyn
Voices from the margins   **016.8**
Ward, Matthew
(il) Willson, Q. Classic American cars   **629.222**
Ward, Nancy, 1738?-1822
About
Furbee, M. R. Wild Rose: Nancy Ward and the Cherokee Nation   **92**
Ward, Paul, 1959-
Wild bears of the world   **599.78**
Wardlaw, Lee, 1955-
101 ways to bug your teacher   **Fic**
The desk
In Tripping over the lunch lady and other school stories p97-117   **S C**
Warfare. Chrisp, P.   **355**
Warhol, Andy, 1928?-1987
About
Greenberg, J. Andy Warhol (7 and up)   **92**
Warhol, Tom
Eagles   **598**
Warren, Andrea
Escape from Saigon   **92**
Orphan train rider (4 and up)   **362.7**
Surviving Hitler (5 and up)   **940.53**
We rode the orphan trains (4 and up)   **362.7**
Warrick, Karen Clemens
John Muir: crusader for the wilderness   **92**
The perilous search for the fabled Northwest Passage in American history   **910.4**
The War of 1812   **973.5**
Warrick, Leanne
Hair trix for cool chix   **646.7**
A **warrior** song. Bruchac, J.
In What a song can do; 12 riffs on the power of music   **S C**
Wartski, Maureen Crane, 1940-
A daughter of the sea
In Join in; multiethnic short stories by outstanding writers for young adults p86-96   **S C**
Washakie, Shoshone Chief, 1797-1900
See/See also pages in the following book(s):
Freedman, R. Indian chiefs (6 and up)   **920**
Washington, Booker T., 1856-1915
Up from slavery   **92**
Washington, Denzel
About
Hill, A. E. Denzel Washington (7 and up)   **92**
Washington, George, 1732-1799
About
Adler, D. A. George Washington (5 and up)   **92**
Allen, T. B. George Washington, spymaster   **92**
Ferrie, R. The world turned upside down (5 and up)   **973.3**

Washington, George, 1732-1799—About—*Continued*
Rosenburg, J. M. First in peace: George Washington, the Constitution, and the presidency (7 and up) **92**
See/See also pages in the following book(s):
McPherson, S. S. Martha Washington **92**
Fiction
Rinaldi, A. Taking liberty **Fic**
Washington, Martha, 1731-1802
About
McPherson, S. S. Martha Washington **92**
Washington (D.C.)
Elish, D. Washington, D.C.
In Celebrate the states **973**
Stein, R. C. Washington, D.C.
In America the beautiful, second series **973**
Fiction
Cummings, P. Saving Grace (5 and up) **Fic**
Washington (State)
Blashfield, J. F. Washington
In America the beautiful, second series **973**
Stefoff, R. Washington
In Celebrate the states **973**
Fiction
Holm, J. L. Boston Jane: an adventure **Fic**
Martin, N. Flight of the Fisherbird (5 and up) **Fic**
Mochizuki, K. Beacon Hill boys (7 and up) **Fic**
Wasow, Omar, 1970-
See/See also pages in the following book(s):
Haskins, J. African American entrepreneurs **920**
Waste. Bowden, R. **363.7**
Waste disposal. Morgan, S. **628.4**
Waste products
See also Recycling
Watch and wake. Anderson, M. T.
In Gothic!; ten original dark tales **S C**
The **watcher**. Howe, J. **Fic**
Water
Farndon, J. Buoyancy **532**
Gallant, R. A. Water (5 and up) **553.7**
Meiani, A. Water (4 and up) **532**
See/See also pages in the following book(s):
Knapp, B. J. Materials science **620.1**
Water. Wolff, V. E.
In Girls got game; sports stories and poems **810.8**
Water animals *See* Marine animals
Water birds
See also Geese
Water horse. McKinley, R.
In McKinley, R. and Dickinson, P. Water: tales of elemental spirits p119-69 **S C**
Water pollution
Bryan, N. Danube (5 and up) **363.7**

The **water** pot and the necklace. Jaffe, N.
In Jaffe, N. and Zeitlin, S. J. The cow of no color: riddle stories and justice tales from around the world p128-33 **398.2**
Water power
Graham, I. Water power **620.1**
Water sky. George, J. C. **Fic**
Water Spirit's gift of horses. Brown, D. A.
In Brown, D. A. Dee Brown's folktales of the Native American; retold for our times p99-101 **398.2**
Water supply
Bowden, R. Water supply **363.6**
Water: tales of elemental spirits. McKinley, R. **S C**
Watergate Affair, 1972-1974
See/See also pages in the following book(s):
Barron, R. Richard Nixon (7 and up) **92**
Goldman, M. S. Richard M. Nixon (7 and up) **92**
Waterlow, Julia
The Yangtze (4 and up) **951.2**
The **watermillion** patch. Van Laan, N.
In Van Laan, N. With a whoop and a holler; a bushel of lore from way down south p33-38 **398**
Waters, Muddy, 1915-1983
See/See also pages in the following book(s):
Lester, J. The blues singers (5 and up) **920**
Water's edge. Simner, J. L.
In Half-human p47-63 **S C**
Watership Down. Adams, R. **Fic**
The **waterstone**. Rupp, R. **Fic**
Watie, Stand, 1806-1871
Fiction
Keith, H. Rifles for Watie **Fic**
Watkins, Richard Ross
Slavery: bondage throughout history (7 and up) **326**
Watkins, Sam *See* Watkins, Samuel R., 1839-1901
Watkins, Samuel R., 1839-1901
The diary of Sam Watkins, a confederate soldier (5 and up) **973.7**
Watkins, Yoko Kawashima
My brother, my sister, and I (6 and up) **Fic**
So far from the bamboo grove (6 and up) **Fic**
Watson, Annah Robinson, b. 1848
Eleanor's colonel
In The Boy of Chancellorville and other Civil War stories p95-102 **S C**
Watson, Esther
(ed) The Pain tree, and other teenage angst-ridden poetry. See The Pain tree, and other teenage angst-ridden poetry **811.008**
Watson, James D., 1928-
About
Edelson, E. James Watson and Francis Crick and the building blocks of life (7 and up) **92**
Hamilton, J. James Watson **92**

The **Watsons** go to Birmingham—1963. Curtis, C.
P.   **Fic**

Watt, James, 1736-1819
About
Sproule, A. James Watt   92

Watt, Susan
Mercury
In The Elements   546

Watt-Evans, Lawrence, 1954-
Richie
In Vampires: a collection of original stories
p211-25   S C

Watts, James, 1955-
(il) Curry, J. L. Hold up the sky: and other Native American tales from Texas and the
Southern Plains   398.2

Watts, Julia, 1969-
Finding H.F (7 and up)   **Fic**

Watts history of sports [series]
Stewart, M. Basketball   **796.323**
Stewart, M. Hockey   **796.962**
Stewart, M. Soccer   **796.334**
Stewart, M. World Series   **796.357**

Watts library [series]
Anderson, M. K. North American Indian games
    970.004
Bonar, S. Small wildcats   **599.75**
Bredeson, C. Pluto   **523.4**
Collard, S. B., III. Birds of prey   **598**
Dramer, K. The Mekong River   **959.7**
Greenberg, A. Asthma   **616.2**
Kent, D. Animal helpers for the disabled
    636.088
Kent, D. Athletes with disabilities   **371.9**
McPhee, A. T. AIDS   **616.97**
Miller, S. S. Amazing amphibians   **597.8**
Miller, S. S. Radical reptiles   **597.9**
Perry, P. J. Animals that hibernate   **591.56**
Perry, P. J. Animals under the ground
    591.56
Rawlins, C. The Colorado River   **979.1**
Santella, A. Henry Hudson   **92**
Silverstein, A. Lyme disease   **616.9**
Smith, K. Exploring for shipwrecks   **930.1**
Sonneborn, L. Samuel de Champlain   **92**
Souza, D. M. Freaky flowers   **582.13**
Souza, D. M. What is a fungus?   **579.5**
Spangenburg, R. Mercury   **523.4**
Spangenburg, R. The sun   **523.7**
Spangenburg, R. Venus   **523.4**
Staub, F. J. The signs animals leave   **590**
Trueit, T. S. Earthquakes   **551.2**
Trueit, T. S. Fossils   **560**
Trueit, T. S. Rocks, gems, and minerals   **552**
Trueit, T. S. Volcanoes   **551.2**
Whitcraft, M. The Hudson River   **974.7**
Whitcraft, M. The Tigris and Euphrates Rivers
    935

Watts reference [series]
Barber, N. Music: an A-Z guide   **780.3**
Fischer, D. The encyclopedia of the Summer
Olympics   **796.48**

Wawiorka, Matthew
(il) Krizmanic, J. A teen's vegetarian cookbook
    641.5

The **way** a door closes. Smith, H. A.   **811**
The **way** cool license plate book. Wise, L.
    793.7
The **way** it was. Freeman-Villalobos, T. M.
In Talking leaves; contemporary native
American short stories   S C

Way people live [series]
Blackwood, G. L. Life on the Oregon Trail
    979.5
Cartlidge, C. Life of a Nazi soldier   **940.54**
Einfeld, J. Life in the Australian Outback
    994
Netzley, P. D. Life during the Renaissance
    940.2
Nnoromele, S. Life among the Ibo women of
Nigeria   **966.9**
Stewart, G. Life under the Taliban   **958.1**
The **way** science works. Kerrod, R.   **507.8**
The **way** things work. See Macaulay, D. The new
way things work   **600**

Wayland, April Halprin, 1954-
Girl coming in for a landing (7 and up)
    811

A **wayside** comedy. Kipling, R.
In McCaffrey, A. {The Pern series}   S C

WCTU *See* Woman's Christian Temperance
Union

We all fall down. Cormier, R.   **Fic**
We are all one. Yep, L.
In Yep, L. The rainbow people p72-78
    398.2
We are Americans. Hoobler, D.   **325.73**
We are witnesses. Boas, J.   **940.53**
We hunted and we hollered. Van Laan, N.
In Van Laan, N. With a whoop and a holler;
a bushel of lore from way down south
p65   **398**
We interrupt this broadcast. Garner, J.   **070.1**
We loved Lucy. Krisher, T.
In Time capsule: short stories about teenagers
throughout the twentieth century p112-38
    S C
We remember the Holocaust. Adler, D. A.
    940.53
We rode the orphan trains. Warren, A.   **362.7**
We shall not be moved. Dash, J.   **331.4**
We shall overcome. Finlayson, R.   **323.1**
We the people. Katz, B.   **811**
We were there, too!. Hoose, P. M.   **973**
Wealth
Fiction
Ferris, J. Love among the walnuts (7 and up)
    Fic
Roberts, W. D. The kidnappers (4 and up)
    Fic
Weapons
Byam, M. Arms & armor (4 and up)   **355.8**
Weapons of mass destruction: opposing view-
points   **358**
History
Weapons   **623.4**
Weapons   **623.4**

Weapons & warfare. Meltzer, M.　　355

Weapons and weaponry *See* Military weapons

Weapons of mass destruction: opposing viewpoints　　358

Weapons of peace. Blohm, C. E.　　327.1

Weapons of war. Hamilton, J.　　623.4

Weapons of war. Nardo, D.　　973.3

Weapons satellites. Wolny, P.　　358

Weate, Jeremy
　A young person's guide to philosophy (5 and up)　　100

Weather
　　　See also Meteorology
　Engelbert, P. The complete weather resource　　551.5
　Gardner, R. Science projects about weather (7 and up)　　551.5
　Kahl, J. D. National Audubon Society first field guide: weather (4 and up)　　551.5
　Oxlade, C. Weather　　551.5
　Silverstein, A. Weather and climate　　551.5
　Stein, P. Macmillan encyclopedia of weather　　551.5

　　　　Statistics
　Weather almanac　　551.6

Weather almanac　　551.6

Weather and climate. Silverstein, A.　　551.5

Weather and climate on file　　551.5

Weatherford, Carole Boston, 1956-
　Remember the bridge　　811

Weatherly, Lee
　Missing Abby　　Fic

Weatherly, Myra, 1926-
　William Marshal, medieval England's greatest knight [biography of William Marshal, earl of Pembroke]　　92

Weaver, Michael, 1962-
　(il) Adoff, A. The basket counts　　811

Weaver, Will
　Bad blood
　　In Destination unexpected: short stories
　　　　　S C
　Bootleg summer
　　In Time capsule: short stories about teenagers throughout the twentieth century p39-59
　　　　　S C
　Stealing for girls
　　In Ultimate sports; short stories by outstanding writers for young adults p93-116
　　　　　S C
　WWJD
　　In On the fringe p145-61　　S C

The **weaver** of Yzad. Goldin, B. D.
　In Goldin, B. D. Journeys with Elijah; eight tales of the Prophet p29-37　　222

Weaver's daughter. Bradley, K. B.　　Fic

Weaving
　Monaghan, K. You can weave! (4 and up)　　746.41

Weaving a library Web. Blowers, H.　　025.04

Web-based instruction. Smith, S. S.　　005.7

Web sites
　Blowers, H. Weaving a library Web　　025.04
　Haycock, K. Neal-Schuman authoritative guide to kids' search engines, subject directories, and portals　　025.04
　Hill, A. Tooting your own horn　　021.7
　Lindsay, D. Dave's quick n' easy web pages　　005.7
　Smith, S. S. Web-based instruction　　005.7
　Souter, G. Creating animation for your Web page (4 and up)　　006.6
　See/See also pages in the following book(s):
　Braun, L. W. Teens.library　　027.62
　　　　Fiction
　Tashjian, J. The gospel according to Larry (7 and up)　　Fic

Webb, Del
　See/See also pages in the following book(s):
　Aaseng, N. Business builders in real estate　　920

Webb, Lois Sinaiko, 1922-
　Holidays of the world cookbook for students (5 and up)　　641.5
　(jt. auth) Albyn, C. L. The multicultural cookbook for students　　641.5

Webb, Sophie, 1958-
　Looking for seabirds　　598
　My season with penguins (4 and up)　　598

Weber, EdNah New Rider
　Rattlesnake Mesa (4 and up)　　92

Webster, Daniel, 1782-1852
　　　　About
　Harvey, B. C. Daniel Webster　　92
　See/See also pages in the following book(s):
　Kennedy, J. F. Profiles in courage　　920

Webster, David, 1930-
　(jt. auth) Gardner, R. Science project ideas about animal behavior　　591.5
　(jt. auth) Gardner, R. Science projects about weather　　551.5

Webster's dictionary of synonyms. See Merriam-Webster's dictionary of synonyms　　423

Webster's geographical dictionary. See Merriam-Webster's geographical dictionary　　910.3

Webster's student thesaurus. See Merriam-Webster's school thesaurus　　423

Webster's third new international dictionary of the English language, unabridged　　423

Wee, Jessie
　The Philippines　　959.9

Wee, Patricia Hachten, 1948-
　World War II in literature for youth　　016.9

Wee, Robert James, 1938-
　(jt. auth) Wee, P. H. World War II in literature for youth　　016.9

The **Wee** Free Men. Pratchett, T.　　Fic

Weeding library collections. Slote, S. J.　　025.2

Weeks, Kent R.
　See/See also pages in the following book(s):
　Greenberg, L. Digging into the past　　920

Weeks, Sarah
　Experts, Incorporated
　　In Tripping over the lunch lady and other school stories p30-40　　S C

Weeks, Sarah—*Continued*
So B. it (5 and up)   Fic
Weems, Anne-Marie
Fiction
Carbone, E. L. Stealing freedom   Fic
Weems, Carrie Mae
See/See also pages in the following book(s):
Sills, L. In real life: six women photographers
(7 and up)   920
Weetamoo, heart of the Pocassets. Smith, P. C.
Fic
Wegener, Alfred Lothar, 1880-1930
See/See also pages in the following book(s):
Carruthers, M. W. Pioneers of geology   920
Wehlage, Gary
(jt. auth) Zweizig, D. Lessons from Library
Power   027.8
Weigel, Marlene
(ed) U.X.L encyclopedia of biomes. See U.X.L
encyclopedia of biomes   577.8
Weight control *See* Weight loss
Weight lifting
Brzycki, M. Wrestling strength: prepare to win
796.4
Brzycki, M. Wrestling strength: the competitive
edge   796.4
Porter, D. Winning weight training for girls (7
and up)   613.7
Weight loss
Drohan, M. I. Weight-loss programs (7 and up)
616.85
Frissell, S. Eating disorders and weight control
(7 and up)   616.85
Turck, M. Healthy eating for weight manage-
ment   613.7
Walker, P. Understanding the risk of diet drugs
616.85
See/See also pages in the following book(s):
Schwager, T. The right moves (7 and up)
613.7
Fiction
Lipsyte, R. One fat summer (7 and up)   Fic
Whytock, C. My cup runneth over   Fic
Weight-loss programs. Drohan, M. I.   616.85
Weights and measures
Clark, J. O. E. Under the microscope: science
tools   530.8
Weihenmayer, Erik
See/See also pages in the following book(s):
Kaminsky, M. Uncommon champions   920
Weihs, Erika
(il) Perl, L. The great ancestor hunt   929
(il) Perl, L. Mummies, tombs, and treasure
393
Weihs, Jean Riddle
(jt. auth) Intner, S. S. Standard cataloging for
school and public libraries   025.3
Wein, Elizabeth E., 1964-
The Winter Prince (7 and up)   Fic
Weir, Christina
(jt. auth) DeFilippis, N. Once in a blue moon
741.5
Weiringo, Mike
(jt. auth) Dezago, T. Tellos, Vol. 1   741.5

Weisberg, Barbara
Susan B. Anthony   92
Weiss, Ann E., 1943-
Adoptions today (7 and up)   362.7
Wekesser, Carol, 1963-
(ed) Chemical dependency: opposing viewpoints.
See Chemical dependency: opposing view-
points   362.29
(ed) Smoking. See Smoking   362.29
Welch, Bob, 1956-
See/See also pages in the following book(s):
Kaminsky, M. Uncommon champions   920
Welch, Catherine A.
Margaret Bourke-White   92
Welch, James, 1940-2003
Fools crow [excerpt]
In Talking leaves; contemporary native
American short stories   S C
Welch, Janet, 1953-
(jt. auth) Lerch, M. T. Serving homeschooled
teens and their parents   027.6
Welcome. Sebestyen, O.
In Sixteen; short stories by outstanding writ-
ers for young adults p47-59   S C
Welcome to the Ark. Tolan, S. S.   Fic
Welfare reform (7 and up)   361.6
The **well**. Taylor, M. D.   Fic
The **well** at the world's end. Philip, N.
In Philip, N. Celtic fairy tales p121-24
398.2
Welles, Toby
(il) Duffy, T. The clock   681.1
Wells, Donna Koren
Live aware, not in fear (7 and up)   155.5
Wells, H. G. (Herbert George), 1866-1946
The war of the worlds (7 and up)   Fic
Wells, Haru
(il) Paterson, K. The master puppeteer Fic
Wells, Herbert George *See* Wells, H. G. (Herbert
George), 1866-1946
Wells, Ida B. *See* Wells-Barnett, Ida B., 1862-
1931
Wells, Rosemary, 1943-
Mary on horseback [biography of Mary Breckin-
ridge] (4 and up)   92
Wells-Barnett, Ida B., 1862-1931
About
Davidson, S. Getting the real story: Nellie Bly
and Ida B. Wells   92
Lisandrelli, E. S. Ida B. Wells-Barnett (7 and
up)   92
See/See also pages in the following book(s):
Dubovoy, S. Civil rights leaders (7 and up)
920
Hansen, J. Women of hope (4 and up)   920
Pinkney, A. D. Let it shine (4 and up) 920
Welton, Jude
Henri Matisse   92
The **wendigo**. Schwartz, A.
In Schwartz, A. Scary stories to tell in the
dark p49-53   398.2
Wenger, Jennifer
Teen knitting club (7 and up)   746.43

Wenzel, David, 1950-
(jt. auth) Busiek, K. The wizard's tale   **741.5**
(il) Dixon, C. Hobbit: an illustrated edition of the fantasy classic   **741.5**
Wepman, Dennis
Immigration (7 and up)   **325.73**
Werblowsky, R. J. Zwi (Raphael Jehudah Zwi), 1924-
(ed) The Oxford dictionary of the Jewish religion. See The Oxford dictionary of the Jewish religion   **296.03**
The **werewolf**. Osborne, M. P.
In Osborne, M. P. Favorite medieval tales p42-49   **398.2**
Werewolves
Fiction
Jennings, P. The wolving time   **Fic**
Werlin, Nancy, 1961-
Black mirror (7 and up)   **Fic**
Double helix (7 and up)   **Fic**
Locked inside (7 and up)   **Fic**
Shortcut
In On the fringe p49-60   **S C**
Wertz, Michael
(il) Cerullo, M. M. The truth about great white sharks   **597**
West (U.S.)
Edmondson, J. R. Jim Bowie   **92**
See/See also pages in the following book(s):
Faber, D. Calamity Jane (5 and up)   **92**
Sandler, M. W. Vaqueros   **973**
Biography
Calvert, P. Daniel Boone   **92**
Pendergast, T. Westward expansion: biographies (7 and up)   **920**
Exploration
See also Overland journeys to the Pacific
Blumberg, R. The incredible journey of Lewis and Clark (5 and up)   **978**
Blumberg, R. York's adventures with Lewis and Clark (5 and up)   **978**
Calvert, P. Zebulon Pike (5 and up)   **92**
Clark, W. Off the map   **978**
Faber, H. John Charles Frémont   **92**
Faber, H. Lewis and Clark   **978**
Hirschfelder, A. B. Photo odyssey: Solomon Carvalho's remarkable Western adventure, 1853-54   **92**
Kimmel, E. C. As far as the eye can reach (4 and up)   **978**
Patent, D. H. Animals on the trail with Lewis and Clark (4 and up)   **978**
Patent, D. H. The Lewis and Clark trail (4 and up)   **978**
Patent, D. H. Plants on the trail with Lewis and Clark (4 and up)   **978**
See/See also pages in the following book(s):
St. George, J. Sacagawea (4-6)   **92**
Fiction
Blakeslee, A. R. A different kind of hero   **Fic**
Durbin, W. The journal of Sean Sullivan (5 and up)   **Fic**
Karr, K. The great turkey walk (5 and up)   **Fic**
Myers, W. D. The journal of Joshua Loper (5 and up)   **Fic**
Nixon, J. L. Ghost town   **S C**
Smith, R. The captain's dog   **Fic**
Wallace, B. Eye of the great bear   **Fic**
History
The American frontier (7 and up)   **978**
Blackwood, G. L. Outlaws   **364.1**
Brown, D. A. Bury my heart at Wounded Knee   **970.004**
Cox, C. The forgotten heroes   **978**
Davis, L. Medicine in the American West   **610.9**
DeAngelis, G. The black cowboys   **978**
Ehrlich, A. Wounded Knee: an Indian history of the American West (6 and up)   **970.004**
Galford, E. The trail West (5 and up)   **978**
Josephson, J. P. Growing up in pioneer America, 1800 to 1890   **978**
Katz, W. L. Black women of the Old West (5 and up)   **978**
Ketchum, L. Into a new country (7 and up)   **920**
Lawlor, L. Window on the West (7 and up)   **978**
McGowen, T. African-Americans in the Old West   **978**
Pendergast, T. Westward expansion: almanac   **978**
Pendergast, T. Westward expansion: primary sources (7 and up)   **978**
Sakurai, G. Asian-Americans in the old West (4 and up)   **978**
Schlissel, L. Black frontiers   **978**
Sonneborn, L. The American West: an illustrated history (7 and up)   **978**
Stanley, J. Cowboys & longhorns   **636.2**
Stefoff, R. The opening of the West   **978**
Stovall, T. The Buffalo Soldiers   **978**
Tunis, E. Frontier living (5 and up)   **978**
Westward expansion [Eyewitness history series]   **978**
Westward expansion [Interpreting primary documents] (7 and up)   **978**
See/See also pages in the following book(s):
Marker, S. Plains Indian wars (7 and up)   **973.5**
Social life and customs
Patent, D. H. Homesteading (4 and up)   **978**
West (U.S.) in art
Danneberg, J. Women artists of the West   **920**
Galford, E. The trail West (5 and up)   **978**
West Indies
Anthony, S. West Indies   **972.9**
West Point (Military academy) *See* United States Military Academy
West to a land of plenty. Murphy, J.   **Fic**
West Virginia
Fazio, W. West Virginia
In America the beautiful, second series   **973**
Hoffman, N. West Virginia
In Celebrate the states   **973**
Fiction
Naylor, P. R. Shiloh (4-6)   **Fic**

West Virginia—Fiction—*Continued*
Rylant, C. Missing May (5 and up)   **Fic**
Yep, L. Dream soul   **Fic**
Westerfeld, Scott
The secret hour (7 and up)   **Fic**
So yesterday (7 and up)   **Fic**
Uglies (7 and up)   **Fic**
Western Europe *See* Europe
Western States *See* West (U.S.)
The **Westing** game. Raskin, E.   **Fic**
Westmark. Alexander, L.   **Fic**
Westmoreland, William C.
See/See also pages in the following book(s):
Roberts, R. Leaders and generals   **920**
Weston, Carol
For teens only   **305.23**
Private and personal   **305.23**
Weston, Martha, 1947-
(il) James, E. Social smarts   **395**
Weston, Reiko
Cooking the Japanese way
In Easy menu ethnic cookbooks   **641.5**
Westward expansion [Eyewitness history series]
    978
Westward expansion [Interpreting primary documents] (7 and up)   **978**
Westward expansion: biographies. Pendergast, T.
    920
Westward expansion: primary sources. Pendergast, T.   **978**
Westward movement *See* West (U.S.)—History
Wet hens. Wittlinger, E.
In Shelf life: stories by the book p91-107   **S C**
Wet moccasins. Kenny, M.
In Talking leaves; contemporary native American short stories   **S C**
Wetterer, Charles M.
The Fourth Amendment (7 and up)   **345**
Wexler, Sanford
The civil rights movement (7 and up)   **323.1**
(ed) Westward expansion. See Westward expansion [Eyewitness history series]   **978**
Whale talk. Crutcher, C.   **Fic**
Whales
Carwardine, M. Whales, dolphins, and porpoises (7 and up)   **599.5**
Greenberg, D. A. Whales   **599.5**
Woog, A. The whale (7 and up)   **599.5**
See/See also pages in the following book(s):
Sayre, A. P. Secrets of sound p11-23 (4 and up)   **591.59**

Fiction
Jennings, R. W. The great whale of Kansas   **Fic**
Mikaelsen, B. Stranded   **Fic**
Velmans, H. Isabel of the whales (5 and up)   **Fic**
Whales, dolphins, and porpoises. Carwardine, M.   **599.5**
Whaling
McKissack, P. C. Black hands, white sails (5 and up)   **639.2**

Philbrick, N. Revenge of the whale (7 and up)   **910.4**
Fiction
George, J. C. Water sky (5 and up)   **Fic**
Whalley, Paul Ernest Sutton
Butterfly & moth (4 and up)   **595.7**
What a great idea!. Tomecek, S.   **609**
What a song can do (7 and up)   **S C**
What a song can do. Levithan, D.
In What a song can do; 12 riffs on the power of music   **S C**
What American women did, 1789-1920. Coppens, L. M.   **305.4**
What are my rights? Jacobs, T. A.   **346**
What are you? (7 and up)   **305.8**
What are you good at? Townley, R.
In The Color of absence; 12 stories about loss and hope p17-38   **S C**
What child is this? Cooney, C. B.   **Fic**
What do fish have to do with anything? Avi
In Avi. What do fish have to do with anything? and other stories p9-32   **S C**
What do fish have to do with anything? and other stories. Avi   **S C**
What do you know about [series]
Sanders, P. Anorexia and bulimia   **616.85**
Sanders, P. Divorce and separation   **306.89**
What do you really want? Bachel, B. K.   **153.8**
What every girl (except me) knows. Baskin, N. R.   **Fic**
What happened in the cemetery. Mazer, N. F.
In Visions: nineteen short stories by outstanding writers for young adults p64-75   **S C**
What happened on Planet Kid. Conly, J. L.   **Fic**
What have you lost? (7 and up)   **808.81**
What I believe. Birdseye, D. H.   **200**
What is a fungus? Souza, D. M.   **579.5**
What is a hate crime? (7 and up)   **364.1**
What it all goes back to. Wallace, R.
In Wallace, R. Losing is not an option: stories   **S C**
What means switch. Jen, G.
In Who do you think you are?; stories of friends and enemies p96-118   **S C**
What my mother doesn't know. Sones, S.   **Fic**
What teens need to succeed. Benson, P. L.   **305.23**
What the birds see. Hartnett, S.   **Fic**
What the cat contemplates while pretending to clean herself. Boutilier, N.
In Girls got game; sports stories and poems   **810.8**
What to do when you're scared & worried. Crist, J. J.   **152.4**
What's a fellow to do. Karr, K.
In Shelf life: stories by the book p81-90   **S C**
What's an "A" anyway? Terkel, M.   **371.2**

What's cooking? Whitman, S.   **394.1**
What's going on down there? Gravelle, K.
    612.6
What's inside. Avi
  In Avi. What do fish have to do with any-
  thing? and other stories p153-72   **S C**
What's Michael? Vol. 10: Sleepless nights.
  Kobayashi, M.   **741.5**
What's real, what's ideal. Davis, B.   **616.85**
What's so scary about R.L. Stine? Jones, P.
    813.009
What's the deal? Jefferson, Napoleon and the
  Louisiana Purchase. Blumberg, R.   **973.4**
What's the worst that could happen? Coville, B.
  In 13; thirteen stories that capture the agony
  and ecstasy of being thirteen   **S C**
What's your story? Bauer, M. D.   **808.3**
Wheatley, Phillis, 1753-1784
      About
  Richmond, M. A. Phillis Wheatley   **92**
  Salisbury, C. Phillis Wheatley   **92**
      Fiction
  Rinaldi, A. Hang a thousand trees with ribbons
    Fic
Wheaton, Elizabeth
  Ms: the story of Gloria Steinem   **92**
Wheeler, Jill C.
  September 11, 2001: the day that changed
  America   **973.931**
Wheeler, Mortimer *See* Wheeler, Sir Robert Eric
  Mortimer, 1890-1976
Wheeler, Sir Robert Eric Mortimer, 1890-1976
See/See also pages in the following book(s):
  Greenberg, L. Digging into the past   **920**
Wheelock, Anne
  (ed) The Information-powered school. See The
  Information-powered school   **027.8**
Whelan, Gloria
  Angel on the square   **Fic**
  Burying the sun   **Fic**
  Chu Ju's house   **Fic**
  Goodbye, Vietnam (4 and up)   **Fic**
  Homeless bird (6 and up)   **Fic**
  The impossible journey   **Fic**
When a friend dies. Gootman, M. E.   **155.9**
When Dad killed Mom. Lester, J.   **Fic**
When eagles fall. Casanova, M.   **Fic**
When freedom came. Lester, J.
  In Lester, J. Long journey home: stories from
  black history p105-28   **S C**
When I was a soldier. Zenatti, V.   **92**
When I was older. Freymann-Weyr, G.   **Fic**
When Johnny went marching. Wisler, G. C.
    973.7
When Kambia Elaine flew in from Neptune. Wil-
  liams, L. A.   **Fic**
When life stinks. Piquemal, M.   **305.23**
When my name was Keoko. Park, L. S.   **Fic**
When nothing matters anymore. Cobain, B.
    155.9
When objects talk. Friedlander, M. P.   **363.2**

When something feels wrong. Pledge, D. S.
    362.7
When the beginning began. Lester, J.   **296.1**
When the brain dies first. Hyde, M. O.   **616.8**
When the Chenoo howls. Bruchac, J.   **398.2**
When the legends die. Borland, H.   **Fic**
When the rain sings   **811.008**
When the sun and the moon were children.
  Delacre, L.
  In Delacre, L. Golden tales; myths, legends,
  and folktales from Latin America p31-35
    398.2
When the train comes. Wicomb, Z.
  In Somehow tenderness survives; stories of
  Southern Africa p61-76   **S C**
When will I stop hurting? Myers, E.   **155.9**
When will this cruel war be over? Denenberg, B.
    Fic
When Zachary Beaver came to town. Holt, K. W.
    Fic
Where are you going, where have you been?
  Oates, J. C.
  In Oates, J. C. Small avalanches and other
  stories   **S C**
  also in Who do you think you are?; stories of
  friends and enemies p14-35   **S C**
Where credit is due. Shields, N. E.   **808**
Where I want to be. Griffin, A.   **Fic**
Where I'd like to be. Dowell, F. O.   **Fic**
Where in the world. French, S.   **Fic**
Where the action was. Colman, P.   **070.4**
Where the bald eagles gather. See Patent, D. H.
  The bald eagle returns   **598**
Where the broken heart still beats. Meyer, C.
    Fic
Where the ground meets the sky. Davies, J.
    Fic
Where the lillies bloom. Cleaver, V.   **Fic**
Where the red fern grows. Rawls, W.   **Fic**
Where the sidewalk ends. Silverstein, S.   **811**
Which way freedom? Hansen, J.   **Fic**
While no one was watching. Conly, J. L.   **Fic**
The **whipping** boy. Fleischman, S.   **Fic**
Whipple, Laura
  If the shoe fits (5 and up)   **811**
Whirligig. Fleischman, P.   **Fic**
Whisper and shout (4 and up)   **811.008**
Whistle! Volume 1. Higuchi, D.   **741.5**
Whistler, James McNeill, 1834-1903
      About
  Berman, A. James McNeill Whistler (7 and up)
    92
Whitaker, John O., Jr.
  National Audubon Society field guide to North
  American mammals   **599**
Whitcraft, James E.
  (il) Farlow, J. O. Bringing dinosaur bones to life
    567.9
Whitcraft, Melissa
  The Hudson River   **974.7**
  The Tigris and Euphrates Rivers   **935**

White, Andrea
Surviving Antarctica (7 and up)   **Fic**

White, Deborah Gray
Let my people go: African Americans, 1804-1860 (7 and up)   **305.8**

White, Ellen Emerson
Kaiulani   **Fic**

White, Margaret Bourke- *See* Bourke-White, Margaret, 1904-1971

White, Michael
Galileo Galilei   **92**
Isaac Newton   **92**

White, Ruth
Belle Prater's boy (5 and up)   **Fic**
Memories of Summer (7 and up)   **Fic**

White, T. H. (Terence Hanbury), 1906-1964
The candle in the wind
In White, T. H. The once and future king
   Fic
The ill-made knight
In White, T. H. The once and future king
   Fic
The once and future king   **Fic**
The Queen of Air and Darkness
In White, T. H. The once and future king
   Fic
The sword in the stone
In White, T. H. The once and future king
   Fic
The witch in the wood
In White, T. H. The once and future king
   Fic

White, Terence Hanbury *See* White, T. H. (Terence Hanbury), 1906-1964

White balloons. Ortiz Cofer, J.
In Ortiz Cofer, J. An island like you; stories of the barrio p144-65   **S C**

White collar crimes
DeAngelis, G. White-collar crime (7 and up)
   364.1

White Fang. London, J.   **Fic**

White Fox. Curry, J. L.
In Curry, J. L. Hold up the sky: and other Native American tales from Texas and the Southern Plains p123-27   **398.2**

White girl. Olsen, S.   **Fic**

White House (Washington, D.C.)
Feinberg, B. S. The changing White House
   975.3

White lilacs. Meyer, C.   **Fic**

White midnight. Calhoun, D.   **Fic**

The **White** Mountains. Christopher, J.   **Fic**

White-out. Wolf, P.
In Talking leaves; contemporary native American short stories   **S C**

The **white** seal. Kipling, R.
In Kipling, R. The jungle books   **S C**

White Sox (Baseball team) *See* Chicago White Sox (Baseball team)

White supremacy movements
See/See also pages in the following book(s):
Roleff, T. L. Hate groups (7 and up)   **364.1**

White-water canoeing
Fiction
Hobbs, W. Downriver (7 and up)   **Fic**

White-water rafting. George, C.   **797.1**

Whitebear Whittington
In Hearne, B. G. Beauties and beasts p76-83
   398.2

Whitelaw, Nancy
Clara Barton   **92**
The shot heard round the world   **973.3**
Thomas Jefferson (7 and up)   **92**

Whiteman, Roberta Hill, 1947-
Summer girl
In Talking leaves; contemporary native American short stories   **S C**

Whitesel, Cheryl Aylward
Rebel   **Fic**

Whiteside, Michael
Health and illness
In Being human   **612**

Whitfield, Peter
History of science   **509**

Whitfield, Philip J.
(ed) Animals. See Animals   **596**

Whitman, Sylvia, 1961-
What's cooking? (5 and up)   **394.1**

Whitman, Walt, 1819-1892
Walt Whitman (7 and up)   **811**
In The Blackbirch treasury of American poetry p193-237   **811.008**
About
Kerley, B. Walt Whitman (4 and up)   **92**
Meltzer, M. Walt Whitman (7 and up)   **92**
Reef, C. Walt Whitman (7 and up)   **92**

Whittington, Mary K.
Ahvel
In Vampires: a collection of original stories p121-33   **S C**
Somewhere a puppy cries
In The Haunted house: a collection of original stories   **S C**

WHO *See* World Health Organization

Who am I without him? Flake, S. G.   **S C**

Who are you? Nixon, J. L.   **Fic**

Who came first. Lauber, P.   **970.01**

Who do you think you are?   **S C**

Who is Carrie? Collier, J. L.   **Fic**

Who is Jesse Flood? Doyle, M.   **Fic**

Who ordered the jumbo shrimp? and other oxymorons. Agee, J.   **793.73**

Who said that? Burleigh, R.   **808.88**

Who the man. Lynch, C.   **Fic**

Who were the founding fathers? Jaffe, S. H.
   973.3

Who will tell my brother? Carvell, M.   **Fic**

Who wrote that? [series]
Cammarano, R. Betsy Byars   **92**
Davenport, J. C.S. Lewis   **92**
Dean, T. Theodor Geisel   **92**
Ludwig, E. Judy Blume   **92**
Wagner, H. L. Jane Austen   **92**

Who you!. Hamilton, V.
In Hamilton, V. Her stories; African
American folktales, fairy tales, and true
tales p45-50 **398.2**

The **Whole** school library handbook **027.8**

Whole story [series]
Poe, E. A. The pit and the pendulum and other
stories **S C**

Who's afraid? Pearce, P.
In Read all about it!; great read-aloud stories,
poems, and newspaper pieces for preteens and teens p230-35 **808.8**

Who's Hu? [excerpt] Namioka, L.
In American dragons: twenty-five Asian
American voices p48-64 **810.8**

Why are people prejudiced? Senker, C. **303.3**

Why Bear waddles when he walks. Curry, J. L.
In Curry, J. L. Hold up the sky: and other
Native American tales from Texas and
the Southern Plains p15-19 **398.2**

Why Brer Bull growls and grumbles. Lester, J.
In Lester, J. The last tales of Uncle Remus
p119-23 **398.2**

Why Brer Fox's legs are black. Lester, J.
In Lester, J. The last tales of Uncle Remus
p64-66 **398.2**

Why Brer Possum has no hair on his tail. Lester,
J.
In Lester, J. The last tales of Uncle Remus
p41-44 **398.2**

Why Brer Possum loves peace. Lester, J.
In Lester, J. The last tales of Uncle Remus
p44-46 **398.2**

Why Bush Cow and Elephant are bad friends.
Bryan, A.
In Bryan, A. Ashley Bryan's African tales,
uh-huh p54-69 **398.2**

Why chickens scratch in the dirt. Lester, J.
In Lester, J. The last tales of Uncle Remus
p147-49 **398.2**

Why Coyote stopped imitating his friends. Brown,
D. A.
In Brown, D. A. Dee Brown's folktales of the
Native American; retold for our times
p150-53 **398.2**

Why do people fight wars? Brownlie, A. **355**

Why do people join gangs? Johnson, J. **364.1**

Why does the coqui sing? Polikoff, B. G. **Fic**

Why dogs are tame. Lester, J.
In Lester, J. The last tales of Uncle Remus
p76-82 **398.2**

Why dogs have long tongues. Brown, D. A.
In Brown, D. A. Dee Brown's folktales of the
Native American; retold for our times
p26-28 **398.2**

Why don't you come live with me: it's time.
Oates, J. C.
In Oates, J. C. Small avalanches and other
stories **S C**

Why Frog and Snake never play together. Bryan,
A.
In Bryan, A. Ashley Bryan's African tales,
uh-huh p81-92 **398.2**

Why guinea fowls are speckled. Lester, J.
In Lester, J. The last tales of Uncle Remus
p88-93 **398.2**

Why not, Lafayette? Fritz, J. **92**

Why on this night? Musleah, R. **296.4**

Why the cricket has elbows on his legs. Lester, J.
In Lester, J. The last tales of Uncle Remus
p3-8 **398.2**

Why the earth is mostly water. Lester, J.
In Lester, J. The last tales of Uncle Remus
p8-12 **398.2**

Why the goat has a short tail. Lester, J.
In Lester, J. The last tales of Uncle Remus
p136-38 **398.2**

Why the Guineas stay awake. Lester, J.
In Lester, J. The last tales of Uncle Remus
p93-94 **398.2**

Why the hawk likes to eat chickens. Lester, J.
In Lester, J. The last tales of Uncle Remus
p98-102 **398.2**

Why the moon is free. Gerson, M.-J.
In Gerson, M.-J. Fiesta femenina; celebrating
women in Mexican folktale **398.2**

Why the rude visitor was flung by walrus. Norman, H.
In Norman, H. The girl who dreamed only
geese, and other tales of the Far North
398.2

Whyte, Mariam
Bangladesh (5 and up) **954.92**

Whytock, Cherry
My cup runneth over **Fic**

Wick, Walter, 1953-
Walter Wick's Optical tricks (4 and up)
152.14

Wicked poems (4 and up) **811.008**

Wicomb, Zoë, 1948-
When the train comes
In Somehow tenderness survives; stories of
Southern Africa p61-76 **S C**

Wide awake: a Buddhist guide for teens. Winston,
D. **294.3**

The **widow** and the Spriggans of Trenscrom Hill.
Climo, S.
In Climo, S. Magic & mischief; tales from
Cornwall p25-30 **398.2**

Wiese, Jim, 1948-
Spy science **363.2**

Wiesel, Elie, 1928-
The accident
In Wiesel, E. Night, Dawn, The accident:
three tales p205-318 **Fic**
Dawn
In Wiesel, E. Night, Dawn, The accident:
three tales **Fic**
Night
In Wiesel, E. Night, Dawn, The accident:
three tales **Fic**
Night, Dawn, The accident: three tales (7 and
up) **Fic**

Wiesner, David
See/See also pages in the following book(s):
Marcus, L. S. A Caldecott celebration **741.6**

Wiesner, David—*Continued*
The Newbery & Caldecott medal books, 1986-2000 **028.5**
(il) Yep, L. The rainbow people **398.2**
Wife abuse
Fiction
Byars, B. C. Cracker Jackson (5 and up) **Fic**
Hoffman, N. K. A stir of bones (7 and up) **Fic**
Kwasney, M. D. Baby Blue **Fic**
The **wife** of Bath's tale. Cohen, B.
In Cohen, B. Canterbury tales **821**
Wigoder, Geoffrey, 1922-1999
(ed) The Holocaust. See The Holocaust **940.53**
(ed) The Oxford dictionary of the Jewish religion. See The Oxford dictionary of the Jewish religion **296.03**
The **wigwam** and the longhouse. Yue, C. **970.004**
Wilcox, Charlotte
Mummies, bones & body parts (5 and up) **393**
Wild bears of the world. Ward, P. **599.78**
Wild cats
See also Cats; Lions; Pumas; Tigers
Alderton, D. Wild cats of the world (7 and up) **599.75**
Bonar, S. Small wildcats **599.75**
Saign, G. The African cats **599.75**
Thomas, P. Big cat conservation **333.95**
Fiction
Taylor, T. Lord of the Kill **Fic**
Wild cats of the world. Alderton, D. **599.75**
Wild children
Fiction
Mazer, H. The wild kid (4 and up) **Fic**
Wild country. Harrison, D. L. **811**
Wild dogs
Fiction
Salisbury, G. Jungle dogs **Fic**
Wild flowers
Niehaus, T. F. A field guide to Pacific states wildflowers **582.13**
Ryden, H. Wildflowers around the year (5 and up) **582.13**
Spellenberg, R. National Audubon Society field guide to North American wildflowers, western region **582.13**
Thieret, J. W. National Audubon Society field guide to North American wildflowers: eastern region **582.13**
Wild horses I have known. Ryden, H. **599.66**
The **wild** kid. Mazer, H. **Fic**
Wild Man Island. Hobbs, W. **Fic**
Wild meat and the bully burgers [excerpt] Yamanaka, L.-A.
In American eyes; new Asian-American short stories for young adults p8-12 **S C**
Wild Rose: Nancy Ward and the Cherokee Nation. Furbee, M. R. **92**
Wild shots. Aaseng, N. **778.9**

Wilder, Laura Ingalls, 1867-1957
About
Anderson, W. T. Laura Ingalls Wilder (4 and up) **92**
Wilderness areas
Hart, J. Walking softly in the wilderness **796.51**
Malaspina, A. Saving the American wilderness **333.72**
See/See also pages in the following book(s):
Netzley, P. D. Issues in the environment (7 and up) **333.7**
Wilderness survival
Dewey, J. Finding your way **796.5**
Fiction
George, J. C. Julie of the wolves (6 and up) **Fic**
George, J. C. The talking earth **Fic**
Hobbs, W. Far North (7 and up) **Fic**
Hobbs, W. Wild Man Island **Fic**
Houston, J. A. Frozen fire (6 and up) **Fic**
Mazer, H. Snow bound (7 and up) **Fic**
Mikaelsen, B. Touching Spirit Bear **Fic**
O'Dell, S. Island of the Blue Dolphins (5 and up) **Fic**
Vanasse, D. Out of the wilderness **Fic**
Wildfires
Bryan, N. Los Alamos wildfires (5 and up) **363.34**
Wildfires. Simon, S. **577.2**
Wildflowers around the year. Ryden, H. **582.13**
Wildlife
Lewin, T. Tooth and claw (4 and up) **590**
Encyclopedias
International wildlife encyclopedia **590.3**
Wildlife and plants of the world **578**
Wildlife conservation
See also Birds—Protection
Arnold, C. On the brink of extinction (4 and up) **598**
The Atlas of endangered species **333.95**
Bortolotti, D. Panda rescue (4 and up) **639.9**
Bortolotti, D. Tiger rescue (4 and up) **333.95**
Fridell, R. The search for poison-dart frogs (4-6) **597.8**
Lasky, K. Monarchs (4 and up) **595.7**
Salmansohn, P. Saving birds (5 and up) **333.95**
Swinburne, S. R. Once a wolf (4 and up) **333.95**
Thomas, P. Big cat conservation **333.95**
Thomas, P. Bird alert **333.95**
Thomas, P. Marine mammal preservation (5 and up) **639.9**
Turner, P. S. Gorilla doctors (5 and up) **333.95**
Vergoth, K. Endangered species **578.68**
See/See also pages in the following book(s):
Africa: opposing viewpoints **960**
Wildlife of the world. See Wildlife and plants of the world **578**

Wiley and the Hairy Man [play] Zeder, S.
  In Theatre for young audiences; 20 great
    plays for children p142-69   **812.008**

Wiley, his mama, and the Hairy Man. Hamilton,
  V.
  In Hamilton, V. The people could fly;
    American black folktales p90-103
                      398.2

Wilhelm, Doug
  The revealers   **Fic**

Wilkens, Frances
  Egypt   **962**

Wilkes, Angela
  Children's quick & easy cookbook   **641.5**
  Dangerous creatures (5 and up)   **591.6**

Wilkinson, Beth
  Coping with the dangers of tattooing, body
    piercing, and branding   **617.9**

Wilkinson, Brenda Scott, 1946-
  My sweet sixteenth
  In Join in; multiethnic short stories by out-
    standing writers for young adults p128-
    40   **S C**

Wilkinson, Carole, 1950-
  Dragon keeper (5 and up)   **Fic**

Wilkinson, Philip, 1955-
  Buddhism (4 and up)   **294.3**
  Building (4 and up)   **690**
  Illustrated dictionary of mythology   **201**

Will you be an astronaut? Van Eekhout, G.
  In New skies: an anthology of today's science
    fiction   **S C**

Will you, won't you? Haas, J.   **Fic**

Willard, Nancy, 1936-
  (comp) Step lightly. See Step lightly   **808.81**

Willett, Edward, 1959-
  Alzheimer's disease (7 and up)   **616.8**
  Ebola virus   **616.9**
  J.R.R. Tolkien   **92**
  Meningitis (7 and up)   **616.8**

William, Kate *See* Armstrong, Jennifer, 1961-

William Marshal, medieval England's greatest
  knight [biography of William Marshal, earl of
  Pembroke] Weatherly, M.   **92**

William Shakespeare & the Globe. Aliki
                      792.09

William Shakespeare's A midsummer night's
  dream. Coville, B.   **822.3**

Williams, Barbara
  World War II, Pacific (5 and up)   **940.54**

Williams, Betty, 1943-
  See/See also pages in the following book(s):
  Hacker, C. Nobel Prize winners   **920**

Williams, Brian
  (jt. auth) Wood, M. Ancient America   **970.01**

Williams, Carol Lynch, 1959-
  If I forget, you remember   **Fic**

Williams, Eli
  (jt. auth) Huddleston, C. Decoy   **741.5**

Williams, Jean Kinney
  The Amish (7 and up)   **289.7**
  The Christian Scientists (7 and up)   **289.5**
  The Quakers (7 and up)   **289.6**

The Shakers (7 and up)   **289**
South Korea (7 and up)   **951.95**

Williams, Juan
  Eyes on the prize: America's civil rights years,
    1954-1965 (7 and up)   **323.1**

Williams, Lori Aurelia
  Black holes and basketball sneakers
  In 13; thirteen stories that capture the agony
    and ecstasy of being thirteen   **S C**
  When Kambia Elaine flew in from Neptune (7
    and up)   **Fic**

Williams, Lucinda
  See/See also pages in the following book(s):
  Orgill, R. Shout, sister, shout! (6 and up)
                      920

Williams, Maiya
  The golden hour   **Fic**

Williams, Marcia, 1945-
  Tales from Shakespeare   **822.3**

Williams, Mary E., 1960-
  (ed) Abortion: opposing viewpoints. See Abor-
    tion: opposing viewpoints   **363.46**
  (ed) Civil rights. See Civil rights   **323.1**
  (ed) Culture wars: opposing viewpoints. See
    Culture wars: opposing viewpoints   **306**
  (ed) The Death penalty: opposing viewpoints.
    See The Death penalty: opposing viewpoints
                      364.66
  (ed) Discrimination: opposing viewpoints. See
    Discrimination: opposing viewpoints   **305.8**
  (ed) Epidemics: opposing viewpoints. See Epi-
    demics: opposing viewpoints   **614.4**
  (ed) The Family: opposing viewpoints. See The
    Family: opposing viewpoints   **306.8**
  (ed) Marriage and divorce. See Marriage and di-
    vorce   **306.8**
  (ed) The Middle East: opposing viewpoints. See
    The Middle East: opposing viewpoints
                      956
  (ed) Sex: opposing viewpoints. See Sex: oppos-
    ing viewpoints   **306.7**
  (ed) Terminal illness: opposing viewpoints. See
    Terminal illness: opposing viewpoints
                      362.1

Williams, Mary Lou, 1910-1981
  See/See also pages in the following book(s):
  Mour, S. I. American jazz musicians   **920**

Williams, Phyllis S.
  (jt. auth) Kenda, M. Math wizardry for kids
                      793.7

Williams, Raymond, 1921-1988
  (jt. auth) Mann, G. S. Buddhists, Hindus, and
    Sikhs in America   **294**

Williams, Roger, 1604?-1683
                About
  Gaustad, E. S. Roger Williams (7 and up)
                      92

Williams, Serena, 1981-
  (jt. auth) Williams, V. How to play tennis
                      796.342
  (jt. auth) Williams, V. Venus & Serena   **92**

Williams, Venus, 1980-
  How to play tennis (5 and up)   **796.342**
  Venus & Serena (7 and up)   **92**

Williams-Garcia, Rita
Into the game
In Join in; multiethnic short stories by out-
standing writers for young adults p3-11
S C

Like sisters on the homefront (7 and up)
Fic
No laughter here (7 and up)　　　　Fic
A woman's touch
In Necessary noise: stories about our families
as they really are p131-42　　　S C

Willis, Connie
A letter from the Clearys
In New skies: an anthology of today's science
fiction　　　　　　　　　　　S C

Willis, Roy G.
(ed) World mythology. See World mythology
201

Willis, Terri
Democratic Republic of the Congo (5 and up)
967.51

The **Willoughby** Spit wonder. Fuqua, J. S.　Fic

Willson, Quentin
Classic American cars (7 and up)　629.222
The ultimate classic car book　　629.222

Wiloch, Thomas
Everything you need to know about protecting
yourself and others from abduction　613.6

Wilsdon, Christina
National Audubon Society first field guide: insects (4 and up)　　　　　　595.7

Wilson, Alex
(il) Platt, R. Shipwreck　　　　910.4

Wilson, Antoine
S.E. Hinton　　　　　　　　92

Wilson, Bernice
Art of the ancient Mediterranean world
In International encyclopedia of art　703

Wilson, Darryl Babe, 1939-
Diamond Island: Alcatraz
In Talking leaves; contemporary native
American short stories　　　S C

Wilson, Don E.
(ed) Animal. See Animal　　　590.3

Wilson, Edith Bolling Galt, 1872-1961
About
Flanagan, A. K. Edith Bolling Galt Wilson,
1872-1961　　　　　　　　92

Wilson, Gahan
Mister ice cold
In Beware!; R.L. Stine picks his favorite
scary stories p199-207　　　808.8

Wilson, George, 1920-
(jt. auth) Moss, J. Profiles in American history
973

Wilson, Jacqueline
The suitcase kid　　　　　　Fic

Wilson, John, 1951-
And in the morning (7 and up)　　Fic

Wilson, Kathleen
(ed) Short stories for students. See Short stories
for students　　　　　　　809.3

Wilson, Nancy Hope, 1947-
Mountain pose (5 and up)　　　Fic

Wilson, Patricia J. (Patricia Jane)
Center stage　　　　　　　027.8

Wilson, Robert Charles, 1953-
The great goodbye
In New skies: an anthology of today's science
fiction　　　　　　　　　S C

Wilson, Suzan
Stephen King: king of thrillers and horror
92

Wilson, Thomas H.
City states of the Swahili coast　　967.6

Wilson, Woodrow, 1856-1924
See/See also pages in the following book(s):
Flanagan, A. K. Edith Bolling Galt Wilson,
1872-1961　　　　　　　　92

The **Wilson** chronology of Asia and the Pacific
950

The **Wilson** chronology of ideas. Ochoa, G.
909

The **Wilson** chronology of science and technology.
Ochoa, G.　　　　　　　502

The **Wilson** chronology of the arts. Ochoa, G.
700

The **Wilson** chronology of the world's religions
200

The **Wilson** chronology of women's achievements.
Franck, I. M.　　　　　　305.4

Wiltshire, Paula
Dyslexia (5 and up)　　　　616.85

Wimmer, Mike
(il) Fritz, J. Bully for you, Teddy Roosevelt!
92

Winckler, Suzanne, 1946-
Planting the seed　　　　　635

Wind power
Graham, I. Wind power　　　621.4

Windling, Terri, 1957-
(ed) The Green Man: tales from the mythic forest. See The Green Man: tales from the mythic forest　　　　　　　808.8

Window on the West. Lawlor, L.　　978

Windows on the world. Heath, A.　394.2

Winds
Friend, S. Earth's wild winds (5 and up)
551.51

Windsor, Patricia, 1938-
Moon kill
In Night terrors; stories of shadow and sub-
stance　　　　　　　　S C

Windsor, House of *See* House of Windsor

Winerip, Michael
Adam Canfield of the Slash (5 and up)　Fic

Winfield, Julia *See* Armstrong, Jennifer, 1961-

Winfrey, Oprah
See/See also pages in the following book(s):
Haskins, J. African American entrepreneurs
920

Jeffrey, L. S. Great American businesswomen
920

Wing nut. Auch, M. J.　　　　Fic

Wingman, fly me down. Taylor, T.
   In Taylor, T. Rogue wave and other red-
     blooded sea stories   **S C**

Winick, Judd, 1970-
   Pedro and me (7 and up)   **362.1**

Winkelman, Barbara Gaines
   The Panama Canal   **972.87**

Winkler, Allan M., 1945-
   The Cold War   **909.82**

Winner, Cherie
   Erosion   **551.3**

Winning. Adler, C. S.   **Fic**

Winning authors. Bostrom, K. L.   **920**

Winning his way. Coffin, C. C.
   In The Boy of Chancellorville and other Civil
     War stories p23-39   **S C**

Winning lacrosse for girls. Swissler, B.
     796.34

Winning track and field for girls. Housewright, E.
     796.42

Winning volleyball for girls. Crisfield, D.
     796.325

Winning weight training for girls. Porter, D.
     613.7

Winston, Diana
   Wide awake: a Buddhist guide for teens
     294.3

Winter, Jane Kohen, 1959-
   Chile (5 and up)   **983**
   Italy (5 and up)   **945**
   Venezuela   **987**

Winter, Laurel
   The flying woman
   In Firebirds: an anthology of original fantasy
     and science fiction; an anthology of orig-
     inal fantasy and science fiction   **S C**

The **winter** hibiscus. Ho, M.
   In Join in; multiethnic short stories by out-
     standing writers for young adults p239-
     56   **S C**

The **winter** of red snow. Gregory, K.   **Fic**

The **winter** people. Bruchac, J.   **Fic**

The **Winter** Prince. Wein, E. E.   **Fic**

The **winter** room. Paulsen, G.   **Fic**

Winter sports
   See also Olympic games; Snowboarding

Winterdance. Paulsen, G.   **798.8**

Wintering. Durbin, W.   **Fic**

Wintering well. Wait, L.   **Fic**

Winters, Paul A., 1965-
   (ed) Cloning. See Cloning [At issue]   **174.2**
   (ed) The Collapse of the Soviet Union. See The
     Collapse of the Soviet Union   **947.085**
   (ed) Death and dying: opposing viewpoints. See
     Death and dying: opposing viewpoints
     155.9

Winthrop, John, 1588-1649
     About
   Aronson, M. John Winthrop, Oliver Cromwell,
     and the Land of Promise (7 and up)   **92**

Winyan Ohitika. Mayer, M.
   In Mayer, M. Women warriors; myths and
     legends of heroic women p67-69   **398**

"Wireless". Kipling, R.
   In McCaffrey, A. {The Pern series}   **S C**

Wiretapping
   See/See also pages in the following book(s):
   MccGwire, S. Surveillance (7 and up)
     323.44

Wirths, Claudine G.
   Coping with confrontations and encounters with
     the police (7 and up)   **363.2**

Wisconsin
   Blashfield, J. F. Wisconsin
   In America the beautiful, second series
     973
   Zeinert, K. Wisconsin
   In Celebrate the states   **973**
     Fiction
   Bauer, J. Hope was here (7 and up)   **Fic**
   Carter, A. R. Crescent Moon   **Fic**

Wisdom for sale. Kimmel, E. A.
   In Kimmel, E. A. The jar of fools: eight Ha-
     nukkah stories from Chelm p42-55
     S C

Wisdom tales from around the world. Forest, H.
     398.2

Wise, Leonard, 1940-
   The way cool license plate book (4 and up)
     793.7

The **wise** dove. Lee, J. M.
   In Lee, J. M. I once was a monkey; stories
     Buddha told   **294.3**

The **wise** king. Jaffe, N.
   In Jaffe, N. and Zeitlin, S. J. The cow of no
     color: riddle stories and justice tales from
     around the world p118-21   **398.2**

The **wise** men of Chelm [play] Asher, S. F.
   In Theatre for young audiences; 20 great
     plays for children p217-43   **812.008**

The **wise** men of Chelm [play] Asher, S.
   In Theatre for young audiences; 20 great
     plays for children p217-43   **812.008**

Wise words of Paul Tiulana. Tiulana, P.   **92**

The **wish.** Dahl, R.
   In Dahl, R. Skin and other stories   **S C**

The **wish.** Levine, G. C.   **Fic**

The **wish** giver. Brittain, B.   **Fic**

The **wish** house. Kipling, R.
   In McCaffrey, A. {The Pern series}   **S C**

A **wish** named Arnold. De Lint, C.
   In De Lint, C. Waifs and strays p83-92
     S C

Wishes
     Fiction
   Brittain, B. The wish giver   **Fic**

Wishing moon. Tunnell, M. O.   **Fic**

Wisler, G. Clifton, 1950-
   Caleb's choice   **Fic**
   Red Cap (4 and up)   **Fic**
   Run the blockade   **Fic**
   When Johnny went marching (5 and up)
     973.7

Wisniewski, David
See/See also pages in the following book(s):
The Newbery & Caldecott medal books, 1986-2000 **028.5**

Wit and humor
See also Humorous poetry
Twain, M. The adventures of Tom Sawyer (5 and up) **Fic**
The **witch** in the wood. White, T. H.
In White, T. H. The once and future king **Fic**
The **witch** in the wood. See White, T. H. The Queen of Air and Darkness
The **witch** of Blackbird Pond. Speare, E. G. **Fic**

Witchbirds. San Souci, R.
In San Souci, R. A terrifying taste of short & shivery; thirty creepy tales p68-72 **398.2**

Witchcraft
See also Magic
Black magic and witches **133.4**
Fremon, D. K. The Salem witchcraft trials in American history **133.4**
Kallen, S. A. The Salem witch trials (7 and up) **133.4**
Roach, M. K. In the days of the Salem witchcraft trials (4 and up) **133.4**
Fiction
Horowitz, A. Raven's gate (7 and up) **Fic**
Jarvis, R. The alchemist's cat (5 and up) **Fic**
Lasky, K. Beyond the burning time (7 and up) **Fic**
Speare, E. G. The witch of Blackbird Pond (6 and up) **Fic**

Witches
Fiction
Gruber, M. The witch's boy (7 and up) **Fic**
Jones, D. W. Charmed life **Fic**
Pratchett, T. The Wee Free Men **Fic**
The **witches**. Dahl, R.
In Beware!; R.L. Stine picks his favorite scary stories p101-19 **808.8**
Witches and witch-hunts. Meltzer, M. **133.4**
The **witch's** head. San Souci, R.
In San Souci, R. A terrifying taste of short & shivery; thirty creepy tales p77-81 **398.2**

With a whoop and a holler. Van Laan, N. **398**
With courage and cloth. Bausum, A. **305.4**
With every drop of blood. Collier, J. L. **Fic**
With love. Goodall, J. **599.8**
With needle and thread. Bial, R. **746.46**
With the night mail. Kipling, R.
In McCaffrey, A. {The Pern series} **S C**
With their eyes (7 and up) **812**
Withern Rise [series]
Lawrence, M. A crack in the line **Fic**
Within reach: my Everest story. Pfetzer, M. **796.52**

Without benefit of clergy. Kipling, R.
In McCaffrey, A. {The Pern series} **S C**
Witness. Armstrong, J.
In Shattered: stories of children and war p133-38 **S C**
Witness. Hesse, K. **Fic**
Witness to history [series]
Barr, G. Pearl Harbor **940.54**
Barr, G. World War II home front **940.53**
Downing, D. Apartheid in South Africa **968**
Witness to our times. Schulke, F. **92**
Witnesses
Fiction
Woodson, J. Hush **Fic**
Witnesses to war. Leapman, M. **940.53**
Witschonke, Alan
(il) Mann, E. Hoover Dam **627**
Wittlinger, Ellen, 1948-
Hard love (7 and up) **Fic**
Noodle soup for nincompoops
In 13; thirteen stories that capture the agony and ecstasy of being thirteen **S C**
Stevie in the mirror
In On the edge: stories at the brink p1-20 **S C**
Tourist trapped
In Destination unexpected: short stories **S C**
Wet hens
In Shelf life: stories by the book p91-107 **S C**
Zigzag (7 and up) **Fic**
Wizards of the game. Lubar, D. **Fic**
The **wizard's** tale. Busiek, K. **741.5**
WJHC: on the air!. Fisher, J. S. **741.5**
Wobblies *See* Industrial Workers of the World
Woff, Richard, 1953-
The ancient Greek Olympics (4 and up) **796.48**
Wolf, Allan
New found land (7 and up) **Fic**
Wolf, Phyllis
White-out
In Talking leaves; contemporary native American short stories **S C**
Wolf and birds and the Fish-Horse. Hamilton, V.
In Hamilton, V. The people could fly; American black folktales p43-49 **398.2**
A **wolf** and Little Daughter. Hamilton, V.
In Hamilton, V. The people could fly; American black folktales p60-64 **398.2**
Wolf by the ears. Rinaldi, A. **Fic**
Wolf children *See* Wild children
The **wolf** girl. Schwartz, A.
In Schwartz, A. Scary stories 3; more tales to chill your bones p47-50 **398.2**
Wolf on the fold. Clarke, J. **Fic**
Wolf rider. Avi **Fic**

Wolf-Sampath, Gita
(jt. auth) Rao, S. Sophocles' Oedipus the King
Fic

Wolff, Lisa, 1954-
Teen depression **616.85**

Wolff, Tobias, 1945-
This boy's life [excerpt]
In Who do you think you are?; stories of
friends and enemies p83-91 **S C**

Wolff, Virginia Euwer
Brownian motion
In Ultimate sports; short stories by outstand-
ing writers for young adults p207-36
S C

Chair: a story for voices
In The Color of absence; 12 stories about loss
and hope p91-102 **S C**
Make lemonade **Fic**
The Mozart season (6 and up) **Fic**
Probably still Nick Swansen (7 and up) **Fic**
Water
In Girls got game; sports stories and poems
810.8

Wolfman, Ira
Climbing your family tree **929**

Wolfsgruber, Linda
(il) Lottridge, C. B. Stories from the life of Jesus **232.9**

Wolfson, Evelyn
From Abenaki to Zuni (4 and up) **970.004**

Wolinsky, Art
Internet power research using the Big6 approach
(5 and up) **025.04**
Safe surfing on the Internet (4 and up)
004.6

Wolk-Stanley, Jessica
(il) Campbell, A. The New York Public Library
incredible Earth **550**

Wollstonecraft, Mary, 1759-1797
About
Miller, C. C. Mary Wollstonecraft and the rights
of women (7 and up) **92**

Wolny, Philip
Weapons satellites **358**

The **wolverine's** secret. Norman, H.
In Norman, H. The girl who dreamed only
geese, and other tales of the Far North
398.2

Wolves
Swinburne, S. R. Once a wolf (4 and up)
333.95

Fiction
George, J. C. Julie (6 and up) **Fic**

Wolves and the mermaids. Aiken, J.
In Aiken, J. Shadows and moonshine; stories
S C

The **wolves** of Willoughby Chase. Aiken, J.
Fic

The **wolving** time. Jennings, P. **Fic**

The **Woman**, Adam, and the fruit. Lester, J.
In Lester, J. When the beginning began; stories about God, the creatures, and us
p81-85 **296.1**

Woman and Man started even. Hamilton, V.
In Hamilton, V. Her stories; African
American folktales, fairy tales, and true
tales p69-74 **398.2**

The **woman** in the wall. Kindl, P. **Fic**

Woman's Christian Temperance Union
Harvey, B. C. Carry A. Nation: saloon smasher
and prohibitionist **92**

A **woman's** touch. Williams-Garcia, R.
In Necessary noise: stories about our families
as they really are p131-42 **S C**

Womb to tomb. Lynch, C.
In Lynch, C. All the old haunts p58-78
S C

Women
See also and women of particular racial or
ethnic groups, e.g. *African American women;*
and women in various occupations and pro-
fessions
Women's almanac **305.4**
Biography
Chin-Lee, C. Amelia to Zora (4 and up)
920
Hacker, C. Nobel Prize winners **920**
Jones, V. B. Government & politics **920**
Stewart, G. Great women comedians **920**
Civil rights
See Women's rights
Employment
Colman, P. Rosie the riveter (5 and up)
331.4
Dash, J. We shall not be moved (7 and up)
331.4
Dean, R. Women of the Middle Ages (7 and up)
940.1
Schwager, T. Cool women, hot jobs . . . and
how you can go for it, too! (7 and up)
650.14
Folklore
Gerson, M. J. Fiesta femenina (4 and up)
398.2
Mayer, M. Women warriors (5 and up)
398.2
San Souci, R. Cut from the same cloth (4 and
up) **398.2**
Tchana, K. H. The serpent slayer: and other sto-
ries of strong women **398.2**
Health and hygiene
Diamond, S. N. Everything you need to know
about going to the gynecologist (7 and up)
618.1
See/See also pages in the following book(s):
Gray, H. M. Real girl/real world (7 and up)
305.23
Jukes, M. It's a girl thing (5 and up)
305.23
History
Dean, R. Women of the Middle Ages (7 and up)
940.1
Franck, I. M. The Wilson chronology of wom-
en's achievements (7 and up) **305.4**
Thomson, M. Women of the Renaissance
940.2
Women in history on file **305.4**

Women—*Continued*
Law and legislation
Frost-Knappman, E. Women's rights on trial

346

Poetry
More spice than sugar (4 and up)   **811.008**
Political activity
See also Women politicians
Psychology
Rutledge, J. Z. Dealing with the stuff that makes life tough (7 and up)   **305.23**
Religious life
Braude, A. Women and American religion (7 and up)   **200.9**
Social conditions
Coppens, L. M. What American women did, 1789-1920 (7 and up)   **305.4**
Heinemann, S. The New York Public Library amazing women in American history (5 and up)   **305.4**
Macdonald, F. Women in 19th-century America

305.4
Macdonald, F. Women in 19th-century Europe

305.4
Suffrage
Adams, C. Women's suffrage   **305.4**
Bausum, A. With courage and cloth   **305.4**
Frost-Knappman, E. Women's suffrage in America (7 and up)   **324.6**
Monroe, J. The Susan B. Anthony women's voting rights trial   **324.6**
Weisberg, B. Susan B. Anthony   **92**
Suffrage—Fiction
Lasky, K. A time for courage   **Fic**
Europe
Macdonald, F. Women in 19th-century Europe

305.4
India—Fiction
Whelan, G. Homeless bird (6 and up)   **Fic**
Middle East
Harik, R. M. Women in the Middle East

305.4
Nigeria
Nnoromele, S. Life among the Ibo women of Nigeria (7 and up)   **966.9**
Rome
Nardo, D. Women of ancient Rome (7 and up)

937
United States
Adams, C. Women's suffrage   **305.4**
Hartman, H. Girlwonder (5 and up)   **305.23**
United States—History
33 things every girl should know about women's history (5 and up)   **305.4**
Bausum, A. With courage and cloth   **305.4**
Coppens, L. M. What American women did, 1789-1920 (7 and up)   **305.4**
Cullen-DuPont, K. Encyclopedia of women's history in America   **305.4**
Frost-Knappman, E. Women's suffrage in America (7 and up)   **324.6**
Heinemann, S. The New York Public Library amazing women in American history (5 and up)   **305.4**
Kendall, M. E. Failure is impossible!   **305.4**

Macdonald, F. Women in 19th-century America

305.4
Matthews, G. American women's history

305.4
Miller, B. M. Good women of a well-blessed land   **305.4**
Slavicek, L. C. Women of the American Revolution (7 and up)   **973.3**
Zeinert, K. Those courageous women of the Civil War (7 and up)   **973.7**
Zeinert, K. Those remarkable women of the revolution (7 and up)   **973.3**
West (U.S.)
Alter, J. Extraordinary women of the American West   **920**
Ketchum, L. Into a new country (7 and up)

920

Women air pilots
Hart, P. S. Up in the air: the story of Bessie Coleman   **92**
Nathan, A. Yankee doodle gals   **940.54**
Women and American religion. Braude, A.

200.9

Women artists
Danneberg, J. Women artists of the West

920
Lyons, M. E. Talking with Tebé: Clementine Hunter, memory artist (4-6)   **92**
Laidlaw, J. A. Frida Kahlo (5 and up)   **92**
Morris, J. Tending the fire: the story of Maria Martinez (4 and up)   **92**
Sills, L. Visions (5 and up)   **920**
Women artists of the West. Danneberg, J.   **920**

Women astronauts
Bredeson, C. Shannon Lucid   **92**
Jeffrey, L. S. Christa McAuliffe   **92**
Yannuzzi, D. A. Mae Jemison   **92**

Women astronomers
Anderson, D. Maria Mitchell, astronomer (7 and up)   **92**
Gormley, B. Maria Mitchell (7 and up)   **92**

Women athletes
Freedman, R. Babe Didrikson Zaharias (5 and up)   **92**
Girls got game (5 and up)   **810.8**
Green, M. Y. A strong right arm: the story of Mamie "Peanut" Johnson (4 and up)   **92**
Hasday, J. L. Extraordinary women athletes

920
Lannin, J. A history of basketball for girls and women   **796.323**
Shea, P. D. Ekaterina Gordeeva   **92**
Stewart, M. Jackie Stiles (4 and up)   **92**
Teitelbaum, M. Great moments in women's sports   **796**
Williams, V. Venus & Serena (7 and up)

92

Dictionaries
Woolum, J. Outstanding women athletes

920.003
Encyclopedias
Encyclopedia of women and sport in America

796.03
Poetry
Smith, C. R. Hoop queens   **811**

Women authors
Anderson, W. T. Laura Ingalls Wilder (4 and up)   92
Bauer, M. D. A writer's story (7 and up)   92
Byars, B. C. The moon and I (4 and up)   92
Cammarano, R. Betsy Byars (4 and up)   92
Cleary, B. A girl from Yamhill: a memoir (6 and up)   92
Cleary, B. My own two feet   92
Cook, J. Natural writer: a story about Marjorie Kinnan Rawlings   92
Cuffie, T. A. Maya Angelou (7 and up)   92
Fritz, J. Harriet Beecher Stowe and the Beecher preachers (5 and up)   92
George, J. C. A tarantula in my purse (4-6)   92
Giff, P. R. Don't tell the girls (4 and up)   92
Harper, J. E. Maya Angelou   92
Haskins, J. Toni Morrison (4 and up)   92
Kenschaft, L. Lydia Maria Child (7 and up)   92
Kite, L. P. Maya Angelou   92
Lowry, L. Looking back (5 and up)   92
Ludwig, E. Judy Blume   92
Meigs, C. L. Invincible Louisa [May Alcott]   92
Miller, C. C. Mary Wollstonecraft and the rights of women (7 and up)   92
Mirriam-Goldberg, C. Sandra Cisneros   92
Nixon, J. L. The making of a writer   92
Ruth, A. Jane Austen   92
Ruth, A. Louisa May Alcott   92
Shields, C. J. Amy Tan   92
Trachtenberg, M. P. Anne McCaffrey   92
Wagner, H. L. Jane Austen   92
Women composers
Reich, S. Clara Schumann (5 and up)   92
Women executives
Jeffrey, L. S. Great American businesswomen   920
Women hall of famers in mathematics and science [series]
Alagna, M. Mae Jemison   92
Women in 19th-century America. Macdonald, F.   305.4
Women in 19th-century Europe. Macdonald, F.   305.4
Women in business *See* Businesswomen
Women in history [series]
Dean, R. Women of the Middle Ages   940.1
Nardo, D. Women of ancient Rome   937
Slavicek, L. C. Women of the American Revolution   973.3
Thomson, M. Women of the Renaissance   940.2
Women in history on file   305.4
Women in medicine
DeAngelis, G. Science & medicine   920
Lindop, L. Scientists and doctors (7 and up)   920
Stille, D. R. Extraordinary women of medicine   920

Women in Military Service for America Memorial (Arlington, Va.)
Ashabranner, B. K. A date with destiny   355
Women in politics
Axelrod-Contrada, J. Women who led nations (7 and up)   920
Gulotta, C. Extraordinary women in politics   920
Jones, V. B. Government & politics   920
Hewitt, K. Lives of extraordinary women (4 and up)   920
Price-Groff, C. Twentieth-century women political leaders (7 and up)   920
Zeinert, K. Women in politics   320
Women in profile [series]
Hacker, C. Nobel Prize winners   920
Women in science [series]
Anderson, D. Maria Mitchell, astronomer   92
Cullen, J. H. Barbara McClintock, geneticist   92
Ferry, J. Maria Goeppert Mayer, physicist   92
Kozleski, L. Jane Goodall   92
Nicholson, L. Dian Fossey   92
Women in the armed forces
See also Women soldiers
Anderson, M. K. So proudly they served   940.54
Ashabranner, B. K. A date with destiny   355
Kuhn, B. Angels of mercy (5 and up)   940.54
Nathan, A. Count on us   355
Fiction
Efaw, A. Battle dress (7 and up)   Fic
Women in the Bible
Daughters of the desert   220.9
Ward, E. M. Old Testament women (5 and up)   221.9
Women in the Koran
Daughters of the desert   220.9
Women in the Middle East. Harik, R. M.   305.4
Women inventors
Thimmesh, C. Girls think of everything (5 and up)   920
Women journalists
Colman, P. Where the action was   070.4
Davidson, S. Getting the real story: Nellie Bly and Ida B. Wells   92
Price-Groff, C. Extraordinary women journalists   920
Women mathematicians
Celebrating women in mathematics and science   920
Dictionaries
Yount, L. A to Z of women in science and math   920.003
Women of achievement [series]
Hasday, J. L. Madeleine Albright   92
Shields, C. J. Amy Tan   92
Women of adventure. McLean, J.   920
Women of ancient Rome. Nardo, D.   937
Women of hope. Hansen, J.   920

Women of our time [series]
Meltzer, M. Mary McLeod Bethune   **92**
Women of the American Revolution. Slavicek, L.
C.   **973.3**
Women of the frontier [series]
Furbee, M. R. Anne Bailey   **92**
Women of the Middle Ages. Dean, R.   **940.1**
Women of the Renaissance. Thomson, M.
                                    940.2
Women photographers
Partridge, E. Restless spirit: the life and work of
Dorothea Lange (6 and up)   **92**
Rubin, S. G. Margaret Bourke-White **92**
Sills, L. In real life: six women photographers
(7 and up)   **920**
Welch, C. A. Margaret Bourke-White **92**
Wooten, S. M. Margaret Bourke-White **92**
Women physicians
See also Women in medicine
Stille, D. R. Extraordinary women of medicine
                                    920
Women poets
Dommermuth-Costa, C. Emily Dickinson   **92**
It's a woman's world (7 and up)   **808.81**
Rhynes, M. E. Gwendolyn Brooks (7 and up)
                                    92
Richmond, M. A. Phillis Wheatley   **92**
Salisbury, C. Phillis Wheatley   **92**
Women politicians
Axelrod-Contrada, J. Women who led nations (7
and up)   **920**
Hasday, J. L. Madeleine Albright   **92**
Howard, M. Madeleine Albright   **92**
Price-Groff, C. Twentieth-century women politi-
cal leaders (7 and up)   **920**
Women scientists
Birch, B. Marie Curie   **92**
Celebrating women in mathematics and science
                                    920
Cullen, J. H. Barbara McClintock, geneticist (7
and up)   **92**
DeAngelis, G. Science & medicine   **920**
Di Domenico, K. Super women in science
                                    920
Ferry, J. Maria Goeppert Mayer, physicist (7
and up)   **92**
Fine, E. H. Barbara McClintock (7 and up)
                                    92
Gogerly, L. Dian Fossey   **92**
Hamilton, J. Lise Meitner   **92**
Kozleski, L. Jane Goodall (7 and up)   **92**
Lassieur, A. Marie Curie   **92**
Lindop, L. Scientists and doctors (7 and up)
                                    920
MacLeod, E. Marie Curie (5 and up) **92**
Matthews, T. L. Light shining through the mist:
a photobiography of Dian Fossey (4 and up)
                                    92
Nicholson, L. Dian Fossey (7 and up)   **92**
Notable women scientists (7 and up)
                                    920.003
Ottaviani, J. Dignifying science: stories about
women scientists   **741.5**
Pasachoff, N. E. Marie Curie and the science of
radioactivity   **92**

Poynter, M. Marie Curie: discoverer of radium
(4 and up)   **92**
Reynolds, M. D. American women scientists (7
and up)   **920**
Ross, M. E. Fish watching with Eugenie Clark
(4 and up)   **92**
Senker, C. Rosalind Franklin (5 and up)   **92**
Sullivan, O. R. African American women scien-
tists and inventors   **920**
Thimmesh, C. The sky's the limit (5 and up)
                                    500
Dictionaries
Yount, L. A to Z of women in science and math
                                    920.003
Women singers *See* Singers
Women soldiers
Zenatti, V. When I was a soldier (7 and up)
                                    92
Women warriors. Mayer, M.   **398.2**
Women who dared series
Davidson, S. Getting the real story: Nellie Bly
and Ida B. Wells   **92**
Women who led nations. Axelrod-Contrada, J.
                                    920
Women's almanac   **305.4**
Women's hall of fame series
Di Domenico, K. Super women in science
                                    920
The **women's** house. Ochiltree, D.
In Don't cramp my style; stories about that
time of the month p68-100   **S C**
Women's rights
33 things every girl should know about wom-
en's history (5 and up)   **305.4**
Adams, C. Women's suffrage   **305.4**
Kendall, M. E. Failure is impossible!   **305.4**
Fiction
Jocelyn, M. Mable Riley (5 and up)   **Fic**
Krisher, T. Uncommon Faith   **Fic**
Women's rights on trial. Frost-Knappman, E.
                                    346
Women's suffrage. Adams, C.   **305.4**
Women's suffrage in America. Frost-Knappman,
E.   **324.6**
Wonder beasts. Nigg, J.   **398**
Wonders *See* Curiosities and wonders
Wonders and miracles. Kimmel, E. A.   **296.4**
The **wonders** of biodiversity. Gallant, R. A.
                                    333.95
Wonders of the world [series]
Kallen, S. A. Gems   **553.8**
Kallen, S. A. Mummies   **393**
Mann, E. Hoover Dam   **627**
Wonders of the world book [series]
Mann, E. The Roman Colosseum   **937**
Wong, Janet S., 1962-
Behind the wheel (7 and up)   **811**
Wong, Tony
Ultraman Tiga, Vol. 1: Return of the warrior
                                    741.5

Wong-Staal, Flossie, 1947-
See/See also pages in the following book(s):
Yount, L. Asian-American scientists (7 and up)
    920

Wood, Elaine
(jt. auth) Walker, P. The digestive system
    612.3
(jt. auth) Walker, P. The immune system
    616.07

Wood, Gail
How to study (7 and up)   371.3

Wood, Ian, 1946-
Platinum
  In The Elements   546

Wood, Irene
(ed) Culturally diverse videos, audios, and CD-ROMS for children and young adults. See Culturally diverse videos, audios, and CD-ROMS for children and young adults
    011.6

Wood, June Rae, 1946-
The man who loved clowns   Fic

Wood, Marion
Ancient America (5 and up)   970.01

Wood, Richard J. (Richard John)
(jt. auth) Hoffmann, F. W. Guide to popular U.S. government publications   015.73

Wood, Ted, 1965-
Iditarod dream (4 and up)   798.8

Wood, Tim
The Renaissance (4 and up)   940.2

Wood
See/See also pages in the following book(s):
Knapp, B. J. Materials science   620.1

Wood carving
          Fiction
Carter, A. R. Crescent Moon   Fic

Wooden, Lenny
(il) San Souci, R. A terrifying taste of short & shivery   398.2

Wooden bones. De Lint, C.
  In De Lint, C. Waifs and strays p93-108
    S C

Woodford, Chris, 1943-
Atoms and molecules (5 and up)   540
Electricity (5 and up)   537

Wooding, Chris, 1977-
The haunting of Alaizabel Cray (7 and up)
    Fic

Woodland Indians
Yue, C. The wigwam and the longhouse
    970.004

Woodpeckers
Hoose, P. M. The race to save the Lord God Bird (7 and up)   598

Woodruff, Elvira
Dear Austin   Fic

Woods, Brenda
The red rose box (5 and up)   Fic

Woods, Geraldine, 1948-
Science in ancient Egypt (4 and up)   509
Science of the early Americas (4 and up)
    509

Woods, Granville, 1856-1910
See/See also pages in the following book(s):
Aaseng, N. Black inventors (7 and up)   920
Haskins, J. African American entrepreneurs
    920

Woods, Ron
The hero   Fic

Woods and forests. Martin, P. A. F.   577.3
The **woods** scientist. Swinburne, S. R.   591.7

Woodson, Carter Godwin, 1875-1950
          About
Durden, R. F. Carter G. Woodson (7 and up)
    92

Woodson, Jacqueline
Beanie
  In Girls got game; sports stories and poems
    810.8
Behind you (7 and up)   Fic
The house you pass on the way (7 and up)
    Fic
Hush   Fic
I hadn't meant to tell you this   Fic
If you come softly (7 and up)   Fic
July Saturday
  In Places I never meant to be; original stories by censored writers   S C
Locomotion (4 and up)   811
Miracle's boys   Fic
The Rialto
  In The Color of absence; 12 stories about loss and hope p185-204   S C

Woodson, Sarah Jane
See/See also pages in the following book(s):
Katz, W. L. Black pioneers   920

Woodsong. Paulsen, G.   796.5

Woodward, John, 1958-
(ed) Israel: opposing viewpoints. See Israel: opposing viewpoints   956.94

Woody, Elizabeth, 1959-
Homecooking
  In Talking leaves; contemporary native American short stories   S C

Woog, Adam, 1953-
Fidel Castro   92
A history of the Elizabethan theater   792.09
A sweatshop during the industrial revolution
    331.2
The whale (7 and up)   599.5

Woolf, Alex
Death and disease (5 and up)   610
Education (5 and up)   940.1

Woolls, E. Blanche
The school library media manager   027.8
(ed) The Whole school library handbook. See The Whole school library handbook   027.8

Woolum, Janet, 1955-
Outstanding women athletes   920.003

Wooten, Sara McIntosh
Margaret Bourke-White   92

Word games
Agee, J. Sit on a potato pan, Otis!   793.73
Agee, J. Who ordered the jumbo shrimp? and other oxymorons   793.73

Words of faith. Lubar, D.
 In Soul searching: thirteen stories about faith
  and belief p90-111 **S C**
The **words** of Martin Luther King, Jr. King, M. L.
  323.1
Words of power. Yolen, J.
 In Visions: nineteen short stories by outstand-
  ing writers for young adults p170-85
  S C
Words of the ancient Romans. Nardo, D. **937**
Words that changed history [series]
 Damon, D. Mein Kampf **943.086**
 Tackach, J. The Emancipation Proclamation
  973.7
Words with wings (4 and up) **811.008**
Wordsworth, William, 1770-1850
 (jt. auth) Liu, A. William Wordsworth **821**
Work
 See/See also pages in the following book(s):
 The information revolution **303.4**
Work stoppages *See* Strikes
A **worker** on the transcontinental railroad. Barter,
 J. **331.7**
Working dogs
 Gorrell, G. K. Working like a dog (4 and up)
  636.7
Working life [series]
 Barter, J. A Renaissance painter's studio
  759.5
 Barter, J. A worker on the transcontinental rail-
  road **331.7**
 Currie, S. An actor on the Elizabethan stage
  792.09
 Uschan, M. V. The cavalry during the Civil War
  973.7
 Woog, A. A sweatshop during the industrial
  revolution **331.2**
Working like a dog. Gorrell, G. K. **636.7**
Working with computers. McAlpine, M. **004**
Working women *See* Women—Employment
World, End of the *See* End of the world
The **world** according to dog. Sidman, J. **810.8**
The **world** according to horses. Budiansky, S.
  636.1
The **World** almanac and book of facts **031.02**
The **World** almanac for kids **031.02**
**World Almanac Library of American govern-
 ment** [series]
 Horn, G. The Congress **328**
 Horn, G. The presidency **352.23**
 Horn, G. The Supreme Court **347**
World art & culture [series]
 Bingham, J. African art & culture **709.6**
 Bingham, J. Indian art & culture **709.5**
 Khanduri, K. Japanese art & culture **709.52**
 Lewis, E. Mexican art & culture **709.72**
The **world** at her fingertips: the story of Helen
 Keller. Dash, J. **92**
World authors, 1900-1950 **920.003**
World authors, 1950-1970 **920.003**
World authors, 1970-1975 **920.003**
World authors, 1975-1980 **920.003**

World authors, 1980-1985 **920.003**
World authors, 1985-1990 **920.003**
World authors, 1990-1995 **920.003**
World authors, 1995-2000 **920.003**
World Bank
 January, B. Globalize it! (7 and up) **337**
The **world** before this one. Martin, R. **398.2**
The **World** Book encyclopedia **031**
The **World** Book encyclopedia of science **503**
World Book looks at [series]
 World Book looks at the sea and its marvels
  577.7
World Book looks at the sea and its marvels
  577.7
The **World** Book multimedia encyclopedia. See
 The World Book encyclopedia **031**
World Book of America's presidents **920**
World Book's biographical encyclopedia of scien-
 tists **920.003**
World Book's science year in review. See The
 World Book encyclopedia **031**
World Book's year in review. See The World
 Book encyclopedia **031**
World crafts [series]
 Doney, M. Festivals **745.5**
 Doney, M. Masks **745.59**
 Doney, M. Puppets **745.592**
World habitats [series]
 Pipes, R. Rain forests **577.3**
World health. Foley, R. **362.1**
World Health Organization
 Foley, R. World health (7 and up) **362.1**
 Grahame, D. A. World Health Organization
  610.6
World historical atlases [series]
 Stefoff, R. The ancient Mediterranean **938**
 Stefoff, R. The ancient Near East **939**
 Stefoff, R. The Asian empires **950**
 Stefoff, R. Exploration **910**
 Stefoff, R. The medieval world **909.07**
World history
 George, L. S. 800 **909.07**
 History of the modern world **909.08**
 The Kingfisher history encyclopedia (5 and up)
  909
 Galens, J. Middle ages: almanac **909.07**
 Roberts, J. M. The illustrated history of the
  world (7 and up) **909**
 Tomaselli-Moschovitis, V. Junior timelines on
  file **902**
 World history on file **909**
   13th century
 Service, A. 1200 **909.07**
   16th century
 Schomp, V. 1500 **909.08**
   18th century
  See also Enlightenment
 Dunn, J. M. The Enlightenment (7 and up)
  940.2
   19th century
 Ashby, R. 1800 **909.8**

World history—*Continued*
20th century
Children's history of the 20th century
909.82
Bibliography
Beck, P. GlobaLinks: resources for world
studies, grades K-8   016.9
Encyclopedias
Junior worldmark encyclopedia of the nations
910.3
Lands and peoples   910.3
Worldmark encyclopedia of the nations
910.3
World history by era [series]
The Renaissance   940.2
World history on file   909
World history series
Altman, L. J. The creation of Israel   956.94
Bachrach, D. The Crimean War   947
Corrick, J. A. The Industrial Revolution
909.81
Corrick, J. A. The Louisiana Purchase   973.4
Corzine, P. The Black Death   614.5
Dunn, J. M. The Enlightenment   940.2
Kallen, S. A. The Salem witch trials   133.4
Kronenwetter, M. America in the 1960s
973.92
Nardo, D. The Mexican-American War
973.6
Schaffer, D. The Iran-Iraq War   956.7
Tackach, J. The abolition of American slavery
326
Yancey, D. The internment of the Japanese
940.53
World in ancient times [series]
Mellor, R. The ancient Roman world   937
World in conflict, Middle East [series]
Gunderson, C. G. The need for oil   338.2
World leaders past & present [series]
Bruns, R. Julius Caesar   92
Humphrey, J. Genghis Khan   92
World life library [series]
Gamble, C. Leopards   599.75
Ovsyanikov, N. Polar bears   599.78
Ripple, J. Sea turtles   597.9
World mythology   201
World of animals [series]
Amphibians and reptiles   597.9
Birds   598
Fish   597
Insects and other invertebrates   595.7
Morris, P. Mammals   599
The **world** of architectural wonders. Corbishley,
M.   720
The **world** of King Arthur and his court. Crossley-
Holland, K.   942.01
World organizations [series]
Perkins, R. International Red Cross   361.7
Prior, K. UNICEF   362.7
A **world** painted by birds. Vaz, K.
In The Green Man: tales from the mythic for-
est p168-88   808.8

World politics
1945-
Blohm, C. E. Weapons of peace   327.1
Ross, S. The causes of the Cold War
327.73
1945-1991
Burgan, M. Cold War (7 and up)   909.82
Collier, C. The United States in the Cold War:
1945-1989   327.73
Speakman, J. The Cold War (7 and up)
327.73
Taylor, D. The Cold War   909.82
1991-
Gunderson, C. G. The need for oil   338.2
Encyclopedias
Worldmark encyclopedia of the nations
910.3
World records
Ash, R. The top 10 of everything   031.02
World religions [series]
Brown, S. F. Protestantism   280
Gordon, M. Islam   297
Hartz, P. Baha'i Faith   297
Hartz, P. Native American religions   299.7
Hartz, P. Taoism   299.5
Wangu, M. B. Hinduism   294.5
World series (Baseball)
Stewart, M. World Series   796.357
The **World** through children's books   011.6
**World Trade Center (New York, N.Y.) terrorist
attack, 2001**
See also September 11 terrorist attacks,
2001
**World Trade Center Bombing, New York, N.Y.,
1993**
Pellowski, M. The terrorist trial of the 1993
bombing of the World Trade Center   974.7
Shields, C. J. The 1993 World Trade Center
bombing   364.1
World Trade Organization
January, B. Globalize it! (7 and up)   337
The **world** turned upside down. Ferrie, R.
973.3
World War, 1914-1918
Adams, S. World War I (4 and up)   940.3
Collier, C. The United States enters the world
stage: from the Alaska Purchase through
World War I, 1867-1919   973.8
Feldman, R. T. World War I   940.3
Gay, K. World War I (5 and up)   940.3
Hatt, C. World War I, 1914-18 (7 and up)
940.3
History of World War I   940.3
Pendergast, T. World War I almanac (7 and up)
940.3
Pendergast, T. World War I primary sources (7
and up)   940.3
Ross, S. The technology of World War I
940.3
Ruggiero, A. World War I   940.3
World War I [Turning points in world history
series] (7 and up)   940.3
Biography
Pendergast, T. World War I: biographies (7 and
up)   920

World War, 1914-1918—*Continued*
Fiction

Breslin, T. Remembrance (7 and up)   **Fic**
Havill, J. Eyes like Willy's   **Fic**
Lawrence, I. Lord of the nutcracker men (5 and up)   **Fic**
Morpurgo, M. Private Peaceful (7 and up)   **Fic**
Wilson, J. And in the morning (7 and up)   **Fic**

Naval operations

Preston, D. Remember the Lusitania (5 and up)   **940.4**

Personal narratives

Kirchberger, J. H. The First World War (7 and up)   **940.3**

Sources

Coetzee, F. World War I: a history in documents (7 and up)   **940.3**

Women

Zeinert, K. Those extraordinary women of World War I   **940.3**

United States

Bosco, P. I. World War I (7 and up)   **940.3**
Brown, G. Conflict in Europe and the Great Depression   **973.9**

World War, 1939-1945

Aaseng, N. Navajo code talkers   **940.54**
Adams, S. World War II (4 and up)   **940.53**
Ambrose, S. E. The good fight (5 and up)   **940.53**
Durrett, D. Unsung heroes of World War II (7 and up)   **940.54**
Feldman, G. World War II: almanac   **940.53**
Goldstein, M. J. World War II, Europe (5 and up)   **940.53**
Hatt, C. World War II, 1939-45 (7 and up)   **940.53**
Lawton, C. Hiroshima (5 and up)   **940.54**
Levy, P. M. The home front in World War II (7 and up)   **940.53**
McGowen, T. World War II (4 and up)   **940.53**
O'Neill, W. L. World War II: a student companion (7 and up)   **940.53**
Ruggiero, A. World War II   **940.53**
Sheehan, S. The technology of World War II   **940.54**
Tanaka, S. Attack on Pearl Harbor (4 and up)   **940.54**
Williams, B. World War II, Pacific (5 and up)   **940.54**
World War II [Turning points in world history series] (7 and up)   **940.53**

Aerial operations

George, L. The Tuskegee Airmen   **940.54**
McGowen, T. Air raid   **940.54**
McGowen, T. Assault from the sky   **940.54**
McGowen, T. Carrier war   **940.54**
Nathan, A. Yankee doodle gals   **940.54**
See/See also pages in the following book(s):
Haskins, J. Black eagles (5 and up)   **629.13**

African Americans

Bruning, J. R. Elusive glory   **920**

Battles, sieges, etc.

See World War, 1939-1945—Aerial operations; World War, 1939-1945—Campaigns; World War, 1939-1945—Naval operations

Bibliography

Wee, P. H. World War II in literature for youth   **016.9**

Biography

Howes, K. K. World War II: biographies   **920**
Ross, S. Leaders of World War II   **920**

Campaigns

See also names of battles, campaigns, sieges, etc.

Stein, R. C. World War II in Europe   **940.54**
World War II battles and leaders   **940.54**

Campaigns—France

Drez, R. J. Remember D-day (5 and up)   **940.54**

Campaigns—Pacific Ocean

Stein, R. C. World War II in the Pacific   **940.54**

Causes

See also National socialism

Children

Gottfried, T. Children of the slaughter (7 and up)   **940.53**
Leapman, M. Witnesses to war (5 and up)   **940.53**
Tunnell, M. O. The children of Topaz (5 and up)   **940.53**

Fiction

Avi. Don't you know there's a war on? (4 and up)   **Fic**
Bat-Ami, M. Two suns in the sky (7 and up)   **Fic**
Bradley, K. B. For freedom   **Fic**
Bruchac, J. Code talker   **Fic**
Bunting, E. Spying on Miss Müller (5 and up)   **Fic**
Chan, G. A foreign field (7 and up)   **Fic**
Cormier, R. Heroes (7 and up)   **Fic**
Davies, J. Where the ground meets the sky   **Fic**
Denenberg, B. Early Sunday morning   **Fic**
Denenberg, B. The journal of Ben Uchida, citizen #13559, Mirror Lake internment camp   **Fic**
Elliott, L. Under a war-torn sky (7 and up)   **Fic**
Gaeddert, L. B. Friends and enemies   **Fic**
Giff, P. R. Lily's crossing (4 and up)   **Fic**
Greene, B. Summer of my German soldier (6 and up)   **Fic**
Griffis, M. L. The Feester filibuster (4 and up)   **Fic**
Hahn, M. D. Following my own footsteps (5 and up)   **Fic**
Hahn, M. D. Stepping on the cracks (5 and up)   **Fic**
Hughes, D. Soldier boys   **Fic**
Isaacs, A. Torn thread (7 and up)   **Fic**
Kerr, M. E. Slap your sides (7 and up)   **Fic**
Lawrence, I. B for Buster (7 and up)   **Fic**
Levitin, S. Journey to America (4 and up)   **Fic**

World War, 1939-1945—Fiction—*Continued*
Levitin, S. Room in the heart   **Fic**
Lisle, J. T. The art of keeping cool (5 and up)   **Fic**
Lowry, L. Autumn Street (4 and up)   **Fic**
Lowry, L. Number the stars (4 and up)   **Fic**
Lurie, A. Dancing in the streets of Brooklyn   **Fic**
Maguire, G. The good liar (4 and up)   **Fic**
Matas, C. Greater than angels (7 and up)   **Fic**
Matas, C. In my enemy's house (7 and up)   **Fic**
Mazer, H. The last mission (7 and up)   **Fic**
Mazer, N. F. Good night, Maman (5 and up)   **Fic**
Myers, W. D. The journal of Scott Pendleton Collins (5 and up)   **Fic**
Napoli, D. J. Stones in water (5 and up)   **Fic**
Park, L. S. When my name was Keoko (5 and up)   **Fic**
Paulsen, G. The cookcamp (5 and up)   **Fic**
Salisbury, G. Under the blood-red sun   **Fic**
Tunnell, M. O. Brothers in valor   **Fic**
Watkins, Y. K. My brother, my sister, and I (6 and up)   **Fic**
Watkins, Y. K. So far from the bamboo grove (6 and up)   **Fic**
Whelan, G. Burying the sun   **Fic**
Wulffson, D. L. Soldier X (7 and up)   **Fic**

Jews
See also Holocaust, 1933-1945
Adler, D. A. We remember the Holocaust   **940.53**
Boas, J. We are witnesses (7 and up)   **940.53**
Frank, A. The diary of a young girl (6 and up)   **92**
Frank, A. The diary of a young girl: the definitive edition (6 and up)   **92**
Lyman, D. Holocaust rescuers   **920**
Müller, M. Anne Frank (7 and up)   **92**
Reiss, J. The upstairs room (5 and up)   **92**
Siegal, A. Upon the head of the goat: a childhood in Hungary, 1939-1944   **92**

Jews—Rescue
Gottfried, T. Heroes of the Holocaust (7 and up)   **940.53**
Kustanowitz, E. The hidden children of the Holocaust   **940.53**
Levine, E. Darkness over Denmark   **940.53**
Meltzer, M. Rescue: the story of how Gentiles saved Jews in the Holocaust (6 and up)   **940.53**
Opdyke, I. G. In my hands (7 and up)   **940.53**
Rescue and resistance: portraits of the Holocaust   **940.53**
Talbott, H. Forging freedom (4 and up)   **940.53**

Journalists
Colman, P. Where the action was   **070.4**
Naval operations
McGowen, T. Carrier war   **940.54**

McGowen, T. Sink the Bismarck (5 and up)   **940.54**
Nelson, P. Left for dead (7 and up)   **940.54**
Personal narratives
Allen, T. B. Remember Pearl Harbor (5 and up)   **940.54**
Hautzig, E. R. The endless steppe: growing up in Siberia   **92**
Opdyke, I. G. In my hands (7 and up)   **940.53**
Reparations
Alonso, K. Korematsu v. United States (7 and up)   **323.1**
Resistance movements
  See World War, 1939-1945—Underground movements
Sources
World War II: primary sources   **940.53**
Underground movements
Gottfried, T. Heroes of the Holocaust (7 and up)   **940.53**
Women
Anderson, M. K. So proudly they served   **940.54**
Colman, P. Where the action was   **070.4**
Kuhn, B. Angels of mercy (5 and up)   **940.54**
Germany
McGowen, T. Germany's lightning war (5 and up)   **940.54**
Japan
Maruki, T. Hiroshima no pika   **940.54**
Poland
Opdyke, I. G. In my hands (7 and up)   **940.53**
United States
Barr, G. World War II home front   **940.53**
Collier, C. The United States in World War II: 1941-1945   **940.53**
Colman, P. Rosie the riveter (5 and up)   **331.4**
Cooper, M. L. Fighting for honor (6 and up)   **940.53**
Cooper, M. L. Remembering Manzanar   **940.53**
Houston, J. W. Farewell to Manzanar (7 and up)   **940.53**
Isserman, M. World War II (7 and up)   **940.53**
Perl, L. Behind barbed wire   **940.53**
Yancey, D. The internment of the Japanese   **940.53**
See/See also pages in the following book(s):
Trotter, J. W. From a raw deal to a New Deal? African Americans, 1929-1945 (7 and up)   **305.8**

World War I. Bosco, P. I.   **940.3**
World War I. Feldman, R. T.   **940.3**
World War I. Gay, K.   **940.3**
World War I. Ruggiero, A.   **940.3**
  [Turning points in world history series] (7 and up)   **940.3**
World War I, 1914-18. Hatt, C.   **940.3**

World War I: a history in documents. Coetzee, F.
940.3

World War I primary sources. Pendergast, T.
940.3

World War II. Adams, S.   940.53

World War II. Isserman, M.   940.53

World War II. McGowen, T.   940.53

World War II. Ruggiero, A.   940.53

World War II, 1939-45. Hatt, C.   940.53

World War II: almanac. Feldman, G.   940.53

World War II battles and leaders   940.54

World War II home front. Barr, G.   940.53

World War II in Europe. Stein, R. C.   940.54

World War II in the Pacific. Stein, R. C.
940.54

World War II, Pacific. Williams, B.   940.54

World War II: primary sources   940.53

World War I. Adams, S.   940.3

World War I: biographies. Pendergast, T.   920

World War II [Turning points in world history series] (7 and up)   940.53

World War II: a student companion. O'Neill, W. L.   940.53

World War II, Europe. Goldstein, M. J.
940.53

World wars [series]
  Levy, P. M. The home front in World War II
940.53
  Ross, S. Leaders of World War II   920
  Ross, S. The technology of World War I
940.3
  Sheehan, S. The technology of World War II
940.54

World Wide Web
  Benson, A. C. Connecting kids & the Web
004.6
  Cooper, G. New virtual field trips   025.5
  Minkel, W. Delivering Web reference services to young people   025.04

World wide web sites See Web sites

World writers [series]
  Hart, J. Native son: the story of Richard Wright
92
  Miller, C. C. Mary Wollstonecraft and the rights of women   92
  Rhynes, M. E. Gwendolyn Brooks   92
  Schoell, W. Remarkable journeys: the story of Jules Verne   92
  Somervill, B. A. Ida Tarbell   92

Worldmark encyclopedia of the nations   910.3

Worldmark encyclopedia of the states   973.03

Worlds afire. Janeczko, P. B.   Fic

Worlds beyond [series]
  Miller, R. Earth and the moon   525
  Miller, R. Extrasolar planets   523
  Miller, R. Jupiter   523.4
  Miller, R. Mercury and Pluto   523.4
  Miller, R. Saturn   523.4
  Miller, R. The sun   523.7

World's hot spots [series]
  The Palestinians and the disputed territories
956.04

Worms, Penny
  (jt. auth) Tym, K. Coping with your emotions
152.4
  (jt. auth) Tym, K. School survival   371.8

Worms
  Pascoe, E. Earthworms   592

Wormser, Richard, 1933-
  American Islam (7 and up)   297
  Defending the accused (7 and up)   345
  The rise and fall of Jim Crow (7 and up)
305.8

Worry
  Crist, J. J. What to do when you're scared & worried (5 and up)   152.4

Worth, Charles Frédéric, 1826-1895
  See/See also pages in the following book(s):
  Kent, J. Business builders in fashion   920

Worth, Richard, 1945-
  The great empire of China and Marco Polo in world history   92
  The insanity defense (7 and up)   345
  Slave life on the plantation (7 and up) 326
  The slave trade in America (7 and up) 326
  The Spanish Inquisition in world history (7 and up)   272

Worth. LaFaye, A.   Fic

Worth the risk. Erlbach, A.   302

Wortis, Avi See Avi, 1937-

Wounded Knee: an Indian history of the American West. Ehrlich, A.   970.004

Wounds and injuries
  See also Burns and scalds; Wounds and injuries
  Crash   617.1
  Johansson, P. Carpal tunnel syndrome and other repetitive strain injuries (7 and up)   616.8
  Sports injuries information for teens (7 and up)   617.1

Wozniak, Stephen, 1950-
  See/See also pages in the following book(s):
  Northrup, M. American computer pioneers
920

The wreckers. Lawrence, I.   Fic

Wrede, Patricia C., 1953-
  Dealing with dragons (6 and up)   Fic
  Sorcery and Cecelia, or, The enchanted chocolate pot (7 and up)   Fic

Wren, Laura Lee
  Pirates and privateers of the high seas 920

Wrestling
  Brzycki, M. Wrestling strength: prepare to win
796.4
  Brzycki, M. Wrestling strength: the competitive edge   796.4
  Gallagher, J. The composite guide to wrestling
796.8

Fiction
  Hayes, D. No effect   Fic
  Spinelli, J. There's a girl in my hammerlock (5 and up)   Fic
  Wallace, R. Wrestling Sturbridge (7 and up)
Fic

Wrestling strength: prepare to win. Brzycki, M.
796.4

Wrestling strength: the competitive edge. Brzycki, M. **796.4**

Wrestling Sturbridge. Wallace, R. **Fic**

Wright, Amy Bartlett
  (il) Latimer, J. P. Butterflies **595.7**
  (il) Latimer, J. P. Caterpillars **595.7**

Wright, Betty Ren
  Out of the dark (4 and up) **Fic**

Wright, Cora M.
  More hot links **011.6**

Wright, David K., 1943-
  Frank Lloyd Wright **92**
  Paul Robeson **92**

Wright, Frank Lloyd, 1867-1959
  About
  Rubin, S. G. Frank Lloyd Wright (7 and up) **92**
  Wright, D. K. Frank Lloyd Wright **92**

Wright, Joseph P., 1939-
  (jt. auth) Salvadori, M. G. Math games for middle school **510.7**

Wright, Katharine See Haskell, Katharine Wright, 1874-1929

Wright, Orville, 1871-1948
  About
  Carson, M. K. The Wright Brothers for kids (4 and up) **629.13**
  Collins, M. Airborne: a photobiography of Wilbur and Orville Wright (4 and up) **92**
  Freedman, R. The Wright brothers: how they invented the airplane **92**
  Maurer, R. The Wright sister [biography of Katharine Wright Haskell] (5 and up) **92**
  Sproule, A. The Wright brothers **92**

Wright, Rachel
  The Viking news **948**

Wright, Richard, 1908-1960
  About
  Hart, J. Native son: the story of Richard Wright (7 and up) **92**

Wright, Wilbur, 1867-1912
  About
  Carson, M. K. The Wright Brothers for kids (4 and up) **629.13**
  Collins, M. Airborne: a photobiography of Wilbur and Orville Wright (4 and up) **92**
  Freedman, R. The Wright brothers: how they invented the airplane **92**
  Maurer, R. The Wright sister [biography of Katharine Wright Haskell] (5 and up) **92**
  Sproule, A. The Wright brothers **92**

The **Wright** brothers. Sproule, A. **92**

The **Wright** Brothers for kids. Carson, M. K. **629.13**

The **Wright** brothers: how they invented the airplane. Freedman, R. **92**

The **Wright** sister [biography of Katharine Wright Haskell] Maurer, R. **92**

Wrigley, Chris
  Winston Churchill: a biographical companion (7 and up) **92**

Wringer. Spinelli, J. **Fic**

A **wrinkle** in time. L'Engle, M. **Fic**

Write grants, get money. Anderson, C. **025.1**

Writers See Authors

Writers for young adults **920.003**

A **writer's** story. Bauer, M. D. **92**

Writing
  See also Picture writing

Writing (Authorship) See Authorship; Creative writing; Journalism

Writing on the wall. Rees, C.
  In Gothic!; ten original dark tales **S C**

Writing stories. Harrison, D. L. **808.3**

Writing winning reports and essays. Janeczko, P. B. **808**

Writing with style. Young, S. **808**

Writings of teenagers See Teenagers' writings

WTO See World Trade Organization

Wu, Chien Shiung, 1912-1997
  See/See also pages in the following book(s):
  Di Domenico, K. Super women in science **920**
  Lindop, L. Scientists and doctors (7 and up) **920**
  Yount, L. Asian-American scientists (7 and up) **920**

Wu, William F., 1951-
  Black powder
  In American dragons: twenty-five Asian American voices p211-34 **810.8**

Wukovits, John F., 1944-
  Anne Frank (7 and up) **92**
  The encyclopedia of world sports **796.03**
  Oskar Schindler **92**
  Stephen King (7 and up) **92**

Wulffson, Don L., 1943-
  The kid who invented the trampoline **609**
  Soldier X (7 and up) **Fic**
  Toys! (4 and up) **688.7**

Wunsch, Susi Trautmann
  The adventures of Sojourner **629.43**

Wurman, Joshua
  About
  Grace, C. O. Forces of nature (4 and up) **551.2**

WWJD. Weaver, W.
  In On the fringe p145-61 **S C**

Wyborny, Sheila, 1950-
  Virtual reality **006.8**

Wyeth, Andrew, 1917-
  About
  Meryman, R. Andrew Wyeth (7 and up) **92**

Wyeth, Sharon Dennis
  A piece of heaven **Fic**

Wynne-Jones, Tim
  The boy in the burning house **Fic**
  Dawn
  In Leaving home: stories p91-114 **808.8**
  Stephen Fair (7 and up) **Fic**
  A thief in the house of memory (7 and up) **Fic**

Wyoming
  Baldwin, G. Wyoming
  In Celebrate the states **973**

Wyoming—*Continued*
Kent, D. Wyoming
In America the beautiful, second series
973
Kent, D. Wyoming
In America the beautiful, second series
973
Fiction
Ehrlich, G. A blizzard year   **Fic**

X

X-men (Comic strip)
Sanderson, P. Ultimate X-men   **741.5**
X-rays
McClafferty, C. K. The head bone's connected
to the neck bone (7 and up)   **616.07**
The **xenocide** mission. Jeapes, B.   **Fic**
Ximen Bao and the river spirit. Jaffe, N.
In Jaffe, N. and Zeitlin, S. J. The cow of no
color: riddle stories and justice tales from
around the world p18-22   **398.2**

Y

Y2K.CHATRM43. Carter, A. R.
In Time capsule: short stories about teenagers
throughout the twentieth century p205-19
S C
Yaakov, Juliette
(ed) Senior high school library catalog. See Se-
nior high school library catalog   **011.6**
Yabu, Julie
A lesson from the heart
In American dragons: twenty-five Asian
American voices p161-65   **810.8**
Yahk fahn, Auntie. Lum, D. H. Y.
In American dragons: twenty-five Asian
American voices p5-13   **810.8**
Yahoo! Inc.
Sherman, J. Jerry Yang and David Filo   **92**
Yai. Hirunpidok, V.
In American dragons: twenty-five Asian
American voices p168-84   **810.8**
Yakami. Mayer, M.
In Mayer, M. Women warriors; myths and
legends of heroic women p61-64   **398**
Yakwawiak. Bruchac, J.
In Bruchac, J. and Bruchac, J. When the
Chenoo howls; native American tales of
terror   **398.2**
Yalow, Rosalyn S. (Rosalyn Sussman), 1921-
See/See also pages in the following book(s):
Celebrating women in mathematics and science
920
Lindop, L. Scientists and doctors (7 and up)
920
Yamanaka, Lois-Ann, 1961-
Wild meat and the bully burgers [excerpt]
In American eyes; new Asian-American short
stories for young adults p8-12   **S C**

Yamauchi, Wakako
And the soul shall dance
In American dragons: twenty-five Asian
American voices p144-54   **810.8**
Yancey, Diane
Al Capone   **92**
Frederick Douglass   **92**
The internment of the Japanese   **940.53**
Life of an American soldier   **959.704**
Tuberculosis (7 and up)   **616.2**
Yang, Chen-ning, 1922-
See/See also pages in the following book(s):
Yount, L. Asian-American scientists (7 and up)
920
Yang, Jerry, 1968-
About
Sherman, J. Jerry Yang and David Filo   **92**
The **Yangtze**. Waterlow, J.   **951.2**
Yangtze River valley (China)
Waterlow, J. The Yangtze (4 and up)   **951.2**
Yankee doodle gals. Nathan, A.   **940.54**
Yankee girl. Rodman, M. A.   **Fic**
Yannuzzi, Della A.
Ernest Hemingway   **92**
Mae Jemison   **92**
Yara-ma-yha-who. San Souci, R.
In San Souci, R. A terrifying taste of short &
shivery; thirty creepy tales p6-11
398.2
Yates, Adam
Guide to wild dinosaurs   **567.9**
Yates, Elizabeth, 1905-2001
Amos Fortune, free man   **92**
A **year** down yonder. Peck, R.   **Fic**
Year of impossible goodbyes. Choi, S. N.   **Fic**
The **year** of secret assignments. Moriarty, J.
Fic
The **year** of the hangman. Blackwood, G. L.
Fic
The **year** they burned the books. Garden, N.
Fic
The **year** without Michael. Pfeffer, S. B.   **Fic**
A **year** without rain. Love, D. A.   **Fic**
The **yearling**. Rawlings, M. K.   **Fic**
Yee, Lisa
Millicent Min, girl genius (5 and up)   **Fic**
Yee, Paul
Tales from Gold Mountain (4 and up)   **S C**
See/See also pages in the following book(s):
Ellis, S. From reader to writer   **372.6**
The **yellow** boat. Saar, D.
In Theatre for young audiences; 20 great
plays for children p535-78   **812.008**
The **yellow** face. Doyle, Sir A. C.
In Doyle, Sir A. C. The complete Sherlock
Holmes   **S C**
Yellow fever
Murphy, J. An American plague (5 and up)
614.5
Fiction
Anderson, L. H. Fever, 1793 (5 and up)   **Fic**
The **yellow** jar. Atangan, P.   **741.5**

Yellow journalism. Cohen, D.   **302.23**

Yemen

  Hestler, A. Yemen (5 and up)   **953.3**

Yeoman, John

  The Seven voyages of Sinbad the Sailor (5 and up)   **398.2**

Yep, Laurence

  Angelfish (5 and up)   **Fic**

  The case of the Goblin Pearls   **Fic**

  Child of the owl (5 and up)   **Fic**

  Dragon's gate (6 and up)   **Fic**

  Dragonwings (5 and up)   **Fic**

  Dream soul   **Fic**

  Hiroshima (4 and up)   **Fic**

  The lost garden (5 and up)   **92**

  The rainbow people (4 and up)   **398.2**

  Thief of hearts (5 and up)   **Fic**

  The traitor (5 and up)   **Fic**

  See/See also pages in the following book(s):

  Author talk (4 and up)   **028.5**

  (ed) American dragons: twenty-five Asian American voices. See American dragons: twenty-five Asian American voices   **810.8**

Yeshi Dorjee

  See/See also pages in the following book(s):

  Major, J. S. Caravan to America p[1]-13 (4 and up)   **920**

Yesner, Bernice L.

  Operating and evaluating school library media programs   **027.8**

Yin, Saw Myat

  Myanmar (5 and up)   **959.1**

Yolen, Jane

  Armageddon summer (7 and up)   **Fic**

  Briar Rose   **Fic**

  Cards of grief

    In New skies: an anthology of today's science fiction   **S C**

  Centaur field

    In Half-human p117-37   **S C**

  Color me a rhyme (4 and up)   **811**

  The devil's arithmetic (4 and up)   **Fic**

  Girl in a cage   **Fic**

  Jason and the Gorgon's blood   **Fic**

  The king's dragon

    In Fire and wings: dragon tales from East and West p112-16   **S C**

  Mama gone

    In Vampires: a collection of original stories p202-10   **S C**

  Mightier than the sword (4 and up)   **398.2**

  Contents: The magic brocade; The young man protected by the river; The devil with the three golden hairs; Eating with trolls; Knee-high man; Language of the birds; Thick-head; The fisherman and the chamberlain; Jack and his companions; The truthful shepherd; And who cured the princess?; The false knight on the road; Hired hands; Mighty mikko

  Night wolves

    In The Haunted house: a collection of original stories   **S C**

  O Jerusalem (4 and up)   **811**

  Our Lady of the Greenwood

    In Sherwood: original stories from the world of Robin Hood p6-16   **S C**

  Passager   **Fic**

  Prince across the water   **Fic**

  The queen's own fool   **Fic**

Sacred places   **811**

Sword of the rightful king   **Fic**

Words of power

  In Visions: nineteen short stories by outstanding writers for young adults p170-85   **S C**

See/See also pages in the following book(s):

MacRae, C. D. Presenting young adult fantasy fiction (7 and up)   **813.009**

(ed) The Haunted house: a collection of original stories. See The Haunted house: a collection of original stories   **S C**

(ed) Sherwood: original stories from the world of Robin Hood. See Sherwood: original stories from the world of Robin Hood   **S C**

(ed) Vampires: a collection of original stories. See Vampires: a collection of original stories   **S C**

Yolonda's genius. Fenner, C.   **Fic**

Yong, Teo Chuu

  (jt. auth) Shelley, R. Japan   **952**

Yoon, Steve Chan-No

  Stoplight

    In American dragons: twenty-five Asian American voices p14-25   **810.8**

York, ca. 1775-ca. 1815

About

  Blumberg, R. York's adventures with Lewis and Clark (5 and up)   **978**

  See/See also pages in the following book(s):

  Haskins, J. Against all opposition (5 and up)   **920**

York, Sherry, 1947-

  Children's and young adult literature by Latino writers   **028.5**

York's adventures with Lewis and Clark. Blumberg, R.   **978**

Yorktown (Va.)

History—Siege, 1781

  Ferrie, R. The world turned upside down (5 and up)   **973.3**

Yoshida, Minosuke, 1933-

  See/See also pages in the following book(s):

  Hamanaka, S. In search of the spirit (5 and up)   **920**

Yoshina, Joan M.

  (jt. auth) Harada, V. H. Inquiry learning through librarian-teacher partnerships   **371.1**

You are the juror. Aaseng, N.   **345**

You be me (7 and up)   **305.23**

You can weave!. Monaghan, K.   **746.41**

You come too: favorite poems for young readers. Frost, R.   **811**

You don't know me. Klass, D.   **Fic**

You gotta try this!. Cobb, V.   **507.8**

You hear me? (7 and up)   **810.8**

You may be the next . . . Schwartz, A.

  In Schwartz, A. Scary stories 3; more tales to chill your bones p89   **398.2**

Young, Ed

  See/See also pages in the following book(s):

  The Newbery & Caldecott medal books, 1986-2000   **028.5**

  (il) Grimes, N. Tai chi morning   **811**

Young, Jeff C., 1948-
Dwight D. Eisenhower   **92**

Young, Karen Romano, 1959-
The Beetle and me (7 and up)   **Fic**

Young, Marilyn Blatt
The Vietnam War: a history in documents (7 and up)   **959.704**

Young, Robyn V.
(ed) Notable mathematicians. See Notable mathematicians   **920.003**

Young, Sue
The new comprehensive American rhyming dictionary   **423**
Writing with style (5 and up)   **808**

Young actor series
Lamedman, D. 111 one-minute monologues   **812.008**
Shakespeare, W. One hundred and eleven Shakespeare monologues   **822.3**
Surface, M. H. Short scenes and monologues for middle school actors   **812**

Young Adult Library Services Association
Carter, B. Best books for young adults   **028.1**
Kan, K. Sizzling summer reading programs for young adults   **027.62**
New directions for library service to young adults. See New directions for library service to young adults   **027.62**

Young adult literature
Read all about it!   **808.8**
Writers for young adults   **920.003**
    Bibliography
Anderson, V. Fiction sequels for readers 10 to 16   **016.8**
Best books for young adult readers   **011.6**
Bodart, J. R. Radical reads   **028.5**
Carter, B. Best books for young adults   **028.1**
Day, F. A. Lesbian and gay voices   **016.8**
Helbig, A. Many peoples, one land   **016.8**
Herald, D. T. Teen genreflecting   **016.8**
Jones, P. Connecting young adults and libraries   **027.62**
Jones, P. A core collection for young adults   **011.6**
Jweid, R. Building character through literature   **028.5**
Knowles, E. Reading rules!   **028.5**
Makowski, S. Serious about series   **016.8**
McCaffery, L. H. Building an ESL collection for young adults   **016.4**
New York Public Library. Books for the teen age   **011.6**
Rosow, L. V. Light 'n lively reads for ESL, adult, and teen readers   **011.6**
Schon, I. Recommended books in Spanish for children and young adults, 2000 through 2004   **011.6**
Senior high school library catalog   **011.6**
Sullivan, E. T. Reaching reluctant young adult readers   **028.5**
Ward, M. Voices from the margins   **016.8**
York, S. Children's and young adult literature by Latino writers   **028.5**

Your reading   **011.6**
    Bio-bibliography
Drew, B. A. The 100 most popular young adult authors   **810.9**
    History and criticism
Brown, J. Declarations of independence   **028.5**
Crew, H. S. Is it really Mommie Dearest?   **813.009**
Donelson, K. L. Literature for today's young adults   **028.5**
Stephens, C. G. Coretta Scott King Award books   **028.5**
    Technique
Peck, R. Invitations to the world   **808.06**

Young adults' libraries
Braun, L. W. Technically involved   **027.62**
Braun, L. W. Teens.library   **027.62**
Bromann, J. Booktalking that works   **028.5**
Edwards, K. Teen library events   **027.62**
Honnold, R. 101+ teen programs that work   **027.62**
Information literacy skills, grades 7-12   **027.62**
Jones, P. Connecting young adults and libraries   **027.62**
Jones, P. Do it right!   **027.62**
Kan, K. Sizzling summer reading programs for young adults   **027.62**
Lerch, M. T. Serving homeschooled teens and their parents   **027.6**
New directions for library service to young adults   **027.62**
O'Dell, K. Library materials and services for teen girls   **027.62**
Reid, R. Something funny happened at the library   **027.62**
Taney, K. B. Teen spaces   **022**

The **young** baseball player. Smyth, I.   **796.357**

Young Boy Chief and his sister. Curry, J. L.
  In Curry, J. L. Hold up the sky: and other Native American tales from Texas and the Southern Plains p133-41   **398.2**

Young enthusiast [series]
Smyth, I. The young baseball player   **796.357**

The **young** equestrian. Davis, C.   **798.2**

The **young** man and the sea. Philbrick, W. R.   **Fic**

The **young** man protected by the river. Yolen, J.
  In Yolen, J. Mightier than the sword; world folktales for strong boys p11-17   **398.2**

Young Merlin trilogy [series]
Yolen, J. Passager   **Fic**

Young musicians in world history. Earls, I.   **920**

The **young** nation: America 1787-1861. Brownstone, D. M.   **973**

The **young** Oxford book of archaeology. Moloney, N.   **930.1**

The **young** Oxford book of the human being. Glover, D. M.   **612**

Young Oxford history of African Americans [series]
Bair, B. Though justice sleeps **305.8**
Frankel, N. Break those chains at last: African Americans, 1860-1880 **305.8**
Grossman, J. R. A chance to make good **305.8**
Littlefield, D. C. Revolutionary citizens **305.8**
Trotter, J. W. From a raw deal to a New Deal? African Americans, 1929-1945 **305.8**
White, D. G. Let my people go: African Americans, 1804-1860 **305.8**
The **Young** Oxford Library of science **503**
A **young** patriot. Murphy, J. **973.3**
Young people's letters to the president. Greenberg, J. E. **973**
Young people's libraries See Young adults' libraries
A **young** person's guide to philosophy. Weate, J. **100**
The **young** person's guide to Shakespeare. Ganeri, A. **822.3**
The **young** person's guide to the opera. Ganeri, A. **792.5**
The **young** person's guide to the orchestra. Ganeri, A. **784.2**
Young person's occupational outlook handbook **331.7**
Young readers' history of the Civil War [series]
Ray, D. Behind the Blue and Gray **973.7**
Ray, D. A nation torn **973.7**
Young royals [series]
Meyer, C. Mary, Bloody Mary **Fic**
The **young** writer's guide to getting published. Henderson, K. **808**
Youngerman, Barry
The truth about alcohol. See The truth about alcohol **362.292**
Yount, Lisa
A to Z of women in science and math **920.003**
Antoni van Leeuwenhoek **92**
Asian-American scientists (7 and up) **920**
Biotechnology and genetic engineering **303.4**
Cancer (7 and up) **616.99**
Your government—how it works [series]
Mintzer, R. The National Institutes of Health **362.1**
Mintzer, R. The National Transportation Safety Board **363.1**
Your legal rights. Landau, E. **346**
Your move, J.P.!. Lowry, L. **Fic**
Your reading **011.6**
Your travel guide to ancient Israel. Sherman, J. **933**
You're not a winner unless your picture's in the paper. Avi
    In The Color of absence; 12 stories about loss and hope p147-66 **S C**
You're on!: seven plays in English and Spanish (4 and up) **812.008**

You're smarter than you think. Armstrong, T. **153.9**
Yourgrau, Barry
Have no fear, Crumpot is here!
    In Gothic!; ten original dark tales **S C**
Youth
    See also Teenagers
Hoose, P. M. We were there, too! (5 and up) **973**
Alcohol use
    See also Teenagers—Alcohol use
Gottfried, T. The facts about alcohol **362.292**
Employment
    See also Teenagers—Employment
Fiction
Leaving home: stories **808.8**
Health and hygiene
Child and youth security sourcebook **362.7**
Crump, M. Don't sweat it! **613**
Law and legislation
Greenberg, K. E. Adolescent rights (7 and up) **346**
Jacobs, T. A. What are my rights? (7 and up) **346**
Sexual behavior
Pregnancy (7 and up) **362.7**
Youth violence (7 and up) **364.36**
Youths' writings
Night is gone, day is still coming (7 and up) **808.8**
Yucht, Alice H.
Flip it! **025.5**
Yue, Charlotte
The igloo (4 and up) **728**
The wigwam and the longhouse **970.004**
Yue, David
(jt. auth) Yue, C. The igloo **728**
(jt. auth) Yue, C. The wigwam and the long-house **970.004**
Yuen, Charles
(il) Lagasse, E. Emeril's there's a chef in my family! **641.5**
Yugoslav War, 1991-1995
O'Grady, S. F. Basher five-two (5 and up) **949.7**
War-torn Bosnia (7 and up) **949.7**
Yugoslavia
    See also Bosnia and Hercegovina; Croatia; Serbia
History
Andryszewski, T. Kosovo **949.7**
History—Civil War, 1991-1995
    See Yugoslav War, 1991-1995
Yukon Territory
Ferry, S. Yukon Territory
    In Exploring Canada **971**
History
    See also Klondike River valley (Yukon)—Gold discoveries
Poetry
Service, R. W. The cremation of Sam McGee (4 and up) **811**

Yumoto, Kazumi
The letters (7 and up)   Fic

Z

Z for Zachariah. O'Brien, R. C.   Fic
Zaharias, Babe Didrikson, 1911-1956
           About
Freedman, R. Babe Didrikson Zaharias (5 and up)   92
Zallinger, Jean
(il) Sattler, H. R. The book of North American owls   598
Zambia
Holmes, T. Zambia (5 and up)   968.94
Zambreno, Mary Frances, 1954-
At fountain abbey
     In Sherwood: original stories from the world of Robin Hood p100-18   S C
Miss Emily's roses
     In Vampires: a collection of original stories p64-80   S C
Zamojska-Hutchins, Danuta
Cooking the Polish way
     In Easy menu ethnic cookbooks   641.5
Zamora, Pedro, 1972-1994
           About
Winick, J. Pedro and me (7 and up)   362.1
Zanger, Mark H.
The American ethnic cookbook for students   641.5
Zap! blink! taste! think!. Chahrour, J.   507.8
Zarembka, Arlene
(jt. auth) McKissack, P. C. To establish justice   342
Zazoo. Mosher, R.   Fic
Zeaman, John
Birds   636.5
Overpopulation (7 and up)   363.9
Zebra. Potok, C.
     In Potok, C. Zebra and other stories p1-25   S C
Zebra and other stories. Potok, C.   S C
Zeder, Suzan
Wiley and the Hairy Man [play]
     In Theatre for young audiences; 20 great plays for children p142-69   812.008
Zeinert, Karen, 1942-2002
Cults (7 and up)   209
Those courageous women of the Civil War (7 and up)   973.7
Those extraordinary women of World War I   940.3
Those remarkable women of the revolution (7 and up)   973.3
Tragic prelude: bleeding Kansas (7 and up)   978.1
Wisconsin
     In Celebrate the states   973
Women in politics   320
Zeises, Lara M.
Contents under pressure (7 and up)   Fic

Zeitlin, Steven J.
The four corners of the sky (5 and up)   201
(jt. auth) Jaffe, N. The cow of no color: riddle stories and justice tales from around the world   398.2
Zel. Napoli, D. J.   Fic
Zelinsky, Paul O.
See/See also pages in the following book(s):
The Newbery & Caldecott medal books, 1986-2000   028.5
(il) Cleary, B. Dear Mr. Henshaw   Fic
(il) Cleary, B. Strider   Fic
Zelzah: a tale from long ago. Mazer, N. F.
     In Leaving home: stories p179-99   808.8
Zenatti, Valérie, 1970-
When I was a soldier (7 and up)   92
           About
Zenatti, V. When I was a soldier (7 and up)   92
Zenobia, Queen of Palmyra
See/See also pages in the following book(s):
Meltzer, M. Ten queens (5 and up)   920
Zephaniah, Benjamin
Face (7 and up)   Fic
Zhang, Ange
Red land, yellow river (5 and up)   951.05
Zheng Yi Sao *See* Cheng, Yi Sao, d. 1844
Zhukov, Georgiĭ Konstantinovich, 1896-1974
See/See also pages in the following book(s):
Ross, S. Leaders of World War II   920
Zia. O'Dell, S.   Fic
Zickgraf, Ralph
Laos   959.4
Zielin, Lara, 1975-
Make things happen   302.2
Zigzag. Wittlinger, E.   Fic
Zillah and Lot. Myers, W. D.
     In Myers, W. D. A time to love; stories from the Old Testament p87-102   S C
Zim, Herbert S.
(jt. auth) Robbins, C. S. Birds of North America   598
Zimbabwe
Sheehan, S. Zimbabwe (5 and up)   968.91
           Fiction
Farmer, N. The Ear, the Eye, and the Arm (6 and up)   Fic
Farmer, N. A girl named Disaster (6 and up)   Fic
Zimmermann, Karl R.
Steam locomotives (4 and up)   385
The zimwi. San Souci, R.
     In San Souci, R. A terrifying taste of short & shivery; thirty creepy tales p62-67   398.2
Zindel, Paul
Love and centipedes
     In Places I never meant to be; original stories by censored writers   S C
The Pigman (7 and up)   Fic
Zink. Bennett, C.   Fic
Zinnen, Linda
The dragons of Spratt, Ohio (5 and up)   Fic

Zinnen, Linda—*Continued*
The truth about rats, rules, and seventh grade
Fic

Zionism
Altman, L. J. The creation of Israel (7 and up)
956.94
Blumberg, A. The history of Israel (7 and up)
956.94
Israel: opposing viewpoints **956.94**
Schroeter, D. J. Israel (7 and up) **956.94**

Zlata's diary. Filipovic, Z. **92**

Zoell, Bob
(il) Hirsch, R. F E G: ridiculous stupid poems
for intelligent children **821**

Zoeller, Chuck
(ed) Flash!: the Associated Press covers the
world. See Flash!: the Associated Press covers the world **070.4**

Zohorsky, Janet R., 1958-
Medieval knights and warriors **940.1**

Zoos
Fiction
Taylor, T. Lord of the Kill **Fic**

Zorich, Chris, 1969-
See/See also pages in the following book(s):
Kaminsky, M. Uncommon champions **920**

Zucker, Naomi Flink
Benno's bear **Fic**

Zuehlke, Jeffrey
Egypt in pictures (5 and up) **962**

Zug, Mark
(il) Sage, A. Magyk . **Fic**

Zulu (African people)
Stanley, D. Shaka, king of the Zulus (4 and up)
92

Zusak, Markus, 1975-
Fighting Ruben Wolfe (7 and up) **Fic**

Zweifel, Frances W.
(il) Bonnet, R. L. Science fair projects: chemistry **540.7**

Zweizig, Douglas
Lessons from Library Power **027.8**